3rd EDITION

standard catalog of

AMERICAN CARS

1946-1975

Edited by

John Gunnell

krause publications

700 E. State St., Iola, WI 54990-0001

(715) 445-2214

THIRD EDITION

International Standard Book Number: 0-87341-204-4

Library of Congress Number: 82-084065

ABBREVIATIONS

AAA	American Automobile Assoc.
Aero	Aerodynamic
Air	Air Conditioning
AM	AM Radio
AM	American Motors Corp.
Amp	Amperes
AMX	American Motors Experimental
B-Pillar	Second roof pillar
Brghm/Brgm	Brougham
Br2	Breezeway
BSW	Black Sidewall Tires
Bus	Business
Cabr	Cabriolet
Cam	Camshaft
CC	Cubic Centimeters
cid	cubic inch displacement
CJ	Cobra Jet
clb	club
Co.	Company
Conv.	Convertible
Corp	Corporation
Cpe	Coupe
C-Pillar	third roof pillar
cr	Cross (AMC)
cr	Crown(Ford)
cty/ctry	Country
cus	custom
cyl	cylinder
del	deluxe
DeV	DeVille or deVille
Div	division
d/l	deluxe level
dly	delivery
dpl	diplomat (AMC)
dr	door(s)
DSO	District Sales Office
EFI	Electronic Fuel Injection
Eight	Eight cylinder auto
Eldo	Eldorado
ESA	Economic Stabilization Agency
Est	Estate
Exec	executive
Fam	Family (Family Sedan)
FLO	Flow
Fltwd	Fleerwood
FM	FM Radio
Fml	Formal
FoMoCo	Ford Motor Co.
FsBk	Fastback
FT	Formal Top
GI	WWII Soldiers
GM	General Motors Corp.
Go-Pack	AMC performance options
GS	Gran Sport
GT	Gran Turismo
Hatch	hatchback
HO	High-output
Holly	Hollywood (Hudson)
Hp	Horsepower
HT	hardtop
I	Inline
I.O.	Identification
Imp	Imperial
L4	L-head four cylinder
LAN	Landau
LAPD	Los Angeles Police Dept.
LdCr	Land Cruiser
LeB	LeBaron
L-head	valve in block motor
Limo	limousine
LTO	Limited
LWB	Long Wheel Base
Mk	Mark
MM	millimeters
mpg	miles per gallon
mph	miler per hour
MTL	metal
NASA	type of hood scoop
NASCA	Nat. Assoc. Stock Car Racing
NHP	Net horsepower
NHRA	Nat. Hot Rod Assoc.
NPA	National Price Administration
Notch	notchback
OHV	overhead valve(s)
Ont.	Ontario, Canada
OSRV	Outside readview (mirror)
O/W	opera window
P	passenger (GP=6-passenger)
Pacer	Indy Pace Car nickname
Phae	Phaeton
Rbt	Runabout
Rds	roadster
PRM	Revolutions per minute
RWL	raised white letter
SAE	Society Automotive Engineer
SC/360	AMC Model Name
SCCA	Sports Car Club of Amer.
SCJ	Super Cobra Jet
Sed	Sedan
Six	Six-cylinder model
Sky	Skyliner (a last op or retractable)
SL	Sunliner (Ford conv)
SM	Sportsman (Ford)
SOHC	Single overhead camshaft
Spec.	Special
Spl.	Special
Spt.	Sport(s)
Sptmn	Sportman (DeSoto)
Sq	Squire
Sub/Suburb	Suburban
SST	Super Sport Touring AMC Model
Sta	Station
Star	Starliner
Tach	Tachometer
Taxi	Taxicab
T-Bird	Thunderbird
T&C	Town & Country
Trans AM	Trans American Race
Trav.	Traveler (Kaiser)
Tu-Tone	two-tone
Twn	Town
US.	United States
USA	United States of America
USAC	U.S. Auto Racing Club
UTL	utility
Veed	V-shaped
V-8	V-8 cylinder engine
Vic	Victoria
Vir	Virginian
V-Shaped	Shaped like a V
Wag	Wagon
Wis	Wisconsin
WL	white letter
w/o	without

INTRODUCTION

Re-editing THE STANDARD CATALOG of AMERICAN CARS 1946-1975 has been like restoring a vehicle that a hobbyist would call "a really good car to start with." In automotive terms, the idea was to go from a 90-plus point show car to 99.9 points...near perfect.

To achieve this, we knew that the catalog had to become more factual, more fact-filled and easier to use. A new cover and a couple of additional photos just wouldn't do the trick.

Step one was to review the previous edition. More than 60 members of the Society of Automotive Historians who specialize in particular brands of cars were asked to go over the catalog to check the facts. They poured over their personal archives to document serial numbers, production totals and other details.

Second came the job of adding new information to the data base. Museum curators, restorers, club technical advisors and individual car owners joined the historians in contributing fresh information.

Making the catalog easier to use fell to the editorial and production staffs of Krause Publication's Automotive Division. Photo pages were arranged differently to break the sections better. All current pricing was moved to the back of the book to make looking up the latest values a simpler job. In many sections, the organization of data has been rearranged, grouping all serial numbers at the beginning of a section and all engine specifications near the end. The amount of footnotes used has been reduced. The remaining footnotes are presented more clearly, making them easier to use.

THE STANDARD CATALOG of AMERICAN CARS 1946-1975 continues to provide students of the postwar car field, from novice hobbyists to advanced collectors, with a handy guide to this automotive era. It is full of a great deal of detailed information that the practicing historian or professional car restorer will not find in any other single reference source.

This edition brings us closer to the "perfect" book — a goal for which we constantly strive. In reality, this goal will always remain unobtainable, but we feel that this third edition marks a major contribution towards enhancing general knowledge about the exciting automobiles built during the postwar era.

This third edition is the result of a year's work and planning. We sincerely believe it will answer thousands of questions which have been put to the editors of OLD CARS and OLD CARS PRICE GUIDE over the past 22 years. At the same time, we expect it will raise new questions and bring forth new facts that were not unearthed in the countless hours of research by our team.

Should you, as an individual or member of a club, have access to expanded information you wish to share, contact the editors in care of: Krause Publications, 700 East State St., Iola, WI 54990. Every effort will be made to include improvements or corrections in future catalogs.

CONTENTS

HOW TO USE THIS CATALOG

APPEARANCE AND EQUIPMENT: Word descriptions help identify postwar cars down to details such as styling features, trim and interior appointments. Standard equipment lists usually begin with low-priced base models. Then, subsequent data blocks cover higher-priced car-lines of the same year.

VEHICLE I.D. NUMBERS: The third edition features expanded data explaining the basic serial numbering system used by each postwar car manufacturer. This data reveals where, when and in what order your car was built. There is much more information on assembly plant, body style and original engine codes.

SPECIFICATIONS CHART: The first chart column gives series or model numbers for postwar cars. The second column gives Body/Style Number codes revealing type of body and trim. The third column tells number of doors, body type and passenger capacity ("4-dr Sed-6P" means "four-door sedan six-passenger"). The fourth column gives factory suggested retail price of the car when new. The fifth column gives the car's original shipping weight. The sixth column provides model year production totals (if available) or makes reference to additional notes found below the specifications chart. When the same car came with different engines or trim levels at different prices and weights, slashes (/) are used to separate the low price or weight from the high one. In some cases, model numbers are also presented this way. In rare cases where data is non-applicable or not available the abbreviation "NA" appears.

BASE ENGINE DATA: According to make of car, engine data will be found either below the data block for each series or immediately following the specifications chart for the last car-line. Displacement, bore and stroke and horsepower ratings are listed, plus a lot more data where available. This edition has more complete engine listings for many models. In other cases, extra-cost engines are listed in the "options" section.

CHASSIS FEATURES: The main data compiled here consists of wheelbase, overall length and tire size. Front and rear tread widths are given for most cars through the early 1960s and some later models. Overall width and height appears in some cases, too.

OPTIONAL EQUIPMENT LISTS: This section includes data blocks listing all types of options and accessories. In some instances, there are multiple data blocks for different cars (i.e. compact, intermediate, full-size, sports/personal). A great deal of attention has been focused on cataloging both the availability and the original factory retail prices of optional equipment for postwar cars. Emphasis has been placed on RPOs (Regular Production Options), rather than dealer-installed or special-order equipment. Because of size and space limitations, a degree of selectivity has been applied by concentrating on those optional features of greatest interest to collectors. Important option packages have been covered and detailed as accurately as possible in the given amount of space. Some contributors have provided the exact price of the options (down to the last penny). Others have rounded-off prices to the nearest whole dollar.

HISTORICAL FOOTNOTES: Postwar cars - especially low-production models and high-performance types - are already recognized as an important part of America's automotive heritage. Revealing statistics; important dates and places; personality profiles; performance milestones; and other historical facts are highlighted in this "automotive trivia" section.

CORONET SERIES — (ALL ENGINES) — The 1959 Dodges were easily recognizeable as Dodges, even though the styling of the 1957-1958 models was simply exaggerated. The fins were longer and higher, the brows over the headlights were much larger and the entire car was longer, lower and wider than in previous years. Dodge continued to be a major factor in the great horsepower race of the '50s. This year's offering in the high-horsepower category was the first of the famous 383 cid V-8 engines, which Chrysler used for more than a decade. The 383 boasted 345 hp when equipped with the extremely rare electronic fuel-injection. Also new for 1959 was the swivel seat option. A simple motion of the lever at the side of the seat and the unit swung out to meet the occupant. Even though this option met with limited acceptance, it made enough of an impression on the auto industry that GM introduced their own version of the swivel seat on the 1973 intermediate line. The Coronet continued to be the base trim level and included chrome windshield and rear window moldings, a single horizontal chrome strip along the bodyside and chrome trim at the lower edge of the fender fin. The Dodge name, in block letters, appeared on the trunk lid (directly below a combination Dodge crest and trunk handle). The Coronet name, in script, appeared on the front fenders.

DODGE I.D. NUMBERS: The VIN is stamped and embossed on a stainless steel plate attached to the left front door pillar. [CORONET] Coronet sixes assembled in Detroit began at M302100001 and went up. Those assembled in Newark began at M305100001 and went up. V-8 powered models assembled in Detroit began at M312100001 and went up and those assembled in Newark began at M315100001 and went up. V-8 models assembled in California began at M314100001 and went up. [ROYAL] Royal models assembled in Detroit began at M332100001 and went up. Those assembled in Newark began at M33510001 and went up. Those assembled in California began at M334100001 and went up. [CUSTOM ROYAL] Custom Royal models assembled in Detroit began at M352100001 and went up. Those assembled in Newark began at M355100001 and went up. Those assembled in California began at M354100001 and went up.

CORONET SERIES

Model Number	Body/Style Number	Body Type & Seating	Factory Price	Shipping Weight	Production Total
MD1/2-L	41	4-dr Sed-6P	2537/2657	3425/3615	Note 1
MD1/2-L	21	2-dr Clb Sed-6P	2466/2586	3375/3565	Note 1
MD1/2-L	23	2-dr Lancer HT-6P	2594/2714	3395/3590	Note 1
MD2-L	43	4-dr Lancer HT-6P	2792	3620	Note 1
MD2-L	27	2-dr Conv-6P	3039	3775	Note 1

NOTE 1: A total of 96,782 Coronet models were produced during calendar 1959. Exactly 151,851 Dodges were built for the 1959 model year. In slightly rounded-off figures, the model year output of Coronets was counted at 96,900 units. See historical footnotes for available body style production totals, which are not broken-out by series.

ENGINES

(Six) L-head. Inline. Six-cylinder. Cast iron block. Displacement: 230 cid. Bore and stroke: 3.25 x 4.38 inches. Compression ratio: 8.0: 1. Brake hp: 135 at 3600 rpm. Four main bearings. Solid valve lifters. Carburetion: Stromberg single-barrel.

(V-8) Red Ram V-8. Overhead valves. Cast iron block. Displacement: 326 cid. Bore and stroke: 3.95 x 3.31 inches. Compression ratio: 9.21. Brake hp: 255 at 4400 rpm. Five main bearings. Hydraulic valve lifters. Carburetion: Carter two-barrel.

(Optional V-8) Ram Fire V-8. Overhead valves. Cast iron block. Displacement: 361 cid. Bore and stroke: 4.12 x 3.38 inches. Compression ratio: 10.1:1. Brake hp: 295 at 4600 rpm on Royal and Sierra models, 305 at 4600 rpm on Custom Royal and Custom Sierra models. Five main bearings. Hydraulic valve lifters. Carburetion: Carter four-barrel.

(Optional D500 V-8*) Overhead valves. Cast iron block. Displacement: 383 cid. Bore and stroke: 4.25 x 3.38 inches. Compression ratio: 10.1:1. Brake hp: 320 at 4600 rpm (four-barrel), 345 at 5000 rpm (dual four-barrel). Five main bearings. Hydraulic valve lifters. Carburetion: Carter four-barrel (two four-barrels on higher horsepower engine).

(Optional D500 V-8) Super D500 V-8. Overhead valves. Cast iron block. Displacement: 383 cid. Bore and stroke: 4.25 x 3.38 inches. Compression ratio: 10.0:1, Brake hp: 345 at 5000 rpm. Five main bearings. Hydraulic valve lifters. Carburetion: Electronic fuel injection.

CHASSIS FEATURES: Wheelbase: 122 inches. Overall length: 217.4 inches. (216.4 inches on station wagons). Tires: 7.50 x 14 on Coronet models: 8.00 x 14 tubeless black sidewalls on all others.

OPTIONS: TorqueFlite transmission, all V-8 models ($226.90). PowerFlite transmission, Coronet and Royal ($189.10). Power steering, V-8 only ($92.15). Power brakes ($42.60). Power window lifts ($102.30). Power tailgate windows, twoseat wagons ($34.10). Six-Way power seat ($95.70). Dual Exhaust ($30.90), Pushbutton Radio ($86.50). Rear speaker ($14.95). Radio with dual antennas ($14.05). Heater and defroster ($93.55). Tires: white sidewall 7.50 x 14, Coronet except convertible ($33.35); 8.00 x 14, other models ($41.75). Two-tone paint, standard colors ($18.55): DeLuxe ($34.10). Solex glass ($42.60); windshield only ($18.55). Backup lights ($10.70). Wheel covers ($14.30); DeLuxe ($30.50). Electric clock ($15.95). Windshield washer ($11.80). Variable speed windshield wipers ($6.60). Windshield washer and Vari-speed wipers ($18.25). Front and rear Air Foam seat ($10.70). Undercoating ($12.85). Air conditioning with heater, V-8s only ($468.55): wagons ($662.95). Carpets ($11.80). Rear window defroster ($20.60). Sure-Grip differential, all except convertible ($49.70). Padded instrument panel ($20.00). Padded sun visors ($8.00). Automatic headlight beam changer ($49.70). Heavy-duty 70-amp battery ($8.60). Custom trim package, Coronet except convertible ($56.00). D500, 320 hp, 383 cid four-barrel carb package with dual exhaust and torqueflite transmission, Coronet convertible ($368.00): Coronet V-8 except convertible ($398.90). Royal and Sierra wagons ($,328.10); Custom Royal convertible ($273.35) Royal and Custom wagons ($304.15). Super D500, 345 hp engine, Coronet V-8 except convertible ($540.45); Coronet convertible ($509.60); Royal and Sierra wagons ($469.65); Custom Royal convertible ($414.95); Custom Royal and Custom wagons ($445.75. Level Flite, V-8s only ($127.55). Outside rearview mirror ($6.45).

HISTORICAL FOOTNOTES: The 1959 Dodges were introduced on Oct. 10, 1958. Model year production peaked at 151,851 units, of which approximately 15,600 were sixes and 136,200 were V-8 powered. A breakout of model year production by body style is available, although the figures do not tell us how many of each body style were made in a specific series. Dodge assembled 13,515 two-door sedans; 65,752 four-door sedans; 29,610 two-door hardtops; 16,704 four-door hardtops: 2,733 convertibles; 13,515 four-door two-seat station wagons and 10,022 four-door three-seat station wagons in the 1959 model year. We cannot however, for example, tell how many of the 2,733 ragtops were Coronets and how many were Custom Royal convertibles. Dodge Div.'s calendar year output was 192,798 units this year, accounting for a 3.44 percent share of the total market. M.C. Patterson continued as vice-president and general manager of Dodge Div. this season. For the model run, about 94 percent of all Dodges had automatic transmission 68.9 percent had power steering; 27.4 percent had power brakes; 23.2 percent had windshield washers; 84.7 percent had back-up lights; 4.5 percent had air conditioning and only 0.7 percent had the rare air suspension, an option that did not last very long.

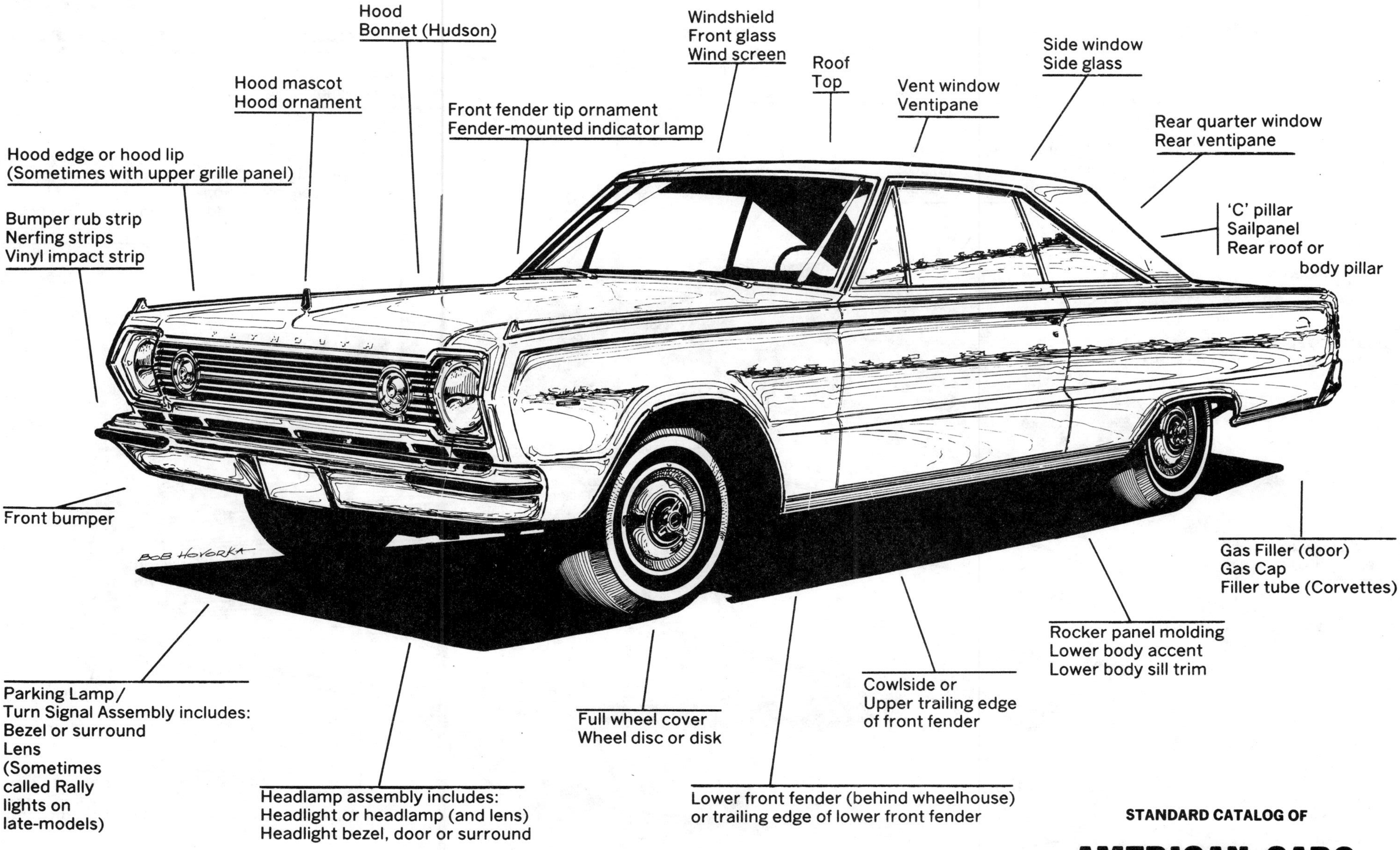
Hood
Bonnet (Hudson)
Windshield
Front glass
Wind screen
Roof
Top
Side window
Side glass
Vent window
Ventipane
Hood mascot
Hood ornament
Front fender tip ornament
Fender-mounted indicator lamp
Rear quarter window
Rear ventipane
Hood edge or hood lip
(Sometimes with upper grille panel)
'C' pillar
Sailpanel
Rear roof or
body pillar
Bumper rub strip
Nerfing strips
Vinyl impact strip
Front bumper
BOB HOVORKA
Gas Filler (door)
Gas Cap
Filler tube (Corvettes)
Rocker panel molding
Lower body accent
Lower body sill trim
Parking Lamp/
Turn Signal Assembly includes:
Bezel or surround
Lens
(Sometimes
called Rally
lights on
late-models)
Cowlside or
Upper trailing edge
of front fender
Full wheel cover
Wheel disc or disk
Headlamp assembly includes:
Headlight or headlamp (and lens)
Headlight bezel, door or surround
Lower front fender (behind wheelhouse)
or trailing edge of lower front fender

STANDARD CATALOG OF

AMERICAN CARS

1946-1975

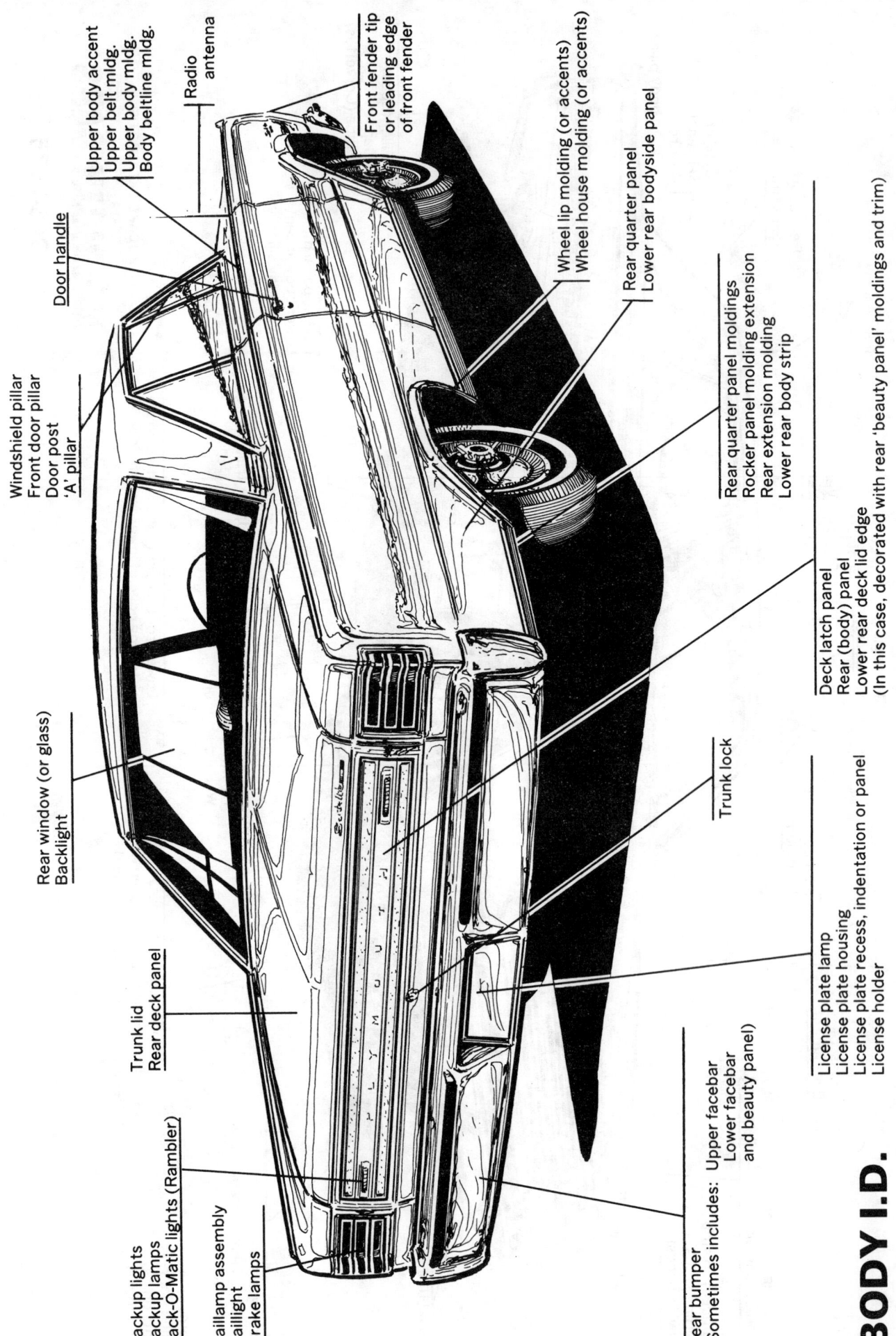

Upper body accent
Upper belt mldg.
Upper body mldg.
Body beltline mldg.

Radio antenna

Front fender tip or leading edge of front fender

Wheel lip molding (or accents)
Wheel house molding (or accents)

Rear quarter panel
Lower rear bodyside panel

Door handle

Windshield pillar
Front door pillar
Door post
'A' pillar

Rear quarter panel moldings
Rocker panel molding extension
Rear extension molding
Lower rear body strip

Deck latch panel
Rear (body) panel
Lower rear deck lid edge
(In this case, decorated with rear 'beauty panel' moldings and trim)

Rear window (or glass)
Backlight

Trunk lock

Trunk lid
Rear deck panel

License plate lamp
License plate housing
License plate recess, indentation or panel
License holder

Backup lights
Backup lamps
Back-O-Matic lights (Rambler)

Taillamp assembly
Taillight
Brake lamps

Rear bumper
(Sometimes includes: Upper facebar
                        Lower facebar
                        and beauty panel)

BODY I.D.
GUIDE

Standard Catalog of American Cars

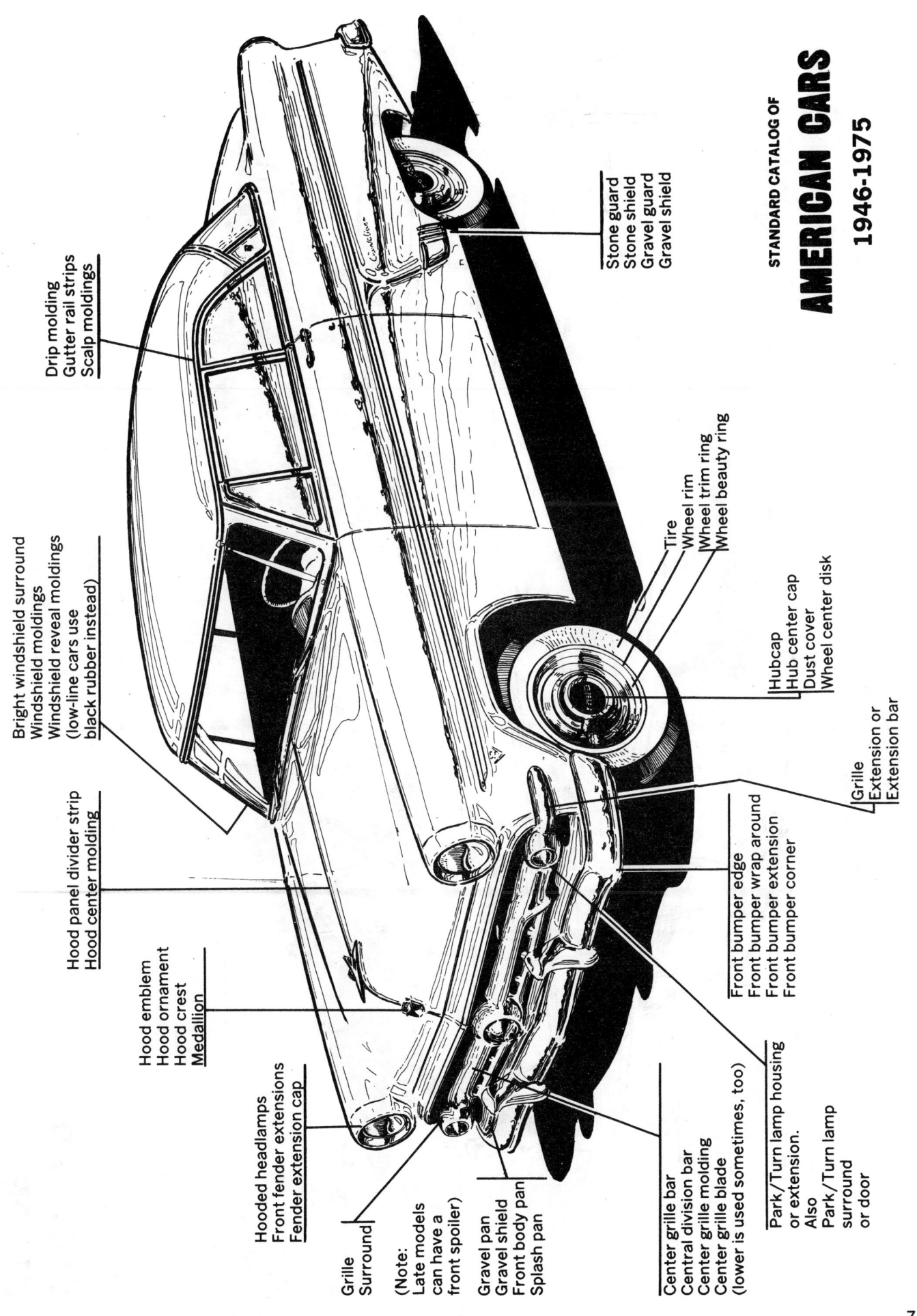

Stone guard
Stone shield
Gravel guard
Gravel shield

Drip molding
Gutter rail strips
Scalp moldings

Tire
Wheel rim
Wheel trim ring
Wheel beauty ring

Bright windshield surround
Windshield moldings
Windshield reveal moldings
(low-line cars use
black rubber instead)

Hubcap
Hub center cap
Dust cover
Wheel center disk

Grille
Extension or
Extension bar

Hood panel divider strip
Hood center molding

Hood emblem
Hood ornament
Hood crest
Medallion

Front bumper edge
Front bumper wrap around
Front bumper extension
Front bumper corner

Hooded headlamps
Front fender extensions
Fender extension cap

Park/Turn lamp housing
or extension.
Also
Park/Turn lamp
surround
or door

Grille
Surround

(Note:
Late models
can have a
front spoiler)

Gravel pan
Gravel shield
Front body pan
Splash pan

Center grille bar
Central division bar
Center grille molding
Center grille blade
(lower is used sometimes, too)

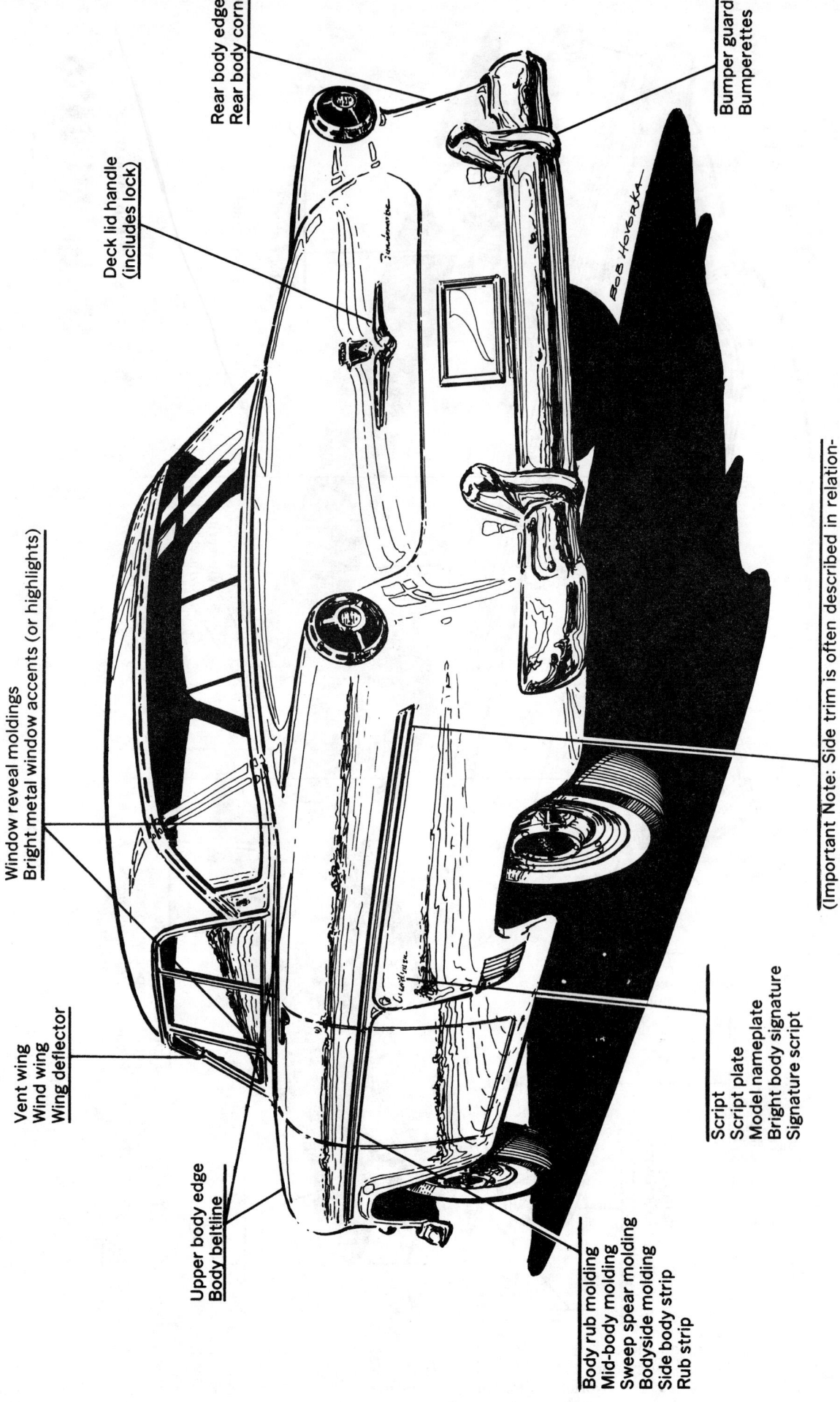

Rear body edge
Rear body corner

Bumper guards
Bumperettes

Deck lid handle
(includes lock)

Window reveal moldings
Bright metal window accents (or highlights)

Vent wing
Wind wing
Wing deflector

Upper body edge
Body beltline

Script
Script plate
Model nameplate
Bright body signature
Signature script

Body rub molding
Mid-body molding
Sweep spear molding
Bodyside molding
Side body strip
Rub strip

(Important Note: Side trim is often described in relationship to rear design elements, even though it's positioned
on the body side. For example, this mid-body molding, or
sweep spear, might be described as ending just ahead of
the rear body corner, below the taillamp)

BODY I.D. GUIDE

AMC • RAMBLER

1958-1965

In many ways the 1958 and later models of the Rambler marked a second coming of the marque.

The history of the modern Rambler goes back to 1950, when it was offered as the first successful modern compact car. In 1954, American Motors Corp. (AMC) was formed when Nash-Kelvinator and Hudson merged. Just before the start of 1958, AMC decided to discontinue Nash and Hudson. Instead, it would concentrate on selling a revised series of cars, including a new version of the original Rambler compact.

Still affectionately known as the "Nash-Rambler" and heralded as such on the 1958 record "Beep Beep" by the Playmates, the little car enjoyed a fair amount of popularity in its new "American" identity (adopted because "Rambler" had become the name of a larger, fancier model line).

Release of this "old-but-new" American was particularly well-timed. It came out immediately after a 1957 economic recession. As a result, high sales of the model increased AMC's industry market share substantially.

By Larry Daum

In 1958, AMC offerings included more than the just the American, though. The 1957 Rambler model was facelifted. It had a nine inch stretch in wheelbase and overall length. The

Ambassador was AMC's full-size car, continuing a model begun in 1932 by Nash. The Ambassador used the 327 cid V-8 formerly used in top of the line Nashes, not to be confused with the unrelated Chevrolet 327 cid engine.

AMC was the only major U.S. automaker to increase sales in the recession year of 1958. Every other make was down substantially that year. The consumer trend was to smaller cars and the Rambler was the only U.S. compact car around. AMC was at the right place at the right time.

In 1959, the two-door station wagon was revived in the American line and slight styling changes were made to the Rambler, Rebel and Ambassador models. Rambler registrations doubled for 1959, as the introduction of the Studebaker Lark went virtually unnoticed at the AMC factory in Kenosha, Wis.

Things got more competitive in 1960. New compacts were introduced by Ford, Plymouth and Chevrolet. AMC countered with a four-door American. All companies were emphasizing station wagons for 1960. AMC was right there too, with 14 of them, including three-seat models in all but the American series. As a result, AMC held its own for 1960 despite the threats from the "Big Three."

Even more competition came in 1961 as Pontiac, Oldsmobile, Buick and Dodge introduced new smaller cars. The intermediate-size models were called Rambler Classics for 1961. But the most exciting news from AMC was the completely

face-lifted Rambler American series with a four-door station wagon and a convertible added. The American and Classic series came in three levels of trim: Deluxe, Super, and Custom. The Custom Classic had an overhead valve conversion of the Nash L-head six, plus a short-lived aluminum version of the same motor.

Two things disappeared from 1962 AMCs. One was an optional 250 cid V-8 in Classics. The other was the shrinking of the 117 inch Ambassador wheelbase. It now had the 108 inch span of the Classic, but trim and upholstery differences separated the two car lines. The Super line was discontinued as a middle-market designation and "400" identification was used for a new top-of-the line model designation. Two-door sedans were added to the Classic and Ambassador series. It was the first time that Rambler offered the body style in this size car since 1957.

A two-door hardtop was added to the American Series for 1963. The Classic and Ambassador got completely new bodies. A restyling included all-new curved side glass. Wheelbases of the new models increased four inches, but overall length was shorter. Model names were revamped. Deluxe and Custom designations were replaced with numbers: American 220, 330 and 440; Classic 550, 660 and 770; and Ambassador 880 and 990.

In 1964, the Rambler American was completely restyled. It looked somewhat like Chrysler's famous turbine car. The wheelbase was increased to 106 inches. The Classic and Ambassador received a minor facelift, including new front grille and rear end designs. A special model of the Classic called the Typhoon was used to introduce AMC's new Torque-Command six-cylinder engine.

The 1965 American was little changed. Classics and Ambassadors got crisper lines in a major facelift. The Ambassador grew four inches in wheelbase and five overall. Convertibles were added to the Classic 770 and Ambassador 990 lines. Much publicity was devoted to the new Marlin, which was introduced as a midyear 1965 model and competitor to the Mustang and Barracuda. It was essentially the Classic with a fastback roof.

The Marlin and Ambassador continued in 1966, but the Rambler name was not applied to them. They were "AMC" models, now. Ads in magazines had blue and red stripes in the lower right-hand corner signifying the new brand name. The copy advised interested buyers to drive the car of their choice at their "American Motors/Rambler dealer." The rest of the AMC story continues in the next section of this catalog.

1959 Rambler, Ambassador Custom, four-door hardtop, V-8

1961 Rambler American Custom, two-door convertible, 6-cyl

1959 Rambler Custom Six, four-door Cross-Country station wagon, 6-cyl

1962 Rambler Classic, four-door sedan, 6-cyl

1959 Rambler, American Super two-door station wagon, 6-cyl

1963 Rambler Classic 660, four-door station wagon, eight-passenger, 6-cyl

Standard Catalog of American Cars

1958 RAMBLER

1958 Rambler, American two-door sedan, 6-cyl

RAMBLER AMERICAN — (6-CYL) — SERIES 01 — The 1955 Nash Rambler was brought back into production as the 1958 American, joining the model lineup in January. It had minor styling revisions. They included a small grille with a rounded-off rectangular shape and plain bodysides. A two-door sedan was the only model available and came in Super and Deluxe trim levels. The former featured bright metal windshield and beltline trim to distinguish it from Deluxes. The 195.6 cid six was used, but had the water pump moved to the front.

RAMBLER I.D. DATA: Serial number under hood on firewall's right dash panel; right-hand wheelhouse panel. Six-cylinder motor number on upper left front corner of engine block. V-8 motor number on top at front of block; or front of block; or center, left side of block, above oil pan. [American] Starting serial number M-1001 for Kenosha, Wis. Starting engine number E-1001. [Rambler Six] Starting serial number D-409001. Starting engine numbers B-145001 (standard engine); or CB9001 (power-pack engine). [Rebel] Starting Serial Number for the Rebel V-8 was A-16001. Starting engine number was G-24001. [Ambassador] Starting Serial Number for the Ambassador V-8 was V-27001. Starting engine number was N-17001.

RAMBLER AMERICAN SERIES 01

Model Number	Body/Style Number	Body Type & Seating	Factory Price	Shipping Weight	Production Total
DELUXE LINE					
01	5802	2-dr Bus Cpe-3P	1775	2439	184
01	5806	2-dr Sed-5P	1789	2463	15,765
SUPER LINE					
01	5806-1	2-dr Sed-5P	1874	2475	14,691

1958 Rambler, Super Cross Country four-door station wagon, 6-cyl

RAMBLER SIX — (6-CYL) — SERIES 10 — The Rambler Six received new front and rear fenders. It represented a major restyle of the 108 inch wheelbase Rambler body. The new front fenders featured quad headlights on all, but Deluxes, which had single headlights standard/dual optional. Several states still had laws against dual headlights. The Rambler's rear fenders featured small, restrained tailfins. This was a move towards conforming with current styling trends. The Rambler line was one of the last to add tailfins and one of the first to drop them. The Custom and Super models also featured new side trim moldings. All models had Rambler nameplates just above the grille. Custom models had Custom nameplates on the rear deck or tailgate, dual sidespear moldings on front fenders and both doors, with a single molding on the rear fenders. Sedans and hardtops had paint inside dual front moldings and wagons had simulated wood-grain trim. Super models had Super nameplates on front fenders and single full-length bodyside moldings. Deluxe models had no nameplates or side moldings. Deluxes included directional signals, hood or fender ornaments, ashtray, baked enamel colors, fuel filter, bumper jack and wheel lug wrench and hubcaps. In addition, Supers had dual horns, step-on parking brake, cigar lighter and door armrests.

RAMBLER SIX SERIES 10

Model Number	Body/Style Number	Body Type & Seating	Factory Price	Shipping Weight	Production Total
DELUXE LINE					
10	5815	4-dr Sed-6P	2047	2947	12,723
10	5818	4-dr Crs Cty Wag-6P	2376	3056	78
SUPER LINE					
10	5815-1	4-dr Sed-6P	2212	2960	29,699
10	5819-1	4-dr Cty Clb HT-6P	2287	2983	983
10	5818-1	4-dr Crs Cty Wag-6P	2506	3069	26,452
CUSTOM LINE					
10	5815-2	4-dr Sed-6P	2327	2968	16,850
10	5818-2	4-dr Crs Cty Wag-6P	2621	3079	20,131

1958 Rambler, Rebel Custom four-door hardtop sedan, V-8

RAMBLER REBEL — (V-8) — SERIES 20 — The Rebel shared the styling of the Rambler six, with the biggest difference being the powertrain. Rebel Customs carried V-8 front fender emblems. New was a deep-dip rustproofing process. A wide side trim panel with a 'half-spear-tip' front shape was used. It had a contrasting beauty insert strip. Split fin hood ornaments were used on both Rebels and Rambler sixes, while side trim of the type described above appeared on Custom models up.

RAMBLER REBEL SERIES 20

Model Number	Body/Style Number	Body Type & Seating	Factory Price	Shipping Weight	Production Total
DELUXE LINE (FLEET)					
20	4825	4-dr Sed-6P	2177	3287	22
SUPER LINE					
20	5825-1	4-dr Sed-6P	2342	3300	2,146
20	5828-1	4-dr Crs Cty Wag-6P	2636	3410	1,782
CUSTOM LINE					
20	5825-2	4-dr Sed-6P	2457	3313	2,595
20	5828-2	4-dr Crs Cty Wag-6P	2751	3418	3,101
20	5829-2	4-dr Cty Clb HT-6P	2532	3328	410

AMBASSADOR — (V-8) — SERIES 80 — The 1958 Ambassador was built off of the 108 inch Rambler chassis by adding nine inch longer front end sheet metal. The dropping of the Nash and Hudson names from the Ambassador was a last minute decision made by George Romney and American Motor's upper management. A number of cars were made with Nash and Hudson emblems ahead of the Ambassador nameplates on the sides of the front fenders. Factory photos exist which show the Nash Ambassador nameplates on these cars. Early factory literature also has noticeable airbrushing of the Nash emblems out of the catalogs. The 1958 Ambassador carried model identification just above the grille, on front fenders and on the rear deck lid. Side trim featured dual jet-stream side moldings, which were painted a contrasting color. The tone used for the insert harmonized with body colors used on Super models. Silver aluminum side trim was used inside the moldings on Custom models, which also featured model nameplates on the rear deck lid or tailgate. There were three bright metal windsplits on the rear window pillars of hardtops and sedans and on the wide pillars of station wagons. Super nameplates were on rear fenders of Super models.

AMBASSADOR SERIES 80

Model Number	Body/Style Number	Body Type & Seating	Factory Price	Shipping Weight	Production Total
SUPER LINE					
80	5885-1	4-dr Sed-6P	2587	3456	2,774
80	5888-1	4-dr Sta Wag-6P	2881	3544	1,051
CUSTOM LINE					
80	5885-2	4-dr Sed-6P	2732	3462	6,369
80	5889-2	4-dr HT Sed-6P	2822	3475	1,340
80	5888-2	4-dr Sta Wag-6P	3026	3568	2,742
80	5883-2	4-dr HT Wag-6P	3116	3586	294

BASE ENGINES

(RAMBLER AMERICAN) Inline, L-head Six: Cast iron block. Displacement: 195.6 cid. Bore and stroke: 3-1/8 x 4-1/4 inches. Compression ratio: 8.0:1. Brake hp: 90 at 3800 rpm. Four main bearings. Solid valve lifters. Carburetor: Carter Type YF-2014S one-barrel.

(AMBASSADOR) V-8: Overhead valves. Cast iron block. Displacement: 327 cid. Bore and stroke: 4 x 3-1/4 inches. Compression ratio: 9.7:1. Brake hp: 270 at 4700 rpm. Five main bearings. Hydraulic valve lifters. Carburetor: Holley four-barrel Model 4150C.

(RAMBLER SIX) Inline Six: Overhead valves. Cast iron block. Displacement: 195.6 cid. Bore and stroke: 3-1/8 x 4-1/4 inches. Compression ratio: 8.7:1. Brake hp: 127 at 4200 rpm. Four main bearings. Solid valve lifters. Carburetor: Carter Type YF one-barrel Model 2014S.

(REBEL V-8 ENGINE) V-8: Overhead valves. Cast iron block. Displacement: 250 cid. Bore and stroke: 3-1/2 x 3-1/4 inches. Compression ratio: 8.7:1. Brake hp: 215 at 4900 rpm. Five main bearings. Solid valve lifters. Carburetor: Holley four-barrel Model 4150C.

CHASSIS FEATURES: Wheelbase: (American) 100 inches; (Rambler and Rebel) 108 inches; (Ambassador) 117 inches. Overall length: (American) 178.32 inches; (Rambler and Rebel) 191.14 inches; (Ambassador) 200.14 inches. Add 7.75 inches to overall length for Rambler and Ambassador with continental tire carrier. Front tread: (American) 54.62 inches; (Rambler and Ambassador) 57.75 inches; (Rebel) 58.75 inches. Rear tread: (American) 55 inches; (Rambler) 58 inches; (Rebel and Ambassador) 59.13 inches. Tires: (American) 5.90 x 15; (Rambler six) 6.40 x 15; (Rambler Rebel) 7.50 x 14; (Ambassador) 8.00 x 14.

OPTIONS: Power brakes ($38). Power steering ($85). Air conditioning ($369). Weather-Eye heater ($72). Tinted glass ($27). Wheel discs ($16). Rearview mirror ($4). Two-tone paint ($16). Continental tire ($60). Undercoating ($15). Oil filter ($9). Reclining seat ($15). Whitewall

tires ($40). Manual radio ($58). Clock ($18). Deluxe push-button radio ($90). Rear foam cushion. Left outside rearview mirror. Custom steering wheel. Heavy-duty rear springs and shocks. Windshield washer. Ambassador V-8 Power Saver fan. Power windows. Back-O-Matic lights. Inside anti-glare mirror. Heavy-duty springs and shock absorbers. Padded instrument panel and sun visor. Dealer accessories: Seat belts. Travel rack straps. Child guard door locks. Three-speed manual transmission was standard. Overdrive transmission ($112.50). Flash-O-Matic transmission ($200). Push-button Flash-O-Matic transmission ($219.50). Rambler "Power-Pack" 195.6 cid/138 hp two-barrel engine. Dual exhausts ($18.50). Positive traction rear axle ($39.50). Oil bath air cleaner ($7.15). Heavy-duty radiator ($19.85). Available rear axle gear ratios (standard) 4.10:1; (optional) 4.44:1; 3.55:1 and 3.15:1. Size 6.40 x 15 tires for American.

HISTORICAL FOOTNOTES: The full-sized Ramblers were introduced Oct. 22, 1957 and the American appeared in dealer showrooms the same day. Model year production peaked at 162,182 units. Calendar year sales of 199,236 cars were recorded. George Romney was the chief executive officer of the company this year. R.D. Chapin was executive vice president and general manager of the automotive division. The company made a $26 million profit after two straight years of losses. An expansion program was initiated by year's end.

1959 RAMBLER

1959 Rambler, American two-door sedan, 6-cyl

RAMBLER AMERICAN — (6-CYL) — SERIES 01 — The American continued as a compact model with the smooth, rounded styling that dated to 1954. There were front fender namescripts, but no side moldings were seen. The grille had a rectangular shape and was surrounded by a chrome housing with rounded corners. A fine, grid type insert was used, the vertical members looking slightly more prominent. A round medallion was housed in the center. Super models had bright metal trim around the windshield and rear window. A chrome molding decorated the upper beltline. Deluxes had black rubber windshield and rear window trim and lacked belt moldings. A handful of panel deliveries were built off the station wagon platform. One style had glass rear side windows, the second had metal panels in the same location. The Super two-door sedan was rated for one more passenger than other non-commercial models.

RAMBLER I.D. DATA: Serial number under hood on firewall right dash panel; right-hand wheelhouse panel. Six-cylinder motor number on upper left front corner of engine block. V-8 motor number on top at front of block; or front of block; or center, left side of block, above oil pan. [American] Starting serial number M-32001 for Kenosha, Wis. Starting engine number E-33001. [Rambler Six] Starting serial number D-516001. Starting engine numbers B-227001 (standard engine); or CB36001 (power-pack engine). [Rebel] Starting Serial Number for the Rebel V-8 was A-26001. Starting engine number was G-34501. [Ambassador] Starting Serial Number for the Ambassador V-8 was V-41501. Starting engine number was N-32501.

RAMBLER AMERICAN SERIES 01

Model Number	Body/Style Number	Body Type & Seating	Factory Price	Shipping Weight	Production Total
PANEL DELIVERY LINE					
01	5904-7	2-dr Glass Dly	—	—	3
01	5904-8	2-dr Steel Dly	—	—	3
DELUXE LINE					
01	5902	2-dr Bus Sed-5P	1821	2435	443
01	5904	2-dr Sta Wag-5P	2060	2554	15,256
01	5906	2-dr Sed-5P	1835	2476	29,954
SUPER LINE					
01	5904-1	2-dr Sta Wag-5P	2145	2570	17,383
01	5906-1	2-dr Sed-6P	1920	2492	28,449

RAMBLER SIX — (6-CYL) — SERIES 10 — Rambler had new grilles, new arrangements of side trim and re-contoured rear tailfins. The new fender treatment blended the fins into the upper beltline in a smooth, down-curving line. On all models, a horizontal gap ran above the upper grille bar and between the dual headlamps. Stand-up chrome letters spelling the word Rambler appeared in the gap. The manufacturer's name also decorated the deck lid tailgate. Custom models had Custom nameplates at the front of the rear missile-shaped side molding. A narrower, straight molding extended along the upper bodyside from just behind the headlamps to the missile-shaped molding. Super models had Super nameplates within the tip of the 'missile.' On these cars the straight front molding stopped just beyond the middle of the front door, without hitting the rear trim. Deluxes had no series nameplates or side trim and dual headlamps were optional. The lower grille insert was of cellular-grid design.

RAMBLER SIX SERIES 10

Model Number	Body/Style Number	Body Type & Seating	Factory Price	Shipping Weight	Production Total
DELUXE LINE					
10	5915	4-dr Sed-6P	2098	2934	26,157
10	5918	4-dr Crs Cty Wag-6P	2427	3047	422
SUPER LINE					
10	5915-1	4-dr Sed-6P	2268	2951	72,577
10	5919-1	4-dr HT Sed-6P	2343	2961	2,683
10	5918-1	4-dr Crs Cty Wag-6P	2562	3082	66,739
CUSTOM LINE					
10	5915-2	4-dr Sed-6P	2383	2956	35,242
10	5918-2	4-dr Crs Cty Wag-6P	2677	3097	38,761

1959 Rambler, Rebel Custom four-door sedan, V-8

RAMBLER REBEL — (V-8) — SERIES 20 — The Rebel shared the same body styling features as the Rambler six. The major external difference was that the Custom models had Rebel V-8 emblems on the front fenders, ahead of the wheel openings. The scripts placed within the missile-shaped rear molding panel carried the name of the trim line, except on the plain-looking Deluxes, which had no script.

RAMBLER REBEL V-8 SERIES 20

Model Number	Body/Style Number	Body Type & Seating	Factory Price	Shipping Weight	Production Total
DELUXE LINE					
20	5925	4-dr Sed-6P	2228	3283	113
SUPER LINE					
20	5925-1	4-dr Sed-6P	2398	3287	3,488
20	5928-1	4-dr Crs Cty Wag-6P	2692	3398	3,634
CUSTOM LINE					
20	5925-2	4-dr Sed-6P	2513	3295	4,046
20	5929-2	4-dr HT Sed-6P	2588	3338	691
20	5928-2	4-dr Crs Cty Wag-6P	2807	3407	4,427

AMBASSADOR EIGHT — (V-8) — SERIES 80 — The 1959 Ambassador retained the same basic styling seen in 1958, with changes being comparable to those seen on Rambler and Rambler Rebel. The wide gap above the upper grille bar had Ambassador spelled out in stand-up block letters. Similar lettering appeared on the deck lid or tailgate. Custom models had silver aluminum trim inside dual side moldings. ScotchLite reflecting sections were found on the rear face of the back fenders. The four-door hardtop had Custom Country Club written on the rear fender tips. Other cars, depending on trim line, read Custom or Super in the same spot. The front of the side trim spear had Ambassador lettering at its tip. The side trim, although similar to the Rambler type, had more of a lightning bolt shape than a missile shape. The upper molding 'zigged' (but the lower molding did not 'zag') upwards, just below the rear side window. The Ambassador grille was distinctive in that it had a full-width horizontal central bar, instead of a cellular grid type insert. The bar had a V-shaped dip at its center.

1959 Rambler, Ambassador four-door hardtop sedan, V-8

AMBASSADOR EIGHT SERIES 80

Model Number	Body/Style Number	Body Type & Seating	Factory Price	Shipping Weight	Production Total
DELUXE LINE					
20	5985	4-dr Sed-6P	—	3428	155
SUPER LINE					
20	5985-1	4-dr Sed-6P	2587	3428	4,675
20	5988-1	4-dr Crs Cty Wag-6P	2881	3546	1,782

CUSTOM LINE

20	5985-2	4-dr Sed-6P	2732	3437	10,791
20	5989-2	4-dr Cty Clb HT-6P	2822	3483	1,447
20	5988-2	4-dr Cty Clb HT Wag-6P	3026	3562	4,341
20	5983-2	4-dr Crs Cty Wag-6P	3116	3591	578

BASE ENGINES

(RAMBLER AMERICAN) Inline, L-head Six: Cast iron block. Displacement: 195.6 cid. Bore and stroke: 3-1/8 x 4-1/4 inches. Compression ratio: 8.0:1. Brake hp: 90 at 3800 rpm. Four main bearings. Solid valve lifters. Carburetor: Carter Type YF-2014S one-barrel.

(RAMBLER SIX) Inline Six: Overhead valves. Cast iron block. Displacement: 195.6 cid. Bore and stroke: 3-1/8 x 4-1/4 inches. Compression ratio: 8.7:1. Brake hp: 127 at 4200 rpm. Four main bearings. Solid valve lifters. Carburetor: Carter Type YF one-barrel Model 2014S.

(REBEL V-8 ENGINE) V-8: Overhead valves. Cast iron block. Displacement: 250 cid. Bore and stroke: 3-1/2 x 3-1/4 inches. Compression ratio: 8.7:1. Brake hp: 215 at 4900 rpm. Five main bearings. Solid valve lifters. Carburetor: Holley four-barrel Model 4150C.

(AMBASSADOR) V-8: Overhead valves. Cast iron block. Displacement: 327 cid. Bore and stroke: 4 x 3-1/4 inches. Compression ratio: 9.7:1. Brake hp: 270 at 4700 rpm. Five main bearings. Hydraulic valve lifters. Carburetor: Holley four-barrel Model 4150C.

CHASSIS FEATURES: Wheelbase: (American) 100 inches, (Rambler/Rebel) 108 inches; (Ambassador) 117 inches. Overall length: (American) 178.32 inches; (Rambler/Rebel) 191.15 inches; (Ambassador) 200.15 inches. Front tread: (American) 54.62 inches; (Rambler/Ambassador) 57.75 inches; (Rebel) 58.75 inches. Tires: (American station wagon) 6.40 x 15; (American passenger car) 5.90 x 15; (Rambler six) 6.40 x 15; (Rebel V-8) 7.50 x 14; (Ambassador) 8.00 x 14.

OPTIONS

(AMERICAN): Weather-Eye heater ($72). Oil-bath cleaner ($7.15). Oil filter ($9.30). Solex glass ($26.95). Front or rear foam seat cushions ($9.95). Reclining seat ($14.95). Manual radio and antenna with single speaker ($57.70). Size 5.90 x 15, four-ply rayon tires on sedans ($32.50); size 6.40 x 15 four-ply rayon tires on sedans ($52.80); size 6.40 x 15 four-ply rayon tires on station wagons ($36.05). Undercoating ($14.95). Windshield washer ($11). Wheel discs ($15.25). Electric clock ($15.25). Outside rearview mirror ($3.95). Inside tilt mirror ($4.95). Custom steering wheel ($7.70). Heavy-duty springs and shocks ($4.00). Two-tone paint on sedans ($15.95). Two-tone paint on station wagons ($17.95). Continental tire carrier ($59.50). Heavy-duty cooling system ($12.50). Three-speed manual transmission was standard. Overdrive transmission, in American ($102). Flash-O-Matic automatic transmission, in American ($179)).

RAMBLER/REBEL: Flash-O-Matic push-button transmission with Rambler six ($199.50); with Rebel V-8 ($219.50). Overdrive ($112.50). Power steering with Rambler six ($69.50); with Rebel V-8 ($79.50). Power windows lifts ($99.50). Power brakes ($37.95). Oil filter ($9.75). Oil bath air cleaner on Rambler six ($7.50). Radio with manual antenna and single speaker ($75.65); with dual speaker ($86.40). Weather-Eye heater and ventilator ($76). Size 6.40 x 15 four-ply tires on Rambler six ($35.90); six 6.70 x 15 four-ply tires on Rambler six ($48.30); size 7.50 x 14 four-ply tires on Rebel ($39.90). Wheel discs ($15.95). Two-tone paint on Deluxe sedans ($16.95); on Super sedans ($18.95); on Custom sedans ($22.95); on Super wagons ($18.95); on Custom wagons ($29.95) and on station wagon solid with Di-Noc ($49.95). Solex tinted glass ($33). Backup lights ($9.95). Continental tire carrier ($69.50). Front or rear foam cushion ($12.50). Reclining front seat ($25.50). Windshield washer ($11.50). Electric clock ($15.95). Padded instrument panel with visors ($19.95). Rambler six power pack ($19.50). Undercoating ($14.95). Left or right headrests ($12). Air conditioning ($369). Rambler Rebel V-8 Power-Lok differential ($39.50). Inside rearview mirror ($4.95). Outside rearview mirror ($5.25). Rebel dual exhausts ($15.50). Deluxe six-cylinder dual headlights ($23.50). Rear air coil suspension ($98.50). Self-adjusting brakes ($7.45). Three-speed manual transmission was standard. Overdrive transmission, in American ($102); all other models ($113). Flash-O-Matic automatic transmission, in American ($179); in Rambler six ($200); in Rebel V-8 ($220); in Ambassador ($230). Two-barrel carburetor, in Rambler six ($20). Power-Lok positive traction rear axle, in Rambler ($40); in Ambassador ($43). Heavy-duty air cleaner, in Rambler six ($8); in Ambassador (standard). Optional rear axle gear ratios available at no extra charge.

AMBASSADOR: Flash-O-Matic push-button transmission ($229.50). Overdrive ($114.50). Power steering ($89.50). Power window lifts ($99.50). Power brakes ($39.95). Radio and antenna with dual speakers ($91.90); on station wagons ($87.10). Weather-Eye heater and ventilator ($82.50). Size 8 x 15 four-ply rayon tires ($43.55); size 8 x 15 four-ply nylon tires ($67.30). Wheel discs ($16.95). Two-tone paint on Super and Custom ($22.95). Solid with Di-Noc on station wagons ($59.95). Solex tinted glass ($33). Backup lights ($9.95). Continental tire carrier ($76.50). Rear foam cushion ($14.35). Reclining front seat ($25.50). Windshield washer ($11.50). Electric clock ($17.95). Padded instrument panel and visors ($19.95). Undercoating ($14.95). Air conditioning ($398). Power-Lok differential ($42.50). Inside rearview mirror ($4.95). Outside rearview mirror ($5.25). Power-Saver fan ($19.50). Heavy-duty radiator ($8). Self-adjusting brakes ($7.45). Heavy-duty cooling system ($19.85). Dual exhausts ($18.50). Adjustable front seats ($20). Left and right headrests ($24). Three-speed manual transmission was standard. Power-Lok positive traction rear axle ($43). Heavy-duty air cleaner standard in Ambassador. Optional rear axle gear ratios available at no extra charge.

HISTORICAL FOOTNOTES: The full-sized Ramblers were introduced Oct. 8, 1958 and the Americans appeared in dealer showrooms the same day. Model year production peaked at 374,240 units. Calendar year sales of 401,446 cars were recorded. George Romney was the chief executive officer of the company this year. A record profit of $60,341,823 was earned. Rambler qualified as America's fourth-ranked maker. Resale value on Ramblers was considered high at this time, a point Rambler salesmen often stressed. America was in a recession and a small economy car trend had begun. Rambler benefited greatly, achieving net sales of $869,849,704.

1960 RAMBLER

RAMBLER AMERICAN — (6-CYL) — SERIES 01 — Annual styling revisions included removal of upper beltline moldings from below the windows of all Americans. A new four-door sedan was introduced in this series. A rooftop luggage rack was standard on the station wagons. A minor change was an increase in the door opening angle, from 55- to 75-degrees. Supers had a horizontal front spear on the doors and fenders and American front fender scripts. Customs had a similar chrome spear and, like Supers, used chrome windshield and rear window surrounds. Deluxe models had no side trim or bright metal window surrounds. Custom, Super or Deluxe scripts appeared at the rear of all cars and all had either American or Rambler American scripts on the front fendersides.

RAMBLER I.D. DATA: VIN on plate on right wheelhouse panel below hood. First symbol identified series: A=Rebel V-8; B=American; C=Rambler; H=Ambassador. Second through fifth symbols were sequential production number. Starting serial numbers were: [American] B-100001; [American for knocked-down export] BK-10001; [Rambler] C-100001; [Rambler for knocked-down export] CK-10001; [Rebel V-8] A-100001 and [Rebel V-8 for knocked-down export] AK-10001; [Ambassador V-8] H-100001; [Ambassador V-8 for knocked-down export]. for Ambassador V-8, HK-10001 for Ambassador V-8 for unassembled export. Body number plate riveted to left front door hinge pillar has additional data. First line indicates body production sequence number. Second line indicates "Model No." consisting of first two symbols indicating model year and additional symbols indicating body style and series. Complete "Model No." corresponds to column two of charts below. Third line gives trim data. Fourth line gives paint color data. Six-cylinder motor number on upper left front corner of engine block. V-8 motor number on top at front of block; or front of block; or center, left side of block, above oil pan. Starting in late 1959 for the 1960 model year, AMC discontinued engine serial numbers. An "Engine Day Build Code" system gave all engines of a type the same six symbol code. The first symbol of the engine day built code is a single digit number code for the year of manufacture starting with 1=1959; 2=1960; 3=1961; 4=1962; 5=1963; 6=1964; 7=1965; etc. The second and third symbols indicated month of build: 01=Jan.; 02=Feb.; etc. The numbers differed in the fourth symbol, a letter code designating the engine displacement and carburetion. Letter codes were: A=195.6cid/90 hp L-head six; B=195.6 cid/127 hp aluminum OHV six; C=195.6 cid/127 hp cast-iron OHV six; D=195.6 cid/138 hp six 2V; E=327 cid/250 hp V-8 2V; F=327 cid/270 hp V-8 4V; G="287" engine. The fifth and sixth symbols indicated day of manufacture as appropriate. In motor number 201A22: first symbol 2=1960; 01=Jan.; A=195.6 cid/90 hp six and 22=22nd day of month.

RAMBLER AMERICAN SERIES 01

Model Number	Body/Style Number	Body Type & Seating	Factory Price	Shipping Weight	Production Total
DELUXE LINE					
01	6005	4-dr Sed-5P	1844	2474	22,593
01	6006	2-dr Sed-5P	1795	2451	23,960
01	6004	2-dr Sta Wag-5P	2020	2527	12,290
01	6002	2-dr Bus Cpe-3P	1781	2428	630
SUPER LINE					
01	6005-1	4-dr Sed-6P	1929	2490	21,108
01	6006-1	2-dr Sed-5P	1880	2462	17,233
01	6004-1	2-dr Sta Wag-6P	2105	2549	15,093
CUSTOM LINE					
01	6005-2	4-dr Sed-6P	2059	2551	3,272
01	6006-2	2-dr Sed-5P	2010	2523	2,994
01	6004-2	2-dr Sta Wag-5P	2235	2606	1,430

RAMBLER SIX — (6-CYL) — SERIES 10 — The Rambler's tailfins were lowered and canted out slightly. A convex lower rear fender contour was new. The Rambler grille was redesigned. It had two rows of 'cells' in its gridwork, instead of three. Stand-up chrome letters still spelled out Rambler in the horizontal space between the head lamps, above the grille. The word Rambler was also on the rear. Customs had a suitable script on the rear also, plus full-length trim moldings that widened into dual moldings between the wheel housings. Supers had different model identifying scripts at the rear and full-length side trim moldings. Deluxe models had a suitable rear scripts, but no side trim. Dual headlamps were optional on Deluxes. On all lines, the twin fin hood ornaments of the past were gone and were not replaced.

RAMBLER SIX SERIES 10

Model Number	Body/Style Number	Body Type & Seating	Factory Price	Shipping Weight	Production Total
DELUXE LINE					
10	6015	4-dr Sed-6P	2098	2912	37,666
10	6018	4-dr Sta Wag-6P	2427	3051	24,001
SUPER LINE					
10	6015-1	4-dr Sed-6P	2268	2930	88,004
10	6018-1	4-dr Sta Wag-6P	2562	3054	59,491
10	6018-3	4-dr Sta Wag-8P	2687	3117	8,456
CUSTOM LINE					
10	6015-2	4-dr Sed-6P	2883	2929	38,003
10	6910-2	4-dr HT Sed-6P	2458	2981	3,937
10	6018-2	4-dr Sta Wag-6P	2677	3057	32,092
10	6018-4	4-dr Sta Wag-8P	2802	3137	5,718

1960 Rambler, Custom Country Club four-door hardtop, 6-cyl

RAMBLER REBEL — (V-8) — SERIES 20 — Rebels had the same general styling changes as Rambler sixes. They included lower, canted fins; convex rear fenders; grille with two rows of cellular grids; side trim revisions; and deletion of hood ornaments. Rambler sales features for 1960 included single unit-body construction; deep-dip rustproofing; deep coil spring ride; self-adjusting brakes (optional); push-button automatic gear shift selection (optional); and optional 'Air Liner' reclining seats. Rebel V-8 emblems appeared on front fenders again this year. A new base powerplant was used. The former 215 hp four-barrel V-8 (with standard dual exhausts) became optional. A number of Ramblers were built for export this year. These cars were shipped overseas in completely knocked-down (CKD) form, or in other words, unassembled. This meant that the importing country was providing employment for workers who would assemble the cars there. Such cars had a two symbol alphabetical serial number prefix, with the second letter 'K' indicating 'CKD' sales.

RAMBLER REBEL V-8 SERIES 20

Model Number	Body/Style Number	Body Type & Seating	Factory Price	Shipping Weight	Production Total
DELUXE LINE					
20	6025	4-dr Flt Sed-6P	2217	3252	143
SUPER LINE					
20	6025-1	4-dr Sed-6P	2387	3270	3,826
20	6028-1	4-dr Sta Wag-6P	2681	3391	3,328
20	6028-3	4-dr Sta Wag-8P	2806	3446	718
CUSTOM LINE					
20	6025-2	4-dr Sed-6P	2502	3278	3,969
20	6029-2	4-dr HT Sed-6P	2577	3319	579
20	6028-2	4-dr Sta Wag-6P	2796	3395	3,613
20	6028-4	4-dr Sta Wag-8P	2921	3447	886

1960 Rambler, Ambassador Country Club four-door HT, V-8

AMBASSADOR SERIES — (V-8) — SERIES 80 — On the top line series the letters above the grille spelled Ambassador, a name which appeared on the deck lid or tailgate as well. This series featured the new compound wraparound windshield and a distinctive grille design. Fashioned of aluminum, the lower insert ran fully across the car with a pattern of medium sized square openings stamped out of the metal. Bombsight style front fender ornaments were seen. Side trim consisted of dual moldings running in a tapering line from the middle of the extreme rear body corner and coming to a point just in back of the dual headlamps. On Customs an aluminum beauty panel insert was placed within the moldings and, on all models, the word Ambassador appeared at the tip. In addition, scripts placed on the deck lid of passenger models or tailgate of station wagons identified Supers or Customs. Foam rear seat cushions; full wheel discs; electric clock; padded dashboard and padded sun visors were standard on Customs. A cheap Deluxe sedan was built in limited numbers for fleet use only and not cataloged with regular cars.

AMBASSADOR EIGHT SERIES 80

Model Number	Body/Style Number	Body Type & Seating	Factory Price	Shipping Weight	Production Total
DELUXE LINE					
80	6085	4-dr Flt Sed-6P	2395	3384	302
SUPER LINE					
80	6085-1	4-dr Sed-6P	2587	3395	3,990
80	6088-1	4-dr Sta Wag-6P	2881	3531	1,342
80	6088-3	4-dr Sta Wag-8P	3006	3581	637
CUSTOM LINE					
80	6085-2	4-dr Sed-6P	2732	3408	10,949
80	6089-2	4-dr Cty Clb HT-6P	2822	3465	1,141
80	6088-2	4-dr Sta Wag-6P	3026	3538	3,849
80	6083-2	4-dr Cty Clb HT Wag-6P	3116	3583	435
80	6088-4	4-dr Sta Wag-8P	3151	3592	1,153

BASE ENGINES

(RAMBLER AMERICAN) Inline, L-head Six: Cast iron block. Displacement: 195.6 cid. Bore and stroke: 3-1/8 x 4-1/4 inches. Compression ratio: 8.0:1. Brake hp: 90 at 3800 rpm. Four main bearings. Solid valve lifters. Carburetor: Carter Type YF-2014S one-barrel.

(RAMBLER SIX) Inline Six: Overhead valves. Cast iron block. Displacement: 195.6 cid. Bore and stroke: 3-1/8 x 4-1/4 inches. Compression ratio: 8.7:1. Brake hp: 127 at 4200 rpm. Four main bearings. Solid valve lifters. Carburetor: Holley model 1904-FC one-barrel.

(REBEL V-8) V-8: Overhead valves. Cast iron block. Displacement: 250 cid. Bore and stroke: 3-1/2 x 3/1-4 inches. Compression ratio: 8.7:1. Brake hp: 200 at 4900 rpm. Five main bearings. Hydraulic valve lifters. Carburetor: Holley model 2040 two-barrel.

(AMBASSADOR EIGHT) V-8: Overhead valves. Cast iron block. Displacement: 327 cid. Bore and stroke: 4 x 3-1/4 inches. Compression ratio: 8.7:1. Brake hp: 250 at 4700 rpm. Five main bearings. Hydraulic valve lifters. Carburetor: Holley model 2040 two-barrel.

CHASSIS FEATURES: Wheelbase: (Rambler/Rebel) 108 inches; (American) 100 inches; (Ambassador) 117 inches. Overall length: (American) 178.32 inches; (Rambler/Rebel) 189.5 inches; (Ambassador) 198.5 inches. Front tread: (Rambler/Rebel) 58.75 inches; (Ambassador) 57.75 inches. Rear tread: (Rambler/Rebel) 59.13 inches; (Ambassador) 59.13 inches. Tires: (American standard passenger car) 5.90 x 15; (American Custom and station wagon) 6.40 x 15; (Rambler six) 6.40 x 15; (Rambler Rebel) 7.50 x 14; (Ambassador) 8.00 x 14.

OPTIONS

AMERICAN: Anti-freeze ($3.80). Two-tone color on sedans ($15.95); on station wagons ($17.95); special application (except Fleet) ($29.50). Overdrive transmission ($102). Lever control Flash-O-Matic transmission ($178.50). Weather-Eye ($72). Power steering ($69.50). Oil bath air cleaner ($7.15). Oil filter ($9.30). Solex glass ($26.95). Front and rear Deluxe foam rubber seat cushions ($19.90); front only ($9.95); rear only ($9.95). Reclining seat ($14.65). Manual radio and antenna ($57.70). Size 5.90 x 15 four-ply rayon white sidewall tires on sedans ($27.40); size 6.40 x 15 four-ply rayon white sidewall tires on sedans ($44.45); size 6.40 x 15 four-ply nylon white sidewall tires on sedans ($60.80) size 6.40 x 15 four-ply rayon white sidewall tires on sedans ($30.35); size 6.40 x 15 four-ply nylon white sidewall tires on wagons ($46.70). Undercoating ($14.95). Windshield washer ($11). Back-up lights ($9.95); Wheel discs ($15.25). Electric clock ($15.25). Continental tire carrier on sedans ($59.50). Self-adjusting brakes ($7.45). Inside "tilt" rearview mirror ($4.95). Outside left or right rearview mirror ($3.95); left and right ($7.90). Custom steering wheel ($7.70). Twin-Grip differential ($29.50). Pair of license plate frames ($4.05); rear only ($2.05). Heavy-duty front and rear shocks ($2.70). Heavy-duty front and rear shocks and rear springs ($4). Heavy-duty radiator ($3.00). Heavy-duty cooling system ($12.50). Three-speed manual transmission was standard. Overdrive transmission ($102). Automatic transmission ($179). Custom American six-cylinder 195.6 cid 125 hp two-barrel engine. Heavy-duty air cleaner. Available rear axle gear ratios.

RAMBLER/REBEL: Flash-O-Matic push-button transmission on Rambler six ($199.50); on Rebel V-8 ($219.50). Overdrive ($112.50). Power steering on Rambler six ($69.50); on Rebel V-8 ($79.50). Power windows lifts ($99.50). Power brakes ($37.95). Oil filter ($9.75). Oil-bath air cleaner on Rambler six ($7.50). Radio with manual antenna and single speaker ($75.65); with dual speaker ($86.40). Weather-Eye heater and ventilator ($76). Solex tinted glass ($33). Back-up lights ($9.95). Continental tire carrier ($69.50). Front or rear foam cushion ($12.50); reclining front seat ($25.50). Windshield washer ($11.50). Electric clock ($15.95). Padded instrument panel and visors ($19.95). Undercoating ($14.95). Left or right headrests ($12). Air conditioning ($369). Inside rearview mirror ($4.95). Outside rearview mirror ($5.25). Deluxe six-cylinder dual headlights ($23.50). Rear air coil suspension ($98.50). Self-adjusting: brakes ($7.45). Wheel discs ($15.95). Twin grip differential on six-cylinder ($34.50); on V-8 ($39.50). Parking brake warning light ($3.95). Light package including trunk or cargo, two courtesy, parking and brake warning lights) ($9.95). Two-tone paint on sedans, except Custom ($19.95); two-tone paint on Custom ($24.95); two-tone paint on wagons except Custom ($21.95); two-tone paint on Custom wagons ($29.95); solid with Di-Noc ($59.95). Power Pak on six-cylinder ($19.50); on V-8 ($37.50). Size 6.40 x 15 rayon white sidewall four-ply tires on six-cylinder except three-seat wagon ($30.30); Size 6.40 x 15 nylon ($46.70); size 6.70 x 15 rayon ($40.50). Size 7.50 x 14 white sidewall four-ply V-8 except three-seat wagon ($32.10); size 7.50 x 14 nylon ($49.15). Size 6.40 x 15 nylon white sidewall four-ply Captive Air for three-seat wagons on six-cylinder ($28.10); size 7.50 x 14 nylon four-ply on V-8 ($29.50). Three-speed manual transmission was standard. Overdrive transmission ($113). Automatic transmission ($200). Rebel V-8 250 cid 215 hp four-barrel engine ($80). Positive traction rear axle available at extra cost. Heavy-duty air cleaner available on some as standard equipment; others as extra cost. Available rear axle gear ratios.

AMBASSADOR: Overdrive transmission ($114.50). Push-button Flash-O-Matic transmission ($229.50). Power Pack ($229.50). Weather-Eye ($37.50). Air conditioning and heavy-duty cooling system ($398.00). Power brakes ($39.95). Power steering ($89.50). Power window lifts ($99.50). Solex glass ($99.50). Front foam rubber seat cushions ($14.35). Rear foam rubber seat cushions ($14.35). Reclining seat ($25.50). Left and right headrests ($24). Left or right headrest ($12). Individually adjustable front seats ($20). Radio and antenna with front speakers for wagons ($75.65); for sedans ($91.90). Size 8.00 x 14 white sidewall rayon four-ply tires for station wagons (except three-seat wagon) ($35.25); size 8.00 x 14 white sidewall nylon four-ply ($54.15); Captive Air nylon tires, size 8.00 x 14 white sidewall (four tires) ($113.70); Size 8.00 x 14 white sidewall (five tires) ($169.45); size 8.00 x 14 (four) white sidewall for three-seat wagons ($32.40). Undercoating ($14.95). Windshield washer ($11.50). Back-up lights ($9.95). Wheel discs ($16.95). Electric clock ($16.95). Parking brake warning light ($3.95). Padded instrument panel and sun visors ($19.95). Self-adjusting brakes ($7.45). Inside "tilt" rearview mirror ($4.95). Left or right outside rearview mirror ($5.25); left and right outside rearview mirror ($10.50). Power-Saver fan ($19.50). Twin-Grip differential ($42.50). Pair of license plate frames ($4.05); rear only ($2.05). Light package ($9.95). Heavy-duty front and rear shocks ($3.80). Heavy-duty front and rear shocks and front springs with heavy-duty rear springs in sedans ($5.00). Extra heavy-duty springs in sedans ($7.25). Heavy-duty rear springs on wagon ($6.50). Air-Coil ride rear suspension ($98.50). Heavy-duty radiator ($8.00). Heavy-duty cooling system ($19.85). Two-tone, Deluxe sedans ($22.95); two-tone, Super and Custom sedans ($24.95); two-tone, Super and Custom wagons ($29.95); solid paint with Di-Noc on wagons ($59.95). Three-speed manual transmission was standard. Overdrive transmission ($115). Automatic transmission. Ambassador V-8 327 cid 270 hp four-barrel engine ($90). Positive traction rear axle available at extra cost. Heavy-duty air cleaner available on some as standard equipment; others as extra cost. Available rear axle gear ratios.

HISTORICAL FOOTNOTES: The 1960 Ramblers were introduced Oct. 14, 1959. Model year production peaked at 458,841 units. Calendar year sales of 485,745 cars were recorded. George Romney was the chief executive officer of the company this year. Annual sales topped the billion dollar mark for the first time in the company's six-year history. A new lakefront body plant was constructed for 1961 assemblies. Of all 1960 Ramblers built, 49.4 percent had automatic transmission; 8.9 percent had V-8 engines; 9.4 percent had power brakes; 0.4 percent had power windows; 7.5 percent had tinted glass; 3.8 percent had air-conditioning; 1.6 percent had dual exhausts; and 14.6 percent used overdrive transmissions.

1961 RAMBLER

1961 Rambler, American two-door convertible, 6-cyl

RAMBLER AMERICAN — (6-CYL) — SERIES 01 — America's recognized economy king was all new in style and beauty for 1961. The American was even more compact than ever and easier to park. Features included all welded, single unit construction, deep-dip rustproofing and a ceramic armored muffler and tailpipe guaranteed to the original owner for the life of the car. Styling features included a new trapezoidal grille insert. It was made of perforated aluminum lattice work. The hood carried a stand-up 'R' ornament. The simple rear end design featured circular taillamps and optional round back-up lamps. A new body style was a two-door convertible. Standard equipment on Deluxe models included air cleaner; front

armrests; front ashtray; cigar lighter; dual sun visors; turn signals; black floor mats; black rubber cargo mats on wagons; and black tubeless tires. Super models had all of the above, plus rear door armrests; rear ashtray; colored rubber mats on wagons; colored floor mats; automatic dome switches on front doors; station wagon travel rack; front foam cushion; and chrome horn ring. Custom models had all of the above plus oil- bath air cleaner; colored carpet on station wagons; dual horn; two-tone steering wheel; and wheel discs.

RAMBLER I.D. DATA: VIN on plate on right wheelhouse panel below hood. First symbol identified series: A=Rebel V-8; B=American; C=Rambler; H=Ambassador. Second through last symbols were sequential production number. Starting serial numbers were: [American] B-221001; [American for knocked-down export] CK-10701; [Rambler] C-400001; [Rambler for knocked-down export] CK-10401; [Rebel V-8] A-118001 and [Rebel V-8 for knocked-down export] AK-10001; [Ambassador V-8] H-125001; [Ambassador V-8 for knocked-down export]. for Ambassador V-8, HK-10001 for Ambassador V-8 for unassembled export. Body number plate riveted to left front door hinge pillar has additional data. First line indicates body production sequence number. Second line indicates "Model No." consisting of first two symbols indicating model year and additional symbols indicating body style and series. Complete "Model No." corresponds to column two of charts below. Third line gives trim data. Fourth line gives paint color data. Six-cylinder motor number on upper left front corner of engine block. V-8 motor number on top at front of block; or front of block; or center, left side of block, above oil pan. Continuing in 1961, AMC employed an "Engine Day Build Code" system giving all engines of a type the same six symbol code. The first symbol of the engine day built code is a single digit number code for the year of manufacture starting with 3=1961. The second and third symbols indicated month of build: 01=Jan.; 02=Feb.; etc. The numbers differed in the fourth symbol, a letter code designating the engine displacement and carburetion. Letter codes were: A=195.6 cid/90 hp L-head six; B=195.6 cid/125 hp aluminum OHV six; C=195.6 cid/127 hp cast-iron OHV six; n.a.=195.6 cid/138 hp six 2V; n.a.=250 cid/200 hp V-8; n.a.=250 cid/215 hp V-8; E=327 cid/250 hp V-8 2V; F=327 cid/270 hp V-8 4V; G="287" engine. The fifth and sixth symbols indicated day of manufacture as appropriate. In motor number 301A22: first symbol 3=1961; 01=Jan.; A=195.6 cid/90 hp six and 22=22nd day of month.

RAMBLER AMERICAN SERIES 01

Model Number	Body/Style Number	Body Type & Seating	Factory Price	Shipping Weight	Production Total
DELUXE LINE					
01	6102	2-dr Flt Bus Cpe-3P	1831	2454	355
01	6106	2-dr Sed-6P	1845	2480	28,555
01	6105	4-dr Sed-6P	1894	2513	17,811
01	6108	4-dr Sta Wag-6P	2129	2583	7,260
01	6104	2-dr Sta Wag-6P	2080	2539	5,666
SUPER LINE					
01	6105-1	4-dr Sed-6P	1979	2520	15,741
01	6106-1	2-dr Sed-6P	1930	2489	14,349
01	6108-1	4-dr Sta Wag-6P	2214	2590	10,071
01	6104-1	2-dr Sta Wag-6P	2165	2546	5749
CUSTOM LINE					
01	6105-2	4-dr Sed-6P	2109	2578	5,920
01	6105-2	4-dr Cus Sed-5P	—	—	1,629
01	6106-2	2-dr Sed-6P	2060	2547	4,883
01	6107-2	2-dr Conv-6P	2369	2732	10,855
01	6107-2	2-dr Cus Conv-5P	—	2745	2,063
01	6108-2	4-dr Sta Wag-6P	2344	2648	3,679
01	6104-2	2-dr Sta Wag-6P	2295	2607	1,417

NOTE 1: Customs have five-passenger, bucket seating.

1961 Rambler, Classic four-door station wagon, 6-cyl

RAMBLER CLASSIC SIX — (6-CYL) — SERIES 10 — The Rambler six was renamed for 1961. It received a new front end featuring a one-piece rectangular, extruded aluminum grille with the letters Rambler underneath, just above the bumper. The park/turn lights were located just below the front bumper. New front and rear bumpers were also used along the new side trim. Deluxe Series standard equipment included: turn signals; twin panel ashtrays; air cleaner; front armrests; cigar lighter; dual headlamps; dual sun visors; station wagon travel rack; and five black tubeless tires. Super Series models were equipped the same as above, plus dual horns; rear door armrests; front foam cushions; and rear ashtrays. Custom Series models were equipped with all above, plus wheel discs; electric clock; glovebox light; two-tone steering wheel; carpets; and rear vent window. A major engineering change and a first for the industry was the introduction of a die-cast aluminum six-cylinder engine for Classic Custom models. The special die-cast block was made of an innovative aluminum-silicon alloy with centrifugal cast iron cylinders bonded to the block. This was advertised as "America's first Die-Cast aluminum six" and was optional on Deluxe and Super models in the Classic Series. Other highlights for this line were freshly sculptured side styling and one-piece bumpers.

RAMBLER CLASSIC SIX SERIES 10

Model Number	Body/Style Number	Body Type & Seating	Factory Price	Shipping Weight	Production Total
DELUXE LINE					
10	6115	4-dr Sed-6P	2098	2905	40,398
10	6118	4-dr Sta Wag-6P	2437	3014	19,848
SUPER LINE					
10	6115-1	4-dr Sed-6P	2268	2923	62,563
10	6118-3	5-dr Sta Wag-8P	2697	3087	4,465
10	6118-1	4-dr Sta Wag-6P	2572	3047	38,370
CUSTOM LINE					
10	6115-2	4-dr Sed-6P	2413	2898	26,497
10	6115-2	4-dr Cus Sed-5P	—	2853	2,901
10	6118-2	4-dr Sta Wag-6P	2717	2984	16,394
10	6118-4	5-dr Sta Wag-8P	2842	3023	2,741

NOTE 1: Customs have five-passenger, bucket seating.

RAMBLER CLASSIC EIGHT — (V-8) — SERIES 20 — Like the Classic six, the Rambler Classic V-8 gave buyers the best of both worlds, big car room and comfort, compact car economy and handling ease. Styling for both lines was the same, as was the availability of three different levels of trim: Deluxe, Super and Custom. As on American and Classic six models, a chrome signature placed on the right-hand lower corner of the deck lid identified the line that each car was in. A Classic script was attached to the front fendersides, below the tapering dual side moldings. Cars with the V-8 had large badges attesting to the fact located under the namescript directly behind the front wheel opening. This motor was advertised as a 'high-performance' option.

RAMBLER CLASSIC EIGHT SERIES 20

Model Number	Body/Style Number	Body Type & Seating	Factory Price	Shipping Weight	Production Total
DELUXE LINE					
20	6125	4-dr Sed-6P	2227	3237	121
SUPER LINE					
20	6125-1	4-dr Sed-6P	2397	3255	2,156
20	6128-1	4-dr Sta Wag-6P	—	—	1,964
20	6128-3	5-dr Sta Wag-8P	2826	3408	382
CUSTOM LINE					
20	6125-2	4-dr Sed-6P	2512	3252	2,071
20	6128-4	5-dr Sta Wag-8P	2941	3420	382
20	6128-2	4-dr Sta Wag-6P	2816	3378	1,777
CUSTOM 400 LINE					
20	6125-5	4-dr Sed-6P	2662	3283	109

1961 Rambler, Ambassador four-door sedan, V-8

AMBASSADOR EIGHT — (V-8) — SERIES 80 — The 1961 Ambassador was promoted as a high-performance luxury compact. The body styling was highly revised at the front end. Although based on Rambler Classic type sheet metal, the front wheel panels were extended into a highly sculptured, bullet-shaped panel which blended into protruding and flat, bullet-shaped fender ends. The entire front panel of the car was set back several inches from the fender tips and incorporated a new one-piece aluminum grille, one-piece front bumper and bold dual headlights. The grille was 'veed' on its horizontal plane and angled backwards on its vertical axis. This gave the front of the car a 'shovel nose' look. There were seven fine horizontal bars, a trapezoidal outer surround and a gold Ambassador script in the lower left corner. An identification shield also appeared at the center of the hood, above the grille. Side trim included series identification scripts (Super or Custom) ahead of the front wheel openings; a horizontal side spear that branched out into a dual molding on the rear doors and fenders; anodized aluminum insert on Customs; identification shields on the roof pillar; and fin-shaped front fendertop ornaments with bright metal extensions towards the rear. The Ambassador Deluxe had all equipment that was standard on Classic Deluxe, plus dual horns. The Ambassador Super series has, in addition to Super equipment listed for Classic, hood insulation, glovebox light and rear door vent window. Ambassador Custom models have all Classic Custom features, plus Handi-Pak Carrier, padded dash and visors, rear foam cushion and hood insulation.

AMBASSADOR EIGHT SERIES 80

Model Number	Body/Style Number	Body Type & Seating	Factory Price	Shipping Weight	Production Total
DELUXE LINE					
80	6185	4-dr Flt Sed-6P	2395	3343	273
SUPER LINE					
80	6185-1	4-dr Sed-6P	2537	3361	3,299
80	6188-1	4-dr Sta Wag-6P	2841	3493	1,099
80	6188-3	5-dr Sta Wag-8P	2966	3560	277
CUSTOM LINE					
80	6185-2	4-dr Sed-6P	2682	3370	9,269
80	6188-2	4-dr Sta Wag-6P	2986	3495	3,010
80	6188-4	5-dr Sta Wag-8P	3111	3566	784
CUSTOM 400 LINE					
80	6185-5	4-dr Sed-5P	2812	3387	831

NOTE 1: Customs have five-passenger, bucket seating.

NOTE 2: AMC called wagon with side-hinged tailgate a five-door station wagon.

BASE ENGINES

(AMERICAN SIX) Inline, L-head Six: Cast iron block. Displacement: 195.6 cid. Bore and stroke: 3-1/8 x 4-1/4 inches. Compression ratio: 8.0:1. Brake hp: 90 at 3800 rpm. Four main bearings. Solid valve lifters. Carburetor: Carter Type YF-2014S one-barrel.

(DELUXE/SUPER SIX) Inline, L-head Six: Cast iron block. Displacement: 195.6 cid. Bore and stroke: 3-1/8 x 4-1 /4 inches. Compression ratio: 8.0: 1. Brake hp: 90 at 3800 rpm. Four main bearings. Solid valve lifters. Carburetor: Carter Type YF one-barrel Model 2014S.

(CUSTOM SIX) Inline Six: Overhead valves. Cast iron block. Displacement: 195.6 cid. Bore and stroke: 3-1/8 x 4-1/4 inches. Compression ratio: 8.7:1. Brake hp: 125 at 4200 rpm. Four main bearings. Solid valve lifters. Carburetor: Holley one-barrel Model 1908-FC.

(CLASSIC SIX) Inline Six: Overhead valves. Cast aluminum block. Displacement: 195.6 cid. Bore and stroke: 3.125 x 4.25 inches. Compression ratio: 8.7:1. Brake hp: 127 at 4200 rpm. Four main bearings. Solid valve lifters. Carburetor: Holley one-barrel Model 1908FC.

(REBEL V-8) V-8: Overhead valves. Cast iron block. Displacement: 250 cid. Bore and stroke: 3-1/2 x 3/1-4 inches. Compression ratio: 8.7:1. Brake hp: 200 at 4900 rpm. Five main bearings. Hydraulic valve lifters. Carburetor: Holley model 2040 two-barrel.

(AMBASSADOR EIGHT) V-8: Overhead valves. Cast iron block. Displacement: 326.7 cid. Bore and stroke: 4.00 x 3.25 inches. Compression ratio: 8.7:1. Brake hp: 250 at 4700 rpm. Five main bearings. Hydraulic valve lifters. Carburetor: Holley two-barrel Model H-2040.

CHASSIS FEATURES: Wheelbase: (American) 100 inches, (Classic) 108 inches, (Ambassador) 117 inches. Overall length: (American) 173.1 inches; (Classic) 189.8 inches; (Ambassador) 199 inches. Overall width: (American) 70.0 inches; (Classic) 72.4 inches. (Ambassador) 73.6 inches. Tires: (American) 6.00 x 15 inches: (Classic six) 6.50 x 15; (Classic Eight) 7.50 x 14; (Ambassador) 8.00 x 14).

OPTIONS

AMERICAN: Anti-freeze ($3.80). Two-tone paint on sedans ($15.95); on station wagons ($17.95); Special application (29.50). Overdrive transmission ($102). Lever control Flash-O-Matic ($164.85). Weather-Eye ($74). Overhead valve engine ($59.50). Air conditioning with heavy-duty cooling system ($359). Power brakes ($37.95). Power steering ($72). Oil-bath air cleaner ($7.15). Oil filter ($9.30). Solex glass ($26.95). Front and rear Deluxe foam rubber seat cushion ($19.90); front only ($9.95); rear only ($9.95). Reclining seat ($25.50). Undercoating ($14.95). Windshield washer ($11). Back-up lights ($9.95). Wheel discs ($15.25). Electric clock ($15.25). Continental tire carrier on sedans ($59.50). Self-adjusting brakes ($7.45). Inside 'tilt' rearview mirror ($4.95). Left- or right-hand outside rearview mirror ($3.95); Left- and right-hand outside rearview mirror ($7.90). Custom steering wheel ($7.70). Twin-Grip differential ($29.50). Pair of license plate frames ($4.05); rear only ($2.05). Heavy-duty front and rear shocks ($2.70). Heavy-duty front and rear shocks and rear springs ($4). Heavy-duty radiator ($3). Heavy-duty cooling system ($12.50). Push-button radio and antenna ($58.50); Manual radio ($53.95). Individually adjusted front seats ($20). Crankcase ventilation system ($3.25). Padded instrument panel ($12.75). Size 6.00 x 15 four-ply rayon white sidewall tires ($28.35), size 6.50 x 15 four-ply rayon black sidewall tires ($14.65); size 6.50 x 15 four-ply rayon white sidewall tires ($46); size 6.50 x 15 four-ply nylon black sidewall tires ($28.40): size 6.50 x 15 four-ply nylon white sidewall tires ($62.90).

RAMBLER/REBEL: Flash-O-Matic push-button transmission for six-cylinder ($199.50); for V-8 ($219.50). Overdrive ($112.50). Power steering for six-cylinder ($74.00); for V-8 ($79.50). Power window lifts ($99.50). Power brakes ($39.95). Oil filter on Classic six Deluxe and Super ($9.75). Oil-bath air cleaner for six-cylinder models ($9.75). Radio with manual antenna and front speaker ($69.95); with front and rear speaker ($80.70). Weather-Eye heater and ventilator ($76). Solex tinted glass ($33). Back-up lights ($9.95). Continental tire carrier ($69.50). Front and rear foam cushions ($12.50). Reclining front seat ($25.50). Windshield washer ($11.50). Electric clock ($15.95); Padded instrument panel and visors ($21.50). Undercoating ($14.95). Left or right headrests ($12). Air conditioning ($369). Inside rearview mirror ($5.25). Self-adjusting brakes ($7.45). Wheel discs ($15.95). Twin grip differential for six-cylinder ($34.50): for V-8 models ($39.50). Parking brake warning light ($3.95). Light package ($3.95). Two-tone paint on sedans ($19.95); on Custom ($24.95); on wagons ($21.95); on Custom wagons ($29.95); on Special (except Fleet) ($29.50). Power Pack on two-barrel six-cylinder models ($12); on four-barrel and dual exhaust V-8 models ($47.50). Individually adjustable front seats ($20). Crankcase ventilation system ($3.25). Side hinged tailgate on two-seat wagons ($39.50). Lock-O-Matic door locks on four-doors ($29.85). Pair of license plate frames ($4.05). Front and rear heavy-duty shocks ($3.80); with heavy-duty front and rear springs on sedans ($5). Heavy-duty rear springs on wagons ($7.25). Heavy-duty radiator on six-cylinder ($5); on V-8 ($9.50). Heavy-duty cooling system on six-cylinder ($15.35); on V-8 ($19.85). Aluminum die-cast six-cylinder engine and oil filter on Classic six, Deluxe and Super ($30).

AMBASSADOR: Overdrive transmission ($114.50). Push-button Flash-O-Matic transmission ($229.50). Power Pack ($47.50). Weather-Eye ($82.50). Air conditioning and heavy-duty cooling system ($398). Power brakes ($41.95). Power steering ($89.50). Power window lifts ($99.50). Solex glass ($33). Front foam rubber seat cushions ($14.35). Rear foam rubber seat cushions ($14.35). Reclining seat ($25.50). Left and right headrests ($24); Left or right headrest ($12). Individually adjustable front seats ($20). Radio and antenna with front speaker in station wagons ($69.95). Radio and antenna with front and rear speakers in sedans ($86.20). Crankcase ventilation system ($3.25). Undercoating ($14.95). Windshield washer ($11.50). Back-up lights ($9.95). Wheel discs ($16.95). Electric clock ($17.95). Parking brake warning light ($3.95). Padded instrument panel and sun visors ($21.50). Side hinged tailgate for two-seat wagons ($39.50). Lock-O-Matic door locks in four-doors ($29.85). Self-adjusting brakes ($7.45). Inside 'tilt' rearview mirror ($4.95). Left or right outside rearview mirror ($5.25). Left and right outside rearview mirror ($10.50). Power-saver fan ($19.50). Twin-grip differential ($42.50). Pair of license plate frames ($4.05); rear only ($2.05). Light package ($9.95). Heavy-duty front and rear shocks ($3.80). Heavy-duty front and rear shocks and front springs with heavy-duty rear springs in sedans ($5.00). Extra heavy-duty rear springs on sedans ($7.25). Heavy-duty rear springs on wagons ($6.50). Heavy-duty radiator ($9.50). Heavy-duty cooling system ($19.85). Plus a variety of tire and paint options too numerous to list.

HISTORICAL FOOTNOTES: The full-size Ramblers were introduced Oct. 5, 1961. Model year production peaked at 377,900 units. Calendar year sales of 380,525 cars recorded. R.E. Cross was the chief executive officer of the company this year. American Motors Corp. announced the introduction of the Custom 400 entries (bucket seat four-door sedans) in late April, 1961.

1962 RAMBLER

RAMBLER AMERICAN — (6-CYL) — SERIES 6200 — The 1962 Rambler American had no major styling changes. The Super models were dropped and replaced by a '400' which had the overhead valve engine standard. Bucket seats were optional only with the '400'. A new Canadian assembly plant was opened in Brampton, Ontario, Canada to build Americans and Classics. Standard equipment for Deluxe models included air cleaner, oil filter, front armrests, front ashtray, dual sun visors, turn signals, black rubber floor mats, black rubber cargo mats on wagons and five black tubeless tires, self-adjusting brakes, front foam cushion. Custom models feature all of the above, plus rear door armrests, rear ashtray, colored carpet on wagons, automatic dome switches on front doors, station wagon travel rack, chrome horn ring and cigar lighter. 400 models had all above plus, dual horn, two-tone steering wheel, wheel discs, chrome front seat trim, vinyl pleated upholstery, padded instrument panel and visors, metallic door panel insert, door scuff plate, trim and vinyl, glovebox lock and overhead valve engine including 45 amp. battery.

1962 Rambler, American two-door convertible, 6-cyl

RAMBLER I.D. DATA: VIN on plate on right wheelhouse panel below hood. First symbol identified series: B=American; C=Rambler; 2=Super; 5=400; H=Ambassador. Second through last symbols were sequential production number. Starting serial numbers were: [American] B-375001; [American for knocked-down export] BK-13001; [Canadian-built Americans] BT-100201; [Rambler] C-625001; [Rambler for knocked-down export] CK-11501; [Canadian-built Rambler] CT-206001; [Ambassador V-8] H-160001; [Ambassador V-8 for knocked-down export]. for Ambassador V-8, HK-10301 for Ambassador V-8 for unassembled export. Body number plate riveted to left front door hinge pillar has additional data. First line indicates body production sequence number. Second line indicates "Model No." consisting of first two symbols indicating model year and additional symbols indicating body style and series. Complete "Model No." corresponds to column two of charts below. Third line gives trim data. Fourth line gives paint color data. Six-cylinder motor number on upper left front corner of engine block. V-8 motor number on top at front of block; or front of block; or center, left side of block, above oil pan. Continuing in 1962, AMC employed an "Engine Day Build Code" system giving all engines of a type the same six symbol code. The first symbol of the engine day built code is a single digit number code for the year of manufacture starting with 4=1962. The second and third symbols indicated month of build: 01=Jan.; 02=Feb.; etc. The numbers differed in the fourth symbol, a letter code designating the engine displacement and carburetion. Letter codes were: A=195.6 cid/90 hp L-head six; B=195.6 cid/125 hp aluminum OHV six; C=195.6 cid/127 hp cast-iron OHV six; n.a.=195.6 cid/138 hp six 2V; E=327 cid/250 hp V-8 2V; F=327 cid/270 hp V-8 4V; G="287" engine. The fifth and sixth symbols indicated day of manufacture as appropriate. In motor number 401A22: first symbol 4=1962; 01=Jan.; A=195.6 cid/90 hp six and 22=22nd day of month.

RAMBLER AMERICAN SERIES

Model Number	Body Style Number	Body Type & Seating	Factory Price	Shipping Weight	Production Total
Deluxe Line					
6200	6202	2-dr Bus Cpe-3P	1832	2454	281
6200	6205	4-dr Sed-6P	1895	2500	17,758
6200	6206	2-dr Sed-6P	1846	2480	29,665
6200	6208	4-dr Sta Wag-6P	2130	2573	6,304
6200	6204	2-dr Sta Wag-6P	2081	2555	4,434
Custom Line					
6200	6205-2	4-dr Sed-6P	1958	2512	13,884
6200	6206-2	2-dr Sed-6P	1909	2492	12,710
6200	6208-2	4-dr Sta Wag-6P	2190	2600	8,998
6200	6204-2	2-dr Sta Wag-6P	2141	2565	4,398
400 Line					
6200	6205-5	4-dr Sed-6P	2089	2585	5,773
6200	6206-5	2-dr Sed-6P	2040	2558	4,840
6200	6207-5	2-dr Conv-5P	2344	2735	13,497
6200	6208-5	4-dr Sta Wag-6P	2320	2692	3,134

1962 Rambler, Classic two-door sedan, 6-cyl

RAMBLER CLASSIC — (6-CYL) — SERIES 6210 — The 1962 Rambler Classic Six had all but the smallest trace of tailfins removed from the rear end. There were new, round taillights, a new front grille and new side trim and moldings. The die-cast aluminum block was standard on all Classic Sixes and optional on the Custom and Deluxe lines. Other innovations for the

year were a new brake system with tandem master cylinder and a hydraulic tilting front seat. Standard equipment for the Classic Six Deluxe Series included turn signal, air cleaner, front armrests, cigar lighter, dual headlamps, dual sun visors, station wagon travel rack, front ashtrays, oil filter, front foam cushion, and five black tubeless tires. The Classic Six Custom Series had all above features, plus electric clock, glovebox light, carpets, rear armrests, rear ashtrays, dual horns, automatic dome light switch. Three-seat station wagons have four black Captive Air nylon tires. Classic Six 400 Series included all above features, plus padded dash and visors, rear door vent windows, two-tone steering wheel, wheel discs, wagon robe rail and aluminum engine. (Cast iron engine optional at no cost.)

RAMBLER CLASSIC SERIES

Model Number	Body Style Number	Body Type & Seating	Factory Price	Shipping Weight	Production Total
Deluxe Line					
6210	6215	4-dr Sed-6P	2050	2888	38,082
6210	6216	2-dr Sed-6P	2000	2866	14,811
6210	6218	4-dr Sta Wag-6P	2380	3014	28,203
Custom Line					
6210	6215-2	4-dr Sed-6P	2200	2898	68,699
6210	6216-2	2-dr Sed-6P	2150	2876	12,652
6210	6218-2	4-dr Sta Wag-6P	2492	3024	53,671
6210	6218-4	5-dr Sta Wag-6P	2614	3094	6,322
400 Line					
6210	6215-5	4-dr Sed-6P	2349	2853	31,255
6210	6216-5	2-dr Sed-6P	2299	2841	5,521
6210	6218-5	4-dr Sta Wag-6P	2640	2985	21,281

1962 Rambler, Ambassador four-door station wagon, V-8

RAMBLER AMBASSADOR — (V-8) — SERIES 6180 — The Rambler Ambassador, for 1962, used the Rambler Classic Six body and running gear with the same minimal styling changes. Both models now shared use of the 108 inch wheelbase. This was basically the 1962 Rambler Rebel V-8 with a new name. At the same time, the 117 inch wheelbase Ambassador was dropped. The Ambassador V-8 Deluxe came standard with an air cleaner, front armrests. front ashtrays, cigar lighter, dual headlamps, dual horns, oil filter, front foam cushion. The Ambassador V-8 Custom had all features listed for Ambassador Deluxe, plus rear armrests, rear ashtrays, carpets, electric clock, glovebox light, hood insulation, automatic dome light switch, rear door vent windows, station wagon travel rack. The Ambassador V-8 400 had all features listed for Ambassador Deluxe and Custom, plus Handi-Pak Carrier, padded dash and visors, station wagon robe rail, rear foam cushion, wheel discs and four black nylon Captive Air tires on three seat station wagon.

RAMBLER AMBASSADOR SERIES

Model Number	Body Style Number	Body Type & Seating	Factory Price	Shipping Weight	Production Total
Deluxe Line (Fleet Only)					
6280	6285	4-dr Sed-6P	2336	3249	421
6280	6286	2-dr Sed-6P	2282	3227	45
6280	6288	4-dr Sta Wag-6P	2648	3375	77
Custom Line					
6280	6285-2	4-dr Sed-6P	2464	3259	7,398
6280	6286-2	2-dr Sed-6P	2410	3237	659
6280	6288-2	4-dr Sta Wag-6P	2760	3385	4,302
400 Line					
6280	2605-5	3283 Sed-6P	15,120		
6280	6286-5	2-dr Sed-6P	2551	3261	459
6280	6288-5	4-dr Sta Wag-6P	2901	3408	6,401
6280	6288-6	4-dr Sta Wag-8P	3023	3471	1,289

BASE ENGINES

(AMERICAN SIX) Inline, L-head Six: Cast iron block. Displacement: 195.6 cid. Bore and stroke: 3-1/8 x 4-1/4 inches. Compression ratio: 8.0:1. Brake hp: 90 at 3800 rpm. Four main bearings. Solid valve lifters. Carburetor: Carter Type YF-2014S one-barrel.

(DELUXE/SUPER SIX) Inline, L-head Six: Cast iron block. Displacement: 195.6 cid. Bore and stroke: 3-1/8 x 4-1 /4 inches. Compression ratio: 8.0:1. Brake hp: 90 at 3800 rpm. Four main bearings. Solid valve lifters. Carburetor: Carter Type YF one-barrel Model 2014S.

(CUSTOM SIX) Inline Six: Overhead valves. Cast iron block. Displacement: 195.6 cid. Bore and stroke: 3-1/8 x 4-1/4 inches. Compression ratio: 8.7:1. Brake hp: 125 at 4200 rpm. Four main bearings. Solid valve lifters. Carburetor: Holley one-barrel Model 1908-FC.

(CLASSIC SIX) Inline Six: Overhead valves. Cast aluminum block. Displacement: 195.6 cid. Bore and stroke: 3.125 x 4.25 inches. Compression ratio: 8.7:1. Brake hp: 127 at 4200 rpm. Four main bearings. Solid valve lifters. Carburetor: Holley one-barrel Model 1908FC.

(REBEL V-8) V-8: Overhead valves. Cast iron block. Displacement: 250 cid. Bore and stroke: 3-1/2 x 3/1-4 inches. Compression ratio: 8.7:1. Brake hp: 200 at 4900 rpm. Five main bearings. Hydraulic valve lifters. Carburetor: Holley model 2040 two-barrel.

(AMBASSADOR EIGHT) V-8: Overhead valves. Cast iron block. Displacement: 326.7 cid. Bore and stroke: 4.00 x 3.25 inches. Compression ratio: 8.7:1. Brake hp: 250 at 4700 rpm. Five main bearings. Hydraulic valve lifters. Carburetor: Holley two-barrel Model H-2040.

CHASSIS FEATURES: Wheelbase: (American) 100 inches; (Classic/Ambassador) 108 inches. Overall length: (American) 173.1 inches; (Classic/Ambassador) 190 inches. Front tread: (American) 54.6 inches; (Classic/Ambassador) 57.8 inches. Rear tread: (American) 55 inches; (Classic/Ambassador) 58 inches. Tires: (American) 6:00 x 15; (Classic) 6.50 x 15; (Ambassador) 7.50 x 14.

OPTIONS

AMERICAN: Anti-freeze ($4.25). Two-tone paint on sedans ($15.95); on station wagons ($17.95); special application [except fleet] (29.50). Overdrive transmission ($102). Lever control Flash-O-Matic ($164.85). Weather-Eye ($74.20). Overhead valve engine. Oil-bath cleaner and 45 amp. battery ($59.50). Air conditioning with heavy-duty cooling system ($360). Power brakes ($39.95). Power steering ($72.20). Oil-bath air cleaner ($7.15). Solex glass ($26.95); windshield only ($8.95). Seat Cushion, foam rubber, rear ($9.95). Reclining seat ($25.50). Undercoating ($11.95). Windshield washer ($11). Back-up lights ($9.95). Wheel discs ($14.95). Electric clock ($15.30). Inside rearview 'tilt' mirror ($4.95). Left or right outside rearview mirror ($3.95); left and right outside rearview mirror ($7.90). Twin-Grip Differential ($29.60). Pair of license plate frames ($3.50); rear only ($1.75). Heavy-duty front and rear shocks ($2.70). Heavy-duty front and rear shocks and rear springs ($4). Heavy-duty radiator ($3.05). Heavy-duty cooling system with radiator fan shroud ($12.50). Push-button radio and antenna ($58.50); manual ($52.50). Individually adjusted front seats ($20). Crankcase ventilation system, required on all California cars ($4.95). Padded instrument panel and visors ($17.60). 6.00 x 15 4-ply rayon whitewall tires ($28); 6.50 x 15 4-ply rayon blackwall tires ($8.10); 6.50 x 15 4-ply rayon whitewall tires ($37.45). Bucket seats ($59.50). Right lounge-tilt seat and headrest ($20.00). Left or right headrests ($12.00); left and right ($24.00). Load levelers only ($25); load levelers with heavy-duty front shocks ($27.10). Two front seat belts ($20.60); four belts, front and rear ($41.20). E-stick transmission (automatic clutch, only available with standard and overdrive transmissions) ($59.50). Light package [trunk, cargo or glovebox] with two courtesy lamps, parking brake warning lamp and automatic dome light on Deluxes ($9.95). Parking brake warning light ($3.95).

CLASSIC/AMBASSADOR: Air conditioning, All-Season on Classic [tinted glass required] ($370); on Ambassador (tinted glass required) ($399). Back-up lights ($9.95). Bucket seats in 400s ($59.50). Electric clock on Classic Deluxe ($15.95). Two-tone paint for Sedans ($19.95); for Wagons ($21.95); Special Application ($29.50). Dowgard coolant for Classic ($4.25); for Ambassador ($6.25). Heavy-duty cooling system, on Classic ($15.35); on Ambassador ($19.85). Crankcase ventilation system ($4.95). Aluminum six-cylinder engine on Classic Deluxe and Custom ($30). Rear foam cushions [standard in Ambassador 400] ($9.95). Individually adjustable front seats ($20); reclining front seat ($25.50). Tinted glass ($37.65); windshield tinted glass ($11.50). Left or right headrest ($12.00). Two license plate frames ($3.50); rear license plate frame ($1.75). Light package ($9.95). Load levelers ($32.15); same with heavy-duty front shocks ($36.00); same with heavy-duty front shocks and springs ($38.70). Inside tilt mirror ($4.95). Left or right outside mirror ($5.30). Padded instrument panel and visors ($21.60). Parking brake warning light ($3.95). Power brakes on Classic ($41.95); on Ambassador ($43.95). Two-door power door locks on Classic ($23.45). Four-door power door locks on Classic and Ambassador ($29.85). Power pack on Classic ($12); on Ambassador ($47.50). Power Saver fan on Classic ($47.50). Power Saver fan on Ambassador ($19.60). Power steering on Classic ($74.20); on Ambassador ($81.20). Power windows ($102.25). Heavy-duty radiator for Classic ($5.05); for Ambassador ($9.55). Single speaker radio and antenna for Classic, Ambassador wagon ($64.95); dual speaker for Classic and Ambassador sedans ($77.25). Two front seat belts ($20.60); four seat belts rear and front ($41.20). Seat lounge tilt with headrest ($20.75). Heavy-duty front and rear shocks ($3.85). Heavy-duty springs and shocks, except wagons ($5.05). Extra-heavy-duty springs and shocks, rear, except wagons ($7.30); wagons ($6.55). Side hinge tailgate on Classic and Ambassador six-passenger wagons ($39.60). Tires: Classic: 6.50 x 15 - 4-ply whitewall rayon, except nine-passenger wagons ($29.60); 6.70 x 15 - 4 -ply black rayon, except nine-passenger wagons ($8.70); 6.70 x 15 - 4-ply rayon whitewall, except nine-passenger wagons ($39.90); 6.50 x 15 - 4-ply whitewall nylon Captive Air (four) on nine-passenger wagon ($27.30); 6.70 x 15 - 4-ply black nylon Captive Air (four) on nine-passenger wagon ($7.50); 6.70 x 15 - 4-ply whitewall nylon Captive Air (four) on nine-passenger wagon ($36.30). Ambassador: 7.50 x 14 - 4 ply white sidewall rayon except nine-passenger wagons ($31.40); 7.50 x 14 - 4 ply white sidewall nylon Captive Air (4) on nine-passenger wagons ($28.95); 8.00 x 14 - 4 ply black rayon except nine-passenger wagons ($14.20); 8.00 x 14 - 4 ply white sidewall rayon except nine-passenger wagons ($48.35); 8.00 x 14 - 4 ply black nylon Captive Air (4) on 9-pass. wagons ($12.95); 8.00 x 14 - 4 ply white sidewall nylon Captive Air (4) on nine-passenger wagons ($44.50);, plus a variety of tire options too numerous to list here. Flash-O-Matic transmission on Classic ($186.50); on Ambassador ($219.50). Overdrive transmission on Classic ($108.50); on Ambassador ($114.95). Twin Grip differential on Classic ($34.60); on Ambassador ($42.70). Undercoating ($14.95). Weather eye heater ($76). Wheel discs (Std. 400) ($14.95). Windshield washer ($11.95).

HISTORICAL FOOTNOTES: The full-sized Ramblers were introduced Oct. 6, 1961 and the compact Americans appeared in dealer showrooms the same day. Model year production peaked at 442,300 units. Calendar years sales of 434,788 cars were recorded. R.E. Cross was the chief executive officer of the company this year. The 2,000,000 Rambler built since 1902 was produced on Feb. 1, 1962 in Kenosha, Wis. In June of the same year a strike by the supplier ended availability of aluminum engines for 1962. The next season, four suppliers and four different versions of such engines were seen. Low installation rate options included V-8 engines (8.2 percent); power brakes (7.9 percent); bucket seats (13.4 percent); air conditioning (6.5 percent) and dual exhausts (1.5 percent).

1963 RAMBLER

RAMBLER AMERICAN — (6-CYL) — SERIES 6301 — The addition of a pair of two-door hardtops to the 100 inch wheelbase American marked the return of this body style in a Rambler. American Motor's last pillarless coupe had been offered in 1960. New grilles and trim were evident. The grille was of the same trapezoidal shape as in 1962, but had an insert with a pattern of closely-spaced vertical bars. At the rear end several changes were noticeable. First, the license plate bracket was moved from the center of the rear deck lid panel to a position below the middle of the back bumper bar. Second, the Rambler lettering across the edge of the 1962 deck lid was replaced with a logo nameplate mounted where the license plate had been. A redesigned power convertible top; transistorized radio; dual-braking system improvements; new wheel discs; a self-adjusting clutch for the semi-automatic 'E-stick' transmission; and better heating and air conditioning units were other notable advances. Model designations were changed to American 220, American 330 and American 440 instead of Deluxe, Custom and 400 respectively. A new two-door hardtop called the 440-H was introduced. It had a special roof pillar badge; ridged type roof; and contrast-finished side insert panel. Standard equipment on Americans included five 6.00x15 blackwall tires; front foam

cushions; front armrests; sun visors; oil filter; and roof luggage rack on station wagons. Custom models also had carpets; a cigarette lighter; and rear armrests; "400" models also had wheelcovers; two-tone steering wheel; glovebox lock; padded dash and sun visors; dual horns; and front door dome light switches.

1963 Rambler, American two-door convertible, 6-cyl

RAMBLER I.D. DATA: VIN on plate on right wheelhouse panel below hood. First symbol identified series: B=American; G=Classic Six; Z=Classic Eight; H=Ambassador Eight. Second through last symbols were sequential production number. Starting serial numbers were: [American] B-515001; [American for knocked-down export] BK-15001; [Canadian-built Americans] BT-110001; [Classic Six] G-100001; [Classic Six for knocked-down export] GK-10001; [Canadian-built Classic Six]; GT-220001 [Classic Eight] Z-100001; [Classic Eight knocked-down for export] ZK-1001; [Ambassador V-8] H-210001; [Ambassador V-8 for knocked-down export]. for Ambassador V-8, HK-11001 for Ambassador V-8 for unassembled export. Body Number plate riveted to left front door hinge pillar has additional data. First line indicates body production sequence number. Second line indicates "Model No." consisting of first two symbols indicating model year and additional symbols indicating body style and series. Complete "Model No." corresponds to column two of charts below. Third line gives trim data. Fourth line gives paint color data. Six-cylinder motor number on upper left front corner of engine block. V-8 motor number on top at front of block; or front of block; or center, left side of block, above oil pan. Continuing in 1963, AMC employed an "Engine Day Build Code" system giving all engines of a type the same six symbol code. The first symbol of the engine day built code is a single digit number code for the year of manufacture starting with 5=1963. The second and third symbols indicated month of build: 01=Jan.; 02=Feb.; etc. The numbers differed in the fourth symbol, a letter code designating the engine displacement and carburetion. Letter codes were: A=195.6 cid/90 hp L-head six; B=195.6 cid/125 hp aluminum OHV six; C=195.6 cid/127 hp cast-iron OHV six; n.a.=195.6 cid/138 hp six 2V; E=327 cid/250 hp V-8 2V; F=327 cid/270 hp V-8 4V; G=287 cid/198 hp V-8 engine. The fifth and sixth symbols indicated day of manufacture as appropriate. In motor number 501A22: first symbol 5=1963; 01=Jan.; A=195.6 cid/90 hp six and 22=22nd day of month.

RAMBLER AMERICAN SERIES 6301

Model Number	Body/Style Number	Body Type & Seating	Factory Price	Shipping Weight	Production Total
AMERICAN 220 (DELUXE) LINE					
6301	6305	4-dr Sed-6P	1895	2485	14,419
6301	6306	2-dr Sed-6P	1846	2472	27,780
6301	6302	2-dr Bus Sed-3P	1832	2446	162
6301	6308	4-dr Sta Wag-6P	2130	2549	4,436
6301	6304	2-dr Sta Wag-6P	2081	2528	3,312
AMERICAN 330 (CUSTOM) LINE					
6301	6305-2	4-dr Sed-6P	1958	2500	9,666
6301	6308-2	4-dr Sta Wag-6P	2190	2561	6,848
6301	6304-2	2-dr Sta Wag-6P	2141	2539	3,204
AMERICAN 440 LINE					
6301	6305-5	4-dr Sed-6P	2089	2575	2,937
6301	6306-5	2-dr Sed-6P	2040	2556	1,486
6301	6309-5	2-dr HT-6P	2136	2550	5,101
6301	6309-7	2-dr 440H-4P	2281	2567	9,749
6301	6307-5	2-dr Conv-5P	2344	2743	4,750
6301	6308-5	4-dr Sta Wag-6P	2320	2638	1,874

NOTE 1: The 440H hardtop came with bucket seats and 138 hp 'power pack' six.

RAMBLER CLASSIC SIX — (6-CYL) — SERIES 6310 — The Rambler Classic for 1963 was completely redesigned. It had a very clean, lower and narrower box shape on a longer 112 inch wheelbase. The front grille consisted of a double convex surface of fine U-shaped vertical bars with Rambler across the front. It was a one-piece aluminum stamping. New curved glass side windows were used along with new push-button door handles. New series identification numbers were placed in the center of the trunk lid. There was also Rambler identification trim below the trunk lid, A new tri-pose engine mounting system was used. It replaced a four-point system used earlier. At the beginning of the 1963 model year, only a Classic Six was available and it came in Deluxe, Custom and 400 series. After the release of the Classic Eight series, in January, the series names were changed to 550, 660 and 770. The base Classic 550 models compared to Deluxe models and had no side trim. Standard equipment included directional signals; dual headlamps; air cleaner; five 6.50 x 15 blackwall tires; front foam cushions; front armrests; sun visors; and oil filter. The one-step-up Classic 660s compared to Custom models. They had a dual horizontal molding on front fender and single molding from the front door back. In addition to base equipment, "660s" had front door dome light switches; rear armrests; rear ashtrays; glovebox lock; electric clock; carpet; dual horns; and luggage rack on station wagons (blackwall Captive Air nylon tires on nine-passenger station wagons). The top-of-the-line Classic 770s compared to the "400" range cars and carried a full-length dual molding with contrasting insert. The Classic 770 had all of this, plus electric clock; padded dash and visors; rear door vent window; wheel discs; two-tone steering wheel; station wagon robe rail; foam cushions; and the die-cast aluminum six (with cast-iron engine as a no-cost option).

1963 Rambler, Classic 770 four-door station wagon, 6-cyl

RAMBLER CLASSIC SIX SERIES 6310

Model Number	Body/Style Number	Body Type & Seating	Factory Price	Shipping Weight	Production Total
CLASSIC SIX 550 LINE					
6310	6315	4-dr Sed-6P	2105	2729	43,315
6310	6316	2-dr Sed-6P	2055	2720	14,417
6310	6318	4-dr Sta Wag-6P	2435	2893	26,261

Series Number	Body/Style Number	Body Type & Seating	Factory Price	Shipping Weight	Production Total
CLASSIC SIX 660 LINE					
6310	6315-2	4-dr Sed-6P	2245	2740	71,646
6310	6316-2	2-dr Sed-6P	2195	2725	11,064
6310	6318-4	5-dr Sta Wag-8P	2609	2885	5,752
6310	6318-2	4-dr Sta Wag-6P	2537	2890	46,282
CLASSIC SIX 770 LINE					
6310	6315-5	4-dr Sed-6P	2349	2686	35,281
6310	6316-5	2-dr Sed-6P	2299	2663	5,496
6310	6318-5	4-dr Sta Wag-6P	2640	2828	19,319

RAMBLER CLASSIC EIGHT — (V-8) — SERIES 6350 — The Rambler Classic V-8 shared the same all-new styling as the Rambler Classic Six. The main trim difference was the attachment of V-8 emblems on the front fenders, behind the wheel openings. As on the six-cylinder models, features included redesigned grilles: curved side glass, a sharper silhouette and an advanced type of unitized construction that reduced the number of parts and welds in the assembly by 30 percent. The Classic took on the semi-automatic 'E-stick' transmission and it was in early February that the V-8 (287 cid) was introduced at the Chicago Automobile show as a running addition to the 1963 line that created this new series. Numbering on either the center edge of the deck lid or center of tailgate identified each car as a 550, 660 or 770 Classic. Side molding treatments for each of the lines were the same ones described for the Classic Sixes of a comparable trim level. A 'Twin Stick' five-speed (overdrive) floor-mounted transmission was offered in some models. The right-hand lever was for locking the overdrive function in or out, while the left-hand lever was the floor shifter. Standard equipment for each series was the same as installed in Classic Six series, except for different engine.

RAMBLER CLASSIC V-8 SERIES 6350

Model Number	Body/Style Number	Body Type & Seating	Factory Price	Shipping Weight	Production Total
CLASSIC V-8 550 LINE					
6350	6355	4-dr Sed-6P	2210	3109	3,444
6350	6356	2-dr Sed-6P	2160	3100	992
6350	6358	4-dr Sta Wag-6P	2540	3273	2,318
CLASSIC V-8 660 LINE					
6350	6355-2	4-dr Sed-6P	2345	3120	11,067
6350	6356-2	2-dr Sed-6P	2300	3105	1,369
6350	6358-4	5-dr Sta Wag-9P	2714	3265	1,150
6350	6358-2	4-dr Sta Wag-6P	2642	3340	7,237
CLASSIC V-8 770 LINE					
6350	6355-5	4-dr Sed-6P	2454	3130	7,869
6350	6356-5	2-dr Sed-6P	2404	3113	1,341
6350	6358-5	4-dr Sta Wag-6P	2754	3208	4,399

1963 Rambler, Ambassador two-door sedan, V-8

AMBASSADOR — (V-8) — SERIES 6380 — The Ambassador was on the same platform as the Rambler Classic and varied mainly in terms of trim. The grille had a horizontal center blade which carried an Ambassador nameplate at its middle. A lower band of horizontal trim decorated the body, between the two wheel housings. Ambassador scripts were carried on the side of the back fenders and the rear treatment included a vertically ribbed, horizontal

Standard Catalog of American Cars

beauty panel. Rambler Classic type taillamps with chrome division bars were added. There were center-mounted Ambassador nameplates and a logo badge on the top center edge of the trunk. At the beginning of the 1962 model year, Ambassadors were available in Custom and 400 series. After the rearrangement of the Rambler Classic series in January, the Ambassadors also changed to three distinct levels of trim. The Ambassador 800 models were somewhat similar to previous low-rung Customs. Standard equipment was comprised of five 7.50 x 14 blackwall tires; sun visors; air cleaner; front armrests; front ashtray; cigar lighter; dual headlamps; dual horns; oil filter; front foam cushions and station wagon travel rack. Ambassador 880 was a new mid-range series, offering more trim and equipment than the base Ambassador, but not quite as many extras as the former 400. It had all 800 features, plus front and rear armrests; ashtrays; carpets; hood insulation; automatic dome light switch and chrome horn ring. The top of the line Ambassador 990 had everything found on the lower-priced lines, plus, electric clock; padded dashboard; padded sun visors; station wagon robe rail; rear front seat cushions; full wheel discs; and Captive Air tires on nine-passenger station wagon.

AMBASSADOR SERIES 6380

Model Number	Body/Style Number	Body Type & Seating	Factory Price	Shipping Weight	Production Total
AMBASSADOR 800 LINE					
6380	6385	4-dr Sed-6P	2391	3140	437
6380	6386	2-dr Sed-6P	2337	3110	41
6380	6388	4-dr Sta Wag-6P	2703	3270	113
AMBASSADOR 880 LINE					
6380	6385-2	4-dr Sed-6P	2519	3145	7,667
6380	6386-2	2-dr Sed-6P	2465	3116	1,042
6380	6388-2	4-dr Sta Wag-6P	2815	3275	4,929
AMBASSADOR 990 LINE					
6380	6385-5	4-dr Sed-6P	2660	3158	14,019
6380	6386-5	2-dr Sed-6P	2606	3132	1,764
6380	6388-6	5-dr Sta Wag-9P	3018	3305	1,687
6380	6388-5	4-dr Sta Wag-6P	2956	3298	6,112

BASE ENGINES

(AMERICAN 220/330) Inline Six: Cast iron block. Displacement: 1956 cid. Bore and stroker 3.125 x 4.25 inches. Compression ratio: 8.0:1. Brake hp: 90 at 3800 rpm. Four main bearings. Solid valve lifters. Carburetor: Carter Type RBS one-barrel Model 3487S.

(AMERICAN 440/RAMBLER CLASSIC SIX) Inline Six: Overhead valve. Cast iron block. Displacement; 195.6 cid. Bore and stroke: 3.125 x 4.25 inches. Compression ratio: 8.7:1. Brake hp: 126 at 4200 rpm. Four main bearings. Solid valve lifters. Carburetor: Holley one-barrel Model 1909-2555.

(AMERICAN 440H) Inline Six: Cast iron or aluminum block. Displacement: 195-6 cid. Bore and stroke: 3.125 x 4.25 inches. Compression ratio: 8.7:1. Brake hp: 138 at 4500 rpm. Four main bearings. Solid valve lifters. Carburetor: Carter Type WCD two-barrel Model 3434S.

(RAMBLER CLASSIC EIGHT) V-8: Overhead valves. Cast iron block. Displacement: 287 cid. Bore and stroke: 3-3/4 x 3-1/4 inches. Compression ratio: 8.7:1. Brake hp: 198 at 4700 rpm. Five main bearings. Hydraulic valve lifters. Carburetor: Holley two-barrel Model 2209-2699.

(AMBASSADOR EIGHT) V-8: Overhead valves. Cast iron block. Displacement: 326.7 cid. Bore and stroke: 4.00 x 3.25 inches. Compression ratio: 8.7:1. Brake hp: 250 at 4700 rpm. Five main bearings. Hydraulic valve lifters. Carburetor: Holley two-barrel Model H-2040.

CHASSIS FEATURES: Wheelbase: (American) 100 inches; (Classic/Ambassador) 112 inches. Overall length: (American) 173.1 inches; (Classic/Ambassador) 189.3 inches. Front tread: (American) 54.6 inches; (Classic) 58.2 inches; (Ambassador) 58.6 inches. Rear tread: (American) 55 inches; (Classic) 57.4 inches; (Ambassador) 57.5 inches. Tires: (American) 6.00 x 15; (Classic eight-passenger wagon) 7.00 x 14; (other Classics) 6.50 x 15; (Ambassadors) 7.50 x 14.

OPTIONS

AMERICAN: Antifreeze ($4.25). Two-tone colors on sedans ($15.95); two-tone color on station wagons ($17.95), two-tone color on hardtops except 440H ($37.90); two-tone color on convertible ($21.95), special color application ($29.50). Overdrive transmission ($102). Lever control Flash-O-Matic ($164.85). Weather-Eye ($74.20). Overhead valve engine ($59.50). Air conditioning including heavy-duty cooling system ($360). Power brakes ($39.95). Power steering ($72.20). Oil-bath air cleaner ($7.15). Solex glass ($26.95). Solex windshield only ($8.95). Rear foam rubber seat cushion ($9.95). Reclining seat ($25.50). Undercoating ($14.95). Windshield washer ($11.95). Back-up lights ($10.70). Wheel discs ($14.95). Electric clock ($15.30). Inside 'tilt' rearview mirror ($4.95). Left or right outside rearview mirror ($3.95); left and right outside rearview mirror ($7.90). Twin-grip differential ($29.60). Pair of license frames ($3.50): rear license frame only ($1.75). Front and rear heavy-duty shocks ($2.70). Heavy-duty front and rear shocks and rear springs ($4). Heavy-duty radiator ($3.55). Heavy-duty cooling system ($12.50). Push-button radio and antenna ($58.50); manual radio and antenna ($52.50). Individually adjusted front seats ($20). Padded instrument panel and visors ($17.60). Bucket seats on American 440 ($99.50); left and right bucket seats on American 440 ($24). Rear load levelers ($32.15). Load levelers with heavy-duty front shocks ($34.85). Two front seat belts ($17.85); four front and rear seat belts ($37). E-Stick transmission, automatic clutch available only with standard or overdrive gearboxes ($59.50). Visibility group A ($21.25). Light group ($19.60). Chrome horn ring ($7.70). Heavy-duty batter ($6.50). Air conditioning adaptor group ($20.55). 33 amp. alternator ($12). Vinyl seat upholstery ($15). Left or right-hand lounge-tilt seat and headrest ($21). Left- and right-hand lounge-tilt seat and headrest ($42). Power-Pack, twin throat carburetor ($12). Twin-stick floor shift transmission and overdrive ($134.50).

CLASSIC/AMBASSADOR: All-Season air conditioning ($380-$399). Alternator ($12). Back-up lights ($10.70). Heavy-duty battery ($6.50). Bucket seats ($99.50) Electric clock ($15.95). Two-tone color on sedans ($19.95); two-tone color on wagons ($21.95), special color applications ($29.50). Coolant Dowgard ($4.25-$6.25). Heavy-duty cooling system ($17.20-$19.85). Six-cylinder aluminum engine ($30). Rear foam cushions ($9.95). Adjustable front seats ($20). Reclining front seat ($25.50). Front lounge-tilt seat with headrest ($21). Tinted glass ($39.50-$45.50). Tinted windshield ($15.95). Left or right headrest ($12). Chrome horn ring ($7.70). Light group ($19.60). Load levelers ($32.15). Load levelers with heavy-duty front shocks ($36). Load levels with heavy-duty front shocks and springs ($38.70). Inside 'tilt' mirror ($4.95). Outside left or right mirror ($5.30). Outside rearview remote control mirror ($11.95). Padded instrument panel and visors ($19.95). Power brakes ($42.95-$43.95). Power door locks on two-doors ($23.45); power door locks on four-doors ($29.85). Power Pack ($12.00-$23.75). Power Saver fan ($19.60). Power steering ($19.60-$81.20). Power windows ($102.25). Heavy-duty radiator ($5.55-$9.55). Single speaker radio and antenna ($64.95). Dual speaker radio and antenna ($77.25). Front seat belts ($17.85). Front and rear seat belts ($37). Heavy-duty springs and shocks ($5.05). Extra-heavy-duty springs and rear shocks ($7.30). Heavy-duty springs and shocks ($6.55). Side hinge tailgate ($39.60). Twin stick transmission ($141.00$147.50). Flash-O-Matic transmission ($186.50-$219.50). Overdrive transmission ($108.50-$114.95). Twin grip differential ($37.50-$42.70). Undercoating ($14.95). Visibility group A ($22.50). Visibility group B ($28.85). Weather-Eye Heater ($78). Wheel discs ($14.95). Windshield washer ($11.95). Numerous tire choices.

HISTORICAL FOOTNOTES: The 1963 Rambler line was introduced Oct. 5, 1962 and the Rambler Classic V-8 appeared in dealer showrooms during February. Model year production peaked at 464,000 units. Calendar year sales of 441,508 cars were recorded in the United States. R.E. Cross was the chief executive officer of the company this year. Options and accessories seeing low installation rates included: power windows (0.5 percent). V-8 engines (17 percent); power brakes (8.1 percent): bucket seats (9.6 percent) and air conditioning (8.2 percent). A Rambler took top honors in the Mobilgas Economy Run. The 1963 Rambler line was picked as 'Car of the Year' by MOTOR TREND magazine.

1964 RAMBLER

1964 Rambler, American 440-H two-door hardtop, 6-cyl

RAMBLER AMERICAN — (6-CYL) — SERIES 6401 — The Rambler American for 1964 was totally redesigned. Wheelbase was increased from 100 inches to 106 inches. The new styling was cleaner with the corners more rounded. The front fenders were rounded near the front headlights and styled similarly to Chrysler's famous experimental turbine car. Front foam seat cushions; a cigarette lighter (except 220); and five 6.45 x 14 blackwall tires were standard in all Americans. 220s and 330s had the 90 horsepower six-cylinder engine. American 440s featured the 125 hp six. In addition, the 440-H had wide reclining bucket seats; rear foam cushions; front seat belts; wheel discs; and, on station wagons, a roof luggage rack.

RAMBLER I.D. DATA: VIN on plate on right wheelhouse panel below hood. First symbol identified series: B=American; G=Classic Six; Z=Classic Eight; H=Ambassador Eight. Second through last symbols were sequential production number. Rambler American Series 6401 starting Serial Numbers were B-650001 for cars built in Kenosha, Wis., BK-16001 for unassembled export and BT-115401 for Brampton, Ontario, Canada. Rambler Classic Series 6410 starting Serial Numbers were G-500001 for cars built in Kenosha, Wis. and GK-14001 for unassembled export. Starting Serial Numbers for Rambler Classic V-8s were Z-155001 for cars built in Kenosha, Wis. and ZK-11001 for unassembled export. All Classics built in Brampton, Ontario, Canada had a starting Serial Number of GT-239001. Rambler Ambassador Series 6380 starting Serial Numbers were H-255001 for cars built in Kenosha, Wis. and HK-12001 for unassembled export. Starting serial numbers for all Rambler Ambassador V-8 built in Brampton, Ontario, Canada were HT-33301. Body Number plate riveted to left front door hinge pillar has additional data. First line indicates body production sequence number. Second line indicates "Model No." consisting of first two symbols indicating model year and additional symbols indicating body style and series. Complete "Model No." corresponds to column two of charts below. Third line gives trim data. Fourth line gives paint color data. Six-cylinder motor number on upper left front corner of engine block. V-8 motor number on top at front of block; or front of block; or center, left side of block, above oil pan. Continuing in 1964, AMC employed an "Engine Day Build Code" system giving all engines of a type the same six symbol code. The first symbol of the engine day built code is a single digit number code for the year of manufacture starting with 6=1964. The second and third symbols indicated month of build: 01=Jan.; 02=Feb.; etc. The numbers differed in the fourth symbol, a letter code designating the engine displacement and carburetion. Letter codes were: A=195.6 cid/90 hp L-head six; B=195.6 cid/125 hp aluminum OHV six; C=195.6 cid/127 hp cast-iron OHV six; n.a.=195.6 cid/138 hp six 2V; E=327 cid/250 hp V-8 2V; F=327 cid/270 hp V-8 4V; G=287 cid/198 hp V-8; L=232 cid/145 hp six. The fifth and sixth symbols indicated day of manufacture as appropriate. In motor number 601A22: first symbol 6=1964; 01=Jan.; A=195.6 cid/90 hp six and 22=22nd day of month.

RAMBLER AMERICAN SERIES 6401

Model Number	Body/Style Number	Body Type & Seating	Factory Price	Shipping Weight	Production Total
AMERICAN 220					
6401	6405	4-dr Sed-6P	1964	2527	18,225
6401	6406	2-dr Sed-6P	1907	2506	32,716
6401	6408	4-dr Sta Wag-6P	2240	2661	8,062
AMERICAN 330					
6401	6405-2	4-dr Sed-6P	2057	2526	19,379
6401	6406-2	2-dr Sed-6P	2000	2504	15,171
6401	6408-2	4-dr Sta Wag-6P	2324	2675	20,587
AMERICAN 440					
6401	6405-5	4-dr Sed-6P	2150	2572	6,590
6401	6409-5	2-dr HT-6P	2133	2596	19,495
6401	6409-7	2-dr 440-H HT-5P	2292	2617	14,527
6401	6407-5	2-dr Conv-6P	2346	2752	8,907

RAMBLER CLASSIC SIX — (6-CYL) — SERIES 6410 — The major styling changes for the Classic line was a new grille. It had six stacks of short, bright metal 'dashes' running between dual outboard headlamps. The headlights were horizontally positioned in rounded rectangular

housings. The entire ensemble was surrounded by a barbell-shaped chrome grille shell with Rambler lettering stamped into the upper bar. Side trim varied by line. Classic 550 models had a bright rocker panel strip, but no lower beltline molding. Classic 660 models added a horizontal mid-bodyside strip, of constant width, which ran from the headlights to the taillights. The Classic 770 models used the same basic trim, but had a 'butter knife' shaped front tip on the molding. This tip was horizontally ribbed and carried '770' numbering. All three lines had a Classic script plate on the back edge of the rear fender. A 232 cid six-cylinder engine was introduced in a limited number of Classic two-door hardtops beginning in late April, 1964. All of these special cars were painted Solar Yellow (with black roofs) and only 2,520 were built. They had distinctive 'Typhoon' rear fender badges, in place of the regular Classic script. However, the Typhoon six-cylinder motor was also provided, as a $59.95 powertrain option, in Classic 770 models. It produced 145 brake hp at 4300 rpm. Standard equipment in all Rambler Classic 550s included front foam cushions; dual headlights; and five 6.95 x 14 blackwall tires. Classic 660s also had automatic dome lights; rear armrests; glovebox lock; carpets; and dual horns. Classic 770s had such extras as an electric clock; padded dash and visors; two-tone steering wheel; and full wheel discs.

RAMBLER CLASSIC SIX SERIES 6410

Model Number	Body/Style Number	Body Type & Seating	Factory Price	Shipping Weight	Production Total
CLASSIC 550					
6410	6415	4-dr Sed-6P	2116	2755	21,310
6410	6416	2-dr Sed-6P	2066	2732	6,454
6410	6418	4-dr Sta Wag-6P	2446	2915	13,164
CLASSIC 660					
6410	6415-2	4-dr Sed-6P	2256	2758	37,584*
6410	6416-2	2-dr Sed-6P	2206	2736	3,976
6410	6418-2	4-dr Sta Wag-6P	2548	2916	26,671
CLASSIC 770					
6410	6415-5	4-dr Sed-6P	2360	2763	14,337*
6410	6416-5	2-dr Sed-6P	2310	2740	1,278*
6410	6419-5	2-dr Typ HT-6P	2397	2789	8,996*
6410	6419-7	2-dr HT-5P	2509	2818	2,520
6410	6418-5	4-dr Sta Wag-6P	2651	2921	10,523*

NOTE 1: (*) indicates limited number of cars had optional Typhoon six.
NOTE 2: According to Body Style Number, the following number of Typhoon six attachments were recorded: 6415-2 (6); 6415-5 (2,025); 6416-5 (71); 6418-2 (4); 6418-5 (1,720) and 6419-5 (429).

1964 Rambler, Classic 770 four-door station wagon, V-8

RAMBLER CLASSIC EIGHT — (V-8) — SERIES 6410 — The styling and equipment features of the Rambler Classic, when equipped with V-8 power, were the same as for the Classic Six, except for the engine and engine identification badges. The optional V-8 was a 287.2 cid 198 hp engine. Cars with this engine installed received V-8 fender badges which were placed behind the front wheelhousing and under the lower beltline molding.

RAMBLER CLASSIC EIGHT SERIES 6410

Model Number	Body/Style Number	Body Type & Seating	Factory Price	Shipping Weight	Production Total
CLASSIC 550					
6410	6415	4-dr Sed-6P	2221	3115	2,760
6410	6416	2-dr Sed-6P	2171	3092	545
6410	6418	4-dr Sta Wag-6P	2551	3275	2,199
CLASSIC 660					
6410	6415-2	4-dr Sed-6P	2361	3118	11,374
6410	6416-2	2-dr Sed-6P	2311	3096	873
6410	6418-2	4-dr Sta Wag-6P	2653	3276	10,908
CLASSIC 770					
6410	6415-5	4-dr Sed-6P	2465	3123	9,451
6410	6416-5	2-dr Sed-6P	2415	3100	669
6410	6418-5	4-dr Sta Wag-6P	2756	3281	8,835
6410	6419-5	2-dr HT-6P	2502	3149	11,872

RAMBLER AMBASSADOR 990 — (V-8) — SERIES 6480 — The 1964 Ambassador 990 looked like a Rambler Classic with some of its teeth knocked out. At the center of each stack of chrome grille dashes, a few dashes were omitted. This left a gap which was filled with Ambassador lettering. Seen on the hood, above the center of the grille, was a winged medallion. Side trim consisted of rocker sill moldings; full-length horizontal lower beltline strips; horizontal chrome slashes on the rear roof pillar; and vertical louvers on the front fenders behind the wheel openings. The deck lid or tailgate was decorated with a horizontal beauty panel that matched the general texture of the front grille. A chrome extension panel appeared between the rear bumper and wheelhousing. Ambassador standard equipment included front foam cushions; dual headlights; five 7.35 x 14 blackwall tires; V-8 engine; electric clock; rear foam cushions; and wheel discs. An optional feature on Ambassador 990 was a bucket seat combination with a special between-the-seat cushion permitting a third person to ride in front. Ambassador scripts were positioned at the lower rear side of the back fenders. The special Ambassador 990-H two-door hardtop came standard with front and rear armrests; front and rear seat cushions; and wheel opening moldings. The 990 convertible had wheel opening moldings and a power top. Ambassador wagons had a rooftop luggage carrier.

1964 Rambler, Ambassador 990-H two-door hardtop, V-8

RAMBLER AMBASSADOR 990 SERIES 6480

Model Number	Body/Style Number	Body Type & Seating	Factory Price	Shipping Weight	Production Total
6480	6485-5	4-dr Sed-6P	2671	3204	9,827
6480	6489-5	2-dr HT-6P	2736	3213	4,407
6480	6489-7	2-dr 990-H HT-6P	2917	3255	1,464
6480	6488-5	4-dr Sta Wag	2985	3350	2,995

BASE ENGINES

(AMERICAN 220/330) Inline Six: Cast iron block. Displacement: 195.6 cid. Bore and stroker 3.125 x 4.25 inches. Compression ratio: 8.0:1. Brake hp: 90 at 3800 rpm. Four main bearings. Solid valve lifters. Carburetor: Carter Type RBS one-barrel Model 3708S.

(AMERICAN 440) Inline Six: Overhead valve. Cast iron block. Displacement; 195.6 cid. Bore and stroke: 3.125 x 4.25 inches. Compression ratio: 8.7:1. Brake hp: 125 at 4200 rpm. Four main bearings. Solid valve lifters. Carburetor: Holley one-barrel Model 1909-2555-3.

(AMERICAN 440H) Inline Six: Cast iron or aluminum block. Displacement: 231.9 cid. Bore and stroke: 3.125 x 4.25 inches. Compression ratio: 8.7: 1. Brake hp: 138 at 4600 rpm. Four main bearings. Solid valve lifters. Carburetor: Carter Type WCD two-barrel Model 3706S.

(CLASSIC 550/660/770) Inline Six: Cast iron block. Displacement: 195.6 cid. Bore and stroke: 3.125 x 4.25 inches. Compression ratio: 8.7:1. Brake horsepower: 127 at 4200 rpm. Four main bearings. Solid valve lifters. Carburetor: Carter RBS one-barrel Model 2727S.

(RAMBLER CLASSIC EIGHT) V-8: Overhead valves. Cast iron block. Displacement: 287.2 cid. Bore and stroke: 3-3/4 x 3-1/4 inches. Compression ratio: 8.7:1. Brake hp: 198 at 4700 rpm. Five main bearings. Hydraulic valve lifters. Carburetor: Holley 2209-3305 two-barrel.

(AMBASSADOR EIGHT) V-8: Overhead valves. Cast iron block. Displacement: 326.7 cid. Bore and stroke: 3.75 x 3.25 inches. Compression ratio: 8.7:1. Brake hp: 250 at 4700 rpm. Five main bearings. Hydraulic valve lifters. Carburetor: Holley 2300-2442-1 two-barrel.

(AMBASSADOR 990-H) V-8: Overhead valves. Cast iron block. Displacement: 326.7 cid. Bore and stroke: 4.00 x 3.25 inches. Compression ratio: 9.7:1. Brake hp: 270 at 4700 rpm. Five main bearings. Hydraulic valve lifters. Carburetor: Holley four-barrel Model 4150-1957-1.

CHASSIS FEATURES: (American) 106 inches; (Classic/Ambassador) 112 inches. Overall length: (American) 177.3 inches; (Classic station wagon) 190 inches; (Classic passenger cars) 190.5 inches; (Ambassador station wagon) 190 inches; (Ambassador passenger cars) 190.5 inches. Width: (American) 68.6 inches; (all other models) 71.3 inches. Height: (American sedan) 54.5 inches; (Classic sedan) 54.6 inches; (Ambassador sedan) 55.3 inches. Tires: (Ambassador) 7.50 x 14: (American) 6.00 x 14: (Classic) 6.50 x 14.

OPTIONS

AMERICAN: Antifreeze ($4.25). Two-tone colors on sedans ($15.95); two-tone color on station wagons ($17.95); two-tone color on hardtops except 440H ($37.90); two-tone color on convertible ($21.95); special color application ($29.50). Overdrive transmission ($102). Lever control Flash-O-Matic ($164.85). Weather-Eye ($74.20). Overhead valve engine ($59.50). Air conditioning including heavy-duty cooling system ($360). Power brakes ($39.95). Power steering ($72.20). Oil-bath air cleaner ($7.15). Solex glass ($26.95). Solex windshield only ($8.95). Rear foam rubber seat cushion ($9.95). Reclining seat ($25.50). Undercoating ($14.95). Windshield washer ($11.95). Back-up lights ($10.70). Wheel discs ($14.95). Electric clock ($15.30). Inside 'tilt' rearview mirror ($4.95). Left or right outside rearview mirror ($3.95); left and right outside rearview mirror ($7.90). Twin-grip differential ($29.60). Pair of license frames ($3.50): rear license frame only ($1.75). Front and rear heavy-duty shocks ($2.70). Heavy-duty front and rear shocks and rear springs ($4). Heavy-duty radiator ($3.55). Heavy-duty cooling system ($12.50). Push-button radio and antenna ($58.50); manual radio and antenna ($52.50). Individually adjusted front seats ($20). Padded instrument panel and visors ($17.60). Bucket seats on American 440 ($99.50); left and right bucket seats on American 440 ($24). Rear load levelers ($32.15). Load levelers with heavy-duty front shocks ($34.85). Two front seat belts ($17.85); four front and rear seat belts ($37). E-Stick transmission, automatic clutch available only with standard or overdrive gearboxes ($59.50). Visibility group A ($21.25). Light group ($19.60). Chrome horn ring ($7.70). Heavy-duty battery ($6.50). Air conditioning adaptor group ($20.55). 33 amp. alternator ($12). Vinyl seat upholstery ($15). Left or right-hand lounge-tilt seat and headrest ($21). Left- and right-hand lounge-tilt seat and headrest ($42). Power-Pack, twin throat carburetor ($12). Twin-stick floor shift transmission and overdrive ($134.50).

CLASSIC/AMBASSADOR: All-Season air conditioning ($380-$399). Alternator ($12). Back-up lights ($10.70). Heavy-duty battery ($6.50). Bucket seats ($99.50) Electric clock ($15.95). Two-tone color on sedans ($19.95); two-tone color on wagons ($21.95), special color applications ($29.50). Coolant Dowgard ($4.25-$6.25). Heavy-duty cooling system ($17.20-$19.85). Six-cylinder aluminum engine ($30). Rear foam cushions ($9.95). Adjustable front seats ($20). Reclining front seat ($25.50). Front lounge-tilt seat with headrest ($21). Tinted glass ($39.50-$45.50). Tinted windshield ($15.95). Left or right headrest ($12). Chrome horn ring ($7.70). Light group ($19.60). Load levelers ($32.15). Load levelers with heavy-duty front shocks ($36). Load levels with heavy-duty front shocks and springs ($38.70). Inside 'tilt' mirror ($4.95). Outside left or right mirror ($5.30). Outside rearview remote control mirror ($11.95). Padded instrument panel and visors ($19.95). Power brakes ($42.95$43.95). Power door locks on two-doors ($23.45); power door locks on four-doors ($29.85). Power Pack ($12.00-$23.75). Power Saver fan ($19.60). Power steering ($19.60-$81.20). Power windows ($102.25). Heavy-duty radiator ($5.55-$9.55). Single speaker radio and antenna ($64.95). Dual speaker radio and antenna ($77.25). Front seat belts ($17.85). Front and rear seat belts ($37). Heavy-duty springs and shocks ($5.05). Extra-heavy-duty springs and rear shocks ($7.30). Heavy-duty springs and shocks ($6.55). Side hinge tailgate ($39.60). Twin stick transmission ($141.00$147.50). Flash-O-Matic transmission ($186.50-$219.50). Overdrive trans-

mission ($108.50-$114.95). Twin grip differential ($37.50-$42.70). Undercoating ($14.95). Visibility group A ($22.50). Visibility group B ($28.85). Weather-Eye Heater ($78). Wheel discs ($14.95). Windshield washer ($11.95). Numerous tire choices.

HISTORICAL FOOTNOTES: The 1964 Ramblers were introduced Oct. 65, 1963. Model year registrations peaked at 379,412 units. Calendar year production of 393,863 cars was recorded. R.E. Cross was the chief executive officer of the company this year. A new option was Adjust-O-Tilt steering.

1965 RAMBLER

1965 Rambler, American 440 two-door hardtop, 6-cyl

RAMBLER AMERICAN — (SIX) — SERIES 01 — The 1965 Rambler American retained the same basic styling as in 1964. The front horizontal bar grille now had indentations made in it. This gave the appearance that it was divided into three parts. Rocker panel moldings were added to all lines, except '220's. New chrome side trim was also used on all, but '220' models, which did not have bodyside moldings. Standard equipment on '220' models included turn signals, heavy-duty lights; front armrests; dual sun visors; rubber floor mats; front foam seat cushions; front seat belts; one front ashtray; dome or pillar lamps; Fresh-Air ventilation; two coat hooks; 60 amp. battery and blue/green panel illumination. The '330' models had all of these items, plus rear armrests; cigarette lighter; rear ashtrays; carpets and station wagon luggage rack. The '440' models added richer appointments and trim, plus a lockable glovebox. Standard or base technical features of all 1965 Ramblers included column-mounted three-speed manual transmission; self-adjusting Double-Safety brakes; oil, gas and fuel pump filters; power booster fuel pump; Anti-Smog system and ceramic armoured exhaust system. A new '232' engine was available and the E-Stick transmission was dropped.

RAMBLER I.D. DATA: VIN on plate on right wheelhouse panel below hood. First symbol identified series: B=American; G=Classic Six; Z=Classic Eight; H=Ambassador Eight. Second through last symbols were sequential production number. [American] Starting Serial Numbers were P-100001 for cars with the '196' six; PK-100001 for export models with the '196' six; W-100001 for cars with the '232' six; WK-100001 for export models with the '232' six. The starting serial numbers for Canadian production were as follows: PT-500001 for '196' six QT-500001 for '199' six; VVT-500001 for '232' six. [Classic] Starting Serial Numbers were J-100001 for cars with the '199' six; JK-100001 for export models with the '199' six; L-1500001 for cars with the '232' six; LK-100001 for export models with the '232' six; Z-275001 for cars with the '287' V-8; ZK-12001 for export models with the '287'; U-100001 for cars with the '327' V-81 UK-100001 for export models with the '327' V-8. The starting serial numbers for Canadian production were as follows: JT-500001 for cars with the '199' six; LT-500001 for cars with '232' six; ZT-500001 for cars with the '287' six. [Marlin] Starting serial numbers were 2K-100001 for cars with the '232' six; 4-100001 for cars with the '327' V-8; 4K-10001 for Export models with the '327' V-8. [Ambassador] Starting Serial Numbers were S-100001 for cars with the '232' six and SK-10001 for export models with the same engine; E-100001 for cars with the '287' V-8 and EK-10001 for export cars with the same engine; H-100001 for cars with the '327' V-8 and HK-13001 for export cars with the same engine. The starting serial numbers for Canadian built cars were as follows: ST-500001 for cars with the '232'; ET-500001 for cars with the '287' V-8; and HT-500001 for cars with the '327' V-8. Body Number plate riveted to left front door hinge pillar has additional data. First line indicates body production sequence number. Second line indicates "Model No." consisting of first two symbols indicating model year and additional symbols indicating body style and series. Complete "Model No." corresponds to column two of charts below. Third line gives trim data. Fourth line gives paint color data. Six-cylinder motor number on upper left front corner of engine block. V-8 motor number on top at front of block; or front of block; or center, left side of block, above oil pan. Continuing in 1965, AMC employed an "Engine Day Build Code" system giving all engines of a type the same six symbol code. The first symbol of the engine day built code is a single digit number code for the year of manufacture starting with 7=1965. The second and third symbols indicated month of build: 01=Jan.; 02=Feb.; etc. The numbers differed in the fourth symbol, a letter code designating the engine displacement and carburetion. Letter codes were: A=195.6 cid/90 hp L-head six; B=195.6 cid/125 hp six; B=195.6 cid/138 hp OHV six; F=327 cid/270 hp V-8 4V; G=287 cid/198 hp V-8; L=232 cid/145 hp six; L=232 cid/155 hp six; J=199 cid/128 hp six. The fifth and sixth symbols indicated day of manufacture as appropriate. In motor number 701A22: first symbol 7=1965; 01=Jan.; A=195.6 cid/90 hp six and 22=22nd day of month.

RAMBLER AMERICAN SERIES 01

Series Number	Body/Style Number	Body Type & Seating	Factory Price	Shipping Weight	Production Total
220 SERIES					
01	6505	4-dr Sed-6P	2036	2518	13,700
01	6506	2-dr Sed-6P	1979	2495	26,409
01	6508	2-dr Sta Wag-6P	2312	2684	5,224
330 SERIES					
01	6505-2	4-dr Sed-6P	2129	2522	15,148
01	6506-2	2-dr Sed-6P	2072	2490	9,065
01	6508-2	2-dr Sta Wag-6P	2396	2682	12,313

440 SERIES

Series Number	Body/Style Number	Body Type & Seating	Factory Price	Shipping Weight	Production Total
01	6505-5	4-dr Sed-6P	2222	2580	5,194
01	6507-5	2-dr Conv-5P	2418	2747	3,882
01	6509-5	2-dr HT Cpe-6P	2205	2596	13,784
01	6509-7	2-dr 440H HT-4P	2327	2622	8,164

1965 Rambler, Classic 770 two-door convertible, 6-cyl

RAMBLER CLASSIC — (SIX) — SERIES 10 — Rambler Classics received a completely restyled front end for 1965, plus new rear end sheet metal. The front featured new fenders and a grille having 'veed-out' horizontal bars, with three vertical division bars that created four sections. Dual horizontal headlamps flanked the grille on either side. The rear was squared-off and had wraparound, rectangular taillamps. Three trim levels were provided: '550', '660' and '770'. Five body styles were offered, including a new convertible. Standard equipment on '550' models included front armrests; dual visors; cigar lighter; one front ashtray; rubber floor covering (and trunk mat): front foam seat cushions; dome or pillar lights; front seat belts; Fresh Air ventilation; station wagon luggage rack; two coat hooks; 60 amp. battery; and blue/green panel lighting. The '660' models had all of the above, plus rear armrests; two front ashtrays; rear ashtrays; carpets; and locking glovebox. The '770' had all above features, except no coat hooks on convertibles. Trim bars were seen on the rear roof pillar and '770' trim and appointments were richer. A 199 cid six was standard in the '550'. A 232 cid six was base power plant for the other lines. A 287 cid V-8 was extra in '550s,' a 327 cid V-8 in other lines.

RAMBLER CLASSIC SERIES 10

Series Number	Body/Style Number	Body Type & Seating	Factory Price	Shipping Weight	Production Total
550 SERIES					
10	6515	4-dr Sed-6P	2192	2987	30,869
10	6516	2-dr Sed-6P	2142	2963	7,082
10	6518	4-dr Sta Wag-6P	2522	3134	13,759
660 SERIES					
10	6515-2	4-dr Sed-6P	2287	2882	50,638
10	6516-2	2-dr Sed-6P	2282	2991	4,561
10	6518-2	4-dr Sta Wag-6P	2624	3155	32,444
770 SERIES					
10	6515-5	4-dr Sed-6P	2436	3029	23,603
10	6519-5	2-dr HT Cpe-6P	2436	3063	14,778
10	6519-7	2-dr 770H HT-5P	2548	3089	5,706
10	6517-5	2-dr Conv-6P	2696	3169	4,953
10	6518-5	4-dr Sta Wag-6P	2727	3180	15,623

MARLIN — (SIX) — SERIES 50 — The 1965 Marlin was introduced in February, 1965 as a midyear addition to the line. It was basically a Rambler Classic with special fastback roof styling. Different taillights were used, but the grille was of the Classic type with the vertical division bars removed. A special Marlin hood ornament was seen. The Marlin was American Motors Corp.'s answer to the Ford Mustang, but could accommodate six passengers, as opposed to only four in the Mustang.

MARLIN SERIES 50

Series Number	Body/Style Number	Body Type & Seating	Factory Price	Shipping Weight	Production Total
50	6559-7	2-dr HT FsBk-6P	3100	3234	10,327

1965 Rambler, Ambassador 990 four-door sedan, V-8

RAMBLER AMBASSADOR — (SIX) — SERIES 80 — The 1965 Ambassador had a totally new front end with a four-inch longer wheelbase than Classics. The front featured vertical, quad headlamps and a grille of numerous horizontal bars which 'veed' slightly outwards along the horizontal plane. Bright metal side trim ran from the rear along the top edge of the body and around the front of the car (crossing the grille). The taillamps wrapped around the body corners and could be seen from both the rear and the side. A convertible, four-door sedans, station wagons, two-door sedans and hardtops were offered in specific lines. A new Ambassador Six marked the first time since 1956 that a six-cylinder motor had been offered in Ambassadors.

RAMBLER AMBASSADOR SERIES 80

Series Number	Body/Style Number	Body Type & Seating	Factory Price	Shipping Weight	Production Total
AMBASSADOR 880 SERIES					
80	6585-2	4-dr Sed-6P	2565	3120	10,564
80	6586-2	2-dr Sed-6P	2512	3087	1,301
80	6588-2	4-dr Sta Wag-6P	2879	3247	3,812
AMBASSADOR 990 SERIES					
80	6585-5	4-dr Sed-6P	2656	3151	24,852
80	6587-5	2-dr Conv-6P	2955	3265	3,499
80	6588-5	4-dr Sta Wag-6P	2970	3268	8,701
80	6589-5	2-dr HT Cpe-6P	2669	3168	5,034
80	6589-7	2-dr 990H HT-5P	2837	3198	6,382

BASE ENGINES

(AMERICAN 220/330) Inline Six: Cast iron block. Displacement: 195.6 cid. Bore and stroke: 3.125 x 4.25 inches. Compression ratio: 8.0:1. Brake hp: 90 at 3800 rpm. Four main bearings. Solid valve lifters. Carburetor: Carter Type RBS one-barrel Model 3708S.

(AMERICAN 440/440-H) Inline Six: Overhead valve. Cast iron block. Displacement: 195.6 cid. Bore and stroke: 3.125 x 4.25 inches. Compression ratio: 8.7:1. Brake hp: 125 at 4200 rpm. Four main bearings. Solid valve lifters. Carburetor: Holley one-barrel Model 1909-2555-3.

(CLASSIC 550) Inline Six: Cast iron block. Displacement: 198.8 cid. Bore and stroke: 3.75 x 3.25 inches. Compression ratio: 8.5:1. Brake horsepower: 128 at 4400 rpm. Four main bearings. Solid valve lifters. Carburetor: Holley 1909-25555-3 one-barrel.

(CLASSIC 660/770/MARLIN SIX) Inline Six: Cast iron block. Displacement: 231.9 cid. Bore and stroke: 3.75 x 3.25 inches. Compression ratio: 8.5:1. Brake horsepower: 145 at 4300 rpm. Carburetor: Carter WCD-3882 two-barrel.

(CLASSIC 660/770/MARLIN EIGHT) V-8: Overhead valves. Cast iron block. Displacement: 287 cid. Bore and stroke: 3-3/4 x 3-1/4 inches. Compression ratio: 8.7:1. Brake hp: 198 at 4700 rpm. Five main bearings. Hydraulic valve lifters. Carburetor: Holley 2209-2699.

(AMBASSADOR 990 SIX) Inline Six: Cast iron block. Displacement: 231.9 cid. Bore and stroke: 3.75 x 3.50 inches. Compression ratio: 8.5:1. Brake horsepower: 155 at 4400 rpm. Carburetor: Carter WCD-3888S two-barrel.

(AMBASSADOR EIGHT) V-8: Overhead valves. Cast iron block. Displacement: 326.7 cid. Bore and stroke: 3.75 x 3.25 inches. Compression ratio: 8.7:1. Brake hp: 250 at 4700 rpm. Five main bearings. Hydraulic valve lifters. Carburetor: Holley four-barrel.

CHASSIS FEATURES: Wheelbase: (Americans) 106 inches; (Classic/Marlin) 112 inches; (Ambassadors) 116 inches. Overall length: (Americans) 177.25 inches; (Classic station wagon) 193 inches; (other Classic/Marlin) 195 inches; (Ambassador station wagon) 197 inches. Front tread: (Ambassador/Marlin) 58.6 inches; (American) 56 inches; (Classic) 58.2 inches. Rear tread: (Ambassador/Marlin) 57.6 inches; (American) 55 inches; (Classic) 57.4 inches. Tires: (Ambassador/Marlin) 7.35 x 14; (American) 6.45 x 14; (Classic) 6.95 x 14.

OPTIONS: Air conditioner adaptor group with heavy-duty radiator and seven ampere battery ($19). All-Season air conditioner, in American ($295.85), in Classic ($312.05), in Ambassador, with power-saver fan required with V-8 ($321). 40-amp. alternator ($8.95). Appearance Group A for Americans except 440H and wagons, includes rocker panel molding, deck molding, rear fender moldings and spinner wheel discs ($55.54); same on 440H ($39.75). Appearance Group A for Classics except not available on 770H, includes rocker panel moldings, wheel opening moldings and spinner wheel discs ($58.05); same for Classic 880 ($60.30). Appearance Group B, includes same as above except wire wheelcovers: for Americans, except 440H and wagon ($92.65); for 440H ($76.95); for Classic, except 770H ($92.65); and for Classic 880 ($94.90). Back-up lights ($10.70). Heavy-duty battery ($6.50). Front disc brakes for Classic/Ambassador, includes power assist ($79.95). Slim bucket seats with console, 440 and 770 ($99.50); 440H and 770H with reclining bucket seats required ($40). Slim bucket seats with front armrest and cushion in Ambassador, with reclining seats required

($99.50). Wide bucket seats without console, 440/770 reclining seats required [standard in 440H/770H] ($59.50). Slim front bucket seats with armrest and console in Ambassador 990, requires reclining seats ($119.50); same in 990H ($20). Front bumper guards ($11.50). Front and rear bumper guards, except wagons ($23). Two-barrel carburetor with 232 cid engine ($11.55). Electric clock ($15.95). Two-tone paint on American sedans and hardtops ($16.95); on American wagons ($18.95); on Classic/Ambassador hardtops and sedans ($19.95). on Classic/Ambassador wagons ($21.95). Special paint color application, except fleet cars ($29.50). Simulated Ambassador wagon woodgrain trim ($22.20). Dowgard coolant ($5). Heavy-duty cooling system, six ($10.95); eight ($14.95). California crankcase ventilation ($5.05). L-head 196 cid engine in 220/330 ($38.55). 232 cid two-barrel engine in 220/330 with automatic required ($84.95); in 440/440H with automatic required ($49.95); in 550 only ($39.95). 327 cid V-8 four-barrel engine in Classic and Ambassador small V-8s ($81.95). Rear foam cushion ($9.95). Individually adjustable front seats ($20). Reclining front seat ($25.50). Tinted glass, in American ($27.95); in Classic/Ambassador cars ($45.50); in Classic/Ambassador wagon ($39.50). Tinted windshield only, in American ($12.95); in Classic and Ambassador ($19.95). Headrest ($12). Light Group ($19.60). Inside tilt mirror ($4.95). Outside mirror, either side ($5.30). OSRV mirror with remote-control ($11.95). Oil-bath air cleaner with L-head ($7.15). Padded panel and visors ($19.95). Padded dash panel, convertible ($17.50). Padded visors ($4.50). Power brakes, in American/Classic ($42.95), in Ambassador ($43.95). Power Saver fan ($19.60). Power steering, in American/Classic ($85.95); in Ambassador ($96.90). Power tailgate window ($31.95). American convertible power top ($49.95). Front power windows, except Americans and convertibles and hardtops ($59.50). Station wagon power front windows and power tailgate window, except Americans ($91.45). Power front and rear windows, except Americans, not available on two-door sedans or convertibles ($102.25). Wagons, except Americans, power front, rear and tailgate windows ($134.20). Radio and manual antenna in Americans ($49.50). Push-button radio and antenna in Americans ($56.50). Push-button AM radio in Classic/Ambassador ($58.50). Push-button AM/FM radio in Classic/Ambassador ($129.30). DuoCoustic rear speaker in Classic/Ambassador sedans and hardtops ($12.60). VibraTone rear speaker in Classic/Ambassador sedans and hardtops ($40.50). Heavy-duty radiator in American ($3.35). Heavy-duty radiator in Classic/Ambassador ($5.35). Airliner reclining seats in American, standard 440H, others ($25.50). Adjustable front seat in Americans, requires reclining seats ($20). Front seat belt deletion ($11 credit). Retractable front seat belts ($7.50). Retractable front and non-retractable rear seat belts ($26.70). Retractable seat belts front and rear ($45.80). Front and rear shocks in American ($2.70). Front and rear shocks in Classic/Ambassador ($3.85). Heavy-duty front and rear springs, in American ($5.15 cars/$6.55 wagons). Heavy-duty front and rear shocks and rear springs in Classic/Ambassador cars ($5.05). Heavy-duty front and rear extended springs, in Classic/Ambassador ($7.30 cars/$6.55 wagons). Adjustable steering wheel in Classic/Ambassador, requires automatic transmission ($43). Custom steering wheel in 220/550 ($7.70). Side hinge tailgate, except Americans (($39.60, but standard with third seat). Station wagon third seat, except American and 550 ($85). Flash-O-Matic transmission, in American ($171.25); in Classic Six ($186.50); in Classic Eight ($193.65); in Ambassador Six ($212.35); in Ambassador Eight ($219.50). Overdrive transmission, in Americans without 232 cid engine ($105.50); in Classic Six, ($108.50); in Classic Eight or Classic with 232 cid engine ($11.35); in Ambassador ($114.95). Flash-O-Matic Shift Command transmission, in American with 232 cid engine and slim bucket seats ($186.25); in Classic with 232 cid two-barrel engine requires slim bucket seats ($201.50); in Classic V-8 requires slim bucket seats ($208.65); in Ambassador Six, requires bucket seats and console ($227.30). In Ambassador V-8, requires bucket seats and console ($234.50). Twin Stick transmission ($134.50 to $147.50). Twin Grip differential (($37.55-$42,70). Undercoating ($17.20). Wheel discs ($20.55). Wheel discs with spinners ($14.05-$34.55). Wire wheelcovers ($48.70-$69.15). Wire wheelcovers with spinners ($11.95). Electric wipers ($8.95 American/$10.95 others). Vinyl upholstery ($15-$24.50). Credit for Weather Eye heater deletion ($72-$79). Various tire options.

HISTORICAL FOOTNOTES: The full-sized Ramblers were introduced in September, 1964 and the Americans appeared in dealer showrooms at the same time. Calendar year registrations of 324,669 cars were recorded. Calendar year sales were counted at 346,367 units. American Motors was the country's ninth largest automaker this season. The 'Rambulance', a station wagon conversion for the economy class emergency vehicle market, was available again this year. A total of 246 such vehicles were sold to police and fire departments in small towns between 1960 and 1965.

1965 Rambler, Ambassador 880, two-door sedan, V-8

1965 Rambler, American 440, two-door convertible, 6-cyl

1966 AMC, Ambassador 990, two-door convertible, V-8

1967 AMC, Ambassador DPL, two-door hardtop V-8

1968 AMC, Rambler Rogue, two-door hardtop V-8

1971 AMC, Ambassador Brougham four-door station wagon, V-8

1972 AMC, Hornet "Gucci" four-door Sportabout, 6-cyl

1973 AMC, Gremlin "Levis" two-door hatchback coupe, 6-cyl

AMC
1966-1975

1972 Javelin AMX, two-door fastback coupe, V-8.

In February, 1962, George Romney resigned as president and chairman of American Motors Corp. (AMC) to campaign successfully for Governor of Michigan. The board of directors elected him vice-chairman and granted him a leave of absence. Richard E. Cross was named board chairman, and Roy Abernethy became president.

Data Compiled by Larry Daum

During the next few years, AMC invested $300 million in new advanced-designed engines, bodies and plant facilities. Romney had been the primary driving force behind AMC's small car program. When he left, Abernathy, a former Packard sales manager, began going into direct competition with the "big three" automakers.

An entirely new line of larger cars was introduced in the 1967 model year, with the Classic series becoming the Rebel. New luxury models, including convertibles, were introduced. Roy D. Chapin, Jr., son of a founder of Hudson Motor Car Co., was made chairman and chief executive officers on Jan. 9, 1967 with William V. Luneburg as president and chief operating officer. Chapin stalked out a new and bold direction for American Motors. Among the many forward steps taken to strengthen confidence in the company was a sharp reduction in delivered prices of the low-priced Rambler American models to make them more competitive with imports, which again

were on the rise. Chapin pledged to introduce six new models in the next 18 months. The first was the Javelin, bowing on Sept. 26, 1967 as a 1968 model. A two-passenger sport car, the AMX, bowed in February, 1968. Both cars were designed to change AMC's image from a company that had once advertised, "The only race we are interested in is the human race." Now the ads said, "We just haven't been the same since we discovered racing."

In July, 1968, AMC sold its Kelvinator appliance business to White Consolidated Industries of Cleveland, Ohio. The company could now devote its full and complete energy to the automotive business. The Hornet replaced the Rambler American in the fall of 1969, as a 1970 model. The Rambler name was discontinued. A new sub-compact, the Gremlin, bowed in April, 1970, as the first American sub-compact.

On Feb. 5, 1970, AMC acquired Kaiser-Jeep Corp. in a transaction involving cash debentures and American Motors stock. The deal was part of planned expansion and acquisition program. Kaiser-Jeep became the Jeep Div. of AMC and is the leading worldwide manufacturer of four-wheel-drive vehicles.

In March, 1971, a wholly owned subsidiary, AM General Corp., was created by AMC. The company assumed the assets of both AMC's former U.S. government contracts and that of Kaiser-Jeep's General Products Div., whose plants are in Mishawaka, Indianapolis, and South Bend, Ind. Cruse W. Moss was named president of AM General, which made tac-

tical wheeled vehicles for the military and delivery vehicles for the U.S. Postal Service in Studebaker's old Chippewa Ave. plant in South Bend, Ind.

In 1971, AM General announced that it planned to enter the urban transit bus field, with production in the AM General plant in Michawaha, Ind. A deal had been arranged to manufacture a bus originally designed by Canadian Flyer. In 1973, AM General began bidding successfully on contracts, including one to build buses for the Washington D.C. Mass Transit District.

1971 also marked the redesign of the Javelin and a major facelift and change of the name for the intermediates from Rebel to Matador. Also new was a station wagon version of the Hornet, called the Sportabout. It sold extremely well. A sport model of the Hornet, the SC360, that did not sell well, was also introduced.

The year 1972 brought little change to AMC's model line-up, but a gas crisis in 1972 and 1973 brought on by an Arab oil embargo increased AMC's sales of its smaller more economical models. A special model in an AMC "designer series" of cars, was the Pierre Cardin Javelin. Inspired by fashion designer Pierre Cardin, it was available in 1972 and 1973. Another designer car, for 1972 only, was the Gucci Sportabout in the Hornet series.

In 1973, the Hornet series received a new body style. Its hatchback body style had many imitators after 1973.

The two-door Matador received a major facelift, in 1974, making it into a sleek new body style aimed at NASCAR racing. With its fastback body style, it came in two special models. The Matador X was a special sporty model and the Cassini Matador, inspired by fashion designer Oleg Cassini, was a luxury model. Four-door station wagon versions of the Matador received few changes and remained basically the same as the year before. The Ambassador made its last appearance in 1974. Then it was discontinued.

The big news at AMC for 1975 was the introduction of the Pacer in March 1975 at the Chicago Auto Show. The Pacer was AMC's first new-from-the-ground-up car to come along in a long time. It featured a unique hatchback body with larger passenger side door then driver side door, a high glass area, and a sloping hood. It had originally been intended as a front-wheel drive, rotary-engined car, but GM's discontinuance of its rotary engine program forced a return to a conventional drivetrain layout. Also for 1975, a special 'Touring' package was offered on the Sportabout, including special interior and exterior trim.

1966 AMC, American 440 four-door station wagon, 6-cyl

1967 AMC, Rambler Rebel SST two-door convertible, V-8

1968 AMC, Rambler Rebel Rogue two-door hardtop, V-8

1970 AMC, Rebel SST two-door hardtop, V-8

1971 AMC, Matador four-door station wagon, V-8

1971 AMC, Ambassador SST, four-door sedan, V-8

Standard Catalog of American Cars

1966 AMC

1966 AMC, Rambler Rogue two-door hardtop coupe, V-8

RAMBLER AMERICAN — (SIX) — SERIES 01 — The 1966 American was redesigned. It had a squared-off front end. The '330' models and the old 196.5 cid overhead valve six were dropped. A new top-of-the-line model, called the Rambler Rogue, was introduced. Rear taillamps were larger. At the Chicago Automobile Show, in mid-season, a new 290 cid overhead valve V-8 was announced and a four-speed manual transmission was introduced.

VIN: Stamped on plate welded to right fender below hood. First symbol A = AMC. Second symbol 6 = 1966. Third symbol identifies assembly plant: K = Kenosha, Wis.; B = Brampton, Ont. (Canada); Fourth symbol identifies transmission. Fifth symbol identifies body type (corresponds to fourth digit in Body/Style Number column of charts in this catalog). Sixth symbol identifies car-line (corresponds to Model Number suffix in charts). Seventh symbol identifies series and engine. Last six symbols are sequential production number starting at 100001.

RAMBLER AMERICAN

Series Number	Body/Style Number	Body Type & Seating	Factory Price	Shipping Weight	Production Total
220 LINE					
01	6605-0	4-dr Sed-6P	2086	2574	15,940
01	6606-0	2-dr Sed-6P	2017	2554	24,440
01	6608-0	4-dr Sta Wag-6P	2369	2740	5,809
440 LINE					
01	6605-5	4-dr Sed-6P	2203	2582	14,543
01	6606-5	2-dr Sed-6P	2134	2562	5,252
01	6607-5	2-dr Conv-6P	2486	2782	2,092
01	6608-5	4-dr Sta Wag-6P	2477	2745	6,603
01	6609-5	2-dr HT Cpe-6P	2227	2610	10,255
01	6609-7	2-dr Rogue HT-5P	2370	2630	8,718

1966 AMC, Rambler Marlin two-door fastback hardtop, V-8

MARLIN — (SIX) — SERIES 50 — The 1966 Marlin received a few changes. A new grille was used and many features, formerly standard, were now optional. This included power steering and brakes. The price dropped by nearly $500. And the Rambler nameplate was deleted from the rear of the car.

MARLIN

Series Number	Body/Style Number	Body Type & Seating	Factory Price	Shipping Weight	Production Total
50	6659-7	2-dr FsBk-6P	2601	3050	4,547

1966 AMC, Rambler Ambassador 990 four-door sedan, V-8

RAMBLER AMBASSADOR — (SIX) — SERIES 80 — The 1966 Ambassadors had a new roof, larger and more visible taillamps and new chrome trim pieces alongside the car, on the tip of the front fenders. They took the form of a small, ribbed rectangle. The top-level Ambassador was now called the Ambassador DPL, which would soon become 'Diplomat.'

AMBASSADOR

Series Number	Body/Style Number	Body Type & Seating	Factory Price	Shipping Weight	Production Total
880 LINE					
80	6685-2	4-dr Sed-6P	2455	3006	Note 1
80	6686-2	2-dr Sed-6P	2404	2970	Note 1
80	6688-2	4-dr Sta Wag-6P	2759	3160	Note 1
990 LINE					
80	6685-5	4-dr Sed-6P	2574	3034	Note 1
80	6689-5	2-dr HT Cpe-6P	2600	3056	Note 1
80	6687-5	2-dr Conv-5P	2968	3432	(1,798)
80	6688-5	4-dr Sta Wag-6P	2880	3180	Note 1
DPL LINE					
80	6689-7	2-dr HT Cpe-5P	2756	3090	Note 1

NOTE 1: Total 1966 Rambler Ambassador Series production was 34,222 units. No breakout per body style (except for convertible) is currently available.

BASE ENGINES: Inline Six. Overhead valves. Cast iron block. Displacement: 198.8 cid. Bore and stroke: 3.75 x 3.00 inches. Compression ratio: 8.5:1. Brake hp: 128 at 4400 rpm. Seven main bearings. Hydraulic valve lifters. Carburetor: Holley one-barrel.

1966 AMC, Rambler Classic 770 two-door convertible, V-8

RAMBLER CLASSIC — (SIX) — SERIES 10 — The 1966 Classic received a new grille, new roof and larger taillights on the same basic 1965 body. The top-level model was a two-door hardtop called the Rebel. The '660' Series designation was dropped. During the last three months of production the 290 cid V-8 took the place of the 287 cid V-8, as the smallest optional eight-cylinder engine.

RAMBLER CLASSIC

Series Number	Body/Style Number	Body Type & Seating	Factory Price	Shipping Weight	Production Total
550 LINE					
10	6615-0	4-dr Sed-6P	2238	2885	22,485
10	6616-0	2-dr Sed-6P	2189	2860	5,505
10	6618-0	4-dr Sta Wag-6P	2542	3070	9,390
770 LINE					
10	6615-5	4-dr Sed-6P	2337	2905	46,044
10	6619-5	2-dr HT Cpe-6P	2363	2935	8,736
10	6617-5	2-dr Conv-5P	2616	3070	1,806
10	6618-5	4-dr Sta Wag-6P	2629	3071	24,528

CHASSIS FEATURES: Wheelbase: (Americans) 106 inches; (Classic/Rebel/Marlin) 112 inches; (Ambassador) 116 inches. Overall length: (Americans) 181 inches; (Classic/Rebel/Marlin) 195 inches; (Ambassador station wagons) 200 inches; (other Ambassadors/DPL) 199 inches. Tires: (Americans) 6.45 x 14; (other station wagons) 7.35 x 14; (all other models) 6.95 x 14.

OPTIONS: Power brakes ($42). Power steering ($84). Air conditioning, Americans ($303); Classic ($319); Ambassador ($328). Power steering, Ambassador ($95). Front disc brakes ($91). Two-tone paint. Wheel disc, standard on Rogue/Rebel/DPL and Marlin. Turbo-cast wheelcovers. Wire wheelcovers with spinners. Slim band whitewall tires. Bumper guards with rubber facings. Black vinyl covered hardtop roof. Reclining seats, bucket-type standard on Rogue/Rebel/DPL. Safety headrests. Tachometer. Vinyl upholstery in station wagons. Side-hinged tailgate, Classic/Ambassador wagons only. Simulated woodgrain wagon paneling, Ambassadors only. Appearance group with wheel discs, rocker and wheelhouse moldings, standard on '990' and DPL. Rear seat foam cushions, standard on 770/Rebel/990/DPL/Marlin. Electric clock, standard in Rebel/990/DPL and Marlin. Cruise Command speed control, automatic transmission mandatory. Special black two-tone paint, for Rogue with vinyl roof. AM all-transistor radio, in Americans. Air-Guard, exhaust emissions control system. Four-Way hazard warning signals. Custom steering wheel, standard on all except '220' models. Remote control left-hand outside rearview mirror. AM/FM all transistor radio, for all except Americans.

Three-speed manual transmission was standard. Automatic transmission ($187). Four-speed manual floor shift transmission was optional. American six-cylinder 232 cid 155 hp two-barrel engine ($51). All Series V-8 287 cid 198 hp two-barrel engine ($106). V-8 327 cid 250 hp two-barrel engine ($32). V-8 327 cid 270 hp four-barrel engine ($65). Positive traction rear axle was optional.

HISTORICAL FOOTNOTES: The 1966 Ramblers were introduced Oct. 7, 1965 and the Marlin appeared in dealer showrooms around midyear. Model year production peaked at 295,897 units. Calendar year sales of 346,367 cars were recorded. R.D. Chapman, Jr. was the chief executive officer of the company this year. A total of 45,235 AMC models were made with 327 cid V-8s. Only 623 cars were built with 290 cid V-8s during the 1966 model year. The 287 cid V-8 was used in 44,300 additional units. AMC held a 3.71 percent share of the total market this year. Bucket seats were installed in 11.5 percent of all 1966 Ramblers; 27.6 percent had V-8s; 4.3 percent had disc brakes; 3.4 percent had movable steering columns; 10.9 percent had limited-slip differentials; 12.1 percent had air conditioning and only one percent had power windows.

1967 AMC

1967 AMC, Rambler Rogue two-door convertible, V-8

RAMBLER AMERICAN — (SIX) — SERIES 01 — The 1967 Rambler American used the same body styling as the previous year's models, with only minor changes. New taillamps were of the same, rectangular shape, but were shorter and higher. A new side molding was used on the 440 and Rogue models. It was positioned lower on the beltline. A 343 cid V-8 with four-barrel carburetion was available as optional equipment. This was also the last season for the Rambler American convertible. Only seven convertibles were assembled with the 343 cid engine. All 1967 Ramblers and Ambassadors were marketed in six-cylinder series, with V-8 engines as options.

VEHICLE IDENTIFICATION NUMBERS: Starting in 1967 (but also found on some 1966 models), American Motors used a new vehicle identification system. There are 13 symbols in the Vehicle Identification Number, which was located below the hood, on the top right-hand inner fender panel. The first symbol designated the manufacturer: A = American Motors. The second symbol designated the model year: 7 = 1967. The third symbol designated the assembly plant, B = Brampton, Canada; K = Kenosha, Wis. The fourth symbol designated the type of transmission, as follows: S = three-speed manual on column; O = three-speed manual with overdrive; A = automatic transmission on column; C = three-speed manual with floor shift; F = four-speed manual with console and floor shift and M = four-speed manual with floor shift and no center console. The fifth symbol designated Body Style, 5 = four-door sedan; 7 = two-door sedan; 8 = four-door station wagon and 9 = two-door hardtop. The sixth symbol designated class of body: 0 = 220/550; 2 = 880; 5 = 440/770/990 and 7 = Rogue/SST/DPL/Marlin. The seventh symbol designated series and engine type, as follows: (American 01 Series) A = 199 cid six with one-barrel carburetor; B = 232 cid six with two-barrel carburetor; C = 290 cid V-8 with two-barrel carburetor; D = 290 cid V-8 with four-barrel carburetor; E = 232 cid six with one-barrel carburetor and X = 343 cid V-8 with four-barrel carburetor. (Ambassador 80 Series) M = 232 cid six with one-barrel carburetor; N = 290 cid V-8 with two-barrel carburetor; P = 232 cid six with one-barrel carburetor; Q = 343 cid V-8 with four-barrel carburetor and R = 343 cid V-8 with four-barrel carburetor. (Rebel Series 10) F = 232 cid six with one-barrel carburetor; G = 232 cid six with two-barrel carburetor; H = 290 cid V-8 with two-barrel carburetor; J = 343 cid V-8 with two-barrel carburetor and K = 343 cid V-8 with four-barrel carburetor. (Marlin Series 50) S = 232 cid six with one-barrel carburetor; T = 232 cid six with two-barrel carburetor; U = 290 cid V-8 with two-barrel carburetor; V = 343 cid V-8 with two-barrel carburetor and W = 343 cid V-8 with four-barrel carburetor. The remaining symbols were six digits representing the sequential serial number and starting with 100001 for domestic cars; 700001 for Canadian cars and 10001 for export cars.

RAMBLER AMERICAN SERIES 01

Series Number	Body/Style Number	Body Type & Seating	Factory Price	Shipping Weight	Production Total
AMERICAN 220 LINE					
01	6705	4-dr Sed-6P	2142	2621	10,362
01	6706	2-dr Sed-6P	2073	2591	24,834
01	6708	4-dr Sta Wag-6P	2425	2767	2,489
AMERICAN 440 LINE					
01	6705-5	4-dr Sed-6P	2259	2613	7,523
01	6706-5	2-dr Sed-6P	2191	2586	3,317
01	6709-5	2-dr HT Cpe-6P	2283	2643	4,970
01	6708-5	4-dr Sta Wag-6P	2533	2769	4,135
AMERICAN ROGUE LINE					
01	6709-7	2-dr HT Cpe-5P	2426	2663	4,129
01	6707-7	2-dr Conv-6P	2611	2821	921

1967 AMC, Rambler Rebel SST two-door hardtop, V-8

RAMBLER REBEL — (SIX) — SERIES 10 — Rebel nameplates now adorned the cars that used to be called Classics, as the series' name was changed this year. The Rambler Rebel was also a totally redesigned automobile poised on a longer, 114 inch wheelbase. The top-of-the-line entry was known as the SST, which stood for Super Sport Touring (not Super Sonic Transport). New body styling featured slightly rounded body contours with a semi-fastback roof on two-door styles. In February, 1967 AMC introduced three special, limited-production station wagons. The first was called the Briarcliff and 400 examples were sold only in the Eastern portion of the United States. The second was the Mariner, marketed to just 600 buyers in coastal areas. Finally, there was the Westerner, which found 500 customers in the Midwest. A new 'venturi' styled grille was one appearance highlight. The 550 models had the lowest level of trim and Rebel signatures low on the sides of the cowl, behind the front wheel opening. On 770 models a lower body molding traversed and entire length of the body, arching up over both front and rear wheelhousings. The SST was adorned with simulated air intake scoops ahead of the rear wheel openings and upper beltline accent trim, but no lower body moldings. A five year or 50,000 mile warranty covered the 1967 engines and drivetrains.

RAMBLER REBEL SERIES 10

Series Number	Body/Style Number	Body Type & Seating	Factory Price	Shipping Weight	Production Total
REBEL 550 LINE					
10	6715	4-dr Sed-6P	2319	3055	10,249
10	6716	2-dr Sed-6P	2294	3089	9,121
10	6718	4-dr Sta Wag-6P	2623	3287	6,845
REBEL 770 LINE					
10	6715-5	4-dr Sed-6P	2418	3053	24,057
10	6719-5	2-dr HT Cpe-6P	2443	3092	9,685
10	6718-5	4-dr Sta Wag-6P	2710	3288	18,240
REBEL SST LINE					
10	6719-7	2-dr HT Cpe-5P	2604	3109	15,287
10	6717-7	2-dr Conv-5P	2872	3180	1,686

1967 AMC, Rambler Marlin two-door fastback hardtop coupe, V-8

RAMBLER MARLIN — (SIX) — SERIES 50 — The 1967 Marlin was longer, lower and wider and had a two-inch increase in wheelbase. The sporty Rambler entry retained its distinctive fastback roof styling and semi-elliptical side window openings. It was basically an Ambassador with a fastback roof, instead of being a streamlined Rambler Classic. American Motors hoped to increase Marlin sales by upgrading the car in this manner. It was also quite a distinctive product: a large, six-passenger sports car aimed at the family man with a 'Walter Mitty' complex. There were smoother bodysides, a new rectangular gas filler door and Rally lights incorporated into the grille. Side marker lights could be seen on the trailing edge of the rear fenders, just ahead of the wraparound rear bumper ends. A full-length lower body molding helped create a slim appearance and followed the pattern seen on Rebels, arching up over both wheelhousings. The rear deck area was cleaned-up a bit, by removal of the large, round medallion. Marlins (and other Ramblers) with V-8 power had V-shaped emblems at the forward edge of the front fenders. Unfortunately, the Marlin again had problems in the marketplace, as sales dropped to even lower levels.

RAMBLER MARLIN SERIES 50

Series Number	Body/Style Number	Body Type & Seating	Factory Price	Shipping Weight	Production Total
50	6759-7	2-dr FsBk Cpe-6P	2963	3342	2,545

AMBASSADOR — (SIX) — SERIES 80 — The 1967 Ambassador was the top American Motors' model, but it actually shared the basic body of the new Rebel. The major difference was that the front end stretched four inches longer. It had vertically stacked quad headlights flanking a horizontal bar grille. Ambassador scripts were placed on the sides of the front fenders (behind the wheel opening) and on the left-hand side of the hood. There was also a new stand-up hood ornament and segmented vertical taillamps. The basic 880 had low level trim and appointments with almost bare bodysides. The 770 models had a full-length lower

side molding similar to that described for other lines. The starring role went to the DPL, which carried a horizontal center grille divider and integral Rally lights up front. This was the final season before the curtain dropped on the Ambassador convertible.

AMBASSADOR SERIES 80

Series Number	Body/Style Number	Body Type & Seating	Factory Price	Shipping Weight	Production Total
AMBASSADOR 880 LINE					
80	6785-2	4-dr Sed-6P	2657	3279	9,772
80	6786-2	2-dr Sed-6P	2619	3310	3,623
80	6788-2	4-dr Sta Wag-6P	2962	3486	3,540
AMBASSADOR 990 LINE					
80	6785-5	4-dr Sed-6P	2776	3324	17,809
80	6789-5	2-dr HT Cpe-6P	2803	3376	6,140
80	6788-5	4-dr Sta Wag-6P	3083	3545	7,919
AMBASSADOR DPL LINE					
80	6789-7	2-dr HT Cpe-5P	2958	3394	12,552
80	6787-7	2-dr Conv-5P	3143	3434	1,260

BASE ENGINES

INLINE SIX: Overhead valves. Cast iron block. Displacement: 199 cid. Bore and stroke: 3-3/4 x 3 inches. Compression ratio: 8.5:1. Brake hp: 128 at 4400 rpm. Seven main bearings. Hydraulic valve lifters. Carburetors: Carter Type RBS one-barrel or Holley one-barrel Model 1931C-3705.

INLINE SIX: Overhead valves. Cast iron block. Displacement: 232 cid. Bore and stroke: 3.75 x 3.50 inches. Compression ratio: 8.5:1. Brake hp: 145 at 4400 rpm. Seven main bearings. Hydraulic valve lifters. Carburetor: Carter Type RBS one-barrel or Holley one-barrel Model 1931C-3705.

INLINE SIX: Overhead valves. Cast iron block. Displacement: 231.9 (232) cid. Bore and stroke: 3.75 x 3.50 inches. Compression ratio: 8.5:1. Brake hp: 145 at 4300 rpm. Seven main bearings. Hydraulic valve lifters. Carburetor: Holley one-barrel.

V-8: Overhead valves. Cast iron block. Displacement: 287.2 cid. Bore and stroke: 3.75 x 3.25 inches. Compression ratio: 8.7:1. Brake hp: 198 at 4700 rpm. Five main bearings. Hydraulic valve lifters. Carburetor: Carter WCD or Holley two-barrel.

CHASSIS FEATURES: Wheelbase: (American) 106 inches; (Rebel) 114 inches; (Ambassador/Marlin) 118 inches. Overall length: (American station wagon) 181 inches; (American passenger) 181 inches; (Rebel station wagon) 198 inches; (Rebel passenger) 197 inches; (Marlin) 201.45 inches; (Ambassador station wagon) 203 inches; (Ambassador passenger) 202.5 inches. Front tread: (American) 56 inches; (Rebel Six) 58.2 inches; (all other models) 58.6 inches. Rear tread: (American) 55 inches; (all other models) 58.5 inches. Tires: (American passenger) 6.45 x 14; (American station wagon) 6.95 x 14; (all other passenger models) 7.35 x 14; (all other station wagons) 7.75 x 14.

RAMBLER AMERICAN OPTIONS: All-transistor manual radio ($49). All-transistor push-button radio ($57). Tachometer. All-Season air conditioning ($311). Twin-Grip differential ($37). Electric washer/wipers, electric wipers mandatory with V-8 ($18). Power steering ($84). Power brakes ($42). Power tailgate window ($31). All-vinyl upholstery, standard equipment in Rogue ($24). Exterior appearance group, includes rocker moldings and wheelcovers ($77). Full wheel discs, standard on Rouge ($21). Turbo-cast wheelcovers ($61). Reclining seats for 220/440 models ($25). Reclining bucket seats with center armrest and cushion, for Rogue convertible, standard on Rogue hardtop ($98). Safety headrests ($15). Custom steering wheel for American 220, standard on other models ($8). V-8 handling package. Sports steering wheel, 440 and Rogue only ($11). Black or white vinyl roof for hardtops ($75).

AMBASSADOR/MARLIN OPTIONS: Adjust-O-Tilt steering wheel ($42). Cruise-Command automatic speed control ($44). Power disc brakes ($91). All-Season air conditioning ($350). Stereo system with 8-track tape ($133). Custom Trim package for DPL hardtop, includes: Morocco Brocade fabric in five colors for seats and door panels; two matching pillows and Custom nameplates ($49). Black or white vinyl roof, for hardtops and 990 sedan ($75). Two-tone paint ($19). Station wagon woodgrained exterior paneling ($100). Reclining bucket seats, standard in DPL hardtop ($142). Individually adjustable reclining seats, standard in DPL convertible ($45). Center console, with bucket seats and console shift options only ($113). Electric clock ($16). Tachometer ($48). Passenger third seat for station wagons ($112). Sports steering wheel; standard in DPL models ($16). Safety headrests ($45). AM/FM all-transistor radio ($134). Vinyl upholstery, standard in DPL convertible ($25). Full wheel discs, standard on Marlin and DPL ($21). Turbo-cast wheelcovers ($40). Light Group, standard in DPL ($16).

REBEL OPTIONS: All-Season air conditioning ($350). Adjust-O-Tilt steering wheel ($42). Cruise-Command automatic speed control ($44). Eye-level 6,000 rpm. tachometer $48). New 8-track stereo tape player, in sedans and hardtops with rear speaker ($134). Black or white vinyl roof, on hardtops and 770 sedan ($75). Two-tone paint ($26). Simulated woodgrain station wagon trim ($100). Vibra-Tone rear seat speakers for all-transistor radios ($52). Power steering ($84). Power brakes ($42). Power disc brakes for V-8 models ($91). Power tailgate window ($32). Station wagon third passenger seat ($112). Reclining, individually adjustable seats, standard in SST convertible ($45). Reclining bucket seats, standard in SST hardtop and not available in 550 model ($78). Vinyl upholstery, standard in SST convertible ($25). Solex glass, all window ($34); windshield only ($21). Sports steering wheel, in 770 and SST only ($16). Electric clock ($16). Rear foam seat cushion, standard in 770 and SST models and on third station wagon seat ($11). Wheel discs, standard on SST ($21). Turbo-cast wheelcovers ($61).

POWERTRAIN OPTIONS: Three-speed manual transmission was standard. Three-speed manual transmission with overdrive, in American Six ($109); others ($115). Automatic transmission, in American ($174); in Rebel ($186); in Ambassador/Marlin ($217). Four-speed manual transmission, with V-8 engines only ($184). Shift-Command automatic transmission with thumb-button operated floor shift, in Rogue with buckets and console ($192); in 770 and SST ($205); in Ambassador 880/Marlin ($217). Six-cylinder 232 cid 145 hp engine, in American ($39). Six-cylinder 232 cid 155 hp two-barrel engine, in American ($51); in other models ($12). V-8 290 cid 200 hp two-barrel engine, in American ($119). V-8 290 cid 225 hp four-barrel engine, in American ($32). V-8 343 cid 235 hp two-barrel engine, in Marlin/Rebel/Ambassador ($58). V-8 343 cid 280 hp four-barrel engine, in Marlin/Rebel/Ambassador ($91). 'Air Guard' exhaust emissions control system for V-8s ($45). 'Engine Mod' system for sixes, mandatory smog-control option for California ($11). Closed crankcase ventilation system. mandatory in California ($50). Heavy-duty clutch for V-8 with manual transmission ($5). Dual exhausts ($26).

HISTORICAL FOOTNOTES: The full-sized models were introduced Oct. 6, 1966 and the American appeared in dealer showrooms the same day. Model year production peaked at 235,522 units. Calendar year sales of 229,058 cars were recorded. R.D. Chapin, Jr. was the chief executive officer of the company this year. American Motor's financial branch, called Redisco, Inc., was sold to Chrysler this year. A new advertising agency, Wells, Rich, Greene, Inc., of New York City, was engaged by AMC's brand new management team and came up with a series of humorous, but effective ad campaigns that focused on product advantages. A total of 1.2 percent of all AMC products had four-speed manual transmissions; 16.3 percent had bucket seats, 45 percent V-8 powerplants and 11.2 percent vinyl tops.

1968 AMC

RAMBLER AMERICAN — (SIX) — SERIES 01 — The 1968 Rambler American used the same body styling as the 1966 and 1967 models. There were several changes in decorative trim. A new grille featured a single horizontal strip of chrome across the insert with a Rambler nameplate at the left-hand side. Signature scripts on the sides of front fenders were moved, from in back of the headlights, to a point behind the wheel opening. Rectangular side markers were seen on both front and rear fenders. Squarish taillamps were set into the rear panel and a Rambler badge was placed near the right taillight lens. The base American 220 came as a four-door sedan or the year's only two-door sedan. This car had no side body moldings and equipment consisted of a Weather-Eye heater; front armrests; front seat foam cushions and dome or side pillar lights. The American 440 had a single, wide strip of ribbed chrome molding positioned high on the bodysides. It connected the front and rear side markers. There was also a bright metal horizontal strip between the taillamps; carpeting; rear armrests; cigarette lighter; glove box lock; dual horns and Custom steering wheel. The station wagon came with all-vinyl upholstery and larger tires. The top model was the Rogue two-door hardtop which had all American 440 features, plus a larger base six-cylinder engine; special Rogue identification scripts (in place of American signatures) and higher level interior appointments. All Americans were marketed as sixes, with V8s available as optional equipment.

VIN: The 1968 serial numbers were located on top of the right front wheelhouse panel. The unit body data plate was riveted to the left front door, below the latch mechanism. In 1968, American Motors refined the 13 symbol identification code system introduced the previous year. The third symbol was now a letter designating transmission type, instead of a number designating the assembly plant. (The transmission codes themselves were unchanged.) The fourth symbol was a number designating car-line, as follows: 0 = American; 1 = Rebel, 3 = AMX; 7 = Javelin and 8 = Ambassador. The fifth symbol designated body type, using the 1967 number codes. The sixth symbol designated the series or class of body, as follows: 0 = American 220/Rebel 550; 2 = Ambassador; 5 = American 440/Rebel 770/Ambassador DPL and 7 = AMX/Rogue/SST Ambassador. The seventh symbol was a letter designating engine type (without regard to car-line), as follows: A = 199 cid six one-barrel; B = 232 cid six one-barrel; C = 232 cid six two-barrel; M = 290 cid V-8 two-barrel; N = 290 cid V-8 four-barrel; S = 343 cid V-8 two-barrel; T = 343 cid V-8 four-barrel; W = 390 cid V-8 two-barrel and X = 390 cid V-8 four-barrel. The following group of symbols was the sequential serial number and began with 100001 for cars built in Kenosha, Wis. and 700001 for cars built in Brampton, Ontario, Canada.

1968 AMC, Rambler American 440 four-door station wagon, V-8

RAMBLER AMERICAN SERIES 01

Series Number	Body/Style Number	Body Type & Seating	Factory Price	Shipping Weight	Production Total
AMERICAN 220 LINE					
01	6805	4-dr Sed-6P	2024	2638	16,595
01	6806	2-dr Sed-6P	1946	2604	53,824
AMERICAN 440 LINE					
01	6805-5	4-dr Sed-6P	2166	2643	11,116
01	6808-5	4-dr Sta Wag-6P	2426	2800	8,285
AMERICAN ROGUE LINE					
01	6809-7	2-dr HT Cpe-6P	2244	2678	4,549

NOTE: Prices on many American Motor cars were increased around May 1, 1968. The above prices are those in effect at the end of the model year.

RAMBLER REBEL — (SIX/V-8) — SERIES 10 — Offering the only convertible left in the AMC stable, the Rebel was modestly restyled for 1968. The Rambler name was removed from the hood and the taillamps now took the form of three horizontal, curved rectangles, instead of the two large rectangles seen the year before. Square, recessed door handles were another new feature and bodyside moldings were eliminated. The base Rebel 550 models carried this designation below the signature scripts on the sides of front fenders and on the right-hand corner of the trunk lid's rear face. More than a dozen safety changes, enacted to satisfy government regulations, included new front side marker lamps and a preset door locking system. Regular equipment on 550s included all standard safety features; heater; front armrests (on four-doors); cigar lighter; dual headlamps; front seat foam cushions and dome or side pillar lamps. Station wagons came with a rooftop travel rack and all-vinyl upholstery and convertibles featured power operated tops. Rebel 770 models had all above items, plus rear ashtrays; rear armrests; Custom steering wheel; glove box lock; dual horns and cloth and vinyl or all-vinyl seats. The 770 station wagons also had a hidden stowage compartment and vertical tailgate with power window on three-seat options. Model identification numbers were seen in the usual places and read '770.' The Rebel SST came only with V-8 power, exclusively in sport body styles, and represented the top of the line. Trim and equipment distinctions included SST lettering (below front fenderside scripts); wheelhouse trim moldings; simulated chrome air vents ahead of rear wheel opening; individually adjustable reclining seats and special interior appointments. Wheel discs were standard on the SST, as was underhood

insulation. This was the final season for Rambler convertibles and the two low-production Rebel ragtops were the last that American Motors would ever offer, at least during the years covered by this catalog.

RAMBLER REBEL SERIES 10

Series Number	Body/Style Number	Body Type & Seating	Factory Price	Shipping Weight	Production Total
REBEL 550 LINE					
10	6815	4-dr Sed-6P	2443	3062	14,712
10	6817	2-dr Conv-6P	2736	3195	377
10	6818	4-dr Sta Wag-6P	2729	3301	7,427
10	6819	2-dr HT Cpe-6P	2454	3117	7,377
REBEL 770 LINE					
10	6815-5	4-dr Sed-6P	2542	3074	22,938
10	6818-5	4-dr Sta Wag-6P	2854	3306	11,375
10	6819-5	2-dr HT Cpe-6P	2556	3116	4,420
REBEL SST LINE (V-8)					
10	6817-7	2-dr Conv-6P	2999	3427	823
10	6819-7	2-dr HT Cpe-6P	2775	3348	9,876

NOTE 1: The Rebel SST came only with the 'Typhoon' 290 cid V-8 as base powerplant.
NOTE 2: See 1968 American Series note. The above prices are those in effect at the end of the model year.

1968 AMC, Ambassador SST two-door hardtop coupe, V-8

AMBASSADOR — (SIX/V-8) — SERIES 80 — The 1968 Ambassador had a grille with squarer corner extensions, a grid style insert with black-out finish and a wider horizontal center divider that gave a twin slot look. Side molding treatments remained basically unchanged and consisted of a full-length chrome strip, mounted low on the body, which arched up over the wheel openings. The stand-up hood ornament was eliminated. Taillights were now divided horizontally, instead of vertically. Cars with 'Typhoon' power had V-shaped rear fender ornaments. The new paddle type AMC door handles were used. In a move that was very heavily promoted, air conditioning became standard Ambassador equipment. The base model was no longer called the 880 (although these numbers still appeared as the last three symbols in the series designation) and was simply referred to as the Ambassador. It came with All-Season air conditioning; all standard safety features; 60 ampere battery; heater; front and rear armrests; cigarette lighter; front and rear ashtrays; carpets; front foam seat cushions; dome or side pillar lights; glove box lock; dual horns and headlights (still vertically stacked) and a Custom steering wheel. Ambassador wagons had a roof rack and lockable stowage compartment, plus power tailgate window on three-seat types. The Ambassador DPL carried these three letters on a nameplate located below the side fender scripts and featured full wheel discs and upgraded appointments. Both the Ambassador and Ambassador DPL models were marketed as six-cylinder cars, with V-8 options. The flagship of the fleet was the Ambassador SST which had all DPL items, plus custom interior and exterior trim; individually adjustable reclining seats; woodgrain look paneling on dashboard; electric clock; headlights-on warning buzzer; rear foam seat cushions and a 200 hp two-barrel V-8 engine. The Ambassador SST hardtop featured a special grille treatment, with integral Rally lights, and interior courtesy lamps.

AMBASSADOR SERIES 80

Model Number	Body/Style Number	Body Type & Seating	Factory Price	Shipping Weight	Production Total
AMBASSADOR LINE					
80	6885-2	4-dr Sed-6P	2820	3193	8,788
80	6889-2	2-dr HT Cpe-6P	2842	3258	3,360
AMBASSADOR DPL LINE					
80	6885-5	4-dr Sed-6P	2920	3265	13,265
80	6889-5	2-dr HT Cpe-6P	2941	3321	3,696
80	6888-5	4-dr Sta Wag-6P	3207	3475	10,690
AMBASSADOR SST LINE (V-8)					
80	6885-7	4-dr Sed-6P	3151	3476	13,387
80	6889-7	2-dr HT-6P	3172	3530	7,686

NOTE 1: The Ambassador SST came only with the 290 cid V-8 as base powerplant.
NOTE 2: See 1968 American Series note. The above prices are those in effect at the end of the model year.

1968 AMC, Javelin SST two-door hardtop coupe, V-8

JAVELIN — (SIX/V-8) — The new Javelin filled the slot vacated by the unsuccessful Marlin. It was American Motors Corp.'s entry into the Pony Car market that Ford created, with the Mustang, in 1964. The car was 189 inches long and on a 109 inch wheelbase platform. Power came from either the 232 cid six or the 343 cid V-8 in standard form. Styling characteristics included a split grille with black-out treatment and form-fitting bumper; single, square headlamp housings integrated into fenders; round parking lamps integrated into bumper (below headlights); clean-lined body with smooth-flowing lines and a semi-fastback roofline with wide, flat sail panels. The profile exhibited a 'venturi' silhouette. A full-width rear bumper; horizontal, rectangular taillights and a black-out rear panel treatment characterized the rear. Javelin chrome signature scripts were seen in the left-hand grille insert; on the front fenders behind the wheel opening and in the center of the deck latch panel. Standard equipment included all regulation safety features; Custom steering wheel; heater; Flo-Thru ventilation; dual paint stripes along upper beltline; front armrests; cigarette lighter; front ashtray; carpeting; bucket seats with front foam cushions; compartment lights; glove box lock; dual horns; wide profile tires and, for V-8s, a performance suspension with sway bar. There was also a Javelin SST, with all the above, plus reclining front bucket seats; wood-look Sports steering wheel and door panel trims; full wheel discs and moldings for the rocker panels, side windows and hood scoop. The Javelin went on sale Sept. 26, 1967 and by January a total of 12,390 had been sold. The company took the Javelin to Daytona Beach and other race tracks to show that it could really go. Later, the car showed promise in the new Trans-American racing series and, with full factory backing, narrowly missed unseating the championship Ford Mustang factory team. The Javelin was the last American Pony Car introduced and many enthusiasts thought it to be the best.

JAVELIN SERIES 70

Series Number	Body/Style Number	Body Type & Seating	Factory Price	Shipping Weight	Production Total
JAVELIN					
70	6879-5	2-dr FsBk-4P	2482	2826	29,097
JAVELIN SST					
70	6879-7	2-dr FsBk-4P	2587	2836	26,027

NOTE 1: The Javelin was introduced as a six-cylinder Series, with optional V-8s available at extra cost. Prices above are those in effect at the end of the model year.

1968 AMC, AMX two-door fastback sports coupe, V-8

AMX — (V-8) — SERIES 30 — Round number two in the AMC revitalization program officially kicked-off on Feb. 24, 1968 with the midyear introduction of the AMX two-seater sports car at the Chicago Automobile Show. Actually, the car had made its initial public appearance about a week earlier, when it was press previewed at Daytona Raceway in Daytona Beach, Fla. The model designation stood for "American Motors Experimental" and it was the first American two-passenger, steel-bodied production type sports car to be seen since the 1955-1957 Ford Thunderbird. A kid brother to the Javelin, the AMX was built off a 97 inch wheelbase version of the same platform. Features included thin shell reclining bucket seats; carpeted interior; woodgrained steering wheel and door panel trim; the 290 cid 225 hp V-8; four-speed manual transmission; special suspension; glass-belted Goodyear tires; and four-barrel carburetor. Power options included the 343 cid V-8 and a 390 cid engine with 315 hp that turned the little sportster into a real speed demon. It looked like a short Javelin with louvered hood bulges and a non-divided grille treatment. It carried special model identification within a large ring of chrome, on the sail panels. Craig Breedlove established 106 world speed records with a 1968 AMX at Goodyear's Texas test track in February, 1968. The following month, the AMX was seen in dealer showrooms, hoping to go half as fast in the race for sales. It was, however, primarily an image car designed to exhibit AMC's new approach to design, engineering, styling and marketing. A number of replica Craig Breedlove model AMXs with red, white and blue paint jobs and the 290 V-8 and four-speed transmission were sold. The number of Craig Breedlove Special AMXs made is believed to have been 50 cars.

AMX SERIES 30

Model Number	Body/Style Number	Body Type & Seating	Factory Price	Shipping Weight	Production Total
30	6839-7	2-dr FsBk-2P	3245	3097	6,725

NOTE: Prices above are introductory prices. The AMX was a midyear model and its retail pricing did not change when retails for other lines increased in the spring.

BASE ENGINES

INLINE SIX: Overhead valves. Cast iron block. Displacement: 199 cid. Bore and stroke: 3-3/4 x 3 inches. Compression ratio: 8.5:1. Brake hp: 128 at 4400 rpm. Seven main bearings. Hydraulic valve lifters. Carburetors: Carter Type RBS one-barrel or Holley one-barrel Model 1931C-3705.

INLINE SIX: Overhead valves. Cast iron block. Displacement: 232 cid. Bore and stroke: 3.75 x 3.50 inches. Compression ratio: 8.5:1. Brake hp: 145 at 4400 rpm. Seven main bearings. Hydraulic valve lifters. Carburetor: Carter Type RBS one-barrel or Holley one-barrel Model 1931C-3705.

V-8: Overhead valves. Cast iron block. Displacement: 290 cid. Bore and stroke: 3.75 x 3.25 inches. Compression ratio: 9.0:1. Brake hp: 200 at 4600 rpm. Five main bearings. Hydraulic valve lifters. Carburetor: AMC two-barrel Model 8HM2.

AMX V-8: Overhead valves. Cast iron block. Displacement: 290 cid. Bore and stroke: 3.75 x 3.25 inches. Compression ratio: 10.0:1. Brake hp: 225 at 4700 rpm. Five main bearings. Carburetor: Carter type AFB four-barrel 4660S.

CHASSIS FEATURES: Wheelbase: (American) 106 inches; (Javelin) 109 inches; (Rebel) 114 inches; (Ambassador) 118 inches; (AMX) 97 inches. Overall length: (American) 181 inches; (Javelin) 189.2 inches; (Rebel wagon) 198 inches; (Rebel) 197 inches; (Ambassador wagon) 203 inches; (Ambassador) 202.5 inches; (AMX) 177.2 inches. Front tread: (Javelin) 57.9 inches; (AMX) 58.4 inches; (other models) See 1967 specifications. Rear tread: (Javelin and AMX) 57 inches; (other models) See 1967 specifications. Tires: (American) 6.45 x 14; (American wagon) 6.95 x 14; (Javelin Six) 6.95 x 14; (Rebel and Ambassador Six) 7.35 x 14; (Rebel/Ambassador Six wagon) 7.75 x 14; (Rebel V-8) 7.35 x 14; (Ambassador V-8) 7.75 x 14; (AMX) E70-14.

AMERICAN OPTIONS: Power brakes ($42). Power steering ($84). Air conditioning ($311). Power disc brakes, V-8 only ($97). Solex glass, all windows ($29); windshield only ($16). Front and rear bumper guards ($23); front bumper guards only ($12). Vinyl top, hardtops only ($79). Individually reclining seats ($49). Sports steering wheel ($21). Custom steering wheel in 220 models ($9). Tachometer, with V-8 only ($48). Column shift automatic transmission ($174). Four-speed manual transmission, with V-8 ($184). Vinyl seat upholstery, standard on wagon ($24). Turbo-cast wheelcovers ($61). Wire wheelcovers ($66). Full wheel discs, all ($21). Electric windshield wipers ($12). Wide profile high-performance tires, exchange ($64). Push-button radio and antenna ($61). Rooftop station wagon travel rack ($39). Pair of headrests ($35). Special application paint colors ($28). Three-speed manual transmission was standard. Overdrive transmission was available for American. Automatic transmission was optional on all with floor control on specific models. Four-speed manual floor shift transmission, standard AMX; optional, with V-8 only, on other models. American six-cylinder 232 cid 145 hp one-barrel engine ($45). American V-8 290 cid 200 hp two-barrel engine ($119). American V-8 290 cid 225 hp four-barrel engine ($45).

REBEL OPTIONS: Power brakes ($42). Power steering ($84). Air conditioning ($356). Power disc brakes, V-8 only ($97). Solex glass, all windows ($34); windshield only ($21). Front and rear bumper guards ($23). Pair of headrests, bench seat ($35); bucket seats ($49). Two-tone paint ($32). Station wagon exterior woodgrained, 770 only ($100). SST exterior paint stripe ($14). AM push-button radio, all ($58). AM/FM push-button radio, all ($134). Black, blue or off-white vinyl roof, hardtop or sedan ($79). SST reclining bucket seat with center armrest ($91). Station wagon third rear-facing seat, includes power tailgate window ($112). Stereo 8-track player with two rear speakers ($134). Adjust-O-Tilt steering, with automatic only ($42). Speed control system, with automatic only ($44): Tachometer, with V-8 only ($48). SST Shift-Command console, with V-8 only ($249). Four-speed manual floor shift ($184). SST undercoating ($17). Vinyl seats, standard in convertible and wagon ($24). Sports steering wheel ($21). Turbo-cast wheelcovers; SST ($40); others ($51). Wire wheelcovers, SST ($45); other models ($66). Wheel discs, standard on SST ($45). Power windows, SST only ($100). Three-speed manual transmission was standard. Overdrive transmission was available for Rebel. Automatic transmission was optional on all with floor control on specific models. Four-speed manual floor shift transmission optional, with V-8 only. Rebel V-8 290 cid 200 hp two-barrel engine ($106). Rebel V-8 343 cid 235 hp two-barrel engine ($45). Rebel V-8 343 cid 280 hp four-barrel engine ($76).

AMBASSADOR OPTIONS: Power brakes ($43). Power steering ($95). Power disc brakes ($97). Twin-Grip differential ($42). Engine block heater ($18). Two-tone paint, standard color ($32). DPL Special paint with painted side panel and accent trim ($45). Simulated woodgrain side paneling, DPL only ($100). Exterior paint strip, SST only ($14). AM/FM push-button radio ($58). Vinyl top, hardtop or sedan only, three colors ($79). Reclining bucket seat with center armrest cushion ($91). Adjust-O-Tilt steering wheel ($42). Sports steering wheel ($21). Stereo 8-track with twin rear speakers ($134). Shift-Command console for V-8, SST only ($250). Four-speed manual transmission ($184). Turbo-cast wheelcovers, SST/DPL ($40); others ($61). Wire wheelcovers, SST/DPL ($45); others ($66). Station wagon power side and tailgate windows, DPL only ($134). Power side windows, except base models ($100). Station wagon power tailgate window only ($33). Station wagon rear facing third seat with power tailgate window ($95). Tachometer, V-8 only ($48). Visibility option package ($41). Light Group option package ($22). Engine cooling option package ($16). Handling option package ($10). Two front shoulder belts, all ($23). Three-speed manual transmission was standard. Overdrive transmission was available for Ambassador. Automatic transmission was optional on all with floor control on specific models. Four-speed manual floor shift transmission, standard AMX; optional, with V-8 only, on other models. Ambassador V-8 290 cid 200 hp two-barrel engine ($16). Ambassador V-8 343 cid 235 hp two-barrel engine ($58). Ambassador V-8 343 cid 280 hp four-barrel engine ($91). Four-barrel carburetor. Positive traction rear axle. Heavy-duty clutch. NOTE: Prices for V-8s other than base 200 hp engine are in addition to basic cost of V-8 attachment.

JAVELIN OPTIONS: Power brakes ($42). Power steering ($85). Air conditioning ($356). Dual exhausts, V-8 ($21). Solex glass, all windows ($31); windshield only ($21). Headrest, with bench seat ($35); with buckets ($49). Power discs brakes, V-8 ($97). Power steering ($84). Stereo 8-track player ($195). Individually adjusting seat ($49). White vinyl seat upholstery ($20). Adjust-O-Tilt steering ($42). Shift-Command automatic transmission with floor shift and console ($269). Twin-Grip differential ($42). Vinyl roof ($85). Turbo-Cast wheelcovers, SST ($51); base model ($65). Handling package ($17). 'GO Pack' performance package includes: 343 cid V-8; dual exhausts; power disc brakes; E-70 wide profile tires; Handling Package and Rally stripes ($266). Visibility Group package ($27). FM push-button radio and antenna ($61). AM/FM push-button radio and antenna ($134). Quick-ratio manual steering ($16). Four-speed manual transmission with floor shift ($184). Wire wheelcovers, SST ($51); base Javelin ($75). Three-speed manual transmission was standard, except AMX. Overdrive transmission was available for American/Ambassador/Rebel. Automatic transmission was optional on all with floor control on specific models. Four-speed manual floor shift transmission, standard AMX; optional, with V-8 only, on other models. Four-barrel carburetor. Positive traction rear axle. Heavy-duty clutch. NOTE: Prices for V-8s other than base 200 hp engine are in addition to basic cost of V-8 attachment.

AMX OPTIONS: Specific prices for AMX options are not available. The options list was about the same as for Javelin (at about the same prices) plus, over-the-top striping; chrome steel mag wheels and dealer accessory 'Rally Pak' gauge cluster. Automatic transmission was optional on all with floor control on specific models. Four-speed manual floor shift transmission, standard AMX; optional, with V-8 only, on other models. Four-barrel carburetor. Positive traction rear axle. Heavy-duty clutch. NOTE: Prices for V-8s other than base 200 hp engine are in addition to basic cost of V-8 attachment.

HISTORICAL FOOTNOTES: The AMC models were introduced Sept. 26, 1967 and the AMX appeared in dealer showrooms during March, 1968. Model year production peaked at 272,726 units. Calendar year sales of 269,334 cars were recorded. R.D. Chapin, Jr. was the chief executive officer of the company this year. For the first time since 1965, American Motors Corp. operated in the black for 1968 (although no dividends were paid). This compared to a loss of 75.8 million in 1967. The company sold its Kelvinator division to White Consolidated Industries. Each AMC built in 1968 carried a metal dashboard plate bearing a special number (numbers 000001 to 006175 were used). This was intended to designate its rather special nature. However, the first 550 units, assembled in calendar 1967, did not have this feature.

1969 AMC

1969 AMC, SC/Rambler two-door hardtop, V-8

RAMBLER — (SIX/V-8) — SERIES 01 — Formerly the Rambler American, the 1969 base model got a shortened name. It retained its compact dimensions and overall styling in line with AMC's new policy of maintaining design continuity from year to year for its low-priced models. American nameplates were gone from the grille and a new chrome side molding was used. Some of the mechanical improvements earmarked for the more expensive AMC products were incorporated in the Rambler. They included a new accelerator cable linkage; suspended accelerator pedal; 'Clear Power 24' battery and parking lamps that remained on with headlamps. Regular equipment included all regulation safety features; front armrests; front ashtrays; heater and defroster; head restraints; front foam seat cushions; a 199 cid six and 6.45 x 14 blackwall tires. The Rambler 440 models also had rear armrests and ashtrays; cigarette lighter; glove box lock; and dual horns. The Rogue featured carpeting; 'Air Guard' system and 232 cid six. Rambler wagons had 6.95 x 14 blackwall tires. With the help of Hurst Products Corp., a special Rogue offering was built exclusively during 1969. It was called the Hurst SC/Rambler and came only with the AMX type 390 cid 315 hp V-8 engine; four-speed manual floor shift transmission; and a host of other performance items as standard equipment. The retail price was $2,988. Original programming called for a limited run of just 500 units, but supply was far outstripped by demand. Ultimately, three runs of this model were made and the total output hit 1,512 units. The first batch, or 'A' Group, had the major portion of the bodysides painted red, with a blue racing stripe traveling down the middle of the body and across the roof and deck. There was also a large blue arrow, pointing towards the hood scoop. The paint code for such cars was '00.' The second, or 'B' Group of Hurst SC/Ramblers where finished more conservatively. They had a largely white exterior, with narrow red and blue stripes. These cars had either a special ('SPEC') or regular P-72 white paint code. The third group reverted to the original or 'A' style, so of the three groups, the 'A' style is predominant.

VEHICLE IDENTIFICATION NUMBERS: The numbering system and code locations were the same as on previous models. The second symbol was changed to a '9' to indicate 1969 model year. The code 'F' (four-speed manual transmission with floor shift and console) was no longer used as a third symbol. The code '7' (convertible) was also deleted. Otherwise, no changes were seen over previous nomenclature.

RAMBLER SERIES 01

Series Number	Body/Style Number	Body Type & Seating	Factory Price	Shipping Weight	Production Total
RAMBLER					
01	6905	4-dr Sed-6P	2076	2638	16,234
01	6906	2-dr Sed-6P	1998	2604	51,062
RAMBLER 440					
01	6905-5	4-dr Sed-6P	2218	2643	11,957
01	6908-5	2-dr Sed-6P	2478	2800	13,233
RAMBLER ROGUE					
01	6909-7	2-dr HT Cpe-6P	2296	2296	3,543
HURST SC/RAMBLER (V-8)					
01	6909-7	2-dr HT Cpe-6P	2998	2988	1,512

NOTE 1: The SC/Rambler came only with V-8 power. A total of 1,012 A-Group editions were built. A total of 500 B-Group editions were built.

1969 AMC, Rebel SST four-door station wagon, V-8

REBEL — (SIX) — SERIES 10 — The Rebel's track was increased to 60 inches for 1969. There were styling revisions including a new grille, deck lid and taillights. The outboard headlamps were housed separately in square surrounds, while the inner lamps were part of the main grille. A horizontal bar pattern insert was used in both the main opening and the outboard headlamp surrounds. The taillamps wrapped around the rear body corners. On SST models, the fake air scoops ahead of the rear wheel opening were replaced by four chrome side strips. Rebels were offered in six models; sedan, hardtop and wagon in the base series and the same three styles with SST equipment and trim. Basic equipment included standard safety features; head restraints; front armrests in two-doors; front and rear armrests in four-doors; front styling; cigar lighter; dual headlights; heater and defroster; front foam seat cushions; 7.35 x 14 blackwall tires; and the 145 hp 232 cid six. For all Rebels, V-8 engines were classed as optional equipment. The Rebel SST came with all the above items, plus carpets; rear armrests in two-door styles; rear ashtray; Custom steering wheel; glove box light; and dual horns. Wagons also featured a secret, lockable rear storage compartment; roof luggage rack; dual hinged tailgate; and 7.75 x 14 blackwall tires.

REBEL SERIES 10

Series Number	Body/Style Number	Body Type & Seating	Factory Price	Shipping Weight	Production Total
REBEL					
10	6915	4-dr Sed-6P	2484	3062	10,885
10	6919	2-dr HT Cpe-6P	2496	3117	5,396
10	6918	4-dr Sta Wag-6P	2817	3301	8,569
REBEL SST					
10	6915-7	4-dr Sed-6P	2584	3074	20,595
10	6919-7	2-dr HT Cpe-6P	2598	3140	5,405
10	6918-7	4-dr Sta Wag-6P	2947	3306	9,256

1969 AMC, AMX two-door fastback sports coupe, V-8

AMX — (V-8) — SERIES 30 — The 1969 AMC was described as being "more racy looking than ever," but was really little changed. Its introduction as a late 1968 entry precluded major revisions for its second year. There was a new 140 mph speedometer and tachometer with a larger face. Many minor running changes evolved as the year progressed, the most obvious being the addition of a hooded dash panel cover in most 1969s. New convenience items included a passenger grab handle above the glove box and a between-the-seats package tray. Leather upholstery trims were a new option. The 290 cid four-barrel V-8 engine was the base powerplant and motors with displacements of 343 and 390 cid were available. Standard equipment included all safety items; front and rear ashtrays and armrests; cigarette lighter; collapsable spare tire; Sports steering wheel; courtesy lights; dual exhausts; carpets; Flo-Thru ventilation; glove box lock; dual horns; instrument panel gauge cluster with tachometer; rear traction bars; front head restraints; reclining bucket seats; front foam cushions; wheel discs; heavy-duty suspension; E70 x 14 fiberglass-belted blackwall tires; four-speed manual transmission with floor-shift; and 225 hp, four-barrel V-8. Introduced as a midyear entry was the 'Big Bad AMX.' This option-created-model came in three colors and had the bumpers painted the same shade as the body. A total of 284 orange-colored Big Bad AMXs were built, as well as 195 similar models finished in blue and 283 additional cars done in green. A limited number of 52 or 53 Super Stock AMXs were made by the Hurst Corp. for AMC as special turn-key NHRA drag racing cars.

AMX SERIES 30

Series Number	Body/Style Number	Body Type & Seating	Factory Price	Shipping Weight	Production Total
AMX (V-8)					
30	6939-7	2-dr FsBk Cpe-2P	3297	3097	8,293

JAVELIN — (SIX) — SERIES 70 — The 1969 Javelin had a new twin venturi grille with a round, 'bull's-eye' emblem on the left-hand side. Otherwise, it was largely unchanged. The side stripes were redesigned. There had formerly been two, narrow, parallel stripes running full-length along the beltline. Now there was a larger 'C' stripe traveling down the mid-side of the car and turning downward at the trailing edge of the front wheelhousing. This change was put into effect on Jan. 9, 1969, so both designs appeared on 1969 models. Another Javelin revision was a new trim treatment for the instrument panel in standard-level cars and

extensive use of woodgrained paneling in the Javelin SST interior. Introduced as a midyear addition was the 'Mod Javelin,' which came in the same colors as the Big Bad AMX. Many Mod Javelins were marketed with the 'Craig Breedlove' options package. It included a rooftop spoiler and simulated exhaust rocker mountings. A limited number of Javelins and some Rambler 440s were built, in Germany, by Karmann. Standard equipment included the safety group; carpets; head restraints; front ashtray and armrests; cigarette lighter; Custom steering wheel; compartment lights; 'Air Guard' system; Flo-Thru ventilation; glove box lock; heater and defroster; dual horns; front bucket seats; foam front cushions; 6.95 x 14 blackwall tires; three-speed manual transmission with floor-mounted control and the 223 cid/145 hp six. Optional V-8s were available. The Javelin SST had all base items, plus a Sports steering wheel; reclining bucket seats; full wheelcovers; twin colored side stripes; and mag-styled wheels

1969 AMC Javelin SST two-door hardtop

JAVELIN SERIES 70

Series Number	Body/Style Number	Body Type & Seating	Factory Price	Shipping Weight	Production Total
JAVELIN					
70	6979-5	2-dr FsBk Cpe-4P	2512	2826	17,389
JAVELIN SST					
70	6979-7	2-dr FsBk Cpe-4P	2633	2836	23,286

1969 AMC, Ambassador SST, four-door sedan, V-8

AMBASSADOR — (SIX/V-8) — SERIES 80 — The 1969 Ambassador received a major facelift for 1969, with an all-new frontal treatment featuring horizontal, quad headlamps. The wheelbase was increased to 122 inches, a four inch gain. The track was widened to 60 inches. The new front end had a sculptured hood and a new plastic grille with twin, oblong-shaped inserts finished in black-out style. An Ambassador signature was placed at the left-hand side of the upper insert. Horizontal taillamps were set into a rear deck beauty panel. There were also notch style taillight lenses integral with the rear fender extension caps and viewable from the side of the car. They served as side marker lamps and, directly ahead of them, there was another bright metal Ambassador script. The Ambassador had the same equipment as the Rebel SST, plus standard air conditioning; front sway bar; 8.25 x 14 blackwall tires; and a 155 hp two-barrel version of the 232 cid six. The Ambassador DPL also wore wheel discs; DPL interior trim; and special, lower body exterior moldings with vinyl inserts. The Ambassador SST came standard with a clock; individually adjustable reclining seats; column-controlled Shift-Command automatic transmission; and a 200 hp, two-barrel V-8, plus all DPL equipment. There was also an SST station wagon with simulated woodgrain exterior paneling on the sides and rear of the body. New custom velour seats and stainless steel side trim were among package options for the SST. All Ambassadors had a higher capacity air conditioning system, too. In most ads of the year, an SST Ambassador was shown with a uniformed chauffeur. "To make an appointment for a test ride," said the copy. "Visit your American Motors dealer. A number of them have chauffeurs available."

AMBASSADOR SERIES 80

Series Number	Body/Style Number	Body Type & Seating	Factory Price	Shipping Weight	Production Total
AMBASSADOR					
80	6985-2	4-dr Sed-6P	2914	3276	14,617
AMBASSADOR DPL					
80	6985-5	4-dr Sed-6P	3265	3358	12,665
80	6988-5	4-dr Sta Wag-6P	3504	3561	8,866
80	6989-5	2-dr HT Cpe-6P	3182	3403	4,504
AMBASSADOR SST (V-8)					
80	6985-7	4-dr Sed-6P	3605	3508	18,719
80	6988-7	4-dr Sta Wag-6P	3998	3732	7,825
80	6989-7	2-dr HT Cpe-6P	3622	3566	8,998

BASE ENGINES

AMERICAN: Inline six. Overhead valves. Cast iron block. Displacement: 198.8 cid. Bore and stroke: 3.75 x 3.00. Compression ratio: 8.5:1. Brake hp: 128 at 4400 rpm. Seven main bearings. Hydraulic valve lifters. Carburetor: Carter RBS-4633S one-barrel.

ROGUE/JAVELIN: Inline six. Overhead valves. Cast iron block. Displacement: 231.9 (232) cid. Bore and stroke: 3.75 x 3.50 inches. Compression ratio: 8.5:1. Brake hp: 145 at 4300 rpm. Seven main bearings. Hydraulic valve lifters. Carburetor: Carter Type RBS one-barrel Model 4631S.

AMBASSADOR SIX: Inline six. Overhead valves. Cast iron block. Displacement: 231.9 (232) cid. Bore and stroke: 3.75 x 3.50 inches. Compression ratio: 8.5:1. Brake hp: 155 at 4400 rpm. Seven main bearings. Hydraulic valve lifters. Carburetor: Carter Type WCD two-barrel Model 4667S.

BASE V-8: Overhead valves. Cast iron block. Displacement: 289.8 (290) cid. Bore and stroke: 3.75 x 3.28 inches. Compression ratio: 10.0:1. Brake hp: 225 at 4700 rpm. Five main bearings. Hydraulic valve lifters. Carburetor: Carter Type AFB four-barrel Model 4660S.

OPTIONAL V-8: Overhead valves. Cast iron block. Displacement: 343.1 cid. Bore and stroke: 4.08 x 3.28 inches. Compression ratio: 10.0:1. Brake hp: 280 at 4800 rpm. Five main bearings. Hydraulic valve lifters. Carburetor: Carter Type AFB four-barrel Model 4662S.

HIGH-PERFORMANCE V-8: Overhead valves. Cast iron block. Displacement: 390 cid. Bore and stroke: 4.17 x 3.57 inches. Compression ratio: 10.2:1. Brake hp: 315 at 4600 rpm. Five main bearings. Hydraulic valve lifters. Carburetor: Carter Type AFB four-barrel Model 4665S.

CHASSIS FEATURES: Wheelbase: (Rambler/Rogue) 106 inches; (Rebel) 114 inches; (Javelin) 109 inches; (AMX) 97 inches; (Ambassador) 122 inches. Overall length: (Rambler/Rogue) 181 inches; (Rebel wagon) 198 inches; (Rebel) 197 inches; (Javelin) 182.2 inches; (AMX) 177.2 inches; (Ambassador wagon) 207 inches; (Ambassador) 206.5 inches. Front tread: (Rebel/Ambassador) 60 inches; (other models) See 1968. Rear tread: (Rebel/Ambassador) 60 inches; (other models) See 1968. Tires: (all models) See text.

POWERTRAIN OPTIONS: Three-speed manual transmission was standard in most models. Automatic transmission was standard in Ambassador SST with base engine. Overdrive transmission, optional in Rambler and Rebel six ($116). Automatic transmission, optional in all, ($171-223); in Ambassador SST with '343' or '390' V-8 ($22-$32). Four-speed manual floor shift transmission, in Rogue with 225 hp V-8 ($193). Javelin/close-ratio four-speed manual transmission with floor shift ($205). Rambler six-cylinder 223 cid 145 hp one-barrel engine ($45). Rebel/six-cylinder 223 cid 155 hp two-barrel engine ($16). Rogue-Javelin/V-8 290 cid 225 hp four-barrel engine ($45). Rebel-Ambassador/V-8 343 cid 280 hp four-barrel engine ($80). Rebel-Ambassador/V-8 309 cid 235 hp two-barrel engine ($52). Javelin/V-8 343 cid 280 hp four-barrel engine ($91). AMX/V-8 343 cid 280 hp four-barrel engine ($45). AMX/V-8 390 cid 315 hp four-barrel engine ($123). Javelin SST/Ambassador SST/V-8 380 cid 315 hp four-barrel engine ($168). Heavy-duty 70 ampere battery ($8). Heavy-duty battery and 55 ampere generator ($26). Heavy-duty cooling system ($53). Dual exhaust as separate V-8 option ($31). Positive traction rear axle ($42). Heavy-duty clutch, in Rambler with three-speed ($5); in Javelin with 200 hp V-8 ($11). Available rear axle gear ratios ($5).

RAMBLER CONVENIENCE OPTIONS: Power brakes ($42). Power steering ($90). Air conditioning ($324). Front and rear bumper guards, except wagon ($25). Special paint color application ($39). Two-tone paint in standard colors ($24). Tinted glass, (Javelin same price), all windows ($32); windshield ($23). Push-button radio and antenna, same price all AMC models ($61). Station wagon rooftop travel rack ($39). Individually adjusting reclining bench seats ($52). Custom steering wheel, standard in Rambler 440 and Rogue ($12). Sports steering wheel, available Rambler Rogue only ($30). Automatic transmission oil cooler ($18). Column-Shift Shift-Command automatic transmission in Rambler six ($171). Column-Shift Shift-Command automatic transmission in '440' with V-8 ($190). Four-speed manual floor shift in Rogue with 225 hp V-8 ($193). Undercoating and underhood insulation pad ($21). Black or white vinyl roof, Rogue only ($79). Full-wheel discs ($21). Electric windshield wipers, required in V-8 Ramblers ($15). Air conditioning package includes Solex glass and power steering ($387). Code 56-4 Appearance Group with sill moldings and wheel discs ($39). Code 70-1 Handling Package with heavy-duty sway bar, shocks and springs ($17). Light Group, includes door switches, trunk, courtesy, glove box and other lamps ($23). Visibility Group with outside rearview remote control mirror, electric window/washer etc. ($29). Rambler sedan/hardtop, Size 6.45 x 14 two-ply whitewalls, exchange ($32). Rambler station wagon, six 6.95 x 14 two-ply whitewalls, exchange ($32). Rambler V-8, Size 6.95 x 14 two-ply whitewalls, exchange ($32).

HURST SC/RAMBLER OPTION PACKAGE: Standard equipment on the Group 'A' SC/Rambler included: AMX 390 cid V-8; four-speed all-synchromesh close-ratio transmission; special Hurst shift linkage with T-handle; Sun tach mounted on steering column; dual exhaust system with special mufflers and chrome extensions; functional hood scoop for cold-air induction; Twin-Grip differential; 10-1/2 inch diameter clutch; 3.54:1 axle ratio; front power disc brakes; rear axle torque links; handling package with heavy-duty sway bar, springs and shocks; heavy-duty radiator and cooling system; 20.0:1 manual steering ratio; special application red, white and blue exterior finish; hood lock pins; dual racing mirrors; black-out grille; special emblems on front fenders/rear panel; 14x6 inch color-keyed mag-style wheels; five E70 x 14 Goodyear Polyglas wide-tread tires; Sports steering wheel; red, white and blue headrests; all-vinyl charcoal trim; full carpeting; individually adjustable reclining seats and more.

AMX/JAVELIN CONVENIENCE OPTIONS: Power brakes ($42). Power steering ($95). Air conditioning ($369). Rear bumper guards only ($13). Special application paint colors ($39). Console, all Javelin with Shift-Command/column shift ($53). Javelin, instrument cluster with tachometer and 140 mph speedometer ($50). Automatic transmission oil cooler ($18). Javelin, Rally Side paint stripes, replacing pin stripes ($27). Stereo 8-track tape player, with manual radio ($195). All except Ramblers; AM/FM push-button radio and antenna ($134). Center armrest seat with cushion, bucket seats mandatory, in AMX, with four-speed ($35). Leather, upholstery trim, AMX only ($79). Quick ratio manual steering ($16). Shift-Command, column control, in Javelins except SST with '343' V-8 ($223). Shift-Command, floor control, in Javelins with 200/280 hp V-8s ($287). Four-speed close-ratio manual floorshift, except with 200 hp V-8 ($205). Twin-Grip differential ($42). Air-Command ventilation, not available with air conditioning ($41). Wire wheelcovers, 14-inch, base Javelin ($72); Javelin SST and AMX ($51). Black, white or blue vinyl roof, all Javelins/not AMX ($100). Turbo-cast wheelcovers, base Javelin ($67); Javelin SST and AMX ($46). 'Mag' styled wheelcovers, base Javelin only ($94). Six-inch extra-wide wheel rims ($72). Full wheel discs, all Javelins; not AMX ($21). Handling Package group ($19). AMX, higher-rate front and rear springs, 1-3/16. Heavy-Duty shocks ($19). Light Group; AMX ($20); all Javelins ($23). Electric clock plus, visibility package group ($43). Javelin E70 x 14 redline tires ($75); same AMX ($34). A desirable option is the 'Go Package' (Code 39-1), which retailed for $233.15 on cars with the '343' V-8 and $310.85 on cars with the '390' engine. It included power disc brakes; E70 redline tires; six inch wide wheel rims; handling package; Twin-Grip; heavy-duty cooling system and black, white, red, blue or silver 'over-the-top' racing stripe. The Javelin 'Go Package' (code 39-1/2) retailed for $265.50 when the '343' V-8 was ordered and $343.25 when the '390' engine was specified. It included the V-8; dual exhausts; power disc brakes; E70 wide profile redline tires; six inch wide wheel rims; handling package; and black fiberglass hood scoops.

REBEL/AMBASSADOR CONVENIENCE OPTIONS: Power brakes, Rebel ($42); Ambassador ($43). Power steering ($100). Rebel air conditioning ($376). Front and rear bumper guards, except wagons ($32). Automatic speed control, V-8/automatic ($52). SST Rebel station wagon, simulated woodgrain exterior paneling ($113). All tinted windows, in Ambassador ($39); in Rebel ($36). Automatic transmission oil cooler, standard Ambassador SST ($18). Exterior paint stripe, except SST models and DPL ($14). Power side windows, Ambassador SST/DPL cars ($105); wagons ($140). Duo-coustic rear speakers ($13). Stereo 8-track tape with manual radio, sedans/hardtops only ($134). Individually adjustable reclining seats ($58). Reclining bucket seats with front armrest and center cushion, SSTs only ($111). Station wagon third seat, includes power tailgate window ($118). Custom velour trim, Ambassador SST sedan, includes stainless trim insert ($68). All-vinyl seat upholstery, bench or individual cushion, standard in wagon ($24). Adjust-O-Tilt steering, automatic required ($45). Rebel Custom steering wheel, standard in SST ($13). Rebel SST and all Ambassadors, Sport type steering wheel ($30). Shift-Command with column control, standard Ambassador SST ($201). Shift-Command with column control, Rebel/Ambassador (except SST) with '343' V-8 ($223). Shift-Command, Ambassador SST with '343' V-8 ($22); with '390' V-8 ($37). Shift-Command with floor control, Ambassador (except SST) and Rebel SST ($280). Shift-Command with floor control, Ambassador SST with '343' V-8 ($69); with '390' V-8 ($79). Black, white or blue vinyl roof, Rebel SST except wagon ($90); Ambassador SST/DPL ($100). Wire wheelcover, SST and DPL ($51); other models ($72). Turbo-cast wheelcovers, SST and DPL ($46); other models ($67). Full wheel discs, standard SST and DPLs ($21). Visibility Group with electric clock, Ambassador SST ($29); others ($43).

HISTORICAL FOOTNOTES: The full-sized Ramblers were introduced Oct. 1, 1968 and the compact lines appeared in dealer showrooms the same day. Model year production peaked at 275,350 units. Calendar year production of 242,898 cars was recorded. R.D. Chapin was the chief executive officer of the company this year. This was the final season that the Rambler nameplate would appear. A total of 4,204,925 Ramblers were sold 1950-1969. Operations were profitable for the second year in a row, although AMC's net earnings were only $4.9 million, compared to $11.8 million one year earlier. Retail sales totaled 239,548 cars, an 11.1 percent decrease from 1968 levels. A total of 17,147 cars were made with 390 cid engines during the model year. Four and one-half percent had four-speed manual transmissions; 8.2 percent had disc brakes: 22.2 percent had bucket seats; 15.8 percent had vinyl roofs and five percent had styled steel wheels.

1970 AMC

1970 AMC, Hornet SST four-door sedan, 6-cyl

HORNET — (SIX) — SERIES 01 — In 1970, the Rambler (American) was replaced with a new car that revived an old name. This was the Hornet, which reminded some people of the days when an AMC family member - Hudson Motors - had championed in stock car racing. The Hornet, however, was not a performance car in its basic form. It was a compact, economy model with a modern, but conventional styling theme. It was basically the Rambler/American with a major facelift and more rounded body contours. The new Hornet was offered in two body styles, two- and four-door sedan, and in base or SST trim levels. Standard equipment, in addition to all regulation safety features, included front armrests and ashtrays, 6.45-14 blackwall tires and a 128 hp 199 cid six. The Hornet SST also had rear armrests; cigarette lighter; Custom steering wheel; colored carpets; rubber trunk mat; glove box light; package tray; front foam seat cushions and a larger, 232 cid six that put out 145 hp.

VEHICLE IDENTIFICATION NUMBERS: The numbering system and code locations were the same as on previous models. The second symbol was changed to '0' to indicate 1970 model year. The third symbol '0' (indicating overdrive transmission) was no longer used. A new range of seventh symbols (indicating engine types) was adopted, as follows: 'A' = 199 cid six; 'B' = low-compression 199 cid six; 'E' = 232 cid six with one-barrel carburetor; 'F' = low-compression 232 cid six with one-barrel carburetor; 'G' = 232 cid six with two-barrel carburetor; 'Q' = low-compression 232 cid six with two-barrel carburetor; 'H' = 304 cid V-8 with two-barrel carburetor; 'I' = low-compression 304 cid V-8 with two-barrel carburetor; 'M' = low-compression 304 cid V-8 with four-barrel carburetor; 'N' = 360 cid V-8 with two-barrel carburetor; 'P' = 360 cid V-8 with four-barrel carburetor; 'S' = 390 cid V-8 with four-barrel carburetor and 'X' = 'Rebel Machine' 390 cid V-8 with four-barrel carburetor. The new Hornet adopted the Rambler/American Series 01 nomenclature. The midyear Gremlin had new Series 40 nomenclature. Other coding and nomenclature was unchanged from the past.

HORNET SERIES 01

Series Number	Body/Style Number	Body Type & Seating	Factory Price	Shipping Weight	Production Total
HORNET					
01	7005-0	4-dr Sed-6P	2072	2748	17,948
01	7006-0	2-dr Sed-6P	1994	2677	43,610
HORNET SST					
01	7005-7	4-dr Sed-6P	2221	2765	19,786
01	7006-7	2-dr Sed-6P	2144	2705	19,748

1970 AMC, Rebel 'Machine' two-door hardtop, V-8

REBEL — (SIX/V.8) — SERIES 10 — The 1970 Rebel received new rear quarter panel styling and a more massive rear bumper. There were two large, horizontal-rectangular taillights with Rebel spelled out between them. There was a new vertically split and horizontally segmented grille. The Rebel SST had a bright metal molding on the front fenders, between the door handle and side marker lights. Model identification lettering was placed behind the front wheel opening and, on SST, below the rear roof pillar. There was similar Rebel lettering on the left lip of the hood. Standard Rebel features began with the regulation safety equipment (used in all 1970 AMC models), plus front and rear armrests (except two-door); front ashtray; cigarette lighter; dome or side lights; rubber trunk mat; dual headlights; front foam cushions; E78-14 fiberglass-belted blackwall tires and 145 hp 232 cid six. The Rebel SST also had rear ashtrays; glove box lock; dual horns and Custom steering wheel. Another special, Rebel-based model was developed, for AMC, by the Hurst products company. The 'Rebel Machine' was introduced at the National Hot Rod Association World Championship Drag Race, in Dallas, Texas, during October, 1969. Standard on this model were all Rebel SST features (except rear armrests and ashtrays); high-back bucket seats; Space-Saver spare tire; power front disc brakes; Ram-Air hood scoop; Handling Package; heavy-duty cooling system with Power-Flex fan; carpeting; 15 x 7 inch styled steel wheel; E60-15 fiberglass-belted tires with raised white letters; four-speed manual floor shift transmission and a 340 hp, 390 cid four-barrel V-8 with dual exhausts. The 'Machine' had the highest output motor ever used in an American Motor's product offered for public sale. Of a total of 2,326 car run, approximately the first 1,000 units were finished in white, with the lower beltline and hood done in blue. A red stripe traveled down the front fender and along the car to the deckside region. From there, the stripe crossed over the trunk and came back along the opposite bodyside. There were also blue and white stripes over the trunk, behind the red one and integrated into it. Later editions of the model were finished in a choice of solid colors and featured a black-out hood treatment with silver pinstriping, plus optional red, white and blue graphics that could be added on the grille and body. The 'Machine' was actually a bigger and faster car than it should have been.

REBEL SERIES 10

Series Number	Body/Style Number	Body Type & Seating	Factory Price	Shipping Weight	Production Total
REBEL					
10	7015-0	4-dr Sed-6P	2626	3129	11,725
10	7019-0	2-dr HT Cpe-6P	2660	3148	1,791
10	7018-0	4-dr Sta Wag-6P	2766	3356	8,183
REBEL SST					
10	7015-7	4-dr Sed-6P	2684	3155	13,092
10	7019-7	2-dr HT Cpe-6P	2718	3206	6,573
10	7018-7	4-dr Sta Wag-6P	3072	3375	6,846
REBEL 'MACHINE' (V-8)					
10	7019-7	2-dr HT Cpe-6P	3475	3650	1,936

1970 AMC, AMX two-door fastback sports coupe, V-8

AMX — (V-8) — SERIES 30 — The 1970 AMX got new rear lamps and a completely restyled front end and that was shared with Javelin performance models. The frontal treatment featured a grille that was flush with the hood and redesigned bumper housing squarish parking lamps. A horizontally divided, cross-hatched grille insert, with prominent bright vertical moldings, was used and also incorporated circular rally lights. The restyled hood had a large Ram-Air induction scoop that took in cold air for the engine. Height was reduced about one inch, while overall length grew about two inches. Standard equipment included all items used with Javelin SST models, plus a heavy-duty 60 ampere battery; courtesy lights; rear traction bar; Space-Saver spare tire; tachometer; 140 mph speedometer; 14 x 6 inch styled steel wheels; E78-14 blackwall tires; four-speed manual floor-shift transmission and 290 hp 360 cid four-barrel V-8 with dual exhaust system. The metal dashboard plates affixed to 1970 models were numbered 014469 to 18584. This was the final year for the original type AMX, although the nameplate would be used again on performance image Javelin and Hornet-based models.

Series Number	Body/Style Number	Body Type & Seating	Factory Price	Shipping Weight	Production Total
AMX					
30	7039-7	2-dr FsBk Cpe-2P	3395	3126	4,116

1970 AMC, Gremlin two-door sedan, 6-cyl

GREMLIN — (SIX) — SERIES 40 — Introduced Weds., April 1, 1970, the AMC Gremlin was hailed as the first modern U.S.-built sub-compact car. This unique entry was basically a Hornet from the trailing edge of the door forward, and there really wasn't much left after that. The rear styling had a slanted, Kammback theme. It angled from a foot, or so, behind the rear wheel opening (at the bottom) to a point on the roof that was nearly plumb with the rear wheel centerline. Model identification came from a front fender cartoon badge and model name script on the sail panel (between two angular windsplit depressions). The rear was decorated with a circular medallion set into a rectangular depression panel that arched over it. Recessed, rectangular taillamps were seen. A hatch style rear window was featured on a four-passenger version. The two available models were a two-passenger commuter and the four-passenger job with fold-down rear seat. Standard features included front armrests; front ashtray; 35 ampere alternator (55 ampere with air conditioner); dome light; exhaust emissions control system; rubber floor and trunk mats; heater and defroster; split-back front foam seat cushion; wheel trim hubcaps; dual pinstripes: 'B'-rated 6.00 x 13 blackwall Polyester tires. The four-passenger model used the rear window liftgate feature and had a foam cushioned rear seat (with folding backrest). Gremlins optionally equipped with the 232 cid six came standard with floorshift transmission controls. A selection of 30 factory-installed options or accessories, plus seven packages was provided. The Gremlin may have been undersized, but it sure wasn't under-equipped.

GREMLIN SERIES 40

Series Number	Body/Style Number	Body Type & Seating	Factory Price	Shipping Weight	Production Total
40	7046-0	2-dr Sed-2P	1879	2497	872
40	7046-5	2-dr Sed-4P	1959	2557	27,688

1970 AMC, Javelin SST two-door hardtop-sports coupe, V-8

JAVELIN — (SIX/V-8) — SERIES 70 — The new Javelin shared its basic styling features with AMX, but retained its own twin venturi type grille without the previous 'bull's-eye' badge. The headlights were better integrated into the nose, sharing a common upper border molding with the main grille. It had the same front bumper, front parking lights and hood as the AMX and, like the two-seat 'mini-mite', was an inch lower and two inches longer. Standard equipment began with all items (except package tray) that were found on the Hornet SST. Additional features included compartment lights; dual horns; high-back bucket seats; C78-14 tires (D78-14 with V-8) and three-speed manual gearbox with shift control off the floor. The Javelin SST also had a Sports steering wheel with horn-blow rim and full wheel discs. Two-limited production Javelin SSTs were offered. The Javelin 'Trans Am' had all SST equipment (minus sill moldings and paint stripes), plus front lower and rear deck spoilers; black vinyl interior; '390' Go-Package; F70-14 glass-belted tires with raised white letters; 14 x 6 inch mag styled wheels; Space-Saver tire with regular spare wheel; AM push-button radio; tachometer and 140 mph speedometer: Visibility Group; Light Group; power steering; Twin-Grip differential; 3.91:1 axle ratio; four-speed box with Hurst floor shifter and 390 cid four-barrel V-8 with heavy-duty cooling system. These cars were replicas of the Ronnie Kaplan Trans-Am Racing Team's competition machines and were finished in a three-segment red, white and blue paint scheme created by industrial designer Brooks Stevens. Only 100 cars were built, the amount necessary to make this model eligible for the Sports Car Club of America's popular Trans-Am races under 1969 'formulas.' In early 1970, the SCCA formulas were changed and so were the AMC drivers. The new rules demanded 2,500 replicas built to certain specifications. This led to the production of the 'Mark Donohue' Javelin SST. The majority of these cars had a special, thick-walled, 360 cid V-8 and all featured a unique 'duck-tail' rear spoiler with 'Mark Donohue' signature script at the right-hand side.

JAVELIN SERIES 70

Series Number	Body/Style Number	Body Type & Seating	Factory Price	Shipping Weight	Production Total
JAVELIN					
70	7079-5	2-dr FsBk Cpe-4P	2720	2845	8,496

JAVELIN SST					
70	7070-7	2-dr FsBk Cpe-4P	2848	2863	19,714
JAVELIN/SST 'TRANS AM' (V-8)					
70	7079-7	2-dr FsBk Cpe-4P	3995	3340	(100)
MARK DONOHUE JAVELIN SST (V-8)					
70	7079-7	2-dr FsBk Cpe-4P	—	—	(2,501)*

NOTE 1: *The total of 19,714 Javelin SSTs includes both the Trans-Am and Mark Donohue Javelin models, as these were package models based on the Javelin SST.)

AMBASSADOR — (SIX/V-8) — SERIES 80 — A new cross-hatched grille insert pattern characterized the 1970 Ambassador line. The rear quarter panels and bumper were also restyled. A large, rectangular taillamp crossed the back of the car. Trim distinctions between the various models followed the 1969 pattern. Standard equipment for the base Ambassador was the same as for the Rebel SST, plus 55 ampere alternator; air conditioning; F78-14 blackwall tires and 155 hp 232 cid six. The Ambassador DPL also had full wheel discs; Shift-Command automatic transmission (with base V-8) and a 210 hp 304 cid two-barrel V-8 engine. A standard extra Ambassador SST was individually adjustable reclining front seats. Ambassador DPL station wagons had all regular DPL features, plus cargo area carpets; rooftop travel rack and Dual-Swing tailgate. The Ambassador SST station wagon also had individually adjustable reclining front seats; woodgrained inside door panels a woodgrained side and rear exterior paneling.

1970 AMC, Ambassador SST, four-door station wagon, V-8

AMBASSADOR SERIES 80

Series Number	Body/Style Number	Body Type & Seating	Factory Price	Shipping Weight	Production Total
AMBASSADOR					
80	7085-2	4-dr Sed-6P	3020	3328	9,565
AMBASSADOR DPL (V-8)					
80	7085-5	4-dr Sed-6P	3588	3523	6,414
80	7089-5	2-dr HT Cpe-6P	3605	3555	2,036
80	7088-5	4-dr Sta Wag-6P	3946	3817	8,270
AMBASSADOR SST (V-8)					
80	7085-7	4-dr Sed-6P	3722	3557	19,687
80	7089-7	2-dr HT Cpe-6P	3739	3606	8,255
80	7088-7	4-dr Sta Wag-6P	4122	3852	5,714

NOTE 1: The exact model year output of 1970 Ambassadors was 59,941 cars.
NOTE 2: In figures rounded-off to the nearest hundred, the model year output included the following: 3,500 base Ambassador sixes; 6,100 base Ambassador V-8s; 8,400 Ambassador DPLs (V-8 only); 27,900 Ambassador SSTs (V-8 only); 1,000 Ambassador station wagons with six-cylinder power and 13,000 Ambassador station wagons with V-8s.

ENGINES

(BASE SIX) Inline Six: Overhead valves. Cast iron block. Displacement: 199 cid. Bore and stroke: 3.75 x 3 inches. Compression ratio: 8.5:1. Brake hp: 128 at 4400 rpm. Seven main bearings. Hydraulic valve lifters. Carburetor: Carter Type YF one-barrel.

(BASE SIX) Inline Six: Overhead valves. Cast iron block. Displacement: 232 cid. Bore and stroke: 3.75 x 3.50 inches. Compression ratio: 8.5:1. Brake hp: 155 at 4400 rpm. Seven main bearings. Hydraulic valve lifters. Carburetor: Carter Type WCD two-barrel.

(BASE V-8) V-8. Overhead valves. Cast iron block. Displacement: 304 cid. Bore and stroke: 3.75 x 3.44 inches. Compression ratio: 9.0:1. Brake hp: 210 at 4400 rpm. Five main bearings. Hydraulic valve lifters. Carburetor: Autolite two-barrel Model 2100.

(REBEL 'MACHINE' V-8) V-8. Overhead valves. Cast iron block. Displacement: 390 cid. Bore and stroke: 4.17 x 3.57 inches. Compression ratio: 10.0:1. Brake hp: 340 at 3600 rpm. Five main bearings. Hydraulic valve lifters. Carburetor: Autolite four-barrel Model 4300.

(AMX V-8) V-8. Overhead valves. Cast iron block. Displacement: 360 cid. Bore and stroke: 4.08 x 3.44 inches. Compression ratio: 10.0:1. Brake hp: 290 at 4800 rpm. Five main bearings. Hydraulic valve lifters. Carburetor: Autolite four-barrel Model 4300.

(JAVELIN/SST 'TRANS AM' V-8) V-8. Overhead valves. Cast iron block. Displacement: 390 cid. Bore and stroke: 4.17 x 3.57 inches. Compression ratio: 10.0:1. Brake hp: 325 at 5000 rpm. Five main bearings. Hydraulic valve lifters. Carburetor: Autolite four-barrel Model 4300.

('MARK DONOHUE' JAVELIN V-8) V-8. Overhead valves. Cast iron thick-wall block. Displacement: 360 cid. Bore and stroke: 4.08 x 3.44 inches. Compression ratio: 10.0:1. Brake hp: 290 at 4800 rpm. Five main bearings. Hydraulic valve lifters. Carburetor: Autolite four-barrel Model 4300.

CHASSIS FEATURES: Wheelbase: (Gremlin) 96 inches; (AMX) 97 inches; (Javelin) 109.9 inches; (Hornet) 108 inches; (Rebel) 114 inches; (Ambassador) 122 inches. Overall length: (Gremlin) 161-1/4 Inches; (AMX) 179 inches; (Javelin) 191 inches; (Hornet) 179.3 inches; (Rebel) 199 inches; (Wagon) 198 inches; (Ambassador) 208 Inches; (Wagon) 207 inches. Front tread: (Gremlin) 57.5 inches; (AMX and Javelin) 59.1 inches; (Hornet) 57.2 inches; (Rebel and Ambassador) 59.7 inches. Rear tread: (Gremlin) 57 inches; (AMX, Javelin and Hornet) 56.6 inches; (Rebel and Ambassador) 60 inches. Tires: See text.

POWERTRAIN OPTIONS: Three-speed manual transmission was standard in most AMC models. Automatic transmission was standard in Ambassador DPL and SST. Shift-Command automatic transmission was optional on all models at various prices. Four-speed manual floor shift transmission, in Javelin '360' and '390' V-8s. Close-ratio four-speed manual transmission with floor shift was standard in Rebel 'Machine' and AMX. Hornet/Gremlin six-cylinder 232 cid 145 hp one-barrel engine ($45). Base Hornet six-cylinder 232 cid 155 hp two-barrel engine ($65). Hornet SST/Rebel six-cylinder 232 cid 155 hp two-barrel engine ($19). Javelin / Ambassador / Rebel (except 'Machine') V-8 360 cid 245 hp two-barrel engine ($41). Javelin / Ambassador / Rebel (except 'Machine') V-8 360 cid 290 hp four-barrel engine ($86). Ambassador DPL/SST/Rebel SST/Javelin V-8 390 cid 325 hp four-barrel engine ($168). AMX V-8 390 cid 325 hp four-barrel engine ($11). Heavy-duty 70 ampere battery ($13). Axle ratios, all optional ($10). Heavy-duty cooling, standard with air ($16). Dual exhaust, as separate option ($31). Twin-Grip positive traction rear axle ($43). NOTE: Overdrive was no longer available. Three-speed manual floor shift with Gremlin V-8s only (as standard equipment).

GREMLIN/HORNET OPTIONS: Power brakes ($43). Power steering ($96). Air conditioning ($381). Front and rear bumper guards ($25). Locking gas cap ($6). Engine block heater ($16). Gremlin rooftop luggage rack ($39). Special application paint ($39). AM push-button radio ($62). Gremlin white, black or red Rally side stripes ($25). Custom steering wheel, Gremlin ($12). Gremlin Shift-Command with column controls ($195). Wheel disc covers ($25). Electric washer/wipers, Gremlin and Hornet ($20). Tinted glass, Gremlin, all windows ($34); windshield only ($26). Electric clock, in base Hornet only ($16). Air Command ventilation system, Hornet Group only ($41). Tinted glass, Hornet all windows ($34); windshield only ($26). Vinyl insert scuff side molding, Hornet Group ($27). Hornet SST two-tone paint ($24). Hornet Group exterior body striping ($19). Front disc brakes, Hornet Group, except base series ($84). Hornet SST caranaby plaid interior trim ($78). Hornet SST, individual seats, fabric trim ($52); vinyl trim ($71). Hornet SST, bench seat, vinyl trim/standard base model ($20). Hornet base models, bench seat, cloth trim/standard SST ($13). Handling Package, Hornet Group ($23). Hornet Group Decor Package, with/Air ($34); without Air ($58). Hornet Light Group Package ($25). Hornet SST, vinyl roof ($84).

REBEL/AMBASSADOR OPTIONS: Power brakes ($43). Power steering ($105). Air conditioning, Rebel Group ($380). Cruise Control, Rebel and Ambassador, with automatic ($60). Front and rear bumper guards, except station wagons ($32). Tinted glass, all windows, Ambassador ($42); Rebel ($37). Tinted windshield, Ambassador ($32); Rebel ($30). Two-tone paint, Rebel/Ambassador sedans and hardtops ($27). Bodyside accent panels and moldings, wagons except Style 7088-7 ($65). Special paint, other than standard ($39). Power side windows, Ambassador DPL/SST passenger cars ($105). Power side and tailgate window, Ambassador DPL/SST wagons ($140). Power tailgate window, standard with third wagon seat ($35). AM push-button radio ($62). AM/FM push-button radio, all AMC except Hornets ($134). Eight-track stereo tape, all Ambassador, except wagons ($134). Third seat, Rebel SST and Ambassador DPL/SST wagons, with extras ($118). Vinyl bench seat, Ambassador style 70852 and base Rebel ($24). Individual seat, fabric, Ambassador (standard SST) and Rebels, except 'Machine' ($64). Velour Individual cushion interior, Ambassador SST sedan ($68). Bucket seats fabric or vinyl, Rebel/Ambassador SST hardtop ($123). Sports steering wheel with horn-blow, Ambassador, Rebel SST ($37). Tilt-O-Just steering wheel, Rebel/Ambassador with automatic ($45). Shift-Command; with floor shift, Rebel 'Machine' with '390' V-8 ($188). Black, white or blue vinyl roof, Ambassador DPL/SST, except wagons ($106). Black, white or blue vinyl roof, Rebel SST hardtop and sedan ($95). Turbo-cast wheelcovers, Rebel (except 'Machine'); Ambassador 7085-2 ($74). Wire wheelcovers, Rebel (except 'Machine'); Ambassador Style 7085-2 ($74). Turbo-cast or wire wheelcovers, Ambassador SST or DPL ($49).

JAVELIN/AMX OPTIONS: Power brakes ($43). Power steering ($102). Air conditioning ($380). Rear bumper guards ($13). Command Air ventilation system, w/o air ($41). Center console, Javelin Group with column automatic shift only ($53). Tinted glass, Javelin/AMX prices same as Hornet. Simulated exhaust type rocker panel moldings, Javelin SST ($32). Simulated exhaust type rocker panel moldings, base Javelin ($50). AMX two-tone finish with 'black shadow' treatment ($52). Rally side stripes, solid color Javelin/AMX ($32). Power front disc brakes, V-8 engine required ($84). Eight-track stereo tape with manual radio/twin rear speakers ($195). Corduroy fabric bucket seats, Javelin SST only ($50). Leather trimmed bucket seats, AMX only ($84). Leather trimmed bucket seats, Javelin SST only ($127). quick-ratio manual steering, for racing ($16). Javelin Code 533 spoiler roof, not available with vinyl top ($33). Tachometer and 140 mph speedometer with V-8 ($50). Shift-Command, column control, Javelin with '304' V-8 ($200). Shift-Command, column control, Javelin with '360' V-8 ($233). Shift-Command, column control, Javelin six ($195). Shift-Command, floor control, Javelin with '304' V-8 ($264). Shift-Command, floor control, Javelin with '360' V-8 ($287). Shift-Command, floor control, AMX with '390' V-8 ($118). Four-speed floor-shift, Javelins with 290/325 hp V-8 ($205). Black, white or blue vinyl roof, Javelin only ($84). Turbo-cast wheelcovers; base Javelin ($74); Javelin SST ($49). Wire wheelcovers; base Javelin ($74); Javelin SST ($49). Styled steel wheels, 14 x 6 inch, base Javelin ($98); Javelin SST ($72). A desirable option was the code 391/2 'Go-Package', which retailed for $298.85 on the '360' AMX and $383.90 on the '390' AMX. It included one of these engines; power front disc brakes; F70-14 blackwall tires with raised white letters; Handling Package; heavy-duty cooling system and functional Ram-Air induction scoop. A desirable Javelin option was the Code 391/2 'Go Package' which retailed for $321.65 on the '360' Javelin and $409.75 on the '390' Javelin. Features included one of these engines; power front disc brakes: E70-14 redline tires; six inch wheel rims; Handling Package: AMX Ram-Air hood and dual exhausts.

HISTORICAL FOOTNOTES: The AMC line was introduced Sept. 25, 1969 and the 1970 Gremlin appeared in dealer showrooms April 1, 1970. Model year production peaked at 242,664 units. Calendar year production of 276,110 cars was recorded. R.D. Chapin, Jr. was the chief executive officer of the company this year. A total of 11,125 AMC products, built in the 1970 model year, were equipped with 390 cid V-8 engines. Twenty percent of all AMC cars had bucket seats; 14.9 percent had vinyl roofs; styled wheels were ordered by 4.6 percent of 1970 buyers and four-speed transmission installations were made in 2.6 percent of all cars. The company referred to itself as "the new American Motors" in advertisements and presented buyers with the catch line, "If you had to compete with GM, Ford and Chrysler, what would you do?"

1971 AMC

HORNET — (SIX/V-8) — SERIES 01 — The 1971 Hornet received no major styling changes for 1971. Two new models were added, however, along with some springtime equipment packages. The new styles were a SST four-door Sportabout station wagon and a Hornet V-8 performance car called the SC/360 two-door sports sedan. Standard equipment on base Hornets was the same as that found on 1971 Gremlins, plus color-keyed rubber floor mats and larger, 6.45 x 14 blackwall tires. The Hornet SST models also had color-keyed carpets; cigarette lighter; Command-Air ventilation; glove box; full width package tray; Custom steering wheel; and movable rear quarter windows. The Sportabout added a carpeted cargo area; rear liftgate; cargo compartment lock; and Space-Saver spare tire. The SC/360 sports sedan had the same equipment as Hornet SST passenger models, plus front sway bar; slot style wheels; Space-Saver spare tire; D70-14 raised white letter tires; and a 245 hp 360 cid two-barrel V-8.

Springtime changes included price increases for all Hornet SST V-8s and a Sportabout D/L package including color-keyed woodgrain side and rear panels; roof rack with integral air deflector; Custom wheelcovers; individual reclining seats; woodgrained instrument cluster trim; Sports rim-blow steering wheel; and D/L decals. In addition, free sun roofs were provided as part of several Hornet packages. The SC/360 stands out as the most collectable car in the group. It was designed as a low-priced performance car that could pass as a compact and, thus, side-step rising insurance rates affecting the owners and buyers of such vehicles. Its trim included special around-the-beltline decals with SC/360 call-outs at the trailing edge of rear fenders. Optional, at $199, was a 'Go-Package' that consisted of four-barrel carburetor; Ram-Air induction system; dual exhausts; Handling Package; tachometer; and Polyglas white letter tires. It included a wide hood scoop with black-out paint treatment. American Motors had programed the model for 10,000 sales, but only 784 buyers were interested. Many expressed hopes that the new 401 cid V-8 be offered in this car, but insurance and marketing considerations precluded this. The SC/360 was sold only in 1971.

1971 AMC, Hornet SC/360 two-door sedan, V-8

VEHICLE IDENTIFICATION NUMBERS: The numbering system and code locations were the same as on previous models. The second symbol was changed to a '1' to indicate 1971 model year. A new third symbol was 'F' (indicating three-speed manual transmission with floor shift). New sixth symbols, designating class of body, were as follows: '0' = Hornet and base Gremlin; '1' = Hornet SC/360. New seventh symbols (indicating engine types) were as follows: 'A' = 258 cid six with one-barrel carburetor; 'B' = 258 cid six, low-compression, with one-barrel carburetor; 'Z' = 401 cid V-8 with four-barrel carburetor.

HORNET SERIES 01

Series Number	Body/Style Number	Body Type & Seating	Factory Price	Shipping Weight	Production Total
HORNET					
01	7106-0	2-dr Sed-6P	2174	2654	19,395
01	7105-0	4-dr Sed-6P	2234	2731	10,403
HORNET SST					
01	7106-7	2-dr Sed-6P	2324	2732	8,600
01	7105-7	4-dr Sed-6P	2274	2691	10,651
01	7108-7	4-dr Sta Wag-6P	2594	2827	73,471
HORNET SST SC/360 (V-8)					
01	7106-1	2-dr Spt Sed-6P	2663	3300	784

MATADOR — (SIX) SERIES 10 — The former AMC Rebel became the Matador for 1971. The renamed product was significantly restyled with changes to taillamps; hood; grille; front fenders; bumper and valance panel. Wheelbase was increased to 118 inches. The Matador appearance was characterized by an integrated bumper/grille; horizontal, double-venturi grille insert and triple-rectangular taillight lenses integrated into a horizontal rear beauty panel. Body style offerings were limited to a two-door hardtop, four-door sedan and four-door station wagon marketed in a single level of trim, but with many available options packages including the high-performance 'Go Machine' group. Standard equipment was the same as for base Javelins, plus rear armrests; rear ashtray; full-back bench seat cushion in sedans and wagon/split-back in hardtop; hardtop pillar lights; color-keyed cargo area carpets in wagon (and Dual-Swing tailgate) and three-speed transmission with column shift. The Matador was marketed as a six, with V-8 options. Additional equipment, installed when a V-8 with automatic transmission was ordered, included a transmission oil cooler.

1971 AMC, Matador four-door station wagon, V-8

MATADOR SERIES 10

Series Number	Body/Style Number	Body Type & Seating	Factory Price	Shipping Weight	Production Total
10	7118-0	4-dr Sed-6P	2770	3165	5
10	7119-0	2-dr HT Cpe-6P	2799	3201	1
MATADOR					
10	7115-7	4-dr Sed-6P	3163	3437	24,918
10	7119-7	2-dr HT-6P	3129	3360	7,661
10	7118-7	4-dr Sta Wag-6P	3493	3596	10,740

GREMLIN — (SIX) — SERIES 40 — Introduced as a midyear 1970 model, the Gremlin was unchanged for 1971 in terms of appearance. A technical revision was seen in the use of the 232 cid six as base engine and the smaller 199 cid six went out of production. There was also an attractive new Gremlin 'X' option package. It was provided only for the four-passenger model at a price of $300 with blackwall tires or $334.35 with raised white letter tires. Included were 'Spear' side stripes; black-painted grille; 14 x 6 inch slot style wheels; Space-Saver spare; Custom interior appointments; front bucket seats; special 'X' decals and D70-14 size tires (with raised white letter style considered as option-within-option). Standard equipment on all Gremlins included 35 ampere alternator; front armrests and ashtray; 50 ampere battery; dome light; exhaust emissions control; rubber floor mats; bench seats; split-back front foam seat cushion; exterior paint stripes; and 6.00 x 13 black sidewall Polyester tires. The four-passenger model also featured a glove box door; liftgate type rear window; and rear foam seat cushion with fold-down back. The 135 hp 232 cid six was base engine, with a bigger six optional.

1971 AMC, Gremlin 'X' two-door sedan, 6-cyl

GREMLIN SERIES 40

Series Number	Body/Style Number	Body Type & Seating	Factory Price	Shipping Weight	Production Total
40	7146-0	2-dr Sed-2P	1899	2503	2,145
40	7146-5	2-dr Sed-4P	1999	2552	74,763

1971 AMC, Javelin AMX, two-door hardtop sports coupe, V-8

JAVELIN — (SIX/V-8) — SERIES 70 — The 1971 Javelin was completely restyled. There were highly sculptured raised fenders, a twin-canopy roof with air spoiler type rear window lip, and new full-width taillamps. The interior was completely redesigned and upgraded. It featured a curved cockpit type instrument panel inspired by aircraft motifs. Three levels of trim were provided in one two-door hardtop style: base Javelin; Javelin SST and Javelin AMX. This new AMX was a four-place automobile, replacing the former two-seater. A rear-facing cowl-induction hood, flush wire mesh grille and optional front and rear spoilers were claimed as the design work of race driver Mark Donohue, who raced Javelins successfully in SCCA Trans-Am competition. Standard equipment on the Javelin was the same as for Hornets, plus Custom steering wheel; color-keyed carpets; glove box lock; dual horns; high-back bucket seats; three-speed manual transmission with floor-shift; C78-14 glass-belted tires; cigar lighter; and automatic transmission oil cooler with V-8s. The Javelin SST also had rear ashtray; rim-blow Sports steering wheel; rubber trunk mat; and wheelcovers. The AMX featured all this equipment, plus electric clock; center console (without armrest); rear deck mounted spoiler; slot style wheels; E70-14 glass-belted tires; and 245 hp 360 cid two-barrel V-8.

JAVELIN SERIES 70

Series Number	Body/Style Number	Body Type & Seating	Factory Price	Shipping Weight	Production Total
JAVELIN					
70	7179-5	2-dr FsBk Cpe-6P	2879	2887	7,105
JAVELIN SST					
70	7179-7	2-dr FsBk Cpe-6P	2999	2890	17,707
JAVELIN/AMX (V-8)					
70	7179-8	2-dr FsBk Cpe-4P	3432	3244	2,054

1971 AMC, Ambassador Brougham two-door hardtop, V-8

AMBASSADOR — (SIX/V-8) — SERIES 80 — The 1971 Ambassador received a new, die-cast rectangular grille. There were also new front end caps incorporating side marker lights visible in face or profile view. Car-line nameplates were downgraded one notch to make it seem that each line was one level higher. The Ambassador six sedan became the DPL. Offered in SST and top-level Brougham trims were the two-door hardtop and four-door sedans and station wagon. Along with air conditioning (as before) the standard equipment list was expanded to include automatic transmission. The Ambassador six came with all Matador features, plus 55 ampere alternator: front bumper guards; All-Season air conditioning; Shift-Command transmission; and a 258 cid six. Ambassador SSTs had, in addition, full wheel-covers and a 210 hp 304 cid V-8. Ambassador Broughams also had individually adjustable reclining seats and, for wagons, woodgrained exterior panels on the sides and rear.

AMBASSADOR SERIES 80

Series Number	Body/Style Number	Body Type & Seating	Factory Price	Shipping Weight	Production Total
AMBASSADOR DPL SIX					
80	7185-2	4-dr Sed-6P	3616	3315	6,675
AMBASSADOR SST (V-8)					
80	7185-5	4-dr Sed-6P	3852	3520	5,933
80	7189-5	2-dr HT Cpe-6P	3870	3561	1,428
80	7188-5	4-dr Sta Wag-6P	4253	3815	4,465
AMBASSADOR BROUGHAM (V-8)					
80	7185-7	4-dr Sed-6P	3983	3541	13,115
80	7189-7	2-dr HT Cpe-6P	3999	3580	4,579
80	7188-7	4-dr Sta Wag-6P	4430	3862	5,479

BASE ENGINES

(SIX) Inline Six: Overhead valves. Cast iron block. Displacement: 232 cid. Bore and stroke: 3.75 x 3.50 inches. Compression ratio: 8.0:1. Brake hp: 135 at 4400 rpm. Seven main bearings. Hydraulic valve lifters. Carburetor: Carter Type YF one-barrel.

(SC/360 V-8) V-8. Overhead valves. Cast iron block. Displacement: 360 cid. Bore and stroke: 4.08 x 3.44 inches. Compression ratio: 8.5:1. Brake hp: 245 at 4400 rpm. Five main bearings. Hydraulic valve lifters: Carburetor: Autolite two-barrel Model 2100.

(DPL SIX) Inline Six: Overhead valves. Cast iron block. Displacement: 258 cid. Bore and stroke: 3.75 x 3.90 inches. Compression ratio: 8.0:1. Brake hp: 150 at 3800 rpm. Seven main bearings. Hydraulic valve lifters. Carburetor: Carter Type YF one-barrel.

(BASE V-8) V-8. Overhead valves. Cast iron block. Displacement: 304 cid. Bore and stroke: 3.75 x 3.44 inches. Compression ratio: 8.4:1. Brake hp: 210 at 4400 rpm. Five main bearings. Hydraulic valve lifters. Carburetor: Autolite Model 2100 two-barrel.

POWERTRAIN OPTIONS: Automatic transmission was standard in Ambassador SST and Ambassador Brougham. Three-speed manual transmission with floor-shift was standard in the Javelin Group. Three-speed manual transmission with column-shift was standard in other models. Shift-Command with column shift, in Gremlin ($200); in Hornet six ($210); in Hornet '304' V-8 ($216); in Hornet SC/360 ($238); in Javelin/Matador six ($217); in Javelin/Matador with '304' V-8 ($223); in Ambassador SST/Brougham with '304' V-8 ($6); in Matador/Javelin with '360' V-8, except AMX ($246); in DPL with '360' V-8 ($29); in other Ambassadors with '360' V-8 ($23); in Matador with '401' V-8 ($256) and in non-DPL Ambassadors with '401' V-8 ($33). Shift Command with floor-shift and console, in Matador/Javelin with '304' V-8 and bucket seats ($279); in Brougham with '304' V-8 ($56); in non-AMX Javelin and Matador with '360' V-8 ($302); in AMX with '360' V-8 ($246); in Brougham with '360' V-8 ($79); in non-AMX Javelin and Matador with '401 'V-8 ($312); in AMX with '401 'V-8 ($256) and in '401' Ambassador Brougham ($89). Four-speed manual transmission with floorshift, available only in Matador with 'Go-Machine' package and Javelin Group with 285/330 hp V-8s ($209). (NOTE: Some transmission attachment prices increased $4-$7 at midyear). Six-cylinder 360 cid 150 hp engine, in Gremlin and Hornet, except SC/360 ($54); in Javelin and Matador, except AMX ($50). Two-barrel 360 cid 245 hp V-8 in all, except Gremlin/Hornet and except standard in AMX ($48). Four-barrel 360 cid 285 hp V-8 in Javelin AMX ($49); in Matadors, Ambassadors and other Javelins ($97). Four-barrel 401 cid 330 hp V-8 in Javelin AMX ($137); in Matador; Ambassadors and other Javelins ($137). Optional axle ratios ($12-$14). Heavy-duty 70-ampere battery ($14-$15). Twin-Grip differential in Gremlin and Hornet ($43); in all other models ($47). Dual exhausts, in all with '360' four-barrel V-8 ($31). Dual exhausts were standard with the '401' V-8. Engine block heater ($12). Cooling system including heavy-duty radiator, Power flex fan and fan shroud ($16). Cold Start package ($18-19).

CONVENIENCE OPTIONS: Power brakes ($45-$49). Power steering ($100-$111). Air conditioning ($399). Speed control, Matador/Ambassador ($63). Front and rear bumper guards, Gremlin/Hornet ($20); Javelin/Matador ($32). Locking type gas cap, Gremlin ($6). Electric clock, in base Hornet only ($17). Electric rear defogger, Javelin/Matador/Ambassador passenger ($52). Front manual disc brakes, Javelin V-8 ($40). Engine block heater, all ($12). Heavy-duty cooling system, all ($16-$18). Tinted glass, all windows; Gremlin ($37); Hornet ($40); Matador/Javelin ($44); Ambassador ($47); Tinted windshield, Gremlin/Hornet ($30); Javelin ($32); Matador ($36); Ambassador ($38); Headlight delay system ($23). Roof luggage rack, Gremlin ($40); Matador wagon ($58). Deck luggage rack, Javelin ($35); Hornet sedan ($32); Sportabout ($47). Bodyside scuff molding, Gremlin/Hornet ($27); Javelin/Ambassador ($31). Two-tone paint, Hornet SST ($28); Matador/Ambassador sedan ($31); wagon ($71); Rally stripe, Javelins except AMX ($37); Gremlin ($30); Hornet (standard). Exterior paint stripe, basic Hornet - standard Hornet SST - ($10). Power front disc brakes, SC/360 and Hornet SST V-8 ($84); other V-8 ($89). Power side windows, Ambassador cars ($120); wagons with tailgate ($157). AM push-button radio, Gremlin/Hornet ($67); all others ($72). AM/FM Multiplex stereo, Javelin Group including AMX ($224). AM/FM push-button radio, Matador/Ambassador ($143). AM/radio with 8-track and two speakers, Javelin Group ($207). AM radio with 8-track and two-speakers Matador/Ambassador ($140). Leather bucket seats, Javelin SST/AMX ($84). Corduroy fabric bucket seats, Javelin SST/AMX ($52). Serape fabric reclinable seats, Matador hardtop ($71). Center console, Javelin Group, except standard. AMX ($58). Vinyl center armrest bucket seats, Ambassador Style 7189-7 and Matador Style 7119-7 ($136). Fabric reclinable seats, Ambassador SST wagon ($96). 'Harem' fabric reclinable seats, Ambassador Brougham passenger models ($75). Third station wagon seat with power tailgate and extras ($118). Custom steering wheel, Gremlin/Hornet ($14). Rim-blow Sports steering wheel, Gremlin/Hornet ($37); Matador/Ambassador ($40). Adjust-O-Tilt steering, Javelin/Matador/Ambassador ($49). Tachometer, Hornet SC/360 only ($50). Station wagon tailgate air deflector, Gremlin ($49); others ($22). Air adjustable rear suspension, Matador/Ambassador ($42). Undercoating, Hornet SC/360 ($18). Undercoating and hood insulation, Gremlin/Hornet ($22). Black, white, blue or green vinyl top, Matador ($97); Ambassador ($108). Standard wheelcovers ($27-$30). Custom wheelcovers ($25-$54). Turbo-cast or wire wheelcovers ($52-$75). Styled steel wheels, Gremlin 'X'/AMX with 'Go-Package' ($34-$37). Styled steel wheels, most other models ($99-$108); SC/360 ($46). Rear quarter vent windows, basic Hornet ($30). Electric wiper/washers, Gremlin/Hornet, except SC/360 ($21). Electric wiper/washers, Javelin/Matador/Ambassador ($22). Matador station wagon, woodgrained side panels ($117). Black, white, blue or green vinyl roof, Hornet, except SC/360 ($88); Javelin ($89). Calvary Twill recliner seat, Matador wagon ($96). Center armrest and cushion, Javelin without console ($51).

OPTION PACKAGES: (Matador 'Go-Machine') $373 on Matador hardtops with '360' V-8/ $461.10 on Matador hardtops with '401' V-8, includes selected engine; four-barrel carburetion; dual exhausts; Handling Package; power disc brakes; E60-15 Polyglass tires with raised white letters; 15 x 7 inch styled steel wheels and Space-Saver spare tire. (Javelin/AMX 'Go Package') $410.90 on Javelin/AMX with '360' V-8/$498.95 on Javelin/AMX with '401' V-8, includes specified engine; four-barrel carburetor; dual exhausts; hood 'T' stripe decal; Rally-Pac instrumentation: Handling Package; Cowl-Air carburetor induction system; heavy-duty cooling components; Twin-Grip differential; power disc brakes; E60-15 Polyglas raised white letter tires; styled-steel wheels of 15 x 7 inch size and Space-Saver spare.

HISTORICAL FOOTNOTES: The full-sized AMC models were introduced Oct. 6, 1970 and the Gremlin appeared in dealer showrooms the same date. Model year production peaked at 244,758 units. Calendar year sales of 256,963 cars were recorded. R.D. Chapin, Jr. was the chief executive officer of the company this year.

1972 AMC

1972 AMC, Hornet Sportabout 'D/L' four-door station wagon, 6-cyl

HORNET SST — (SIX/V-8) — SERIES 01 — All Hornets were SST models this year. In addition, all were marketed in six and V-8 series for the first time. Physical changes were minor, consisting mainly of trim and ornamentation revisions. One was a 'silver line' treatment for the molded plastic radiator grille. There were also new taillights and an aluminum overlay panel below the trunk lid. Two model-creating options packages were available and served to upgrade the level of trim in specific attachments. For example, there was the Sportabout D/L (Deluxe) package which included color-keyed, woodgrained side and rear paneling; roof rack with air deflector; Custom wheelcovers; individually reclining seats; and 'D/L' decals. It could be had, on the station wagon only, two different ways. With vinyl upholstery, the price tag was $236.25 and with 'Scorpio' fabric upholstery the retail price was $283.55. A sporty 'X' package, priced at $118.55, included Sports steering wheel; Rally stripes; wide rocker panel moldings; slot styled wheels; C78 x 14 tires; and special 'X' emblems. The two-door sedan 'X' package included the same equipment, less wide rocker panel moldings, at the same price. A designer series Hornet Sportabout was created by famed Italian fashion genius Dr. Aldo Gucci. It featured beige seats and door panels trimmed with red and green stripes. The Gucci crest appeared on the inside door panel, front fenders and headliners. Available in just four exterior colors - Snow white; Hunter green; Grasshopper green and Yuca tan - the Gucci Sportabout registered sales of 2,583 units. Standard Hornet equipment features began with all items found in Gremlins plus, rear armrest; rear ashtray; cigarette lighter; two coat hooks; color-keyed carpets; cargo mat; 16 gallon gas tank, glove box; full-width package tray; Custom steering wheel; and three-speed manual transmission with column shift. The Hornet Sportabout also had carpeting in the rear cargo area; rear liftgate; cargo compartment lock; and Space-Saver spare tire. A Space-Saver spare was also standard on any Hornet with optional styled steel wheels. The 232 cid six-cylinder engine was the base powerplant and tire sizes varied with each different engine. Size 6.45 x 14 blackwall tires came as regular equipment with sixes. However, 6.95 x 14 tires were used with sixes having an air conditioner and were standard with V-8 powered sedans and Sportabouts. An improved type of Torque-Command automatic transmission was optionally available this year. A special Hornet Rallye model trim package was available in 1972 only with a special Hornet Rallye stripe treatment along the lines of the 1972 SC/360 stripe treatment, on two-door Hornets. It consists of pleated vinyl bucket seats; manual disc brakes; handling package; 20:1 quick-ratio manual steering; fully-synchromesh three-speed manual transmission; three-spoke sports steering wheel (15"); and 'Rallye' emblems on rear fenders.

VEHICLE IDENTIFICATION NUMBERS: The numbering system and code locations were the same as on previous models. The second digit was changed to a '2' to indicate 1972 model year. A new third symbol was the Code 'E' (indicating fully synchronized three-speed manual floor shift). There were also several new possibilities for the sixth symbol, (indicating class of body) as follows: '5' = Gremlin or Ambassador SST; '7' = Hornet SST, Sportabout, Matador, Javelin SST or Ambassador Brougham; '8' = Javelin AMX. New seventh symbols (indicating engine type) were as follows: 'M' = 304 cid V-8 with low-compression and two-barrel carburetor (instead of 'I'). Other codes were carried over from earlier years without change.

HORNET SST SERIES 01

Model Number	Body/Style Number	Body Type & Seating	Factory Price	Shipping Weight	Production Total
01	7206-7	2-dr Sed-6P	2199/2337	2627/2861	27,122
01	7205-7	4-dr Sed-6P	2265/2403	2691/2925	24,254
01	7208-7	4-dr Sta Wag-6P	2587/2725	2769/2998	34,065

NOTE 1: Data above slash for six/below slash for V-8.

1972 AMC, Matador two-door hardtop coupe, 6-cyl

MATADOR — (SIX/V-8) — **SERIES 10** — The Matador was also marketed as a six/V-8 Series for the first time this year. The 1972 Matador was fighting an identity crisis and was sometimes promoted as, "A car you probably never heard of." In attempting to give it an image, AMC redesigned the grille. Ads highlighted the Matador's use by the Los Angeles Police Department. A horizontally lined, segmented pattern grille insert with three color-keyed bars amounted to the major frontal change. The rear also had new lamps and center panel trim, while the side of the car had a dual length pinstripe treatment. Old-fashioned cable controls in the heating system were switched to a vacuum operated type. Standard equipment was the same as used on 1972 Javelins, plus a front sway bar and 19.5 gallon fuel tank. The hardtop came with two side pillar lights and split-back bench seat. Station wagons had four plastic coat hooks; cargo compartment lock; Dual-Swing tailgate; and a larger, 258 cid, base six. Tires were E78 x 14 blackwalls on passenger car models; G78 x 14 on station wagons. The base V-8 was the same as the Hornet SST's base V-8.

MATADOR SERIES 10

Model Number	Body/Style Number	Body Type & Seating	Factory Price	Shipping Weight	Production Total
10	7215-7	4-dr Sed-6P	2784/2883	3171/3355	36,899
10	7219-7	2-dr HT Cpe-6P	2818/2917	3210/3394	7,306
10	7218-7	4-dr Sta Wag-6P	3140/3239	3480/3653	10,448

NOTE 1: Data above slash for six/below slash for V-8.

1972 AMC, Gremlin 'X' two-door sedan, 6-cyl

GREMLIN — (SIX/V-8) — **SERIES 40** — Since it was essentially a chopped-off Hornet, it made sense to market the Gremlin the same way: as a six or V-8. The two-seater was dropped, though. Stuffing the 304 cid engine into such a small package did require some engineering modifications. Special drivetrain and suspension components were used. Standard equipment included front armrests and ashtrays; 50 ampere battery; dome light; rubber floor mats and trunk mat; glove box door; heater and defroster; foam seat cushions; split-back front seat; fold down rear seat; 21 gallon fuel tank; opening type tailgate; three-speed manual gearbox (with choice of column or floor controls); hubcaps; 37 ampere alternator; exhaust emissions controls; exterior paint stripe; and blackwall tires. Size 6.00 x 13 rubber was used with the basic six; size 6.45 x 14 with air-conditioning or V-8s. Also found on V-8 equipped models were a front sway bar and rear deck '5-Litre V-8' badge. A few new pieces of safety equipment used on all AMC products this year were three-point seat belts linked to a seat belt warning buzzer. As you can tell, the Gremlin, though small, was very well built and equipped. POPULAR MECHANICS magazine wrote, "The best put-together cars out of Detroit this year may come out of Wisconsin... where American Motors makes them."

GREMLIN SERIES 40

Model Number	Body/Style Number	Body Type & Seating	Factory Price	Shipping Weight	Production Total
40	7246-5	2-dr Sed-4P	1999/2153	2494/2746	94,808

NOTE 1: Data above slash for six/below slash for V-8.
NOTE 2: Exactly 10,949 Gremlin V-8s were built in the model year.

1972 AMC, Javelin SST two-door hardtop sports coupe, V-8

JAVELIN SST — (SXI/V-8) — **SERIES 70** — Small styling changes were the order of the year on Javelin SST. A new taillight treatment and grille were seen. The grille was a gridwork formed by three long, horizontal bright moldings and 11 shorter vertical bars. At the rear, there was full-width cross-hatch type decorative patterning in two rows on both Javelin and Javelin/AMX. The Javelin AMX, however, used a different radiator grille design, which matched the center-bulge horizontal blade pattern of 1971. For the, 1972 Javelin SST French fashion designer Pierre Cardin created the Cardin-Javelin option. It featured an interior of multi-colored pleated stripes in Chinese red, plum, white and silver on a black background. Five exterior color choices were: Snow white; Stardust silver; Diamond blue; Trans-Am red; and Wild plum. Experts say that a few Cardin-Javelins left the factory with midnight black finish. The crest of the House of Cardin was applied to door panels and front fenders. Production amounted to 4,152 units for the designer special. Performance, too, was part of 1972 Javelin history, as George Follower won a second SCCA Trans-Am title for AMC this year. The standard equipment list for the Javelin SST was the same as for Hornets, with several deletions or additions. For example, no rear armrest was used. There were, however, such items as a glove box lock; dual horns; high-back bucket seats with front foam cushions; three-speed manual (full-synchromesh) transmission with floor control; Custom steering wheel; and C78-14 blackwall tires on sixes (D78-14s on V-8s). The Javelin AMX also had a Sports steering wheel; deck mounted spoiler; slot style wheels with E70-14 blackwall tires; and standard 304 cid V-8.

JAVELIN SERIES 70

Model Number	Body/Style Number	Body Type & Seating	Factory Price	Shipping Weight	Production Total
JAVELIN SST					
70	7279-7	2-dr FsBk Cpe-4P	3807/2901	2875/3118	22,964*
JAVELIN AMX (V-8)					
70	7279-8	2-dr FsBk Cpe-4P	3109	3149	3,220

NOTE 1: Prices and weights above slash are for six/below slash for V-8.
***NOTE 2:** Totals include 100 Javelin '401' Alabama State Police Interceptors.

1972 AMC, Ambassador Brougham, four-door station wagon, V-8

AMBASSADOR — (V-8) — **SERIES 80** — The 1972 Ambassador received just a few changes, the most noticeable one being a new radiator grille. It incorporated three heavy horizontal bright blades which, together with thinner vertical blades, formed a grid of large, square openings. There was an Ambassador chrome signature script at the left-hand side. The rearview also reflected two changes: new taillights and an attractive center trim panel. Six styles were provided in two levels of trim: SST or Brougham. A six was not available. Standard equipment began with all items found in or on Matadors, plus a big 55 ampere alternator (to provide a strong electrical system with standard air conditioning); rear armrests; front and rear bumper guards on hardtops and sedans; inside hood release; power brakes; Torque Command gearbox; and the '304' V-8. The Brougham also had wheelcovers. All models, except station wagons, used E78 x 14 blackwall tires. Wagons came without the rear bumper guards, but had carpeted cargo spaces; rooftop luggage racks; and H78 x 14 tires. Brougham wagons had a tailgate air deflector and woodgrained exterior paneling. With prices beginning under $4,000, the Ambassador Eight was a good bargain.

AMBASSADOR EIGHT SERIES 80

Model Number	Body/Style Number	Body Type & Seating	Factory Price	Shipping Weight	Production Total
AMBASSADOR SST					
80	7285-5	4-dr Sed-6P	3885	3537	11,929
80	7289-5	2-dr HT Cpe-6P	3902	3579	986
80	7288-5	4-dr Sta Wag-6P	4270	3833	5256
AMBASSADOR BROUGHAM					
80	7285-7	4-dr Sed-6P	4002	3551	16,432
80	7289-7	2-dr HT Cpe-6P	4018	3581	4137
80	7288-7	4-dr Sta Wag-6P	4437	3857	5624

BASE ENGINES

NOTE: SAE net horsepower (nhp) ratings measuring output at the rear of the transmission with all accessories installed and operating are now used.

(BASE SIX) Inline Six: Overhead valves. Cast iron block. Displacement: 232 cid. Bore and stroke: 3.75 x 3.50 inches. Compression ratio: 8.0:1. SAE nhp: 100 at 3600 rpm. Seven main bearings. Hydraulic valve lifters. Carburetor: Carter Type YF one-barrel.

(BASE STATION WAGON SIX) Inline Six: Overhead valves. Cast iron block. Displacement: 258 cid. Bore and stroke: 3.75 x 3.90 inches. Compression ratio: 8.0:1. SAE Net hp: 110 at 3500 rpm. Seven main bearings. Hydraulic valve lifters. Carburetor: Carter Type YF one-barrel.

(BASE V-8) V-8. Overhead valves. Cast iron block. Displacement: 304 cid. Bore and stroke: 3.75 x 3.44 inches. Compression ratio: 8.4:1. SAE Net hp: 150 at 4400 rpm. Five main bearings. Hydraulic valve lifters. Carburetor: Autolite two-barrel Model 2100.

CHASSIS FEATURES: Wheelbase: (Gremlin) 96 inches; (Hornet) 108 inches; (Javelin) 110 inches; (Matador) 118 inches; (Ambassador) 122 inches. Overall length: (Gremlin) 161.3 inches; (Hornet) 179.3 inches; (Javelin) 191.8 inches; (Matador) 206 inches; (Ambassador) 210.8 inches. Front tread: (Gremlin and Hornet) 57.5 inches; (Javelin) 59.3 inches; (Matador and Ambassador) 59.9 inches. Rear tread: (Gremlin and Hornet) 57 inches; (Javelin, Matador and Ambassador) 60 inches.

POWERTRAIN OPTIONS: Torque-Command transmission was standard in Ambassador Series models with the base V-8 and was optional in other models at 15 different prices determined by series and engine attachment. The prices ranged from $200 for Gremlin/Hornet sixes to $257 for Matadors with the '401' V-8. In addition, Torque-Command was a $23 option for Ambassadors with the '360' V-8 and $35 extra in those with the big '401' V-8. Three-speed manual transmission with floor shift was available, as an option in Gremlin/Hornet models ($32). Torque-Command with floor shift was optional in Javelins, with the '304' V-8 ($282); with the '360' V-8 ($293) and with the '401' V-8 ($305). Four-speed manual was optional in Javelins only in combination with the four-barrel '360' V-8 or '401' V-8 ($188). The big 258 cid six was optional, in Gremlin/Hornet Group ($51); in Javelin SST ($43); in Matador passenger cars ($46). The 360 cid two-barrel V-8 was optional in Hornet/Javelin Group ($42). The 360 cid four-barrel V-8 was optional in Javelin ($85); in Matador/Ambassador ($89). The 401 cid four-barrel V-8 was optional in Javelin Group ($162) and in Matador/Ambassador Group models only when F78 x 14 tires were also used ($170). Optional axle ratios, all models ($12-$14). Heavy-duty 70 ampere battery ($14-$15). Twin-Grip differential ($43-$46). Dual exhaust with '360' V-8 and four-barrel, standard with '401' V-8 ($28-$31). Heavy-duty cooling system ($16). A cowl-air induction system was included in 'Go-Package' option groups.

CONVENIENCE OPTIONS: All-Season air conditioning, all models except Ambassador ($377). Gremlin/Hornet air conditioning package ($473). Front and rear bumper guards, Gremlin/Hornet ($21); Javelin ($29); Matador/Ambassador ($31). Center armrest cushion, Javelin without console ($54). Rear window defogger, Javelin ($45); Matador/Ambassador ($48). Front manual disc brakes, Gremlin/Hornet with 14 inch wheels ($47); Javelin ($47); Matador/Ambassador ($50). Engine block heater, Matador/Ambassador ($16); all others ($14). Tinted glass, all windows; Gremlin ($37); Hornet/Javelin ($40); Matador ($42); Ambassador ($49). Tinted windshield only, Gremlin/Hornet/Javelin ($30); Matador ($35). Tinted glass standard with air conditioned Ambassador. Headlights-off delay ($21). Gremlin, locking gas cap ($6). Station wagon rooftop luggage rack, Matador ($56). Sportabout, including air deflector ($61). Rear deck luggage rack, Hornet sedan ($32); Javelin SST ($32). Rally side stripes, Gremlin/Javelin SST ($33-$39). Hood 'T' Stripe AMX ($39). Color-keyed woodgrain panels, Sportabout ($95), Matador wagon ($113). Power brakes, Gremlin/Hornet/Javelin ($44) and Matador ($47). Power front disc brakes, Hornet with Rallye package ($32); Hornet/Gremlin ($79); Javelin ($77); Matador ($81) and Ambassador ($50). Power steering, Gremlin/Hornet, with 14 inch wheels only. ($99); Javelin ($106) and Matador/Ambassador ($111). Power side window lifts, Matador/Ambassador only ($123). Power tailgate window, in Matador/Ambassador wagons without third seat ($35). All power windows package Ambassador wagon only ($158). AM push-button radio, Gremlin/Hornet/Javelin ($66); AM/FM Multiplex stereo with two rear speakers, Javelin ($196); Matador/Ambassador ($230). Stereo tape player in Javelin with manual radio ($190). Gremlin bench seat with Custom trim ($79). Gremlin bucket seats with Custom trim ($117). Hornet Group 'Scorpio' fabric trim with reclining seats ($109). 'Harem' fabric trim in Ambassador Brougham ($69); in Ambassador Brougham wagon, ($96). Matador/Ambassador wagon third seat, includes two safety belts, cargo mat and power tailgate window ($108). Adjustable rear air shocks, Matador/Ambassador ($40). Functional lower front spoiler, Javelin/AMX with disc brakes ($31). Quick-ratio manual steering, 20:1 ratio with Gremlin/Hornet ($11); Javelin Group, 16:1 ratio ($15). Adjust-O-Tilt steering wheel, Gremlin/Hornet with Torque-Command and Javelin ($43); Matador/Ambassador ($46). Three-spoke Sports steering wheel, Gremlin ($33); Hornet/Javelin, standard AMX, ($19); Matador/Ambassador ($20). Sun roof, Hornet two-door sedan without vinyl top, Sportabout and Gremlin ($142). Black; white; blue; green or brown vinyl roof, on Hornet/Javelin ($88); on Matador passenger models ($91) and Ambassador passenger ($109). Full wheelcovers ($72-29). Custom wheelcovers ($50-$53). Turbo-Disc wheelcovers, Hornet D/L ($25); most other models ($75-$78) and Ambassador Brougham ($50). Spoke style wheels (including Space-Saver spare on all except Matador/Ambassador), for cars with options packages that include special spoke wheel prices ($34-$50); on others ($99-$104).

OPTION PACKAGES: Gucci Sportabout package featured beige seats and door panels trimmed with red and green stripes. The Gucci crest appeared on the inside door panel, front fenders and headliners. Available in special exterior colors. Javelin Cardin bucket seats and Cardin trim, for Javelin SST only ($85). Individual reclining seat with Hornet Sportabout Gucci trim ($142). Code 391 Javelin AMX '360 Go-Package,' includes: specified engine; dual exhausts; hood 'T' stripe decal; black-out rear panel; Rally-Pack instrumentation; Handling Package; Cowl-Air induction; heavy-duty cooling; Twin-Grip; power disc brakes; E60-15 Polyglas raised white-letter tires; 15 x 7 inch styled steel wheels; and Space-Saver spare with regular 14 inch wheels ($428). Code 392 Javelin AMX '401 Go-Package,' includes all above with 401 cid V-8 ($505). Code 633 Hornet sedan Rally-Package, includes vinyl bucket seats; manual front disc brakes; Handling Package; quick 20:1 ratio manual steering; three-speed floor-shift transmission; Sports steering wheel; and 'Rallye' emblems ($119). Gremlin 'X' package, includes: full-length spear decal; painted grille; 14 x 6 inch slotted wheels; D70 x 14 tires; Space-Saver spare; Custom bucket seat interior; cargo region insulation; 15 inch Sports

steering wheel; and interior appointments package with special decals ($285.10 w/regular tires; $319.55/with RWL tires).

HISTORICAL FOOTNOTES: The 1972 AMC models were introduced Sept. 22, 1971. Calendar year production peaked at 279,132 units. AMC set a record dollar sales total of $1.4 billion and pulled-down a $30.2 million profit. The AMC Buyer Protection Plan was an excellent 1972 sales motivation tool.

1973 AMC

1973 AMC, Hornet two-door hatchback coupe, 6-cyl

HORNET — (SIX/V-8) — American Motor's popular compact, was offered in 1973, with a new hatchback model. This brought to four the number of Hornet body styles. The third 'door' combined the functions of window and trunk lid. It was top hinged and fully counter-balanced for easy opening and closing. The Hornet had new front fenders, a recessed hood with raised center crease line, and a new full-length grille. CAR and DRIVER magazine called the 1973 Hornet Hatchback "The styling coup of '73" and this was used by AMC in one of its advertisements. An interesting Levi's Jean-style interior was added as a new option on June 20, 1973. The Hornet offered plenty of interior room, good economy, and a high degree of mechanical reliability. Standard equipment and trims continued in the pattern of earlier years.

VEHICLE IDENTIFICATION NUMBERS: The numbering system and code locations were the same as on previous models. The first symbol was changed to a '3' to indicate 1973 model year. The third symbol 'F' was no longer used. It had previously designated three-speed manual transmission with non-synchromesh first gear. A new fifth symbol was '3', used to designate the new three-door hatchback body. There were several variations in sixth symbols, as follows: '5' = Gremlin; '7' = Hornet hatchback, Hornet Sportabout, Matador, Ambassador Brougham and '8' = Javelin AMX. The coding system was otherwise unchanged.

HORNET SERIES 01

Model Number	Body/Style Number	Body Type & Seating	Factory Price	Shipping Weight	Production Total
01	7306-7	2-dr Sed-6P	2298/2436	2777/2990	23,187
01	7305-7	4-dr Sed-6P	2343/2481	2854/3067	25,452
01	7303-7	2-dr Hatch-5P	2449/2587	2818/3031	40,110
01	7308-7	4-dr Sta Wag-6P	2675/2813	2921/3134	44,719

NOTE 1: Data above slash for six/below slash for V-8.

MATADOR — (SIX/V-8) — SERIES 10 — The Matador received a new grille. It consisted of four groups of slim rectangles stacked triple high. In the center of each rectangle was a short horizontal molding. There were new interior colors and fabrics, too. It was marketed with carryover sixes and V-8s. The Matador was again a hit with the LAPD, which added more Matadors to the fleet.

MATADOR SERIES 10

Model Number	Body/Style Number	Body Type & Seating	Factory Price	Shipping Weight	Production Total
10	7315-7	4-dr Sed-6P	2814/2853	3289/3502	33,822
10	7318-7	4-dr Sta Wag-6P	3197/3278	3627/3815	11,643
10	7319-7	2-dr HT Cpe-6P	2887/2986	3314/3527	7,067

Note 1: Data above slash for six/below slash for V-8.

1973 AMC, Matador four-door station wagon, 6-cyl

1973 AMC, Gremlin 'X' two-door sedan, V-8

GREMLIN — (SIX/V-8) — The basic Gremlin remained the same as last year's model. About the only significant changes were new safety bumpers and 6.45 x 17 standard sized tires. Equipped with the base 258 cid six, the Gremlin had lots of 'guts' and averaged about 20 mpg of gas...excellent for 1973. The Gremlin was a lot heavier than other early subcompacts and better-suited to sustained high-speed touring. It was, however, plagued by typical ills, like carburetion; cooling; squeaking; and rattles. It was also quite prone to rust. New for 1973 were several optional equipment changes. A new bodyside trim design had the stripe 'hopping up' behind the rear wheel opening and continuing to the rear of the fender at the higher level. It was used on the Gremlin 'X,' which also had special decals; painted grille; Custom interior appointments; bucket seats; slotted styled wheels; Space-Saver spare tire; and added cargo area sound insulation. A Levi's Gremlin package was also available, reproducing an authentic 'blue jeans' look in a spun nylon version of denim for seats, door inserts and map storage pockets. There was also orange stitching and copper rivets, just like on real jeans. Standard equipment features for 1973 were essentially unchanged

GREMLIN SERIES 40

Model Number	Body/Style Number	Body Type & Seating	Factory Price	Shipping Weight	Production Total
40	7346-5	2-dr Sed-4P	2098/2252	2642/2867	122,844

NOTE 1: 11,672 V-8 Gremlins made in calendar 1973.
NOTE 2: Prices and weights above slash are for six/below slash for V-8.

GREMLIN SERIES 40 ENGINES: See 1972 Gremlin Series engines.

1973 AMC, Javelin two-door fastback coupe, V-8

JAVELIN — (SIX/V-8) — SERIES 70 — The Javelin and Javelin AMX sports hardtops featured a new, smooth roofline. A new taillight treatment, with twin-pod lamps at each side of the car, was adopted. The Javelin AMX was unchanged otherwise, but the Javelin base models had a recessed plastic grille that was distinctive from the past. It was flush with the front of the car and incorporated rectangular Rally lights. Bucket seats were standard in both Javelin and Javelin AMX lines, along with interior packaging of the aircraft cockpit type. Both cars featured spoiler lips over the rear window, with a rear spoiler optional on AMX. Standard equipment was similar to that offered in 1972. A special model called the 'Trans Am Victory Javelin' was offered in 1973. It had a decal on the rear of the front fenders stating that the Javelin had won the SCCA Trans-AM championship for 1971 and 1972. Besides the decal, 14 inch slot-style wheels with E70-14 RWL tires and space saver spare were included at no extra charge. An advertisement featured George Follomer and Roy Woods, who had won the championship for AMC in 1972.

JAVELIN SERIES 70

Model Number	Body/Style Number	Body Type & Seating	Factory Price	Shipping Weight	Production Total
JAVELIN					
70	7379-7	2-dr FsBk Cpe-4P	2889/2983	2868/3104	25,195
JAVELIN AMX					
70	7379-8	2-dr FsBk Cpe-4P	3191	3170	5,707

NOTE1: Data above slash for six/below slash for V-8.

AMBASSADOR — (V-8) — SERIES 80 — Luxury was a key word in describing the 1973 Ambassador line of hardtop, sedan and station wagon. The SST Series was discontinued and Broughams were exclusively retained. A 304 cid V-8; automatic transmission; power steering; power front disc brakes; white sidewall tires; tinted glass; and AM radio were all standard Ambassador Brougham features. Guard-rail steel door beams, for side impact protection, were part of the construction after Jan. 1, 1973. In addition, a quieter type of seat belt warning buzzer was used. Styling features included a slightly redesigned grille with heavier vertical and horizontal moldings. The Ambassador signature was gone from the left side. On the front bumper, a black, rubber impact strip appeared. There was a hood insulation pad; left outside rearview remote-control mirror; visor vanity mirror; electric clock; and electric, variable-speed windshield wipers on every 1973 Ambassador sold. All cars were also undercoated, for protection against rust. Three optional V-8s were offered.

AMBASSADOR SERIES 80 V-8

Model Number	Body/Style Number	Body Type & Seating	Factory Price	Shipping Weight	Production Total
80	7385-7	4-dr Sed-6P	4461	3763	31,490
80	7389-7	2-dr HT Cpe-6P	4477	3774	5,534
80	7388-7	4-dr Sta Wag-6P	4861	4054	12,270

NOTE 1: Data above slash for six/below slash for V-8.

1973 AMC, Ambassador Brougham two-door hardtop coupe, V-8

BASE ENGINES

NOTE: SAE net horsepower (nhp) ratings measuring output at the rear of the transmission with all accessories installed and operating are now used.

(BASE SIX) Inline Six: Overhead valves. Cast iron block. Displacement: 232 cid. Bore and stroke: 3.75 x 3.50 inches. Compression ratio: 8.0:1. SAE nhp: 100 at 3600 rpm. Seven main bearings. Hydraulic valve lifters. Carburetor: Carter Type YF one-barrel.

(BASE STATION WAGON SIX) Inline Six: Overhead valves. Cast iron block. Displacement: 258 cid. Bore and stroke: 3.75 x 3.90 inches. Compression ratio: 8.0:1. SAE nhp: 110 at 3500 rpm. Seven main bearings. Hydraulic valve lifters. Carburetor: Carter Type YF one-barrel.

(BASE V-8) V-8. Overhead valves. Cast iron block. Displacement: 304 cid. Bore and stroke: 3.75 x 3.44 inches. Compression ratio: 8.4:1. SAE Net hp: 150 at 4400 rpm. Five main bearings. Hydraulic valve lifters. Carburetor: Autolite two-barrel Model 2100.

CHASSIS FEATURES: Wheelbase: (Gremlin) 96 inches; (Hornet) 108 inches; (Javelin) 110 inches; (Matador) 118 inches; (Ambassador) 122 inches. Overall length: (Gremlin) 165.5 inches; (Javelin) 192.3 inches; (Ambassador) 212.9 inches; (Matador) 208.5 inches; (Hornet) 184.9 inches. Front tread: (Gremlin) 57.5 inches; (Hornet) 56.4 inches; (Javelin) 59.3 inches. Rear tread: (Gremlin/Hornet) 57 inches; (Javelin/Ambassador/Matador) 60 inches. Tires: (Hornet) 6.95 x 14; (Matador) E78 x 14; (Ambassador) F78 x 14; (Javelin) D78 x 14 and (Gremlin) 6.45 x 14.

POWERTRAIN OPTIONS: Torque-Command automatic transmission with column control was standard in Ambassador Broughams. Three-speed manual transmission with full-synchromesh first gear and floor shift was standard in Gremlins - optional in all other models, except Ambassadors. Other available transmissions for AMC cars included Torque-Command with column control; Torque-Command with floor shift; three-speed manual with column control (standard in all except Gremlin/Javelin/Ambassador) and, in selected applications, four-speed manual with floor-mounted Hurst heavy-duty shifter. Engine choices for Gremlins were the 100 hp 232 cid six; 110 hp 258 cid six and 150 hp 304 cid V-8. These engines, plus a 175 hp 360 cid two-barrel V-8, were available in Hornets. Specific Matador models could also be ordered with a 195 hp 360 cid four-barrel V-8 or a 255 hp 401 cid four-barrel V-8. These same choices were also available for Javelin and Javelin AMX. In the Ambassador Brougham were the 150, 175, 195 and 255 hp engines (all V-8) with similar specifications. Optional rear axle ratios: 2.73: 1; 2.87:1 and 3.54:1.

CONVENIENCE OPTIONS: Gremlin 'X' package ($285). Sportabout D/L package ($284). 'Gucci' vinyl interior, in Hornet ($142). Javelin AMX '360' Go-Package ($428). Javelin AMX '401' Go-Package ($476). Power brakes, standard in Ambassador ($44). Power disc brakes, standard in Ambassador ($79). Manual disc brakes ($47). Sun roof ($142). Station wagon third seat, includes two safety belts and power tailgate window ($108). Reclining seats, average price ($80). Bucket seats, in selected models ($131). Power steering, Gremlin ($99). Factory air conditioning, Gremlin ($377). Vinyl roof, on Hornet ($88). Factory air conditioning, Javelin/Javelin AMX ($377). AM/FM stereo, Javelin/Javelin AMX ($196). Vinyl covered top, Javelin/AMX ($88). AM/FM stereo, in Matador ($230). Vinyl covered top, on Matador, except station wagon ($91). Power windows ($123). AM/FM stereo, in Ambassador ($61). Vinyl covered top, on Ambassador ($109).

HISTORICAL FOOTNOTES: Model year output for 1973 American Motors' models was registered at exactly 320,786 cars. The company held only a 3.3 percent share of the total car business. R.D. Chapin, Jr. continued as the firm's chief executive officer this year. Introduced on the American Motor's Jeep Wagoneer line this year was the innovative 'Quadra-Trac' full-time four-wheel-drive system.

1974 AMC

HORNET — (SIX/V-8) — SERIES 01 — The styling seen on 1974 AMC Hornets was slightly revised. A new energy-absorbing front bumper looked much the same as before, but the full-width, vinyl impact strip was replaced by rubber-faced bumper guards spaced widely apart, just inboard of the grille-mounted Rally lights. The grille itself still consisted of many fine, vertical louvers, but the horizontal center bar that integrated the lamps was now finished in black. A new side trim treatment featured a thin, straight upper beltline molding that ran from the taillamps to the front fender tip and, then, down around the side marker light, with a shape paralleling the front fender edge contour. A second full-length molding ran from below the taillamp (and above the rear bumper end) to a point under the front side marker light. This

molding was also straight, except in those places where it curved over the front and rear wheel openings. The Hornet nameplate was removed from the lip of the hood. Model nameplates seen alongside of the car were moved from their 1973 position (on the upper cowlsides) to a point just behind the front side marker lights. Standard equipment for the basic Hornet began with all items found on Gremlins, plus rear ashtray; color-keyed carpets; 16 gallon fuel tank; full-width package tray; Custom steering wheel; foam front bench seat; full-flow oil filter; three-speed manual column shifted transmission; 6.95 x 14 blackwall tires and, on all models except the hatchback, rear armrests. The Sportabout wagon and hatchback models also had cargo area carpeting; fold-down rear seats and a rear liftgate. Standard equipment in Hornet V-8s was a front sway bar. On cars with the optional 360 cid two-barrel V-8, a 60 ampere battery was used in place of the regular 50 ampere type.

1974 AMC, Hornet two-door sedan, 6-cyl

VEHICLE IDENTIFICATION NUMBERS: The numbering system and code locations were the same as on previous models. The second symbol was changed to a '4' to indicate 1974 model year. There were several possible changes in other symbols. The range of sixth symbols, indicating model, was modified as follows: '5' = Gremlin; '7' = Hornet; Javelin; Matador or Ambassador Brougham; '8' = Javelin AMX or Matador X; '9' = Matador Brougham; 'P' = police car and 'T' = taxicab. The range of seventh symbols, indicating type of engine, was modified as follows: 'A' = 258 cid one-barrel six; 'E' = 232 cid one-barrel six; 'H' = 304 cid two-barrel V-8; 'N' = 360 cid two-barrel V-8; 'P' = 360 cid four-barrel V-8 and 'Z' = 401 cid four-barrel V-8. The range of eighth symbols was modified as follows: Cars coded 1-6 were built in Kenosha, Wis. and those coded 7-9 were built in Brampton, Ontario, Canada. Other coding was as in the past.

HORNET SERIES 01

Series Number	Body/Style Number	Body Type & Seating	Factory Price	Shipping Weight	Production Total
01	7403-7	2-dr Hatch-5P	2849/2987	2815/3042	55,158
01	7406-7	2-dr Sed-6P	2774/2912	2774/3001	29,950
01	7405-7	4-dr Sed-6P	2824/2962	2841/3068	29,754
01	7408-7	4-dr Sta Wag-6P	3049/2987	2908/3135	71,413

NOTE 1: Data above slash for six/ below slash for V-8.

1974 AMC, Matador 'X' two-door sedan, V-8

MATADOR — (SIX/V-8) — SERIES 10 — AMC drastically restyled the Matador two-door coupe. Sedans and wagons had modest changes with new grilles and front/rear bumpers. A big difference in appearance was the dropping of the integrated bumper/grille for a centrally divided unit with vertical louvers, square headlamp surrounds with Argent silver finish; round parking lamps mounted in grille (inboard of headlights) and Matador lettering on the left-hand hood lip. The front bumper was a shelf-like affair with center license plate indent flanked by rubber-faced bumper guards. Side trim on the sedans and wagons consisted of a thin, straight, three-quarter length molding. It ran from behind the front wheel opening to above the rear side marker light. There were model nameplates on the front fender, behind the wheel cutout. Standard equipment was the same as on base Javelins, plus front sway bar; full insulation package including undercoating; 19.5 gallon fuel tank; side molding vinyl inserts; Custom steering wheel; full-back bench seats; and base six or V-8 engine. The 232 cid one-barrel six or 304 cid two-barrel V-8 were standard in sedans along with E78 x 14 blackwall tires. The base station wagon also included a rubber cargo area mat; lockable hidden storage compartment; Dual-Swing tailgate; H78 x 14 tires and bigger 258 cid one-barrel base six. Vinyl inserts were not used on side moldings on woodgrained wagons. The two-door Matador coupe was unique with its long, low, fast-looking silhouette. AMC enthusiasts compare it the Jensen Interceptor. Major styling features were a long fast-sloping hood and a short rear deck. It was conceived with stock car racing in mind. After Mark Donohue captured the SCCA's Trans-Am Series championship in 1971, AMC created a factory racing team with Donohue as driver and Roger Penske as team manager. By the time the car hit the production stage the Energy Crunch had negated the effect of performance on sales. But, 6,165 coupes with a fancy "Cassini" package were produced in 1974 and 1,817 more the following season. Matador coupes had a shorter wheelbase, than sedans and wagons. They also had some equipment differences over these models, including split-back front seats and front door light switches. There was also a special Matador 'X'. It was a full-fledged sub-model (not an option like the Gremlin 'X') with extras including a three-spoke Sports steering wheel; wide bodyside stripes; hood stripes; slot styled wheels; blacked-out grille; Matador 'X' cowl nameplates;

automatic transmission; and two-barrel '304' V-8. Finally, for the low-buck luxury buyer, there was the Matador Brougham coupe with all base equipment, plus black vinyl bumper nerfing strips and full wheelcovers.

MATADOR SERIES 10

Series Number	Body/Style Number	Body Type & Seating	Factory Price	Shipping Weight	Production Total
MATADOR					
10	7415-7	4-dr Sed-6P	3052/3151	3444/3659	27,608
10	7416-7	2-dr Cpe-6P	3096/3195	3459/3674	31,169
10	7416-9	2-dr Brgm Cpe-6P	3249/3348	3486/3701	21,026
10	7418-7	4-dr Sta Wag-6P	3378/3477	3769/3957	9709
MATADOR 'X' (V-8)					
10	7416-8	2-dr Cpe-6P	3699	3674	10,074

NOTE 1: Data above the slash for six/ below slash for V-8.

GREMLIN — (SIX/V-8) — SERIES 40 — There was a new grille for the 1974 Gremlin, but it didn't look totally fresh and new. A multitude of thin, horizontal blades filled a slightly taller opening. The molding around the entire insert was different. The side pieces had a bend instead of being straight. To complement the grille pattern, there were horizontal grooves on the headlight door/fender extension panels. They began just outside the grille surround and swept around the front body corners, with the upper grooves being interrupted by the headlamp lenses. A new bumper, of the energy-absorbing type, was used. It had a shelf-like appearance and black, rubber-faced guards. A Gremlin script was again placed on the left front face of the scoop-like hood bulge. Several new trim variations could be seen on the side of the Gremlin. The thin moldings, formerly used around the windsplits on the rear sail panels, were removed. In addition, the bodyside stripes were entirely redone. The overall effect was somewhat like that of a hockey stick with a pointed handle lying on its bottom edge. Changes in the rear included a thinner bumper; an AMC letter badge on the left side of the indentation panel; new, rubber-faced guards; and chrome bullet-shaped lamps surrounding the license plate (which was in a new location at the center). Standard equipment on the basic Gremlin included all regulation safety features; front armrests and ashtrays; 50 ampere battery; dome light; rubber floor and trunk mats; glove box door; heater and defroster; foam-cushioned splitback front seat; rear seat with fold-down back; 21 gallon fuel tank; opening type rear liftgate; three-speed manual transmission with floor-shift; hubcaps; 35 ampere alternator; exterior paint stripes; and either the base '232' six or '304' V-8. Standard tires were 6.45 x 14 blackwalls and V-8s also had a front suspension sway bar.

1974 AMC, Gremlin two-door sedan, 6-cyl

GREMLIN SERIES 40

Series Number	Body/Style Number	Body Type & Seating	Factory Price	Shipping Weight	Production Total
40	7446-5	2-dr Sed-4P	2481/2635	2855/3094	171,128

NOTE 1: Data above slash for six/below slash for V-8.
NOTE 2: A total of 14,137 Gremlin V-8 were produced in model year 1974.

JAVELIN — (SIX/V-8) — SERIES 70 — Very few cars see major changes in their last season. The Javelin, which was about to bite the dust, followed this long tradition for 1974. About the best way to tell 1973 and 1974 base models apart is to drive them. In the '74, you'll immediately notice the new three-point lap/shoulder harness with ignition interlock. In addition, the later cars may go faster due to emissions control advances. There were federally mandated bumper design changes, to insure the cars could meet five mph impacts. This was done with the addition of shock-absorber mountings and black rubber bumper guards. The molding around the grille insert had an inverted trapezoid shape. On the AMX, red, white and blue letters were placed in the center of the grille. Circular rally-style parking lamps were set into larger circles creating a 'bombsight' appearance. Standard equipment included all found on base Hornets (except rear armrest), plus dual horns; foam-cushioned high-back front bucket seats; front and rear bumper guards; manual front disc brakes; rubber trunk mat; D78 x 14 blackwall tires; three-speed manual floor-shift transmission; a 232 cid six or 304 cid V-8 engine; and a front sway bar. Extra standard equipment for the AMX included a Sports steering wheel; deck mounted rear spoiler; and slotted styled wheels. Javelin AMX 'Go-Packages' were supplied, with the price depending on what kind of tires the customer ordered and which engine was installed.

JAVELIN SERIES 70

Series Number	Body/Style Number	Body Type & Seating	Factory Price	Shipping Weight	Production Total
JAVELIN					
70	7479-7	2-dr FsBk Cpe-4P	2999/3093	2875/3117	22,556
JAVELIN AMX (V-8)					
70	7479-8	2-dr FsBk Cpe-4P	3299	3184	4980

NOTE 1: Data above slash for six/below slash for V-8.
NOTE 2: Javelins and AMXs were never assembled in Canada, though some were assembled in foreign plants from U.S. made parts.

AMBASSADOR BROUGHAM — (V-8) — SERIES 80 — The 1974 Ambassador received a completely new frontal treatment, which was more squared-off and designed to meet a new federal five mile per hour barrier crash test. The grille surround was completely straight (though not flat) on top and bottom and outlined the entire grille including the dual headlights. These units had round lenses mounted in square bezels. A fine-grid pattern insert was divided, horizontally, by two thicker bright moldings forming three levels of background gridwork. There was a stand-up hood ornament and Ambassador lettering on the left-hand

hood lip. The new bumper, which no longer housed the park/turn lamps, was slightly thicker at the center and had an overall shelf-like look. There was a license plate indentation at the middle, flanked by a chrome and rubber guard on each side. Vinyl nerfing strips appeared at each end, wrapping around the corners. Side trim consisted of a straight, three-quarter length strip of chrome running from behind the front wheel opening to the rear of the car; rocker panel moldings; Ambassador nameplates in back of the front wheels; and, on station wagons, redesigned woodgrained paneling positioned higher on the bodysides. Two-door Ambassadors were dropped due to the Matador coupe's restyling. The two previously shared sheetmetal from the cowl back. It was felt the new coupe was not suitable for the Ambassador market. Remaining were sedans and wagons, available in only Brougham level trim. Standard equipment included all items found on base Hornets, plus a 62 ampere generator; front and rear bumper guards; inside hood release; air conditioning; full insulation package; light group; visibility group; undercoating and hood insulation; power front disc brakes; power steering; push-button AM radio; tinted glass in all windows; dual headlights; wheel opening moldings; bright metal rocker panel accents; and the '304' two-barrel V-8. Ambassador Brougham station wagons came with an in-the-floor lockable cargo compartment; Dual Swing-tailgate; durable color-keyed carpeting for cargo area; exterior woodgrained trim; rooftop travel rack and tailgate air deflector. It was the last season that the Ambassador would be offered.

AMBASSADOR BROUGHAM SERIES 80 (V-8)

Series Number	Body/Style Number	Body Type & Seating	Factory Price	Shipping Weight	Production Total
80	7485-7	4-dr Sed-6P	4559	3872	17,901
80	7488-7	4-dr Sta Wag-6P	4960	4115	7,070

BASE ENGINES

NOTE: SAE net horsepower (nhp) ratings measuring output at the rear of the transmission with all accessories installed and operating are now used.

(BASE SIX) Inline Six: Overhead valves. Cast iron block. Displacement: 232 cid. Bore and stroke: 3.75 x 3.50 inches. Compression ratio: 8.0:1. SAE nhp: 100 at 3600 rpm. Seven main bearings. Hydraulic valve lifters. Carburetor: Carter Type YF one-barrel.

(BASE STATION WAGON SIX) Inline Six: Overhead valves. Cast iron block. Displacement: 258 cid. Bore and stroke: 3.75 x 3.90 inches. Compression ratio: 8.0:1. SAE Net hp: 110 at 3500 rpm. Seven main bearings. Hydraulic valve lifters. Carburetor: Carter Type YF one-barrel.

(BASE V-8) V-8. Overhead valves. Cast iron block. Displacement: 304 cid. Bore and stroke: 3.75 x 3.44 inches. Compression ratio: 8.4:1. SAE Net hp: 150 at 4400 rpm. Five main bearings. Hydraulic valve lifters. Carburetor: Autolite two-barrel Model 2100.

CHASSIS FEATURES: Wheelbase: (Hornet) 108 inches; (Matador coupe) 114 inches; (other Matadors) 118 inches; (Gremlin) 96 inches; (Javelin) 110 inches; (Ambassador) 122 inches. Overall length: (Hornet) 187 inches; (Matador coupe) 209 inches; (other Matadors) 215.5 inches; (Matador 'X') 209.4 inches; (Gremlin) 170.3 inches; (Javelin) 195.3 inches; (Ambassador) 219.3 inches. Front tread: (Gremlin) 57.5 inches; (Hornet) 56.4 inches; (Javelin) 59.3 inches. Rear tread: (Gremlin/Hornet) 57 inches; (Javelin/Ambassador/Matador) 60 inches. Tires: (Hornet) 6.95 x 14; (Matador) E78 x 14; (Ambassador) F78 x 14; (Javelin) D78 x 14 and (Gremlin) 6.45 x 14.

POWERTRAIN OPTIONS: Torque-Command automatic transmission with column control was standard in Ambassador Broughams with the base '304' V-8. Torque-Command was also standard in the Matador 'X' with the base '304' V-8. Three-speed all-synchromesh manual transmission with floor control standard in Gremlin/Javelin groups. Three-speed all-synchromesh manual transmission with column control was standard in all other models. Torque-Command was optional in Ambassador Broughams and Matador 'X' with '360' or '401' V-8s ($13-$35). Torque-Command was optional in all other models, with prices and attachments governed by series and type of engine ($200-$257). Torque-Command with floor-shift control was optional in Hornet/Gremlin groups with prices and attachments governed by model and type of engine ($220-$251). Torque-Command with floor-shift control and center console was optional in Javelins ($280-$305); in Matadors ($291-$316) and in Matador 'X' ($59-$84) with price depending on choice of the 304, 360 or 401 V-8s; not available in sixes. Four-speed manual transmission with floor-shift control was optional in Javelins with the '232' one-barrel six or '304' two-barrel V-8 ($188). Four-speed manual transmission with Hurst floor-shifter was available in the Javelin AMX only as part of the 'Go-Package' option. A 51 ampere alternator was optional in Hornet/Gremlin/Matador groups ($13) and with air conditioning. A 62 ampere generator was optional in the Matador group ($48). An 80 ampere heavy-duty battery was optional in Ambassador/Matador groups ($21). A 10 inch heavy-duty clutch was optional in Gremlin/Hornet/Matador six ($12). A coolant recovery system was optional in Matador/Ambassador ($19). Heavy-duty cooling system, in Matador/Ambassador ($17). Dayco 'DS-7' fan belt ($5). Heavy-duty '360'-and '401' V-8, in Matador/Ambassador with heavy-duty Torque-Command only ($32). Manual low gear lock-out, with Matador V-8 and automatic transmission only (no charge). Dual exhausts were available as a separate option for the '360' V-8 and were standard with the '401' V-8. Engine option choices for the year included: 304 cid V-8 two-barrel with 150 nhp at 4200 rpm; 360 cid V-8 two-barrel with 175 nhp at 4000 rpm; 360 cid V-8 four-barrel with 195 nhp at 4400 rpm (single exhaust) and 220 nhp at 4400 rpm (dual exhausts); and 401 cid V-8 four-barrel with 235 nhp at 4600 rpm (single exhausts) and 315 nhp at 3100 rpm (dual exhausts). The 360 cid two-barrel engine was the minimum required engine size for cars sold in California. Prices for powertrain options now based on engine/transmission package (i.e. Matador X/360 V-8/Torque-Command with floor shift and console package was $71.35 above Matador base price, which included regular Torque-Command and a 304 V-8).

POPULAR CONVENIENCE OPTIONS: Air conditioning, except Ambassador ($400). Air conditioning package, in Gremlin/Hornet ($490). Matador wagon vinyl roof ($100). Gremlin 'X' hatchback package ($227). Gremlin 'X' hatchback package with Levi's trim ($298). Hornet Sportabout D/L package, with vinyl trim ($284); with Custom fabric trim ($333). Hornet Sportabout 'X' package ($139). Rooftop travel rack on Matador wagon ($56). Scuff side molding, except specific models ($38). Two-tone paint, on Hornets, except Sportabout ($30); on Matador/Ambassador, except wagons ($37). Special paint application, including painted bodyside panels and accent moldings, on Matador wagon ($69). Rally side stripes, on Gremlins ($33); on base Javelin ($38). Hood 'T' stripes on Javelin AMX without 'Go Package' - standard with ($39). Color-keyed woodgrained exterior paneling, on Sportabout ($95); on Matador wagon, including rear panel ($113). Power brakes, except Matador/Javelin/Ambassador groups ($44). Front power disc brakes ($32-$81). Power steering ($99-$111). Power side windows, Ambassador only ($123). Power tailgate window, Matador/Ambassador two-seat wagons ($35); three-seat wagons (no charge). AM push-button radio ($66-$70). AM/FM push-button radio ($179); AM/FM Multiplex radio with four speakers, in Javelin/Matador/Ambassador ($161-$230). Stereo tape player, Javelin/Ambassador ($196-$200). Domino fabric trim in Hornet hatchback ($99); in Javelin ($47); in Hornet hatchback 'X' ($50). Individual reclining seats with Venetian fabric special interior in Hornets ($109). Third seat with belts and power windows, Matador/Ambassador wagons ($108). Adjust-O-Tilt steering wheel ($43-46). Sports steering wheel, in Gremlin ($33). Aluminum trim rings and hubcaps, Gremlin/Javelin ($33). Black, white, blue, green, brown or cinnamon vinyl roof, on Matadors ($91); on Ambassadors ($109); on Hornet/Javelin coupes ($88). Full wheelcovers ($27-$29). Custom wheelcovers ($23-$50). Javelin 19 x 7 inch slotted wheels ($205). Spoke-style 6 x 14 inch wheels on cars with 'D/L', 'X' or 'Go' packages ($34-$49); as a separate option, ($74-$104). Vent rear quarter windows in Gremlin/Hornet coupe ($28). Deluxe, intermittent electric windshield wipers ($23-$24).

1974 AMC Hornet "Levis" hatchback

OPTION PACKAGES: Gremlin Custom trim, includes: Custom door and seat trim in pleated vinyl; carpeting; extra insulation; Custom steering wheel; wheel opening and drip moldings; and cargo insulation, with bench seat ($109), with bucket seat ($147). Gremlin 'X' package, includes: spear side decal; 6 x 14 inch slot wheels; Space Saver spare with base D70-14 tires; Custom trim with bucket seats: cargo insulation; carpeting; 15 inch steering wheel; special interior appointments; and decals, with base tires ($314), with RWL tires ($349), with whitewall radial tires ($298), and with RWL radials ($410). Handling package ($23-$30). Hornet hatchback 'X', includes: sports steering wheel; rally stripes; slot wheels; 'X' emblems, insulation; vinyl bucket seats; Space-Saver spare; and hidden compartment ($207). Levi's Custom trim package, includes: bucket seats with blue denim trim and Levi's buttons; special door trim; sun visors; insulation; denim litter container; blue headliner: front fender Levi's emblem; and, in Gremlin, carpets; cargo insulation and Custom steering wheel, in Gremlin ($165), in Hornet hatchback ($150), in Hornet hatchback 'X' ($101). Levi's Custom trim package, in Gremlin 'X' ($50). Rally-Pac instrumentation, in Javelin ($77). Gremlin/Hornet hatchback Rally 'X' package, includes: three-speed floor-shift or automatic; power steering; manual front disc brakes; gauges; black dash cluster; and leather Sports steering wheel, 'X' models only, with air conditioning ($100); without ($199). Sportabout D/L package, includes: Sports steering wheel; rally stripes; slot wheels; and 'X' emblems, with vinyl trim ($264), with Custom fabric trim ($313). Designer series Cassini Matador Brougham included Custom wheelcovers with copper-colored inserts; scuff moldings; a copper-colored vinyl roof; copper grille and headlamp bezels; black-carpeted trunk compartment and tire cover; special black seat and door trim with copper buttons; black headliner; black instrument panel with copper dials and overlays; black steering wheel with copper inserts in horn rim; and copper-colored floor carpeting ($299). The upholstery in this model was quite lavish, with the individually reclining seats covered in a rich, black nylon knit fabric having a tufted look. The "Oleg Cassini of Paris, France" crest was embroidered on each front headrest and also appeared, in medallion form, on the trailing edge of front fenders below the 'dipping' feature line molding. Javelin/AMX 'Go-Package included: (with 360 V-8) hood 'T' stripe decal; black-finished rear panel; Rally-Pac instrumentation; Handling Package; heavy-duty cooling system; Twin-Grip differential; power disc brakes; slot styled wheels; Space-Saver spare; and FR78-14 RWL tires on 14 inch wheels ($372.30). Same with E60 x 15 tires and 15 inch slot-styled wheels ($413.35). '401 Go-Package' includes the same features, but bigger V-8 ($420.50 or $461.55, respectively). AMC also offered specially-priced, factory-installed fleet options and fleet option packages.

HISTORICAL FOOTNOTES: Model year production introductions were scheduled for Sept. 15, 1973. Model year production was an all-time high of 509,496 units. Calendar year production peaked at 351,398 cars. Only 3,734 AMC models had 401 cid V-8 engines installed this year. Calendar year sales by dealer franchises in the United States totaled 355,093. Model year ended in November of 1974 instead of June 1974, to take advantage of easier 1974 emission laws. This partly accounts for the large model year production figures. R.D. Chapin, Jr. was chairman and chief executive officer of AMC. A net profit of $28.6 million was made in a season that saw an energy conscious public shun the purchase of all new cars and, especially those reputed to be gas guzzlers. Luckily, AMC's traditional image did not place it deeply into this group. All 1974 AMC engines were designed to run on regular leaded, low-lead or no-lead fuels.

1975 AMC

HORNET — (SIX/V-8) — SERIES 01 — Four models made up the compact Hornet Series for 1975: hatchback; Sportabout sedan/station wagon and two-door sedan. A new grille featured a bold, six segment motif and had five bright vertical division bars against blacked-out vertical louvers within each segment. The outboard divisions contained new rectangular parking lamps. There was also a slightly different look to the front bumper, which was smoother and rounder in general appearance. Six trim packages were available; the sedan offering a new D/L group with individually reclining front seats and cut-pile carpets. It also included a bodyside molding (between the wheelwells at mid-body height), wheelcovers and special emblems. Then, there was the Hornet 'X' group with such items as slot styled wheels: 'X' emblems and full-length Rally striping along the upper feature line. The hatchback and Sportabout could be had with the all-new 'Touring' option. Cars with extra-cost decor trim had a different side molding treatment than described in the 1974 section. Basically, the full-length lower molding was gone. Standard equipment for the base Hornet followed the same pattern described in detail for 1974 models, plus electronic ignition. Identification came from Hornet nameplates right behind the front side marker lamps and on the right rear panel. There were also AMC badges on the left-hand side of the rear panel.

1975 AMC, Hornet Sportabout four-door station wagon, 6-cyl

VEHICLE IDENTIFICATION NUMBERS: The numbering system and code locations were the same as for previous models with the second symbol changed to a '5' to indicate 1975 model year. There were several possible changes in other symbols. The range of third symbols was modified as follows: the symbol 'M' (for four-speed manual transmission) was dropped; the symbol 'D' (three-speed manual floor-shift with overdrive) and 'O' (three-speed manual column-shift with overdrive) were added. The range of fourth symbols now included '6' (for Series 60, Pacer). The fifth symbol '9' (two-door hardtop) was no longer used. Sixth symbols were now as follows: '5' = Gremlin; '7' = Hornet/Matador/Pacer; 'P' = police and 'T' = Taxi. All other coding was the same used previously.

HORNET SERIES 01

Series Number	Body/Style Number	Body Type & Seating	Factory Price	Shipping Weight	Production Total
01	7503-7	2-dr Hatch-5P	3174/3312	2839/3085	13,441
01	7505-7	4-dr Sed-6P	3124/3262	2881/3147	20,565
01	7506-7	2-dr Sed-6P	3074/3212	2815/3061	12,392
01	7508-7	4-dr Sta Wag-6P	3374/3512	3844/3878	39,563

NOTE 1: Model year output totaled 85,961 units. Of these cars 77,886 were sixes and 8,075 were V-8s.
NOTE 2: Prices and weights above slash are for six/ below slash for V-8.

1975 AMC, Matador 'X' two-door coupe, V-8

MATADOR (COUPE) — (SIX/V-8) — SERIES 10 — After 1974, the Matador coupe was distinct from the four-door styles. This year, American Motors emphasized the difference, by placing the two types into different series. The sedan and wagon were moved into the 80 Series slot, vacated by the Ambassador Brougham. That left the Matador coupe, by itself, in Series 10. Newly styled road wheels; front disc brakes and radial tires were standard equipment in the Matador 'X' coupe. Styling changes included a new grille with full-length horizontal bars forming a rectangular pattern. The standard engine was the 258 cid six, with three V-8s optional. 89 cars left the factory with 401 cid engines though that motor was not on the normal equipment list. Factory records indicate four 401s were Matador Coupes. The other 84 were used in Series 80 four-door sedans and wagons, probably law enforcement models. The electronic ignition system was now standard. Other regular features were the same as 1974. The Matador 'X' coupe was, technically, an option package, with a $199 price tag. Also remaining available were the Cassini Coupe of which 1,817 found buyers this season.

MATADOR (COUPE) SERIES 10

Series Number	Body/Style Number	Body Type & Seating	Factory Price	Shipping Weight	Production Total
10	7516-7	2-dr Cpe-6P	3446/3545	3562/3734	22,368

NOTE 1: Prices and weights above slash are for six/below slash for V-8.

GREMLIN — (SIX/V-8) — SERIES 40 — The Gremlin was basically unchanged for 1975. Standard equipment was the same as the previous year, plus electronic ignition. Mechanical detail changes included a sturdier manual transmission and the optional availability of overdrive combined with six-cylinder attachments only. Also provided again, at extra-cost, were the Levis, Rally and Gremlin 'X' packages. The 'hockey stick' striping pattern was carried over on cars so-equipped. New body colors and radial-ply tires could be added. A slightly cleaner looking front bumper was used. Its upper edge had a single-bevel appearance, compared to the triple-bevel 1974 type. Also, the sail panel windsplit indentations were now in a slanted, vertical position and the flared wheel treatment was more subdued. Very close inspection would also reveal that the bumper guards had a more wedge-shaped contour. Even with such refinements, nobody had trouble spotting the Gremlin in a crowd. An interesting fact is that the price of the V-8 now came in at a dollar per pound.

GREMLIN SERIES 40

Series Number	Body/Style Number	Body Type & Seating	Factory Price	Shipping Weight	Production Total
40	7546-5	2-dr Sed-4P	2798/2952	2694/2952	56,011

NOTE 1: Model year output totaled 56,011 units. Of these 52,601 were sixes and 3,410 were V-8s.
NOTE 2: Prices and weights above slash are for the six/ below slash for V-8.

1975 AMC, Gremlin two-door Levi's sedan, 6-cyl

PACER — (SIX) — SERIES 60 — The AMC Pacer was introduced on March 1, 1975, as a midyear model. It was billed as the first wide, small car, as it was 77 inches wide but had a short 100 inch wheelbase. The Pacer used many unique features including a passenger side door that was larger than the driver's door and one of the first rack and pinion steering systems available on a U.S. built car. The car was available, for 1975, only as a two-door hatchback. It had a very short, fast-sloping hood, since is was originally designed to use GM's front-wheel-drive Wankle rotary power unit. The cancellation of that program, by GM, forced AMC to re-engineer the car on short notice. It was transformed into a rear wheel-drive piston-engine configuration. The only powerplant provided was the 232 cid six. Although its overall length was a compact-sized 171.5 inches, the Pacer's interior roominess matched or exceeded that of its full-sized contemporaries. It had a very low beltline and large expanses of glass, giving extremely good visibility (and excellent motivation for air conditioning sales). The unconventional body featured a large rear window liftgate with dual, gas-filled cylinders for easy opening. With the rear seat folded, the cargo area expanded to nearly 30 cubic feet. Classified as a two-door sedan, buyers could order-up the 'bubbly' vehicle as a base-trim model; a sporty Pacer 'X;' or a lavish little Pacer 'D/L.' All three editions were sure to get attention in 1975 and still draw interest today.

PACER SERIES 40

Series Number	Body/Style Number	Body Type & Seating	Factory Price	Shipping Weight	Production Total
BASE PACER					
60	7566-7	2-dr Sed-6P	3299	2995	72,158
PACER 'X' OPTION					
60	7566-7	2-dr Spt Sed-5P	3638	NA	N/A
PACER 'D/L' OPTION					
60	7566-7	2-dr DeL Sed-6P	3588	NA	(19,050)

NOTE 1: Factory literature indicates that the optional reclining seats were available only as part of the Pacer D/L package. Industry records show that 26 percent of all 1975 Pacers had these seats. Based on these facts, it can be estimated that 19,050 Pacer D/L models were built during the 1975 model year.

MATADOR — (SIX/V-8) — SERIES 80 — Moved to a higher-numbered series, the Matador four-door styles featured new hoods, grilles and bumpers. The hood was flatter and the center crease ran into the upper grille surround molding. The redesigned grille featured full-width, horizontal blades, with eight bright vertical divider moldings positioned along the protruding center section only. The horizontal blades extended right to the round headlamp lenses, making them seem better integrated into the overall appearance. The front bumper was smoother and rounder looking, eliminating the triple-bevel look of 1974. Another change was to rectangular parking lamps. Identification came from name badges on the front fendersides, behind the wheel openings. Side trim consisted of a three-quarter length belt molding, running from a point above the name badge to the rear. Standard equipment features matched those of the previous season, plus electronic ignition. A Brougham options package was available on both models, but at two different prices. The sedan was the basis of specially-assembled taxi-cab and police car models. The latter group carried 84 of the 89 - 401 cid V-8s installed in AMC products in the 1975 model year.

MATADOR SERIES 80

Series Number	Body/Style Number	Body Type & Seating	Factory Price	Shipping Weight	Production Total
80	7585-7	4-dr Sed-6P	3452/3551	3586/3746	27,522
80	7588-7	4-dr Sta Wag-6P	3844/3943	3878/4038	9,692

NOTE 1: Data above slash for six/below slash for V-8.
NOTE 2: Model year output totaled 59.582 units built in Kenosha, Wis. Of these cars, 10,965 were sixes and 48,617 were V-8s.
NOTE 3: The six-cylinder total includes 9,390 passenger cars and 1,575 station wagons. The V-8 total includes 40,500 passenger cars and 8,117 station wagons.

BASE ENGINES

(BASE SIX) Inline Six: Overhead valves. Cast iron block. Displacement: 232 cid. Bore and stroke: 3.75 x 3.50 inches. Compression ratio: 8.0:1. SAE Net hp: 90 at 3050 rpm. Seven main bearings. Hydraulic valve lifters. Carburetor: one-barrel.

(BIG SIX) Inline Six: Overhead valves. Cast iron block. Displacement: 258 cid. Bore and stroke: 3.75 x 3.90 inches. Compression ratio: 8.0:1. SAE Net hp: 95 at 3050 rpm. Seven main bearings. Hydraulic valve lifters. Carburetor: one-barrel.

(BASE V-8) Overhead Valves: Cast iron block. Displacement: 304 cid. Bore and stroke: 3.75 x 3.44 inches. Compression ratio: 8.0:1. SAE Net hp: 120 at 3200 rpm. Five main bearings. Hydraulic valve lifters. Carburetor: two-barrel.

CHASSIS FEATURES: Wheelbase: (Gremlin) 96 inches; (Pacer) 100 inches; (Hornet) 108 inches; (Matador Series 10) 114 inches; (Matador Series 80) 118 inches. Overall length: (Gremlin) 170.3 inches; (Pacer) 171.5 inches; (Hornet) 187 inches; (Matador Coupe) 209.3 inches; (Matador sedan) 216 inches; (Matador wagon) 215.5 inches. Front tread: (Pacer) 61.2 inches; (other models) See 1972 Chassis Features. Rear tread: (Pacer) 60.2 inches; (other models) See 1972 Chassis Features. Tires: (Gremlin) 6.45 x 14; (Pacer/Hornet) 6.95 x 14; (Matador coupe) ER78 x 14; (Matador sedan) FR78 x 14; (Matador wagon) HR78 x 14.

POWERTRAIN OPTIONS: Three-speed manual transmission was standard. Overdrive transmission, for six. Three-speed manual floor shift transmission. Hornet/Gremlin six-cylinder 258 cid 95 hp one-barrel engine. Pacer six-cylinder 258 cid 95 hp one-barrel engine. Hornet/Gremlin 304 cid 120 hp two-barrel engine. Matador Coupe V-8 304 cid 120 hp two-barrel engine (no charge). Matador Coupe V-8 360 cid 140 hp two-barrel engine. Matador Coupe V-8 360 cid 180 hp four-barrel engine. Matador sedan V-8 304 cid 120 hp one-barrel engine. Matador sedan V-8 360 cid 140 hp two-barrel engine. Matador sedan V-8 360 cid 180 hp four-barrel engine. Matador wagon V-8 304 cid 120 hp two-barrel engine. Matador wagon V-8 360 cid 140 hp two-barrel engine. Matador wagon V-8 360 cid 180 hp four-barrel engine. Positive traction rear axle. Heavy-duty clutch, for six.

HORNET/GREMLIN/MATADOR OPTIONS: Power steering, in Gremlin/Hornet ($119). Air conditioning, in Gremlin/Hornet group ($400). Gremlin 'X' package ($201). Gremlin Levis Custom trim package ($220). Gremlin Rallye option package ($133). AM/FM stereo, all except Matador Group ($179). Styled Road wheels, Gremlin/Hornet group ($115). Hornet D/L package, on sedan ($299); on Sportabout ($293). Hornet Levis Custom trim package ($125). Hornet 'X' hatchback option package ($227). Hornet Sportabout 'X' package ($139). Sportabout rooftop travel rack ($75). Hornet Rallye option package ($125). Matador air conditioning ($450). Matador AM/FM stereo system ($230). Matador AM/FM stereo with 8-track tape player ($300). Matador station wagon, third seat equipment ($121). Matador station wagon. Rooftop travel rack ($59). Matador 'X' package ($199). Oleg Cassini coupe trim package ($299). Styled road wheels, on Matador group ($121). Matador Brougham package, wagon ($145); others ($105). Gremlin/Hornet group Econo-Miser package ($225). Gremlin, Custom trim package ($135). Reclining seats, as option ($75).

PACER OPTIONS: 'X' package ($339). 'D/L' package ($289). Decor package ($49). 232 CID six, one-barrel carburetor engine (standard). 258 CID six, one-barrel carburetor engine ($69). Torque-Command, Column-Shift ($239.95). Torque-Command with floor-shift, available only with bucket or reclining seats ($259.95). Three-speed manual, column shift (standard). Three-speed manual floor shift ($19.95). Three-speed manual with overdrive, column shift ($149). Twin-Grip differential ($46). Power steering ($119). Power front disc brakes ($79.35). Manual front disc brakes ($47.45). AM push-button radio ($69). AM/FM stereo radio, with four speakers ($179). Entertainment center with AM/FM stereo and tape player ($299). Hidden compartment ($29). Bucket seats ($99). Individual reclining seats, 'D/L' only. Air conditioning system ($399.95). Tinted glass, all windows ($49). Rear window defogger ($59.95). Rear window washer and wiper ($49.95). Roof rack ($49.95). Cruise-command speed control with automatic transmission only ($65). Adjust-O-Tilt steering column with automatic transmission column shift only ($49). Visibility group ($49.95). Deluxe electric windshield wipers with inter-mittent action ($24.95). Light group ($34.95). Door vent windows ($29.95). Sports steering wheel ($18.90). Wheel discs ($29.95). Styled road wheels ($115); with 'X' package ($50); with 'D/L' package ($85.05). Aluminum styled wheels ($200); with 'X' package ($135); with 'D/L' package ($170.05). Slot-styled wheels ('X' only). Extra quiet insulation ($29.95). Protection group ($34.95). Bumper nerfing strips ($19). Handling package, includes: heavy-duty springs, shocks and front sway bar ($29.95). Handling package with 'X' or 'D/L' package ($15). Front sway bar ($14.95). Vinyl roof ($99.95). Two-Tone paint ($49). Whitewall tires ($34.45).

HISTORICAL FOOTNOTES: The AMC models made their debut Nov. 15, 1974 and the Pacer was introduced Feb. 28, 1975. The unique 'bubble car' went on sale March 1, 1975. American Motors Corp.'s model year output hit 244,941 units. Calendar year production was recorded as 323,704 cars. Sales by U.S. dealers, for 1975 models only, were reported as 268,526 vehicles. R.D. Chapin, Jr. remained at the head of the company. Richard A. Teague, vice-president of styling gets the credit for the Pacer's unique and attractive appearance.

1975 AMC Matador four-door sedan

BUICK
1946-1975

Buick entered the post-World War II market with a product for which there was enormous pent-up demand. During the years just prior to the war, Buick had become one of America's favorite cars. Large, but fast, and with sporting lines, the prewar Buick symbolized upward mobility. In 1946, many veterans came home with a dream of a family, a home in suburbia — and a Buick in the driveway. "So nice to come home to," a 1943 ad had proclaimed — using a yellow 1942 Roadmaster convertible for the illustration.

The Buick's role as part of the postwar dream was more than an ad man's pitch. This was born out by public acceptance of Buick's 1946-1948 models, although they were little more than warmed-over 1942s. Indeed, Buick's convertible styles, in Roadmaster and Super trim, were extremely popular. They are, today, treasured collector cars.

By Terry V. Boyce

Though the styling hadn't changed for 1948, there was an important innovation — Dynaflow automatic drive. Optional on the 1948 Roadmaster, it would soon power all Roadmasters and become a very popular option for other series.

New styling, still drawing on traditional design elements, appeared in 1949. Ventiports made their initial appearance on Buick front fenders. Mid-1949 saw the unveiling of a new Riviera hardtop which led the way towards acceptance of this design. The two-door hardtop coupe was destined to be one of the most popular models of the '50s.

Then came 1950. According to many marque enthusiasts, Buick went a step too far. It was the year of the "bucktooth Buick," with a grille cavity full of large bumper guards. Actually, this new design had appeared during mid-calendar 1949, in a new "1950" Special line. There had been Specials from 1946 on, but they had been largely ignored by Buick's sales staff, which concentrated on the more expensive Supers and Roadmasters. As late as the beginning of 1949, the Buick Special had been almost identical to 1942 models. The time had come for a new push into the low-priced field, so the Special got the new styling first.

The 1950-'52 Buicks were solidly built and heavily trimmed. Yet, they were somehow a bit lacking in excitement and, even today, are not ranked among the most popular models. The straight eight era ended for the larger cars in 1952, when a four-barrel carbureted, 170 hp Roadmaster version made a fitting farewell.

Whatever excitement had been missing from Buick was back in 1953. The big news was under the hood — a 322 cid overhead valve V-8 for Super and Roadmaster models. For the first time ever (except two sedans), all Buicks shared a

common wheelbase. Celebrating their 50th anniversary, the Buick Division of General Motors offered an Anniversary Convertible, also known as the Skylark, for a cool $5,000. Just 1,690 were sold. Today, many still survive and are in great demand by collectors.

Buick chassis engineering began to catch up with the new V-8 in 1954. The updated cars were lower and wider, with greatly improved handling. Even the Special now had V-8 power. The Skylark returned for an unsuccessful encore, but the year was otherwise a smashing performance saleswise. The next year, 1955, was even better. Buick broke all the old records. A popular model line was the Century, which had returned in 1954. A new four-door Riviera pillarless hardtop debuted midyear.

By 1957, Buick styling had began to lag. Sales started to slump. An over-chromed, overweight 1958 edition proved even less palatable to consumer tastes. It was a time of rapid change. The year 1959 brought new Buicks, with new series designations replacing those used since 1936. Wildly finned, and lacking almost any sort of continuity with Buick's past, the 1959 Buicks continued to get a cool reception in the showrooms. Buick was committed to the same basic body for 1960, but completely changed its look by blunting edges everywhere.

For 1961, Buicks looked lighter and cleaner. A new compact, the Special, was introduced and would soon be joined by a fancier Skylark Sport Coupe version. There was little real news for 1962, but the season's offerings were attractive and well-executed. A Buick highpoint, in the '60s, came the next year, with the introduction of the 1963 Riviera. It was a four-passenger sporting car that was immediately, and correctly, termed a classic design.

By 1965, the Special/Skylark had grown to intermediate proportions and was wrapped in a very handsome package. The larger Buicks, too, were restyled. Increasingly distinctive was the mid-range, Buick performance line — offering the Wildcat. Continuing through 1970, the Wildcat series, provided extra performance and style. Beginning in 1963, the largest Buicks, (Electras and Electra 225s) were given styling touches of their own, including unique rear fenders with skirts, distinctive bright trim and even specific grillework. They obtained a following that lasted for two decades.

A new Riviera, with some of the smoothest lines ever rendered by GM stylists, came in 1966. A GS or Gran Sport equipment option was continued, from 1965, and would be

a rare option for the rest of the decade. The GS badge also appeared on a high-performance Skylark late in 1965, and evolved into a series designation by 1966.

By the end of the '60s, Buick had strong followings in many segments of the market. Never a large part of the sales picture, but still catered to with great care, were Buick's performance buyers. A 1970-'71 GSX option for the GS 455 coupe featured special paint colors, wild stripes and performance touches. The GSX may become the most sought after Buick of the '70s. Buick lovers also said goodbye to the prestige Buick convertible in 1970, with discontinuation of the Electra 225 edition marked that year.

Buick Division shocked the automotive world, in 1971, with a new tapered-deck 'boattail' Riviera. This design, built through 1973, will always stand out on the road. A new Centurion line also replaced the Wildcat, as Buick's full-size luxury performance line. The Centurion convertible became Buick's plushest, most expensive open car and is sure to be increasingly appreciated by collectors.

Skylark/GS models continued with little change from 1970 to 1972, although the potent GS 455s, with their Stage I engine option topping most performance cars in sheer acceleration, were detuned for 1971 to run on regular gas and decrease emissions. The Skylark/GS Sport Coupes and Convertibles, when optioned with desirable accessories, are sure bets for enthusiast attention.

An interesting series of Buick station wagons were issued throughout the post-World War II era. The Roadmaster Estates of 1947-'53 are among the most sought after of all wood-bodied cars. The 1953 model's combination of V-8 power and traditional wood sportiness presents a stunning combination. The all-steel wagons of 1954-'56 are rare. A four-door hardtop Caballero version followed in 1957. Innovative styling continued on Buick wagons into the '60s. The famous Skyroof Sport Wagons featured raised, glass-paneled roof sections, making them true specialty cars.

Buicks from any postwar year abound with the fine touches that make the cars interesting and collectible. From the showboats of the late '40s to the compact, but well-trimmed and gutsy Skylarks of the early '60s, to the boattail Riviera of the '70s, plenty of appreciation for restoration, or conservator's efforts are assured. For thousands of collector car enthusiasts, the question, "Wouldn't you really rather have a Buick?" is still answered with a resounding, "Yes."

1949 Buick, Super two-door convertible, 8-cyl

1954 Buick, Century two-door convertible, V-8

1961 Buick, Electra 225, two-door convertible, V-8

1968 Buick, Wildcat Custom, two-door hardtop coupe, V-8

1964 Buick, Riviera two-door hardtop Sports Coupe, V-8

1969 Buick, GS-400 two-door hardtop, V-8

1968 Buick, GS-400 two-door hardtop coupe, V-8

1970 Buick, GSX two-door hardtop, V-8

Standard Catalog of American Cars

NOTE: Through 1950 Buick provided separate production totals for cars built for export. These are given In brackets on the charts.

SPECIAL — SERIES 40 — The Special was Buick's lowest priced line. It was the only Buick line continuing the Fisher B-body fastback styles from 1941-'42 into the postwar era. Standard equipment included an automatic choke, ash receiver and turn signals. Exterior bright trim echoed 1942 models with twin strips of stainless steel flowing from the front wheelhouse to the rear edge of the standard rear wheelhouse skirts. Bright rocker moldings were also standard. Interiors featured rubber floor mats and painted instrument panels with round gauges. Series identification was found between the bumper guards, front and rear, on the crossbar. A cloisonne emblem carried the Special signature.

SPECIAL I.D. NUMBERS: The serial numbers for the 1946 Special series were the same as for other 1946 Buick series, which were mixed in production. They were: (Flint) 1436445 to 14524130, (Calif.) 24380001 to 24511494, (N.J.) 34390001 to 34429256, (Kans.) 44415001 to 44419786. Motor numbers began at 4558037-4 and up, the suffix '4' denoting a Series 40 motor.

Model Number	Body/Style Number	Body Type & Seating	Factory Price	Shipping Weight	Production Total
41	46-4409	4-dr Sed-6P	1580 (1)	3720	1,649
46S	46A407	2-dr S'dn't-6P	1522	3670	1,350

ENGINE: Eight-cylinder. Inline. Overhead valve. Cast iron block. Displacement: 248.0 cid. Bore and stroke: 3-3/32 x 4-1/8 inches. Compression ratio: 6.3: 1. Brake horsepower: 110 at 3600 rpm. Five main bearings. Mechanical valve lifters. Carburetor: Stromberg AAV-16 number 380106 two-barrel or Carter 608 or 663 two-barrel.

SUPER — SERIES 50 — Buick combined the large Series 70 body with the economical Series 40 powerplant to create the Super Series 50 line. Basic styling was continued from 1942, but now sedans had the front fender sweep across the doors to the rear fenders as did sedanettes and convertible styles. A stamped grille with vertical bars dominated the frontal ensemble. Single stainless body trim lines began on the front fenders and ended at the rear edge of the standard rear wheelhouse shields. Standard equipment was the same as the series 40, but Series 50 Buicks had two-tone, woodgrained, instrument panels. Exterior series identification was found on the crossbar between the bumper guards, front and rear. Cloisonne emblems carried the super signature.

SUPER I.D. NUMBERS: The serial number sequence was the same for all series (see Special — Series 40). Motor numbers began at 4558037-5 and up. The suffix '5' denoting a Series 50 motor.

Model Number	Body/Style Number	Body Type & Seating	Factory Price	Shipping Weight	Production Total
51	46-4569	4-dr Sed-6P	1822	3935	74,045 (3679)
56S	46-4507	2-dr S'dn't-6P	1741	3795	34,235 (190)
56C	46-4567	2-dr Conv Cpe-6P	2046	3576	40505,931 (456)
59	(Ionia)	4-dr Sta Wag-6P	2594		4170786 (12)

ENGINE: Specifications were the same as previously listed for the 1946 Special — Series 40.

ROADMASTER — SERIES 70 — The Roadmaster was Buick's biggest and fastest car. It's larger and longer straight eight required five inches more wheelbase and longer front fenders and hood. Exterior trim was identical to the Super, except for the longer stainless moldings on the frontal sheetmetal. Standard equipment was the same as for the Super, but richer interior fabrics were used. The instrument panel was two-toned with woodgrains except on convertibles, which used body-colored panels. Series identification was found on cloisonne emblems centered in the bumper guard crossbars front and rear.

ROADMASTER I.D. NUMBERS: The serial number sequence was the same for all series (see Special — Series 40). Motor numbers began at 455829-7 and up.

Model Number	Body/Style Number	Body Type & Seating	Factory Price	Shipping Weight	Production Total
71	46-4769	4-dr Sed-6P	2110	4165	20,597 (267)
76S	46-4707	2-dr S'dn't-6P	2014	4095	8,226 (66)
76C	46-4767	2dr-Conv Cpe-6P	2347	4345	2,576 (11)

ENGINE: Eight-cylinder. Inline. Overhead valve. Cast iron block. Displacement: 320.2 cid. Bore and stroke: 3-7/16 x 4-5/16 inches. Compression ratio: 6.6: 1. Brake horsepower: 144 at 3600 rpm. Five main bearings. Mechanical valve lifters. Carburetor: Stromberg AAV-26 number 380097 two-barrel or Carter 609 or 664 two-barrel.

CHASSIS FEATURES: Wheelbase: Series 40- 121 inches; Series 50 — 124 inches; Series 70 — 129 inches. Overall length: Series 40 - 207-1/2 inches; Series 50 212-3/8 inches; Series 70 — 217-1/8 inches. Front tread: Series 40 — 58-7/8 inches; Series 50 and 70 — 59-1/8 inches. Rear tread: Series 40 — 61-15/16 inches; Series 50 and 70 — 62-3/16 inches. Tires: Series 40 and 50, 6.50 x 16; Series 70, 7.00 x 15.

POWERTRAIN OPTIONS: A three-speed manual transmission with steering column mounted shift lever was standard on all series. There were no optional gearboxes.

CONVENIENCE OPTIONS: Spotlite. Sonomatic radio. Weather-Warden heater/defroster. Side-view mirror. E-Z-I non-glare rearview mirror. Prismatic inside rear-view mirror. Vanity visor mirror. Seat covers. Auxiliary driving lights. Multipurpose trouble lamp. "Breeze-Ease" draft deflectors.

HISTORICAL FOOTNOTES: Calendar year production of 156,080 units gave Buick a 7.2 percent market share and fifth place in sales. Model year output stood at 158,728 cars.

NOTE: Through 1950 Buick provided separate production totals for cars built for export. These are given In brackets on the charts.

SPECIAL — SERIES 40 — Buick's lowest-priced line continued to use the Fisher B-body design from before World War II this year. A new stamped grille with separate upper bar distinguished 1947 Buicks from their 1946 predecessors. Standard equipment included an automatic choke, ash receiver and turn signals. Front and rear bumper guards were standard and the series designation was found, filled in red, on the chrome buttons centered in the guards' crossbars. Twin stainless moldings continued to be a Special hallmark, along the body and onto the standard rear fender wheelhouse skirts. Interiors featured round gauges with control switches flanking a center grille on the instrument panel. Rubber floor mats were standard.

SPECIAL I.D. NUMBERS: The serial numbers for the 1947 Special Series 40 were the same as for other 1947 Buick series, which were mixed in production. They were: Flint — 14524131 to 14801264, Calif. — 24530001 to 24775798, N.J. — 3454001 to 34776843, and Kans. 44536001 to 44774870. Special Series 40 motor numbers were continued from 1946, ending at 4999880-4, the suffix 4 denoting a Series 40 motor.

Model Number	Body/Style Number	Body Type & Seating	Factory Price	Shipping Weight	Production Total
41	47-4409	4-dr Sed-6P	1673	3720	1,136 (1,295)
46	47-4407	2-dr S'dn't-6P	1611	3670	14,278 (325)

ENGINE: Eight-cylinder. Inline. Overhead valve. Cast iron block. Displacement: 248.0 cid. Bore and stroke: 3-3/32 x 4-1/8 inches. Compression ration: 6.3:1. Brake horsepower: 110 at 3600 rpm. Five main bearings. Mechanical valve lifters. Carburetor: Stromberg AAV-16 number 380106 two-barrel or Carter 608 or 663 two-barrel.

1947 Buick, Super two-door convertible coupe, 8-cyl (AA)

SUPER I.D. NUMBERS: The serial number sequence was the same for all series (see Special — Series 40). Motor numbers continued from 1946, ending at 4999880-5 and up, the suffix 5 denoting a Series 50 motor.

SUPER — SERIES 50 — Combining big Buick room and ride with an economical Special engine continued to make an American favorite. The 1947 Super was little changed from its 1946 counterpart, except for a new stamped grille that had a separate upper bar and a new emblem. Stainless lower body moldings made a single line along the body and continued onto the standard rear wheelhouse shields. A white Tenite steering wheel was standard, while the instruments were round and set in a two-toned dash panel. Exterior series identification was found on the crossbars between the standard bumper guards. A chrome emblem with the series script embossed and filled with red was used.

Model Number	Body/Style Number	Body Type & Seating	Factory Price	Shipping Weight	Production Total
51	47-4569	4-dr Sed-6P	1929	3920	76,866 (6710)
56S	47-4507	2-dr S'dn't-6P	1843	3795	46,311 (606)
56C	47-4567	2-dr Conv Cpe-6P	2333	4050	27,796 (501)
59	Ionia	4-dr Sta Wag-6P	2594	4170	786 (12)

ENGINE: Specifications were the same as previously listed for the 1947 Special Series 40.

ROADMASTER — SERIES 70 — Buick's master of the road was a large car which continued basically unchanged from 1946. A new grille, shared with other series, was used. Exterior trim continued to be the same as used on the Super, except that the Roadmaster's longer wheelbase and front dog house required longer moldings ahead of the doors. Standard equipment was the same as found on the Super, but richer interior fabrics were used. Two-tone, neutral colored instrument panels were employed, except on convertibles, which had body-colored panels. The Roadmaster name appeared in red-filled script on a chrome button within the bumper guard crossbars, front and rear.

ROADMASTER I.D. NUMBERS: The serial number sequence was the same for all series (see Special — Series 40). Motor numbers continued from 1946, ending at 499980-7. The suffix 7 denoting a Series 70 motor.

1947 Buick, Roadmaster two-door sedanette, 8-cyl

Model Number	Body/Style Number	Body Type & Seating	Factory Price	Shipping Weight	Production Total
71	47-4769	4-dr Sed-6P	2232	4190	46,531 (621)
76S	47-4707	2-dr S'dn't-6P	2131	4095	18,983 (229)
76C	47-4767	2-dr Conv Cpe-6P	2651	4345	11,947 (127)
79	(Ionia)	4-dr Sta Wag-6P	3249	4445	300

ENGINE: Eight-cylinder. Inline. Overhead valve. Cast iron block. Displacement-. 320.2 cid. Bore and stroke: 3-7/16 x 4-5/16. Compression ratio: 6.6:1. Brake horsepower: 144 at 3600 rpm. Five main bearings. Mechanical valve lifters. Carburetor: Stromberg AAV-26 number 380097 or Carter 609 or 664 two-barrel.

CHASSIS FEATURES: Wheelbase: Series 40 — 121 inches, Series 50 — 124 inches. Series 70 — 129 inches. Overall length: Series 40 — 207-1/2 inches-, Series 50 — 212-3/8 inches; Series 70 — 217-1/8 inches. Front tread: Series 40 — 58-7/8 inches-, Series 50 and 70 — 59-1/8 inches. Rear tread: Series 40 — 61-15/ 16 inches, Series 50 and 70 — 63-3/16 inches. Tires: Series 40 and 50, 6.50 x 16; Series 70, 7.00 x 15.

POWERTRAIN OPTIONS: A three-speed manual transmission with steering column mounted shift lever was standard on all series. There were no optional gearboxes.

CONVENIENCE OPTIONS: Spotlite. Sonomatic radio. Weather-Warden heater/defroster. Side view mirror. E-Z-I non-glare rearview mirror. Prismatic inside rearview mirror. Vanity visor mirror. Seat covers. Auxiliary driving lights. Multi-purpose trouble lamp. "Breeze-Ease" draft deflectors.

HISTORICAL FOOTNOTES: Calendar year production was 267,830 units, earning Buick 7.5 percent of the total domestic market. Model year production stood at 277,134 cars. Models 59 and 79 were Estate Wagons, with wooden upper bodies by Ionia.

1948 BUICK

NOTE: Through 1950 Buick provided separate production totals for cars built for export. These are given in brackets on the charts.

SPECIAL — SERIES 40 — Even more bright metal trim adorned the 1948 Special, as a full length upper body molding was added. Dual stainless bands along the lower body, fenders and rear skirts were continued. Inside, new nickel grey garnish moldings and a black Tenite steering wheel were featured. Sedans were carpeted in the rear, while front compartment mats had a simulated carpet insert. Leatherette seat risers and scuff pads were standard. Equipment included an automatic choke, turn signals and an ash receiver. Series identification was found within a round emblem in the bumper guard crossbars.

SPECIAL I.D. NUMBERS: The serial numbers for the 1948 Special Series 40 were the same as for other 1948 Buick series, which were mixed in production. They were-. (Flint) 14801266 to 15020983, (Calif.) 2482001 to 25003031, (N.J.) 34824001 to 5004975, (Kans.) 4483001, (Ga.) 64834001 to 64987817. Series 40 motor numbers were 4999881-4 to 52220971-4, the suffix 4 denoting a Series 40 motor.

1948 Buick, Special two-door sedanette, 8-cyl(AA)

Model Number	Body/Style Number	Body Type & Seating	Factory Price	Shipping Weight	Production Total
41	48-4409	4-dr Sed-6P	1809	3705	13,326 (815)
46S	48-4407	2-dr S'dn't-6P	1735	3635	10,775 (401)

ENGINE: Eight-cylinder. Inline. Overhead valve. Cast iron block. Displacement: 248.0 cid. Bore and stroke: 3-3/32 x 4-1/8 inches. Compression ratio: 6.3: 1. Brake horsepower: 110 at 3600 rpm. Five main bearings. Mechanical valve lifters. Carburetor: Stromberg AAV-167 number 380225 or Carter 608 or 663 two-barrel.

1948 Buick, Super four-door sedan, 8-cyl

SUPER — SERIES 50 — The main external change to the 1948 Super from its 1947 counterpart was the Super script on each front fender. Other series identification continued to be carried on the bumper guard crossbar. The car was a bit lower than in 1947, rolling on new 7.60 x 15 tires mounted on wheels with trim rings and small hubcaps. Super identification was also found on the center crest of the new black Tenite steering wheel. New cloth interiors featured leatherette scuff pads and trim risers. The instrument panel was redone, using silvertone instruments on a two-tone grey panel. The sedan was carpeted in the rear, with a carpet insert also found in the front rubber mat. The Model 56C featured cloth and leather interior trim, with power top, seat and front windows standard.

SUPER I.D. NUMBERS: The serial number sequence was the same for all series (see Special-Series 40). Motor numbers continued from 1947, running from 4999881-5 to 5220971-5, the suffix (5) denoting a Series 50 motor.

Model Number	Body/Style Number	Body Type & Seating	Factory Price	Shipping Weight	Production Total
51	48-4569	4-dr Sed-6P	2087	3855	47,991 (5456)
56S	48-4507	2-dr S'dn't-6P	1987	3770	32,860 (959)
56C	48-4567	2-dr Conv Cpe-6P	2518	4020	18,311 (906)
59	(Ionia)	4-dr Sta Wag-6P	3124	4170	1,955 63)

ENGINE: Specifications were the same as previously listed for the 1948 Special Series 40, except that compression ratio was 6.6: 1, brake horsepower was 115 at 3600 rpm.

1948 Buick, Roadmaster two-door convertible, 8-cyl(AA)

ROADMASTER — SERIES 70 — Exterior appearance of the 1948 Roadmaster was changed only by the addition of series script to the front fenders. Other series identification continued to be found on the bumper guards' crossbars and within the steering wheel center medallion. The wheel was now black Tenite, coordinated with the new two-tone grey instrument panel with silver tone instruments. Chrome full wheel discs were standard, along with features found on lesser Buicks. Interiors were cloth, with plusher grades of material available. A new optional Custom Trim was offered, consisting of cloth upholstery with leather bolsters; the robe cord cover, and lower door panels were done in leatherette. The Model 76C convertible coupe included power windows, seat and top in its standard equipment.

ROADMASTER I.D. NUMBERS: The serial number sequence was the same for all 1948 series (see Special-Series 40). Series 70 motor numbers were 4999881-7 to 5220971-7, the suffix (7) denoting a Series 70 motor.

Model Number	Body/Style Number	Body Type & Seating	Factory Price	Shipping Weight	Production Total
71	48-4769	4-dr Sed-6P	2418	4160	47,042 (527)
76S	48-4707	2-dr S'dn't-6P	2297	4065	20,542 (107)
76C	48-4767	2-dr Conv Cpe-6P	2837	4315	11,367 (136)
79	(Ionia)	4-dr Sta Wag-6P	3433	4460	344 (6)

ENGINE: Eight-cylinder. Inline. Overhead valve. Cast iron block. Displacement: 320.2 cid. Bore and stroke: 3-7/16 x 4-5/16 inches. Compression ratio: 6.6:1. Brake horsepower: 144 at 3600 rpm. Five main bearings. Mechanical valve lifters. Carburetor: Stromberg AAV-267 #380226 or Carter 609 or 664 two-barrel.

CHASSIS FEATURES: Wheelbase: Series 40-121 inches; Series 50-124 inches; Series 70-129 inches. Overall length: Series 40- 207-1/2 inches; Series 50-212-1/2 inches; Series 70 217-1/2 inches. Front tread: Series 40- 58-7/8 inches; Series 50 and 70- 59-1/8 inches. Rear tread: Series 40- 61-15/16 inches, Series 50 and 70- 62-3/16 inches. Tires: Series 40- 6.50 x 16: Series 50- 7.60 x 15; Series 70- 8.20 x 15.

POWERTRAIN OPTIONS: A three-speed manual transmission with column-mounted shift lever was standard on all series. Dynaflow automatic transmission was optional on Series 70. Cars so equipped also had 6.9:1 compression ratio, 150 brake horsepower motors.

CONVENIENCE OPTIONS: Spotlite. Sonomatic radio. Weather-Warden heater/defroster. Side-view mirror. Tissue dispenser. Vanity visor mirror. E-Z-I non-glare rearview mirror. Prismatic inside rear-view mirror. Seat covers. Auxiliary driving lights. Multipurpose trouble lamp. "Breeze-Ease" draft deflectors. NoRol assembly. Automatic windshield washer. Back-up lights. Polaroid visor. Rear window wiper. Power Pak fire extinguisher/tire inflator.

HISTORICAL FOOTNOTES: Calendar year production of 275,503 units gave Buick a seven percent market share and fourth place in sales. Model year output stood at 229,718 cars. Harlow Curtice became a General Motors executive vice-president. His job as Buick general manager was filled by Ivan Wiles. Dynaflow Drive was introduced. Model 59 was the Estate Wagon, with upper wooden body by Ionia.

1949 BUICK

NOTE: Through 1950 Buick provided separate production totals for cars built for export. These are given In brackets on the charts.

SERIES 40 — The Special was continued from 1948 production without change, until midyear. Data plates, however, have '49' prefix. The second series 1949 Special was continued into 1950 and its specifications may be found under that year.

SPECIAL I.D. NUMBERS: The serial numbers for the 1949 Special Series 40 were mixed in production with other 1949 series. They were: (Flint) 15020984 to 15348304, (Calif.) 25030001 to 25332419, (N.J.) 35036001 to 35333911. (Kans.) 45043001 to 45335606. (Del.) 55050001 to 55417948 and 55417001 to 55417948, (Mass.) 75057001 to 75338786, (Ga.) 65054001 to 65337687. Series 40 motor numbers were 5220972-4 to 5259136-4, the suffix 4 denoting a Series 40 motor.

Model Number	Body/Style Number	Body Type & Seating	Factory Price	Shipping Weight	Production Total
41	49-4409	4-dr Sed-6P	1861	3695	5,777 (163)
46S	49-4407	2-dr S'dn't-6P	1787	3625	4,631 (56)

ENGINE: Eight-cylinder. Inline. Overhead valve. Cast iron block. Displacement: 248.0 cid. Bore and stroke: 3-3/32 x 4-1/8 inches. Compression ratio: 6.3: 1. Brake horsepower: 110 at 3600 rpm. Five main bearings. Mechanical valve lifters. Carburetor: Stromberg AAV-167 number 380225 or Carter 608 or 663 two-barrel.

SUPER — SERIES 50 — Shared a new General Motors C-body with the Roadmaster, but on a shorter wheelbase. It featured three chromed ventiports on each front fender. Super script was found just above the full-length body/fender molding on the front fenders. New fender-edge taillamps were featured, while rear fender skirts remained a Buick standard. New fender-top parking lamps, harking back to 1941 styling, appeared. Full wheel trim discs were standard, along with such features as a cigar lighter, ashtray and automatic choke. Cloth interiors were standard, except for the Model 56C which was trimmed in leather and leatherette and had a power top, seat and windows as standard equipment.

SUPER I.D. NUMBERS: The serial number sequence was the same for all series (see Special — Series 40). Motor numbers were 5220972-5 to 5659598-5, the suffix '5' denoting a Series 50 motor.

Model Number	Body/Style Number	Body Type & Seating	Factory Price	Shipping Weight	Production Total
51	49-4569	4-dr Sed-6P	2157	3835	131,514 (4909)
56S	49-4507	2-dr S'dn't-6P	2059	3735	65,395 (865)
56C	49-4567	2-dr Conv Cpe-6P	2583	3985	21,426 (684)
59	(Ionia)	4-dr Sta Wag-6P	3178	4100	1,830 (17)

ENGINE: Specifications were the same as listed for the 1949 Special Series 40, except the compression ratio was 6.6:1 and brake horsepower was 115 at 3600 rpm.

1949 Buick, Super four-door Estate Wagon, 8-cyl (AA)

ROADMASTER — SERIES 70 — Shared the new General Motors C-body, which used closed quarters in sedan roofs and fastback sedanette styling for coupes. Roadmasters had longer front fenders and four ventiports per side, with series script below, and also within, bumper guard crossbar centers. Skirted rear wheelhouse openings were standard, as were all features found on the Super Series 50. Interior fabrics were plusher, with a Custom trim option again offered. A new instrument panel was used that continued Buick's centered radio grille flanked by operational switches. Windshield panels were curved, but still had a division bar. The Model 79R Estate Wagon had mahogany veneer panels inside, with leather upholstery and carpeted floors and cargo area, while the Model 76C was upholstered in leather and had standard power windows, seat and top. The midyear Model 76R Riviera was upholstered in leather and cloth and also had standard power windows.

1949 Buick, Roadmaster Riviera two-door hardtop coupe, 8-cyl(AA)

ROADMASTER I.D. NUMBERS: The serial number sequence was the same for all 1949 series (see Special — Series 40). Series 70 motor numbers were 5220972-7 to 5548366-7, the suffix '7' denoting a Series 70 motor.

Model Number	Body/Style Number	Body Type & Seating	Factory Price	Shipping Weight	Production Total
71	49-4769	4-dr Sed-6P	2735	4205	54,674 (568)
76S	49-4707	2-dr S'dn't-6P	2618	4115	18,415 (122)
76R	49-4737	2-dr HT Cpe- 6P	3203	4420	4,314 (29)
76C	49-4767	2-dr Conv Cpe- 6P	3150	4370	8,095 (149)
79	(Ionia)	4-dr Sta Wag-6P	3734	4490	632 (21)

ENGINE: Eight cylinder. Inline. Overhead valve. Cast iron block. Displacement: 320.2 cid. Bore and stroke: 3-7/16 x 4-4/16. Compression ratio: 6.9:1. Brake horsepower: 150 at 3600 rpm. Five main bearings. Mechanical valve lifters. Carburetor: Stromberg AAV-267 #380226 and Carter 609 or 664.

CHASSIS FEATURES: Wheelbase: Series 40 and 50 — 121 inches; Series 70 — 126 inches. Overall length: Series 40 — 207-1/2 inches; Series 50 — 209-1/2 inches; Series 70 — 214-1/8 inches. Front tread: Series 40 — 58-7/8 inches; Series 50 and 70 — 59-1/8 inches. Rear Tread: Series 40 — 61-15/16 inches, Series 50 and 70 — 62-3/16 inches. Tires: Series 40 — 6.50 x 15; Series 50 — 7.60 x 15; Series 70 — 8.20 x 15.

POWERTRAIN OPTIONS: Three-speed manual transmission standard on Series 40 and 50. Dynaflow drive standard on Series 70. Column-mounted shift levers. Dynaflow drive optional on Series 50; cars so equipped have 6.9:1 compression ratio, 120 brake horsepower motors.

CONVENIENCE OPTIONS: Spotlite (Series 40). Spotlamp with mirror. Sonomatic radio. Weather Warden heater/defroster. Seat covers. NoRol assembly. Windshield washer. E-Z-I or Prismatic rearview mirrors. Vanity visor mirror. Tissue dispenser. Auxiliary driving lamps. Multi-purpose trouble lamp. All-rubber floor mats.

HISTORICAL FOOTNOTES: This all-time record production year saw 398,482 vehicles built in the calendar year. This gave Buick a 7.7 percent market share. Model year assemblies came to 409,138. Models 59 and 79 were Estate Wagons. Model 76R was the Riviera, a midyear model.

1950 BUICK

NOTE: Through 1950 Buick provided separate production totals for cars built for export. These are given In brackets on the charts.

SPECIAL — SERIES 40 — Introduced as late 1949 style. The first Special with postwar styling previewed the basic styling for 1950. Most prominent and memorable was the car's "bucktooth" grille, consisting of bumper guards. Specials had three rectangular ventiports on each hoodside. A unique feature of the late 1949 cars was that the hood was opened through a ventiport key and slot system; 1950 production cars had inside hood releases. Specials had no side body moldings. Special Deluxe models had plusher interiors, a full-length bodyside molding, bright window outlines and Special script on the front fenders. They were identified by the code 'D' in the model number.

SPECIAL I.D. NUMBERS: The serial numbers for the 1950 Special Series 40 were mixed in production with other 1950 series. They were: Flint 15360001-up, N.J. 35374001-up, Kans. 45380001-up, Del. 55388001-up (except 55417001 to 55417948), Ga. 65393001-up, Mass. 7539001-up. Series 40 motor numbers were 5568000A up, the suffix 4 denoting a Series 40 motor.

Model Number	Body/Style Number	Body Type & Seating	Factory Price	Shipping Weight	Production Total
43	50-4408	4-dr Sed-6P	1909	3715	58,700
41	50-4469	4-dr Sed-6P	1941	3710	1,141
465	50-4407	2-dr S'dn't-6P	1856	3655	42,935
46	50-4407B	2-dr Cpe-6P	1803	3615	2,500
430	50-4408D	4-dr Sed-6P	1952	3720	14,335
41D	50-4469D	4-dr Sed-6P	1983	3735	141,396
460	50-4407D	2-dr S'dn't-6P	1899	3665	76,902

ENGINE: Eight cylinder. Inline. Overhead valve. Cast iron block. Displacement: 248.0 cid. Bore and stroke: 3-3 /32 x 3-1 /8 inches. Compression ratio: 6.3: 1. Brake horsepower: 110 at 3600 rpm. Five main bearings. Mechanical valve lifters. Carburetor: Stromberg AA UVB 267 #380309 or Carter 725 and 782.

SUPER — SERIES 50 — Supers shared other series' totally new, all-bumper guard grille and more rounded styling. Super scripts appeared on front fenders, just above the full-length lower bodyside moldings. A new, long wheelbase sedan featured a plusher interior than most Supers, which normally had cloth interiors of finer material than the Special. Supers had three ventiports on each hoodside. The Model 56C convertible had leather power seats, plus power windows and top.

1950 Buick, Super four-door sedan, 8-cyl(AA)

SUPER I.D. NUMBERS: The serial number sequence was the same for all 1950 series (see Special — Series 40). Motor numbers began at 5628758-5 (manual transmission) and 5624743-5 (Dynaflow), the suffix '5' denoting a Series 50 motor.

Model Number	Body/Style Number	Body Type & Seating	Factory Price	Shipping Weight	Production Total
51	50-4569	4-dr Sed-6P	2139	3745	55,672
565	50-4507	2-dr S'dn't-6P	2041	3645	10,697
56R	50-4537	2-dr HT Cpe-6P	2139	3790	56,030
56C	50-4567	2-dr Conv Cpe	2476	3965	12,259
59	(Ionia)	4-dr Sta Wag-6P	2844	4115	2,480
52	50-4519	4-dr Sed-6P	2212	3870	114,745

ENGINE: Eight cylinder. Inline. Overhead valve. Cast iron block. Displacement: 263.3 cid. Bore and stroker 3-3 /16 x 4-1/8 inches. Compression ratio: 6.6:1. Brake horsepower: 124 at 3600 rpm. Five main bearings. Carburetor: Stromberg AA UVB #380309 or Carter 725 and 782.

ROADMASTER — SERIES 70 — Buick's finest cars had larger engines and plusher interior trims than comparable Super models. They were readily identified by the four ventiports on the hoodsides. A Roadmaster script was found above the full-length bodyside molding on cars so equipped. Cars with sweepspear moldings had Roadmaster script engraved in the upper body trim strip, behind the door trim, except on the Model 79 and 72R (which received the sweepspear at midyear). Deluxe models had plusher interiors and hydraulic window and seat controls. They were identified by an 'X' suffix in their style numbers.

ROADMASTER I.D. NUMBERS: The serial numbers sequence was the same for all 1950 series (see Special — Series 40). Series 70 motor numbers began at 5635021 -up.

1950 Buick, Roadmaster two-door convertible, 8-cyl(AA)

Model Number	Body/Style Number	Body Type & Seating	Factory Price	Shipping Weight	Production Total
71	50-4769	4-dr Sed-6P	2633	4135	6,738
765	50-4707	2-dr S'dn't-6P	2528	4025	2,968
75R	50-4737	2-dr HT Cpe-6P	2633	4135	2,300
76C	50-4767	2-dr Conv Cpe-6P	2981	4345	2,964
79	(Ionia)	4-dr Sta Wag-6P	3407	4470	420
72	5-4719	4-dr Sed-6P	2738	4220	51,212 (incl. 72)
2R	50-4737X	4-dr Sed-6P	2854	4245	
76R	50-4737X	2-dr HT Cpe-6P	2764	4215	8,432

ENGINE: Eight cylinder. Inline. Overhead valve. Cast iron block. Displacement: 320.2 cu. in. Bore and stroke: 3-71 16 x 4-5/ 16. Compression ratio: 6.9: 1. Brake horsepower: 152 at 3600 rpm. Hydraulic valve lifters. Carburetor: Stromberg AAVG-267 #380258 or Carter 726.

CHASSIS FEATURES: Wheelbase: Series 40 — 121-1/2 inches- Series 50 — 121-1/2 inches (except Model 52, which was 125.5 inches), Series 70 — 126-1/4 inches (except Models 72 and 72R which were 130-1/4 inches). Overall length: Series 40 — 204 inches, Series 50 — 209-1/2 inches (except Model 52, 213-1/2 inches)- Series 70 — 214-7/8 inches (except Models 72 and 72R 217-1/2 inches). Front tread: Series 40 — 59.1 inches. Series 50 and 70 — 59-1/8 inches. Rear tread: Series 40 — 62.2 inches. Series 50 and 70 — 62-2/3 inches. Tires: Series 40 and 50 — 7.60 x 15: Series 70 — 8.00 x 15.

POWERTRAIN OPTIONS: Three-speed manual transmission standard on Series 40 and 50. Dynaflow drive standard on Series 70, optional on Series 40 and 50. Series 40 cars so equipped had 6.9:1 compression ratio, 120 brake horsepower motors. Series 50 cars with Dynaflow had 6.9:1 compression ratio and 124 brake horsepower.

CONVENIENCE OPTIONS: Parking brake release warning light. Cushion toppers. License frames. Handy-Mats. Visor vanity mirror. Tool kit. Full wheelcovers (standard on Series 70). "Breeze-Ease" draft deflectors. Outside rearview mirror. Safety Spotlite with mirror. Multi-purpose trouble lamp. Tissue dispenser. Glare-proof inside rearview mirror. Seat covers. All-rubber floor mat. Auxiliary driving lamps. Exhaust pipe trim. Polish cloth kit.

HISTORICAL FOOTNOTES: Calendar year production was 552,827 cars, keeping Buick at fourth place in the sales charts. Model year production totaled a record 588,439 units. Body Styles 50-4408 and 50-4408D were Jetback sedans. Body styles 50-4537 and 50-4747 were Riviera hardtops. Body styles 50-4519, 50-4719 and 50-4719X were Riviera sedans. Models 59 and 79 were Estate Wagons.

1951 BUICK

1951 Buick, Special Deluxe four sedan, 8-cyl(AA)

SPECIAL — SERIES 40 — Standard and Deluxe trims were offered on the Special Series. The low-priced models had only bright rear fender trim moldings and three ventiports on each fender. Deluxe models had a full-length sweepspear molding leading into the rear fender trim. A new, vertical bar grille with a more conventional bumper was used on all 1951 Buicks. Interiors were cloth, with a plusher grade used on Deluxe models. Specials had a unique instrument panel, with speedometer and gauges housed in two large, round units flanking the steering column notch. Controls were centered vertically, flanking the radio speaker grille. The standard Specials were the only 1951 Buicks to have a two-piece windshield, Deluxe and other lines had a new one-piece type.

SPECIAL I.D. NUMBERS: Serial numbers were located on the front side of dash, under the hood on the right and on the left front hinge pillar post. The first symbol was a number indicating assembly plant as follows: 1= Flint, Mich.; 2 = Southgate, Calif.; 3 = Linden, N.J.; 4 = Kansas City, Mo.; 5 = Wilmington, Del.; 6 = Atlanta, Ga.; 7 = Framingham, Mass. The next seven symbols were numbers indicating sequential production number. Serial numbers were mixed in production with other 1951 series. Numbers were Flint 16740001 to 17214106, (Calif.) 26765001 to 27214776; (N.J.) 36774001 to 37217064; (Kans.) 46783001 to 47224950; (Del.) 56799001 to 57226180; (Ga.) 66808001 to 67228458; (Mass.) 76815001 to 77228805. Engine numbers were stamped in various locations on the crankcase, usually, or on the cylinder block. All 1951 motor numbers start at 62400100, Series 40 motors have suffix-4.

Model Number	Body/Style Number	Body Type & Seating	Factory Price	Shipping Weight	Production Total
41	51-4367	4-dr Sed-6P	2139	3605	999
46S	51-4327	2-dr Spt Cpe-6P	2046	3600	2,700
Deluxe Models:					
41D	51-4369	4-dr Sed-6P	2185	3680	87,848
48D	51-4311D	2-dr Sed-6P	2127	3615	54,311
45R	51-4337	2-dr HT Cpe-6P	2225	3645	16,491
46C	51-4367X	2-dr Conv Cpe-6P	2561	3830	2,099

ENGINE: Eight cylinder. Inline. Overhead valve. Cast iron block. Displacement: 263.3 cid. Bore and stroke: 3-3/16 x 4-1/8 inches. Compression ratio: 6.6: 1. Brake horsepower 120 at 3600 rpm. Five main bearings. Hydraulic valve lifters. Carburetor: Stromberg AAUVB 267 or Carter two-barrel 725 and 882 two-barrel.

1951 Buick, Super four-door Estate Wagon, 8-cyl(AA)

SUPER — SERIES 50 — Supers had larger bodies than Specials, but looked very similar with three round ventiports per front fender, a full-length sweepspear, molding and broad, bright rear fender shields. Series script was found on the deck lid and within the steering wheel center. Supers were trimmed in materials similar to Special Deluxes, except for in the plush Model 52 Super Riviera sedan. Front turn signals were within the bumper guard "bombs," while rear signals shared the stop lamps' housing on the rear fender edges. The Model 56C and Model 59 were trimmed in leather.

SUPER I.D. NUMBERS: Serial numbers were mixed with other 1951 series (see 1951 Special ID Numbers above). Motor numbers were mixed in production, but Super motors have suffix 5.

Model Number	Body/Style Number	Body Type & Seating	Factory Price	Shipping Weight	Production Total
51	51-4569	4-dr Sed-6P	2356	3755	10,000
565	51-4507	2-dr S'dn't-6P	2248	2685	1,500
56R	51-4537	2-dr HT Cpe-6P	2356	3765	54,512
56C	51-4567X	2-dr Conv Cpe-6P	2728	3965	8,116
59	(Ionia)	4-dr Sta Wag-6P	3133	4100	2,212
52	51-4519	4-dr Sed	2563	3825	92,886

ENGINE: Specifications were the same as those listed for the 1951 Special Series 40, except manual transmission cars had 6.9:1 compression ratio and 124 brake horsepower.

1951 Buick, Roadmaster Riviera two-door hardtop coupe, 8-cyl(AA)

ROADMASTER — SERIES 70 — Buick's longest and most Deluxe models featured a new grille ensemble for 1951. Roadmasters had the series designation script on the rear deck, with additional identification coming from four ventiports on each front fender. Full-length, wide rocker panel moldings were used with the sweepspear molding found on cheaper models. Cloth interiors in closed models were plusher than lower priced series, with carpeting used on the floors. The Model 76C and Model 79 used leather seats. Standard equipment on the Model 76C convertible included power top, windows and seat. A Custom interior option for the Roadmaster included leatherette door panel trim. Full wheelcovers were standard.

ROADMASTER I.D. NUMBERS: Serial numbers were mixed with other 1951 series (see 1951 Special ID Numbers above). Motor numbers were mixed in production, but Roadmaster motors have suffix 7.

Model Number	Body/Style Number	Body Type & Seating	Factory Price	Shipping Weight	Production Total
76R	51-4737X	2-dr HT Cpe-6P	3143	4235	12,901
76MR	51-4737	2-dr Del HT Cpe-6P	3051	4185	809
76C	51-4767X	2-dr Conv Cpe-6P	3453	4395	2,911
79R	(Ionia)	4-dr Sta Wag-6P	3977	4505	679
72R	51-4719X	4-dr Sed-6P	3200	4285	48,758

ENGINE: Eight cylinder. Inline. Overhead valve. Cast iron Block. Displacement: 320.2 cid. Bore and stroke: 3-7/16 x 4-5/16 inches. Compression ratio: 7.2:1. Brake horsepower: 152 at 3600 rpm. Five main bearings. Hydraulic valve lifters. Carburetor: Stromberg AAVB267, Carter 726 two barrel.

CHASSIS FEATURES: Wheelbase: Series 40 and 50 — 121-1/2 inches (except Model 52 which was 125-1/2 inches); Series 70 — 126-1/4 inches (except Model 72R which was 130-1/4 inches). Overall length: Series 40 and 50 — 206.2 inches (except Model 52 which was 210.2 inches); Series 70 — 211 inches (except Model 72R which was 215 inches). Front tread: Series 40 — 59 inches; Series 50 and 70 — 59 inches. Rear tread: Series 40 — 59 inches; Series 50 and 70 — 62 inches. Tires: Series 40 and 50 — 7.60 x 15; Series 70 — 8.00 x 15.

POWERTRAIN OPTIONS: A three-speed manual transmission was standard on Series 40 and 50. Dynaflow drive was standard on Series 70, optional on Series 40 and 50. Cars equipped with optional Dynaflow had 7.2:1 compression ratio and 128 horsepower engines.

CONVENIENCE OPTIONS: Parking brake release signal light. Took kit. Cushion topper. Electric clock (Series 50 and 70). License frames. Remote control outside rearview mirror. Visor vanity mirror. Handy mats. Full wheelcovers (standard on Series 70).

HISTORICAL FOOTNOTES: Calendar year production was 404,695 units, the second highest in Buick history up to this point. This represented 7.5 percent of total industry output and made Buick America's fourth largest automaker. Model year output was 404,657. Convertibles represented 9.4 percent of Buick's business. Body Styles 51-4337, 51-4537, 51-4737 and 51-4737 are Riviera hardtops. Styles 51-4519 and 51-4719X are Riviera four-door sedans (pillared). An X in the style number indicates hydraulic control of the seat, windows and (convertibles) top. Models 59 and 79R are Estate Wagons.

1952 BUICK

SPECIAL — SERIES 40 — Buick Special styling changed little from 1951. A new sweepspear molding, now incorporating the rear fender gravel guard, was used. Three round chrome ventiports on each front fender continued to be Series 40 hallmark and were also found on Series 50 models. Specials were again divided into standard and Deluxe categories. The standard models (41 and 46S) had a windshield center division bar and lacked the bright rocker panel molding of Deluxe models. Interiors were spartan on the standard models, while Deluxe models were trimmed in a plusher cloth. The Special continued to use a distinctive instrument panel with two large dials containing the indicators. Special script was now found on rear fenders and Deluxe models had bright fender fins.

SPECIAL I.D. NUMBERS: Serial numbers were located on the front side of dash, under the hood on the right and on the left front hinge pillar post. The first symbol was a number indicating assembly plant as follows: 1 = Flint, Mich.; 2 = Southgate, Calif.; 3 = Linden, N.J.; 4 = Kansas City, Mo.; 5 = Wilmington, Del.; 6 = Atlanta, Ga.; 7 = Framingham, Mass. The next seven symbols were numbers indicating sequential production number. Serial numbers were mixed in production with other 1952 series. Numbers were: (Flint) 1643001 to 16739745, (Calif.) 26456001 to 26714109, (N.J.) 36464001 to 36717383, (Kans.) 46471001 to 46722742, (Del.) 56483001 to 56726449, (Ga.) 66490001 to 66729512, (Mass.) 76496001 to 76730564. Motor numbers were found in various locations on the crankcase, usually, or on the cylinder block. All 1952 motor numbers start at 6646230, Series 40 motor numbers have suffix 4.

Model Number	Body/Style Number	Body Type & Seating	Factory Price	Shipping Weight	Production Total
41	52-4369	4-dr Sed-6P	2209	3650	317
46S	52-4327	2-dr Spt Cpe-6P	2115	3605	2,206
Deluxe Models:					
41D	52-4369D	4-dr Sed-6P	2255	3665	63,346
48D	52-4311D	2-dr Sed-6P	2197	3620	32,684
45R	52-4337	2-dr HT Cpe-6P	2295	3665	21,180
46C	52-4367X	2-dr Conv Cpe-6P	2634	3850	600

ENGINE: Eight cylinder. Inline. Overhead valve. Cast iron block. Displacement: 263.3 cid. Bore and stroke: 3-3/16 x 4-1/8 inches. Compression ratio: 6.6:1. Brake horsepower: 120 at 3600 rpm. Five main bearings. Hydraulic valve lifters. Carburetor: Stromberg AAUBV267 or Carter 882.

1952 Buick, Super Riviera two-door hardtop, 8-cyl(AA)

SUPER — SERIES 50 — Buick's mid-sized line resembled the Series 40 with three ventiports per fender and new sweepspear rocker panel trim. Super script on the rear fenders aided identification. The Super was built with the larger General Motors C-body, however. The full-flowing fenderline dipped deeper on this body and rear fenders had a crease line absent on the B-body Specials. A new deck lid gave a more squared-off appearance. Like other Buick series, it was a near carbon copy year for 1952. Chromed rear fender fins gave distinction to 1952 Supers. Interiors were cloth, except on the Models 56C and 59, which were trimmed with leather. The Super used a different instrument panel than the Special. It was distinguished by a large center speedometer housing flanked by smaller gauge housings. Series identification was found within the steering wheel center.

SUPER I.D. NUMBERS: Serial numbers were mixed with other 1952 series (see 1952 Special ID Numbers above). Motor numbers were mixed in production, but Super motors have suffix 5.

Model Number	Body/Style Number	Body Type & Seating	Factory Price	Shipping Weight	Production Total
56R	52-4537	2-dr HT Cpe-6P	2478	3775	55,400
56C	52-4567X	2-dr Conv Cpe-6P	2869	3970	6,904
59	(Ionia)	4-dr Sta Wag-6P	3296	4105	1,641
52	52-4519	4-dr Sed-6P	2563	3825	71,387

ENGINE: Specifications were the same as those listed for the 1952 Special, except manual transmission cars had 6.9:1 compression ratio with 124 brake horsepower.

1952 Buick, Roadmaster four-door sedan, 8-cyl (AA)

ROADMASTER — SERIES 70 — Roadmasters are easy to spot by their longer front fenders and hood, and four ventiports on each side. A rehash of 1951 styling, with new sweepspear moldings and bright rocker trim provided distinction. Series identification appeared on rear fenders. New deck lids gave a higher, more substantial rear end appearance, while the frontal view was unchanged from 1951. Roadmasters continued to be the plushest Buicks. Custom trim options were available for even more richness. Quality cloth was used in sedans, while the Models 76C and 79R were trimmed in leather. The specially-lengthened, extra-posh Model 72R Riviera sedan continued to be the most popular Roadmaster style. All Roadmasters had the popular 1952 Buick "sombrero" wheel disc as standard equipment.

ROADMASTER I.D. NUMBERS: Serial numbers were mixed with the other 1952 series (see 1952 Special ID numbers above). Motor numbers were mixed in production, but Roadmaster motors have suffix 7.

Model Number	Body/Style Number	Body Type & Seating	Factory Price	Shipping Weight	Production Total
76R	52-4737X	2-dr HT Cpe-6P	3306	4235	11,387
76C	52-4767X	2-dr Conv Cpe-6P	3453	4395	2,402
79R	(Ionia)	4-dr Sta Wag-6P	3977	4505	359
72R	52-4719X	4-dr Sed-6P	3200	4285	32,069

ENGINE: Eight cylinder. Inline. Overhead valve. Cast iron block. Displacement: 320.2 cid. Bore and stroke: 3-7/16 x 4-5/16 inches. Compression ratio: 7.5:1. Brake horsepower: 170 at 3800 rpm. Five main bearings. Hydraulic valve lifters. Carburetor: Stromberg 4AUV267 or Carter 894S-5A four-barrel.

POWERTRAIN OPTIONS: A three-speed manual transmission was standard on Series 40 and 50. Dynaflow drive was standard on Series 70. Series 40 and 50 cars equipped with the $193 Dynaflow option had 7.2:1 compression ratio and 128 brake horsepower engines.

CONVENIENCE OPTIONS: Power steering, Series 70, ($199). Parking brake release signal light. Cushion toppers. Electric clock (Series 50-70). License plate frames. Remote control rearview mirror. Visor vanity mirror. Full wheelcovers (standard on Series 70). Handy-Spot. Seat covers. Auto-Jack case.

HISTORICAL FOOTNOTES: A steel strike, Korean War production quotas and a long model changeover combined to hold Buick's calendar year production to 321,048 units in 1952. This kept the company in fourth spot on the sales charts with a 7.4 percent market share. Model year output was 303,745 cars. Buick was the largest builder of hardtops and the third largest convertible maker. Body Styles 52-4337, 52-4537 and 52-4737X are Riviera hardtop coupes. Styles 52-4519 and 52-4719 are Riviera four-door sedans (pillared). An 'X' suffix to the style number indicates hydraulic control of the seat, windows and (convertible) top. Models 59 and 79R are Estate Wagons.

1953 BUICK

1953 Buick, Special two-door convertible, 8-cyl (AA)

SPECIAL — SERIES 40 — The Series 40 was Buick's only line carrying a straight eight in 1953. The small series Buick had its own version of the 1953 frontal look. Since it was a narrower car, the grilles, bumpers and sheet metal parts did not interchange with larger models. On the fenders were new teardrop-shaped ventiports, three to a side. The hood bombsight ornament had no vee on the Special. All 1953 Specials were Deluxe models, with

bright sweepspears and rocker panel moldings. Interiors were cloth, with the unique Special instrument panel continuing for another year. Model 46C, the convertible, was trimmed in leather. Series call-outs were on the rear deck emblem.

SPECIAL I.D. NUMBERS: Serial numbers were located on the hinge pillar post and on the dash under the hood. The first symbol was a number indicating assembly plant as follows: 1 = Flint, Mich.; 2 = Southgate, Calif.; 3 = Linden, N.J.; 4 = Kansas City, Mo.; 5 = Wilmington, Del.; 6 = Atlanta, Ga.; 7 = Framingham, Mass. The next seven symbols were numbers indicating sequential production number. Serial numbers were mixed in production with other 1953 series. Numbers were: (Flint) 1674001 to 17214106; (Calif.) 26765001 to 27214776; (N.J.) 36774001 to 37127064; (Kans.) 46783001 to 47224950; (Del.) 56799001 to 57226180; (Ga.) 66808001 to 67228458; (Mass.) 76815001 to 77228805. Motor numbers were stamped in various locations on the crankcase, usually, or on the cylinder block. All 1953 motors start at 6950620, Series 40 motor numbers have suffix 4.

Model Number	Body/Style Number	Body Type & Seating	Factory Price	Shipping Weight	Production Total
41D	53-4369D	4-dr Sed-6P	2255	3710	100,312
48D	53-4311D	2-dr Sed-6P	2197	3675	53,796
45R	53-4337	2-dr HT Cpe-6P	2295	3705	58,780
46C	53-4367X	2-dr Conv Cpe-6P	2553	3815	4,282

ENGINE: Eight cylinder. Inline. Overhead valve. Cast iron block. Displacement: 263.3 cid. Bore and stroke: 3-3/16 x 4-1/8 inches. Compression ratio: 6.6:1. Brake horsepower: 120 at 3600 rpm. Five main bearings. Hydraulic valve lifters. Carburetor: Stromberg AAUVB267 or Carter 882S.

SUPER — SERIES 50 — Buick's middle-priced line shared the Roadmaster's new V-8 and, for this year, the Roadmaster shared the Super and Special's 121.5 inch wheelbase. The Super carried a horizontal trim bar on its rear fenders that distinguished it from Series 70 Roadmasters. Otherwise, its side trim was identical, although the Super had only three ventiports on each front fender. Series identification was found on the deck emblem. Full wheelcovers were now standard. The vee in the bombsight ornament signified the V-8 power under the hood. Interiors of most models were in nylon and silky broadcloth. The Model 56C and Model 59 were trimmed in leather. Model 56C, the convertible, had power windows, seat and top as standard equipment.

SUPER I.D. NUMBERS: Serial numbers were mixed with other 1953 series (see 1953 Special ID numbers above). Motor numbers began with V-2415-5.

Model Number	Body/Style Number	Body Type & Seating	Factory Price	Shipping Weight	Production Total
56R	53-4567	2-dr HT Cpe-6P	2611	3845	91,298
56C	53-4567X	2-dr Conv Cpe-6P	3002	4035	6,701
59	(Ionia)	4-dr Sta Wag-6P	3430	4150	1,830
52	53-4519	4-dr Sed-6P	2696	3905	90,685

ENGINE: V-8: Overhead valve. Cast iron block. Displacement: 322 cid. Bore and stroke: 4.0 x 3.2 inches. Compression ratio: 8.0:1. Brake horsepower: 164 at 4,000 rpm. Five main bearings. Hydraulic valve lifters. Carburetor: Stromberg AAVB267 or Carter 2017S two-barrel.

1953 Buick Roadmaster four-door sedan (AA)

ROADMASTER — SERIES 70 — Buick's finest had a fore-shortened nose in 1953, to emphasize the compact power of the new V-8 under the hood. Roadmasters had chrome rear fender gravel shields between the rear wheelhouse and the bumper, in addition to the same sweepspear used on the Super. However, the upper horizontal trim strip on Super rear fenders was absent. Series call-outs were found within the deck emblem and on the steering wheel hub. Full wheelcovers were standard. Interiors were nylon, broadcloth or leather, depending on the model. Foam-backed Roxpoint nylon carpeting was standard, as were power steering, power brakes and Dynaflow drive. Color-keyed instrument panels with damascene-patterned lower panels were used. A very special 1953 Roadmaster model was the Model 76X Skylark Anniversary Convertible. It was on the Roadmaster chassis, but had its own fenders with open wheelhouses painted white or red. It did not have any ventiports. A lowered top, 40-spoke Kelsey-Hayes wire wheels and a full complement of luxury accessories were included. The Skylark had its own slim, cast sweepspear moldings and special bodyside emblems on the rear quarters. Interiors were in leather.

ROADMASTER I.D. NUMBERS: Serial numbers were mixed with other 1953 series (see 1953 Buick Special ID numbers above). Motor numbers began with V-2001-7.

1953 Buick, Roadmaster Skylark sport convertible, V-8 (AA)

Model Number	Body/Style Number	Body Type & Seating	Factory Price	Shipping Weight	Production Total
76R	53-4737	2-dr HT Cpe-6P	3358	4125	22,927
76C	53-4767X	2-dr Conv Cpe-6P	3506	4250	3,318
79R	(Ionia)	4-dr Sta Wag-6P	3254	4100	670
72R	53-4719	4-dr Sed-6P	4031	4315	50,523
76X	53-4767SX	2-dr Sky Conv Cpe-6P	5000	4315	1,690

ENGINE: Specifications were the same as those listed for the 1953 Super, except compression ratio was 8.5:1 and brake horsepower was 188 at 4,000 rpm. Carburetors were Stromberg 4AUV267 or Carter 996 or 2082 S 4-barrel.

CHASSIS FEATURES: Wheelbase: Series 40, 50 and 70: 121-1/2 inches (except Models 52 and 72R which were 125-1/2 inches). Overall length: Series 40 — 205.8 inches. Series 50 and 70 — 207.6 inches (except Model 52 and 72R — 211.6 inches). Front tread: Series 40 — 59 inches; Series 50 and 70 — 60 inches. Rear tread: Series 40 — 59 inches, Series 50 and 70 — 62 inches. Tires: Series 40 and 50 — 6.70 x 15; Series 70 — 8.00 x 15.

POWERTRAIN OPTIONS: Three-speed manual transmission was standard on Series 40 Specials and Series 50 Supers. Dynaflow drive was an option on Specials and Supers at $193 extra, but was standard in the Roadmaster prices. Specials equipped with Dynaflow had 7.2:1 compression powerplants with 128 brake horsepower. Supers equipped with Dynaflow had 8.l:l compression powerplant with 170 brake horsepower.

CONVENIENCE OPTIONS: Power steering ($177) [standard on Series 70]. Power brakes (standard on Series 70). Simulated wire wheelcovers (Buick shield center type on Series 40; bright vee with black background type on Series 50 and 70). Full wheelcovers (standard on Series 50 and 70). Eight-inch rear seat speaker. Tool kit. Handy spot. Dor-Gard. Cushion toppers. Selectronic radio (optional Series 50 and 70 and standard Model 76X). Electric clock. License frames. Right-hand outside rearview mirror. Left-hand remote control outside mirror. Handy mats. Air conditioning (Series 50 and 70). Fold-down tissue dispenser.

HISTORICAL FOOTNOTES: This was Buick's 50th anniversary. The company retained fourth rank, with a 7.9 percent market share. Calendar year production was 485,353 units. Model year production was 488,755 units. The seven millionth Buick was built June 13, 1953. Dynaflow was used in 80 percent of the Buicks of 1953. The new V-8 engine went into 55 percent of the cars made, even though it wasn't available in the Specials. Styles 53-4337, 53-4537 and 53-4737X were Riviera hardtop coupes. Style 53-4767SX was the Skylark Anniversary convertible. Models 59 and 79R were Estate wagons. An X suffix to the style number indicates hydraulic control of the seat, windows and (convertible) top.

1954 BUICK

1954 Buick, Special four-door Estate Wagon, V-8 (AA)

SPECIAL — SERIES 40 — The Special had a new body for 1954, lower and wider, on a new V-8-powered chassis. Series identification was found on the rear quarters and within the deck ornament. Three oval ventiports adorned each front fender. Stainless (sweepspears) on the bodysides arched over the rectangular rear wheelhouses of the sedans or station wagons and the rounded rear wheel opening of the Riviera hardtop and convertible. Rear fenders had a blunted fin at their rear edge, with dual 'bullet' taillamps below. A new Panoramic windshield, with slanting side pillars was used. Specials were upholstered in nylon (two-tones in the Riviera hardtop), except for the Model 46C, which had leather trim and an outside rearview mirror as standard equipment, along with a power top, windows and front seat.

Serial numbers were located on the hinge pillar post and on dash under the hood. The first symbol was a number indicating series, as follows: 4 = Series 40 Special; 6 = Series 60 Century; 5 = Series 50 Super; 7 = Series 70 Roadmaster and 8 = Series 80 Limited/Electra or 4 = 4400 (Special); 6 = 4600 (Century); 7 = 4700 (Roadmaster). The second symbol was a letter indicating year as follows: A=1954. The third symbol was a number indicating assembly plant: 1 = Flint, Mich.; 2 = Southgate, Calif.; 3 = Linden, N.J.; 4 = Kansas City, Kan.; 5 = Wilmington, Del.; 6 = Atlanta, Ga.; 7 = Framingham, Mass.; 8 = Arlington, Tex. The remaining symbols represented the sequential production number. Buick Special serial numbers were mixed in production with other 1954 Series. Numbers used at the beginning of the season were as follows: (Flint)-A-1001001-up; (Calif.)-A-2001001-up; (N.J.)-A-3001001-up; (Kans.)-A-4001001up; (Del.)-A-5001001-up; (Ga.)-A-6001001-up; (Mass.)-A-7001001-up and Texas (Tex.)-A-8001001-up. Effective April 1, 1954 beginning numbers changed as follows: (Flint)-4AI-056800-up; (Calif.)-4A2-014905-up; (N.J.)-6A3-020700-up; (Kan.)-7AA021783-up; (Del.)-7A5-013983-up; (Ga.)-7A6-012742-up; (Mass.)-6A7-010471-up and (Tex.)-7A8-002765-up. Motor numbers were stamped in various locations on the crankcase, usually, or on the cylinder block. Motor numbers were also mixed in production, beginning with number Y-273956.

Model Number	Body/Style Number	Body Type & Seating	Factory Price	Shipping Weight	Production Total
41D	54-4469D	4-dr Sed-6P	2265	3735	70,356
48D	54-441 1 D	2-dr Sed-6P	2207	3690	41,557
46R	54-4437	2-dr HT Cpe-6	2305	3740	71,186
46C	54-4467X	2-dr Conv Cpe-6P	2563	3810	6,135
49	54-4481	4-dr Sta Wag-6	3163	3905	1,650

ENGINE: V-8. Overhead valve. Cast iron block. Displacement: 264 cid. Bore and stroke: 3.625 x 3.2 inches. Compression ratio: 7.2: 1. Brake horsepower: 143 at 4200 rpm. (150 w/ automatic transmission). Five main bearings. Hydraulic valve lifters. Carburetor: Stromberg AAVB267 or Carter 2081 or 2179 two-barrel.

1954 Buick, Century two-door hardtop coupe, V-8

CENTURY — SERIES 60 — Revived for the first time since 1942, the new Century shared the Series 40 Special body and basic chassis, but carried the Roadmaster engine. The new performance car carried three ventiports per fender and was identical to the Special in most other exterior trim, except for the Century scripts on the quarter panels and the series designation within the deck ornament. It shared the Special's instrument panel, with gages set into twin round housings. Nylon cloth upholstery, with foam cushions (two-tones in Riviera hardtops), were standard. The Model 66C convertible was trimmed in leather and had an outside rearview mirror and power operated windows, seat and top as part of its base equipment.

CENTURY I.D. NUMBERS: Serial numbers were mixed with other 1954 series (see 1954 Special ID Numbers above). Motor numbers were mixed in production.

Model Number	Body/Style Number	Body Type & Seating	Factory Price	Shipping Weight	Production Total
61	54-4669	4-dr Sed-6P	2520	3805	31,919
66R	54-4637	2-dr HT Cpe-6P	2534	3795	45,710
66C	54-4667X	2-dr Conv Cpe-6P	2963	3950	2,790
69	54-4681	4-dr Sta Wag-6P	3470	39 75	1,563

ENGINE: V-8. Overhead valve. Cast iron block. Displacement. 322 cid Bore and stroke: 4.0 x 3.2 inches. Compression ratio. 72:1 Brake horsepower 195 at 4100 rpm. Five main bearings. Hydraulic valve lifters. Carburetor Stromberg 4AUV267 or Carter 2082S four-barrel.

1954 Buick, Super four-door sedan, V-8

SUPER — SERIES 50 — Using the new, larger General Motors C-body, with vertical windshield pillars and the new Panoramic windshield, the Super for 1954 was a big Buick for the budget minded. Identified by its three ventiports per fender, the Super script on quarters and the series designation within the deck ornament, the Super shared other brightwork with the Roadmaster. Interiors were nylon and were plainer than in the Roadmasters. The Super did have the expensive car's horizontal speedometer instrument panel. Model 56C, the line's convertible, was upholstered in leather and had power-operated windows, seat and top, along with an outside rearview mirror on the left, as standard equipment.

SUPER I.D. NUMBERS: Serial numbers were mixed in 1954 production (see 1954 Special ID Numbers above). Motor numbers were also mixed in production.

Model Number	Body/Style Number	Body Type & Seating	Factory Price	Shipping Weight	Production Total
52	54-4519	4-dr Sed-6P	2711	4105	41,756
56R	54-4567	2-dr HT Cpe-6P	2626	4035	73,531
56C	54-4537X	2-dr Conv Cpe-6P	2964	4145	3,343

ENGINE: Specifications were the same as listed for the 1954 Century except a 7.2:1 compression ratio was used. Brake horsepower was 177 at 4100 rpm. Carburetors: Stromberg AAVB267 or Carter 2081 or 2179 two-barrel.

ROADMASTER — SERIES 70 — The top-of-the line Buick looked like the cheaper Super from the outside, with the exception of a fourth ventiport on each front fender, Roadmaster script on the rear quarters and series identification within the deck ornament. Inside, though, the upholstery was much posher, with various nylon, broadcloth and leather combinations available depending on the model. Seats had chrome bands on the two-door models and all cars were fully carpeted. Power steering, brakes and Dynaflow were standard features, as was a rear seat armrest on the sedan. All had the new instrument panel with horizontal speedometer. Models 76C and 76R had an outside rearview mirror on the left and the 76C convertible was additionally equipped with power-operated windows, (vertical) seat adjustment and top.

ROADMASTER I.D. NUMBERS: Serial and motor numbers were mixed with other 1954 series (see 1954 Special ID Numbers above).

Model Number	Body/Style Number	Body Type & Seating	Factory Price	Shipping Weight	Production Total
72R	54-4719	4-dr Sed-6P	3269	4250	26,862
76RX	54-4737X	2-dr HT Cpe-6P	3373	4215	20,404
76CX	54-4767X	2-dr Conv Cpe-6P	3521	4355	3,305

ENGINE: Specifications were the same as those listed for the 1954 Century, except compression ratio was 8.0: 1 and brake horsepower was 200 at 4100 rpm.

1954 Buick, Skylark Sport two-door convertible, V-8 (AA)

SKYLARK — SERIES 100 — Buick's wild prestige convertible was the only model in this series. A new tapered deck with big chrome fins was grafted onto the 1954 Century body to create the 1954 Skylark. Specific front fenders with wide-open wheelhouse, echoed at the rear wheelhouse, had no ventiports. Forty-spoke Kelsey-Hayes wire wheels were standard, along with leather trim, special emblems, power brakes, power steering, Dynaflow, 4-way powered seat, power top, power windows, Selectronic radio with power antenna, Easy-Eye glass, heater-defroster and whitewall tires.

Model Number	Body/Style Number	Body Type & Seating	Factory Price	Shipping Weight	Production Total
100	54-4667SX	2-dr Spt Conv	4355	4260	836

ENGINE: Specifications were the same as those listed for the 1954 Century, except compression ratio was 8.0:1 and brake horsepower was 200 at 4100 rpm.

CHASSIS FEATURES: Wheelbase: Series 40, 60 and 100 — 122 inches; Series 50 and 70 — 127 inches. Overall length: Series 40, 60 and 100 — 206.3 inches; Series 50 and 70 — 216-4/5 inches. Front tread: Series 40, 60 and 100 — 59 inches; Series 50 and 70 — 59 inches. Rear tread: Series 40, 60 and 100 — 59 inches; Series 50 and 70 — 62-1/5 inches. Tires: Series 40, 60, 50 and 100 — 6.70 x 15; Series 70 — 8.00 x 15.

POWERTRAIN OPTIONS: Three-speed manual transmission standard on Series 40, 50 and 60. Dynaflow drive standard on Series 70 and 100. Series 40 cars equipped with Dynaflow option had 8.0:1 compression ratio and 150 brake horsepower. Series 50 cars equipped with Dynaflow had 8.0:1 compression ratio and 182 brake horsepower. Series 60 cars equipped with Dynaflow had 8.0:1 compression ratio and 200 brake horsepower.

CONVENIENCE OPTIONS: Full wheelcovers (standard Series 70). Set of five genuine 40-spoke wire wheels for Series 50, 60 and 70 (standard for Model 100). Power brakes (standard Series 70 and Model 100). Power steering (standard Series 70 and Model 100). Dor-Gard. Rear fender gas door guard. Windshield washer. Tool kit. Handy-Spot. Cushion toppers. Electric radio antenna (standard Model 100). Sonomatic radio. Selectronic radio (standard Model 100). Rear seat speaker (except convertibles, station wagons). Electric clock. License frames. Inside optional rearview mirror. Glare-proof outside rearview mirrors, right and left-hand. Visor vanity mirror. Handy mats. Air conditioning (except convertibles, Model 48). Hydraulic-electric windows (standard on Models 76RX, 76CX, 100). Horizontal front seat adjustment (standard, Model 100).

HISTORICAL FOOTNOTES: Calendar year production was 531,463. This represented a 9.6 percent market share and gave Buick third place in industry. Model year production was 444,609 units. During 1954, Buick became the first automaker to build one-half million hardtops. The two millionth Dynaflow was built on May 3. Styles number 54-4437, 54-4537, 54-4637 and 54-4737X were Riviera hardtop coupes. Styles number 54-4481 and 55-4681 were all-steel Estate Wagons. An X suffix to the Style Number indicates hydraulic control of the seat, windows, and convertible top.

1955 BUICK

1955 Buick, Special Riviera two-door hardtop coupe, V-8 (AA)

SPECIAL — SERIES 40 — A major facelift, with new rear fenders housing 'tower' taillights, new front fenders and a new oval grille opening (housing a textured grille panel and a large horizontal emblem bar) distinguished the 1955 Buicks. Sweepspear moldings on the Special were the same as in 1954, but new round ventiports were grouped by threes on each front fender. Series script was found on the rear quarters and within the grille emblem. Cordaveen upholstery was used. The distinctive Series 40 and 60 instrument panel, with twin round gauge pods was continued. Tubeless tires were now standard, as were directional signals, front and rear side armrests, sliding sunshades, a Step-On parking brake and heavy insulation.

SPECIAL I.D. NUMBERS: Serial numbers were located on the hinge pillar post and on dash under the hood. The first symbol was a number indicating series, as follows: 4= Series 40 Special; 6=Series 60 Century; 5=Series 50 Super; 7=Series 70 Roadmaster or 4 = 4400 (Special); 6=4600 (Century); 7=4700 (Roadmaster). The second symbol was a letter indicating year as follows: B=1955. The third symbol was a number indicating assembly plant: 1=Flint, Mich.; 2=Southgate, Calif.; 3=Linden, N.J.; 4=Kansas City, Kan.; 5=Wilmington, Del.; 6=Atlanta, Ga.; 7=Framingham, Mass.; 8=Arlington, Tex. The remaining symbols represented the sequential production number. Serial numbers were mixed in production with other 1955 series. Beginning numbers were: (Flint) 5Bl001001-up; (Cal.) 582001001-up; (N.J.) 4B3001001-up; (Kans.) 4B4001001-up; (Del.) 4B5001001-up-, (Ga.) 586001001-up; (Mass.) 5B7001001-up; and (Texas) 488001001-up. Motor numbers were in various locations on the crankcase, usually, or on cylinder block. Motor numbers were mixed in production.

Model Number	Body/Style Number	Body Type & Seating	Factory Price	Shipping Weight	Production Total
41	55-4469	4-dr Sed-6P	2291	3745	84,182
43	55-4439	4-dr HT-6P	2409	3820	66,409
48	55-4411	2-dr Sed-6P	2233	3715	61,879
46R	55-4437	2-dr HT Cpe-6P	2332	3720	155,818
46C	55-4467	2-dr Conv Cpe-6P	2590	3825	10,009
49	55-4481	4-dr Sta Wag-6P	2974	3940	2,952

ENGINE: V-8. Overhead valve. Cast iron block. Displacement: 264 cid. Bore and stroke: 3.625 x 3.2 inches. Compression ratio: 8.4:1. Brake horsepower: 188 at 4800 rpm. Five main bearings. Hydraulic valve lifters. Carburetor: Stromberg AAVB267, AA7-102 or Carter 2179 or 2292 two-barrel.

1955 Buick, Century four-door Riviera hardtop, V-8 (AA)

CENTURY — SERIES 60 — Buick's new performance car combining Roadmaster power and the Special's lighter, the Century had a more agile body, shared in the facelift given other 1955 Buicks. Century models were easily identified by their four ventiports per fender, the Century script on rear quarters and the series designation within the deck emblem. Inside, damascene panels were inset on the instrument panel and a quilted metallic door panel section was featured. The Century had a round Red Liner speedometer with a trip mileage indicator. An electric clock was also standard, along with features found on the Special. Interiors were cloth and Cordaveen except for the Model 66C convertible, which was trimmed in leather and had power windows and a power horizontal seat adjuster as standard equipment. During 1955, Buick made 268 unique police cars for the California Highway Patrol. They were based on the Special two-door sedan body, but from the firewall forward they were Centurys and Buick

listed them with Century production. All had the 322 cid/236 hp V-8 used in Century and Roadmaster models. About half had three-speed manual transmission and the others were equipped with Dynaflow drive.

CENTURY I.D. NUMBERS: Serial numbers were mixed with other 1955 series (see 1955 Special ID Numbers above). Motor numbers were mixed in production.

Model Number	Body/Style Number	Body Type & Seating	Factory Price	Shipping Weight	Production Total
61	55-4669	4-dr Sed-6P	2548	3825	13,629
63D	55-4639	4-dr HT-6P	2733	3900	55,088
66R	55-4637	2-dr HT Cpe-6P	2601	3805	80,338
66C	55-4667X	2-dr Conv Cpe-6P	2991	3950	5,588
69	55-4681	4-dr Sta Wag-6P	3175	3995	4,243
68	55-4611	2-dr Sed-6P	-	-	268

ENGINE: V-8: Overhead valve. Cast iron block. Displacement: 322 cid. Bore and stroke: 4 x 3.2 inches. Compression ratio: 9.1:1. Brake horsepower: 236 at 4600 rpm. Five main bearings. Hydraulic valve lifters. Carburetor: Carter 2197 or 2358 four-barrel.

SUPER — SERIES 50 — Buick's popular Super combined the large C-body interior expanse with medium-bracket interiors and performance. Supers had four of the new round ventiports per fender this year, with additional series script found on rear quarters and within the deck emblem. The side sweepspear was unchanged from 1954. The larger bodied Buicks were readily identifiable by their more rounded contours, straight up windshield pillars and sedan rear quarter windows. Series 50 and 70 headlamp bezels also housed parking lights. Inside, a new Red Liner speedometer lay horizontally across the instrument panel. Interiors were trimmed in nylon/Cordaveen combinations, except for the Model 56C convertible, which featured leather seats. Standard Super equipment included trip mileage indicator, electric clock and, on the Model 56C convertible, a power horizontal seat adjuster.

SUPER I.D. NUMBERS: Serial numbers were mixed in 1955 production (see 1955 Special ID Numbers above). Motor numbers were also mixed in production.

Model Number	Body/Style Number	Body Type & Seating	Factory Price	Shipping Weight	Production Total
52	55-4569	4-dr Sed-6P	2876	4140	43,280
56R	55-4537	2-dr HT Cpe-6P	2831	4075	85,656
56C	55-4567X	2-dr Conv Cpe-6P	3225	4280	3,527

ENGINE: Specifications were the same as listed for the 1955 Century.

1955 Buick, Roadmaster four-door sedan, V-8 (AA)

ROADMASTER — SERIES 70 — Buick's prestige car was given more distinction for 1955. Broad, bright lower rear fender bands, gold-colored Roadmaster deck script and hood ornament, bars on the wheelcovers and a gold-accented grille set the car apart. Four round ventiports were found on each front fender of the C-bodied Buicks, which were distinguished by vertical windshield posts and headlamp rims containing the parking lamp units as well. Interiors were plusher, with 10 choices, including brocaded fabrics. The Model 76C convertible had a standard leather interior. Standard features of all Roadmasters included Variable-pitch Dynaflow, power steering, back-up lights, brake warning signal light, electric clock, windshield washer, Custom wheelcovers, double-depth foam seat cushions, plus features found on other Buick series.

ROADMASTER I.D. NUMBERS: Serial numbers were mixed with other 1955 Series (see 1955 Special ID Numbers above). Motor numbers were mixed in production.

Model Number	Body/Style Number	Body Type & Seating	Factory Price	Shipping Weight	Production Total
72	55-4769	4-dr Sed-6P	3349	4300	31,717
76R	55-4737	2-dr HT Cpe-6P	3453	4270	28,071
76C	55-4767X	2-dr Conv Cpe-6P	3552	4415	4,730

ENGINE: Specifications were the same as listed for the 1955 Century.

CHASSIS FEATURES: Wheelbase: Series 40 and 60 — 122 inches; Series 50 and 70 127 inches. Overall length: Series 40 and 60 — 206.7 inches; Series 50 and 70 — 216 inches. Front tread: Series 40 and 60 — 59 inches; Series 50 and 70 — 59 inches. Read tread: Series 40 and 60 — 59 inches; Series 50 and 70 — 62.2 inches. Tires: Series 40 — 7.10 x 15; Series 60 and 50 — 7.60 x 15; Series 70 — 8.00 x 15.

POWERTRAIN OPTIONS: A three-speed manual transmission was standard on the Special. Series 40; Century, Series 60; and Super. Series 50. Dynaflow drive was standard on the Roadmaster, Series 70, optional on other series ($193). Every 1955 Dynaflow unit contained 20 variable pitch stator blades which opened wide for quick acceleration and returned to normal position for cruising. This new feature also gave greater gasoline economy.

CONVENIENCE OPTIONS: Two-tone and tri-tone paint. Windshield washer. Whitewall tubeless tires. Easy-Eye glass. Outside rearview mirrors. Deluxe Handy mats. Sonomatic radio. Selectronic radio. Electric antenna. Full wheelcovers (standard on 70). Genuine 40-spoke wire wheels (except Series 40). Spotlite. Tissue dispenser. Dor-Gard. Gas door guard. Visor vanity mirror. Red Liner speedometer with trip mileage indicator (for Series 40 — standard other Series). Power steering ($108 — standard Series 50 and 70). Air conditioning. Safety group (back-up lights, brake warning light, windshield washer — standard Series 70). Accessory group (for Series 40) — electric clock, rear license frame, full wheelcovers, trunk light.

HISTORICAL FOOTNOTES: Calendar year production of 781,296 cars was an all-time record, putting Buick in third place. Model year output was 738,814. On March 16, the one millionth Buick V-8 was built. On April 5, the eighth millionth Buick was built (it was also the three-and-a-half millionth Buick since World War II.) On Aug. 3, the one millionth Buick hardtop was made. During 1955, Buick took the only two wins in NASCAR Grand National

stock car racing that it would see for many years. Buick Roadmasters were capable of going 0-to-60 mph in 11.2 seconds. The Century could do the same in 9.8 seconds and cover the quarter-mile in 17.5 seconds. A Century hit 110.425 mph in the Flying Mile competition at Daytona SpeedWeeks. Buick had a new X-braced frame, but continued to use torque tube drive. Body styles 55-4437, 55-4637, 55-4537 and 55-4737 are Riviera hardtop coupes. Styles 55-4439 and 55-4639 are Riviera hardtop sedans (pillarless) introduced midyear. Body styles 55-4481 and 55-4681 are Estate Wagons with all-steel bodies. An 'X' suffix to the Style Number indicates power-operated windows.

1956 BUICK

SPECIAL — SERIES 40 — The Special continued to use the popular sweepspear side motif in 1956. But, now all models, including sedans and wagons, had round rear wheelhouse cutouts. Facelifting included new taillights and a new, slightly forward thrusting grille. Series script continued to appear on rear quarters and within the deck and grille emblems. Specials had three oval ventiports per front fender this year, as was traditional. Closed car interiors were vinyl/Cordaveen combinations, while the Model 46C convertible was upholstered in all-Cordaveen. Standard Special equipment included directional signals, front and rear armrests, sliding sunshades, cigarette lighter, glove compartment light, map light, dual horns, Step-On parking brake, a new horizontal Red Liner speedometer and a trip mileage indicator.

1956 Buick, Special four-door Estate Wagon, V-8 (AA)

SPECIAL I.D. NUMBERS: Serial numbers were located on the hinge pillar post and on dash under the hood. The first symbol was a number indicating series, as follows: 4 = Series 40 Special; 5 = Series 60 Century; 7 = Series 50 Super; 7 = Series 70 Roadmaster or 4 = 4400 (Special); 6 = 4600 (Century); 7 = 4700 (Roadmaster). The second symbol was a letter indicating year as follows: C=1956. The third symbol was a number indicating assembly plant: 1 = Flint, Mich.; 2 = Southgate, Calif.; 3 = Linden, N.J.; 4 = Kansas City, Kan.; 5 = Wilmington, Del.; 6 = Atlanta, Ga.; 7 = Framingham, Mass.; 8 = Arlington, Tex. The remaining symbols represented the sequential production number. Serial numbers were mixed in production with other 1956 series. Numbers were: (Flint) 4Cl001001 to 4C1207895; (Calif.) 4C2001001 to 4C2064441; (N.J.) 4C3001001 to 4C3068989; (Kans.) 4C4001001 to 4C4060680; (Del.) 4C5001001 to 4C5053478; (Atlanta) 4C6001001 to 4C6055767; (Mass.) 4C7001001 to 4C7028493; (Texas) 4C8001001 to 4C8040281. Engine numbers were stamped on various locations on the crankcase or on cylinder block.

Model Number	Body/Style Number	Body Type & Seating	Factory Price	Shipping Weight	Production Total
41	56-4469	4-dr Sed-6P	2416	3790	66,977
43	56-4439	4-dr HT-6P	2528	3860	91,025
48	56-4411	2-dr Sed-6P	2537	2750	38,672
46R	56-4437	2-dr HT Cpe-6P	2457	3775	113,861
46C	56-4467	2-dr Conv Cpe-6P	2740	3880	9,712
49	56-4481	4-dr Sta Wag-6P	2775	3945	13,770

ENGINE: V-8. Overhead valve. Cast iron block. Displacement: 322 cid. Bore and stroke: 4 x 3.2 inches. Compression ratio: 8.9:1. Brake horsepower: 220 at 4400 rpm. Five main bearings. Hydraulic valve lifters. Carburetor: Stromberg 7-104 (manual trans), 7-105 (Dynaflow); Carter 2378 (manual trans), 2400 (Dynaflow).

1956 Buick, Century two-door convertible, V-8

CENTURY — SERIES 60 — The Century relied chiefly on a fourth oval ventiport on each front fender, its series script on the rear quarters, and the series designations within the deck and grille emblems, for its exterior identity. It shared the General Motors B-Body, recognizable by its reverse slanting windshield pillars, with the Series 40 Special. All bright moldings interchanged. Colorful nylon/Cordaveen interior combinations were used in duo and tri-tones. The

convertible, Model 66C, was once more trimmed in leather. Standard features, in addition to those found on the Special, included foam seat cushions, a trunk light, electric clock and rear license frame. Model 66C, the convertible, had a power top, windows and horizontal seat adjuster included in its equipment.

CENTURY I.D. NUMBERS: Serial numbers were mixed with other 1956 Series (see 1956 Special ID Numbers above). Motor numbers were mixed in production.

Model Number	Body/Style Number	Body Type & Seating	Factory Price	Shipping Weight	Production Total
63	56-4639	4-dr HT-6P	3025	4000	20,891
63D	56-4639D	4-dr Del HT-6P	3041	4000	35,082
66R	56-4637	2-dr HT Cpe-6P	2963	3890	33,334
66C	56-4667X	2-dr Conv Cpe-6P	3306	4045	4,721
69	56-4681	4-dr Sta Wag-6P	3256	4080	8,160

ENGINE: Specifications were the same as listed for the 1956 Special, except compression ratio was 9.5:1, brake horsepower was 255 at 4400 rpm and the carburetor was a Carter 2347 or Rochester 7009200-9900 four-barrel.

1956 Buick, Super Riviera four-door hardtop, V-8 (AA)

SUPER — SERIES 50 — Although the Super was a larger Buick, with vertical windshield posts and four ventiports per fender, it had a deep sweepspear similar to the smaller Series 40 and 60 cars. Series script was found on rear quarters and within the deck and grille emblems. Interiors were Cordaveen and patterned nylon, except for the Model 56C which was all-Cordaveen trimmed and had power windows, horizontal seat adjustment, and a power top in its standard form. Dynaflow was now standard on all Supers, along with foam seat cushions, a trunk light and electric clock, plus features found on the lower-priced Special.

SUPER I.D. NUMBERS: Serial numbers were mixed in 1956 production (see 1956 Special ID Numbers). Motor numbers were also mixed in production.

SUPER SERIES 50

Model Number	Body/Style Number	Body Type & Seating	Factory Price	Shipping Weight	Production Total
52	56-4569	4-dr Sed-6P	3250	4200	14,940
53	56-4539	4-dr HT-6P	3340	4265	34,029
56R	56-4537	2-dr HT Cpe-6p	3204	4140	29,540
56C	56-4567	2-dr Conv Cpe-6P	3544	4340	2,489

ENGINE: Specifications are the same as listed for the 1956 Century.

ROADMASTER — SERIES 70 — An effort was made to further distinguish the first class Buick for 1956. Roadmasters had a shallow sweepspear that didn't dip to the rocker panel, as on other series. Twin chrome strips graced the deck lid, with Roadmaster spelled out in block letters between. Roadmaster script was found on the front doors and beneath the vent windows. Fendertop dual bombsights were standard and the grille emblem carried further series identification. Standard Roadmaster equipment included a perimeter heating system, Variable-Pitch Dynaflow, power steering, power brakes, back-up lights, windshield washers, glare-proof rearview mirror, parking brake signal release light, electric clock, Deluxe wheelcovers, foam-cushioned seats, foam-backed carpets and dash pad. Interiors included Custom Nylon and cord combinations and leather in the convertible, Model 76C. Two-door models had bright front seat cushion bands and Models 76R and 76C had power windows and seat adjuster as standard equipment.

1956 Buick, Roadmaster four-door sedan, V-8 (AA)

ROADMASTER I.D. NUMBERS
Serial numbers were mixed in production with other 1956 series (see 1956 Special ID Numbers above). Motor numbers were mixed in production.

Model Number	Body/Style Number	Body Type & Seating	Factory Price	Shipping Weight	Production Total
72	56-4769	4-dr Sed-6P	3503	4280	11,804
73	56-4739	4-dr HT-6P	3692	4355	24,770
76R	56-4737	2-dr HT Cpe-6P	3591	4235	12,490
76C	56-4767	2-dr Conv Cpe-6P	3704	4395	4,354

ENGINE: Specifications were the same as listed for the 1956 Century.

CHASSIS FEATURES: Wheelbase: (Series 40 and 60) 122 inches; (Series 50 and 70) 127 inches. Overall length: (Series 40 and 60) 205 inches; (Series 50 and 70) 213.6 inches. Front tread: (All) 59 inches. Rear tread: (All) 59 inches. Tires: (Series 40) 7. 10 x 15; (Series 60 and 50) 7.60 x 15; (Series 70) 8.00 x 15.

POWERTRAIN OPTIONS: Three-speed manual transmission standard on Series 40 and 60. Dynaflow drive standard on Series 50 and 70, optional ($204) on Series 40 and 60.

CONVENIENCE OPTIONS: Power steering ($108 — standard on Series 50 and 70). Air conditioning ($403). Spotlite. Carpet cover. Cushion topper. Exhaust pipe trim. DorGard. Gas door guard. Rear seat speaker. Tissue dispenser. Visor Vanity mirror. License frame (open top). Seat belts. Custom Cordaveen interior on Series 40, 60 and 50. Power windows (standard on Models 66C, 56C, 76C, 76R, available all other except Model 48). Wire wheels (set of five) on Series 60-50-70. Padded instrument panel (standard Series 70, available for Series 50). Six-way power seat. Sonomatic radio. Selectronic radio. Electric antenna. 30/70 rear seat (Model 49 and 69 wagons).

HISTORICAL FOOTNOTES: Buick captured third place in industry popularity with production of 535,364 units for the calendar year. That equated to a 8.9 percent market share. Model year output was 572,024 units or 9.1 percent of industry production. For the first time, all Buicks used the same engine. Dynaflow transmission was found in 96.7 percent of the cars. A new feature was a foot-operated side-lift jack. The Roadmaster was good for 0-to-60 mph in 11.7 seconds. The 1956 Century could do 0-to-60 in 9.6 seconds and cover the quarter-mile in 17.1. It was the fastest Century ever. All 1956 Buicks were capable of 110 mph. Ivan Wiles was named to replace Edward T. Ragsdale as Buick general manager. Ragsdale (the "father of the hardtop") was promoted to a GM executive position. The Centuriam Motorama show car was seen in 1956. Body styles 56-4437, 56-4537, 56-4637 and 56-4737X are Riviera hardtop coupes. Styles 56-4439, 56-4539, 56-4639 and 56-4739 are Riviera hardtop sedans (Pillarless). Body styles 56-4481 and 56-4681 are Estate wagons. The symbol 'X' after Body Style Number indicates power windows.

1957 BUICK

SPECIAL — SERIES 40 — A new, wider and lower body graced the 1957 Special. A red-filled bright sweepspear lined the bodysides and a chromed rear fender lower panel filled the area between wheelhouse and bumper end. A new centered fuel filler door was found in the rear bumper, the ends of which the single or optional dual exhausts passed through. Three ventiports were found on each front fender. Series script was found within the deck and grille emblems. Closed models were upholstered in nylon/Cordaveen combinations except for the Model 49D Estate Wagon which had cloth and Cordaveen upholstery. The Model 46C convertible was trimmed in two-tone Cordaveen. Standard Special equipment included a Red Liner speedometer, glovebox lamp, dual horns, trip mileage indicator, directional signals, dual sunshades, color-coordinated dash panel and, on Model 46C only, an outside left-hand rear-view mirror.

SPECIAL I.D. NUMBERS: Serial numbers were located on the hinge pillar post and on dash under the hood. The first symbol was a number indicating series, as follows: 4 = Series 40 Special; 6 = Series 60 Century; 5 = Series 50 Super; 7 = Series 70 Roadmaster and 8 = Series 75 Roadmaster (Special); 6 = 4600 (Century); 7 = 4700 (Roadmaster/Electra) and 8 = (4800 Roadmaster 75). The second symbol was a letter indicating year as follows: D=1957. The third symbol was a number indicating assembly plant: 1 = Flint, Mich.; 2 = Southgate, Calif.; 3 = Linden, N.J.; 4 = Kansas City, Kan.; 5 = Wilmington, Del.; 6 = Atlanta, Ga.; 7 = Framingham, Mass.; 8 = Arlington, Tex. The remaining symbols represented the sequential production number. Serial numbers were mixed in production with other 1957 Series. Numbers were: (Flint) 4DI000989 to 4DI149460; (Calif.) 4D2001001 to 4D2038462; (N.J.) 4D3001001 to 4D3047645, (Kans.) 4D4001001 to 4D4046155, (Del.) 4D5001001 to 4D5039991, (Ga.) 4D6001001 to 4D6042248. (Mass.) 4D7001001 to 4D7018900 (Tex.) 4D8001001 to 4D8030225.

SPECIAL SERIES 40

Model Number	Body/Style Number	Body Type & Seating	Factory Price	Shipping Weight	Production Total
41	57-4469	4-dr Sed-6P	2660	4012	59,739
43	57-4439	4-dr HT-6P	2780	4041	50,563
48	57-4411	2-dr Sed-6P	2596	3955	23,180
46R	57-4437	2-dr HT Cpe-6P	2704	3956	64,425
46C	57-4467	2-dr Conv Cpe-6P	2987	4082	8,505
49D	57-4481	4-dr Riv Sta Wag-6P	3167	4309	6,817
49	57-4482	4-dr Sta Wag-6P	3047	4292	7,013

ENGINE: V-8. Overhead valve. Cast iron block. Displacement: 364 cid. Bore and stroke: 4.125 x 3.4 inches. Compression ratio: 9.5:1. Brake horsepower: 250 at 4400 rpm. Five main bearings. Hydraulic valve lifters. Carburetor: Stromberg two-barrel, model 7-106 or Carter 2529 or 2536.

1957 Buick, Century Riviera two-door hardtop, V-8 (AA)

CENTURY — SERIES 60 — Buick's performance star was very similar to the Special in exterior trim, except for an identifying fourth ventiport on each front fender. Series designation was also found on the rear quarters or doors and within front and rear emblems. Interiors were plusher, with Rivieras upholstered in nylon/Cordaveen combinations and the Model 66C convertible being trimmed in Cordaveen and leather (Power windows and seats were standard on this model). Regular features, in addition to those found on the Special, included foam rubber seat cushions and an automatic trunk lamp.

CENTURY I.D. NUMBERS: Serial numbers were mixed with other 1957 Series (See 1957 Special ID Numbers above). Motor numbers were mixed in production.

CENTURY SERIES 60

Model Number	Body/Style Number	Body Type & Seating	Factory Price	Shipping Weight	Production Total
61	57-4669	4-dr Sed-6P	3316	4241	8,075
63	57-4639	4-dr HT-6P	3436	4267	26,589
66R	57-4637	2-dr HT Cpe-6P	3368	4182	17,029
66C	57-4667X	2-dr Conv Cpe-6P	3680	4302	4,085
69	57-4682	4-dr Sta Wag-6P	3831	4498	10,186

ENGINE: Specifications were the same as listed for the 1957 Special, except compression ratio was 10.0:1, brake horsepower was 300 at 4600 rpm (330 hp with high performance kit) and the four-barrel carburetor was a Carter 2507 or Rochester 7010070 (late — 7011570).

SUPER — SERIES 50 — The Super used a new C-Body treatment for 1957. Larger than the Series 40-60 bodies, the Riviera styles had different roof treatments as well. Supers had a group of three Chevrons on each rear quarter or door for series identification, in addition to the normal wording within the grille and deck emblems. Four ventiports were used on each front fender. Closed models were upholstered in Nylon/Cordaveen combinations, while the Model 56C convertible had an all-Cordaveen interior and featured power windows and seat controls as part of its equipment. Standard Super equipment approximated that of the Century.

SUPER I.D. NUMBERS: Serial numbers were mixed in 1957 production (see 1957 Special ID numbers above). Motor numbers were also mixed in production.

SUPER SERIES 50

Model Number	Body/Style Number	Body Type & Seating	Factory Price	Shipping Weight	Production Total
53	57-4539	4-dr HT-6P	3681	4356	41,665
56R	57-4537	2-dr HT Cpe-6P	3536	4271	26,529
56C	57-4567	2-dr Conv Cpe-6P	3981	4414	2,056

ENGINE: Specifications are the same as listed for the 1957 Century.

1957 Buick, Roadmaster two-door convertible, V-8 (AA)

ROADMASTER — SERIES 70 — The Roadmaster Rivieras featured a new body and revised rooflines, with chrome bands sweeping over the top and down division bars on the three-piece rear windows. Consumer resistance led to the optional deletion of these bars and substitution of a one-piece rear window (Models 73A and 76A). Roadmasters had four ventiports per fender. Two-door models had the trio of Chevrons on the rear quarters like the Super, but the four-door styles had a Roadmaster emblem nestled within the sweepspear's dip. Interiors were broadcloth and nylon in the four-door, nylon in the Rivieras and leather in the Model 76C convertible. A padded instrument panel was among the extra touches of luxury found in the Roadmaster.

ROADMASTER I.D. NUMBERS: Serial numbers were mixed in production with other 1957 series (see 1957 Special ID Numbers above). Motor numbers were mixed in production.

ROADMASTER SERIES 70

Model Number	Body/Style Number	Body Type & Seating	Factory Price	Shipping Weight	Production Total
73	57-4739	4-dr HT-6P	4053	4469	11,401
73A	57-4739A	4-dr HT-6P	4053	4455	10,526
76A	57-4737A	2-dr HT Cpe-6P	3944	4370	2,812
76R	57-4737	2-dr HT Cpe-6P	3944	4374	3,826
76C	57-4767X	2-dr Conv Cpe-6P	4066	4500	4,364

ENGINE: Specifications were the same as listed for the 1957 Century.

ROADMASTER 75 — SERIES 75 — A new line for 1957, introduced to cap the prestigious Roadmaster line. Both models used one-piece rear windows and differed from the Roadmaster only by the use of Roadmaster 75 script on the rear quarters or doors on the exterior. Inside, a plusher custom design interior was found. Roadmaster 75s included almost every power assist in their standard price, except for air conditioning.

ROADMASTER 75 I.D. NUMBERS: Serial numbers were mixed in production (see 1957 Special ID Numbers above). Motor numbers were mixed in production.

Model Number	Body/Style Number	Body Type & Seating	Factory Price	Shipping Weight	Production Total
75	57-4839	4-dr HT Sed	4483	4539	12,250
75R	57-4847	2-dr HT Cpe-6P	4373	4427	2,404

ENGINE: Specifications were the same as listed for the 1957 Century.

CHASSIS FEATURES: Wheelbase: (Series 40 and 60) 122 inches; (Series 50, 70 and 75) 127.5 inches. Overall length: (Series 40 and 60) 208.4 inches; (Series 50, 70 and 75) 215.3 inches. Front tread: (All) 59.5 inches. Rear tread: (Series 40 and 60) 59.5 inches; (Series 50, 70 and 75) 61.0 inches. Tires: (Series 40) 7.10 x 15; (Series 60 and 50) 7.60 x 15; (Series 70 and 75) 8.00 x 15.

POWERTRAIN OPTIONS: Three-speed manual standard on Series 40. Dynaflow optional at $220. Dynaflow standard on Series 50, 60, 70 and 75.

CONVENIENCE OPTIONS: Included Power steering ($107 — standard on Series 50 and 70). Air conditioning ($430). Spotlite. Carpet cover. Cushion topper. Dor-Gard. Rear seat speaker. Front bumper guards. Rear seat speaker. Sonomatic radio. Selectronic radio. Electric antenna. Seat belts. Tissue dispenser. Visor Vanity mirror. License frames. Padded instrument panel (standard Series 70). Six-way power seat.

HISTORICAL FOOTNOTES: Calendar year production was 407,271 units, a 24 percent decline. Buick dropped to fourth place in the industry, being passed by Plymouth in sales. Model year production was 405,086 units. Of all Buicks, 61.9 percent had power steering and 56.1 percent had power brakes. On July 7, 1957, the ninth millionth Buick was built. The 1957 Century was a bit slower than the '56. It did 0-to-60 in 10.1 seconds and covered the quarter-mile in 17.6 seconds. Body styles 57-4437, 57-4637, 57-4537 and 57-4737 are Riviera hardtop coupes. Styles 57-4439, 57-4539, 57-4639 and 57-4739 are Riviera hardtop sedans. Styles 57-4481 and 57-4482 are Estate wagons. Style 57-4682 is the Caballero station wagon.

1958 BUICK

1958 Buick, Special two-door Convertible Coupe, V-8 (AA)

SPECIAL — SERIES 40 — Bulkier, more heavily chromed styling adorned the 1958 Special chassis. New Lucite paints were used in many colors. For the first time since 1948, there were no distinguishing ventiports on Buick's front fenders. At the front a new "drawer-pull" grille, made up of rectangular chrome squares, was used. The Special name was spelled out across the deck lid, while a bright sweepspear and a large rear fender bright flash was similar to other models. All 1958 Buicks had four headlamps. Standard features on the Special included an ignition key light, glovebox, cigar lighter, trip mileage indicator, geared vent panes, bumper guards, variable-speed wipers, Step-On parking brake and on the Model 46C convertible an outside left-hand rearview mirror. Special interiors were trimmed with grey cloth and vinyl or Cordaveen and vinyl, or all Cordaveen in the convertible. A plusher Custom interior was available at extra cost.

SPECIAL I.D. NUMBERS: Serial numbers were located on the hinge pillar post and on dash under the hood. The first symbol was a number indicating series, as follows: 4 = Series 40 Special; 6 = Series 60 Century; 5 = Series 50 Super; 7 = Series 70 Roadmaster and 8 = Series 80 Limited or 4 = 4400 (Special); 6 = 4600 (Century); 7 = 4700 (Roadmaster) and 8 = (4800 Limited). The second symbol was a letter indicating year as follows: E=1958. The third symbol was a number indicating assembly plant: 1 = Flint, Mich.; 2 = Southgate, Calif.; 3 = Linden, N.J.; 4 = Kansas City, Kan.; 5 = Wilmington, Del.; 6 = Atlanta, Ga.; 7 =- Framingham, Mass.; 8 = Arlington, Tex. The remaining symbols represented the sequential production number. Serial numbers were mixed in production with other 1958 series. Numbers were: (Flint) 4EI000985 to 4EI09I650, (Calif.) 4E2001001 to 4E2020239, (N.J.) 4E3001001 to 4E3026555, (Kans.) 4E4001001 to 4E4031146, (Del.) 4E5001001 to 4E5022304, (Ga.) 4E6001001 to 4E6027283, (Mass.) 4E7001001 to 4E7011105 and (Tex.) 4E8001001 to 4E8019510.

SPECIAL SERIES

Model Number	Body/Style Number	Body Type & Seating	Factory Price	Shipping Weight	Production Total
41	584469	4-dr Sed-6P	2700	4115	48,238
43	584439	4-dr HT-6P	2820	4180	31,921
48	584411	2-dr Sed-6P	2636	4063	11,566
46R	584437	2-dr HT Cpe-6P	2744	4058	34,903
46C	584467	2-dr Conv Cpe-6P	3041	4165	5,502
49D	584482	4-dr Riv Sta Wag-6P	3265	4408	3,420
49	584481	4-dr Sta Wag-6P	3145	4396	3,663

ENGINE: V-8: Overhead valve. Cast iron block. Displacement: 364 cid. Bore and stroke: 4.25 x 3.4 inches. Compression ratio: 9.5:1. Brake horsepower: 250 at 4400 rpm. Five main bearings. Hydraulic valve lifters. Carburetors: Stromberg two-barrel Model WW7-109B — also — Carter two-barrel (with Synchro) Model 2674; (with Dynaflow) Model 2675.

1958 Buick, Century Caballero hardtop station wagon, V-8 (AA)

1958 Buick, Limited four-door hardtop sedan, V-8 (AA)

CENTURY — SERIES 60 — The Century shared the Special's bulky new sheetmetal and had as much plated brightwork. In addition to the Century name spelled out in block lettering on the deck lid, the 60 Series had Century script within the rear fender flashes. Standard equipment, in addition to features found on the Special, included Variable-Pitch Dynaflow, full wheelcovers, carpeting, padded dash, foam rubber cushions, electric clock and dual horns. Custom-interiors were trimmed in nylon, except for the Model 69 Estate Wagon, which was upholstered in Cordaveen. The model 46C convertible had electric windows and two-way seat controls.

CENTURY I.D. NUMBERS: Serial numbers were mixed with other 1958 Series (see 1958 Special ID Numbers above). Motor numbers were mixed in production.

CENTURY SERIES

Model Number	Body/Style Number	Body Type & Seating	Factory Price	Shipping Weight	Production Total
61	584669	4-dr Sed-6P	3316	4241	7,421
63	584639	4-dr HT-6P	3436	4267	15,171
66R	584637	2-dr HT-6P	3368	4182	8,110
66C	584667X	2-dr Conv Cpe-6P	3680	4302	2,588
69	584682	4-dr Sta Wag-6P	3831	4498	4,456

ENGINE: Specifications were the same as listed for the 1958 Special, except compression ratio was 10.0:1, brake horsepower was 300 at 4600 rpm and the four-barrel carburetor was a Carter model 2800 or Rochester models 7011600 or (late) 7013100.

SUPER — SERIES 50 — The once most popular Buick line was reduced to two models for 1958. Side trim was similar to lesser series, except for the Super lettering on the rear fender flashes, but Supers were longer than the Series 40 and 60 models. The Super name was also lettered across the deck lid. Standard equipment included Variable-Pitch Dynaflow, power steering, power brakes, a safety-cushion instrument panel, fully carpeted floor, courtesy lights and other items found on lesser models.

SUPER I.D. NUMBERS: Serial numbers were mixed in 1958 production (see 1958 Special ID Numbers above). Motor numbers were also mixed in production.

SUPER SERIES

Model Number	Body/Style Number	Body Type & Seating	Factory Price	Shipping Weight	Production Total
53	584539	4-dr HT-6P	3789	4500	28,460
56R	584537	2-dr HT-6P	3644	4392	13,928

ENGINE: Specifications were the same as listed for the 1958 Century.

ROADMASTER — SERIES 75 — The Roadmaster carried all the brightwork of the Super and added bright wheelhouse moldings, a ribbed rocker panel molding and ribbed inserts to the rear fender flashes. All 1958 Roadmasters were in the 75 series, as attested by the script and numerals on the fender flashes. On the rear deck, Roadmaster was spelled out in block lettering beneath a Buick emblem housing the trunk lock keyway. Standard Roadmaster features, in addition to those found on lesser Buicks, included power windows, a power six-way front seat, safety cushion dash, carpeted floors and lower doors, Glare-proof rearview mirror, safety buzzer, brake warning light and Deluxe wheelcovers. Interiors were cloth or cloth and leather except for the convertible, trimmed in all leather.

ROADMASTER I.D. NUMBERS: Serial numbers were mixed in production with other 1958 Series (see 1958 Special ID Numbers above). Motor numbers were mixed in production.

ROADMASTER SERIES

Model Number	Body/Style Number	Body Type & Seating	Factory Price	Shipping Weight	Production Total
75	584739X	4-dr HT-6P	4667	4668	10,505
75R	584737X	2-dr HT-6P	4557	4568	2,368
75C	584767X	2-dr Conv Cpe-6P	4680	4676	1,181

ENGINE: Specifications were the same as listed for the 1958 Century.

LIMITED — SERIES 700 — Buick resurrected a grand old nameplate for a new extra-long luxury line in 1958. Twelve vertical louvers, set within the rear fenders' rocket-like trim motif, distinguished the Limited. All the chrome associated with other 1958 Buicks was present as well. The Limited had its own massive, louvered taillamps. Limited script was found on the rear doors or quarters, and a Buick badge flanked by four chrome bars was found on the Limited, which featured ultra-plush cloth, cloth and leather and in the case of the Model 756 Convertible, all-leather upholstery.

LIMITED I.D. NUMBERS: Serial numbers were mixed in production with other 1958 series (see 1958 Special ID Numbers above). Motor numbers were mixed in production.

LIMITED SERIES

Model Number	Body/Style Number	Body Type & Seating	Factory Price	Shipping Weight	Production Total
750	584839X	4-dr HT-6P	5112	4710	5,571
755	584837X	2-dr HT-6P	5002	4691	1,026
756	584867X	2-dr Conv Cpe-6P	5125	4603	839

ENGINE: Specifications were the same as listed for the 1958 Century.

CHASSIS FEATURES: Wheelbase: (Series 40 and 60) 122 inches; (Series 50, 75 and 700) 127.5 inches. Overall length: (Series 40 and 60) 211.8 inches; (Series 50 and 75) 219.1 inches; (Series 700) 227.1 inches. Front tread: (Series 40, 60 and 50) 59.5 inches; (Series 75 and 700) 60 inches. Rear tread: (Series 40, 60 and 50) 59 inches. (Series 75 and 700) 61 inches. Tires: (Series 40) 7.10 x 15 (Models 46C and 49) 7.60 x 15; (Series 60 and 50) 7.60 x 15; (Series 75 and 700) 8.00 x 15.

POWERTRAIN OPTIONS: Three-speed manual standard on Series 40. Variable-Pitch Dynaflow optional at $220. Variable-Pitch Dynaflow standard on Series 60 and 50. Flight Pitch Dynaflow standard on Series 75 and 700, optional on other series ($296 Series 40, $75 — Series 60 and 50). Dual exhausts optional.

CONVENIENCE OPTIONS: Power steering ($108 — standard Series 50, 75. 700). Power brakes (standard Series 50, 75, 700). Air Poise air suspension. In-dash or under-dash air conditioning. Sonomatic radio. Wonder Bar signal-seeking radio. Power windows (standard Model 66C, all Series 75 and 700). Perimeter heater/defroster. Autronic Eye. Electric radio antenna. Windshield washer (standard Series 75 and 700). E-Z Eye glass. Safety group — back-up lights, lower instrument panel pad, parking brake warning light, glare-proof inside rearview mirror (standard on Series 75 and 700). Upper instrument panel pad (for Series 40, standard other series). Six-way power seat (standard Series 75, 700). Series 40 accessory group-electric clock, full wheelcovers, automatic trunk light, rear license frame.

HISTORICAL FOOTNOTES: Calendar year production was 257,124 units. Buick slid into fifth rank in the industry, with Oldsmobile capturing fourth. Model year production was 241,892 units, for a 5.7 percent market share. The four millionth Dynaflow transmission was built and 98.5 percent of all Buicks had this feature; 97.6 percent had heaters and 87.6 percent had radios. The one millionth Buick power brake installation was made. Buick dealers were authorized to sell the German Opel. A special "Tales of Wells Fargo" Buick with a western motif was built for actor Dale Robertson. It still exists today in the collection of Wally Rank, a Milwaukee, Wis. Buick dealer. Body styles 584437, 584637, 584537, 584737 and 584837X are Riviera coupes. Styles 584439, 584639, 584539, 584739, and 584839X are Riviera sedans. Styles 584482 and 584682 are Riviera Estate Wagons. An X in the style designation indicates electric controls of the windows, front seat, and in convertibles, the top.

1959 BUICK

LESABRE — SERIES 4400 — New series names and totally new styling greeted the 1959 Buick buyer. These were the wildest Buicks yet, with blade fins sweeping from the front of the body rearward. One of the few continued hallmarks from 1958 was the grille made up of rectangular squares. On the sides, bright trim strips ran the length of the LeSabre body. Taillights were low and round. Interiors were trimmed in Barbary cloth and Cordaveen, except on Models 4467 and 4435, which were all-Cordaveen. An optional Balfour Cloth and Cordaveen Custom combination was offered on all, except the convertible and station wagon. Standard LeSabre equipment included a glovebox light, dual horns, electric wipers, horizontal Red Liner speedometer, trip mileage indicator and an outside rearview mirror on the Model 4467 Convertible.

LESABRE I.D. NUMBERS: Serial numbers were located on the hinge pillar post and on dash under the hood. The first symbol was a number indicating series, as follows: 4 = 4400 (LeSabre); 6 = 4600 (Invicta); 7 = 4700 (Electra) and 8 = 4800 (Electra 225). The second symbol was a letter indicating year as follows: F=1959. The third symbol was a number indicating assembly plant: 1 = Flint, Mich.; 2 = Southgate, Calif.; 3 = Linden, N.J.; 4 = Kansas City, Kan.; 5 = Wilmington, Del.; 6 = Atlanta, Ga.; 7 = Framingham, Mass.; 8 = Arlington, Tex. The remaining symbols represented the sequential production number. Serial numbers began with 4F1001001.

LESABRE SERIES

Series Number	Model Number	Body Type & Seating	Factory Price	Shipping Weight	Production Total
4400	4419	4-dr Sed-6P	2804	4229	51,379
4400	4439	4-dr HT-6P	2925	4266	46,069
4400	4411	2-dr Sed-6P	2740	4159	13,492
4400	4437	2-dr HT-6P	2849	4188	35,189
4400	4467	2-dr Conv Cpe-6P	3129	4216	10,489
4400	4435	4-dr Sta Wag-6P	3320	4565	8,286

ENGINE: V-8. Overhead valve. Cast iron block. Displacement: 364 cid. Bore and stroke: 4.25 x 3.4 inches. Compression ratio: 10.5:1. Brake horsepower: 250 at 4400 rpm. Five main bearings. Hydraulic lifters. Carburetor: Stromberg two-barrel Model WW7112A or Carter two-barrels (with Synchromesh) model 2847; (with Dynaflow) Model 2838 or Rochester two-barrel model 7019042.

INVICTA — SERIES 4600 — Replacing the Century Series 60 for 1959 was this new performance line. The exterior was distinguished by a bright rocker panel molding and Invicta scripts on the front fenders. Inside, standard trim was Balfour cloth in a more intricate weave than the LeSabre and in four color combinations. The Estate Wagon was trimmed in Saran Balfour and Cordaveen, and the convertible was upholstered in all-Cordaveen. Standard equipment on the Invicta, in addition to features found on the LeSabre, included Foamtex seat cushions, electric clock, Deluxe steering wheel, full wheelcovers, and an instrument panel cover.

INVICTA I.D. NUMBERS: Serial numbers were distinguished by the use of the numeral '6' as the first symbol of the number. The rest of the number was coded as explained under the 1959 LeSabre ID Number section above.

1959 Buick, Invicta four-door hardtop sedan, V-8 (AA)

INVICTA SERIES

Series Number	Model Number	Body Type & Seating	Factory Price	Shipping Weight	Production Total
4600	4619	4-dr Sed-6P	3357	4331	10,566
4600	4639	4-dr HT-6P	3515	4373	20,156
4600	4637	2-dr HT-6P	3447	4274	11,451
4600	4667	2-dr Conv Cpe-6P	3620	4317	5,447
4600	4635	4-dr Sta Wag-6P	3841	4660	5,231

ENGINE: V-8: Overhead valve. Cast iron block. Displacement: 401 cid. Bore and stroke: 4.1875 x 3.64 inches. Compression ratio: 10.5:1. Brake horsepower: 325 at 4400 rpm. Five main bearings. Hydraulic lifters. Carburetor: Carter four-barrel model 2840 or Rochester four-barrel model 7013044-15900.

ELECTRA — SERIES 4700 — A Roadmaster by another name, the Electra was trimmed with bright rocker moldings, wheelhouse moldings and Electra script on the front fenders, in addition to the brightwork found on other Buicks. Standard features, in addition to those found on lower-priced Buicks, included a Safety Pad dash, power steering, power brakes, two-speed electric wipers, and dual exhausts. Interiors were plusher, being trimmed in nylon Mojave cloth or Broadcloth combinations with Cordaveen.

ELECTRA I.D. NUMBERS: Serial numbers were distinguished by the use of the numeral '7' as the first symbol of the number. The rest of the number was coded as explained under the 1959 LeSabre ID Numbers section above.

ELECTRA SERIES

Series Number	Model Number	Body Type & Seating	Factory Price	Shipping Weight	Production Total
4700	4719	4-dr Sed-6P	3856	4557	12,357
4700	4739	4-dr HT-6P	3963	4573	20,612
4700	4737	2-dr Conv Cpe-6P	3818	4465	11,216

ENGINE: Specifications are the same as those listed for the 1959 Invicta.

1959 Buick, Electra 225 two-door convertible, V-8 (AA)

ELECTRA 225 — SERIES 4800 — The First Electra 225 (with the 225 coming from the overall length of this stretched-body luxury car) was a big Buick. Exterior distinction came from extra-wide moldings, with a massive Electra emblem on the front fender extension. Electra 225 script was found on the front fenders, ahead of the wheelhouse. The four-door models had a lower bright rear fender molding, as well. Standard features, in addition to those found on lesser Buicks, included plusher interiors (leather in the convertible), power windows and top for the convertible, Safety group, Super Deluxe wheelcovers and an outside rearview mirror.

ELECTRA 225 I.D. NUMBERS: Serial numbers were distinguished by the use of the number '8' as the first symbol of the number. The rest of the number was coded as explained under the 1959 LeSabre ID Numbers section above.

ELECTRA 225 SERIES

Series Number	Model Number	Body Type & Seating	Factory Price	Shipping Weight	Production Total
4800	4829	4-dr Sed-6P	4300	4632	6,324
4800	4839	4-dr HT-6P	4300	4641	10,491
4800	4867	2-dr Conv Cpe-6P	4192	4562	5,493

ENGINE: Specifications were the same as those listed for the 1959 Invicta.

CHASSIS FEATURES: Wheelbase: (Series 4400 and 4600) 123 inches; (Series 4700 and 4800) 126.3 inches. Overall length: (Series 4400 and 4600) 217.4 inches; (Series 4700 and 4800) 220.6 inches; (Series 4800 225.4 inches). Front tread: (All series) 62 inches. Rear tread: (All series) 60 inches. Tires: (Series 4400 and 4600) 7.60 x 15; (Series 4700 and 4800) 8.00 x 15 tubeless.

POWERTRAIN OPTIONS: A three-speed manual transmission was standard on Series 4400, Twin Turbine Dynaflow (standard on Series 4600, 4700, 4800) was optional at $220. Triple Turbine Dynaflow was optional on all Series at $296 on Series 4400 and $75 on all others. A Positive Traction differential was offered.

CONVENIENCE OPTIONS: Power steering and power brakes were optional on Series 4400 models (with automatic transmission only) and on Series 4600 models. Both features were standard on Series 4700 and 4800 models. Air conditioning. Power seat (except Style 441 1). Safety Pad dash on Series 4400. Heater/Defroster. Automatic heat fresh air control. Wonderbar signal-seeking radio. Transistor portable radio. Sonomatic radio. Electric antenna. Rear seat speaker. Speed control safety buzzer. Deluxe steering wheel on Series 4400. Deluxe wheelcovers on Series 4400. Super Deluxe wheelcovers on Series 4400, 4600, 4700. Two-speed electric wipers on Series 4400 and 4600. E-Z-Eye glass (windshield only or all glass). Bucket seats (Electric 225 convertible only). Power windows. Power vents. Autronic Eye. Electric rear window for Estate Wagon. Junior third seat for Estate Wagon. Safety Group — safety buzzer, back-up lights, glare-proof inside rearview mirror, parking brake warning light, and map light (standard Series 4800). Accessory group for Series 4400 — electric clock, trunk light, license frame.

HISTORICAL FOOTNOTES: The 1959 Buick was called "The Year's Most Changed Car." Calendar year output was 232,579. Model year production hit 285,089, for a 5.1 percent share of market. Of all Buicks built in 1959, 11 percent were convertibles. A 1959 Buick served as Indy 500 pace car. In the spring, Ed Ragsdale retired and Edward T. Rollert was named Buick general manager. The two millionth Buick hardtop was presented to Sarah Ragsdale upon her husband's retirement. The one millionth Opel was imported by Buick in May, 1959. The Wildcat III show car was seen this season. Models 4435 and 4635 are Estate Wagons. Model 4829 is the Riviera sedan.

1960 BUICK

1960 Buick, LeSabre four-door sedan, V-8 (AA)

LESABRE — SERIES 4400 — Buick rounded and softened the lines of its 1960 models. Clipping the wild fins of 1959 gave the car a shortened, heavier appearance. Ventiports returned for 1960, with a trio of the highly stylized ornaments on each LeSabre front fender. Series identification was further enhanced by LeSabre name bars on each front fender ahead of the wheelhouse. A bright lower body molding accented the car's other bright metal. Interiors were of Cordaveen and cloth (all-Cordaveen on the station wagon). A plusher Custom interior featuring deep-pile carpeting, padded instrument panel, Deluxe door handles, window cranks and armrests, was optional. Standard features of all Specials included Mirromatic adjustable speedometer, electric windshield wipers, trip mileage indicator, cigar lighter, dual sunshades, Step-On parking brake, dual horns and a single-key locking system.

LESABRE I.D. NUMBERS: Serial numbers were located on the hinge pillar post, left side, above instrument panel. Serial numbers began with 4G( )001001. The first symbol identified the series, as follows: 4=4400; 6=4600; 7=4700 and 8=4800. The second symbol was a letter indicating model year, G for the 1960 model year. The third symbol was a number indicating the assembly plant code, as follows: 1=Flint, Mich.; 2=Southgate, Calif.; 3=Linden, N.J.; 4=Kansas City, Kan.; 5=Wilmington, Del.; 6=Atlanta, Ga.; 7=Framingham, Mass.; 8=Arlington, Texas. The last six symbols are the numerical sequence of the assembly at the coded plant, with series mixed in production. Engine numbers were stamped in various locations on crankcase, usually, or cylinder block. Engine production codes were stamped on right side of engine block. Engine codes were as follows: 3G=364 cid/210 or 250 or 300 hp; L3G=364 cid/235 hp; 4G=401 cid/325 hp.

Series Number	Model Number	Body Type & Seating	Factory Price	Shipping Weight	Production Total
4400	4419	4-dr Sed-6P	2870	4219	54,033
4400	4439	4-dr HT-6P	2991	4269	35,999
4400	4411	2-dr Sed-6P	2756	4139	14,388
4400	4437	2-dr HT-6P	2915	4163	26,521
4400	4467	2-dr Conv Cpe-6P	3145	4233	13,588
4400	4445	4-dr Sta Wag-8P	3493	4574	2,222
4400	4435	4-dr Sta Wag-6P	3386	4568	5,331

ENGINE: V-8. Overhead valve. Cast iron block. Displacement: 364 cid. Bore and stroke: 4.125 x 3.4 inches. Compression ratio: 10.25:1. Brake horsepower: 250 at 4400 rpm. Five main bearings. Hydraulic lifters. Carburetor: two-barrels. Stromberg model WW7-1 1A; Carter model 2979 (syncromesh) or model 2980 (automatic); or Rochester model 7019042.

INVICTA — SERIES 4600 — "The most spirited Buick," said the sales catalog of the Invicta. Wearing three ventiports per front fender, the Invicta had all of the LeSabre's brightwork plus bright metal wheelhouse moldings. The front fender plaques carried Invicta lettering, of course. Interiors were cloth and Cordaveen with all-Cordaveen color-coordinated trim optional (standard in the convertible). Station wagon styles were trimmed in Saran cloth and Cordaveen. Standard Invicta features in addition to those found on the LeSabre included Twin Turbine automatic transmission, Foamtex seat cushions, electric clock, trunk light, Deluxe steering wheel, Deluxe wheelcovers, license plate frames and a glovebox light.

1960 Buick, Invicta four-door station wagon, V-8

INVICTA I.D. NUMBERS: Serial numbers were distinguished by the use of the numeral '6' as the first symbol of the number. The rest of the number was coded as explained under the 1960 LeSabre Series 4400 ID Number section.

INVICTA SERIES

Series Number	Model Number	Body Type & Seating	Factory Price	Shipping Weight	Production Total
4600	4619	4-dr Sed-6P	3357	4324	10,839
4600	4639	4-dr HT-6P	3515	4365	15,300
4600	4637	2-dr HT-6P	3447	4255	8,960
4600	4667	2-dr Conv Cpe-6P	3620	4347	5,236
4600	4645	4-dr Sta Wag-8P	3948	4679	1,605
4600	4635	4-dr Sta Wag-6P	3841	4644	3,471

ENGINE: V-8. Overhead valve. Cast iron block. Displacement: 401 cid. Bore and stroke: 4.1875 x 3.640 inches. Compression ratio: 10.25:1. Brake horsepower: 325 at 4400 rpm. Five main bearings. Hydraulic lifters. Carburetor: four-barrel Carter model 29825 or Rochester 7015040.

ELECTRA — SERIES 4700 — A larger Buick, identified by its four ventiports per front fender, had wider rocker panel bright moldings and the Electra script on the front tenders, ahead of the wheelhouse. Electras had plusher cloth and Cordaveen interiors and featured power steering, power brakes and all the features found on the Invicta and LeSabre models as standard.

ELECTRA I.D. NUMBERS: Serial numbers were distinguished by the use of the numeral '7' as the first symbol of the number. The rest of the number was coded as explained under the 1960 LeSabre 4400 ID Number section.

ELECTRA SERIES

Series Number	Model Number	Body Type & Seating	Factory Price	Shipping Weight	Production Total
4700	4719	4-dr Sed-6P	3856	4544	13,794
4700	4739	4-dr HT-6P	3963	4554	14,488
4700	4737	2-dr HT-6P	3818	4453	7,416

ENGINE: Specifications were the same as those listed for the 1960 Invicta.

ELECTRA 225 — SERIES 4800 — Buick's plushest, fanciest model was outstanding this year with its broad, ribbed, lower body bright trim panels. An Electra 225 badge was circled on the deck lid. The Electra 225 name was found on front fenders. Brisbane cloth interiors graced closed models while the convertible was trimmed in leather, with bucket seats for front passenger optional. All of Buick's standard features were found on the Electra, plus back-up lights, a glare proof rearview mirror, parking brake signal light, safety buzzer, map light, Super Deluxe wheelcovers and a two-way power seat adjuster and power windows for the convertible.

ELECTRA 225 I.D. NUMBERS: Serial numbers were distinguished by the use of the numeral '8' as the first symbol of the number. The rest of the number was coded as explained under the 1960 LeSabre Series 4400 ID Number section.

1960 Buick, Electra 225, four-door hardtop sedan, V-8 (AA)

ELECTRA 225 SERIES

Series Number	Model Number	Body Type & Seating	Factory Price	Shipping Weight	Production Total
4800	4829	4-dr Sed-6P	4300	4653	8,029
4800	4839	4-dr HT-6P	4300	4650	4,841
4800	4867	2-dr Conv Cpe-6P	4192	4571	6,746

ENGINE: Specifications were the same as those listed for the 1960 Invicta.

CHASSIS FEATURES: Wheelbase (4400/4600) 123 inches; (4700) 126.3 inches; (4800) 126.3 inches. Overall length: (4400/4600) 217.9 inches; (4700) 221.2 inches; (4800) 225.9 inches. Front tread: (all) 62.2 inches. Rear tread: (all) 60 inches. Tires: (4400/4600) 7.60 x 15; (4700/4800) 8.00 x 15.

POWER TRAIN OPTIONS: A regular fuel Wildcat 375E V-8 was optional on Series 4400 models. This engine featured a 9.1:1 compression ratio and produced 235 brake horsepower at 4400 rpm and cost $52 extra. A high-performance Wildcat 405 four-barrel V-8 was also optional on Series 4400 models with three-speed manual transmission. This combination featured 300 horsepower at 4400 rpm and cost $220 additional. (Buick's engine ID numbers were based on the torque rating, rather than the horsepower rating.)

CONVENIENCE OPTIONS: Power steering was standard on Series 4700 and 4800 models and optional on Series 4400 and 4600 models ($108). Power brakes were standard on Series 4700 and 4800 models, optional on others. ($43). Air conditioning ($430). Twilight Sentinel automatic headlamp dimmer ($29). Tissue dispenser. Compass. Visor vanity mirror. Trunk mat (plastic foam-backed). Deluxe handy mats. Litter basket. Six-Way power seat ($52-103). Six/Two-Way Power seat ($69). Four-Way power seat ($65). Two-Way power seat ($37). Bucket seats ($108). Power vent windows ($54). Power windows ($108). Sonotone radio with manual antenna ($99); with electric antenna ($121). Wonder Bar radio with manual antenna ($135); with electric antenna ($158). Rear seat speaker ($17). Guidematic ($43). Deluxe steering wheel on LeSabre ($16). Deluxe wheelcovers on LeSabre ($19). Super Deluxe wheelcovers ($17-37). Heater and defroster ($99). Easy Eye glass ($29-43). White sidewall tires. Custom exterior moldings ($13-41). Station wagon electric rear window ($27). Station wagon luggage rack ($100). Standard two-tone finish ($16-43). Special order two-toning ($97). Dual exhausts ($31). Turbine Drive transmission ($220). Dual-speed windshield washers/wipers ($19). Accessory group including trunk compartment light, electric clock and license plate frame for LeSabre ($22). Safety accessory group including Glare-Proof mirror. back-up lights, parking brake warning signal and safety buzzer light for 4400-4600-4700 Series ($34).

HISTORICAL FOOTNOTES: Calendar year production was 307,804 for a 4.65 percent share of market, putting Buick in ninth place. It was the lowest industry ranking for the company since 1905! Model year production was 253,999 units or 4.2 percent of the industry total. Buick firsts for 1960 included a K-type Buick chassis, Twilight Sentinel, Mirrormagic adjustable angle instrument dials and separate heater controls for rear seat passengers. A 1960 Buick was taken to the Daytona Beach Speedway and run for three-and-a-half days (10,000 miles) at an average of 120.12 mph. At times the car hit over 130 mph. After this impressive performance feat, Buick decided not to advertise or promote the results of the trial, due to the Automobile Manufacturer's Assoc. (AMA) ban on high-performance advertising. Models 4435, 4445, 4635 and 4645 are Estate Wagons. Model 4829 is the Riviera sedan.

1961 BUICK

1961 Buick, Special four-door sedan, V-8 (AA)

SPECIAL — SERIES 4000 STANDARD 4100 AND 4300 DELUXE — Buick's new quality car in a small package immediately found an enthusiastic following. Styling was related to the larger 1961 Buicks. Specials had three ventiport appliques per front fender. Trim was minimal on the Special. Standard features of the Special included dual sun visors, dual armrests, cigar lighter and electric windshield wipers. The base Special was trimmed in cloth and vinyl. Deluxe models had richer Custom interiors of cloth and vinyl (all-vinyl in the station wagon), plush carpeting, rear armrests, rear ashtrays and a Deluxe steering wheel. They were distinguished by Custom exterior moldings, which included a highlight bright strip on the upper body. A midyear Skylark Sport Coupe was added (Model 4317) that featured unique taillamp housings, additional lower body bright moldings and Turbine wheelcovers. An even plusher all-vinyl interior, came with optional bucket front seats and unique taillamp housings. A vinyl top was standard.

SPECIAL I.D. NUMBERS: Serial numbers were located on the hinge pillar post, left side, above instrument panel. They were also stamped on the top surface of the engine block, left side, ahead of valve cover. Serial numbers began with OH( ) 501001-up. The first symbol indicated series, as follows: 0=4000; 1=4100; or 3=4300. The second symbol was a letter indicating model year, H=1961. The third symbol was a number indicating the plant code, as follows: 1=Flint, Mich.; 2=Southgate, Calif.; 3=Linden, N.J.; 4=Kansas City, Kan.; 5=Wilmington, Del.; 6=Atlanta, Ga.; 8=Arlington, Texas. The last six symbols were the numerical sequence of assembly at the coded plant, with series mixed in production. Engine production codes stamped upside down on right front of engine block, opposite serial number. Production codes were as follows: (Special) 215 cid V-8 = H, LH; (Special Del.) Same; (Skylark) same.

SPECIAL STANDARD MODELS

Series Number	Model Number	Body Type & Seating	Factory Price	Shipping Weight	Production Total
4000	4019	4-dr Sed-6P	2384	2610	18,339
4000	4027	2-dr Spt Cpe-6P	2330	2579	4,232
4000	4035	4-dr Sta Wag-6P	2681	2775	6,101
4000	4045	4-dr Sta Wag-8P	2762	2844	798

SPECIAL DELUXE MODELS

Series Number	Model Number	Body Type & Seating	Factory Price	Shipping Weight	Production Total
4100	4119	4-dr Sed-6P	2519	2632	32,986
4100	4135	4-dr Sta Wag-6P	2816	2794	11,729
4300	4317	2-dr Spt Cpe-5P	2621	2687	12,683

ENGINE: V-8. Overhead valve. Cast aluminum block. Displacement: 215 cid. Bore and stroke: 3.50 x 2.80 inches. Compression ratio: 8.8: 1. Brake horsepower 155 at 4600 rpm. Five main bearings. Hydraulic lifters. Carburetor: two-barrel Rochester model 7019090 (automatic) or model 7019093 (manual).

NOTE: Skylark was equipped with four-barrel Rochester model 7020043 (automatic) or model 7020045 (manual) and had 10.25:1 compression ratio, 185 brake horsepower.

LESABRE — SERIES 4400 — A new slimmer and trimmer image was presented by Buick's sales leading series for 1961. Body sculpturing allowed for a relatively light application of exterior brightwork, with a single narrow bright molding along the upper body. LeSabre script was found on the front fenders, along with three ventiports. Turbine drive automatic transmission was standard on the 1961 LeSabre, along with a revised Mirromagic instrument panel, direction signals, full-flow oil filter, electric windshield wipers, a Deluxe steering wheel, trip mileage indicator, cigar lighter, Step-On brake, dual armrests, cloth and vinyl trim combinations and carpeting on some models. Estate station wagons had a standard all-vinyl interior, with cloth and vinyl optional. A power rear window was standard on the three-seat Estate Wagon.

1961 Buick, LeSabre four-door hardtop sedan, V-8 (AA)

LESABRE I.D. NUMBERS: Buick serial numbers were located on the hinge pillar post, left side, above instrument panel and on top surface of engine block, ahead of valve cover on left. The first symbol indicated series, as follows: (LeSabre) 4=4400; (Invicta) 6=4600; (Electra) 7=4700; and (Electra 225) 8=4800. The second symbol was a letter indicating model year, H=1961. The third symbol was a number indicating the plant code, as follows: 1=Flint, Mich.; 2=Southgate, Calif.; 3=Linden, N.J.; 4=Kansas City, Kan.; 5=Wilmington, Del.; 6=Atlanta, Ga.; 8=Arlington, Texas. The last six symbols are the numerical sequence of assembly at the coded plant, with series mixed in sequence. Engine production codes stamped upside down on right front of block opposite serial number. Engine production codes are as follows: (LeSabre) 364 cid V-8=3H or L3H; (Invicta/Electra) 401 cid V-8=4H or 4LH.

LESABRE SERIES

Series Number	Model Number	Body Type & Seating	Factory Price	Shipping Weight	Production Total
4400	4469	4-dr Sed-6P	3107	4102	35,005
4400	4439	4-dr HT-6P	3228	4129	37,790
4400	4411	2-dr Sed-6P	2993	4033	5,959
4400	4437	2-dr HT-6P	3152	4054	14,474
4400	4467	2-dr Conv Cpe-6P	3382	4186	11,971
4400	4435	4-dr Sta Wag-6P	3623	4450	5,628
4400	4445	4-dr Sta Wag-9P	3730	4483	2,423

ENGINE: V-8. Overhead valve. Cast iron block. Displacement: 364 cid. Bore and stroke: 4.25 x 3.4 inches. Compression ratio: 10.25:1. Brake horsepower: 250 at 4400 rpm. Five main bearings. Hydraulic lifters. Carburetor: Carter model 3089 four-barrel.

INVICTA — SERIES 4600 — Buick's slightly sportier performance line was graced with double belt moldings, in 1961, to set it apart from the LeSabre, with which it shared three ventiports per front fender. Invicta nameplates were used on each front fender, as well as the rear deck. Full wheelcovers, an electric clock, automatic trunk light and license frame were additional standard features of the Invicta over lesser models. Standard trim was cloth and vinyl, except for the Convertible which was all-vinyl. An optional Custom interior featured leather trim, while another featured vinyl with contrasting vertical stripes and front bucket seats with a storage consolex and power two-way seat adjustment.

INVICTA I.D. NUMBERS: Serial numbers were distinguished by the use of the numeral '6' as the first symbol of the number. The rest of the number was coded as explained under the 1961 LeSabre ID Number section.

1961 Buick, Invicta two-door hardtop coupe, V-8 (AA)

INVICTA SERIES

Series Number	Model Number	Body Type & Seating	Factory Price	Shipping Weight	Production Total
4600	4639	4-dr HT-6P	3515	4179	18,398
4600	4637	2-dr HT-6P	3447	4090	6,382
4600	4667	2-dr Conv Cpe-6P	3620	4206	3,953

ENGINE: V-8. Overhead valve. Cast iron block. Displacement: 401 cid. Bore and stroke: 4.1875 x 3.640 inches. Compression ratio: 10.25:1. Brake horsepower: 325 at 4400 rpm. Five main bearings. Hydraulic lifters. Carburetor: four-barrel Carter model 3088S.

ELECTRA — SERIES 4700 — Buick's first step up to the larger models featured bright rocker panel and wheelhouse moldings for 1961. Four ventiports per front fender were a hallmark, with identification spelled out on the front fender plaques. Interiors were trimmed in fabric. Standard Electra features included those of lower-priced Buicks, plus power steering, power brakes, a two-speed windshield wiper/washer system, glovebox light, Custom-padded seat cushions and Deluxe wheelcovers. Two-tone Electras had a color accent on the rear cove.

ELECTRA I.D. NUMBERS: Serial numbers were distinguished by the use of the numeral '7' as the first symbol of the number. The rest of the number was coded as explained under the 1961 LeSabre ID Number section.

ELECTRA SERIES 4700

Series Number	Model Number	Body Type & Seating	Factory Price	Shipping Weight	Production Total
4700	4719	4-dr Sed-6P	3825	4298	13,818
4700	4739	4-dr HT-6P	3932	4333	8,978
4700	4737	2-dr HT-6P	3818	4260	4,250

ENGINE: Specifications were the same as those listed for the 1961 Invicta.

1961 Buick, Electra 225 two-door convertible, V-8 (AA)

ELECTRA 225 — SERIES 4800 — Buick's plushest model had a wide strip of bright trim along the lower body, with vertical "hash marks" interrupting behind the wheelhouse of the rear fender. Electra 225 nameplates were found on the front fenders. Calais cloth or leather trim was found inside. Standard equipment was the same as the Electra except for the addition of back-up lights, Glare-proof rearview mirror, Parking brake signal light, safety buzzer, courtesy lights, two-way power seat, Super Deluxe wheelcovers with gold accents and power windows.

ELECTRA 225 I.D. NUMBERS: Serial numbers were distinguished by the use of the numeral '8' as the first symbol of the number. The rest of the number was coded as explained under the 1961 LeSabre ID Number section.

ELECTRA SERIES 4800

Model Number	Body/Style Number	Body Type & Seating	Factory Price	Shipping Weight	Production Total
4800	4829	4-dr HT Sed-6P	4350	4417	13,719
800	4867	2-dr Conv Cpe-6P	4192	4441	7,158

ENGINE: Specifications were the same as listed for the 1961 Invicta.

CHASSIS FEATURES: Wheelbase: (4000, 4100 and 4300) 112 inches; (4400 and 4600) 123 inches; (4700 and 4800) 126 inches. Overall length: (4000, 4100 and 4300) 188.4 inches; (4400 and 4600) 213.2 inches; (4700 and 4800) 219.2 inches. Front tread: (Special) 56 inches; (Others) 62 inches. Rear tread: (Special) 56 inches; (Others) 61 inches. Tires: (400, 4100 and 4300) 6.50 x l3; (4400 and 4600) 7.60 x 15; (4700 and 4800 8.00 x 15.

POWER TRAIN OPTIONS: A three-speed manual transmission was standard on Series 4000, 4100 and 4300. Dual-path Turbine Drive was optional at $189. A four-speed manual transmission was also an option for the Series 4300 Skylark. A regular fuel V-8 was optional for the Series 4400 and was the same basic 364 cid engine with two-barrel carburetor, 9.0:1 compression and 235 brake horsepower at 4400 rpm. Dual exhausts were standard on the Series 4700 two-door hardtop and Series 4800 Convertible, optional on all other full-size models. Positive traction differential was offered.

CONVENIENCE OPTIONS included Power steering on 4000, 4100, 4300 ($86); and 4400-4600 ($108-standard on 4700 and 4800). Power brakes ($43, standard with 4700 and 4800). Air conditioning ($378 on 4000-4100-4300; $430 on full-size models). Size 7.00 x 13 tires on 4300. Power windows ($108, standard on 4800). Four-way power seat adjustment ($65). Sonotone radio ($90). Wonderbar radio ($127). Twilight Sentinel ($29). Guide-matic dimmer ($43). Heater/Defroster ($99). Deluxe Special wheelcovers ($15). Back-up lights (standard on 4800). Cool-Pak air conditioning on 4000, 4100 and 4300. Luggage rack on Estate Wagons ($100). Power rear window on six-passenger Estate Wagon ($27).

HISTORICAL FOOTNOTES: The big news of 1961 was the return of the Special name. It was also the first time, since 1907, that Buicks did not have torque tube drive and the first time, since 1934, that the accelerator was not mounted on the starter. Calendar year production was 291,895 units for a 5.28 market share. Model year production was 277,422 units for a 5.1 percent share of industry output. Buick held the eigth place in popularity. Model 4829 was the Riviera sedan. Models 4435 and 4445 were Estate Wagons.

1962 BUICK

SPECIAL — SERIES 4000 — The second edition of Buick's compact Special was little changed from the 1961 version. Once again the basic Special had no bright side trim except for three ventiports per front fender and a Special script ahead of the front wheelhouses. Small hubcaps were standard, as were dual sun visors, dual armrests, cigar lighter and electric windshield wipers, directional signals, heater and defroster and outside rearview mirror on convertible. Interiors were cloth and vinyl.

SPECIAL I.D. NUMBERS: Serial numbers were on the hinge pillar post, left side, above instrument panel and stamped on left side, top of engine block, ahead of valve cover. The first symbol was a letter or number denoting the series, as follows: (6-Cyl.) A=4000; B=4100; C=4300; (V-8) 0=4000; 1=4100; 3=4300. The second symbol indicated model year, I for 1962. The third symbol ( ) is a number indicating the assembly plant code, as follows: 1=Flint, Mich.; 2=Southgate, Calif.; 3=Linden, N.J.; 4=Kansas City, Kan.; 5=Wilmington, Del.; 6=Atlanta, Ga.; 8=Arlington, Texas. The last six symbols are the numerical sequence of assembly at the coded plant, with series mixed in production. Engine numbers were located in various places on the crankcase, usually, or on the cylinder block. Along with serial number, the engines carried a production code with a prefix identifying engine and year, then a four symbol sequential production number: (V-8s) stamped front right of block opposite serial number; (V-6) on front of block below left cylinder head gasket. Special engine codes were as follows: (198 cid V-6) 6I; (215 cid V-8)=I, LI, HI.

Series Number	Model Number	Body Type & Seating	Factory Price	Shipping Weight	Production Total
4000	4019	4-dr Sed-6P	2358	2666	23,249
4000	4027	2-dr Sed-6P	2304	2638	19,135
4000	4067	2-dr Conv-6P	2587	2858	7,918
4000	4045	4-dr Sta Wag-8P	2736	2896	2,814
4000	4035	4-dr Sta Wag-6P	2655	2876	7,382

ENGINE: V-6. Overhead valve. Cast-iron block. Displacement: 198 cid. Bore and stroke: 3.625 x 3.2 inches. Compression ratio: 8.8:1. Brake horsepower: 135 at 4600 rpm. Four main bearings. Hydraulic lifters. Carburetor: Rochester 2GC two-barrel.

ENGINE: V-8. Overhead valve. Cast aluminum block. Displacement: 215 cid. Bore and stroke: 3.50 x 2.80 inches. Compression ratio: 9.0:1. Brake horsepower: 155 at 4600 rpm. Five main bearings. Hydraulic lifters. Carburetor: Rochester 2GC two-barrel.

SPECIAL DELUXE — SERIES 4100 — A slightly plusher Special, with a bright strip along the body, nicer vinyls and fabrics inside, and full carpeting. Rear armrests, rear ashtrays, a Deluxe steering wheel, foam seat cushions, cigarette lighter, oil filter and dual horns and visors were addition features found on the Deluxe.

SPECIAL DELUXE I.D. NUMBERS: Serial numbers were distinguished by the use of a B (6-cyl.) or 1 (V-8) as first symbol of the number. The rest of the number was coded as explained under the 1962 Special Series 4000 ID Number section.

SPECIAL DELUXE SERIES

Series Number	Model Number	Body Type & Seating	Factory Price	Shipping Weight	Production Total
4100	4119	4-dr Sed-6P	2593	2648	31,660
4100	4167	2-dr Conv-6P	2879	2820	8,332
4100	4135	4-dr Sta Wag-6P	2890	2845	10,300

ENGINE: Specifications were the same as listed for the 1962 Special Series 4000 V-8.

SKYLARK — SERIES 4300 — Buick's most refined compact featured a new convertible model and slightly changed styling for 1962. The hardtop coupe was of true "hardtop" design this year, without a side window. The Skylark had a Buick emblem centered in the grille and a Skylark badge on each front fender, along with the three ventiports. Taillamp housings wrapped around onto the rear fenders. Lower body bright rocker and wheelhouse moldings accented the Skylark, which came with Turbine wheelcovers. Interiors were all-vinyl, with front

bucket seats. Standard features, in addition to those found on the lesser Specials, included a padded dash, Skylark steering wheel, heater and defroster, rear courtesy lamps and, on the convertible, a power top.

1962 Buick, Skylark two-door coupe, V-8 (AA)

SKYLARK I.D. NUMBERS: Serial numbers were distinguished by the use of a C (6-cyl.) or 3 (V-8) as first symbol of the number. The rest of the number was coded as explained under the 1962 Special Series 4000 ID Number section.

SKYLARK SERIES

Series Number	Model Number	Body Type & Seating	Factory Price	Shipping Weight	Production Total
4300	4347	2-dr HT-6P	2787	2707	34,060
4300	4367	2-dr Conv-5P	3012	2871	8,913

ENGINE: V-8. Specifications were the same as those listed for the 1962 Special — Series 4000 V-8 except compression ratio was 11.0: 1, a four-barrel Rochester 4GC carburetor was used and brake horsepower was 190 at 4800 rpm.

1962 Buick, LeSabre two-door hardtop sport coupe, V-8 (AA)

LESABRE — SERIES 4400 — Refreshing new lines graced the 1962 LeSabre, although its body structure was unchanged from 1961. Still sporting a trio of ventiports on each front fender, LeSabres were identified by script on the front fenders and emblems front and rear. The two-door hardtop featured a new landau style top simulating a raised convertible top, but it was steel and fixed in position. Standard features included directional signals, full-flow oil filter, electric windshield wipers, a Deluxe steering wheel, cigar lighter, Step-On parking brake, dual armrests, Turbine drive transmission, padded dashboard, heater and defroster and glovebox light. Interiors were cloth and vinyl combinations.

LESABRE I.D. NUMBERS: Buick serial numbers were on the hinge pillar post, left side, above instrument panel and stamped on left side, top of engine block, ahead of valve cover. The first symbol was a a number indicating the series, as follows: (LeSabre) 4=4000 series; (Invicta) 6=4600 series; (Electra) 7=4700 series and (Electra 225) 8=4800 series. The second symbol indicated model year, I for 1962. The third symbol ( ) is a number indicating the assembly plant code, as follows: 1=Flint, Mich.; 2=Southgate, Calif.; 3=Linden, N.J.; 4=Kansas City, Kan.; 5=Wilmington, Del.; 6=Atlanta, Ga.; 8=Arlington, Texas. The last six symbols are the numerical sequence of assembly at the coded plant, with series mixed in production. Engine numbers were located in various places on the crankcase, usually, or on the cylinder block. Along with serial number, the engines carried a production code with a prefix identifying engine and year, then a four symbol sequential production number. Numbers stamped on front right of block opposite serial number. Engine codes were as follows: (401 cid V-8) 2I, L2I, 4I, L4I.

LESABRE SERIES

Series Number	Model Number	Body Type & Seating	Factory Price	Shipping Weight	Production Total
4400	4469	4-dr Sed-6P	3227	4104	56,783
4400	4439	4-dr HT Sed-6P	3369	4156	37,518
4400	4411	2-dr Sed-6P	3091	4041	7,418
4400	4447	2-dr HT-6P	3293	4054	25,479

ENGINE: V-8. Overhead valve. Cast-iron block. Displacement: 401 cid. Bore and stroke: 4.1875 x 3.64 inches. Compression ratio: 10.25:1. Brake horsepower: 280 at 4400 rpm. Five main bearings. Hydraulic lifters. Carburetor: Rochester two-barrel model 2GC.

Standard Catalog of American Cars

1962 Buick, Invicta four-door Estate station wagon, V-8 (AA)

INVICTA — SERIES 4600 — The Invicta models had all LeSabre features, plus Deluxe wheelcovers and the engine 'Power Pak' (four-barrel induction system). The four-door hardtop and two-door hardtop also had the Code 06 Accessory Group (trunk light, electric clock and license plate frames) as standard equipment, plus padded cushions. The distinctive Invicta nine-passenger station wagon offered a power tailgate as a regular feature and the convertible in the line came equipped with an outside rearview mirror. All models in this line were generally plusher than LeSabres, although both series shared the same body shell. Exterior distinction came from the use of Invicta front fender badges, with other trim items matching the LeSabre theme.

NOTE: The Wildcat sport coupe was part of the Invicta line, featuring Custom equipment including a Deluxe steering wheel, all-vinyl front bucket seats with a center console housing the Turbine drive transmission lever, a tachometer, and rear floor lamp. An electric clock, chrome roof bows and license frames were other Wildcat equipment. The Wildcat Sport Coupe had a vinyl top covering, with Wildcat emblems on the roof quarter panels and special wheelcovers. Custom bright metal exterior moldings, including lower body rocker panel and wheelhouse bright trim, were used. Dual exhausts were standard. The Wildcat was included with the Invicta hardtop coupe's 13,471 production figure and shared its 4647 model number. However, Wildcat listed for $3,927 and weighed 4,150 pounds.

INVICTA I.D. NUMBERS: Serial numbers were distinguished by the use of a 6 as first symbol of the number. The rest of the number was coded as explained under the 1962 LeSabre Series ID Number section.

INVICTA SERIES

Series Number	Model Number	Body Type & Seating	Factory Price	Shipping Weight	Production Total
4600	4639	4-dr HT Sed-6P	3667	4159	16,443
4600	4547	2-dr HT Cpe-6P	3733	4077	12,355
4600	4667	2-dr Conv-6P	3617	4217	13,471
4600	4645	4-dr Sta Wag-8P	3917	4505	4,617
4600	4635	4-dr Sta Wag-6P	3836	4471	9,131

NOTE: Wildcat- see reference in text in note above.

ENGINE: Specifications were the same as the LeSabre Series 4400 except brake horsepower was 325 and a Rochester 4GC or Carter AFB four-barrel carburetor was used.

1962 Buick, Electra 225 two-door hardtop sport coupe, V-8 (AA)

ELECTRA 225 — SERIES 4800 — The big Buick for 1962 carried four ventiports per front fender and featured a rakish, sculptured restyle of its 1961 guise. The hardtop coupe and new Model 4839 hardtop sedan featured a convertible-inspired semi-formal roofline, while the Model 4829 Riviera sedan continued to use a six-window pillarless configuration. Electra 225 rear fenders had a group of vertical hash marks, with Electra 225 spelled out in block letters just above. A full-length bright strip crowned the upper body ridge, while the tower rocker moldings and wheelhouses were accented with bright trim. Wheelcovers had a gold accent ring. Interiors were of the finest cloth and, on the convertible, leather was used. Standard features, in addition to those found on the less expensive Buicks, included back-up lights, power steering, Glare-proof rearview mirror, power brakes, parking brake signal light, safety buzzer, courtesy lights, two-way power seats, power windows, dual speed washer/wipers, Super Deluxe wheelcovers, Safety option group, custom padded cushions, Accessory Group options and custom moldings.

ELECTRA 225 I.D. NUMBERS: Serial numbers were distinguished by the use of the numeral '8' as the first symbol of the number. The rest of the number was coded as explained under the 1962 LeSabre ID Number section.

ELECTRA 225 SERIES

Series Number	Model Number	Body Type & Seating	Factory Price	Shipping Weight	Production Total
4800	4819	4-dr Sed-6P	4051	4304	13,523
4800	4829	4-dr Riv Sed-6P	4448	4390	15,395
4800	4839	4-dr HT Sed-6P	4186	4309	16,734
4800	4847	2-dr HT Cpe-6P	4062	4235	8,922
4800	4867	2-dr Conv-6P	4366	4396	7,894

ENGINE: Specifications were the same as those listed for the 1962 Invicta Series 4600.

CHASSIS FEATURES: Wheelbase: (Series 4000, 4100 and 4300) 112.1 inches; (Series 4400 and 4600) 123 inches; (Series 4800) 126 inches. Overall length: (Series 4000, 4100 and 4300) 188.4 inches; (Series 4400 and 4600) 214.1 inches; (Series 4800) 220.1 inches; (Estate

wagons) 213.6 inches. Front tread: (Series 4000, 4100 and 4300) 56 inches; (Series 4400, 4600 and 4800) 62.1 inches. Rear Tread: (Series 4000, 4100 and 4300) 56 inches; (Series 4400, 4600 and 4800) 61 inches: Tires: (Series 4000, 4100 and 4300) 6.50 x 13; (Series 4400 and 4600) 7.60 x 15; (Series 4800) 8.00 x 15.

POWERTRAIN OPTIONS: A three-speed manual transmission was standard on Series 4000, 4100 and 4300. Turbine drive was optional at $189. A four-speed was optional for V-8s at $200. The 190 brake horsepower Skylark V-8 was optional on the Special at $145 and on the Special Deluxe at $39. A regular fuel V-8 was optional on the LeSabre Series 4400; It was the same basic 401 cid engine with 9.0:1 compression ratio and 265 brake horsepower. The Wildcat 325 horsepower 401 cubic inch V-8 was optional on the LeSabre. Also available was a 280 horsepower 401 cubic inch engine. Turbine drive was standard on Series 4400, 4600 and 4800.

BUICK CONVENIENCE OPTIONS: Air conditioning ($430). Air conditioning modification ($24). PCV system ($5). Custom padded cushions as option ($23). Divided rear seat on station wagons ($38). Chrome door guards two-door/four-door ($5/9). Posi Traction ($48). Dual exhausts as option ($31). Tinted glass, all windows/windshield only ($43/29). Guide-Matic ($29). Luggage locker for station wagon ($22). Station wagon luggage rack ($100). Outside remote control rearview mirror ($12). Power brakes ($43). Power door locks ($70). Four-barrel Power-Pack ($22). Six-Way power seat ($97). Six/Two-Way power seat ($69). Four-Way power seat ($65) Four/Two-Way power seat ($37). Power steering ($108). Power trunk release ($10). Sonotone radio with manual/electric antennas ($90/116). Wonder Bar radio with manual/electric antennas ($127/153). Rear seat speaker ($17). Convertible buckets seats w/console ($229). Coupe bucket seats w/console ($296). Power bucket seat option ($129 extra). Twilight Sentinel ($29). Code 06 Accessory Group ($22). Safety Options Group (glare-proof mirror, back-up lamps, parking brake warning signal, safety buzzer light, courtesy lights) $40.

BUICK SPECIAL CONVENIENCE OPTIONS: Air conditioning ($351). Code W1 185 horse-power engine — Series 4000 ($145)/Series 4100 ($39). Backup lights ($1 1). Padded dash ($13-26). Two-tone finish ($16). Power brakes ($43). Power steering ($86). Power windows ($102). Bucket seats Series 4000/4100 ($96/70). Turbine drive ($189). Four-speed manual transmission ($200). Deluxe wheelcovers ($15).

HISTORICAL FOOTNOTES: Not since 1956 had Buick built and sold as many cars as delivered in 1962. Calendar year deliveries were 415,892, while model year production stood at 400,150 for six percent of industry. The company captured 6.1 percent of U.S. sales and the Special series gained 65 percent over the previous year. The new V-6 gave the Special a price edge in the growing domestic small car market. It was the first production V-6 in an American car and was available only in base series Specials. It was developed in just six months. MOTOR TREND named the 1962 Buick V-6 the "Car of the Year." Tooling for the V-6 was later sold to American Motors for use in the Jeep. It was then repurchased, by Buick, in 1974 to use in more energy efficient cars. In 1962, Dan Gurney drove a Buick V-8 powered race car, built by Mickey Thompson, in the Indy 500. The car qualified at 147.88 mph and completed 92 laps before being forced out with mechanical difficulties to the rear axle. The Buick-powered Apollo sports car (See "Minor Makes" section) bowed in 1962. It was first built in Italy. On standard Buicks the engines were moved four inches forward, decreasing the size of floor humps. Style Numbers 4645 and 4635 were called Estate Wagons. Style Number 4829 was known as the Riviera sedan.

1963 BUICK

1963 Buick, Special two-door coupe, V-8 (AA)

SPECIAL — SERIES 4000 — An almost complete lack of brightwork on the bodysides of a new, slightly larger and much more square-cut body shell was a 1963 Special hallmark. There were three bright metal ventiports on each front fender. A vertical bar grille was spread across the car's flat face. Special series script appeared high on the rear fender. Interiors were done in cloth and vinyl, except for the convertible, which had all vinyl upholstery.

SPECIAL I.D. NUMBERS: Serial numbers were on the hinge pillar post, left side, above instrument panel and stamped on left side, top of engine block, ahead of valve cover. The first symbol was a letter or number denoting the series, as follows: (6-Cyl.) A=4000; B=4100; C=4300; (V-8) 0=4000; 1=4100; 3=4300. The second symbol indicated model year, J for 1963. The third symbol (   ) is a numer indicating the assembly plant code, as follows: 1=Flint, Mich.; 2=Southgate, Calif.; 3=Linden, N.J.; 4=Kansas City, Kan.; 5=Wilmington, Del.; 6=Atlanta, Ga.; 8=Arlington, Texas. The last six symbols are the numerical sequence of assembly at the coded plant, with series mixed in production. Engine numbers were located in various places on the crankcase, usually, or on the cylinder block. Along with serial number, the engines carried a production code with a prefix identifying engine and year, then a four symbol sequential production number: (V-8s) stamped front right of block opposite serial number; (V-6) on front of block below left cylinder head gasket. Special engine codes were as follows: (198 cid V-6) JL, JZ; (215 cid V-8) =JM, JN, JP.

SPECIAL SERIES 4000

Series Number	Model Number	Body Type & Seating	Factory Price	Shipping Weight	Production Total
4000	4019	4-dr Sed-6P	2363	2696	21,733
4000	4027	2-dr Sed-6P	2309	2661	21,866
4000	4067	2-dr Conv-6P	2591	2768	8,082
4000	4045	4-dr Sta Wag-8P	2740	2903	2,415
4000	4035	4-dr Sta Wag-6P	2659	2866	5,867

ENGINE: V-6. Overhead valves. Cast iron block. Displacement: 198 cid. Bore and stroke: 3.625 x 3.2 inches. Compression ratio: 8.8:1. Brake horsepower: 135 at 4600 rpm. Four main bearings. Hydraulic valve lifters. Rochester 2GC two-barrel carburetor.

V-8: Overhead valves. Cast aluminum block. Displacement: 215 cid. Bore and stroke: 3.5 x 2.8 inches. Compression ratio: 8.8:1. Brake horsepower: 155 at 4600 rpm. Five main bearings. Hydraulic lifters. Rochester 2GC two-barrel carburetor.

SPECIAL DELUXE — SERIES 4100 — Exterior distinction for Deluxe models came from a narrow, full-length bodyside molding. Otherwise the trim was identical to the base line, except on the interior where upholstery combinations were richer.

SPECIAL DELUXE SERIES 4100 I.D. NUMBERS: Serial numbers for cars equipped with the V-6 began with BJ( )501001. Serial numbers for cars equipped with the V-8 began with 1J( )501001. The number coded as explained under the 1963 Special Series 4000 ID Number section.

SPECIAL DELUXE SERIES 4100

Series Number	Model Number	Body Type & Seating	Factory Price	Shipping Weight	Production Total
4100	4119	4-dr Sed-6P	2592	2684	37,695
4100	4135	4-dr Sta Wag-6P	2889	2858	8,771

ENGINE: See 1963 Buick Series 4000 engine data.

SKYLARK — SERIES 4300 — Full-length bodyside moldings graced the 1963 Skylark, which was further identified on the coupe by rear quarter roof pillar emblems. A Buick insignia was centered in the grille and another was found in the bright rear cove insert. All-vinyl interior trim was standard in the convertible and optional in the coupe. Front bucket seats were optional.

SKYLARK SERIES 4300 I.D. NUMBERS: Serial numbers began with 3J( )501001 and were otherwise coded as explained under the 1963 Special Series 4000 ID Number section.

SKYLARK SERIES 4300

Series Number	Model Number	Body Type & Seating	Factory Price	Shipping Weight	Production Total
4300	4347	2-dr HT Cpe-5P	2857	2757	32,109
4300	4367	2-dr Conv-5P	3011	2810	10,212

ENGINE: Powerplant specifications were the same as those listed for the 1963 Special Series 4000 V-8, except the compression ratio was raised to 11: 1 providing 200 horsepower at 5000 rpm in combination with the use of a four-barrel Rochester 4GC carburetor.

LESABRE — SERIES 4400 — A revised styling theme was featured for 1963 with vertical taillights capping the rear fenders. A new stamped grille was seen up front. Side trim was minimal, with a narrow bright strip running horizontally along the rear body and triple ventiports on each front fender. The word LeSabre was spelled out in script on the rear fenders. Standard features included directional signals, electric windshield wipers, cigar lighter, Step-On parking brake, dual armrests and carpeting. Bayonne cloth with vinyl bolsters was used for the interior, except for the convertible, which was trimmed in all-vinyl. LeSabre identification was found on the glovebox door. Station wagons had all-vinyl trim and full carpeting.

LESABRE I.D. NUMBERS: Buick serial numbers were on the hinge pillar post, left side, above instrument panel and stamped on left side, top of engine block, ahead of valve cover. The first symbol was a a number indicating the series, as follows: (LeSabre) 4=4000 series; (Invicta) 6=4600 series; (Electra) 7=4700 series and (Electra 225) 8=4800 series. The second symbol indicated model year, J for 1963. The third symbol ( ) is a number indicating the assembly plant code, as follows: 1=Flint, Mich.; 2=Southgate, Calif.; 3=Linden, N.J.; 4=Kansas City, Kan.; 5=Wilmington, Del.; 6=Atlanta, Ga..; 8=Arlington, Texas. The last six symbols are the numerical sequence of assembly at the coded plant, with series mixed in production. Engine numbers were located in various places on the crankcase, usually, or on the cylinder block. Along with serial number, the engines carried a production code with a prefix identifying engine and year, then a four symbol sequential production number. Numbers stamped on front right of block opposite serial number. Engine codes were as follows: (LeSabre 401 V-8) JR, JS, JT, JU; (Wildcat/Invicta 401 V-8) JT, JU; (Electra 225 401 V-8) JT, JU; (Riviera 401 V-8) JT, JU; (Riviera 425 V-8) JW.

LESABRE SERIES 4400

Series Number	Model Number	Body Type & Seating	Factory Price	Shipping Weight	Production Total
4400	4469	4-dr Sed-6P	3004	3970	64,995
4400	4439	2-dr HT Sed-6P	3146	4007	50,420
4400	4411	2-dr Sed-6P	2869	3905	8,328
4400	4447	2-dr Spt Cpe-6P	3070	3924	27,977
4400	4467	2-dr Conv-6P	3339	4052	9,975
4400	4445	4-dr Sta Wag-8P	3606	4340	3,922
4400	4435	4-dr Sta Wag-6P	3526	4320	5,566

ENGINE: V-8. Overhead valves. Cast iron block. Displacement: 401 cid. Bore and stroke: 4.1875 x 3.64 inches. Compression ratio: 10.25:1. Brake horsepower 280 at 4400 rpm. Five main bearings. Hydraulic valve lifters. Carburetor: Rochester 2GC two-barrel.

WILDCAT — SERIES 4600 — A plusher, more sporting Buick line for 1963 grew from success of the 1962 Wildcat Sport Coupe. Standard Wildcat features for 1963 included an electric clock, Deluxe steering wheel, trunk light, license frames, padded instrument panel, foam-rubber headliner, tachometer (except on hardtops with bench seats), bucket seats (optional on four-door hardtop, standard other models), and a center console. Wildcat script was found on rear fenders and within the rear cove, while the name was lettered across the hood. A brushed finish bright insert began on the front fenders and contained the three ventiports on each fender. Bright wheelhouse and rocker moldings were used. A special grille, with distinct horizontal heavy bars and a center emblem, further distinguished the Wildcat. Sport coupes had roof rear quarter emblems with the Wildcat logo, while the same badge was placed on the rear flanks of convertibles. Bucket seat interiors were all-vinyl. Specific full wheelcovers were used.

NOTE: Also in the 4600 series was the Invicta Estate Wagon, Model 4635. This station wagon had a plusher interior than the 4400 wagons and was available in two-seat form only. A full-length narrow bodyside molding was used, along with bright wheelhouse and rocker moldings and chromed roof bars. All standard Wildcat features were included.

WILDCAT AND INVICTA — SERIES 4600 — I.D. NUMBERS: Serial numbers began with 6J( )001001. The number was coded as explained under the 1963 LeSabre ID Number section.

WILDCAT/INVICTA SERIES 4600

Series Number	Model Number	Body Type & Seating	Factory Price	Shipping Weight	Production Total
4600	4639	4-dr HT Cpe-6P	3871	4222	17,519
4600	4647	2-dr Spt Cpe-6P	3849	4123	12,185
4600	4667	C2-dr Conv-6P	3961	4228	6,021
4600	4635	4-dr Sta Wag-6P	3969	3897	3,495

ENGINE: Specifications were the same as those listed for the 1963 LeSabre Series 4400, except compression ratio was 10.25:1. Brake horsepower was 325 at 4400 rpm and a four-barrel Rochester 4GC or Carter AFB carburetor was used.

1963 Buick, Electra 225 four-door hardtop sedan, V-8

ELECTRA 225 — SERIES 4800 — Buick's largest, plushest and most expensive models were redesigned for 1963, with distinctive rear fenders cumulating in a sharp vertical edge housing narrow back-up lights. The taillights were horizontally placed in the vertical deck cove. A unique cast grille was used at the front. Bright wheelhouse and lower body moldings, with ribbed rear fender panels, were used. Red-filled Electra 225 badges were found on the rear fenders, while four ventiports lent status to the front units. Interiors were cloth and vinyl combinations, while a Custom interior in vinyl and leather, with front bucket seats and a storage console, was available for the convertible and sport coupe. Standard equipment, in addition to items found on lower-priced Buicks, included power steering; power brakes; back-up lights; power brake signal light; map light; safety buzzer; Custom padded seat cushions; Super Deluxe wheelcovers; power windows and two-way seat adjustment on the convertibles (these two features were included with the Custom interior on closed models).

ELECTRA 225 SERIES I.D. NUMBERS: Serial numbers began with 8J( )1001001. The number was coded as explained under the 1963 LeSabre ID Number section.

ELECTRA 225 SERIES 4800

Series Number	Model Number	Body Type & Seating	Factory Price	Shipping Weight	Production Total
4800	4819	4-dr Sed-6P	4051	4241	14,628
4800	4829	4-dr HT Sed-6P	4254	4284	11,468
4800	4839	4-dr HT Sed-6P	4186	4272	19,714
4800	4847	2-dr Spt Cpe-6P	4062	4153	6,848
4800	4867	2-dr Conv-6P	4365	4297	6,367

ENGINE: Specifications were the same as those listed for the 1963 LeSabre Series 4400 except compression ratio was 10.25:1, brake horsepower was 325 at 4400 rpm and a four-barrel Rochester 4GC or Carter AFB carburetor was used.

RIVIERA — SERIES 4700 — A new sports/luxury model for 1963, issued only in a stunning sport coupe body style. From the front fenders, whose leading edges were vertical grilles, to the razor-edged rear contours, the Riviera looked both elegant and fast. A car for Buick's most affluent customers, the Riviera was delivered with a host of standard features, including two-speed wipers with washers; back-up lights; Glareproof inside mirror; parking brake signal light; safety buzzer; Riviera wheelcovers; electric clock; license frame; padded instrument panel; trip mileage odometer; smoking set; front and rear bucket seats; courtesy lamps; deep-pile carpet; foam-padded seat cushions; center console; heater and defroster; and frameless side windows.

RIVIERA SERIES 4700 I.D. NUMBERS: Serial numbers began with 7J( )001001. The number was coded as explained under the 1963 LeSabre ID Number section.

RIVIERA SERIES 4700

Series Number	Model Number	Body Type & Seating	Factory Price	Shipping Weight	Production Total
4700	4747	2-dr Spt Cpe-4P	4333	3998	40,000

ENGINE: Specifications were the same as listed for the 1963 Electra 225 Series 4800.

CHASSIS FEATURES: Wheelbase- (Series 4000, 4100 and 4300) 112.1 inches; (Series 4400 and 4600) 123 inches; (Series 4800) 126 inches; (Series 4700) 117 inches. Overall length: (Series 4000, 4100 and 4300) 192.1 inches; (Series 4400 and 4600) 215.7 inches; (Series 4800) 221.7 inches; (Series 4700) 208 inches. Front tread: (Series 4000, 4100 and 4300) 56 inches; (Series 4400, 4600, 4800 and 4700) 62 inches. Rear tread: (Series 4000, 4100 and 4300) 56 inches; (Series 4400, 4600, 4800 and 4700) 61 inches. Tires: (Series 4000, 4100 and 4300) 6.50 x 13; (Series 4400 and 4600) 7.60 x 15; (Series 4800) 8.00 x 15; (Series 4700) 7.10 x 15.

POWERTRAIN OPTIONS: A three-speed manual transmission was standard on Series 4000, 4100, 4300, 4400 and 4600. Turbine drive was standard on Series 4800 and 4700 and optional on other Series at $231. A four-speed manual transmission was optional on Series 4300 , 4400 and 4600 models at $200-$263. The Series 4300 200 hp V-8 was optional on Series 4000 and 4100 models. A 9.0:1 compression 265 horsepower regular fuel engine was a no-cost option in all Series 4400 models. A 425 cubic inch, 340 brake horsepower V-8 was optional on Series 4700. Positive traction differental optional on all models.

CONVENIENCE OPTIONS: Power steering (standard on Series 4800, 4700). Power brakes (standard on Series 4700 and 4800). Air conditioning. Cruise control on Model 4747. Wire wheelcovers. Cloth/vinyl or leather/vinyl trim on Model 4747. Seven-position tilt steering wheel on Series 4400, 4600, 4800. Electro-Cruise. Cornering lights. Power door locks. Auto trunk release. Seat belts. Sonomatic radio. Wonderbar radio. Rear seat speaker. Soft-Ray glass. Rear window defroster. Chrome door guards. Remote control outside rearview mirror. White-wall tires. Power windows (standard on Electra 225 Convertible and Custom interior). Guide-

Matic dimmer. Twilight Sentinel. Gas door guard. Compass. Litter basket. Tissue dispenser. Seat covers. Spotlite. Carpet covers. Carpet savers. Trunk mat. Ski rack. Heater/Defroster delete. Divided rear seat, luggage rack and luggage locker for station wagons.

HISTORICAL FOOTNOTES: Calendar year production was 479,399, putting Buick in seventh rank in the auto industry. Model year production stood at 458,606 units or 6.3 percent share of market. The big news was introduction of the Thunderbird-fighting Riviera sports/personal car. A Skylark SR200 show car with racing stripes and braking cooling ducts represented one of the first signs of forthcoming high-performance series. Two Riviera "Silver Arrow" show cars were also seen, both being slightly different. CAR LIFE magazine tested a 425 cid/340 hp Riviera for a 0-to-60 time of 7.7 seconds. The 401 cid/325 hp Riviera could do the same in about 8.1 seconds and cover the quarter-mile in 16.01 seconds. Due to production costs, the 1961-1963 aluminum V-8 was dropped for 1964 models. The engine tooling was sold to Rover, which still uses it today in England. Models 4445, 4435 and 4635 are Estate Wagons

1964 BUICK

SPECIAL SERIES 4000 V-6 AND V-8 — A new, larger and more flowing body was used for the 1964 Special, now classed as an intermediate in the GM family. Except for the Special script on rear fenders and trio of ventiports on front fenders, the Special was devoid of bright ornamentation. Interiors were in Brigade cloth. Standard features included electric windshield wipers, ashtrays, directional signals, Step-On parking brake, dome lights and, on the convertible only, carpeting.

SPECIAL I.D. NUMBERS: Serial numbers were on the hinge pillar post, left side, above instrument panel and stamped on left side, top of engine block, ahead of valve cover. On base Buick Specials equipped with the V-6, the numbers began with AK( )501001-up. On base Buick Specials equipped with a V-8, the numbers began with 0K( )501001-up. The first symbol was a letter or number denoting the series, as follows: (6-Cyl.) A=4000; B=4100; C=4300; (V-8) 0=4000; 1=4100; 3=4300. The second symbol indicated model year, K for 1964. The third symbol ( ) is a number indicating the assembly plant code, as follows: 1=Flint, Mich.; 2=Southgate, Calif.; 3=Fremont, Calif.; 4=Kansas City, Kan.; 5=Wilmington, Del.; 6=Atlanta, Ga.; 7=Baltimore, Md.; 8=Kansas City, Mo. The last six symbols are the numerical sequence of assembly at the coded plant, with series mixed in production. Engine numbers were located in various places on the crankcase, usually, or on the cylinder block.- Along with serial number, the engines carried a production code with a prefix identifying engine and year, then a four symbol sequential production number: (V-8s) stamped front right of block opposite serial number; (V-6) on front of block below left cylinder head gasket. Special engine codes were as follows: (225 cid V-6) KH, KJ; (300 cid V-8)= KL, KM, KP and KR.

SPECIAL SERIES 4000

Series Number	Model Number	Body Type & Seating	Factory Price	Shipping Weight	Production Total
4000	4069	4-dr Sed-6P	2397	3000	17,983
4000	4027	2-dr Sed-6P	2343	2983	15,030
4000	4067	2-dr Conv-6P	2605	3099	6,308
4000	4035	4-dr Sta Wag-6P	2689	3258	6,270

NOTE: The V-8 line was considered a sub-series, not an option. Factory prices were $71 higher for V-8s than the prices listed above for the V-6. Shipping weights were 16 pounds heavier for the V-8 than those listed above for the V-6. Production figures include both V-6 and V-8.

ENGINE: V-6. Cast iron block. Displacement: 225 cid. Bore and stroke: 3.75 x 3.4 inches. Compression ratio: 9.0:1. Brake horsepower: 155 at 4400 rpm. Four main bearings. Hydraulic lifters. Two-barrel Rochester BC carburetor.

V-8: Cast iron block. Displacement: 300 cid. Bore and stroke: 3.75 x 3.4 inches. Compression ratio: 9.0:1. Brake horsepower: 210 at 4600 rpm. Five main bearings. Hydraulic lifters. Two-barrel Rochester 2GC carburetor.

1964 Buick, Special Deluxe four-door sedan, V-8

SPECIAL DELUXE — SERIES 4100 — V-6 AND V-8 — A narrow bright bodyside molding swept the full length of the Special Deluxe models, which were plusher inside. There was carpeting, cloth and vinyl combinations over foam-padded seats, and a padded instrument panel. Other line features were a Deluxe steering wheel, dual armrests, dual horns and additional dome lights.

SPECIAL DELUXE SERIES 4100 I.D. NUMBERS: Serial numbers for cars equipped with the V-6 began with BK( )001001. Serial numbers for cars equipped with the V-8 began with 1K( )001001. The numbers were coded as explained under the I964 Special Series 4000 ID Number section.

SPECIAL DELUXE SERIES 4100

Series Number	Model Number	Body Type & Seating	Factory Price	Shipping Weight	Production Total
4100	4169	4-dr Sed-6P	2490	3018	31,742
4100	4127	2-dr Sed-6P	2457	2998	11,962
4100	4135	4-dr Sta Wag-6P	2787	3277	9,467

NOTE: Cars equipped with V-8s listed for $71 more than the V-6 prices given above and they weighed 16 pounds more than the weights given for the V-6. Production totals include both V-6s and V-8s.

ENGINE: Specifications were the same as those listed for the 1964 Special Series 4000.

SPORT WAGONS — SERIES 4200 AND 4300 — A new, long-wheelbase station wagon debuted for 1964. Offered in two stages of trim, the wagons were numbered in 4200 and 4300 (Skylark) series. Both Standard and Custom models had tinted transparent panels above the rear passenger compartment. The Custom models were trimmed like the Skylarks in the 4300 Series (see Skylark Series 4300). Interiors were all-vinyl.

SPORT WAGON I.D. NUMBERS: Serial numbers correspond to the numbers used for the Series 4100 and 4300 cars as detailed above.

SERIES 4200/4300 SPORT WAGONS

Series Number	Model Number	Body Type & Seating	Factory Price	Shipping Weight	Production Total
4200	4265	4-dr Cus Sta Wag-3S	3124	3689	2,586
4200	4255	4-dr Cus Sta Wag-2S	2989	3557	2,709
4300	4365	4-dr Sta Wag-3S	3286	3727	4,446
4300	4355	4-dr Sta Wag-2S	3161	3595	3,913

ENGINE: Specifications were the same as those listed for the 1964 Special Series 4000 V-8.

SKYLARK — SERIES 4300 — Buick's plushest version of their sporty intermediate had considerably more pizzaz this year with its new body and flashier trim. The Skylark emblem and signature were found on roof quarters (rear fenders on the convertible), while Skylark script was on the deck. A round Buick emblem dominated the grille. Another round emblem was housed in the deck cove, which was finished with a brushed metallic insert. Bright rocker moldings and a wider bright bodyside molding, with a brushed metallic insert, gave further distinction. Sport Coupes had twin bright strips on the roof. Standard features, in addition to those found on Special and Special Deluxe series, included instrument panel safety padding, paddle-type armrests, Skylark steering wheel, Skylark wheelcovers and full carpeting. An all-vinyl interior with bucket seats was standard for the convertible and optional for the Sport Coupe. The sedan came in a cloth and vinyl combination with all-vinyl available as a substitution.

SKYLARK I.D. NUMBERS: Serial numbers began with CK( )001001 on cars equipped with the V-6. Serial numbers began with 3K( )001001 on cars equipped with the V-8. The number was coded as explained under the 1964 Special Series 4000 ID Number section.

SKYLARK SERIES 4300

Series Number	Model Number	Body Type & Seating	Factory Price	Shipping Weight	Production Total
4300	4369	4-dr Sed-6P	2669	3062	19,635
4300	4347	2-dr Spt Cpe-6P	2680	3049	42,356
4300	4367	2-dr Conv-5P	2834	3169	10,255

NOTE: Cars equipped with V-8s listed for $71 more than the V-6 prices given above and they weighed six pounds more than the weights given for the V-6s. Production figures combine V-6 and V-8 production.

ENGINE: Specifications were the same as those listed for the 1964 Special Series 4000.

LESABRE — SERIES 4400 — Refined body sculpturing, with fresh frontal and rear treatments, set the 1964 LeSabre apart. A unique stamped grille was used. A narrow bright bodyside molding was found on the rear one-third of the body, with the series signature residing above it, near the fender end. Standard LeSabre features included electric windshield wipers; Step-On parking brake; padded instrument panel; directional signals; front and rear armrests; dual sunshades; smoking set; courtesy lights; dual horns and cloth upholstery. Cloth and vinyl trim was optional. The convertible was trimmed in all-vinyl, with front bucket seats optional. A Custom trim package option included full-length bright bodyside moldings, with a brushed metallic insert.

LESABRE I.D. NUMBERS: Buick serial numbers were on the hinge pillar post, left side, above instrument panel and stamped on left side, top of engine block, ahead of valve cover. The first symbol was a a number indicating the series, as follows: (LeSabre) 4=4000 series; (Invicta) 6=4600 series; (Electra) 7=4700 series and (Electra 225) 8=4800 series. The second symbol indicated model year, K for 1964. The third symbol ( ) is a number indicating the assembly plant code, as follows: 1=Flint, Mich.; 2=Southgate, Calif.; 3=Fremont, Cal.; 4=Kansas City, Kan.; 5=Wilmington, Del.; 6=Atlanta, Ga.; 7=Baltimore, Md.; 8=Kansas City, Mo. The last six symbols are the numerical sequence of assembly at the coded plant, with series mixed in production. Engine numbers were located in various places on the crankcase, usually, or on the cylinder block. Along with serial number, the engines carried a production code with a prefix identifying engine and year, then a four symbol sequential production number. Numbers stamped on front right of block opposite serial number. Engine codes were as follows: (LeSabre/Wildcat/Electra 224 401 V-8) KT, KV; (LeSabre/Wildcat/Riviera 425 V-8) KW, KX; .

LESABRE SERIES 4400

Series Number	Model Number	Body Type & Seating	Factory Price	Shipping Weight	Production Total
4400	4469	4-dr Sed-6P	2980	3693	56,729
4400	4439	4-dr HT Sed-6P	3122	3730	37,052
4400	4447	2-dr Spt Cpe-6P	3061	3629	24,177
4400	4467	2-dr Conv-6P	3314	3787	6,685

ENGINE: Specifications were the same as those listed for the Special Series 4000 V-8.

LESABRE — SERIES 4600 — Two hybrid station wagons made up this curious series. They were trimmed as LeSabres, but had the Wildcat's chassis and power. Leather grain vinyl or vinyl and cloth (two-seater only) were trim choices. A power tailgate window was standard.

LESABRE SERIES 4600 I.D. NUMBERS: Serial numbers began with 4KC( )001001. The numbers were coded as explained under the 1964 LeSabre Series ID Number section.

LESABRE SERIES 4600

Series Number	Model Number	Body Type & Seating	Factory Price	Shipping Weight,	Production Total
4600	4645	4-dr Sta Wag-3S	3635	4362	4,003
4600	4635	4-dr Sta Wag-2S	3554	4352	6,517

ENGINE: Specifications were the same as those listed for the Wildcat Series 4600.

WILDCAT — SERIES 4600 — Sportier and plusher, the 1964 Wildcat was liberally trimmed with brightwork, including a ribbed, wide lower body molding; a trio of stacked, streamlined ventiports behind each front wheelhouse; a unique grille, with heavy horizontal wing bars, and a center emblem. There was Wildcat lettering on the deck lid and another emblem centered within the deck cove, which had a bright metallic insert with bright horizontal stripes. Wildcat badges appeared on roof quarters (except on the convertible, which had them on the fenders) and within the full wheelcovers. Standard and Custom trim choices were available, including bucket seats and a console. Carpeting was standard, in addition to all the features found on the LeSabre.

WILDCAT SERIES 4600 I.D. NUMBERS: Serial numbers began with 6K( )001001. The number was coded as explained under the 1964 LeSabre ID Number section.

WILDCAT SERIES 4600

Series Number	Model Number	Body Type & Seating	Factory Price	Shipping Weight	Production Total
4600	4669	4-dr Sed-6P	3164	4021	20,144
4600	4639	2-dr HT-6P	3327	4058	33,358
4600	4647	2-dr Spt Cpe-6P	3267	4003	22,893
4600	4667	2-dr Conv-6P	3455	4076	7,850

ENGINE: V-8. Overhead valves. Cast iron block. Displacement: 401 cid. Bore and stroke: 4.18 x 3.64. Compression ratio: 10.25:1. Brake horsepower: 325 at 4400 rpm. Five main bearings. Hydraulic lifters. Four-barrel Rochester 4GC or Carter AFB carburetor.

1964 Buick, Electra 225 two-door hardtop, V-8

ELECTRA 225 — SERIES 4800 — The large General Motors C-Body was used to create the Electra 225, Buick's richest full-size car. Vertical, narrow taillamps were found in the nearly straight-cut rear fender ends, and the so-called "Deuce-and-a-Quarter" came with fender skirts. Four traditional ventiports were found on the front fenders, with a heavy die-cast grille accenting the frontal aspect. Wide full length lower body moldings were used along with a bright deck cove insert. Electra 225 lettering was found on rear fenders and specific full wheelcovers were featured. Vinyl and brocade cloth interior trims were found in closed models, while leather upholstery was offered for seats in the convertible. Among the Electra's exclusive standard equipment were power steering; power brakes; two-speed electric wipers with windshield washer; foam-padded seats; electric clock; license frame; trunk light; two-way power seat and power windows for the convertible; a safety buzzer; and additional courtesy lights.

ELECTRA 225 SERIES 4800 I.D. NUMBERS: Serial numbers began with 8K( )001001. The numbers were coded as explained under the 1964 LeSabre ID Number section.

ELECTRA 225 SERIES 4800

Series Number	Model Number	Body Type & Seating	Factory Price	Shipping Weight	Production Total
4800	4819	4-dr Sed-6P	4059	4212	15,968
4800	4829	4-dr Pillarless Sed-6P	4261	4238	11,663
4800	4839	4-dr HT Sed-6P	4194	4229	24,935
4800	4847	2-dr Spt Cpe-6P	4070	4149	9,045
4800	4867	2-dr Conv-6P	4374	4280	7,181

ENGINE: Specifications were the same as those listed for the 1964 Wildcat Series 4600.

RIVIERA — SERIES 4700 — The 1963 Riviera was immediately recognized as a classic design and Buick saw little need for change in 1964. A new, stand-up hood ornament and revised Riviera scripts on the front fenders and right-hand deck were the major changes. The simulated rear fender cooling vents were outlined in bright metal and a thin, bright highlight line continued to follow the bodyside crease, jumping over the wheelhouse in passing. The beautiful, twin grill, with eggcrate center grille frontal ensemble, continued without alteration. The stylized letter 'R' appeared in wheelcover centers. Standard features were similar to those listed for the Electra 225, but also included deep-pile carpeting, foam-padded front and rear bucket seats and a center console with transmission selector lever. Interiors were trimmed in vinyl with wood accents.

1964 Buick, Riviera two-door hardtop sport coupe, V-8

RIVIERA SERIES 4700 I.D. NUMBERS: Serial numbers began with 7K( )001001. The numbers were coded as explained under the 1964 LeSabre ID Number section.

RIVIERA SERIES 4700

Series Number	Model Number	Body Type & Seating	Factory Price	Shipping Weight	Production Total
4700	4747	2-dr HT Cpe	4385	3951	37,958

ENGINE: V-8. Overhead valve. Cast iron block. Displacement: 425 cid. Bore and stroke: 4.3125 x 3.64 inches. Compression ratio: 10.25 to 1. Brake horsepower: 340 at 4400 rpm. Five main bearings. Hydraulic lifters. Four-barrel Carter AFB carburetor.

CHASSIS FEATURES: Wheelbase (Series 4000, 4100, 4200, 4300) 115 inches; (Series 4300 wagon) 120 inches; (Series 4400 and 4600) 123 inches; Series (4800) 126 inches; (Series 4700) 117 inches. Overall length: (Series 4000, 4100, 4200 and 4300) 203.5 inches; (Series 4400 and 4600) 218.5 inches; (Series 4800); (Series 4700) 208 inches. Front tread: (Series 4000, 4100, 4300, and 4200) 58 inches; (Series 4400, 4600 and 4800) 62.1 inches; (Series 4700) 60 inches. Rear tread: (Series 4000, 4100 and 4300) 58 inches; (Series 4400, 4600 and 4800) 61 inches; (Series 4700) 59 inches. Tires: (Series 4000, 41000 and 4300) 6.50 x 14; (Series 4200 wagon) 7.00 x 14; (Series 4300 wagons) 7.50 x 14; (Series 4400 and 4700) 7.1 0 x 15; (Series 4600) 7.60 x 15; (Series 4800) 8.00 x 15.

POWERTRAIN OPTIONS: A three-speed manual transmission was standard on Series 4000, 4100, 4200, 4300, 4400 and 4600. Turbine 300 automatic was optional on Series 4000, 4100, 4200, 4300, 4400 and 4600. Turbine 400 was optional on Series 4600, standard on Series 4700 and 4800. A four-speed manual transmission was optional for Series 4000, 4100, 4300, 4200, 43 and 4400. A 250 brake horsepower 300 cid V-8 was optional for Series 4000, 4100 and 4300. The 340 brake horsepower, 425 cid V-8 was optional for Series 4600, 4800 and 4600 Estate wagons. A 360 brake horsepower, 425 cid V-8 with dual four-barrel carburetors was an option for Series 4600, 4700, and 3800.

CONVENIENCE OPTIONS: Power brakes (standard 4700 and 4800). Power steering (standard 4700 and 4800). Power windows (not available Special station wagon). Power seat control. Air conditioning. Seven-position tilt steering wheel. Carpeting (4000 Series). Bucket seats with console and storage bin on 4600. 'Formula Five' chromed steel wheel. Whitewall tires. Custom fabric roof cover. Bucket seats in Electra 225 convertible. AM radio in 4000, 4100 and 4300. Sonomatic radio. Wonder Bar radio. AM-FM radio on 4400, 4600, 4700 and 4800. Seat belts. Remote control inside rearview mirror. Electro-cruise. Cornering lights. Power door locks. Automatic trunk release. Rear seat speaker. Rear window defroster. Guide-Matic headlight dimmer. Compass. Litter basket. Tissue dispenser. Ski rack. Luggage rack for Estate Wagons. Heater-defroster deletion..

NOTE: Power windows standard on Electra 225 convertible.

HISTORICAL FOOTNOTES: Calendar year production was 482,685 for seventh position in the auto industry. Model year output stood at 511,666 units. Models 4645 and 4635 are called Estate Wagons.

1965 BUICK

SPECIAL — SERIES 43300 (V-6) — A very slightly facelifted car of intermediate size was marketed by Buick under the Special name for 1965. Still largely devoid of side trim, the Special did have its name in script on the rear flanks and had a trio of ventiports on each front fender. A Buick emblem was found at the rear, while the front horizontal grille bars were bare. Interiors were of cloth and vinyl. Standard equipment included electric windshield wipers, directional signals, dual sunshades, ashtray/lighter set, dual armrests on sedans, courtesy lights, Step-On parking brake and carpeting in the convertible.

SPECIAL I.D. NUMBERS: Serial numbers were located on the hinge pillar post, left side, above the instrument panel and stamped on left side, top of engine block, ahead of valve cover. The first five symbols were the model number. The first symbol was a "4" indicating Buick Motor Div. products. The second through fifth symbols indicated the series and body style (see model numbers on tables below). The sixth symbol was a number indicating model year, 5=1965. The seventh symbol was a letter representing the plant code, as follows: B=Baltimore, Md.; C=Southgate, Calif.;D=Donaville, Ga.; H=Flint, Mich.; K=Leeds, Mo.; X=Fairfax, Kan.; Y=Wilmington, Del.; Z=Fremont, Ohio; V=Bloomfield, Mich.. The last six symbols were numerals representing the plant sequential production number, with series mixed in production. Engine numbers were stamped in various positions on the crankcase, usually, or on the cylinder block. Along with serial number, the engines carried a production code with a prefix identifying engine and year, then a four symbol sequential production number: (V-8s) stamped front right of block opposite serial number; (V-6) on front of block below left cylinder head gasket. Special engine codes were as follows: (225 cid V-6) LH, LJ; (300 cid V-8)=LL, LM, LP.

SPECIAL SERIES 43300

Series Number	Model Number	Body Type & Seating	Factory Price	Shipping Weight	Production Total
43300	43369	4-dr Sed-6P	2345	3010	12,945
43300	43327	2-dr Sed-6P	2292	2977	13,828
43300	43367	2-dr Conv-6P	2549	3087	3,357
43300	43335	4-dr Sta Wag-6P	2631	3258	2,868

ENGINE: V-6. Overhead valve. Cast iron block. Displacement: 225 cid. Bore and stroke: 3.75 by 3.4 inches. Compression ratio: 9.0:1. Brake horsepower: 155 at 4200 rpm. Four main bearings. Hydraulic valve lifters. Two-barrel Rochester BC carburetor.

SPECIAL — SERIES 43400 (V-8) — Identical externally to the 1965 V-6 Special described above, the V-8 Specials were numbered as a separate series.

SPECIAL I.D. NUMBERS: Serial numbers began with 434005 ( ) 100001.The numbers were coded as explained under the 1965 Special Series 43300 ID Number section.

SPECIAL SERIES 43400

Series Number	Model Number	Body Type & Seating	Factory Price	Shipping Weight	Production Total
43400	43469	4-dr Sed-6P	2415	3117	5,309
43400	43427	2-dr Sed-6P	2362	3080	8,121
43400	43467	2-dr Conv-6P	2618	3197	3,365
43400	43435	4-dr Sta Wag-6P	2699	3365	3,676

ENGINE: V-8. Overhead valve. Cast-iron block. Displacement: 300 cid. Bore and stroke: 3.75 x 3.4 inches. Compression ratio: 9.0:1. Brake horsepower: 210 at 4600 rpm. Five main bearings. Hydraulic valve lifters. Two-barrel Rochester 2GC carburetor.

SPECIAL DELUXE — SERIES 43500 (V-6) — A Special with a little more dressing, the Special Deluxe had bright bodyside moldings, bright window surrounds and a rear cove insert panel. Interiors were plusher vinyls with some cloth combinations. Floors were carpeted and the instrument panel was padded. Dual horns added to the standard equipment list.

SPECIAL DELUXE V-6 I.D. NUMBERS: Serial numbers began with 43500( )100001. The numbers were coded as explained under the 1965 Special Series 43300 ID Number section.

SPECIAL DELUXE SERIES 43500 (V-6)

Series Number	Model Number	Body Type & Seating	Factory Price	Shipping Weight	Production Total
43500	43569	4-dr Sed-6P	2436	3016	10,961
43500	43535	4-dr Sta Wag-6P	2727	3242	1,677

ENGINE: Specifications were the same as those listed for the 1965 Special Series 43300.

SPECIAL DELUXE — SERIES 43600 (V-8) — Identical externally to the 1965 Special Deluxe V-6 described above, the V-8 Special Deluxes were numbered as a separate series.

SPECIAL DELUXE I.D. NUMBERS: Serial numbers began with 43600( )10001. The numbers were coded as explained under the 1965 Special Series 43300 ID Number section.

SPECIAL DELUXE SERIES 43600 (V-8)

Series Number	Model Number	Body Type & Seating	Factory Price	Shipping Weight	Production Total
43600	43669	4-dr Sed-6P	2506	3143	25,675
43600	43635	4-dr Sta Wag-6P	2796	3369	9,123

ENGINE: Specifications were the same as those listed for the 1965 Special V-8 Series 43400.

SKYLARK — SERIES 44300 (V-6) — Buick's intermediate in its plushest form. Specific full wheelcovers, bright rocker and wheelhouse moldings, a unique cove treatment with full-width taillamps and emblems centered front and rear signified Skylark-level trim on the outside. The Skylark badge appeared on front fenders, deck lid and roof quarters (rear fenders on convertible); Interiors were plusher cloth and vinyl, or leather-grain all-vinyl. Front buckets were optional. Standard equipment on Skylark in addition to that found on lesser series included: foam-padded seats, paddle-type armrests, rear passenger courtesy lights on two doors, ashtray, glove compartment lights and full carpeting.

NOTE: A mid-1965 option was the Skylark Gran Sport, an option package offered on the two-door coupe, Sport Coupe and convertible. A 401 cid V-8 that produced 325 hp at 4400 rpm was the heart of the option. It had a 10.25:1 compression ratio and a single Carter AFB four-barrel carburetor. A heavy-duty crossflow radiator and dual exhaust manifolds with over-sized pipes were included. Exterior identification was provided by red-filled Gran Sport badges on the grille, deck and roof quarters (rear fenders on convertibles). Another badge was affixed to the instrument panel. The Skylark GS featured 7.75x14 tires on 6JK rims.

SKYLARK V-6 I.D. NUMBERS: Serial numbers began with 443005( )100001. The numbers were coded as explained under the 1965 Special Series 43300 ID Number section.

SKYLARK SERIES 44300 (V-6)

Series Number	Model Number	Body Type & Seating	Factory Price	Shipping Weight	Production Total
44300	44369	4-dr Sed-6P	2611	3086	3,385
44300	44327	2-dr Sed-6P	2482	3035	4,195
44300	44337	2-dr Spt Cpe-6P	2622	3057	4,501
44300	44367	2-dr Conv-6P	2773	3149	1,181

ENGINE: Specifications were the same as those listed for the 1965 Special Series 43300 V-6.

SKYLARK V-8 SERIES 44400 — Externally identical to the 1965 Skylark V-6 described above, the V-8 Skylarks were numbered as a separate series.

SKYLARK V-8 I.D. NUMBERS: Serial numbers began with 44405( )100001. Numbers were coded as explained under the 1965 Special Series 43300 ID Number section.

SKYLARK SERIES 44400 (V-8)

Series Number	Model Number	Body Type & Seating	Factory Price	Shipping Weight	Production Total
44400	44469	4-dr Sed-6P	2681	3194	22,239
44400	44427	2-dr Sed-6P	2552	3146	11,877
44400	44437	2-dr Spt Cpe-6P	2692	3198	46,698
44400	44467	2-dr Conv-6P	2842	3294	10,456

ENGINE: Specifications were the same as those listed for the 1965 Special V-8 Series 43400.

1965 Buick, Skylark four-door Sport Wagon, V-8

SPORTWAGON: Buick's stretched wheelbase station wagon continued to feature the unusual Skyroof with shaded glass panels in a raised area above the rear compartment. The increased headroom allowed a three-seat version to be marketed. Cargo area was 95.6 cubic feet. Interiors were all-vinyl. Models 44465 and 44455 were Custom models and featured most Skylark equipment, but had only a full-length bright metal side molding. A tailgate lamp was also standard.

SPORT WAGON I.D. NUMBERS: Serial numbers began with the model number (sample: 44265( )10001) and were coded as explained under the 1965 Special Series ID Number section.

SPORT WAGON SERIES 44200/44400

Series Number	Model Number	Body Type & Seating	Factory Price	Shipping Weight	Production Total
44200	44265	4-dr Sta Wag-9P	3056	3750	4,664
44200	44255	4-dr Sta Wag-6P	2925	3642	4,226
44400	44465	4-dr Cus Sta Wag-9P	3214	3802	11,166
44400	44455	4-dr Cus Sta Wag-9P	3092	3690	8,300

ENGINE: Specifications were the same as those listed for the 1965 Special Series 43400 V-8.

LESABRE — SERIES 45200 — Buick's full-sized price leaders featured a new body with a wider appearance and softer, bulgy lines. A bright narrow lower body molding was used, along with a trio of ventports on each front fender. The LeSabre signature appeared on rear body quarters. An extruded aluminum grille was used at the front. Standard equipment included electric windshield wipers; instrument panel safety pad directional signals; glove compartment light; dual armrests front and rear; door-operated courtesy lights; full carpeting and a map light. Interiors were cloth or vinyl.

LESABRE I.D. NUMBERS: Buick serial numbers were located on the hinge pillar post, left side, above the instrument panel and stamped on left side, top of engine block, ahead of valve cover. The first five symbols were the model number. The first symbol was a "4" indicating Buick Motor Div. products. The second through fifth symbols indicated the series and body style (see model numbers on tables below). The sixth symbol was a number indicating model year, 5=1965. The seventh symbol was a letter representing the plant code, as follows: B=Baltimore, Md.; C=Southgate, Calif.;D=Donaville, Ga.; H=Flint, Mich.; K=Leeds, Mo.; X=Fairfax, Kan.; Y=Wilmington, Del.; Z=Fremont, Calif.; V= Bloomfield, Mich. The last six symbols were numerals representing the plant sequential production number, with series mixed in production. Engine numbers were stamped in various positions on the crankcase, usually, or on the cylinder block. Along with serial number, the engines carried a production code with a prefix identifying engine and year, then a four symbol sequential production number. Numbers stamped on front right of block opposite serial number. Engine codes were as follows: (400 cid GS 400 V-8) LR, NA; (Wildcat/Electra 225/Riviera 401 cid V-8) LT, LV; (Wilcat/Electra/Riviera 425 cid V-8) LW and LX.

LESABRE SERIES 45200

Series Number	Model Number	Body Type & Seating	Factory Price	Shipping Weight	Production Total
45200	45269	4-dr Sed-6P	2888	3788	37,788
45200	45239	4-dr HT Sed-6P	3027	3809	18,384
45200	45237	2-dr Spt Cpe-6P	2968	3753	15,786

ENGINE: Specifications were the same as those listed for the 1965 Special Series 43400 V-8.

LESABRE CUSTOM — SERIES 45400 — Custom interior fabrics of cloth and vinyl set the Custom series apart. The convertible had a standard outside rearview mirror. Exterior trim was like the LeSabre Series 45200.

LESABRE CUSTOM — SERIES 45400 I.D. NUMBERS: Serial numbers began with 454005( )10001. Numbers were coded as explained under the 1965 LeSabre Series ID Number section.

LESABRE CUSTOM SERIES 45400

Series Number	Model Number	Body Type & Seating	Factory Price	Shipping Weight	Production Total
45400	45469	4-dr Sed-6P	2962	3777	20,052
45400	45439	4-dr HT Sed-6P	3101	3811	23,394
45400	45237	2-dr Spt Cpe-6P	3037	3724	21,049
45400	45467	2-dr Conv-5P	3257	3812	6,543

ENGINE: Specifications were the the same as those listed for the 1965 Special Series 43400 V-8.

WILDCAT — SERIES 46200 — Buick's medium-priced line, still equipped for superior performance, shared the LeSabre's new 1965 body. It was distinguished by a die-cast grille having a large center emblem, large simulated bright front fender vents and Wildcat script on the quarter panels and deck. Inside, Wildcat emblems appeared on door panels. The full wheelcovers also used the Wildcat emblem. Standard equipment, in addition to that found on the LeSabre, included a smoking set and rear seat ashtrays. Interiors were cloth or vinyl.

WILDCAT I.D. NUMBERS: Serial numbers began with 462005( )10001. Numbers were coded as explained under the 1965 LeSabre Series ID Number section.

WILDCAT SERIES 46200

Series Number	Model Number	Body Type & Seating	Factory Price	Shipping Weight	Production Total
46200	42269	4-dr Sed-6P	3117	4058	10,184
46200	46239	4-dr HT Sed-6P	3278	4089	7,499
46200	46237	2-dr Spt Cpe-6P	3219	3988	6,031
46200	46267	2-dr Conv-6P	3431	3812	4,616*

NOTE: The symbol (*) indicates that convertible production total also includes Wildcat Deluxe convertibles.

ENGINE: V-8. Overhead valve. Cast iron block. Displacement: 401 cid. Bore and stroke: 4.18x 3.64 inches. Compression ratio: 10.25: 1. Brake horsepower: 325 at 4600 rpm. Five main bearings. Hydraulic lifters. Four-barrel Carter AFB or Rochester 4GC carburetor.

WILDCAT DELUXE — SERIES 46400 — This was a trim variation on the Wildcat Series 46200, with slightly plusher interior combinations available.

WILDCAT DELUXE SERIES 46400 I.D. NUMBERS: Serial numbers began with 464005( )10001. Numbers were coded as explained under the 1965 LeSabre ID Number section.

WILDCAT DELUXE SERIES 46400

Series Number	Model Number	Body Type & Seating	Factory Price	Shipping Weight	Production Total
46400	46469	4-dr Sed-6P	3218	4045	9,765
46400	46439	4-dr HT Sed-6P	3338	4075	13,903
46400	46437	2-dr Spt Cpe-6P	3272	4014	11,617
46400	46467	2-dr Conv-6P	3651	4064	4,616*

NOTE: Symbol (*) indicates that Wildcat Deluxe convertible total also includes Series 46200 Wildcat convertibles.

ENGINE: Specifications were the same as those listed for the 1965 Wildcat Series 46200.

WILDCAT CUSTOM — SERIES 46600 — This was the plushest of all Wildcats, with interiors featuring vinyl bucket seats or notch-back full-width seats in cloth. Offered only on three styles, this was essentially a trim option. Production figures are included with those given for corresponding Wildcat Deluxe figures.

WILDCAT CUSTOM I.D. NUMBERS: Serial numbers began with 466005( )1001.Numbers were coded as explained under the 1965 LeSabre Series ID Number section.

WILDCAT CUSTOM SERIES 46600

Series Number	Model Number	Body Type & Seating	Factory Price	Shipping Weight	Production Total
46600	46639	4-dr HT Sed-6P	3552	4160	—
46600	46637	2-dr Spt Cpe-6P	3493	4047	—
46600	46667	2-dr Conv-6P	3431	4069	—

ENGINE: Specifications were the same as those listed for the 1965 Wildcat Series 45200.

ELECTRA — SERIES 48200 — The largest Buick was equipped with totally new styling for 1965, although the hallmark rear wheelhouse skirts and wide, ribbed lower body moldings

were retained. A distinctive cross-hatch textured cast grille was used at the front. Interiors were fabrics or vinyls, with woodgrain dash accents. Standard Electra features, in addition to those found on less costly Buicks, included Super Turbine transmission; power steering; power brakes; Deluxe steering wheel; two-speed electric wipers with washer; electric clock; license frames; trip mileage indicator; cigar lighter in rear; Safety buzzer; back-up lights, and power brake signal lamp. Convertibles had two-way power seat control and outside rearview mirror.

ELECTRA SERIES 48200

Series Number	Model Number	Body Type & Seating	Factory Price	Shipping Weight	Production Total
48200	48269	4-dr Sed-6P	3989	4261	12,459
48200	48239	4-dr HT Sed-6P	4121	4284	12,842
48200	48237	2-dr Spt Cpe-6P	3999	4208	6,302

ENGINE: Specifications were the same as those listed for the 1965 Wildcat Series 45200.

ELECTRA I.D. NUMBERS: Serial numbers began with 482005( )100001. Numbers were coded as explained under the 1965 LeSabre Series ID Number section.

ELECTRA CUSTOM: A plusher car than the Electra, the Custom featured elegant interior appointment with fine vinyls and fabrics used for trimming.

ELECTRA CUSTOM I.D. NUMBERS: Serial numbers began with 484005( )100001. Numbers were coded as explained under the 1965 LeSabre ID Number section.

ELECTRA CUSTOM SERIES 48400

Series Number	Model Number	Body Type & Seating	Factory Price	Shipping Weight	Production Total
48400	48469	4-dr Sed-6P	4168	4292	7,197
48400	48439	4-dr HT Sed-6P	4300	4344	29,932
48400	48437	2-dr Spt Cpe-6P	4179	4228	9,570
48400	48467	2-dr Conv-6P	4350	4325	8,508

ENGINE: Specifications were the same as those listed for the 1965 Wildcat Series 45200.

1965 Buick, Riviera two-door hardtop sport coupe, V-8 (AA)

RIVIERA — SERIES 49447 — The last recycle of the original Riviera body was also the most distinctive. Headlamps were now stacked vertically behind the fender grilles, which opened when the lamps were turned on. Taillamps were housed in the bumper bar, giving a cleaner rear deck appearance. Riviera script appeared on the front fenders and deck lid. Standard Riviera features included: Super Turbine transmission; power steering; power brakes; two-speed electric wipers with washer; back-up lights; glare-proof rearview mirror; parking brake signal light; Safety buzzer; map light; electric clock; tilt steering wheel; automatic trunk light; license plate frames; upper and lower instrument panel safety pads; full carpeting; double door release handles; console-mounted gear selector; Walnut paneling on instrument panel and individual front bucket seats. Optional Custom interiors included carpeted lower doors.

RIVIERA I.D. NUMBERS: Serial numbers began at 494005( )900001. Numbers were coded as explained under the 1965 LeSabre Series ID Number section.

RIVIERA SERIES 48400

Series Number	Model Number	Body Type & Seating	Factory Price	Shipping Weight	Production Total
49400	49447	Spt Cpe-4P	4318	4036	34,586

ENGINE: Specifications were the same as those listed for the 1965 Wildcat Series 45200.

NOTE: A Gran Sport option was available for the 1965 Riviera. It included a 360 brake horsepower Super Wildcat V-8 with dual four-barrel carburetors, large diameter dual exhausts, positive traction differential and bright metal engine accents including a large plated air cleaner and polished ribbed valve covers. Exterior identification was provided by the use of GS full wheelcovers and Gran Sport lettering below the Riviera script on the deck lid and on the front fenders.

CHASSIS FEATURES: Wheelbase: (Series 43300, 43400, 44300, 44400) 115 inches; (Series 44200 and 44400 Sport Wagons) 120 inches; (Series 45200 and 45400) 123 inches; (Series 46200, 46400, 46600, 48200 and 48400) 126 inches; (Series 474447) 119 inches. Overall length: (Series 43300, 43400, 44300 and 44400) 203.2 inches; (Series 43400 Station Wagon) 203.4 inches; (Series 44200 and 44400 Sport Wagon) 208.2 inches; (Series 45200 and 45400) 123 inches; (Series 46200, 46400, 46600) 219.8 inches; (Series 48200 and 48400) 224.1 inches; (Series 47447) 209 inches. Front tread: (Series 43300, 43400, 44400 and 44200) 58 inches; (Series 45200 and 45400) 63 inches; (Series 46200, 46400 , 46600, 48200 and 48400) 63.4 inches; (Series 47447) 60 inches. Rear tread: (Series 43300, 43400, 44400 and 44200) 58 inches; (Series 45200, 45400, 46200, 46400, 46600, 48200 and 48400) 62 inches; (Series 47447) 59 inches. Tire sizes: Series 43300, 43400, 44300, 43400) 6.95 x 14; (Series 44400 and 44200) 7.75 x 14; (Series 45200 and 45400) 8.15 x 5; (Series 46200, 46400 and 46600) 8.45 x 15; (Series 48200 and 48400) 8.75 x 15; and (Series 47447) 8.45 x 15.

POWERTRAIN OPTIONS: A three-speed transmission was standard on Series 43300, 43400. 44300, 43400, 44200, 44400, 45200, 45400, 46200. 46400 and 46600. Super Turbine Drive was optional on the preceding Series and standard on Series 48200, 48400 and 47747. A four-speed manual transmission was optional for Series 43300, 43400, 44300, 44200, 44400, 46200, 46400 and 46600. A 250 brake horsepower 300 cid V-8 was optional for Series 43300, 43400, 44300, 44200, 44400, 45200 and 45400. The 340 brake horsepower, 425 cid V-8 was optional for the Series 46200, 46400, 46600, 48200, 48400 and 47747. A 360 brake horsepower, 425 cid V-8 equipped with dual four-barrel carburetors was a dealer option for Series 46200, 46400, 46600, 48200, 48400 and 47747. This 360 hp V-8 was included with Riviera Gran Sport option. The 325 hp 401 cid V-8 was included with the Skylark Gran Sport option.

CONVENIENCE OPTIONS: Power steering (standard on 46000, 48000 and 47747 Series). Power brakes (standard on 46000, 48000 and 47747 Series). Power windows (standard on Electra Custom convertible, not offered for 4300 and 4400 Series). Power seat controls (4-way or 6-way; a 2-way power seat was standard on the Electra convertible). Air conditioning. AM radio. AM-FM radio (full-size only). Seven-position tilt steering wheel (standard on 47747). Remote control outside rearview mirror. Tinted glass. Four-note horn. Tachometer. Automatic trunk release (full-size only). Electro cruise (full size only). Cornering lights (Full-size only). Consoles for Skylark bucket seats. Luggage rack for Sport Wagons. Front seat belt deletion. Heater/Defroster deletion.

HISTORICAL FOOTNOTES: Calendar year production was 653,838 units, allowing Buick to slip by Dodge and Oldsmobile into fourth place in the industry. Model year production was 600,787. In July, Edward T. Rollert ("father of theSkylark") moved to a GM executive position and Robert L. Kessler became Buick general manager. The Riviera Gran Sport was advertised as "An iron fist in a velvet glove" and had a top speed of 125-130 mph. The Skylark Gran Sport was advertised as a "Howitzer with windshield wipers." 44200 and 44400 Series station wagons that had raised roof section, were called Sport Wagons.

1966 BUICK

SPECIAL — SERIES 43300 (V-6) — A new body, with more sheet metal sculpting, graced the 1966 Special. Each front fender had three ventiports. Rear fenders carried Special lettering. Otherwise, the car was almost completely devoid of bright metal trim on the sides. Small hubcaps were standard. Regular equipment included a heater and defroster; directional signals; ashtray; cigar lighter; dual key locking system; Step-On parking brake; front door-operated courtesy light; upper instrument panel pad; outside rearview mirror; two-speed wipers with washer; padded sun visors; front and rear seat belts and back-up lamps. Interiors were vinyl and cloth, with an all-vinyl trim optional.

SPECIAL I.D. NUMBERS: Serial numbers began with 433006( )10001 and up. The first five symbols were numerals representing the style. The sixth symbol was a numeral '6' representing the 1966 model year. The seventh symbol was a letter representing the plant code and the last six symbols were numerals representing sequential plant production number, with series mixed in production.

SPECIAL I.D. NUMBERS: Serial numbers were located on the hinge pillar post, left side, above the instrument panel and stamped on the engine block. The first five symbols were the model number. The first symbol was a "4" indicating Buick Motor Div. products. The second through fifth symbols indicated the series and body style (see model numbers on tables below). The sixth symbol was a number indicating model year, 6=1966. The seventh symbol was a letter representing the plant code, as follows: B=Baltimore, Md.; C=Southgate, Calif.;D=Donaville, Ga.; H=Flint, Mich.; I=Oshawa, Ont., Canada; K=Leeds, Mo.; V=Bloomfield, Mich.; X=Fairfax, Kan.; Y=Wilmington, Del.; Z=Fremont, OH. The last six symbols were numerals representing the plant sequential production number, with series mixed in production. Engine numbers were stamped in various positions on the crankcase, usually, or on the cylinder block. Engine production codes, stamped on right-hand side of block, were as follows: (6-cyl.) MH,MK; (300 cid V-8) ML, MM; (340 cid V-8) MB, MC, MA; (GS 400/400 cid V-8) MR; (401 cid V-8) MT, MV; (425 cid V-8) MV, MW, MZ.

Series Number	Model Number	Body Type & Seating	Factory Price	Shipping Weight	Production Total
43300	43369	4-dr Sed-6P	2401	3046	8,797
43300	43307	2-dr Cpe-6P	2348	3009	9,322
43300	43367	2-dr Conv-6P	2604	3092	1,357
43300	43335	4-dr Sta Wag-6P	2695	3296	1,451

ENGINE: V-6. Overhead valve. Cast iron block. Displacement: 225 cid. Bore and stroke 3.75 x 3.4 inches. Compression ratio 9.0:1. Brake horsepower: 160 at 4200 rpm. Four main bearings. Hydraulic lifters. Rochester 2GC two-barrel carburetor.

SPECIAL — SERIES 43400 V-8 — Identical externally to the 1966 Special V-6 described above, the V-8 Specials were numbered as a separate series.

SPECIAL V-8 I.D. NUMBERS: Serial numbers began with 434006( )100001. Numbers were coded as explained under the Special Series ID Number section.

SPECIAL SERIES 43400

Series Number	Model Number	Body Type & Seating	Factory Price	Shipping Weight	Production Total
43400	43469	4-dr Sed-6P	2471	3148	9,355
43400	43407	2-dr Cpe-6P	2418	3091	5,719
43400	43467	2-dr Conv-6P	2671	3223	2,036
43400	43435	4-dr Sta Wag-6P	2764	3399	3,038

ENGINE: V-8. Overhead valve. Cast iron block. Displacement: 300 cid. Bore and stroke: 3.75 x 3.4 inches. Compression ratio: 9.0:1. Brake horsepower: 210 at 4600 rpm. Five main bearings. Hydraulic lifters. Rochester 2GC two-barrel carburetor.

SPECIAL DELUXE — SERIES 43500 V-6 — The Special Deluxe had the same body as the Special, but with slightly more brightwork, including a rear quarter bright spear with Special lettering above it (over the wheelhouse), bright window reveals and a stand-up hood ornament. Special Deluxe models had additional standard features including: rear ashtray; Deluxe steering wheel; dual armrests; carpeting and dual horns. Sedan interiors were cloth and vinyl, while the other models were trimmed in all-vinyl material. A notchback all-vinyl front seat was optional for the coupe and sport coupe.

SPECIAL DELUXE I.D. NUMBERS: Serial numbers began with 435006( )10001. Numbers were coded as explained under the 1966 Special Series 43300 ID Number section.

SPECIAL DELUXE SERIES 43500

Series Number	Model Number	Body Type & Seating	Factory Price	Shipping Weight	Production Total
43500	43569	4-dr Sed-6P	2485	3045	5,501
43500	43507	2-dr Cpe-6P	2432	3009	2,359
43500	43517	2-dr Spt Cpe-6P	2504	3038	25,071
43500	43535	4-dr Sta Wag-6P	2783	3290	824

ENGINE: Specifications were the same as those listed for the 1966 Special Series 43300.

SPECIAL DELUXE V-8 — SERIES 43600 — Identical externally to the Special Deluxe V-6 described above, the V-8 Special Deluxes were numbered as a separate series.

SPECIAL DELUXE SERIES 43600

Series Number	Model Number	Body Type & Seating	Factory Price	Shipping Weight	Production Total
43600	43669	4-dr Sed-6P	2555	3156	26,773
43600	43607	2-dr Cpe-6P	2502	3112	4,908
43600	43617	2-dr Spt Cpe-6P	2574	3130	10,350
43600	4635	2-dr Sta Wag-6P	2853	3427	7,592

ENGINE: Specifications were the same as those listed for the 1966 Special Series 43400 V-8.

1966 Buick, Skylark four-door hardtop sedan, V-8

SKYLARK — SERIES 44300 V-6 — Buick's plushest intermediate was the recipient of additional exterior bright moldings. They included a lower body molding that ran full-length, with wheelhouse kickups, simulated vent grids on front fenders, Skylark script and emblems on rear fenders and a specific rear cove panel. A notchback front seat was standard on the four-door hardtop, optional on other models. Bucket seats, with a reclining passenger seat, were optional, as were headrests. Trim was all-vinyl or cloth and vinyl combinations. All Skylarks had the following additional standard equipment: Custom-padded seat cushions, Deluxe specific wheelcovers, ashtray and glove compartment lights and front interior courtesy lamps.

SKYLARK V-6 I.D. NUMBERS: Serial numbers began with 44300( )10001. Serial numbers were coded as explained under the 1965 Special Series 43300 ID Number section.

SKYLARK SERIES 44300

Series Number	Model Number	Body Type & Seating	Factory Price	Shipping Weight	Production Total
44300	44339	4-dr HT Sed-6P	2846	3172	1,422
44300	44307	2-dr Cpe-6P	2624	3034	1,454
44300	44317	2-dr Spt Cpe-6P	2687	3069	2,456
44300	44367	2-dr Conv-6P	2837	3158	608

ENGINE: Specifications were the same as those listed for the 1966 Special Series 44300 V-6.

SKYLARK — SERIES 44400 V-8 — Identical externally to the 1966 Skylark V-6 described above, the V-8 Skylarks were numbered as a separate series.

SKYLARK SERIES 44400

Series Number	Model Number	Body Type & Seating	Factory Price	Shipping Weight	Production Total
44400	44-439	4-dr HT Sed-6P	2916	3285	18,729
44400	44-4307	2-dr Cpe-6P	2694	3145	6,427
44400	44417	2-dr Spt Cpe-6P	2757	3152	33,086
44400	44467	2-dr Conv-6P	2904	3259	6,129

ENGINE: Specifications were the same as listed for the 1966 Special Series 43400 V-8.

SKYLARK GRAN SPORT — SERIES 44600 — Buick moved a step closer to a muscle car image with the 1966 Gran Sport. Equipped like the Skylark, the sporting image was pursued via a black matte finish rear cove panel, Skylark GS emblems on quarters and instrument panel, Gran Sport nameplates on the grille and deck, and whitewall or redline 7.75 x 14 tires. Bright simulated air scoops, side paint stripes and a blacked-out grille gave further identity. There was no hood ornament. Interiors were all-vinyl, with a notchback front seat standard and bucket front seats optional. The Skylark had a 401 cid V-8 as standard equipment. However, this engine was listed as a 400 cid motor, to get around the GM restriction on over 400 cid engines in mid-size bodies.

SKYLARK GRAN SPORT I.D. NUMBERS: Vehicle Identification Numbers began with 446006( )100001. Numbers were coded as explained under the 1966 Special Series ID Number section.

SKYLARK GRAN SPORT SERIES 44600

Series Number	Model Number	Body Type & Seating	Factory Price	Shipping Weight	Production Total
44600	44607	2-dr Cpe-6P	2956	3479	1,835
44600	44617	2-dr Spt Cpe-6P	3019	3428	9,934
44600	44667	2-dr Conv-6P	3167	3532	2,047

ENGINE: V-8. Overhead valves. Cast iron block. Displacement: 401 cid (advertised as 400 cid). Bore and stroke: 4.18 x 3.64 inches. Compression ratio: 10.25:1. Brake horsepower: 325 at 4400 rpm. Five main bearings. Hydraulic lifters. Four-barrel Carter AFB carburetor.

SPORT WAGON AND SPORT WAGON CUSTOM — SERIES 44200 AND 44400 V-8 — Buick's popular intermediate wagons continued to feature a glass skyroof and two- or three-seat configuration. The Sport Wagon had most Special Deluxe features, plus brush-finished wiper arms, Sport Wagon quarter panel scripts and specific taillights. Interiors were all-vinyl. The Custom versions had satin finished lower body moldings, Deluxe steering wheel and tailgate lamps. Custom padded seat cushions and Custom interior trim, featuring plusher upholstery and carpeting extending to the lower doors, was used.

SPORT WAGON AND SPORT WAGON CUSTOM I.D. NUMBERS: Serial numbers began with 442006( )100001 for the Sport Wagon and 444006( )100001 on the Sport Wagon Custom. Numbers were coded as described under the 1966 Special Series ID Number section.

SPORT WAGONS SERIES 44200/44400

Series Number	Model Number	Body Type & Seating	Factory Price	Shipping Weight	Production Total
44200	44265	4-dr Sta Wag-3S	3173	3811	2,667
44200	44255	4-dr Sta Wag-2S	3025	3713	2,469
44400	44465	4-dr Cus Sta Wag-3S	3293	384-4	9,510
44400	44455	4-dr Cus Sta Wag-2S	3155	3720	6,964

ENGINE: V-8. Overhead valve. Cast iron block. Displacement: 340 cid. Bore and stroke: 3.75 x 3.85 inches. Compression ratio: 9.0:1. Brake horsepower: 220 at 4000 rpm. Five main bearings. Hydraulic lifters. Two-barrel Rochester 2GC carburetor.

LESABRE-SERIES 45200 — Slightly face-lifted from 1965, the lowest-priced, full- sized Buick had three ventiports on each front fender and LeSabre scripts on the quarter panels. Narrow lower body moldings of bright metal were used. Interiors were vinyl and cloth. Standard equipment included front and rear seat belts, Step-On parking brake, door operated courtesy lamps, dual armrests, dual horns and carpeting.

LESABRE I.D. NUMBERS: Vehicle identification Numbers began with 45200( )10001. Numbers were coded as explained under the 1966 Buick Special Series ID Number section.

LESABRE SERIES 45200

Series Number	Model Number	Body Type & Seating	Factory Price	Shipping Weight	Production Total
45200	45269	4-dr Sed-6P	2942	3796	39,146
45200	45239	4-dr HT Sed-6P	3081	3828	17,740
45200	45237	2-dr HT Cpe-6P	3022	3751	13,843

ENGINE: Specifications were the same as listed under 1966 Sport Wagon and Sport Wagon Custom engine data.

LESABRE CUSTOM — SERIES 45400 — Custom models had plusher interiors with Deluxe steering wheel, two-speed wiper and washer equipment, and back-up lamps. Optional Custom trim included bucket seats with black accents.

LESABRE CUSTOM I.D. NUMBERS: Vehicle Identification Numbers began with 454006( )100001. Numbers were coded as explained under the 1966 Buick Special Series ID Number section.

LESABRE CUSTOM SERIES 45400

Series Number	Model Number	Body Type & Seating	Factory Price	Shipping Weight	Production Total
45400	45469	4-dr Sed-6P	3035	3788	25,932
45400	45439	4-dr HT Sed-6P	3174	3824	26,914
45400	45437	2-dr HT Cpe-6P	3109	3746	18,830
45400	45467	2-dr Conv-6P	3326	3833	4,994

ENGINE: Specifications were the same as those listed under 1966 Sport Wagon and Sport Wagon Custom engine data.

WILDCAT — SERIES 46400 — Buick's middle-priced, full-sized car again pursued a performance image. A specific grille with vertical texturing was used. There was a Wildcat hood ornament above it. Wildcat lettering appeared across the deck lid and on rear quarter panels. Simulated air intake grids appeared behind the front wheelhouses. Interiors were cloth and vinyl, or all-vinyl. Standard features included the LeSabre's accoutrements plus a glovebox light.

WILDCAT I.D. NUMBERS: Vehicle Identification Numbers began with 464006 900001. Numbers were coded as explained under the 1966 Special Series ID Number section.

WILDCAT SERIES 46400

Series Number	Model Number	Body Type & Seating	Factory Price	Shipping Weight	Production Total
46400	46469	4-dr Sed-6P	3233	4070	14,389
46400	46439	4-dr HT Sed-6P	3391	4108	15,081
46400	46437	2-dr HT Cpe-6P	3326	4003	9,774
46400	46467	2-dr Conv-6P	3480	4065	2,690

ENGINE: V-8. Overhead valve. Cast iron block. Displacement: 401 cid. Bore and stroke: 4.18 x 3.64 inches. Compression ratio: 10.25:1. Brake horsepower: 325 at 4600 rpm. Five main bearings. Hydraulic lifters. Four-barrel Carter AFB carburetor.

WILDCAT CUSTOM — SERIES 46600 — A plusher Wildcat, with Deluxe steering wheel, padded-type armrests, outside rearview mirror and Custom headlining (except convertible). Plusher cloth and vinyl or all-vinyl trim was used, with notchback or Strato bucket front seat (reclining passenger seat with the latter) and headrests.

WILDCAT CUSTOM I.D. NUMBERS: Vehicle Identification Numbers began with 466006( )900001. Numbers were coded as explained under the 1966 Special Series ID Number Section.

WILDCAT CUSTOM SERIES 46600

Series Number	Model Number	Body Type & Seating	Factory Price	Shipping Weight	Production Total
46600	46639	4-dr HT Sed-6P	3606	4176	13,060
46600	46637	2-dr HT Cpe-6P	3547	4018	10,800
46600	46667	2-dr Conv-6P	3701	4079	2,790

ENGINE: Specifications were the same as those listed under Wildcat Series 46400 engine data.

WILDCAT GRAN SPORT: In 1966, a Wildcat Gran Sport option was offered for the one, and only, time. It was available for the base or Custom two-door Sport Coupe or convertible. Ingredients included a chrome-plated air cleaner; cast aluminum rocker arm covers; dual exhausts; heavy-duty front and rear suspension; positive traction rear axle and GS identification plates for the front and rear of the car.

1966 Buick, Electra 225 four-door hardtop sedan, V-8 (AA)

ELECTRA 225 — SERIES 48200 — The largest Buick, with a distinctly bigger body, was similar to 1965. Fender skirts were standard, with a full-length lower body molding wider than those of other Buicks. Electra 225 script appeared on the rear fenders. The car's prestige was further enhanced by the use of four ventiports per fender. Standard features, in addition to those of lower-priced Buicks, included Custom-padded seat cushions; Custom front seat belts with retractors; electric clock; parking brake signal lamp; glovebox and map lights; Glareproof mirror; power steering; power brakes and Super Turbine automatic transmission. Interiors were cloth and vinyl combinations.

ELECTRA 225 I.D. NUMBERS: Vehicle identification Numbers began with 482006( )100001. Numbers were coded as explained under the 1966 Special Series ID Numbers section.

ELECTRA 225 SERIES 48200

Series Number	Model Number	Body Type & Seating	Factory Price	Shipping Weight	Production Total
48200	48269	4-dr Sed-6P	4022	4255	11,692
48200	48239	4-dr HT Sed-6P	4153	4271	10,792
48200	42837	2-dr HT Cpe-6P	4032	4176	4,882

ENGINE: Specifications were the same as listed under 1966 Wildcat Series 46400 engine data.

ELECTRA 225 CUSTOM — SERIES 48400 — An even plusher Electra 225, with Custom notchback front seat, in cloth, or Strato buckets, in vinyl, for the convertible. All Custom interiors had carpeted lower door panels. Although basically a trim option, Electra 225 Customs were numbered as a separate series.

ELECTRA 225 CUSTOM I.D. NUMBERS: Vehicle Identification Numbers began with 484006( )100001. Numbers were coded as explained under the 1966 Buick Special Series ID Number section.

ELECTRA 225 CUSTOM SERIES 48400

Series Number	Model Number	Body Type & Seating	Factory Price	Shipping Weight	Production Total
48400	48469	4-dr Sed-6P	4201	4292	9,368
48400	48439	4-dr HT Sed-6P	4332	4323	34,149
48400	48437	2-dr HT Cpe-6P	4211	4230	10,119
48400	48467	2-dr Conv-6P	4378	4298	7,175

ENGINE: Specifications were the same as those listed under 1966 Wildcat Series 46400 engine data.

RIVIERA — SERIES 49487 — A sleek new body graced the first totally restyled Riviera since 1963. Headlamps were once again horiztonally paired, unlike 1965. Now, they retracted above the grille when not in use. The body's clean lines were enhanced by the lack of vent windows. Inside, a new instrument panel was found, with a unique, vertical, drum-type speedometer and a full complement of gauges. Standard equipment included power steering, power brakes; Super Turbine transmission; tilt steering wheel; dual exhausts; full carpeting; padded instrument panel; dual-speed wipers and washer; back-up lamps; outside rearview mirror; shatter-resistant inside mirror and front and rear seat belts. Bucket or bench-style front seats were standard at the purchaser's choice. Strato-buckets with Custom all-vinyl trim were available, as were other Custom trim options.

NOTE: Gran Sport equipment was offered for the 1966 Riviera. This year it consisted of a chromed air cleaner and aluminum rocker covers for the standard 340 brake horsepower, 425 cid V-8; plus heavy-duty shocks front and rear, 8.45 x 15 red or white line tires, positive traction differential and GS emblems on front fenders and instrument panel. Also available as a "dealer kit" was a 360 hp version of the 425 cid V-8 with dual four-barrel carburetors.

RIVIERA I.D. NUMBERS: Vehicle Identification Numbers began with 494876 900001. Numbers were coded as explained under the 1966 Special Series ID Number section.

RIVIERA SERIES 49400

Series Number	Model Number	Body Type & Seating	Factory Price	Shipping Weight	Production Total
49400	49487	2-dr Spt Cpe-4P	4424	4180	45,348

ENGINE: V-8. Overhead valve. Cast iron block. Displacement: 425 cid. Bore and stroke: 4.3125 x 3.64 inches. Compression ratio: 10.25:1. Brake horsepower: 340 at 4400 rpm. Five main bearings. Hydraulic lifters. Four-barrel Rochester 4MC carburetor.

CHASSIS FEATURES: Wheelbase: (Series 43300,43400,43500,43600,44300,44400, 44600) 115 inches; (Series 44200 and 44400 Sport Wagons) 120 inches; (Series 45200 and 45400) 123 inches; (Series 46400 and 46600) 126 inches; (Series 49487) 119 inches. Overall length: (Series 43300, 43400, 43500, 43600, 443000, 44400, 44600) 204 inches; (Series 44200 and 44400 Sport Wagons) 209 inches; (Series 45200 and 45400) 216.9 inches; (Series 46400 and 46600) 219.9 inches; (Series 48200 and 48400) 223.4 inches; (Series 494-87) 211.2 inches. Front tread: (Special) 58 inches; (LeSabre) 63 inches; (Wildcat/Electra/Riviera) 63.4 inches. Rear tread: (Special) 59 inches; (All others) 63 inches. Tires: (Series 43300, 43500) 6.95 x 14; (Series 43400, 43600 and 44400) 7.35 x 14; (Series 44600) 7.75 x 14; (Series 44200 and 44400 Sport Wagons) 8.25 x 14; (Series 45200 and 45400) 8.45 x 15; (Series 46400 and 46600) 8.45 x 15; (Series 48200 and 48400) 8.85 x 15; (Series 49487) 8.45 x 15.

POWERTRAIN OPTIONS: A three-speed manual transmission was standard on Series 43300, 43400, 43500, 44300, 44400, 44200, 44600, 45200, 45400, 46400 and 46600. Super Turbine automatic transmission was standard on Series 48200 and 49487 and optional on Series 46400 and 46400. Turbine transmission was optional for all other models. A four-speed manual transmission was optional for Series 44400 and 44600. A 260 brake horsepower, 340 cid V-8 was optional for Series 43400, 44300, 44400, 44200, 45200 and 45400. The 340 horsepower, 425 cid V-8 standard on Model 49487 and optional on Series 46400, 46600, 48200 and 48400. A 360 hp, 425 cid engine with dual four-barrel carburetors could be dealer-installed on 49487.

CONVENIENCE OPTIONS: Power steering ($121, standard on 48000 and 49487). Power brakes ($42, standard on 48000 and 49487). Power windows ($105). Four-way/Six-way power seat controls ($69/$95). Air conditioning ($421). AM radio ($88). AM/FM radio ($175). Seven-position tilt steering wheel ($42). Remote control outside rearview mirror ($7). Tinted glass ($42). Tinted windshield only ($28). Four-note horn ($16). Automatic trunk release ($13). Electro cruise ($56-$63). Cornering lights, full-size only ($34). Simulated wire wheelcovers ($58). Five-spoke chromed wheels ($89). Heater/defroster deletion ($96 cr). Luggage rack for Sport Wagons.

NOTE: Typical option prices for midsize models. Prices vary slightly for compacts and full-size models.

HISTORICAL FOOTNOTES: Calendar year production was 580,421 units. Buick fell to sixth position and Oldsmobile became the fifth largest automaker in the U.S. Model year production was 558,870 units. The Riviera GS could do the quarter-mile in 16.4 seconds at 87 mph and had a top speed of 125 mph. The Skylark GS could do 0-to-60 in 7.6 seconds and cover the quarter-mile in 14.13 at 95.13 mph. The Wildcat GS, offered only in 1966, was even faster. It did 0-to-60 in 7.5 seconds and had a top speed of 125 mph.

1967 BUICK

SPECIAL — SERIES 43300 V-6 — A re-hash of the 1966 style, distinguished by a new grille, the 1967 Special continued with rear quarter model name lettering and triple ventiports on front fenders. These lowest-priced Buicks were lacking in bright trim. Even the window surrounds were plain. Standard equipment included heater and defroster; ashtray; directional signals; cigar lighter; Step-On parking brake; front and rear seat belts; front door operated courtesy light; upper instrument panel safety pad; outside rearview mirror; dual speed wipers and washer; padded sun visors; back-up lamps and other mandated safety items. Vinyl and cloth upholstery was standard, while an all-vinyl interior was optional.

SPECIAL I.D. NUMBERS: Serial numbers were located on the hinge pillar post, left side, above the instrument panel and stamped on the engine block. The first five symbols were the model number. The first symbol was a "4" indicating Buick Motor Div. products. The second through fifth symbols indicated the series and body style (see model numbers on tables below). The sixth symbol was a number indicating model year, 7=1967. The seventh symbol was a letter representing the plant code, as follows: B=Baltimore, Md.; C=Southgate, Calif.;D=Donaville, Ga.; H=Flint, Mich.; I=Oshawa, Ont., Canada; K=Leeds, Mo.; V=Bloomfield, Mich.; X=Fairfax, Kan.; Y=Wilmington, Del.; Z=Fremont, OH. The last six symbols were numerals representing the plant sequential production number, with series mixed in production. Engine numbers were stamped in various positions on the crankcase, usually, or on the cylinder block. Engine production codes, stamped on right-hand side of block, were as follows: (6-cyl.) NH; (300 cid V-8) NL, NM; (340 cid V-8) NB, NX, NA; (GS 400/400 cid V-8) NR; (430 cid V-8) ND, MD, NE.

SPECIAL SERIES 43300

Series Number	Model Number	Body Type & Seating	Factory Price	Shipping Weight	Production Total
43300	43369	4-dr Sed-6P	2462	3077	4,711
43300	43307	2-dr Cpe-6P	2411	3071	6,989
43300	43335	4-dr Sta Wag-6P	2742	2812	908

ENGINE: V-6. Overhead valve. Cast-iron block. Displacement: 225 cid. Bore and stroke: 3.75 x 3.4 inches. Compression ratio: 9.0:1. Brake horsepower: 160 at 4200 rpm. Four main bearings. Hydraulic lifters. Two-barrel Rochester 2GC carburetor.

SPECIAL — SERIES 43400 V-8 — The Buick Special equipped with a V-8 engine was externally identical to the 1967 Special V-6 described above, except in regard to vehicle coding. The V-8 Specials were numbered as a separate series.

SPECIAL SERIES 43400 V-8 I.D. NUMBERS: Vehicle Identification Numbers began with 434007( )600001. Numbers were coded as explained under the 1967 Special V-6 Series ID Number section.

SPECIAL SERIES 43400

Series Number	Model Number	Body Type & Seating	Factory Price	Shipping Weight	Production Total
43400	43469	4-dr Sed-6P	2532	3196	5,793
43400	43407	2-dr Cpe-6P	2481	3173	8,937
43400	43435	4-dr Sta Wag-6P	2812	3343	1,688

ENGINE: V-8. Overhead valve. Cast iron block. Displacement: 300 cid. Bore and stroke: 3.75 x 3.4 inches. Compression ratio: 9.0:1. Brake horsepower: 210 at 4600 rpm. Five main bearings. Hydraulic lifters. Two-barrel Rochester 2GC carburetor.

SPECIAL DELUXE V-6 — SERIES 43500 — A slightly plusher Special, with bright wheelhouse moldings, full-length bodyside bright moldings, black-accented rear cove panel and bright metal window surrounds. Special lettering appeared on the front fenders. Standard equipment was the same as the Special, plus a rear seat ashtray, Deluxe steering wheel, dual side armrests, full carpeting and dual horns. Interiors were cloth and vinyl or all-vinyl.

SPECIAL DELUXE SERIES 43500 V-6 I.D. NUMBERS: Vehicle Identification Numbers began with 435007( )600001. Numbers were coded as explained under the 1967 Special Series ID Number section.

SPECIAL DELUXE SERIES 43500

Series Number	Model Number	Body Type & Seating	Factory Price	Shipping Weight	Production Total
43500	43569	4-dr Sed-6P	2545	3142	3,602
43500	43517	2-dr HT Cpe-6P	2566	3127	2,333

ENGINE: See 1967 Buick Special Series 43300 engine data.

SPECIAL DELUXE V-8 — SERIES 43600 — Externally identical to the V-6 powered Special Deluxe described above, the V-8 Special Deluxes were numbered as a separate series. The Sportwagon was available only with a 340 cid V-8.

SPECIAL DELUXE SERIES 43600 I.D. NUMBERS: Vehicle identification numbers began with 436007( )100001 and up. Numbers were coded as explained under 1967 Special Series ID Number section.

SPECIAL SERIES 43600 DELUXE V-8

Series Number	Model Number	Body Type & Seating	Factory Price	Shipping Weight	Production Total
43600	43669	4-dr Sed-6P	2615	3205	25,361
43600	43617	2-dr HT Cpe-6P	2636	3202	14,408
43600	43635	4-dr Sta Wag-6P	2901	3317	6,851

ENGINE: See 1967 Buick Special Series 43400 engine data.

SKYLARK — SERIES 44307 V-6 — Only one model, the coupe, was offered with the V-6 for the 1967 Skylark. Standard equipment was the same as described for the 1967 Skylark V-8 Series 44400 below.

SKYLARK V-6 SERIES 44307 I.D. NUMBERS: Vehicle Identification Numbers began with 443077( )600001. Numbers were coded as explained under the 1967 Special Series ID Number section.

SKYLARK SERIES 44307 V-6

Series Number	Model Number	Body Type & Seating	Factory Price	Shipping Weight	Production Total
44300	44307	2-dr Cpe-6P	2665	3137	894

ENGINE: See 1967 Buick Special Series 43300 engine data.

70 Standard Catalog of American Cars

SKYLARK — SERIES 44400 V-8 — Exterior distinction was gained by the use of rear fender skirts, a full-length lower body bright molding, simulated front fender vents, a ribbed rear cove panel and a grille with more horizontal bars. Skylark script was used on the rear quarters and Skylarks had no ventiports. Cloth and vinyl trim with bench front seats were standard, except on the convertible, which was all-vinyl trimmed. All-vinyl was optional for other models and bucket seats with consoles were also offered as an option.

SKYLARK — SERIES 44400 V-8 I.D. NUMBERS: Vehicle Identification Numbers began with 44407( )600001. Numbers were coded as explained under the 1967 Special Series ID Number section.

SKYLARK V-8 SERIES 44400

Series Number	Model Number	Body Type & Seating	Factory Price	Shipping Weight	Production Total
44400	44407	2-dr Cpe-6P	2735	3229	3,165
44400	44469	4-dr Sed-6P	2767	3324	9,123
44400	44439	4-dr HT Sed-6P	2950	3373	13,673
44400	44417	2-dr HT Cpe-6P	2798	3199	40,940
44400	44467	2-dr Conv-5P	2945	3335	6,319

ENGINE: Specifications for the Skylark Series 44400 models were the same as engine data listed for 1967 Buick Skylark Series 43400 models, except in the case of the four-door hardtop sedan and Sportwagon. These cars came standard with a 340 cid V-8 having 3.75 x 3.85 inch bore and stroke measurements, 9.0:1 compression and 220 horsepower at 4400 rpm with a Rochester 2GC two-barrel carburetor.

SPORTWAGON — SERIES 44200 AND 44400 — Now spelled as one word, the series name 'Sportwagon' appeared in script on station wagon rear fenders. These long-wheelbase wagons continued to feature the glass Skyroof raised roofline. They used the Skylark grille, but had ventiports and bright rocker and wheelhouse moldings. Specific taillights were used. Standard equipment was similar to that of the Special Deluxe. Interiors were vinyl. Models in the 44400 series had Custom interiors, with padded seat cushions and a tailgate lamp.

SPORTWAGON SERIES 44200/44400 I.D. NUMBERS: Vehicle Identification Numbers began with 442007( )600001 or 444007( )600001. Numbers were coded as explained under the 1967 Special Series ID Number section.

SPORTWAGON SERIES 44200/44300

Series Number	Model Number	Body Type & Seating	Factory Price	Shipping Weight	Production Total
44200	44255	4-dr Sta Wag-6P	3025	3713	5,440
44200	44265	4-dr Sta Wag-9P	3173	3811	5,970
44400	44255	4-dr Cus Sta Wag-6P	3202	3772	3,114
44400	44265	4-dr Cus Sta Wag-9P	3340	3876	4,559

ENGINE: V-8. Overhead valve. Cast iron block. Displacement: 340 cid. Bore and stroke: 3.75 x 3.85 inches. Compression ratio: 9.0:1. Brake horsepower: 220 at 4400 rpm. Five main bearings. Hydraulic valve lifters. Carburetor: Rochester two-barrel Model 2GC.

SKYLARK GS 340 — SERIES 43417 — A hybrid, the GS 340 was numbered in the Special V-8 series, but was trimmed as a low-cost GS. Broad rally stripes and hood scoops were red, as was the lower deck molding. Two body colors, white or platinum mist, were offered. An optional "Sport Pac" included specific front and rear shocks, heavy-duty springs and a large diameter stabilizer bar. Standard features included 15:1 ratio steering, 7.75 x 14 Rayon Cord tires on red 14-inch Rally-style wheels and a two-speed Super Turbine automatic or four-speed manual transmission. Interiors were similar to the Special 43400 Series and black, all-vinyl upholstery was the only choice.

SKYLARK GS 340 SERIES 43417 I.D. NUMBERS: Vehicle Identification Numbers were the same as used on Skylark Series 44400 V-8 models.

SKYLARK GS 340 SERIES 43417

Series Number	Model Number	Body Type & Seating	Factory Price	Shipping Weight	Production Total
43400	43417	2-dr HT Cpe-6P	2845	3283	(3,692)

NOTE: The production total for the GS 340 is shown in parenthesis, since these cars are also included in the Buick Special V-8 series production totals given above.

ENGINE: The GS 340 used a 340 cid/260 hp engine with 10.25:1 compression and a Rochester 4MV four-barrel carburetor.

SKYLARK GS 400 — SERIES 44600 — The high-performance Skylark took its name from its 400 cid V-8. Three- or four-speed manual or three-speed Super Turbine automatic transmissions were offered. Exterior appearance was strengthened by the use of twin hood scoops, Rally stripes and a special grille. The GS name appeared in red letters on the grille and rear deck. F70 x 14 Wide Oval red or white stripe tires were standard. GS 400s had no fender skirts; rear wheelhouses were open, unlike other Skylark models (except GS 340). Interiors were all-vinyl and standard equipment was the same as the Skylark 44400 Series.

SKYLARK GS 400 SERIES 44600 I.D. NUMBERS: Vehicle Identification Numbers began with 446007( )100001. Numbers were coded as explained under the 1967 Special Series ID Number section.

SKYLARK GS 400 SERIES 44600

Series Number	Model Number	Body Type & Seating	Factory Price	Shipping Weight	Production Total
44600	44607	2-dr Cpe-6P	2956	3439	1,014
44600	44617	2-dr HT Cpe-6P	3019	3500	10,659
44600	44667	2-dr Conv-6P	3167	3505	2,140

ENGINE: V-8. Overhead valve. Cast iron block. Displacement: 401 cid (advertised as 400 cid). Bore and stroke: 4.04 x 3.90 inches. Compression ratio: 10.25:1. Brake horsepower: 340 at 5000 rpm. Five main bearings. Hydraulic lifters. Four-barrel Rochester 4MV carburetor.

LESABRE — SERIES 45200 — A new body shell, with a revised sweepspear sculpted into the sheetmetal, was featured for 1967. A horizontal, multiple bar grille was used. Bright lower body moldings, with rear fender extensions on some models, were used. The traditional trio of ventiports was once again found on front fenders. LeSabre script appeared on the rear fenders and deck lid. Standard equipment included heater; defroster; front and rear seat belts; Step-On parking brake; front door operated courtesy lamps; smoking set; rear seat ashtrays; dual front and rear armrests; dual-key locking system and other federally mandated safety features.

LESABRE SERIES 45200 I.D. NUMBERS: Vehicle identification Numbers began with 452007( )100001. Numbers were coded as explained under the 1967 Special Series ID Number section.

LESABRE SERIES 45200

Series Number	Model Number	Body Type & Seating	Factory Price	Shipping Weight	Production Total
45200	45269	4-dr Sed-6P	3002	3847	36,220
45200	45239	4-dr HT Sed-6P	3142	3878	17,464
45200	45287	2-dr HT Cpe-6P	3084	3819	13,760

ENGINE: Specifications for the 340 cid/220 hp LeSabre engine were the same as listed for the 1967 Skylark four-door sedan and Sportwagon.

LESABRE CUSTOM — SERIES 45400 — A slightly plusher LeSabre, with Custom quality cloth and vinyl interior trim. The hardtop coupe was equipped with standard all-vinyl, front bucket seat interior. Standard equipment was the same as in the LeSabre, except for the addition of the Deluxe steering wheel, outside rearview mirror, an upper instrument panel safety pad and a cross flow radiator.

LESABRE CUSTOM I.D. NUMBERS: Vehicle Identification Numbers began with 454007( )100001. Numbers were coded as explained under the 1967 Special Series ID Number section.

LESABRE CUSTOM SERIES 45400

Series Number	Model Number	Body Type & Seating	Factory Price	Shipping Weight	Production Total
45400	45469	4-dr Sed-6P	3096	3855	27,930
45400	45439	4-dr HT Sed-6P	3236	3873	32,526
45400	45487	2-dr HT Cpe-5P	3172	3853	11,871
45400	45467	2-dr Conv-6P	3388	3890	2,913

ENGINE: See 1967 Buick Sportwagon Series engine data.

WILDCAT — SERIES 46400 — A specific, more open grille set the Wildcat apart from the LeSabre at the front. Side trim used a heavier bright lower body molding, that continued across the standard rear fender skirts as a lip molding. The molding flowed out of the front fender's large simulated vent intakes. Wildcat lettering appeared on the rear quarters and deck. Interiors were vinyl and cloth, of a plusher grade than the LeSabre, which featured the same standard equipment.

WILDCAT I.D. NUMBERS: Vehicle Identification Numbers began with 464007 100001. Numbers were coded as explained under the 1966 Special Series ID Number section

WILDCAT SERIES 46400

Series Number	Model Number	Body Type & Seating	Factory Price	Shipping Weight	Production Total
46400	46469	4-dr Sed-6P	3277	4008	14,579
46400	46439	4-dr HT Sed-6P	3437	4069	15,510
46400	46487	2-dr HT Cpe-6P	3382	4021	10,585
46467	46467	2-dr Conv-6P	3536	4064	2,276

ENGINE: V-8. Overhead valve. Cast iron block. Displacement: 430 cid. Bore and stroke: 4.19 x 3.90 inches. Compression ratio: 10.25:1. Brake horsepower: 360 at 5000 rpm. Five main bearings. Hydraulic lifters. Four-barrel Rochester 4MV carburetor.

WILDCAT CUSTOM — SERIES 46600 — A Custom interior, with plusher materials, paddle-type armrests and custom headlining (except convertible) set the Custom Wildcats apart. All-vinyl bucket seats or cloth notchback seats for front seat passengers were standard.

WILDCAT CUSTOM SERIES 46600 I.D. NUMBERS: Vehicle Identification Numbers began with 466007( )100001. Numbers were coded as explained under the 1967 Special Series ID Number section.

WILDCAT CUSTOM SERIES 46600

Series Number	Model Number	Body Type & Seating	Factory Price	Shipping Weight	Production Total
46600	46639	4-dr HT Sed-6P	3652	4119	13,547
46600	46687	2-dr HT Cpe-5P	3603	4055	11,571

ENGINE: See 1967 Buick Wildcat Series 46400 engine data.

ELECTRA 225 — SERIES 48200 — Buick's largest, most luxurious series was restyled for 1967, sharing with lesser, full-sized Buicks, a return to sweepspear bodyside motifs. The Electra used a larger body, however, with its own horizontal-bar grille, distinct squared-off rear fenders and four ventiports on each front fender. The lower body was lined with bright metal bumper to bumper, continuing even across the lip of the fender skirts. Full-width taillights were used at the rear. Electra 225 script appeared on the rear fenders. Standard features included most items found on less costly Buicks plus, power steering; power brakes; custom padded seat cushions; front seat belt retractors; electric clock; trunk light; license frames and mandated safety features. Interiors were cloth and vinyl.

ELECTRA 225 SERIES 48200 I.D. NUMBERS: Vehicle Identification Numbers began with 482007 ( ) 100001. Numbers were coded as explained under the 1966 Special Series ID Number section.

ELECTRA 225 SERIES 48200

Series Number	Model Number	Body Type & Seating	Factory Price	Shipping Weight	Production Total
48200	48269	4-dr Sed-6P	4054	4246	10,787
48200	48239	4-dr HT Sed-6P	4184	4293	12,491
48200	48287	2-dr Spt Cpe-6P	4075	4197	6,845

ENGINE: See 1967 Buick Wildcat Series 4600 engine data.

ELECTRA 225 CUSTOM — SERIES 48400 — Plusher, Custom grade interiors in cloth and vinyl set the Custom models apart. Vinyl bucket seats were an option for the Custom convertible.

NOTE: Custom Limited equipment was available for the Style Number 48439 four-door hardtop sedan. Cars so equipped had Madrid grain or Bavere cloth and Madrid grain vinyl upholstery, with etched Electra 225 emblems; walnut door and instrument panel inserts and dual storage compartments on the front seatbackrest. Limited scripts were affixed to the roof sail panels. This package retailed for $149.27, but the number of cars so equipped was not individually recorded.

ELECTRA 225 CUSTOM I.D. NUMBERS: Vehicle Identification Numbers began with 484007( )100001. Numbers were coded as explained under the 1967 Special Series ID Number section.

ELECTRA 225 CUSTOM SERIES 48400

Series Number	Model Number	Body Type & Seating	Factory Price	Shipping Weight	Production Total
48400	48469	4-dr Sed-6P	4270	4312	10,106
48400	48439	4-dr HT Sed-6P	4363	4336	40,978
48400	48487	2-dr Spt Cpe-6P	4254	4242	12,156
48400	48467	2-dr Conv-6P	4421	4304	6,941

ENGINE: See 1967 Buick Wildcat Series 46400 engine data.

1967 Buick, Electra 225 four-door sedan, V-8 (TVB)

RIVIERA — SERIES 49487 — A new grille was used with the basic 1966 body to very slightly facelift the Riviera. Rocker moldings were altered and new taillamps were installed. Riviera script appeared on front fenders and the deck lid. Standard equipment included Super Turbine transmission; power steering; power brakes; tilt steering wheel; dual exhausts; heater/defroster; Custom padded seats; retractable seat belts; electric clock; trunk and glovebox lights; Glareproof mirror; outside rearview mirror; license frames and carpeting. A bench or bucket seat all-vinyl interior was used.

NOTE: Gran Sport equipment was offered for the 1967 Riviera at $138. This consisted of heavy-duty front and rear shocks, positive traction differential, Wide Oval red or white stripe tires and front fender and instrument panel GS monograms. The standard engine was used.

RIVIERA I.D. NUMBERS: Vehicle Idenfification Numbers began with 494877( )90001. Numbers were coded as explained under the 1967 Special Series ID Number section.

RIVIERA SERIES 49400

Series Number	Model Number	Body Type & Seating	Factory Price	Shipping Weight	Production Total
49400	49487	2-dr HT Cpe-5P	4469	4189	42,799

ENGINE: See 1967 Buick Wildcat 46400 Series engine data.

CHASSIS FEATURES: Wheelbase: (Series 43300, 43400, 43500, 43600, 44300, 44400, 44600) 115 inches; (Series 43200 and 43400 Sportwagons) 120 inches; (Series 45200 and 45400) 123 inches; (Series 46400, 46600, 48200 and 48400) 126 inches; (Series 49487) 119 inches. Overall length: (Series 43300, 43400, 43500, 43600, 44300, 44400 and 44600) 205 inches. (Station wagons) 209.3 inches. (Series 44200 and 44400 Sportwagons) 214. inches; (Series 45200 and 45400) 217.5 inches; (Series 46400 and 46600) 220.5 inches; (Series 48200 and 48400) 223.9 inches; (Series 49487) 211.3 inches. Tread: (Series 44300, 43400, 43500, 43600, 44300, 44400, 44600 and 44200) 58 inches front, 59 inches rear. (Series 45200, 45400, 46400 and 46600) 63 inches front and rear. (Series 48200, 48400 and 49487) 63.4 inches front, 63 inches rear Tires-. (Series 43300, 43400, 43500, 43600, 44300, 44400 and 44600) 7.75 x 14; (Series 44200 and 44400 Sportwagons) 8.25 x 14; (Series 45200, 45400, 46400 and 46600) 8.45 x 15; (Series 48200 and 48400) 8.85 x 15; (Series 49487) 8.45 x 15.

1967 Buick, Riviera two-door hardtop sport coupe, V-8 (TVB)

POWERTRAIN OPTIONS: A three-speed manual transmission was standard on Series 43300, 43400, 43500, 43600, 44300, 44400, 44600, 44200, 45200, 45400, 46400 and 46600. Super Turbine automatic transmission was standard on Series 48200, 48400 and 49487 and was optional on Series 46400 and 46600. An automatic transmission was optional on all other Models. A four-speed manual transmission was optional on the GS 340 and GS 400 at $184. A '400' package, linking the 260 horsepower 340 cid V-8 with four-barrel to a Super Turbine 400 transmission was offered for the Sportwagon and LeSabre models at a cost of $263. The 260 horsepower 340 cid V-8 was also optional with other power teams in intermediates and LeSabres. No engine options were cataloged for Wildcat, Electra 225 or Riviera models.

CONVENIENCE FEATURES: Power steering (standard Electra 225, Riviera). Power brakes (standard Electra 225s, Riviera). Front power disc brakes (except Electra 225s). Automatic air conditioning (full-size only). Air conditioning. Five-spoke plated sport wheels. Wire wheelcovers. Deluxe wheelcovers. Front seat headrests. Power door locks. Tilt steering wheel (standard on Riviera). Full-length console with bucket seats (automatic transmission equipped Skylark, GS 340, GS 400, Wildcat, Riviera). AM radio. AM/FM radio. Stereo radio (full size only). Reclining bucket seat. Reclining Strato bench seat (Riviera only). Power seat adjustment. Electro-cruise (automatic transmission only, not available on GS 400 or Sportwagon with 400 option). Power windows. Overhead courtesy lamps (LeSabre, Wildcat). Four-note horn. Remote control mirror. Automatic trunk release (except 115-120 inch wheelbase). Rear window defroster (except convertibles and station wagons). Vinyl roof cover (specific models). Speed alert. Power tailgate for station wagons. Cornering lights (full-size models). Station wagon luggage rack.

HISTORICAL FOOTNOTES: Calendar year production was 573,866 units. Model year production was 562,507 units. The GS-340 model was introduced at midyear, during the Chicago Automobile Show. A new model sold by Buick dealers this year was the Opel Rallyee Kadett coupe. The GS-400 was a true muscle car capable of going from 0-to-60 in 6.9 seconds

72

with an automatic transmission or 6.6 seconds with a four-speed transmission. Its top speed was 122 mph. The Riviera GS could move too...0-to-60 in 7.8 seconds and 86 mph in the quarter-mile.

1968 BUICK

SPECIAL DELUXE SERIES 43300/43400 — The basic Buick was upgraded to Deluxe status this year, as reflected by more brightwork on the restyled bodies, which now featured their own version of Buick's sculpted sweepspear. A trio of ventiports remained as a series hallmark, while more brightwork appeared on the window surrounds and on the lower body and wheelhouse moldings. Special Deluxe script was found on the rear fenders. Cloth and vinyl was used in the coupe and sedan. All-vinyl upholstery was used in the station wagon and was optional on the other models. Standard equipment included heater and defroster; cigar lighter; front and rear ashtrays; energy-absorbing steering column; lane change feature in directional signals; shoulder and seat belts; inside day/night mirror; side marker lamps and other mandated safety equipment. Wipers were recessed below the hood line.

BUICK I.D. NUMBERS: The serial number (VIN) was located on hinge pillar post, left side, top of instrument panel and stamped on the engine block. The first symbol was a '4' for Buick. The second and third symbols indicated series, as follows: 33=Special DeL.; 34=Special Deluxe/GS 350; 35=Skylark; 44=Skylark Custom/Sportwagon; 46=GS 400; 52=LeSabre; 54=LeSabre Custom; 64=Wildcat; 66=Wildcat Custom; 82=Electra 225; 84=Electra 225 Custom; 94=Riviera. The fourth and fifth symbols indicated body style, as follows: 27=2-dr cpe; 35=4-dr two-seat sta wag; 37=2-dr HT; 39=4-dr HT; 55=4-dr two-seat Sportwagon; 57=2-dr HT; 65=4-dr three-seat Sportwagon; 67=2-dr Conv; 69=4-dr Sedan and 87=2-dr Riv HT. Combined, the first five symbols were the model number, as reflected in tables below. The sixth symbol indicated model year, 8=1968. The seventh symbol was a letter representing the assembly plant, as follows: B=Baltimore, Md.; C=South Gate, Calif; D=Doraville, Ga.; H=Flint, Mich.; I=Oshawa, Ont., Canada; K=Kansas City, Mo.; V=Bloomfield, Mich.; X=Kansas City, Kan.; Y=Wilmington, Del.; z=Fremont, Ohio. The last six digits represent the sequential assembly number at the plant with series mixed in production. In addition to the VIN, the right side of the engine block is stamped with a production code which has letters identifying the engine and numbers indicating production date codes. The letters were as follows: (250 cid six-cyl.) NA, PO; (350 cid V-8) PO, PW, PP; (GS 350 V-8) PP only; (GS 400/Sportwagon 400 cid V-8) PR; (430 cid V-8) PD or PE.

SPECIAL DELUXE SERIES 43300/43400

Series Number	Model Number	Body Type & Seating	Factory Price	Shipping Weight	Production Total
43300	43327	2-dr Cpe-6P	2513	3125	21,988
43300	43369	4-dr Sed-6P	2564	3217	16,571
43400	43435	4-dr Sta Wag-6P	3001	3670	10,916

V-8 NOTE: Special Deluxe also offered in 43400 V-8 series. On V-8s, the third symbol in model number changes to '4.' Add $105 and 153 pounds for V-8s; wagon is V-8 only.

Calif. GS NOTE: The California GS, detailed in the GS-350 section below, carried the same model number as a Special Deluxe V-8 coupe.

ENGINES: Six-Cyl. Inline. Overhead valve. Cast iron block. Displacement: 250 cid. Bore and stroke: 3.875 x 3.53 inches. Compression ratio: 8.5: 1. Brake horsepower: 155 at 4200 rpm. Hydraulic lifters. Rochester MV one-barrel carburetor.

V-8. Overhead valve. Cast iron block. Displacement: 350 cid. Bore and stroke: 3.8 x 3.85 inches. Compression ratio: 9.0:1. Brake horsepower: 230 at 4400 rpm. Five main bearings. Hydraulic lifters. Rochester 2GV two-barrel carburetor.

SKYLARK — SERIES 43500/44500 — More similar to the Special Deluxe than previous Skylarks, the 1968 version relied on a bright metal Sweepspear line, Skylark roof quarter panel emblems and Skylark script on the rear fenders for distinction. In place of the traditional ventiports, there were triple-stacked horizontal bars mounted low on each fender. Inside was a Deluxe steering wheel, lighted ashtray and glovebox, and full carpeting, in addition to Special Deluxe features. Cloth and vinyl or all-vinyl upholstery was offered for the sedan. An all-vinyl front bench or notchback seat was offered for the two-door hardtop.

SKYLARK SERIES 43500/44500 I.D. NUMBERS: On cars with V-6 power Vehicle Identification Numbers (VINs) started with 435008( )600001. On V-8 equipped cars the VINs started with 445008( )100001 up. An explanation of the VIN codes can be found under the 1968 Special Deluxe Series ID Number section.

SKYLARK SERIES 43500

Series Number	Model Number	Body Type & Seating	Factory Price	Shipping Weight	Production Total
43500	43569	4-dr Sed-6P	2666	3282	27,384
43500	43537	2-dr HT-6P	2688	3194	32,795

V-8 NOTE: Skylark also offered in 44500 V-8 series. On V-8s, the second symbol in model number changes to '4.' Add $105 and 153 pounds for V-8s.

ENGINE: V-6 and V-8 specifications were the same as those listed for the 1968 Special Deluxe Series 43300.

SKYLARK CUSTOM — SERIES 44400 — More trim and fender skirts were added to the plushest Skylark series. The sweepspear molding continued onto the skirts and a Custom signature appeared below Skylark script on the rear fenders. All wheelcovers were featured. Interiors were refined with Custom padded seat cushions. The sedan was trimmed in plusher all-vinyl or vinyl and cloth and a notchback seat was available for the hardtop sedan. Convertibles came with all-vinyl trim and front bench seats with bucket seats optionally available. Custom seats had brushed metallic side braces, except on the bucket type. Standard equipment was otherwise similar to the Skylark.

SKYLARK CUSTOM SERIES 44400 I.D. NUMBERS: Vehicle Identification Numbers started at 44408( )100001. An explanation of the VIN code may be found under the 1968 Special Series ID Number section.

SKYLARK CUSTOM SERIES 44400

Series Number	Model Number	Body Type & Seating	Factory Price	Shipping Weight	Production Total
44400	44469	4-dr Sed-6P	2924	3377	8,066
44400	44437	2-dr HT Cpe-6P	3108	3481	44,143
44400	44439	4-dr HT Sed-6P	2956	3344	12,984
44400	44467	2-dr Conv-6P	3098	3394	8,188

ENGINES: Specifications were the same as those listed for the 1968 Special Deluxe V-8.

GS 350 — SERIES 43400 — Trimmed like the Skylark Custom inside, the GS 350 had a more muscular outer appearance. It was coded as a Skylark Custom, although more related to the GS 400. Finned simulated air intakes were seen on the front fenders, while a lower body paint accent stripe replaced the bright molding. Bright wheelhouse moldings were used, but rear fender skirts were not. A GS 350 plaque was found on the center of the deck lid and further identification was seen on the grille and rear fenders with GS monograms appearing in such places, and also on the door panels. All-vinyl, foam-padded seats were standard equipment and bucket seats were optional. A specific grille with bright crossbar and textured background was used. An upper level instrument panel ventilation system was a new feature that eliminated the use of front ventipanes, or so Buick claimed. The hood had a scoop at the rear and concealed wipers.

NOTE: Another GS, the California GS two-door coupe, was similar to the GS 350 in that it was actually numbered in the Special Deluxe line (body style number 43327). Standard California GS equipment included chrome-plated "Super Sport" wheels, vinyl roof covering, Deluxe steering wheel, California script with GS emblems on the grille, roof panels and rear fenders. A GS emblem was centered in the deck lid lip. Cloth and vinyl or horizontally pleated all-vinyl seating surfaces were offered. Standard features included crank-operated vent windows, chrome exterior trim and a two-speed automatic transmission. Production figures and prices are not available.

GS 350 SERIES 43400

Series Number	Model Number	Body Type & Seating	Factory Price	Shipping Weight	Production Total
43400	43437	2-dr HT Cpe-6P	2926	3375	8,317

ENGINE: Specifications were the same as listed for the 1968 Special Series 33300 V-8, except compression ratio was 10.25:1, brake horsepower was 280 at 4600 and a four-barrel Rochester 4MV carburetor was used.

GS 400 — SERIES 44600 — Yet another version of the new 1968 Buick 112 inch wheelbase intermediate coupe, the GS 400 was identified by a GS 400 plaque on each front fender, wide oval F70 x 14 white stripe tires, fake fender vents and functional hood scoops. Folding seatback latches were standard, with all-vinyl, bench front seating or optional front bucket seats.

GS 400 I.D. NUMBERS: Vehicle Identification Numbers began with 446008 100001. An explanation of the VIN code may be found under the 1968 Special Deluxe Series 43300 listing.

GS 400 SERIES 44600

Series Number	Model Number	Body Type & Seating	Factory Price	Shipping Weight	Production Total
44600	44637	2-dr HT Cpe-6P	3127	3514	10,743
44600	44667	2-dr Conv-6P	3271	3547	2,454

ENGINE: V-8. Overhead valve. Cast iron block. Displacement: 400 cid. Bore and stroke: 4.04 x 3.90 inches. Compression ratio: 10.25:1. Brake horsepower: 340 at 5000 rpm. Five main bearings. Hydraulic lifters. Four-barrel Rochester 4MV four-barrel carburetor with chromed air cleaner top.

SPORTWAGON CUSTOM — SERIES 44400/44800 — Still on a stretched wheelbase and using the Skyroof treatment, the intermediate station wagons followed the sweepspear theme into 1968. All were Custom trimmed. Rear fender skirts were not used. Triple ventiports replaced the lower stacked fender bars that other models used. A full-length lower body highlight with wheelhouse moldings was seen. Sportwagon script decorated the rear quarters and tailgate. The all-vinyl interior had full-carpeting and included 100 cubic feet of cargo space. Models with woodgrain bodyside transfers had their own style numbers.

SPORTWAGON SERIES 44400/44800

Series Number	Model Number	Body Type & Seating	Factory Price	Shipping Weight	Production Total
44400	44455	4-dr Sta Wag-2S	3341	3975	5,916
44400	44465	4-dr Sta Wag-3S	3499	4118	6,063
44800	44855	4-dr Cus Sta Wag-2S	3711	3975	4,614
44800	44865	4-dr Cus Sta Wag-3S	3869	4118	6,295

SPORTWAGON SERIES 44400/44800 I.D. NUMBERS: Vehicle Identification Numbers began with 444008( )100001. An explanation of the VIN code may be found under the 1968 Special Deluxe Series ID Number section.

ENGINE: Specifications were the same as listed under 1968 Special Deluxe Series 43300 V-8.

LESABRE — SERIES 45200 — Revised only slightly from 1967, the LeSabre was chiefly facelifted by the use of a new grille with more prominent center division and a textured background. The traditional trio of front fender ventiports was again a trademark. Bright rocker panel and wheelhouse moldings were used. Series designations were found on the rear fenders and instrument panel. Cloth and vinyl upholstery was standard. Regular features included shoulder belts (except convertible); glovebox light; interior courtesy lights; smoking set; rear seat ashtrays; two-speed wipers with washer and recessed arms; outside rearview mirror; energy absorbing steering column and other mandated safety features.

LESABRE SERIES 45200 I.D. NUMBERS: Vehicle Identification Numbers began with 452008( )100001. An explanation of VIN codes may be found under the 1968 Special Series ID Number section.

LESABRE SERIES 45200

Series Number	Model Number	Body Type & Seating	Factory Price	Shipping Weight	Production Total
45200	45269	4-dr Sed-6P	3141	3946	37,433
45200	45287	2-dr HT Cpe-6P	3281	3980	14,922
45200	45239	4-dr HT Sed-6P	3223	3923	10,058

ENGINE: Specifications were the same as those listed for the 1968 Special Deluxe V-8.

LESABRE CUSTOM — SERIES 45400 — Custom interiors of plusher cloth and vinyl, with more ornate door panels, were used. All-vinyl was available and was standard in the convertible. Bucket seats were optional for the convertible and two-door hardtop. Deluxe full wheelcovers were included.

LESABRE CUSTOM SERIES 45400 I.D. NUMBERS: Vehicle Identification Numbers started with 454008( )100001. An explanation of VIN codes appears in the 1968 Special Deluxe Series ID Number section.

LESABRE CUSTOM SERIES 45400

Series Number	Model Number	Body Type & Seating	Factory Price	Shipping Weight	Production Total
45400	45469	4-dr Sed-6P	3235	3950	34,112
45400	45487	2-dr HT-6P	3311	3932	29,596
45400	45439	4-dr HT-6P	3375	4007	40,370
45400	45467	2-dr Conv-6P	3504	3966	5,257

ENGINE: Specifications were the same as listed for the 1968 Special Deluxe V-8.

WILDCAT — SERIES 46400 — A new grille and revised bodyside moldings helped give the 1968 Wildcat a new look. Simulated air vents continued on front fenders. Narrow lower bodyside highlights and wheelhouse moldings were used to make a full-length bright lower strip. Wildcat lettering was found on the rear fenders, on the deck lid and on the instrument panel. An outside rearview mirror and back-up lamps were additional standard equipment inherited from lower-priced Buicks. Interiors were cloth and vinyl, with all-vinyl optional. Bucket seats upholstered in vinyl were a two-door hardtop option.

WILDCAT I.D. NUMBERS: Vehicle Identification Numbers began with 464008 100001. An explanation of the VIN code may be found under the 1968 Special Deluxe Series ID Number section.

WILDCAT SERIES 46400

Series Number	Model Number	Body Type & Seating	Factory Price	Shipping Weight	Production Total
46400	46469	4-dr Sed-6P	3416	4076	15,201
46400	46487	2-dr HT-6P	3521	4065	10,708
46400	46439	4-dr HT-6P	3576	4133	15,173
46400	46667	2-dr Conv-6P	3707	4118	3,572

ENGINE: V-8. Overhead valves. Cast iron block. Displacement: 430 cid. Bore and stroke: 4.19 x 3.9 inches. Compression ratio: 10.25:1. Brake horsepower: 360 at 5000 rpm. Five main bearings. Hydraulic lifters. Four-barrel Rochester 4MV carburetor.

LESABRE SERIES 45200 I.D. NUMBERS: Vehicle Identification Numbers began with 452008( )100001. An explanation of VIN codes may be found under the 1968 Special Series ID Number section.

LESABRE SERIES 45200

Series Number	Model Number	Body Type & Seating	Factory Price	Shipping Weight	Production Total
45200	45269	4-dr Sed-6P	4066	3956	37,433
45200	45287	2-dr HT Cpe-6P	4145	3923	14,922
45200	45239	4-dr HT Sed-6P	4203	3946	10,058

ENGINE: Specifications were the same as those listed for the 1968 Special Deluxe V-8.

LESABRE CUSTOM — SERIES 45400 — Custom interiors of plusher cloth and vinyl, with more ornate door panels, were used. All-vinyl was available and was standard in the convertible. Bucket seats were optional for the convertible and two-door hardtop. Deluxe full wheelcovers were included.

LESABRE CUSTOM SERIES 45400 I.D. NUMBERS: Vehicle Identification Numbers started with 454008( )100001. An explanation of VIN codes appears in the 1968 Special Deluxe Series 43300 listing.

LESABRE CUSTOM SERIES 45400

Series Number	Model Number	Body Type & Seating	Factory Price	Shipping Weight	Production Total
45400	45469	4-dr Sed-6P	4157	3950	34,112
45400	45487	2-dr HT-6P	4233	3932	29,596
45400	45439	4-dr HT-6P	4297	4007	40,370
45400	45467	2-dr Conv-6P	4426	3966	5,257

ENGINE: Specifications were the same as listed for the 1968 Special Deluxe V-8.

WILDCAT — SERIES 46400 — A new grille and revised bodyside moldings helped give the 1968 Wildcat a new look. Simulated air vents continued on front fenders. Narrow lower bodyside highlights and wheelhouse moldings were used to make a full-length bright lower strip. Wildcat lettering was found on the rear fenders, on the deck lid and on the instrument panel. An outside rearview mirror and back-up lamps were additional standard equipment inherited from lower-priced Buicks. Interiors were cloth and vinyl, with all-vinyl optional. Bucket seats upholstered in vinyl were a two-door hardtop option.

WILDCAT I.D. NUMBERS: Vehicle Identification Numbers began with 464008 100001. An explanation of the VIN code may be found under the 1968 Special Deluxe Series 43300 listing.

WILDCAT SERIES 46400

Series Number	Model Number	Body Type & Seating	Factory Price	Shipping Weight	Production Total
46400	46469	4-dr Sed-6P	4372	4107	15,201
46400	46487	2-dr HT-6P	4477	4125	10,708
46400	46439	4-dr HT-6P	4532	4171	15,173
46400	46667	2-dr Conv-6P	4829	4122	3,572

ENGINE: V-8: Overhead valves. Cast iron block. Displacement: 430 cid. Bore and stroke: 4.18 x 3.9 inches. Compression ratio: 10.5:1. Brake horsepower: 360 at 5000 rpm. Five main bearings. Hydraulic lifters. Four-barrel carburetor.

WILDCAT CUSTOM — SERIES 46600 — A plusher interior was the heart of the Custom Series. Brushed metallic door panel inserts were seen with cloth and vinyl trim combinations. A notchback seat with bright side braces was used, as were paddle-type armrests and Custom headlining (except the convertible), All-vinyl trim was optional, except for the convertible, where it was standard. All-vinyl bucket seats were an option.

WILDCAT CUSTOM SERIES 46600 I.D. NUMBERS: Vehicle Identification Numbers began with 466008( )100001. An explanation of VIN codes appears with the 1968 Special Deluxe Series 43300 listing.

WILDCAT CUSTOM SERIES 46600

Series Number	Model Number	Body Type & Seating	Factory Price	Shipping Weight	Production Total
46600	46687	2-dr HT Cpe-6P	4698	4134	11,276
44600	44639	4-dr HT Sed-6P	4747	4253	14,059
46600	46667	2-dr Conv-6P	4829	4122	3,572

ENGINE: Specifications were the same as listed for the 1968 Wildcat Series 46400.

1968 Buick, Electra 225 two-door hardtop, V-8 (TVB)

ELECTRA 225 — SERIES 48200 — The largest Buick was mildly restyled for 1968. New eggcrate textured grilles, divided by a color-accented panel, were up front. Squared rear fenders were tied together by a bumper housing the taillamps. Four ventiports continued to crown the largest of Buick fenders. Full-length lower body moldings continued across the fender skirts. Specific full wheelcovers were used. Electra 225 script was found on rear fenders and instrument panel, while the Series badge was found on the roof quarter panels (except the convertible). Standard features included power steering; power brakes; automatic transmission; custom padded seat cushions; electric clock; parking brake signal light; Deluxe steering wheel and carpeted floors and lower doors.

ELECTRA 225 SERIES 48200 NUMBERS: Vehicle Identification Numbers began with 482008( )100001. An explanation of the VIN code appears with the 1968 Special Deluxe Series 43300 ID Number section.

ELECTRA 225 SERIES 48200

Series Number	Model Number	Body Type & Seating	Factory Price	Shipping Weight	Production Total
48200	48269	4-dr Sed-6P	4200	4253	12,723
48200	48257	2-dr HT-6P	4330	4270	10,705
48200	48239	4-dr HT-6P	4221	4180	15,376

ENGINE: Specifications were the same as listed for the 1968 Wildcat Series 46400.

ELECTRA 225 CUSTOM — SERIES 48400 — Essentially a trim package, the Custom models were plusher inside. Cloth and vinyl combinations were used in the four-door hardtop, with an all-vinyl interior available. All-vinyl notchback seating was standard in the coupe and convertible, with all-vinyl buckets an option.

NOTE: Custom 'Limited' equipment was available for the Model 48439 four-door hardtop sedan and 48457 two-door hardtop. Cars so equipped had plusher cloth and vinyl upholstery with special accents. 'Limited' script appeared on the roof quarter panels. Production and price figures are not known.

ELECTRA 225 CUSTOM SERIES 48400

Series Number	Model Number	Body Type & Seating	Factory Price	Shipping Weight	Production Total
48400	48469	4-dr Sed-6P	4415	4304	10,910
48400	48457	2-dr HT Cpe-6P	4400	4273	6,826
48400	48439	4-dr HT Sed-6P	4509	4314	50,846
48400	48467	2-dr Conv-6P	4541	4285	7,976

ENGINE: Specifications were the same as listed for the 1968 Wildcat Series 46400.

RIVIERA — SERIES 49487 — Once again using the same body shell, the Riviera had a new frontal appearance. Large parking lamps were housed within the bumper, which also framed the low, textured grille. Headlamps retracted above until needed. A wide, full-length lower body molding with bright wheelhouse moldings was used. Specific full wheelcovers were seen. Riviera lettering appeared on front fenders and deck. Standard equipment included power steering; power brakes; tilt steering column; brake warning light; Custom-padded seat cushions; license frames and mandated safety features. Interior were bench or bucket seats in all-vinyl trim. Plusher Custom grade interiors were offered with fancier door panels incorporating the Riviera 'R' logo and all-vinyl Strato-bench or bucket seats, or cloth and vinyl Strato-bench front seats.

NOTE: Gran Sport equipment was offered for the 1968 Riviera. This consisted of heavy-duty front and rear suspension, positive traction differential. H70 x 15 red or white stripe tires and front fender GS monograms. The GS signature was also found on the instrument panel.

RIVIERA I.D. NUMBERS: Vehicle Identification Numbers began with 494878 900001. An explanation of the VIN code may be found under the 1968 Special Deluxe Series ID Number section.

RIVERIA SERIES 49400

Series Number	Model Number	Body Type & Seating	Factory Price	Shipping Weight	Production Total
49400	49487	2-dr HT Cpe-6P	5245	4222	49,284

ENGINE: Specifications were the same as listed for the 1968 Wildcat Series 46400.

CHASSIS FEATURES: Wheelbase: (Series 43300, 43500, 44400, 43400, and 44600 coupe and convertible) 112 inches: (Series 43300, 43500, 44400, 43400 and 44600 sedans and Special Deluxe station wagon) 116 inches; (Sportwagons) 121 inches; (Series 45200 and 45400) 123 inches; (Series 46400 and 46600) 126 inches; (Series 49487) 119 inches. Overall length: (Series 43300, 43500, 44400, 43400 and 46600 coupe and convertible) 200.7 inches; (Series 43300, 43500, 44400, 43400 and 46600 sedan) 204.7 inches; (Sportwagon) 209.1 inches; (Series 45200 and 45400) 217.5 inches; (Series 46400 and 46600) 220.5 inches; (Series 48200 and 48400) 224.9 inches; (Series 49487) 215.2 inches. Tread: (Series 43300, 43500, 44400, 43400 and 44600) 59.35 inches front, 59.0 inches rear; (Series 45200 and 45400) 63 inches front and rear; (Series 46400, 46600, 48400 and 49487) 63.4 inches front, 63 inches rear. Tires: (Series 43300, 43500, 44400, 43400 and 44600) 7.75 x 14; (Sportwagon and Series 45200, 45400, 46400, 46600 and 49487) 8.45 x 15; (Series 48200 and 48400) 8.85 x 15.

POWERTRAIN FEATURES: Three-speed manual transmission was standard in all except Electras and Rivieras. The GS 350 came with three-speed column shift or four-speed floor shift optional. The GS 400 came with three-speed or four-speed manual transmission on floor. Four-speed manual transmission was available in GS 350/GS 400. Super Turbine automatic transmission was standard in Electra and Riviera, available in all others. Console automatic shifter was available with GS 350, GS 400, Wildcat and Riviera. The GS 350 V-8 was available in Special Deluxe, Skylark Custom, Sportwagon and LeSabre models. The GS 400 V-8 was available in Sportwagons.

COVENIENCE FEATURES: Power steering (standard Series 48200, 48400 and 49487). Power brakes (standard on Series 48200, 48400 and 49487). Power windows (not offered for Special Deluxe six-cyl.) Four-way power seat. Six-way power seat (full-size). Air conditioning. Vinyl top (special models). Seven-position tilt steering column. Limited trim on Electra Custom hardtops. AM/FM stereo radio. Tape deck. Strato seats (Series 49487) Chrome road wheels. AM radio. AM/FM radio. Whitewall tires. Deluxe wheelcovers. Soft-Ray glass. Cruise Master. GS 350/GS 400 consolette, tachometer, for manual transmission. Full-length console (bucket seats and Super Turbine transmission required). Cornering lights (full-size only). Automatic Climate Control. Power front disc brakes. Automatic door locks. Trailer hitch. Rear window defroster. Remote control outside rearview mirror. Speed alert. Super Deluxe wheelcovers. Radial ply tires. Power tailgate window on station wagons. Luggage rack for station wagons.

HISTORICAL FOOTNOTES: Calendar year production was 652,049 units. Model year production was 651,823 units. Buick was fifth largest automaker this year. GS production climbed 55 percent, reflecting the popularity of the sporty Skylark models. The V-6 was discontinued and replaced with an inline six built by Chevrolet. New federally mandated safety features for 1968 included larger outside rearview mirrors, side marker lights on front and rear fenders, safety armrests and improved door latches. A new Opel Kadette Sport Sedan was available from Buick dealers this year. The GS 400 had a top speed of 120 mph, down slightly from the previous year due to increased weight. The Riviera could do 0-to-60 in 8.1 seconds and had a top speed of 125-132 mph, depending on which car magazine you read. MECHANIX ILLUSTRATED said it was "Just about the best of any 1968 cars we have tested." Styles 44855 and 44865 are Sportwagons with woodgrain sides. Style 43327 was the California GS.

1969 BUICK

SPECIAL DELUXE — SERIES 43300 — The basic Buick for 1969 appeared with a minimum of change from its 1968 counterpart. A trio of bright outlined ventiports and bright housings for the side marker lamps were part of the minimal bodyside brightwork. Special Deluxe script appeared on the rear fenders. Among the standard features, many being mandated by new federal safety standards, were back-up lamps, a left-hand outside rearview mirror and seat belts.

BUICK I.D. NUMBERS: The serial number (VIN) was located on a plate, attached to top of dash on driver's side and viewable through outside of windshield. It was also stamped on the engine block. The first symbol was a '4' for Buick. The second and third symbols indicated series, as follows: 33=Special DeL.; 34=Special Deluxe/GS 350; 35=Skylark; 44=Skylark Custom/Sportwagon; 46=GS 400; 52=LeSabre; 54=LeSabre Custom; 64=Wildcat; 66=Wildcat Custom; 82=Electra 225; 84=Electra 225 Custom; 94=Riviera. The fourth and fifth symbols indicated body style, as follows: 27=2-dr cpe; 35=4-dr two-seat sta wag; 36=4-dr two-seat sta wag; 37=2-dr HT; 39=4-dr HT; 56=4-dr two-seat Sportwagon; 57=2-dr HT; 66=4-dr three-seat Sportwagon; 67=2-dr Conv; 69=4-dr Sedan and 87=2-dr Riv HT. Combined, the first five symbols were the model number, as reflected in tables below. The sixth symbol indicated model year, 9=1969. The seventh symbol was a letter representing the assembly plant, as follows: B=Baltimore, Md.; C=South Gate, Calif; D=Doraville, Ga.; H=Flint, Mich.; I=Oshawa, Ont., Canada; K=Kansas City, Mo.; V=Bloomfield, Mich.; X=Kansas City, Kan.; Y=Wilmington, Del.; Z=Fremont, Ohio. The last six digits represent the sequential assembly number at the plant with series mixed in production. In addition to the VIN, the right side of the engine block is stamped with a production code which has letters identifying the engine and numbers indicating production date codes. The letters were as follows: (250 cid six-cyl.) NA; (350 cid V-8) RO, RW, RP; (GS 350 V-8) RP only; (GS 400 V-8) RR, RS or Stage 1; (Sportwagon 400 cid V-8) RR; (430 cid V-8) RO or RE.

SPECIAL DELUXE SERIES 43300/43400

Series Number	Model Number	Body Type & Seating	Factory Price	Shipping Weight	Production Total
43300	43327	2-dr Cpe	2562	3126	15,268
43300	43369	4-dr Sedan	2613	3182	11,113
43400	43455	4-dr Sta Wag-2S	3092	3783	2,590
43400	43436	4-dr Sta-Wag-2S	3124	3736	6,677

V-8 NOTE: Special Deluxe also offered in 43400 V-8 series. On V-8s, the third symbol in model number changes to '4.' Add $111 and 119 pounds for V-8s; wagon is V-8 only.

ENGINES: Six. Inline. Overhead valves. Cast-iron block. Displacement: 250 cid. Bore and stroke: 3.875 x 3.53 inches. Compression ratio: 8.5:1. Brake horsepower: 155 at 4200 rpm. Hydraulic valve lifters. One-barrel Rochester MV carburetor.

V-8. Overhead valves. Cast iron block. Displacement: 350 cid. Bore and stroke: 3.80 x 3.85 inches. Compression ratio: 9.0:1. Brake horsepower: 230 at 4400 rpm. Five main bearings. Hydraulic valve lifters. Two-barrel Rochester 2GV carburetor.

NOTE: Style 43327 was also built in California GS trim, with bright wheelhouse moldings, a vinyl top with GS monograms on the roof quarters and a GS emblem on the deck lid. A functional hood scoop, with the opening near the windshield, was included as well. The word California was spelled out in script on the rear fenders. The California GS coupes had vent windows. The California GS was powered by the GS 350 engine linked to a standard Turbo-Hydramatic 350 transmission. Production of this option was 4,831 units. This production number is included with the Special Deluxe coupe on table above.

SKYLARK — SERIES 43500 — Reduced to a two model line for 1969, the Skylark featured minimal side trim, with a trio of leaning vertical bright bars on each front fender. Skylark script appeared on the rear fenders. The grille had a horizontal division bar.

SKYLARK SERIES 43500 I.D. NUMBERS: Serial numbers began with 435009( )600001 on cars equipped with the V-6. Serial numbers began with 435009( )100001 on V-8 cars. An explanation of the VIN code may be found under the 1968 Special Deluxe Series ID Number section.

SKYLARK SERIES 43500

Series Number	Model Number	Body Type & Seating	Factory Price	Shipping Weight	Production Total
43500	43537	2-dr HT Cpe-6P	2736	3179	38,658
43500	43569	4-dr Sed-6P	2715	3209	22,349

V-8 NOTE: Skylarks also offered in 43500 V-8 series. On V-8s, the third symbol in model number changes. Add $111 and 119 pounds for V-8s

ENGINES: Six-Cylinder and V-8 specifications were the same as listed for the 1969 Special Deluxe Series 43300.

SKYLARK CUSTOM — SERIES 44400 — The plushest intermediate Buick, had better quality vinyl and cloth or all-vinyl interiors, a bright lower body molding and wheelhouse moldings. A chrome sweepspear molding was optional and, at the front, a Buick emblem was centered in the grille.

SKYLARK CUSTOM SERIES 44400 I.D. NUMBERS: Vehicle Identification Numbers began with 444009( )100001. VINs were coded as explained under the 1969 Special Deluxe Series ID Number section.

SKYLARK SERIES 43500

Series Number	Model Number	Body Type & Seating	Factory Price	Shipping Weight	Production Total
43500	43537	2-dr Cpe-6P	2847	3298	38,658
43500	43569	4-dr Sed-6P	2826	3328	22,349

ENGINES: Six-cylinder and V-8 specifications were the same as listed for the 1969 Special Deluxe Series 43300.

SKYLARK CUSTOM — SERIES 44400 — The plushest intermediate Buick had better quality vinyl and cloth or all-vinyl interiors, a bright lower body molding and wheelhouse moldings. A chrome sweepspear molding was optional and, at the front, a Buick emblem was centered in the grille.

SKYLARK CUSTOM SERIES 44400 I.D. NUMBERS: Vehicle Identification Numbers began with 444009( )100001. VINs were coded as explained under the 1969 Special Deluxe Series ID Number section.

Series Number	Model Number	Body Type & Seating	Factory Price	Shipping Weight	Production Total
44400	44437	2-dr Spt Cpe-6P	3009	3341	35,639
44400	44439	4-dr HT Sed-6P	3151	3477	9,609
44400	44467	2-dr Conv-6P	3152	3398	6,552
44400	44469	4-dr Sed-6P	2978	3397	6,423

ENGINE: V-8 specifications were the same as listed for the 1969 Special Deluxe Series 43300.

GS 350 — SERIES 43437 — A one-style series for 1969 was the GS 350. Once again this car combined the Skylark Custom's interior accoutrements with a sporting car's exterior. Front fenders carried neither ventiports or vents this year, while the wheelhouse moldings were continued. A more prominent hood scoop was hooked to a special air cleaner with twin snorkels. Buick claimed this cold air induction system boosted power eight percent and increased torque 6.5 percent. However, the factory ratings did not change. A GS 350 plaque was used on the center of the deck lid, with monograms on the grille and door panels. All-vinyl, foam-padded seats were standard, with the bucket versions an option. Upper level ventilation, without vent windows, was a distinctive feature.

GS 350 SERIES 43437 I.D. NUMBERS: Vehicle Identification Numbers began with 434379( )100001. An explanation of VIN codes appears in the 1969 Special Deluxe ID Number section.

GS 350 SERIES 43437

Series Number	Model Number	Body Type & Seating	Factory Price	Shipping Weight	Production Total
43400	43437	2-dr Spt Cpe-5P	2980	3406	4.933

ENGINE: Specifications were the same as listed for the 1969 Special Deluxe Series 43300 V-8, except the compression ratio was 10.25:1, brake horsepower was 280 at 4600 rpm and a four-barrel Rochester 4MV carburetor was used.

1969 Buick, GS-400 two-door hardtop sport coupe, V-8 (TVB)

GS 400 — SERIES 44600 — Similar to the GS 350, the most potent Buick had 400 numerals on the hood scoop and rear quarters. A Deluxe steering wheel was standard, along with foam-padded seats, ashtray light, glovebox light and upper interior light. Interiors were all-vinyl, with a bench front seat standard and buckets available optionally. There was a unique GS 400 grille and a cold air induction package. A hot, dealer-installed option was the Stage 1 package including a 400 cid V-8 with 11.0:1 compression that was rated for 345 hp at 4800 rpm and 440 lbs.-ft. of torque at 3200 rpm. Experts said the actual output of this motor was closer to 400 hp.

GS 400 SERIES 44600 I.D. NUMBERS: Vehicle Identification Numbers began with 44600( )100001. An explanation of the VIN codes appears under the 1969 Special Deluxe Series ID Number section.

GS 400 SERIES 44600

Series Number	Model Number	Body Type & Seating	Factory Price	Shipping Weight	Production Total
44600	44637	2-dr HT Cpe-6P	3181	3549	6,356
44600	44667	2-dr Conv-6P	3325	3594	1,176

ENGINE: V-8: Overhead valve. Cast iron block. Displacement: 400 cid. Bore and stroke: 4.04 x 3.90 inches. Compression ratio: 10.25:1. Brake horsepower: 340 at 5000 rpm. Hydraulic lifters: Four-barrel carburetor.

SPORTWAGON CUSTOM — SERIES 44400 — Numbered in the Skylark Custom series, but with varied trim, these wagons had bright wheelhouse and rocker panel moldings, woodgrain side trim and Sportwagon script on the rear fenders. They were fully carpeted, including the cargo areas and used expanded vinyl trimming. A Deluxe steering wheel, Custom padded seat cushions and the features of the Custom Skylark were used.

SPORTWAGON CUSTOM SERIES 44400 I.D. NUMBERS: Vehicle Identification Numbers began with 444009HI000I. VIN numbers were coded as explained under the 1969 Special Deluxe Series ID Number section.

SPORTWAGON CUSTOM SERIES 44400

Series Number	Model Number	Body Type & Seating	Factory Price	Shipping Weight	Production Total
44400	44456	4-dr Sta Wag-2S	3465	4106	9,157
44400	44466	4-dr Sta Wag-3S	3621	4231	11,513

ENGINE: Specifications were the same as those listed for the Special Deluxe V-8. Series 43300/43400.

1969 Buick, LeSabre four-door hardtop sedan, V-8 (TVB)

LESABRE — SERIES 45200 — A new body greeted LeSabre buyers for 1969. Styling was refined and lighter than in immediately preceding years. The LeSabre still wore its trio of front fenders ventiports and a narrow argent accent strip rocker panel was used. LeSabre script appeared on the rear fenders, with further series identification found on the instrument panel. Standard equipment included upper level ventilation system (instead of ventipanes); door-operated interior lights; glove compartment light; smoking set; rear seat ashtray; front and rear armrests and full carpeting.

NOTE: The LeSabre '400' option, offered for LeSabre and LeSabre Custom models, included a 280 horsepower, 350 cid V-8 and Turbo-Hydramatic transmission. Cars so equipped had '400' emblems on the rear fenders, below the LeSabre script.

LESABRE SERIES 45200 I.D. NUMBERS: Vehicle Identification Numbers began with 452009( )100001. VIN numbers were coded as explained under the 1969 Special Deluxe Series ID Number section.

LESABRE SERIES 45200

Series Number	Model Number	Body Type & Seating	Factory Price	Shipping Weight	Production Total
45200	45269	4-dr Sed-6P	3216	3966	36,664
45200	45237	2-dr HT-6P	3298	3936	16,201
45200	45239	4-dr HT-6P	3356	3983	17,235

ENGINE: Specifications were the same as listed for the 1969 Special Deluxe V-8 Series 43300/43400.

LESABRE CUSTOM — SERIES 45400 — This represented a plusher edition of the popular LeSabre. A broader metal rocker panel molding, with rear fender extension, was used with bright wheelhouse moldings to accent Custom level trim. Custom Script appeared on the rear fenders beneath the LeSabre signatures. Inside, plusher cloth and vinyl trim combinations were found, or an all-vinyl interior could be chosen. Bucket seats were optional for the Custom Sport Coupe.

LESABRE CUSTOM SERIES 45400 I.D. NUMBERS: Vehicle Identification Numbers began with 454009( )100001. VINs were coded as explained under the 1969 Special Deluxe ID Number section.

LESABRE CUSTOM SERIES 45400

Series Number	Model Number	Body Type & Seating	Factory Price	Shipping Weight	Production Total
45400	45469	4-dr Sed-6P	3310	3941	37,136
45400	45437	2-dr HT Cpe-6P	3386	4018	38,887
45400	45439	4-dr HT Sed-6P	3450	4073	48,123
45400	45469	2-dr Conv-6P	3579	3958	3,620

ENGINE: Specifications are the same as listed for the Special Deluxe V-8 Series 43300/43400.

WILDCAT — SERIES 46400 — Sharing the LeSabre's sheetmetal, but with styling touches suggesting a more powerful, sporting automobile, the Wildcat had a distinctive grille with vertical texturing. A bright, broad rocker molding with fender extensions and wheelhouse moldings was used. Wildcat script appeared above groups of five vertical bars on each front fender. Standard equipment was the same as the LeSabre except for the addition of a Deluxe steering wheel. Interiors were cloth and vinyl or all-vinyl. Bucket seats, with all-vinyl seating surfaces, were offered for the Sport Coupe.

WILDCAT SERIES 46400 I.D. NUMBERS: Vehicle Identification Numbers began with 464009( )100001. VINs were coded as explained under the 1969 Special Deluxe Series ID Number section.

WILDCAT SERIES 46400

Series Number	Model Number	Body Type & Seating	Factory Price	Shipping Weight	Production Total
46400	46469	4-dr Sed-6P	4448	4102	13,126
46400	46437	2-dr HT Cpe-6P	4553	3926	12,416
46400	46439	4-dr HT Sed-6P	4608	4204	13,805

ENGINE: V-8: Overhead valves. Cast iron block. Displacement: 430 cid. Bore and stroke: 4.19 x 3.9 inches. Compression ratio: 10.25:1. Brake horsepower: 360 at 5000 rpm. Five main bearings. Hydraulic valve lifters. Four-barrel Rochester 4MV carburetor.

WILDCAT CUSTOM — SERIES 46600 — Custom quality cloth and vinyl or all-vinyl interiors were the hallmark of the custom series, with notchback front seats featured. Otherwise, the cars were the same as the Wildcat Series 45200 models.

WILDCAT CUSTOM SERIES 46600 I.D. NUMBERS: Vehicle Identification Numbers began with 466009( )100001. VINs were coded as explained under the 1969 Special Deluxe listing.

WILDCAT CUSTOM SERIES 46600

Series Number	Model Number	Body Type & Seating	Factory Price	Shipping Weight	Production Total
46600	46637	2-dr HT-6P	3817	4134	12,136
46600	46639	4-dr HT-6P	3866	4220	13,596
46600	46667	2-dr Conv-6P	3948	4152	2,374

ENGINE: Specifications were the same as listed for the 1969 Wildcat Series 46400.

ELECTRA 225 SERIES 48200 — A large, yet graceful, body was used for Buick's biggest models in 1969. A tapering sweepspear sculpture line and rear fender skirts contributed to the smooth-flowing Electra lines. A group of four ventiports were lined out on each front fender. The lower body was swathed in bright metal from the front bumper to the rear, with a kick-up over the front wheelhouse lip. A specifically designed grille texture was used. Rear taillamps were horizontal and were behind bright grids. Electra 225 emblems were on the rear fenders and deck. Round rear fender marker lights were exclusive to the Electra 225 styles. Standard features in addition to those found on the Wildcat, included power steering; power brakes; automatic transmission; Custom padded seat cushions; electric clock; carpeted floors and lower doors and side coat hooks. Interiors were cloth and vinyl or all-vinyl, with front bench seats.

ELECTRA 225 SERIES 48200 I.D. NUMBERS: Vehicle Identification Numbers began with 482009HI00001. VINs were coded as explained under the 1969 Special Deluxe Series ID Number section.

ELECTRA 225 SERIES 48200

Series Number	Model Number	Body Type & Seating	Factory Price	Shipping Weight	Production Total
48200	42869	4-dr Sed-6P	4302	4236	14,521
48200	48257	2-dr HT Cpe-6P	4323	4203	13,128
48200	48239	4-dr HT Sed-6P	4432	4294	15,983

ENGINE: Specifications were the same as listed for the 1969 Wildcat Series 46400.

ELECTRA 225 CUSTOM — SERIES 48400 — A more refined interior was the basis of the Custom Electra. Expanded vinyl notchback front seats were used in the two-door hardtop and four-door hardtop, while vinyl and cloth bench or notchback type front seats were found in sedans. Expanded vinyl trim, with notchback front seat, power windows and two-way power seat adjustments were standard on the Custom Convertible.

NOTE: Custom Limited equipment was available for the two-door hardtop and four-door hardtop. Cars so-equipped had better quality vinyl and cloth or all-vinyl interior trims with a 60/40 front deck. Limited scripts appeared on the roof quarters.

ELECTRA 225 CUSTOM SERIES 48400 I.D. NUMBERS: Vehicle Identification Numbers began with 484009HI00001. VINs were coded as explained under the 1969 Special Deluxe Series ID Number section.

ELECTRA 225 CUSTOM SERIES 48400

Series Number	Model Number	Body Type & Seating	Factory Price	Shipping Weight	Production Total
48400	48469	4-dr Sed-6P	4517	4281	14,434
48400	48457	2-dr HT Cpe-6P	4502	4222	27,018
48400	48439	4-dr HT Sed-6P	4611	4328	65,240
48400	48467	2-dr Conv-6P	4643	4309	8,294

ENGINE: Specifications were the same as listed for the 1969 Wildcat Series 46400.

RIVIERA — SERIES 49487 — A slight facelift was seen for 1969 as the sleek Riviera continued to be offered only in sport coupe form. Retractable headlamps and an intregral front bumper/grille continued to distinguish the front of the Riviera. New bodyside trims using bright wheelhouse moldings and bright lower body moldings with argent accents were utilized. Expanded vinyl with front bench or bucket seats was standard Custom interiors with bench, buckets or notchback front seats in plusher vinyl or vinyl and cloth combinations was available. Standard Riviera features included all items found on other Buicks, plus woodgrained dash accents and trunk lights.

NOTE: A new Riviera GS option package sold for $131.57 at retail. It included chrome covered air cleaner; front and rear heavy-duty suspension; performance axle with positive traction differential; and white sidewall tires. Cars with the package installed were outwardly distinguished by special narrow rocker panel covers, the lack of gravel deflectors, and a thin side trim molding.

RIVIERA I.D. NUMBERS: Vehicle Identification Numbers began with 494879H900001. VINs were coded as explained under the 1969 Special Deluxe Series ID Number section.

RIVIERA SERIES 49487

Series Number	Model Number	Body Type & Seating	Factory Price	Shipping Weight	Production Total
49400	49487	2-dr Spt Cpe-5P	4701	4199	52,872

ENGINE: Specifications were the same as listed for the 1969 Wildcat Series 46400.

CHASSIS FEATURES: Wheelbase: (Series 43300, 43500, 44400, 43400, 44600 two-door styles) 112 inches; (four-door styles) 116 inches; (Sportwagon) 121 inches; (Series 45200, 45400, 46400 and 46600) 123.2 inches; (Series 48200 and 48400) 126.2 inches; (Series 49487) 119 inches. Overall length: (Series 43300, 43500, 44400, 43400 and 44600 two-door styles) 200.7 inches; (four-door styles) 204.7 inches; (Station wagon) 209 inches; (Sportwagon) 214 inches; (Series 45200, 45400, 46400 and 46600) 218.2 inches. Tread: (Series 43300, 43500, 44400, and 43300 and 44600) 59 inches front and rear; (Series 42500, 45400, 46400 and 46600) 63.5 inches front and 63 inches rear; (Series 48200, 48400 and 49487) 63.4 inches front and 63 inches rear. Tires: (Series 43300, 43500, 44400, 43400 and 46600) 7.75 x 14; (Sportwagon) 8.55 x 14; (Series 45200, 45400, 46400, 46600, 48200, 48400 and 49487) 8.55 x 15.

POWERTRAIN OPTIONS: A three-speed manual transmission with column shift was standard on Special Deluxe, Skylark, Skylark Custom, GS 350, LeSabre, and Wildcat models. A three-speed manual transmission with floor shift was standard on GS 400 models and optional on California GS and GS 350 models. A four-speed manual transmission was optional on California GS, GS 350 and GS 400 models. Super Turbine 300 automatic transmission was optional for Special Deluxe, Skylark, Skylark Custom and LeSabre models. Turbo-Hydramatic 350 automatic transmission was optional for Special Deluxe, Skylark, Skylark Custom and GS 350 models. Turbo-Hydramatic 400 automatic transmission was optional for GS 400 and Wildcat models and was standard on Electra 225, Electra Custom and Riviera models. A 280 brake horsepower, 350 cid V-8 was optional for the Special Deluxe, Skylark, Skylark Custom and LeSabre. A '400' option package for the LeSabre series included the 280 horsepower 350 V-8 an Turbo-Hydramatic 400 transmission. Cars so equipped had '400' emblems below the rear fender LeSabre scripts. A 'Stage I' option was offered for the GS 400. It included a high-lift camshaft, special carburetor and large diameter dual exhausts, along with a 3.64 rear axle. Cars so equipped had 'Stage I' emblems on the front fenders.

CONVENIENCE OPTIONS included air conditioning ($376 on intermediate, $437 on full-size). Power windows. Vinyl top. Seven-position tilt wheel. AM radio. AM/FM radio. AM/FM radio with stereo tape. Five-spoke Sport Wheels (chrome). Strato bucket seats on specific models. Limited Trim option for Electra 225 Custom ($231). Map light on rearview mirror. 60/40 seat (Electra 225 styles). Electric window defogger (Riviera). Protective bodyside moldings (full-size). Power door locks. Power steering (standard Electra 225, Electra 225 Custom and Riviera). Power brakes (standard Electra 225, Electra 225 Custom and Riviera). Climate-control air (full-size). Center console with bucket seats on Skylark Custom, GS 350, GS 400 and Wildcat when equipped with THM-350 or THM-400 automatic transmission. Four-way power seat. Six-way power seat. (Electra 225, Wildcat, LeSabre). Trailering packages. Dual Action tailgate on station wagons.

HISTORICAL FOOTNOTES: A record year with 713,832 units made in the calendar year. Model year production stood at 665,422. The only bigger year for Buick, to this point, was 1955. The company went into fourth place in production. New features included Turbo-Hydramatic transmission, Accu-Drive suspension, electric fuel pump on Riviera, new anti-theft ignition lock, headrests, ventless windows (on some models) and a redesigned collapsible steering wheel.The Century Cruiser, a radical show car, was exhibited at the New York Auto Show. The California GS did 0-to-60 in 9.5 seconds and had a 110 mph top speed. The Riviera GS did 0-to-60 in 9.2 seconds and topped out at 132 mph. Model 43536 was a station wagon with dual-action tailgate and plusher interior. On April 7, 1969, Lee N. Mayes succeeded Robert L. Kessler as Buick general manager.

1970 BUICK

SKYLARK — SERIES 43300 — A new look was used for 1970, with crisper lines and more open wheelhouses. The sweepspear look was once again relegated to retirement, with horizontal sculpturing taking its place. The basic Buick had a vertically textured grille with a grid overlay. Narrow lower body moldings and wheelhouse bright moldings were used. Skylark emblems were on the roof sail panels and side marker lamps were rectangular. The Skylark signature appeared on rear fenders. Interiors were spartan with vinyl and cloth combinations on bench seats standard. All-vinyl was no-cost option for the coupe and an extra cost option for the sedan. Standard equipment included a host of mandated safety features, including left-hand outside rearview mirror and back-up lights.

BUICK I.D. NUMBERS: The serial number (VIN) was located on a plate, attached to top of dash on driver's side and viewable through outside of windshield. It was also stamped on the engine block. The first symbol was a '4' for Buick. The second and third symbols indicated series, as follows: 33=Skylark; 34=Sportwagon/GS; 35=Skylark 350; 44=Skylark Custom; 46=GS 455; 52=LeSabre; 54=LeSabre Custom; 60=Estate Wagon; 64=LeSabre Custom 455; 66=Wildcat Custom; 82=Electra 225; 84=Electra 225 Custom; 94=Riviera. The fourth and fifth symbols indicated body style, as follows: 27=2-dr cpe; 35=4-dr two-seat sta wag; 36=4-dr two-seat sta wag; 37=2-dr HT; 39=4-dr HT; 46=4-dr three-seat sta wag; 47= 4-dr HT; 56=4-dr two-seat Sportwagon; 57=2-dr HT; 66=4-dr three-seat Sportwagon; 67=2-dr Conv; 69=4-dr Sedan and 87= 2-dr Riv HT. Combined, the first five symbols were the model number, as reflected in tables below. The sixth symbol indicated model year, 0=1970. The seventh symbol was a letter representing the assembly plant, as follows: C=South Gate, Calif; D=Doraville, Ga.; G=Framingham, Mass.; H=Flint, Mich.; K=Leeds, Mo.; X=Fairfax, Kan.; Y=Wilmington, Del.; Z=Fremont, Calif. The last six digits represent the sequential assembly number at the plant with series mixed in production. In addition to the VIN, the engine block is stamped with a production code. These numbers were found on different locations: (6-cyl.) right side to rear of distributor; (350 cid V-8) on front of left bank of cylinders and between front two spark plugs and left exhaust manifold; (455 cid V-8) between front two spark plugs and exhaust manifold and production code between two left rear spark plugs and exhaust manifold. The production code has letters identifying the engine and numbers indicating production date codes. The letters were as follows: (250 cid six-cyl.) SA; (350 cid/285 hp V-8) SB; (350 cid/230 hp V-8) SO; (350 cid/315 hp V-8) SP; (400 cid/400 hp V-8) RR; (455 cid/370 hp V-8) SF; (455 cid/350 hp V-8) SR and (455 cid/360 hp V-8) SS.

SKYLARK SERIES 43300

Series Number	Model Number	Body Type & Seating	Factory Price	Shipping Weight	Production Total
43300	43327	2-dr Cpe-6P	2685	3155	18,620
43300	43369	4-dr Sed-6P	2736	3214	13,420

NOTE: Add $111 and 195 pounds for V-8s.

ENGINES: Six-cyl. Overhead valves. Cast-iron block. Displacement: 250 cid. Bore and stroke: 3.875 x 3.53 inches. Compression ratio: 8.5:1. Brake horsepower: 155 at 4200 rpm. Five main bearings. Hydraulic valve lifters. Rochester 1MV one-barrel carburetor.

V-8. Overhead valve. Cast iron block. Displacement: 350 cid. Bore and stroke: 3.8 x 3.85 inches. Compression ratio: 9.0:1. Brake horsepower: 260 at 4600 rpm. Five main bearings. Hydraulic valve lifters. Two-barrel Rochester 2GV carburetor.

SKYLARK 350 — SERIES 43500 — Identical to the Skylark, except for the addition of 350 emblems to the body and a Buick emblem for the center grille.

SKYLARK 350 SERIES 43500 I.D. NUMBERS: Vehicle Identification Numbers began with 43500( )100001. VIN codes are explained under the 1970 Skylark Series ID Number section.

SKYLARK SERIES 43500

Series Number	Model Number	Body Type & Seating	Factory Price	Shipping Weight	Production Total
43500	43569	4-dr Sed-6P	2838	3223	30,281
43500	43537	2-dr HT-6P	2859	3180	70,918

NOTE: Add $111 and 195 pounds for V-8.

ENGINE: Specifications were the same as listed for the 1970 Skylark Series 43300 V-8.

SKYLARK CUSTOM — SERIES 44400 — The plushest intermediate model had a Buick emblem centered in the grille, lower body and wheelhouse moldings and Skylark signatures on the hood, deck and rear fenders. The Custom badge appeared beneath the rear fender signatures. Interiors were done in all-vinyl or Kenora cloth and vinyl. A bench seat was standard, with bucket front seats available for the convertible and coupe.

SKYLARK CUSTOM SERIES 44400 I.D. NUMBERS: Vehicle Identification Numbers began with 44400( )100001. VIN codes are explained under the 1970 Skylark Series 33300 ID Number section.

SKYLARK CUSTOM SERIES 44400

Series Number	Model Number	Body Type & Seating	Factory Price	Shipping Weight	Production Total
44400	44469	4-dr Sed-6P	3101	3499	7,113
44400	44437	2-dr HT Cpe-6P	3132	3435	36,367
44400	44439	4-dr HT Sed-6P	3220	3565	12,411
44400	44467	2-dr Conv-6P	3275	3499	4,954

ENGINES: Six-cyl. and V-8 specifications were the same as listed for the 1970 Skylark Series 43300.

1970 Buick, GS-455 two-door hardtop coupe, V-8 (TVB)

GRAN SPORT — SERIES 43437 — A one-model series constituted Buick's cosmetic musclecar for 1970. This was a mild-mannered intermediate with the trimmings of a rip-roaring charger. A textured black grille was used, with hood scoops on the panel above. GS signatures appeared on the left-hand grille, front fenders and deck. All-vinyl bench seats in sandalwood, blue or black were standard. An all-vinyl notchback seat was optional, as were individual front bucket seats. Standard equipment approximated that found on the Skylark Custom and also included dual exhausts, a full-flow oil filter, three-speed manual transmission, heavy-duty shocks and springs and a semi-enclosed cooling system.

GRAN SPORT SERIES 43400 I.D. NUMBERS: Vehicle Identification Numbers began with 434370( )100001. VINs were coded as explained under the 1970 Skylark Series 33300 ID Number section.

GRAN SPORT SERIES 43400

Series Number	Model Number	Body Type & Seating	Factory Price	Shipping Weight	Production Total
43400	43437	2-dr HT Cpe-6P	3098	3434	9,948

ENGINE: V-8: Specifications were the same as the Skylark Series 33300 V-8 except the compression ratio was 10.25:1, brake horsepower was 315 at 4800 rpm and dual exhausts were standard.

GRAN SPORT 445 — SERIES 44600 — This was the truly muscular Buick, with a new big block V-8 and Hurst-shifted performance transmissions. Functional hood scoops dumped cold air into the big V-8's intake. Chrome red-filled lower body and wheelhouse moldings were used with five-spoke 14 x 6 inch chrome wheels standard. A GS 455 emblem appeared on the left-hand blacked-out grille, with others showing up on the front fenders and a GS monogram appearing on the deck lid. Standard interior appointments were the same as on the GS. A number of mandated safety features were standard.

GRAN SPORT SERIES 46600 I.D. NUMBERS: Vehicle Identification Numbers began with 46600( )100001. VINs were coded as explained under the 1970 Skylark Series ID Number section.

GRAN SPORT 455 SERIES 46600

Series Number	Model Number	Body Type & Seating	Factory Price	Shipping Weight	Production Total
44600	44637	2-dr HT-6P	3283	3562	8,732
44600	44667	2-dr Conv-6P	3469	3619	1,416

GSX SUB-SERIES

44600	44637	2-dr HT-5P	4479	n.a.	(678)
44600	44667	2-dr Conv-5P	4665	n.a.	(678)

NOTE: "Production total" indicates number of option package installations.

ENGINE: V-8: Overhead valves. Cast-iron block. Displacement: 455 cid. Bore and stroke: 4.3 x 3.9 inches. Compression ratio: 10.0:1. Brake horsepower: 350 at 4600 rpm. Hydraulic valve lifters. Five main bearings. Four-barrel Rochester 4MV carburetor.

STAGE I/STAGE II NOTE: Stage I equipment, consisting of a high-lift camshaft, 10.5:1 compression pistons, positive traction rear axle, special four-barrel carburetor and low-restriction dual exhaust increased brake horsepower to 360 at 4600 rpm. Cars so equipped have Stage I badges in place of 455 emblems and a logo replacing the 455 emblem in the left-hand grille. The GS 455 produced 510 lbs.-ft. of torque at 2800 rpm! There was also a Stage II dealer-installed package with a hotter cam, 12.0:1 forged pistons, Edelbrock B4B manifold, Holley carb, Mickey Thompson headers and 4.78 differential gears.

GSX NOTE: At midyear, Buick introduced its ultra-high-performance GSX package as a $1,196 option for the GS-455. It included a hood tach with available lighting control; G60 x 15 tires on seven-inch wide chrome rims; molded plastic front/rear spoilers; twin OSRV mirrors; four-speed Hurst shifter; front disc brakes; heavy-duty suspension and black vinyl bucket seats. It was available with both the 350 V-8 and the Stage I engine.

SPORTWAGON — SERIES 43400 — The traditional roof panel with glass inserts was missing from 1970 Sportwagons, which had flat roofs. Narrow lower body moldings were used with bright wheelhouse moldings. Sportwagon script appeared on the rear fenders. Interiors were similar to the corresponding Skylark models, with all-vinyl trimming. Fiberglass belted tires were standard.

SPORTWAGON SERIES 43400 I.D. NUMBERS: Vehicle Identification Numbers began with 434000( )100001. VINs were coded as explained under the 1970 Skylark Series ID Number section.

SPORTWAGON SERIES 43400

Series Number	Model Number	Body Type & Seating	Factory Price	Shipping Weight	Production Total
43400	43435	4-dr Sta Wag-2S	3210	3775	2,239
43400	43436	4-dr Sta Wag-2S	3242	3898	10,002

NOTE: Prices and weights for V-8s are given. Deduct $111 for 6-cylinder models.

ENGINES: Specifications for 6-cyl and V-8 were the same as listed under 1970 Skylark Series 43300 ID Number section.

LESABRE — SERIES 45200 — The lowest-priced full-size Buick featured a very minor face-lift for 1970. A new grille-bumper combination with horizontal textured grille was at the front, while at the rear the taillights dropped into the bumper assembly. A lower body bright molding was used, but there were no wheelhouse moldings. The LeSabre name appeared in script on the rear fenders and triple ventiports were found on the front. Cloth and vinyl seating surfaces were standard with a front bench. The LeSabre signature was on the right-hand instrument panel. Standard equipment included Comfort-Flo ventilation; heater and defroster; front-door operated interior light; glove compartment light; smoking set; rear seat ashtray and carpeting front and rear.

LESABRE SERIES 45200 I.D. NUMBERS: Vehicle Identificaton Numbers began with 452200( )100001. VINs were coded as explained under the 1970 Skylark Series ID Number section.

LESABRE SERIES 45200

Series Number	Model Number	Body Type & Seating	Factory Price	Shipping Weight	Production Total
45200	45269	4-dr Sed-6P	3337	3970	35,404
45200	45237	2-dr HT Cpe-6P	3419	3866	14,163
45200	45239	4-dr HT Sed-6P	3477	4018	14,817

ENGINE: Specifications were the same as listed for the 1970 Skylark Series 33300.

LESABRE CUSTOM — SERIES 45400 — A plusher LeSabre was seen this year. It had wheelhouse moldings in addition to bright lower body moldings, which now extended onto the rear fenders. Custom badges appeared below the rear fender LeSabre scripts. Richer cloth and vinyl or all-vinyl (convertible) interiors were standard.

LESABRE CUSTOM SERIES 45200 I.D. NUMBERS: Vehicle Identification Numbers began with 45200( )100001. VINs were coded as explained under the 1970 Skylark Series ID Number section.

LESABRE CUSTOM SERIES 45400

Series Number	Model Number	Body Type & Seating	Factory Price	Shipping Weight	Production Total
45400	45469	4-dr Sed-6P	3431	3950	36,682
45400	45437	2-dr HT Cpe-6P	3507	3921	35,641
45400	45439	4-dr HT Cpe-6P	3571	3988	43,863
45400	45467	2-dr Conv-6P	3700	3947	2,487

ENGINE: Specifications were the same as listed for the 1970 Skylark Series 43300.

LESABRE CUSTOM — SERIES 45600 — Identical to the LeSabre Custom externally, this model had rear fender badges signifying use of the big 455 cid V-8 and was numbered as a separate series. The convertible was not available in this series.

LESABRE CUSTOM 455 SERIES 45400 I.D. NUMBERS: Vehicle Identification Numbers began with 456000( )100001. VINs were coded as explained under the 1970 Skylark Series ID Number section.

LESABRE CUSTOM 455 SERIES 45600

Series Number	Model Number	Body Type & Seating	Factory Price	Shipping Weight	Production Total
45600	45669	4-dr Sed-6P	3599	4107	5,555
45600	45637	2-dr HT Cpe-6P	3675	4066	5,469
45600	45639	4-d HT Sed-6P	3739	4143	6,541

ENGINE: V-8. Overhead valves. Cast iron block. Displacement: 455 cid. Bore and stroke: 4.3 x 3.9 inches. Compression ratio: 10.0:1. Brake horsepower: 370 at 4600 rpm. Five main bearings. Hydraulic valve lifters. Four-barrel Rochester 4MV carburetor.

1970 Buick, Estate Wagon four-door station wagon, V-8 (TVB)

ESTATE WAGONS — SERIES 46000 — A full-size Buick wagon was marketed for the first time since 1964. It had the basic LeSabre body, but wore four ventiports on the front fenders. The LeSabre Custom's bright rocker, wheelhouse and rear lower fender moldings were used. Woodgraining was an option for the bodysides Interiors were all-vinyl in a Custom grade.

ESTATE WAGON SERIES 46000 I.D. NUMBERS: Vehicle Identification Numbers began with 460000( )100001. VINs were coded as explained under the 1970 Skylark Series ID Number section.

ESTATE WAGON SERIES 4600

Series Number	Model Number	Body Type & Seating	Factory Price	Shipping Weight	Production Total
46000	46036	4-dr Sta Wag-2S	3923	4691	11,427
46000	46046	4-dr Sta Wag-2S	4068	4779	16,879

ENGINE: Specifications were the same as those listed for the 1970 LeSabre Custom 455.

WILDCAT CUSTOM — SERIES 46600 — The Wildcat came only with Custom trim for 1970. It shared the LeSabre body with its new intregral grille and front bumper assembly, but a grid-pattern bright overlay on the grille itself distinguished the Wildcat. There were no ventiports, but there was a simulated bright air intake on each front fender. There was also a wide bright molding extending along the lower body, with connecting strips over the wheelhouse, from front to rear. The Wildcat signature appeared on the grille, deck and front fenders above the inlet grids. Vinyl notchback or bucket seats were standard, with a cloth and vinyl combination offered for the four-door hardtop. Standard equipment was the same as on the LeSabre, except for Deluxe steering wheel. The Wildcat signature appeared on the instrument panel.

WILDCAT CUSTOM SERIES 46600 I.D. NUMBERS: Vehicle Identification Numbers began with 466000( )100001. VINs are coded as explained under the 1970 Skylark Series ID Number section.

WILDCAT CUSTOM SERIES 4600

Series Number	Model Number	Body Type & Seating	Factory Price	Shipping Weight	Production Total
46600	46637	2-dr HT Cpe-6P	3949	4099	9,477
46600	46639	4-dr HT Sed-6P	3997	4187	12,924
46600	46667	2-dr Conv-6P	4079	4214	1,244

ENGINE: Specifications were the same as those listed for the 1970 LeSabre Custom 455.

ELECTRA 225 — SERIES 48200 — The largest Buicks were also the least changed for 1970. A new grille with bright grid overlay represented the chief distinction from a 1969 edition. Once again four ventiports graced the front fenders, while a strip of bright trim ran along the lower body from front to rear and extended across the fender skirts. Standard Electra features included those found on less expensive Buicks, plus Custom padded seat cushions; electric clock; trunk light; smoking set; rear seat ashtrays; carpeting on floors and lower doors and front and rear armrests. Cloth and vinyl bench seats were standard on the Electra.

ELECTRA 225 SERIES 48200 I.D. NUMBERS: Vehicle Identification Numbers began with 48200( )100001. VINs were coded as explained under the 1970 Skylark Series ID Number section.

ELECTRA 225 SERIES 48200

Series Number	Mode Number	Body Type & Seating	Factory Price	Shipping Weight	Production Total
48200	48269	4-dr Sed-6P	4461	4274	12,580
48200	48257	2-dr HT Cpe-6P	4482	4214	12,013
48200	48239	4-dr HT Sed-6P	4592	4296	14,338

ENGINE: Specifications were the same as listed for the 1970 LeSabre Custom 455.

ELECTRA 225 CUSTOM — SERIES 48400 — Plusher interiors with side coat hooks and additional interior lighting made up the Custom series differences.

NOTE: 'Limited' Custom trim was available on Body Styles 48457 and 48439. The finest Buick interiors, with notchback or 60/40 notchback front seats were standard. Limited script appeared on the roof sail panels when this optional package was ordered.

ELECTRA 225 CUSTOM SERIES 48400 I.D. NUMBERS: Vehicle Identification Numbers began with 484000( )100001. VINs were coded as explained under the 1970 Skylark Series ID Number section.

ELECTRA 225 CUSTOM SERIES 48400

Series Number	Model Number	Body Type & Seating	Factory Price	Shipping Weight	Production Total
48400	48469	4-dr Sed-6P	4677	4283	14,109
48400	48457	2-dr HT Cpe-6P	4661	4297	26,002
48400	48439	4-dr HT Sed-6P	4771	4385	65,114
48400	48467	2-dr Conv-6P	4802	4341	6,045

ENGINE: Specifications were the same as listed for the 1970 LeSabre Custom 455.

RIVIERA — SERIES 49487 — A new vertical textured grille, within the front bumper ensemble, updated the 1970 Riviera front end. At the sides, a new version of the famous Buick sweepspear was created with new bodyside moldings. Fender skirts were standard equipment for the first, and only, time on a Riviera. The headlamps were flanking the grille and did not retract. Bright metal outlined the lower body and fender skirt lip, continuing in a narrow line to the rear bumper. Riviera script appeared on the hood, deck, roof and sail panels, while the 'R' trademark appeared within the round rear fender sidemarkers. Standard equipment included every feature found on less expensive Buicks, plus padded seat cushions; full carpeting; smoking set; and an electric clock. Vinyl bench or bucket seating surfaces were standard. An optional Custom interior was available, with Strato notchback seating in all-vinyl or a vinyl and cloth combination.

NOTE: A Gran Sport option was offered for the Riviera. Cars so equipped had heavy-duty suspension; positive traction differential; H78 x 15 fiberglass belted white sidewall tires and GS monograms on the front fenders and instrument panel. The Stage I version of the 455 cid V-8 was an extra-cost option.

RIVIERA SERIES 49400 I.D. NUMBERS: Vehicle Identification Numbers began with 494870 ( )100001. VINs were coded as explained under the 1970 Skylark Series ID Number section.

RIVIERA SERIES 49487

Series Number	Model Number	Body Type & Seating	Factory Price	Shipping Weight	Production Total
49400	49487	2-dr HT Cpe-5P	4854	4216	37,366
49400	49487	2-dr GS HT Cpe-5P	4986	n.a.	n.a.

ENGINE: Specifications were the same as listed for the 1970 LeSabre custom 455.

CHASSIS FEATURES: Wheelbase: (Series 43300, 43400, 44400, 44500 and 44600 two-door styles) 112 inches; (four-door styles) 116 inches; (Series 45300, 45400, 45600, 46000 and 46600) 124 inches; (Series 48200 and 48400) 127 inches: (Series 49487) 119 inches. Overall length: (Series 43300, 43400, 44400, 44500 and 46600 two-door styles) 202.2 inches; (four-door styles) 206.2 inches; (Series 45200, 45400, 45600, 46000 and 46600) 220.2 inches; (Series 48200 and 48400) 225.8 inches; (Series 49487) 215.5 inches. Front Tread: (Skylark) 59 in.; (LeSabre) 63 in.; (GS) 59 in.; (GS-455) 59.4 in.; (Wildcat/Electra) 63.5 in.; (Riviera) 63.4 in. Rear Tread: (Skylark/GS/GS-455) 59 in.; (All others) 63 in. Tire size: (Series 43300, 43400, 44400. 45400, 44600) G78 x 14; (Series 45200, 45400, 45600 and 49487) H78 x 15; (Series 46000) L78 x 15; (Series 48200 and 48400) J78 x 15.

POWER OPTIONS: A three-speed manual transmission with column shift was standard on Skylark, Skylark 350, Skylark Custom, Gran Sport, LeSabre and Wildcat styles. A three-speed manual transmission with floor-mounted shifter was standard on GS 455. A four-speed manual transmission was optional on the GS and GS 455. Turbo-Hydramatic 350 was available with Skylark series and the GS. Turbo-Hydramatic 400 was optional for GS 455, LeSabre Custom 455 and Wildcat and was standard on Electra 225 Series and Riviera. A 285 brake horsepower, 350 cid V-8 was optional for the Skylark Custom, as was a 315 horsepower version of the same engine when ordered with the "high performance group." The 360 hp Stage I version of the 455 cid V-8 was available in specific Skylark and Riviera models.

CONVENIENCE OPTIONS: GSX package for Gran Sport models including, hood-mounted tachometer; Rally steering wheel; front and rear spoilers; outside sport mirrors; power front disc brakes; G60 x 15 tires; 15 x 7 inch chrome spoke wheels; black bucket seat interior; GSX ornament on instrument panel and grille; GSX decals and body stripes; black-finished hood panels; heavy-duty suspension; special 350 horsepower 455 cid V-8 and Saturn Yellow or Apollo White exterior finish ($1196). Air conditioning. ($486 intermediate; $457 full-size). Power steering (standard on Electra 225s, Riviera). Power brakes (standard on Electra 225s, Riviera). Power windows. Vinyl top covering. AM radio. AM/FM radio. Stereo tape player. Tilt steering wheel. Limited trim for Electra 225 Custom ($318). Strato bench seats (Riviera). Five-spoke chromed wheels. Console with shifter (Riviera). Consoles (bucket seats on GS; GS 455). Automatic Climate Control (full-size). Rearview mirror map light. Cornering lights (full-size). Automatic level control (specific models). Protective bodyside moldings (except Riviera and GS/GS 455). Soft-ray tinted glass. Rim-mounted horn control. Remote control outside rearview mirror. Four-way or six-way power seat control. Electric door locks. Tow Master trailering package. Electric trunk release. Chrome luggage rack twoway door gate power rear window for Estate and Station Wagon styles.

HISTORICAL FOOTNOTES: Calendar year production was 459,931. Model year production was 666,501. Buick came in fourth in the production race. The five millionth Buick was built at the Doraville, Ga. factory, near Atlanta. The GS-455 could do 0-to-60 in 6.5 seconds and had a 129.5 mph top speed. The Riviera GS could do 0-to-60 in 7.9 seconds and had a 125 mph top speed. Buick discontinued the California GS option this year. Style 43436 is the Sportwagon with dual-action tailgate. Styles 46036 and 46046 are Estate Wagons.

1971 BUICK

1971 Buick, Skylark Custom two-door hardtop, V-8

SKYLARK — SERIES 43300 — The basic 1970 styling was continued for another year. The Skylark had its own grille and used bright metal wheelhouse and lower body moldings of a very narrow width. Standard Skylark features included front and rear ashtrays. heater and defroster, Step-On parking brake, padded head restraints and other features mandated by federal safety standards. Interiors were cloth and vinyl or all-vinyl.

BUICK I.D. NUMBERS: The serial number (VIN) was located on a plate, attached to top of dash on driver's side and viewable through outside of windshield. It was also stamped on the engine block. The first symbol was a '4' for Buick. The second and third symbols indicated series, as follows: 33=Skylark; 34=Sportwagon/GS; 44=Skylark Custom; 52=LeSabre; 54=LeSabre Custom; 60=Estate Wagon; 71=Centurian; 82=Electra 225; 84=Electra 225 Custom; 94=Riviera. The fourth and fifth symbols indicated body style, as follows: 27=2-dr cpe; 35=4-dr two-seat sta wag; 36=4-dr two-seat sta wag; 37=2-dr HT; 39=4-dr HT; 45=4-dr three-seat sta wag; 47= 2-dr HT; 57=2-dr HT Spt Cpe; 67=2-dr Conv; 69=4-dr Sedan and 87= 2-dr Riv HT. Combined, the first five symbols were the model number, as reflected in tables below. The sixth symbol indicated model year, 1=1971. The seventh symbol was a letter representing the assembly plant, as follows: C=South Gate, Calif; G=Framingham, Mass.; H=Flint, Mich.; I=Oshawa, Ont., Canada; X=Fairfax, Kan.; Y=Wilmington, Del.; Z=Fremont, Calif. The last six digits represent the sequential assembly number at the plant with series mixed in production. In addition to the VIN, the engine block is stamped with a production code. These numbers were found on different locations: (6-cyl.) right side to rear of distributor; (350 cid V-8) on front of left bank of cylinders and production code between front two spark plugs and left exhaust manifold; (455 cid V-8) between front two spark plugs and exhaust manifold and production code between two left rear spark plugs and exhaust manifold. The production code has letters identifying the engine and numbers indicating production date codes. The letters were as follows: (250 cid I-6/145 hp) DF; (250 cid I-6/155 hp) EA; (350 cid/230 hp V-8) TO, TC; (350 cid/260 hp V-8) TD, TB; (350 cid/315 hp V-8) TP; (455 cid/335 hp V-8) TA; (455 cid/310 hp V-8) TR; and (455 cid/345 hp V-8) TS.

SKYLARK SERIES 43300

Series Number	Model Number	Body Type & Seating	Factory Price	Shipping Weight	Production Total
43300	43327	2-dr Cpe-6P	2847	3144	14,500
43300	43337	2-dr HT Cpe-6P	2918	3163	61,201
43300	43369	4-dr Sed-6P	2897	3216	34,037

NOTE: Add $121 and 219 pounds for V-8s.

ENGINES: Six-cyl. Overhead valves. Cast iron block. Displacement: 250 cid. Bore and stroke: 3.875 x 3.53 inches. Compression ratio: 8.5:1. Brake horsepower: 145 at 4200 rpm. Hydraulic valve lifters. Five main bearings. One-barrel Rochester 1MV carburetor.

V-8. Overhead valves. Cast iron block. Displacement: 350 cid. Bore and stroke: 3.8 x 3.85 inches. Compression ratio: 8.5:1. Brake horsepower: 230 at 4200 rpm. Five main bearings. Hydraulic lifters. Two-barrel Rochester 2GV carburetor.

SKYLARK CUSTOM — SERIES 44400 — A plusher Skylark, with Comfort-Flo ventilation system, Deluxe steering wheel, glovebox light and plusher interiors with full carpeting. An additional rocker panel molding was used, along with a bright applique on the front fenders. Custom badges appeared below the Skylark rear fender scripts and on the grille. Skylark emblems were on the roof sail panels.

SKYLARK CUSTOM SERIES 44400 I.D. NUMBERS: Vehicle Identification Numbers began with 444001( )100001. VINs were coded as explained under the 1971 Skylark Series ID Number section.

SKYLARK CUSTOM SERIES 44400

Series Number	Model Number	Body Type & Seating	Factory Price	Shipping Weight	Production Total
44400	44438	2-dr HT Cpe-6P	3317	3391	29,536
44400	44469	4-dr Sed-6P	3288	3455	8,299
44400	44439	4-dr HT Sed-6P	3397	3547	20,418
44400	44467	2-dr Conv-6P	3462	3431	3,993

NOTE: Add $121 and 219 pounds for V-8s.

ENGINE: Six-cyl. and V-8 specifications were the same as those listed for the 1971 Skylark Series 43300.

SPORTWAGON — SERIES 43436 — The Sportwagon shared the Skylark chassis and its improvements for 1971. The Sportwagon did not have bright wheelhouse moldings, using only a lower body bright molding for trim. Power front disc brakes were standard, as was an all-vinyl interior with front bench seat. The dual-action tailgate was now standard on this model only. Sportwagon script appeared on the rear fenders.

SPORTWAGON SERIES 43436 I.D. NUMBERS: Vehicle Identification Numbers began with 43461( )100001. VINs were coded as explained under the 1971 Skylark Series ID Number section.

SPORTWAGON SERIES 43446

Series Number	Model Number	Body Type & Seating	Factory Price	Shipping Weight	Production Total
43400	43436	Sta Wag-2S	3515	3928	12,525

ENGINE: Specifications were the same as listed for the 1971 Skylark Series 43300 V-8.

GS AND GS 455 — SERIES 43400 — Buick combined these two series into one for 1971. These muscular Buicks had blacked-out grilles with bright trim, bright wheelhouse moldings and bright rocker panel moldings with red-filled accents. Dual, functional hood scoops were ahead of the windshield. GS monograms appeared on the front fenders, deck and hood. Cars equipped with the 455 cid or 455 Stage I options had additional emblems. Standard equipment was the same as the Skylark Custom, but bucket or notchback front seats, in all-vinyl trim were optional. A GSX appearance package was available at extra-cost. It included a painted hood, accent striping, special emblems, blacked-out grille and dual, funtional hood air scoops.

GS AND GS 455 SERIES 43400 I.D. NUMBERS: Vehicle Identification Numbers began with 434001( )100001. VINs were coded as explained under the 1971 Skylark Series ID Number section.

GS/GS 455 SERIES 43400

Series Number	Model Number	Body Type & Seating	Factory Price	Shipping Weight	Production Total
43400	43437	2-dr HT-5P	3285	3461	8,268
43400	43467	2-dr Conv-5P	3476	3497	902

NOTE: Prices and weights are for GranSports with 350 cid engines. Production numbers include both GS and GS 455 cars.

ENGINES: GS V-8. Specifications were the same as listed for the 1971 Skylark 350 cid V-8, except brake horsepower was 260 and a four-barrel carbureted V-8 with dual exhausts was used. The GS 455 engine produced 315 hp. The Stage I engine produced 345 hp.

GS 455 V-8. Overhead valve. Cast iron block. Displacement: 455 cid. Bore and stroke: 4.3 x 3.9 inches. Compression ratio: 8.5:1. Brake horsepower: 315 at 4600 rpm. Five main bearings. Hydraulic valve lifters. Four-barrel Rochester 4MV carburetor.

LESABRE — SERIES 45200 — A new, larger body was used on the 1971 LeSabre. Full-Flo ventilation with deck lid louvers was standard. The new body, with a sweeping side sculpture, used the customary Buick ventiports in groups of three on each front fender. Bright metal lower body and wheelhouse moldings were used. The LeSabre had its own grille. Interiors were fabric and vinyl. Standard equipment included armrests; rear ashtrays; glovebox light; interior lights; front and rear carpeting; full-foam seat cushions; inside hood release; power front disc brakes, seat belts and other mandated federal safety features. LeSabre script appeared on the front fenders.

LESABRE SERIES 45200 I.E. NUMBERS: Vehicle Identification Numbers began with 45200( )100001. VINs were coded as explained under the 1971 Skylark Series ID Number section.

LESABRE SERIES 45200

Series Number	Model Number	Body Type & Seating	Factory Price	Shipping Weight	Production Total
45200	45269	4-dr Sed-6P	3992	4078	26,348
45200	45257	2-dr HT Cpe-6P	4061	4049	13,385
45200	45239	4-dr HT Cpe-6P	4119	4109	41,098

ENGINE: Specifications were the same as listed for the 1971 Skylark Series 43300 V-8.

LESABRE CUSTOM AND CUSTOM 455 — SERIES 45400 — A plusher Buick with more luxurious interiors. The convertible, offered only in this series, had a new top that folded inward on retracting. Custom models had a Custom badge beneath the LeSabre front fender script, unless they were equipped with the 455 cid V-8, in which case they had that engine's insignia instead.

LESABRE CUSTOM SERIES 45400 I.D. NUMBERS: Vehicle Identification Numbers began with 454001( )100001. VINs were coded as explained under the 1971 Skylark Series ID Number section.

LESABRE CUSTOM SERIES 45400

Series Number	Model Number	Body Type & Seating	Factory Price	Shipping Weight	Production Total
45400	45469	4-dr Sed-6P	4085	4410	26,970
45400	45457	2-dr HT Cpe-6P	4149	4095	29,944
45400	45439	4-dr HT Sed-6P	4213	4147	41,098
45400	45467	2-dr Conv-6P	4342	4086	1,856

ENGINES: 350 V-8: Specifications were the same as listed for the 1971 Skylark Series 43300 V-8.

455 V-8: Specifications were the same as listed for the 1971 GS 455 Series 43400 V-8.

1971 Buick, Centurion two-door hardtop sport coupe, V-8 (TVB)

CENTURION — SERIES 46600 — A new line for Buick, replacing the Wildcat series. The Centurion was a masculine, performance image machine that went for the clean look. Side trim was minimal, with only a bright rocker panel molding and wheelhouse moldings. There were no ventiports on the Centurion. The grille was of a special texture and the taillights had bright grids over them. Centurion lettering appeared on the front fenders and the round Centurion medallion was used on closed model roof sail panels. It also appeared on the deck and hood. The Formal Coupe (two-door hardtop) included a vinyl top covering. Standard equipment was the same as on the LeSabre, plus a Deluxe steering wheel. Interiors were vinyl and fabric combinations, with bench or notchback front seats.

CENTURION SERIES I.D. 46600 NUMBERS: Vehicle Identification Numbers began with 466001( )100001. VINs were coded as explained under the 1971 Skylark Series ID Number section.

CENTURION SERIES 46600

Series Number	Model Number	Body Type & Seating	Factory Price	Shipping Weight	Production Total
46600	46647	2-dr HT Cpe-6P	4678	4195	11,892
46600	46639	4-dr HT-6P	4564	4307	15,345
46600	46667	2-dr Conv-6P	4678	4227	2,161

ENGINE: V-8: Specifications were the same as listed for the 1971 GS 455 Series 43400.

ELECTRA 225 — SERIES 48200 — The biggest Buicks were freshly styled for 1971 with a longer, wider look predominating. Four ventiports again indicated the car's prestige in the Buick line. Series identification appeared on the deck lid and roof sail pillars. Standard equipment included Full-Flo ventilation with deck lid louvers; Custom foam seats; heater and defroster; Deluxe steering wheel; plush pile carpeting; variable ratio power steering; power brakes; remote control outside rearview mirror; windshield radio antenna and a fully-padded instrument panel. A number of mandated safety features were also included.

ELECTRA 225 SERIES 48200 I.D. NUMBERS: Vehicle Identification Numbers began with 482001( )100001. VINs were coded as explained under the 1971 Skylark Series ID Number section.

ELECTRA 225 SERIES 48200

Series Number	Model Number	Body Type & Seating	Factory Price	Shipping Weight	Production Total
48200	48237	2-dr HT Cpe-6P	4801	4345	8,662
48200	48239	4-dr HT-6P	4915	4381	17,589

ELECTRA 225 CUSTOM — SERIES 48400 — Custom models had a plusher interior than the regular Electra 225 with woodgrain inserts used liberally on door panels and the instrument panel. Exterior appearance was identical to the 48200 Series.

ELECTRA 225 CUSTOM SERIES 48400 I.D. NUMBERS: Vehicle Identification Numbers began with 484001( )100001. Numbers were coded as explained under the 1971 Skylark Series ID Number section.

ELECTRA 225 CUSTOM SERIES 48400

Series Number	Model Number	Body Type Seating	Factory Price	Shipping Weight	Production Total
48400	48437	2-dr HT-6P	4980	4359	26,831
48400	48439	4-dr HT-6P	5093	4421	72,954

NOTE: 'Limited' interiors were offered for both Custom Electra 225 styles. Cars so equipped had even plusher interiors, with bench seats or 60/40 notchback front seats. 'Limited' badges were applied to the roof sail panels when this option was included.

ENGINE: V-8: Specifications were the same as listed for the 1971 GS 455 Series 43400.

ESTATE WAGONS — SERIES 4600 — A new Estate Wagon was built on the 127 inch wheelbase Electra 225 chassis. Standard equipment was the same as the Electra 225, with Custom-grade all-vinyl interior trimming. Woodgrain sides were available. All wagons had the Glide-Away tailgate, Full-Flo ventilation with louvers in the tailgate, bright rocker panel and wheelhouse moldings and four ventiports on each front fender.

ESTATE WAGON SERIES 46000 I.D. NUMBERS: Vehicle Identification Numbers began with 466001( )100001. VINs were coded as explained under the 1971 Skylark Series ID Number section.

ESTATE WAGON SERIES 46000

Series Number	Model Number	Body Type & Seating	Factory Price	Shipping Weight	Production Total
46000	46035	4-dr Sta Wag-2S	4640	4906	8,699
46000	40645	4-dr Sta Wag-3S	4786	4965	15,335

ENGINE: V-8: Specifications were the same as listed for the 1971 GS 455 — Series 43400.

1971 Buick, Riviera two-door hardtop sport coupe, V-8 (TVB)

1972 Buick, Skylark 350 'Sun Coupe' two-door hardtop, V-8 (TVB)

RIVIERA — SERIES 49487 — A sensational new Riviera debuted for 1971. A large car with a boattail rear roof and window section and sweeping side sculpture greeted 1971's Riviera customers. Wheelhouses were wide open, after a year of skirted fenders. Riviera shared Full-Flo ventilation with other 1971 Buicks and had the louvers on the deck lid. Standard features were numerous and included heater and defroster; Custom padded contoured seats; deep pile carpeting; electric clock; smoking set; head restraints; new seat belt system; inside hood lock release; variable ratio power steering; Turbo-Hydramatic; power front disc brakes and dual exhausts.

NOTE: A Gran Sport option was available for the Riviera. Cars so equipped had a 330 horsepower 455 cid V-8 with chrome air cleaner top linked to a specially calibrated Turbo-Hydramatic 400 transmission; heavy-duty suspension; positive traction differential; H78 x 15 Bias-belted whitewall tires and Riviera GS monogram on front fenders and instrument panel. This model also included heavy-duty suspension.

RIVIERA SERIES 49400 I.D. NUMBERS: Vehicle Identification Numbers began with 494871( )10001. Numbers were coded as explained under the 1971 Skylark Series ID Number section.

RIVIERA SERIES 49400

Series Number	Model Number	Body Type & Seating	Factory Price	Shipping Weight	Production Total
49400	49487	2-dr Spt Cpe-5P	5253	4325	33,810

ENGINE: Specifications were the same as listed for the 1971 GS 455 Series 43400 models.

CHASSIS FEATURES: Wheelbase: (Series 43300, 44400 and 43400) two-door styles 112 inches; four-door styles 116 inches; (Series 45200, 45400, 46400) 124 inches; (Series 48200, 48400 and 46000) 127 inches; (Series 48487) 112 inches. Overall length: (Series 43300, 44400. 43400) two-door styles 203.3 inches; four-door styles 207.3 inches; (Sportwagons) 213.7 inches; (Series 45200, 45400 and 46400) 221.9 inches; (Series 48200, 48400) 227.9 inches; (Series 46000) 228.3 inches; (Series 48487) 218.3 inches. Tire size: (Skylark) F78 x 14; (Skylark Custom, Sportwagon, GS and GS 455) G78 x 14; (LeSabre, Centurion and Riviera) H78 x 15; (Electra 225) J78 x 15; (Estate Wagons) L78 x 15.

POWERTRAIN OPTIONS: Three-speed manual transmission was standard in Series 43300, 44400, 43400. 45200,45400 and 46600. Four-speed manual transmission was optional in Series 43400 only. Turbo-Hydramatic 350 was optional for cars with six-cylinder or 350 cid V-8 engines. Turbo-Hydramatic 400 was optional for cars equipped with the 455 cid V-8 and was also standard in Series 48200, 48400 and 49487. A 260 brake horsepower 350 cid V-8 was optional for Series 43300, 44400, 43400, 45200 and 45400. A 330 brake horsepower 455 cid V-8 with four-barrel induction was optional for Series 43400, 45200, 45400, 46600, 48200 and 48400. Max-Trac all-weather traction control rear axles were optional in Series 49487 models.

CONVENIENCE AND APPEARANCE FEATURES: Air conditioning. Power windows ($116). Vinyl top. Tilt steering wheel. Strato bucket seats (Riviera — $187). Chrome five spoke wheels ($95). Limited trim (Electra 225 Custom — $284). Custom Trim (Estate Wagon woodgrain — $199). AM radio. AM/FM radio. AM/FM stereo ($239). Speed alert control. Cornering lights (full size). Bumper guards (except Riviera and Estate Wagon). Protective bodyside moldings (except Riviera). Console (Riviera, GS, and Skylark Custom with bucket seats). Six-way power seats. GSX equipment for GS 455 including bodyside stripes; black hood panels; GSX grille emblem; body color headlamp bezels; black rocker moldings and rear spoiler. Sport mirrors (GS and GSX). Instrument panel gauges (GS and GSX). Hood-mounted tachometer (GS and GSX). Front spoiler (GS and GSX). Automatic Climate Control. Rear window defogger. Custom interior trim (Riviera). Electric trunk release. Special sport steering wheel. Ralley steering wheel (GS and GSX). Deluxe steering wheel (LeSabre). Power door locks. Child safety seat. Chrome luggage rack (Estate Wagon). Power Glide-Away tailgate (Estate Wagon). Intermittent wipers. Auto Level Control. Remote outside rearview mirror (standard, Electra 225s).

HISTORICAL FOOTNOTES: Model year production was 551,188 units. A new "Silver Arrow" Riviera show car was exhibited. The Riviera GS could still do 0-to-60 in a respectable 8.1 seconds and had a 120 mph top speed. Style 46647 was the Centurion Formal Coupe. Style 46035 was the two-seat Estate Wagon. Style 46045 was the three-seat Estate Wagon.

1972 BUICK

SKYLARK AND SKYLARK 350 — SERIES 43300 — A very mild facelift was done on the 1972 Skylark. The front bumper was redesigned with bumper guards now standard. At the rear, black vinyl surrounds were added to the taillamp/bumper assembly. The Skylark had a narrow lower body molding and bright wheelhouse molding. Skylark script appeared on the rear fenders, with a 350 badge added when equipment included the four-barrel 175 brake horsepower 350 cid V-8. Standard Skylark features were front ashtray; heater and defroster; side terminal energizer battery; padded Instrument panel and mandated safety features. Skylark 350 had Deluxe cloth and vinyl seats, carpeting, rear ashtrays, armrests, Deluxe steering wheel and dual horns.

BUICK I.D. NUMBERS: VIN was located on top of dash, on driver's side, visible through windshield. The first symbol was a '4' for Buick. The second symbol identified the series, as follows: D=Skylark; F=Sport Wagon; G=GS; H=Skylark Custom; L=LeSabre; N=LeSabre Custom; P=Centurion; R=Estate Wagon; U=Electra 225; V=Electra 225 Custom; Y=Riviera. The third and fourth symbols identified the body style. They appear as last two digits of model number in tables below. The fifth symbol indicated engine type, as follows: (250 cid six) D; (350 cid V-8) G, H, J, K; (455 cid V-8) P, R, T, U, V, W. The sixth symbol indicated model year, 2=1972. The seventh symbol indicated assembly plant, as follows: C=Southgate, Calif.; G=Framingham, Mass.; H=Flint, Mich.; X=Fairfax, Kan.; Y=Wilmington, Del.; and Z=Fremont, Calif. The last six symbols were the sequential production number at the assembly plant.

SKYLARK/SKYLARK 350 SERIES 43300

Series Number	Model Number	Body Type & Seating	Factory Price	Shipping Weight	Production Total
43300	43327	2-dr Cpe-6P	2925	3436	14,552
43300	43337	2-dr HT-6P Cpe-6P	2993	3442	84,868
43300	43369	4-dr Sed-6P	2973	3491	42,206

ENGINE: Skylark V-8. Overhead valve. Cast iron block. Displacement: 350 cid. Bore and stroke: 3.8 x 3.85 inches. Compression ratio: 8.5: 1. Net horsepower: 150 at 3800 rpm. Five main bearings. Hydraulic valve lifters. Two-barrel Rochester 2GV carburetor.

Skylark 350 V-8. Specifications were the same as above, except a four-barrel carburetor was used and net horsepower was 175.

SKYLARK CUSTOM — SERIES 44400 — A plusher Skylark, distinguished on the exterior by a grid-textured bright grille, wider black rocker panel moldings with rear stone guard extensions and wheelhouse moldings. Plusher Custom interiors were of cloth and viny, or all-vinyl. The Sport Wagon featured a standard dual-action tailgate.

SKYLARK CUSTOM I.D. NUMBERS: Serial numbers began with 4H002( )100001 for Skylark Customs and 4F362( )100001 for Sport Wagons. See ID Number section in the 1972 Skylark Series 43300 listing.

SKYLARK CUSTOM SERIES 44400

Series Number	Model Number	Buy Type & Seating	Factory Price	Shipping Weight	Production Total
44400	44437	2-dr HT Cpe-6P	3255	3487	34,271
44400	44469	4-dr Sed-6P	3228	3532	9,924
44400	44467	2-dr Conv-6P	3393	3550	3,608
44400	44439	4-dr HT Sed-6P	3331	3625	12,925
44400	43436	4-dr Sta Wag-6P	3443	4003	14,417

ENGINES: Specifications were the same as those listed under 1972 Skylark and Skylark 350 engine data.

GS 350 AND GS 455 — SERIES 43400 — These sport coupe and convertible styles featured dual exhausts, functional dual hood scoops, heavy-duty springs, shocks, and stabilizer bar in conjunction with a muscular look. Appearance was enhanced by wide bright rocker moldings, wheelhouse moldings and GS monograms on the front fenders and deck. When cars had the 455 cid V-8 installed, suitable emblems were attached. Vinyl bench seats were standard (black on the convertible). Bucket seats were available at extra cost.

GS 350 AND GS 455 SERIES 43400 I.D. NUMBERS: Vehicle Identification Numbers began with 46002( )100001. See I.D. Number section in the 1972 Skylark Series 43300 listing.

GS 350/455 SERIES 43400

Series Number	Model Number	Body Type & Seating	Factory Price	Shipping Weight	Production Total
43400	43437	2-dr HT-6P Cpe-6P	3226	3487	7,723
43400	43467	2-dr Conv-6P	3406	3541	852

NOTE: Add $165 to above prices for 455 cid V-8.

ENGINES: GS 350 V-8. Specifications were the same as listed under 1972 Skylark 350 cid V-8 engine data, except a Rochester 4MV four-barrel carburetor was used and horsepower was rated 190 nhp at 4000 rpm..

GS 455 V-8. Overhead valve. Cast-iron block. Displacement: 455 cid. Bore and stroke: 4.3 x 3.9 inches. Compression ratio: 8.5:1. Net horsepower: 225 at 4000 rpm. Five main bearings. Hydraulic valve lifters. Four-barrel Rochester 4MV carburetor. A high-performance GS-455 engine with 270 hp at 4400 rpm was optional at extra-cost.

LESABRE — SERIES 45200 — Little changed from 1971, the LeSabre had no deck louvers for the Full-Flo ventilation this year. A trio of ventiports did continue on the front fenders. Standard exterior trim included bright rocker panel moldings, but no wheelhouse moldings. LeSabre script appeared on front fenders. Interiors were of Kalmora cloth and Madrid vinyl. Standard equipment now included power front disc brakes and variable ratio power steering, plus numerous mandated federal safety features.

LESABRE SERIES 45200 I.D. NUMBERS: Vehicle Identification Numbers began with 4L002( )100001. See I.D. Number section in the Skylark Series 43300 listing.

LESABRE SERIES 45200

Series Number	Model Number	Body Type & Seating	Factory Price	Shipping Weight	Production Total
45200	45257	2-dr Spt Cpe-6P	4024	4184	14,001
45200	45269	4-dr Sed-6P	3958	4219	29,505
45200	45239	4-dr HT Sed-6P	4079	4229	15,160

ENGINE: Specifications were the same as listed under 1971 Skylark 350 cid, two-barrel V-8 engine data.

LESABRE — CUSTOM — SERIES 45400 — The Custom featured a plusher interior of vinyl and fabric or all vinyl. A broader lower body molding was used with bright wheelhouse moldings. Custom plaques were used beneath the LeSabre signatures on the front fenders.

LESABRE CUSTOM SERIES 45400 I.D. NUMBERS: Vehicle Identification Numbers began with 4N002( )100001. See I.D. Number section in the 1972 Skylark Series 43300 listing.

LESABRE CUSTOM SERIES 45400

Series Number	Model Number	Body Type & Seating	Factory Price	Shipping Weight	Production Total
45400	45457	2-dr Spt Cpe-6P	4107	4199	36,510
45400	45469	4-dr Sed-6P	4047	4239	35,295
45400	45469	4-dr HT Sed-6P	4168	4244	50,804
45400	45467	2-dr Conv-6P	4291	4253	2,037

ENGINES: Specifications were the same as listed under the 1972 Skylark 350 cid, two-barrel V-8 engine data.

CENTURION — SERIES 46600 — A new vertical grille giving the hood more of a domed effect distinguished the 1972 Centurion. Side trim continued to be minimal with a bright metal lower body strip and wheelhouse moldings taking care of most superfluous touches. A Centurion medallion appeared on closed body roof sail panels and on all decks and hoods. Centurion lettering was used on the front fenders. There were no ventports. Standard equipment duplicated that of the LeSabre, but interiors were of a more luxurious vinyl and fabric combination with notchback front seat standard.

CENTURION SERIES 46600 I.D. NUMBERS: Vehicle Identification Numbers began with 4P002( )100001. See I.D. Number section under the 1972 Skylark Series 43300 listing.

CENTURION SERIES 46600

Series Number	Model Number	Body Type & Seating	Factory Price	Shipping Weight	Production Total
46600	46647	2-dr Spt Cpe-6P	4579	4358	14,187
46600	46639	4-dr HT Sed-6P	4508	4426	19,582
46600	46667	2-dr Conv-6P	4616	4235	2,396

ENGINE: Specifications were the same as listed under 1972 GS 455 V-8 engine data.

ESTATE WAGON — SERIES 46000 — These big wagons shared the Electra body and an Electra-like grille. All-vinyl interiors with a bench front seat were standard. A notchback front seat was optional on the nine-passenger, three-seat version. Standard equipment was the same as on the LeSabre, plus a four-jet windshield washer assembly.

ESTATE WAGON SERIES 46000 I.D. NUMBER: Vehicle Identification Numbers began with 4R002( )100001. See I.D. Number section in the 1972 Skylark Series 43300 listing.

ESTATE WAGONS SERIES 46000

Series Number	Model Number	Body Type & Seating	Factory Price	Shipping Weight	Production Total
46000	46035	4-dr Sta Wag-2S	4589	4995	10,175
46000	46045	4-dr Sta Wag-3S	4728	5080	18,793

ENGINE: Specifications were the same as listed under 1972 GS 455 V-8 engine data.

ELECTRA 225 — SERIES 48200 — A new grille was one of the facelift features of the 1972 Electra 225. Bumper guards front and rear promised better collision protection. The traditional four ventports per fender remained. Fender skirts were again standard with their lower lip molding providing a link for the bright metal lower body strip that ran full-length. The Electra 225 emblem appeared on the grille and deck this year. Interiors were cloth and vinyl with bench front seat. Standard features included those of lower-priced Buicks, plus such touches as variable ratio power steering, power front disc brakes and remote control outside rearview mirror.

ELECTRA 225 SERIES 48200 I.D. NUMBERS: Vehicle Identification Numbers began with 40002( )100001. V.I.Ns were coded as explained in the 1972 Skylark Series 43300.

ELECTRA 225 SERIES 48200

Series Number	Model Number	Body Type & Seating	Factory Price	Shipping Weight	Production Total
48200	48237	2-dr HT Cpe-6P	4781	4465	9,961
48200	48239	4-dr HT Sed-6P	4889	4535	19,433

ENGINE: Specifications were the same as listed under 1972 GS 455 V-8 engine data.

ELECTRA 225 CUSTOM LIMITED — SERIES 48400 — A plusher interior of cloth and vinyl with fold-down center armrest for front seat passengers was standard. A notchback 60/40 seat was optional. Limited script appeared on the roof sail panels of this plushest of all Buicks. Exterior trim was otherwise identical to the Electra 225 Series 48200.

ELECTRA 225 CUSTOM LIMITED SERIES 48400 I.D. NUMBERS: Vehicle Identification Numbers began with 4V002( )100001. See I.D. Number section in the Skylark Series 43300 listing.

ELECTRA 225 CUSTOM LIMITED SERIES 48400

Series Number	Model Number	Body Type & Seating	Factory Price	Shipping Weight	Production Total
48400	48437	2-dr HT Cpe-6P	4951	4475	37.974
48400	48439	4-dr HT Sed-6P	5059	4550	104,754

ENGINE: Specifications were the same as listed under 1972 GS 455 V-8 engine data.

1972 Buick, Riviera two-door hardtop sport coupe, V-8 (TVB)

RIVIERA — SERIES 49487 — A slightly restyled Riviera with the same boattail body was marketed in 1972. A new eggcrate grille thrust forward with the 'R' emblem on the left. A similar emblem was centered on the deck lid, which this year made a clean, without the ill-fated Full-Flo ventilation louvers of 1971. Vinyl bodyside moldings were standard. Interiors were available with all-vinyl bench seats or in Custom trim with 60/40 notchback or bucket front seating. Standard features included all items found on the Electra 225.

NOTE: Riviera Gran Sport equipment was available at $200. Included was a 260 net horsepower 455 cid V-8 with dual exhausts, positive traction differential and GS monograms for the front fenders. An engine turned instrument panel insert was featured.

RIVIERA SERIES 49400 I.D. NUMBERS: Vehicle Identification Numbers began with 4Y002( )100001.See I.D. Number section in the Skylark Series 43300 listing.

RIVIERA SERIES 49400

Series Number	Model Number	Body Type & Seating	Factory Price	Shipping Weight	Production Total
49400	49487	2-dr Spt Cpe-6P	5149	4368	33,728

ENGINE: Specifications were the same as listed under 1972 GS 455 except net horsepower was 250.

CHASSIS FEATURES: Wheelbase: (Series 43300, 44400 and 43400) 112 inches; two-door styles, 116 inches, four-door styles. (Series 45200, 45400 and 46600) 124 inches; (Series 48200, 48400 and 4600) 127 inches; (Series 49487) 122 inches. Overall length: (Series 43300, 44400 and 43400) two-door styles 203.3 inches; four-door styles 207.3 inches. (Sportwagon) 213.7 inches; (Series 45200, 45400 and 46600) 221.9 inches; (Series 46000) 228.3 inches; (Series 48200 and 48400) 227.9 inches; (Series 48487) 218.3 inches. Tire Sizes: (Skylark, Skylark Custom, GS 350 and GS 455) G78 x 14; (LeSabre, Riviera and Centurion) H78 x 15; (Electra 225s) J78 x 15; (Estate Wagons) L78 x 15.

POWERTRAIN OPTIONS: A three-speed manual transmission was standard in Series 43300, 44400 and 43400. A four-speed manual transmission was optional for Series 43400. Turbo-Hydramatic 350 was an automatic transmission option for Series 43300, 44400 and 43400 with 350 cid V-8. Turbo-Hydramatic 400 was optional for Series 43400 with 455 cid V-8 and Series 46200 and 45400 with 455 cid V-8 option; it was standard in Series 46600, 46000, 48200 and 49487. Turbo-Hydramatic 375B was standard with LeSabre. Max-Trac differential was offered for all full-size Buicks. Maintenance-free battery was available for Series 48200, 48400 and 49487.

CONVENIENCE AND APPEARANCE OPTIONS: Customline hard boot cover (LeSabre and Centurion Convertible). Protective impact strips. Folding vinyl sun roof (Sun Coupe on Skylark 350 Sport Coupe with roof sail panel emblems) Steel panel sun roof, electrically operated (Riviera and Electra 225). Front light monitors (full-size). AM radio. AM/FM radio. AM/FM radio with stereo and tape player ($363). Center console (Skylark, GS 350 and 455, Riviera with bucket seats). Climate Control. Automatic Climate Control (full-size). Power windows. Electric trunk release. Child safety seat. Remote control outside rearview mirror (standard on Electra 225 and Riviera). Custom seat and shoulder belts. Custom vinyl top with halo molding for Skylark Custom Sport Coupe; Sport Vinyl top for Skylark 350 Coupe and Riviera; full vinyl top for other specific styles. Soft-ray tinted glass. Rear window defroster. Mirror map light. Electric clock. Power tailgate window. Tilt steering wheel. (standard on Riviera). Cornering lights (full-size). Speed alert. Luggage rack for station wagons. Five-spoke chrome sport wheels ($70 Riviera). Trailer towing packages. Automatic Level Control.

HISTORICAL FOOTNOTES: Style 43436 was the Sportwagon. Styles 46035 and 46045 were Estate Wagons.

1973 BUICK

APOLLO SERIES — SIX AND V-8 — Introduced as a midyear model, on April 12, 1973, the Apollo marked Buick's re-entry into the compact car market. The new car was based on the Chevrolet Nova X-body shell with Buick trim and styling motifs added. Features included unit construction from the cowl back, with a bolted-on front stub frame. Single round headlamps in large, square bezels flanked a low, rectangular grille insert of a vertical-dash type design. Square parking lamps were set into either side of the grille and a Buick medallion was placed at the center. Buick block lettering appeared on the hood; slit type cornering lamps on the front fender and three thin, rectangular ventports on the upper rear side of front fenders. The base engine was a Chevrolet six and Apollos with the Buick 350 cid V-8 were grouped as a separate series.

BUICK I.D. NUMBERS: Vehicle identification numbers began with 43( )100001 up. The first symbol '4' indicated Buick. The second symbol, a letter, indicated the series. The third and fourth symbols indicated the body style and correspond to the numbers in column two of the charts. The fifth symbol designated type of engine. The sixth symbol, a '3' designated 1973

model year. The seventh symbol was the assembly plant code with Apollo production quartered at Willow Run, Michigan (W) or Los Angeles. Van Nuys (L), which were GMAD factories, not Buick. The last group of six digits indicated the sequential production number.

1973 Buick, Apollo two-door hatch back coupe, 6-cyl (TVB)

APOLLO SERIES SIX/V-8

Model Number	Body/Style Number	Body Type & Seating	Factory Price	Shipping Weight	Production Total
4XB	B69	4-dr Sed-5P	2628/2746	3152/3326	8,450
4XB	B27	2-dr Notch-5P	2605/2723	3108/3282	14,475
4XB	B17	2-dr Hatch-5P	2754/2872	3210/3384	9,868

NOTE: Style B27 is a two-door notchback coupe; Style B17 a two-door hatchback coupe. Factory prices and shipping weights above slash are for sixes; below slash for V-8s.

ENGINES: Inline six. Overhead valves. Cast iron block. Displacement: 250 cid. Bore and stroke: 3.87 x 3.50 inches. Compression ratio: 8.25:1. SAE net horsepower: 100 at 3600 rpm. Hydraulic valve lifters. Carburetor: one-barrel. (Chevrolet manufacture).

V-8. Overhead valves. Cast iron block. Displacement: 350 cid. Bore and stroke: 3.8 x 3.85 inches. Compression ratio: 8.5:1. SAE net horsepower: 150 at 3800 rpm. Hydraulic valve lifters. Carburetor: two-barrel (Buick V-8).

1973 Buick, Century Regal 2-dr colonnade coupe, V-8 (TVB)

CENTURY/LUXUS/REGAL SERIES — (V-8) — The Buick Century lines represented a new intermediate range of offerings on the GM A-Body platform. The cars rode on a new chassis and had disc brakes up front as standard equipment. Styling features included GM's 'Colonnade' pillared hardtop look. There were single round headlights in square bezels flanking a thin crosshatch grille with three bright horizontal division bars. In between the headlamps and grille were medium size round parking lamps. The Century 350 passenger cars were in the AD Series with comparable station wagons forming Series AF. These cars had '350' front fender tip nameplates. The Luxus line (Series AH passenger models and Series AK station wagons) had richer interior appointments and horizontal beltline moldings along the trailing edge of front fenders and on the front door. The Regal coupe (Series AJ) had a distinctive grille, with a vertically segmented design and special crest emblems on the front fendersides. A Gran Sport package, with special styling and suspension features, was available as a sports/performance option. It included electric clock; wheel opening moldings; instrument gauges; glovebox ashtray and courtesy lamps as standard extras.

CENTURY/LUXUS/REGAL SERIES

Model Number	Body/Style Number	Body Type & Seating	Factory Price	Shipping Weight	Production Total
CENTURY 350					
4AD	D29	4-dr HT Sed-6P	3057	3780	38,202
4AD	D37	4-dr HT Cpe-6P	3057	3713	56,154
4AF	F45	4-dr Sta Wag-9P	3601	4192	Note 1
4AF	F35	4-dr Sta Wag-6P	3486	4156	7,760
LUXUS					
4AH	H29	4-dr HT Sed-6P	3326	3797	22,438
4AH	H57	2-dr HT Cpe-6P	3331	3718	71,712
4AK	K45	4-dr Sta Wag-9P	3767	4227	Note 1
4AK	K35	4-dr Sta Wag-6P	3652	4190	10,645
REGAL					
4AJ	J57	2-dr HT Cpe-5P	3470	3743	91,557

NOTE 1: Production totals for six and nine-passenger station wagons are counted together, with no breakouts per seating configuration.

ENGINE: See 1973 Apollo Series V-8 engine data. Base engine for Century models was the optional Apollo 350 cid V-8.

LESABRE CENTURION SERIES — (V-8) — LeSabres, LeSabre Customs and Centurions were built off the same 124 inch wheelbase platform with different levels of appointments and trims. Two Estate wagons were based on a 127 inch wheelbase version of the Electra chassis and grouped into their own separate series as well. Styling features for the entire group of cars included new energy absorbing front bumpers, dual headlamps set in square bezels, a low grille with short vertical bars and Buick medallions at the center of the hood. Standard equipment on all models included Turbo-Hydramatic transmission, power steering and brakes.

LeSabres had series identification scripts behind the front wheel cutouts. Custom LeSabres included standard extras such as Custom steering wheel, Deluxe wheelcovers, vinyl notchback seats and a four-barrel carburetor. There were Custom nameplate badges placed under the LeSabre scripts on the one-step-up models. Centurions represented a slightly cleaner styled rendition of the LeSabre body, having the traditional Buick ventiports removed from the hoods. Centurion lettering was placed behind the front wheel cutout and a four-barrel V-8 was the base powerplant. An exclusive Centurion body style was the convertible. Estate wagons came with woodgrain exterior body panelling and were trimmed comparable to Custom LeSabres, except that model identification took the form of Estate Wagons block lettering on the upper rear fender tips. They had lower rear bumper ends than other standard Buicks, with taillamps notched into the blade-shaped body edges.

LESABRE CENTURION SERIES

Model Number	Body/Style Number	Body Type & Seating	Factory Price	Shipping Weight	Production Total

ENGINE: See 1973 Apollo Series V-8 engine data. Base engine for LeSabre and LeSabre Custom models was the two-barrel 350 cid V-8.

LESABRE

Model Number	Body/Style Number	Body Type & Seating	Factory Price	Shipping Weight	Production Total
4BL	L69	4-dr Sed-6P	3998	4234	29,649
4BL	L39	4-dr HT Sed-6P	4125	4259	13,413
4BL	L57	2-dr HT Spt Cpe-6P	4067	4210	14,061
CUSTOM LESABRE					
4BN	N69	4-dr Sed-6P	4091	4264	42,845
4BN	N39	4-dr HT Sed-6P	4217	4284	55,879
4BN	N57	2-dr HT Spt Cpe-6P	4154	4225	41,425

ENGINE: Base engine for Centurions was the 350 cid V-8 with four-barrel carburetion and 175 horsepower at 4000 rpm.

ESTATE WAGON					
4BR	R35	4-dr Sta Wag-6P	4645	4952	12,282
4BR	R45	4-dr Sta Wag-9P	4790	5021	23,513
CENTURION					
4BP	P39	4-dr HT Sed-6P	4390	4329	22,354
4BP	P57	2-dr HT Spt Cpe-5P	4336	4260	16,883
4BP	P67	2-dr Conv-5P	4534	4316	5,739

ENGINE: V-8. Overhead valves. Cast iron block. Displacement: 455 cid. Bore and stroke: 4.3 x 3.9 cid. Compression ratio: 8.5:1. Brake horsepower: 225 at 4000 rpm. Hydraulic valve lifters. Carburetor: four-barrel.

1973 Buick, Electra 225 Limited four-door hardtop, V-8 (TVB)

ELECTRA 225/ELECTRA 225 CUSTOM SERIES — (V-8) — The Electra series was a two model line, split into two sub-series, Electra 225 and Electra 225 Custom. A Limited trim package was available for the upper level. Standard equipment was the same as on Centurions plus electric clock; license frames; all courtesy and safety lights; foam seats; remote control OSRV mirror; Super Deluxe wheelcovers; Custom safety belts and some changes in technical features. Custom models had carpeted lower door panels and special trims. The Limited had wide, bright metal body underscores.

ELECTRA 225/ELECTRA CUSTOM SERIES

Model Number	Body/Style Number	Body Type & Seating	Factory Price	Shipping Weight	Production Total
ELECTRA 225					
4CT	T39	4-dr HT Sed-6P	4928	4581	17,189
4CT	T37	2-dr HT Spt Cpe-6P	4815	4488	9,224
ELECTRA 225 CUSTOM					
4CV	V39	4-dr HT Sed-6P	5105	4603	107,031
4CV	V37	2-dr HT Spt Cpe-6P	4993	4505	44,328

ENGINE: V-8. Overhead valves. Cast iron block. Displacement: 455 cid. Bore and stroke: 4.313 x 3.900 inches. Compression ratio: 8.5:1. SAE net horsepower: 225 at 4000 rpm. Hydraulic valve lifters. Carburetor: four-barrel.

RIVIERA SERIES — (V-8) — Along with the other regular-size cars from Buick Division, the Riviera had a new front and rear treatment with new hood. fenders, grille and lights. Standard equipment included new Accu Drive; variable-ratio power steering; power brakes with front discs; new, durable stamped steel rocker arms; computer selected springs; new windshield washer; radiator overflow coolant reservoirs; solenoid activated throttle stop and exhaust gas recirculation (EGR) emissions control system; integral voltage regulator and Delcotron and brake proportioning valve. The boattail body featured thicker rocker panel trim covers, which overlapped the lower door edge. New, notch style front cornering lamps were seen. Riviera scripts appeared on the lower front fenders, with Riviera emblems on the roof pillar.

RIVIERA SERIES

Model Number	Body/Style Number	Body Type & Seating	Factory Price	Shipping Weight	Production Total
4EY	Y87	2-dr HT Spt Cpe-5P	5221	4486	34,080

ENGINE: V-8. Overhead valves. Cast iron block. Displacement: 455 cid. Bore and stroke: 4.313 x 3.900. Compression ratio: 8.5:1. SAE net horsepower: 250 at 4000 rpm. Carburetor: four-barrel.

CHASSIS FEATURES: Wheelbase: (Apollo) III inches; (Century, Luxus, Regal two-door) 112 Inches; (Century, Luxus four-door) 116 Inches; (LeSabre, Custom LeSabre, Centurion) 124 inches; (Estate Wagon) 127 Inches; (Electra, Electra 225) 127 inches; (Riviera) 122 inches. Overall length: (Apollo) 197.5 inches; (Century, Luxus, Regal two-door) 210.7 inches; (Century, Luxus four-door) 212.4 inches; (LeSabre, Custom LeSabre. Centurion) 224.2 inches; (Estate wagon) 229.5 inches; (Electra, Electra 225) 229.8 inches; (Riviera) 223.4 inches. Tires: (Apollo) ET8 x 14; (Century) G78-14; (LeSabre) 8.78 x 14; (Centurion) L78 x 15; (Electra) J78-15; (Riviera) J78 x 15.

POWERTRAIN OPTIONS: The 150 horsepower '350' V-8 was optional in Apollo. The 175 horsepower '350' V-8 was optional in all A-Body Buicks and in LeSabre/Customs. A 190 horsepower '350' V-8 was available in Century Grand Sport coupes. The 225 horsepower '455' V-8 was optional in Centurys / Luxus / Regal / LeSabre / Custom / Centurion / Electra 225 / 225 Custom. A 260 horsepower '455' V-8 was optional in Rivieras. A 270 horsepower '455' V-8 was optional in the Century Grand Sport Coupe.

CONVENIENCE OPTIONS: Vinyl top ($99). AM/FM stereo ($233). AM/FM stereo with tape ($363). Power seats ($103). Century Gran Sport package ($173). Power windows ($129). Vinyl top ($123). Riviera Stage I package ($139). Electra 225 Custom Limited trim ($174). 60/40 seats in Electra Custom ($77). Sun roof ($589). Riviera chrome styled wheels ($70). Apollo air-conditioning ($381). Century Stage I package ($546). Apollo Sport wagon disc brakes ($68). Disc brakes, other models ($46). Max trac ($89). Riviera Gran Sport package ($17 1).

HISTORICAL FOOTNOTES: Dealer introductions took place on September 21, 1972. Model year sales by U.S. dealers peaked at a record 726,191 cars. It was the second best season in Buick history. New 'Colonnade' styling was seen on Buick Century, Century Luxus and Regals in 1973. This type of design was essentially hardtop styling with a center pillar added to better satisfy federal roll over standards. G.R. Elges was general manager of Buick Motor Division this year. The Centurion nameplate disappeared at. the end of the 1973 model run.

1974 BUICK

1974 Buick, Apollo two-door hatch back sedan, V-8 (TVB)

APOLLO SERIES — SIX AND V-8 — Styling changes for the second year Apollo included a new, vertically segmented grille; a redesigned hood that dropped all the way to the upper grille header bar and the positioning of the front license plate bracket below the center of the bumper. A new, circular medallion was set into the center of the grille. Power for the base, six-cylinder series again came from an inline Chevrolet engine. Apollos with the 350 cid Buick V-8 were considered a separate series. An Apollo GSX trim option was available for $96 extra.

BUICK I.D. NUMBERS: All Buicks continued to use the same type of serial numbers as in 1973. The sixth symbol was changed to a '4' to indicate 1974 model year.

APOLLO SERIES (SIX/V-S)

Model Number	Body/Style Number	Body Type & Seating	Factory Price	Shipping Weight	Production Total
4XB	B69	4-dr Sed-5P	3060/3184	3256/3469	16,779
4XB	B27	2-dr Notch-5P	3037/3161	3216/3429	28,286
4XB	B17	2-dr Hatch-5P	3160/3284	3321/3534	11,644

NOTES: Style B27 is the two-door notchback coupe; Style B17 the two-door hatchback coupe. Factory prices and shipping weights above slash are for sixes; below slash for V-8s.

ENGINES: See 1973 Apollo Series engine data.

1974 Buick, Century Luxus two-door colonnade coupe, V-8 (TVB)

CENTURY/LUXUS/REGAL/SERIES — (V-8) — The 'Colonnade' styled A-Body Buicks were mildly facelifted. A larger grille with rectangular grid insert was seen. The front bumper guard arrangement of 1973 was replaced by a flat license plate holder. The guards became optional and, when used, were spaced wider apart. Century nameplates appeared behind the front wheel opening on Century 350 models. Luxus models had enriched trims and bright rocker moldings. Regals had a front fender crest hood crest and more delicately crosshatched grille insert. The A-Body station wagons were again designated Sport Wagons. Four different Gran Sport packages were optionally available on the Century Sport Coupe. The base GS group ($108) included GS styling and suspension components; instrument gauge cluster; clock, wheel opening moldings; glovebox; ashtray and courtesy lights. The GS 455 (code A5) package included all of the above plus a four-barrel 455 cid V-8; dual exhausts and power front disc brakes for $292. The GS 455 (code A9) package included all of the above plus a dual snorkel air cleaner for $338. The ultimate option was the GS Stage I package ($558) including a performance modified 455 cid V-8. all Gran Sport features; high energy ignition, dual snorkel air cleaner: positive traction axle; power front disc brakes and dual exhausts. The Turbo-Hydramatic 400 transmission was mandatory on Century GS Stage I models.

CENTURY/LUXUS/REGAL SERIES

Model Number	Body/Style Number	Body Type & Seating	Factory Price	Shipping Weight	Production Total
CENTURY 350					
4AD	D29	4-dr HT Sed-6P	3836	3890	22,856
4AD	D37	2-dr HT Cpe-6P	3790	3845	33,166
4AF	F45	4-dr Sta Wag-9P	4320	4305	Note 1
4AF	F35	4-dr Sta Wag-6P	4205	4272	4,860
LUXUS					
4AD	H29	4-dr HT Sed-6P	4109	3910	11,159
4AH	H57	2-dr HT Cpe-6P	4089	3835	44,930
4AK	K45	4-dr Sta Wag-9P	4486	4345	Note 1
4AK	K35	4-dr Sta Wag-6P	4371	4312	6,791
REGAL					
4AJ	J57	2-dr HT Cpe-6P	4201	3900	57,512
4AJ	J29	4-dr HT Sed-6P	4221	3930	9,333

NOTE 1: Production totals for six and nine-passenger station wagons are counted together. with no breakouts per seating configuration.

ENGINE: See 1973 Century/Luxus/Regal Series engine data.

LESABRE, LESABRE LUXUS SERIES — (V-8) — A very noticeable facelift marked the 1974 LeSabre. Round headlights were now set into individual square bezels which were separated by a body colored panel. The grille stretched across the car from end to end, but ran below and in between the headlamp bezels. The front, lower gravel pan was redesigned, having twin horizontal slots on either side of a center panel and horizontal parking lamps at the outboard ends. Cornering lamps were notched into the front fender tips. Buick lettering appeared on the upper grille shell header bar. LeSabre scripts were mounted at the trailing edge of the rear fenders. The rear end had a slanting, sweptback look and side body sculpturing was of a crisper style. Standard LeSabre features included power brakes (front disc); power steering; Turbo-Hydramatic; Accu Drive; full-flow ventilation; semi-closed cooling system; time modulated choke; EGR system; air injection reactor: front and rear ashtrays; full-foam .seats; carpeting; Deluxe steering wheel; recessed wipers; glovebox light; automatic interior lamp; bumper guard strips and the two-barrel '350'V-8. The Luxus models also had Custom steering wheel: Deluxe wheelcovers: vinyl notchback seat (except convertiblr); Lexus trim and four-barrel '350' V-9s.

1974 Buick, LeSabre four-door sedan, V-8 (TVB)

LESABRE/LESABRE LUXUS SERIES

Model Number	Body/Style Number	Body Type & Seating	Factory Price	Shipping Weight	Production Total
LESABRE					
4BN	N69	4-dr Sed-6P	4355	4337	18,572
4BN	N39	4-dr HT Sed-6P	4482	4387	11,879
4BN	N57	2-dr HT Cpe-6P	4424	4297	12,522
LESABRE LUXUS					
4BP	P69	4-dr Sed-6P	4466	4352	16,039
4BP	P39	4-dr HT Sed-6P	4629	4397	23,910
4BP	P57	2-dr HT Cpe-6P	4575	4307	27,243
4BP	P67	2-dr Conv-6P	4696	4372	3,627
ESTATE WAGON					
4BR	R45	4-dr Sta Wag-9P	5163	5182	9,831
4BR	435	4-dr Sta Wag-6P	5019	5082	4,581

ENGINE: See 1973 LeSabre Series engine data. A 210 horsepower 455 cid V-8 was standard equipment for Estate wagons.

ELECTRA 225/ELECTRA 225 CUSTOM SERIES — (V-8) — Styling changes for the big Buicks paralleled those seen on LeSabres with individual headlamp bezels and slot style front gravel pans. A wide, chrome header bar was added to the grille and had the word Buick lettered at the center. Notch style cornering lamps were set into the front corners of the body. Standard equipment was the same as on LeSabre Luxus models, plus accessory lamp group (less sunshade lamp); foam padded seats; remote control OSRV mirror; Super Deluxe wheel-covers; seat belt restrainers; Custom safety belts; evaporative emissions control system; integral voltage regulator and Delcotron; Turbo-Hydramatic 400 transmission; J78-15 blackwall

tires and the four-barrel '455' V-8. Custom trimmed Electra 225s had carpeted lower door panels and Custom exterior and interior trim. The Limited was now a separate series identified by wide rocker panel moldings, plus all other Custom features.

ELECTRA 222/ELECTRA 225 CUSTOM SERIES

Model Number	Body/Style Number	Body Type & Seating	Factory Price	Shipping Weight	Production Total
ELECTRA 225					
4CT	T39	4-dr HT Sed-6P	5373	4682	5,750
4CT	T37	2-dr HT Cpe-6P	5260	4607	3,339
ELECTRA 225 CUSTOM					
4CV	V39	4-dr HT Sed-6P	5550	4702	29,089
4CV	V37	2-dr HT Cpe-6P	5438	4682	15,099
ELECTRA LIMITED					
4CX	X39	4-dr HT Sed-6P	5921	4732	30,051
4CX	X37	2-dr HT Cpe-6P	5886	4682	16,086

ENGINE: V-8. Overhead valves. Cast iron block. Displacement: 455 cid. Bore and stroke: 4.31 x 3.9. Compression ratio: 8.0: 1. SAE net horsepower: 2 1 0. Hydraulic valve lifters. Carburetor: four-barrel.

1974 Buick, Riviera two-door hardtop sport coupe, V-8 (TVB)

RIVIERA SERIES — (V-8) — A new vertical grille with the Riviera name above it was seen as part of the 1974 restyling. An all-new notchback roofline appeared. A stand-up hood ornament was added. At the rear, the fender line sloped downward, dropping below the upper contour of the deck lid. Slanted, rectangular taillamps were horizontally mounted and decorated with a grid work of bright metal strips. Equipment features started at the Electra 225 level, except that wire wheel hubcaps were standard and Custom safety belts were not. Standard extras included a tilt steering wheel; dual exhausts; foam contoured seats; digital clock; courtesy and glovebox lights; dual front lighted ashtrays and H78-15 blackwall bias belted tires. The Gran Sport ride and handling package ($108) included a rear stabilizer bar; J78-15 whitewall steel-belted tires, radial roadability suspension and specific body insulation and ornamentation. The Riviera Stage I option ($139) included a performance modified '455' V-8; positive traction axle and chrome plated air cleaner.

RIVIERA SERIES

Model Number	Body/Style Number	Body Type & Seating	Factory Price	Shipping Weight	Production Total
4EY	Y87	2-dr HT Spt Cpe-5P	5678	4572	20,129

ENGINE: V-8. Overhead valves. Cast iron block. Displacement: 455 cid. Bore and stroke: 4.31 x 3.9. Compression ratio: 8.25:1. SAE net horsepower: 210. Carburetor: four-barrel.

CHASSIS FEATURES: Wheelbase: (Apollo) 111 inches; (Century f our-door) 116 inches; (Century two-door) 112 inches; (LeSabre) 123.5 inches, (Estate Wagon and Electra) 127 inches; (Riviera) 122 inches. Overall lengths: (Apollo) 200.2 inches; (Century four-door) 212 inches; (Sport Wagons) 218.2 inches; (Century two-door) 209.5 inches; (LeSabre) 225.9 inches; (Estate Wagon) 231.1 inches; (Electra) 231.5 inches; (Riviera) 226.4 inches. Tires: (Apollo) E78-14; (Century) G78-14; (Sport Wagon) H78-14; (LeSabre) H78-15; (Estate Wagon) L78-14; (Electra) J78-15; (Riviera) J78-15.

POWERTRAIN OPTIONS: Heavy-duty air cleaner ($9). Heavy-duty Delco energizer ($15). Dual exhausts ($30). Emission test, required for California sale ($20). Apollo '350' two-barrel V-8 ($118). Apollo '350' four-barrel V-8 ($164). Four-barrel '350' V-8 in Century or LeSabre ($46). Two-barrel '455' V-8 in LeSabre and Century ($184). Performance-modified '455' V-8 in Electras ($96); in Estate Wagons ($152); in LeSabres ($322). Four-barrel '455' V-8 in Sport Wagons ($184); in other Centurys ($230); in LeSabres ($170). Engine block heater in Apollo ($10); in other models ($5); High-energy ignition in Apollo/Century ($77); in other models ($56). Instrument gauges and clock in Centurys, except Sport Wagons ($38). Positive traction axle ($43). Max track wheel spin control ($89). Turbo-Hydramatic 350 transmission in Apollo Six ($196) in Apollo '350' V-8 ($206). Turbo-Matic 400 transmission in Century ($21). Heavy-duty radiator in Apollo ($14); in other models ($21). Heavy-duty 80-Amp Delcotron ($31-35).

CONVENIENCE OPTIONS: Air-conditioning ($396-446). Air cushion restraint system ($181-225). Station wagon air deflector ($21). Automatic climate control ($488-522). Custom safety belts ($11-37). Apollo bumper impact strips ($13). Riviera bumper reinforcement ($12). Electra rear bumper reinforcement ($6). Cargo area carpeting in Sport Wagons ($19); in Estate Wagons ($51). Trunk carpet in Electras and Riviera ($41). Electric clock, Apollo ($16); Century ($18). Full-length console for Century and Riviera two-doors ($61). Mini console in Century two-doors ($36). Convenience center console ($26). Customline convertible cover ($36). Cruise control in Century ($65). Rear window defogger ($33). Electric rear window defogger ($64). Tinted glass ($3050). Tinted windshield ($30-35). Front and rear bumper guards ($31-35). Automatic level control ($77). Buick cornering lights ($36). Front monitors ($22). Front and rear monitors ($48). Station wagon luggage rack ($64-84). Sports mirrors, right and left ($22-44). Special order paint ($113). Apollo body striping ($21). Riviera body striping ($31). Wide rocker moldings for LeSabre Luxus and Electra 225s, except Limited ($28). Custom bodyside trim ($24-46). Custom door/window trim ($21-27). Twotone paint ($27-43). Wide rocker panel group for LeSabre and Estate. including lower rear quarter, front and rear wheel well moldings ($69). Six-way right-hand and left-hand power seats of 60/40 design or 40/40 design ($211). Other six-way seat options ($80-106). Electric sunroof in Century ($325); in all Sports Coupes ($589). AM radio with stereo tape and dual rear speakers ($203-216). AM/FM stereo radio with stereo tape and front and rear dual speakers ($363). Rallye suspension ($30). Super lift shock absorbers ($41). Speed Alert ($11-17). Manual sunroof in Century ($275); in Sport Coupes ($539). Vinyl trim with Custom bucket seats ($124); with lumbar-support reclining bucket seats ($236); vinyl bucket seats ($119), all in

Century two-doors only. Vinyl roofs, Custom Apollo ($82); Custom Century ($99); Custom Century short type ($84); Custom padded Electra ($385); Custom Landau Riviera ($385); Custom Landau Electra Sport Coupe ($525); Custom with moldings on Estate ($138); Custom Regal Landau ($310); Custom padded with moldings on Electra/LeSabre/Riviera ($123-138). Deluxe wheelcovers ($26); Wire wheelcovers ($56-82). Super Deluxe wheelcovers ($34-56). Deluxe wire wheelcovers ($60-108). Chrome wheels ($66-118). Woodgrain exterior station wagon panelling on Estate ($177); Luxus ($136); Century 168). Code V4 accessory group-($26-36). Code VI convenience group ($12-27).

Ride and handling package ($15). LeSabre Luxus ride and performance package ($423-575). (Note: Prices for certain options and accessories varied by Series or body style. In such cases, the low-to-high range is reflected above).

HISTORICAL FOOTNOTES: Model year introductions took place on September 27, 1974. Calendar year production peaked at 400,262 cars or 5.49 percent of industry output. Model year production hit 495,063 units. Buick dealers also marketed Opels this year. George R. Elges remained Buick's general manager in 1974 and P.C. Bowser was chief engineer.

1975 BUICK

1975 Buick, Skyhawk 2-dr hatch back coupe, V-6 (TVB)

SKYHAWK SERIES — (V-6) — An all new car, the sub-compact Skyhawk was the smallest Buick in more than 60 years. It weighed below 3,000 pounds and stood less than four feet high. The Skyhawk shared the GM H-Body platform — featuring torque arm rear suspension and super sleek 2 + 2 styling — with the Chevrolet Monza. Under the hood, however, was a 231 cid Buick V-6. This engine had started its life as a 225 cid Buick powerplant for the Special Series in the early 1960s. In 1968, the tooling for the engine was sold to American Motors Corporation. Now, with a displacement increased, the motor was back in the Buick stable and many of its parts were interchangeable with a 260 cid V-8. Mounted on a 97 inch wheelbase, the Skyhawk was 179.3 inches long (21 inches shorter than the Apollo) and came with all features of larger GM cars, including the Efficiency System and a full list of options.

BUICK I.D. NUMBERS: Vehicle identification numbers and number locations followed the previous system. The sixth symbol was changed to a '5' for 1975 model year.

SKYHAWK SERIES

Model Number	Body/Style Number	Body Type & Seating	Factory Price	Shipping Weight	Production Total
4H	HT07	2-dr 'S' Hatch-4P	3860	2851	Note 1
4H	HS07	2-dr Hatch-4P	4173	2891	Note I

NOTE 1: Buick Skyhawks were manufactured exclusively in Canada this ear. Buick reported U.S. dealer model year sales of 29,448 examples of the new 'H' car. No breakout was provided for the two trim levels.

ENGINE: V-6. Overhead valves. Cast iron block. Displacement: 231 cid. Bore and stroke: 3.80 x 3.40. Compression ratio: 8.0: 1. SAE net horsepower: 110 at 4000 rpm. Overhead valves. Carburetor: two-barrel.

1975 Buick, Apollo two-door notchback sedan, V-6 (TVB)

APOLLO/SKYLARK SERIES — (L-6/V-6/V-8) — The Apollo lineup was the most extensively revised 1975 Buick series. Topped by the revived Skylark two-door coupe, other X-car models included a two-door hatchback coupe and a thin pillared four-door sedan. New styling gave the Apollo a European flair, with a low beltline, full-width grille, wraparound parking and directional lamps and large, horizontal taillamps. Both standard and luxury 'R/S' models were on a

111 inch wheelbase with Apollos offering the 250 cid Chevrolet L-head Six as base power-plant. Cars with V-8 power were considered to be in a separate series. The 260 cid V-8 was the base V-8 and the 350 cid job was optional. Base engine in the Skylark was the "new" V-6. Signature scripts below the rear tender belt moldings were helpful in identifying the various models.

ENGINES: L-6. Overhead valves. Cast iron block. Displacement: 250 cid. Bore and stroke: 3.87 x 3.5 inches. Compression ratio: 8.0:1. Brake horsepower: 105 at 4000 rpm. Carburetor: one-barrel.

V-6. See 1975 Skyhawk Series engine data.

V-8. Overhead valves. Cast iron block. Displacement: 260 cid. Bore and stroke: 3.5 x 3.385 inches. Compression ratio: 8.0: 1. Brake horsepower: 110 at 4000 rpm. Carburetor: two-barrel.

APOLLO/SKYLARK SERIES

Model Number	Body/Style Number	Body Type & Seating	Factory Price	Shipping Weight	Production Total
(APOLLO SUB-SERIES)					
4BX	B69	4-dr Sed-5P	3436/3514	3366/3511	21,138
(SKYLARK 'S' SUB-SERIES)					
4WX	W27	2-dr Notch-5P	3234/3260	3309/3502	Note 1
(SKYLARK SUB-SERIES)					
4BX	B27	2-dr Notch-5P	3463/3489	3341/3537	27,689
4BX	B17	2-dr Hatch-5P	3586/3612	3438/3587	6,814
(APOLLO 'SR' SUB-SERIES)					
4CX	C69	4-dr Sed-5P	4092/4170	3383/3574	2,241
(SKYLARK 'SR' SUB-SERIES)					
4CX	C27	2-dr Notch-5P	4136/4162	3309/3498	3,746
4CX	C17	2-dr Notch-5P	4253/4279	3441/3586	1,505

NOTE 1: No breakout is provided for production of the Skylark 'S' notchback coupe.

NOTE 2: A total of 504 Apollos were manufactured in Canada, late in the 1975 calendar year, to 1976 specifications. In the chart above Factory Prices and Shipping Weights above slash are for Sixes; below slash for V-8s. The L-6 was used in Apollos; the V-6 in Skylarks. The base V-8 was the 260 cubic-inch Buick motor.

1975 Buick, Century 2-dr colonnade coupe w/'Free Spirit' pkg, V-8

CENTURY/REGAL SERIES — (V-6/V-8) — The Intermediate size Buick A-Body lineup offered the biggest selection of models for 1975. The Century was again the base level in terms of trim and appointments, with an equipment list comparable to similar 1974 models. A one-step up Century Custom was comparable to the 1974 Luxus, with the same type of features and extra decorative touches. The Gran Sport was no longer a separate sub-series, but 'GS' type equipment was available as a $171 options package. Basic styling changes from a year earlier included a wider grille that varied in design from line to line. On Century Specials it had a horizontal double-deck look, with vertical-dash type insert and vertically-mounted rectangular parking lamps housed, within the grille, at its outboard ends. On Centurys and Century Customs, the horizontal divider was deleted. On Regals, there was a shorter grille with vertical blades only and the same type of parking lamps were seen outside the grille, between the chrome surround and the headlamps. Regals had a model identification script on the left-hand side of the grille, while other models had Buick block lettering. The Century Special was marketed as a low-rung economy job with less basic equipment than other models, allowing it to be advertised at an attractive price. As in the past, the two-door A-Body cars were shorter, in wheelbase and overall length, than four-doors on this platform.

CENTURY/REGAL SERIES

Model Number	Body/Style Number	Body Type & Seating	Factory Price	Shipping Weight	Production Total
(CENTURY/SPECIAL V-6)					
4AE	E37	2-dr Cpe-6P	3815	3613	Note 1
(CENTURY V-6/V-8)					
4AD	D29	4-dr Sed-6P	3944/4022	3730/3906	22,075
4AD	D37	2-dr Cpe-6P	3894/3972	3674/3850	39,556
4AF	F45	4-dr Sta Wag-9P	4751	4370	Note 2
4AF	F35	4-dr Sta Wag-6P	4636	4320	4,416
(CENTURY CUSTOM V-6/V-8)					
4AH	H29	4-dr Sed-6P	4211/4289	3763/3939	9,995
4AH	H57	2-dr Cpe-6P	4154/4232	3671/3847	32,966
4AK	K45	4-dr Sta Wag-9P	4917	4400	Note 2
4AK	K35	4-dr Sta Wag-6P	4802	4350	7,078
(REGAL V-6/V-8)					
4AJ	J29	4-dr Sed-6P	4311/4389	3800/3976	10,726
4AJ	J57	2-dr Cpe-6P	4257/4335	3733/3909	56,646

NOTE 1: The Century Special came only with V-6 power and was technically an equipment-deleted model and not a distinct body style. Production of this car, Style Number E37, is counted with Style Number D37.

NOTE 2: Station Wagons came only with V-8 power. Production of six and nine-passenger station wagons was counted as a single total. ADDITIONAL NOTE: Factory Prices and Shipping Weights above slash are for Sixes; below slash for V-8s. Cars with V-8 power were considered to be in a separate series.

ENGINES: V-6. See 1975 Skyhawk Series engine data.

V-8. Overhead valves. Cast iron block. Displacement: 350 cid. Bore and stroke: 3.8 x 3.85 inches. Compression ratio: 8.0:1. Brake horsepower: 145 at 3800 rpm. Carburetor: two-barrel.

LESABRE/LESABRE CUSTOM/ESTATE WAGON SERIES — (V-8) — Both LeSabre and LeSabre Custom series offered B-Body two and four-door hardtops, plus four-door thin-pillar styles. A convertible was exclusive to the Custom level line. All LeSabres were on a 123.5 inch wheelbase with either a standard 350 cid V-8 or optional '455'. The Estate Wagons shared the 127 inch Electra wheelbase and luxury appointments. As on all Buicks, the GM Efficiency System was standard and included High-energy ignition a catalytic convertor and steel-belted radial tires. Styling updates included a new grid-style grille with under the headlamp extensions. The square headlamp housings returned to a side-by-side type mounting; ventiports were moved from the hood to the front fendersides and Buick block lettering was the only decoration on the lower lip of the hood. Equipment variations between the various sub-series were comparable to the previous year with Custom replacing the Luxus designation.

1975 Buick, LeSabre four-door hardtop sedan, V-8 (TVB)

LESABRE/LESABRE CUSTOM/ESTATE WAGON SERIES

Model Number	Body/Style Number	Body Type & Seating	Factory Price	Shipping Weight	Production Total
(LESABRE)					
4BN	N69	4-dr Sed-6P	4771	4355	14,088
4BN	N39	4-dr HT Sed-6P	4898	4411	9,119
4BN	N57	2-dr HT Cpe-6P	4840	4294	8,647
(LESABRE CUSTOM)					
4BP	P69	4-dr Sed-6P	4936	4388	17,026
4BP	P39	4-dr HT Sed-6P	5061	4439	30,005
4BP	P57	2-dr HT Cpe-6P	5007	4316	25,016
4BP	P67	2-dr Conv-6P	5133	4392	5,300
(ESTATE WAGON)					
4BR	R45	4-dr Sta Wag-9P	5591	5135	9,612
4BR	R35	4-dr Sta Wag-6P	5447	5055	4,128

LESABRE/LESABRE CUSTOM

The 350 cid V-8 was the standard engine in LeSabre and LeSabre Customs. General specifications were the same as for the Century '350' except that a four-barrel carburetor was used and the output was 165 horsepower at 4000 rpm.

ESTATE WAGON ENGINE: V-8. Overhead valves. Cast iron block. Displacement: 455 cid. Bore and stroke: 4.313 x 3.9 inches. Compression ratio: 7.9: 1. Brake horsepower: 205 at 3800 rpm. Carburetor: Four-barrel.

ELECTRA 225 CUSTOM/ELECTRA 225 LIMITED SERIES — (V-8) — Buick's most prestigious series was reduced to four models, as full-sized cars continued to be de-emphasized by General Motors. These C-Body models were built off a 127 inch wheelbase platform. The 455 cid V-8 was standard as were Efficiency System features. Rectangular headlamps were a styling change along with a Classic-looking eggcrate grille that extended below the headlamps. Also new were monogrammed hood ornaments; large opera style rear quarter windows; shag carpeting and soft velour upholstery and headliners. An especially luxurious Park Avenue option package was available for the Limited hardtop sedan. as well as an even richer Park Avenue Deluxe group.

ELECTRA 225 CUSTOM/ELECTRA 225 LIMITED

Model Number	Body/Style Number	Body Type & Seating	Factory Price	Shipping Weight	Production Total
(CUSTOM)					
4CV	V39	4-dr HT Sed-6P	6201	4706	27,357
4CV	V37	2-dr HT Cpe-6P	6041	4582	16,145
(LIMITED)					
4CX	X39	4-dr HT Sed-6P	6516	4762	33,778
4CX	X37	2-dr HT Cpe-6P	6352	4633	17,650

ENGINE: See 1975 Estate Wagon engine data.

1975 Buick, Riviera hardtop sport coupe, V-8 (TVB)

RIVIERA SERIES — (V-8) — The Riviera remained as Buick's personal luxury off ering. A major redesign was seen up front. Changes to the bumper, grille and trim and new rectangular headlamps were seen. Overall length was 3-1/2 inches shorter. The ultra luxurious and sporty 'GS' option remained available and standard equipment was the same as the previous season, plus High-Energy ignition; Efficiency System features and steel-belted radial ply tires. Annual styling changes included closer together vertical blades in the Neo-Classic grille shell; clear cornering lamp lenses; a slotted-center bumper design and a Riviera script plate on the left-hand side of the grille.

RIVIERA SERIES

Model Number	Body/Style Number	Body Type & Seating	Factory Price	Shipping Weight	Production Total
4EZ	Z87	2-dr HT Spt Cpe-5P	6420	4539	17.306

ENGINE: See 1975 Estate Wagon engine data.

CHASSIS FEATURES: Wheelbase: (Skyhawk) 97 inches; (Apollo/Skylark) 111 inches; (Century two-door) 1 12 inches; (Century four-door) 116 inches; (LeSabre) 124 inches; (Electra and Estate) 127 inches; (Riviera) 122 inches. Overall length: (Skyhawk) 179.3 inches; (Apollo and Skylark) 200.3 inches; (Century two-door) 209.5 inches; (Century four-door) 213.5 inches; (Century station wagon) 218.2 inches; (Regal two-door) 212 inches; (Regal four-door) 216 inches; (LeSabre) 226.9 inches; (Estate Wagon) 233.4 inches; (Electra) 233.4 inches; (Riviera) 223 inches. Tires: (Skyhawk) BR78-13; (Skylark and Apollo) FR78-14; (Century) GR78-15; (Estate Wagon) LR78-15; (LeSabre) HR78-15; (Electra and Riviera) JR78-15.

POWERTRAIN OPTIONS: Optional engines for Apollos included the two and four-barrel versions of the 350 cid V-8. Optional engines for Century/Regal models were the two and four-barrel versions of the 350 cid V-8 (145 and 165 horsepower, respectively). The 350 cid, four-barrel engine was standard in Century station wagons, with no other choices available. The four-barrel 455 cid V-8 (205 horsepower) was optional in LeSabres. There were no engine options for Electras or Rivieras. A 400 cid 185 horsepower engine was optional in LeSabres and was, most likely, released only for use in cars built for California sale. The horsepower rating indicates this is a Pontiac-built motor, although standard reference sources are unclear on this point.

CONVENIENCE OPTIONS: Skyhawk air conditioning ($398). Skyhawk AM/FM stereo ($214). Apollo air conditioning ($435). Apollo AM/ FM stereo ($233); with tape player ($363). Century AM/FM stereo ($233); with tape player ($363). Century Six-Way power seat ($117). Century sun roof ($256). Gran Sport package ($171). Regal S/R package ($256). Station Wagon luggage rack ($68). LeSabre Six-Way power seat ($117). LeSabre power windows ($149). Station wagon woodgrain applique ($182). Estate Wagon luggage rack ($89). Riviera 'GS' ride and handling package ($73). Electra and Riviera sun roof ($644). Park Avenue option group ($495). Power brakes in Apollo ($55). Rear window defroster ($60). Electra rear window defroster ($73). Bucket seats ($75). Regal sun roof ($350). Custom trim ($165). Air bags ($275). Park Avenue Deluxe package ($1,675). Electra and Riviera cornering lamps ($38). Heavy padded vinyl roof ($389).

HISTORICAL FOOTNOTES: Dealer introductions were held September 27, 1974. Calendar year production (U.S. built models only) peaked at 545.820 cars or 7.99 percent of the total industry output. Model year sales of domestically-built models peaked at 481,768 units. D.C. Collier was named general manager of Buick Division this year. A total of 49,226 Opels were also sold from Buick dealer showrooms this season. In late 1975, assemblies of Skyhawks built to 1976 specifications began at the GMAD plant in Southgate, California.

1970 Buick, Gran Sport GSX two-door hardtop coupe, V-8

1974 Buick, Apollo two-door sedan, 6-cyl

1970 Buick, Wildcat Custom, two-door hardtop coupe, V-8

1974 Buick, Electra Limited four-door hardtop sedan, V-8

Standard Catalog of American Cars

STANDARD CATALOG OF
CADILLAC
1946-1975

The years 1946-1975 were good ones for Cadillac. The company entered postwar times selling about 30,000 updated 1942 models each year and competing, with Packard, for the top rank in America's luxury car market. The battle was a short one. The famous, aircraft-inspired tailfin look debuted on selected 1948 models and, from then on, Cadillac became the style innovator in the high-priced field. Sales hit 100,000 units in 1950, passing those of other prestige makes and remaining out front for more than 25 years. By 1975, Cadillac's annual sales volume was some 265,000 cars.

By John A. Gunnell

Trendsetting engineering seemed, always, to be part and parcel of the motoring masterpieces turned out, with remarkable consistency, by the Cadillac styling studio. In 1949, a compact, but exceptionally sturdy, overhead valve V-8 became the brand's new power source. It was an engine that would last some 30 years without growing stale, becoming always more monsterous in size and output as time rolled by. Tailfins and big motors would characterize the marque, year after year, right through the early 1960s, but annually reblended in a product that seemed constantly new and ever more exciting.

The Golden Era of the automotive stylist is a good way to describe the early 1950s, a period which gave birth to such

Cadillac innovations as the 'Florentine Curve' roof; bumper tip dual exhaust exits; purposeful-looking eggcrate grilles and the simulated air vent rear fenderline treatment.

Derived from the Motorama parade of futuristic dream machines, the Cadillac Eldorado convertible became a production line reality in 1953. This 'Eldo,' like many top dollar Cadillacs, came only fully equipped. It featured a profile that belonged more to a sports car than an elegant ragtop. Exactly 532 buyers had the foresight to place orders for a copy, while 109,000 others made their picks from the balance of Cadillac's 1953 fleet. New that season was the bullet-shaped bumper/grille 'bomb' which saw immediate popularity and imitation.

After celebrating its 50th season as an automaker, in 1952, Cadillac marked its 40th consecutive year of V-8 availability in 1954. A far cry from the 70 horsepower Type 51 motor of 1914, the 1954 powerplant had a 331 cid piston displacement, four-barrel carburetion, 8.25:1 compression ratio and 230 hp output rating. Unlike other manufacturers, the company did not enlarge engine size each year, but usually managed a power boost through compression or induction refinements. The cars themselves, however, did tend to grow a bit larger annually.

Sales for 1955 peaked at a record 141,000 deliveries. The product line started at the rich level and included the traditional, long-wheelbased limousines for upper crust society. Features like automatic transmission and power brakes were

taken for granted. Power seats, steering and window lifts came at no additional cost in some models. Air conditioning was far from rare. For several years, the Eldorado was marketed with styling touches that the rest of the line would adopt a year or two later. This allowed the company to test forthcoming design changes, before putting them into full production.

After 1956, this system was also used on the Eldorado's closed-bodied counterpart, the super luxurious Seville hardtop coupe. At this point in time Packard was gasping its final breaths, Imperial was having an identity crisis and Lincoln was just incubating its fabulous Continental Mark II. Meanwhile, Cadillacs found 155,000 buyers, virtually dominating the top rung of the domestic market spectrum.

The big news for 1957 was all-new styling and technology combined with the release of another show car come to life. The Eldorado Brougham, with its advanced airplane fuselage styling, was priced above $13,000 and came with every conceivable option, plus a few features never before seen on any car.

The 1958-1960 era could easily be called the 'Wurlitzer Jukebox' period of automotive design and, like other makers, Cadillac was guilty of excessive use of towering tailfins, unnecessary tinsel and overpowering size. To some, the 'Batmobile' look of 1959 will always be regarded as the ultimate of this era. On the other hand, the cars of this vintage are precious to collectors now.

Like an Edsel, the 1959 Cadillac has come to represent a cultural symbol of its day. The following model, though somewhat similar, was clearly a move towards the more sophisticated styling of the 1960s.

Clean, crisp lines and a modest attempt at down-sizing characterized the 1961 model year. Slowly, but surely, the tailfin started to descend back towards earth. Sculptural body feature lines took the place of unneeded chromium sweep spears. Increasing emphasis was placed on more attractive roofline treatments, interior design reflecting subdued elegance and the creation of cars equipped for safer, more comfortable and ultra-convenient driving. Cadillac's 1964 introduction of the Comfort Control heating and air conditioning system set a new industry standard.

Finless rear fenders appeared on a long, low and even more luxurious line of Cadillacs for 1965. A new Fleetwood Brougham, with a vinyl covered roof as standard equipment, was introduced. Outstanding performance was, as usual, an accepted fact. The latest V-8, of 340 hp, came with the best power-to-weight ratio of any engine used as base equipment in a domestic car. Sales climbed to nearly 200,000 units, a barrier level that finally fell by the wayside during 1966.

The highlight of model year 1967 was a radically new front-wheel-drive Eldorado coupe aimed at the growing sports/personal car segment of the high-priced field. Its slotted wheelcovers, hidden headlamps and long hood/short deck configuration quickly endeared the sporty new Cadillac to the wealthy who were young at heart. By 1968, the Eldorado was attracting over 25,000 buyers a year, while the more conventional Cadillacs continued to follow a conservative pattern of annual styling and engineering refinements that won more customers each season. Between 1963 and 1968, Cadillac Division established a new sales record each year.

This ever-upward trend was temporarily broken in 1969, the year in which the front vent window disappeared. This was not a very popular styling change and may have accounted, in some measure, for the modest drop in sales. In 1970, however, Cadillac bounced back with a massive 500 cid engine and deliveries of a record 239,000 units. Three long-standing models, the Sixty Special sedan and the DeVille sedan and convertible passed from the scene, as the company adapted to a more streamlined marketing program for its seventh decade.

A growing emphasis on safety keynoted the completely restyled Cadillacs of 1971, which were also larger than ever before. Even the Eldorado was dressed in entirely new sheetmetal that further accented the 'big car' look. In coupe form, it could now be had with a sun roof, a feature not seen on Cadillacs since 1941. To keep a watchdog government happy, Cadillac adopted massive front safety bumpers and a 8.5:1 compression ratio to permit utilization of low-lead or lead-free gasoline.

To celebrate its 70th anniversary in 1972, Cadillac built and sold 267,000 cars for the calendar year. One of these — a Fleetwood Eldorado Coupe — became a gift to the late Leonid Brezhnev from U.S. President Richard M. Nixon. Although the Cadillac image changed little, from year-to-year, in the early 1970s, sales continued to climb. The company had abandoned its former role as innovator and was now virtually an institution: the king of the luxury car market. A degree of conservatism seemed to go with the new role.

The king, of course, reigned supreme. More than 300,000 Cadillacs were sold in 1973, a year in which a white Eldorado convertible paced the 57th running of the Indianapolis 500 Mile Race. Not since 1937 had a Cadillac product been given this particular honor.

Modern technology was very obvious in the facelifted Cadillacs presented to buyers in the 1974 model year. Not only was a digital dashboard clock standard equipment, but an expanded list of options included the air bag safety restraint system, steel-belted radial tires, High-Energy electronic ignition and pulsating windshield wipers. In addition, a number of extremely high-priced luxury options packages were offered. They could convert various models into ultra-elegant Cabriolet, D'Elegance or Talisman editions. Sales, however, took a plunge to the 242,000 unit level as a result of the Arab nations' embargo upon the flow of oil to the United States. Of course, this eco-political situation affected all automakers and Cadillac wound up with a larger market share, even though volume sales were off.

In 1975, Cadillac's superiority over competitors in the prestige class was once again demonstrated, when Chrysler Corp. announced that it was discontinuing production of the Imperial (later revived). This left the top of the market to Cadillac and Lincoln, both of which had seen a nearly tenfold increase, in sales, since 1946. Yet, in terms of overall volume, Cadillac continued to play the king's role by outselling the 'fancy Ford' via a wide margin.

A seasonal highlight was the midyear release of an international-sized Seville on a 114 inch wheelbase platform. A completely new concept, the 'baby' Cadillac found more than 16,000 buyers waiting. For the big cars, another midyear innovation was the offering of an optional, electronic fuel-injection setup, on the 500 cid V-8.

Today, the collector, historian and old car hobbyist are likely to regard the latest Cadillacs as a reflection of a great company's decline. And, to a large degree, the viewpoint is a sound one. The Cadillac of 1992 simply does not embody the distinction and high quality level associated with the marque in the past. However, the models built by Cadillac Division in the first 30 years after World War II were, for the most part, outstanding machines that maintained the brand's traditional position as a 'Standard' of the automotive world.

1949 Cadillac, Series 62 four-door sedan, V-8

1953 Cadillac, Series 62 two-door convertible, V-8

1958 Cadillac, Series 62 two-door convertible, V-8

1961 Cadillac, Series 62 two-door convertible, V-8

1970 Cadillac, two-door Convertible DeVille, V-8

1975 Cadillac, Fleetwood Eldorado, two-door convertible, V-8

1946 CADILLAC

1946 Cadillac, Fleetwood 75 limousine, V-8, AA

SERIES 61 — (V-8) — All 1946 Cadillacs were a continuation of prewar styling and engineering with the unpopular 63 and 67 Series being dropped. Features common to each series included dual downdraft carburetors; Torbend disc clutch; directional signals; knee action wheels; double ride stabilizers; permanently lubricated universals; ball bearing steering; mechanical fuel pump; oil bath air cleaner; intake silencer; automatic choke; Synchromesh transmission; sealed beam lighting; front coil springs; Super-Safe hydraulic brakes; wax lubricated rear springs; hypoid rear axle; slotted disc wheels; low pressure tires; large luggage compartments and safety plate glass throughout. Cadillac's lowest-priced Series 61 line was based on the General Motors' B-Body,' also used on cars in the Buick 40, Olds 70 and Pontiac 26 and 28 series. Fastback styling characterized the two available body styles, which saw a late production startup in May, 1946. Standard features included small hubcaps; a wider, more massive grille; bullet-shaped front and rear fenders; skirted rear wheel openings and chrome-plated rear fins. The gas filler cap was located under the rear signal lamp.

SERIES 61 I.D. NUMBERS: Cadillac serial numbers matched the motor numbers and were used for all license, insurance and identification purposes. For 1946 they were located on the right-hand side of the engine crankcase, just above the water pump, and on the right frame side member, behind the motor support. Numbers 5400001 to 5402975 appeared on Series 61 models.

SERIES 61

Model Number	Body/Style Number	Body Type & Seating	Factory Price	Shipping Weight	Production Total
46-61	6107	2-dr Clb Cpe-5P	2052	4145	800
46-61	6109	4-dr Sed-5P	2176	4225	2,200
46-61	—	Chassis only	—	—	1

1946 Cadillac, Series 62 four-door sedan, V-8 (AA)

SERIES 62 — (V-8) — Series 62 Cadillacs were based on the General Motors' C-Body, also used on the Cadillac 60S, Buick 50 and 70 and Oldsmobile 90 series. Notchback styling characterized the racy-looking cars in this line except for the Club Coupe, which had fastback styling. The Series 62 four-door sedan was the first Cadillac to enter production after WWII. Styling and technical features were similar to those seen on lower priced models, but on a longer chassis with slightly richer interior appointments.

SERIES 62 I.D. NUMBERS: Motor serial numbers 8400001 to 8418566 appeared on 1946 models.

SERIES 62

Model Number	Body/Style Number	Body Type & Seating	Factory Price	Shipping Weight	Production Total
46-62	6207	2-dr Clb Cpe-5P	2284	4215	2,323
46-62	6267D	2-dr Conv Cpe-5P	2556	4475	1,342
46-62	6269	4-dr Sed-5P	2359	4295	14,900
46-62	—	Chassis only	—	—	1

SERIES 60 SPECIAL FLEETWOOD — (V-8) — The Series 60 Special Fleetwood line included only one model, a four-door sedan also based on the corporate C-Body. However, each door was made two inches wider, amounting to an overall four inch extension over the standard Series 62 sedan. For easy identification, there were four slanting louvers on the rear roof pillar and a distinctive type of roof drip molding, which was separate for each door opening.

SERIES 60 SPECIAL FLEETWOOD I.D. NUMBERS: Motor serial number 6400001 to 6405679 appeared on 1946 models.

SERIES 60 SPECIAL FLEETWOOD

Model Number	Body/Style Number	Body Type & Seating	Factory Price	Shipping Weight	Production Total
46-60S	6069	4-dr Sed-6P	3099	4420	5,700

SERIES 75 FLEETWOOD — (V-8) — Cadillac's Fleetwood long-wheelbase line used totally distinctive bodies which were not shared with other General Motors' divisions. They were generally characterized by a prewar appearance and came in five different touring sedan configurations: with quarter windows; with auxiliary (jump) seats; business; Imperial 7-passenger and Imperial 9-passenger (the latter two both having jump seats). Standard equipment included large wheel discs, fender skirts, hood, side and lower beltline moldings and stainless steel running boards.

SERIES 75 FLEETWOOD I.D. NUMBERS: Motor I.D. serial numbers 3400001 to 640579 appeared on 1946 models.

SERIES 75 FLEETWOOD

Model Number	Body/Style Number	Body Type & Seating	Factory Price	Shipping Weight	Production Total
46-75	7519	4-dr Sed-5P	4298	4860	150
46-75	7523	4-dr Sed-7P	4475	4905	225
46-75	7523L	4-dr Bus Sed-9P	4153	4920	22
46-75	7533L	4-dr Imp Bus Sed-9P	4346	4925	17
46-75	7533	4-dr Imp Sed-7P	4669	4925	221
46-75	—	Commercial Chassis	—	—	1,292

NOTE: Commercial chassis featured a 163 inch wheelbase.

ENGINE: V-8: L-head. Cast iron block. Displacement: 346 cid. Bore and stroke: 3-1/2 x 4-1/2 rpm.. inches. Compression ratio: 7.25:1. Brake hp: 150 at 3400 rpm. Three main bearings. Hydraulic valve lifters. Carburetor: Carter WCD two-barrel (models 595S or 595SA) or Stromberg AAV-26 two-barrel (models 380154 or 380871).

CHASSIS FEATURES: Wheelbase: (Series 61) 126 inches; (Series 62) 129 inches; (Series 60S) 133 inches; (Series 75) 136 inches. Overall length: (Series 61) 215 inches, (Series 62) 220 inches; (Series 60S) 224 inches; (Series 75) 227 inches. Front tread: (All) 59 inches. Rear tread: (All) 63 inches. Tires: (Series 75) 7.50 x 16; (All others) 7.00 x 15.

POWER TRAIN OPTIONS: None available.

CONVENIENCE OPTIONS: Hydra-Matic transmission ($176). Large wheel discs ($19). White sidewall disc. Fog lights. Safety spotlight. And more.

HISTORICAL FOOTNOTES: Division windows between front and rear seats were available on Fleetwood models for limousine use. Commercial chassis were provided for makers of hearses and ambulances. A limited number of dual-cowl phaetons were also constructed on Cadillac chassis this year. The Classic Car Club of America recognizes all 1946 Series 75 models as classic cars.

1947 CADILLAC

SERIES 61 — (V-8) — A minor styling facelift characterized 1947 Cadillacs, which now had grilles with five massive horizontal blades instead of the six used the previous year. A new identification feature was a striped field for the V-shaped hood crest. Sombrero style wheel-covers were an attractive new option seen on many Cadillacs. In the logo, department, a script type nameplate replaced the block lettering used on the sides of front fenders in 1946. Upholstery and paint combinations were generally revised and steering wheel horn rings were changed to a semi-circular design. The old style rubber stone shields were replaced with a bright metal type and a new winged trunk ornament was used on all models except the Series 60 Fleetwood Special sedan. Other features were basically unchanged over last year's cars. The Series 61 models continued to utilize the GM B-Body with fastback styling.

SERIES 61 I.D. NUMBERS: Cadillac serial numbers again matched motor numbers and were used for all license, insurance and identification purposes. They were placed in the same locations as before. Motor serial numbers 5420001 to 5428555 appeared on 1947 Series 61 models.

SERIES 61

Model Number	Body/Style Number	Body Type & Seating	Factory Price	Shipping Weight	Production Total
47-61	6107	2-dr Clb Cpe-5P	2200	4080	3,395
47-61	6109	4-dr Sed-5P	2324	4165	5,160

SERIES 62 — (V-8) — Series 62 Cadillacs were again based on the GM C-Body and had a slightly sleeker appearance than models in the other lines. Notchback styling was seen on all models, except the fastback coupe. However, it was easy to distinguish this car from a 61 coupe, as the door skins did not flare out above the rocker panels; the side window openings were lower and the reveal moldings circled each window individually instead of looping around all windows, as on the smaller car. The 62 sedan also had door skins, which mated flush with the rocker panels, and featured ventipanes on both the front and rear windows. The 62 convertible was the only open-bodied Cadillac available.

SERIES 62 I.D. NUMBERS: Motor serial numbers 8420001 to 8459835 appeared on 1947 Series 62 models.

1947 Cadillac, Series 62 two-door sedanette, V-8, AA

SERIES 62

Model Number	Body/Style Number	Body Type & Seating	Factory Price	Shipping Weight	Production Total
47-62	6207	2-dr Clb Cpe-5P	2446	4145	7,245
47-62	6267	2-dr Conv Cpe-5P	2902	4455	6,755
47-62	6269	4-dr Sed-5P	2523	4235	25,834
47-62	—	Chassis only	—	—	1

1947 Cadillac, Fleetwood 60 Special sedan, V-8, AA

SERIES 60 SPECIAL FLEETWOOD — (V-8) — Two-inch wider doors were again seen on the Series 60 Special Fleetwood line, giving this car a custom look, as compared to standard Series 62 sedans based on the same GM C-Body shell. A heavy upper beltline molding, individual window loop moldings and four slanting louvers on the rear roof pillar were identification features as was the new Fleetwood trunk ornament, which varied from that seen on lower models. Bright metal stone guards were adopted this season and skirted rear fenders were used again.

SERIES 60S FLEETWOOD I.D. NUMBERS: Motor serial numbers 6420001 to 6428500 appeared on 1947 series 60S models.

SERIES 60S FLEETWOOD

Model Number	Body/Style Number	Body Type & Seating	Factory Price	Shipping Weight	Production Total
47-60	6069	4-dr Sed-6P	3195	4370	8,500

SERIES 75 FLEETWOOD — (V-8) — Unchanged in all but minor details for 1947, the big Fleetwood 75 series continued to use the touring sedan body with a stately, prewar appearance. It came in the same five configurations marketed the year before and had the same assortment of standard equipment geared to the luxury class buyer.

SERIES 75 FLEETWOOD I.D. NUMBERS: Motor serial numbers 3420001 to 3425036 appeared on 1947 series 75 models.

SERIES 75 FLEETWOOD

Model Number	Body/Style Number	Body Type & Seating	Factory Price	Shipping Weight	Production Total
47-75	7519	4-dr Sed-5P	4340	4875	300
47-75	7523	4-dr Sed-7P	4517	4895	890
47-75	7523L	4-dr Bus Sed-9P	4195	4790	135
47-75	7533-L	4-dr Imp Bus Sed-9P	4388	4800	80
47-75	7533	4-dr Imp Sed-7P	4711	4930	1,005
47-75	—	Chassis only	—	—	3
47-75	—	Commercial Chassis	—	—	2,423
47-75	—	Business Chassis	—	—	200

NOTE: The Commercial Chassis and Business Chassis featured a 163 inch wheelbase.

ENGINE: V-8: L-head. Cast iron block. Displacement: 346 cid. Bore and stroke: 3-1/2 x 4-1/2 inches. Compression ratio: 7.25:1. Brake hp: 150 at 3400 rpm.. Three main bearings. Hydraulic valve lifters. Carburetor: Carter WCD two-barrel (models 595S or 595SA) or Stromberg AAV-26 two-barrel (models 380154 or 380871).

CADILLAC CHASSIS FEATURES: Wheelbase: (Series 61) 126 inches; (Series 62) 129 inches; (Series 60S) 133 inches; (Series 75) 136 inches. Overall length: (Series 61) 215 inches; (Series 62) 220 inches; (Series 60S) 224 inches; (Series 75) 227 inches. Front tread: (All) 59 inches. Rear tread: (All) 63 inches. Tires: (Series 75) 7.50 x 16; (All others) 7.00 x 15.

POWER TRAIN OPTIONS: None available.

CONVENIENCE OPTIONS: Hydra-Matic transmission ($186). Large wheel discs ($25). White sidewall discs. Fog lights. Safety spotlight. Fender mounted radio antenna. And more.

HISTORICAL FOOTNOTES: Division windows between front and rear windows were available on some Fleetwood models for limousine use. Commercial and business chassis were provided to professional car makers. The Classic Car Club of America recognizes all 1947 Series 75 models as classic cars.

SERIES 61 — (V-8) — Major design changes marked the short wheelbase Cadillacs for 1948. They featured General Motors first all-new postwar body with styling advances including tailfins inspired by the Lockheed P-38 fighter plane. There was also an attractive eggcrate grille which was higher in the middle than on the sides. The front of the car was protected by a heavier and more massive bumper bar which curved around the fenders. The Cadillac crest was centered low in a 'V' above the radiator grille. Chrome headlamp rims were used. Cars in the 61 series lacked bright metal front fender shields and under-taillight trim. A new dashboard with 'rainbow' style instrument cluster and leather grained panels extending to the carpets was seen only this year.

SERIES 61 I.D. NUMBERS: Cadillac serial numbers again matched motor numbers and were used for all license, insurance and identification purposes. They were placed in the same locations as before. Motor serial numbers 48100001 to 486148663 appeared on 1948 Series 61 models.

SERIES 61

Model Number	Body/Style Number	Body Type & Seating	Factory Price	Shipping Weight	Production Total
48-61	6169	4-dr Sed-5P	2833	4150	5,081
48-61	6107	2-dr Clb Cpe-5P	2728	4068	3,521
48-61	—	Chassis only	—	—	1

SERIES 62 — (V-8) — The Series 62 was now on the same wheelbase as the lowest priced line, making the club coupe and sedan practically identical to similar models in the Series 61 range except for trim and appointments. Distinguishing features included grooved, bright metal front fender gravel guards, rocker panel brightwork, chevron style chrome slashes below taillights and slightly richer interior trim. The convertible coupe was an exclusive offering in this line.

SERIES 62 I.D. NUMBERS: Motor serial numbers 486200001 to 486252704 appeared on 1948 Series 62 models.

SERIES 62

Model Number	Body/Style Number	Body Type & Seating	Factory Price	Shipping Weight	Production Total
48-62	6269	4-dr Sed-5P	2996	4179	23,997
48-62	6207	2-dr Clb Cpe-5P	2912	4125	4,764
48-62	6267	2-dr Conv Cpe-5P	3442	4449	5,450
48-62	—	Chassis only	—	—	2

1948 Cadillac, Fleetwood 60 Special Derham sedan, V-8 (AA)

SERIES 60 SPECIAL FLEETWOOD — (V-8) — The Series 60 Special Fleetwood sedan was again based on an extended General Motors C-Body shell with two-inch wider front and rear doors. The tailfins, built-in rear bumper design and eggcrate grille seen on the lower-priced lines were used. Appearing again, on the rear roof pillar, were four slanting chrome slashes. Instead of the standard wide stone shields, the 60 Special had a thinner type which curved upwards along the forward contour of the rear fender and incorporated an attractive ribbed insert panel. At the rear of the car, a band of chrome extended across the bottom of the fender skirts and quarter panels. Standard equipment included cloth and leather upholstery combinations and leather-grained doors and instrument panel.

SERIES 60 SPECIAL FLEETWOOD I.D. NUMBERS: Motor serial numbers 486000001 to 486052706 appeared on 1948 Series 60S Fleetwood models.

SERIES 60 SPECIAL FLEETWOOD

Model Number	Body/Style Number	Body Type & Seating	Factory Price	Shipping Weight	Production Total
48-60S	6069	4-dr Sed-6P	3820	4356	6,561

SERIES 75 FLEETWOOD — (V-8) — Consideration was given to the deletion of the long-wheelbase line this year, but competitive pressures from Packard in the luxury class market dictated the retention of these models. Again, they featured General Motors' old-fashioned 'Turret Top' styling, a throwback to the prewar years. Minor revisions on the outside of the cars included a new background for the V-shaped hood emblem and Cadillac scripts-replacing block lettering-low on the fenders behind the front wheel opening. Buyers ordering fog lamps got rectangular parking lamps in place of the smaller round style. Stainless steel runningboards were seen once more and the 75s also had the new dashboard treatment, but with burled leather trim.

SERIES 75 FLEETWOOD I.D. NUMBERS: Motor serial numbers 487500001 to 487546088 appeared on 1948 Series 75 Fleetwood models.

SERIES 75 FLEETWOOD

Model Number	Body/Style Number	Body Type & Seating	Factory Price	Shipping Weight	Production Total
48-75	7519X	4-dr Sed-5P	4779	4875	225
48-75	7523X	4-dr Sed-7P	4999	4878	499
48-75	7523L	4-dr Bus Sed-9P	4679	4780	90
48-75	7533X	4-dr Imp Sed-7P	5199	4959	382
48-75	7533L	4-dr Bus Imp-9P	4868	4839	64
48-75		Chassis only	—	—	2

NOTE: The commercial chassis featured a 163 inch wheelbase.

ENGINE: V-8: L-head. Cast iron block. Displacement: 346 cid. Bore and stroke: 3-1/2 x 4-1/2 inches. Compression ratio: 7.25:1. Brake hp: 150 at 3400 rpm. Three main bearings. Hydraulic valve lifters. Carburetor: Carter WCD two-barrel (models 595S or 595SA) or Stromberg AAV-26 two-barrel (models 380154 or 380871).

CADILLAC CHASSIS FEATURES: Wheelbase: (Series 61 and 62) 126 inches: (Series 60S) 133 inches; (Series 75) 136 inches. Overall length: (Series 61 and 62) 214 inches; (Series 60S) 226 inches; (Series 75) 226 inches. Front tread: (All) 59 inches. Rear tread: (All) 63 inches. Tires: (Series 75) 7.50 x 16; (All others) 8.20 x 15.

POWER TRAIN OPTIONS: None available.

CONVENIENCE OPTIONS: Hydra-Matic transmission ($174). Whitewall tires, Radio and antenna. Fog lamps. Safety spotlight. Rear window defroster. And more.

HISTORICAL FOOTNOTES: Division windows between front and rear seats were available on some Fleetwood models for limousine use. Commercial and business chassis were supplied to professional carmakers. The Classic Car Club of America recognizes all 1948 Series 75 models as Classic Cars. The following models are recognized as Milestones by the Milestone Car Society: Series 61 coupe (sedanette); Series 62 coupe (sedanette); Series 62 convertible; Series 60S Fleetwood Special sedan.

1949 CADILLAC

SERIES 61 — (V-8) — The big news at Cadillac in 1949 centered on engineering, with the release of a new overhead valve V-8 engine. Only minor appearance changes were seen. They included a more massive grille treatment with grooved extension panels housing the front parking lights and chevron slashes below the taillamps on Series 61 coupes. Once again, the cars in this line lacked front fender gravel shields and rocker panel moldings and had plainer interior trims. A larger luggage compartment lid was seen on all sedans, except very early production units. Standard equipment now included twin back-up lamps mounted on the deck lid latch panel.

SERIES 61 I.D. NUMBERS: Cadillac serial numbers again matched motor numbers. They appeared stamped on a boss at the front right-hand face of the engine block and on the right frame side member behind the motor support. Motor serial numbers 496100000 to 496192552 were used on 1949 Series 61 models.

SERIES 61

Model Number	Body/Style Number	Body Type & Seating	Factory Price	Shipping Weight	Production Total
49-61	6169	4-dr Sed-5P	2893	3915	15,738
49-61	6107	2-dr Clb Cpe-5P	2788	3838	6,409
49-61		Chassis only	—	—	1

1949 Cadillac, Series 62 two-door sedanette, V-8 (AA)

SERIES 62 — (V-8) — The major difference between Series 61 and Series 62 models of similar body style was minor trim variations. The higher-priced series again had grooved, front fender stone shields and bright rocker panel moldings. Chevrons below the taillights were no longer seen. The convertible was an exclusive offering, as was a new pillarless two-door 'convertible hardtop' called the Coupe DeVille. A plusher interior was featured and power window lifts were standard on the convertible coupe and optional with other styles.

SERIES 62 I.D. NUMBERS: Motor serial numbers 496200000 to 496292554 appeared on 1949 Series 62 models.

SERIES 62

Model Number	Body/Style Number	Body Type & Seating	Factory Price	Shipping Weight	Production Total
49-62	6269	4-dr Sed-5P	3050	3956	37,617
49-62	6207	2-dr Clb Cpe-5P	2966	3862	7,515
49-62	6237	2-dr Cpe DeV-5P	3496	4033	2,150
49-62	6267X	2-dr Conv Cpe-5P	3497	4218	8,000
49-62	6269	4-dr Export Sed	3050	3956	360
49-62		Chassis only	—	—	1

NOTE: The sedan for export was shipped in completely-knocked-down (CKD) form to foreign countries.

1949 Cadillac, Fleetwood 60 Special four-door sedan, V-8 (AA)

SERIES 60 SPECIAL FLEETWOOD — (V-8) — The car with the big doors, the 60 Special Fleetwood sedan, again had four chrome slashes on the rear roof pillar, thinner rear fender stone guards with front and rear extensions and Cadillac scripts mounted high on the front fenders, above the crease line. The new grille design with parking lamp extensions was seen along with standard back-up lamps. Hydraulic window lifts were also regular equipment on this car. A more conventional dashboard design appeared on all Cadillacs this year, featuring a horizontal speedometer.

SERIES 60 SPECIAL FLEETWOOD I.D. NUMBERS: Motor serial numbers 496000000 to 496088221 appeared on 1949 Series 60S Fleetwood models.

SERIES 60 SPECIAL FLEETWOOD

Model Number	Body/Style Number	Body Type & Seating	Factory Price	Shipping Weight	Production Total
49-60S	6069X	4-dr Sed-5P	3828	4129	11.399
49-60S	6037X	2-dr Spl Cpe DeV-5P			1

SERIES 75 FLEETWOOD — (V-8) — To accomodate luxury-class buyers, the long wheelbase Fleetwood models were carried over without any basic changes, except for revisions to the dashboard design which followed those on other models.

SERIES 75 FLEETWOOD I.D. NUMBERS: Motor serial numbers 497500000 to 497577135 appeared on 1949 Series 75 models.

SERIES 75 FLEETWOOD

Model Number	Body/Style Number	Body Type & Seating	Factory Price	Shipping Weight	Production Total
49-75	7519X	4-dr Sed-5P	4750	4579	220
49-75	7523X	4-dr Sed-7P	4970	4626	595
49-75	7523L	4-dr Bus Sed-9P	4650	4522	35
49-75	7533X	4-dr Imp Sed-7P	5170	4648	626
49-75	7533L	4-dr Bus Imp-9P	4839	4573	25
49-75	—	Chassis only	—	—	1
49-75	—	Commercial chassis			1,861

NOTE: The commercial chassis featured a 163 inch wheelbase and was offered to professional car makers for the construction of funeral vehicles, ambulances, etc.

ENGINE: V-8: Overhead valves. Cast iron block. Displacement: 331 cid. Bore and stroke: 3-13/16 x 3-5/8 inches. Compression ratio: 7.5:1. Brake hp: 160 at 3800 rpm. Five main bearings. Hydraulic valve lifters. Carburetor: Carter WCD two-barrel Model 742S.

CADILLAC CHASSIS FEATURES: Wheelbase: (Series 61 and 62) 126 inches; (Series 60S) 133 inches; (Series 75) 136 inches. Overall length: (Series 61 and 62) 214 inches; (Series 60S) 226 inches; (Series 75) 226 inches. Front tread: (All) 59 inches. Rear tread: (All) 63 inches. Tires: (Series 75) 7.50 x 16; (All others) 8.20 x 15.

CADILLAC POWER TRAIN OPTIONS: None available.

CONVENIENCE OPTIONS: Hydra-Matic transmission ($174). Whitewall tires. Radio and antenna. Heating and ventilating system. Chrome wheel discs. Fog lights. Safety spotlights. Other standard accessories.

HISTORICAL FOOTNOTES: The Milestone Car Society recognizes the following 1949 Cadillacs as Milestone Cars: Series 61 coupe (sedanette); Series 62 coupe (sedanette); Series 62 convertible; Series 60 Special Fleetwood sedan.

1950 CADILLAC

SERIES 61 — (V-8) — Cadillacs had extensive styling changes this year. They looked generally heavier and had low, sleek contours with longer rear decks, more sweeping front fenders and a broken rear fender line. The hood protruded further out at the front and was underlined by an even more massive eggcrate grille. Round parking lights were used, but as in the past, when buyers chose fog lamps, an additional bulb and larger housing were used. This setup combined the fog lamps and directional signals. One-piece windshields were introduced and the leading edge of the rear fender, which had a broken-off look, was highlighted by chrome imitation air slots. The rear fenders were longer and ended in a swooping tailfin design. A Cadillac script again appeared on the sides of front fenders, but was now positioned closer to the front door opening gap. As far as Series 61 models went, a big styling change was a return to marketing this line on a shorter wheelbase than used on the 62s. This led to some styling differences. For example, the Series 61 sedan had no rear ventipanes and featured a wraparound backlight. An identifying feature on both models was the absence of rocker panel moldings and rear quarter panel chrome underscores. Cars in Cadillac's lowest-priced range also had bodies which were four inches shorter than the previous season.

SERIES 61 I.D. NUMBERS: Cadillac serial numbers again matched motor numbers and were used for all license, insurance and identification purposes. They were located on a boss on the right-hand face of the engine block and on the right frame side member behind the motor support. Motor serial numbers 506100000 to 5061103853 appeared on 1950 Series 61 models.

SERIES 61

Model Number	Body/Style Number	Body Type & Seating	Factory Price	Shipping Weight	Production Total
50-61	6169	4-dr Sed-5P	2866	3822	14,619
50-61	6137	2-dr Clb Cpe-5P	2761	3829	11,839
50-61	6169	4-dr Exp Sed-5P	2866	3822	312
50-61	—	Chassis only	—	—	2

NOTE: The sedan for export was shipped in completely-knocked-down (CKD) form to foreign countries.

SERIES 62 — (V-8) — Cars in the Cadillac next-step-up line were identified by slightly richer interior appointments and by chrome underscores running the full length of the body at the bottom. Hydra-Matic drive was now standard in this line. The Series 62 sedan incorporated rear ventipanes. Exclusive models in this range were the convertible coupe and Coupe DeVille, both with dual hydraulic window lifts.

SERIES 62 I.D. NUMBERS: Motor serial numbers 506200000 to 5062103857 appeared on 1950 Series 62 models.

1950 Cadillac, Coupe DeVille two-door hardtop coupe, V-8 (AA)

SERIES 62

Model Number	Body/Style Number	Body Type & Seating	Factory Price	Shipping Weight	Production Total
50-62	6219	4-dr Sed-5P	3234	4012	41,890
50-62	6237	2-dr Clb Cpe-5P	3150	3993	6,434
50-62	6237DX	2-dr Cpe DeV-5P	3523	4074	4,507
50-62	6267	2-dr Conv Cpe-5P	3654	4316	6,986
50-62	—	Chassis only	—	—	1

SERIES 60 SPECIAL FLEETWOOD — (V-8) — Eight vertical chrome louvers on the rear fenders characterized the Series 60S sedan. It was built on the same platform as the previous year, but had all the new styling features. It looked lower than the 62 because of the extra length and had a different rear deck contour. Hydra-Matic drive and power windows were standard.

SERIES 60 SPECIAL FLEETWOOD I.D. NUMBERS: Motor serial numbers 506000000 to 5060103850 appeared on 1950 Series 60S models.

SERIES 60 SPECIAL FLEETWOOD

Model Number	Body/Style Number	Body Type & Seating	Factory Price	Shipping Weight	Production Total
50-60S	6019X	4-dr Sed-5P	3797	4136	13,755

SERIES 75 FLEETWOOD — (V-8) — An all-new postwar body, which conformed to the other lines for the first time since 1941, was introduced on the luxury-class models this year. It featured six-window styling and a 'high-headroom' limousine type appearance. Jump seats were used in the seven-passenger sedan and the Imperial limousine. Surprisingly, Hydra-Matic drive was optional, but power windows were standard equipment.

1950 Cadillac, Fleetwood 75 Limousine, V-8 (AA)

SERIES 75 FLEETWOOD I.D. NUMBERS: Motor serial numbers 507500000 to 507510387 were used on 1950 Series 75 Fleetwood models.

SERIES 75 FLEETWOOD

Model Number	Body/Style Number	Body Type & Seating	Factory Price	Shipping Weight	Production Total
50-75	7523X	4-dr Sed-7P	4770	4555	716
50-75	7533X	4-dr Imp Sed-7P	4959	4586	743
50-75	7523L	4-dr Bus Sed-7P	—	—	1
50-75	86	Commercial chassis	—	—	2,052

NOTE: The commercial chassis featured a 157 inch wheelbase and was supplied to professional car makers for the construction of funeral cars, ambulances, etc.

ENGINE: V-8: Overhead valves. Cast iron block. Displacement: 331 cid. Bore and stroke: 3-13/16 x 3-5/8 inches. Compression ratio: 7.5:1. Brake hp: 160 at 3800 rpm. Five main bearings. Hydraulic valve lifters. Carburetor: Carter WCD two-barrel Models 682S or 722S.

CADILLAC CHASSIS FEATURES: Wheelbase: (Series 61) 122 inches; (Series 62) 126 inches; (Series 60S) 130 inches; (Series 75) 146-3/4 inches. Overall length: (Series 61) 211-7/8 inches; (Series 62) 215-7/8 inches, (Series 60S) 224-7/8 inches; (Series 75) 236-5/8 inches. Front tread: (All) 59 inches. Rear tread: (All) 63 inches. Tires: (Series 75) 8.20 x 15; (All others) 8.00 x 15.

POWER TRAIN OPTIONS: None available.

CONVENIENCE OPTIONS: Hydra-Matic drive on Series 61 and 75 ($174). Power windows (on specific models). Heating and ventilating system. Radio and antenna. Chrome wheel discs (Sombrero). Windshield washers. Fog lamps. White sidewall tires. Other standard accessories.

HISTORICAL FOOTNOTES: Stainless steel Sombrero wheelcovers replaced the chrome plated type this year, although the stampings were identical. An hydraulic seat was standard on the Coupe DeVille. The one-millionth Cadillac ever produced was a 1950 Coupe DeVille assembled Nov. 25, 1949. An all-time Cadillac production record was set.

1951 CADILLAC

1951 Cadillac, Series 61 four-door sedan, V-8

SERIES 61 — (V-8) — A minor facelift and small trim variations were the main Cadillac styling news this year. Miniature eggcrate grilles were set into the outboard grille extension panels below the headlights. Larger, bullet shaped style bumper guards were used. The features list included handbrake warning lamp: key start ignition; steering column cover; Delco-Remy generator: knee-action front suspension; directionals; mechanical fuel pump; dual downdraft carburetion; slipper type pistons; rubber engine mountings; oversize brakes; Super Cushion tires; one-piece windshield; intake silencer; 160 hp engine; oil bath air cleaner; equalized manifolding; automatic choke and luxury appointments. On the dashboard, 'idiot lights' were used to monitor oil pressure and electrical charge rate instead of gages. The smaller body was again used on 61s and again identified by the lack of full-length chrome underscores. However, a new medallion now appeared on the rear roof pillar of these cars, above the upper beltline molding.

SERIES 61 I.D. NUMBERS: Cadillac serial numbers again matched motor numbers and were used for all license, insurance and identification purposes. They were located on a boss at the front right-hand face of the engine block and on the right frame side member behind the motor support. Motor serial numbers for 1951 Series 61 models began at 51610000000. The ending number for all Cadillac series was 110340 (preceeded by applicable model year and series code for final unit.)

SERIES 61

Model Number	Body/Style Number & Seating	Body Type Factory Price	Shipping Weight	Production Total
51-61	6169	4-dr Sed-5P	2917	3827	2300
51-51	6137	2-dr Clb Cpe-5P	2810	3829	2400

1951 Cadillac, Series 62 four-door sedan, V-8 (AA)

SERIES 62 — (V-8) — Series 62 models had full-length chrome underscores on the rocker panels, rear fender skirts and lower rear quarters. The sedan had a conventional backlight and featured rear ventipanes. A new Coupe DeVille script was seen on the rear roof pillar of this model which, like the convertible, was an exclusive Series 62 offering. The script clearly distinguished the more luxurious DeVille from the plainer club coupe, a distinction not emphasized in 1950. Hydra-Matic drive was regular equipment on all models (with a new type dial) and power windows were standard on the convertible and Coupe DeVille.

SERIES 62 I.D. NUMBERS: Motor serial numbers 516200000 and up appeared on 1951 Series 62 models.

SERIES 62

Model Number	Body/Style Number	Body Type & Seating	Factory Price	Shipping Weight	Production Total
51-62	6219	4-dr Sed-5P	3528	4102	54,596
51-62	6219	4-dr Exp Sed-5P	—	—	756
51-62	6237	2-dr Clb Cpe-5P	3436	3993	10,132
51-62	6237DX	2-dr Cpe DeV-5P	3843	4074	10,241
51-62	6267	2-dr Conv Cpe-5P	3987	4316	6,117
51-62	126	Chassis only	—	—	2

NOTE: The export sedan was shipped in completely-knocked-down (CKD) form to foreign countries.

1951 Cadillac, Fleetwood 60 Special four-door sedan, V-8 (AA)

SERIES 60 SPECIAL FLEETWOOD — (V-8) — The 60 Special Fleetwood sedan was facelifted to conform with the minor changes in other models. Eight vertical chrome louvers on the forward edge of the rear fenders continued to identify this car. All 1951 Cadillacs with full wheel discs featured a new type design lacking the popular Sombrero look. Hydra-Matic and power windows were standard on Sixty Specials.

SERIES 60 SPECIAL FLEETWOOD I.D. NUMBERS: Motor serial numbers 516000000 and up appeared on 1951 Series 60S models.

SERIES 60 SPECIAL FLEETWOOD

Model Number	Body/Style Number	Body Type & Seating	Factory Price	Shipping Weight	Production Total
51-60	6019	4-dr Sed-5P	4142	4136	18,631

SERIES 75 FLEETWOOD — (V-8) — The Series 75 Fleetwood models were also facelifted to conform to the minor changes seen in other lines. Jump seats were used in both the seven-passenger sedan and Imperial limousine. Hydra-Matic drive was optional and hydraulic window lifts were standard. Business sedans were built in limited numbers on a special order basis.

SERIES 75 FLEETWOOD I.D. NUMBERS: Motor serial numbers 517500000 and up appeared on 1951 Series 75 Fleetwood models.

SERIES 75 FLEETWOOD

Model Number	Body/Style Number	Body Type & Seating	Factory Price	Shipping Weight	Production Total
51-75	7523X	4-dr Sed-8P	5200	4555	1,090
51-75	7533X	4-dr Imp Sed-8P	5405	4586	1,085
51-75	7523L	4-dr Bus Sed-8P	—	—	30
51-75	86	Commercial chassis	—	—	2,960

NOTE: The commercial chassis featured a 157 inch wheelbase and was supplied to professional car makers for construction.

ENGINE: V-8: Overhead valves. Cast iron block. Displacement: 331 cid. Bore and stroke: 3-3/16 x 3-5/8 inches. Compression ratio: 7.5:1. Brake hp: 160 at 3800 rpm. Five main bearings. Hydraulic valve lifters. Carburetor: Carter WCD two-barrel Model 845S — also — Rochester BB two-barrel Model 7004200.

CADILLAC CHASSIS FEATURES: Wheelbase: (Series 61) 122 inches; (Series 62) 126 inches; (Series 60S) 130 inches; (Series 75) 146-3/4 inches. Overall length: (Series 61) 211-7/8 inches; (Series 62) 215-7/8 inches; (Series 60S) 224-7/8 inches; (Series 75) 236-5/8 inches. Front tread: (All) 59 inches. Rear tread: (All) 63 inches. Tires: (Series 75) 8.20 x 15; (All others) 8.00 x 15.

POWERTRAIN OPTIONS: None available.

CONVENIENCE OPTIONS: Hydra-Matic drive on Series 61 and 75 ($186). Power windows (specific models). Heating and ventilating system. Radio and antenna. Chrome wheel discs. Windshield washers. Fog lamps. White sidewall tires (availability limited).

HISTORICAL FOOTNOTES: The Series 61 line was discontinued in the middle of the year due to lagging sales.

1952 CADILLAC

SERIES 62 — (V-8) — This was Cadillac's 50th anniversary year. Only minor styling and trim changes were seen, but some were specially planned to commemorate the occasion. For example, the V-shaped hood and deck emblems were done as gold castings. The Series 62 sedan was also characterized by a distinct, higher rear deck lid contour. This provided additional luggage space. Back-up lights were standard equipment and were now incorporated in the taillights. The grille wraparound panels were redesigned once again. They now had broad chrome trim below each headlight with side scoop styling and a gold-colored winged emblem mounted in the center. At the rear, all models adopted a new Cadillac

trademark, a through-the-bumper dual exhaust system. Deck ornamentation varied by series and, on 62s, took the form of a Cadillac crest over a broad golden 'V.' The Coupe DeVille again had a script nameplate on the rear roof pillar. New standards included self-winding clocks, dual-range Hydra-Matic drive, improved direction signal indicators, glare-proof mirrors, stannate treated pistons, four-barrel carburetion and all other features seen the year before. Hydraulic window lifts remained as regular equipment on convertibles and Coupe DeVilles.

1952 Cadillac, Series 62 convertible, V-8 (AA)

CADILLAC I.D. NUMBERS: Serial numbers and engine numbers were again one and the same. They appeared on the right-hand side of the crankcase above the 'water pump and on the right frame side bar behind the engine support. The first two symbols were '52' for 1952. The next two symbols indicated the series as follows: '62', '60S' or '75'. The remaining digits represented the consecutive unit number and began with 00000 for all series. All series had the same ending number.

SERIES 62

Model Number	Body/Style Number	Body Type & Seating	Factory Price	Shipping Weight	Production Total
52-62	6219	4-dr Sed-5P	3636	4151	42,625
52-62	6237	2-dr Clb Cpe-5P	3542	4174	10,065
52-62	6237 DX	2-dr Cpe DeV-5P	3962	4205	11,165
52-62	6267X	2-dr Conv Cpe-5P	4110	4419	6,400

SERIES SIXTY SPECIAL FLEETWOOD — (V-8) — The Sixty Special Fleetwood sedan had the same general styling changes seen in other lines, plus minor trim and appointment variations. For example, the word Fleetwood appeared on the rear deck lid (instead of a Cadillac crest) and the eight vertical fender louvers were seen again. Hydra-Matic drive and hydraulic windows were installed at no extra cost to buyers.

SERIES SIXTY SPECIAL FLEETWOOD

Model Number	Body/Style Number	Body Type & Seating	Factory Price	Shipping Weight	Production Total
52-60	6019	4-dr Sed-5P	4720	4258	16,110

1952 Cadillac, Fleetwood 75 Limousine, V-8 (AA)

SERIES 75 FLEETWOOD — (V-8) — Styling changes on the long-wheelbase series also conformed to the theme for the year with the Golden Anniversary aspect highlighted. Equipment features were the same as before and no business sedans were built.

SERIES 75 FLEETWOOD

Model Number	Body/Style Number	Body Type & Seating	Factory Price	Shipping Weight	Production Total
52-75	7523X	4-dr Sed-8P	5361	4699	1,400
52-75	7533X	4-dr Imp Sed-8P	5572	4734	800
52-76	86	Commercial chassis	—	—	1,694

NOTE: The commercial chassis was built off a 157 inch wheelbase and was provided to makers of professional vehicles for construction of funeral cars, ambulances, etc.

ENGINE: V-8: Overhead valves. Cast iron block. Displacement: 331 cid. Bore and stroke: 3-13/16 x 3-5/8 inches. Compression ratio: 7.5:1. hp: 190 at 4000 rpm. Five main bearings. Hydraulic valve lifters. Carburetor: Carter WFCB four-barrel Model 896S — also — Rochester 4GC four-barrel 7004500.

CADILLAC CHASSIS FEATURES: Wheelbase. (Series 62) 126 inches; (Series 60S) 130 inches; (Series 75) 147 inches. Overall length: (Series 62 sedan) 215-1/2 inches; (All other 62s) 200-1/2 inches; (Series 60S) 224-1/2 inches; (Series 75) 236-1/4 inches. Front tread: (All) 59 inches. Rear tread: (All) 63 inches. Tires: (Series 75) 8.20 x 15; (Other series) 8.00 x 15. Dual exhausts standard. Real axle ratio: 3.07: 1.

POWERTRAIN OPTIONS: None available.

CONVENIENCE OPTIONS: Hydra-Matic drive on Series 75 ($186). Wheel discs ($28). Windshield washer ($11). Oil filter ($11). Fog lamps ($37). License frames ($4). Outside mirror ($6). Vanity mirror ($2). E-Z Eye glass ($46). Heater and blower ($114). Push-button radio

and rear speaker ($112). Signal-seeking radio and rear speaker ($129). Power steering ($198). Autronic Eye headlight beam control ($53). White sidewall tires Series 62 and 60S ($34). Automatic window regulators ($139). Wheel trim rings ($11).

HISTORICAL FOOTNOTES: Cadillac had the most powerful car in the American industry this year. The 1,300,000th Cadillac of all time was built. Military orders for T4IEl Walker Bulldog tanks and T41 twin 40-mm gun motor carriages were secured by the division this year as part of the Korean war buildup. Hydraulically controlled power seats were standard on Coupe DeVille.

1953 CADILLAC

1953 Cadillac, Coupe DeVille two-door hardtop coupe, V-8 (AA)

SERIES 62 — (V-8) — Changes seen in 1953 included a redesigned grille with heavier integral bumper and bumper guards, the repositioning of parking lamps directly under the headlights, chrome 'eyebrow' type headlamp doors and one-piece rear windows without division bars. Wheel discs were fashioned in an attractive new dished design. Series 62 models were identified by non-louvered rear fenders, the use of thin bright metal underscores on the bottom rear of the cars only and the decoration of both hood and deck lid with Cadillac crests and V-shaped ornaments. As was the practice since 1951, Series 62 sedan bodies measured five inches less than the other styles. A Coupe DeVille roof pillar script was seen again on this luxury hardtop. Standard equipment included all items featured the year before. Late in the production year the limited-edition Eldorado luxury convertible was added to this model range. A full assortment of Deluxe accessories, including wire wheels, were standard on this specialty car which introduced the wraparound windshield for production models. On Aug. 12. a fire at the Hydra-Matic transmission factory in Livonia, Mich. broke out and would bring a damaging halt to production within a week. It was September 8 before Cadillacs began leaving the factory again.

1953 Cadillac, Eldorado convertible, V-8 (AA)

CADILLAC I.D. NUMBERS: Serial numbers and engine numbers were again one and the same. They appeared on the right-hand side of the crankcase above the water pump and on the right frame side bar behind the engine support. The first two symbols were '53' for 1953. The next two symbols indicated the series as follows: '62', '60' or '75.' The remaining digits represented the consecutive unit number and began with 00000 for all series. All series had the same ending number, which would be misinterpreted if listed.

SERIES 62

Model Number	Body/Style Number	Body Type & Seating	Factory Price	Shipping Weight	Production Total
53-62	6219(X)	4-dr Sed-5P	3666	4201	47,316
53-62	6219(X)	4-dr Sed-5P	3666	4201	324
53-62	6237(X)	2-dr Cpe-5P	3571	4189	14,353
53-62	6237DX	2-dr Cpe Dev-5P	3995	4252	14,550
53-62	6267X	2-dr Conv Cpe-5P	4144	4476	8,367
53-62	62	Chassis only	—	—	4

ELDORADO SPECIAL

Model Number	Body/Style Number	Body Type & Seating	Factory Price	Shipping Weight	Production Total
53-62	6267SX	Spt 2-dr Conv Cpe-5P	7750	4799	532

NOTES: The export sedan was shipped in CKD form to foreign countries. The symbol X in brackets indicates hydraulic window lifts optional, without brackets indicates this feature standard.

1953 Cadillac, Fleetwood 60 Special four-door sedan, V-8 (AA)

SERIES SIXTY SPECIAL FLEETWOOD — (V-8) — Eight vertical louvers on the lower rear fenders directly behind the fender breakline once again characterized the wide door Cadillac sedan. This model was also distinguished by exclusive extra-wide full length chrome underscores and a Fleetwood insignia on the rear deck lid.

SERIES SIXTY SPECIAL FLEETWOOD

Model Number	Body/Style Number	Body Type & Seating	Factory Price	Shipping Weight	Production Total
53-60	6019X	4-dr Sed-5P	4305	4337	20,000

SERIES 75 FLEETWOOD — (V-8) — Styling facelifts on the cars in the 75 Fleetwood line conformed to those seen on the other models. Appearance features and equipment were about the same as in previous years. Regular production models included the Imperial eight-passenger limousine with glass partition or eight-passenger sedan, both with jump seats.

SERIES 75 FLEETWOOD

Model Number	Body/Style Number	Body Type & Seating	Factory Price	Shipping Weight	Production Total
53-75	7523X	4-dr Sed-8P	5604	4801	1,435
53-75	7533X	4-dr Imp Sed-8P	5818	4853	765
53-86	8680S	Commercial chassis	—	—	2,005

NOTE: The commercial chassis featured a 157 inch wheelbase and was provided to makers of professional vehicles for construction of funeral cars, ambulances, etc.

ENGINE: V-8. Overhead valves. Cast iron block. Displacement: 331 cid. Bore and stroke: 3-15/16 x 3-5/8 inches. Compression ratio: 8.25: 1. Brake hp: 210 at 4150 rpm. Five main bearings. Hydraulic valve lifters. Carburetors: (Hydra-Matic) Carter WCFB four-barrel Model 2005S — also — Rochester 4GC four-barrel Model 7005100. (Dynaflow) Carter WCFB four-barrel Models 2088S, 2119S and 2119SA also — Rochester 4GC four-barrel Model 7006215.

CHASSIS FEATURES: Wheelbase: (Series 62) 126 inches; (Series 60S) 130 inches; (Series 75) 146-3/4 inches. Overall length: (Series 62 sedan) 215.8 inches; (Other 62s) 220.8 inches; (Series 60S) 224.8 inches; (Series 75) 236.5 inches. Tires: (Series 75) 8.20 x 15; (Others) 8.00 x 15. Dual exhaust system standard. Rear axle ratios: (Series 62 and 60S) 3.07: 1; (Series 75) 3.77: 1.

POWERTRAIN OPTIONS: None available.

CONVENIENCE OPTIONS: Hydra-Matic drive on Series 75 ($186). Hydraulic window lifts optional on some Series 62 models. Heating and ventilation system ($199). Power steering ($177). Signal-seeking radio with preselector and antenna ($132). Remote control signal-seeking radio with preselector and antenna ($214). Five white sidewall tires ($48 exchange). Tinted E-Z-Eye glass ($46). Autronic Eye Automatic headlamp beam control ($53). Chrome wire wheels ($325). Air conditioning ($620). Other standard G.M. accessories.

HISTORICAL FOOTNOTES: Standard equipment on the Style Number 6267S Eldorado sport convertible included Hydra-Matic drive, wraparound windshield, special cut-down doors, rich leather-and-cloth upholstery, wire wheels, white sidewall tires, fog lamps. vanity and side mirrors, metal tonneau cover and signal-seeking radio. The Style Number 7533 Series 75 Fleetwood Imperial sedan was fitted with an hydraulically operated glass driver's partition. The Style Number 6267S Eldorado sport convertible is a certified Milestone Car. The futuristic Cadillac LeMans show car convertible was displayed this year and would heavily influence styling of the 1954 Eldorado. It has a special 270 hp V-8 with dual four-barrel carburetion and a fiberglass body. Also, 28,000 Cadillacs were built with Buick Dynaflow transmission after GM's Hydramatic plant burned to the ground.

1954 CADILLAC

SERIES 62 — (V-8) — Many appearance improvements marked the 1954 Cadillacs. They included a lower, sleeker body, a new cellular grille insert, inverted gull-wing front bumpers and tapered dagmar style bumper guards. Round, jet-style dual exhaust outlets were incorporated into the vertical bumper extensions and the rear bumper was entirely redesigned. An Eldorado type wraparound windshield was seen on all models. Sedans used a distinctive type of window reveal molding which created a built-in sun visor effect. For coupes, a smoothly curved wraparound backlight was referred to as the 'Florentine' style rear window. A wide ventilator intake now stretched across the base of the windshield on all models and the chrome visored headlamp look was emphasized. The Series 62 chassis had a brand new, longer wheelbase. One identifying feature of this line was the lack of rear fender louvers. V-shaped ornaments and crests were used on the hood and deck lid and there were full-length body underscores in bright metal. Coupe DeVille scripts were seen on the rear corner pillars of the luxury hardtop, which also had wider sill moldings. The Eldorado had golden identifying crests centered directly behind the air-slot fenderbreaks and wide, fluted beauty panels to decorate the lower rear bodysides. These panels were made of extruded aluminum and also appeared on a unique, one-of-a-kind Eldorado coupe built for the president of the Reynolds Aluminum Co. Also included on the production convertible were monogram plates on the doors, wire wheels and custom interior trimmings with the Cadillac crest embossed on the seat bolsters. Automatic windshield washers, power steering, 12-volt electrical system and

aluminum alloy pistons made the long standard equipment list this year. The Series 62 four-door sedan was now seven inches shorter than other models in this range. Another one-off creation was an exclusive Sedan DeVille.

1954 Cadillac, Coupe DeVille two-door hardtop coupe, V-8 (AA)

CADILLAC I.D. NUMBERS: Serial numbers and engine numbers were again one and the same. They appeared on the right-hand of the crankcase above the water pump and on the right frame side bar behind the engine support. The first two symbols were '54' for 1954. The next two symbols indicated series as follows: '62', '60' or '75'. The remaining digits represented the consecutive unit number and began with 00000 for each series. All series had the same ending number, which would be misinterpreted if listed.

SERIES 62

Model Number	Body/Style Number	Body Type & Seating	Factory Price	Shipping Weight	Production Total
54-62	6219(X)	4-dr Sed-5P	3933	4330	33,845
54-62	6219(X)	4-dr Exp Sed-5P	3933	4330	408
54-62	6219SX	4-dr Sed DeV-5P	-	-	1
54-62	6237(X)	2-dr Cpe-5P	3838	4347	17,460
54-62	6237DX	2-dr Cpe DeV-5P	4261	4409	17,170
54-62	6267X	2-dr Conv Cpe-5P	4404	4598	6,310
54-62	62	Chassis only	—	—	1

ELDORADO SPECIAL

Model Number	Body/Style Number	Body Type & Seating	Factory Price	Shipping Weight	Production Total
54-62	6267SX	2-dr Spt Conv Cpe-5P	5738	4809	2,150

NOTES: The export sedan was shipped in CKD form to foreign countries. The symbol X after Body Style Number with brackets indicates hydraulic window lifts optional equipment; without brackets indicates this feature is standard.

1954 Cadillac, Fleetwood 60 Special four-door sedan, V-8 (AA)

SERIES SIXTY SPECIAL FLEETWOOD — (V-8) — The Sixty Special sedan had luxurious Fleetwood style interior appointments. Identifiers included the traditional fender louvers, V-shaped ornaments on the hood and rear deck and a Fleetwood script in the latter location. Wheelbase measurements returned to 133 inches for the first time since 1949. Also seen were a panoramic (wraparound) windshield, new grille, longer more sweeping fenders and all other 1954-style appearance innovations. The newly expanded equipment list appeared on the 60S sedan, too.

SERIES SIXTY SPECIAL FLEETWOOD

Model Number	Body/Style Number	Body Type & Seating	Factory Price	Shipping Weight	Production Total
54-60	6019X	4-dr Sed-5P	4683	4490	16,200

SERIES 75 FLEETWOOD — (V-8) — The big Fleetwood 'high headroom' job came as an eight-passenger limousine with driver's partition or eight-passenger sedan without partition, both having jump seats. V-shaped ornaments appeared on the hood and deck with a Fleetwood script in the latter location. Wheelbase increased to 149.8 inches. Styling changes conformed with those seen on other lines.

SERIES 75 FLEETWOOD

Model Number	Body/Style Number	Body Type & Seating	Factory Price	Shipping Weight	Production Total
54-75	7523X	4-dr Sed-8P	5875	5031	889
54-75	7533X	4-dr Imp Sed-8P	6090	5093	611
54-86	8680	Commercial chassis	—	—	1,635

NOTE: The commercial chassis featured a 158 inch wheelbase and was provided to professional car makers for construction of funeral cars, ambulances, etc.

ENGINE: V-8: Overhead valves. Cast iron block. Displacement: 331 cid. Bore and stroke: 3-13/16 x 3-5/8 inches. Compression ratio: 8.25:1. Brake hp: 230 at 4400 rpm. Five main bearings. Hydraulic valve lifters. Carburetors: Carter WCFB four-barrel Models 2143S, 2109S and 2110S — also — Rochester 4GC four-barrel (with Air) Model 7006963; (without Air) Model 7006962.

CHASSIS FEATURES: Wheelbase: (Series 62) 129 inches; (Series 60S) 133 inches; (Series 75) 149.8 inches. Overall length: (Series 62 sedan) 216.4 inches; (All other 62s) 223.4 inches; (Series 60S) 227.4 inches; (Series 75) 237.1 inches. Front tread: (All) 60 inches. Rear tread: (All) 63.1 inches. Standard tires: (Series 75) 8.20 x 15; (Eldorado) 8.20 x 15 whitewalls; (Others) 8.00 x 15. Optional tires (Series 60 and 62 except 6267S) 8.20 x 15 whitewall. Dual exhaust system standard. Rear axle ratios: (Standard) 3.07: 1; (Standard with air conditioning; optional without) 3.36:1.

POWER TRAIN OPTIONS: None available.

CONVENIENCE OPTIONS: Hydra-Matic drive on Series 75 ($186). Power brakes ($48). Radio ($120). Heater ($129). Air-conditioning ($620). Power operated window and seat ($124). Chrome wire wheels ($325). White sidewall tires ($49 exchange). E-Z-Eye tinted glass. Autronic Eye automatic headlamp dimmer. Vertical front seat adjuster. Horizontal front seat adjuster (standard on Coupe DeVille, convertible, Eldorado, Series 60S and Series 75). Other standard GM options and accessories.

HISTORICAL FOOTNOTES: Assembly of 1954 models began January 4, 1954 after a 25-day halt for changeover to new production specifications. Fiberglass-bodied Cadillac show cars appearing at the GM Motorama this year included the Park Avenue four-door sedan. El Camino coupe and La Espada convertible.

1955 CADILLAC

1955 Cadillac, Coupe DeVille two-door hardtop coupe, V-8 (AA)

SERIES 62 — (V-8) — While no major appearance changes were seen on Cadillacs this year, a number of refinements were apparent. The grille was redesigned with wider spaces between the blades and the parking lamps were repositioned directly below the headlights. On the sides of the body the rub-rail moldings formed a right angle with the vertical trim on the rear doors or fenders of Series 62 and 60S models. This accentuated a character line in the sheet-metal. The Florentine curve rear window treatment was adopted for sedans. Three chrome moldings bordered the rear license plate and deck lid decorations consisted of a V-shaped ornament and a Cadillic crest. The Coupe DeVille had a golden script nameplate at the upper body belt just forward of the rear window pillar. The Eldorado sport convertible featured extras such as wide chrome body belt moldings, a distinctive rear fender design with twin round taillights halfway up the fenders and flatter. pointed tailfins. Tubeless tires were a new feature throughout the line.

CADILLAC I.D. NUMBERS: Serial numbers and engine numbers were the same again and were found in the same locations. The first two symbols were '55' to designate 1955 model production. The next two symbols indicated the series as follows: '62', '60' or '75.' The remaining digits represented the consecutive unit number and began at 00000 for each series. All series had the same ending number.

1955 Cadillac, Eldorado Biarritz convertible, V-8

SERIES 62

Model Number	Body/Style Number	Body Type & Seating	Factory Price	Shipping Weight	Production Total
55-62	6219(X)	4-dr Sed-6P	3977	4375	44,904
55-62	6219(X)	4-dr Exp Sed-6P	3977	4375	396
55-62	6237(X)	2-dr HT Cpe-6P	3882	4364	27,879
55-62	6237DX	2-dr Cpe DeV-6P	4305	4428	33,300
55-62	6267X	2-dr Conv Cpe-6P	4448	4631	8,150
55-62	62	Chassis only	—	—	7

ELDORADO SPECIAL

55-62	6267SX	2-dr Spt Conv Cpe-5P	6286	4809	3,950

NOTES: The export sedan was shipped in CKD form to foreign countries. The symbol X in brackets after Body Style Number indicates hydraulic window lifts optional; without brackets indicates this feature standard.

SERIES SIXTY SPECIAL FLEETWOOD — (V-8) — This model now had 12 vertical louvers at the rear lower side of the back fenders and continued with a Fleetwood script on the rear deck. The special 'glamour' upholstery used in the 60S was similar to the metallic thread fabric with genuine leather trim combination used in the Series 62 Coupe DeVille. Standard equipment included directional signals, back-up lights, oil bath air cleaner, automatic choke, full-pressure lubrication, 12-volt electrical system, knee-action front suspension, hypoid semi-floating rear axle, wheel discs and push-button automatic windshield washers.

SERIES SIXTY SPECIAL FLEETWOOD

Model Number	Body/Style Number	Body Type & Seating	Factory Price	Shipping Weight	Production Total
55-60	6019X	4-dr Sed-6P	4728	4545	18,300

1955 Cadillac, Fleetwood 75 limousine, V-8 (AA)

SERIES 75 FLEETWOOD — (V-8) — The trim on Fleetwood long-wheelbase models was distinctive from other lines. A horizontal rub molding ran from the front parking light housings to the trailing edge of the front door and stopped. A full-length vertical air-slot style fenderbreak molding was placed directly behind the rear gap of the back doors. The two moldings did not meet at right angles. Other styling alterations, such as grille design changes, conformed to the new 1955 themes. A Fleetwood script appeared on the deck lid. The high headroom appearance was seen again. Both models continued to feature auxiliary seats for extra passenger carrying capacity and the Imperial sedan limousine had an hydraulically operated glass driver's partition.

SERIES 75 FLEETWOOD

Model Number	Body/Style Number	Body Type & Seating	Factory Price	Shipping Weight	Production Total
55-75	7523X	4-dr Sed-7P	6187	5020	1.075
55-75	7533X	4-dr Imp Sed-8P	6402	5113	841
55-86	8680S	Commercial chassis	—	—	1,975

ENGINE: V-8. Overhead valves. Cast iron block. Displacement: 331 cid. Bore and stroke: 3.81 x 3.63 inches. Compression ratio: 9.0: 1. Brake hp: 250 at 4600 rpm. Five main bearings. Hydraulic valve lifters. Carburetors: Carter WCFB four-barrel, Models 2355S, 2354S. 2185S. 2186S, 2266S, 2267S, and 2255 — also — Rochester 4GC four-barrel, (Less air conditioning) Model 7007970; (With air conditioning) Model 7007971.

ELDORADO ENGINE: The Eldorado engine had the following changes from above specifications: Brake hp: 270 at 4800 rpm. Carburetors: Two (2) Rochester 4GC four-barrels, (front) Model 7007240; (rear, less air conditioning) Model 7007240; (rear, with air conditioning) Model 7007241.

CHASSIS FEATURES: Wheelbase: (Series 62) 129 inches; (Series 60S) 133 inches; (Series 75) 149.8 inches. Overall length: (Series 62 sedan) 216.3 inches; (Other 62s) 223.2 inches; (Series 60S) 227.3 inches; (Series 75) 237.1 inches. Front tread: (All) 60 inches. Rear tread: (All) 63.1 inches. Tires: (Series 75) 8.20 x 15 six-ply; (Eldorado) 8.20 x 15 four-ply whitewalls; (Others) 8.00 x 15. Standard dual exhausts. Rear axle ratios: (Standard) 3.36: 1; (Optional) 3.07: 1.

POWER TRAIN OPTIONS: The 270 hp Eldorado engine was available as an optional 'Power Package' in other models for $161 extra.

CONVENIENCE OPTIONS: Radio and antenna ($132). Heating and ventilation system ($129). Power brakes ($48).Four-way adjustable power seat ($70). Vertically adjustable power seat ($54). Power windows ($1O8). Air conditioning ($620). White sidewall tires. E-Z-Eye safety glass. Autronic Eye automatic headlamp dimmer. Other standard GM options and accessories available.

HISTORICAL FOOTNOTES: Standard equipment on the Eldorado special sport convertible included customized interior and rear body styling; 270 hp dual four-barrel inducted V-8; radio and antenna; heater; power brakes; power seat; power windows; whitewall tires; metal tonneau cover; custom trim and ornamentation; individual circular tail and rear directional lights and saber-spoke wheels. The 1955 Eldorado is a certified Milestone Car. The Park Avenue sedan, a futuristic show car which became the predecessor to the Eldorado Brougham, appeared at the New York Motorama on January 19, 1955. It was built in less than 74 days! Another show car seen this year was the Celebrity hardtop coupe. MOTOR TREND magazine reported fuel consumption figures of 12.9 miles per gallon (stop-and-go) for a Series 62 sedan with the standard 250 hp V-8. Total 1955 model year output reached 140,777 units, a new record high for Cadillac Division.

1956 CADILLAC

SERIES 62 — (V-8) — Although a facelift was the major restyling news for 1956, there were still many changes in the Series 62 lineup and especially in the Eldorado sub-series. The annual 'beauty treatment' consisted of a new grille with finer textured insert and the repositioning of parking lights in the bumper, below the wing guards. Buyers were given a choice of a standard satin finish grille or optional gold finish, both selections decorated with Cadillac script on the left-hand side. On the rear side fenders of Series 62 models a narrow chrome molding and nine vertical louvers were seen. The Coupe DeVille had a model nameplate and Cadillac crest on the sides of front fenders, while the more standard cars had only the crest. An Eldorado script appeared, with a fender crest on the luxury convertible, which also featured a twin-fin hood ornament. Other extras on this car — now known as the Biarritz — were a ribbed chrome saddle molding extending from the windshield to the rear window pillar along the beltline and flat, pointed rear fender fins. Totally new models included a pillarless four-door called the Sedan DeVille and an Eldorado Coupe Seville. The latter represented an especially luxurious hardtop coupe, which was built to Eldorado standards and similarly priced. As usual, the standard four-door 62 sedan was seven inches shorter than the other cars in the same series. Both cars in the Eldorado sub-series were slightly longer this year.

1956 Cadillac, Eldorado Seville two-door hardtop, V-8 (AA)

CADILLAC I.D. NUMBERS: Serial numbers and engine numbers were the same again and were found in the same locations. The first two symbols were '56' to designate 1956 model production. The next two symbols indicated the series as follows: '62', '60' or '75.' The remaining digits represented the consecutive unit number and began at 00000 for each series. All series had the same ending number.

1956 Cadillac, Series 62 four-door sedan, V-8

SERIES 62

Model Number	Body/Style Number	Body Type & Seating	Factory Price	Shipping Weight	Production Total
55-62	6219(X)	4-dr Sed-6P	4241	4430	26,222
55-62	6219(X)	4-dr Exp Sed-6P	4241	4430	444
55-62	6239DX	4-dr Sed DeV-6P	4698	4550	41,732
55-62	6237(X)	2-dr HT Cpe-6P	4146	4420	26,649
55-62	6237DX	2-dr Cpe DeV-6P	4569	4445	25,086
55-62	6267X	2-dr Conv Cpe-6P	4711	4645	8,300
55-62	62	Chassis only	—	—	19

ELDORADO (SUB-SERIES)

Model Number	Body/Style Number	Body Type & Seating	Factory Price	Shipping Weight	Production Total
55-62	6237DX	4-dr Cpe Sev-6P	6501	4665	3,900
55-62	6267SX	2-dr Conv Biarritz-6P	6501	4880	2,150

NOTE: The symbol X in brackets after Body Style Number indicates hydraulic window lifts optional; without brackets indicates this feature standard.

SERIES SIXTY SPECIAL FLEETWOOD — (V-8) — Cadillac's non-limousine style Fleetwood model carried the Sixty Special designation in script below the Cadillac crest on the sides of the front fenders. A Fleetwood name also appeared on the rear face of the deck lid. Solid chrome extension trim moldings were seen on the rear fenders.

SERIES SIXTY SPECIAL FLEETWOOD

Model Number	Body/Style Number	Body Type & Seating	Factory Price	Shipping Weight	Production Total
55-62	6019X	4-dr Sed-6P	6019	4992	17,000

SERIES 75 FLEETWOOD — (V-8) — Side trim on the long-wheelbase Fleetwood models was about the same as 1955, except for the addition of exhaust extension moldings on the rear fender. This trim ran along a tapering conical flare from above the wheel housing to the rear bumper. A Fleetwood script appeared on the deck lid and limousine styling was seen again. Changes in grilles and bumpers conformed to those used with other series. Both models had auxiliary seats and the Imperial sedan again featured a glass driver's partition. Standard equipment on all Cadillacs was comparable to that included the previous year.

SERIES 75 FLEETWOOD

Model Number	Body/Style Number	Body Type & Seating	Factory Price	Shipping Weight	Production Total
55-75	7523X	4-dr Sed-7P	6558	5050	1095
55-75	7533X	4-dr Imp Sed-8P	6773	5130	955
55-86	8680S	Commercial chassis	—	—	2,025

NOTE: The commercial chassis featured a 158 inch wheelbase and was provided to makers of professional cars for construction of funeral cars and ambulances, etc.

ENGINES: STANDARD V-8: Overhead valves. Cast iron block. Displacement: 365 cid. Bore and stroke: 4.0 x 3.63 inches. Compression ratio 9.75:1. hp rating: 285 at 4600 rpm. Five main bearings. Hydraulic valve lifters. Carburetor: Carter WCFB four-barrel, Model 2370S.

ELDORADO V-8: The Eldorado engine had the following changes from the above specifications: Brake hp: 305 at 4700 rpm. Carburetors: Two (2) Carter WCFB four-barrel. Model 2371 S.

CHASSIS FEATURES: Wheelbase: (Series 62) 129 inches; (Series 60S) 133 inches; (Series 75) 149.75 inches. Overall length: (Eldorados) 222.2 inches; (Series 62 sedan) 214.9 inches; (Other 62s) 221.9 inches; (Series 60S) 225.9 inches; (Series 75) 235.7 inches. Front tread: (All) 60 inches. Rear tread: (All) 63.1 inches. Tires: (Series 75) 8.20 x 15 black; (Eldorado) 8.20 x 15 whitewall; (Others) 8.00 x 15. Standard dual exhausts.

POWER TRAIN OPTIONS: The 305 hp Eldorado engine was available in other models at extra cost.

CONVENIENCE OPTIONS: Air conditioning. White sidewall tires. E-Z-Eye safety glass. Autronic eye automatic headlamp dimmer. Signal-seeking radio with preselector and antenna. Heating and ventilation system. Power window lifts (specific models). Gold finish grille. Two-way posture power seat ($81). Six-way power seat ($97). Other standard GM accessories available. (Note: Posture power adjustable seat on convertible, DeVilles and Series 60S only. Six-way seat on 62 Coupe and sedan and standard for Eldorado).

HISTORICAL FOOTNOTES: The Cadillac Series 62 Sedan DeVille four-door hardtop and Eldorado Seville two-door hardtop were introduced to the public almost a month earlier than other models on October 24, 1955. The remaining cars in the line were introduced the following month on November 18. The 1956 Hydra-Matic transmission incorporated changes that increased its size and smoothed out shifting qualities. It was developed by GM at a cost of $35 million. The 1956 line set records in sales and production moving Cadillac from 10th to ninth position in the American sales race. On Aug. 5, 1956 the division announced the purchase of the former Hudson Motor Car plant on Detroit's east end.

1957 CADILLAC

SERIES 62 — (V-8) — For 1957 Cadillac adopted a tubular X-frame, without side rails, on all models. This resulted in greater structural rigidity and provided for lower body lines without loss of useable space. New front end styling was marked by rubber bumper guard tips and dual, circular parking lamps set into the lower bumper section. Side trim was revised and a dual taillight theme was used throughout the line. By utilizing different center frame sections the wheelbases and overall lengths of specific body styles was altered. In the 62 lineup, including the Eldorado sub-series, three different overall measurements appeared on cars with matching wheelbases. The Sedan DeVille was bigger than 'standard' models and the Eldorado Coupe Seville and Biarritz convertible were larger still. Identifying the 'standard' 62 models were vertical bright metal moldings, just forward of the rear wheel openings, highlighted by seven horizontal windsplits. At the upper end this fenderbreak trim joined a horizontal molding that ran along a conical flare extending forward from the taillamps. A crest medallion was seen on the forward angled rear fins. Coupe DeVilles and Sedan DeVilles had special nameplates on the front fenders. Eldorados were further distinguished by the model name above a V-shaped rear deck ornament and on the front fenders. The rear fender and deck contour was sleekly rounded and the wheel housing was trimmed with broad, sculptured stainless steel beauty panels. Also seen were pointed, 'shark' style fins pointing towards the back of the cars. A three-section built-in front bumper was another exclusive trait of the two luxury cars, which came with a long list of standard accessories.

1957 Cadillac, Series 62 convertible, V-8 (AA)

CADILLAC I.D. NUMBERS: Serial numbers and engine numbers were the same again. They appeared on a boss on the front right-hand face of the engine block; on the lubrication plate on the left front door pillar (1953-1957) and on the right frame side member behind the motor support. The first pair of symbols were '57' to designate the model year. The next two symbols

indicated series as follows: '62', '60', '70' and '75.' The immediately following numbers, beginning at 00000 for each series, indicated the production sequence in consecutive order. Ending numbers were the same for all series since the engines were installed in mixed production fashion.

1957 Cadillac, Eldorado Biarritz convertible, V-8 (AA)

SERIES 62

Model Number	Body/Style Number	Body Type & Seating	Factory Price	Shipping Weight	Production Total
57-62	6239(X)	4-dr HT Sed-6P	4713	4595	32,342
57-62	6239(X)	4-dr Exp Sed-6P	4713	4595	384
57-62	6239DX	4-dr DeV HT-6P	5188	4655	23,808
57-62	6237(X)	2-dr HT Cpe-6P	4609	4565	25,120
57-62	6237DX	2-dr Cpe DeV-6P	5048	4620	23,813
57-62	6267X	2-dr Conv Cpe-6P	5225	4730	9,000
57-62	62	Chassis only	—	—	1

SERIES 62 ELDORADO SPECIALS

Model Number	Body/Style Number	Body Type & Seating	Factory Price	Shipping Weight	Production Total
57-62	6237SDX	2-dr Cpe Sev-6P	7286	4810	2,100
57-62	6267SX	2-dr Biarritz Conv-6P	7286	4930	1,800
57-62	6239SX	4-dr Sed Sev-6P	—	—	4

NOTES: The export sedan was shipped in CKD form to foreign countries. The Eldorado Sedan Seville was a special order model built in limited quantities. The symbol 'X' after Body Style Number in brackets indicates power windows optional; without brackets indicates this feature standard.

1957 Cadillac, Fleetwood 60 Special four-door hardtop, V-8 (AA)

SERIES SIXTY SPECIAL FLEETWOOD — (V-8) — The 60S Fleetwood long-deck four-door hardtop sedan featured a wide, ribbed bright metal fairing extending from the lower rear half of the door to the back bumper. A Fleetwood nameplate appeared on the rear deck lid, which also housed the back-up lamps on this car.

SERIES SIXTY SPECIAL FLEETWOOD

Model Number	Body/Style Number	Body Type & Seating	Factory Price	Shipping Weight	Production Total
57-60	6039	4-dr HT Sed-6P	5539	4755	24,000

1957 Cadillac, Eldorado Brougham four-door hardtop, V-8 (AA)

SERIES 70 ELDORADO BROUGHAM — (V-8) — Announced in December, 1956 and released around March, 1957, the Eldorado Brougham was a hand-built, limited-edition four-door hardtop sedan derived from the Park Avenue and Orleans show cars of 1953-1954. Designed by Ed Glowacke, the Brougham featured America's first completely pillarless four-door body styling. Even ventipanes were absent. The Brougham was further distinguished by a brushed stainless steel roof, the first appearance of quad headlights and totally unique trim. The exterior ornamentation included wide, ribbed lower rear quarter beauty panels (extending

along the full rocker sills) and a rectangularly sculptured side body 'cove' highlighted with five horizontal windsplits on the rear doors. Tail styling treatments followed the Eldorado theme and 'suicide' type hanging was used for the rear doors. Standard equipment included all possible accessories such as a dual four-barrel V-8; air-suspension; low-profile tires with thin whitewalls; automatic trunk lid opener; automatic 'memory' seat; Cruise Control; high-pressure cooling system; polarized sun visors; Signal-Seeking twin speaker radio; electric antenna; automatic-release parking brake; electric door locks; dual heating system; silver magnetized glovebox drink tumblers; cigarette and tissue dispensers; lipstick and cologne; ladies' compact with powder puff, mirror and matching leather notebook, comb and mirror; Arpege atomizer with Lanvin perfume; automatic starter (with re-start function); Autronic-Eye; drum-type electric clock; power windows; forged aluminum wheels and air conditioning. Buyers of Broughams had a choice of 44 full leather interior trim combinations and could select such items as Mouton, Karakul or lambskin carpeting.

SERIES 70 ELDORADO BROUGHAM

Model Number	Body/Style Number	Body Type & Seating	Factory Price	Shipping Weight	Production Total
57-70	7059X	4-dr HT Sed-6P	13,074	5315	400

SERIES 75 FLEETWOOD — (V-8) — Long-wheelbase Cadillacs came in Fleetwood limousine or nine-passenger sedan configurations, both with auxiliary seats. Side trim was the same as on Series 62 models, except that no Cadillac crest was used on the rear fins.

SERIES 75 FLEETWOOD

Model Number	Body/Style Number	Body Type & Seating	Factory Price	Shipping Weight	Production Total
57-75	7523X	4-dr Sed-9P	7348	5340	1,010
57-75	7533X	4-dr Imp Sed-9P	7586	5390	890
57-86	8680S	Commercial chassis	—	—	2,169

NOTE: The commercial chassis featured a 156 inch wheelbase and was provided to professional car makers for construction of funeral cars and ambulances, etc.

ENGINES: STANDARD V-8: Overhead valves. Cast iron block. Displacement: 365 cid. Bore and stroke: 4.00 x 3.625 inches. Compression ratio: 10.0:1. Brake hp: 300 at 4800 rpm. Five main bearings. Hydraulic valve lifters. Carburetor: Rochester fourbarrel Model 7015701.

ELDORADO V-8: Overhead valves. Cast iron block. Displacement: 365 cid. Bore and stroke: 4.00 x 3.625. Compression ratio: 10.0:1. Brake hp: 325 at 4800 rpm. Five main bearings. Hydraulic valve lifters. Carburetors: Two (2) Carter four-barrel (Front) Model 2584S; (Rear) Model 2583S.

CHASSIS FEATURES: Wheelbase: (Series 62) 129.5 inches; (Series 60S) 133 inches; (Series 70) 126 inches; (Series 75) 149.7 inches. Overall length: (Series 62 sedans) 215.9 inches; (Series 62 coupes and convertibles) 220.9 inches; (Series 62 Eldorados) 222.1 inches; (Series 60S) 224.4 inches; (Series 70) 216.3 inches; (Series 75) 236.2 inches. Front and rear tread: (All models) 61 inches. Tires: (Series 75) 8.20 x 15 six-ply blackwall; (Series 62 Eldorados) 8.20 x 15 whitewalls; (Series 70) 8.40 x 15 high-speed type; (Other models) 8.00 x 15 blackwall. Standard dual exhausts.

POWERTRAIN OPTIONS: The 325 hp Eldorado Brougham dual four-barrel V-8 was optional on the Eldorado Seville and Biarritz only. In normal attachments on these models the front carburetor was changed to a Carter four-barrel Model 258S. When air conditioning was also installed the front carburetor was the same model use in the Brougham, which came standard with air conditioning.

CONVENIENCE ACCESSORIES: Hydra-Matic drive, power steering and power brakes were standard in all Cadillacs. Many models (designated by non-bracketed 'X' suffix in charts above) also had standard power window lifts. Fore-and-Aft power seats were standard on the same models. Six-Way power seats were regularly featured on Eldorados and Sixty Specials. Air-conditioning, radios, heaters, etc. were optional on most other models (standard in Brougham) along with regular GM factory and dealer installed extras.

HISTORICAL FOOTNOTES: The 1957 Eldorado Brougham was designed to compete with the Lincoln-Continental Mark II. The new dual quad headlamps seen on the Brougham were illegal in some states during 1957. The Brougham air suspension system proved unreliable and Cadillac later released a kit to convert cars to rear coil spring type suspension. This makes Broughams with the feature rarer and more valuable today. The Brougham is a certified Milestone Car. Series 62 sedans were short-deck models with trunks five inches shorter than 60S sedans. Ball joint suspension was a new technical feature adopted this year. Model year sales amounted to 146,841 deliveries earning Cadillac Division ninth industry ranking for two years in a row.

1958 Cadillac, Park Avenue four-door hardtop, V-8 (AA)

SERIES 62 — (V-8) — Cadillacs for 1958 were basically carryover models with a facelift on all but the Brougham. There was a new grille featuring multiple round 'cleats' at the intersection of horizontal and vertical members. The grille insert was wider and the bumper guards were positioned lower to the parking lamps. New dual headlamps were seen throughout all lines and small chrome fins decorated front fenders. Tailfins were a bit less pronounced and trim attachments were revised. The word Cadillac appeared, in block letters, on the fins of Series 62 base models. On the sides of the cars there were five longer horizontal windsplits ahead of the unskirted rear wheel housings; front fender horizontal moldings with crests placed above at the trailing edge and no rocker sill trim. The convertible, Coupe DeVille and Sedan DeVille used solid metal trim on the lower half of the conical projectile flares, while other models had a thin ridge molding in the same location. On Series 62 Eldorados, a V-shaped ornament and model identification script were mounted to the deck lid. The two luxury Cadillacs also had 10 vertical chevron slashes ahead of the open rear wheel housings and crest medallions on the flanks of tailfins. Broad, sculptured beauty panels decorated the lower rear quarters on Eldorados and extended around the wheel opening to stretch along the body sills. Standard equipment was the same as the previous year. All new was an extended deck Series 62 sedan, which was 8.5 inches longer than other models.

1958 Cadillac, Eldorado Biarritz convertible, V-8 (AA)

CADILLAC I.D. NUMBERS: Serial numbers now used a three symbol prefix. The first pair of numerical symbols '58' designated model year. A one-letter alphabetical code (included as part of model number in charts below) indicated model and series. Each prefix was followed by the consecutive unit number which started at 000001 and up. The serial number was located at the front of the left-hand frame side bar. Motor serial numbers again matched and were found on the center left-hand side of the block above the oil pan.

SERIES 62

Model Number	Body/Style Number	Body Type & Seating	Factory Price	Shipping Weight	Production Total
58K-62	6239(X)	4-dr HT Sed-6P	4891	4675	13,335
58K-62	6239(X)	4-dr Exp Sed-6P	4891	4675	204
58N-62	6239E(X)	4-dr Ext Sed-6P	5079	4770	20,952
58L-62	6239EDX	4-dr Sed DeV-6P	5497	4855	23,989
58G-62	6237(X)	2-dr HT Cpe-6P	4784	4630	18,736
58J-62	6237DX	2-dr Cpe DeV-6P	5231	4705	18,414
58F-62	6267X	2-dr Conv Cpe-6P	5454	4845	7,825
58-62	62	Chassis only	—	—	1

SERIES 62 ELDORADO SPECIAL

Model Number	Body/Style Number	Body Type & Seating	Factory Price	Shipping Weight	Production Total
58H-62	6237SDX	2-dr Cpe Sev-6P	7500	4910	855
58E-62	6267SX	2-dr Biarritz Conv-6P	7500	5070	815
58-62	6267SSX	2-dr Spl Eldo Cpe-6P	—	—	1

NOTES: The export sedan was shipped in CKD form to foreign countries. The Special Eldorado Coupe was special order model built in limited quantities. Five specially equipped Eldorado Biarritz convertibles were also built (See historical footnotes for details). The symbol 'X', in brackets after Body Style Number, indicates power windows and seat optional; without brackets indicates these features are standard. Style Number 6239E(X) is the new Extended Deck Sedan (Listed above as 4-dr Ext Sed-6P).

SERIES SIXTY SPECIAL FLEETWOOD — (V-8) — The Sixty Special was very distinctive and rich-looking this year. Broad ribbed stainless steel fairings decorated the entire rear quarter panel, below the conical flare. Even the fender skirts featured this type of trim, which extended fully forward along the body sills. Sixty Special scripts appeared on the sides of the tailfins and a Fleetwood script nameplate adorned the rear deck lid. Standard equipment included Hydra-Matic, power brakes, power steering, power windows and fore-and aft power front seat.

SERIES SIXTY SPECIAL FLEETWOOD

Model Number	Body/Style Number	Body Type & Seating	Factory Price	Shipping Weight	Production Total
58M-60	6039X	4-dr HT Sed-6P	6232	4930	12,900

SERIES 70 FLEETWOOD ELDORADO BROUGHAM — (V-8) — The major change for the Eldorado Brougham was seen inside the car. The interior upper door panels were now finished in leather instead of the metal finish used in 1957. New wheelcovers also appeared. Forty-four trim combinations were available, along with 15 special monotone paint colors. This was the last year for domestic production of the handbuilt Brougham at Cadillac's Detroit factory, as future manufacturing of the special bodies was transferred to Pininfarina of Turin, Italy.

SERIES 70 FLEETWOOD ELDORADO BROUGHAM

Model Number	Body/Style Number	Body Type & Seating	Factory Price	Shipping Weight	Production Total
58P-70	7059X	4-dr HT Sed-6P	13.074	5,315	304

1958 Cadillac, Fleetwood 75 limousine, V-8 (AA)

SERIES 75 FLEETWOOD — (V-8) — The limousine or nine-passenger long-wheelbase sedans were available once again, both with auxiliary seats and the same basic side trim as Series 62 models.

SERIES 75 FLEETWOOD

Model Number	Body/Style Number	Body Type & Seating	Factory Price	Shipping Weight	Production Total
58R-75	7523X	4-dr Sed-9P	8460	5360	802
58S-75	4533X	4-dr Imp Sed-9P	8675	5475	730
58-86	8680S	Commercial chassis	—	—	1,915

NOTE: The commercial chassis features a 156 inch wheelbase and was provided to professional car makers for construction of funeral cars and ambulances, etc.

ENGINE: STANDARD V-8: Overhead valves. Cast iron block. Displacement: 365 cid. Bore and stroke: 4 x 3.625 inches. Compression ratio: 10.25:1. Brake hp: 310 at 4800 rpm.. Five main bearings. Hydraulic valve lifters. Carburetor: Carter AFB four-barrel Model 2862S.

ENGINE: Same general specifications as above except for following changes: Brake hp: 355 at 4800 rpm.. Carburetors: Three (3) Rochester two-barrel Model 7015801.

1958 Cadillac, Fleetwood 60 Special four-door hardtop, V-8 (AA)

CHASSIS FEATURES: Wheelbase: (Series 62) 129.5 inches: (Series 60S) 133 inches; (Series 70) 126 inches; (Series 75) 149.7 inches. Overall length: (58K) 216.8 inches; (58G, 58J and 58F) 221.8 inches; (58N and 58L) 225.3 inches; (58M) 225.3 inches; (58H and 58E) 223.4 inches; (58R and 58S) 237.1 inches. Front and rear tread: (All Models) 61 inches. Tires: (Series 75) 8.20 x 15 six-ply blackwall; (Series 62 Eldorados) 8.20 x 15 whitewalls; (Series 70) 8.40 x 15 high-speed thin whitewalls; (Other models) 8.00 x 15 blackwalls.

POWERTRAIN OPTIONS: The 335 hp Eldorado engine with triple two barrel carburetion was used on all Eldorados as standard equipment. This engine was also optional for all other Cadillacs. See 1958 Cadillac Series 62 Eldorado engine data for specifications.

CONVENIENCE ACCESSORIES: Radio with antenna and rear speaker ($164). Radio with rear speaker and remote control on Series 75 only ($246). Automatic heating system for Series 75 ($179); for other models ($129). Posture seat adjuster ($81). Six Way seat adjuster ($103). Power window regulators ($108). E-Z-Eye Glass ($46). Fog lamps ($41). Automatic headlamp beam control ($48). Five (5) sabre spoke wheels ($350). White sidewall 8.20 x 15 four-ply tires ($55). Gold finish grille on Eldorado (no charge); on other models ($27). Four-door door guards ($7). Two-door door guards ($4). Remote control trunk lock ($43). License plate frame ($8). Air conditioning ($474). Series 75 air conditioner ($625). Eldorado engine in lower models ($134). Air suspension ($214). Electric door locks on coupes ($35); on sedans ($57). Local dealer options: Utility kit ($15). Monogram ($12). Blue Coral waxing ($25). Under-coating ($5). Lubrication agreement ($34).

HISTORICAL FOOTNOTES: Five special Eldorado Biarritz convertibles were built with completely automatic top riser mechanisms and metal tonneaus and incorporated humidity sensors which activated the top riser mechanism in case of rain. These cars had four place bucket seating and custom leather interior trims including driveshaft tunnel coverings. The 1958 Eldorado Brougham is a certified Milestone Car.

1959 CADILLAC

SERIES 6200 — (V-8) — No single automotive design better characterizes the industry's late '50s flamboyance than the 1959 Cadillac, which incorporated totally new styling. Large tailfins, twin bullet taillamps, two distinctive rooflines and roof pillar configurations, new jewel-like grille patterns and matching deck latch lid beauty panels personified these cars. The former 62 line was now commonly called the 6200 Series and was actually comprised of three sub-series, all with similar wheelbases and lengths. Each will be treated individually here. The five base models were identified by their straight body rub moldings, running from front wheel openings to back bumpers, with crest medallions below the tip of the spear. A one-deck jeweled rear grille insert was seen. Standard equipment included power brakes; power steering; automatic transmission; dual back-up lamps; windshield washers and two-speed wipers; wheel discs; outside rearview mirror; vanity mirror and oil filter. The convertible also had power windows and a Two-Way power seat. Plain fender skirts covered rear wheels and sedans were available in four-window (4W) and six-window (6W) configurations.

1959 Cadillac, Series 62 four-door 6-window hardtop, V-8 (AA)

CADILLAC I.D. NUMBERS: The motor serial number system adopted in 1958 was used again with numbers in the same locations. The first pair of symbols changed to '59' to designate model year. The third symbol (a letter listed as a Body Style Number suffix in charts below) identified model and series. Consecutive unit numbers began at 000001 and up.

SERIES 6200

Model Number	Body/Style Number	Body Type & Seating	Factory Price	Shipping Weight	Production Total
59-62	6229K	4-dr 6W Sed-6P	5080	4835	23,461
59-62	6229K	4-dr Exp 6W Sed-6P	5080	4835	60
59-62	6239A	4-dr 4W Sed-6P	5080	4770	14,138
59-62	6237G	2-dr HT Cpe-6P	4892	4690	21,947
59-62	6267F	2-dr Conv Cpe-6P	5455	4855	11,130

NOTES: The Export Sedan was shipped in CKD form to foreign countries and is indicated by the abbreviation Exp 6W Sed.

DEVILLE SUB-SERIES 6300 — (V-8) — The DeVille models, two sedans and a coupe, had script nameplates on the rear fenders, thus eliminating the use of the front fender crest medallions. They were trimmed like 6200s otherwise. The DeVilles also had all of the same standard equipment listed for 6200s, plus power windows and Two-Way power seats.

DEVILLE SUB-SERIES 6300

Model Number	Body/Style Number	Body Type & Seating	Factory Price	Shipping Weight	Production Total
59-63	6329L	4-dr 6W Sed-6P	5498	4850	19,158
59-63	6339B	4-dr 4W Sed-6P	5498	4825	12,308
59-63	6337J	2-dr Cpe-6P	5252	4720	21,924

SERIES 6200 AND 6300 ENGINES

V-8: Overhead valves: Cast iron block. Displacement: 390 cid. Bore and stroke: 4 x 3.875 inches. Compression ratio: 10.5:1. Brake hp: 325 at 4800 rpm.. Five main bearings. Hydraulic valve lifters. Carburetor: Carter AFB four-barrel Model 2814S.

1959 Cadillac, Eldorado Biarritz convertible, V-8 (AA)

SUB-SERIES 6400/6900 ELDORADO/BROUGHAM — (V-8) — As if to cause confusion, the 6400 Eldorado Sub-series included two 6400 models, the Seville and Biarritz, and one 6900 model, the Brougham. (Whoever said automakers are logical?) All were characterized by a three-deck, jeweled, rear grille insert, but other trim and equipment features varied. The Seville and Biarritz had the Eldorado model name spelled out below the front wheel opening and featured broad, full-length body sill highlights which curved over the rear fender profile and back along the upper beltline region. Standard equipment included all items found on DeVilles plus, heater; fog lamps; 345 hp V-8; remote control deck lid; radio with antenna and rear speaker; power vent windows; Six-Way power seat; air suspension; electric door locks and license frames. The Brougham was now incorporated into the line as an Italian-bodied, limited production car. A vertical crest medallion with Brougham script plate appeared on the front fenders and a single, thin molding ran from front to rear along the mid-sides of the body. Styling on this car was not as radical as in the past and predicted the 1960 themes used on other Cadillacs. The standard equipment list was pared down to match those of other Eldorados, plus Cruise Control, Autronic Eye, air conditioning and E-Z-Eye glass.

1959 Cadillac, Eldorado Brougham four-door hardtop, V-8 (AA)

SUB-SERIES 6400/6900 ELDORADO/BROUGHAM

Model Number	Body/Style Number	Body Type & Seating	Factory Price	Shipping Weight	Production Total
59-64	6437H	2-dr Sev HT-6P	7401	4855	975
59-64	6467E	2-dr Biarritz Conv-6P	7401	5060	1,320
59-69	6929P	4-dr Brougham HT-6P	13075	—	99

SERIES SIXTY SPECIAL FLEETWOOD — (V-8) — On this line Fleetwood lettering was used on the front fenders and on the trim strip crossing the bottom of the deck lid. A rear facing, bullet-shaped, scoop-like convex panel was used on the rear doors and fenders and was trimmed by a similarly shaped body rub molding that extended to the front wheel well, at the bottom, and to the headlamps, at the top. Pillared, six window styling was seen and a three-deck jeweled rear grille was featured. The rear wheels were skirted and wheelbase was now identical to all but the 'Seventy-Five' models. The standard equipment list included all 6200 and 6300 features plus, power front windows and dual outside mirrors.

SERIES SIXTY SPECIAL FLEETWOOD

Model Number	Body/Style Number	Body Type & Seating	Factory Price	Shipping Weight	Production Total
59-60	6029M	4-dr HT Sed-6P	6233	4890	12,250

SERIES 6700 FLEETWOOD 75 — (V-8) — The long wheelbase Fleetwoods were still called Seventy-Fives, although a new numerical series designation was in official use. Production models again were a nine-passenger sedan and Imperial sedan/limousine with auxiliary jump seats. Fleetwood lettering appeared on the rear deck lid trim strip. Single side trim moldings extended from the front wheel housing to the rear of the car. Standard equipment included all items found on the Sixty Special Fleetwood line.

SERIES 6700 FLEETWOOD 75

Model Number	Body/Style Number	Body Type & Seating	Factory Price	Shipping Weight	Production Total
59-67	6723R	4-dr Sed-9P	9533	5490	710
59-67	6733S	4-dr Imp Sed-9P	9748	5570	690
59-68	6890	Commercial chassis	—	—	2,102

NOTE: The commercial chassis featured a 156 inch wheelbase and was provided to professional car makers for construction of funeral cars and ambulances, etc.

SERIES 6400/6900 ELDORADO/BROUGHAM ENGINE

V-8: Overhead valves. Cast iron block. Displacement: 390 cid. Bore and stroke: 4 x 3.875 inches. Compression ratio: 10.5:1. Brake hp: 345 at 4800 rpm.. Five main bearings. Hydraulic valve lifters. Carburetion: Three (3) Rochester two-barrel Model 7015901.

CHASSIS FEATURES: Wheelbase: (Series 75) 149.75 inches; (All others) 130 inches. Overall length: (Series 75) 244.8 inches; (All others) 225 inches. Tires: (Eldorados and Series 75) 8.20 x 15; (All others) 8.00 x 15. Dual exhausts standard. Rear axle ratios: (Series 75) 3.36:1 standard; 3.77:1 optional; 3.21:1 with air conditioning: (All others) 2.94:1 standard; 3.21:1 optional or mandatory with air conditioning.

POWER TRAIN OPTIONS: The 345 hp Eldorado V-8 was optional on all other Cadillacs at $134.30 extra.

CONVENIENCE OPTIONS: Radio with rear speaker ($165). Radio with rear speaker and remote control ($247). Automatic heating system on Series 75 ($179); on other models ($129). Six-Way power seat on 6200s, except convertible ($188). Six-Way power seat on 60-6300-6400 and 6200 convertible ($89). Power window regulators ($73). Power vent regulators ($73). Air conditioning, on Series 75 ($624); on other models ($474). Air suspension ($215). Autronic Eye ($55). Cruise Control ($97). Electric door locks, on two-doors ($46); on four-doors ($70). E-Z-Eye glass ($52). Fog lamps ($46). White sidewall tires 8.20 x 15 four-ply ($57 exchange); 8.20 x 15 six-ply ($65 exchange). Door guards on four-doors ($7) on two-doors ($4). Remote control trunk lock ($59). License plate frame ($8). Local options: Utility kit ($15); Monogram ($12). Acrylic Lustre finish ($20). Undercoating ($25). Radio foot switch ($10). Gas cap lock ($4). Pair of rugs for front ($8); for rear ($5). Note: Bucket seats were a no-cost option on the Biarritz convertible.

HISTORICAL FOOTNOTES: Assembly of 142,272 units was counted for the 1959 model year. This was the next to last season for selling the Brougham. Flat-top roof styling was used on four-window sedans; six-window jobs had sloping rooflines with rear ventipanes. Power steering and shock absorbers were improved this year.

1960 CADILLAC

SERIES 6200 — (V-8) — The 1960 Cadillacs exhibited a smoother, more subtle rendition of the styling theme introduced one year earlier. General changes included a full-width grille; the elimination of pointed front bumper guards; increased restraint in the application of chrome trim; lower tailfins with oval shaped nacelles (which enclosed stacked taillights and back-up lamps) and front fender mounted directional indicator lamps. Series 6200 base models had

plain fender skirts, thin three-quarter length bodyside spears and Cadillac crests and lettering on short horizontal front fender bars mounted just behind the headlights. Four-window (4W) and six-window (6W) sedans were offered again. The former featured a one-piece wraparound backlight and flat-top roof, while the latter had a sloping rear window and roofline. Standard equipment on 6200 models included power brakes; power steering; automatic transmission; dual back-up lamps; windshield washers and dual speed wipers; wheel discs; outside rearview mirror; and oil filter. Added extras on convertibles included power windows and Two-Way power seats. Technical highlights were comprised of finned rear drums, a vacuum operated automatic-releasing floor controlled parking brake and tubular X-frame construction. Interiors were done in Fawn, Blue or Gray Cortina Cord or Turquoise, Green, Persian Sand or Black Caspian cloth with Florentine vinyl bolsters. Convertibles were upholstered in Florentine leather single or two-tone combinations or monochromatic Cardiff leather combinations.

1960 Cadillac, Series 62 convertible, V-8 (AA)

CADILLAC I.D. NUMBERS: Motor serial numbers took the same form used in 1959 with the first pair of symbols changed to '60' to indicate 1960 model year. The applicable codes were stamped in the same locations on cars.

SERIES 6200

Model Number	Body/Style Number	Body Type & Seating	Factory Price	Shipping Weight	Production Total
60-62K	6229K	4-dr 6W Sed-6P	5080	4805	26,824
60-62K	6229K	4-dr Exp 6W Sed-6P	5080	4805	36
60-62A	6239A	4-dr 4W Sed-6P	5080	4775	9,984
60-62G	6237G	2-dr HT Cpe-6P	4892	4670	19,978
60-62F	6267F	2-dr Conv-6P	5455	4850	14,000
60-62( )	62	Chassis only	—	—	2

NOTE: The Export (Exp) six-window sedan was shipped in CKD form to foreign countries. All sedans were pillarless hardtop sedans.

DEVILLE SUB-SERIES 6300 — (V-8) — Models in the DeVille sub-series were trimmed much like 6200s, but there was no bar medallion on the front fenders and special script nameplates appeared on the rear fenders. Standard equipment included all base model features, plus power windows and Two-Way power seat. Interiors were done in Chadwick cloth or optional Cambray cloth and leather combinations.

DEVILLE SUB-SERIES 6300

Model Number	Body/Style Number	Body Type & Seating	Factory Price	Shipping Weight	Production Total
60-63	6329L	4-dr 6W Sed-6P	5498	4835	22,579
60-638	6339B	4-dr 4W Sed-6P	5498	4815	9,225
60-63J	6337J	2-dr HT Cpe-6P	5252	4705	21,585

NOTE: All DeVille sedans were pillarless hardtop sedans.

1960 Cadillac, Eldorado Seville two-door hardtop, V-8 (AA)

ELDORADO/BROUGHAM SUB-SERIES 6400/6900 — (V-8) — External variations on the Seville two-door hardtop and Biarritz convertible coupe took the form of bright body sill highlights that extended across the lower edge of fender skirts and Eldorado lettering on the sides of front fenders, just behind the headlamps. Standard equipment was the same as on 6300 models, plus heater; fog lamps; Eldorado engine; remote control trunk lock; radio with antenna and rear speaker; power vent windows; Six-Way power seat; air suspension; electric door locks; license frames; and five whitewall tires. A textured vinyl fabric top was offered on the Eldorado Seville and interior trim choices included cloth and leather combinations. The Brougham continued as an Italian-bodied four-door hardtop with special Brougham nameplates above the grille. It did not sport Eldorado front fender letters or body sill highlights, but had a distinctive squared-off roofline with rear ventipanes — a prediction of 1961 styling motifs for the entire Cadillac line. A fin-like crease, or 'skeg', ran from behind the front wheel opening to the rear of the car on the extreme lower bodysides and there were special vertical crest medallions on the trailing edge of rear fenders. Cruise Control, a Guide-Matic headlight dimmer, air conditioning and E-Z-Eye glass were regular equipment.

ELDORADO/BROUGHAM SUB-SERIES 6400/6900

Model Number	Body/Style Number	Body Type & Seating	Factory Price	Shipping Weight	Production Total
60-64H	6437H	2-dr Sev HT Cpe-6P	7401	4855	1,075
60-64E	6467E	2-dr Biarritz Conv-6P	7401	5060	1,285
60 69P	6929P	4-dr Brougham-6P	13075	—	101

SERIES SIXTY SPECIAL FLEETWOOD — (V-8) — The Sixty Special Fleetwood sedan had the same standard equipment as the 6200 convertible and all 6300 models. This car was outwardly distinguished by a Fleetwood script on the rear deck, nine vertical bright metal louvers on rear fenders, vertical crest medallions on front fenders and wide full-length bright metal sill underscores, which extended to the fender skirts and lower rear quarter panels.

SERIES SIXTY SPECIAL FLEETWOOD

Model Number	Body/Style Number	Body Type & Seating	Factory Price	Shipping Weight	Production Total
60-60M	6029M	4-dr HT Sed-6P	6233	4880	11,800

1960 Cadillac, Fleetwood 75 limousine, V-8

SERIES 6700 FLEETWOOD SEVENTY-FIVE — (V-8) — The long wheelbase sedan and limousine had auxiliary jump seats, high-headroom formal six-window styling, broad ribbed roof edge beauty panels and trim generally similar to 6200 Cadillacs in other regards. The limousine passenger compartment was trimmed in either Bradford cloth or Bedford cloth, both in combinations with wool. Florentine leather upholstery was used in the chauffer's compartment.

SERIES 6700 FLEETWOOD SEVENTY-FIVE

Model Number	Body/Style Number	Body Type & Seating	Factory Price	Shipping Weight	Production Total
60-67R	6723R	4-dr Sed-9P	9533	5475	718
60-67S	6733S	4-dr Limo-9P	9748	5560	832
60-68	6890	Commercial chassis	—	—	2,160

NOTE: The commercial chassis featured a 156 inch wheelbase and was provided to professional car makers for construction of funeral cars and ambulances, etc.

ENGINES: STANDARD V-8: Overhead valves. Cast iron block. Displacement: 390 cid. Bore and stroke: 4 x 3.875 inches. Compression ratio: 10.5:1. Brake hp: 325 at 4800 rpm.. Five main bearings. Hydraulic valve lifters. Carburetors: Carter two-barrel Model 2814S.

ELDORADO/BROUGHAM ENGINE: V-8: Overhead valves. Cast iron block. Displacement: 390 cid. Bore and stroke: 4 x 3.875 inches. Compression ratio: 10.5:1. Brake hp: 345 at 4800 rpm.. Five main bearings. Hydraulic valve lifters. Carburetion: Three (3) Rochester two-barrel Model 701 590 1.

CHASSIS FEATURES: Wheelbase: (Series 75) 149.75 inches; (All others) 130 inches. Overall length: (Series 75) 244.8 inches; (All others) 225 inches. Tires: (Eldorados and Series 75) 8.20 x 15; (All others) 8.00 x 15. Dual exhausts standard. Rear axle ratios: (Series 75) 3.36:1 standard; 3.77:1 optional; 3.21:1 with air conditioning: (All others) 2.94:1 standard; 3.21:1 optional or mandatory with air conditioning.

POWERTRAIN OPTIONS: The 345 hp Eldorado V-8 with three two-barrel carburetors was $134.40 extra installed in any other Cadillac model.

CONVENIENCE OPTIONS: Air conditioning on Series 62 or 60 ($474); on Series 75 ($624). Air suspension on non-Eldorados ($215); standard on Eldorado. Autronic Eye ($46). Cruise Control ($97). Door guards on two-door ($4); on four-door ($7). Electric door locks on two-door ($46); on four-door ($70); standard on Eldorado. E-Z-Eye glass ($52). Fog lamps ($43). Automatic heating system on Series 62 or 60 ($129); on Series 75 ($279). License plate frame ($6). Six-Way power seat ($85-113) depending on style number. Power window regulators ($118). Power vent windows ($73). Radio with rear speaker ($165); with rear speaker and remote control ($247). Remote control trunk lock ($59). White sidewall tires, size 8.20 x 15 four-ply ($57 exchange); size 8.20 x 15 six-ply ($64). Antifreeze -20 degrees ($8); -40 degrees ($9). Accessory Group 'A' included whitewalls, heater, radio and E-Z-Eye glass for $402 extra and air suspension, cruise control and Eldorado engine at regular prices. Accessory Group 'B' included air conditioner, whitewalls, heater, radio and E-Z-Eye glass at $876 extra and Six-Way power seat, power vent windows and power windows at regular prices. Gas and oil delivery charge was $7 and district warehousing and handling charges averaged $15. Note: Eldorado standard equipment features specified above are those not previously mentioned in text. Consult both sources for complete list.

HISTORICAL FOOTNOTES: CAR LIFE magazine selected the 1960 Cadillac as its "Best buy in the luxury field." This was the last year for air suspension and for wraparound windshields, except on the Series 75 Fleetwood models. According to contemporary road tests, gas economy ratings for 1960 Cadillacs were approximately 14 miles per gallon at a steady 60 mph.

1961 CADILLAC

SERIES 6200 — (V-8) — Cadillacs were restyled and re-engineered for 1961. The new grille slanted back towards both the bumper and the hood lip, along the horizontal plane, and sat between dual headlamps. New forward slanting front roof pillars with non-wraparound windshield glass were seen. The revised backlight treatment had crisp, angular lines with thin pillars on some models and heavier, semi-blind-quarter roof posts on others. A new short-deck sedan was situated in the 6300 lineup. It was ostensibly created for rich San Francisco dowagers with small parking stalls in their luxury apartment houses. The DeVille models were retained as the 6300 sub-series (which was technically part of the Sixty-Two line), but the Eldorado Seville and Brougham were dropped. This moved the Eldorado Biarritz convertible into the DeVille sub-series. Standard equipment on base 6200 models included power brakes; power steering; automatic transmission; dual back-up lights; windshield washer and dual speed wipers; wheel discs; plain fender skirts; outside rearview mirror; vanity mirror; and oil filter. Rubberized front and rear coil springs replaced the trouble-prone air suspension system. Wheelbases were decreased on most models. Four-barrel induction systems were now the sole power choice and dual exhausts were no longer available. Series designation trim appeared on the front fenders.

1961 Cadillac, Series 62 convertible, V-8 (AA)

CADILLAC I.D. NUMBERS: Motor serial numbers took the same form used in 1960 with the first pair of symbols changed to '61' to indicate model year. Applicable codes were stamped in the same locations on the cars. The alphabetical code 'C' identified the new Series 6300 short-deck sedan.

SERIES 6200

Model Number	Body/Style Number	Body Type & Seating	Factory Price	Shipping Weight	Production Total
61-62A	6239A	4-dr 4W Sed-6P	5080	4660	4,700
61-62K	6229K	4-dr 6W Sed-6P	5080	4680	26,216
61-62G	6237G	2-dr HT Cpe-6P	5892	4560	16,005
61-62F	6267F	2-dr Conv-6P	5455	4720	15,500

NOTE: All 6200 sedans were pillarless hardtop sedans.

SERIES 62 DEVILLE 6300 SUB-SERIES — (V-8) — DeVille models featured front fender series designation scripts and a lower body 'skeg' trimmed with a thin three-quarter length spear molding running from behind the front wheel opening to the rear of the car. Standard equipment was the same used on 6200 models, plus Two-Way power seat and power windows. The Biarritz convertible also had power vent windows, whitewall tires, Six-Way power bench seat (or bucket seats) and remote control trunk lock. The new short-deck four-door hardtop appeared in mid-season and is often referred to as the Town Sedan.

SERIES 62 DEVILLE 6300 SUB-SERIES

Model Number	Body/Style Number	Body Type & Seating	Factory Price	Shipping Weight	Production Total
61-63B	6339B	4-dr 4W Sed-6P	5498	4 715	4,847
61-63L	6329L	4-dr 6W Sed-6P	5498	4710	26,415
61-63C	6399C	4-dr Twn Sed-6P	5498	4670	3,756
61-63J	6337J	2-dr HT Cpe-6P	5252	4595	20,156

SERIES 62 ELDORADO 6300 MODEL

Model Number	Body/Style Number	Body Type & Seating	Factory Price	Shipping Weight	Production Total
61-63E	6367E	2-dr Biarritz Conv-6P	6477	4805	1,450

NOTES: The Style Number 6399C Town Sedan was the short-deck four-window pillarless hardtop sedan introduced at midyear. The Style Number 6337J was the Coupe DeVille. All 6300 sedans were pillarless hardtop sedans.

1961 Cadillac, Fleetwood 60 Special four-door hardtop, V-8 (AA)

SERIES SIXTY-SPECIAL FLEETWOOD — (V-8) — The Sixty Special Fleetwood sedan featured semi-blind-quarter four-door hardtop styling with an angular roofline that approximated a raised convertible top. Six chevron slashes appeared on the rear fender sides at the trailing edge. A model nameplate was seen on the front fender. Standard equipment was the same used on 6300 models including power seats and windows.

SERIES SIXTY-SPECIAL FLEETWOOD

Model Number	Body/Style Number	Body Type & Seating	Factory Price	Shipping Weight	Production Total
61-60M	6039M	4-dr HT Sed-6P	6233	4770	15,500

SERIES 6700 FLEETWOOD 75 — (V-8) — The limousine and big sedan for 1961 sported the all-new styling motifs. Standard equipment was the same used on 6300 models including power seats and windows.

SERIES 6700 FLEETWOOD 75

Model Number	Body/Style Number	Body Type & Seating	Factory Price	Shipping Weight	Production Total
61-67R	6723R	4-dr Sed-9P	9533	5390	699
61-67S	6733S	4-dr Imp Sed-9P	9748	5420	926
61-68	6890	Commercial chassis	—	—	2,204

NOTE: The commercial chassis featured a 156 inch wheelbase and was provided to professional car makers for construction of funeral vehicles and ambulances, etc. Series 6700 sedans were full-pillared models with six-window styling. A high-headroom roofline was used on these models.

ENGINE: V-8: Overhead valves. Cast iron block. Displacement: 390 cid. Bore and stroke: 4 x 3-8/8 inches. Compression ratio: 10.5:1. Brake hp: 325 at 4800 rpm.. Five main bearings. Hydraulic valve lifters. Carburetion: Rochester four-barrel Model 701930.

CHASSIS FEATURES: Wheelbase: (Series 75) 149.8 inches, (All others) 129.5 inches. Overall length: (Series 75) 242.3 inches; (Town Sedan) 215 inches; (All others) 222 inches. Single exhaust only. Tires: (Eldorado and 75) 8.20 x 15; (All others) 8.00 x 15.

POWERTRAIN OPTION: None available.

CONVENIENCE OPTIONS: Air conditioning Series 62 or 60 ($474); Series 75 ($624). Autronic Eye ($46). Cruise Control ($97). Door guards on two-door ($4); on four-door ($7). Electric door locks on two-door ($46); on four-door ($70). E-Z-Eye glass ($52). Pair of fog lamps ($43). Automatic heating system on Series 62 or 60 ($129); on Series 75 ($179). License plate frame ($6). Six-Way power seat ($85-113). Power vent windows ($73). Radio with rear speaker ($16); with remote control ($247). Remote control trunk lock ($59). Five white sidewall tires size 8.20 x 15 four-ply ($58 exchange), standard on Eldorado, size 8.20 x 15 six-ply for Series 75 ($64 exchange). Permanent anti-freeze -20 degrees ($8); -40 degrees ($9). Accessory groups A and B included mostly the same features as 1960 at the combined total of individual prices listed above.

HISTORICAL FOOTNOTES: Total model year output for 1961 amounted to 138,379 units. A limited slip differential was optional at $53.70.

1962 CADILLAC

SERIES 62 — (V-8) — A mild facelift characterized Cadillac styling trends for 1962. A flatter grille with a thicker horizontal center bar and more delicate cross-hatched insert appeared. Ribbed chrome trim panels, seen ahead of the front wheel housings in 1961, were now replaced with concerning lamps and front fender model and series identification badges were eliminated. More massive front bumper end pieces appeared and housed rectangular parking lamps. At the rear, taillamps were now housed in vertical nacelles designed with an angled peak at the center. On Series 6200 models a vertically ribbed rear beauty panel appeared on the deck lid latch panel. Cadillac script also appeared on the lower left side of the radiator grille. The short-deck Town Sedan was switched to the base 6200 lineup, while a similar model was still part of the DeVille sub-series. Standard equipment on 6200 models included power brakes; power steering; automatic transmission; dual back-up lamps; windshield washer and dual speed wipers; wheel discs; fender skirts; remote control outside rearview mirror; left vanity mirror; oil filter; five tubeless blackwall tires; heater and defroster and front cornering lamps.

1962 Cadillac, Series 62 four-door hardtop, V-8 (AA)

CADILLAC I.D. NUMBERS: Motor serial numbers took the same form used in 1961 with the first pair of symbols changed to '62' to indicate model year. Applicable codes were stamped in the same locations on the cars. The alphabetical code 'C' now identified the Town Sedan in the 6200 series, while the code 'D' was adopted to identify the similar short-deck DeVille sedan added to the lineup this year.

SERIES 6200

Model Number	Body/Style Number	Body Type & Seating	Factory Price	Shipping Weight	Production Total
62-62A	6239A	4-dr 4W Sed-6P	5213	4645	17,314
62-62K	6229K	4-dr 6W Sed-6P	5213	4640	16,730
62-62C	6289C	4-dr Twn Sed-6P	5213	4590	2,600
62-62G	6237G	2-dr HT Cpe-6P	5025	4530	16,833
62-62F	6268F	2-dr Conv-6P	5588	4630	16,800

NOTE: All 6200 sedans were pillarless four-door hardtops. The Town Sedan was of four-window design.

1962 Cadillac Series 62 convertible

1962 Cadillac, Coupe DeVille two-door hardtop, V-8 (AA)

SERIES 62 DEVILLE 6300 SUB-SERIES — (V-8) — The DeVille lineup was much more of a separate series this year and some historical sources list it as such. Others list it as a 6200 sub-series. The latter system is utilized here. The new model for 1962 was a variation of Town Sedan, introduced the previous season, with a new Style Number and name. It was now Body Style 6289D and referred to as the Park Avenue four-window sedan. DeVilles were trimmed very similar to base 6200 models. They had all of the same standard equipment, plus Two-Way power seat and power windows. The Style Number 6367E Biarritz convertible also featured power vent windows, white sidewall tires and a Six-Way power bench seat. Buyers could substitute bucket seats, in place of the last item, at no cost.

SERIES 6200 DEVILLE 6300 SUB-SERIES

Model Number	Body/Style Number	Body Type & Seating	Factory Price	Shipping Weight	Production Total
62-63B	6339B	4-dr 4W Sed-6P	5631	4675	27,378
62-62L	6329L	4-dr 6W Sed-6P	5631	4660	16,230
62-63D	6389D	4-dr Park Ave Sed-6P	5631	4655	2,600
62-63J	6347J	2-dr HT Cpe-6P	5385	4595	25,675

SERIES 62 ELDORADO 6300 MODEL

Model Number	Body/Style Number	Body Type & Seating	Factory Price	Shipping Weight	Production Total
62-63E	6367E	2-dr Biarritz Conv-6P	6610	4620	1,450

NOTES: The Park Ave sedan was a short-deck DeVille sedan. The Style Number 6347J was the Coupe DeVille. All Sedan DeVilles were pillarless hardtop sedans.

SERIES SIXTY-SPECIAL FLEETWOOD — (V-8) — The Sixty-Special Fleetwood sedan stood apart in a crowd. It had chevron slash moldings on the rear roof pillar and a distinctly cross-hatched rear deck latch panel grille. Standard equipment comprised all features found on closed cars in the 6300 DeVille sub-series.

SERIES SIXTY-SPECIAL FLEETWOOD

Model Number	Body/Style Number	Body Type & Seating	Factory Price	Shipping Weight	Production Total
62-60W	6039	4-dr HT Sed-6P	6366	4710	13,350

SERIES 6700 FLEETWOOD 75 — (V-8) — The limousine and big sedan for 1962 sported the new styling motifs. Standard equipment was the same used on Sixty-Special Fleetwoods. A distinctive high-headroom look was seen again.

SERIES 6700 FLEETWOOD 75

Model Number	Body/Style Number	Body Type & Seating	Factory Price	Shipping Weight	Production Total
62-67R	6723R	4-dr Sed-9P	9722	5325	696
62-67S	6733S	4-dr Limo-9P	9937	5390	904
62-68	6890	Commercial chassis	—	—	2,280

NOTE: The commercial chassis featured a 156 inch wheelbase and was provided to professional car makers for construction of funeral cars and ambulances. etc. Series 6700 sedans and limousines were full-pillared models with six-window styling.

CADILLAC V-8: Overhead valves. Cast iron block. Displacement: 390 cid. Bore and stroke: 4 x 3.875 inches. Compression ratio: 10.5:1. Brake hp: 325 at 4800 rpm.. Five main bearings. Hydraulic valve lifters. Carburetors: Carter two-barrel Model 2814S.

CHASSIS FEATURES: Wheelbase: (Series 75) 149.8 inches, (All others) 129.5 inches. Overall length: (Series 75) 242.3 inches; (Town Sedan) 215 inches; (All others) 222 inches. Single exhaust only. Tires: (Eldorado and 75) 8.20 x 15; (All others) 8.00 x 15. (Note: The Park Avenue sedan had the same wheelbase and length as the 1961 Town Sedan.)

CONVENIENCE OPTIONS: Air conditioning on Series 62 or 60 ($474); on Series 75 ($624). Air suspension on non-Eldorados ($215); standard on Eldorado. Autronic Eye ($46). Cruise Control ($97). Door guards on two-door ($4); on four-door ($7). Electric door locks on two-door ($46); on four-door ($70); standard on Eldorado. E-Z-Eye glass ($52). Fog lamps ($43). Automatic heating system on Series 62 or 60 ($129); on Series 75 ($279). License plate frame ($6). Six-Way power seat ($85-113) depending on series number. Power window regulators ($118). Power vent windows ($73). Radio with rear speaker ($165); with rear speaker and remote control ($247). Remote control trunk lock ($59). White sidewall tires, size 8.20 x 15 four-ply ($57 exchange); size 8.20 x 15 six-ply ($64). Antifreeze -20 degrees ($8); -40 degrees ($9). Accessory Group 'A' included whitewalls, heater, radio and E-Z-Eye glass for $402 extra and air suspension, cruise control and Eldorado engine at regular prices. Accessory Group 'B' included air conditioner, whitewalls, heater, radio and E-Z-Eye glass at $876 extra and Six-Way power seat, power vent windows and power windows at regular prices. Gas and oil delivery charge was $7 and district warehousing and handling charges averaged $15. Bucket seats were available for 6267F, 6339B, 6347J or 6389D as an option ($108).

1963 CADILLAC

SERIES 62 — (V-8) — In overall terms, 1963 Cadillacs were essentially the same as the previous models. Exterior changes imparted a bolder and longer look. Hoods and deck lids were redesigned. The front fenders projected 4-5/8 inches further forward than in 1962, while the tailfins were trimmed down somewhat to provide a lower profile. Bodyside sculpturing was entirely eliminated. The slightly v-shaped radiator grille was taller and now incorporated outer extensions that swept below the flush-to-fender dual headlamps. Smaller, circular front parking lights were mounted in these extensions. A total of 143 options, including bucket seats with wool, leather or nylon upholstery fabrics and wood veneer facings on dash, doors and seatbacks, set an all-time record for interior appointment choices. Standard equipment for cars in the 62 Series (6200 models) included power brakes; power steering; automatic transmission; dual back-up lamps; windshield washers; dual speed wipers, wheel discs; remote control outside rearview mirrors; left-hand vanity mirror; oil filter; five tubeless black tires; heater; defroster and cornering lights. Convertibles were equipped with additional features, also used on all 6300 models.

CADILLAC I.D. NUMBERS: Motor serial numbers took the same form used in 1962, with the first pair of symbols changed to '63' to indicate the new model year. Applicable codes were stamped in the same locations on the cars. The alphabetical body identification code 'C' was no longer used, since the short-deck Town Sedan was dropped from the 62 Series. However, the short-deck 6300 model, called the Sedan DeVille Park Avenue, was retained and used the same 'D' body identification symbol. Rooflines on two-door hardtops were restyled, which brought a change in body style coding, but not in the alphabetical suffix.

SERIES 62 (6200 MODELS)

Model Number	Body/Style Number	Body Type & Seating	Factory Price	Shipping Weight	Production Total
62-63K	6229K	4-dr 6W Sed-6P	5214	4610	12,929
63-62G	6257G	2-dr Cpe-6P	5026	4505	16,786
63-62N	6239N	4-dr 4W Sed-6P	5214	4595	16,980
63-62F	6267F	2-dr Conv-6P	5590	4544	17,600
63-62	6200	Chassis only	—	—	3

NOTE: All 6200 Series sedans are pillarless four-door hardtops.

1963 Cadillac, Eldorado two-door sport convertible, V-8 (AA)

SERIES 62 — DEVILLE 6300 SUB-SERIES — (V-8) — This line reflected Series 62 styling revisions, but incorporated a DeVille signature script above the lower beltline molding, near the rear of the body. Standard features on DeVilles (and on base 6200 convertibles) were the same as on closed body 6200 models, plus two-way power seats and power windows. Model 6367E, the Eldorado Biarritz convertible, had special styling with untrimmed bodysides, full-length stainless steel underscores and a rectangular grid pattern rear decorative grille. Power vent windows, white sidewall tires and Six-Way power seats (in bench seat models) were standard in Eldorados.

SERIES 62 DEVILLE 6300 SUB-SERIES

Model Number	Body/Style Number	Body Type & Seating	Factory Price	Shipping Weight	Production Total
63-63L	6329L	4-dr 6W Sed-6P	5633	4650	15,146
63-63J	6357J	2-dr Cpe DeV-6P	5386	4520	31,749
63-63B	6339B	4-dr 4W Sed-6P	5633	4065	30,579
63-63D	6389D	4-dr Park Ave-6P	5633	4590	1,575

SERIES 62 ELDORADO BIARRITZ 6300 MODEL

Model Number	Body/Style Number	Body Type & Seating	Factory Price	Shipping Weight	Production Total
63-63E	6367E	2-dr Spt Conv-6P	6609	4640	1,825

NOTES: The Park Avenue was a short-deck DeVille sedan. The Style Number 6357J was the Coupe DeVille. All Sedan DeVilles were pillarless four-door hardtops.

1963 Cadillac, Fleetwood 60 special four-door hardtop, V-8 (AA)

SERIES SIXTY-SPECIAL FLEETWOOD — (V-8) — The Sixty-Special Fleetwood sedan was, again, distinguished by chevron slashes of bright metal on the sides of the roof 'C' pillars. Also seen were full-length bright metal underscores, clean side styling, a rear end quadrant pattern grille and Cadillac crest medallions towards the back of the rear fenders. Standard equipment included all normal 6300 sub-series features, plus power ventipanes.

SERIES SIXTY-SPECIAL FLEETWOOD

Model Number	Body/Style Number	Body Type & Seating	Factory Price	Shipping Weight	Production Total
63-60M	6039M	4-dr HT Sed-6P	6366	4690	14,000

SERIES 6700 — FLEETWOOD 75 — (V-8) — Cadillac's extra-long nine-passenger cars were the only pillared four-door sedans in the line. Standard equipment was the same as on base 6300 models and Series 62 convertibles. Trimmings Included a full-length lower beltline molding of a simple, but elegant design. Convertible top-like rooflines and windshields with forward 'dog leg' style pillars were 1962 carryovers seen exclusively on this line.

SERIES 6700 FLEETWOOD 75

Model Number	Body/Style Number	Body Type & Seating	Factory Price	Shipping Weight	Production Total
63-67R	6723R	4-dr Sed-9P	9724	5240	680
63-67S	6733S	4-dr Limo-9P	9939	5300	795
63-68	6890	Commercial chassis	—	—	2,527

NOTE: The commercial chassis featured a 156 inch wheelbase and was provided to professional car makers for construction of funeral cars. ambulances, etc.

ENGINES: V-8. Overhead valves. Cast iron block. Displacement: 390 cid. Bore and stroke: 4.0 x 3.875 inches. Compression ratio: 10.5:1. hp: 325 at 4800 rpm. Five main bearings. Hydraulic valve lifters. Carburetion: Rochester four-barrel model 710930.

NOTE: Although neither engine displacement or output changed, the 1963 Cadillac V-8 was completely redesigned. Quieter, smoother and more efficient, the new motor was one-inch lower, four inches narrower and 1-1/4 inches shorter than the 1962 V-8. It was also some 82 pounds lighter, due to the use of aluminum accessory drives.

CHASSIS FEATURES: Wheelbase: (Series 75) 149.8 inches. (all other series) 129.5 inches. Overall length: (Series 75) 243.3 inches; (Park Ave) 215 inches; (all other models) 223 inches. Tires: (Series 75) 8.20 x 15; (all other series) 8.00 x 15. Rear axle ratio: (Series 75) 3.36: 1; (all other series) 2.94:1.

CONVENIENCE OPTIONS: Air conditioner for Series 60-62 ($474). Air conditioner for Series 75 ($624). Automatic headlight control ($45). Bucket seats in styles 6267F. 6339B, 6357J or 6389D with leather upholstery required ($188). Controlled differential ($54). Cruise Control ($97). Door guards for two-door styles ($4); for four-door styles ($97). Electric door locks for two-door styles ($46); for four-door styles ($70). E-Z-Eye Glass ($52). Leather upholstery for styles 6339B, 6357J. 6389D or 6039M ($134). License plate frame ($6). Padded roof for style 6357J ($91); for style 6039M ($134). Six-way power seat ($85 or $113 depending on body style). Power window regulators as an option ($118). Power ventipanes as an option ($73). Radio with rear seat speaker ($165). Radio with rear seat speaker and remote control ($247). AM/FM radio ($191). Front seat belts in Series 60-62 models ($22). Rear seat belts in same models ($22). Adjustable steering wheel ($48). Remote control trunk lock ($53). Five white sidewall tires, 8.20 x 15 four-ply on Series 60-62; standard on Eldorado ($57 exchange). Five white sidewall tires. 8.20 x 15 six-ply on Series 75 models ($64 exchange).

1964 CADILLAC

SERIES 62 — (V-8) — It was time for another facelift this year and, really, a very minor one. New up front was a bi-angular grille that formed a V-shape along both its vertical and horizontal planes. The main horizontal grille bar was now carried around the bodysides. Outer grille extension panels again housed the parking and cornering lamps. It was the 17th running season for Cadillac tailfins, with a new, fine-blade design carrying this tradition on. Performance improvements, including a larger V-8, were the dominant changes for the model run. Equipment features replicated those of 1963 for the most part. Introduced as an industry first was Comfort Control, a completely automatic heating and air-conditioning system controlled by a dial thermostat on the instrument panel.

CADILLAC I.D. NUMBERS: Motor serial numbers were located on the left side of the engine block and left-hand frame side bar. The first two symbols. '63' identified the model year. The third symbol, a letter, designated body type. The last six numerical symbols indicated unit production sequence. The short-deck Park Avenue sedan. formerly coded with a 'D', was discontinued.

SERIES 62 (6200 MODELS)

Model Number	Body/Style Number	Body Type & Seating	Factory Price	Shipping Weight	Production Total
64-62K	6229K	4-dr 6W Sed-6P	5236	4575	9,243
64-62N	6239N	4-dr 4W Sed-6P	5236	4550	13,670
64-62G	6257G	2-dr Cpe-6P	5048	4475	12,166

NOTE: All 6200 Sedans were pillarless four-door hardtops.

1964 Cadillac, Sedan DeVille four-door hardtop, V-8 (AA)

SERIES 62 — DEVILLE 6300 SUB-SERIES — (V-8) — Styling changes for new DeVilles followed the Series 62 pattern. Equipment features were about the same as the year before. Performance gains from the new engine showed best in the lower range, at 20 to 50 mph traffic driving speeds. A new technical feature was Turbo-HydraMatic transmission, also used in Eldorado convertibles and Sixty-Special sedans. A DeVille script, above the lower belt molding at the rear, was continued as an identifier.

SERIES 62 — DEVILLE 6300 SUB-SERIES

Model Number	Body/Style Number	Body Type & Seating	Factory Price	Shipping Weight	Production Total
64-63L	6329	4-dr 6W Sed-6P	5655	4600	14,627
64-63B	6339B	4-dr 4W Sed-6P	5655	4575	39,674
64-63J	6357J	2-dr HT Cpe-6P	5408	4495	38,195
64-63F	6267F	2-dr Conv-6P	5612	4545	17,900

SERIES 62 ELDORADO BIARRITZ 6300 MODEL

Model Number	Body/Style Number	Body Type & Seating	Factory Price	Shipping Weight	Production Total
64-63P	6367P	2-dr Spt Conv-6P	6630	4605	1,870

NOTE: Style Number 6357J was the Coupe DeVille. All Sedan DeVilles were pillarless four-door hardtops. The Convertible DeVille was coded similar to 6200 models, but was considered a 6300.

SERIES SIXTY-SPECIAL FLEETWOOD — (V-8) — The 1964 Sixty-Special Fleetwood sedan had the new styling features combined with carryover trims. Standard equipment was the same as the previous year.

SERIES SIXTY-SPECIAL FLEETWOOD

Model Number	Body/Style Number	Buy Type & Seating	Factory Price	Shipping Weight	Production Total
64-60M	6039M	4-dr HT Sed-6P	6388	4680	14,550

SERIES 6700 — FLEETWOOD 75 — (V-8) — This line featured the same limousine type styling seen in 1963, combined with a new frontal treatment, angular taillamps and revised rear sheetmetal. The back fenders swept rearward in a straighter and higher line, while the fins began with a more pronounced kickup and housed new notch-shaped taillamp lenses.

SERIES 6700 FLEETWOOD 75

Model Number	Body/Style Number	Body Type & Seating	Factory Price	Shipping Weight	Production Total
63-67R	6723R	4-dr Sed-6P	9746	5215	617
63-67S	6733S	4-dr Limo-9P	9960	5300	808
63-67Z	6890Z	Commercial chassis	—	—	2,527

NOTE: The commercial chassis featured a 156 inch wheelbase and was provided to professional car makers for construction of funeral cars, ambulances, etc.

ENGINES: V-8. Overhead valves. Cast iron block. Displacement: 429 cid. Bore and stroke: 4.13 x 4.0 inches. Compression ratio: 10.5:1. hp: 340 at 4600 rpm. Five main bearings. Hydraulic valve lifters. Carburetion: Carter AFB four-barrel model 3655S.

CHASSIS FEATURES: Wheelbase (Series 75) 149.8 inches; (all other series) 129.5 inches. Overall length: (Series 75 and Eldorado) 243.8 inches; (all other series) 223.5 inches. Tires: (Series 75 and Eldorado) 8.20 x 15; (all other series) 8.00 x 15. Rear axle ratio: (Series 75) 3.36:1; (all other series) 2.94:1.

CONVENIENCE OPTIONS: Air conditioner for Series 60-62 ($474). Air conditioner for Series 75 ($624). Automatic headlight control ($45). Bucket seats in styles 6267F. 6339B, 6357J or 6389D with leather upholstery required ($188). Controlled differential ($54). Cruise Control ($97). Door guards for two-door styles ($4); for four-door styles ($7). Electric door locks for two-door styles ($46); for four-door styles ($70). E-Z-Eye Glass ($52). Leather upholstery for styles 6339B, 6357J. 6389D or 6039M ($134). License plate frame ($6). Padded roof for style 6357J ($91); for style 6039M ($134). Six-way power seat ($85 or $113 depending on body style). Power window regulators as an option ($118). Power ventipanes as an option ($73). Radio with rear seat speaker ($165). Radio with rear seat speaker and remote control ($247). AM/FM radio ($191). Front seat belts in Series 60-62 models ($22). Rear seat belts in same models ($22). Adjustable steering wheel ($48). Remote control trunk lock ($53). Five white sidewall tires, 8.20 x 15 four-ply on Series 60-62; standard on Eldorado ($57 exchange). Five white sidewall tires, 8.20 x 15 six-ply on Series 75 models ($64 exchange).

1965 CADILLAC

CALAIS SERIES — (V-8) — The Calais Series replaced the Sixty-Two line for 1965, as one of numerous Cadillac changes. A broader, more unified grille and vertically mounted headlamps featured the styling improvements. The Cadillac tailfin was said to be gone, but symmetrical rear fender forms tapered to very thin edges, top and bottom, giving a very traditional visual impression. Curved side windows with frameless glass were new and convert-

ibles had tempered glass backlights. Last seen in 1956, the standard wheelbase pillared sedan made a return this year. Perimeter frame construction allowed repositioning of engines six inches forward in the frame, thus lowering transmission hump and increasing interior room. Standard Calais equipment was comprised of power brakes; power steering; automatic transmission; dual back-up lights; windshield washers and dual speed wipers; full wheel discs; remote controlled outside rearview mirror; visor vanity mirror; oil filter; five tubeless black tires; heater; defroster; lamps for luggage, glove and rear passenger compartments; cornering lights and front and rear seat safety belts.

CADILLAC I.D. NUMBERS: Vehicle numbers were now located on the right or left-hand side of the forward frame crossmember. The original engine serial number was the same as the vehicle identification number. The first symbol was a letter (see Body Style Number suffixes) indicating series and body style. The second symbol was a number designating the model year. The following six numbers designated the sequential production code and started with 100001 and up. Body Style Numbers were revised to reflect a more rational arrangement of models. The new five digit codes began with '68' except in the case of Fleetwood Seventy-Five models and early production Fleetwood Eldorado convertibles, all of which were coded '69'. The third number was a '2' on Calais; a '3' on DeVilles; a '4' on Eldorados; a '0' on 60 Specials and a '7' on 75 limousines. The final two symbols corresponded to Fisher Body Division Style Number codes. The five digit numbers were found on the vehicle data plate, affixed to engine side of the firewall, and may have been followed by a letter suffix corresponding to those on the charts below.

CALAIS SERIES 682

Model Number	Body/Style Number	Body Type & Seating	Factory Price	Shipping Weight	Production Total
65-682	68257-G	2-dr HT Cpe-6P	5059	4435	12,515
65-682	68239-N	4-dr HT Sed-6P	5247	4500	13,975
65-682	68269-K	4-dr Sed-6P	5247	4490	7,721

DEVILLE SERIES — (V-8) — DeVilles kept their rear fender signature scripts for distinctions of trim. One auto writer described this feature as "Tiffany-like". Standard equipment matched that found in Calais models, plus power window lifts.

DEVILLE SERIES 683

Model Number	Body/Style Number	Body Type & Seating	Factory Price	Shipping Weight	Production Total
65-683	68367-F	2-dr Conv-6P	5639	4690	19,200
65-683	68357-J	2-dr HT Cpe-6P	5419	4480	43,345
65-683	68339-B	4-dr HT Sed-6P	5666	4560	45,535
65-683	68369-L	4-dr Sed-6P	5666	4555	15,000

NOTES: Style Number 68357-J was called the Coupe DeVille. Other models were Convertible or Sedan DeVilles. Some sources quote substantially lower factory list prices for 1965 Cadillacs. This may be due to a strike that occurred very early in the year, which probably brought $1 price increases after it was settled. The UAW walkout closed the company's newly expanded Clark Avenue (Detroit) factory from September 25, 1964 through the following December and created a decline in production and sales for the 1964 calendar year. The higher retail prices are being used in this book.

FLEETWOOD SIXTY-SPECIAL SUB-SERIES — (V-8) — Poised on a new 133 inch wheelbase, the Sixty-Special sedan wore Fleetwood crests on the hood and deck. All features found in lower priced Cadillacs were standard, as well as power ventipanes, glare-proof rearview mirror and automatic level control. Like Calais and DeVilles, the Fleetwood Sixty-Special had an improved Turbo-HydraMatic transmission with a variable stator. A new Fleetwood Brougham trim option package was introduced at a price of $199. Its main feature was a more richly appointed interior.

FLEETWOOD SIXTY-SPECIAL SUB-SERIES 680

Model Number	Body/Style Number	Body Type & Seating	Factory Price	Shipping Weight	Production Total
65-680	680-69-M	4-dr Sed-6P	6479	4670	18,100

FLEETWOOD ELDORADO SUB-SERIES — (V-8) — Under a new model arrangement, the Eldorado became a one-car Fleetwood sub-series, but was really less distinguished than before. Fleetwood hood and deck lid crests were the main difference in outer trim. Additional standard equipment, over that found in Sixty-Specials, included white sidewall tires and a six-way power seat for cars with regular bench seating.

FLEETWOOD ELDORADO SUB-SERIES 684

Model Number	Body/Style Number	Body Type & Seating	Factory Price	Shipping Weight	Production Total
65-684	68467-E	2-dr Eldo Conv-6P	6754	4660	2,125

1965 Cadillac, Fleetwood 75 commercial chassis ambulance, V-8

FLEETWOOD 75 SUB-SERIES — (V-8) — Cadillac's longest, heaviest, richest and highest priced models were, again, more conventionally engineered than the other lines. For example, the new perimeter frame was not in use and neither was the improved automatic transmission. In addition, automatic level control was not featured. Even the annual styling facelift did not affect these tradition-bound luxury cars. They came with all power controls found in Eldorados and added courtesy and map lights to the standard equipment list. Sales of commercial chassis earned an increase of 30 units, while limousine deliveries tapered slightly downward and the popularity of the nine-passenger sedan saw a considerable decline.

FLEETWOOD 75 SUB-SERIES 697

Model Number	Body/Style Number	Body Type & Seating	Factory Price	Shipping Weight	Production Total
65-697	69723-R	4-dr Sed-9P	9746	5190	455
65-697	69733-S	4-dr Limo-9P	9960	5260	795

FLEETWOOD 75 SUB-SERIES 698

Model Number	Body/Style Number	Body Type & Seating	Factory Price	Shipping Weight	Production Total
65-698	69890-Z	Commercial chassis	—	—	2,669

ENGINE: V-8. Overhead valves. Cast iron block. Displacement: 429 cid. Bore and stroke: 4.13 x 4.0 inches. Compression ratio: 10.5:1. Brake hp: 340 at 4600 rpm. Five main bearings. Hydraulic valve lifters. Carburetor: Carter AFB four-barrel, model 3903S.

CHASSIS FEATURES: Wheelbase: (Commercial chassis) 156 inches; (Series 75) 149.8 inches; (Series 60 Special) 133 inches (all other series) 129.5 inches. Overall length: (Series 75) 243.8 inches; (Series 60 Special) 227.5 inches; (all other series) 224 inches. Front tread: (all series) 62.5 inches. Rear tread: (all series) 62.5 inches. Automatic level control standard where indicated in text. A new engine mounting system and patented quiet exhaust were used. Tires: (Series 75) 8.20 x 15, (Eldorado) 9.00 x 15; (all others) 8.00 x 15.

CONVENIENCE OPTIONS: Air conditioner, except 75 Series models ($495). Air conditioner, 75 Series model ($624). Bucket seats with console in F-J-B models with leather upholstery ($188). Controlled differential ($54). Cruise Control ($97). Door guards on two-door models ($4); on four-door models ($7). Fleetwood Brougham option on M model ($199). Soft Ray tinted glass ($52). Delete-option heater and defroster on 75 Series models ($135 credit), on other models ($97 credit). Leather upholstery on J-B-L-M models ($141). License plate frame ($6). Padded roof on J model ($124); on B or L models ($140). Left-hand four-way power bucket seat on F-J-B models ($54). Power door locks on G-F-J-E models ($46); on N-K-B-L-M models ($70). Power headlight control on R-S models ($46); on other models ($51). Six-way power front seat on G-N-K models ($113); on F-J-B-L-M models ($85). Power window regulators on G-N-K models ($119). Power vent window regulator option ($73). Radio with rear speaker ($165). Radio with rear speaker and remote control ($246). AM/FM radio ($191). Rear seat belts ($18). Front seat belt delete-option. ($17 credit). Adjustable steering wheel, except on R-S models ($91). Remote control trunk lock, except on R-S models ($53). Twilight Sentinal, except on E-R-S models ($57). Five white sidewall tires 9.00 x 15 size with four-ply construction, except E-R-S models ($57 exchange). Five white sidewall tires 9.00 x 15 size with six-ply construction. on R-S models only ($64 exchange).

HISTORICAL FOOTNOTES: Vinyl roofs for Coupe and Sedan DeVilles came in four different colors. A tilt telescope steering wheel option was highlighted this season. The Cadillac factory closed July 8, 1964 for the changeover to 1965 model production. This was 22 days earlier than usual, as a 471,000 square foot expansion of facilities was planned. The plant reopened August 24, when production of cars to 1965 specifications commenced. It was the longest plant shutdown in Cadillac history and the new manufacturing potential of 800 cars per day was an all-time high. The three millionth Cadillac was built this season and a new engineering center was dedicated. The Fleetwood Sixty Special Brougham was frequently referred to as a separate model.

1966 CADILLAC

CALAIS — (V-8) — SERIES 682 — For 1966 Cadillac offered 12 models in three series, Calais, DeVille and Fleetwood. Cadillac 'firsts' seen this season included variable ratio steering and optional front seats with carbon cloth heating pads built into cushions and seatbacks. Comfort and convenience innovations were headrests, reclining seats and an AM/FM stereo system. Engineering improvements made to the perimeter frame increased ride and handling ease. Newly designed piston and oil rings were adoped and new engine and body mountings were employed. All models, except the 75 Series limousines. were mildly facelifted. Changes included a somewhat coarser mesh for the radiator grille insert, which was now divided by a thick, bright metal horizontal center bar housing rectangular parking lamps at its outer ends. A Cadillac crest and V-shaped molding trimmed the hood of Calais. Separate, rectangular side marker lamps replaced the integral grille extension designs. There was generally less chrome on all Cadillac this year.

1966 Cadillac, Calais four-door hardtop sedan, V-8

CADILLAC I.D. NUMBERS: Vehicle numbers were found on the left center pillar post. The original engine serial number was the same as the vehicle identification number. The numbering system was the same employed a year earlier with the second symbol changed to a '6' for 1966 model year. All Eldorados now utilized the first two symbols '68' for their Style Number. The Sixty-Special Brougham was now a separate model of the Fleetwood Series with a 'P' Style Number suffix applied.

CALAIS SERIES 682

Model Number	Body/Style Number	Body Type & Seating	Factory Price	Shipping Weight	Production Total
66-682	68269-K	4-dr Sed-6P	5171	4460	4,575
66-682	68239-N	4-dr HT Sed-6P	5171	4465	13,025
66-682	68257-G	2-dr HT Cpe-6P	4986	4390	11,080

DEVILLE — (V-8) — SERIES 683 — Following the general styling theme found on Calais models, the DeVille series was again distinguished with Tiffany-like scripts above the rear tip of the horizontal body rub moldings. Standard equipment additions followed the pattern of previous years. Cadillac crests and V-shaped moldings, front and rear, were identifiers.

1966 Cadillac, two-door convertible DeVille, V-8

DEVILLE SERIES 683

Model Number	Body/Style Number	Body Type & Seating	Factory Price	Shipping Weight	Production Total
66-683	68369-L	4-dr Sed-6P	5581	4535	11,860
66-683	68339-B	4-dr HT Sed-6P	5581	4515	60,550
66-683	68357-J	2-dr Cpe DeV-6P	5339	4460	50,580
66-683	68367-F	2-dr Conv Cpe-6P	5555	4445	19,200

1966 Cadillac, Fleetwood 60 Special Brougham four-door sedan, V-8

FLEETWOOD SIXTY-SPECIAL — (V-8) — SUB-SERIES 680/681 — Models in this range were characterized by traditional standard equipment additions and by emblems containing a Cadillac shield encircled by a laurel wreath, which appeared on the hood and center of the deck. Fleetwood designations, in block letters, were also found at the right-hand side of the deck. The Brougham had the wreath-style medallions on the roof pillar, along with Tiffany scripts in the same location to identify this extra-rich model.

FLEETWOOD SIXTY-SPECIAL SUB-SERIES 680/681

Model Number	Body/Style Number	Body Type & Seating	Factory Price	Shipping Weight	Production Total
66-680	68069-M	4-dr Sed-6P	6378	4615	5,445
66-681	68169-P	4-dr Brghm-6P	6695	4616	13,630

FLEETWOOD ELDORADO — (V-8) — SUB-SERIES 684 — Fleetwood type trim was seen again on the Eldorado. Equipment additions included white sidewall tires and a six-way power front bench seat. It was to be the last season that conventional engineering characterized this model.

FLEETWOOD ELDORADO SUB-SERIES 684

Model Number	Body/Style Number	Body Type & Seating	Factory Price	Shipping Weight	Production Total
66-684	68567-E	2-dr Eldo Conv-6P	6631	4500	2,250

FLEETWOOD SEVENTY-FIVE — (V-8) — SERIES 697/698 — Fleetwood exterior trim and Fleetwood interior appointments enriched the cars in Cadillac's high-dollar lineup. The first major restyling since 1959 was seen on these models, as well as perimeter type frames. The new look brought the appearance of the big sedan and the limousine up to date, so that it matched the visual impression of other Cadillac lines. A big jump in sales for both regular production models, but not the commercial chassis, was the result.

FLEETWOOD 75 SUB-SERIES 697

Model Number	Body/Style Number	Body Type & Seating	Factory Price	Shipping Weight	Production Total
66-697	69723-R	4-dr Sed-9P	10,312	5320	980
66-697	69733-S	4-dr Limo-9P	10,521	5435	1,037

FLEETWOOD 75 SUB-SERIES 698

Model Number	Body/Style Number	Body Type & Seating	Factory Price	Shipping Weight	Production Total
66-698	69890-Z	Commercial chassis	—	—	2,463

ENGINE: V-8. Overhead valves. Cast iron block. Displacement: 429 cid. Bore and stroke: 4.13 x 4.0 inches. Compression ratio: 10.5:1. Brake hp: 340 at 4600 rpm. Five main bearings. Hydraulic valve lifters. Carburetor: Carter AFB four-barrel, model 3903S.

CHASSIS FEATURES: Chassis features for 1966 Cadillacs were about the same as for 1965 Cadillacs, except that the overall length of all models increased slightly as follows: (Series 75) 244.5 inches; (Series 60-Special) 227.7 inches; (Eldorado) 224.2 inches and (all other Series) 224.2 inches. Fleetwood 75s now had the perimeter frame. See 1965 Cadillac chassis features for other details.

CONVENIENCE OPTIONS: Air conditioner, except 75 Series models ($495). Air conditioner, 75 Series model ($624). Bucket seats with console in F-J-B models with leather upholstery ($188). Controlled differential ($54). Cruise Control ($97). Door guards on two-door models ($4); on four-door models ($7). Fleetwood Brougham option on M model ($199). Soft Ray tinted glass ($52). Delete-option heater and defroster on 75 Series models ($135 credit), on other models ($97 credit). Leather upholstery on J-B-L-M models ($141). License plate frame ($6). Padded roof on J model ($124); on B or L models ($140). Left-hand four-way power bucket seat on F-J-B models ($54). Power door locks on G-F-J-E models ($46); on N-K-B-L-M models ($70). Power headlight control on R-S models ($46); on other models ($51). Six-way power front seat on G-N-K models ($113); on F-J-B-L-M models ($85). Power window regulators on G-N-K models ($119). Power vent window regulator option ($73). Radio with rear speaker ($165). Radio with rear speaker and remote control ($246). AM/FM radio ($191). Rear seat belts ($18). Front seat belt delete-option. ($17 credit). Adjustable steering wheel, except on R-S models ($91). Remote control trunk lock, except on R-S models ($53). Twilight Sentinal, except on E-R-S models ($57). Five white sidewall tires 9.00 x 15 size with four-ply construction, except E-R-S models ($57 exchange). Five white sidewall tires 9.00 x 15 size with six-ply construction. on R-S models only ($64 exchange). A new seat warmer sold for $60.20. The recliner seat with head rest was $64.20 extra and was available only in F-J-B-H models with Eldorado bench seats or optional bucket seats. Headrests were a separate, $40.15 option for all Cadillacs.

HISTORICAL FOOTNOTES: Best ever sales and production year in Cadillac history. Second year running for sales increases, despite a downturn in the overall market for U.S. cars. First season for delivery of more than 200,000 new units. A record of 5.570 one-week builds was marked December 5 and a record one-day output of 1,017 cars was achieved October 27. The 1966 models were introduced October 14, 1965. Towards the end of the summer, in 1966, a new assembly line was set up to manufacture front-wheel-drive Eldorados conforming to 1967 model specifications.

1967 CADILLAC

1967 Cadillac, Calais two-door hardtop coupe, V-8

CALAIS — (V-8) — SERIES 682 — New at Cadillac for 1967 was a redesigned side panel contour that created a longer look and more sculptured appearance. The coupe roof structure was restyled after the Florentine show car and gave added privacy to rear seat passengers. Technical improvements included a revised engine valve train, different carburetor, Mylar printed circuit instrument panel, re-tuned body mounts and a new engine fan with clutch for quieter operation. A squarer cornered radiator grille insert had a cross-hatch pattern that appeared both above the bumper and through a horizontal slot cut Into it. Rear end styling revisions were highlighted by metal divided taillamps and a painted lower bumper section. The new front grille had a forward angle and blades that seemed to emphasize its vertical members. Rectangular parking lamps were housed at the outer ends. Listed as standard equipment for cars in this line were automatic transmission; power brakes; power steering; heater and defroster; reflectors; full wheel discs; three-speed windshield wipers and washers; left-hand remote control outside rearview mirror; inside non-glare rearview mirror; visor vanity mirror; cigarette lighter; electric clock; cornering lights; lamps for the rear compartment, glovebox and luggage compartment; interior courtesy lamps; and all standard GM safety features. Also included at base price were Automatic Climate Controls; rear cigarette lighter (except coupes); padded dashboard; Hazard Warning system; and front and rear seat belts with outboard retractors.

CADILLAC I.D. NUMBERS: Took the same general form and were found in the same locations as In 1966 models. Second symbol was changed to a '7' for 1967 model year.

CALAIS SERIES 682

Model Number	Body/Style Number	Body Type & Seating	Factory Price	Shipping Weight	Production Total
67-682	68269-K	4-dr Sed-6P	5215	4520	2,865
67-682	68249-N	4-dr HT Sed-6P	5215	4550	9,880
67-682	68247-G	2-dr Cpe-6P	5040	4445	9,085

CADILLAC V-8: A Rochester Quadrajet four-barrel carburetor and de-clutching cooling fan were new. Most other specifications were carried over from 1966. See 1966 Cadillac engine data.

DEVILLE — (V-8) — SERIES 683 — Minor trim variations and slightly richer interiors separated DeVilles from Calais. For example, Tiffany style chrome signature scripts were again found above the bodyside molding on the rear fenders. DeVille equipment lists were comprised of all the same features found in Calais models, plus power operated window

regulators; rear cigarette lighters in all styles; and two-way power front seats. An innovative slide-out fuse box and safety front seatback lock for two-door models were additional Cadillac advances for the 1967 model year.

DEVILLE SERIES 683

Model Number	Body/Style Number	Body Type & Seating	Factory Price	Shipping Weight	Production Total
67-683	68369L	4-dr Sed-6P	5625	4675	8,800
67-683	68349-B	4-dr HT Sed-6P	5625	4550	59,902
67-683	68347-J	2-dr Cpe DeV-6P	5392	4505	52,905
67-683	68367-F	2-dr Conv-6P	5608	4541	18,200

1957 Cadillac, Fleetwood 60 Special four-door Brougham, V-8

FLEETWOOD SIXTY-SPECIAL — (V-8) — SUB-SERIES 680/681 — Full-length bright metal body underscores; Fleetwood wreath and crest emblems for the hood, trunk and roof pillar, the lack of horizontal lower body rub moldings and Fleetwood block letters on the lower front fenders and passenger side of the deck lid characterized the new Sixty-Specials. The Brougham featured a padded Cordova vinyl top with model identification scripts attached to the roof 'C' pillar. Added to the list of DeVille equipment were Automatic Level Control suspension and power operated ventipanes. The Brougham also included lighted fold-down trays; adjustable reading lamps; and carpeted fold-down footrests.

FLEETWOOD SIXTY-SPECIAL SUB-SERIES 680/681

Model Number	Body/Style Number	Body Type & Seating	Factory Price	Shipping Weight	Production Total
67-680	68069-M	4-dr Sed-6P	6423	4685	3,550
67-681	68169-P	4-dr Brghm-6P	6739	4735	12,750

FLEETWOOD SEVENTY-FIVE — (V-8) — SUB-SERIES 697/698 — The year's new styling was beautifully rendered on the Cadillac long-wheelbase models, which had extra-long rear fenders and an extended 'greenhouse' with a formal, high-headroom look. Fleetwood wreath and crest emblems decorated the hood and the trunk and there were Fleetwood block letters at the right side of the deck lid. A simple horizontal body rub molding, lengthened to fit the elongated sheetmetal, trimmed the sides of these elegant machines. Standard equipment included all found in DeVilles, plus Automatic Level Control; air-conditioning; carpeted fold-down foot rests; and 8.20 x 15, four-ply 8PR black tires.

FLEETWOOD SEVENTY-FIVE SUB-SERIES 697/698

Model Number	Body/Style Number	Body Type & Seating	Factory Price	Shipping Weight	Production Total
67-697	69723-R	4-dr Sed-6P	10.360	5335	835
67-697	69733-S	4-dr Limo-6P	10,571	5450	965
67-698	69890-Z	Commercial chassis	—	—	2333

NOTE: The commercial chassis was built on a 156 inch wheelbase and was provided to professional car builders for the manufacture of hearses and ambulances, etc.

CADILLAC ENGINE: V-8. Overhead valves. Cast iron block. Displacement: 429 cid. Bore and stroke: 4.13 x 4.0 inches. Compression ratio: 10.5:1. Brake hp: 340 at 4600 rpm. Five main bearings. Hydraulic valve lifters. Carburetor: Carter AFB four-barrel, model 3903S.

1967 Cadillac, Fleetwood Eldorado two-door hardtop sport coupe, V-8

FLEETWOOD ELDORADO — (V-8) — SUB-SERIES 693 — The 1967 Cadillac Eldorado was a completely new front-wheel-drive six-passenger coupe. It was described as a "sports-styled" automobile and the first car to combine front-wheel-drive; variable ratio power steering; and automatic level control. Built off the Oldsmobile Toronado platform, utilizing the same basic body shell, the Eldorado was shorter and lower than even the smallest Cadillacs, but could provide full six-passenger seating because of its drivetrain layout. The Cadillac V-8 was fitted to the platform with changes in the oil pan, exhaust manifolds, accessory and drive belt layout and motor mount system. It had dual exhausts, but a single outlet muffler and tailpipe arrangement. An improved fresh-air system eliminated the need for front ventipanes. The Eldorado shared 1967 Cadillac technical changes such as Mylar-backed circuitry; bigger power brake booster; slide-out fuse box; improved automatic headlamp dimmer and braided rayon brake hoses, but was the only model in the line to offer front disc brake option. The typical assortment of Fleetwood extra equipment was standard on Eldorados as well.

FLEETWOOD ELDORADO SUB-SERIES 693

Model Number	Body/Style Number	Body Type & Seating	Factory Price	Shipping Weight	Production Total
67-393	69347-H	2-dr HT Cpe-6P	6277	4590	17,930

CHASSIS FEATURES: Wheelbase: (Series 75) 149.8 inches, (Commercial chassis) 156 inches; (Eldorado) 120 inches; (Sixty-Special) 133 inches; (all other models) 129.5 inches. Overall length: (Series 75) 244.5 inches, (Eldorado) 221 inches; (Sixty-Special) 227.5 inches; (all other models) 224 inches. Rear axle ratio: 2.94:1. Transmission: three-speed Turbo-Hydramatic. Tires: (Series 75) 8.20 x 15: (all other models) 9.00 x 15. Front tread: (Eldorado) 63.5 inches, (all other models) not available. Rear tread: (Eldorado) 63.0 inches; (all other models) not available.

POWERTRAIN OPTIONS: A 3.21:1 rear axle gear ratio was standard on Series Seventy-Five and Eldorado; optional on other models. A controlled differential was $40.15 extra on all models, except Eldorados. An air injection reactor was $34.13 extra on all Cadillacs and required on all cars built for California sale. Closed positive crankcase ventilators were $4 extra on all Cadillacs and required on all cars built for California sale.

CONVENIENCE OPTIONS: Auxiliary horn ($12). Automatic level control option on models G-N-K-F-J-B-L ($79). Automatic Climate Control. except R and S models ($516). Bucket seats with console on models F-J-B-H with leather upholstery required ($184). Firemist finish ($132). Cruise control ($95). Rear window defogger on models G-N-K-J-B-L-M-P ($27). Front disc brakes on Eldorado only ($105). Door guards on model G-F-J-H ($5); on models N-K-B-L-M-P-R-S ($8). Expanded vinyl upholstery on models G-N-K ($42). Soft Ray glass ($51). Guide-Matic headlamp control ($50). Headrests ($53). Leather upholstery, models J-B-L-M-P ($138); model H ($158). License frame, single ($6); pair ($12). Padded roof, models J-H ($132); models B-L ($137). Power door locks, two-door ($47); four-door ($68). Power door locks for Fleetwood 75 models ($116). Power ventipanes, except models H-M-P, power windows required ($72). Rear quarter power ventipanes on Eldorado only ($63). Power windows on Calais models ($116). AM radio ($162). AM/FM radio ($188). AM/FM stereo, except Fleetwood 75 models ($288). AM radio rear controls on Fleetwood 75 models ($242). Reclining front seat with headrests on models F-J-B-H with bucket seats or Eldorado bench seats required ($84). Four-way left-hand power bucket seat on models F-J-B-H ($53). Six-way power front seat on models G-N-K ($11); models F-J-B-L-H-M-P-R ($83). Rear center seat belt ($1 1). Front shoulder straps ($32). Tilt-telescope steering wheel ($90). Remote control trunk lock ($52). Twilight Sentinel on Eldorado ($37); other models ($32). White sidewall tires, size 9.00 x 15, four-ply 8PR-5, except nine-passenger models ($56 exchange). White sidewall tires. size 8.20 x 15, four-ply 8PR-5 on nine-passenger models ($64 exchange).

HISTORICAL FOOTNOTES: Dealer introduction date for 1967 Cadillacs and Eldorados was October 6, 1966. The Eldorado featured concealed, horizontally mounted headlamps. A new assembly line was set up at the Detroit factory to build Eldorados. A third successive year of record production and sales was marked by Cadillac Division in 1967. Based on the Eldorado's popularity, Cadillac sales for a single month passed the 20,000 unit level for the first time in the company's history, setting an all-time high of 22,072 cars in October, 1966. A year later, 23,408 cars conforming to 1968 specifications were built in October, 1967. Calvin J. Werner was general manager of Cadillac; Fred T. Hopkins general sales manager. C.A. Rasmussen was chief engineer and W.J. Knight was public relations director.

1968 CADILLAC

CALAIS — (V-8) — SERIES 682 — Cadillac was not about to alter its popular product in any major way, so the same basic styling and engineering continued into the 1968 model year, with a number of refinements, but no drastic changes. New grilles were added. They had an insert with a finer mesh and step-down outer section, which held the rectangular parking lights just a little higher than before. Rear end styling was very modestly altered. An obvious change was a 6-1/2 inch longer hood, designed to accommodate recessed windshield wipers. The deck lid also had more of a rake. An enlarged engine offered more cubic inches and torque than any other American V-8 and put out 375 hp. Of 20 exterior paint color combinations, 14 were totally new. On the inside, enriched appointments included molded inner door panels and a selection of 147 upholstery combinations, 76 in cloth, 67 in leather and four in vinyl. The Calais four-door pillared sedan was dropped. Standard features for the two remaining styles included Turbo-Hydramatic; power steering; power brakes; power windows; heater and defroster; center armrests; electric clock; dual back-up lamps; cornering lights; front and rear side marker lamps; Light Group; Mirror Group; padded instrument panel; seat belts; trip odometer; ignition key warning buzzer; recessed three-speed wipers and washers and five 9.00 x 15 blackwall tires.

CADILLAC I.D. NUMBERS: Vehicle identification numbers were stamped on the top of the instrument panel this year and were visible through the windshield. The first symbol was a '6' for Cadillac. The second and third symbols correspond to the same symbols in the series code number. The fourth and fifth symbols correspond to the last two symbols in the standard Fisher Body Division code (Style Number, without letter suffix). The sixth symbol was an '8' for 1968 model year. The seventh symbol was an assembly plant code as follows: 'Q' = Detroit, Michigan; 'E' = Linden, New Jersey. The next group of six numbers was the sequential unit production code. The number sequence began with 100001 at each assembly plant. Body Style Numbers, on the vehicle data plate (located on firewall) were prefixed with '68' for 1968 and suffixed with a single letter, which also indicated series and model and corresponds to the letter on the charts below.

CALAIS SERIES 62

Model Number	Body/Style Number	Body Type & Seating	Factory Price	Shipping Weight	Production Total
68-682	68247-G	2-dr Cpe-6P	5315	4570	8,165
68-682	68249-N	4-dr HT Sed-6P	5491	4640	10,025

1968 Cadillac, two-door convertible DeVille, V-8

DEVILLE (V-8) — SERIES 683 — On paper, it seemed that the main distinctions of cars in the DeVille lineup were the installation of a power-operated front seat with horizontal adjustment and the addition of illuminated door panel reflectors. There were, however, richer appointments inside and out, including the traditional rear fender Tiffany-like scripts and, plusher upholstery trims. In addition, twice as many body styles were provided in DeVille level finish.

DEVILLE SERIES 683

Model Number	Body/Style Number	Body Type & Seating	Factory Price	Shipping Weight	Production Total
68-683	68369-L	4-dr Sed-6P	5785	4680	9,850
68-683	68349-8	4-dr HT Sed-6P	5785	4675	72,662
68-683	68347-J	2-dr Cpe DeV-6P	5552	4595	63,935
68-683	68367-F	2-dr Conv DeV-6P	5736	4600	18,025

NOTE: Some sources list lower prices for 1968 Cadillacs, indicating a midyear increase. The higher recorded prices are being used in this book.

1968 Cadillac, Fleetwood 60 Special four-door Brougham, V-8

FLEETWOOD SIXTY-SPECIAL — (V-8) — SUB-SERIES 680/681 — Features distinguishing 1968 Sixty-Specials, in addition to a longer wheelbase, were the same exterior and interior appointments used in 1967 models. Extra items of standard equipment included Automatic Level Control; front and rear power operated ventipanes and, on Broughams, adjustable reading lamp; padded roof with special scripts and emblems; and carpeted folding foot rests.

FLEETWOOD SIXTY-SPECIALS SUB-SERIES 680/681

Model Number	Body/Style Number	Body Type & Seating	Factory Price	Shipping Weight	Production Total
68-680	68069-M	4-dr Sed-6P	6583	4795	3,300
68-681	68169-P	4-dr Brghm-6P	6899	4805	15,300

NOTE: See price increase notation under DeVille specifications chart.

FLEETWOOD SEVENTY-FIVE — (V-8) — SUB-SERIES 697/698 — Again marked by simple extra-long body rub moldings, a formal high-headroom look (with doors cut into roof) and Fleetwood type wreath and crest emblems, the nine-passenger models had the longest Cadillac production car wheelbase, as well as power front ventipanes, Automatic Level Control, right-hand manually operated outside rearview mirrors, 8.20 x I5-8PR blackwall tires and Automatic Climate Control air-conditioning, as standard equipment.

FLEETWOOD SEVENTY-FIVE SUB-SERIES 697/698

Model Number	Body/Style Number	Body Type & Seating	Factory Price	Shipping Weight	Production Total
68-697	69723-R	4-dr Sed-9P	10,629	5300	805
68-697	69733-S	4-dr Limo-9P	10,768	5385	995
68-698	69890-Z	Commercial chassis	—	—	2,413

NOTE: The commercial chassis was built on a 156 inch wheelbase and was provided to professional car builders for the manufacture of hearses and ambulances, etc.

1968 Cadillac, Fleetwood Eldorado two-door hardtop sport coupe, V-8

FLEETWOOD ELDORADO — (V-8) — SUB-SERIES 693 — The 1968 Eldorado had the front parking lamps located to the leading edge of the fenders, where they were mounted vertically. To accommodate recessed windshield wipers, the hood was lengthened by 4-1/2 inches. On the rear fenders, small round safety lamps were now affixed. The design of the lens for the front cornering lamps (formerly vertically ribbed) was modified. The new 472 cid V-8, with 525 foot-pounds of torque, made it possible to spin the front-driven wheels on smooth, dry surfaces. Spring rates were slightly lowered to give a more cushiony ride. Upholstery trims included diamond pattern cloth and vinyl; Deauville cloth with vinyl bolsters in four color choices and genuine leather options. Removed from the rear roof pillar, but not the hood and deck lid, were the familiar wreath and crest style Fleetwood emblems. Regular equipment on the luxury sports type car included all Fleetwood standards, plus power rear quarter venti-panes; power front disc brakes: retractable headlamp covers; and Rosewood pattern dash panel appliques.

FLEETWOOD ELDORADO SUB-SERIES 693

Model Number	Body/Style Number	Body Type & Seating	Factory Price	Shipping Weight	Production Total
68-693	69347-H	2-dr HT Cpe-6P	6605	4580	24,528

NOTE: See price increase notation under DeVille specifications chart.

CADILLAC ENGINE: V-8. Overhead valves. Cast iron block. Displacement: 472 cid. Bore and stroke: 4.30 x 4.06 inches. Compression ratio: 10. 5: 1. Brake hp: 37 5 at 4400 rpm. Five main bearings. Hydraulic valve lifters. Carburetor: Rochester Quadrajet four-barrel model 7028230.

NOTE: The new engine featured a metal temperature monitoring device; air injection emissions control system; integral air-conditioning system (still optional); cast crankshaft and connecting rods; integral water crossover pipe with thermostatic passages; engine bearings with more surface area; and 15-plate battery.

CHASSIS FEATURES: Wheelbase: (Series 75) 149.8 inches, (Commercial chassis) 156 inches; (Eldorado) 120 inches; (Sixty-Special) 133 inches; (all other models) 129.5 inches. Overall length: (Series 75) 245.2 inches, (Eldorado) 221 inches; (Sixty-Special) 228.2 inches; (all other models) 224.7 inches. Rear axle ratio: 2.94:1. Transmission: three-speed Turbo-Hydramatic. Tires: (Series 75) 8.20 x 15: (all other models) 9.00 x 15. Front tread: (Eldorado) 63.5 inches, (all other models) not available. Rear tread: (Eldorado) 63.0 inches; (all other models) not available.

POWERTRAIN OPTIONS: Optional axle ratio data not available. Air injector reactor and closed positive crankcase ventilation standard. Controlled differential was now $52.65 extra on all models except Eldorado.

CONVENIENCE OPTIONS: Auxiliary horn ($16). Automatic level control option on models G-N-K-F-J-B-L ($79). Automatic Climate Control. except R and S models ($516). Bucket seats with console on models F-H with leather upholstery required ($184). Firemist finish ($132). Cruise control ($95). Rear window defogger on models G-N-K-J-B-L-M-P ($27). Front disc brakes on Eldorado only ($105). Door guards on model G-F-J-H ($5); on models N-K-B-L-M-P-R-S ($8). Expanded vinyl upholstery on models G-N-K ($42). Soft Ray glass ($51). Guide-Matic headlamp control ($51). Headrests ($53). Leather upholstery, models J-B-L-M-P ($138); model H ($158). License frame, single ($6); pair ($13). Padded roof, models J-H ($132); models B-L ($137). Power door locks, two-door ($47); four-door ($68). Power door locks for Fleetwood 75 models ($116). Power ventipanes, except models H-M-P, power windows required ($72). Rear quarter ventipanes on Eldorado only ($63). Power windows on Calais models ($116). AM radio ($162). AM/FM radio ($188). AM/FM stereo, except Fleetwood 75 models ($288). AM radio rear controls on Fleetwood 75 models ($242). Reclining front seat with headrests on models F-H with bucket seats or Eldorado bench seats required ($84). Four-way left-hand power bucket seat on models F-J-B-H ($53). Six-way power front seat on models G-N-K ($11l); models F-J-B-L-H-M-P-R ($83). Rear center seat belt ($11). Front shoulder straps ($32). Tilt-telescope steering wheel ($90). Remote control trunk lock ($52). Twilight Sentinel on Eldorado ($37); other models ($32). White sidewall tires, size 9.00 x 15, four-ply 8PR-5, except nine-passenger models ($56 exchange). White sidewall tires. size 8.20 x 15, four-ply 8PR-5 on nine-passenger models ($63 exchange). Four new items of optional equipment were: Twin front and rear floor mats for all models except H-R-S ($17). One-piece front and rear floor mats for Eldorado ($20). Twin front floor mats for Fleetwood 75 models ($10) and front seat warmer for all models except Fleetwood 75s, which came instead with rear seat warmer only, both at ($95).

HISTORICAL FOOTNOTES: Dealer introduction for 1968 Cadillacs and Eldorados took place September 21, 1967. Fourth successive yearly sales record set this year despite 21 day UAW shutdown at Fisher Body Fleetwood plant in Detroit (November 1967). Production was down 1.1 percent, due to same strike. Four-wheel disc brakes with floating calipers optionally available. All-new dashboard design. Larger, shrouded rearview mirrors to eliminate wind buffeting.

1969 CADILLAC

CALAIS — (V-8) — SERIES 682 — Although its overall size and character was largely unchanged, the 1969 Cadillac was restyled in the Eldorado image. An Eldorado like front fender treatment evolved and helped to emphasize a stronger horizontal design line. Rear quarters were extended to give the car a longer look. There was also an all-new grille with dual horizontal headlamps positioned in the outboard, step-down areas of the grille. The hood was again extended, a total of 2-1/2 inches, to add to the impression of extra length. Calais models came with all GM safety features; V-8; Turbo-Hydramatic; variable-ratio power steering; dual power brakes; power windows; center front armrest; electric clock; two front cigarette lighters; twin front and rear ashtrays; a complete set of interior and exterior courtesy, safety and warning lights; Mirror Group; concealed three-speed windshield washers and wipers; and five 900 x 15-4PR black sidewall tires. All regular Cadillac models had a new, squarer roofline and sculptured rear deck and bumper treatments.

CADILLAC I.D. NUMBERS: Serial numbers and motor numbers took the same general form used in 1968. The serial number was in the same location. The sixth symbol was changed to '9' to indicate 1969 model year.

CALAIS SERIES 682

Model Number	Body/Style Number	Body Type & Seating	Factory Price	Shipping Weight	Production Total
69-682	68249N	4-dr HT Sed-6P	5660	4630	6,825
69-682	68247G	2-dr HT Cpe-6P	5484	4555	5,600

NOTE: On January 1, 1969, headrests (restraints) became mandatory on all U.S. cars. Cadillac prices were increased $18, with new prices reflected above.

1969 Cadillac, Coupe DeVille, two-door hardtop, V-8

DEVILLE SERIES — (V-8) — SERIES 683 — DeVilles had all of the features used in Calais, plus rear center armrests; dual rear cigarette lighters and two-way power operated horizontal front seat adjusters. A model identification signature script still sat above the horizontal bodyside rub molding towards the back of the rear fenders.

DEVILLE SERIES 683

Model Number	Body/Style Number	Body Type & Seating	Factory price	Shipping Weight	Production Total
69-683	68369L	4-dr Sed DeV-6P	5954	4640	7,890
69-683	68347J	2-dr Cpe DeV-6P	5721	4595	65,755
69-683	68349B	4-dr Sed DeV-6P	5954	4660	72,958
69-683	68367F	2-dr Conv DeV-6P	5905	4590	16,445

NOTE: On January 1, 1969, head restraints became mandatory on all U.S. cars. Cadillac prices increased $18, with new prices reflected above.

1969 Cadillac, Fleetwood 60 Special four-door Brougham, V-8

FLEETWOOD SIXTY-SPECIAL — (V-8) — SUB-SERIES 680/681 — Fleetwood models had all standard features of DeVilles, except limousine had no front center armrest. Extra regular equipment included Automatic Level Control. The Brougham included adjustable reading lamps and a Dual Comfort front seat. External identification was provided with bright metal body underscores, Fleetwood emblems and lettering and padded Brougham roof. The wheelbase for Sixty-Specials was again 3-1/2 inches longer than on other models. Interior appointments were enriched and new, Eldorado-like, front and rear styling was seen.

FLEETWOOD SIXTY-SPECIAL SUB-SERIES 680/681

Model Number	Body/Style Number	Body Type & Seating	Factory Price	Shipping Weight	Production Total
69-680	68069M	4-dr Sed-6P	6779	4765	2,545
69-681	68169P	4-dr Brghm-6P	7110	4770	17,300

NOTE: On January 1, 1969, head restraints became mandatory on all U.S. cars. Cadillac prices were increased $18, with new prices reflected above.

FLEETWOOD SEVENTY-FIVE — (V-8) — SUB-SERIES 697/698 — Stretched bodies and trim; Fleetwood emblems and embellishments; doors cut into a formal, high headroom roof and generally higher appointment and trim levels continued to mark Cadillac's most luxurious line. All DeVille equipment, plus Automatic Level Control; Automatic Climate Control; rear window defogger; four rear ashtrays and 8.20 x 15 four-ply blackwall tires were standard.

FLEETWOOD SEVENTY-FIVE SUB-SERIES 697/698

Model Number	Body/Style Number	Body Type & Seating	Factory Price	Shipping Weight	Production Total
69-697	69723R	4-dr Sed-6P	10,841	5430	880
69-697	69733S	4-dr Limo-9P	10,979	5555	1,156
69-698	6989OZ	Commercial chassis	—	—	2,550

NOTE: On January 1, 1969, head restraints became mandatory on all U.S. cars. Cadillac prices were increased $18, with new prices reflected above. Dealer preparation charges were $90 on Calais, DeVille and Eldorado; $115 on Fleetwood Sixty-Special and Brougham; $150 on Fleetwood Seventy-Fives. These charges are included in retail prices listed above.

1969 Cadillac, Fleetwood Eldorado two-door hardtop sport coupe, V-8

FLEETWOOD ELDORADO — (V-8) — SUB-SERIES 693 — The front-wheel-drive Eldorado continued to be offered as a single model; a six-passenger, two-door hardtop on a short wheelbase platform. There was a new cross-hatch grille that was separated from the headlights. The dual headlights were now part of the body design and were fully exposed and stationary. Standard equipment included power operated rear quarter vent windows.

FLEETWOOD ELDORADO SUB-SERIES 693

Model Number	Body/Style Number	Body Type & Seating	Factory Price	Shipping Weight	Production Total
69-693	69347H	2-dr HT Cpe-6P	6711	4550	23,333

ENGINE: V-8. Overhead valves. Cast iron block. Displacement: 472 cid. Bore and stroke: 4.3 x 4.06 inches. Compression ratio: 10.5:1. Brake hp: 375 at 4400 rpm.. Five main bearings. Hydraulic valve lifters. Carburetor: Rochester four-barrel Quadrajet, model 7028230.

CHASSIS FEATURES: Wheelbase: (Commercial chassis) 156 inches; (Seventy-Five) 149.8 inches; (Sixty-Special) 133 inches; (Eldorado) 120 inches, (all other models) 129.5 inches. Overall length: (Seventy-Five) 245.5 inches; (Sixty-Special) 228.5 inches; (Eldorado) 221 inches; (all other models) 225 inchs. Front tread; (Eldorado) 63 inches; (all other models) not available. Rear tread: (Eldorado) 63.5 inches; (all other models) not available. Tires: (Seventy-Five) 8.20 x 15 four-ply blackwall; (all other models) 9.00 x 15-PR blackwalls.

POWERTRAIN OPTIONS: All cars used the 472 cid, 375 hp V-8 with no other powerplants available. Turbo-Hydramatic transmission was standard equipment throughout the line. Controlled differential was $52.65 extra on all models except Eldorado. Standard axle ratios: (Seventy-Five) 3.21:1; (Eldorado) 3.07:1; (all other models) 2.94:1.

CONVENIENCE OPTIONS: Automatic Climate Control option ($516). Automatic level control, models G-N-F-J-B-L, ($79). Bucket seats with console, model H with leather upholstery required ($184). Firemist paint ($132). Cruise Control ($95). Rear window defogger, models G-N-H-J-B-L-M-P ($26). Door guards, models G-F-J-H ($5); models N-B-L-M-P-R-S ($8). Dual comfort seat, standard in Brougham, optional models F-J-BM ($105). Twin front and rear floor mats, all models except H-R-S ($17). One-piece front and rear floor mats, model H ($20). Twin front floor mats, models R-S ($10). Soft Ray tinted glass ($53). Guide-Matic headlamp control ($51). Head restraints ($18). Note: Head restraints mandatory after January 1, 1969. Leather upholstery, models J-B-L-M-P ($138); model H ($158). License frame, single ($6); dual ($13). Power door locks, includes electric seatback release, models G-F-J-H ($68); models N-B-L-M-P ($68); models R-S ($116). AM radio ($162). AM/FM radio ($188). AM/FM stereo radio, except models R-S ($288). AM rear-control radio, models R-S ($242). Four-way left-hand bucket seat, model H ($53). Six-way power seat adjuster: front seat, models G-N ($116); front seat, models F-J-B-L-H-M-R, with bench seat only ($90); models F-J-B-M-P, for right-hand Dual Comfort seat, Code Y accessories required, ($116). Front seat warmer, available all models, except rear seat only in models R-S, ($95). Front shoulder belts ($32). Tilt and telescope steering wheel ($95). Trumpet horn ($16). Remote control trunk lock ($32). Twilight Sentinel, Eldorado ($37); other models ($32). Expanded vinyl roof, in standard production colors, models G-N ($42). Vinyl roof, models J-B-L ($153). Padded vinyl roof, model H ($158). Whitewall tires, size 9.00 x 15 four-ply, except models R-S ($57 exchange). Whitewall tires, size 8.20 x 15 four-ply, models R-S only ($63 exchange). Whitewall tires, heavy-duty high mileage type for Eldorado ($83 exchange).

HISTORICAL FOOTNOTES: Dealer introduction for 1969 Cadillacs and Eldorados was held September 26, 1968. Production of the Eldorado body for 1969 was transferred from the Fleetwood plant in Detroit to the Fisher Body plant in Euclid, Ohio. Cadillac enjoyed its fifth consecutive record sales year and built over 250,000 units for the first time in company history. (Calendar year figures). Strikes again affected the 1969 model run and production of cars built to 1969 specifications peaked at 223,267 units, of which 199,934 were regular Cadillacs. Total production fell 2.9 percent over the 1968 model run.

CALAIS — (V-8) — SERIES 682 — A relatively minor restyling marked the 1970 Cadillacs. A facelift included a grille with 13 vertical blades set against a delicately cross-hatched rectangular opening. The bright metal headlamp surrounds were bordered with body color to give a more refined look. Narrow, vertical 'vee' taillights were seen again, but no longer had smaller V-shaped bottom lenses pointing downward below the bumper. Wheel discs and winged crest fender tip emblems were new. A Calais signature script was placed above the rear end of the horizontal lower belt molding, just ahead of the chromed taillight dividers. Standard equipment included Turbo-Hydramatic transmission; power steering; front disc brakes; power windows; center front armrest; electric clock; two front cigarette lighters; twin front and rear ashtrays; complete interior and exterior courtesy lamps; safety, warning and convenience lights; outside remote control left-hand mirror; visor vanity mirror and L78-15 bias-belted fiberglass blackwall tires.

CADILLAC I.D. NUMBERS: Serial numbers and motor numbers took the same general form used in 1969. The serial number was in the same location. The sixth symbol was changed to a '0' to indicate the 1970 model year.

CALAIS SERIES 682

Model Number	Body/Style Number	Body Type & Seating	Factory Price	Shipping Weight	Production Total
70-682	68249N	4-dr HT Sed-6P	5813	4680	5,187
70-682	68247G	2-d HT Cpe-6P	5637	4620	4,724

ENGINE: (STANDARD ENGINE)

1970 Cadillac, Sedan DeVille four-door hardtop, V-8

DEVILLE SERIES — (V-8) — SERIES 683 — DeVilles had all of the same features as Calais models, plus, dual rear cigarette lighters, Two-Way horizontal control front seat adjustment and rear center armrest in all models, except convertibles. Exterior distinction came from a DeVille script above the rear end of the belt molding and from the use of long, rectangular back-up light lenses set into the lower rear bumper, as opposed to the smaller, square lenses used on Calais. A new feature seen this year was a body color border around the edge of the vinyl top covering, when this option was ordered. This treatment had first been seen on 1969 Fleetwoods. The Sedan DeVille and Convertible DeVille were in their last season.

DEVILLE SERIES 683

Model Number	Body/Style Number	Body Type & Seating	Factory Price	Shipping Weight	Production Total
70-683	68369L	4-dr Sed-6P	6118	4690	7,230
70-683	68349B	4-dr HT DeV-6P	6118	4725	83,274
70-683	68347J	2-dr Cpe DeV-6P	5884	4650	76,043
70-683	68367F	2-dr Conv DeV-6P	6068	4660	15,172

1970 Cadillac, Fleetwood 60 Special four-door Brougham, V-8

FLEETWOOD SIXTY-SPECIAL — (V-8) — SUB-SERIES 680/681 — The Fleetwood models had all equipment offered in DeVilles plus, Automatic Level Control. The Brougham also came standard with adjustable reading lights; Dual Comfort front seat with Two-Way power adjustment (left side) and a padded vinyl top. Distinguishing Sixty-Specials externally were bright metal wheelhouse moldings; wide full-length rocker panels with rear extensions and block lettering, denoting the series, positioned in back of the front wheel opening. At the end of the 1970 model run, the 'standard' Sixty-Special sedan was dropped. A noticeable trim change was the use of a thin, horizontal beltline molding on all 1970 Sixty-Specials.

FLEETWOOD SIXTY-SPECIAL SUB-SERIES 680/681

Model Number	Body/Style Number	Body Type & Seating	Factory Price	Shipping Weight	Production Total
70-680	68069M	4-dr Sed-6P	6953	4830	1,738
70-681	68169P	4-dr Brghm-6P	7284	4835	16,913

FLEETWOOD SEVENTY-FIVE — (V-8) — SUB-SERIES 697/698 — Special equipment found on the big Cadillac sedan and limousine included Automatic Level Control; rear window defogger; four rear ashtrays and a manual right-hand outside rearview mirror. Separate Climate Control systems were provided for front and rear compartments. Fleetwood wreath crests appeared at the extreme edge of the rear fenders, above the belt molding, on both models. As usual, the doors on the limousine were cut into the roof and a fixed driver's partition with adjustable glass compartment divider was inside. The front compartment was trimmed in genuine leather, the rear in one of five combinations. Three of these were the more standard Divan cloth trims, while Decordo cloth or Dumbarton cloth with leather were the richest selections available.

FLEETWOOD SEVENTY-FIVE SUB-SERIES 697/698

Model Number	Body/Style Number	Body Type & Seating	Factory Price	Shipping Weight	Production Total
70-697	69723R	4-dr Sed-6P	11,039	5530	876
70-697	69733S	4-dr Limo-9P	11,178	5630	1,240
70-698	6989OZ	Commercial chassis	—	—	2,506

NOTE: The commercial chassis was built on a 156 wheelbase and was provided to professional car builders for the manufacture of hearses and ambulances, etc.

1970 Cadillac, Eldorado two-door hardtop coupe, V-8 (AA)

FLEETWOOD ELDORADO — (V-8) — SUB-SERIES 693 — A new, 500 cid 400 hp V-8 was the big new for the Eldorado this year. A special '8.2 litre' badge was placed on the left-hand side of the redesigned grille to announce the industry's biggest powerplant. The grille itself again had a cross-hatched insert, but horizontal blades were set upon it, emphasizing the V-shape of the front. Thinner vertical taillamps were used, giving a more rakish look. The winged-V emblems used at the front of the fenders on other Cadillacs were added to the Eldorado front parking lamp lenses. Bright rocker panel trim, with front and rear extensions, was used. There was also Eldorado block lettering at the lower front fender, behind the wheel housing.

FLEETWOOD ELDORADO SUB-SERIES 693

Model Number	Body/Style Number	Body Type & Seating	Factory Price	Shipping Weight	Production Total
70-693	69347H	2-dr HT Cpe-6P	6903	4630	23,842

CADILLAC ENGINE: V-8. Overhead valves. Cast iron block. Displacement: 472 cid. Bore and stroke: 4.3 x 4.06 inches. Compression ratio: 10.0:1. Brake hp: 375 at 4400 rpm.. Five main bearings. Hydraulic valve lifters. Carburetor: Rochester four-barrel Quadrajet Model 4MV.

ELDORADO ENGINE: V-8. Overhead valves. Cast iron block. Displacement: 500 cid. Bore and stroke: 4.30 x 4.304 inches. Compression ratio: 10.0:1. Brake hp: 400 at 4400 rpm.. Five main bearings. Hydraulic valve lifters. Carburetor: Rochester four-barrel Quadrajet Model 4MV (Eldorado type).

CHASSIS FEATURES: Wheelbase: (Seventy-Five) 149.8 inches; (Eldorado) 120 inches; (Sixty-Special) 133 inches; (all other models) 129.5 inches. Overall length: (SeventyFive) 245.3 inches; (Sixty-Special) 288.5 inches; (Eldorado) 221 inches; (all other models) 225 inches. Tires: L-78 x 15.

POWERTRAIN OPTIONS: Controlled differential, except Eldorado ($53).

CONVENIENCE OPTIONS: Automatic Climate Control ($516). Automatic Level Control on models G-N-F-J-B-L ($79). Bucket seats with console in Eldorado with leather upholstery required ($184). Bucket seats in Eldorado, with cloth upholstery, as SPO ($292). Special carpets with matching instrument carpet panels in all models except H-R-S, as SPO ($32); in Eldorados, as SPO ($37). Cloth front compartment in limousine, as SPO ($126). Firemist paint, as SPO ($205). Special paint, except Firemist, as SPO ($179). Dual Comfort front seat in Model L, as SPO with standard cloth upholstery ($184). Dual Comfort front seat in Model L, as SPO with production leather upholstery ($316). Vinyl padded roof in models R-S as SPO ($758). Vinyl padded roof with Landau bows in models R-S, as SPO ($2,131). Vinyl padded blind quarter roof in models R-S, without Landau bows, as SPO ($2,026). NOTE The term 'SPO' means "Special Production Option". Cruise control ($95). Rear window defogger ($26-37). Door edge guards ($610). Dual Comfort seat with standard Brougham trim in models F-J-B-M ($105). Soft Ray glass ($53). Guide-Matic headlamp control ($51). Leather upholstery ($156-184). License frame(s) in all models ($6-13). Floor and trunk mats ($11-20). Power door locks in standard wheelbase models ($68); in limousines ($116). Signal seeking radio AM/FM with rear control ($289); without rear control ($222); with stereo, except models R-S ($322). AM/FM radio ($188). Power seats, Eldorado left-hand Four-Way bucket ($53); Six-Way front ($90-116); Six-Way left-hand front with Dual-Comfort ($90116). Shoulder belts ($32). Tilt and telescope steering wheel ($95). Electric powered sun roof in models B-H-J-L-P with vinyl top required and Six-Way seat recommended ($626). Trumpet horn ($15). Remote control trunk

lock ($53). Twilight Sentinel ($37). Expanded vinyl upholstery in models G-N ($42). Vinyl roof in models J-B-L ($153); in Eldorado ($158). White sidewall L78-15 tires models R-S ($46); all other models ($40).

HISTORICAL FOOTNOTES: A total of 238,745 Cadillacs, built for the 1970 model run, set an all-time divisional record. Calendar year sales totals were off the mark, however, due to a major G.M. strike. They peaked at just 152,859 units. George R. Elges became general manager of Cadillac Division this year. Sales of the new Cadillac line began September 18, 1969. The optional Trackmaster skid control system was made available for the Eldorado, subsequent to initial model introductions.

1971 CADILLAC

CALAIS — (V-8) — SERIES 682 — Cadillacs were completely restyled with pairs of individually housed squarish headlamps set wider apart. The V-shaped grille had an eggcrate style insert and was protected by massive vertical guards framing a rectangular license plate indentation. The Calais wheelbase stretched 133 inches long. A wide hood with full-length windsplits, a prominent center crease and hidden windshield wipers was seen. A Cadillac crest decorated the nose and new indicator lamps appeared atop each front fender. A horizontal beltline molding ran from behind the front wheel housing, almost to the rear, stopping where an elliptical bulge in the body came to a point. The rear wheel openings were again enclosed with fender skirts. Calais signature scripts were on front fenders and the right side of the deck lid. Taillamps were of the same general shape as a year earlier, but were no longer divided by a chrome bar. Long, horizontal back-up lamps were set in the bumper, on either side of a deeply recessed license plate housing. Standard Calais equipment included Turbo-Hydramatic transmission; power steering; dual power brakes with front discs: power windows; center front armrest; electric clock; twin front cigarette lighters; twin front and rear ashtrays; complete interior and exterior courtesy, safety, warning and convenience lights; remote control left-hand outside rearview mirror; visor vanity mirror; L-78-15 bias belted tires and the 472 cid four-barrel V-8 engine.

CADILLAC I.D. NUMBERS: Serial numbers and motor numbers took the same general form used in 1970. The serial number was in the same location. The sixth symbol was changed to a '1' to indicate 1971 model year.

CALAIS SERIES 682

Model Number	Body/Style Number	Body Type & Seating	Factory Price	Shipping Weight	Production Total
71-682	68249N	4-dr HT Sed-6P	6075	4715	3,569
71-682	68247G	2-dr HT Cpe-6P	5899	4635	3,360

1971 Cadillac, two-door hardtop Coupe DeVille, V-8

DEVILLE SERIES — (V-8) — SERIES 683 — DeVilles had all equipment standard on Calais models, plus, dual rear cigarette lighters, Two-Way horizontal front seat adjuster and rear center armrests on all styles, except the DeVille. To set them apart visually, DeVilles had thin, bright metal rocker panel strips and signature scripts on front fenders bearing the series name. The bottoms of the rear fenders were decorated with a bright metal beauty panel that was wider than the rocker strips and blended into the molding running along the bottom of the fender skirt. As on Calais, the lower beltline molding ended on the elliptical rear fender bulge, where thin rectangular side markers were placed above and below the chrome strip. Only two body styles remained in this series.

DEVILLE SERIES 683

Model Number	Body/Style Number	Body Type & Seating	Factory Price	Shipping Weight	Production Total
71-683	68349B	4-dr HT Sed DeV-6P	6498	4730	69,345
71-683	68347J	2-dr Cpe DeV-6P	6264	4685	66,081

FLEETWOOD SIXTY-SPECIAL — (V-8) — SUB-SERIES 681 — The Sixty-Special was now a one model line, including only the Brougham sedan. It came with standard extras like Automotive Level Control; adjustable reading lights; Two-Way adjustable Dual Comfort front seat and a padded vinyl roof. New exterior styling was seen along with several new trim features. The windows were cut nearly into the roof in semi-limousine fashion and had softly rounded corners. Vertically angled rectangular coach lamps were a common option incorporated into the rear roof pillar. A broad rocker panel trim plate, with rear extension, was used. The Fleetwood name was block lettered on the front fenders, behind the wheel opening and on the right-hand side of the rear deck lid. The new window styling included a wide pillar separating the front and rear door glass.

1971 Cadillac, Fleetwood 60 Special four-door Brougham, V-8

FLEETWOOD SIXTY-SPECIAL SUB-SERIES 681

Model Number	Body/Style Number	Body Type & Seating	Factory Price	Shipping Weight	Production Total
71-681	68169P	4-dr Brghm-6P	7763	4910	15,200

FLEETWOOD SEVENTY-FIVE — (V-8) — SUB-SERIES 697/698 — The long-wheelbase Fleetwoods came with everything found on DeVilles (except front center armrest in limousine) plus, Automatic Level Control; Automatic Climate Control; rear window defogger; four rear ashtrays and manual right-hand outside rearview mirror. Externally, they had the new Cadillac styling and window treatments similar to those described for the Sixty-Special. However, the rear roof pillar could be custom finished in several different ways, including triangular 'coach' windows or vinyl covered 'blind quarter' looks. Ornamentation included the traditional Fleetwood laurel wreath crests and lettering, plus, thin horizontal belt moldings. However, no rocker sill strips, panels or extension moldings were used. And, of course, the limousine had the doors cut into the roof, special upholstery appointments and a driver's partition with adjustable division window.

FLEETWOOD SEVENTY-FIVE SUB-SERIES 697/698

Model Number	Body/Style Number	Body Type & Seating	Factory Price	Shipping Weight	Production Total
71-697	69723R	4-dr Sed-6P	11,869	5335	752
71-697	69733S	4-dr Limo-9P	12,008	5475	848
71-698	6989Z	Commercial chassis	—	—	2,014

NOTE: The commercial chassis was built off a 157-1/2 inch wheelbase and was provided to professional car builders for the manufacture of hearses and ambulances, etc.

1971 Cadillac, Eldorado two-door convertible, V-8

FLEETWOOD ELDORADO — (V-8) — SUB-SERIES 693 — The second generation of front-wheel-drive Eldorados appeared this year, including a new convertible. Used again was the big 500 cid V-8, but with lower compression ratios and 35 hp less. Rear coil springs were another new technical feature. The Eldorado wheelbase was stretched more than six inches, too. Body styling was heavily sculptured. A vertically textured, rectangular grille was new. Front fenders had a chiselled, cut-off look and a vertical windsplit, that harkened back to the early 1950s, appeared just behind the doors. Fender skirts were something new for Eldorados and added to the old-fashioned, classical image. So did the revival of convertible styling in this line. Trim features included twin vertical front bumper guards; Fleetwood wreaths on the hood and deck; Eldorado scripts on the lower front fenders; short horizontal beltline moldings on front fenders and doors; rocker sill beauty panels and a stand-up hood ornament. Narrow 'coach' windows were cut into the rear roof pillar of the Eldorado coupe. Rear end treatments for the new body included a raised and extended trunk lid appearance; extra large backlight and a massive rear bumper, with a flat in-and-out look, that housed vertical, wraparound taillights at each side. Standard fare for the sporty luxury series included all DeVille equipment, less rear armrests, plus, Automatic Level Control and front-wheel-drive technology.

FLEETWOOD ELDORADO SUB-SERIES 693

Model Number	Body/Style Number	Body Type & Seating	Factory Price	Shipping Weight	Production Total
71-693	69367E	2-dr Conv Cpe-6P	7751	4690	6,800
71-693	69347H	2-dr HT Spt Cpe-6P	7383	4650	20,568

CADILLAC ENGINES

STANDARD V-8: V-8. Overhead valves. Cast iron block. Displacement: 472 cid. Bore and stroke: 4.3 x 4.06 inches. Compression ratio: 10.0:1. Brake hp: 375 at 4400 rpm.. Five main bearings. Hydraulic valve lifters. Carburetor: Rochester four-barrel Quadrajet Model 4MV (standard).

ELDORADO V-8: V-8. Overhead valves. Cast iron block. Displacement: 500 cid. Bore and stroke: 4.30 x 4.304 inches. Compression ratio: 9.0: 1. Brake hp: 365 at 4400 rpm.. Five main bearings. Hydraulic valve lifters. Carburetor: Rochester four-barrel Quadrajet Model 4MV.

CHASSIS FEATURES: Wheelbase: (Commercial chassis) 157-1/2 inches; (Seventy Five) 151-1/2 inches; (Sixty-Special) 133 inches; (Eldorado) 126.3 inches; (all other models) 130 inches. Overall length: (Seventy-Five) 247.3 inches; (Sixty-Special) 228.8 inches; (Eldorado) 221.6 inches; (all other models) 225.8 inches. Tires: L-78 x 15.

POWERTRAIN OPTIONS: Controlled differential, except Eldorado ($58). Trackmaster for Eldorado only ($211).

CONVENIENCE OPTIONS: Automatic Climate Control ($537). Automatic Level Control for Calais and DeVille ($79). Cruise control ($95). Rear window defogger in Eldorado ($37); in other models ($32). Eldorado grid type rear window defogger ($63). Door edge guards in two-door ($6); in four-door ($10). Power door locks for 75s ($118); other models ($71). Power door locks with electric seatback release in coupes and convertibles ($71). DeVille, Dual Comfort front seat ($105). Front and rear floor mats; twin type in 75s ($10); one-piece type in Eldorado ($20); twin type in other models ($17). Soft Ray tinted glass ($59). Guidematic ($51). Lamp monitors ($50). License frames, one ($6); pair ($12). Remote control right mirror ($26). Brougham and 75 opera lamps ($53). Firemist paint ($132). Radios, AM/FM push-button ($138); AM/FM signal-seeking stereo ($328); AM/FM with tape ($416); AM/FM stereo signal-seeking with rear control in 75s ($421). DeVille vinyl roof ($156). Eldorado padded vinyl roof ($161). DeVille and Brougham Six-Way seat ($92). Six-Way seat in DeVille/Brougham/Calais, with passenger Dual-Comfort in DeVille/Brougham ($118). Shoulder belts in convertible front seat or rear seat all models ($32). Tilt and Telescope steering wheel ($95). DeVille/Eldorado/Brougham sun roof with vinyl or padded roof mandatory ($626). Trumpet horn in Eldorado coupe ($16). Remote control trunk lock ($58). Trunk mat ($8). Twilight Sentinel ($41). Expanded vinyl Calais upholstery ($42). Expanded leather upholstery, in DeVille/Brougham ($174); in Eldorado coupe ($184). White sidewall L78-15 tires, in 75s ($49); in others ($42).

HISTORICAL FOOTNOTES: Model year production was curtailed by labor disputes and peaked at 188,537 units. The new models were introduced September 29, 1982. For the first time ever, Cadillac built cars outside of Detroit, Mich. Same 1971 Coupe and Sedan DeVilles were built at a GM Assembly Division (GMAD) factory in Linden, N.J. Sales, for calendar 1971, hit a new high of 267,868 units. Hints of a forthcoming down-sized Cadillac line were heard in Detroit.

1972 CADILLAC

CALAIS — (V-8) — SERIES 682 — In 1972, General Motors kept busy with the task of re-engineering its cars to conform to new fuel and safety standards established by Federal Government mandate. There was little time to pay attention to altering appearances and few styling changes were seen in the latest Cadillacs. A modest frontal revision placed more emphasis on horizontal grille blades. The parking lamps were moved from the bumper to between the square bezeled headlamps, which were now set wider apart. V-shaped emblems made a return appearance on the hood and deck lid. A number of equipment changes were seen. As usual (since 1967) the list of Calais features started with all regulation safety devices, to which was added variable ratio power steering; dual power brakes with front discs; automatic transmission; power windows; all courtesy and warning lights; a new bumper impact system; three-speed wipers and windshield washers; visor vanity mirror; two front cigar lighters; automatic parking brake release; front center armrest; passenger assist straps; side marker and cornering lights; the 472 cid four-barrel V-8; flow-through ventilation and five L78-15 black sidewall bias belted tires. Externally, the Calais was identified by front fender model scripts; thin horizontal belt moldings; fender skirts; full wheelcovers and a script on the right side of the trunk.

CADILLAC I.D. NUMBERS: The GM serial numbering system changed slightly this year to incorporate an alphabetical series code and a new alphabetical code designating engine type. The serial number was again located on top of the instrument panel, where it was visible through the windshield. The first symbol was a number '6' to indicate production by Cadillac. The second symbol was a letter identifying the series as follows: C = Calais; D = DeVille: B = Brougham; L= Eldorado and F= Fleetwood 75. The third and fourth symbols were numbers identifying the body type and they correspond to the numerical portion of the Body Style Numbers used in the charts below. The fifth symbol was a letter identifying the engine, as follows: R = 472 cid V-8; S 500 cid Eldorado V-8. The sixth symbol was a number identifying model year, such as '2' for 1972. The seventh symbol was a letter designating the manufacturing point as follows: Q= Detroit, Michigan and E = Linden, New Jersey. The next group of numbers was the sequential production code. Body Style Numbers were also changed this year on some data plates and factory literature, but not all. The first symbol of the new type of code was the series identifying letter given above. For example, the new system used a 'C' to designate Calais (the old system used the three numbers '682'). The second and third symbols of the new type code were numbers identifying body style. These numbers correspond to the charts below and were the same as the fourth and fifth numbers used in the past. For example, the Body Style Code for a Calais Coupe was 68247 under the old system and C47 under the new system. Of course, despite the new GM system, Cadillac had been using letter codes for different body styles since the mid-1950s and these were used again. They were the same as in the past; G = Calais Coupe; N = Calais sedan; etc. Research shows that GM cars built in 1972 used the new system on the serial number tag and the old system on the vehicle data plate below the hood. From 1973 on, the new system was used in both locations. Also, this new system was used through 1975, the last year covered in this edition of the Standard Catalog of American Cars.

CALAIS SERIES/CALAIS SERIES 682

Model Number	Body/Style Number	Body Type & Seating	Factory Price	Shipping Weight	Production Total
682/C	C49-N	4-dr HT Sed-6P	5938	4698	3,875
682/C	C47-G	2-dr HT Cpe-6P	5771	4642	3,900

NOTE: Body Style Numbers in column two above are the new type used on the serial number tag mounted to top of instrument panel, visable through windshield. Research indicates that the old type Body Style Number was still found on the vehicle data plate below the hood. With the new system the Calais sedan is Body Style Number C49; with the old system 68249. This note applies only to 1972 Cadillacs, as the new system was used in both locations from 1973 on.

1972 Cadillac, Sedan DeVille four-door hardtop, V-8

DEVILLE — (V-8) — SERIES D/SERIES 683 — DeVille standard equipment included all found on Calais plus, rocker panel moldings; rear center armrest and twin rear cigarette lighters. Of course, the rocker panel trim helped in identifying the cars, but there were also new DeVille signature scripts affixed to the sides of the rear roof pillars.

DEVILLE SERIES D/DEVILLE SERIES 683

Model Number	Body/Style Number	Body Type & Seating	Factory Price	Shipping Weight	Production Total
683/D	D49-B	4-dr Sed DeV-6P	6390	4762	99.531
683/D	D47-J	2-dr Cpe DeV-6P	6168	4682	95,280

1972 Cadillac, Fleetwood Sixty-Special four-door Brougham, V-8

FLEETWOOD SIXTY-SPECIAL — (V-8) — SUB-SERIES B/681 — Fleetwood models had all DeVille features plus, Automatic Level Control and, on the Brougham, Dual Comfort front seat; rear seat reading light; carpeted foot rests and a padded vinyl roof with rear window chrome molding. As the only Cadillacs on the 133 inch wheelbase, Broughams were identified by their large, rounded corner, four window styling, Fleetwood front fender lettering and laurel wreath hood and deck badges. Many were sold equipped with the coach lamp option and bright body underscores, with rear extensions, were included as well.

FLEETWOOD SIXTY-SPECIAL SUB-SERIES B/681

Model Number	Body/Style Number	Body Type & Seating	Factory Price	Shipping Weight	Production Total
681/B	B69-P	4-dr Brghm-6P	7637	4858	20,750

FLEETWOOD SEVENTY-FIVE (V-8) — SUB-SERIES F/697 — Fleetwood 75s had all DeVille equipment (less front seat armrest on limousine) plus, Automatic Level Control; carpeted foot rests; fixed ratio power steering; remote control right-hand outside mirror; rear window defogger and Automatic Climate Control. The sedan included folding auxiliary seats. The limousine had the doors cut into the roof and had the traditional partition and glass divider. Trim included bright body underscores with rear extensions; horizontal thin belt moldings; Fleetwood front fender lettering and laurel wreath badges for the hood and deck lid. Several optional rear roof treatments were available. making these models a true factory built semi-custom type vehicles.

FLEETWOOD SEVENTY-FIVE SUB-SERIES F/697

Model Number	Body/Style Number	Body Type & Seating	Factory Price	Shipping Weight	Production Total
697/F	F23-R	4-dr Sed-6/9P	11,948	5620	995
697/F	F33-S	4-dr Limo-9P	12,080	5742	960
698/Z	6989OZ	Commercial chassis	—	—	2,462

NOTE: The commercial chassis was built off a 157-1/2 inch wheelbase platform and was provided to professional car builders for the manufacture of hearses and ambulances, etc.

1972 Cadillac, Eldorado two-door coupe, V-8

FLEETWOOD ELDORADO — (V-8) — SUB-SERIES L/693 — The 1972 Eldorados had a vertical texture grille. The Cadillac name was engraved on the left side of the upper grille surround and Eldorado scripts appeared above the cornering lights on the lower front fender tips. The 8.2 Litre badges were moved to the sides of the body, below the belt molding and behind the front wheel openings. New full wheelcovers with concentric rings were seen. Eight colors of Sierra grain leather were supplied as convertible upholstery selections. Standard equipment included the detuned 1972 version of the 500 cid V-8, front-wheel-drive chassis layout; Automatic Level Control; front center armrest only and 'coach widows' on the hardtop coupe.

FLEETWOOD ELDORADO SUB-SERIES L/693

Model Number	Body/Style Number	Body Type & Seating	Factory Price	Shipping Weight	Production Total
693/L	L67-E	2-dr Conv-6P	7681	4966	7,975
693/L	L47-H	2-dr HT Cpe-6P	7360	4880	32,099

CADILLAC V-8 ENGINE: V-8. Overhead valves. Cast iron block. Displacement: 472 cid. Bore and stroke: 4.3 x 4.06 inches. Compression ratio: 8.5:1. SAE Net hp: 220. Five main bearings. Hydraulic valve lifters. Carburetor: Rochester four-barrel Quadrajet. Note: hp ratings are now expressed in SAE net hp. A gross hp rating of 345 at 4400 rpm. was listed, too.

ELDORADO V-8 ENGINE: V-8. Overhead valves. Cast iron block. Displacement: 500 cid. Bore and stroke: 4.3 x 4.304 inches. Compression ratio: 8.5:1. Brake hp: 365. SAE net hp: 235. Five main bearings. Hydraulic valve lifters. Carburetor: Rochester four-barrel Quadrajet (Eldorado special).

HISTORICAL FOOTNOTES: Introductions of the 1972 line took place in September, 1971 with production continuing until July 7, 1972. Calendar year production peaked at 266,780 cars and model year output hit 267,787 units. It was a record breaking year. Cadillac celebrated its 70th anniversary this season.

1973 CADILLAC

CALAIS — (V-8) — SERIES 6C — New energy absorbing bumpers were seen on GM cars this year and brought Cadillac styling refinements with them. Grilles were widened and had an intricate eggcrate design. Larger, vertical rectangles housed the parking lamps between wide spaced headlamps, which had square bezels, but round lenses. Bumpers ran fully across the front of the cars and wrapped around each end. Vertical guards were spaced much wider apart, at a point outboard of the grille. The rear end had a bumper with a wider, flatter upper section housing an angled license plate recess. Border outline moldings, vertically 'veed', paralled the fender edge shape at the rear bodysides. Single, rectangular rear side marker lamps, horizontally mounted, were placed over and under the rear tip of the thin beltline trim. Cadillac scripts were seen on the front fender sides, below the belt molding, behind the wheel opening. Cloth upholstery was standard and equipment features were comparable to 1972.

CADILLAC I.D. NUMBERS: The serial number system and locations were the same as the previous year with sixth symbol changed to '3' to indicate model year. Calais were numbered 6C( )R3Q 100001 to 350000; DeVilles 6D( )R3Q 100001 to 350000 or 6D4( )R3E 3500001 to 400000; El Dorados 6L( )S3Q 400001 to 450000; Broughams 6B69R3Q 100001 to 350000 and Seventy-Fives 6F( )R3Q 100001 to 350000. The new Body Style Number codes were used on both serial number tags and vehicle data plates.

CALAIS SERIES 6C

Model Number	Body/Style Number	Body Type & Seating	Factory Price	Shipping Weight	Production Total
6C	C47/G	2-dr HT Cpe-6P	5886	4900	4,202
6C	C49/N	4-dr HT Sed-6P	6038	4953	3,798

1973 Cadillac, two-door hardtop Coupe DeVille, V-8

DEVILLE — (V-8) — SERIES 6D — Bright body underscores with rear extensions distinguished the DeVille externally. There were also DeVille signatures on the rear roof pillar. Equipment specifications were comparable to 1972. The DeVille was actually a Calais with added trim, richer appointments, rear armrest and standard power seat.

DEVILLE SERIES 6D

Model Number	Body/Style Number	Body Type & Seating	Factory Price	Shipping Weight	Production Total
6D	D47/J	2-dr Cpe DeV-6P	6268	4925	112,849
6D	D49/N	4-dr Sed DeV-6P	6500	4985	103,394

FLEETWOOD SIXTY-SPECIAL BROUGHAM — (V-8) — SERIES 68 — Standard equipment on the Brougham included DeVille features (with different body underscores); Automatic Level Control; Dual-Comfort front seat; rear reading lights; a new front reading lamp; padded vinyl roof with rear chrome moldings and carpeted, rear compartment foot rests. Four window, rounded corner roof styling, with extra wide center pillars, was seen again. Tires with pencil thin whitewall bands were used.

1973 Cadillac, Fleetwood 60 Special four-door Brougham, V-8

FLEETWOOD SIXTY-SPECIAL BROUGHAM SERIES 6B

Model Number	Body/Style Number	Body Type & Seating	Factory Price	Shipping Weight	Production Total
6B	B69/P	4-dr Sed-6/9P	7765	5102	24,800

FLEETWOOD SEVENTY-FIVE — (V-8) — SERIES 6F — The long-wheelbase, high-dollar Fleetwoods were immense automobiles with low-cut, extra-large. rounded corner side window treatments and rather large 'coach windows' cut into the rear roof pillar. Fleetwoods had the annual Cadillac styling changes plus, thin, horizontal bodyside molding; front fender nameplates; full-length body underscores with rear extensions; and Fleetwood style laurel wreath badge ornamentation. Equipment inclusions were carpeted foot rests; fixed ratio power steering; rear seat window defogger; Automatic Climate Control and right-hand outside rearview mirrors operated by remote control. Bumper impact strips were standard on Seventy-Fives, optional on other Cadillacs.

FLEETWOOD SEVENTY-FIVE SERIES 6F

Model Number	Body/Style Number	Body Type & Seating	Factory Price	Shipping Weight	Production Total
6F	F23/R	4-dr Sed-6P	11,948	5620	1,017
6F	F33/S	4-dr Limo-9P	12,080	5742	1,043
6F	F90/Z	Commercial chassis	—	—	2,212

NOTE: The commercial chassis was built off a 157-1/2 inch wheelbase platform and provided to professional car makers for manufacture of hearses and ambulances.

1973 Cadillac, Eldorado two-door convertible, V-8

FLEETWOOD ELDORADO — (V-8) — SERIES 6L — The front-wheel-drive Eldorados were restyled stem to stern. A new eggcrate grille was seen. The front bumper had an angular, in-and-out look with wide spread vertical guards. Parking lamps wrapped around the body corners. On the sides of the cars, a thin rub molding ran from behind the forward wheel housing and stretched nearly to the round, rear side marker lamps, which had wreath and crest ornamentation. Gone were the vertical rear fender breaks (along with the windsplit trim), but fender skirts and bright underscores were used again. An Eldorado script was seen behind the front wheel opening. The deck lid still bulged up at the top center, but was flatter along its rear face. The rear bumper was flatter and straighter, too. Vertical taillamps looked somewhat like the previous type, but with the heavy chrome housings deleted. They slanted slightly forward at the same angle as the fender line. Standard Eldorado extras included Automatic Level Control, new energy absorbing bumper system, 'coach' windows for coupes and the 500 cid V-8.

FLEETWOOD ELDORADO SERIES 6L

Model Number	Body/Style Number	Body Type & Seating	Factory Price	Shipping Weight	Production Total
6L	L47/H	2-dr HT Cpe-6P	7360	5094	42,136
6L	L67/E	2-dr Conv-6P	7681	5131	9,315

CADILLAC ENGINES

STANDARD V-8: V-8. Overhead valves. Cast iron block. Displacement: 472 cid. Bore and stroke: 4.3 x 4.06 inches. Compression ratio: 10.0:1. Brake hp: 375 at 4400 rpm.. Five main bearings. Hydraulic valve lifters. Carburetor: Rochester four-barrel Quadrajet Model 4MV (standard).

ELDORADO V-8: V-8. Overhead valves. Cast iron block. Displacement: 500 cid. Bore and stroke: 4.30 x 4.304 inches. Compression ratio: 9.0: 1. Brake hp: 365 at 4400 rpm.. Five main bearings. Hydraulic valve lifters. Carburetor: Rochester four-barrel Quadrajet Model 4MV.ELDORADO ENGINE

CHASSIS FEATURES: Wheelbase: (Commercial chassis) 157-1/2 inches; (SeventyFive) 151-1/2 inches; (Sixty-Special) 133 inches; (Eldorado) 126.3 inches; (all other models) 130 inches. Overall length: (Seventy-Five) 251 inches; (Sixty-Special) 232 inches; (Eldorado) 222 inches; (all other models) 231 inches. Width: (all models) 80 inches. Tires: L-78 x 15.

114

POWERTRAIN OPTIONS: Cruise Control ($92). Controlled differential ($56). Eighty Amp generator ($41). Heavy-duty cooling system ($56). Exhaust emissions system, required on all cars built for California sale ($15). Trackmaster ($205). Trailer towing package, Eldorado ($62); all others ($92).

CONVENIENCE OPTIONS: Automatic Climate Control ($523). Automatic Level Control ($77). Rear window defoggers; grid type in Eldorado convertible ($62); standard type in Eldorado coupe ($36); standard type in all others, except regular equipment in 75s ($31). Door edge guards, two-door ($6); four-door ($9). Power door locks, in two-doors, includes automatic seatback release ($69); in 75s ($115); in other four-doors ($69). Dual Comfort seat in DeVille and Eldorado ($103). Front and rear twin rubber floor mats ($16). Front and rear one piece rubber floor mats for Eldorados ($19). Front and rear twin rubber floor mats for 75s ($10). Soft Ray tinted glass ($57). Convertible hard boot ($40). Auxiliary horn ($15). Bumper impact strips ($24). One license frame ($6); two ($11). Remote control right-hand outside rearview mirror, standard on 75s ($26). Roof pillar coach lights on Brougham and 75s ($51). Firemist paint ($128). AM/ FM radios, regular ($183); stereo signal-seeking ($3 20); stereo signal-seeking with rear control in 75s only ($410); stereo with tape player ($406). Full vinyl padded top for DeVilles, including 'halo' on Coupe DeVille ($152). Full vinyl Eldorado padded top ($157). Custom Cabriolet Eldorado Coupe roof ($360). Power seat options ($89-115 depending on model and use of Dual Comfort seats). Twin front shoulder harness in convertible ($31). Tilt & Telescope steering wheel ($92). DeVille/Brougham/Eldorado sun roof, with vinyl top mandatory ($610). Sunroof with Eldorado Coupe Custom Cabriolet treatment ($1,005). White sidewall tires, on 75s ($47); others ($41). Remote control trunk lock ($56). Trunk mat ($8). Twilight Sentinel ($40). Expanded vinyl Calais upholstery ($41). Expanded leather DeVille/Brougham upholstery ($169). Expanded leather Eldorado Coupe upholstery ($179). Steel-belted radial ply tires, size L78 x 15 with Space Saver spare, for all models except Seventy-Fives ($156). Lighted right-hand visor vanity mirror ($430). Theft deterent system ($80). Brougham d'Elegance Group ($750). Deluxe robe and pillow ($85). Left-hand remote control thermometer mirror ($15).

HISTORICAL FOOTNOTES: Dealer introductions were held September 21, 1972. Model year production hit a record 304,839 Cadillacs. The five millionth Cadillac, a blue Sedan DeVille, was built June 27, 1973. A Cotillion white Eldorado convertible paced the Indy 500 with Jim Rathman driving. Robert D. Lund became general manager of Cadillac Division, January 1, 1973.

1974 CADILLAC

CALAIS — (V-8) — SERIES 6C — A major restyling marketed the 'Gas Crunch' era Cadillacs of 1974. A wide eggcrate grille was used. Dual round headlamps were mounted in close together square bezels. Further outboard were double-deck wraparound parking lamps. Shorter vertical grille guards appeared in about the same position as before. Rear fendersides were flatter, without the elliptical bulge. The thin beltline molding was positioned lower by several inches. The rear end had vertical bumper ends with the taillights built in. Both bumpers, especially the rear, protruded further from the body. Coupes sported large, wide 'coach' windows giving a thick center pillar look. A new curved instrument panel housed a digital clock. Standard equipment included variable-ratio power steering; dual power brakes; front disc brakes; automatic transmission; power windows; all courtesy and warning lights; three-speed wipers and electric washers; visor vanity mirror; two front cigar lighters; front and rear armrests; remote control left-hand outside mirror; assist straps; side and cornering lights; automatic parking brake release; front center armrest; litter container; flow-through ventilation; L-78 x 15B blackwall bias belted tires and a 472 cid four-barrel V-8.

CADILLAC I.D. NUMBERS: The serial number system and locations were the same as the previous year with sixth symbol changed to a '4' to indicate 1974 model year. Calais were numbered 6C4( )R4Q 100001 and up; DeVilles 6D5( )R4( ) 100001 and up; Eldorados 6L( )S4Q( ) 400001 and up; Broughams 6B69R4Q 100001 and up and Seventy-Five 6F( )R4Q 100001 to 350000.

CALAIS SERIES 6C

Model Number	Body/Style Number	Body Type & Seating	Factory Price	Shipping Weight	Production Total
6C	C49/N	4-dr HT Sed-6P	7545	4979	2,324
6C	C47/G	2-dr HT Cpe-6P	7371	4900	4,449

1974 Cadillac, two-door coupe DeVille, V-8

DEVILLE — (V-8) — SERIES 60 — DeVilles again had all Calais equipment plus, rocker moldings; rear center armrests; rear cigar lighters and power front seat adjuster. A DeVille script nameplate replaced the Calais signature above the rear tip of the lower belt molding. New options included a DeVille d'Elegance luxury appointments package and a fully padded vinyl Cabriolet roof treatment. Ingredients of the former package were velour upholstery; Deluxe padded doors; front seatback storage pockets; deep pile carpeting; floor mats. The Cabriolet group incorporated a landau style top with bright metal forward divider strip. A Space Saver spare tire was standard when DeVilles were ordered with optional white sidewall steel belted radial tires.

DEVILLE SERIES 6D

Model Number	Body/Style Number	Body Type & Seating	Factory Price	Shipping Weight	Production Total
6D	D49/B	4-dr Sed DeV-6P	8100	5032	60,419
6D	D47/J	2-dr Cpe-6P	7867	4924	112,201

NOTE: At the beginning of the 1974 model year, the following factory retail prices were in effect for Calais and DeVille models: C49/N ($6,327); C47/G ($6,153); D49/B ($6,793); D47/J ($6,560). Midyear price increases, although nothing new to the auto industry, became much more common after the early 1970s.

1974 Cadillac, Fleetwood 60 Special four-door Brougham, V-8

FLEETWOOD BROUGHAM — (V-8) — SERIES 68 — The 1974 Fleetwood Sixty-Special Brougham came with all DeVille standard equipment plus, Automatic Level Control; Dual Comfort front seat; front and rear reading lights; padded vinyl roof with chrome rear window moldings; carpeted foot rests and L78 x 15/B white sidewall tires of biasbelted construction. Fleetwood ornamentation, nameplates and round corner, four window roof styling were seen again. The Brougham d'Elegance option package was available again, including the same type of appointments outlined for the DeVille d'Elegance, but at nearly twice the price on the bigger car. Even more ostentatious was the Talisman group with four-place seating in Medici crushed velour arm chair style seats; full length center consoles with writing set in front and rear vanity; reclining front passenger seat; assist straps; special Turbine wheel discs; seatback pockets; deep-pile carpeting floor mats; stand-up hood ornament and special rear roof pillar Fleetwood Talisman scripts. Even more luxurious was a leather trim Talisman package, an option which cost only $100 less than a brand new 1974 four-cylinder Ford Pinto two-door sedan!

FLEETWOOD BROUGHAM SERIES 6B

Model Number	Body/Style Number	Body Type & Seating	Factory Price	Shipping Weight	Production Total
6B	B69/P	4-dr Sed-6P	9537	5143	18,250

FLEETWOOD SEVENTY-FIVE — (V-8) — SERIES 6F — Standard equipment on 1974 models in the Fleetwood Seventy-Five line began at the DeVille level, plus, Automatic Level Control; carpeted foot rests; fixed ratio power steering; rear seat window defogger: Automatic Climate Control, trailering package and remote control right-hand outside rearview mirror. Black sidewall L78 x 15/D tires (optional on other Cadillacs) were used. Also found on all of the big Fleetwoods were new, gray and white bumper impact strips, which cost extra on other models. Series scripts appeared on the front fenders, behind the wheelhousings, and 'coach' windows appeared in the rear roof pillar. Twilight Sentinel was now featured on all 75s at regular prices.

FLEETWOOD SEVENTY-FIVE SERIES 6F

Model Number	Body/Style Number	Body Type & Seating	Factory Price	Shipping Weight	Production Total
6F	F23/R	4-dr Sed-6P	13,120	5719	895
6F	F33/S	4-dr Limo-9P	13,254	5883	1,005
6F	F90/O	Commercial chassis			2,265

NOTES: The commercial chassis was built off a 157-1/2 inch wheelbase platform and supplied to professional car makers for the manufacture of hearses and ambulances, etc. Introductory factory retail prices for conventional Fleetwood models were as follows: B69/P ($8,083); F23/R ($12.344) and F33/S ($12,478). A midyear price increase resulted in the factory retails shown in the chart above.

1974 Cadillac, Eldorado two-door coupe, V-8

FLEETWOOD ELDORADO — (V-8) — SERIES 6L — A new grille for Eldorados had the opposite design change, compared to other Cadillacs. The eggcrate look was gone and a finer crosshatched insert was used. It also had a wide, brushed aluminum top header bar, providing a neoclassical appearance. A Cadillac signature was engraved on the left side of the header. The rear fender line looked squarer and a bumper/taillight arrangement that telescoped on impact was used. A curved instrument panel was new, too. The equipment list included all

---

DeVilles features plus, L78 x 15/B whitewall bias-belted tires; 'coach' windows on the coupe and the big 500 cid V-8. Expanded leather interiors were standard in what was now America's only production luxury convertible.

FLEETWOOD ELDORADO SERIES 6L

Model Number	Body/Style Number	Body Type & Seating	Factory Price	Shipping Weight	Production Total
6L	L47/H	2-dr HT Cpe-6P	9110	4960	32,812
6L	L67/E	2-dr Conv-6P	9437	5019	7,600

NOTE: Introductory prices for the 1974 front-wheel-drive Eldorados were $7,656 for the coupe and $7,873 for the convertible. A midyear price increase resulted in the factory retails shown in the chart above.

CADILLAC ENGINE: V-8. Overhead valves. Cast iron block. Displacement: 472 cid. Bore and stroke: 4.3 x 4.06 inches. Compression ratio: 8.25: 1. SAE net hp: 205 at 4000 rpm. Hydraulic valve lifters. Carburetor: Four-barrel.

ELDORADO ENGINE: V-8. Overhead valves. Displacement: 500 cid. Bore and stroke: 4.3 x 4.3 inches. Compression ratio: 8.25:1. Brake hp: 210 at 3800 rpm. Hydraulic valve lifters. Carburetor: four-barrel.

CHASSIS FEATURES: Wheelbase: (Commercial chassis) 157-1/2 inches; (Seventy-Five) 151-1/2 inches; (Brougham) 133 inches; (Eldorado) 126 inches; (other models) 130 inches. Overall length: (Seventy-Five) 252 inches; (Brougham) 234 inches; (Eldorado) 224 inches; (other models) 231 inches. Width: (all models) 80 inches. Tires: (Seventy-Five) L78 x 15/D blackwall; (Eldorado and Brougham) L78 x 15/B white sidewall bias-belted; (all others) L78 x 15/B black sidewall bias-belted.

POWERTRAIN OPTIONS: Controlled differential, except Eldorado ($56). Emissions test, required in California ($20). High altitude performance package ($16). High energy electronic ignition ($77). Trackmaster skid control ($214).

CONVENIENCE OPTIONS: Automatic Climate Control, standard in 75s ($523). Airbag restraint system, except 75s and Eldorado convertible ($225). Automatic Level Control on Calais/DeVille ($77). Brougham d'Elegance group ($750). Cruise control ($95). Coupe DeVille Custom Cabriolet, with sun roof ($840); without sun roof ($220). Eldorado Custom Cabriolet Coupe, with sun roof ($1005); without sun roof ($385). Rear window defogger, except 75s and convertible ($64). Deluxe robe and pillow ($85). DeVille d'Elegance group, in Sedan DeVille ($355); in Coupe DeVille ($300). Door edge guards, two-door ($6; four-door ($10). Power door locks, two-door including seatback release ($69); four-door except 75 ($69); 75 sedan and limousine ($115). Dual Comfort front seat in DeVille, Eldorado, 75 Sedan ($108). Fleetwood Brougham Talisman group ($1800). Fleetwood Brougham Talisman group with leather trim ($2450). Front/rear twin floormats in all except Eldorado/75's ($17). Eldorado front and rear one-piece floor mats ($20). Twin rubber front floor mats in 75s ($11). Soft Ray tinted glass ($57). Guidematic headlamp control ($49). Trumpet horn ($15). Bumper impact strips, standard on 75s ($24). Lamp monitors ($48). License frame ($6). Illuminated vanity mirror, ($43). right-hand remote control outside rearview mirror, standard in 75s ($27). Opera lamps on Brougham/75s ($52). Firemist paint ($132). Special Firemist paint ($200). Special non-Firemist paint ($174). Radios (all with power antenna), AM/FM push-button ($203); AM/FM with tape ($426); AM/FM signal seeking ($340); AM/FM stereo with rear control in 75s ($430). Fully-padded vinyl roofs, on DeVille/Calais ($152); Eldorado Coupe ($157); 75s ($741). Six-Way power seat in Calais ($120), in DeVille/Fleetwood, except limousine ($89); passenger seat only, with Dual-Comfort ($120); driver's seat only, with Dual-Comfort ($89). Convertible shoulder harness ($33). Tilt & Telescope steering ($94). Sun roof. DeVille/Brougham/ Eldorado coupe ($610). Theft deterant system ($80). Left-hand remote control thermometer mirror ($15). Tires, L78 x 15/D whitewall, on 75s ($47); others ($41). Tires, LR78 x 15/B whitewall steel belted radial on 75s ($162); on Calais ($156); on DeVille with Space Saver spare ($156). Tires, L78 x 15/B blackwall bias belted with Space Saver spare ($35); whitewall ($63). Eldorado convertible top boot ($40). Trailering package, standard on 75s ($65). Remote control trunk lock ($60). Trunk mat ($80). Twilight Sentinel, standard in 75s ($42). Expanded vinyl upholstery in DeVille/Brougham ($184). Expanded leather upholstery in Eldorado coupe ($195). Special wheel discs, except Eldorado ($40). Controlled cycle windshield wipers ($25).

HISTORICAL FOOTNOTES: Model introductions took place on September 16, 1973. Model year production hit 242,330 cars. All U.S. auto sales were off this season, as a side affect of the Arab oil embargo. Because of this, Cadillac's lower production level was still sufficient to pull down a greater market share.

1975 CADILLAC

1975 Cadillac, Calais four-door hardtop, V-8

CALAIS — (V-8) SERIES 6C — Styling changes for 1975 brought dual, square headlight lenses flanked by rectangular cornering lights wrapping around the body. A new crosshatched grille appeared. Calais Coupes and Sedans had triangular 'coach' windows. Standard equipment was about the same as in 1974, plus, front fender lamp monitors; power door locks;

high-energy ignition; steel-belted radial tires and catalytic converter. Once again, substantial midyear price increases were seen. Also, all cars offered at the beginning of the model run were equipped with 500 cid V-8s and electronic fuel injection became optional in March, 1975.

CADILLAC I.D. NUMBERS: The serial number system and locations were unchanged. The sixth symbol changed to a '5' for 1975. Calais were numbered 6C4( )S5( )100001 up; DeVilles 6D4( )S5( )100001 up; El Dorados 6D4( )S59100001 up; Broughams 6B69S5( )100001 up; Seventy-Fives 6F( )S5( )100001 up and Sevilles 6S69R6Q 4500001 up. (Sevilles sold in 1975 were considered 1976 models and all production of this model was quartered in the Detroit assembly plant, Code 'Q'). Engine code 'R' was now applied to the new 350 cid Seville V-8.

CALAIS SERIES 6C

Model Number	Body/Style Number	Body Type & Seating	Factory Price	Shipping Weight	Production Total
6C	C49/N	4-dr HT Sed-6P	8377	5087	2,500
6C	C47/G	2-dr HT Cpe-6P	8184	5003	5,800

NOTE: Initial 1975 pricing is reflected above. Two rounds of price increases were seen, the sedan going to $8,390 and then $8,806; the coupe going to $8,197 and then $8,613.

1975 Cadillac, two-door Coupe DeVille, V-8

DEVILLE — (V-8) — SERIES 6D — Chrome underscores, DeVille series rear fender nameplates and richer interiors identified Coupe and Sedan DeVille models. They both had slim, triangular rear quarter windows and power front seat adjusters. Luxury level options, including d'Elegance and Cabriolet packages were available again.

DEVILLE SERIES 6D

Model Number	Body/Style Number	Body Type & Seating	Factory Price	Shipping Weight	Production Total
6D	D49/B	4-dr HT Sed-6P	8801	5146	63,352
6D	D47/J	2-dr HT Cpe-6P	8600	5049	110,218

NOTE: At the beginning of the 1975 model year, prices were those seen above. Two rounds of midyear increases were seen, the sedan going to $8,814 and then $9,230; the coupe going to $8,613 and then $9,029.

1975 Cadillac, Fleetwood 60 Special four-door Brougham, V-8

FLEETWOOD BROUGHAM — (V-8) — SERIES 6B — The Sixty-Special designation was retired this year. Identification features for Broughams included front fender scripts, Fleetwood decorative touches and the traditional extra equipment like padded top; automatic leveling; dual-comfort seats and reading lamps, etc. Talisman and d'Elegance option groups were available again. Size was unchanged over 1974.

FLEETWOOD BROUGHAM SERIES 6B

Model Number	Body/Style Number	Body Type & Seating	Factory Price	Shipping Weight	Production Total
6B	B69/P	4-dr Sed-6P	10,414	5242	18,755

NOTE: Initial 1975 pricing is reflected above. Two rounds of price increases were seen, the Brougham going to $10,427 and then $10.843.

FLEETWOOD SEVENTY-FIVE — (V-8) — SERIES 6F — Both long-wheelbase Cadillacs came with two separate climate control systems; automatic leveling air shocks; folding jump seats; rear window defogger; trailering equipment and remote control right-hand OSRV mirrors. The Limousine had a leather front chauffer's compartment and glass partition window. Script identification nameplates were worn on the front fenders, behind the wheel opening. Fleetwood decorative trim was seen. New triangular rear quarter windows, of much slimmer design than before, were seen.

FLEETWOOD SEVENTY-FIVE SERIES 6F

Model Number	Body/Style Number	Body Type & Seating	Factory Price	Shipping Weight	Production Total
6F	F23/R	4-dr Sed-9P	14.218	5720	876
6F	F23/S	4-dr Limo-9P	14,557	5862	795
6F	F90/Z	Commercial Chassis	—	—	1,328

NOTE: Initial 1975 pricing is reflected above. Two rounds of price increases were seen, the 75 sedan going to $14,231 and then $14,647; the 75 limousine going to $14,570 and then $14,986.

1975 Cadillac, Eldorado two-door convertible, V-8

FLEETWOOD ELDORADO — (V-8) — SERIES 6L — The Eldorado lost its rear fender skirts this season and saw a major facelift, as well. Square headlamps were new. Wraparound cornering lamps were gone, being replaced by a narrow, rectangular type, housed in the front fender tips. The parking lamps and directionals were placed in the bumper ends. Larger rear quarter windows appeared on the coupe and a new cross-hatch grille was used on both styles. The rear fender wells were enlarged, causing the horizontal belt molding to end just ahead of the wheel opening. On the coupes, Fleetwood ornaments decorated the roof 'C' pillar. Front-wheel-drive technology was retained.

FLEETWOOD ELDORADO — SERIES 6L

Model Number	Body/Style Number	Body Type & Seating	Factory Price	Shipping Weight	Production Total
6L	L47/H	2-dr HT Cpe-6P	9935	5108	35,802
6L	L67/E	2-dr Conv-6P	10,354	5167	8,950

NOTE: Introductory prices for 1975 are reflected above. Two rounds of price increases were seen, the Eldorado coupe going to $9,948 and then $10,364; the Eldorado convertible going to $10,367 and then $10,783.

SEVILLE — (V-8) — SERIES 6S — The Seville was introduced as a down-sized 1976 Cadillac in April, 1975. It appeared in dealer showrooms the first day of May. It was based on the GM front engine/rear drive 'X' car platform used for the Chevrolet Nova and its derivatives such as Omega, Ventura and Apollo. The exterior panels were, however, exclusive to Cadillac and the equipment and trim level was as rich as possible. Included at a base price of $12,479 were padded vinyl roof; air conditioning; Automatic Level Control; power seats; power windows; power door locks; AM/FM stereo; leather or special cloth upholstery; Tilt and Telescope steering wheel; chimes and GR78-15B steel-belted radial whitewall tires. Sevilles came only as four-door sedans with crisp, angular-curved styling that was purely modern. Square headlamps, wraparound cornering lights and an eggcrate grille with narrow, vertical center division bar, were seen. The base powerplant was a 350 cid Oldsmobile product, to which electronic fuel injection was added.

SEVILLE SERIES 6S

Model Number	Body/Style Number	Body Type & Seating	Factory Price	Shipping Weight	Production Total
6S	6S69	4-dr Sed-6P	12,479	4232	16,355

CADILLAC ENGINE: V-8. Overhead valves. Cast iron block. Displacement: 500 cubic inches. Compression ratio: 8.5:1. SAE net hp: 190 at 4000 rpm. Hydraulic valve lifters. Carburetor: four-barrel.

SEVILLE ENGINE: V-8. Overhead valves. Cast iron block. Displacement: 350 cid. Bore and stroke: 4.057 x 3.385 inches. Compression ratio: 8.0:1. SAE net hp: 180 at 4400 rpm. Induction system: Electronic fuel injection.

CHASSIS FEATURES: Wheelbase: (commercial chassis) 157-1/2 inches; (Seventy-Five) 151-1/2 inches; (Brougham) 133 inches; (Eldorado) 126.3 inches; (Seville) 114.3 inches; (all others) 130 inches. Overall length: (Seventy-Five) 253 inches-, (Brougham) 234 inches; (Eldorado) 225 inches; (Seville) 204 inches; (all others) 231 inches. Width: (Seville) 72 inches; (all others) 80 inches. Tires: (Seville) GR78-15B; (all others) LR78xl5.

POWERTRAIN OPTIONS: Controlled differential ($60). Trackmaster ($250). Fuel injection ($600).

CONVENIENCE OPTIONS: Talisman Brougham ($1788). Astro roof ($843). Sun roof ($668). Rear window defroster, standard on 75s ($73). Automatic Level Control ($84). Cruise control ($100). Eldorado reclining seat ($188). Air cushion restraints ($300). Coupe DeVille Cabriolet, without sun roof ($236). Eldorado Cabriolet Coupe, without sun roof ($413). Brougham d'Elegance Group ($784). DeVille d'Elegance Group ($350). Dual Comfort Six-Way passenger seat ($125). AM/FM stereo with tape ($229). Padded roof on 75s ($745). More.

HISTORICAL FOOTNOTES: Dealer introductions took place September 19, 1974. Model year production was 264,731 cars. Lower axle ratios used for fuel mileage improvements, except on limousines. First time prices on production models surpassed price of 1957-1960 Eldorado Broughams.

CHECKER

1960-1975

1963 Checker Marathon, four-door sedan, 6-cyl

Checker Motors Corp. can be traced back to the DeSchaum Automobile Co. of Buffalo, N.Y. which began building automobiles in 1908. Later, in 1910, DeSchaum became the Suburban Motor Car Co. of Detroit, Mich. In turn, Suburban evolved into the Partin Manufacturing Co. and finally the Checker Cab Manufacturing Co. was founded in 1923. This company absorbed the factories of Dort and Handley-Knight in Kalamazoo, Mich. Checker was engaged, exclusively, in the building of taxicabs from 1923 until 1959. Then it launched a line of modified taxicabs for passenger car use. At one period the firm was a part of the automobile empire put together by E.L. Cord.

By G. Marshall Naul

The company name was changed to Checker Motors Corp. in 1958. The business of manufacturing passenger cars was conducted on a modest scale, at least by Detroit standards, until the early 1980s.

However, the manufacture of Checker taxis and passenger cars continually declined from its high point of production, in 1962. Finally, Checker was forced to announce that it would cease building passenger cars in July, 1982.

The Checker passenger cars, which were first offered to the public late in 1959, were based on the Model A8 taxi, which appeared as early as 1956. With only a few exterior

changes, the four-door sedan remained essentially unchanged from 1960 to 1982.

Small modifications were made to provide a station wagon. Later, in 1963, a stretched version of the sedan provided the chassis for an eight-passenger Custom Limousine and Deluxe Sedan.

The major changes in Checkers over the years 1960-1975 have been in the powerplants used. Checker passenger car engine applications began with an 80 hp, L-head Six. Gradually, the marque switched to V-8s. Overhead valves appeared by the 1970s. Continental engines were originally used for the early six and a later overhead valve version of the L-head. In 1964, Chevrolet Motor Div. became the source for Checker engines, with both overhead valve sixes and V-8s being available. In the period 1963-1964, a number of Checker cars were provided with Chrysler V-8 engines.

The Checker never claimed to be the vision or victim of automotive stylists, but, rather, maintained a reputation for a utilitarian vehicle with a reputation for longevity, endurance and a lack of obsolescence. This is evidenced in Checker's resistance to yearly appearance changes. Gradual improvements were made, though.

The fact that the basic design was offered for 22 years and grew old-fashioned can't be denied. If the company had adopted a Ghia-designed Checker prototype of 1970, it's likely the nameplate would have remained around for some time.

1960 CHECKER

SUPERBA STANDARD/SPECIAL — (6-CYL) — SERIES A10 — The Superba was based on the Checker taxicab, Model A8 of 1956, with the dual headlamps of the 1959 Model A9 included. The Special series had extra trim and script on the side and an upgraded interior. The four-door station wagon used a dash panel controlled switch to lower the rear seat, a feature that was unique to Checker. The L-head six-cylinder engine, which had been a mainstay with Checker cabs, was essentially the same obsolescent design that had been used in Kaisers and Frazers a decade earlier. It was built by Continental Motors Co. For station wagon attachments, the engine builder converted this motor to a six with pushrod-operated overhead valves. This gave slightly more power to move around the 370 pound heavier wagons.

CHECKER I.D. NUMBERS: Serial numbers and engine numbers were found on the upper firewall. Serial and engine codes had three parts. The first identified the model; second part the production order; and third part the chassis or serial numbers. Serial numbers for 1960 were 37396 and up. Although true style numbers were not used, the first part of the serial number served this purpose and a 'W' was added to identify station wagons.

SUPERBA STANDARD/SPECIAL SERIES

Model Number	Body/Style Number	Body Type & Seating	Factory Price	Shipping Weight	Production Total
STANDARD LINE					
A10	A10	4-dr Sed-6P	2542	3410	Note 1
A10	WA10	4-dr Sta Wag-6P	2896	3780	Note 1
SPECIAL LINE					
A10	A10	4-dr Sed-6P	2650	3410	Note 1
A10	WA10	4-dr Sta Wag-6P	3004	3780	Note 1

NOTE 1: Production total for all models combined is estimated at 1,050.

SEDAN ENGINE: Inline. L-head Six. Cast iron block. Displacement: 226 cid. Bore and stroke: 3-5/16 x 4-3/8 inches. Compression ratio: 7.3:1. Brake hp: 80 at 3100 rpm. Four main bearings. Solid valve lifters. Carburetor: Carter Type AS one-barrel Model 2858S.

STATION WAGON ENGINE: Inline. Six. Overhead valves. Cast iron block. Displacement: 226 cid. Bore and stroke: 3-5/16 x 4-3/8 inches. Compression ratio: 8.0:1. Brake hp: 122 at 4400 rpm. Four main bearings. Solid valve lifters. Carburetor: Carter Type AS one-barrel Model 2858S.

CHASSIS FEATURES: Wheelbase: 120 inches. Overall length: 199.5 inches. Front tread: 60 inches. Rear tread: 62-1/2 inches. Overall width: 76 inches. Tires: 6.70 x 15.

OPTIONS: Power steering ($64). Power brakes ($33). Air conditioning ($411). Overdrive ($108). Overhead valve engine ($57). Single range automatic transmission ($222). Dual-range automatic transmission ($248).

HISTORICAL FOOTNOTES: This was the first year Checkers were sold in the private car market. The firm's contribution was small and was not recorded in regular industry publications such as WARD'S AUTOMOBILE YEARBOOK. In fact, the 1961 edition of WARDS did not even list Checker output under their catch-all category, others. The company's plant was in Kalamazoo, Mich.

1961 CHECKER

CHECKER SUPERBA — (6-CYL) — SERIES A10 — In 1960, Checker Motors Corp.'s total output was 6,980 cars, of which an estimated 1,050 went to private buyers. The balance were sold to the taxicab trade. Production for the private sector was considered sufficient to continue marketing cars for this purpose in 1961. The Superba Special was renamed the Marathon and considered a separate series. The standard Superba was the base line this year. The main styling difference between the two was in the placement of front parking lamps. The standard Superba had them mounted on a panel housed within the outboard vertical division of the cross-hatched grille insert. Dual headlamps were used on both cars. The sedan was fitted with 14 inch tires to make it ride lower. Standard equipment included full instrumentation, padded interior and an extra large rear seating compartment with a flat floor and folding jump seats.

CHECKER I.D. NUMBERS: Serial numbers and engine numbers were found on the upper firewall. Serial and engine codes had three parts. The first identified the model; second part the production order; and third part the chassis or serial numbers. Serial numbers for 1961 determined by the year appearing on the registration for each car. Numbers for 1961 began in September, 1960. Style numbers were changed as indicated on charts below.

CHECKER SUPERBA SERIES

Model Number	Body/Style Number	Body Type & Seating	Factory Price	Shipping Weight	Production Total
A10	W/10L	4-dr Sed-6P	2542	3410	Note 1
A10	W/A10	4-dr Sta Wag-6P	2896	3670	Note 1

NOTE 1: A total of 5,683 Checkers were built this year including taxicabs. Of this total, an estimated 860 were private passenger cars or station wagons. This estimate includes both Superbas and Marathons.

CHECKER MARATHON — (6-CYL) — SERIES A10 — The Marathon had the parking lamps outside the grille, below the headlights, and a strip of chrome on the front fenders and doors. A few small extras were included as standard equipment.

CHECKER MARATHON SERIES

Model Number	Body/Style Number	Body Type & Seating	Factory Price	Shipping Weight	Production Total
A10	W10L	4-dr Sed-6P	2650	3410	Note 1
A10	W/A10	4-dr Sta Wag-6P	3004	3720	Note 1

NOTE 1: A total of 5,683 Checkers were built this year including taxicabs. Of this total, an estimated 860 were private passenger cars or station wagons. This estimate includes both Superbas and Marathons.

SEDAN ENGINE: Inline. L-head Six. Cast iron block. Displacement: 226 cid. Bore and stroke: 3-5/16 x 4-3/8 inches. Compression ratio: 7.3:1. Brake hp: 80 at 3100 rpm. Four main bearings. Solid valve lifters. Carburetor: Carter Type AS Model 2858S one-barrel.

STATION WAGON ENGINE: Inline. Six. Overhead valves. Cast iron block. Displacement: 226 cid. Bore and stroke: 3-5/16 x 4-3/8 inches. Compression ratio: 8.0:1. Brake hp: 122 at 4000 rpm. Four main bearings. Solid valve lifters. Carburetor: Carter Type AS Model 2858S one-barrel.

CHASSIS FEATURES: Wheelbase: 120 inches. Overall length: 199.5 inches. Front tread: 60 inches. Rear tread: 62-1/2 inches. Overall width: 76 inches. Tires: (sedans) 6.70 x 14; (station wagons) 6.70 x 15.

OPTIONS: Power steering ($64). Air conditioning ($411). Power brakes ($33). Single range automatic transmission ($222). Dual range automatic transmission ($248). Overdrive ($108). Overhead valve W/A10 engine ($57).

HISTORICAL FOOTNOTES: Kalamazoo, Mich.'s largest automaker remained rather obscure this year. In fact, a special 1961 statistical issue of AUTOMOTIVE NEWS ran a list of all known automakers past and present. Marathon Motor Works (of Cincinnati, circa 1912) was on it, but the builder of the 1961 Marathon wasn't. The same publication did, however, have both monthly and yearly production totals for 1960 Checkers, plus a short publicity release of the current models. The car in the press photo had two-tone finish.

1962 CHECKER

1962 Checker, Superba four-door sedan, 6-cyl

CHECKER SUPERBA — (6-CYL) — SERIES A10 — Checkers were like Volkswagens in one regard; they weren't compacts, but they didn't change much from year to year. Therefore, the 1962 models were nearly identical to the previous cars in all regards, right down to price. There may have been a number of small detail changes, but the only one that's easily documented was a switch to a Zenith one-barrel carburetor in place of the former Carter type. Even this had no effect as far as the horsepower rating went. Also, the station wagon became an eight-passenger model.

CHECKER I.D. NUMBERS: Serial numbers and engine numbers were found on the upper firewall. Serial and engine codes had three parts. The first identified the model; second part the production order; and third part the chassis or serial numbers. Serial numbers for 1962 determined by the year appearing on the registration for each car. Numbers for 1962 began in September, 1961. Style numbers changes reflected on charts below.

CHECKER SUPERBA SERIES

Model Number	Body/Style Number	Body Type & Seating	Factory Price	Shipping Weight	Production Total
A10	W/10L	4-dr Sed-6P	2542	3410	Note 1
A10	W/A10	4-dr Sta Wag-8P	2896	3670	Note 1

NOTE 1: A total of 8,173 Checkers were built this year including taxicabs. Of this total, an estimated 1,230 were non-taxicabs, including all series models.

CHECKER MARATHON — (6-CYL) — SERIES A10 — The 1962 Marathon changed about as much as the new Superba, which is to say very little. And the variations between the two cars were the same as the previous season, mainly different grille treatments and the chrome side spear used to embellish the front fenders and both doors of Marathons.

CHECKER MARATHON SERIES

Model Number	Body/Style Number	Body Type & Seating	Factory Price	Shipping Weight	Production Total
A10	W10L	4-dr Sed-6P	2650	3410	Note 1
A10	W/A10	4-dr Sta Wag-8P	3004	3720	Note 1

NOTE 1: A total of 8,173 Checkers were built this year including taxicabs. Of this total, an estimated 1,230 were non-taxicabs, including all series models.

SEDAN ENGINE: Inline. L-head Six. Cast iron block. Displacement: 226 cid. Bore and stroke: 3-5/16 x 4-3/8 inches. Compression ratio: 7.3:1. Brake hp: 80 at 3100 rpm. Four main bearings. Solid valve lifters. Carburetor: Zenith 0-12469 one-barrel.

STATION WAGON ENGINE: Inline. Six. Overhead valves. Cast iron block. Displacement: 226 cid. Bore and stroke: 3-5/16 x 4-3/8 inches. Compression ratio: 8.0:1. Brake hp: 122 at 4000 rpm. Four main bearings. Solid valve lifters. Carburetor: Zenith 0-12469 one-barrel.

CHASSIS FEATURES: Wheelbase: 120 inches. Overall length: 199.5 inches. Front tread: 60 inches. Rear tread: 62-1/2 inches. Overall width: 76 inches. Tires: (sedans) 6.70 x 14; (station wagons) 6.70 x 15.

OPTIONS: Power steering ($64). Air conditioning ($411). Power brakes ($33). Single range automatic transmission ($222). Dual range automatic transmission ($248). Overdrive ($108). Overhead valve W/A10 engine ($57).

HISTORICAL FOOTNOTES: Checker Motors Corp. had a good year, with sales climbing 1,500 units. This inspired the company to plan some 'big' changes in 1963. A Town Limousine with eight-passenger seating was developed and a new front bumper was redesigned. It should be noted that Checker didn't adhere to annual model year alterations. New features and models were introduced as a running production change and, therefore, some standard reference sources date the above changes to 1962, since they came in that particular calendar year.

1963 CHECKER

CHECKER SUPERBA — (6-CYL) — SERIES A12 — Instead of a straight across, wraparound bumper with two vertical guards placed in front of the Superba parking lights, 1963 models had a more sculptured wraparound bumper with a dip in the center and no bumper guards. The parking lamps remained mounted inside the grille on panels that filled the space between the grille surround and the outboard vertical dividers. As in the past, this gave the appearance of the Superba having a narrower grille with only four vertical segments compared to six on the Marathon. Dual headlamps continued on both lines. A new Rochester two-barrel carburetor was supplied in those Checkers with overhead valve Continental motors. Two engines continued to be offered, the basis for attachment being changed. The 80 hp L-head six was now standard in all models; the overhead valve six, with its new 141 hp rating, was optional in all Checkers at $57 extra. Three-speed manual transmission was standard with both powerplants. Overdrive was optionally available. A single range automatic transmission could be ordered with the L-head Six. Dual-range Hydra-Matic was optional with the 141 hp two-barrel job. A padded dashboard, heater and defroster and heavy-duty battery were standard equipment with the more powerful drivetrain. As in the past, the sedan came with a flat rear floor and folding jump seats.

CHECKER I.D. NUMBERS: Serial numbers and engine numbers were found on the upper firewall. Serial and engine codes had three parts. The first identified the model; second part the production order; and third part the chassis or serial numbers. Serial numbers for 1963 determined by the year appearing on the registration for each car. Numbers for 1963 began in September, 1962. The series number was changed to A12 for conventional models and A19E for the long-wheelbase limousine. The 'E' may have indicated 'Extended Wheelbase'.

CHECKER SUPERBA SERIES

Model Number	Body/Style Number	Body Type & Seating	Factory Price	Shipping Weight	Production Total
A12	A12	4-dr Sed-6P	2642	3485	Note 1
A12	A12W	4-dr Sta Wag-8P	2991	3625	Note 1

NOTE 1: A total of 7,050 Checkers were built this year including taxicabs. Of this total, an estimated 1,080 were not taxicabs.

1963 Checker, Marathon four-door sedan, 6-cyl

CHECKER MARATHON — (6-CYL) — SERIES A12 — The Marathon continued with its wide grille look, the rectangular parking lamps being placed in a horizontal plane midway between the dual headlamps and the horizontally grooved outer grille extensions. The new bumper, with a dip in the center and no guards, was seen. A straight chrome molding ran across the fender sides, above the front wheel opening, and continued back over the doors. Above this molding, on the front fenders, was wording that read Checker in underlined block letters and, on a lower level, Marathon in script. Small, black rubber gravel guards were placed ahead of the front wheel openings. Jump seats were used in the sedan and the station wagon continued as an eight-passenger rated model. Rear decorative treatments included a bumper that looked identical to the front unit. The taillamp treatment consisted of a protruding oblong red lens placed above a round white lens, both of which were set upon a vertically positioned oblong chrome plate. This, then, was mounted on a vertical, paddle-shaped panel that ran from the top of the fender to the bottom.

1963 Checker, Marathon four-door station wagon, 6-cyl (PH)

CHECKER MARATHON SERIES

Model Number	Body/Style Number	Body Type & Seating	Factory Price	Shipping Weight	Production Total
A12	A12	4-dr Sed-6P	2793	3485	Note 1
A12	A12W	4-dr Sta Wag-P	3140	3625	Note 1

NOTE 1: A total of 7,050 Checkers were built this year including taxicabs. Of this total, an estimated 1,080 were not taxicabs.

CHECKER MARATHON TOWN CUSTOM — (6-CYL) — SERIES A19E — The new Town Custom Limousine was on a long 129 inch wheelbase. It had the Marathon grille and trim treatment. Photos of this model seem to indicate the use of extra chrome outside window frame moldings. Two folding jump seats were standard equipment. A glass driver's partition and power-operated accessories were featured. For a Checker product, the price was high and the production is believed to have been extremely low. The car did have a certain market niche, however, since many limousine buyers of this era were dissatisfied with the low styling contemporary to other early '60s cars.

CHECKER MARATHON TOWN CUSTOM

Model Number	Body/Style Number	Body Type & Seating	Factory Price	Shipping Weight	Production Total
A19E	A19E	4-dr Limo-8P	4638	3525	Note 1

NOTE 1: A total of 7,050 Checkers were built this year including taxicabs. Of this total, an estimated 1,080 were not taxicabs.

BASE ENGINE: Inline. L-head Six. Cast iron block. Displacement: 226 cid. Bore and stroke: 3-5/16 x 4-3/8 inches. Compression ratio: 7.3:1. Brake hp: 80 at 3100 rpm. Four main bearings. Solid valve lifters. Carburetor: Zenith 0-12469 one-barrel.

OPTIONAL ENGINE: Inline. Six. Overhead valves. Cast iron block. Displacement: 226 cid. Bore and stroke: 3-5/16 x 4-3/8 inches. Compression ratio: 8.0:1. Brake hp: 141 at 4400 rpm. Four main bearings. Solid valve lifters. Carburetor: Rochester two-barrel Model 7023096.

CHASSIS FEATURES: Wheelbase: (Limousine) 129 inches; (other models) 120 inches. Overall length: (Limousine) 208 inches; (other models) 199.3 inches. Front tread: 60 inches. Rear tread: 62-1/2 inches. Tires: (Limousine) data not available; (sedan) 6.70 x 15; (station wagon) 7.10 x 15.

OPTIONS: Power brakes ($33). Power steering ($64). Air conditioning ($382). Whitewall tires. Full wheel discs. Padded dash. Heater and defroster. Heavy-duty battery. Single range automatic transmission ($222). Dual range automatic transmission ($248). Overdrive transmission ($108). Overhead valve engine in sedan ($57).

HISTORICAL FOOTNOTES: Last year for six-cylinder engines only. The November, 1962 edition of MOTOR TREND magazine carried an article on page 57 about the 1963 Checker line.

1964 CHECKER

CHECKER MARATHON — (6-CYL) — SERIES A12 — The Superba name was dead for 1964 — or was it? There's no disputing the fact that the only standard wheelbase Checker left was the Marathon, but according to at least one source the L-head engine was still referred to as the "Superba Six." This motor was the base powerplant in both the Marathon sedan and station wagon. Styling and equipment features reflected no changes over 1963. Jump seats still came in the sedan, even though it was rated for only six passengers. The station wagon came with three seats for eight place seating. Prices for both cars were 'adjusted' in stages. The sedan was introduced at the same price as 1963, then later increased by $21. The station wagon also started the year with carryover retails, then jumped $20. Identification features included the high, front-side molding and a twin-level Checker/Marathon nameplate on the fender, aside the cowl.

CHECKER I.D. NUMBERS: Serial numbers and engine numbers were found on the upper firewall. Serial and engine codes had three parts. The first identified the model; second part the production order; and third part the chassis or serial numbers. Serial numbers for 1964 determined by the year appearing on the registration for each car. Numbers for 1964 began in September, 1963. The series number was changed to A12 for conventional models and A19E for the long-wheelbase limousine. The 'E' may have indicated 'Extended Wheelbase.' An interesting fact was that for the 1965 model year (beginning September, 1964) all new Checkers or 1964 models left in stock with serial numbers higher than 20,000 were made 1965 models.

CHECKER MARATHON SERIES

Model Number	Body/Style Number	Body Type & Seating	Factory Price	Shipping Weight	Production Total
A12	A12	4-dr Sed-6P	2793	3485	Note 1
A12	A12W	4-dr Sta Wag-8P	3140	3625	Note 1

NOTE 1: A total of 6,310 Checkers were built this year including taxicabs. Of this total, an estimated 960 were not-taxicabs.

NOTE 2: Factory retail prices of $2,814 for the sedan and $3,160 for the station wagon seem to have gone into effect in midyear. Cars with overhead valve attachments (optional) were approximately 95 pounds heavier than base models listed above.

CHECKER MARATHON TOWN CUSTOM — (6-CYL) — SUB-SERIES A12E — The Town Limousine was again available on the extended, 129 inch wheelbase Checker chassis. Styling and equipment features paralleled those of the previous season. A front fender script, attached above the horizontal molding, identified the model. A glass driver's partition and several standard options were included. While specifics aren't available, collectors will have no problem spotting one of these extra-long cars. And, if the serial number is under 20,000, it can be pinpointed as a 1963 or 1964 edition.

CHECKER MARATHON TOWN CUSTOM

Model Number	Body/Style Number	Body Type & Seating	Factory Price	Shipping Weight	Production Total
A12	A12E	4-dr Limo-8P	4638	3525	Note 1

NOTE 1: A total of 6,310 Checkers were built this year including taxicabs. Of this total, an estimated 960 were not-taxicabs.

SUPERBA SIX ENGINE: Inline. L-head Six. Cast iron block. Displacement: 226 cid. Bore and stroke: 3.31 x 4.38 inches. Compression ratio: 7.3:1. Brake hp: 80 at 3100 rpm. Four main bearings. Solid valve lifters. Carburetor: Zenith Type 'O' Model 12469 one-barrel. Engine manufactured by Continental Motor Corp., Muskegon, Mich. Exhaust valve diameter: 1.328 inches. Intake valve diameter: 1.515 inches. Chrome piston rings with 0.0020 inch skirt clearance. Durex 100 bearings with babbitt overlay. Exhaust pipe: two inch diameter. Tailpipe: 1.74 inch diameter. Electrical system: 12-volt negative ground. Spark setting: 4-degrees Before Top Dead Center. Fuel pump pressure: 3 psi. Champion 18 mm Model UD-16 spark plugs. AutoLite generator.

MARATHON OPTIONAL ENGINE: Inline. Six. Overhead valves. Cast iron block. Displacement: 266 cid. Bore and stroke: 3-5/16 x 4-3/8 inches. Compression ratio: 8.0:1. Brake hp: 141 at 4400 rpm. Four main bearings. Solid valve lifters. Carburetor: Rochester Type 2GC Model 7023096. Engine manufactured by Continental Motors Corp., Muskegon, Mich. Exhaust valve diameter: 1.422 inches. Intake valve diameter: 1.781 inches. Chrome piston rings with 0.0015 inch skirt clearance. Durex bearings. Exhaust pipe and tailpipe same as L-head six. Electrical system: 12-volt negative ground. Spark setting: same as L-head six. Fuel pump pressure: 3 psi. Autolite generator. Champion 14 mm spark plugs Model N-8.

CHASSIS FEATURES: Wheelbase: (Town Custom) 129 inches; (Marathon) 120 inches. Overall length: (Town Custom) 208.3 inches; (Marathon) 199.3 inches. Front tread: 60 inches. Rear tread: 62-1/2 inches. Tires: (Town Custom) data not available; (sedan) 6.70 x 15; (station wagon) 7.10 x 15. Standard transmission: Warner Gear three-speed manual with non-synchromesh first gear. Ten inch Auburn coil clutch. Standard rear axle gear ratio: 3.73: 1. Brakes: Eleven inch front and rear drum type with 311 square inch swept area. Manual steering ratio: 26.9:1. Turns lock-to-lock: 5.8. Suspension: (front) coil spring; (rear) 2.50 x 56.0 inch leaf.

OPTIONS: Power steering ($65). Air conditioning ($382). Power brakes ($33). White sidewall tires. Full wheel discs. Padded dashboard. Heater and defroster. Heavy-duty battery. NOTE: Padded dashboard, heater/defroster and power brakes are standard on overhead valve models. Two-speed Hydra-Matic (Neutral-Drive-Low-Reverse), with L-head engine only ($222). Dual-Range Hydra-Matic (Park/Reverse/Neutral/Drive 1/Drive 2/Low), with overhead valve engine only ($248). Overhead valve engine, specifications listed below ($57). Overdrive transmission ($108). Available rear axle ratio: (automatic) 3.31:1; (overdrive) 4.09:1; (other) 3.54:1. Limited slip differential.

HISTORICAL FOOTNOTES: The April 1964 issue of CAR LIFE magazine had a 16-page specifications chart giving details on all U.S. cars, including standard wheelbase Checker models. It provided such obscure facts as the timing chain pitch and the weight of the crankshaft. For Checkers, it is generally very hard to obtain this type of information. One Checker model that is generally outside the scope of this catalog deserves mention in relation to a 1964 change. This is the station-wagon-like eight-door (nine including tailgate) Aerobus, which was designed for airport transportation service. It came with front fender clearance lights, full-length air foil/luggage rack roof 'fins' and a twin-level Checker/Aerobus fender script. Through the end of 1964, all Aerobuses were built with Chrysler V-8 attachments. In 1965, the Aerobus switched to Chevrolet V-8 power. This year was also the last season for the 226 cid Continental Six, as Checkers came with Chevrolet sixes or V-8s from 1965 on. The November, 1963 issue of MOTOR TREND had a Checker article.

1965 CHECKER

1965 Checker, Marathon four-door sedan, 6-cyl (IB)

CHECKER MARATHON — (6-CYL) — SERIES A12 — In a rather strange sounding statement, Checker Motors Corp. announced that all new and unused cars sold after Sept. 1, 1965, with serial numbers larger than 20,000 would be considered 1965 models. Outwardly, there was no change in the product. Below the hood, Chevrolet powerplants were new. The base engine was 230 cid overhead valve six and a 283 cid V-8 was optional. Although not really a physical revision, the sedan was now marketed separately with two seating configurations. Standard six-passenger jobs came with front and rear bench seats and the year's lowest price tag. Carrying a higher retail was the six-/eight-passenger version with two folding jump seats. Marathons were unchanged insofar as styling or identification features and continued to be built on a sturdy X-Frame with five heavy crossmembers. Use of the lighter Chevrolet engine reduced weight by 125 pounds for sedans; 175 pounds for station wagons. Checkers continued with a basically boxy look and plenty of headroom. The overall height of the sedan was 62.8 inches. The 6.3 inch ground clearance was more than on all U.S. cars, except the Kaiser Jeep. Surprisingly, front hip room was only average and rear hip room of 52.5 inches was less than all standard domestic cars. In fact, rear hip room in Mustangs was only slightly less; in Buick Rivieras, just slightly more. So, there wasn't all that much more space in a Checker, but it was arranged somewhat differently than in other makes.

CHECKER I.D. NUMBERS: Serial numbers and engine numbers were found on the upper firewall. Serial and engine codes had three parts. The first identified the model; second part the production order; and third part the chassis or serial numbers. Serial numbers for 1965 determined by the year appearing on the registration for each car. The series number was A12 for conventional models and A19E for the long-wheelbase limousine. The 'E' may have indicated 'Extended Wheelbase.' An interesting fact was that for the 1965 model year (beginning September, 1964) all new Checkers or 1964 models left in stock with serial numbers higher than 20,000 were made 1965 models. The beginning 1965 serial number was 20001 and the ending number was 26636.

CHECKER MARATHON SERIES

Model Number	Body/Style Number	Body Type & Seating	Factory Price	Shipping Weight	Production Total
A12	A12	4-dr Sed-6P	2874	3360	Note 1
A12	A12	4-dr Sed-6/8P	3567	3406	Note 1
A12	A12W	4-dr Sta Wag-6P	3075	3400	Note 1

1965 Checker, Marathon four-door station-wagon, 6-cyl (IB)

NOTE 2: The new 'jump seat' sedan had the same price differential as the 1966 Deluxe Sedan and must have been the same model, although not officially called a Deluxe. This would explain the over $300 spread between it and the regular sedan, which the addition of jump seats alone would not warrant. When equipped with optional jump seats, the station wagon weighed 3450 pounds.

CHECKER MARATHON TOWN CUSTOM — (6-CYL) — SERIES A12E — The Marathon Town Custom limousine was now available on special order only. It increased noticeably in both price and weight, suggesting the inclusion of additional standard features. Styling was the same as in 1964. Power steering and brakes were standard equipment.

CHECKER MARATHON TOWN CUSTOM SERIES

Model Number	Body/Style Number	Body Type & Seating	Factory Price	Shipping Weight	Production Total
A12	A12E	4-dr Limo-6P	5491	4640	Note 1

NOTE 1: A total of 6,136 Checkers were built this year including taxicabs. Of this total, an estimated 930 were not taxicabs.

CHECKER MARATHON ENGINE: Inline. Six. Overhead valves. Cast iron block. 230 cid. Bore and stroke: 3.88 x 3.25 inches. Compression ratio: 8.5:1. Brake hp: 140 at 4400 rpm. Seven main bearings. Hydraulic valve lifters. Carburetor: Carter Model 3933 one-barrel or Rochester Type BC one-barrel Model 7028230.

OPTIONAL V-8 ENGINE: V-8. Overhead valves. Cast iron block. Displacement: 283 cid. Bore and stroke: 3.88 x 3 inches. Compression ratio: 9.25:1. Brake hp: 195 at 4800 rpm. Five main bearings. Hydraulic valve lifters. Carburetor: Rochester Type 2GC two-barrel Model 7028230.

CHASSIS FEATURES: Wheelbase: (Town Custom) 129.5 inches; (Marathons) 120 inches. Overall length: (Town Custom) 208.3 inches; (Marathons) 199.3 inches. Front tread: 60 inches. Rear tread: 62-1/2 inches. Tires: (Town Custom) 9.00 x 15; (Marathons) 7.10 x 15. Overall width: 76 inches.

OPTIONS: Power steering, standard on eight-passenger sedan and Town Custom ($76). Power brakes, standard on above models ($41). Air conditioning ($354). Power-operated forward folding rear seat. Auxiliary jump seats. Station wagon rooftop luggage carrier. Power tailgate. Full wheel discs. White sidewall tires. Heavy-duty shock absorbers. Two-tone paint finish. Chevrolet V-8 engine ($110). A Warner Gear three-speed manual transmission with non-synchromesh first gear was standard equipment. Overdrive transmission was optional ($108). Two-speed Turbo-Hydramatic transmission was optional ($248). A Power-Lok limited slip differential was optional. Available rear axle gear ratios: (standard) 3.73:1; (overdrive) 4.09:1; (Hydramatic) 3.31:1.

HISTORICAL FOOTNOTES: The twelve-passenger Aerobus on the 129 inch wheelbase continued to be offered for commercial use. An article about Checkers appeared in the November, 1964 issue of MOTOR TREND on page 63.

1966 CHECKER

CHECKER MARATHON — (6-CYL) — SERIES A12 — The 1966 Checkers continued to look just like the 1963 models outside. An engineering addition was the optional availability of a 327 cid Chevrolet V-8, plus the 230 cid six (base) or 283 cid V-8 (option). A new tire size was used for standard models. Power brakes and steering were standard on Deluxe sedans.

CHECKER I.D. NUMBERS: Serial numbers and engine numbers were found on the upper firewall. Serial and engine codes had three parts. The first identified the model; second part the production order; and third part the chassis or serial numbers. Serial numbers for 1966 determined by the year appearing on the registration for each car. The series number was A12 for all models. The beginning 1966 serial number was 26637.

CHECKER MARATHON SERIES

Model Number	Body/Style Number	Body Type & Seating	Factory Price	Shipping Weight	Production Total
A12	A12	4-dr Sed-6P	2874	3360	Note 1
A12	A12E	4-dr DeL Sed-6P	3567	3800	Note 1
A12	A12W	4-dr Sta Wag-6P	3075	3500	Note 1

1966 Checker, Marathon four-door sedan, 6-cyl (PH)

NOTE 1: A total of 5,761 Checkers were built this year including taxicabs. Of this total, an estimated 1,056 were not taxicabs.

1966 Checker, Marathon four-door Town Custom limousine, V-8 (IB)

CHECKER MARATHON TOWN CUSTOM — (6-CYL) — SERIES A12E — The Marathon Town Custom Limousine was reinstated as a regularly listed model. There were no changes other than the new optional V-8 and the use of a more expensive optional air conditioning system on this model. On all 'E' suffix models power brakes and steering were standard equipment.

CHECKER MARATHON TOWN CUSTOM SERIES

Model Number	Body/Style Number	Body Type & Seating	Factory Price	Shipping Weight	Production Total
A12	A12E	4-dr Limo-6P	4541	3800	Note 1

NOTE 1: A total of 5,761 Checkers were built this year including taxicabs. Of this total, an estimated 1,056 were not taxicabs.

HISTORICAL FOOTNOTES: A short article about Checkers appeared in the November, 1965, issue of MOTOR TREND on page 87. A Checker road test appeared in the September 1965 issue of MOTOR TREND on pages 45-47. Morris Markin, who had founded the Checker Motor Corp. as a taxicab builder, over 40 years earlier, was still in charge of the firm.

1967 CHECKER

CHECKER MARATHON — (6-CYL) — SERIES A12 — There were no physical or technical changes in the 1967 Checker Marathon. It seemed to be caught in a marathon of unending repetitiveness. The three Chevrolet engines remained available, with the six as base power-plant. Research turns up a few previously unearthed facts, such as that the sedan had a 12.2 cubic foot trunk capacity and both models carried 23 gallon gas tanks. No doubt this is the same as in the past, though not previously mentioned in this catalog. The steering system was, however, slightly modified for 1967. With manual steering 6.14 turns lock-to-lock were required, as opposed to 5.80 the previous year. With power assist, the respective figures moved in the opposite direction to 4.12 from 5.80. The turning circle stayed the same at 37.5 feet. Also, brake swept area decreased to 276 square inches (from 311 square inches previously). In Chevrolets, the horsepower rating of the four-barrel 327 V-8 climbed to 275 hp this year, but it appears that this did not affect Checker immediately. They probably had 250 hp motors in stock. As far as the model lineup, the 'E' suffix models were either dropped or converted into a special order choice. They do not appear in standard reference sources for 1967.

1967 Checker, Marathon four-door sedan, 6-cyl (PH)

CHECKER I.D. NUMBERS: Serial numbers and engine numbers were found on the upper firewall. Serial and engine codes had three parts. The first identified the model; second part the production order; and third part the chassis or serial numbers. Serial numbers for 1966 determined by the year appearing on the registration for each car. The series number was A12 for all models. The beginning 1967 serial number was 26637. New and unused cars sold after Sept. 1, 1966 with serial numbers larger than (6000) 28923 were considered 1967 models.

1967 Checker, Aerobus eight-door station wagon, V-8 (IB)

CHECKER MARATHON SERIES

Model Number	Body/Style Number	Body Type & Seating	Factory Price	Shipping Weight	Production Total
A12	A12	4-dr Sed-6P	2874	3400	Note 1
A12	A12W	4-dr Sta Wag-6P	3075	3500	Note 1

NOTE 1: A total of 5,822 Checkers were built this year including taxicabs. Of this total, an estimated 950 were not taxis.

BASE ENGINE: Inline. Six. Overhead valves. Cast iron block. 230 cid. Bore and stroke: 3.88 x 3.25 inches. Compression ratio: 8.5:1. Brake hp: 140 at 4400 rpm. Seven main bearings. Hydraulic valve lifters. Carburetor: Carter Model 3933 one-barrel or Rochester Type BC one-barrel Model 7028230. (Chevrolet manufacture).

OPTIONAL V-8 ENGINE: V-8. Overhead valves. Cast iron block. Displacement: 283 cid. Bore and stroke: 3.88 x 3 inches. Compression ratio: 9.25:1. Brake hp: 195 at 4800 rpm. Five main bearings. Hydraulic valve lifters. Carburetor: Rochester Type 2GC two-barrel Model 7028230. (Chevrolet manufacture).

OPTIONAL V-8 ENGINE: V-8. Overhead valves. Cast iron block. Displacement: 327 cid. Bore and stroke: 4 x 3.25 inches. Compression ratio: 10.5:1. Brake hp: 250 at 4400 rpm. Five main bearings. Hydraulic valve lifters. Carburetor: Rochester Type 4GC four-barrel. (Chevrolet manufacture).

CHASSIS FEATURES: Wheelbase: (Marathons) 120 inches. Overall length: (Marathons) 199.3 inches. Front tread: 60 inches. Rear tread: 62-1/2 inches. Tires: (Marathons) 8.15 x 15. Overall width: 76 inches.

OPTIONS: Air conditioning ($346). Power brakes ($41). Power steering ($74). Power side windows. Radio. Dash clock. Back-up lights. Parking brake warning light. Safety four-way flashers. Station wagon rooftop luggage rack. Power tailgate window. Wheel discs. Power folding rear seat. Jump seats. White sidewall tires. Heavy-duty shock absorbers. Two-tone paint. Chevrolet 195 hp; V-8 ($108). Chevrolet 250 hp V-8 ($194).

1968 CHECKER

1968 Checker, Marathon four-door station wagon, V-8 (PH)

CHECKER MARATHON — (6-CYL) — Like other manufacturers in America, the Kalamazoo cab maker was forced to bow to Federal Government safety and emissions control regulations this year. Round side marker lamps were added to the front fenders, ahead of the wheel opening. Padded dashboards, outside rearview mirror, windshield washers, front seat head rests, front safety belts, dual master cylinder braking system and four-way safety flashers became part of the standard safety equipment assortment. The standard wheelbase Deluxe sedan was reinstated in the Marathon model lineup. The 275 hp 327 cid Chevrolet V-8 found its way to the Checker stockroom for the 1967 model year. The small V-8 was bored and stroked to 307 cid. Otherwise, things were much the same as before.

CHECKER I.D. NUMBERS: Serial numbers and engine numbers were found on the upper firewall. Serial and engine codes had three parts. The first identified the model; second part the production order; and third part the chassis or serial numbers. New and unused cars sold after Sept. 1, 1967 with serial numbers larger than 1364-8001 were considered 1968 models.

CHECKER MARATHON SERIES

Model Number	Body/Style Number	Body Type & Seating	Factory Price	Shipping Weight	Production Total
A12	A12	4-dr Sed-6P	3221	3390	Note 1
A12	A12W	4-dr Sta Wag-6P	3491	3480	Note 1
A12	A12E	4-dr DeL Sed-8P	3915	3700	Note 1

NOTE 1: A total of 5,477 Checkers were built this year including taxicabs. Of this total, 992 were not taxicabs.

BASE ENGINE: Inline. Six. Overhead valves. Cast iron block. 230 cid. Bore and stroke: 3.88 x 3.25 inches. Compression ratio: 8.5:1. Brake hp: 140 at 4400 rpm. Seven main bearings. Hydraulic valve lifters. Carburetor: Carter Model 3933 one-barrel or Rochester Type BC one-barrel Model 7028230. (Chevrolet manufacture).

OPTIONAL V-8 ENGINE: V-8. Overhead valves. Cast iron block. Displacement: 283 cid. Bore and stroke: 3.88 x 3 inches. Compression ratio: 9.25:1. Brake hp: 195 at 4800 rpm. Five main bearings. Hydraulic valve lifters. Carburetor: Rochester Type 2GC two-barrel Model 7028230. (Chevrolet manufacture)

OPTIONAL V-8 ENGINE: V-8. Overhead valves. Cast iron block. Displacement: 307 cid. Bore and stroke: 3-7/8 x 3-1/4 inches. Compression ratio: 9.0:1. Brake hp: 200 at 4600 rpm. Five main bearings. Hydraulic valve lifters. Carburetor: Rochester two-barrel.

OPTIONAL V-8 ENGINE: V-8. Overhead valves. Cast iron block. Displacement: 327 cid. Bore and stroke: 4 x 3.25 inches. Compression ratio: 10.5:1. Brake hp: 250 at 4400 rpm. Five main bearings. Hydraulic valve lifters. Carburetor: Rochester Type 4GC four-barrel. (Chevrolet manufacture.)

OPTIONAL V-8 ENGINE: V-8. Overhead valves. Cast iron block. Displacement: 327 (326.9) cid. Bore and stroke: 4 x 3-1/4 inches. Compression ratio: 10.25:1. Brake hp: 275 at 4800 rpm. five main bearings. Hydraulic valve lifters. Carburetor: Rochester Type 4MV four-barrel.

CHASSIS FEATURES: Wheelbase: (Marathons) 120 inches. Overall length: (Marathons) 199.3 inches. Front tread: 60 inches. Rear tread: 62-1/2 inches. Tires: (Marathons) 8.15 x 15. Overall width: 76 inches.

OPTIONS: Air conditioning ($346). Power brakes ($41). Power steering ($74). Power side windows. Radio. Dash clock. Back-up lights. Parking brake warning light. Safety four-way flashers. Station wagon rooftop luggage rack. Power tailgate window. Wheel discs. Power folding rear seat. Jump seats. White sidewall tires. Heavy-duty shock absorbers. Two-tone paint. Chevrolet 195 hp: V-8 ($108). Chevrolet 250 hp V-8 ($194).

HISTORICAL FOOTNOTES: A road test of a Checker was done by ROAD & TRACK magazine in their August, 1968 issue (pages 73-76).

1969 CHECKER

CHECKER MARATHON — (6-CYL) — What Uncle Sam had wrought, mere men could not throw asunder. Neither could Checker Motor Corp., so the round fender side markers and safety equipment remained in 1969. So did the limousine, being grouped in a separate Deluxe series with the Deluxe sedan. Both Deluxes were, in fact, now on the 129 inch wheelbase and

---

had Deluxe front fender scripts. The 327 cid V-8 was de-tuned and robbed of 40 hp, but a 350 cid Chevrolet motor was new and put out 300 horses, a high for Checker. The base engine was a new 250 cid Chevrolet six-cylinder.

1969 Checker, Marathon four-door sedan, V-8 (PH)

CHECKER I.D. NUMBERS: Looked like the following sample: A12E 2134 90001. The first group of symbols was the Body Style Number; the second group the Production Number and the third group the Chassis Number.

CHECKER MARATHON SERIES

Model Number	Body/Style Number	Body Type & Seating	Factory Price	Shipping Weight	Production Total
A12	A12	4-dr Sed-6P	3290	3390	Note 1
A12	A12W	4-dr Sta Wag-6P	3560	3480	Note 1

NOTE 1: A total of 5,417 Checkers were built this year including taxicabs. Of this total, 760 were not taxis.

CHECKER DELUXE — (6-CYL) — The new Deluxe series had two long-wheelbase models averaging $1,000 in price over Marathons. Both cars had richer appointments and more regular equipment than the standard series entries. The word Deluxe appeared in script on the fenders. Most were sold with optional V-8 power and many accessories. They still had appeal to more conservative limousine buyers, plus people with large families. Both were priced way below the cheapest Cadillacs or Lincolns. Jump seats were standard in these cars.

CHECKER DELUXE SERIES

Model Number	Body/Style Number	Body Type & Seating	Factory Price	Shipping Weight	Production Total
A12	A12E	4-dr Sed-6/8P	3984	3590	Note 1
A12	A12E	4-dr Limo-6 /8P	4969	3802	Note 1

NOTE 1: A total of 5,417 Checkers were built this year including taxicabs. Of this total, 760 were not taxis.

BASE ENGINE: Inline. Six. Overhead valves. Cast iron block. Displacement: 250 (249.9) cid. Bore and stroke: 3-7/8 x 3-17/32 inches. Compression ratio: 8.5:1. Brake hp: 155 at 4200 rpm. Seven main bearings. Hydraulic valve lifters. Carburetor: Rochester Type MV two-barrel.

OPTIONAL 327 V-8: Optional engine: V-8. Overhead valves. Cast iron block. Displacement: 327 cid. Bore and stroke: 4 x 3-1/4 inches. Compression ratio: 9.0:1. Brake hp: 235 at 4800 rpm. Five main bearings. Hydraulic valve lifters. Carburetor: Rochester four-barrel.

OPTIONAL 350 V-8: V-8. Overhead valves. Cast iron block. Displacement: 350 cid. Bore and stroke: 4 x 3-15/16 inches. Compression ratio: 10.25:1. Brake hp: 300 at 4800 rpm. Five main bearings. Hydraulic valve lifters. Carburetor: Rochester four-barrel.

CHASSIS FEATURES: Wheelbase: (Marathon) 120 inches; (Deluxe) 129 inches. Overall length: (Marathon) 202 inches; (Deluxe) 211 inches. Front tread: 63.6 inches. Rear tread: 63 inches. Tires: 8.25 x 15.

OPTIONS: Air conditioning ($346). Power brakes ($41). Power steering. Automatic transmission. Optional 327 cid V-8 ($108). Optional 350 cid V-8 ($195).

HISTORICAL FOOTNOTES: An article about Checker appeared in CAR and DRIVER magazine June, 1969 (pages 59-61, 88). In addition, an article about a Ghia modified Checker appeared in ROAD & TRACK in January, 1969.

1970 CHECKER

CHECKER MARATHON — (6-CYL) — SERIES A-12 — In 1970, Morris Markin, Checker's founder, died. His son David took over as president of the firm with R.E. Oakland as executive vice-president and treasurer. Only one optional engine, the 350 cid V-8, was offered and its power was down by 17 percent. Two lines were available again: the standard 120 inch wheelbase Marathon and the Marathon Deluxe series, with a nine inch longer stance. All cars were one inch longer, due to minor bumper changes.

CHECKER I.D. NUMBERS: Vehicle Identification code locations were on dash under hood and on top of instrument panel. Serial numbers for 1970 were again a three part code referring to the model, production order and chassis or serial number. Example: A-12-403-00001.

CHECKER MARATHON SERIES

Model Number	Body/Style Number	Body Type & Seating	Factory Price	Shipping Weight	Production Total
A-12	A-12	4-dr Sed-6P	3671	3268	Note 1
A-12	A-12W	4-dr Sta Wag-6P	3941	3470	Note 1

NOTE 1: An estimated 4,000 Checkers were built this year including taxicabs. Of this total, 397 were non-taxicabs including all models in both series.

1970 Checker, Marathon four-door sedan, V-8 (PH)

CHECKER MARATHON DELUXE — (6-CYL) — SERIES A-12E — The long wheelbase models were now called Marathon Deluxes. There were no styling changes to speak of. The cars were one inch longer, which was probably due to a new bumper mounting system. Disc brakes were a new option this year. Jump seats, power steering and power brakes were standard on the big cars.

CHECKER MARATHON DELUXE

Model Number	Body/Style Number	Body Type & Seating	Factory Price	Shipping Weight	Production Total
A-12	A-12E	4-dr Sed-8P	4364	3378	Note 1
A-12	A-12E	4-dr Limo-8P	5338	3578	Note 1

NOTE 1: An estimated 4,000 Checkers were built this year including taxicabs. Of this total, 397 were non-taxicabs including all models in both series.

CHECKER MARATHON ENGINE: Inline. Six. Overhead valves. Cast iron block. Displacement: 250 cid. Bore and stroke: 3.88 x 3.53 inches. Compression ratio: 8.5:1. Brake hp: 155 at 4200 rpm. Seven main bearings. Hydraulic valve lifters. Carburetor: Rochester Type MV two-barrel.

OPTIONAL 327 V-8: Optional engine: V-8. Overhead valves. Cast iron block. Displacement: 327 cid. Bore and stroke: 4 x 3-1/4 inches. Compression ratio: 9.0:1. Brake hp: 235 at 4800 rpm. Five main bearings. Hydraulic valve lifters. Carburetor: Rochester four-barrel.

CHASSIS FEATURES: Wheelbase: (Marathon) 120 inches; (Deluxe) 129 inches. Overall length: (Marathon) 203 inches; (Deluxe) 212 inches. Front tread: 63.6 inches. Rear tread: 63 inches. Tires: (Marathon) 8.25 x 15.

OPTIONS: Power brakes ($41). Power steering. Air conditioning. Disc brakes ($64). Power windows. Three-speed manual transmission was standard. Overdrive transmission. Automatic transmission. V-8 350 cid 250 hp four-barrel engine ($108). Positive traction rear axle.

HISTORICAL FOOTNOTES: The 1970 Checkers were introduced Sept. 1, 1969. David Markin became the chief executive officer of the firm this year, replacing his father Morris, who died. Morris Markin had founded Checker in 1921. The company's address was 2016 North Pitcher St., Kalamazoo, MI 49007. J.J. Love was in charge of sales and advertising. Saburo Hori was vice-president of engineering. R.E. Smigh was vice-president and master mechanic. The 12-passenger Aerobus continued in production as a commercial vehicle.

1971 CHECKER

MARATHON SIX/EIGHT — (6-CYL/V-8) — SERIES A-12 — Checker attempted to market its cars separately as sixes and V-8s after the 1971 model year began. This had the effect of doubling the number of 'models,' although it was not really a true expansion of the line. All Checkers grew another inch in length and G78 x 15 tires were used. They were unchanged otherwise. Round side marker lamps were seen on both the front and rear fenders of all models.

CHECKER I.D. NUMBERS: The numbering system and code locations were the same as for previous models. Checkers continued with a three-part code. The first group of symbols referred to the model; the second group indicated production order number and the third group formed the chassis or Serial numbers. Example: A-12-403-10001. In the final group of symbols the first digit '1' designated 1971 model year. Official Body Style numbers were not used, although the A-12, A-12W and A-12E codes served the same purpose.

1971 Checker, Marathon Deluxe four-door sedan, V-8 (PH)

MARATHON SIX/EIGHT SERIES

Model Number	Body/Style Number	Body Type & Seating	Factory Price	Shipping Weight	Production Total
SIX					
A-12	A-12	4-dr Sed-6P	3843	3400	Note 1
A-12	A-12W	4-dr Sta Wag-6P	4113	3600	Note 1

Model	Body/Style	Body Type & Seating	Factory Price	Shipping Weight	Production Total
EIGHT (V-8)					
A-12	A-12	4-dr Sed-6P	3958	3500	Note 1
A-12	A-12W	4-dr Sta Wag-6P	4228	3700	Note 1

NOTE 1: Total output, including taxicabs was approximately 4,500 vehicles.

MARATHON DELUXE SIX/EIGHT — (6-CYL/V-8) — SERIES A-12E — The long wheelbase cars were also marketed as sixes and V-8s. They grew an inch and used the new sized tires. No styling or standard equipment changes can be discerned.

MARATHON DELUXE SIX/EIGHT SERIES

Model Number	Body/Style Number	Body Type & Seating	Factory Price	Shipping Weight	Production Total
SIX					
A-12	A-12E	4-dr Sed-8P	4536	3700	Note 1
A-12	A-12E	4-dr Limo-8P	5510	3700	Note 1
EIGHT (V-8)					
A-12	A-12E	4-dr Sed-8P	4651	3800	Note 1
A-12	A-12E	4-dr Limo-8P	5626	3800	Note 1

NOTE 1: Total output, including taxicabs was approximately 4,500 vehicles.

MARATHON SIX SERIES ENGINE DATA: Inline. Six. Overhead valves. Cast iron block. Displacement: 250 cid. Bore and stroke: 3.88 x 3.53 inches. Compression ratio: 8.5:1. Brake (SAE NET) hp: 145 at 4200 rpm. Seven main bearings. Hydraulic valve lifters. Carburetor: Rochester Type MC two-barrel.

MARATHON EIGHT SERIES ENGINE DATA: V-8. Overhead valves. Cast iron block. Displacement: 350 cid. Bore and stroke: 4 x 3-15/32 inches. Compression ratio: 9.0:1. Brake hp: 245 at 4800 rpm. Five main bearings. Hydraulic valve lifters. Carburetor: Rochester Type four-barrel.

CHASSIS FEATURES: Wheelbase: (Marathon) 120 inches; (Marathon Deluxe) 129 inches. Overall length: (Marathon) 204 inches; (Marathon Deluxe) 213 inches. Front tread: (All models) 63.6 inches. Rear tread: (All models) 63 inches. Tires: (All models) G78 x 15.

OPTIONS: Power brakes. Power steering. Air conditioning. ($364). Three-speed manual transmission was standard. Overdrive transmission. Automatic transmission. Positive traction rear axle. Heavy-duty clutch.

HISTORICAL FOOTNOTES: The 1971 Checkers were introduced Sept. 1, 1970. David R. Markin was the chief executive officer of the company again this year. A graduate of Bradley University, Markin had entered the auto industry with Checker Motors Corp. in 1948. He had worked in every phase of the business until assuming the presidency upon his father's passing away.

1972 CHECKER

MARATHON SIX/EIGHT — (6-CYL/V-8) — SERIES A-12 — Once again, Checker styling and post 'Federal' era trim features were the same. Automatic transmission and power-operated disc brakes were made standard equipment this year. The firm continued to market sixes and V-8s as separate models. A total of 5,325 miscellaneous brand gas powered cars were manufactured in the United States this year and the majority of these were Checkers.

1972 Checker, Marathon four-door sedan, V-8 (PH)

CHECKER I.D. NUMBERS: The numbering system and code locations were the same as for previous models. They took the form: A-12E-2134-20001. The first group of symbols designated the Body Style Number. The second group of symbols designated the Production Number. The third group of symbol designated the Chassis Number. The '12E' designation indicates a Deluxe 129 inch wheelbase model. The '12' in the Chassis Number indicates a 1972 model.

MARATHON SIX/EIGHT SERIES

Model Number	Body/Style Number	Body Type & Seating	Factory Price	Shipping Weight	Production Total
SIX					
A-12	A-12	4-dr Sed-6P	3654	3522	Note 1
A-12	A-12W	4-dr Sta Wag-6P	3910	3725	Note 1
EIGHT (V-8)					
A-12	A-12	4-dr Sed-6P	3769	3623	Note 1
A-12	A-12W	4-dr Sta Wag-6P	4025	3816	Note 1

NOTE 1: Estimated production of non-taxicabs was 850 units.

MARATHON DELUXE SIX/EIGHT — (6-CYL/V-8) — SERIES A-12E — The Limousine was dropped for the 1972 model year. Available on the 129 inch wheelbase was the Deluxe sedan. It had the same styling, with an extra wide rear door and rear side window. Jump seats were included, too, but the driver's partition was not. Deluxe scripts were attached to the front fender, above the straight, horizontal trim molding.

MARATHON DELUXE SIX/EIGHT SERIES

Model Number	Body/Style Number	Body Type & Seating	Factory Price	Shipping Weight	Production Total
SIX					
A-12	A-12E	4-dr Sed-8P	4312	3722	Note 1
EIGHT (V-8)					
A-12	A-12E	4-dr Sed-8P	4427	3823	Note 1

NOTE 1: Estimated production of non-taxicabs was 850 units.

1972 Checker, Aerobus eight-door station wagon, V-8 (IB)

MARATHON SIX ENGINE: Inline. Six. Overhead valves. Cast iron block. Displacement: 250 cid. Bore and stroke: 3.88 x 3.53 inches. Compression ratio: 8.5:1. Brake hp: 145 at 4200 rpm. Seven main bearings. Hydraulic valve lifters. Carburetor: Rochester Type MV two-barrel.

MARATHON V-8 ENGINE: V-8. Overhead valves. Cast iron block. Displacement: 350 cid. Bore and stroke: 4 x 3-15/32 inches. Compression ratio: 9.0:1. Brake hp: 345 at 4800 rpm. Five main bearings. Hydraulic valve lifters. Carburetor: Rochester Type 4GC four-barrel.

CHASSIS FEATURES: Wheelbase: (Marathon) 120 inches; (Marathon Deluxe) 129 inches. Overall length: (Marathon) 203 inches; (Marathon Deluxe) 212 inches. Front tread: (All models) 63.6 inches. Rear tread: (All models) 63 inches. Tires: (All models) G78 x 15.

OPTIONS: Power steering ($71). Air conditioning ($362). Dual air conditioning ($624). Full wheel discs. White sidewall tires. Vinyl top. Radio. Station wagon roof top luggage carrier. Power side windows. Power tailgate window. Jump seats. Power rear seat in station wagon. Automatic transmission was standard. Positive traction rear axle was available at extra cost.

HISTORICAL FOOTNOTES: The full-sized Checkers were introduced Sept. 1, 1971. David Markin was the chief executive officer of the company this year. R.E. Oakland was first vice-president. R.A. Yealin was secretary treasurer. J.J. Love was vice-president of sales. J.M. Temple was vice-president sales and service. Saburo-Hori was vice-president of engineering. S. Wilson was materials manager. B.B. Herrington was vice-president of manufacturing. Taxicabs and the 12-passenger Aerobus were also produced. General Motors supplied Checker engines (Chevrolet Division) and released both brake and net horsepower ratings for their powerplants in 1972. The six had an output of 110 SAE net hp. The V-8 was rated at 165 SAE net hp.

1973 CHECKER

MARATHON SIX/EIGHT — (6-CYL/V-8) — SERIES A-12 — Checker sales climbed to 5,900 vehicles in 1973, with taxicabs included. It is estimated that private sector deliveries went up by about 50 cars. Tough new federal emissions standards were met in the General Motor's powerplants by reducing compression ratios and adding an exhaust gas recirculating system (EGR) developed by Rochester Products Div. Also, it appears that slightly more oval-shaped parking lamp housings were substituted at about the same time. Not much else was in variance with the past. These changes added $299 to the Marathon's price and 100 pounds more weight.

CHECKER I.D. NUMBERS: The numbering system and code locations were the same as for previous models. They took the form A-12W-2134-30001. The first group of symbols designated the Body Style Number. The second group of symbols designated the Production Number. The third group of symbols designated the Chassis Number. The '12W' designation indicates a station wagon. The '3' in the Chassis Number indicates a 1973 model.

MARATHON SIX/EIGHT SERIES

Model Number	Body/Style Number	Body Type & Seating	Factory Price	Shipping Weight	Production Total
SIX					
A-12	A-12	4-dr Sed-6P	3955	3622	Note 1
A-12	A-12W	4-dr Sta Wag-6P	4211	3825	Note 1
EIGHT (V-8)					
A-12	A-12	4-dr Sed-6P	4070	3723	Note 1
A-12	A-12W	4-dr Sta Wag-6P	4326	2916	Note 1

NOTE 1: A total of 5,900 Checkers were built including taxicabs. Of this total, 900 non-taxicabs were estimated including models in all series.

1973 Checker, Marathon Deluxe four-door sedan, V-8 (IB)

MARATHON DELUXE SIX/EIGHT — (6-CYL/V-8) — SERIES A-12E — The 129 inch wheelbase Deluxe eight-passenger sedan also got a less powerful 'clean air' engine, oval shaped parking lamps. Its price climbed an even $300 and weight went up 100 pounds. Automatic transmission and power disc brakes were used as standard equipment on all Checker products, including taxicabs. Power steering was now standard as well.

MARATHON DELUXE SIX/EIGHT SERIES

Model Number	Body/Style Number	Body Type & Seating	Factory Price	Shipping Weight	Production Total
SIX					
A-12	A-12E	4-dr Sed-6P	4612	3822	Note 1
EIGHT (V-8)					
A-12	A-12E	4-dr Sed-8P	4727	3923	Note 1

NOTE 1: A total of 5,900 Checkers were built including taxicabs. Of this total, 900 non-taxicabs were estimated including models in all series.

MARATHON SIX ENGINE: Inline. Six. Overhead valves. Cast iron block. Displacement: 250 cid. Bore and stroke: 3.88 x 3.53 inches. Compression ratio: 8.25:1. SAE NET hp: 100 at 3600 rpm. Seven main bearings. Hydraulic valve lifters. Carburetor: Rochester two-barrel.

MARATHON EIGHT ENGINE: V-8. Overhead valves. Cast iron block. Displacement: 350 cid. Bore and stroke: 4 x 3-15/32 inches. Compression ratio: 8.5:1. SAE NET hp 145 at 4000 rpm. Five main bearings. Hydraulic valve lifters. Carburetor: Rochester four-barrel.

CHASSIS FEATURES: Wheelbase: (Marathon) 120 inches; (Marathon Deluxe) 129 inches. Overall length: (Marathon) 203 inches; (Marathon Deluxe) 212 inches. Front tread: (All models) 63.6 inches. Rear tread: (All models) 63 inches. Tires: (All models) G78 x 15.

OPTIONS: Air conditioning ($362). Dual air conditioning ($624). Full wheel discs. White sidewall tires. Vinyl top ($121). Radio. Station wagon rooftop luggage carrier. Power side windows. Power tailgate window. Jump seats. Power rear folding seat in station wagon. Automatic transmission was standard. Positive traction rear axle was available at extra cost.

HISTORICAL FOOTNOTES: The full-sized Checkers were introduced Sept. 1, 1972. Model year production peaked at 5,900 units. Calendar year sales of 6,297 cars and taxicabs were recorded. David Markin was the chief executive officer of the company this year. All Checkers had automatic transmissions. A total of just 662 Checkers were manufactured with V-8s. Sixes were employed in 5,259 cars. Discs brakes were standard equipment on all and combined with power assist. Also, all of these cars featured power steering. Twenty-six percent of production, or 1,770 cars, left the factory with air conditioning. A rare option was a vinyl top. Rather surprising is the fact that just a few hundred cars each year had radios installed at the factory. Apparently, most Checker taxicabs weren't delivered with regular radios. The Aerobus remained available.

1974 CHECKER

MARATHON SIX/EIGHT — (6-CYL/V-8) — SERIES A-12 — There were substantial increases in both price and weight this year, as Checker struggled to keep up with a myriad of new government regulations. For the 1973 model year, other manufacturers, who produced in larger numbers, were forced to install front bumpers capable of withstanding five mile per hour crash barrier impact tests. Now, it was Checker's turn to comply with the new regulation. Shunning elaborate polyurethane nose treatments and such, the Kalamazoo company adopted a bulky, shelf-like bumper that looked like something lifted straight from taxicab specifications. The important thing was that it did the job. Pricing and weight jumped substantially and overall length increased by two inches. Styling and standard equipment were basically unaffected. Ornamentation resembled the past. Both model year output and calendar year sales took a dip, although market share increased by 0.01 percent to a whopping 0.07 percent of industry output. The factory installed only 230 radios and added a mere 34 vinyl roofs on 1974 Checkers. The price of the Marathon V-8 station wagon climbed to over $5,000.

CHECKER I.D. NUMBERS: The numbering system and code locations were the same as for previous models. They took the form A-12-2134-40001. The first group of symbols designated the Body Style Number. The second group of symbols designated the Production Number. The third group of symbols designated the Chassis Number. The 'A-12' designation indicates the base Marathon sedan. The '4' in the chassis code indicates a 1974 model.

MARATHON SIX/EIGHT SERIES

Model Number	Body/Style Number	Body Type & Seating	Factory Price	Shipping Weight	Production Total
SIX					
A-12	A-12	4-dr Sed-6P	4716	3720	Note 1
A-12	A-12W	4-dr Sta Wag-6P	4966	3925	Note 1
EIGHT (V-8)					
A-12	A-12	4-dr Sed-6P	4825	3723	Note 1
A-12	A-12W	4-dr Sta Wag-6P	5074	3916	Note 1

NOTE 1: A total of 5,880 Checkers were built this year including taxicabs. Of this total, an estimated 900 were non-taxicabs, including all models in both series.

1974 Checker, Marathon four-door station wagon, V-8 (IB)

MARATHON DELUXE SIX/EIGHT — (6-CYL/V-8) SERIES A-12E — This was the last year for the long wheelbase cars, which measured two inches more end-to-end because of the new 'Federal' bumpers. With the recently emasculated engine, that was a lot of car to get out of its own way when it couldn't. As usual, there was little change in body styling or trim other than the new 'cow catcher' bumper up front. Prices increased an average of $779.

MARATHON DELUXE SIX/EIGHT SERIES

Model Number	Body/Style Number	Body Type & Seating	Factory Price	Shipping Weight	Production Total
SIX					
A-12	A-12E	4-dr Sed-8P	5394	3920	Note 1
EIGHT (V-8)					
A-12	A-12E	4-dr Sed-8P	5503	3923	Note 1

NOTE 1: A total of 5,880 Checkers were built this year including taxicabs. Of this total, an estimated 900 were non-taxicabs, including all models in both series.

MARATHON SIX ENGINE: Inline. Six. Overhead valves. Cast iron block. Displacement: 250 cid. Bore and stroke: 3.88 x 3.53 inches. Compression ratio: 8.25:1. SAE NET hp: 100 at 3600 rpm. Seven main bearings. Hydraulic valve lifters. Carburetor: Rochester two-barrel.

MARATHON V-8 ENGINE: V-8. Overhead valves. Cast iron block. Displacement: 350 cid. Bore and stroke: 4 x 3-15/32 inches. Compression ratio: 8.5:1. SAE NET hp: 145 at 3800 rpm. Five main bearings. Hydraulic valve lifters. Carburetor: Rochester four-barrel.

CHASSIS FEATURES: Wheelbase: (Marathon) 120 inches; (Marathon Deluxe) 129 inches. Overall length: (Marathon) 205 inches; (Marathon Deluxe) 212 inches. Front tread: (all models) 63.6 inches. Rear tread: (all models) 63 inches. Tires: (all models) G78 x 15.

OPTIONS: Air conditioning ($362). Dual air conditioning ($592). Vinyl roof ($145). Radio. Full wheel discs. Whitewall tires. Luggage carrier. Power windows. Power tailgate. Jump seats. Power folding seat in station wagon. Automatic transmission was standard. Positive traction rear axle was available at extra cost.

HISTORICAL FOOTNOTES: The full-sized Checkers were introduced Sept. 1, 1973. Model year production peaked at 5,880 units. Calendar year sales of 5,229 cars and taxicabs were recorded. David Markin was the chief executive officer of the firm this year. No executive changes had been made since 1972. Checkers advertising agency was Baker and Brichta, Inc. of Chicago, Illinois. Equipment having 100 percent installation rates included automatic transmission, power steering and power brakes. A total of 662 cars had V-8 engine installed. Air conditioners were ordered by only 882 Checker buyers this season. Radios were put into 230 production units. A mere 34 Checkers wore vinyl tops.

1975 CHECKER

MARATHON SIX/EIGHT — (6-CYL/V-8) — SERIES A-12 — In 1975, General Motors cars were fitted with catalytic converters. Since Checkers had Chevrolet motors, they received this change, too. As a consequence, both prices and weights increased again. The model and series lineup was also rearranged. The Marathon station wagon was dropped. The Deluxe

series nomenclature also disappeared and the long wheelbase models were dropped. A Deluxe Marathon V-8 sedan on the standard platform replaced it. It was over $700 more expensive than the big car. Styling stayed the same.

CHECKER I.D. NUMBERS: The numbering system and code locations were the same as for previous models. The A-12W Body Style code was no longer used. Serial numbers took the form A-12E-2134-50001. The first group of symbols designated the Body Style Number. The second group of symbols designated the Production Number. The third group of symbols designated the Chassis Number. The 'A-12E' designation indicates a Deluxe sedan. The '5' in the chassis code indicates a 1975 model.

MARATHON SIX/EIGHT SERIES

Model Number	Body/Style Number	Body Type & Seating	Factory Price	Shipping Weight	Production Total
SIX					
A-12	A-12	4-dr Sed-6P	5394	3774	Note 1
EIGHT (V-8)					
A-12	A-12	4-dr Sed-6P	5539	3839	Note 1
A-12	A-12E	4-dr DeL Sed-6P	6216	4137	Note 1

1975 Checker, Marathon four-door sedan, V-8 (IB)

NOTE 1: A total of 3,005 Checkers were built in the 1975 calendar year including taxicabs. Of this total, 450 were estimated to be non-taxicabs including all models above.

MARATHON SIX ENGINE: Inline. Six. Overhead valves. Cast iron block. Displacement: 250 cid. Bore and stroke: 3.88 x 3.53 inches. Compression ratio: 8.25:1. SAE NET hp: 100 at 3600 rpm. Seven main bearings. Hydraulic valve lifters. Carburetor: Rochester two-barrel.

MARATHON V-8 ENGINE: V-8. Overhead valves. Cast iron block. Displacement: 350 cid. Bore and stroke: 4 x 3-15/32 inches. Compression ratio: 8.5:1. SAE NET hp: 145 at 3800 rpm. Five main bearings. Hydraulic valve lifters. Carburetor: Rochester four-barrel.

CHASSIS FEATURES: Wheelbase: (all models) 120 inches. Overall length: (all models) 205 inches. Front tread: (all models) 63.6 inches. Tires: (all models) G78 x 15.

OPTIONS: Air conditioning ($362). Dual air conditioning ($592). Vinyl roof ($145). Radio. Full wheel discs. Whitewall tires. Jump seats. Two-tone paint. Automatic transmission was standard. Positive traction rear axle was available at extra cost.

HISTORICAL FOOTNOTES: The full-sized Checkers were introduced Sept. 1, 1974. Model year production totals were not reported. Calendar year sales of 3,005 cars and taxicabs were recorded. David R. Markin was the chief executive officer of the company this year. No top executives were changed. Checker's share of the U.S. auto market dropped to 0.04 percent. In the first 12 months of the 1975 model year 3,171 Checkers were registered in the U.S. In December, 1975, another 306 units were registered. This compares to respective figures of 4,892 and 230 in the 1974 model year. The company did not report optional equipment installation rates. The Environmental Protection Agency (EPA) gave the Checker with automatic transmission and 250 cid six a fuel economy rating of 17 city/23 highway/19 combined.

Although Chevrolet entered the postwar era with a warmed-over version of its 1942 model, the marque quickly assumed its traditional role as America's best selling car. The 1946-1948 Chevys were conservative in styling and engineering, but earned a reputation as value leaders in the low-price field. The "Stovebolt Six," dating back to 1937, was not a performance engine, but provided dependable service.

By Tony Hossain

Chevrolet's brand new 1949 models were, once again, conservatively styled and ruggedly built. Although arch-rival Ford also fielded a new 1949 model, with more modern slab-sided body lines, Chevrolet remained far ahead in the sales race.

The big news for 1950 was the addition of a sporty Bel Air two-door hardtop and a new option, the fully automatic Powerglide transmission. Sales went over the 1.5 million mark for the first time in history.

Chevrolet strengthened its hold on the low-price field in the early '50s, but these were not exciting years for enthusiasts ... with one notable exception. In 1953, Chevy introduced the fiberglass Corvette sports car. The first Corvette used a Chevy sedan chassis, engine and Powerglide transmission, but the car would soon become a creditable sports car.

Nineteen fifty-five was Chevrolet's renaissance. It was year one for the hot Chevy and marked the division's first assault on the growing youth market. With a sharp new style and a hot new 265 cid V-8 under the hood, as optional power, Chevrolet was no longer Grandma's car. Model year production soared to over 1.7 million, a record figure for any automaker.

Chevrolet built upon a good thing in 1956, with an extensive facelift and some potent new power options for the 265 cid 'Turbo-Fire' V-8. But, if there ever was a 'Classic Chevy', it was the 1957 model. In the '50s, people regarded it as a 'baby Cadillac' and the Bel Air Sport Coupe, convertible and two-door Nomad station wagon quickly developed a cult following that still lasts to this day. In a 1974 advertisement, Chevy referred to the 17-year old car as "the most popular used car in history." It still is.

Performance enthusiasts will remember 1957 as the year Chevy bored-out the small-block V-8 to 283 cid and made available that most prestigious of options, Ramjet Fuel-Injection. Chevy claimed one horsepower per cid.

The 1958 Chevrolet was totally redesigned, inside and out. The new Impala Sport Coupe and convertible joined the Bel Air Series as Chevy's top-of-the-line offering. The Impala was immediately popular and, in ensuing years, would become known as 'the pre-eminent American car.'

Chevrolet called its 1959 models "all new all over again." Although they shared the cruciform frame design, which

debuted in 1958, the 1959 body styling was all new and highly controversial. Especially disconcerting, to many longtime Chevrolet buyers, were the extreme horizontal tailfins and dramatically larger size. The Impala became a separate line, rather than a Bel Air sub-series. While young people scoured used car markets for sharp 1955-1957 models in power-packed form, Chevrolet, responding to criticism of past performance merchandising, toned down the styling of its 1960 models.

The big news for 1960 was the introduction of the compact Corvair. Initially available in four-door sedan form only, the Corvair was a revolution in American automotive design with its rear-mounted aluminum six, fully independent suspension and clean styling. At first, sales were disappointing, but the mid-1960 addition of two-door models and the luxurious Monza Club Coupe, sent sales upward. The Corvair quickly developed a following among automotive enthusiasts.

The Chevrolet product line continued to proliferate in the early '60s, with the addition of the traditionally engineered, compact Chevy II, in model year 1962. Then came the popular Chevelle, two years later. Chevrolets from the early '60s that collectors find particularly appealing today include the 1962-1964 Impala SS (Super Sport), the Corvair Monza Spyder and all Corvettes.

Nineteen sixty-five would be known as the year of records for the Chevrolet Motor Division. Large Chevrolets were restyled with pleasing, flowing lines. Also new, from the ground-up, was the Corvair. With continental-like styling and an all-new suspension system, the new Corvair received rave reviews from the motoring press. The 1965 Corvette received a four-wheel disc brake system and a robust 396 cid V-8 became Chevy's latest stormer.

It replaced the big Chevy's top-option '409;' an engine which had become a legend from 1961 to early 1963.

The late 1960s were years of declining market share for Chevrolet products. Ralph Nader's attack on the Corvair, in 1965, hurt auto sales in general, but had a particularly severe impact on Chevrolet. The Corvair was quietly withdrawn from the market in 1969.

The Camaro, Chevy's belated answer to the enormously successful Ford Mustang, was introduced in model year 1967. First-generation Camaros (1967-1969) are very popular among collectors today. Particularly desirable are the Z28 or SS performance packages and all convertible models.

Chevrolet regained lost market share in the early '70s, with new products and aggressive marketing. New for 1970 was the Monte Carlo and a redesigned Camaro, hailed as a contemporary classic. The smart new, sporty design lasted, with few changes, through the 1981 model year. Chevrolet's combined car and truck sales, in 1971, totalled over three million units.

Chevy had entered the '70s as the world's largest producer of motor vehicles. Notable new entries in 1971 included a redone full-size Chevrolet and the subcompact Vega. Although it was a strong contender in its market segment, the Vega suffered numerous quality and engineering problems and was withdrawn at the end of the 1977 model year. Highly desirable today, however, are the limited edition, high-performance 1975-1976 Cosworth Vegas.

Chevrolets from the 1970s attracting collector interest today include the 1970-1972 Monte Carlos, Chevelle SSs, Camaros of all years and the 1975 Caprice convertible. That car was Chevrolet's last production ragtop for the '70s.

1946 Chevrolet, Fleetline two-door Aerosedan, 6-cyl

1947 Chevrolet, Fleetmaster two-door convertible, 6-cyl

1946 Chevrolet, Fleetline two-door Aerosedan, 6-cyl

1948 Chevrolet, Custom Country Club Coupe, 6-cyl

1948 Chevrolet, Fleetmaster four-door station wagon, 6-cyl

1949 Chevrolet, Fleetline four-door sedan, 6-cyl

1951 Chevrolet, Styleline Special two-door business coupe, 6-cyl

1952 Chevrolet, Styleline Special four-door sedan, 6-cyl

1953 Chevrolet, Two-Ten two-door convertible (custom), 6-cyl

1954 Chevrolet, Bel Air four-door sedan, 6-cyl

1954 Chevrolet, Bel Air four-door station wagon, 6-cyl

1955 Chevrolet, Bel Air two-door convertible, V-8

Standard Catalog of American Cars

1946 CHEVROLET

1946 Chevrolet, Stylemaster four-door sedan, 6-cyl

STYLEMASTER — SIX — SERIES DJ — The 1946 Chevrolet Stylemaster models were updated 1942 Master Deluxes. The grille was modified, the parking lamps were relocated and chrome plated trim features returned to replace plastic parts used in prewar cars. Plain fenders, notchback styling and Stylemaster block lettering on hoodside moldings were identifiers. On the interior, three-spoke steering wheels, painted window sills and a minimum of bright metal trim moldings were used. Pile fabric upholstery, standard rubber floor mats and single left-hand sun visors were seen.

STYLEMASTER I.D. NUMBERS: Serial numbers were stamped on a plate on the right front door hinge pillar. Motor numbers were stamped on the right side of block near fuel pump. The numerical prefix in serial number indicated assembly plant as follows: (1) Flint, Mich.; (2) Tarrytown, N.Y.; (3) St. Louis, Mo., (5) Kansas City, Mo.; (6) Oakland, Calif.; (8) Atlanta, Ga.; (9) Norwood, Ohio; (14) Baltimore, Md.; (21) Janesville, Wis. The letters on the number plate indicated year and model, for example: DJ was for 1946 Stylemasters. A Fisher Body Style Number was located on the vehicle data plate, on engine side of firewall. It began with a two-digit prefix designating model year. followed by a dash and four numbers indicating body type and sometimes having a letter suffix designating trim level or equipment installations. Serial numbers for Michigan built 1946 Stylemasters were DJ-1001 to 56896; motor numbers were DAA1001 to 546865. Chevrolet model numbers appear in second column in charts below.

STYLEMASTER SIX — SERIES DJ

Model Number	Body/Style Number	Body Type & Seating	Factory Price	Shipping Weight	Production Total
46-DJ	1504	2-dr Bus Cpe-2P	1022	3080	14,267
46-DJ	1524	2-dr Spt Cpe-5P	1059	3105	19,243
46-DJ	1502	2-dr Twn Sed-6P	1072	3145	61,104
46-DJ	1503	4-dr Spt Sed-6P	1123	3150	75,349

FLEETMASTER — SIX — SERIES DK — The Fleetmaster series replaced the prewar Special Deluxe group. The moldings on sides of the hood carried this name. Richer upholstery trims were available and included two sun visors; front seat armrests and woodgrained window sills. No business coupe was offered, but a convertible and station wagon were. A Deluxe, two-spoke steering wheel with a stylized "bird" horn button insert was seen.

FLEETMASTER I.D. NUMBERS: Serial, motor and body style coding was based on the Stylemaster system, but different series codes and additional body nomenclature were used. Fleetmasters built in Michigan were numbered DK-1001 to 58678. The first two symbols in the main Style Number were '21' for Fleetmaster DK Series. Engine numbering range same as Stylemaster.

1946 Chevrolet, Stylemaster four-door sedan, 6-cyl

FLEETMASTER SIX SERIES DK

Model Number	Body/Style Number	Body Type & Seating	Factory Price	Shipping Weight	Production Total
46-DK	2124	2-dr Spt Cpe-5P	1130	3120	27,036
46-DK	2134	2-dr Conv-5P	1381	3420	4,508
46-DK	2102	2-dr Twn Sed-6P	1143	3165	56,538
46-DK	2103	4-dr Spt Sed-6P	1194	3200	73,746
46-DK	2109	4-dr Sta Wag-8P	1604	3435	804

FLEETLINE — SIX — SUB-SERIES DK — As was the case in prewar times, a Fleetmaster sub-series was available as the two model Fleetline group. Both of these cars had the fastback GM 'Sport Dynamic' body shell and a Super Deluxe level of trim. Fleetline lettering adorned the hoodside molding. Triple speedline moldings were stacked on the flanks of all fenders. A distinctive bright metal windshield surround was seen. Interior appointments were generally of the Fleetmaster level, with special non-pile 'Fleet weave' fabrics used only in these two models. There was no way to overlook their extra-fancy appearance.

1946 Chevrolet, Fleetline Sportmaster four-door sedan, 6-cyl

FLEETLINE I.D. NUMBERS: As a Fleetmaster sub-series, Fleetlines shared the same numbering system, except for style codes.

FLEETLINE SUB-SERIES DK

Model Number	Body/Style Number	Body Type & Seating	Factory Price	Shipping Weight	Production Total
46-DK	2113	4-dr SptMas Sed-6P	1222	3215	7,501
46-DK	2144	2-dr Aero Sed-6P	1165	3140	57,932

CHEVROLET CHASSIS FEATURES: Three-speed manual transmission was exclusively available. Wheelbase: (all) 207-1/2 inches. Front tread: (all) 57.6 inches. Rear tread: (all) 60 inches. Rear axle ratio: 4.11:1. Tires: 16 x 6.00.

CONVENIENCE OPTIONS: Radio. Heater. Whitewall tire disks. Spotlight. Radio antenna. Fog lamps. Cowl windshield washer. Center bumper guards. Deluxe steering wheel. Deluxe push-button radio. Heater and defroster. Wheel trim rings. Deluxe in-dash heater and defroster.

HISTORICAL FOOTNOTES: First postwar Chevy built Oct. 3, 1945. The business coupe had front seat only. The Fleetmaster station wagon was a true 'woodie' wagon.

1947 CHEVROLET

1947 Chevrolet, Stylemaster four-door sedan, 6-cyl

STYLEMASTER SIX SERIES 1500 EJ — There was minimal change for 1947 at Chevrolet. The radiator grille had a softer, more horizontal appearance with the blades contoured into three distinct sections and Chevrolet lettering on the uppermost bar. A more horizontal hood emblem with bow-tie insignia was used. The horizontal moldings, which ran from hood to rear, were eliminated from all models, but a short, spear-shaped molding at the rear sides of the hood carried the series name in block letters. A three-spoke steering wheel with no horn ring was seen. Pile fabric upholstery was used. The floor mats lacked carpet inserts and a single left-hand sun visor appeared.

STYLEMASTER I.D. NUMBERS: Serial numbers were stamped on a plate on the right front door hinge pillar. Motor numbers were stamped on the right side of block near fuel pump. The numerical prefix in serial number indicated assembly plant as follows: (1) Flint, Mich.; (2) Tarrytown, N.Y.; (3) St. Louis, Mo.; (5) Kansas City, Mo.; (6) Oakland, Calif.; (8) Atlanta, Ga.; (9) Norwood. Ohio: (14) Baltimore, Md.; (21) Janesville, Wis. The letters on the number plate indicated year and model, for example: EJ was for 1947 Stylemaster. A Fisher Body Style Number was located on the vehicle data plate, on engine side of firewall. It began with a two-digit prefix designating model year, followed by a dash and four numbers indicating body type and sometimes having a letter suffix designating trim level or equipment installations. Serial numbers for Michigan built 1947 Stylemasters were EJ-1001 to 56896; motor numbers were EA1001 to 683120. Chevrolet model numbers appear in column two in charts below.

SYTLEMASTER SIX SERIES 1500 EJ

Model Number	Body/Style Number	Body Type & Seating	Factory Price	Shipping Weight	Production Total
47-EJ	1504	2-dr Bus Cpe-2P	1160	3050	27,403
47-EJ	1524	2-dr Spt Cpe-5P	1202	3060	34,513
47-EJ	1502	2-dr Twn Sed-6P	1219	3075	88,534
47-EJ	1503	4-dr Spt Sed-6P	1276	3130	42,571

FLEETMASTER — SIX — SERIES 2100 EK — Quick identification of Fleetmaster models came from the lettering on hoodside spears, the appearance of bright metal window reveal moldings and use of trim below taillamps. A Deluxe two-spoke steering wheel was standard. Two-tone, Bedford cloth upholstery was optional, with leatherette scuff covering used in all trim combinations on doors, front seats and rear seats. Carpet inserts highlighted Fleetmaster front floor mats. Two sun visors were used. An illuminated radio grille and package compartment with lock was featured. Fleetline fastbacks lacked speedline fender trim, but again came with special "Fleetweave" upholstery and all Fleetmaster appointments.

FLEETMASTER I.D. NUMBERS: Followed same general system with new alphabetical codes. Serial numbers EK-1001 to 72404. Motor numbers fit into the same sequence listed for Stylemaster above.

1947 Chevrolet, Fleetline Aerosedan two-door sedanette, 6-cyl

FLEETMASTER SIX SERIES 2100 EK

Model Number	Body/Style Number	Body Type & Seating	Factory Price	Shipping Weight	Production Total
47-EK	2103	4-dr Spt Sed-6P	1345	3185	91,440
47-EK	2102	2-dr Twn Sed-6P	1286	3125	80,128
47-EK	2124	2-dr Spt Cpe-5P	1281	3090	59,661
47-EK	2134	2-dr Conv-5P	1628	3390	28,443
47-EK	2109	4-dr Sta Wag-8P	1893	3465	4,912

FLEETLINE 2100 EK SUB-SERIES

Model Number	Body/Style Number	Body Type & Seating	Factory Price	Shipping Weight	Production Total
47-EK	2113	4-dr SptMas Sed-6P	1371	3150	54,531
47-EK	2144	2-dr Aero Sed-6P	1313	3125	159,407

1947 Chevrolet, Fleetmaster four-door station wagon, 6-cyl

ENGINE: Six-cylinder. Overhead valves. Cast iron block. Displacement: 216.5 cid. Bore and stroke: 3-1/2 x 3-3/4 inches. Compression ratio: 6.5:1. Brake horsepower: 90 at 3300 rpm. Four main bearings. Solid valve lifters. Carburetors: Carter one-barrel as follows: (standard transmission with Climate Control) YF-765S or YF-765SA; (manual choke with standard transmission) YF-787S or YF-787SA or YF-787SB; (all standard transmission) WI-574S or YF-787S or YF-787SB or YF-789S or YF-789SB.

CHEVROLET CHASSIS FEATURES: Three-speed manual transmission. Wheelbase: (all) 116 inches. Overall length: (passenger cars) 197-3/4 inches; (station wagons) 207-1/2 inches. Front tread: (all) 57.6 inches. Rear tread: (all) 60 inches. Rear axle ratio: 4.11:1. Tires: 16 x 6.00.

CONVENIENCE OPTIONS: Heater. Whitewall tire disks. Spotlight. Radio antenna. Fog lamps. Cowl windshield washer. Center bumper guards. Deluxe steering wheel. Deluxe push-button radio. Heater and defroster. Wheel trim rings. Deluxe in-dash heater and defroster.

HISTORICAL FOOTNOTES: Model year sales of 684,145 units made Chevrolet America's number one producer of autos. Dealer introductions held Feb. 8, 1947. The business coupe had a front seat only. The Fleetmaster station wagon was a true 'woodie' wagon.

1948 Chevrolet, Stylemaster two-door sport coupe, 6-cyl

STYLEMASTER SIX SERIES 1500 FJ — A T-shaped vertical center bar was added to the 1947 grille to make a 1948 Chevy. A new hood ornament and slightly revised nose emblem appeared. Black rubber windshield surrounds; plain side fenders; rubber mud guards; and Stylemaster lettering on the rear hoodside spears characterized the exterior of the low-price Chevrolet. Inside was found a three-spoke steering wheel (without horn ring); painted dashboard; unlighted glovebox; plain trim; pile fabric upholstery; plain rubber floor mats; painted window sills and all-cloth seats without leather topped armrests.

STYLEMASTER I.D. NUMBERS: Serial numbers were stamped on a plate on the right front door hinge pillar. Motor numbers were stamped on the right side of block near fuel pump. The numerical prefix in serial number indicated assembly plant as follows: (1) Flint, Mich.; (2) Tarrytown, N.Y.; (3) St. Louis, Mo., (5) Kansas City, Mo.; (6) Oakland, Calif.; (8) Atlanta, Ga.; (9) Norwood. Ohio: (14) Baltimore, Md.; (21) Janesville, Wis. The letters on the number plate indicated year and model, for example: FJ was for 1948 Stylemaster. A Fisher Body Style Number was located on the vehicle data plate, on engine side of firewall. It began with a two-digit prefix designating model year, followed by a dash and four numbers indicating body type and sometimes having a letter suffix designating trim level or equipment installations. Serial numbers for Michigan built 1948 Stylemasters were FJ-1001 to 30590; motor numbers were FA1001 to 825234. Chevrolet model numbers appear in column two in charts below.

STYLEMASTER SIX SERIES 1500 FJ

Model Number	Body/Style Number	Body Type & Seating	Factory Price	Shipping Weight	Production Total
48-FJ	1503	4-dr Spt Sed-6P	1371	3115	48,456
48-FJ	1502	2-dr Twn Sed-6P	1313	3095	70,228
48-FJ	1524	2-dr Spt Cpe-5P	1323	3020	34,513
48-FJ	1504	2-dr Bus Cpe-3P	1244	3045	18,396

1948 Chevrolet, Fleetline two-door Aerosedan, 6-cyl (AA)

FLEETMASTER SIX SERIES 2100 FK — Short, stylized spears on the rear corners of hoods said 'Fleetmaster.' So did the inclusion of features such as chrome windshield surrounds; two-spoke Deluxe steering wheel (with horn ring); woodgrained dashboard and window sills; illuminated glove locker; leatherette rear seat scuff covers; front floor mat carpet inserts and leather-topped front seat armrests. An equipment change was that the clock and cigarette lighter were now considered standard on Fleetmasters and Fleetlines only. A dome lamp with automatic switch at driver's door was also a regular extra feature on these lines. On Fleetmaster, buyers could select two-tone Bedford cloth upholstery options or stick with the standard pile fabric choice. Triple, stacked speedline moldings once again graced front and rear fenders of Fleetline fastbacks. These cars had other Super Deluxe features as well, such as five, vertical slashes of chrome beneath the taillights and Fleetline signature scripts on the center of deck lid. There was also a three-quarter length belt molding.

FLEETMASTER I.D. NUMBERS: Followed the same general system with new alphabetical codes. Serial numbers FK-1001 to 81603. Motor numbers fit into the same sequence listed for Stylemaster above.

FLEETMASTER SIX SERIES 2100 FK

Model Number	Body/Style Number	Body Type & Seating	Factory Price	Shipping Weight	Production Total
48-FK	2103	4-dr Spt Sed-6P	1439	3150	93,142
48-FK	2102	2-dr Twn Sed-6P	1381	3110	66,208
48-FK	2124	2-dr Spt Cpe-6P	1402	3050	58,786
48-FK	2134	2-dr Conv-5P	1750	3340	20,471
48-FK	2109	4-dr Sta Wag-8P	2013	3430	10,171

FLEETLINE 2100 FK SUB-SERIES

48-FK	2113	4-dr SptMas-6P	1492	3150		83,760
48-FK	2144	2-dr Aero Sed-5P	1434	3100		211,861

ENGINE: Six-cylinder. Overhead valves. Cast iron block. Displacement: 216.5 cid. Bore and stroke: 3-1/2 x 3-3/4 inches. Compression ratio: 6.5:1. Brake horsepower: 90 at 3300 rpm. Four main bearings. Solid valve lifters. Carburetors: Carter one-barrel as follows: (standard transmission with Climate Control) YF-765S or YF-765SA; (manual choke with standard transmission) YF-787S or YF-787SA or YF-787SB; (all standard transmission) WI-574S or YF-787S or YF-787SB or YF-789S or YF-789SB.

1948 Chevrolet, Fleetline two-door Aerosedan, 6-cyl

CHEVROLET CHASSIS FEATURES: Three-speed manual transmission. Wheelbase: (all) 116 inches. Overall length: (passenger cars) 197-3/4 inches; (station wagons) 207-1/2 inches. Front tread: (all) 57.6 inches. Rear tread: (all) 60 inches. Rear axle ratio: 4.11:1. Tires: 16 x 6.00.

CONVENIENCE OPTIONS: Standard radio. Deluxe push-button radio. Standard below dash heater and defroster. Deluxe in-dash heater and defroster. White sidewall tires. Spotlight cowl windshield washer. Low-pressure tires on wide rim 15 inch wheels. Bedford cord Fleetmaster upholstery. Front and rear bumper wing guards. Chrome plated gravel shields. Radio antenna. Clock in Stylemaster. Cigarette lighter in Stylemaster. Engine oil filter, external canister type. Oil bath air cleaner. Country Club trim package (see HISTORICAL FOOTNOTES for details). Wheel trim rings. Directional signals. External windshield sun shade (visor).

HISTORICAL FOOTNOTES: Model introductions were held February, 1948. Calendar sales of 775,982 units were recorded for the year. Precision interchangeable main engine bearings were adopted this season, in place of poured babbitt bearings. The business coupe had a front seat only. The Fleetmaster station wagon was a true 'woodie' wagon. A unique accessory sold by Chevrolet dealers this year was the woodgrained 'Country Club' trim package, produced by Engineered Enterprises of Detroit, Mich., but sold only through factory authorized dealers for $149.50. It could be ordered for the Fleetline Aero Sedan and the Fleetmaster Town Sedan or convertible coupe, but very few cars were so-equipped.

1949 CHEVROLET

1949 Chevrolet, Styleline Special business coupe, 6-cyl

SPECIAL SERIES — SIX — 1500 GJ — Series designations were now determined by trim level, not body style. Each line had Styleline (notchback) and Fleetline (fastback) sub-series. All new, postwar designs were seen with integral front fenders and lower styling lines for fenders, roofs and hoods. The grille had a bowed upper bar with Chevrolet lettering; a horizontal center bar with round parking lamps (where bars intersected); and seven, short vertical bars dividing the lower opening. Standard equipment for Specials included dual tail and stop lights; dual license lights; dual windshield wipers; stainless steel body belt molding; body sill molding; rear fender crown moldings; front door push-button handles (with integral key locks); black rubber rear fender shields; gas filler door in left rear fender; hood ornament and emblem; rear deck lid emblem; chrome headlamp rims; five extra-low pressure 6.70 x 15 tires on five-inch rims; front and rear bumpers and guards; and license guard on front bumper. Seats were upholstered with tan, striped-pattern, pile fabric with rubberized backs. Black rubber floor mats were used in the front compartment, carpets in rear of sedans and sport coupes. Three-spoke steering wheels with horn buttons appeared.

SPECIAL I.D. NUMBERS: Serial numbers were stamped on a plate on the right front door hinge pillar. Motor numbers were stamped on the right side of block near fuel pump. The numerical prefix in serial number indicated assembly plant as follows: (1) Flint, Mich.; (2) Tarrytown, N.Y.; (3) St. Louis, Mo., (4) Kansas City, Mo.; (5) Oakland, Calif.; (8) Atlanta, Ga.; (9) Norwood. Ohio: (14) Baltimore, Md.; (21) Janesville, Wis. The letters on the number plate indicated year and model, for example: 'GJ' for Special Series; 'GK' for Deluxe. Number plate locations changed to left-hand door pillar. Engine number also stamped on crankcase to rear of distributor. Serial numbers GJ-1001 to 47213. Motor numbers GA-1001 to 1031807. Fisher Body Style Numbers now appear on second column of charts; Chevrolet model numbers in first column; Series code in head above.

SPECIAL SERIES 1500 GJ

STYLELINE SUB-SERIES

Model Number	Body/Style Number	Body Type & Seating	Factory Price	Shipping Weight	Production Total
1503	49-1269	4-dr Sed-6P	1460	3090	46,334
1502	49-1211	2-dr Sed-6P	1413	3070	69,398
1524	49-1227	2-dr Spt Cpe-6P	1418	3030	40,239
1504	49-1227B	2-dr Bus Cpe-3P	1339	3015	20,337

FLEETLINE SUB-SERIES

Model Number	Body/Style Number	Body Type & Seating	Factory Price	Shipping Weight	Production Total
1553	49-1208	4-dr Sed-6P	1460	3095	58,514
1552	49-1207	2-dr Sed-5P	1413	3060	36,317

1949 Chevrolet, Styleline Deluxe convertible, 6-cyl (AA)

DELUXE SERIES — SIX — 2100 GK — In addition to body equipment found, on Special Series models, Deluxes had series nameplate (Deluxe) on front fenders; stainless steel moldings on front fenders and doors; windshield reveal moldings; stainless steel rear fender shields (gravel guards); window reveal moldings (except station wagon and convertible); short lower belt molding sections; rear wheelcover panels (fender skirts); left-hand outside rearview mirror on convertible and coupe and chrome plated side window frames, also on convertible. Seats were upholstered with tan, striped pattern, flat cloth in sedans and coupe; genuine leather and tan Bedford cord in convertibles; tan leather fabric in station wagon. Also included were Deluxe two-spoke steering wheel, two sun visors, simulated carpet floor mat inserts, two-tone tan and brown dashboard finish and many other Deluxe appointments.

DELUXE SERIES I.D. NUMBERS: Followed same general system with new alphabetical code. Serial numbers GK-1001 to 128201. Motor numbers fit into the same sequence listed for Special Series above.

1949 Chevrolet, Fleetline Deluxe four-door sedan, 6-cyl

DELUXE SERIES 2100 GK

STYLELINE SUB-SERIES

Model Number	Body/Style Number	Body Type & Seating	Factory Price	Shipping Weight	Production Total
2103	49-1069	4-dr Sed-6P	1539	3125	191,357
2102	49-1011	2-dr Sed-6P	1492	3100	147,347
2124	49-1027	2-dr Spt Cpe-6P	1508	3065	78,785
2134	49-1067	2-dr Conv-5P	1857	3355	32,392
2109	49-1061	4-dr Wood Wag-8P	2267	3485	3,342
2119	49-1062	4-dr Steel Wag-8P	2267	3435	2,664

FLEETLINE SUB-SERIES

Model Number	Body/Style Number	Body Type & Seating	Factory Price	Shipping Weight	Production Total
2153	49-1008	4-dr Sed-5P	1539	3135	130,323
2152	49-1007	2-dr Sed-5P	1492	3100	180,251

NOTE 1: Body Style Number 1061, the wood station wagon, was replaced by Style Number 1062, the steel station wagon, in the middle of the model run, with both styles available concurrently early in the year.

ENGINE: Six-cylinder. Overhead valves. Cast iron block. Displacement: 216.5 cid. Bore and stroke: 3-1/2 x 3-3/4 inches. Compression ratio: 6.5:1. Brake horsepower: 90 at 3300 rpm. Four main bearings. Solid valve lifters. Carburetors: Carter one-barrel W1-684.

CHEVROLET CHASSIS FEATURES: Box girder frame. In convertible a 'VK' structure of I-beam members takes place of engine rear support cross member. Knee-action front suspension with direct, double-acting shock absorbers. Ride stabilizer. Rubber insulated semi-elliptic rear springs with metal covers. Direct double-acting hydraulic rear shock absorbers. Four-wheel hydraulic brakes with 11 inch drums. Wheelbase: (all) 115 inches. Overall length: (passenger cars) 197 inches; (station wagon) 198 inches. Front tread: (all) 57 inches. Rear tread: (all) 58-3/4 inches. Rear axle: Semi-floating with hypoid drive and 4.11:1 gear ratio. Torque tube drive with tubular propeller shaft; both fully enclosed. Tires: 6.70 x 15 blackwall on widebase rims.

CONVENIENCE OPTIONS: Standard manual radio. Deluxe push-button radio. Radio antenna. Under dash heater and defroster. In-dash Deluxe heater and defroster. White sidewall tires. Wheel trim rings. Spotlight. Fog lamps. Directional signals. Back-up light. External windshield sun shade (visor), Tan striped pattern, free-breathing pile fabric Deluxe Series upholstery trim. San-Toy seat covers. Outer bumper tips. Master grille guard. Locking gas filler cap. Other standard factory and/or dealer installed accessories.

HISTORICAL FOOTNOTES: Dealer introduction in January, 1949. Interior trims varied per body style and are fully explained in 1949 Chevrolet sales catalogs. Model year production was 1,037,600 cars. Calendar year sales total was 1,109,958 cars. Chevrolet was America's number one automaker again. Steel station wagon (not wood) has front bodyside molding. Business Coupe has black rubber mat on rear compartment floor; single sun visor for driver. Lowerable quarter windows in two-door sedans. Lowerable forward sections and fixed venti-panes in four-door sedan rear door windows. Fixed quarter windows in coupes. Sliding rear quarter windows in sport coupe. Genuine carpet inserts for convertible front floor mat. Convertible features dome light in roof bow. Station wagon has sliding quarter windows; woodgrained leatherette headliner; tan rubber floor mats; tan linoleum cargo area deck and no rear seat armrests, coat hooks or assist straps.

1950 CHEVROLET

SPECIAL SERIES — SIX — 1500 HJ — Few styling changes. New grille deletes vertical division bars, except for new triple ribbed type directly under front parking lamps. Nose and deck lid ornaments restyled; new hood ornament. Deck lid handle slightly revised for easier locking and lifting. Styleline Specials have bustle back; no chrome body strip. Fleetline Specials have sweeping fastback lines; no chrome body strip. Curved windshield with chrome center strip on both. Equipment features similar to list for 1949. Upholstery is gray-striped modern weave flat cloth with dark gray broadcloth; plain light gray fabric back, side and sidewall panels. Light gray control knobs replace ivory type used in 1949. Floor mat, lamp and steering wheel features follow trends of earlier years. Exact equipment varies per model and is fully outlined in 1950 factory sales literature.

SPECIAL I.D. NUMBERS: Serial numbers were stamped on a plate on the right front door hinge pillar. Motor numbers were stamped on the right side of block near fuel pump. The numerical prefix in serial number indicated assembly plant as follows: (1) Flint, Mich.; (2) Tarrytown, N.Y.; (3) St. Louis, Mo.; (5) Kansas City, Mo.; (6) Oakland, Calif.; (8) Atlanta, Ga.; (9) Norwood, Ohio: (14) Baltimore, Md.; (21) Janesville, Wis. The letters on the number plate indicated year and model, for example: HJ was for 1950 Special. A Fisher Body Style Number was located on the vehicle data plate, on engine side of firewall. It began with a two-digit prefix designating model year, followed by a dash and four numbers (shown in second column of charts below) indicating body type and sometimes having a letter suffix designating trim level or equipment installations. Serial numbers for Michigan built 1950 Specials were HJ-1001 to 49801; motor numbers were HA1001 to 1320152.

SPECIAL SERIES 1500 HJ

STYLELINE SUB-SERIES

Model Number	Body/Style Number	Body Type & Seating	Factory Price	Shipping. Weight	Production Total
1503	50-1269	4-dr Sed-6P	1450	3120	55,644
1502	50-1211	2-dr Sed-6P	1403	3085	89,897
1524	50-1227	2-dr Spt Cpe-6P	1408	3050	28,328
1504	50-1227B	2-dr Bus Cpe-3P	1329	3025	20,984

FLEETLINE SUB-SERIES

1553	50-1208	4-dr Sed-6P	1450	3115	23,277
1552	50-1207	2-dr Sed-6P	1403	3080	43,682

NOTE 1: Fisher Body Style Numbers: First two symbols are prefix indicating model year; 50=1950. First two symbols in main number identify series (12=Special). Second two symbols in main number identify body type (69=four-door sedan; 11=two-door sedan, etc.). This number is located on vehicle data plate under hood and is the best way to positively identify Chevrolet body styles.

1950 Chevrolet, Styleline Deluxe four-door sedan, 6-cyl

DELUXE SERIES — SIX — 2100 HK — Styleline Deluxe models have bustle back; fender skirts; chrome body strip; word Deluxe on fender; and same extra equipment features outlined for 1949 Deluxe series. Bel Air 'hardtop convertible,' with three-piece wraparound curved backlight, is a new style. Fleetline Deluxe models have sweeping fastback body with same

higher trim level features inside and out. Bel Air interior features are same as in convertible coupe, except two rear compartment lamps are used at roof quarter panels; neutral gray headliner with chrome roof bows appears; and transmission lever knob is black plastic. Other Deluxe models trimmed with gray striped broadcloth material having 'off shoulder' dark gray broadcloth contrast panels and dark gray front seatback cushions, seat risers, upper sidewalls and center pillars. Light gray headliner and lower sidewalls used. Features vary per body style and are fully detailed in 1950 Chevrolet sales catalogs.

DELUXE SERIES I.D. NUMBERS: Followed same general system with new 'HK' alphabetical code. Serial numbers HK-1001 to 187118. Motor numbers fit into some sequence listed for Special Series above.

1950 Chevrolet, Deluxe Bel Air two-door hardtop coupe, 6-cyl

DELUXE SERIES 2100 HK

STYLELINE SUB-SERIES

Model Number	Body/Style Number	Body Type & Seating	Factory Price	Shipping Weight	Production Total
2103	50-1069	4-dr Sed-6P	1529	3150	316,412
2102	50-1011	2-dr Sed-6P	1482	3100	248,567
2124	50-1027	2-dr Spt Cpe-6P	1498	3090	81,536
2154	50-1037	2-dr BelAir-6P	1741	3225	76,662
2134	50-1067	2-dr Conv-5P	1847	3380	32,810
2119	50-1062	4-dr Sta Wag-8P	1994	3460	166,995

FLEETLINE SUB-SERIES

2153	50-1008	4-dr Sed-6P	1529	3145	124,287
2152	50-1007	2-dr Sed-6P	1482	3115	189,509

NOTE 1: Style Number 50-1037 is a two-door pillarless hardtop coupe.

ENGINE: Six-cylinder. Overhead valves. Cast iron block. Displacement: 216.5 cid. Bore and stroke: 3-1/2 x 3-3/4 inches. Compression ratio: 6.5:1. Brake horsepower: 90 at 3300 rpm. Four main bearings. Solid valve lifters. Carburetors: Rochester one-barrel 7002050.

CHEVROLET CHASSIS FEATURES: Box girder frame. In convertible a 'VK' structure of I-beam members takes place of engine rear support cross member. Knee-action front suspension with direct. double-acting shock absorbers. Ride stabilizer. Rubber insulated semi-elliptic rear springs with metal covers. Direct double-acting hydraulic rear shock absorbers. Four-wheel hydraulic brakes with 11 inch drums. Wheelbase: (all) 115 inches. Overall length: (passenger cars) 197.5 inches; (station wagon) 198.25 inches. Front tread: (all) 57 inches. Rear tread: (all) 58-3/4 inches. Rear axle: Semi-floating with hypoid drive and 4.11:1 gear ratio. Torque tube drive with tubular propeller shaft; both fully enclosed. Tires: 6.70 x 15 blackwall on widebase rims.

POWERTRAIN OPTIONS: Powerglide two-speed automatic transmission was introduced as a $159 option for Deluxe Series only. Cars so equipped were provided with a modified Chevrolet truck engine with 3-9/6 x 3-15/16 inch bore and stroke and 235 cid of piston displacement. Hydraulic valve lifters and larger intake valves were used. Horsepower was rated the familiar 90 at 3300 rpm A slightly lower 3.55:1 rear axle gear ratio was used on Powerglide equipped models. Also, 7.10 x 15 tires ($14.75 extra) were optional for convertibles equipped with Powerglide.

CONVENIENCE OPTIONS: Standard manual radio. Deluxe push-button radio. Radio antenna. Under dash heater and defroster. In-dash Deluxe heater and defroster. White sidewall tires. Wheel trim rings. Spotlight. Fog lamps. Directional signals. Back-up light. External windshield sun shade (visor), Tan striped pattern, free-breathing pile fabric Deluxe Series upholstery trim. San-Toy seat covers. Outer bumper tips. Master grille guard. Locking gas filler cap. Other standard factory and/or dealer installed accessories.

HISTORICAL FOOTNOTES: Dealer introduction Jan. 7, 1950. Model year production 1,371,535. Calendar year sales 1,520,577. Chevrolet is America's number one automaker again. Bel Air hardtop introduced. Powerglide automatic transmission introduced. Hydraulic valve lifters adopted for Powerglide six-cylinder engine. Body style features same as detailed under 1949 footnote. New Rochester carburetor was B or BC type ('C' indicating automatic choke). Some cars also had Stromberg BXVD-2 or BXXD-35 type carburetors.

1951 CHEVROLET

SPECIAL SERIES — SIX — 1500 JJ — A subtle, but attractive facelift characterized the 1951 Chevrolet. By moving the parking lamps into the lower grille opening, under the headlamps, a wider look was achieved. Styleline Specials had bustle backs and no chrome body strip. Fleetline Specials had fastbacks and no chrome body strip. Black rubber mud guards were seen on both Special lines. Two-tone gray interiors with light gray striped pattern cloth upholstery were used. Equipment features followed the 1949-1950 assortment. Variations are fully detailed in factory sales catalogs. New, smaller taillamps with a nearly square red plastic lens were used. A small, round reflector was positioned at the bottom of the same housing. Bendix 'Jumbo Drum' brakes replaced the old Huck units. A simplified trunk ornament bearing the Chevrolet bow-tie emblem was used. Specials still came only with the base engine and conventional transmission.

SPECIAL I.D. NUMBERS: Serial numbers were stamped on a plate on the right front door hinge pillar. Motor numbers were stamped on the right side of block near fuel pump. The numerical prefix in serial number indicated assembly plant as follows: (1) Flint, Mich.; (2) Tarrytown, N.Y.; (3) St. Louis, Mo., (5) Kansas City, Mo.; (6) Oakland, Calif.; (8) Atlanta, Ga.; (9) Norwood. Ohio: (14) Baltimore, Md.; (21) Janesville, Wis. The letters on the number plate indicated year and model, for example: JJ was for 1951 Special. A Fisher Body Style Number was located on the vehicle data plate, on engine side of firewall. It began with a two-digit prefix designating model year, followed by a dash and four numbers (shown in second column of charts below) indicating body type and sometimes having a letter suffix designating trim level or equipment installations. Serial numbers for Michigan built 1951 Specials were JJ-1001 to 32061; motor numbers were JA1001 to 1261301.

1951 Chevrolet, Styleline Deluxe two-door sedan, 6-cyl

SPECIAL SERIES 1500 JJ

STYLELINE SUB-SERIES

Model Number	Body/Style Number	Body Type & Seating	Factory Price	Shipping Weight	Production Total
1503	1269	4-dr Sed-6P	1594	3110	63,718
1502	1211	2-dr Sed-6P	1540	3070	75,566
1524	1227	2-dr Spt Cpe-6P	1545	3060	18,981
1504	1227B	2-dr Bus Cpe-3P	1460	3040	17,020

FLEETLINE SUB-SERIES

1553	1208	4-dr Sed-6P	1594	3130	3,364
1552	1207	2-dr Sed-6P	1540	3090	6,441

1951 Chevrolet, Styleline Deluxe four-door sedan, 6-cyl

DELUXE SERIES — SIX — 2100 JK — Deluxe models also used the newly designed grille which had the lower two horizontal bars extended to form a circular frame for oblong parking lamps with five vertical sectioned bars beside the parking lamps. Chevrolet was written, in script, on the chrome grille frame molding. Deluxes had a stainless steel molding starting above the front wheel openings and extending onto doors with a Deluxe nameplate on front fenders. Chrome rear fender gravel shields and painted fender skirts were standard equipment. Interiors were two-tone gray with gray striped broadcloth upholstery. Four different, special two-tone combinations were offered for Bel Air interiors. Bel Air upholstery was in two-tone gray striped pilecord fabric with genuine deep buff leather bolsters. Station wagons were trimmed with tan imitation pigskin. Cars with Powerglide had a special script, denoting this feature, on deck lids.

DELUXE SERIES I.D. NUMBERS: Followed same general system with new 'JK' alphabetical code. Serial numbers JK-1001 to 174408 motor numbers fit into same sequence listed for Special Series above.

DELUXE SERIES 1500 JK

STYLELINE SUB-SERIES

Model Number	Body/Style Number	Body Type & Seating	Factory Price	Shipping Weight	Production Total
2103	1069	4-dr Sed-6P	1680	3150	380,270
2102	1011	2-dr Sed-6P	1629	3110	262,933
2124	1027	2-dr Spt Cpe-6P	1647	3090	64,976
2154	1037	2-dr BelAir-6P	1914	3215	103,356
2134	1067	2-dr Conv-5P	2030	3360	20,172
2119	1062	4-dr Sta Wag-8P	2191	3450	23,586

FLEETLINE SUB-SERIES

2153	1008	4-dr Sed-6P	1680	3155	57,693
2152	1007	2-dr Sed-6P	1629	3125	131,910

NOTE 1: Style Number 1037 is a two-door pillarless hardtop coupe.

ENGINES

(SIX): Overhead valves. Cast iron block. Displacement: 216.5 cid. Bore and stroke: 3-1/ 2 x 3-3/4 inches. Compression ratio: 6.6:1. Brake horsepower: 92 at 3400 rpm. Four main bearings. Solid valve lifters. Carburetor: Single-barrel Rochester. Carter and Stromberg models used in mixed production.

(POWERGLIDE SIX): Inline six. Overhead valves. Cast iron block. Displacement: 235.5 cid. Bore and stroke: 3-9/16 x 3-15/16 inches. Four main bearings. Hydraulic valve lifters. Compression ratio: 6.7:1. Brake horsepower: 105 at 3600 rpm Carburetor: Rochester one-barrel BC.

CHEVROLET CHASSIS FEATURES: Box girder frame. In convertible a 'VK' structure of I-beam members takes place of engine rear support cross member. Knee-action front suspension with direct. double-acting shock absorbers. Ride stabilizer. Rubber insulated semi-elliptic rear springs with metal covers. Direct double-acting hydraulic rear shock absorbers. Four-wheel hydraulic brakes with 11 inch drums. Wheelbase: (all) 115 inches. Overall length: (passenger cars) 197.75 inches; (station wagon) 198-7/8. Front tread: (all) 57 inches. Rear tread: (all) 58-3/4 inches. Rear axle: Semi-floating with hypoid drive and 4.11:1 gear ratio. Torque tube drive with tubular propeller shaft; both fully enclosed. Tires: 6.70 x 15 blackwall on widebase rims; 7.10 x 15 on convertible.

CONVENIENCE OPTIONS: Directional signals. Dash panel ashtray (standard in Deluxe). Manual radio. Deluxe push-button radio. Under dash heater and defroster. Deluxe in-dash heater and defroster. Full wheel discs. Wheel trim rings. Whitewall tires. Thirty-nine hour stem wind clock (standard in Deluxe). Fender skirts (standard on Deluxe). No-Mar Fuel door guard. Door handle shields. Front and rear bumper wing tips. Master grille guard. Spot light. Fog lamps. External sun shade (visor). Locking as filler door. Front fender stainless steel gravel shields. Impala-style hood ornament. Tissue dispenser. San-Toy seat covers. Left-hand outside rearview mirror (standard in convertible). Right-hand outside rearview mirror. Radio antenna. License plate frame. Back-up lamp. Vacuumatic ashtray. Rubber heel protector. Underhood lamp. Luggage compartment lamp. Other standard factory and dealer-installed accessories. Powerglide, Deluxe only ($169).

HISTORICAL FOOTNOTES: Dealer introductions were held December 9, 1950. Model year production 1,250,803 units. Calendar year sales 1,118,096 cars. Chevrolet remained America's number one automaker. Attractive new dashboard and steering wheel with 'bow tie' spoke and horn ring design (Deluxe type). Parting seam makes first appearance on this body below headlamps.

1952 CHEVROLET

1952 Chevrolet, Styleline Deluxe two-door Sport Coupe, 6-cyl

SPECIAL SERIES — SIX — 1500 KJ — A new grille for 1952 had five vertical bars that soon became known as Chevrolet "teeth." They were mounted to the horizontal center divider bar and equally spaced out from the center. The parking lamps were again in the lower grille opening and again oblong-shaped, but now "floated" in their housings. The word Chevrolet trimmed a wider new nose emblem, which still had a "bow-tie" logo. The Special Series no longer included fastback Fleetline models. Specials had notchback styling, no chrome body molding, rubber gravel deflectors and open rear wheelhousings. Nine exterior colors and four two-tone combinations were provided for all sedans, sport coupes and business coupes, including Styleline Specials. Two-tone gray interiors were featured, with seat upholstery of checkered pattern cloth.

SPECIAL I.D. NUMBERS: Serial numbers were stamped on a plate on the right front door hinge pillar. Motor numbers were stamped on the right side of block near fuel pump. The numerical prefix in serial number indicated assembly plant as follows: (1) Flint, Mich.; (2) Tarrytown, N.Y.; (3) St. Louis, Mo., (5) Kansas City, Mo.; (6) Oakland, Calif.; (8) Atlanta, Ga.; (9) Norwood. Ohio: (14) Baltimore, Md.; (21) Janesville, Wis. The letters on the number plate indicated year and model, for example: KJ was for 1951 Special. A Fisher Body Style Number was located on the vehicle data plate, on engine side of firewall. It began with a two-digit prefix designating model year, followed by a dash and four numbers (shown in second column of charts below) indicating body type and sometimes having a letter suffix designating trim level or equipment installations. Serial numbers for Michigan built 1951 Specials were KJ-1001 to 19286; motor numbers were KA1001 to 860773.

STYLELINE SPECIAL SERIES 1500 KJ

Model Number	Body/Style Number	Body Type & Seating	Factory Price	Shipping Weight	Production Total
1503	1269	4-dr Sed-6P	1659	3115	35,460
1502	1211	2-dr Sed-6P	1603	3085	54,781
1524	1227	2-dr Spt Cpe-6P	1609	3050	8,906
1504	1227B	2-dr Bus Cpe-6P	1519	3045	10,359

1952 Chevrolet, Deluxe Bel Air two-door hardtop coupe, 6-cyl

DELUXE SERIES — SIX — 2100 KK — The new 1952 styling was particularly attractive when packaged in Deluxe trim. Easily noticed distinctions included body rub moldings on front fenders and doors; bright metal rear fender gravel guards (with long extension moldings sweeping up over the fender-skirted wheelhousings) and Deluxe script logos directly above the gravel guards on the rear fender pontoons. Bright metal windshield and window reveals were featured as well. A two-spoke steering wheel, with full blowing ring, replaced the three-spoke Special type with horn button. Deluxes also had ivory plastic control knobs with bright metal inserts; dome lamps with automatic door switches; two inside sun visors and richer interior trims with foam rubber cushions. Upholstery combinations were reversed, with dark gray chevron pattern cloth and lighter toned upper contrast panels. As usual, convertibles, Bel Airs and station wagons had their own exclusive trim. There were also four exterior paint colors for Bel Airs and 11 two-tone combinations, while convertibles came in 10 colors (with five different top tones) and wagons offered four types of finish in combination with woodgrained trim panels. In the model lineup, the two-door Fleetline sedan was the sole fastback car in the Chevrolet line. It came only with Deluxe trim, as did the Powerglide transmission option. Cars with Powerglide again had lettering to the effect attached on the rear deck lid.

DELUXE SERIES I.D. NUMBERS: Followed same general system with new 'KK' alphabetical code. Serial numbers KK-1001 to 115,255. Motor numbers fit into same sequence given for Special Series above.

DELUXE SERIES 2100 KK

STYLELINE SUB-SERIES

Model Number	Body/Style Number	Body Type & Seating	Factory Price	Shipping Weight	Production Total
2103	1069	4-dr Sed-6P	1749	3145	319,736
2102	1011	2-dr Sed-6P	1696	3110	215,417
2124	1027	2-dr Spt Cpe-6P	1715	3100	36,954
2154	1037	2-dr Bel Air-6P	1992	3215	74,634
2134	1067	2-dr Conv-5P	2113	3380	11,975
2119	1062	4-dr Sta Wag-8P	2281	3475	12,756

FLEETLINE SUB-SERIES

Model Number	Body/Style Number	Body Type & Seating	Factory Price	Shipping Weight	Production Total
2152	1007	2-dr Sed-6P	1696	3110	37,164

NOTE 1: Style number 1037 is a two-door pillarless hardtop coupe.

ENGINES

(INLINE SIX): Overhead valves. Cast iron block. Displacement-. 216.5 cid. Bore and stroke: 3-1/2 x 3-3/4 inches Compression ratio: 6 6.1. Brake horsepower: 92 at 3400 rpm. Four main bearings. Solid valve lifters. Carburetor: Rochester one-barrel B or BC (automatic choke on BC); or Stromberg BXOV-2. model number 380286-, or Stromberg BXOV-25. Model number 380270.

(POWERGLIDE SIX): Inline six. Overhead valves. Cast iron block. Displacement: 235.5 cid. Bore and stroke: 3-9/16 x 3-15/16 inches. Four main bearings. Hydraulic valve lifters. Compression ratio: 6.7:1. Brake horsepower: 105 at 3600 rpm Carburetor: Rochester one-barrel BC. (Note: 3.55:1 gear ratio rear axle used with Powerglide transmission both years).

CHEVROLET CHASSIS FEATURES: Box girder frame. In convertible a 'VK' structure of I-beam members takes place of engine rear support crossmember. Knee-action front suspension with direct. double-acting shock absorbers. Ride stabilizer. Rubber insulated semi-elliptic rear springs with metal covers. Direct double-acting hydraulic rear shock absorbers. Four-wheel hydraulic brakes with 11 inch drums. Wheelbase: (all) 115 inches. Overall length: (passenger cars) 197.75 inches; (station wagon) 198-7/8. Front tread: (all) 57 inches. Rear tread: (all) 58-3/4 inches. Rear axle: Semi-floating with hypoid drive and 4.11:1 gear ratio. Torque tube drive with tubular propeller shaft; both fully enclosed. Tires: 6.70 x 15 blackwall on widebase rims; 7.10 x 15 on convertible.

CONVENIENCE OPTIONS: Directional signals. Dash panel ashtray (standard in Deluxe). Manual radio. Deluxe push-button radio. Under dash heater and defroster. Deluxe in-dash heater and defroster. Full wheel discs. Wheel trim rings. Whitewall tires. Thirty-nine hour stem wind clock (standard in Deluxe). Fender skirts (standard on Deluxe). No-Mar Fuel door guard. Door handle shields. Front and rear bumper wing tips. Master grille guard. Spot light. Fog lamps. External sun shade (visor). Locking as filler door. Front fender stainless steel gravel shields. Impala-style hood ornament. Tissue dispenser. San-Toy seat covers. Left-hand outside rearview mirror (standard in convertible). Right-hand outside rearview mirror. Radio antenna. License plate frame. Back-up lamp. Vacuumatic ashtray. Rubber heel protector. Underhood lamp. Luggage compartment lamp. Other standard factory and dealer-installed accessories. Powerglide, Deluxe only ($178). E-Z-Eye glass. ashtray (dash-type) now standard in both series. Availability of whitewalls limited due to Korean War material restrictions.

HISTORICAL FOOTNOTES: Began Jan. 19, 1952. Model year sales 827,317 despite Korean war manufacturing limitations. Calendar year sales 877,947 despite Korea. Whitewall tires uncommon. Inferior chrome plating process used this year. Chevrolet again number one American automaker. In October, 1952 the one millionth Powerglide equipped Chevrolet was assembled, the option was just 34 months old. The 28 millionth U.S. or Canadian Chevrolet car or truck was built in December, 1952.

1953 Chevrolet, Two-Ten four-door sedan, 6-cyl

SPECIAL 150 SERIES — SIX — 1500A — The sub-series designations Styleline and Fleetline were dropped, since there was no fastback Chevrolet for 1953. Cars with Special level features and trim were called One-Fifty or 150 models, this designation coming from the first three digits of the numerical series code. The sport coupe became the 'club coupe' and a 'Handyman' station wagon was a new Special model. New styling details included one-piece curved windshields; new chrome hood ornament and nose nameplate; new grille with three vertical fins on the center horizontal bar and extensions encircling the parking lamps; and new vertical dual stop and taillamps. Easy identifiers included rubber windshield molding; plain bodysides without moldings; rubber gravel guards; no rocker panel molding: unskirted rear wheel housings; and no series nameplate. On the inside of Special 150s there was a standard steering wheel; single sun visor; and plain upholstery. The One-Fifty station wagon had safety sheet side door windows in place of Safety Plate glass and was rated a six-passenger car.

CHEVROLET I.D. NUMBERS: Serial numbers were stamped on a plate on the right front door hinge pillar. Motor numbers were stamped on the right side of block near fuel pump. Style Number was located on the vehicle data plate, on engine side of firewall. It began with a two-digit prefix designating model year, followed by a dash and four numbers (shown in second column of charts below) indicating body type and sometimes having a letter suffix designating trim level or equipment installations. Alphabetical code 'A' for Special Series. Serial numbers A53( )-001001 to A53-228961. Motor numbers LA-1001 to 1183450. The blank space ( ) in serial number was filled with a letter indicating assembly plant as follows: A-Atlanta; B-Baltimore; F-Flint; J-Janesville; K-Kansas City; L-Los Angeles; N-Norwood, Ohio; O-Oakland; S-St. Louis; T-Tarrytown. It should be noted that engine numbers consisted of four to seven numbers with a prefix or suffix. The prefix or suffix indicated year, engine size, factory, type of valve lifter and other peculiarities. It is impossible to tabulate all these codes in a small amount of space. Restorers can consult Chevrolet shop manuals or master parts catalogs for this type of information.

SPECIAL 150 SERIES

Model Number	Body/Style Number	Body Type & Seating	Factory Price	Shipping Weight	Production Total
1503	1269	4-dr Sed-6P	1670	3215	54,207
1502	1211	2-dr Sed-6P	1613	3180	79,416
1524	1227	2-dr Clb Cpe-6P	1620	3140	6,993
1504	1227B	2-dr Bus Cpe-3P	1524	3140	13,555
1509	1262F	4-dr Sta Wag-6P	2010	3420	22,408

NOTE 1: Style Number 1227B has single seat (front), fixed rear quarter windows and rear storage space with raised floor. Style Number 1262F has two seats (folding second seat) and plexiglass 'Safety Seal' side windows.

1953 Chevrolet, Two-Ten four-door station wagon, 6-cyl

SPECIAL 150 SERIES ENGINE: Inline six. Overhead valves. Cast iron block. Displacement: 235.5 cid. Bore and stroke: 3-9/16 x 3-15/16. Compression ratio: 7.1:1. Brake horsepower: 108 at 3600 rpm. Four main bearings. Solid valve lifters. Carburetor: Rochester one-barrel B-type model 7007181 or Carter one-barrel model 2101S.

DELUXE 210 SERIES — SIX — 2100 B — Cars with Deluxe level features and trim were now called Two-Ten or 210 models, the new designation taken from first three digits of numerical series code. The Sport Coupe became the 'Club Coupe.' The pillarless hardtop was not a Bel Air. The six-passenger station wagon with folding second seat was called the 'Handyman' (as was the same version with Special trim). The eight-passenger station wagon was called the 'Townsman.' The Townsman had three seats, the second and third units being stationary, but

completely removable. The 210 convertible was deleted in midyear and the 210 Townsman station wagon was also dropped for 1954, along with the 210 sport coupe. External identification of Two-Tens was afforded by horizontal lower belt moldings running from front to rear; chrome windshield and window moldings; rocker panel moldings; and bright metal rear gravel guards with short spears at the top. A two-spoke steering wheel with horn ring was used. Standard equipment also included cigarette lighter; dash panel ashtray; dual sun visors and 39-hour stem wind clock. Heaters and radios were optional and, when not fitted, blocker plates were used to cover the cutouts on the dashboard for heater and radio controls. Interior door handles used on 210 models had bright metal inserts in the black plastic knobs. Other interior appointments included foam rubber seat cushion pads in front seats and in rear seats of sedans and coupes; front armrests in all models; rear armrests in sedans and coupes; rear compartment ashtray in four-door sedans; one ashtray in each armrest of two-door sedans and coupes; and bright metal moldings on rear quarter panels of sedans and coupes.

DELUXE 210 SERIES I.D. NUMBERS: Followed same general system with new 'B' alphabetical code. Serial numbers B53( ) 001001 to 228961 with blank ( ) showing assembly plant code. Motor numbers fit into same sequence given above for Special 150 Series.

DELUXE 210 SERIES

Model Number	Body/Style Number	Body Type & Seating	Factory Price	Shipping Weight	Production Total
2103	1069W	4-dr Sed-6P	1761	3250	332,497
2102	1011W	2-dr Sed-6P	1707	3215	247,455
2124	1027	2-dr Clb Cpe-6P	1726	3190	23,961
2154	1037	2-dr Spt Cpe-6P	1967	3295	14,045
2134	1067	2-dr Conv-5P	2093	3435	5,617
2109	1062F	4-dr Sta Wag-6P	2123	3450	18,258
2119	1062	4-dr Sta Wag-8P	2273	3495	7,988

NOTE 1: Two-Ten body style numbers are similar to Bel Air Body Style numbers except for suffixes. Style Number 1011W. 1037 and 1067 have lowering rear quarter windows. The Style Number 1062F 210 Townsman station wagon varies from the '150' Townsman in that Safety Plate glass door windows are used.

1953 Chevrolet, Bel Air four-door sedan, 6-cyl (AA)

BEL AIR — SIX — SERIES 2400 C — The Bel Air designation was applied to a four car lineup this season. It now identified a level of trim, instead of a particular body style. The numerical code 2400-C applied to all Bel Air models, but was rarely used in place of the descriptive series name. To identify this new luxury series, Chevrolet added a double molding on the rear fender pontoon. It enclosed a panel which was decorated with a short wide ribbed beauty molding, Bel Air script and Chevrolet crest on the leading edge above a chrome gravel shield. All Two-Ten trim features and equipment were incorporated, plus rear fender skirts; double windshield pillar moldings; extra wide window reveals on sedans; and saddle moldings on sport coupes and convertibles. Exposed bright metal roof bows and dashboard mounted rearview mirrors were standard in Bel Air sport coupes.

BEL AIR SERIES I.D. NUMBERS: Followed the same general system with new 'C' alphabetical code. Serial numbers C53( )-001001 to 228961 with ( ) showing assembly plant code. Note that serial numbers as well as motor number, fit into same sequence given above for Deluxe 210 Series.

BEL AIR 2400 C SERIES

Model Number	Body/Style Number	Body Type & Seating	Factory Price	Shipping Weight	Production Total
2403	1069WD	4-dr Sed-6P	1874	3275	246,284
2402	101IWD	2-dr Sed-6P	1820	3230	144,401
2454	1037D	2-dr Spt Cpe-6P	2051	3310	99,047
2434	1067D	2-dr Conv-5P	2175	3470	24,047

ENGINES

(INLINE SIX): Overhead valves. Cast iron block. Displacement: 235.5 cid. Bore and stroke: 3-9/16 x 3-15/16. Compression ratio: 7.1:1. Brake horsepower: 108 at 3600 rpm. Four main bearings. Solid valve lifters. Carburetor: Rochester one-barrel B-type model 7007181 or Carter one-barrel model 2101S.

(POWERGLIDE INLINE SIX): Overhead valves. Cast iron block. Displacement: 235.5 cid. Bore and stroke: 3-9/16 x 3-15/16 inches. Compression ratio: 7.5:1. Brake horsepower: 115 at 3600 rpm. Four main bearings. Hydraulic valve lifters. Carburetor: Rochester BC type one-barrel model 7007200 or Carter one-barrel model 2101S. (A transmission oil cooler and 3.55:1 axle ratio are used with Powerglide.)

CHEVROLET CHASSIS FEATURES: Wheelbase: (all series) 115 inches. Overall length: (all passenger cars) 195-1/2 inches; (all station wagons) 197-7/8 inches. Front tread: (all) 56.69 inches. Rear tread: (all) 58.75 inches. Tires: (Convertible with Powerglide) 7.10 x 15 four-ply; (Townsman station wagon) 6.70 x 15 six-ply; (all others) 6.70 x 15 four-ply. Standard rear axle ratio: 3.7:1.

CONVENIENCE OPTIONS: Power steering ($178). Custom radio. push-button Custom Deluxe radio. Recirculating heater and defroster (under dash type). Air Flow heater and defroster (dashboard type) E-Z-Eye tinted glass. Autronic Eye automatic headlamp dimmer. White sidewall tires. Directional signals. Back-up lights. Bumper guards (second pair, front or rear). Front fender gravel shields. Door handle shields. Windshield sunshade (visor). Full wheel discs. Accessory. "Bird type", hood ornament. Fender skirts on 150 models. License plate frame. Front and rear bumper tip guards. Stem wind clock on 150 models. Radio antenna. Locking gas filler door. Venti-pane wind deflectors. Left-hand outside rearview

---

mirror. Fog lights. Traffic light viewer. Tissue dispenser. Vacuumatic ashtray. Non-glare rearview mirror. No-Mar fuel door trim. Underhood light. San-Toy seat covers. Powerglide ($178). Other standard factory and dealer-installed accessories.

HISTORICAL FOOTNOTES: Dealer introduction January, 1953. Model year sales 1,356,413. Calendar year sales 1,477,287. Completely new body with wraparound & backlight on all models except club coupe, convertible and station wagon. Chevrolet introduced Corvette marque. Powerglide models now have full-pressure lubrication. Powerglide available in Two-Ten and Bel Air only. Seventeen models are most ever offered by Chevrolet. First year for Chevrolet power steering. Chevrolet remains America's number one automaker.

1954 CHEVROLET

1954 Chevrolet, One-Fifty two-door utility sedan, 6-cyl

SPECIAL 150 SERIES — SIX — 1500 A — Styling improvements for 1954 Chevrolets, although very minor, gave the impression of a wider, more modern car. New was a full-width horizontal center grille bar housing wraparound horizontal parking lamp housings at each outer end. Five vertical teeth were equally spaced from the center of the main bar out. The front bumper was redesigned with its ends bulged out to wraparound the body corners. New bumper guards, headlight rims, front ornament and hood mascot were seen. The taillight housings were hooded to create a fin-like look in profile view. They housed a vertical red and white cigar-shaped lens, the white portion provided in case optional back-up lamp wiring was added. Powerglide was now available in One-Fifty models, cars so equipped having Powerglide badges, in place of the normal Chevrolet scripts, on the deck lid. Inside, the 150 Specials had black window crank knobs and plainer interior appointments described as being "smartly fashioned of durable materials." Rubber windshield moldings; black rubber gravel guards; hubcaps and plain bodysides were a few ways to spot cars in this line. The club coupe was gone and the business coupe was renamed as the 'utility sedan,' which had no back seat. It had a raised rear compartment load floor.

CHEVROLET I.D. NUMBERS: Serial numbers were stamped on a plate on the right front door hinge pillar. Motor numbers were stamped on the right side of block near fuel pump. Style Number was located on the vehicle data plate, on engine side of firewall. It began with a two-digit prefix designating model year, followed by a dash and four numbers (shown in second column of charts below) indicating body type and sometimes having a letter suffix designating trim level or equipment installations. Alphabetical code 'A' for Special Series. Serial numbers A54( )-001001 to A54-174684. Motor numbers 01001Z54 to 1024930. The blank space ( ) in serial number was filled with a letter indicating assembly plant as follows: A-Atlanta; B-Baltimore; F-Flint; J-Janesville; K-Kansas City; L-Los Angeles; N-Norwood, Ohio; O-Oakland; S-St. Louis; T-Tarrytown. It should be noted that engine numbers consisted of four to seven numbers with a prefix or suffix. The prefix or suffix indicated year, engine size, factory, type of valve lifter and other peculiarities. It is impossible to tabulate all these codes in a small amount of space. Restorers can consult Chevrolet shop manuals or master parts catalogs for this type of information.

SPECIAL 150 SERIES

Model Number	Body/Style Number	Body Type & Seating	Factory Price	Shipping Weight	Production Total
1503	1269W	4-dr Sed-6P	1680	3210	32,430
1502	1211W	2-dr Sed-6P	1623	3165	64,855
1509	1262F	4-dr Sta Wag-6P	2020	3455	21,404
1512	1211WB	2-dr Utl Sed-3P	1539	3145	10,770

1954 Chevrolet, Two-Ten Del Ray two-door sedan, 6-cyl

DELUXE 210 SERIES — SIX — 2100 B — Two-Ten identification features were similar to 1953 and included chrome bodyside moldings; chrome windshield molding; chrome window moldings; rocker panel moldings; bright metal gravel guards; genuine carpets in rear compartment; and durable cloth seats with vinyl contrasting panels in four different color schemes. The Two-Ten club coupe was sometimes called the 'Del Ray' and came with all-vinyl, waffle pattern upholstery and matching two-tone door panels. The Two-Ten 'Handyman' station wagon was upholstered with long-wearing vinyl materials of contrasting colors and textures including horizontally ribbed door panel inserts. The Two-Ten convertible and 'Townsman' station wagon were dropped.

DELUXE '210" SERIES I.D. NUMBERS: Followed the same general system. Serial numbers 8-54( )-001001 to 174684. Motor numbers fit into the same sequence given above for special '150' Series.

DELUXE 210 SERIES

Model Number	Body/Style Number	Body Type & Seating	Factory Price	Shipping Weight	Production Total
2103	1069W	4-dr Sed-6P	1771	3230	235,146
2102	1011W	2-dr Sed-6P	1717	3185	194,498
2124	1011WA	2-dr DelRay Cpe-6P	1782	3185	66,403
2109	1062F	4-dr Sta Wag-6P	2133	3470	27,175

NOTE 1: Style Number 1062F was the 'Handyman' station wagon with two seats. The rear most often was a folding type.

1954 Chevrolet, Bel Air convertible, 6-cyl

BEL AIR — SIX — SERIES 2400 C — The new Bel Air had the traditional assortment of extra equipment and features such as full genuine carpeting; newly designed full wheel discs; horizontally ribbed vinyl door panels and an electric clock. The sport coupe had special 'fashion fiesta' two-tone upholstery;' rear pillar courtesy lights; chrome plated inside roof garnish moldings; and rear window frame and bright metal exposed roof bows. The convertible interior seemed even richer, with two-tone all-vinyl trims and snap-on boot cover. The rearview mirror was no longer mounted atop the dashboard. Identifying all Bel Airs externally were full-length sweepspear moldings with double moldings on rear fenders enclosing the name Bel Air and a Chevrolet crest; bright metal double windshield pillar moldings and window molding; body belt molding; rocker panel moldings; bright metal gravel guards; and rear wheel fender skirts.

BEL AIR SERIES I.D. NUMBERS: Followed the same general system. Serial numbers C54( )-001001 to 174684. Motor numbers fit into the same sequence given above for Special 150 Series.

BEL AIR SERIES 2400 C

Model Number	Body/Style Number	Body Type & Seating	Factory Price	Shipping Weight	Production Total
2403	1069WD	4-dr Sed-6P	1884	3255	248,750
2402	1011WD	2-dr Sed-6P	1830	3220	143,573
2454	1037D	2-dr Spt Cpe-6P	2061	3300	66,378
2434	1067D	2-dr Conv-5P	2185	3445	19,383
2419	1062D	4-dr Sta Wag-8P	2283	3540	-8,156

NOTE 1: Style Number 1062D was the Bel Air Townsman station wagon with Di-Noc simulated woodgrain exterior trim and color-keyed interior. It had three stationary seats, the rear two being entirely removable for extra cargo capacity.

ENGINES

(SYNCHROMESH) Inline Six: Overhead valves. Cast iron block. Displacement: 235.5 cid. Bore and stroke: 3-9/16 x 3-15/16. Compression ratio: 7.5:1. Brake horsepower: 115 at 3700 rpm. Four main bearings. Solid valve lifters. Carburetor: Rochester one-barrel 'B' type model 7007181 or Carter one-barrel 2102S.

(POWERGLIDE) Inline Six: Overhead valves. Cast iron block. Displacement: 235.5 cid. Bore and stroke: 3-9/16 x 3-15/16. Compression ratio: 7.5:1. Brake horsepower: 125 at 4000 rpm. Four main bearings. Hydraulic valve lifters. Include transmission oil cooler; new high-lift camshaft; full-pressure lubrication; new aluminum pistons. (Standard with Powerglide and available in all car-lines.)

CHEVROLET CHASSIS FEATURES: Wheelbase: (all series) 115 inches. Overall length: (all passenger cars) 196-7/16 inches; (all station wagons) 198-15/16 inches. Front tread: (all) 56.69 inches. Rear tread: (all) 58.75 inches. Tires: (Convertible with Powerglide) 7.10 x 15 four-ply; (Townsman station wagon) 6.70 x 15 six-ply; (all others) 6.70 x 15 four-ply. Standard rear axle ratio: 3.7:1.

1954 Chevrolet, Bel Air four-door station wagon, 6-cyl

CONVENIENCE OPTIONS: Power steering ($178). Custom radio. push-button Custom Deluxe radio. Recirculating heater and defroster (under dash type). Air Flow heater and defroster (dashboard type) E-Z-Eye tinted glass. Autronic Eye automatic headlamp dimmer. White sidewall tires. Directional signals. Back-up lights. Bumper guards (second pair, front or rear). Front fender gravel shields. Door handle shields. Windshield sunshade (visor). Full wheel discs. Accessory. "Bird type", hood ornament. Fender skirts on 150 models. License plate frame. Front and rear bumper tip guards. Stem wind clock on 150 models. Radio antenna. Locking gas filler door. Venti-pane wind deflectors. Left-hand outside rearview mirror. Fog lights. Traffic light viewer. Tissue dispenser. Vacuumatic ashtray. Non-glare rearview mirror. No-Mar fuel door trim. Underhood light. San-Toy seat covers. Powerglide ($178). Power brakes ($38). Power operated front window lifts ($86). Power operated seat ($86). Power steering ($135). White sidewall tires ($27 exchange).

HISTORICAL FOOTNOTES: Introduced December, 1953. Model year sales 1,151,486. Calendar year sales 1,414,352. Ford actually out produced Chevrolet on a model year basis this season, but Chevrolet 'dumped' cars on dealers to increase factory shipments and capture first place on a calendar year basis. Thus, Ford was America's largest maker, but Chevrolet was the number one selling" American car again. Last season for woodgrained station wagon trim through 1966 model year, when Caprice station wagon reintroduced this feature. First year automatic transmission was available in all Chevrolets. Last year for exclusive use of six-cylinder powerplants in Chevrolet.

1955 CHEVROLET

ONE-FIFTY — SERIES 1500 A — The One-Fifty series was Chevrolet's lowest-priced line. Standard equipment included rubber floor mats front and rear; full-width all-steel seat frames with 'S' springs; all vinyl upholstery for station wagon and one piece wraparound windshield. Exterior bright metal decoration was limited to a Chevrolet script on front fender and standard chrome plated bumpers; grille; door handles; hood ornament; lamp rims; and wheel hub center caps.

ONE-FIFTY I.D. NUMBERS: Serial number stamped on plate on right (front) door hinge pillar. Motor numbers stamped on crankcase to rear of distributor on right side of engine. The beginning serial numbers for the 1955 One-Fifty series were A55-001001 (six-cylinder) and VA55-001001 (V-8). Six-cylinder motor numbers began 01001-55Z and up. V-8 motor numbers began 01001-55G and up.

1955 Chevrolet, Two-Ten four-door sedan, V-8 (AA)

ONE-FIFTY SERIES

Model Number	Body/Style Number	Body Type & Seating	Factory Price	Shipping Weight	Production Total
1503	55-1219	4-dr Sed-6P	1728/1827	3165/3135	29,898
1502	55-1211	2-dr Sed-6P	1685/1784	3110/3080	66,416
1512	55-1211B	2-dr Sed-3P	1593/1692	3085/3055	11,196
1529	55-1263F	2-dr Sta Wag-6P	2030/2129	3290/3260	17,936

NOTE 1: The V-8 was considered a separate series, not an option.
NOTE 2: Data for six above slash/V-8 below slash.

TWO-TEN — SERIES 2100 B — The Two-Ten series was Chevrolet's middle-priced line. Standard equipment included all One-Fifty equipment listed above, plus stainless steel windshield and backlight reveals; chrome front seat and sidewall moldings glove compartment light; ash receptacles; cigarette lighter; armrests; and assist straps. Additional exterior bright metal decoration included upper beltline and rear fender side and sash moldings.

TWO-TEN I.D. NUMBERS: The beginning serial numbers for the 1955 Two-Ten series were B55-001001 (six-cylinder) and VB55-001001 (V-8). The motor number sequence was the same for all series.

1955 Chevrolet, Bel Air two-door hardtop Sport Coupe, V-8

TWO-TEN SERIES 2100 8

Model Number	Body/Style Number	Body Type & Seating	Factory Price	Shipping Weight	Production Total
2103	55-1019	4-dr Sed-6P	1819/1918	3180/3150	317,724
2102	55-1011	2-dr Sed-6P	1775/1874	3145/3125	249,105
2124	55-1011A	2-dr Clb Cpe-6P	1835/1934	3145/3115	115,584
2154	55-1037F	2-dr Spt Cpe-6P	1959/2058	3172/3144	11,675
2129	55-1063F	2-dr Sta Wag-6P	2079/2178	3330/3300	29,918
2109	55-1062F	4-dr Sta Wag-6P	2127/2226	3370/3340	82,303

NOTE 1: The V-8 was considered a separate series, not an option.
NOTE 2: Data for six above slash/V-8 below slash.

1955 Chevrolet, Bel Air two-door convertible coupe, V-8

BEL AIR — SERIES 2400-C — The Bel Air was Chevrolet's top series. Standard equipment included most features found on the lower-priced lines, plus carpets on closed body styles; chrome ribbed headliner on Sport Coupe; richer upholstery fabrics; horizontal chrome strip on sides of front fender and doors; narrow white painted insert on rear fender horizontal side molding; gold Bel Air script and Chevrolet crest behind slanting vertical sash molding; ribbed vertical trim plate on sides above rear bumper ends; wide chrome window and door post reveals; and full wheel discs.

BEL AIR I.D. NUMBERS: The beginning serial numbers for the 1955 Bel Air series were C55-001001 (six-cylinder) and VC55-001001 (V-8). The motor number sequence was the same for all series.

BEL AIR SERIES 2400-C

Model Number	Body/Style Number	Body Type & Seating	Factory Price	Shipping Weight	Production Total
2403	55-1019D	4-dr Sed-6P	1932/2031	3200/3170	345,372
2402	55-1011D	2-dr Sed-6P	1888/1987	3155/3125	168,313
2454	55-1037D	2-dr HT-6P	2067/2166	3195/3165	185,562
2434	55-1067D	2-dr Conv-5P	2206/2305	3315/3285	41,292
2429	55-1064DF	2-dr Nomad Wag-6P	2472/2571	3300/3270	6,103
2409	55-1062DF	4-dr Sta Wag-6P	2262/2361	3385/3355	24,313

NOTE 1: The V-8 was considered a separate series, not an option.
NOTE 2: Data for six above slash/V-8 below slash.

1955 Chevrolet, Bel Air two-door Nomad station wagon, V-8 (AA)

1955 Chevrolet, Bel Air Beauville four-door station wagon, 6-cyl

BASE ENGINES

SIX-CYLINDER: Overhead valve. Cast iron block. Displacement: 235.5 cid. Bore and stroke: 3-9/16 x 3-15/16 inches. Compression ratio: 7.5:1. Brake horsepower: 123 at 3800 rpm (Standard shift); 136 at 4200 rpm (Powerglide). Four main bearings. Solid valve lifters (standard shift); Hydraulic valve lifters (Powerglide). Carburetor: Rochester model 7007181 one-barrel.

V-8: Overhead valve. Cast iron block. Displacement: 265 cid. Bore and stroke: 3-3/4 x 3 inches. Compression ratio: 8.0:1. Brake horsepower: 162 at 4400 rpm. (all V-8s). Five main bearings. Powerglide engine has hydraulic valve lifters. Carburetor: Rochester model 7008006 two-barrel.

POWERTRAIN OPTIONS: A three-speed manual gearbox with column-mounted gear shift was standard on all models. Overdrive was available on the manual transmission at $108 extra. Powerglide two-speed automatic transmission was available at $178 extra. The V-8 engine was available with an optional 'power-pack' that included single four-barrel carburetor and dual exhausts. Optional horsepower rating with 'power-pack' was 180 at 4600 rpm.

CHASSIS FEATURES: Wheelbase: 115 inches. Overall length: (passenger cars) 195.6 inches; (Sta Wags) 197.1 inches. Front tread: 58 inches. Rear tread: 58.8 inches. Tires: 6.70 x 15 tubeless.

CONVENIENCE OPTIONS: Power steering ($92). Power brakes ($38). Directional signals. Electric windshield wipers. Power windows. Power seat. Heater and defroster. Air conditioning. White sidewall tires. Fender antenna. Locking gas cap. Continental tire kit. Outside sun visor. Self deicing wiper blades. Wiring junction block. Electric clock. Compass. Seat covers. Accelerator pedal cover. Wire wheelcovers. Wire wheelcovers. Exhaust extension. Filter and element. License plate frame. Glare-shields. Grille guard. Fender guard. Door edge guard. Gasoline filler guard. Tool kit. Back-up lamps. Courtesy lamps. Cigarette lighter. Floor mats. Outside rearview mirrors. Inside non-glare rearview mirrors. Vanity visor. Body sill. Manual radio. Push-button radio. Signal seeking radio. Automatic top riser. armrests. Wheel trim rings. Safety light with mirror. Sport lamp. Electric shaver. Parking brake signal. Door handle shields. Front fender shields. Rear speaker. Vent shades. Inside sun visor. Traffic light viewer. Foot operated windshield washer. Vacuum operated windshield washer.

HISTORICAL FOOTNOTES: Body style 55-1211 B was a Utility Sedan: Body style 55-1263F was a Handyman station wagon. Body style 55-1062F was a Handyman station wagon. Body style 55-1063F was a Townsman station wagon. Body style 55-1011A was the Del Ray. Body style 55-1037F was a midyear model. Body style 55-1062DF was the Beauville station wagon. Body Style 55-1064DF was the Nomad station wagon, a two-door station wagon with special hardtop styling, introduced as a midyear model.

1956 CHEVROLET

1956 Chevrolet, One-Fifty four-door sedan, V-8 (AA)

ONE-FIFTY — SERIES 1500-A — A minor restyling for 1956 Chevrolets included a full-width grille; large, rectangular front parking lamps; new front and rear bumpers and guards (except station wagons); inward angled dome-shaped taillamp lenses set into chrome ribbed decorative housings (with back-up lamp lens provided); new side trims that varied per series; and squarer headlamp hoods. One-Fifty models had Chevrolet rear fender nameplates; chrome moldings around the windshield and rear window; and a horizontal bodyside molding. This chrome strip ran from just behind the headlamp hood crease line to a point below the rear side window, where it was intersected by a slanting sash molding embossed in windsplit style.

Standard equipment included a two-spoke steering wheel with horn ring; lockable glovebox; dome light; and cloth and vinyl upholstery (all-vinyl on station wagons). Features such as the upholstery fabrics or provision of a dashboard ashtray varied per body style, but all had black rubber floor mats and small hubcaps as standard features. Just one interior sun visor, on the driver's side, was provided as base One-Fifty equipment.

CHEVROLET I.D. NUMBERS: Serial number stamped on plate on right (front) door hinge pillar. Motor numbers stamped on crankcase to rear of distributor on right side of engine. Serial numbers were A56-001001 to 220555 (six-cylinder) and VA56001001 to 220555 (eight-cylinder). Six-cylinder motor numbers 01001-56Z to 525227 were used. V-8 motor numbers 01001-56G to 676997 were used.

ONE-FIFTY SERIES

Model Number	Body/Style Number	Body Type & Seating	Factory Price	Shipping Weight	Production Total
1503	1219	4-dr Sed-6P	1869/1968	3206/3186	29,898
1502	1211	2-dr Sed-6P	1826/3164	3164/3144	66,416
1512	1211B	2-dr Utl Sed-3P	1734/1833	3127/3107	11,196
1529	1263F	2-dr Sta Wag-6P	2171/2270	3309/3289	17,936

NOTE 1: The V-8 was considered a separate series not an option.
NOTE 2: Data for six above slash; for V-8 below slash.

1956 Chevrolet, Two-Ten two-door hardtop Sport Coupe, V-8 (AA)

TWO-TEN — SERIES 2100 B — The Two-Ten Series was Chevrolet's middle-priced line. These cars also carried Chevrolet rear fender nameplates and had chrome moldings around the windshield and backlight, plus on the side window sills. The side trim was distinctive in that the single horizontal molding swept downward, towards the rear bumper end, from the point where the sash molding intersected it below the rear side window. Exterior and interior details varied per body style, but all models had two sunshades (visors), ashtrays and cigarette lighters and richer interior trims. The Del Ray coupe featured deep-pile carpets and all-vinyl upholstery, while others had vinyl coated rubber floor mats and vinyl and cloth trims. A two-spoke steering wheel with horn ring was used. Small hubcaps were standard equipment. Specific interior colors were standard, but custom colored upholstery was optional. A brand new style was a pillarless four-door hardtop, which was called a Sport Sedan.

TWO-TEN I.D. NUMBERS: The Chevrolet numbering system and number locations were used and numbers assigned were the same as on One-Fifty models, except the serial number prefix was a 'B'.

TWO-TEN SERIES

Model Number	Body/Style Number	Body Type & Seating	Factory Price	Shipping Weight	Production Total
2103	1019	4-dr Sed-6P	1955/2054	3212/3192	283,125
2113	1039	4-dr HT	2117/2216	3262/3242	20,021
2102	1011	2-dr Sed-6P	1912/2011	3177/3157	205,545
2124	1011A	2-dr Cpe-6P	1971/2070	3182/3162	56,382
2154	1037	2-dr HT	2063/2162	3204/3184	18,616
2129	1063F	2-dr Sta Wag-6P	2215/2314	3344/3324	22,038
2109	1062F	4-dr Sta Wag-6P	2263/2362	3381/3361	113,656
2119	1062FC	4-dr Sta Wag-9P	2348/2447	3500/3480	17,988

NOTE 1: The V-8 was considered a separate series not an option.
NOTE 2: Data for six above slash; for V-8 below slash.

1956 Chevrolet, Bel Air Nomad two-door station wagon, V-8

BEL AIR — SERIES 2400 C — A real honey of a car, the luxurious Bel Air was richly appointed inside and out. Bel Air nameplates and emblems appeared on rear fenders. The slanting sash molding blended into a horizontal chrome belt that ran forward to the headlamp crease and doubled back, running horizontally to below rear side windows and then, sweeping down towards the rear bumper ends. Chrome wheelcovers were standard equipment. There was an extra chrome treatment around and between all window groups. Three-spoke steering wheels and deep-pile carpets graced all models, but the Beauville nine-passenger station wagon. It had vinyl coated rubber floor mats as standard equipment. Exclusive Bel Air models included a convertible and the Milestone two-door Nomad station wagon, the latter having a unique two-door hardtop roof treatment. All Bel Airs had electric clocks and lighted, lockable glove compartments. All 1956 Chevrolets with V-8 power had large V-shaped emblems below the crest ornaments on the hood and deck, a feature which really looked great on Bel Airs.

CHEVROLET I.D. NUMBERS: Serial number stamped on plate on right (front) door hinge pillar. Motor numbers stamped on crankcase to rear of distributor on right side of engine. The Chevrolet system was also used on Bel Air with the same range of numbers seen for other lines, but with a 'C' prefix for serial numbers.

BEL AIR SERIES

Model Number	Body/Style Number	Body Type & Seating	Factory Price	Shipping Weight	Production Total
2403	1019D	4-dr Sed-6P	2068/2167	3231/3211	269,798
2413	1039D	4-dr HT-6P	2230/2329	3280/3260	103,602
2402	1011D	2-dr Sed-6P	2025/2124	3197/3177	104,849
2454	1037D	2-dr HT-6P	2176/2275	3232/3212	128,382
2434	1067D	2-dr Conv-5P	2344/2443	3340/3320	41,268
2429	1064DF	2-dr Nomad-6P	2608/2707	3362/3342	7,886
2419	1062DF	4-dr Sta Wag-9P	2482/2581	3516/3496	13,268

NOTE 1: The V-8 was considered a separate series not an option.
NOTE 2: Data for six above slash; for V-8 below slash.

1956 Chevrolet, Bel Air four-door hardtop Sport Sedan, V-8

BASE ENGINES

SIX-CYLINDER: Overhead valves. Cast iron block. Displacement: 235.5 cid. Bore and stroke: 3-9/16 x 3-15/16 inches. Compression ratio: 8.0:1. Brake horsepower: 140 at 4200 rpm. Four main bearings. Hydraulic valve lifters. Carburetor: (Powerglide) Rochester model 7007200 one-barrel; or Carter 2101S one-barrel; (standard shift) Rochester model 7007181 one-barrel.

V-8: Overhead valves. Cast iron block. Displacement: 265 cid. Bore and stroke: 3-3/4 x 3 inches. Compression ratio: 8.0:1. Brake horsepower: (standard transmission or 'Touch-down' overdrive) 162 at 4400 rpm.; (Powerglide) 170 at 4400 rpm. Five main bearings. Hydraulic valve lifters. Carburetor: (Powerglide) Carter two-barrel model 2286S; Rochester two-barrel model 7009910; (standard shift) Rochester two-barrel model 7009909.

POWERTRAIN OPTIONS: Three-speed manual transmission with column-mounted control was standard. Overdrive was available on the manual transmission at $108 extra. Powerglide two-speed automatic transmission was available at $189 extra. A four-barrel Super Turbo-Fire V-8 with 205 horsepower and 9.25:1 compression ratio was optional with all transmissions. Also a 225 horsepower dual four-barrel carburetor. Study of the specifications charts will reveal that Chevrolet V-8s were lighter than sixes. The resulting power-to-weight ratio is one reason 1956 Chevrolet V-8s became known as the 'Hot Ones.'

CHASSIS FEATURES: Wheelbase: 115 inches. Overall length: (station wagons) 200.8 inches; (all other models) 197.5 inches. Front tread: 58 inches. Rear tread: 58.9 inches. Tires: (station wagons) 6.70 x 15 six-ply on nine-passenger models; (all other models) 6.70 x 15 four-ply; (optional) 7.10 x 15 four-ply.

CONVENIENCE OPTIONS: Power steering ($92). Power brakes ($38). Accelerator cover. Oil bath air cleaner. Air conditioner (V-8 only). Armrests for One-Fifty. Autronic Eye. Back-up lights. Chrome sill moldings. Park brake signal lamp. Power seat (except One-Fifty). Lighted cigarette lighter. Electric clock (except Bel Air). Eleven inch diameter heavy-duty clutch. Optional colors (paint or convertible top). Compass. Courtesy lights. Custom Color interior. Door edge guards. Door handle shields. Exhaust-extension. Fender guards. Fender top moldings. Floor mats. Locking gas cap. Heavy-duty generators. Deluxe heater and defroster. Recirculating heater and defroster. Tinted glass. Glovebox lamp as option. Six-cylinder governor. Vibrator horn. License frames. Power convertible top. Vanity mirror. Oil filter. Chrome grille guard. Insect screen. Radio antennas. Radios (manual, push-button or signal-seeking). Rear speaker. Rain deflectors. Rearview mirrors (three-types). Seat covers. Ventilated seat pad. Electric shaver. Spotlights. Heavy-duty springs. Right-hand sun visor for One-Fifty. Whitewall and oversize tires. Tissue dispenser. Tool Kit. Traffic light viewer. Trunk light. Underhood light. Continental wheel carrier. Wheelcovers. Wire wheelcovers. Power windows (except One-Fifty). Plastic windshield glare shield. Outside sun visor. Windshield washers (automatic or foot operated). De-icing wiper blades. Dual electric wipers. Wiring junction block.

1956 Chevrolet, Bel Air Beauville four-door station wagon V-8

Standard Catalog of American Cars

HISTORICAL FOOTNOTES: Dealer introductions were held in November, 1955. Model year production equalled 1,574,740 units. Calendar year sales hit 1,621,004. Chevrolet was America's number one automaker. The Two-Ten Club Coupe was called the Del Ray coupe. The One-Fifty utility coupe was the equivalent of traditional business coupe and had a single front bench seat with raised storage compartment platform behind. All four-door hardtops were called Sport Sedans; two-door hardtops were called Sport Coupes. Nine-passenger station wagons were called Beauvilles. Four-door conventional station wagons were called Townsman(s). Two-door conventional station wagons were called Handyman(s). The two-door Nomad station wagon had a slanting pillar roofline, cross ribbed roof and slanting tailgate with seven chrome 'slat' moldings. An innovation on all 1956 Chevrolets was that the left-hand taillamp functioned as the fuel filler door. The Nomad station wagon is a recognized Milestone Car.

1957 CHEVROLET

1957 Chevrolet, One-Fifty two-door sedan, V-8 (AA)

ONE-FIFTY- SERIES 1500 — One of the most popular models in the modern collector car hobby, the 1957 Chevrolet was highlighted by a new oval shaped front bumper grille complete with bomb type bumper guards. Round front parking lamps were seen at each end of a horizontal center bar that seemed to float against the delicately cross-hatched grille insert. A Chevrolet medallion was set into a center cavity within this horizontal bar. Windsplit bulges ran along both sides of the flat hood panel, decorated in front by bombsight ornaments. The headlamps were set into small grilles housed in square-looking fender openings. New side moldings appeared, but varied for each series, looking a little richer as they moved up the scale. The rear fenders were shaped into broad, flat tailfins. Although based on the previous body structure, the new Chevrolet image seemed more modern and sportier. The One-Fifty models were the plainest. They had exclusive use of the 1955-'56 style sash molding (below rear side windows), which intersected an approximately half-length, single horizontal molding. This strip of chrome ran from the front door region to the trailing edge of the tailfins. Chevrolet scripts were affixed to the upper side of the front fender. The fins had only partial outline moldings near their rear tip, which dropped to the taillight housing. The grille insert was done in anodized aluminum finish. Interior trims were the most basic, although the Handyman station wagon had a two-tone look inside. Round horn buttons were used with standard steering wheels.

CHEVROLET I.D. NUMBERS: Serial number stamped on plate on right (front) door hinge pillar. Motor numbers stamped on crankcase to rear of distributor on right side of engine. Serial numbers used on One-Fifty models were A57-100001 to 314393 for sixes; VA57-100001 to 314393 for V-8s. Motor numbers are difficult to catalog and factory shop manuals or master parts catalogs should be consulted.

1957 Chevrolet, Bel Air two-door sedan, V-8

ONE-FIFTY SERIES

Model Number	Body/Style Number	Body Type & Seating	Factory Price	Shipping Weight	Production Total
1503	1219	4-dr Sed-6P	2048/2148	3241/3232	52,266
1502	1211	2-dr Sed-6P	1996/2096	3216/3207	70,774
1512	1211B	2-dr Utl Sed-3P	1885/1985	3168/3159	8,300
1529	1263F	2-dr Sta Wag-6P	2307/2407	3411/3402	14,740

NOTE 1: The V-8 was considered a separate series, not an option.
NOTE 2: V-8s are priced uniformly $100 above six-cylinder models.
NOTE 3: Data for six above slash; for V-8 below.

TWO-TEN — SERIES 2100 — Distinguishing this line from the lowest series was the distinct side trim treatment; richer interiors; and not really much else. The body rub moldings began just behind the headlight area and gently sloped to the rear bumper ends, although the sweep was most pronounced towards the rear half of the body. However, there was a second, upper molding, that branched off just below (and behind) the body belt dip. This top molding just about paralleled the general contour of the fins and ran, rearward, to hit the back edge of the fender. Inside the two moldings, near the taillamp, a Chevrolet script was placed. In many cases, this 'inside' area was painted a contrasting color, as part of many optional two-tone finish schemes. Other trim features were the same used on One-Fifty models. For instance, rear fendertop moldings on the rear third of the fins only and silver aluminized grilles. Three two-tone interior schemes, with cloth and vinyl combinations, were available at standard prices. Despite its kinship to the lowest priced line, this year's Two-Ten looked more Bel Air-like, especially when done up in optional two-tone exterior finish. As in 1956, all Chevrolets with V-8 power had large, V-shaped hood and deck lid ornaments, which were bright metal finished on the lower series.

TWO-TEN I.D. NUMBERS: The only VIN numbering variation for the mid-range models was a 'B' prefix (instead of 'A') for the serial numbers with VB indicating V-8 attachment. The range of numbers was the same used on One-Fifty models, which indicates mixed production runs.

TWO-TEN SERIES

Model Number	Body/Style Number	Body Type & Seating	Factory Price	Shipping Weight	Production Total
2103	1019	4-dr Sed-6P	2174/2274	3275/3266	260,401
2113	1039	4-dr HT Spt Sed-6P	2270/2370	3325/3316	16,178
2102	1011	2-dr Sed-6P	2122/2222	3230/3221	162,090
2124	1011A	2-dr Del Ray Cpe-6P	2162/2262	3225/3216	25,664
2154	1037	2-dr HT Spt Cpe-6P	2204/2304	3265/3256	22,631
2109	1062F	4-dr Sta Wag-6P	2456/2556	3466/3457	27,803
2119	1062FC	4-dr Sta Wag-9P	2563/2663	3566/3557	21,083
2129	1063F	2-dr Sta Wag-6P	2402/2502	3411/3402	17,528

NOTE 1: The V-8 was considered a separate series, not an option.
NOTE 2: V-8s are priced uniformly $100 above six-cylinder models.
NOTE 3: Data for six above slash; for V-8 below.

1957 Chevrolet, Bel Air two-door hardtop Sport Coupe, V-8

BEL AIR — SERIES 2400 C — Extra richness characterized the Bel Air line in all regards. Side trim was arranged as on Two-Tens, except the area between the molding 'branches' was filled with a silver anodized aluminum beauty panel. Three gold chevrons marked the forward side of each front fender. Also done in gold were such things as the grille insert, V-8 ornaments (when used) and Bel Air beauty panel scripts. Rocker sills, roof and window outlines and the entire edge of the fins were all trimmed with bright metal moldings. There were also traditional Chevrolet/Bel Air crests on the rear fenders, near the golden script. Distinctive two-tone interiors were another highlight. The Nomad station wagon had carryover features with new 1957 styling and the convertible was a dream car come true.

BEL AIR I.D. NUMBERS: The Chevrolet numbering system was also used on Bel Air with the same range of numbers seen for other lines, but with 'C' or 'VC' serial number prefixes.

BEL AIR SERIES

Model Number	Body/Style Number	Body Type & Seating	Factory Price	Shipping Weight	Production Total
2403	1019D	4-dr Sed-6P	2290/2390	3281/3272	254,331
2413	1039D	4-dr HT Spt Sed-6P		2364/2464	137,672
2402	1011D	2-dr Sed-6P	2238/2338	3237/3228	62,751
2454	1037D	2-dr HT Spt Cpe-6P	2299/2399	3283/3274	166,426
2434	1067D	2-dr Conv-5P	2511/2611	3414/3405	47,562
2409	1062DFC	4-dr Sta Wag-6P	2580/2680	3465/3456	27,375
2429	1064DF	2-dr Nomad-6P	2757/2857	3470/3461	6,103

NOTE 1: The V-8 was considered a separate series, not an option.
NOTE 2: V-8s are priced uniformly $100 above six-cylinder models.
NOTE 3: Data for six above slash; for V-8 below.

1957 Chevrolet, Bel Air Nomad two-door wagon V-8

BASE ENGINES

SIX-CYLINDER: Overhead valves. Cast iron block. Displacement: 235.5 cid. Bore and stroke: 3-9/16 x 3-15/16 inches. Compression ratio: 8.0:1. Brake horsepower: 140 at 4200 rpm. Four main bearings. Hydraulic valve lifters. Carburetor: (Powerglide) Rochester model 7007200 one-barrel; or Carter 2101S one-barrel; (standard shift) Rochester model 7007181 one-barrel. (The 'Blue Flame' six came with synchromesh, overdrive or Powerglide attachment.)

V-8: Overhead valves. Cast iron block. Displacement: 265 cid. Bore and stroke: 3-3/4 x 3 inches. Compression ratio: 8.0:1. Brake horsepower: (standard transmission or 'Touch-down' overdrive) 162 at 4400 rpm.; (Powerglide) 170 at 4400 rpm. Five main bearings. Hydraulic valve lifters. Carburetor: (Powerglide) Carter two-barrel model 2286S; Rochester two-barrel model 7009910; (standard shift) Rochester two-barrel model 7009909. (Note: This 'Turbo-Fire 265' was available as the base V-8 powerplant for 1957 Chevrolets with synchromesh or overdrive transmissions.) Other engines are listed under Powertrain Options below.

1957 Chevrolet, Two-Ten two-door station wagon V-8 (AA)

POWERTRAIN OPTIONS: According to the 1957 Chevrolet Passenger Car Shop Manual, six extra-cost power options were available in conventional (non-Corvette) models, along with six gearbox selections. This provided a total of 17 optional engine/transmission combinations as follows:

CID Displ.	Comp. Ratio	Carb Barrels	Exhaust	H.P. @ rpm.	Trans Combo	Valve Lifters
TURBO-FIRE V-8						
283	8.5	2V	1	185 @ 4600	3-4	H
SUPER TURBO-FIRE V-8						
283	9.5	4V	2	220 @ 4800	1-2-3-4	H
CORVETTE V-8						
283	9.5	2 x 4V	2	245 @ 5000	1-2-4-5-6	H
283	9.5	F.I.	2	250 @ 5000	1-4-5-6	H
283	9.5	2 x 4V	2	270 @ 6000	5	S
283	10.5	F.I.	2	283 @ 6200	5	S

NOTES: F.I. — Fuel-injection. Transmission choices: (1) Three-speed manual; (2) Overdrive; (3) Regular Powerglide; (4) Turboglide; (S) Close-ratio three-speed and (6) Corvette type Powerglide. H=hydraulic lifters. S=solid (mechanical) lifters. Corvette V-8s were not available in sedan deliveries. Lightweight valves were used only with SR high-performance camshaft and solid lifters. Some collectors maintain that a limited number of 1957 Chevrolet passenger cars came with four-speed manual transmission attachments, perhaps dealer-installed. This cannot be verified with normal factory literature. Cars with fuel-injection engines wore special badges denoting this fact.

CHASSIS FEATURES: Wheelbase: 115 inches. Overall length: 200 inches. Front tread: 58 inches. Rear tread: 58.8 inches. Tires: 7.50 x 14 four-ply tubeless blackwall.

1957 Chevrolet, Bel Air four-door hardtop Sport Sedan, V-8 (AA)

CONVENIENCE OPTIONS: Power brakes ($38). Power steering ($70). Overdrive ($108). Powerglide ($188). Turboglide ($231). Accelerator cover. Oil bath air cleaner. Air conditioner (V-8 only). Armrests for One-Fifty. Autronic Eye. Back-up lights. Chrome sill moldings. Park brake signal lamp. Power seat (except One-Fifty). Lighted cigarette lighter. Electric clock (except Bel Air). Eleven inch diameter heavy-duty clutch. Optional colors (paint or convertible top). Compass. Courtesy lights. Custom Color interior. Door edge guards. Door handle shields. Exhaust-extension. Fender guards. Fender top moldings. Floor mats. Locking gas cap. Heavy-duty generators. Deluxe heater and defroster. Recirculating heater and defroster. Tinted glass. Glovebox lamp as option. Six-cylinder governor. Vibrator horn. License frames. Power convertible top. Vanity mirror. Oil filter. Chrome grille guard. Insect screen. Radio antennas (three-types). Radios (manual, push-button or signal-seeking). Rear speaker. Rain deflectors. Rearview mirrors (three-types). Seat covers. Ventilated seat pad. Electric shaver. Spotlights. Heavy-duty springs. Right-hand sun visor for One-Fifty. Whitewall and oversize tires. Tissue dispenser. Tool Kit. Traffic light viewer. Trunk light. Underhood light. Continental wheel carrier. Wheelcovers. Wire wheelcovers. Power windows (except One-Fifty). Plastic windshield glare shield. Outside sun visor. Windshield washers (automatic or foot operated). Deicing wiper

blades. Dual electric wipers. Wiring junction block. The fuel-injection V-8 was priced $484 over the base price of a six. Safety seat belts and shoulder harnesses were new options this season.

HISTORICAL FOOTNOTES: Dealer introductions for 1957 Chevrolets were held October, 1956. Model year production peaked at 1,515,177 cars. Calendar year sales were counted at 1,522,536 units. Chevrolet outsold Ford by only 136 cars on a calendar year basis, but Ford actually built more 1957 specifications models than Chevrolet. It was a neck-and-neck battle between the two firms this season. Turboglide transmission was a running production change, so some early cars may have had 265 cid V-8s with Powerglide attachment. Chevrolet advertised that its solid lifter fuel-injection V-8 was the first American production car engine to provide one horsepower per cid (283 cid/283 horsepower). This year the Chevrolet gas filler was incorporated into the chrome molding at the rear edge of the left-hand tailfin. Body style nomenclature (Sport Sedan, Sport Coupe, Del Ray; Beauville; Townsman; Handyman and Nomad) was similar, in application, to the year before.

1958 CHEVROLET

1958 Chevrolet, Del Ray two-door sedan, 6-cyl (AA)

DEL RAY — 1100 SERIES (6-CYL) — 1200 SERIES (V-8) — By adopting an all-new Safety Girder chassis for 1958, Chevrolet brought to market a completely re-engineered and restyled line. Body revisions included lower, wider, longer sheet metal; a new front end with dual headlamps and a dream car look; gull-wing rear fender and deck sculpturing; and revamped side trim treatments. New names, identified two series, while models available within each line were altered, too. The sedan delivery was cataloged as a conventional model, but strangely, not with the station wagons, which were now a series unto themselves. Del Ray nameplates marked the rear fender coves (indentations) of four styles in the low-priced line, which had single belt moldings and lacked bright metal side window trim. Del Ray interior appointments were, needless to say, the most basic types with standard steering wheels, rubber floor mats and fewer bright highlights.

CHEVROLET I.D. NUMBERS: Serial numbers were stamped on a plate affixed to the left front door hinge pillar. The first symbol, a letter, identified series as follows: A — Del Ray six; B — Del Ray V-8; C — Biscayne six; D — Biscayne V-8; E — Bel Air six; F — Bel Air V-8. The second and third symbols were '58' for 1958 model year. The fourth symbol indicated assembly plant, as follows: A — Baltimore; F — Flint; J — Janesville; K — Kansas City; L — Los Angeles; N — Norwood; 0 — Oakland; S — St. Louis and T — Tarrytown. The last six symbols were numbers indicating production sequence. Numbers for each series at each factory began at 100001 and up. For example, Number A58(F)100101 — one hundredth Del Ray six manufactured in Flint, Mich. Sedan deliveries used Body Style Number and letter prefix (G — six; H — V-8). For example, 1171G48(F)-100001 for Del Ray six Sedan delivery built at Flint. Engine numbers are not given in general reference sources.

Model Number	Model Number (V-8)	Body Type & Seating	Factory Price	Shipping Weight	Production Total
(PASSENGER CARS)					
1149	1249	4-dr Sed-6P	2155/2262	3439/3442	Note 1
1141	1241	2-dr Sed-6P	2101/2208	3396/3399	Note 1
1121	1221B	2-dr Utl Sed-3P	2013/2120	3351/3356	Note 1
1171	1271	2-dr Sed DeL-1P	2123/2230	3529/3531	Note 1
(STATION WAGONS)					
1193	1293	4-dr Sta Wag-6P	2467/2574	3740/3743	Note 1
1191	1291	2-dr Sta Wag-6P	2413/2520	3693/3696	Note 1

NOTE 1: Most Chevrolet production totals, after 1957, are available only in a form which indicates all series. There are no breakouts per series, model or engine type. For 1958, the totals were: Four-door sedan — 491,441; Two-door sedan 256,182; Four-door station wagon — 170,473; Sports Coupe — 142,592; Sports Sedan — 83,330; Convertible — 55,989 and Two-door station wagon — 16,590.
NOTE 2: Chevrolet station wagons were officially listed as separate series, but will be grouped under passenger cars with the same level of trim in this catalog. Station wagons with Del Ray trim were called Yeoman models.
NOTE 3: The model numbering system changed in 1958. Model numbers and Body Style Numbers are now identical. The first column in chart above shows model/body numbers for sixes. The second column in chart shows model/body numbers for V-8s. This system will be applied post 1958 models.

1958 Chevrolet, Bel Air Impala two-door hardtop Sport Coupe, V-8

BISCAYNE — SERIES 1500 (6-CYL) — 1600 SERIES (V-8) — Only two body styles came under the Biscayne name, although two Brookwood station wagons wore the same level trim. Since sixes and V-8s were considered separate series, the result is eight Biscaynes to catalog. The passenger styles wore Biscayne nameplates at the leading edge of the rear fender cove, but station wagons had Brookwood scripts in the same location. All 1958 Chevrolets with V-8 power had additional, large, V-shaped ornaments on the hood and deck (or tailgate). Biscayne side trim moldings outlined the upper and lower edges of the cove, but did not connect. Ahead of the cove, a bi-level belt molding, with slight forward taper, was seen. It was connected to the single, lower cove outline trim at the rear. Like the Del Ray models, Biscaynes came standard with small hubcaps, no sill moldings, no chevrons and no fender ornaments, but they did feature slightly up-market interior trims.

BISCAYNE SERIES

Model Number	Model Number (V-8)	Body Type & Seating	Factory Price	Shipping Weight	Production Total
(PASSENGER CARS)					
1549	1649	4-dr Sed-6P	2290/2397	3447/3450	Note 1
1541	1641	2-dr Sed-6P	2236/2343	3404/3407	Note 1
(STATION WAGONS)					
1593	1693	4-dr Sta Wag-6P	2571/2678	3748/3751	Note 1
1594	1694	4-dr Sta Wag-9P	2678/2785	3837/3839	Note 1

NOTE 1: Most Chevrolet production totals, after 1957, are available only in a form which indicates all series. There are no breakouts per series, model or engine type. For 1958, the totals were: Four-door sedan — 491,441; Two-door sedan 256,182; Four-door station wagon — 170,473; Sports Coupe — 142,592; Sports Sedan — 83,330; Convertible — 55,989 and Two-door station wagon — 16,590.
NOTE 2: Station wagons with Biscayne trim are Brookwoods and were actually part of the separate Chevrolet station wagon series.
NOTE 3: The V-8 was considered a separate series, not an option. Data for six above slash; for V-8 below; for V-8 below slash.

1958 Chevrolet, Bel Air four-door hardtop Sport Sedan, V-8 (AA)

BEL AIR — 1700 SERIES (6-CYL) — 1800 SERIES (V.8) — This series was enriched over others and was also endowed with two even more luxurious Impala models. The base Bel Air had a series name scripts and Chevrolet crests of the rear of the coves. The upper edge of the indentation was outlined with a single level molding that slashed down and back, below the body belt dip, to intersect an elaborated horizontal molding arrangement. This could best be described as spear-shaped moldings, with indented concave contrast band towards the rear and a horizontally grooved, missile-shaped 'spear tip' at the front. Also seen were four chevrons on the sides of the front fenders; four short vertical strips on the lower rear fender bulge; front fendertop ornaments; chrome outlined side windows; grooved rear roof pillar beauty plates; and full wheel discs. Interior appointments were rich and fancy. The Impala sport coupe and convertible were even more impressive. Trim features included Impala scripts; Insignia and crossed-flag emblems at the front of the cove; broad, ribbed body sill panels; large dummy chrome plated chrome air scoops ahead of rear wheelwells; competition style two-spoke deep hub steering wheels (with Impala medallions); Impala dashboard script; standard rear radio speaker grille (with Impala script and medallion between rear seatback dip); and triple taillamp arrangements (replacing two taillights on other cars; one on all station wagons). The Impala Sport Coupe had a chrome-edged, rear facing dummy air scoop and curved contour crease molded into the back of the roof.

BEL AIR SERIES

Model Number	Model Number (V-8)	Body Type & Seating	Factory Price	Shipping Weight	Production Total
(PASSENGER CARS)					
1749	1849	4-dr Sed-6P	2440/2547	3467/3470	Note 1
1739	1839	4-dr HT Spt Sed-6P	2511/2618	3511/3514	Note 1
1741	1841	2-dr Sed-6P	2386/2493	3424/3427	Note 1
1731	1831	2-dr HT Spt Cpe-6P	2447/2554	3455/3458	Note 1
(IMPALA)					
1747	1847	2-dr HT Spt Cpe-5P	2586/2693	3458/3459	Note 1
1767	1867	2-dr HT Spt Conv-5P	2724/2841	3522/3523	Note 1

(STATION WAGONS)

1793	1893SD	4-dr Nomad-6P	2728/2835	3738/3771	Note 1

NOTE 1: Most Chevrolet production totals, after 1957, are available only in a form which indicates all series. There are no breakouts per series, model or engine type. For 1958, the totals were: Four-door sedan — 491,441; Two-door sedan 256,182; Four-door station wagon — 170,473; Sports Coupe — 142,592; Sports Sedan — 83,330; Convertible — 55,989 and Two-door station wagon — 16,590.
NOTE 2: Impalas were considered part of the Bel Air line and were not listed as a sub-series. The Nomad station wagon was now a four-door style with conventional styling, but high-level trim. The Nomad was actually a part of the separate station wagon series, but had Impala trim with Nomad rear fender nameplates.
NOTE 3: The V-8 was considered a separate series, not an option. Data for six above slash; for V-8 below; slash.

BASE ENGINES

SIX-CYLINDER: Overhead valves. Cast iron block. Displacement: 235.5 cid. Bore and stroke: 3.56 x 3.94 inches. Compression ratio: 8.25:1. Brake horsepower: 145 at 4200 rpm. Four main bearings. Hydraulic valve lifters. Carburetor: Rochester two-barrel model 7012127.

V-8: Overhead valves. Cast iron block. Displacement: 283 cid. Bore and stroke: 3.875 x 3 inches. Compression ratio: 8.5:1. Brake horsepower: 185 at 4600 rpm. Five main bearings. Hydraulic valve lifters. Carburetor: Rochester two-barrel model 7012133.

POWERTRAIN OPTIONS: Optional engine and transmission combinations were as follows:

CID Displ.	Comp. Ratio	Carb Barrels	Exhaust	HPP @ rpm.	Trans Combo	Valve Lifter
SUPER TURBO-FIRE V-8						
283	9.5	4V	1	230 @ 4800	1-2-3-5	H
TURBO-THRUST V-8						
348	9.5	4V	2	250@ 4400	14-5-6	H
SUPER TURBO-THURST V-8						
348	9.5	3 x 2V	2	280 @ 4800	1-4-5	H
348 (M)	11.0	3 x 2V	2	315 @ 5600	1-5	S
RAM-JET FUEL INJECTION V-8						
283	9.5	F.I.	1	250 @ 5000	1-4-5-6	H

NOTES: (M) — Maximum performance V-8. F.I. — fuel Injection. Transmission choices; (1) — Three-speed manual; (2) — Overdrive; (3) — Two-Speed Powerglide; (4) Turbo-glide; (5) — Close-ratio three-speed; (6) — Corvette type Powerglide; H=Hydraulic litters; S=Solid lifters. (M)=Includes special performance type cam shaft and high-speed valve trains. Some of the transmission attachment data that has been interpolated as normal factory literature is not specific about types of three-speed manual or automatic transmission used.

CHASSIS FEATURES: Wheelbase: 117.5 inches. Overall length: 209.1 inches. Overall width: 77.7 inches. Overall height: (Impala Convertible) 56.5 inches; (Impala sport coupe) 56.4 inches; (other models) 57.4 inches. Tires: (convertibles and station wagons) 8.00 x 14; (other models) 7.50 x 14. Full coil spring suspension; high-level ventilation; anti-dive braking and built-in leveling and foot operated parking brakes were used this year.

1958 Chevrolet, Bel Air Impala two-door convertible, V-8 (AA)

CONVENIENCE OPTIONS: Four-barrel carburetor for 283 cid, 230 horsepower V-8 ($27). Turbo-thrust 250 horsepower V-8 ($59). Super Turbo-thrust 280 horsepower V-8 ($70). Base fuel-injection 250 horsepower V-8 ($484). Powerglide transmission ($188). Turbo-glide transmission ($231). Overdrive ($108). Power steering ($70). Power brakes ($38). Power window control ($102). Front power seat ($43). Oil filter ($9). Oil bath air cleaner ($5). Dual exhaust as option ($16). Deluxe heater ($77). Recirculating heater ($49). Whitewall tires, size 7.50 x 14, four-ply ($32). E-Z-I tinted glass ($38). Electric wipers ($7). Safety panel padding ($16). Manual radio ($61). Push-button radio ($84). Air conditioning ($468). Air suspension ($124). Two-tone paint ($32). Posi-traction rear axle with 3.36 or 3.55 ratio ($48). Other standard dealer installed accessories.

HISTORICAL FOOTNOTES: Dealer introductions of 1958 Chevrolets took place October, 1957. Model year total was 1,217,047 cars. Calendar year total was 1,255,935 cars. Gas filler now under door in trunk latch lid panel. On Impalas the center taillamps housed a back-up lamp. A great deal of bright metal trim on 1958 Chevrolets was made of aluminum.

1959 CHEVROLET

BISCAYNE — SERIES 1100 (6-CYL) — 1200 SERIES (V-8) — Chevrolet for 1959 featured new "Slimline Design" styling with wider, roomier bodies; a new radiator grille; "Spread Wing" rear treatment; cat's eye taillights; increased glass area and flat-top roof styling on Sport Sedans. Standard equipment on Biscaynes included rear foam cushions; electric wipers; and oil bath air cleaner for V-8s.

CHEVROLET I.D. NUMBERS: Serial numbers were stamped on a plate affixed to the left front door hinge pillar. The first symbol, a letter, identified series as follows: A — Del Ray six; B — Del Ray V-8; C — Biscayne six; D — Biscayne V-8; E — Bel Air six; F — Bel Air V-8. The second and third symbols were '59' for 1959 model year. The fourth symbol indicated assembly plant, as follows: A — Baltimore; F — Flint; J — Janesville; K — Kansas City; L — Los Angeles; N — Norwood; 0 — Oakland: S — St. Louis; T — Tarrytown; and W — Willow Run, Mich. The last six symbols were numbers indicating production sequence. Numbers for each series at each factory began at 100001 and up. For example, Number A59(F)100101 — one hundredth Biscayne six manufactured in Flint, Mich. Engine numbers are not given in general reference sources.

BISCAYNE SERIES

Model Number	Model Number (V-8)	Body Type & Seating	Factory Price	Shipping Weight	Production Total
(PASSENGER CARS)					
1119	1219	4-dr Sed-6P	2301/2419	3605/3600	Note 1
1111	1211	2-dr Sed-6P	2247/2365	3535/3530	Note 1
1121	1221	2-dr Utl Sed-3P	2160/2278	3480/3490	Note 1
(STATION WAGONS)					
1135	1235	4-dr Brkwd-6P	2638/2756	3955/3955	Note 1
1115	1215	2-dr Brkwd-6P	2571/2689	3870/3860	Note 1

NOTE 1: Chevrolet production totals are now available by body style only. For 1959, the totals were: four-door sedan — 525,461; two-door sedan — 281,924; four-door station wagon — 188,623: Sports Sedan — 182,520; Sports Coupe — 164,901; convertible — 72,765 and two-door station wagon — 20,760. No breakouts by series, model or body style are available.
NOTE 2: First column shows six-cylinder Model Number; second column shows V-8 Model Number.
NOTE 3: Data above slash for six/below slash for V-8.

1959 Chevrolet, Impala two-door convertible, V-8

1959 Chevrolet, Bel Air four-door sedan, 6-cyl (AA)

BEL AIR — SERIES 1500 (6-CYL) — SERIES 1600 (V-8) — Bel Airs had model script nameplates and crests on front fenders. While Biscayne side moldings ran from the headlights to center front doors, Bel Air moldings ran full length and had painted inserts. Another enrichment was front fendertop ornaments. Kingswood and Parkwood station wagons had Bel Air trim, but their own model scripts on front fenders. Standard equipment was the same as Biscayne, plus Deluxe features, front foam seat cushions, Deluxe steering wheel and power tailgate on Kingswood.

BEL AIR SERIES

Model Number	Model Number (V-8)	Body Type & Seating	Factory Price	Shipping Weight	Production Total
(PASSENGER CARS)					
1519	1619	4-dr Sed-6P	2440/2558	3600/3615	Note 1
1539	1639	4-dr HT Spt Sed-6P	2556/2674	3660/3630	Note 1
1511	1611	2-dr Sed-6P	2386/2504	3515/3510	Note 1
(STATION WAGONS)					
1535	1635	4-dr Pkwd-6P	2749/2867	3965/3970	Note 1
1545	1645	4-dr Kgwd-9P	2852/2970	4020/4015	Note 1

NOTE 1: Chevrolet production totals are now available by body style only. For 1959, the totals were: four-door sedan — 525,461; two-door sedan — 281,924; four-door station wagon — 188,623; Sports Sedan — 182,520; Sports Coupe — 164,901; convertible — 72,765 and two-door station wagon — 20,760. No breakouts by series, model or body style are available.
NOTE 2: First column shows six-cylinder Model Number; second column shows V-8 Model Number.
NOTE 3: Data above slash for six/below slash for V-8.

1959 Chevrolet, Impala two-door convertible, V-8 (AA)

IMPALA — SERIES 1700 (6-CYL) — SERIES 1700 (V-8) — For the "upper crust" Chevrolet, identification features included Impala nameplates and crossed racing flags emblems. Both identifiers were mounted inside the painted insert area of the full-length side trim moldings, below the rear side windows. The front fendertop ornaments also had rear extension strips. Bright metal trim marked the deck lid center crease and taillamp lenses. Closed models had simulated Impala-style roof scoops. Nomads had Impala trim with different I.D. scripts. Standard equipment was the same as on Bel Airs, plus electric clock, dual sliding sun visors and aluminum trim.

IMPALA SERIES

Model Number	Model Number (V-8)	Body Type & Seating	Factory Price	Shipping Weight	Production Total
(PASSENGER CARS)					
1719	1819	4-dr Sed-6P	2592/2710	3625/3620	Note 1
1739	1839	4-dr HT Spt Sed-6P	2664/2782	3665/3670	Note 1
1737	1837	2-dr HT Spt Cpe-6P	2599/2717	3570/3580	Note 1
1767	1867	2-dr Conv-5P	2849/2967	3660/3650	Note 1
(STATION WAGONS)					
1735	1835	4-dr Nomad-6P	2891/3009	3980/3975	Note 1

NOTE 1: Chevrolet production totals are now available by body style only. For 1959, the totals were: four-door sedan — 525,461; two-door sedan — 281,924; four-door station wagon — 188,623; Sports Sedan — 182,520; Sports Coupe — 164,901; convertible — 72,765 and two-door station wagon — 20,760. No breakouts by series, model or body style are available.
NOTE 2: First column shows six-cylinder Model Number; second column shows V-8 Model Number.
NOTE 3: Data above slash for six/below slash for V-8.

BASE ENGINES

SIX-CYLINDER: Overhead valves. Cast iron block. Displacement: 235.5 cid. Bore and stroke: 3-9/16 x 3-15/16 inches. Compression ratio: 8.25:1. Brake horsepower: 135 at 4000 rpm. Four main bearings. Hydraulic valve lifters. Carburetor: Rochester two-barrel model 7013003.

V-8: Overhead valves. Cast iron block. Displacement: 283 cid. Bore and stroke: 3.875 x 3 inches. Compression ratio: 8.5:1. Brake horsepower: 185 at 4600 rpm. Five main bearings. Hydraulic valve lifters. Carburetor: Rochester two-barrel model 7013007.

POWERPLANT OPTIONS: Optional engine and transmission combinations were:

CID Displ.	Comp. Ratio	Carb Barrels	Exhaust	HP @ rpm.	Trans Combo	Valve Lifters
SUPER TURBO-FIRE V-8						
283	9.5	4V	1	230 @ 4800	1-2-3-4-5-6	H
RAM-JET FUEL INJECTION V-8						
283	9.5	F.I.	1	250 @ 5000	1-3-4-5-6-7	H
283	10.5	F.I.	1	290 @ 6200	1-5-7	H
TURBO-THRUST V-8						
348	9.5	4V	2	250 @ 4400	1-3-4-5-6-7	H
SUPER TURBO-THRUST V-8						
348	9.5	3x2V	2	280 @ 4800	1-3-4-5-6-7	H
SPECIAL TURBO-THRUST V-8						
348	11.0	4V	2	300@ 5600	1-3-5-6-7	S
SPECIAL SUPER TURBO-THRUST V-8						
348	11.0	3x2V	2	315 @ 5600	1-5-7	S

NOTES: F.I. — Fuel-injection. Transmission choices; (1) Three-speed manual; (2) Overdrive; (3) — Two-Speed Powerglide; (4) — Turboglide; (5) — Close-ratio three-speed; (6) — Corvette type Powerglide; (7) — Four-speed.

CHASSIS FEATURES: Wheelbase: 119 inches. Overall length: 210.9 inches. Overall width: 79.9 inches. Overall height: (hardtops) 54 inches; (sedans) 56 inches; (station wagons) 56.3 inches. Tires: (convertible and station wagons) 8.00 x 14; (all other models) 7.50 x 14.

CONVENIENCE OPTIONS: Powerglide transmission ($199). Turboglide transmission ($242). Overdrive ($108). Super Turbo-fire V-8 ($147). Turbo-thrust V-8 ($199). Super Turbo-thrust V-8 ($269). Power steering ($75). Power brakes ($43). Power windows ($102). Power seat ($102). Oil filter ($9). Oil bath air cleaner ($5). Dual exhausts ($19). Deluxe heater ($80). Recirculating heater ($52). Whitewall 7.50 x 14 tires ($32). Whitewall 8.00 x 14 tires, for convertibles and station wagons ($35); other models ($51). E-Z-I tinted glass ($43). Windshield washer ($12). Padded dash ($18). Manual radio ($65). Push-button radio ($87). Air conditioner including heater ($468). Air suspension ($135). Positraction with 3.36; 3.55 or 4.11 gears ($48). Two-tone paint, on Biscayne ($22); on Brookwood, Bel Air. Impala ($27); on Parkwood, Kingswood, Nomad ($32). Power tailgate window ($32). Deluxe steering wheel ($4). Close-ratio four-speed transmission ($188). Wheel discs ($16). Two-speed wipers and washers ($16). Shaded rear window ($22). Front air foam cushion ($8). Deluxe Group including sun visor; front armrest; fender ornaments and cigarette lighter ($16). Heavy-duty 35-ampere generator($8).

1959 Chevrolet, Bel Air four-door hardtop Sport Sedan, V-8

HISTORICAL FOOTNOTES: Dealer introductions were held October, 1958. The Del Ray name was dropped. Calendar year sales were 1,528,592 units. Model year production equaled 1,481,071 cars. Ford and Chevy ran neck-and-neck, but Chevrolet turned out more cars built to 1959 specifications. Magic-Mirror deep-luster acrylic lacquer introduced, along with improved Safety-Master brakes.

1960 CHEVROLET

BISCAYNE — SERIES 1100/1300 (6-CYL) — SERIES 1200/1400 (V-8) — This year a new oval grille enclosed dual headlamps. Missile inspired side trim was seen. The seagull-like "Spread Wing" fins were more angular. Small circular taillamps were set into a beauty panel at the rear. Identification came from Biscayne front fender scripts; a painted rear beauty panel; and single molding quarter panel trim. Brookwoods, actually part of a separate station wagon series, were trimmed like Biscaynes, except for front fender scripts. Cataloged as standard were dual sun visors, electric wipers, cigarette lighter and front armrests, all formerly considered Deluxe equipment. An economy sub-series for corporate fleet use was provided in two Fleetmasters, which were marketed without these Deluxe type items.

CHEVROLET I.D. NUMBERS: Serial numbers were stamped on a plate affixed to the left front door hinge pillar. The first symbol identified model year, 0=1960. The second and third symbols identified the series (see first two digits of Model Number columns in charts below). The fourth and fifth symbols identified body style (see last two digits of Model Number columns in charts below). The sixth symbol, a letter, indicated assembly plant, as follows: A=Atlanta, Ga.; B=Baltimore, Md.; F=Flint, Mich.; J=Janesville, Wis.; K=Kansas City, Mo.; L=Los Angeles, Calif.; N=Norwood, Ohio; O=Oakland, Calif.; S=St. Louis, Mo.; T=Tarrytown, NY; W=Williiow Run, Mich.; G=Framingham, Mass. The last six symbols are the sequential production number, with numbers for each series at each factory starting at 100001 and up. Fisher Body plate attached to left-hand cowl starts with two-digit model year prefix (60-) and Fisher Body Style Number (Model Number) and also shows factory code, production sequence, trim and body color data. Engine numbers: (six) right side of block behind distributor; (V-8) right front of engine block).

BISCAYNE SERIES

Model Number	Model Number (V-8)	Body Type & Seating	Factory Price	Shipping Weight	Production Total
(BASE PASSENGER CARS)					
1169	1269	4-dr Sed-6P	2316/2423	3500/3505	Note 1
1111	1211	2-dr Sed-6P	2262/2369	3415/3425	Note 1
1121	1221	2-dr Utl Sed-6P	2175/2282	3390/3395	Note 1
NOTE 1 (FLEETMASTER 1300 SUB-SERIES)					
1369	1469	4-dr Sed-6P	2284/2391	3495/3500	Note 1
1311	1411	2-dr Sed-6P	2230/2337	3410/3415	Note 1
(STATION WAGON)					
1145	1245	4-dr Brkwd-9P	2756/2863	3900/3895	Note 1
1135	1235	4-dr Brkwd-6P	2653/2760	3850/3845	Note 1

NOTE 1: Chevrolet production totals are again available by body style only. For 1960, the totals were: four-door sedan — 497,048; two-door sedan — 228,322; Sports Coupe — 204,467; four-door station wagon — 198,066; Sports Sedan — 169,016; convertible — 79,903 and two-door station wagon — 14,663. No breakouts by series, model or engine are available.
NOTE 2: Data for six above slash/for V-8 below slash.

BEL AIR — SERIES 1500 (6-CYL) — SERIES 1600 (V-8) — A shield medallion split the words Bel Air on front fenders. A single rear quarter extension molding flew rearward from the missile ornament. The rear beauty panel was horizontally grooved and outlined with bright metal trim. All Biscayne features were standard, plus front foam cushions; Deluxe steering wheel and power tailgate on Kingswood station wagon.

BEL AIR SERIES

Model Number	Model Number (V-8)	Body Type & Seating	Factory Price	Shipping Weight	Production Total
(PASSENGER CARS)					
1519	1619	4-dr Sed-6P	2438/2545	3565/3580	Note1
1539	1639	4-dr HT Spt Cpe-6P	2554/2661	3605/3620	Note1
1511	1611	2-dr Sed-6P	2384/2491	3490/3505	Note1
1537	1637	2-dr HT Spt Cpe-5P	2489/2596	3515/3530	Note1

Model Number	Model Number (V-8)	Body Type & Seating	Factory Price	Shipping Weight	Production Total
(STATION WAGON)					
1545	1645	4-dr Kgswd-9P	2850/2957	3990/4000	Note 1
1535	1635	4-dr Pkwd-6P	2747/2854	3945/3950	Note1

NOTE 1: Chevrolet production totals are again available by body style only. For 1960, the totals were: four-door sedan — 497,048; two-door sedan — 228,322; Sports Coupe — 204,467; four-door station wagon — 198,066; Sports Sedan — 169,016; convertible — 79,903 and two-door station wagon — 14,663. No breakouts by series, model or engine are available.
NOTE 2: Data for six above slash/for V-8 below slash.

1960 Chevrolet, Bel Air two-door hardtop sports coupe, 6-cyl

IMPALA — SERIES 1700 (6-CYL) — SERIES 1800 (V-8) — The Impala was dressy from stem to stern. A short molding strip extended back from the headlights. Twin pairs of bar moldings were above and below this strip on the fender tips. The quarter panel missile ornaments had two moldings streaking rearward, the area between them filled with a white insert and Impala script with crossed racing flags insignia. Triple taillights and a vertically ribbed aluminum rear beauty panel were seen. All, but convertibles, had simulated vents on the lower rear window molding. Standard equipment was as on Bel Airs, plus parking brake, glove compartment and back-up lights; anodized aluminum trim; electric clock; and, on V-8s, oil filters and oil bath air cleaners.

IMPALA SERIES

Model Number	Model Number (V-8)	Body Type & Seating	Factory Price	Shipping Weight	Production Total
(PASSENGER CARS)					
1719	1819	4-dr Sed-6P	2590/2697	3575/3580	Note 1
1739	1839	4-dr HT Spt Sed-6P	2662/2769	3625/3625	Note 1
1737	1837	2-dr HT Spt Cpe-5P	2597/2704	3540/3530	Note 1
1767	1867	2-dr Conv-5P	2847/2954	3635/3625	Note 1
(STATION WAGON)					
1735	1835	4-dr Nomad-6P	2889/2996	3960/3955	Note 1

NOTE 1: Chevrolet production totals are again available by body style only. For 1960, the totals were: four-door sedan — 497,048; two-door sedan — 228,322; Sports Coupe — 204,467; four-door station wagon — 198,066; Sports Sedan — 169,016; convertible — 79,903 and two-door station wagon — 14,663. No breakouts by series, model or engine are available
NOTE 2: Data for six above slash/for V-8 below slash.

1960 Chevrolet, Impala two-door hardtop sports coupe, V-8 (AA)

BASE ENGINES: There were no changes in specifications from 1959, except in Biscayne V-8 attachments, where a detuned 170 horsepower rating was cataloged for the 283. In other Chevrolets, the base engines were:

SIX-CYLINDER: Overhead valves. Cast iron block. Displacement: 235.5 cid. Bore and stroke: 3-9/16 x 3-15/16 inches. Compression ratio: 8.25:1. Brake horsepower: 135 at 4000 rpm. Four main bearings. Hydraulic valve lifters. Carburetor: Rochester two-barrel model 7013003.

V-8: Overhead valves. Cast iron block. Displacement: 283 cid. Bore and stroke: 3.875 x 3 inches. Compression ratio: 8.5:1. Brake horsepower: 185 at 4600 rpm. Five main bearings. Hydraulic valve lifters. Carburetor: Rochester two-barrel model 7013007.

POWERPLANT OPTIONS: Optional engine and transmission combinations were:

CID Displ.	Comp. Ratio	Carb Barrels	Exhaust	HP @ rpm.	Trans. Combo	Valve Lifters
283	8.5	4V	1	230 @ 4800	1-3-4-5-6	H
348	9.5	4V	1	250 @ 4400	1-3-4-5-6-7	H
348	9.5	3x2V	2	280 @ 4800	1-3-4-5-6-7	H
348	11.25	4V	2	320 @ 5600	1-5-6-7	H
348	11.25	3x2V	2	335 @ 5800	1-5-6-7	H

NOTES: F.I. — Fuel-injection. Transmission choices; (1) Three-speed manual; (2) Overdrive; (3) — Two-Speed Powerglide; (4) — Turboglide; (5) — Close-ratio three-speed; (6) — Corvette type Powerglide; (7) — Four-speed.

CHASSIS FEATURES: Wheelbase: 119 inches. Overall length: 210.8 inches. Overall width: 79.9 inches. Overall height: (hardtops) 54 inches; (sedans) 56 inches; (station wagons) 56.3 inches. Tires: (convertible and station wagons) 8.00 x 14; (all other models) 7.50 x 14.

1960 Chevrolet, Impala two-door convertible, V-8

CONVENIENCE OPTIONS: Oil bath air cleaner ($5). Air conditioner, including heater; requires automatic drive ($468). Positraction ($43). Heavy-duty battery ($8). Biscayne economy carburetor ($8). Heavy-duty clutch for six-cylinder ($5). Foam front cushion ($8). PCV valve ($12). Dual exhausts ($19). Temperature Control fan ($16). Generators, 35-amp ($8); 40-amp ($27). Tinted glass, windshield ($22); all windows ($38); shaded backlight for Sport Coupe ($14). Deluxe heater ($74). Recirculating heater ($46). Padded dash ($18). Non-glare inside mirror ($4). Six-cylinder oil filter ($9). Two-tone paint ($16). Power brakes ($43). Power seat, except 1100/1200/1300/1400, Six-Way ($97); Four-Way ($65). Power steering ($75). Power tailgate window ($32). Power windows, except 1100/ 1200/ 1300/1400 ($102). Manual radio ($56). Push-button radio ($72). Heavy-duty rear coil springs ($3). Deluxe steering wheel ($4). Whitewalls, priced by size and model, ($16-36). Overdrive ($188). Power-glide on six ($188); on V-8 ($199). Turbo-glide V-8 only ($210). Four-speed close-ratio, V-8 only ($188). Wheel discs ($15). Windshield washer ($11). Electric wipers with washer ($16). Super Turbo-fire V-8 ($136). Turbo-thrust V-8 ($188). Special Turbo-thrust V-8 ($268). Special Turbo-glide thrust 320 horsepower V-8 ($311). Super Turbo-thrust V-8 ($258). Special Super Turbo-thrust V-8 ($333). Seat belt ($16). Electric clock ($21). Wheelcovers ($24). Edge guards, two-door ($4); four-door ($7). Lamps, ashtray ($3); back-up ($13); courtesy ($7); glovebox ($3); luggage ($4) and underhood ($7); rear ($7). OSRV mirror, body-mounted ($6). Vanity mirror ($2). Body sill molding ($15). Brake signal ($5). Rear speaker ($15).

HISTORICAL FOOTNOTES: Model introduction October, 1959. Calendar year production 1,863,598. Model year production 1,391,485. Corvair introduced. Totals include Corvettes and Corvairs, which are listed separately in this catalog.

1961 CHEVROLET

BISCAYNE — SERIES 1100/1300 (6-CYL) — SERIES 1200/1400 (V-8) — The 1961 Chevrolets followed the General Motors pattern in adopting a brand new, down-sized body, but varied from the corporate trend In that strictly carryover engineering was used. Grille and front areas were rather flat and square, while the rear end sported a flat V-type fin. At the front, a full-width air slot stretched above the grille, below the beveled front lip of the hood. The bevel line swept around the front body corners and ran, in a straight line, down and back towards the rear quarter panel. There, it angled upwards again, to connect with the flat V-type fin. Biscaynes had twin circular taillamps, small hubcaps and model nameplates on upper rear fender tips, while lacking side body moldings along the bevel line. Rocker panel strips were used on 1100/1200 level cars, but not on the Series 1300/1400 Fleetmaster economy jobs. Standard equipment consisted of dual sun visors, electric windshield wipers, cigarette lighter, front armrests and five 7.50 x 14 black tubeless tires.

CHEVROLET I.D. NUMBERS: Serial numbers were stamped on a plate affixed to the left front door hinge pillar. The first symbol identified model year, 1=1961. The second and third symbols identified the series (see first two digits of Model Number columns in charts below). The fourth and fifth symbols identified body style (see last two digits of Model Number columns in charts below). The sixth symbol, a letter, indicated assembly plant, as follows: A=Atlanta, Ga.; B=Baltimore, Md.; F=Flint, Mich.; J=Janesville, Wis.; K=Kansas City, Mo.; L=Los Angeles, Calif.; N=Norwood, Ohio; O=Oakland, Calif.; S=St. Louis, Mo.; T=Tarrytown, NY; W=Williow Run, Mich.; G=Framingham, Mass. The last six symbols were the sequential production number, with numbers for each series at each factory starting at 100001 and up. Fisher Body plate attached to left-hand cowl starts with two-digit model year prefix (60-) and Fisher Body Style Number (Model Number) and also shows factory code, production sequence, trim and body color data. Engine numbers: (six) right side of block behind distributor; (V-8) right front of engine block).

BISCAYNE SERIES

Model Number	Model Number (V-8)	Body Type & Seating	Factory Price	Shipping Weight	Production Total
(FLEETMASTER LINE)					
1369	1469	4-dr Sed-6P	2284/2391	3495/3500	Note 1
1311	1411	2-dr Sed-6P	2230/2337	3410/3415	Note 1
(DELUXE LINE)					
1169	1269	4-dr Sed-6P	2316/2423	3500/3505	Note 1
1111	1211	2-dr Sed-6P	2262/2369	3415/3425	Note 1
1121	1221	2-dr Utl Sed-3P	2175/2282	3390/3395	Note 1
(STATION WAGONS)					
1145	1245	4-dr Brkwd-9P	2756/2863	3900/3895	Note 1
1135	1235	4-dr Brkwd-6P	2643/2760	3850/3845	Note 1

NOTE 1: Chevrolet production was recorded, by body style only, as follows: four-door sedan — 452,251; Sport Coupe — 177,969; Sport Sedan — 174,141; four-door station wagon — 168,935; two-door sedan — 153,988 and convertible — 64,624. No further breakouts by model, series or engine were provided by Chevrolet, except in the case of Super Sports.
NOTE 2: Industry statistics provide some additional information. First, on a model year basis, approximately 137,300 station wagons were two-seat types and approximately 31,649 others

had three-seat configuration. Second, Chevrolet production by series, again on a model year basis, included the following: (Fleetmaster) 3,000 units; (Biscayne) 201,006 units; (Bel Air) 330,000 units; (Impala) 491,000 units; and (station wagons) 169,000 units. These figures are slightly rounded-off, as is the figure of 513,000 six-cylinder Chevrolets built this season.
NOTE 3: Data above slash for six/below slash for V-8.
NOTE 4: Station wagons were grouped by the manufacturer as a separate series, but are being grouped under passenger cars with similar trim level in this catalog.

1961 Chevrolet, Bel Air four-door sedan, 6-cyl

BEL AIR — SERIES 1500 (6-CYL) — SERIES 1600 (V-8) — A chrome trim bar, extending from the front parking lights rearward to the trunk, distinguished Bel Airs from Biscaynes. Bel Air nameplates appeared at the upper rear fender; twin taillamps were seen; small hubcaps were standard equipment; and no rocker sill strips were used. As in other lines, regular sedans, Sport Sedans, Sport Coupes and station wagons all had individual rooflines with the flat-top look on regular sedans, a formal look on Sport Sedans, a rounded semi-fastback on Sport Coupes and boxy, conventional station wagon styling. Station wagons had Bel Air trim, but Parkwood rear fender scripts. Standard equipment matched that of Biscayne, plus foam seat cushions and Deluxe steering wheel.

BEL AIR SERIES

Model Number	Model Number (V-8)	Body Type & Seating	Factory Price	Shipping Weight	Production Total
(PASSENGER CARS)					
1569	1669	4-dr Sed-6P	2438/2545	3515/3520	Note 1
1539	1639	4-dr HT Spt Sed-6P	2554/2661	3550/3555	Note 1
1511	1611	2-dr Sed-6P	2384/2491	3430/3435	Note 1
1537	1637	2-dr HT Spt Cpe-5P	2489/2596	3475/3480	Note 1
(STATION WAGONS)					
1545	1645	4-dr Pkwd-9P	2850/2957	3910/3910	Note 1
1535	1635	4-dr Pkwd-6P	2747/2854	3865/3860	Note 1

NOTE 1: Chevrolet production was recorded, by body style only, as follows: four-door sedan — 452,251; Sport Coupe — 177,969; Sport Sedan — 174,141; four-door station wagon — 168,935; two-door sedan — 153,988 and convertible — 64,624.
NOTE 2: On a model year basis, approximately 137,300 station wagons were two-seat types and approximately 31,649 others had three-seat configuration. Chevrolet production by series: (Fleetmaster) 3,000 units; (Biscayne) 201,006 units; (Bel Air) 330,000 units; (Impala) 491,000 units; and (station wagons) 169,000 units. These figures are rounded-off, as is the figure of 513,000 six-cylinder Chevrolets.
NOTE 3: Data above slash for six/below slash for V-8.
NOTE 4: Station wagons were grouped by the manufacturer as a separate series, but are being grouped under passenger cars with similar trim level in this catalog.

IMPALA — SERIES 1700 (6-CYL) — SERIES 1800 (V-8) — Impalas were easily identified by their triple taillight treatment. They also had crossed racing flags insignia at the center of the rear deck and at the rear fenders, with model identification scripts in the latter location as well. Deluxe wheel discs and wide side moldings, with contrasting insert panels, were other visual distinctions of the top Chevrolet line. Nomad station wagons had Impala level trim, but Nomad rear fender signatures. Standard equipment lists began with Bel Air features and added parking brake, glovebox and back-up lights; anodized aluminum trim; electric clock; and 8.00 x 14 size tires on convertibles. All 1961 Chevrolet V-8s had oil filters and oil bath type air cleaners, all station wagons had 8.00 x 14 tires and nine-passenger jobs had power tailgates.

IMPALA SERIES

Model Number	Model Number (V-8)	Body Type & Seating	Factory Price	Shipping Weight	Production Total
(PASSENGER CARS)					
1769	1869	4-dr Sed-6P	2590/2697	3530/3525	Note 1
1739	1839	4-dr HT Spt Sed-6P	2662/2769	3575/2570	Note 1
1711	1811	2-dr Sed-6P	2536/2643	3445/3440	Note 1
1737	1837	2-dr HT Spt Cpe-5P	2597/2704	3485/3480	Note 1
1767	1867	2-dr Conv-5P	2847/2954	3605/3600	Note 1
(STATION WAGONS)					
1745	1845	4-dr Nomad-9P	2922/3099	3935/3930	Note 1
1735	1835	4-dr Nomad-6P	2889/2996	3885/3885	Note 1

NOTE 1: Chevrolet production was recorded, by body style only, as follows: four-door sedan — 452,251; Sport Coupe — 177,969; Sport Sedan — 174,141; four-door station wagon — 168,935; two-door sedan — 153,988 and convertible — 64,624. No further breakouts by model, series or engine were provided by Chevrolet, except in the case of Super Sport models, of which 142 were reported as built.
NOTE 2: On a model year basis, approximately 137,300 station wagons were two-seat types and approximately 31,649 others had three-seat configuration. Chevrolet production by series: (Fleetmaster) 3,000 units; (Biscayne) 201,006 units; (Bel Air) 330,000 units; (Impala) 491,000 units; and (station wagons) 169,000 units. These figures are rounded-off, as is the figure of 513,000 six-cylinder Chevrolets.
NOTE 3: Data above slash for six/below slash for V-8.
NOTE 4: Station wagons were grouped by the manufacturer as a separate series, but are being grouped under passenger cars with similar trim level in this catalog.
NOTE 5: The 1961 Super Sport package was a dealer installed kit available on any Impala model. It consisted of 'SS' emblems on rear fenders and deck lid; instrument panel pad; special wheelcovers with spinners; power brakes and steering; heavy-duty springs and shocks; sintered metallic brake linings; 7000 rpm. tachometer and 8.00 x 14 narrow band white sidewall tires. A choice of five performance power teams was available. Price for the equipment package was in the $54 range according to sources.

1961 Chevrolet, Impala two-door convertible, V-8

1961 Chevrolet, Impala two-door convertible, V-8

BASE ENGINES

SIX-CYLINDER: Overhead valves. Cast iron block. Displacement: 235 cid. Bore and stroke: 3.56 x 3.94 inches. Compression ratio: 8.25:1. Brake horsepower: 135 at 4000 rpm. Four main bearings. Hydraulic valve lifters. Carburetor: Rochester one-barrel model 7013003.

V-8: Overhead valves. Cast iron block. Displacement: 283 cid. Bore and stroke: 3.87 5 x 3.00 inches. Compression ratio: 8.5:1. Brake horsepower: 170 at 4200 rpm. Five main bearings. Hydraulic valve lifters. Carburetor: Rochester two-barrel model 7019007.

POWERTRAIN OPTIONS: Six optional engine choices were provided for 1961 Chevrolets as follows:

1961 Chevrolet, Impala four-door hardtop Sport Sedan, V-8

SUPER TURBO-FIRE V-8

CID Displ.	Comp. Ratio	Carb Barrels	Exhaust	HP @ rpm.	Trans Combo	Valve Lifters
283	9.5	4V	1	230 @ 4800	N.A.	H

TURBO-THRUST V-8

348	9.5	4V	2	250 @ 4400	N.A.	H

SPECIAL TURBO-THRUST V-8

348	9.5	4V	2	305 @ 5200	N.A.	S
348	11.25	4V	2	340 @ 5800	N.A.	S

SUPER TURBO-THRUST V-8

348	11.25	3 x 2V	2	280 @ 4800	N.A.	H

SPECIAL SUPER TURBO-THRUST V-8

348	11.25	3 x 2V	2	350 @ 6000	N.A.	S

TURBO-FIRE 409 V-8

409	11.00	1x4V	2	360 @ 5800	N.A.	S

CHASSIS FEATURES: Wheelbase: 119 inches. Overall length: 209.3 inches. Front tread: 60.3 inches. Rear tread: 59.3 inches. Width: 78.4 inches. Height: 55.5 inches.

1961 Chevrolet, Impala two-door convertible, V-8

CONVENIENCE OPTIONS: Oil bath air cleaner ($5). Deluxe air conditioner, with V-8 only, includes heater ($457). Cool pack air conditioner ($317). Positraction rear axle ($43). Heavy-Duty battery ($8). Group A body equipment package including OSRV mirror, front and rear bumper guards, grille guard and inside non-glare mirror, for all models except Impala and Nomad ($48). Group B body equipment package with electric clock, door guards and back-up lights for all models except Impala and Nomad; two-door ($23); four-door ($26). Economy carburetor ($8). Heavy-duty clutch for six-cylinder models ($5). Crankcase ventilation system, required on California cars ($5). Air Foam front seat cushions for Biscayne and Brookwood models ($8). Positive engine ventilation for six-cylinder models ($12). Dual exhausts combined with 230 horsepower V-8 ($25). Temperature controlled radiator fan for V-8 models ($16). Optional generators, three types ($8-97). Tinted glass, all windows ($38); windshield only ($22); shaded rear windows on two-door Sport Coupe ($14). Deluxe heater ($74); recirculating heater ($47). Padded instrument panel ($18). Oil filter with six-cylinder models ($9). Two-tone paint ($16). Power brakes ($43). Six-Way power seat, except Biscayne and Brookwood, ($97); Four-way power seat, except Biscayne and Brookwood, ($65). Power steering ($75). Power tailgate window ($32). Power windows, except Biscayne and Brookwood, ($102). Heavy-duty radiator ($11). Radios, manual ($54), push-button ($62). Heavy-duty rear coil springs ($3). Deluxe steering wheel ($4). Overdrive transmission ($108). Powerglide transmission with six-cylinder ($188). Powerglide transmission with V-8 ($199). Turbo-glide transmission with V-8 ($210). Four-speed, close-ratio manual transmission with V-8 ($188). Wheelcovers ($15). Windshield washers ($11). Two-speed electric windshield wipers and washers ($16). Super Turbo fire V-8 ($136). Turbo-thrust V-8 ($201). Special Turbo-thrust V-8 ($317). Special Turbo-thrust, 340 horsepower V-8 ($344). Super Turbo-thrust V-8 ($271). Special Super Turbo-thrust V-8 ($365).

1961 Chevrolet, Impala two-door hardtop Sport Coupe

1961 Chevrolet, Impala, four-door Nomad station wagon.

HISTORICAL FOOTNOTES: Chevrolets were introduced to the public Oct. 8, 1960. The division's model year production output peaked at 1,204,917 cars, including Corvettes, but excluding 297,881 Corvairs. (See separate catalog listing for Corvettes and Corvairs.) A total of 142 Impalas were manufactured with Super Sport equipment and the 409 cid V-8, which went into production in January 1961. Production of models built to 1961 specifications ceased on Aug. 2, 1961. Calendar year production of 1,604,805 units in all lines made Chevrolet America's number one maker again. Semon E. 'Bunkie' Knudsen was general manager of the division this season. The 1961 Impala SS hardtop with the 409 cid/360 hp was reported capable of 0-to-60 times of 7.8 seconds and 15.8 second quarter-mile runs. The 1961 Bel Air Sports Coupe with the 409 cid/409 hp engine was reported to do the quarter-mile in 12.83 seconds. Don Nicholson was Top Stock Eliminator at the 1961 National Hot Rod Assoc. Winter Nationals in a 409/409 Super Stock Chevy.

1962 CHEVROLET

1962 Chevy II 300 four-door station wagon 6-cyl

CHEVY II — ALL SERIES — Designed to combat the popularity of the Falcon, Ford Motor Co.'s conventional compact car, the Chevy II line made its debut in 1962. This no-nonsense economy job featured simple, squarish styling with unitized body and front stub-frame construction. Major front end components, including fenders, were of bolt-on design for easy replacement. There were 11 basic models arranged in five different series, according to powerplant applications. At the bottom were the 100 (four-cylinder/six cylinder) having, as standard equipment, five 6.00 x 13 tires; heater and defroster; front foam cushions; cigarette lighter; electric windshield wipers; oil filter; and power tailgate on three-seat station wagons. These cars lacked moldings around the side windows, rear deck panel and bodysides and had spartan interiors. The 300 four and six had all moldings mentioned above, plus slightly enriched interiors. The fifth series was the Nova 400, which came only with six-cylinder power. Identification features included Nova rear fender nameplates; side body, window and deck trim; rocker sill strips; front fender tip windsplit moldings and full wheel discs. Nova equipment included all found on the lower series, plus 6.50 x 13 tires (also used on base station wagons); rear foam seat cushions; floor carpets; and special interior upholstery and trim. The engines used in all Chevy IIs were completely new.

CHEVY II I.D. NUMBERS: Vehicle numbers were on the left front body hinge pillar. Motor numbers, for both engines, were on the right side of the block to the rear of distributor. The first symbol was a '2' indicating model year. This was followed by four symbols shown in charts below as Model Numbers. The first pair of symbols in these Model Numbers indicate the series (01=Chevy II 100 four-cylinder; 02=Chevy II 100 six-cylinder; 03=Chevy II 300 four-cylinder and 04=Chevy II 300 and Nova six-cylinder) and the second pair of symbols in the Model Number indicate body style. The next letter (sixth symbol of VIN) shows the assembly plant code with Chevy II production limited to factories coded W (Willow Run, Mich.) and N (Norwood, Ohio.) The last six numbers were the sequential production code starting with 100001 at each plant. A Fisher Body Style plate is under the hood on left and gives Style Number, Body Number, Trim code and Paint code.

1962 Chevrolet, Chevy II Nova two-door convertible, 6-cyl

CHEVY II SERIES (ALL)

SERIES 100 (4-CYL)/SERIES 100 (6-CYL)

Model Number	Model Number (6-CYL)	Body Type & Seating	Factory Price	Shipping Weight	Production Total
0169	0269	4-dr Sed-6P	2041/2101	2445/2535	Note 1
0111	0211	2-dr Sed-6P	2003/2063	2410/2500	Note 1
0135	0235	2-dr Sta Wag-6P	2339/2399	2665/2755	Note 1

SERIES 300 (4-CYL)/SERIES 300 (6-CYL)

Model Number	Model Number (6-CYL)	Body Type & Seating	Factory Price	Shipping Weight	Production Total
0369	0469	4-dr Sed-6P	2122/2182	2460/2550	Note 1
0311	0411	2-dr Sed-6P	2084/2144	2425/2515	Note 1
0345	0445	2-dr Sta Wag-9P	2517/2577	2765/2855	Note 1

SERIES NOVA 400 (6-CYL)

Model Number	Model Number (6-CYL)	Body Type & Seating	Factory Price	Shipping Weight	Production Total
NA	0449	4-dr Sed-6P	2236	2575	Note 1
NA	0441	2-dr Sed-6P	2198	2540	Note 1
NA	0437	2-dr Spt Cpe-5P	2264	2550	Note 1
NA	0467	2-dr Conv-5P	2475	2745	Note 1
NA	0435	4-dr Sta Wag-6P	2497	2775	Note 1

NOTE 1: Production totals were recorded by body style only, with no breakouts by series, model or engine. Totals for 1962 were as follows: four-door sedan — 139,004; four-door station wagons — 59,886; two-door Sport Coupe — 59,586; two-door sedan -44,390 and two-door convertible -23,741.
NOTE 2: First column shows four-cylinder codes and second column shows six-cylinder codes.
NOTE 3: Data above slash for fours/below slash for sixes. Nova 400 is six-cylinder only, no

slashes used.
NOTE 4: There was a factory-offered kit for dealer installation of either a 283 cid or 327 cid V-8 engine, with outputs up to 360 h.p.

BISCAYNE — SERIES 1100 (6-CYL) — SERIES 1200 (V-8) — The plainest full-sized Chevrolet benefited from the bodyside sculpturing of the 1962 design. Standard features included heater and defroster; dual sun visors; crank operated ventipanes; directional signals; parallel action windshield wipers; front door armrests; ashtray; coat hooks; and color-keyed vinyl-coated rubber floor coverings. Interiors were trimmed in cloth and leather grain vinyl with all-vinyl sidewalls. Exterior bright metal decoration included an anodized aluminum grille with pairs of headlamps flanking. Biscaynes had a slender, full-length lower body sill molding and four taillights at the rear. The series script appeared on the rear fenders. Small hubcaps were standard.

CHEVROLET I.D. NUMBERS: Serial numbers were stamped on a plate affixed to the left front door hinge pillar. The first symbol identified model year, 2=1962. The second and third symbols identified the series (see first two digits of Model Number columns in charts below). The fourth and fifth symbols identified body style (see last two digits of Model Number columns in charts below). The sixth symbol, a letter, indicated assembly plant, as follows: A=Atlanta, Ga.; B=Baltimore, Md.; F=Flint, Mich.; G=Framingham, Mass.; J=Janesville, Wis.; K=Kansas City, Mo.; L=Los Angeles, Calif.; N=Norwood, Ohio; O=Oakland, Calif.; S=St. Louis, Mo.; T=Tarrytown, NY; W=Williow Run, Mich. The last six symbols are the sequential production number, with numbers for each series at each factory starting at 100001 and up. Fisher Body plate attached to left-hand cowl starts with two-digit model year prefix (60-) and Fisher Body Style Number (Model Number) and also shows factory code, production sequence, trim and body color data. Engine numbers: (six) right side of block behind distributor; (V-8) right front of engine block).

BISCAYNE SERIES

Model Number	Model Number (V-8)	Body Type & Seating	Factory Price	Shipping Weight	Production Total
(PASSENGER CARS)					
1169	1269	4-dr Sed-6P	2378/2485	3480/3475	Note 1
1111	1211	2-dr Sed-6P	2324/2431	3405/3400	Note 1
(STATION WAGONS)					
1135	1235	4-dr Bis Sta Wag-6P	2725/2832	3845/3840	Note 1

NOTE 1: Production totals were recorded by body style only, with no breakouts by series, model or engine. Totals for 1962 'Regular Chevrolets' were as follows: four-door sedan — 533,349; two-door hardtop Sport Coupe — 323,427; four-door station wagon — 187,566; four-door hardtop Sport Sedan — 176,077; two-door sedan 127,870 and two-door convertible — 75,719.
NOTE 2: In rounded-off figures, production of Biscaynes, excluding station wagons was 166,000 units. Production of all Chevrolet station wagons was 187,600.
NOTE 3: Production of all full-sized Chevy V-8s was 921,900 units. Production of all full-sized Chevy sixes was 502,100 units.
NOTE 4: Data above slash for six/below slash for V-8.
NOTE 5: Model Numbers and Body Style Numbers are the same. The first column in chart shows six-cylinder codes and the second column in chart shows V-8 codes.

1962 Chevrolet, Impala two-door convertible, V-8

BEL AIR — SERIES 1500 (6-CYL) — SERIES 1600 (V-8) — This was Chevrolet's popular mid-priced line. Standard equipment included all Biscayne features, plus extra quality interior appointments; foam front and rear seats; color-keyed carpeting; foam backed luggage compartment mat; and a specific steering wheel hub. Interiors were higher grade cloth and vinyl combinations. A full-length upper bodyside molding was used, with Bel Air script appearing on the rear fenders, just below it. A stainless bright gutter cap molding was another Bel Air feature. Four taillights, arranged two on each side, were seen. A bright rear cove molding added a touch of distinction.

BEL AIR SERIES

Model Number	Model Number (V-8)	Body Type & Seating	Factory Price	Shipping Weight	Production Total
(PASSENGER CARS)					
1569	1669	4-dr Sed-6P	2510/2617	3480/3475	Note 1
1511	1611	2-dr Sed-6P	2456/2563	3410/3405	Note 1
1537	1637	2-dr HT Spt Cpe-6P	2561/2668	3445/3440	Note 1
(STATION WAGONS)					
1545	1645	4-dr Sta Wag-9P	2922/3029	3895/3890	Note 1
1535	1635	4-dr Sta Wag-6P	2819/2926	3845/3840	Note 1

NOTE 1: Production totals were recorded by body style only, with no breakouts by series, model or engine. Totals for 1962 'Regular Chevrolets' were as follows: four-door sedan — 533,349; two-door hardtop Sport Coupe — 323,427; four-door station wagon — 187,566; four-door hardtop Sport Sedan — 176,077; two-door sedan 127,870 and two-door convertible — 75,719.
NOTE 2: In rounded-off figures, production of Bel Airs, excluding station wagons, was 365,500 units. Production of all Chevrolet station wagons was 187,600.
NOTE 3: Production of all full-sized Chevy V-8s was 921,900 units. Production of all full-sized Chevy sixes was 502,100 units.
NOTE 4: Data above slash for six/below slash for V-8.
NOTE 5: Model Numbers and Body Style Numbers are the same. The first column in chart shows six-cylinder codes and the second column in chart shows V-8 codes.

1962 Chevrolet, Bel Air two-door hardtop Sport Coupe, V-8

1962 Chevrolet, Impala four-door sedan, V-8

1962 Chevrolet, Impala four-door hardtop Sport Sedan, V-8

IMPALA — SERIES 1700 (6-CYL) — SERIES 1800 (V-8) — Chevrolet's top models were in the Impala line. Standard equipment included most features found on lower priced lines, plus bright aluminum front seat end panels; bright metal backed rearview mirror; extra-long front and rear armrests (with finger-tip door release handles); built-in door safety panel reflectors; rear seat radio grille (built into Sport Coupe and convertible); and Sports type steering wheel with Impala center emblem. The instrument panel included an electric clock; parking brake warning light; glove compartment light; and bright metal valance panels. Interiors were plusher cloth and leather grain vinyl combinations, with embossed vinyl headlining. Exterior bodyside trim consisted of a full-length bodyside upper molding with color-keyed insert; a wide, ribbed body sill molding; stainless steel window reveals (except convertible); and Impala script badge on the rear fenders. Front fender ornaments were standard, while, at the rear, a brushed aluminum cove panel with six taillamps was found. Back-up lights were built-in. A simulated rear window vent was seen, below the glass, on all styles, but the convertible.

IMPALA SERIES

Model Number	Model Number (V-8)	Body Type & Seating	Factory Price	Shipping Weight	Production Total
(PASSENGER CARS)					
1769	1869	4-dr Sed-6P	2662/2769	3510/3505	Note 1
1739	1839	4-dr HT Spt Sed-6P	2734/2841	3540/3535	Note 1
1747	1847	2-dr HT Spt Cpe-5P	2669/2776	3455/3450	Note 1
1767	1867	2-dr Conv-5P	2919/3026	3565/3560	Note 1
(STATION WAGON)					
1745	1845	4-dr Sta Wag-9P	3064/3171	3935/3930	Note 1
1735	1835	4-dr Sta Wag-6P	2961/3068	3870/3865	Note 1

NOTE 1: Production totals were recorded by body style only, with no breakouts by series, model or engine. Totals for 1962 'Regular Chevrolets' were as follows: four-door sedan — 533,349; two-door hardtop Sport Coupe — 323,427; four-door station wagon — 187,566; four-door hardtop Sport Sedan — 176,077; two-door sedan 127,870 and two-door convertible — 75,719.
NOTE 2: In rounded-off figures, production of Impalas, excluding station wagons, was 704,900 units. Of these, 99,311 had the Super Sport option. Production of all Chevrolet station wagons was 187,600.
NOTE 3: Production of all full-sized Chevy V-8s was 921,900 units. Production of all full-sized Chevy sixes was 502,100 units.
NOTE 4: Production of 409 cid V-8s was 15,019.
NOTE 5: Data above slash for six/below slash for V-8.
NOTE 6: Model Numbers and Body Style Numbers are the same. The first column in chart shows six-cylinder codes and the second column in chart shows V-8 codes.

SUPER SPORT EQUIPMENT: The Option Code 240 Super Sport package added or substituted the following items on regular Impala equipment: Swirl-pattern bodyside moldings; 'SS' rear fender emblems; 'SS' deck lip badge; specific Super Sport full wheel discs with simulated knock-off spinners; locking center console and passenger assist bar. Super Sport equipment was available on the Impala Sport Coupe and convertible at $53.80 extra, plus $102.25 for bucket seats.

BASE CHEVY II ENGINES

FOUR-CYLINDER: Overhead valves. Cast iron block. Displacement: 153.3 cid. Bore and stroke: 3.875 x 3.25 inches. Compression ratio: 8.5:1. Brake horsepower: 90 at 4000 rpm. Five main bearings. Hydraulic valve lifters. Carburetor: Rochester one-barrel model 7020103.

SIX-CYLINDER: Overhead valves. Cast iron block. Displacement: 194.4 cid. Bore and stroke: 3.562 x 3.25 inches. Compression ratio: 8.5:1. Brake horsepower: 120 at 4400 rpm. Seven main bearings. Hydraulic valve lifters. Carburetor: Rochester one-barrel Model 7020105.

BASE CHEVROLET ENGINES

SIX-CYLINDER: Overhead valves. Cast iron block. Displacement: 235 cid. Bore and stroke: 3.56 x 3.94 inches. Compression ratio: 8.25:1. Brake horsepower: 135 at 4000 rpm. Four main bearings. Hydraulic valve lifters. Carburetor: Rochester one-barrel model 7013003.

V-8: Overhead valves. Cast iron block. Displacement: 283.0 cid. Bore and stroke: 3.87 5 x 3.00 inches. Compression ratio: 8.5:1. Brake horsepower: 170 at 4200 rpm. Five main bearings. Hydraulic valve lifters. Carburetor: Rochester two-barrel Model 7020007. Base engines for Impalas were the same as for Biscaynes. See 1962 Biscayne engine data.

CHEVROLET POWERTRAIN OPTIONS: Optional engine choices provided for 1962 were:

CID Displ.	Comp. Ratio	Carb Barrels	Exhaust	H P @ rpm.	Trans Combo	Valve Lifters
327	10.5	4V	2	250 @ 4400	M/PG	H
327	10.5	4V	2	300 @ 5000	M/PG	H
409	11.1	4V	2	380 @ 6000	M	S
409	11.1	4V	2	409 @ 5800	M	S

NOTE: V=venturi; 1=single exhaust; 2=dual exhaust; M=manual transmission; PG=Powerglide automatic transmission; H=hydraulic valve lifters; S=solid valve lifters.

CHASSIS FEATURES: Wheelbase: (Chevy II) 110 inches; (Chevrolet) 119 inches. Overall length: (Chevy II station wagon) 197.4 inches; (all other Chevy IIs) 183 inches; (Chevrolet, all models) 209.6 inches. Front tread: (Chevy II) 56.8 inches; (Chevrolet) 60.3 inches. Rear tread: (Chevy II) 56.3 inches; (Chevrolet) 59.3 inches. Tires: (Chevy II, all station wagons and Sport models) 6.50 x 13; (all other Chevy II) 6.00 x 131; (Biscayne) 7.00 x 14, (Chevrolet station wagons) 8.00 x 14; (all other Chevrolets) 7.50 x 14.

CHEVY II OPTIONS: Air conditioning ($317). Rear armrest for 100 models only ($1 0). Front seat driver's safety belt ($11). Two front seat safety belts ($20). Group A body equipment, station wagons ($29); passenger cars ($34). Heavy-duty brakes ($38). Comfort and Convenience group ($39). Tinted glass, all windows ($27); windshield only ($13). Padded dash ($16). Two-tone paint, except convertible ($11). Power brakes ($43). Power steering ($75). Power tailgate window on six-passenger station wagon ($27). Manual radio and antenna ($48). Push-button radio and antenna ($57). Station wagon divided second seat ($38). Nova 400 front bucket seats, except station wagon ($70). Heavy-duty rear shock absorbers ($1). Heavy-duty springs, front ($1); rear ($3). Whitewall tires ($30). Full wheelcovers ($13) and wire wheelcovers ($38). Rear axles with 3.36 or 3.55 gear ratio ($2). Positraction rear axle ($40). Heavy-duty battery ($8). Heavy-duty clutch ($5). Crankcase ventilation ($4). Generator, 35-amp ($8). Delcotron generator 42-amp ($27). Heavy-duty radiator ($3). Powerglide transmission ($167).

CHEVROLET OPTIONS: Deluxe air conditioning with automatic transmission, includes heater ($364). Cool Pack air conditioner ($317). Group A body equipment including OSRV mirror, rear bumper guards, grille guard and inside non-glare mirror, for station wagons ($29); other models ($34). Heavy-duty metallic-faced brakes ($38). Impala Comfort and Convenience Group ($30); same for Bel Air ($41); same for Biscayne ($44). Air conditioning ($39). Tinted glass, all windows ($38); windshield only ($22). Shaded Sport Coupe backlight ($14). Padded dash ($16). Lockable station wagon rear compartment ($11). Two-tone paint ($16). Power brakes ($43). Six-Way power seat ($97). Power steering ($75). Power tailgate window ($32). Power windows, except Biscayne ($102). Manual radio ($48). Push-button radio ($57). Station wagon divided second seat ($38). Impala Sport Coupe and convertible bucket seats ($102). Heavy-duty front and rear shock absorbers, except station wagons ($1). Heavy-duty front coil springs ($1). Heavy-duty rear coil springs ($3).

Deluxe steering wheel for Biscayne ($4). Tachometer for V-8s ($49). Vinyl trim for Biscayne sedan ($5). Wheel discs ($18). Electric two-speed wipers with washers ($17). Various whitewall and oversize tire options ($31-36). The Option Code 240 Super Sport (SS) package was available on the Impala Sport Coupe and convertible at $53.80 extra, plus $102.25 for bucket seats.Turbo-Fire 250 horsepower 327 cid V-8 with four-barrel carburetor and dual exhausts ($191). Turbo-Fire 300 horsepower 327 cid V-8 with four-barrel carburetor and dual exhausts ($245). Turbo-Fire 380 horsepower 409 cid V-8 with four-barrel carburetor, dual exhausts, high-lift camshaft and solid valve lifters ($428). Turbo-Fire 409 horsepower 409 cid V-8 with dual four-barrel carburetors, lightweight valve train, dual exhausts and solid valve lifters ($484). Economy carburetor ($8). Heavy-duty six-cylinder clutch ($30). Positive crankcase ventilation system ($5). Positive six-cylinder engine ventilation ($12). Heavy-duty battery ($8). Oil bath air cleaner ($5). Temperature controlled 170 horsepower V-8 radiator fan ($16). Generator 35-amp ($8). Delcotron 45-amp generator ($27). Delcotron 52-amp generator, with Deluxe air conditioner ($8); without air ($34).

NOTE: Generator options not available with 409 cid V-8s. Heavy-duty radiator ($11). Positraction rear axle ($43). Overdrive transmission ($108). Six-cylinder Powerglide attachment ($188). V-8 Powerglide attachment, not available with 409 cid engine ($199). Close-ratio four-speed transmission with Turbo-Fire V-8 ($188).

HISTORICAL FOOTNOTES: Chevrolets and Chevy IIs built to 1962 specifications appeared in dealer showrooms Sept. 29, 1961. Model year production hit 1,424,000 units, excluding Corvairs, Corvettes and Chevy IIs. The new Chevy II series saw production of 326,600 additional units for the model year, which included 47,000 cars in the 100 Series (35,500 sixes); 103,200 cars in the 300 Series (92,800 sixes); 116,500 Nova 400s (all sixes) and 59,900 station wagons (57,800 sixes), in rounded-off totals. Calendar year output peaked at 2,161,398 units, making Chevrolet America's Number 1 automaker by a substantial margin. The first Chevrolets with a lightweight Z11 drag racing package were constructed late this year. They had an aluminum hood, aluminum inner fenders and aluminum front fenders. The Bel Air "bubbletop" two-door sedan was the basis of most Chevrolet race cars and came in at about 3,360 pounds with Z11 equipment. Many sources indicate "about 100" Z11s were built (57 is given as the specific number made in 1963). Hayden Profits Z11 took AA/S Stock Eliminator honors at the U.S. Nationals in Indianapolis, Ind. with a run of 12.83 seconds/113.92 mph in the quarter-mile. Top Stock Eliminator in S/S was Dave Stickler's Z11 with a 12.97 second/113.35 mph run. Don Nicholson's B/FX Z11 ran a 12.93 second quarter-mile at 113.63 mph. Ronnie Sox campaigned two Z11s on the East Coast. Chevrolets took 14 NASCAR victories on the short tracks. The 1962 Impala SS two-door hardtop with the 409 cid/409 hp engine was reported to do the quarter-mile in 14.9 seconds. A 1962 Bel Air "bubbletop" with the same engine covered the distance in 12.2 seconds!

1963 CHEVROLET

1963 Chevy II, Nova 400 two-door hardtop Sport Coupe, 6-cyl

CHEVY II/NOVA — ALL SERIES — Detail refinements and new freshness for its basically simple lines were the major exterior changes for this year's Chevy II. On the inside, new upholstery and trim set the cars off. The three series, 100, 300 and Nova 400 were continued with a total of 10 regular models, plus a new Super Sport (SS) option exclusive to Nova 400 Sports models. A new grille consisted of five, slightly thicker horizontal bars. The main divider bar of the previous year was gone. Chevrolet lettering on the front of the hood replaced the thin, wide medallion of 1962. Base level 100 Series models were very plain, without bodyside trim. Series 300 models had moldings along the bodysides, window reveals and edges of the rear cove panel. Novas had similar trim, plus wheel discs and rocker sill moldings, with identification scripts on the rear fenders. Cars with the Super Sport option had special finned wheelcovers, wider bodyside moldings, aluminized rear panels and 'SS' badges on the rear fenders and right-hand side of the deck lid. Standard equipment included five 6.00 x 13 black tubeless tires on most cars (6.50 x 13 on station wagon and Nova 400 SS models); heater; defroster; front foam cushions; cigarette lighter; electric windshield wipers; oil filter and power tailgate windows on three-seat station wagons. In addition, Nova 400s had rear foam seats; floor carpets; special upholstery; Deluxe trims; and back-up lights.

CHEVY II/NOVA I.D. NUMBERS: Vehicle numbers were on the left front body hinge pillar. Motor numbers, for both engines, were on the right side of the block to the rear of distributor. The first VIN symbol was a '3' indicating model year. This was followed by four symbols shown in charts below as Model Numbers. The first pair of symbols in these Model Numbers indicate the series (01=Chevy II 100 four-cylinder; 02=Chevy II 100 six-cylinder; 03=Chevy II 300 four-cylinder and 04=Chevy II 300 and Nova six-cylinder) and the second pair of symbols in the Model Number indicate body style. The next letter (sixth symbol of VIN) shows the assembly plant code with Chevy II production limited to factories coded W (Willow Run, Mich.) and N (Norwood, Ohio.) The last six numbers were the sequential production code starting with 100001 at each plant. A Fisher Body Style plate is under the hood on left and gives Style Number, Body Number, Trim code and Paint code.

CHEVY II/NOVA SERIES (ALL)

Model Number	Model Number (6-CYL)	Body Type & Seating	Factory Price	Shipping Weight	Production Total
SERIES 100 (4-CYL)/SERIES 100 (6-CYL)					
0169	0269	4-dr Sed-6P	2040/2099	2455/2545	Note 1
0111	0211	2-dr Sed-6P	2003/2062	2430/2520	Note 1
0135	0235	4-dr Sta Wag-6P	2338/2397	2725/2810	Note 1
SERIES 300 (4-CYL)/SERIES 300 (6-CYL)					
0369	0469	4-dr Sed-6P	2121/2180	2470/2560	Note 1
0311	0411	2-dr Sed-6P	2084/2143	2440/2530	Note 1
0345	0445	4-dr Sta Wag-9P	2516/2575	2810/2900	Note 1
SERIES NOVA 400 (6-CYL)					
NA	0449	4-dr Sed-6P	2235	2590	Note 1
NA	0437	2-dr HT Spt Cpe-5P	2262	2590	Note 1
NA	0467	2-dr Conv-5P	2472	2760	Note 1
NA	0435	4-dr Sta Wag-6P	2494	2835	Note 1

NOTE 1: Chevy II production totals were recorded by body style only, with no breakouts by series, model or engine. Totals for 1963 were as follows: four-door sedan 146,097; two-door hardtop Sport Coupe — 87,415; four-door station wagon 72,274; two-door sedan — 42,017 and two-door convertible — 24,823.
NOTE 2: Nova SS production — 42,432 Sport Coupes and convertibles (combined).
NOTE 3: Model year production of 1963 Chevy IIs was approximately 375,600 cars. This included 50,400 in the 100 Series (48,200 six-cylinder); 78,800 in the 300 Series (77,700 six-cylinder); 171,100 in the Nova 400 Series and 75,300 station wagons (74,800 six-cylinder). Of these station wagons, 67,347 had two-seats and 7,927 had three-seats. Also, 470 station wagons with four-cylinder engines were made.
NOTE 4: First column above shows four-cylinder Model Number; second column above shows six-cylinder Model Number.
NOTE 5: Data above slash for four-cylinder/below slash for six-cylinder. The Nova 400 line came only with six-cylinder power, so no slashes are used.

1963 Chevrolet, Chevy II Nova SS two-door Sport Coupe, 6-cyl

BISCAYNE — SERIES 1100 (6-CYL) — SERIES 1200 (V-8) — Chevrolet's new 1963 styling was seen as a move to make the company's products look more like luxury cars. Grilles. bumpers, hoods, sculptured side panels and rear deck contours were all new, yet the overall alteration level was minor. Seen in profile, both front and rear fenders had a 'Vee' shape. The basic Biscayne was a little brighter this year with its slender, full-length upper body molding. Standard features included heater and defroster; dual sun visors; crank operated ventipanes; directional signals; parallel action electric windshield wipers; front door armrests; vinyl embossed headliners; ashtray; and color coordinated vinyl-coated rubber front covering. Interiors were trimmed in cloth and leather grained vinyls (all-vinyl on station wagons) with full vinyl door panels. The front seat was foam-cushioned. Exterior brightwork included the full-length body trim strip; anodized bright grille, hood and deck emblems and bright trim rings for the twin unit taillights. A series script and Chevrolet badge were seen on rear fenders and small hubcaps were standard.

CHEVROLET I.D. NUMBERS: Serial numbers were stamped on a plate affixed to the left front door hinge pillar. The first VIN symbol identified model year, 3=1963. The second and third symbols identified the series (see first two digits of Model Number columns in charts below). The fourth and fifth symbols identified body style (see last two digits of Model Number columns in charts below). The sixth symbol, a letter, indicated assembly plant, as follows: A=Atlanta, Ga.; B=Baltimore, Md.; F=Flint, Mich.; G=Framingham, Mass.; J=Janesville, Wis.; K=Kansas City, Mo.; L=Los Angeles, Calif.; N=Norwood, Ohio; O=Oakland, Calif.; R= Arlington, Texas; S=St. Louis, Mo.; T=Tarrytown, NY; W=Willow Run, Mich. The last six symbols are the sequential production number, with numbers for each series at each factory starting at 100001 and up. Fisher Body plate attached to left-hand cowl starts with two-digit model year prefix (60-) and Fisher Body Style Number (Model Number) and also shows factory code, production sequence, trim and body color data. Engine numbers: (six) right side of block behind distributor; (V-8) right front of engine block).

BISCAYNE SERIES

Model Number	Model Number (V-8)	Body Type & Seating	Factory Price	Shipping Weight	Production Total
(PASSENGER CARS)					
1169	1269	4-dr Sed-6P	2376/2483	3280/3415	Note 1
1111	1211	2-dr Sed-6P	2322/2429	3205/3340	Note 1
(STATION WAGON)					
1135	1235	4-dr Sta Wag-6P	2723/2830	3685/3810	Note 1

NOTE 1: Production totals for 1963 'Regular Chevrolets' were as follows: four-door sedan — 561,511; two-door hardtop Sports Coupe — 399,224; four-door station wagon — 198,542; four-door hardtop Sports Sedan — 194,158; two-door sedan 135,636 and two-door convertible — 82,659.
NOTE 2: Model year production (rounded-off) of Biscaynes, excluding station wagons, was approximately 186,500 cars (37,000 V-8s; 149,500 six-cyl.). Production of all station wagons was 198,500 (146,200 V-8s; 52,300 six-cyl.).
NOTE 3: Data above slash for sixes/below slash for V-8s.
NOTE 4: First column in chart above shows six-cylinder model codes and the second column in chart shows V-8 codes.

BEL AIR SERIES — SERIES 1500 (6-CYL) — SERIES 1600 (V-8) — Chevrolet's medium-priced line was refined for 1963. Standard equipment included most Biscayne features, plus extra-quality interior trims; front and rear foam seat cushions; Deluxe steering wheel; glove compartment light; carpets: automatic dome light and dual rear ashtrays. A foam backed luggage compartment mat was another Bel Air additive. A bright metal lower body ridge molding, with accent stripe, was used. Bel Air signature scripts and Chevrolet badges appeared on the rear fenders. Stainless steel drip gutter moldings were found above the side windows. A bright finished rear cove with embossed Chevrolet lettering was seen at the rear, as well as twin unit taillights.

BEL AIR SERIES

Model Number	Model Number (V-8)	Body Type & Seating	Factory Price	Shipping Weight	Production Total
(PASSENGER CARS)					
1569	1669	4-dr Sed-6P	2508/2615	3280/3415	Note 1
1511	1611	2-dr Sed-6P	2454/2561	3215/3345	Note 1

Model Number	Model Number (V-8)	Body Type & Seating	Factory Price	Shipping Weight	Production Total
(STATION WAGONS)					
1545	1645	4-dr Sta Wag-9P	2921/3028	3720/3850	Note 1
1535	1635	4-dr Sta Wag-6P	2818/2925	3685/3810	Note 1

NOTE 1: Production totals for 1963 'Regular Chevrolets' were as follows: four-door sedan — 561,511; two-door hardtop Sports Coupe — 399,224; four-door station wagon — 198,542; four-door hardtop Sports Sedan — 194,158; two-door sedan 135,636 and two-door convertible — 82,659.
NOTE 2: Model year production (rounded-off) of 1963 Bel Airs, excluding station wagons, was approximately 354,100 cars, of which 177,200 were V-8s and 176,900 were sixes. Production of all station wagons was 198,500 (146,200 V-8s; 52,300 six-cyl.).
NOTE 3: Data above slash for sixes/below slash for V-8s.
NOTE 4: First column in chart above shows six-cylinder model codes and the second column in chart shows V-8 codes.

1963 Chevrolet, Impala SS two-door convertible, V-8

IMPALA — SERIES 1700 (6-CYL) — SERIES 1800 (V-8) — Chevrolet's plushest line had most standard equipment found on lower lines, plus bright aluminum front seat end panels; patterned cloth and leather grained vinyl upholstery (in color-coordinated materials); extra thick foam seat cushions; tufted grain and cobble pattern vinyl door and side panels; paddle type armrests with lift-up door releases; bright metal rearview mirror backing; added insulation; and foam backed trunk mats. A specific Sports style steering wheel with half-circle, thumb control horn ring was used. Other extras included electric clock; parking brake warning lamp; glovebox lamp; bright metal, textured instrument cluster accents; and dashboard face panels of similar texture. The steering wheel had duo-tone finish on cars with fawn, aqua, green and blue interiors. Exterior bodyside trim included front fender accent bars; stainless steel belt moldings with stainless steel drip caps (except convertible); a full-length lower body molding with colored insert; and Impala lettering on the rear quarter section. An Impala emblem also appeared high on rear fenders. The rear cove was filled with satin aluminum finish and trimmed by bright metal outline moldings. Triple unit taillight groups were used and incorporated built-in back-up lamps.

IMPALA SERIES

Model Number	Model Number (V-8)	Body Type & Seating	Factory Price	Shipping Weight	Production Total
(PASSENGER CARS)					
1769	1869	4-dr Sed-6P	2662/2768	3310/3435	Note 1
1739	1839	4-dr HT Spt Sed-6P	2732/2839	3350/3475	Note 1
1747	1847	2-dr HT Spt Cpe-5P	2667/2774	3265/3390	Note 1
1767	1867	2-dr Conv-5P	2917/3024	3400/3870	Note 1
(STATION WAGONS)					
1745	1845	4-dr Sta Wag-9P	2063/3170	3745/3870	Note 1
1735	1835	4-dr Sta Wag-6P	2960/3067	3705/3835	Note 1

NOTE 1: Production totals for 1963 'Regular Chevrolets' were as follows: four-door sedan — 561,511; two-door hardtop Sports Coupe — 399,224; four-door station wagon — 198,542; four-door hardtop Sports Sedan — 194,158; two-door sedan 135,636 and two-door convertible — 82,659.
NOTE 2: The 1963 Super Sport equipment package (RPO Z03) was expanded this season. It now included swirl pattern side molding inserts; matching cove inserts; red-filled 'SS' overlays for rear fender Impala emblems; specific full wheelcovers; all-vinyl front bucket seat interiors and also, a center console with locking storage compartment (when optional Powerglide or four-speed manual transmissions were ordered). In addition, the Super Sport's dashboard was trimmed with bright, swirl pattern inserts and 'SS' steering wheel center hubs were used.
NOTE 3: Model year production (rounded-off) of 1963 Impalas, excluding station wagons, was approximately 832,600 cars, of which 735,900 were V-8 and 96,700 were sixes. Production of all station wagons was 198,500 (146,200 V-8s; 52,300 six-cyl.).
NOTE 4: A total of 16,920 cars had the 409 cid V-8 installed during the 1963 model run. Most of these units were Super Sports.
NOTE 5: Chevrolet Motor Division released a figure of 153,271 cars built, in 1963, with the Super Sport equipment package, but no breakout of SS cars per body style.
NOTE 6: Data above slash for sixes/below slash for V-8s.
NOTE 7: First column in chart above shows six-cylinder model codes and the second column in chart shows V-8 codes.

CHEVY II BASE ENGINES

FOUR-CYLINDER: Overhead valves. Cast iron block. Displacement: 153.3 cid. Bore and stroke: 3.875 x 3.25 inches. Compression ratio: 8.5:1. Brake horsepower: 90 at 4000 rpm. Five main bearings. Hydraulic valve lifters. Carburetor: Rochester one-barrel Model 7020103.

SIX-CYLINDER: Overhead valves. Cast iron block. Displacement: 194.4 cid. Bore and stroke: 3.562 x 3.25 inches. Compression ratio: 8.5:1. Brake horsepower: 120 at 4400 rpm. Seven main bearings. Hydraulic valve lifters. Carburetor: Rochester one-barrel Model 7023103.

CHEVROLET BASE ENGINES

SIX-CYLINDER: Overhead valves. Cast iron block. Displacement: 230 cid. Bore and stroke: 3.875 x 3.25 inches. Compression ratio: 9.25:1. Brake horsepower: 140 at 4400 rpm. Seven main bearings. Hydraulic valve lifters. Carburetor: Rochester one-barrel Model 7023003.

V-8: Overhead valves. Cast iron block. Displacement: 283 cid. Bore and stroke: 3.875 x 3.00 inches. Compression ratio: 9.25:1. Brake horsepower: 195 at 4800 rpm. Five main bearings. Hydraulic valve lifters. Carburetor: Rochester two-barrel Model 7023007.

CHEVROLET POWERTRAIN OPTIONS: Optional engine choices provided for 1963 were:

CID Displ.	Comp. Ratio	Carb Barrels	Exhaust	H P @ rpm.	Trans Combo	Valve Lifters
327	10.5	4V	2	250 @ 4400	M/PG	H
327	10.5	4V	2	300 @ 5000	M/PG	H
327	10.5	4V	2	340 @ 6000	M/PG	S
409	11.1	4V	2	400 @ 5800	M	S
409	11.1	2x4V	2	425 @ 6000	M	S
427	13.5	2x4V	2	430 @ 6000	M	S

NOTE: V=venturi; 1=single exhaust; 2=dual exhaust; 2 x 4V= dual four-barrel carburetor; M=manual transmission; PG=Powerglide automatic transmission; H=hydraulic valve lifters; S=solid valve lifters.

CHEVROLET CHASSIS FEATURES: Wheelbase: (Chevy II) 110 inches; (Chevrolet) 119 inches. Overall length: (Chevy II station wagon) 187.4 inches; (other Chevy IIs) 183 inches; (all Chevrolets) 210.4 inches. Front tread: (Chevy II) 56.8 inches; (Chevrolet) 60.3 inches. Rear tread: (Chevy II) 56.3 inches; (Chevrolet) 59.3 inches. Tires: (Chevy II station wagon) 6.50 x 13; (Chevy II) 6.00 x 13; (Chevrolet station wagon) 8.00 x 14; (Chevrolet convertible) 7.50 x 14; (Chevrolet) 7.00 x 14.

1963 Chevrolet, Impala four-door hardtop Sport Sedan, V-8

CHEVY II OPTIONS: Air conditioning ($317). Rear armrests ($10). Pair of front seat belts ($19). Heavy-duty brakes ($38). Comfort and Convenience Group, on Nova ($28); on others ($39). Tinted glass, all windows ($13); windshield only ($13); Grille guard ($15); Rear bumper guard ($10). Padded dash ($16). Station wagon roof luggage rack ($43). Two-tone paint, except convertible ($11). Power brakes ($3). Power steering ($75). Power tailgate window ($27). Power convertible top ($54). Push-button radio with antenna and rear speaker ($70). Manual radio and antenna ($48). Push-button radio and antenna ($57). Station wagon divided second seat ($38). Super Sport equipment for Nova Sports Coupe and convertible ($161). Full wheelcovers ($13). Wire design wheelcovers ($13). Various whitewall and oversize tire options ($9-42). Positraction rear axle ($38). Heavy-duty clutch ($5). Delcotron 42-amp generator ($11). Heavy-duty radiator ($3). Powerglide transmission ($167).

1963 Chevrolet, Impala two-door hardtop Sport Coupe, V-8

CHEVROLET OPTIONS: Deluxe air conditioning, including heater ($364). Cool Pack air conditioning ($317). Driver seat belt ($10). Pair of front seat belts ($19). Heavy-duty brakes with metallic facings ($38). Comfort and Convenience Group, for Impala ($31); for Bel Air ($41), for Biscayne ($44). Biscayne front air foam seat cushion ($8). Tinted glass, all windows ($38); windshield only ($22). Grille guard ($19). Passenger car rear bumper guard ($10). Padded dash ($18). Station wagon luggage rack ($43). Station wagon luggage carrier ($43). Two-tone paint ($16). Power brakes ($43). Six-Way power seat ($97). Power steering, except Biscayne ($75). Power tailgate window ($32). Power windows, except Biscayne ($102). Manual radio ($48). Push-button radio ($57). Push-button radio with antenna and rear speaker ($70). Vinyl roof for Impala Sport Coupes ($75). Station wagon divided second seat ($38). Deluxe steering wheel ($4). Super Sport equipment package ($161). Tachometer with V-8s ($48). Wheel discs ($18). Wire wheel discs on super Sport ($25); on others ($43). Two-speed electric washers and wipers ($17). Turbo-Fire 250 horsepower 327 cid V-8 with four-barrel carburetor and dual exhausts ($191). Turbo-Fire 300 horsepower 327 cid V-8 with four-barrel carburetor and dual exhausts ($245). Turbo-Fire 340 horsepower 327 cid V-8 with four-barrel carburetor and dual exhausts ($349). Turbo-Fire 400 horsepower 409 cid V-8 with four-barrel carburetor, dual exhausts, high-lift camshaft and solid valve lifters ($428). Turbo-Fire 425 horsepower 409 cid V-8 with dual four-barrel carburetors, dual exhausts, high-lift camshaft and solid valve lifters ($484). (Note: 427 cid V-8 came with Z11 package.) Overdrive transmission with six-cylinder or 283 cid V-8 engines ($108). Six-cylinder Powerglide ($188). Powerglide with 283/327 cid V-8s ($199). Close-ratio four-speed manual transmission with 250 horsepower V-8 ($188). Four-speed transmission with 340/400/425 horsepower V-8s ($237). Positraction rear axle ($43). Delcotron 42-amp generator, standard with air condi-

tioning, optional on others at ($11). Heavy-duty radiator ($11). Heavy-duty battery, standard with 340 horsepower V-8, optional on others at ($8). Six-cylinder temperature controlled cooling fan ($16). Delcotron 52-amp generator ($32). Delcotron 62-amp generator ($65-75).

1963 Chevrolet, Impala four-door sedan, V-8

HISTORICAL FOOTNOTES: For 1963 the widest range of Chevrolets ever offered in history was available in dealer showrooms on Sept. 28, 1962. The division sold three out of every 10 cars retailed in the U.S. this season. Model year sales of Chevrolets and Chevy IIs peaked at 1,947,300 units. Calendar year production reached 2,303,343 cars, including Corvettes and Corvairs, which are covered separately in this catalog. Semon E. Knudsen remained General Manager of Chevrolet Motor Div. In July, 1963, prototypes for a new, intermediate-sized line, to be called Chevelle, were introduced at the long-lead press preview. The cast iron crankshaft, used in the all-new seven main bearing six-cylinder engine, was a first for Chevrolet. This was a peak year for factory drag racing options, such an improved-for-'63 lightweight Z11 drag package (RPOZ11). This was available for the model 1847 Impala Sport Coupe. The $1,245 option now had an aluminum front bumper and stripped interior, in addition to the aluminum front fenders, inner fenders, and hood. A new 427 cid/430 hp version of the Chevy big-block used a .100 stroke increase to achieve the extra 18 cubic inches of displacement. It had a bore and stroke of 4.312 x 3.65. This engine also included a new dual four-barrel intake manifold that isolated the intake runners from the engine valves, which were covered by a separate valve cover. The cylinder heads were slightly different on the intake manifold mating the surface, in order to match this new manifold setup. There was also a special cowl induction air cleaner; heavy-duty clutch; four-speed gearbox; Positraction rear axle; semi-metallic brakes and tachometer. On Dec. 1, 1962, Chevrolet issued 25 cars with the Z11 package. On Jan. 1, 1963, the company issued 25 more and seven more were sold soon after that date for a total of 57. The aluminum front end saved 112 lbs. Other weight-saving measures, such as the lack of center bumper backing and bracing helped too. By cutting another 121 lbs., the car weight dropped to about 3,340 lbs. Also in 1963, five Mark II NASCAR 427 "mystery engines" were built and raced at Daytona, winning the two 100-mile preliminary races and setting the track stock car speed record. While these engines were very rare, they were the prototype of the 396 cid 1965 engine that was brought up to 427 cid in 1966 and 454 cid in 1970. These first five engines were closely related to the 409 and the Z11-optioned 427. They even shared crankshaft and piston rods with the Z11, but differed completely in having the combustion chamber in the cylinder head. That means the cylinder block deck surfaces were angled to parallel the piston dome, and also incorporated the stagger-valve or "porcupine" valve layout. The bore and stroke was the same as the Z11, 4.312 x 3.65. The GM decision to adhere strictly to the Auto Manufacturers Association's anti-racing ban put a tragic end to these great engines, but not before the cat was, at least briefly, out of the bag.

1964 CHEVROLET

1964 Chevrolet, Chevy II Nova 4-dr sedan, 6-cyl

CHEVY II/NOVA — ALL SERIES — The 1964 Chevy II had a redesigned grille. Nine vertical bars were equally spaced along the five, full-width horizontal blades. This gave a quadrant effect. Side trim treatments were more like the 1962 look, than the 1963 style. The base level 100 Series models had no belt moldings. The 300 Series was discontinued. Novas had constant-width belt moldings and Nova signature scripts at the upper trailing edge of front fenders. The top series consisted of only one model, the Nova Super Sport Sports Coupe, with

'SS' trim and equipment. Body style and engine availability was shuffled as indicated by the chart below. New technical features included an optional 283 cid V-8 and self-adjusting 9.6 inch drum brakes.

CHEVY II/NOVA I.D. NUMBERS: Vehicle numbers were on the left front body hinge pillar. Motor numbers, for both engines, were on the right side of the block to the rear of distributor. The first VIN symbol was a '4' indicating model year. This was followed by four symbols shown in charts below as Model Numbers. The first pair of symbols in these Model Numbers indicate the series (01=Chevy II 100 four-cylinder; 02=Chevy II 100 six-cylinder; 04=Nova six-cylinder) and the second pair of symbols in the Model Number indicate body style. The next letter (sixth symbol of VIN) shows the assembly plant code with Chevy II production limited to factories coded W (Willow Run, Mich.) and N (Norwood, Ohio.) The last six numbers were the sequential production code starting with 100001 at each plant. A Fisher Body Style plate is under the hood on left and gives Style Number, Body Number, Trim code and Paint code.

CHEVY II ALL SERIES

Model Number	Model Number (6-CYL)	Body Type & Seating	Factory Price	Shipping Weight	Production Total
SERIES 100 (4-CYL)/SERIES 100 (6-CYL)					
0169	0269	4-dr Sed-6P	2048/2108	2495/2580	Note 1
0111	0211	2-dr Sed-6P	201112070	2455/2540	Note 1
NA	0235	4-dr Sta Wag-6P	NA/2406	NA/2840	Note 1
NOVA 400 SERIES (6-CYL)					
NA	0469	4-dr Sed-6P	NA/2243	NA/2595	Note 1
NA	0411	2-dr Sed-6P	NA/2206	NA/2560	Note 1
NA	0437	2-dr Spt Cpe-5P	NA/2271	NA/2660	Note 1
NA	0435	4-dr Sta Wag-6P	NA/2503	NA/2860	Note 1
NOVA SUPER SPORT SERIES					
NA	0447	2-dr Spt Cpe-4P	NA/2433	NA/2675	Note 1

NOTE 1: Production was recorded only by body styles, as follows; four-door sedan 84,846; two-door sedan — 40,348; four-door station wagon — 35,670 and two-door Sport Coupe — 30,827.
NOTE 2: Industry production figures vary by source. One indicates 165,487 sixes; 1,121 fours; and 25,083 V-8s. Another indicates 800 fours in the 100 Series, 52,300 cars in the 100 Series, 102,900 cars in the Nova Series (including Super Sports) and 35,700 station wagons. Apparently, the new V-8 option caused some confusion in record keeping.
NOTE 3: Data above slash for four/below slash for six. A V-8 was optional.
NOTE 4: Top section of charts shows four-cylinder Model Number in first column; six-cylinder Model Number in second column. The Series 100 station wagon and all Novas were available with the base six or optional V-8, but not with the four-cylinder motor.

1964 Chevelle, Malibu 'SS' two-door hardtop, V-8

CHEVELLE/MALIBU — ALL SERIES — Anticipating a general improvement in the market for cars priced and sized below regular models, Chevrolet introduced its all-new Chevelle, a car that fit between the compact Chevy II and full-size models and was soon being called a "senior compact." Assembly was quartered at plants in Baltimore and Kansas City and a brand new factory in Fremont, Calif. The car was styled with square looking lines in the Chevy II model, but curved side window glass and an emphasis on width provided a distinctive look. Eleven models were available in two basic lines called Chevelle 300 and Chevelle Malibu, with a convertible as an exclusive upper level offering. Base editions lacked bodyside moldings. Malibu models had a full-length strip of bright metal along the lower beltline, with an insert at the rear and Malibu rear fender script. A Super Sport option was released and cars so-equipped had no lower belt trim. Instead, there was a molding running along the full-length of the upper body ridge and continuing along the rear fender edge, plus SS rear fender and rear panel badges and specifically styled wheelcovers. Bucket front seats were popular features in the Chevelle Malibu Super Sport.

CHEVELLE/MALIBU I.D. NUMBERS: Vehicle numbers were on the left front body hinge pillar. Motor numbers, for both engines, were on the right side of the block to the rear of distributor. The first VIN symbol was a '4' indicating model year. This was followed by four symbols shown in charts below as Model Numbers. The first pair of symbols in these Model Numbers indicate the series (53=Chevelle six-cylinder; 54=Chevelle V-8; 55=Malibu six-cylinder; 56=Malibu V-8; 57=Malibu SS six-cylinder; 58=Malibu SS V-8) and the second pair of symbols in the Model Number indicate body style. The next letter (sixth symbol of VIN) shows the assembly plant code with Chevelle production limited to factories coded B (Baltimore, Md.); K (Kansas City, Mo.) and Z (Fremont, Calif.) The last six numbers were the sequential production code starting with 100001 at each plant. A Fisher Body Style plate is under the hood on left and gives Style Number, Body Number, Trim code and Paint code.

CHEVELLE/MALIBU ALL SERIES

Model Number	Model Number (V-8)	Body Type & Seating	Factory Price	Shipping Weight	Production Total
(SERIES 300 (6-CYL)/SERIES 300 (V-8)					
5369	5469	4-dr Sed-6P	2268/2376	2850/2980	Note 1
5311	5411	2-dr Sed-6P	2231/2339	2825/2955	Note 1
5335	5435	4-dr Sta Wag-6P	2566/2674	3130/3250	Note 1
5315	5415	2-dr Sta Wag-6P	2528/2636	3050/3170	Note 1
MALIBU SERIES (6-CYL)/MALIBU SERIES (V-8)					
5569	5669	4-dr Sed-6P	2349/2457	2870/2995	Note 1
5537	5637	2-dr Spt Cpe-5P	2376/2484	2850/2975	Note 1
5567	5667	2-dr Conv-5P	2587/2695	2995/3120	Note 1
5545	5645	4-dr Sta Wag-8P	2744/2852	3240/3365	Note 1
5535	5635	2-dr Sta Wag-6P	2647/2755	3140/3265	Note 1

NOTE 1: Production was recorded by body style, as follows: two-door Sport Coupe — 134,670; four-door sedan — 113,816; four-door station wagon — 41,374; two-door convertible — 23,158; two-door sedan — 22,588 and two-door station wagon — 2,710.
NOTE 2: Industry statistical breakouts show 142,034 Chevelle sixes and 196,252 Chevelle V-8s were built.
NOTE 3: Additional statistics record series production, in rounded-off figures, as follows: (Chevelle 300) 53,000 sixes and 15,300 V-8s; (Malibu) 62,100 sixes and 86,900 V-8s; (Malibu SS) 67,100 V-8s and (station wagons) 17,100 sixes and 26,900 V-8s.
NOTE 4: Data above slash for six/below slash for V-8.
NOTE 5: First column on chart shows model codes for sixes and the second column on chart shows model codes for V-8.

BISCAYNE — SERIES 1100 (6-CYL) — SERIES 1200 (V-8) — Chevrolet's most inexpensive line. Standard features included heater and defroster; dual sun visors; color-keyed floor carpeting; foam-cushioned seats; cigarette lighter; glove compartment lock; dual-spoke steering wheel with horn ring; front and rear armrests; ashtray; crank-operated ventipanes; and two coat hooks. Interiors were trimmed in patterned cloth and leather grain vinyl combinations, with all-vinyl door panels and embossed vinyl headliners. Spatter pattern paint was used in the luggage compartment. Exterior bright metal decoration included a full-length lower body molding; rear cove upper molding; twin style taillights; hood and deck emblems and nameplates; Biscayne rear fender signatures with Chevrolet emblems; small wheel center hubcaps; and bright windshield, rear window and ventipane frames.

CHEVROLET I.D. NUMBERS: Serial numbers were stamped on a plate affixed to the left front door hinge pillar. The first VIN symbol identified model year, 4=1964. The second and third symbols identified the series (see first two digits of Model Number columns in charts below). The fourth and fifth symbols identified body style (see last two digits of Model Number columns in charts below). The sixth symbol, a letter, indicated assembly plant, as follows: A=Atlanta, Ga.; B=Baltimore, Md.; F=Flint, Mich.; G=Framingham, Mass.; H=Fremont, Calif.; J=Janesville, Wis.; K=Kansas City, Mo.; L=Los Angeles, Calif.; N=Norwood, Ohio; O=Oakland, Calif.; R=Arlington, Texas; S=St. Louis, Mo.; T=Tarrytown, NY; U=Southgate, Calif.; W=Willow Run, Mich.; Y=Wilmington, Del. The last six symbols are the sequential production number, with numbers for each series at each factory starting at 100001 and up. Fisher Body plate attached to left-hand cowl starts with two-digit model year prefix (60-) and Fisher Body Style Number (Model Number) and also shows factory code, production sequence, trim and body color data. Engine numbers: (six) right side of block behind distributor; (V-8) right front of engine block.

BISCAYNE SERIES

Model Number	Model Number (V-8)	Body Type & Seating	Factory Price	Shipping Weight	Production Total
1169	1269	4-dr Sed-6P	2417/2524	3300/3430	Note 1
1111	1211	2-dr Sed-6P	2363/2471	3230/3365	Note 1
1135	1235	4-dr Sta Wag-6P	2763/2871	3700/3820	Note 1

NOTE 1: Production (for all full-sized Chevrolets) was recorded by body style only, as follows: four-door sedan — 536,329; two-door Sport Coupe — 442,292; four-door Sport Sedan — 200,172; four-door station wagon — 192,827; two-door sedan 120,951 and two-door convertible — 81,897.
NOTE 2: Breakouts show 383,647 Chevrolet sixes and 1,190,821 Chevrolet V-8s were built.
NOTE 3: Rounded-off series production figures were: (Biscayne six) 132,500; (Biscayne V-8) 41,400; (station wagon six) 39,700 and (station wagon V-8) 153,100. The station wagon totals are for Chevrolet wagons of all trim levels and not just Biscaynes.
NOTE 4: Data above slash for six/below slash for V-8.
NOTE 5: First column in chart above shows six-cylinder Model Number; second column shows V-8 Model Number.

BEL AIR — SERIES 1500 (6-CYL) — SERIES 1600 (V-8) — Chevrolet's middle-priced line had less exterior distinction, but a plusher interior for 1964. Standard equipment included all the Biscayne features listed above, plus bright door trim accents; plastic cowl side panels with molded-in ventilation grilles; a bright instrument panel molding; glove compartment light; dome light door switches; Deluxe quality interior handles; and a patterned rubber luggage compartment mat. Interior trim was of a brighter, color-keyed patterned cloth and leather-grained vinyl combination on the seats, with all-vinyl door panels and embossed headliner. A narrow, full-length upper body bright molding and a slender body sill molding were used. Bel Air script and Chevrolet badges appeared on the rear fenders. Dual rear cove moldings were used, with twin-unit taillights. Bright roof drip cap moldings were a Bel Air feature.

BEL AIR SERIES

Model Number	Model Number (V-8)	Body Type & Seating	Factory Price	Shipping Weight	Production Total
1569	1669	4-dr Sed-6P	2519/2626	3305/3440	Note 1
1511	1611	2-dr Sed-6P	2465/2573	3235/3370	Note 1
1535	1635	4-dr Sta Wag-6P	2828/2935	3705/3825	Note 1
1545	1645	4-dr Sta Wag-9P	2931/3039	3845/3865	Note 1

NOTE 1: Production (for all full-sized Chevrolets) was recorded by body style only, as follows: four-door sedan — 536,329; two-door Sport Coupe — 442,292; four-door Sport Sedan — 200,172; four-door station wagon — 192,827; two-door sedan 120,951 and two-door convertible — 81,897.
NOTE 2: Breakouts show 383,647 Chevrolet sixes and 1,190,821 Chevrolet V-8s were built.
NOTE 3: In rounded-off figures Bel Air production, by series, was as follows: (Bel Air six) 137,800 and (Bel Air V-8) 180,300. Bel Air station wagons are included in combined total previously noted.
NOTE 4: Data above slash for six/below slash for V-8.
NOTE 5: First column in chart above shows six-cylinder Model Number; second column shows V-8 Model Number.

1964 Chevrolet, Impala two-door hardtop Sport Coupe, V-8

IMPALA — SERIES 1700 (6-CYL) — SERIES 1800 (V-8) — The separation of Impala Super Sport models into their own series made the regular Impala the second most expensive Chevrolet line for 1964. Standard equipment included most features found on lower-priced lines, plus extra-thick foam cushion seats; bright aluminum front seat end panels; bright instrument panel insert with nameplate molding; electric clock; parking brake warning light; Impala center emblem on steering wheel; chrome-backed rearview mirror; specific paddle-type front and rear armrests (with finger-tip door release lever); dual dome lights; bright windshield, rear window and upper side window interior garnish moldings; and an automatic luggage compartment light. Interiors were of cloth and leather-grain vinyl, in a more intricate design, with bright-accented all-vinyl door panels and vinyl embossed headliner. (Convertible and station wagons had all-vinyl trim). Exterior trim included color-accented bodyside moldings; hood and deck windsplit moldings; rear cove outline moldings; satin-finish anodized cove insert; triple unit taillights (with back-up light built in); Impala lettering and emblem on rear fenders; roof rail and drip cap moldings; bright door windows glass edges (hardtop styles); and bright belt moldings.

1964 Chevrolet, Impala four-door station wagon V-8

IMPALA SERIES

Model Number	Model Number (V-8)	Body Type & Seating	Factory Price	Shipping Weight	Production Total
1769	1869	4-dr Sed-6P	2671/2779	3340/3460	Note 1
1739	1839	4-dr HT Spt Sed-6P	2742/2850	3370/3490	Note 1
1747	1847	2-dr HT Spt Cpe-6P	2678/2786	3295/3415	Note 1
1767	1867	2-dr Conv-6P	2927/3035	3400/3525	Note 1
1735	1835	4-dr Sta Wag-6P	2970/3077	3725/3850	Note 1
1745	1845	4-dr Sta Wag-9P	3073/3181	3770/3895	Note 1

NOTE 1: Production (for all full-sized Chevrolets) was recorded by body style only, as follows: four-door sedan — 536,329; two-door Sport Coupe — 442,292; four-door Sport Sedan — 200,172; four-door station wagon — 192,827; two-door sedan 120,951 and two-door convertible — 81,897.
NOTE 2: Breakouts show 383,647 Chevrolet sixes and 1,190,821 Chevrolet V-8s were built.
NOTE 3: Production, in rounded-off figures, was follows: (Impala six) 73,600 and (Impala V-8) 816,000. Impala station wagons are included in combined total for all wagons.
NOTE 4: Data above slash for six/below slash for V-8.
NOTE 5: First column in chart above shows six-cylinder Model Number; second column shows V-8 Model Number.

1964 Chevrolet, Chevelle, SS two-door convertible, V-8

IMPALA SUPER SPORT — SERIES 1300 (6-CYL) — SERIES 1400 (V-8) — Chevrolet's plushest and most sporting model was available only in two-door styles. Standard equipment approximated that of the Impala, with added interior features including leather-grained vinyl upholstery with individual front bucket seats and locking compartment in a center console. Swirl-pattern instrument panel inserts and moldings were used. A built-in rear seat radio speaker grille was featured. Dual dome and floor courtesy lamps, with automatic door switches or manual instrument panel controls were used. Door safety reflectors were found on the all-vinyl door panels. Special SS emblems appeared on the console and door panels. Exterior distinction came from the use of a wider upper body molding, filled with a swirl-pattern silver anodized insert. Impala lettering and the SS badge appeared on the rear fenders, with another badge appearing on the deck lid. The rear cove outline moldings were filled with silver-anodized inserts. Full wheelcovers of specific Super Sport design were used.

IMPALA SUPER SPORT SERIES

Model Number	Model Number (V-8)	Body Type & Seating	Factory Price	Shipping Weight	Production Total
1347	1447	2-dr HT Spt Cpe-5P	2839/2947	3325/3450	Note 1
1367	1467	2-dr Conv-5P	3088/3196	3435/3555	Note 1

NOTE 1: Chevrolet Motor Div. recorded the production of 185,325 Impala Super Sport models in 1964. There is no breakout, by body style, available at this time. It is most likely that six to 10 percent of these units were convertibles; the rest two-door hardtop Sport Coupes.
NOTE 2: A total of 8,684 Chevrolets were equipped with 409 cid engines during the 1964 model run, the majority being Impala Super Sports.

1964 Chevrolet, Impala SS two-door hardtop, V-8

CHEVY II BASE ENGINES

FOUR-CYLINDER: Overhead valves. Cast iron block. Displacement: 153 cid. Bore and stroke: 3.875 x 2.35 inches. Compression ratio: 8.5:1. Brake horsepower: 90 at 4000 rpm. Five main bearings. Hydraulic valve lifters. Carburetor: Carter one-barrel model 3379.

SIX-CYLINDER: Overhead valves. Cast iron block. Displacement: 194.4 cid. Bore and stroke: 3.562 x 3.25 inches. Compression ratio: 8.5:1. Brake horsepower: 120 at 4400 rpm. Seven main bearings. Hydraulic valve lifters. Carburetor: Rochester one-barrel model 7023105.

CHEVELLE BASE ENGINES

SIX-CYLINDER: Overhead valves. Cast iron block. Displacement: 194.4 cid. Bore and stroke: 3.562 x 3.25 inches. Compression ratio: 8.5:1. Brake horsepower: 120 at 4400 rpm. Seven main bearings. Hydraulic valve lifters. Carburetor: Rochester one-barrel model 7023105.

V-8: Overhead valves. Cast iron block. Displacement: 283 cid. Bore and stroke: 3.875 x 3.00 inches. Compression ratio: 9.25:1. Brake horsepower: 195 at 4800 rpm. four main bearings. Hydraulic valve lifters. Carburetor: Rochester one-barrel model 7024101.

CHEVROLET BASE ENGINES

SIX-CYLINDER: Overhead valves. Cast iron block. Displacement: 230 cid. Bore and stroke: 3.875 x 3.25 inches. Compression ratio: 9.25:1. Brake horsepower: 140 at 4400 rpm. Seven main bearings. Hydraulic valve lifters. Carburetor: Rochester one-barrel Model 7023003.

V-8: Overhead valves. Cast iron block. Displacement: 283 cid. Bore and stroke: 3.875 x 3.00 inches. Compression ratio: 9.25:1. Brake horsepower: 195 at 4800 rpm. Five main bearings. Hydraulic valve lifters. Carburetor: Rochester two-barrel Model 7023007.

CHEVY II/NOVA POWERTRAIN OPTIONS: Optional engines for 1964 were:

CID Displ.	Comp. Ratio	Carb Barrels	Exhaust	H P @ rpm.	Trans Combo	Valve Lifters
(SIX)						
230	8.5	1V	1	155 @ 4400	M/A	H
(V-8)						
283	9.25	2V	1	195 @ 4800	M/A	H

NOTE: V=venturi; 1=single exhaust; M=manual transmission; PG=Powerglide automatic transmission; H=hydraulic valve lifters.

CHEVELLE/MALIBU POWERTRAIN OPTIONS: Optional engines for 1964 were:

CID Displ.	Comp. Ratio	Carb Barrels	Exhaust	H P @ rpm.	Trans Combo	Valve Lifters
(SIX)						
230	8.5	1V	1	155 @ 4400	M/A	H
(V-8)						
283	9.25	4V	2	220 @ 4800	M/A	H
327	10.5	4V	1	250 @ 4400	M/A	H
327	10.5	4V	2	300 @ 5000	M/A	H

NOTE: V=venturi; 1=single exhaust; 2=dual exhaust; M=manual transmission; A=automatic transmission; H=hydraulic valve lifters.

CHEVROLET POWERTRAIN OPTIONS: Optional V-8 engines for 1963 were:

CID Displ.	Comp. Ratio	Carb Barrels	Exhaust	H P @ rpm.	Trans Combo	Valve Lifters
327	10.5	4V	2	250 @ 4400	M/A	H
327	10.5	4V	2	300 @ 5000	M/A	H
327	10.5	4V	2	340 @ 6000	M/A	S
409	11:1	4V	2	400 @ 5800	M	S
409	11:1	2x4V	2	425 @ 6000	M	S

NOTE: V=venturi; 1=single exhaust; 2=dual exhaust; 2 x 4V= dual four-barrel carburetor; M=manual transmission; A=automatic transmission; H=hydraulic valve lifters; S=solid valve lifters.

CHASSIS FEATURES: Wheelbase: (Chevy II) 110 inches; (Chevelle) 115 inches; (Chevrolet) 119 inches. Overall length: (Chevy II station wagon) 187.6 inches; (Chevy II) 182.9 inches; (Chevelle station wagon) 198.8 inches; (Chevelle) 193.9 inches; (Chevrolet station wagon) 210.8 inches; (Chevrolet) 209.9 inches. Width: (Chevy II) 69.9 inches; (Chevelle) 74.6 inches; (Chevrolet) 79.6 inches. Tires: (Chevy II station wagons and Novas) 6.50 x 13; (Chevy II) 6.00 x 13; (Chevelle station wagons) 7.00 x 14; (Chevelles) 6.50 x 14; (Chevrolet station wagons) 8.00 x 14; (other Chevrolet convertibles) 7.50 x 14; (other Chevrolets) 7.00 x 14.

CHEVY II/NOVA OPTIONS: Air conditioning ($317). Rear armrests ($10). Pair of front seat belts ($19). Heavy-duty brakes ($38). Comfort and Convenience Group, on Nova ($28); on others ($39). Tinted glass, all windows ($27); windshield only ($13); Grille guard ($15); Rear bumper guard ($10). Padded dash ($16). Station wagon roof luggage rack ($43). Two-tone paint, except convertible ($11). Power brakes ($3). Power steering ($75). Power tailgate window ($27). Power convertible top ($54). Push-button radio with antenna and rear speaker ($70). Manual radio and antenna ($48). Push-button radio and antenna ($57). Station wagon divided second seat ($38). Super Sport equipment for Nova Sports Coupe and convertible ($161). Full wheelcovers ($13). Wire design wheelcovers ($13). Various whitewall and oversize tire options ($9-42). Positraction rear axle ($38). Heavy-duty clutch ($5). Delcotron 42-amp generator ($11). Heavy-duty radiator ($3). Powerglide transmission ($167).

CHEVELLE/MALIBU OPTIONS: Air conditioning ($317). Rear armrests ($10). Pair of front seat belts ($19). Heavy-duty brakes ($38). Comfort and Convenience Group, on Nova ($28); on others ($39). Tinted glass, all windows ($27); windshield only ($13); Grille guard ($15); Rear bumper guard ($10). Padded dash ($16). Station wagon roof luggage rack ($43). Two-tone paint, except convertible ($11). Power brakes ($3). Power steering ($75). Power tailgate window ($27). Power convertible top ($54). Push-button radio with antenna and rear speaker ($70). Manual radio and antenna ($48). Push-button radio and antenna ($57). Station wagon divided second seat ($38). Super Sport equipment for Nova Sports Coupe and convertible ($161). Full wheelcovers ($13). Wire design wheelcovers ($13). Various whitewall and oversize tire options ($9-42). Positraction rear axle ($38). Heavy-duty clutch ($5). Delcotron 42-amp generator ($11). Heavy-duty radiator ($3). Powerglide transmission ($167). The 230 cid six-cylinder engine with one-barrel carburetor and 155 horsepower was $43 extra. The 283 cid V-8 with four-barrel carburetor, 9.25:1 compression and 220 horsepower returned as a $54 extra. The 327 cid V-8 with four-barrel carburetor, 10.5:1 compression and 250 horsepower was $95 extra. The 327 cid V-8 with four-barrel carburetor, 10.5:1 compression and 300 horsepower was a $138 option.

CHEVROLET OPTIONS: Deluxe air conditioning, including heater ($364). Cool Pack air conditioning ($317). Driver seat belt ($10). Pair of front seat belts ($19). Heavy-duty brakes with metallic facings ($38). Comfort and Convenience Group, for Impala ($31); for Bel Air ($41), for Biscayne ($44). Biscayne front air foam seat cushion ($8). Tinted glass, all windows ($38); windshield only ($22). Grille guard ($19). Passenger car rear bumper guard ($10). Padded dash ($18). Station wagon luggage locker ($11). Station wagon luggage carrier ($43). Two-tone paint ($16). Power brakes ($43). Six-Way power seat ($97). Power steering, except Biscayne ($75). Power tailgate window ($32). Power windows, except Biscayne ($102). Manual radio ($48). Push-button radio ($57). Push-button radio with antenna and rear speaker ($70). Vinyl roof for Impala Sport Coupes ($75). Station wagon divided second seat ($38). Deluxe steering wheel ($4). Super Sport equipment package ($161). Tachometer with V-8s ($48). Wheel discs ($18). Wire wheel discs on super Sport ($25); on others ($43). Two-speed electric washers and wipers ($17). Tilt Steering. Turbo-Fire 250 horsepower 327 cid V-8 with four-barrel carburetor and dual exhausts ($191). Turbo-Fire 300 horsepower 327 cid V-8 with four-barrel carburetor and dual exhausts ($245). Turbo-Fire 340 horsepower 327 cid V-8 with four-barrel carburetor and dual exhausts ($349). Turbo-Fire 400 horsepower 409 cid V-8 with four-barrel carburetor, dual exhausts, high-lift camshaft and solid valve lifters ($428). Turbo-Fire 425 horsepower 409 cid V-8 with dual four-barrel carburetors, dual exhausts, high- lift camshaft and solid valve lifters ($484). Overdrive transmission with six-cylinder or 283 cid V-8 engines ($108). Six-cylinder Powerglide ($188). Powerglide with 283/327 cid V-8s ($199). Close-ratio four-speed manual transmission with 250 horsepower V-8 ($188). Four-speed transmission with 340/400/425 horsepower V-8s ($237). Positraction rear axle ($43). Delcotron 42-amp generator, standard with air conditioning, optional on others at ($11). Heavy-duty radiator ($11). Heavy-duty battery, standard with 340 horsepower V-8, optional on others at ($8). Six-cylinder temperature controlled cooling fan ($16). Delcotron 52-amp generator ($32). Delcotron 62-amp generator ($65-75).

1965 CHEVROLET

BISCAYNE — (6-CYL/V-8) — SERIES 153/154 — Chevrolets had larger bodies for 1965. A new stamped grille had a lower extension below the bumper, which was slightly veed. Curved window glass and taillamps mounted high at the rear characterized the new styling. Rear fender lines had a prominent kick up and a blunter and more rounded shape. Biscaynes had thin body sill moldings, thin rear fender ridge moldings, bright windshield moldings and dual-style rear lamps with the Biscayne script on the rear quarters. Standard equipment for all Biscaynes included heater and defroster; foam-cushioned front seat; oil filter; electric wipers; front seat belts; and five blackwall tires. Convertibles and all 327 cid V-8 cars had 7.75 x 14 tires, station wagons and 409 cid V-8 cars had a 8.25 x 14 tires. Interiors were vinyl and pattern cloth (all-vinyl on station wagons).

CHEVROLET I.D. NUMBERS: VIN located on plate attached to left front door hinge pillar. The number had 13 symbols. The first symbol is a 1 for Chevrolet; the second and third symbols indicate series and the third and fourth symbols indicate body type. (Together, these first five symbols comprised the model number and appear in the Body/Style Number column of charts below.) The sixth symbol indicated model year, 5=1965. The seventh symbol indicated assembly plant: A= Atlanta, Ga.; B=Baltimore, Md.; C=Southgate, Calif.; F=Flint, Mich.;G=-Framingham, Mass.; J=Janesville, Wis.; K=Kansas City, Mo.; L=Los Angeles, Calif; N=Norwood, Ohio; R=Arlington, Texas; S= St. Louis, Mo.; T=Tarrytown, N.Y.; W=Willow Run, Mich.; Y=Wilmington, Del.; Z=Fremont, Calif.; 1=Oshawa, Ontario (Canada); 2=St. Therese, Quebec (Canada) and P=Pontiac, Mich. The last six symbols were the sequential number. A Fisher Body Number tag on the cowl gives the style number, body number, trim and paint codes. Engine codes appear on the right side of six-cylinder blocks behind the distributor and right front of V-8 engine blocks: CHEVY II (153 cid/90 hp four) OA, OC, OG, OH, OJ; (194 cid/120 hp six) OK, OM, OQ, OR; (230 cid/140 hp six) PA,PC, PV,PX, PI; (283 cid/195 hp V-8) PD, PF, PL, PM, PN, PP; (283 cid/220 hp V-8) PB, PE, PG, PK, PO, PQ; (327 cid/250 hp V-8) ZA, ZE, ZK, ZM; (327 cid/300 hp V-8) ZB, ZF, ZL, ZN; CHEVELLE (194 cid/120 hp six) AA, AC, AG, AH, AK, AL, AN, AR; (230 cid/140 hp six) BK, BN, BY, BZ, CA, CB, CC, CD, (283 cid/195 hp V-8) DA, DB, DE; (283 cid/220 hp V-8) DG, DH; (327 cid/250 hp V-8) EA, EE; (327 cid/300 hp V-8) EB, EF; (327 cid/350 hp V-8) EC, ED; (396 cid/375 hp V-8) IX. CHEVROLET (230 cid/140 hp six) FA, FE, FF, FK, FL, FM, FP, FR; (250 cid/150 hp six) FY, FZ; (283 cid/195 hp V-8) GA, GC, GF; (283 cid/220 hp V-8) GK, GL; (327 cid/250 hp V-8) HA, HC; (327 cid/300 hp V-8) HB, HD; (396 cid/325 hp V-8) IA, IB, IC, IE, IF, IG, II, IV, IW; (409 cid/340 hp V-8) JB, JC, JE, JF; (409 cid/400 hp V-8) JA, JD.

BISCAYNE SERIES

Model Number	Body/Style Number	Body Type & Seating	Factory Price	Shipping Weight	Production Total
153/4	15369	4-dr Sed-6P	2417/2524	3365/3515	Note 1
153/4	15311	2-dr Sed-6P	2363/2470	3305/3455	Note 1
153/4	15335	4-dr Sta Wag-6P	2417/2871	3765/3900	Note 2

NOTE 1: Some 107,700 six-cylinder and 37,600 V-8 Biscaynes were built. Total production, in figures rounded-off to the nearest 100 units, was 145,300 excluding station wagons.
NOTE 2: Some 29,400 six-cylinder and 155,000 V-8 Chevrolet station wagons were built during the 1965 model year. Total station wagon output, in figures rounded-off to the nearest 100 units, was 184,400 cars. This includes Biscayne; Bel Air and Impala station wagons.
NOTE 3: V-8s have the number '6' as the third digit of their series, model and serial number.
NOTE 4: Prices and weights above slash for six/below slash for V-8.

BEL AIR — (6-CYL/V-8) — SERIES 155/156 — External decor on the Bel Air included a narrow full-length bodyside molding; roof drip rail moldings; rear accent band; and Bel Air script (with Chevrolet emblems on rear quarters). All features found on Biscaynes were included, plus a glove compartment light and power tailgate window on nine-passenger station wagons. Interiors were plusher, with vinyl and pattern cloth trims.

BEL AIR SERIES

Model Number	Body/Style Number	Body Type & Seating	Factory Price	Shipping Weight	Production Total
155/6	15569	4-dr Sed-6P	2519/2626	3380/3530	Note 1
155/6	15511	2-dr Sed-6P	2465/2573	3310/3460	Note 1
155/6	15535	4-dr Sta Wag-6P	2970/2936	3810/3950	Note 2
155/6	15545	4-dr Sta Wag-6P	3073/303	3765/3905	Note 2

NOTE 1: Some 107,800 six-cylinder and 163,600 V-8 Bel Airs were built. Total production, in figures rounded-off to the nearest 100 units, was 271,400, excluding station wagons (all full-sized Chevrolet station wagons being contained in a separate series).

NOTE 2: Some 29,400 six-cylinder and 155,000 V-8 Chevrolet station wagons were built during the 1965 model year. Total station wagon output, in figures rounded-off to the nearest 100 units, was 184,400 cars. This includes Biscayne; Bel Air and Impala station wagons.

NOTE 3: V-8s have the number '6' as the third digit of their series, model and serial number.

NOTE 4: Prices and weights above slash for six/below slash for V-8.

1965 Chevrolet, Impala two-door convertible, V-8

IMPALA — (6-CYL/V-8) — SERIES 163/164 — Impala features include wide, lower, bright bodyside moldings (with rear fender extensions); bright wheelhouse moldings; bright rear cover panel trim; triple-unit taillamps and full wheelcovers. Interiors are more detailed and plusher. Instrument panels have bright center panel moldings and woodgrained lower panel facings. Bright garnish moldings are seen. Extra features included on Impala are electric clock; parking brake light; trunk and back-up lights. Luxurious vinyl/pattern cloth trim combinations were used in pillared sedan models. Both convertibles and station wagons featured all-vinyl trims. Black, all-vinyl upholstery was available in sport coupes and pillarless sport sedans. The four-door (hardtop) sport sedans had dual roof side rail lamps.

IMPALA SERIES

Model Number	Body/Style Number	Body Type & Seating	Factory Price	Shipping Weight	Production Total
163/4	16369	4-dr Sed-6P	2672/2779	3460/3595	Note 1
163/4	16337	2-dr HT-6P	2678/2785	3385/3630	Note 1
163/4	16339	4-dr HT-6P	2742/2850	3490/3525	Note 1
163/4	16337	2-dr Conv-6P	2943/3051	3470/3605	Note 2
163/4	16335	4-dr Sta Wag-6P	2970/3078	3825/3960	Note 2
163/4	16345	4-dr Sta Wag-9P	3073/3181	3865/4005	Note 2

NOTE 1: Some 56,600 six-cylinder and 746,800 V-8 Impalas were built. Total production, in figures rounded off to the nearest 100, was 803,400. excluding station wagons (all full-sized Chevrolet station wagons being contained in a separate series).

NOTE 2: A total of 72,760 full-sized Chevrolet convertibles were built, including both Impalas and Impala Super Sports. About 45,800 of these were Impalas and about 27,000 were Impala Super Sports.

NOTE 3: V-8s have the number '4' as the third digit of their series, model and serial number.

NOTE 4: Prices and weights above slash for six/below slash for V-8.

CAPRICE CUSTOM SEDAN OPTION PACKAGE: RPO Z-18 was the Caprice Custom Sedan option for model 16439 (Impala four-door hardtop) and included a heavier stiffer frame, suspension changes, black-accented front grille and rear trim panel with Caprice nameplate, slender body sill moldings, Fleur-de-lis roof quarter emblems, color-keyed bodyside stripes, specific full wheelcovers and Caprice hood and dash emblems.

IMPALA SUPER SPORT — (6-CYL/V-8) — SERIES 165/166 — The prestige Chevrolet was noted by its bright wheelhouse moldings (without bright lower body moldings); Super Sport front fender scripts; black-filled rear cove band with Impala SS badge at right; and a similar badge on the radiator grille, at the left. Specific Super Sport full wheelcovers were used. The SS interior featured full carpeting; all-vinyl trim with front bucket seats and bright seatback outline moldings; combination vinyl and carpet door trim (with bright accents); foam cushions, courtesy lights; SS identification on the door panels; and a console with a built-in, Rally-type clock. A vacuum gauge was standard as well.

IMPALA SUPER SPORT

Model Number	Body/Style Number	Body Type & Seating	Factory Price	Shipping Weight	Production Total
165/6	16537	2-dr HT-6P	2839/2947	3435/3570	Note 1
165/6	16567	2-dr Conv-6P	3104/3212	3505/3645	Note 2

NOTE 1: 3,600 six-cylinder and 239,500 V-8 Impala Super Sports were built. Total production was exactly 243,114 units.

NOTE 2: Approximately 27,000 Impala Super Sport convertibles were built.

NOTE 3: V-8 models have the numeral '6' as the third digit of their series, style and serial number.

CHEVELLE 300 — (6-CYL/V-8) — SERIES 131/132 — Chevelles were mildly restyled for their second year. The nose was veed slightly outward and a new grille was seen. At the rear were new taillamps. 300 models had lower body sill moldings; Chevelle 300 rear fender nameplates and emblems; bright ventipanes; windshield and rear window reveal moldings; single unit taillamps with bright bezels; rear bumper back-up light opening covers; and small hubcaps. Interiors were pattern cloth and vinyl trim (all vinyl on station wagons) in a standard grade, with vinyl floor covering. Standard equipment included; heater and defroster; front foam cushions; electric windshield wipers; front seat belts; and five 6.95 x 14 blackwall tires (station wagons had 7.35 x 14 blackwall tires).

CHEVELLE 300

Model Number	Body/Style Number	Body Type & Seating	Factory Price	Shipping Weight	Production Total
131/2	13169	4-dr Sed-6P	2193/2251	2910/3035	Note 1
131/2	13111	2-dr Sed-6P	2156/2215	2870/3010	Note 1
131/2	13115	4-dr Sta Wag-6P	2453/2505	3185/3275	Note 2

NOTE 1: Some 26,500 Chevelle 300 sixes and 5,100 V-8s were built. Total production, in figures rounded-off to the nearest 100 units, was 31,600 cars, excluding station wagons (all Chevelle station wagons being contained in a separate series).

NOTE 2: Some 13,800 six-cylinder and 23,800 V-8 Chevelle station wagons were built during the 1965 model year. Total Chevelle station wagon output, in figures rounded-off to the nearest 100 units, was 37,600 cars. This includes all station wagons in the Chevelle 300, Chevelle 300 Deluxe and Chevelle Malibu Series.

NOTE 3: V-8s have the number '2' as the third digit of their series, model and serial number.

NOTE 4: Prices and weights above slash for six/below slash for V-8.

CHEVELLE 300 DELUXE — (6-CYL/V-8) — SERIES 133/134 — Chevelle 300 Deluxe models had higher bright bodyside trim strips; Chevelle 300 rear fender emblems; roof drip cap moldings; and rear cove outline moldings (except station wagons). Interiors were a plusher vinyl and cloth, with all-vinyl door trim and a unique dual-spoke steering wheel with horn ring. Standard equipment, in addition to that found on the Chevelle 300, included padded armrests.

CHEVELLE 300 DELUXE

Model Number	Body/Style Number	Body Type & Seating	Factory Price	Shipping Weight	Production Total
133/4	13369	4-dr Sed-6P	2220/2236	2910/3050	Note 1
133/4	13311	2-dr Sed-6P	2183/2288	2870/3010	Note 1
133/4	13335	4-dr Sta Wag-6P	2511/2616	3185/3320	Note 2

NOTE 1: Some 32,000 six-cylinder and 9,600 V-8 Chevelle 300 Deluxes were built. Total production, in figures rounded-off to the nearest 100, was 41.600 cars, excluding station wagons (All Chevelle station wagons being contained in a separate series).

NOTE 2: Some 13,800 six-cylinder and 23,800 V-8 Chevelle station wagons were built during the 1965 model year. Total Chevelle station wagon output, in figures rounded-off to the nearest 100 units, was 37,600 cars. This includes all station wagons in the Chevelle 300, Chevelle 300 Deluxe and Chevelle Malibu Series.

NOTE 3: V-8s have the number '4' as the third digit of their series, model and serial number.

NOTE 4: Prices and weights above slash for six/below slash for V-8.

1965 Chevrolet, Impala two-door convertible, V-8

CHEVELLE MALIBU — (6-CYL/V-8) — SERIES 135/136 — Cars in the Malibu series had the following features added to, or replacing, 300 Deluxe equipment: color-accented bodyside moldings; bright wheelhouse moldings; Malibu rear fender scripts (with Chevelle emblems); hood windsplit moldings: ribbed upper and lower cove trim panels; ribbed tailgate lower trim panel on station wagon; back-up lights in rear bumper; luxurious pattern cloth and vinyl interior trims; color-keyed deep twist floor carpeting; foam cushioned rear seat; specific dual-spoke steering wheel (with horn ring); electric clock; bright glove compartment facing molding (with series nameplate); and glovebox light.

CHEVELLE MALIBU

Model Number	Body/Style Number	Body Type & Seating	Factory Price	Shipping Weight	Production Total
135/6	13569	4-dr Sed-6P	2299/2405	2945/3080	Note 1
135/6	13537	2-dr HT-6P	2326/2431	2930/3065	Note 1
135/6	13567	2-dr Conv-6P	2532/2637	3025/3160	Note 2
135/6	13535	4-dr Sta Wag-6P	2590/2695	3225/3355	Note 3

NOTE 1: Some 56,400 six-cylinder and 95,800 V-8 Malibus were built. Total production, in figures rounded-off to the nearest 100 units, was 152,200 cars, excluding station wagons (all Chevelle station wagons being contained in a separate series).

NOTE 2: Exactly 19,765 Chevelle convertibles were built during the 1965 model year. However, this total includes both Malibu and Malibu Super Sport convertibles.

NOTE 3: V-8s have the number '6' as the third digit of their series, model and serial number.

NOTE 4: Prices and weights above slash for six/below slash for V-8.

CHEVELLE SUPER SPORT — (6-CYL/V-8) — SERIES 137/138 — A clean, sporty appearance was obtained by the use of wide bright body sill moldings; rear lower fender moldings; Malibu SS rear fender scripts; deck lid SS emblems; black-accented grille and rear cove (except silver rear cove with black exterior); specific Super Sport full wheelcovers; front bucket seats with bright trim ends; center console with four-speed manual or automatic transmissions; and all-vinyl luxury interiors. Special instrument panel features included temperature, ammeter and oil pressure gauges.

CHEVELLE SS

Model Number	Body/Style Number	Body Type & Seating	Factory Price	Shipping Weight	Production Total
137/8	13737	2-dr HT-6P	2484/2590	2980/3115	Note 1
137/8	13767	2-dr Conv-6P	2690/2796	3075/3210	Note 2

NOTE 1: Some 58,600 six-cylinder and 72,500 V-8 Malibus were built. total production, in figures rounded-off to the nearest 100, was 81,100 units.
NOTE 2: Exactly 19,765 Chevelle convertibles were built during the 1965 model year. However, this total includes both Malibu and Malibu Super Sport convertibles.
NOTE 3: V-8s have the number '8' as the third digit of their series, model and serial number.
NOTE 4: Prices and weights above slash for six/below slash for V-8.

1965 Chevrolet, Malibu SS two-door convertible, V-8

CHEVELLE SS-396

RPO Z16 was the midyear SS-396 package, which included a 396 cid/375 hp V-8 with dual exhausts and chrome accents; four-speed transmission; special shocks and suspension; 160 mph speedometer; and AM/FM stereo multiplex radio. Specific exterior trim included Malibu SS emblems mounted on front fenders; special rear cove panel and '396 Turbo-Jet' front fender emblems. An SS-396 emblem was mounted in the dash. Fifteen inch wide simulated mag style wheelcovers were included. The cost for option package was $1,501 and a total of just 201 cars were equipped with it.

Model Number	Body/Style Number	Body Type & Seating	Factory Price	Shipping Weight	Production Total
138	13837	2-dr HT-5P	4091	NA	Note 1
138	13867	2-dr Conv-5P	4297	NA	Note 1

CHEVY II — 100-4/100-6 — (4-CYL/6-CYL) — SERIES 111/113 — Chevy IIs for 1965 were mildly restyled with a new grille, new rear cove treatment and revised bright trim. Sedans benefited from a new roofline. Chevy II 100 models featured rear fender script emblems; bright ventipane frames; windshield and rear window reveal moldings (side and upper tailgate reveal moldings on station wagons) anodized aluminum grille with special emblems; single unit headlights with anodized aluminum bezels; grille opening moldings with Chevrolet hood nameplate; front fender engine identification emblems (with optional six and V-8); front bumper mounted parking and directional signal lights; small, bright hubcaps; cove divider molding (with nameplate and emblem); single-unit taillights with matching back-up light opening cover plates optional; back-up lights; cloth and vinyl trim interior; all-vinyl interior on station wagons; black rubber floor covering; and dual-spoke steering wheel with horn button. Standard equipment included heater and defroster; front seat belts; foam cushioned front seats; dual sun visors; 6.00 x 13 blackwall tubeless tires on four-cylinder models; and 6.50 x 13 blackwall tires on six-cylinder models. Station wagons had size 7.00 x 13 blackwall tires.

CHEVY II 100 SERIES

Model Number	Body/Style Number	Body Type & Seating	Factory Price	Shipping Weight	Production Total
111	11169	4-dr Sed-6P	2005	2520	Note 1
111	11111	2-dr Sed-6P	1968	2505	Note 1
113	11369	4-dr Sed-6P	2070	2620	Note 1
113	11311	2-dr Sed-6P	2033	2605	Note 1
113	11335	4-dr Sta Wag-6P	2362	2875	Note 2

NOTE 1: Total production, in figures rounded-off to the nearest 100 units, was 40,500 cars (excluding station wagons).
NOTE 2: A total of 21,500 Chevy II station wagons were built during the 1965 model year. This includes station wagons Chevy II '100' and Chevy II Nova Series.
NOTE 3: Six-cylinder models have the numeral '3' as the third digit of the series, style and serial numbers.

CHEVY II NOVA — (6-CYL) — SERIES 115 — Nova features used in place of, or in addition to, Chevy II 100 Series equipment included: full-length, color-accented bodyside moldings; rear quarter crown moldings; Nova nameplates and emblems on rear fenders; roof drip cap moldings; hood windsplit moldings; ribbed cove divider panel with nameplate and emblem; single-unit taillights with matching back-up lights; luxury pattern cloth and vinyl trim (all-vinyl on station wagons); bright accents on sidewall trim panels; armrests with built in ashtrays; series nameplate on glove compartment door; full-width instrument panel trim molding; specific dual-spoke steering wheel with horn ring; and color-keyed deep-twist carpet floor covering.

CHEVY II NOVA

Model Number	Body/Style Number	Body Type & Seating	Factory Price	Shipping Weight	Production Total
115	11569	4-dr Sed-6P	2195	2645	Note 1
115	11537	2-dr HT-5P	2222	2645	Note 1
115	11535	4-dr Sta Wag	2456	2880	Note 2

NOTE 1: Total production, in figures rounded-off to the nearest 100 units, was 51,700 cars (excluding station wagons).
NOTE 2: A total of 21,500 Chevy II station wagons were built during the 1965 model year. This includes station wagons Chevy II '100' and Chevy II Nova Series.
NOTE 3: V-8 models have the numeral '6' as the third digit of the series, style and serial numbers.

CHEVY II NOVA SUPER SPORT — (6-CYL) — SERIES 117 — Additional to, or replacing Nova equipment on Nova SS models were: color-accented bodyside and rear quarter moldings; front and rear wheel opening moldings; belt moldings; Nova SS rear fender nameplates and SS emblems; Nova SS deck lid nameplate and emblem; rear cove outline molding; silver-painted rear cove area; special Super Sport wheelcovers with 14 inch wheels and tires; luxurious all-vinyl trim and headliner; front bucket seats; floor-mounted shift and special trim plate (with optional four-speed and Powerglide transmissions); oil pressure, temperature and ammeter gauges (in place of warning lights); bright front seat outer end panels; SS glove compartment door nameplates; and electric clock.

1965 Chevy II, Nova SS two-door hardtop sports coupe, V-8 (PH)

CHEVY II NOVA SUPER SPORT

Model Number	Body/Style Number	Body Type & Seating	Factory Price	Shipping Weight	Production Total
117	11737	2-dr HT-5P	2381	2690	4,300

CHEVROLET BASE ENGINES

SIX-CYLINDER: Inline six-cylinder. Overhead valves. Cast iron block. Displacement: 230 cid. Bore and stroke: 3.87 x 3.25 inches. Compression ratio: 8.5:1. Brake hp: 140 at 4200 rpm. Seven main bearings. Hydraulic valve lifters. Carburetor: Rochester one-barrel Model 7025003.

V-8: Overhead valves. Cast iron block. Displacement: 283 cid. Bore and stroke: 3.875sx 3.0 inches. Compression ratio: 9.25:1. Brake hp: 195 at 4800 rpm. Five main bearings. Carburetor: Rochester two-barrel Model 7024101.

CHEVELLE BASE ENGINES

SIX-CYLINDER: Inline six-cylinder. Overhead valves. Cast iron block. Displacement: 194 cid. Bore and stroke: 3.563 x 3.25 inches. Compression ratio: 8.5:1. Brake hp: 120 at 4400 rpm. Seven main bearings. Hydraulic valve lifters. Carburetor: Rochester one-barrel Model 7023105.

V-8: Overhead valves. Cast iron block. Displacement: 283 cid. Bore and stroke: 3.875 x 3.00 inches. Compression ratio: 9.25:1. Brake hp: 195 at 4800 R. P. M. Hydraulic valve lifters. Carburetor: Rochester two-barrel Model 7024 101.

CHEVY II 100 SERIES ENGINE DATA

FOUR-CYLINDER: Inline four-cylinder. Overhead valves. Cast alloy iron block. Displacement: 153 cid. Bore and stroke: 3.875 x 3.25 inches. Compression ratio: 8.5:1. Brake hp: 90 at 4000 rpm. Five main bearings. Hydraulic valve lifters. Carburetor: Carter one-barrel Model 3379.

SIX-CYLINDER: Inline six-cylinder. Cast alloy block. Displacement: 194 cid. Bore and stroke: 3.563 x 3.25 inches. Compression ratio: 8.5:1. Brake hp: 177 at 2400 rpm. Seven main bearings. Hydraulic valve lifters. Carburetor: Rochester one-barrel Model 7023105.

CHASSIS FEATURES: Wheelbase: (full-size Chevrolets) 119 inches; (Chevelle) 115 inches; (Chevy II) 110 inches. Overall length: (full-size Chevrolet passenger cars) 213.1 inches; (full-size Chevrolet station wagons) 213.3 inches; (Chevelle passenger cars) 196.6 inches; (Chevelle station wagons) 201.4 inches; (Chevy II passenger cars) 182.9 inches; (Chevy II station wagons) 187.6 inches. Front tread: (full-size Chevrolets) 61.2 inches; (Chevelle) 58.0 inches; (Chevy II) 56.8 inches. Rear tread: (full-size Chevrolets) 61.6 inches; (Chevelle) 58.0 inches; (Chevy II) 56.3 inches. Tires: (full-size six-cylinder passenger cars) 7.35 x 14; (full-size V-8 passenger cars) 7.35 x 14; (convertibles) 7.75 xl4; (full-size station wagons) 8.25 x 14; (Chevelle passenger cars) 6.95 x 14; (Chevelle station wagons) 7.35 x 14; (Chevy II 100-4) 6.00 x 13; (Chevy II, Nova passenger cars) 6.50 x 13; (Chevy II Nova SS) 6.95 x 14; (Chevy II and Nova station wagons) 7.00 x 13.

CHEVROLET OPTIONS: Power brakes ($43). Power steering ($96). Four-season air conditioning, not available with 400 hp 409 ($363). Size 7.75 or larger tires required. Deluxe front seat belts with retractors ($8). Rear window defroster ($22). Tinted glass on all windows ($38); windshield only ($22). Rear bumper guards, not available on wagons ($10). Front bumper guards ($16). Heater/defroster delete ($72 credit). Tri-volume horn ($14). Padded instrument panel ($18.30). Rear luggage compartment lock on six-passenger wagons ($11). Roof luggage rack on wagons ($43). Six-Way power seat, not available on Biscayne, Super Sport or with four-speed transmission ($97). Power windows, not available on Biscayne ($102.25). Manual radio ($50). Push-button radio ($59). AM/FM push-button radio ($137). AM/FM radio with stereo ($244). Rear seat speaker ($13). Vinyl roof cover on Impala, SS sport coupe, Impala Sport Sedan ($75). Foam front seat cushion on Biscayne ($8). Divided second seat on wagons ($38). Sport styled steering wheel ($32). Comfort-lift steering wheel ($43). Vinyl interior on Biscayne sedan ($5). Wire design wheelcovers, not available on Impala SS ($75). Wire wheel design wheelcovers on Impala SS ($57). Electric two-speed windshield wipers with washer ($17). Three-speed manual transmission was standard in all models. Overdrive transmission ($107.60). Automatic transmission. Powerglide on six-cylinder models ($188.30); on V-8 models ($199.10). Turbo-Hydramatic with 327 and 396 V-8s. Four-speed manual floor shift transmission with 240 hp ($188.30); with 300, 340 and 400 hp engine ($236.75). Six-cylinder 250 cid 150 hp L22 engine. V-8 283 cid 220 hp L77 engine. V-8 327 cid 250 hp L30 engine ($95). V-8 327 cid 300 hp L74 engine ($138). V-8 396 cid 325 hp L35 engine. V-8 396 cid 425 hp L78 engine. V-8 409 cid 340 hp L33 engine ($242.10). V-8 409 cid 400 hp L31 engine ($320.65). V-8 425 hp 409 cid L3l-L80. V-8 425 hp 396 cid L78. Positive traction rear axle ($43). Heavy-duty air cleaner ($5.40). Heavy-duty clutch ($11). Available rear axle gear ratios: 3.35:1; 3.55:1.

CHEVELLE OPTIONS: Power brakes ($43). Power steering ($86). Four season air conditioning ($364). Rear antenna, not available on station wagons (no charge). Front bumper guards ($10); rear bumper guards, not available on wagons ($10). Rear windshield defroster ($22). Tinted glass on all windows ($31); windshield only ($20). Heater and defroster deletion ($72 credit, not available with air). Tri-volume horn ($14). Instrument panel safety pad ($18). Luggage rack on station wagons ($43). Two-tone paint ($16). Four-way power seat, not available on four-speed, SS or 300 Series) ($64). Power tailgate window on wagons ($27). Power top on convertible ($54). Power windows, not available on 300 Series ($102). Manual radio ($50). Push-button radio ($58). Push-button radio with rear seat speaker, not available on convertibles ($72). AM/FM radio ($137). Black vinyl roof cover on Sport Coupes ($75). Deluxe seat belts with retractors ($8). Divided second seat on wagons ($38). Sport styled steering wheel ($32). Comfort-lift steering wheel with four-speed or Powerglide ($43). Tachometer on V-8s ($48). Full wheelcovers, excluding Super Sport ($22). Simulated wire wheels, excluding Super Sport ($75). Simulated wire wheelcovers, excluding Super Sport ($57). Three-speed manual transmission was standard. Overdrive transmission ($108). Powerglide automatic transmission on six-cylinder ($188); on V-8s ($199). Four-speed

manual floor shift transmission ($188). Six-cylinder 230 cid 140 hp L26 engine. V-8 283 cid 220 hp RPO L77 engine. V-8 327 cid 250 hp L30 engine. V-8 327 cid 300 hp L74 engine. V-8 327 cid 250 hp L79 engine. Positive traction rear axle ($38). Heavy-duty clutch, on six-cylinder only ($5). Available rear axle gear ratios: 3.08:1; 3.31:1; 4.70:1; 2.73:1.

CHEVY II/NOVA OPTIONS: Power brakes ($43). Power steering, not available on four-cylinder ($86). Air conditioning, not available on four-cylinder ($317). Rear antenna, not available on station wagon (no charge). Rear armrest, 100 Series only ($10, standard on Novas)..Front Custom Deluxe retractable seat belts ($8). Tinted glass on all windows ($27); on windshield only ($13). Grille guard ($15). Rear bumper guard, not available on station wagons ($10). Tri-Volume horn, not available on AC ($14). Padded instrument panel ($16). Roof luggage rack on station wagons ($43). Two-tone paint ($11). Power tailgate window on station wagons ($27). Push-button radio with front speaker ($59). Manual radio ($50). Push-button radio with front and rear speakers ($72). Push-button AM/FM radio ($137). Divided second seat on station wagons ($37). Tachometer ($48). Super Sport wire wheelcovers ($57). Wire wheelcovers on Nova and 100 Series ($75). Wheelcovers, not available on Nova and Super Sport ($13). Wheelcovers for 13 inch wheels ($70). Three-speed manual transmission was standard. Automatic transmission, on V-8s ($178); on six and four-cylinder ($167). four-speed manual floor shift transmission on V-8 only ($188). Six-cylinder 230 cid 140 hp RPO L26 engine. V-8 283 cid 220 hp L77 engine. V-8 327 cid 250 hp L30 engine. V-8 327 cid 300 hp L74 engine. Positive traction rear axle, not available on V-8, AC ($5). Available rear axle gear ratios: 3.08:1; 3.55:1; 3.36:1; 3.07:1.

HISTORICAL FOOTNOTES: Model year production peaked at 2,382,509 units. Calendar year sales of 2,587,487 cars were recorded. E.M. Estes was the chief executive officer of the company this year. Chevy built 155,000 V-8 models including all Chevelle, Chevelle and Chevy II models and station wagons. They built 29,400 six-cylinders. Total production was 184,400 units. Chevy built 59,650 of its 396 cid V-8s and 2,828 of its 409 cid V-8s for 1965. This year was also the end of an era. The great W-block introduced in 1958 as a 348 cid, later the 409 of 1961, was phased out, and the Mark IV production version of the '63 Mark II NASCAR engine in its 396 cid version superseded the 409.

1966 CHEVROLET

BISCYANE — (6-CYL/V-8) — SERIES 153/154 — Chevrolet was in the second season of a totally new body change, so mild face-lift sufficed. Front fenders were given blunt, forward-thrusting shapes, while the four-inch headlamp system was placed in new anodized bezels flanking a revised anodized aluminum grille. At the rear, a break with the now traditional round taillamp units were made; the 1966 full-size cars had horizontal rectangles, with back-up lights built in on Biscayne and Bel Air models. Other Biscayne features included series rear fender script, bright ventipane frames, windshield and rear window reveal moldings, (tailgate and side reveal moldings on station wagons), and grille opening moldings. Interiors were upholstered in vinyl and cloth, with Deluxe door release handles featured, and a foam-cushioned front seat only. A silver-painted shatter-resistant rearview mirror was suspended above the instrument panel, which had a glove compartment lock, bright instrument cluster housing and padding. A dual-spoke steering wheel with horn ring was standard, as was carpeting on the floor, dual sun visors and embossed vinyl headlining. A heater and defroster unit, front and rear ashtrays, front and rear seat belts and five tubeless blackwall tires were included in the base equipment.

CHEVROLET I.D. NUMBERS: VIN located on plate attached to left front door hinge pillar. The number had 13 symbols. The first symbol is a 1 for Chevrolet; the second and third symbols indicate series and the third and fourth symbols indicate body type. (Together, these first five symbols comprised the model number and appear in the Body/Style Number column of charts below.) The sixth symbol indicated model year, 6=1966. The seventh symbol indicated assembly plant: A= Atlanta, Ga.; B=Baltimore, Md.; C=Southgate, Calif.; F=Flint, Mich.;G= Framingham, Mass.; J=Janesville, Wis.; K=Kansas City, Mo.; L=Los Angeles, Calif; N=Norwood, Ohio; R=Arlington, Texas; S= St. Louis, Mo.; T=Tarrytown, N.Y.; U=Lordstown, Ohio; W=Willow Run, Mich.; Y=Wilmington, Del.; Z=Fremont, Calif.; 1=Oshawa, Ontario (Canada); 2=St. Therese, Quebec (Canada) and P=Pontiac, Mich. The last six symbols were the sequential number. A Fisher Body Number tag on the cowl gives the style number, body number, trim and paint codes. Engine codes appear on the right side of six-cylinder blocks behind the distributor and right front of V-8 engine blocks: CHEVY II (153 cid/90 hp four) OA, OC, OG, OH, OJ; (194 cid/120 hp six) OK, OQ, OR, OS, OT; ZV, ZW, ZX, ZY; (230 cid/140 hp six) PC, PV,PX, PI; (283 cid/195 hp V-8) PO, PF, PL, PM, PE, PG, PQ, PS, PN, PP, PV, PO; (283 cid/220 hp V-8) QA, QB, QC, QF, PK, PP, QD, QE; (327 cid/275 hp V-8) ZA, ZB, ZC, ZD, ZF, ZK, ZM; (327 cid/350 hp V-8) ZG, ZH, ZI, ZJ; CHEVELLE (194 cid/120 hp six) AA, AC, AG, AH, AK, AL, AN, AR, AS, AT, AU, AV, AW, AX, AY; (230 cid/140 hp) CA, CB, CC, CD, BL, BM, BN, BO (283 cid/195 hp V-8) DA, DB, DE, DF, DK, DI, DJ (283 cid/220 hp V-8) DG, DH, DL, DM; (327 cid/250 hp V-8) EA, EB, EC, EE; (396 cid/325 hp V-8) ED, EH, EK, EM; (396 cid/360 hp V-8) EF, EJ, EL, EN; (396 cid/375 hp V-8) EG. CHEVROLET (250 cid/155 hp six) FA, FE, FF, FK, FL, FM, FP, FR, FV, FW, FX, FY, FZ, GP, GQ, GR; (283 cid/195 hp V-8) GA, GC, GF, GK, GS, GT; (283 cid/220 hp V-8) GL, GW, GX, GZ; (327 cid/275 hp V-8) HA, HB, HC, HF; (327 cid/230 hp V-8) ID; (396 cid/325 hp V-8) IA, IB, IC, IG, IV, IN; (427 cid/390 hp V-8) IH, II, IJ; (427 cid/425 hp V-8) ID, IO.

BISCAYNE SERIES

Model Number	Body/Style Number	Body Type & Seating	Factory Price	Shipping Weight	Production Total
153/4	15369	4-dr Sed-6P	2431/2537	3375/3510	Note 1
153/4	15311	2-dr Sed-6P	2379/2484	3310/3445	Note 1
153/4	15335	4-dr Sta Wag-6P	2772/12877	3770/3895	Note 1

NOTE 1: 83,200 six-cylinder Biscaynes and 39,200 V-8 Biscaynes were built, excluding station wagons.
NOTE 2: V-8 models have the numeral '4' as the third digit of their model, series, style and serial numbers.
NOTE 3: Prices and weights above slash for six/below slash for V-8.

BEL AIR — (6-CYL/V-8) — SERIES 155/156 — One step up Chevrolet's price and prestige ladder was the Bel Air, readily distinguished from the Biscayne by its full-length bodyside molding along the dent-prone bodyside flare. In addition, Bel Air script and Chevrolet emblems were used on the rear fenders, while roof drip gutter moldings and a deck lip molding were also added. Interiors were a bit plusher, in cloth and vinyl (except the station wagon, which was all-vinyl) and features added to or replacing Biscayne equipment included: a glovebox lamp, automatic front door courtesy/dome lamp switches, third seat courtesy lamp and third seat foam padding on station wagons.

BEL AIR SERIES

Model Number	Body/Style Number	Body Type & Seating	Factory Price	Shipping Weight	Production Total
155/6	15569	4-dr Sed-6P	2531/2636	3390/3525	Note 1
155/6	15511	2-dr Sed-6P	2479/2584	3315/3445	Note 1
155/6	15545	4-dr Sta Wag-9P	2948/3053	3815/3990	Note 1
155/6	15535	4-dr Sta Wag-6P	2835/2940	3770/3895	Note 1

NOTE 1: 236,600 Bel Airs were built, (excluding station wagons), of which 164,500 had V-8 engines and 72,100 had six-cylinder engines.
NOTE 2: V-8 models had the numeral '6' as the third digit of their series, style and serial numbers.
NOTE 3: Prices and weights above slash for six/below slash for V-8.

1966 Chevrolet, Impala four-door station wagon, V-8

IMPALA — (6-CYL/V-8) — SERIES 163/164 — A more Deluxe Chevrolet, with a color-accented full-length bodyside molding on the body flare peak, body sill bright moldings, front and rear wheel opening moldings, bright side window accents, Impala front fender nameplates and emblems, belt moldings, deck lid molding with color accent, triple-unit wraparound rear taillamps (dual unit on station wagon), back-up lamps in the rear bumper, hood windsplit molding and station wagon lower reveal molding. Interiors were plusher cloth and vinyl (all-vinyl on station wagon and convertible), with the following features added to, or replacing, Bel Air equipment: brushed aluminum lower instrument panel insert with bright bezel, fingertip door releases, foam cushioned rear seat, bright aluminum seat end panels, chrome-plated rearview mirror housings, bright windshield header (on convertible), rear seat speaker grille (convertible and two-door hardtop), and dual roof rear quarter panel interior lights on two-door hardtops (which also had dual instrument panel courtesy lamps along with the convertible).

IMPALA SERIES

Model Number	Body/Style Number	Body Type & Seating	Factory Price	Shipping Weight	Production Total
163/4	16369	4-dr Sed-6P	2678/2783	3425/3565	Note 1
163/4	16339	4-dr HT-5P	2747/2852	3525/3650	Note 1
163/4	16337	2-dr HT-6P	2684/2789	3430/3535	Note 1
163/4	16367	2-dr Conv-6P	2935/3041	3485/3610	Note 1
163/4	16345	4-dr Sta Wag-9P	3083/3189	3860/3985	Note 1
163/4	16335	4-dr Sta Wag-6P	2971/3076	3805/3930	Note 1

NOTE 1: Impala production totalled 654,900, of which 33,100 were six-cylinders and 621,800 were V-8s.
NOTE 2: V-8 models have the numeral '4' as the third digit of their series, model and serial numbers.
NOTE 3: Prices and weights above slash for six/below slash for V-8.

IMPALA SUPER SPORT — (6-CYL/V-8) — SERIES 167/168 — The sporting Impala lost some of its exterior distinction this year, with only the addition of Super Sport front fender nameplates, grille Impala SS indention bar, deck badge and specific tri-bar Super Sport wheelcovers giving distinction. Interiors again featured all-vinyl trim, with front bucket seats, console and SS identification on the instrument panel. Standard features added to those found on base-line Chevrolets were the same as on the Impala models.

1966 Chevrolet, Impala two-door convertible, V-8

IMPALA SUPER SPORT SERIES

Model Number	Body/Style Number	Body Type & Seating	Factory Price	Shipping Weight	Production Total
167/8	16737	2-dr HT-6P	2842/2947	3460/3485	Note 1
167/8	16767	2-dr Conv-6P	3093/3199	3505/3630	Note 1

NOTE 1: Impala Super Sport production totalled 119,300 of which 900 were six-cylinder and 118,400 were V-8s.
NOTE 2: V-8 models have the numeral '8' as the third digit of their series, model and serial numbers.
NOTE 3: Prices and weights above slash for six/below slash for V-8.

1966 Chevrolet, Caprice two-door hardtop coupe, V-8

CAPRICE — (V-8) — SERIES 166 — A very popular Sport Sedan option in 1965, the Caprice was expanded to series status for 1966. It included a new Custom Coupe with special formal roofline and two station wagon models with woodgrained bodyside trim. Interiors were plush cloth in the four-door hardtop Sport Sedan (bench front seat standard, Strato-back front seat optional), all-vinyl or cloth in the two-door hardtop Custom Coupe, and all-vinyl in the station wagons. A wood-look lower instrument panel insert was used, with wood-accented combination vinyl and carpet door panels (except on wagons) added. Exterior distinction came from color-keyed bodyside striping, wide, ribbed body sill moldings, Caprice front fender and deck signatures, wraparound rear taillamps with bright horizontal ribs, specific Caprice wheelcovers, roof rear quarter emblems, twin simulated exhaust ports below Custom Coupe backlight and a Caprice tailgate nameplate on the Custom Wagons.

CAPRICE SERIES

Model Number	Body/Style Number	Body Type & Seating	Factory Price	Shipping Weight	Production Total
166	16639	4-dr HT-6P	3063	3675	Note 1
166	16647	2-dr Cpe-6P	3000	3585	Note 1
166	16645	4-dr Sta Wag-9P	3347	4020	Note 1
166	16635	4-dr Sta Wag-6P	3234	3970	Note 1

NOTE 1: 181,000 Caprices were built, excluding station wagons.

CHEVELLE 300 — (6-CYL/V-8) — SERIES 131/132 — A new body graced 1966 Chevelles, with forward thrusting front fenders, new body contour lines, wider-appearing anodized aluminum grille and new rear body cove treatment. Chevelle 300 models were relatively lacking in ornamentation with series rear fender emblems, bright ventipane frames, windshield and rear window moldings, outside rearview mirror, four headlamps with anodized aluminum bezels, grille outline moldings, rear cove Chevelle nameplate, front bumper mounted park/turn lights, small hubcaps, single-unit rear lights (with bright bezels) and built-in back-up lights. Interiors were pattern cloth and vinyl trimmed, black rubber floor covering, plus all GM safety features and five blackwall tires, heater and defroster.

CHEVELLE 300 SERIES

Model Number	Body/Style Number	Body Type & Seating	Factory Price	Shipping Weight	Production Total
131/2	13169	4-dr Sed-6P	2202/2308	2935/3080	Note 1
131/2	13111	2-dr Sed-6P	2165/2271	2895/3040	Note 1

NOTE 1: A total of 28,600 Chevelle '300 Deluxes' were built of which 23,300 were six-cylinders and 5,300 were V-8s.
NOTE 2: V-8 models have the numeral '2' as the third digit of their serial numbers and style numbers.
NOTE 3: Prices and weights above slash for six/below slash for V-8.

CHEVELLE 300 DELUXE — (6-CYL/V-8) — SERIES 133/134 — A slightly upgraded Chevelle 300 with full-length bodyside moldings, Chevelle 300 Deluxe rear fender nameplates and painted rear cove Chevelle reveal moldings, bright tailgate molding and emblem on station wagon. A dual-spoke steering wheel with a horn ring was specific to this model, as was the color-keyed upper instrument panel with bright lower panel trim strip. Doors had bright accents on the trim panels and the rear armrests had built in ashtrays. Interiors were cloth and vinyl upholstered.

CHEVELLE 300 DELUXE SERIES

Model Number	Body/Style Number	Body Type & Seating	Factory Price	Shipping Weight	Production Total
133/4	13369	4-dr Sed-6P	2276/2382	2945/3095	Note 1
133/4	13311	2-dr Sed-6P	2239/2345	2910/3060	Note 1
133/4	13335	4-dr Sta Wag-6P	2575/2681	3210/3350	Note 1

NOTE 1: A total of 37.500 Chevelle '300s' were built (excluding station wagons), of which 27,100 were six-cylinders and 10,500 were V-8s.
NOTE 2: V-8 models had the numeral '4' as the third digit of their style and serial numbers.
NOTE 3: Prices and weights above slash for six/below slash for V-8.

CHEVELLE MALIBU — (6-CYL/V-S) — This nicely trimmed series added to or replaced equipment on the Chevelle 300 Deluxe as follows: slender body sill and wheelhouse moldings were added, along with Malibu rear fender nameplates and a hood windsplit molding. A rear cove outline molding surrounded the single-unit rear lights with built-in back-up lamps (vertical light units were used on the station wagons). A rear cove emblem was used, with Chevrolet script above on the deck lid. Station wagons in this series had a full-width ribbed molding and emblem and tailgate Chevelle nameplate. Interiors were plusher cloth and vinyl (all-vinyl on convertible and station wagon). A distinctive dual-spoke steering wheel was used. Black crackle-finish was used on the instrument panel upper section. A glove compartment light, bright-backed rearview mirror, bright roof rails and floor carpeting were additional Malibu features.

CHEVELLE MALIBU

Model Number	Body/Style Number	Body Type & Seating	Factory Price	Shipping Weight	Production Total
135/6	13569	4-dr Sed-6P	2352/2458	2960/3110	Note 1
135/6	13569	4-dr HT-6P	2458/2564	3035/3180	Note 1
135/6	13517	2-dr HT-6P	2378/2484	2935/3075	Note 1
135/6	13567	2-dr Conv-6P	2588/2693	3030/3175	Note 1
135/6	13535	4-dr Sta Wag-6P	2651/2756	2651/3375	Note 1

NOTE 1: A total of 241,500 Chevelle Malibus were built (excluding station wagons), of which 52,300 were six-cylinders and 189,300 were V-8s.
NOTE 2: V-8 models had the numeral '6' as the third digit of their style and serial numbers.
NOTE 3: Prices and weights above slash for six/below slash for V-8.

1966 Chevelle, SS-396 two-door hardtop sports coupe, V-8

CHEVELLE SS-396 — (V-8) — SERIES 138 — Chevelle's performance package for this year included twin simulated air intakes, ribbed color-accented body sill and rear fender lower moldings, SS-396 grille and rear cover emblems and Super Sport script on the rear fenders. Specific wheelcovers were included, as were five nylon red-stripe tires. Interiors were all-vinyl, with bench front seat standard and included all Malibu features (except for color-keyed vinyl-coated cargo floor mat and textured vinyl cargo area sidewalls.)

CHEVELLE SS-396 (SERIES 138)

Model Number	Body/Style Number	Body Type & Seating	Factory Price	Shipping Weight	Production Total
136	13617	2-dr HT-6P	2276	3375	Note 1
136	13667	2-dr Conv-6P	2984	3470	Note 1

NOTE 1: Chevelle Super Sport production was 72,272 units in both body styles.
NOTE 2: All 1966 Chevelle Super Sports were SS-396s.

CHEVY II — 100-4/100-6 — (4-CYL/6-CYL) — SERIES 111/113 — A new body was used for 1966 featuring single unit headlamps in new bright bezels, a refined anodized aluminum front grille, and turn directional signal lights in the front bumper. At the rear were new vertical-type taillights, of the single unit type with built-in back-up lamps. Chevy II '100' models had Chevy II rear fender emblems, bright ventipane frames, windshield and rear window reveal moldings, bright outside rearview mirror, grille opening moldings, small bright hubcaps, deck lid Chevy II emblem tailgate on wagons and cloth and vinyl interiors (all-vinyl on station wagons) and cloth and vinyl interiors (all-vinyl on station wagon). Standard features included a dual spoke steering wheel with horn button, padded instrument panel, glove compartment lock, vinyl door and sidewall trim panels, Deluxe type door handles and regulators, foam-cushioned front seat, dual sun visors, two coat hooks and other convenience items.

CHEVY II

Model Number	Body/Style Number	Body Type & Seating	Factory Price	Shipping Weight	Production Total
111/3	11169	4-dr Sed-6P	2065/2127	2535/2635	Note 1
111/3	11111	2-dr Sed-6P	2028/2090	2520/2630	Note 1
113	11335	4-dr Sta Wag-6P	2430	2855	Note 1

NOTE 1: Six-cylinder and optional V-8 units had the numeral '3' as the third digit of their style and serial numbers.
NOTE 2: A total of 47,000 Chevy II '100s' were produced, of which 44,500 were six-cylinders and 4,900 were optional V-8s.
NOTE 3: Prices and weights above slash for four-cylinder/below slash for six-cylinder.

CHEVY II NOVA — (6-CYL) — SERIES 115 — Plusher models, with exterior distinction derived from a color accent-full length bodyside molding, body sill moldings, Nova rear fender script and model badge, hood emblem, roof drip gutter bright moldings, door and rear quarter upper side moldings (on two-door hardtop Sport Coupe), bright roof rear quarter belt molding (on sedan), and full width-color accented deck trim with Chevy II nameplate. Interiors were cloth and vinyl (all vinyl on sport coupe and station wagon), with the following features added to equipment found on the Chevy II '100': distinctive dual-spoke steering wheel with horn ring, glove compartment door trim panel and nameplate, bright accents on door and sidewall trim, rear armrests with built-in ashtrays, foam cushioned rear seat, color-keyed floor carpeting and automatic front door dome light switches.

1966 Chevy II, Nova Super Sport two-door hardtop sports coupe, V-8

CHEVY II NOVA SERIES

Model Number	Body/Style Number	Body Type & Seating	Factory Price	Shipping Weight	Production Total
115	11569	4-dr Sed-6P	2245	2640	Note 1
115	11537	2-dr HT-6P	2271	2675	Note 1
115	11535	4-dr Sta Wag-6P	2518	2885	Note 1

NOTE 1: A total of 73,900 Chevy II Novas were built, excluding station wagons. Of these, 54,300 were six-cylinders and 19,600 were V-8s.
NOTE 2: V-8s were a Nova option, and are listed under options.

NOVA SS — (6-CYL) — SERIES 117 — The sporty Nova SS was identified on the exterior by color-accented wide body sill moldings, front and rear wheel opening moldings with extensions on both lower fenders, door and rear quarter upper bodyside moldings, an SS grille emblem, Nova SS rear fender scripts, a full width ribbed rear deck panel with Chevy II nameplate, and SS badge and special 14 inch Super Sport wheelcovers. Interiors included all-vinyl front bucket seats (console with four-speed or automatic) and most features found on Nova models. An SS emblem was found on the glovebox door.

NOVA SS SERIES

Model Number	Body/Style Number	Body Type & Seating	Factory Price	Shipping Weight	Production Total
117	11737	2-dr HT	2430	2740	10,100

NOTE 1: V-8s were a Nova SS option and are included in Powertrain Options.

CHEVROLET BASE ENGINES

(SIX-CYLINDER) Inline Six. Overhead valves. Cast-iron block. Displacement: 250 cid. Bore and stroke: 3.87 x 3.53 inches. Compression ratio: 8.5:1. Brake hp: 155 at 4200 rpm. Hydraulic valve lifters. Carburetor: Downdraft single-barrel.

(V-8) Overhead Valves. Cast iron block. Displacement: 283 cid. Bore and stroke: 3.875 x 3.0 inches. Compression ratio: 9.25:1. Brake hp: 195 at 4800 rpm. Five main bearings. Carburetor: Downdraft two-barrel.

CHEVELLE BASE ENGINES

(SIX-CYLINDER) Inline six-cylinder. Overhead valves. Cast iron block. Displacement: 194 cid. Bore and stroke: 3.563 x 3.25 inches. Compression ratio: 8.5:1. Brake hp: 120 at 4400 rpm. Seven main bearings. Hydraulic valve lifters. Carburetor: Rochester one-barrel Model 7023105.

(V-8) Overhead valves. Cast iron block. Displacement: 283 cid. Bore and stroke: 3.875 x 3.00 inches. Compression ratio: 9.25:1. Brake hp: 195 at 4800 R. P. M. Hydraulic valve lifters. Carburetor: Rochester two-barrel Model 7024 101.

SS-396 ENGINE: V-8. Overhead valves. Cast iron block. Displacement: 396 cid. Bore and stroke: 4.094 x 3.76 inches. Compression ratio: 10.25:1. Brake hp: 325 at 4800 rpm. Five main bearings. Hydraulic valve lifters. Downdraft four-barrel carburetor.

CHEVY II BASE ENGINES

FOUR-CYLINDER: Inline four-cylinder. Overhead valves. Cast alloy iron block. Displacement: 153 cid. Bore and stroke: 3.875 x 3.25 inches. Compression ratio: 8.5:1. Brake hp: 90 at 4000 rpm. Five main bearings. Hydraulic valve lifters. Carburetor: Carter one-barrel Model 3379.

SIX-CYLINDER: Inline six-cylinder. Cast alloy block. Displacement: 194 cid. Bore and stroke: 3.563 x 3.25 inches. Compression ratio: 8.5:1. Brake hp: 177 at 2400 rpm. Seven main bearings. Hydraulic valve lifters. Carburetor: Rochester one-barrel Model 7023105.

CHASSIS FEATURES: Wheelbase: (full-size Chevrolets) 119.0 inches; (Chevelle) 115.0 inches; (Chevy II) 110.0 inches. Overall length: (full-size Chevrolet) 213.2; (full-size wagons) 212.4 inches; (Chevelle) 197.0 inches; (wagons) 197.6 inches; (Chevy II) 183.0 inches; (wagons) 187.4 inches. Front tread: (full-size Chevrolet) 62.5 inches; (full-size wagons) 63.5 inches; (Chevelle) 58.0 inches; (Chevy II) 56.8 inches; (wagons) 56.3 inches. Rear tread: (full-size Chevrolet) 62.4 inches; (full-size wagons) 63.4 inches; (Chevelle) 58.0 inches; (Chevy II) 56.3 inches; (wagons) 55.8 inches. Tires: (full-size Chevrolet) 7.35 x 14, 7.75 x 14, 8.25 x 14, 8.55 x 14 (depending on model, engine and options); (Chevelle) 6.95 x 14 or 7.35 x 14, (SS-396) 7.75 x 14; (Chevy II) six-cylinder 6.50 x 13; on V-8 6.95 x 14.

CHEVROLET OPTIONS: Power brakes ($42). Power steering ($95). Four-Season comfort air conditioning. Power rear antenna ($28). Rear window defroster. Emergency road kit. Tinted Soft-Ray glass on all windows ($37); windshield only ($21). Front bumper guards ($16); rear bumper guards ($16). Stratoease front seat headrests ($53). Deletion heater and defroster ($71 credit). Tri-volume horn ($14). Special instrumentation ($79). Spare wheel lock. AM/FM push-button radio with front antenna ($134). AM/FM push-button radio with front antenna and rear speaker ($147). AM/FM push-button stereo radio with front antenna ($239). AM push-button radio with front antenna ($57). AM push-button radio with front antenna and rear speaker ($71). Vinyl roof cover in black or beige ($79). Front and rear Custom Deluxe color matched seat belts with front retractors. Four-Way power drivers seat ($70). Comfort-Tilt steering wheel ($42). Sport-styled steering wheel ($32). Tilt-telescopic steering wheel. Tachometer. Traffic hazard warning system. Set of five 14-inch wheels with 6JK rims ($21). Mag style wheelcovers ($53). Simulated wire wheelcovers ($56). Power windows ($100). A three-speed manual transmission, with column shift was standard on six-cylinder and 283 and 327 cid V-8 models. A heavy-duty three-speed, with floor shift was optional (required) with 396 and 427 cid V-8s ($79). Overdrive was optional for standard engines ($115). A four-speed manual transmission was optional for V-8 engines ($184). Close ratio version (2.20:1 low) was available for 396-427 V-8s. Powerglide two-speed automatic transmission was available with column shift (floor lever on bucket-seat equipped Series 163, 163, 166 cars) for six-cylinder ($184); for 283, 327 and 325 hp 396 V-8s ($195). Turbo Hydra-Matic was optional on 396 V-8 and 390 hp 427 cid V-8 ($226). Optional engines included: 283 cid, 220 hp Turbo-Fire V-8 (RPO L77). 327 cid, 275 hp Turbo-Fire V-8 (RPO-L30) ($93). 396 cid, 325 hp Turbo-Jet V-8 (RPO L35) ($158). 427 cid, 390 hp Turbo-Jet V-8 (RPO L36) ($316). 427 cid, 425 hp Turbo-Jet V-8 (RPO L72).

CHEVELLE/CHEVY II OPTIONS: Power brakes ($42). Power steering ($84). Four-Season air conditioning on Chevelle; All-Weather on Chevy II ($310). Center console for strato-bucket seats. Rear window defroster. Tinted Soft-Ray glass on all windows ($31); on windshield only ($21). Front bumper guards ($10); rear bumper guards ($10). Strato-Rest headrest ($53). Tri-volume horn. AM/FM push-button radio, not available in Chevy II. AM/FM push-button radio with rear speaker, not available in Nova. AM push-button radio ($57). AM push-button radio with rear seat speaker ($71). Vinyl roof cover ($74). Custom Deluxe color matched seat belts ($8). Four-way power front seat, not available in Chevy II. Strato-bucket front seats, not available in Chevy II. Comfort-Tilt steering wheel, not available in Chevy II. Sportsstyled steering wheel ($32). Tachometer, not available in Chevy II. Power operated convertible top. Wheelcovers ($21). Mag styled wheelcovers ($74). Simulated wire wheelcovers ($73). Power windows, Chevelle only. (CHEVELLE): A three-speed manual transmission, with column mounted shift, was standard on all Chevelle models. Overdrive was optional with standard engines ($116). A four-speed manual transmission, close ratio or wide range with floor shift was available for all V-8s ($184; $105 on SS-396). Powerglide two-speed automatic transmission was offered for six-cylinder and all cataloged V-8 engines except the 360 hp, 396 cid V-8 ($184; $195 on SS-396). Optional engines included: 230 cid/140 hp six-cylinder RPO L26 ($37). 283 cid/220 hp V-8 RPO L77. 327 cid/275 hp V-8 RPO L30 ($93). 327 cid/350 hp V-8 RPO L79 ($198). 396 cid/360 hp V-8 RPO L34 ($105). 396 cid/375 hp V-8 RPO L78 for SS-396 only. (CHEVY II): A three-speed manual transmission was standard in all models. A four-speed manual transmission was optional for cars equipped with V-8s ($184). Powerglide two-speed automatic transmission was optional for all engines ($164-$174). Optional engines included: 230 cid/140 hp six-cylinder RPO L26 ($37). 283 cid/220 hp V-8 RPO L77. 327 cid/275 hp V-8 RPO L30 ($93). 327 cid/350 hp V-8 RPO L79) (only 200 built).

HISTORICAL FOOTNOTES: Model year production peaked at 2,215,979 units. Calendar year sales of 2,202,758 cars were recorded. E.M. Estes was the chief executive officer of the company this year. Of the total production of 1966 Chevrolets, 1,499,876 were full-size cars; 18,100 were six-cylinder station wagons; 167,400 were full-size V-8 Chevrolet station wagons, 8,900 were six-cylinder Chevelles; 23,000 were V-8 Chevelles; 16,500 were six-cylinder Chevy II/Novas; and 4,900 were Chevy II/Nova V-8s. Chevrolet called their two-door hardtops 'Sport Coupes' in all lines. Style 16647 was the Caprice Custom Coupe.

1967 CHEVROLET

BISCAYNE — (6-CYL/V-8) — SERIES 153/154 — Chevrolet featured a new body for 1967. The Biscayne was the base line. It had an anodized aluminum grille with a bright bumper carrying the parking/turn signal lamps. Grille opening moldings were used, as were bright windshield and rear window reveal moldings. Biscayne script appeared on the rear fenders, while Chevrolet script was found on the deck lid and hood. Small bright metal hubcaps were standard and a chrome outside rearview mirror was included. Ventipane frames were plated. Dual unit taillamps were found at the rear with built-in back-up lights. Station wagons had tailgate reveal moldings and script on the tailgate. Interiors were cloth and vinyl or all-vinyl on station wagons. Standard features included a brake system warning light: cigarette lighter; illuminated heater control panel; padded instrument panel; glove compartment lock; front door armrests; rear armrests with built-in ashtrays; foam-cushioned front seat (with seatback latches on two-door models); and color-keyed floor carpeting.

BISCAYNE SERIES

Series Number	Body/Style Number	Body Type & Seating	Factory Price	Shipping Weight	Production Total
153/154	69	4-dr Sed-6P	2484/2589	3410/3525	Note 1
153/154	11	2-dr Sed-6P	2442/2547	3335/3465	Note 1
153/154	35	4-dr Sta Wag-6P	2817/2923	3765/3885	Note 2

NOTE 1: Some 92,800 Biscayne passenger cars were built in the 1967 model year. In figures rounded-off to the nearest 100 units, this includes 54,200 sixes and 38,600 V-8s. This does not include station wagons.
NOTE 2: Some 155,100 full-sized station wagons were built in the 1968 model year. In figures rounded-off to the nearest 100 units, this included 11,400 sixes and 140,700 V-8s. Since production of all station wagons was grouped together, this includes Biscayne, Bel Air, Impala and Caprice output.
NOTE 3: Data above slash for six/below slash for V-8.

BEL AIR — (6-CYL/V-8) — SERIES 155/156 — The middle-priced Chevrolet line had a narrow full-length bodyside molding; roof drip cap moldings; triple unit taillamps with center back-up lights; lower deck lid or tailgate moldings; and Bel Air script on the rear fenders to give it distinction. Interiors were somewhat refined and standard equipment, added to that found on the Biscaynes, included a glove compartment light; illuminated ignition switch and the following station wagon features: foam-cushioned third seat; color-keyed textured vinyl cargo area sidewalls (except two-seat wagon); and a third seat courtesy light.

BEL AIR SERIES

Series Number	Body/Style Number	Body Type & Seating	Factory Price	Shipping Weight	Production Total
155/156	69	4-dr Sed-6P	2484/2689	3395/3535	Note 1
155/156	11	2-dr Sed-6P	2542/2647	3340/3470	Note 1
155/156	45	4-dr Sta Wag-9P	2993/3098	3825/3940	Note 2

NOTE 1: Some 179,700 Bel Air passenger cars were built in the 1967 model year. In figures rounded-off to the neatest 100 units, this total included 41,500 sixes and 138,200 V-8s.
NOTE 2: Some 155,100 full-sized station wagons were built in the 1968 model year. In figures rounded-off to the nearest 100 units, this included 11,400 sixes and 140,700 V-8s. Since production of all station wagons was grouped together, this includes Biscayne, Bel Air, Impala and Caprice output.
NOTE 3: Data above slash for six/below slash for V-8.

1967 Chevrolet, Impala SS two-door convertible, V-8

IMPALA (6-CYL/V-8) — SERIES 163/164 — Exterior items giving the Impala its status included bright lower bodyside moldings; roof drip cap and reveal moldings on hardtops; bright side window accents on station wagon and sedan; deck lid center panel accents in silver (with Chevrolet center emblem flanking rear cove); black accented-taillamp surrounds and lower tailgate reveal molding (on the station wagon). Full wheelcovers were included. Interiors were cloth and vinyl or all-vinyl, depending on the model. These features were added to (or replaced) the equipment found on lower-priced lines: a brushed metal bright-outlined lower instrument panel facing; electric clock; finger-tip door releases; foam-cushioned rear seat;

bright seat end panels; bright garnish moldings on hardtop styles; bright foot pedal trim outlines (with power brakes); roof side rail lights; courtesy lamps under instrument panel (on two-door hardtop and convertible); and a power-operated convertible top.

IMPALA SERIES

Series Number	Body/Style Number	Body Type & Seating	Factory Price	Shipping Weight	Production Total
163/164	69	4-dr Sed-6P	2723/2828	3455/3575	Note 1
163/164	39	4-dr HT-6P	2793/2899	3540/3660	Note 1
163/164	37	2-dr HT-6P	2740/2845	3475/3590	Note 1
163/164	67	2-dr Conv-6P	2991/3097	3515/3625	Note 2
163/164	45	4-dr Sta Wag-9P	3129/3234	3860/3980	Note 3
163/164	35	4-dr Sta Wag-6P	3016/3122	3805/3920	Note 3

NOTE 1: Some 575,600 Impala passenger cars were built in the 1967 model year. In figures rounded-off to the nearest 100 units, this includes 18,800 sixes and 556,800 V-8s. It covers convertibles, but not station wagons.
NOTE 2: Exactly 29,937 full-sized Chevrolet convertibles were built in the 1967 model year. This total is included in Note 1. It covers both Impala and Impala SS convertibles with sixes and V-8s.
NOTE 3: Some 155,100 full-sized station wagons were built in the 1968 model year. In figures rounded-off to the nearest 100 units, this included 11,400 sixes and 140,700 V-8s. Since production of all station wagons was grouped together, this includes Biscayne, Bel Air, Impala and Caprice output.

1967 Chevrolet, Impala SS two-door hardtop Sport Coupe, V-8

IMPALA SUPER SPORT — (6 CYL/V-8) — SERIES 167/168 — The sporting Impala once again featured an all-vinyl interior, with front Strato bucket seats and a division console housing the shift lever as standard equipment (Strato bench seating was a no charge substitution). Exterior identification was made by the use of black accents on the grille (with bright horizontal bars remaining); front and rear wheelhouse moldings; black-accented body sill and lower rear fender bright moldings; a black-accent deck lid latch panel; SS deck lid and grille badges and specific Impala SS full wheelcovers.

IMPALA SUPER SPORT

Series Number	Body/Style Number	Body Type & Seating	Factory Price	Shipping Weight	Production Total
167/168	37	2-dr HT-6P	2898/3003	3500/3615	66,510
167/168	67	2-dr Conv-6P	3149/3254	3535/3650	9,545

NOTE 1: In figures rounded-off to the nearest 100 units, total model year production of Impala Super Sports included some 400 sixes and 75,600 V-8s.
NOTE 2: A total of exactly 2,124 Impala Super Sports were equipped with the SS-427 option.
NOTE 3: Data above slash for six/below slash for V-8.

CAPRICE — (V-8) — SERIES 116 — This posh Chevrolet included these exterior features on the Custom Sedan and Custom Coupe: font fender lights; front and rear wheelhouse moldings; bright lower bodyside moldings with rear quarter extensions; color-keyed bodyside stripes, belt reveal molding on Custom Coupe; black-accented deck lid panel with bright highlight trim; triple-unit taillights with back-up lights in the rear bumper; Caprice deck lid signatures; roofside panel nameplates; and specific Caprice full wheelcovers. Interiors were very plush, being trimmed in cloth; cloth and vinyl or all-vinyl, depending on model. Caprice Custom station wagons had wood panels, plus bright outline moldings on the bodysides and tailgate, plus Caprice tailgate nameplates. Interior features, in addition to (or replacing) those found on lower-priced models, included walnut-look lower instrument panel facing (with bright outline); pattern cloth and vinyl door panels; wood-look door panel trim in sedan and coupe (wagons were all-vinyl); and front seat fold-down center armrest (on sedans).

CAPRICE SERIES

Model Number	Body/Style Number	Body Type & Seating	Factory Price	Shipping Weight	Production Total
166	39	4-dr HT-6P	3130	3710	Note 1
166	47	2-dr HT-6P	3078	3605	Note 1
166	45	4-dr Sta Wag-9P	3413	3990	Note 2
166	35	4-dr Sta Wag-6P	3301	3935	Note 2

NOTE 1: In figures rounded-off to the nearest 100 units, a total of some 124,500 Caprice passenger cars were built in the 1967 model year. All were V-8 powered. This does not include Caprice station wagons.
NOTE 2: Some 155,100 full-sized station wagons were built in the 1968 model year. In figures rounded-off to the nearest 100 units, this included 11,400 sixes and 140,700 V-8s. Since production of all station wagons was grouped together, this includes Biscayne, Bel Air, Impala and Caprice output.

CHEVELLE 300 — (6-CYL/V-8) — SERIES 131/132 — Very slight sheetmetal changes, primarily in the front and rear fender edges, were made for Chevelle in 1967. A new anodized aluminum grille was used and all Chevelles had grille opening moldings with a Chevrolet badge; front bumper-mounted parking and directional signals; windshield bright reveal moldings; bright ventipane frames; rear window reveal moldings; and back-up lights in the rear bumper. Chevelle 300 models had rear fender series identification; single-unit taillights with bright bezels; a chromed outside rearview mirror; and Chevelle lettering in the deck cove. Interiors were trimmed in cloth and vinyl and included these features: parking brake and brake system warning light; cigarette lighter; glove compartment lock; lever-type door handles; front door armrests; foam-cushioned front seat; padded sun visors; black rubber floor covering; day/night rearview mirror; four-way hazard flasher system; and center dome light.

CHEVELLE 300 SERIES

Series Number	Body/Style Number	Body Type & Seating	Factory Price	Shipping Weight	Production Total
131/132	69	4-dr Sed-6P	2250/2356	2955/3090	Note 1
131/132	11	2-dr Sed-6P	2221/2326	2935/3360	Note 1

NOTE 1: Some 24.700 Chevelle 300 models were built for the 1967 model year.
NOTE 2: In figures rounded-off to the nearest 100 units, production included 19,900 sixes and 4,800 V-8s.
NOTE 3: Data above slash for six/below slash for V-8.

CHEVELLE 300 DELUXE — (6-CYL/V-S) — SERIES 133/134 — A slightly embellished Chevelle series featured (in addition to or replacing Chevelle 300 equipment) bright exterior body sill moldings; rear cove lower trim moldings on the sedan; Chevelle 300 Deluxe rear fender nameplates; and a rear cove or tailgate center emblem. Interiors were cloth and vinyl (all-vinyl in station wagon) and the instrument panel had a silver-finished upper accent. Rear armrests had built-in ashtrays, while the floor was covered with color-keyed vinyl-coated rubber. Automatic interior light switches were found on the door jambs. Bodies had "Flush & Dry" rocker panels and inner fenders.

CHEVELLE 300 DELUXE SERIES

Series Number	Body/Style Number	Body Type & Seating	Factory Price	Shipping Weight	Production Total
133/134	69	4-dr Sed-6P	2324/2930	2980/3110	Note 1
133/134	11	2-dr Sed-6P	2295/2400	2955/3090	Note 1
133/134	35	4-dr Sta Wag-6P	2619/2725	3230/3360	Note 2

NOTE 1: Some 26,300 Chevelle 300 Deluxe models were built during the 1967 model year.
NOTE 2: In figures rounded-off to the nearest 100 units, production included 19,300 sixes and 7,000 V-8s. (Station wagons not included.)
NOTE 3: Some 27,300 Chevelle station wagons were built during the 1967 model year.
NOTE 4: In figures rounded-off to the nearest 100 units, station wagon production included 5,900 sixes and 21,400 V-8s including both Chevelle 300 Deluxe, Chevelle Malibu and Concours wagons.
NOTE 5: Data above slash for six/below slash for V-8.

MALIBU — (6-CYL/V-8) — SERIES 135/136 — A nicely appointed Chevelle, the Malibu found exterior distinction by the use of bright lower bodyside and rear quarter moldings; roof drip cap molding; bright rear quarter window reveal moldings (on station wagons); Malibu rear fender nameplates; black-accented rear cove outline panel; single-unit taillights with black-accented bezels and bright horizontal strips; rear cove or tailgate Chevelle badge (to the right); and a tailgate molding on the station wagon. Full wheelcovers were included. Interiors were plusher and included a specific steering wheel; a walnut-finish upper panel on the instrument panel; illuminated heater control panel; electric clock; bright accents on the vinyl sidewall and door panel trim; bright bases on front armrests; a foam-cushioned rear seat; color-keyed floor carpeting; and courtesy lights in the convertible.

MALIBU SERIES

Series Number	Body/Style Number	Body Type & Seating	Factory Price	Shipping Weight	Production Total
135/136	69	4-dr Sed-6P	2400/2506	3000/3130	Note 1
135/136	17	2-dr HT-6P	2434/2540	2980/3115	Note 1
135/136	67	2-dr Conv-6P	2637/2743	3050/3185	Note 2
135/136	35	4-dr Sta Wag-6P	2695/2801	3260/3390	Note 3
135/1361	39	4-dr HT-6P	2506/2611	3065/3200	Note 1

NOTE 1: Some 227,800 Malibu passenger cars were built during the 1967 model year.
NOTE 2: In figures rounded-off to the nearest 100 units, this total included 40,600 sixes and 187,200 V-8s. (Does not include station wagons.)
NOTE 3: Some 27,300 Chevelle station wagons were built during the 1967 model year.
NOTE 4: In figures rounded-off to the nearest 100 units, station wagon production included 5,900 sixes and 21,400 V-8s including Chevelle 300 Deluxe, Chevelle Malibu and Concours wagons.
NOTE 5: Exactly 12,772 convertibles were built in the 1967 model year including Chevelle Malibu and Malibu SS models. This figure is included in the rounded-off totals given above. There is no SS breakout available.
NOTE 6: Data above slash for six/below slash for V-8.

1967 Chevelle, Concours Estate, four-door station wagon, V-8

CONCOURS — (6-CYL/V-S) — SERIES 137/138 — This was a luxury station wagon of the Chevelle line, featuring special black-accented grille; synthetic woodgrain exterior side and tailgate panelling (with bright outline trim); front and rear wheelhouse moldings; ribbed, grey-accented, body sill moldings; tailgate emblem, badge for Concours identification; and rear fender Concours script. Interiors were trimmed in textured vinyl. The passenger floor was carpeted and the cargo load floor had a vinyl coating.

CONCOURS SERIES

Series Number	Body/Style Number	Body Type & Seating	Factory Price	Shipping Weight	Production Total
137	38	35 Sta Wag-6P	2827/2933	3270/3405	Note 1

NOTE 1: Some 27,300 Chevelle station wagons were built during the 1967 model year.
NOTE 2: In figures rounded-off to the nearest 100 units, station wagon production included 5,900 sixes and 21,400 V-8s including Chevelle 300 Deluxe, Chevelle Malibu and Concours wagons.
NOTE 3: Data above slash for six/below slash for V-8.

CHEVELLE SS-396 — (V-8) — SERIES 138 — The Chevelle SS-396 had a youthful flair and was identifiable by these exterior additions or changes from other Chevelles: special black-accented grille with SS-396 badge; front and rear wheelhouse bright outlines; ribbed, gray-accented body sill moldings; color-keyed bodyside accent stripes; simulated air intakes on a domed hood; Super Sport rear fender emblems; black-painted rear cove panel (with SS-396 center medallion); five Red-Stripe special tires; and specific full wheelcovers. Interiors were all-vinyl, with a black-accent upper panel on the instrument board. Bucket seats were an option.

CHEVELLE SS-396 SERIES

Series Number	Body/Style Number	Body Type & Seating	Factory Price	Shipping Weight	Production Total
138	17	2-dr HT-6P	2825	3415	Note 1
138	67	2-dr Conv-6P	3033	3495	Notes 1/2

NOTE 1: Exactly 63,006 Chevelle SS-396 models were built during the 1967 model year. This includes both hardtop coupes and convertibles. All were V-8 powered. No further body style breakouts are currently available.
NOTE 2: No more than 29,937 Chevelle SS-396 convertibles were built.

CHEVY II 100 — (4-CYL./6-CYL) — SERIES 111/113 — Very minor trim changes occurred for the second year of the styling cycle. A new anodized aluminum grille had a distinct horizontal center bar motif, with a Chevy II nameplate to the driver's side. Chevy II '100' standard items included grille opening moldings-, front bumper mounted parking and directional signal lamps; windshield bright reveal molding; small, bright hubcaps; bright ventipane frames; chromed outside rearview mirror; vertical, single-unit taillights (with built-in back-up lights); rearview reveal molding; and deck lid or tailgate Chevy II emblems. Chevy II rear fender emblems gave side identification. Interiors were trimmed in cloth and vinyl or all-vinyl, depending on model. Standard interior features included bright instrument cluster bezel; brake system warning light; glove compartment lock; front door armrests; foam-cushioned front seat; folding front seatback latches (on two-door sedan); black rubber floor covering; four-way hazard flasher; and center dome light.

CHEVY II '100' SERIES

Series Number	Body/Style Number	Body Type & Seating	Factory Price	Shipping Weight	Production Total
111/113	69	4-dr Sed-6P	2120/2182	2560/2650	Note 1
111/113	11	2-dr Sed-6P	2090/2152	2555/2640	Note 1
111/113	35	4-dr Sta Wag-6P	2478	2865	Note 2

NOTE 1: Some 35,900 Chevy II '100' passenger cars were built for the 1967 model year.
NOTE 2: In figures rounded-off to the nearest 100 units, production included 480 fours, 33,720 sixes and 1,700 V-8s. (Does not include station wagons.)
NOTE 3: Some 12,900 Chevy II station wagons were built during model year 1967. In figures rounded-off to the nearest 100 units, this included 10,000 sixes and 2,900 V-8s. This includes Chevy II '100' and Nova wagons.
NOTE 4: Data above slash for four/below slash for six. (V-8s optional)

CHEVY II NOVA — (6-CYL) — SERIES 115 — A more Deluxe Chevy II, the Nova had these features in addition to (or replacing) those found on the Chevy II '100:` black-accented bodyside moldings; body sill moldings; roof drip cap bright moldings; door and rear quarter moldings on two-door hardtops; bright roof rear quarter belt molding on sedan; full-width deck lid or tailgate trim panel (with Chevy II badge and emblem); and bright metal extensions under station wagon rear lights. Interiors were cloth and vinyl (all-vinyl in station wagon). Standard features, in addition to those on lower-priced models, included an illuminated heater control panel; cigarette lighter; glove compartment door trim panel; glove compartment light; instrument panel nameplate; more distinctive door panels and sidewall trim (with bright accents); bright bases on front padded armrests; rear armrest bright bases and built-in ashtrays; foam cushioned rear seat; color-keyed floor carpeting; and automatic front door dome light switches.

CHEVY II NOVA SERIES

Series Number	Body/Style Number	Body Type & Seating	Factory Price	Shipping Weight	Production Total
115	69	4-dr Sed-6P	2298	2660	Note 1
115	37	2-dr HT Cpe-6P	2330	2660	Note 1
115	35	4-dr Sta Wag-6P	2566	2890	Note 2

NOTE 1: Some 47,600 Nova passenger cars were built in the 1967 model year.
NOTE 2: In figures rounded-off to the nearest 100 units, this production included 34,400 sixes and 13,200 V-8s. (Does not include station wagons).
NOTE 3: Some 12,900 Chevy II station wagons were built during model year 1967. In figures rounded-off to the nearest 100 units, this included 10,000 sixes and 2,900 V-8s. This includes Chevy II '100' and Nova wagons.

1967 Chevy II, Nova SS two-door hardtop sports coupe, V-8 (AA)

NOVA SUPER SPORT — (6-CYL) — SERIES 117 — Revised for 1967, the taut, small Nova continued to make an excellent high-performance car when equipped with this model-option. The 1967 Nova Super Sport had these exterior distinctions: special black-accented grille (with Nova SS emblem low on the driver's side); lower body moldings (above black-painted sill area); bodyside accent stripes; front and rear bright wheelhouse moldings (with extensions along lower fender edges); specific Super Sport full wheelcovers; Super Sport rear fender scripts; and full-width color accent deck lid trim panel (with center emblem and Nova SS signature). Interiors were all-vinyl, with front Stratobucket seats and bright seat end panels standard. A floor shift trim plate was included on cars with four-speed or automatic transmission. A three-spoke steering wheel was used. Other standard features were the same as Nova.

CHEVY II NOVA SUPER SPORT SERIES

Series Number	Body/Style Number	Body Type & Seating	Factory Price	Shipping Weight	Production Total
117	11737	2-dr HT Cpe-5P	2487	2690	10,100

NOTE 1: Total Nova SS production for the 1967 model year was 10,100 units.
NOTE 2: In figures rounded-off to the nearest 100 units, production included 1,900 sixes and 8,200 V-8s.

CAMARO — (6-CYL/V-8) — SERIES 123/124 — Chevrolet entered the pony car race with their sporty Camaro for 1967. A 'building block' system of option packages allowed the creation of many varied and distinctive vehicles. The base model featured: slender body sill moldings; black plastic grille; single-unit headlights; grille-mounted parking lights; small, bright metal hubcaps; taillights with bright bezels and built-in back-up lights; windshield pillar and rear belt moldings; and manual-operation top (on convertible). Standard interior features included color-keyed all-vinyl trim with Strato-bucket front seats; scuff-resistant cowlside panels with ventilator grilles; color-keyed carpeting; front armrests with bright bases; cigarette lighter; built-in instrument panel ashtray; automatic front door switches for dome or courtesy lights; locking glove compartment; friction-type ventipanes; and, in convertibles, built-in armrests and dual courtesy lights.

CAMARO SERIES

Series Number	Body/Style Number	Body Type & Seating	Factory Price	Shipping Weight	Production Total
123/124	37	2-dr HT Cpe-5P	2466/2572	2770/2920	195,765
123/124	67	2-dr Conv-5P	2704/2809	3025/3180	25,141

NOTE 1: Production included 602 Camaro Z-28 coupes; 64,842 Rally Sports (10,675 RS convertibles); 34,411 Super Sports coupes and convertibles (many with Rally Sport option also).
NOTE 2: Approximately 100-200 Indy Pace Cars and 200-300 Z-10 Pace Car replica hardtops were produced.

1967 Chevrolet, Camaro SS two-door hardtop, V-8

CHEVROLET BASE ENGINES

(SIX-CYLINDER) Inline six. Overhead valves. Cast-iron block. Displacement: 250 cid. Bore and stroke: 3.87 x 3.53 inches. Compression ratio: 8.5:1. Brake hp: 155 at 4200 rpm. Hydraulic valve lifters. Carburetor: Rochester model 7026027 single-barrel. (Base equipment for Biscayne/Bel Air/Impala/Impala SS)

(V-8) Overhead valves. Cast iron block. Displacement: 283 cid. Bore and stroke: 3.875 x 3.0 inches. Compression ratio: 9.25:1. Brake hp: 195 at 4800 rpm. Five main bearings. Carburetor: Rochester model 7027101 two-barrel. (Base V-8 equipment for Biscayne/Bel Air/Impala/Impala SS and standard in Caprice).

CHEVELLE BASE ENGINES

(SIX-CYLINDER) Inline six-cylinder. Overhead valves. Cast iron block. Displacement: 230 cid. Bore and stroke: 3.875 x 3.25 inches. Compression ratio: 8.5:1. Brake hp: 140 at 4400 rpm. Seven main bearings. Hydraulic valve lifters. Carburetor: Rochester one-barrel model 7027003. (Base engine all Chevelle models, except SS-396).

(V-8) Overhead valves. Cast iron block. Displacement: 283 cid. Bore and stroke: 3.875 x 3.00 inches. Compression ratio: 9.25:1. Brake hp: 195 at 4800 rpm. Hydraulic valve lifters. Carburetor: Rochester two-barrel Model 7027101. (Base V-8 equipment for all Chevelle models, except SS-396).

(SS-396 V-8) Overhead valves. Cast iron block. Displacement: 396 cid. Bore and stroke: 4.094 x 3.76 inches. Compression ratio: 10.25:1. Brake hp: 325 at 4800 rpm. Five main bearings. Hydraulic valve lifters. Carburetor: Rochester model 7027201 Quadra-Jet four-barrel. (Standard in SS-396 and not available in Chevelles otherwise).

CHEVY II/NOVA BASE ENGINES

(FOUR-CYLINDER) Inline four-cylinder. Overhead valves. Cast alloy iron block. Displacement: 153 cid. Bore and stroke: 3.875 x 3.25 inches. Compression ratio: 8.5:1. Brake hp: 90 at 4000 rpm. Five main bearings. Hydraulic valve lifters. Carburetor: Carter one-barrel model 3905971. (Base engine Chevy II 100 series)

(SIX-CYLINDER) Inline Six-cylinder. Cast alloy block. Displacement: 187.6 cid. Bore and stroke: 3.50 x 3.25 inches. Compression ratio: 8.5:1. Brake hp: 120 at 4000 rpm. Seven main bearings. Hydraulic valve lifters. Carburetor: Rochester one-barrel Model 7025105. (Base six for Chevy II 100 series and standard in Nova/Nova SS)

(V-8) Overhead Valves: Cast iron block. Displacement: 326.7 cid. Bore and stroke: 4.00 x 3.25 inches. Compression ratio: 10.0:1. Brake hp: 275 at 4800 rpm. Five main bearings. Hydraulic valve lifters. Carburetor: Rochester four-barrel. (There was not a Chevy II V-8 series, but this was the base V-8 option).

CAMARO BASE ENGINES

(SIX-CYLINDER) Inline Six-cylinder: Overhead valves. Cast iron block. Displacement: 230 cid. Bore and stroke: 3.88 x 3.25 inches. Compression ratio: 8.5:1. Brake hp: 140 at 4400 rpm. Seven main bearings. Hydraulic valve lifters. Carburetor: Downdraft one-barrel. (Base six for all Camaros).

(V-8) Overhead Valves: Cast iron block. Displacement: 327 cid. Bore and stroke: 4.0 x 3.25 inches. Compression ratio: 8.8:1. Brake hp: 210 at 4600 rpm. Five main bearings. Carburetor: Downdraft two-barrel. (Base V-8 for Camaros.)

CHASSIS FEATURES: Wheelbase: (full-size Chevrolets) 119.0 inches; (Chevelle) 115.0 inches: (Chevy II) 110.0 inches; (Camaro) 108.1 inches. Overall length: (full-size Chevrolet cars) 213.2 inches; (full-size Chevrolet wagons) 212.4 inches; (Chevelle) 197.0 inches; (Chevy II) 183.0 inches; (Camaro) 184.6 inches. Front tread: (full-size Chevrolet cars) 62.5 inches; (full-size Chevrolet wagons) 63.5 inches; (Chevelle) 58.0 inches; (Chevy II) 56.8 inches; (Chevy II wagons) 56.3 inches; (Camaro) 59.0 inches. Rear tread: (full-size Chevrolet cars) 62.4 inches; (full-size Chevrolet wagons) 63.4 inches; (Chevy II cars) 56.3 inches; (Chevy II wagons) 55.8 inches; (Camaro) 58.9 inches. Tires: (full-size Chevrolets) 8.25 x 14; (with disc brakes) 8.15 x 15; (Impala SS-427) 6.70 x 15; (Chevrolet station wagons) 8.55 x 14; (Chevelles) 7.35 x 14; (Chevelle 384 Sport Sedan/convertible/with 327 V-8s/and wagons) 7.75 x 14; (SS-396) F70 x 14; (Chevy II) 6.95 x 14; (Camaro) 7.35 x 14; (Camaro SS-350) D70 x 14; and (Camaro Z-28) 7.75 x 15.

FULL-SIZE CHEVROLET OPTIONS: Power brakes ($42). Power steering ($95). Four-Season air conditioning ($356). Comfort-On air conditioning ($435). Rear window air deflector on wagons ($19). Rear manual antenna, not available on wagons or with AM/FM radio ($9.50). Custom Deluxe front and rear seat belts ($6). Front shoulder belts ($23). Load area carpets on Caprice and Impala wagons ($53). Electric clock on Biscayne and Bel Air ($16). Rear window defroster ($21). Tinted glass on all windows ($37); windshield only ($21). Door edge guards on two-doors ($3); on four-doors ($6). Rear bumper guards ($16). Front bumper guards ($16). Head rest with Strato-Back or bucket seats ($53). Head rests with standard bench front seats ($42). Heater and defroster deletion ($71 credit). Tri-Volume horn ($14). Special instrumentation, V-8 only ($79). Automatic superlift level control, not available on six-cylinder ($79). Roof luggage rack on wagons ($42). Color-keyed floor mats ($11). Left-hand outside remote control mirror ($10). Two-tone paint ($16). Rear power antenna ($28). Six-Way power seat, not available on Biscayne or with bucket seats ($95). Four-Way power seat on Impala, Super Sport with bucket seats ($70). Power tailgate window, standard on three-seat wagons ($32). Power windows, not available on Biscayne ($100). Push-button radio with front antenna ($57).Push-button AM/FM radio with front antenna. ($134).Push-button AM/FM radio with front antenna and rear speaker ($147). AM/FM stereo radio with front antenna ($239). Rear seat speaker ($13). Vinyl roof cover on black or beige hardtops ($79). Divided second seat on wagons ($37). Strato-back vinyl seat in Caprice Custom sedan ($116). Strato-back vinyl seat in Impala SS (no charge). Strato-back cloth seat, Caprice Custom sedan and coupe ($105). Strato-back seats, including console. Floor-mounted shift ($158). Rear fender skirts ($26). Speed and cruise control ($50). Speed warning indicator ($11). Comfort-lift steering wheel with Powerglide. Hydramatic or four-speed transmission required ($42). Sport styled steering wheel ($32). Stereo tape system with four speakers ($129). Wheelcovers, not available on Impala SS or Caprice ($21). Mag style wheelcovers, on all Chevrolets except Impala SS and Caprice ($74). Mag style wheelcovers, Impala SS and Caprice ($53). Simulated wire wheelcovers on Impala SS and Caprice ($56). Simulated wire wheelcovers, all except Impala SS and Caprice ($74). A three-speed manual transmission with floor shift was standard with six-cylinder and 283/327 cid V-8s. A three-speed manual transmission with floor shift was optional for 396/427 cid V-8s (RPO M13). Overdrive was optional for the base six-cylinder and base 283 V-8 ($116). A four-speed manual transmission with floor shift coded RPO M20 was optional for all V-8 engines ($184). Powerglide two-speed automatic transmission was optional for all engines, except the 427 cid V-8 ($184 with six-cylinder; $195 with V-8). Turbo-Hydramatic ($226). Three-speed automatic transmissions were available with 327/396/427 cid V-8s. Optional engines included: [RPO L30] 327 cid/275 hp V-8 ($92.70). [RPO L35] 396 cid/325 hp V-8 ($158). [RPO L36] 427 cid/385 hp V-8 (included with SS 427 package for $316 total). Posi-Traction rear axle.

CHEVELLE/CHEVY II OPTIONS: Power brakes ($42). Power steering ($84). Four-Season air conditioning, Chevelle ($356). All-Weather air conditioning, Chevy II ($311). Rear antenna ($10). Custom Deluxe front and rear seat belts ($6). Driver and passenger front shoulder belts, standard type ($23); Custom Deluxe type ($26). Front bumper guards, Chevelle ($13); Chevy II ($10). Rear bumper guards, Chevelle ($13, but not available on wagons); Chevy II ($10). Electric clock, Chevelle 300 and 300 Deluxe ($16); Chevy II and Nova ($16). Rear window defroster, sedan and sport coupes ($21). Door edge guards, two-doors ($3); four-doors ($6). Tinted glass, all windows ($31); windshield only ($21). Driver and passenger Strato-Ease headrests, in Chevelle with bucket seats and Nova SS ($53), in Chevelle/Nova/100 with standard bench front seat ($42). Heater and defroster deletion ($70 credit). Tri-Volume horn, all Chevelle except 300 ($14). Special instrumentation on Chevelle V-8 sport coupes and convertibles ($79). Luggage rack, wagons ($42). Front and rear color-keyed floor mats ($11). Left-hand outside remote control mirror ($10). Two-tone paint ($16). Power tailgate window, wagons ($32). Push-button radio with front antenna and rear speaker ($71). Push-button radio with front antenna ($57). Push-button AM/FM radio with front antenna, Chevelle only ($134). Rear speaker ($13). Vinyl roof cover, Chevelle ($74). Strato bucket seats, Chevelle sport coupe and convertible ($111). Speed and cruise control, Chevelle V-8 models ($60). Speed warning indicator ($10). Sport styled steering wheel ($32). Stereo tape system with four speakers, Chevelle ($129). Tachometer in Chevelle V-8 models ($47). Wheelcovers, not available with disc brakes ($21). Mag styled wheelcovers for Chevy II/Nova SS/Chevelle SS-396, not available with disc brakes, ($53). Same for Nova/Chevy II 100/Chevelle models ($74). Simulated wire wheelcovers on Chevy II/Nova SS/SS-396/ without disc brakes ($56);same on Nova/Chevy II 100/Chevelle models ($74). A three-speed manual transmission, with column shift, was standard on all Chevy II/Novas. A four-speed manual transmission was available with optional Chevy II/Nova V-8s ($184). Powerglide two-speed automatic transmission was available with all Chevy II/Nova engines ($164 or $174 with V-8). Optional Chevy II/Nova engines included; [RPO L22] 250 cid/155 hp six-cylinder ($37). [RPO L30] 327 cid/275 hp V-8 ($93). Chevy II/Nova Posi-Traction rear axle ($42). A three-speed manual transmission, with column shift, was standard on Chevelles with six-cylinder engines and 283 or 327 cid V-8s. A three-speed, heavy-duty manual transmission, with floor shift, was standard with Chevelle SS-396s (optional other models for $79). An overdrive transmission was available with for Chevelles with base sixes and 283 V-8s ($116). A four-speed manual transmission, with floor shift, was optional for all Chevelle V-8 engines (wide- or close- ratio SS-396 for $105; others for $184). Powerglide two-speed automatic transmission was available with all Chevelle engines, except SS-396 ($116 with six; $195 with V-8). Turbo-HydraMatic three-speed automatic transmission was available with 396 cid V-8s ($147). Optional engines included: [RPO L22] 250 cid/155 hp six-cylinder ($26). [RPO L30] 327 cid/275 hp V-8 ($198). [RPO L79] 327 cid/325 hp V-8 ($93). [RPO L34] 396 cid/ 350 hp V-8 ($105; SS-396 only). Chevelle Posi-Traction rear axle ($42.15).

CAMARO OPTIONS: All-weather air conditioning ($356). Manual rear antenna, not available with AM-FM radio ($10). Custom Deluxe seat belts ($6). Standard front shoulder belts ($23). Custom Deluxe front shoulder belts ($26). Electric clock, not available with stereo ($16). Floor console with shifter ($47). Rear window defroster, coupe ($21). Tinted glass on all windows ($31); windshield only ($21). Rear bumper guards ($10). Front bumper guards ($13). Door edge guards ($3). Strato-Ease headrests ($53). Heater and defroster deletion ($32 credit). Tri-Volume horn, coupe only ($14). Ashtray light, coupe only ($1.60). Courtesy lights ($4). Glove compartment light, when not included ($2.65). Front and rear floor mats ($42). Power steering ($84). Power windows ($100). Manual push-button radio ($57). Manual push-button radio with rear seat speaker ($71). AM-FM radio ($133). Vinyl roof cover, black or beige for sport coupe only ($74). Folding rear seat ($32). Strato-back front seat, not available on convertible with console ($26). Speed and cruise control with V-8 on Powerglide only ($50). Speed warning indicator ($11). Comfort-tilt steering wheel ($42). Sports style steering wheel ($32). Stereo tape system with four speakers ($128). Simulated wire wheelcovers, not available with disc brake ($74). Simulated mag wheelcovers, not available with disc brakes ($74). Special instrumentation group included ammeter, temperature, oil and fuel gauges; electric clock mounted on console; fuel indicator light and tachometer in instrument panel ($79). A three-speed manual transmission was standard on all models, except Z-28. A three-speed heavy-duty manual transmission with floor shift was available for 350/396 cid V-8 engines. A four-speed manual transmission was optional for all engines ($184 with SS-350). Powerglide two-speed automatic transmission was available for six-cylinder ($184) and 327/350 cid V-8s ($195). Turbo-Hydramatic was optional with 396 cid/325 hp V-8. Optional engines included: [RPO Z28] 302 cid/290 hp V-8 (see Z28 package price). [RPO L30] 327 cid/ 275 hp V-8 ($93). [RPO L48] 350 cid/295 hp V-8 (see L-48 package below). [RPO L35] 396 cid/325 hp V-8. [RPO L78] 396 cid/375 hp V-8. Posi-Traction rear axle ($42).

CAMARO OPTION PACKAGES

(Z10): Indy Pace Car coupe package. Installed for a special promotional run of 200-300 cars made during the period of just a couple of weeks.

(Z21): Style trim group RPO Z21 adds front and rear wheel house moldings, drip gutter moldings on coupe, and bodyside accent stripes. ($29).

(Z23) Special interior group RPO Z23 replaces standard equipment with these items: bright pedal pad frames, windshield pillar moldings in bright metal and roof rail moldings in coupe ($11).

(Z87) Custom interior RPO Z87 replaces standard equipment with these special items: roof rear quarter dome lights on sport coupe, recessed door handles, color-keyed accent bands on front and rear seats, special front armrests. glove compartment light, three-spoke oval steering wheel with ornaments, carpeted scuff panels on doors, molded luggage compartment mat ($95).

(Z22) Camaro Rally Sport RPO Z22 includes style trim group and parking lights below bumper, special grille with electrically controlled panels concealing headlamps, 'RS' grille, fender and gas cap emblems, wide lower body moldings, hood drip bright moldings on coupe, bodyside accent strips, black-painted specific taillight bezels and back-up lights below rear bumper ($105).

(L48) Camaro SS-350 option RPO L48 features these additions: 295 hp Turbo-Fire 350 V-8. 'SS' grille. fender and gas cap emblems (even when 'RS' group is included), special hood and simulated intake grids, front hood stripes and five special D70 x 14 red-stripe tires ($105).

(L34) The high-performance SS-396 package coded RPO L34 included equipment similar to the SS-350 package, plus the bigger engine.

(Indy Pace Car) Actual Official Pace Cars for the 1967 Indianapolis 500-Mile Race were equipped with TR 732-Z bright blue custom interior; matching top boot; Rallyee wheels; D70-14 nylon cord redline tires; and a blue nose stripe. Under the hood was an L35 396 Turbo-Jet V-8 hooked to an M-40 Turbo-Hydramatic and 3.07:1 positraction rear axle. Chevrolet's May 1967 PACE CAR ACTIVITY BOOK listed 43 Camaro Pace Car convertible replicas built as "Festival" cars, plus 10 replicas for use by Indianapolis Motor Speedway officials and about 25 "Brass Hat" Camaro Pace Car convertibles for VIPs. Including the three actual Pace Cars, a total of at least 81 Camaro Pace Car convertible replicas were made for speedway activities. A total of 86 cars are known to exist and 19 of those have the 396 cid V-8. Information about the Camaro Pace Car Registry can be obtained from the International Camaro Owners Club, 2001 Pittston Ave., Scranton, PA 18503 or by calling (717) 347-5839.

HISTORICAL FOOTNOTES: All Chevrolets appeared in dealer showrooms Sept. 29, 1966. Model year production peaked at 1,900,049 units. Calendar year sales of 1,978,550 cars were recorded. E.M. Estes was the chief executive officer of the company this year. In addition to Camaro convertible Pace Cars, Chevrolet supplied eight to 18 Impala station wagons, 10 three-quarter ton trucks and five half-ton pickups for official use during the Indianapolis 500.

1968 CHEVROLET

BISCAYNE — (SIX/V-8) — SERIES 153/154 — Chevrolets grew longer in 1968, with the addition of some bumper, grille, hood and fender modifications. The change that stood out the most was in the taillamp design, which now featured recessed lenses housed in rear bumper apertures. The hood was restyled to cover recessed windshield wipers. The front end featured a 'floating' type bumper design, in which a grille with slightly finer gridwork showed through below the bumper bar. Headlights were now mounted in rectangular bezels. The size of the parking lamps, notched into the front corners of the body, was reduced from 1967 and the lens was now smooth and light colored. Biscayne was the base series with standard equipment including all GM safety features; front seat shoulder belts; door-actuated light switches; heater and defroster; cigarette lighter; locking glovebox; carpeting; armrests; center dome light; Flush and Dry rocker panels; and either the base six or V-8. Passenger cars wore 8.25 x 14 blackwall tires, while station wagons had size 8.55 x 14.

CHEVROLET I.D. NUMBERS: VIN on plate on left front door pillar. First three symbols indicate make and series and appear as Series Number in first column of charts below. For example, first car listed has numbers 153 (1=Chevrolet Div.; 53=Biscayne six) for six-cylinder series and 154 (1=Chevrolet Div.; 54=Biscayne V-8) for eight-cylinder series. Fourth and fifth symbols indicate body type and appear as Body/Style Number in second column of charts below. Sixth symbol indicates model year 8=1968. Seventh symbol identifies assembly plant: A=Atlanta, Ga.; B=Baltimore, Md.; C=Southgate, Calif; D=Doraville, Ga.; F=Flint, Mich.; G=Framingham, Mass.; J=Janesville, Wis.; K=Kansas City, Mo.; U=Lordstown, Ohio; L=Los Angeles, Calif.; N=Norwood, Ohio; R=Arlington, Texas; S=St. Louis, Mo.; T=Tarrytown, N.Y.; W=Willow Run, Mich.; Y=Wilmington, Del.;Z=Fremont, Calif,; 2=St. Therese, Canada. Next six symbols are sequential production number. Body Number tag riveted to cowl indicates some of the same information, plus trim and paint codes. Engine numbers are stamped on front right side of V-8 blocks and right side of six-cylinder block behind distributor. Consult factory or aftermarket sources for numerous Chevrolet engine codes.

BISCAYNE SERIES

Series Number	Body/Style Number	Body Type & Seating	Factory Price	Shipping Weight	Production Total
153/154	69	4-dr Sed-6P	2484/2589	3395/3525	Note 1
153/154	11	2-dr Sed-6P	2442/2547	3335/3465	Note 1
153/154	35	4-dr Sta Wag-6P	2817/2923	3765/3885	Note 3

NOTE 1: In rounded-off total, 82,100 Biscayne 1968 passenger cars built.
NOTE 2: Rounded-off total includes 44,500 sixes and 3,600 V-8 non-wagons.
NOTE 3: Rounded-off total of 175,600 full-size station built in all lines.
NOTE 4: Wagon total includes 7,700 sixes/167,900 V-8s, but no series breakout.
NOTE 5: Data above slash for six/below slash for V-8.

BEL AIR — (SIX/V-8) — SERIES 155/156 — The Bel Air Series was Chevrolet's moderate-priced, full-size line for 1968. Bel Air had all standard equipment found in Biscaynes, plus mid-bodyside moldings; bright metal rear window, roof drip and windshield moldings; front and rear side marker lamps; glovebox and ignition switch lights; and upgraded interior trims. Station wagons featured all-vinyl interior; seat belts for all passengers; and automatic ignition key alarms. The three-seat station wagon also had a power tailgate window.

BEL AIR SERIES

Series Number	Body/Style Number	Body Type & Seating	Factory Price	Shipping Weight	Production Total
155/156	69	4-dr Sed-6P	2723/2828	3466/3582	Note 1
155/156	11	2-dr Sed-6P	2681/2786	3404/3518	Note 1
155/156	45	4-dr Sta Wag-9P	3183/3238	3878/3981	Note 3
155/156	35	4-dr Sta Wag-6P	3020/3125	3823/3926	Note 3

NOTE 1: In rounded-off total 152,200 Bel Air 1968 passenger cars built.
NOTE 2: Rounded-off total includes 28,900 sixes and 123,400 V-8 non-wagons.
NOTE 3: Rounded-off total of 175,600 full-size station wagons in all lines.
NOTE 4: Wagon total includes 7,700 sixes/167,900 V-8s, but no series breakout.
NOTE 5: Data above slash for six/below slash for V-8

1968 Chevrolet, Impala two-door convertible, V-8.

IMPALA — (SIX/V-8) — SERIES 163/164 — The Impala Series was Chevrolet's top-selling full-sized line. It had the same general styling features as the other big cars, except that a new formal-type roofline treatment was available. This gave buyers a choice between a fastback or "coach" style top. Standard equipment began with everything included for the Bel Air. However, bright roof drip moldings were not used on Impala two-door sedans or four-door sedans and station wagons. Additional features for the volume series included Deluxe steering wheel; door and window frame moldings; ignition switch and luggage lights; and front and rear foam seat cushions. The Impala sport coupe had thin, bright metal rocker panel accent moldings below its doors and bright metal wheel lip trim. The convertible featured courtesy lights, all-vinyl upholstery and carpeting on lower door panels. The three-seat Impala station wagon had a built-in rear bumper step. Super Sport equipment returned to its original status as an optional equipment package.

IMPALA SERIES

Series Number	Body/Style Number	Body Type & Seating	Factory Price	Shipping Weight	Production Total
163/164	69	4-dr Sed-6P	2846/2951	3513/3623	Note 1
163/164	39	4-dr HT Sed-6P	2917/3022	3601/3711	Note 1
163/164	87	2-dr HT Cpe-6P	2863/2968	3517/3623	Note 1
164	47	2-dr FT Cpe-6P	3021	3628	Note 1
164	67	2-dr Conv-6P	3197	3677	Note 5
164	45	4-dr Sta Wag-9P	3358	4042	Note 3
164	35	4-dr Sta Wag-6P	3245	3984	Note 3

NOTE 1: In rounded-off total, 710,900 Impala 1968 passenger cars built.
NOTE 2: Rounded-off total includes 11,500 sixes and 699,500 V-8 non-wagons.
NOTE 3: Rounded-off total of 175,600 full-size station built in all lines.
NOTE 4: Wagon total includes 7,700 sixes/167,900 V-8s, but no series breakout.
NOTE 5: Impala convertible production was 24,730 for model year.
NOTE 6: Data above slash for six/below slash for V-8

1968 Chevrolet, Caprice two-door hardtop sports coupe, V-8

1968 Chevrolet, Caprice two-door hardtop sports coupe, V-8 (GM)

CAPRICE — (V-8) — SERIES 166 — The Caprice represented the top of the full-sized Chevrolet line. Its equipment assortment began with all Impala features, plus full wheelcovers; courtesy and ashtray lamps; Caprice signature scripts; fender lights; distinctive side moldings; electric clock; and front center armrest seat. The Caprice coupe also included the Astro Ventilation system. Caprice station wagons had instrument panel courtesy lamps and, in three-seat styles, courtesy lights in the auxiliary passenger area.

CAPRICE SERIES

Series Number	Body/Style Number	Body Type & Seating	Factory Price	Shipping Weight	Production Total
166	39	4-dr HT Sed-6P	3271	3754	Note 1
166	47	2-dr FT Cpe-6P	3219	3648	Note 1
166	45	4-dr Sta Wag-9P	3570	4062	Note 2
166	35	4-dr Sta Wag-6P	3458	4003	Note 2

NOTE 1: In rounded-off total, 115,500 Caprice 1968 passenger cars built.
NOTE 2: Rounded-off total of 175,600 full-size station built in all lines.
NOTE 3: Wagon total includes 7,700 sixes/167,900 V-8s, but no series breakout.
NOTE 4: Data above slash for six/below slash for V-8.

CHEVELLE 300 — (SIX/V-S) — SERIES 131/132 — The Chevelle was completely and very attractively restyled for model year 1968, with one additional body style added to the line in a new station wagon. Characteristics of the latest appearance included long hood/short deck characteristics with the front fenders swept back and cut under the feature line. Two wheelbases were provided, the shorter for two-doors and the longer for four-doors. The standard V-8 now displaced 307 cid. Lowest in price was the base 300 line on which, other than the windshield surround and ventipane frames, practically no chrome moldings were used. A new front bumper was straighter-lined, with the only openings being large squares flanking the license plate, plus smaller, outboard rectangles incorporating amber parking light lenses. The horizontal, dual headlamps were mounted in individual, bright metal bezels of square shape and the full-width grille featured a fine gridwork of cross-hatched moldings with black-finished air slot directly above. Chevelle scripts appeared on the front fenders behind the wheel openings (at mid-body height) and above the left headlight. Standard equipment included all GM safety features, front armrests; heater and defroster; base six or V-8 and 7.35 x 14 two-ply (four-ply rated) tires. Base station wagons, however, used 7.75 x 14 blackwalls. Standard interiors were all textured vinyl in blue, gold or black.

CHEVELLE 300 SERIES

Series Number	Body/Style Number	Body Type & Seating	Factory Price	Shipping Weight	Production Total
131/132	27	2-dr Cpe-6P	2341/2447	3988/3124	Note 1
131/132	35	4-dr Nomad Wag-6P	2625/2731	3350/2731	Note 3

NOTE 1: In rounded-off total 12,600 Chevelle 300 1968 passenger cars built.
NOTE 2: Rounded-off total includes 9,700 sixes and 2,900 V-8 non-wagons.
NOTE 3: Rounded-off total of 45,500 Chevelle wagons built in all lines.
NOTE 4: Wagon total includes 10,700 sixes/34,800 V-8 but no series breakouts.
NOTE 5: Data above slash for six/below slash for V-8.

CHEVELLE 300 DELUXE — (SIX/V-8) — SERIES 133/134 — The easiest way to distinguish the Chevelle 300 Deluxe was to look for the ribbed, bright metal rocker panels below the door. These were promoted as the 'Flush and Dry' type. Other equipment, above the most basic assortment, included a left-hand outside rearview mirror; front shoulder belts; Chevrolet badge on grille center and rear deck latch panel; door switch dome lamp; lane change turn signals; keyless door locking; suspended accelerator pedal; back-up lights and self-adjusting brakes. Four-doors had chrome window sill moldings, while two-doors had chrome trim along the upper window frame. As on all Chevelles, when the base V-8 was added, a black, rectangular engine call-out badge was positioned ahead of the front fender side marker lens and framed in the same band of bright metal. The all-vinyl textured seating surfaces used in Chevelle 300 Deluxes came only in black, although blue, black or gold fabric/vinyl combinations were also provided.

CHEVELLE 300 DELUXE SERIES

Series Number	Body/Style Number	Body Type & Seating	Factory Price	Shipping Weight	Production Total
133/134	69	4-dr Sed-6P	2445/2550	3071/3207	Note 1
133/134	37	2-dr HT Cpe-6P	2479/2584	3036/3171	Note 1
133/134	27	2-dr Cpe-6P	2415/2521	3005/3141	Note 1
133/134	35	4-dr Nomad Wag-6P	2736/2841	3409/3554	Note 3

NOTE 1: In rounded-off total 43,200 Deluxe 300 1968 passenger cars built.
NOTE 2: Rounded-off total includes 24,500 sixes and 17,700 V-8 non-wagons.
NOTE 3: Rounded-off total of 45,500 Chevelle wagons built in all lines.
NOTE 4: Wagon total includes 10,700 sixes/34,800 V-8 but no series breakouts.
NOTE 5: Data above slash for six/below slash for V-8.

1968 Chevelle, Malibu four-door sedan, V-8

CHEVELLE MALIBU — (SIX/V-8) — SERIES 135/136 — The new Malibu was trimmed to play its role as the top non-super-high-performance car in the Chevelle lineup. Like the 300 Deluxe, a Chevrolet insignia was carried in the center of its grille. The Malibu however, did not have the 300 Deluxe's matching insignia on the rear deck latch panel. Instead, the panel was banded in chrome, with a Chevelle signature near the right rear taillamp. The taillamps themselves were different, as Malibu back-up lights were repositioned into the back bumper. Other added highlights included Malibu scripts on the front fendersides; chrome trim along the front feature line (also extending along the lower side feature line); twin pinstripes along the upper side feature line; and additional window frame accents. Standard equipment began at the Deluxe level and added hide-away two-speed wipers; Deluxe steering wheel; illuminated heater controls; ignition alarm system; crank-operated ventipanes; side marker lights; high-level ventilation; and wheelcovers. Interior trim choices varied with body style and there was also a special Concours four-door hardtop. It came with all-vinyl seating; lockable glovebox with light; extra-thick foam-cushioned seats; color-keyed wall-to-wall carpeting; black-accented wheel openings; black-trimmed lower body accents; ribbed bright metal rear deck lid latch panel plate; Concours signature scripts; chrome wheel lip moldings; special oval steering wheel with horn tabs; and woodgrained dash panel inlays. It was called the Concours Sport Sedan and had a lot of extra appeal. Malibu interior trims included the regular fabric/vinyl patterns in gold, black, blue and grey-green; or all-vinyl in teal, gold, black, blue, red and parchment/black or the Concours Sport Sedan's special Custom fabric choice in gold, blue, black or grey-green.

MALIBU SERIES

Series Number	Body/Style Number	Body Type & Seating	Factory Price	Shipping Weight	Production Total
135/136	69	4-dr Sed-6P	2524/2629	3090/3223	Note 1
135/136	39	4-dr HT Sed-6P	2929/2735	3165/3298	Note 1
135/136	37	2-dr HT Cpe-6P	2558/2663	3037/3170	Note 1
135/136	67	2-dr Conv-6P	2757/2863	3115/3245	Note 5
135/136	35	4-dr Sta Wag-6P	2846/2951	3421/3554	Note 3

NOTE 1: In rounded-off total 266,400 Malibu 1968 passenger cars built.
NOTE 2: Rounded-off total includes 33,100 sixes and 233,200 V-8 non-wagons.
NOTE 3: Rounded-off total of 45,500 Chevelle wagons built in all lines.
NOTE 4: Wagon total includes 10,700 sixes/34,800 V-8 but no series breakouts.
NOTE 5: Combined Malibu and SS-396 convertible production was 10,800.
NOTE 6: Data above slash for six/below slash for V-8.

CHEVELLE CONCOURS — (SIX/V-8) — SERIES 137/138 — In addition to the Concours Sport Sedan in the regular model line there was a separate Concours Estate station wagon sub-series. It included only one luxury wagon model, which was specially-trimmed. It came standard with all GM safety features, plus all-vinyl upholstery; lighted glovebox light; extra-thick foam cushioned seats; simulated Walnut exterior side and rear paneling; hide-away two-speed wipers; chrome wheel lip moldings; and special oval steering wheel with the horn tabs.

CONCOURS ESTATE SUB-SERIES

Series Number	Body/Style Number	Body Type & Seating	Factory Price	Shipping Weight	Production Total
137/138	35	4-dr Cus Sta Wag-6P	2978/3083	3543/3561	Note 1

NOTE 1: Concours Estate production included with that of all Chevelle wagons.

CHEVELLE SS-396 — (V-8) — SERIES 138 — Quick-size convenience; floor-mounted shift; vinyl upholstery; carpeting; and brand-new looks characterized the high-performance Chevelle SS-396 Series. Other standard extras on the two models in the line included fender-mounted side marker lamps; lower bodyside moldings with front and rear extensions; black-accented finish below the feature line, front to rear; specific SS-396 identification at grille and latch panel centers; black-out grille treatment; black-finished deck panel plate; F70 x 14 four-ply rated special Red Stripe (or White Stripe) tires; concealed windshield wipers; 325 hp 396 cid V-8; full wheelcovers with SS center medallions; and "Turbo-Jet 396" engine call-out badges ahead of side marker lenses.

CHEVELLE SS-396 SERIES

Series Number	Body/Style Number	Body Type & Seating	Factory Price	Shipping Weight	Production Total
138	37	2-dr HT Cpe-6P	2899	3475	Note 1
138	67	2-dr Conv-6P	3102	3551	Notes 1/3

NOTE 1: Rounded-off calendar production total was 57,600 Chevelle SS-396s
NOTE 2: Model year production was 62,785 Chevelle SS-396s.
NOTE 3: No body style breakouts available.
NOTE 4: Chevy built 131,700 Turbo-Jet 396 V-8s in model year 1968 (all lines).

1968 Nova, two-door sedan, V-8

CHEVY II NOVA — (FOUR/SIX) — SERIES 111/113 — Chevrolet's senior-compact underwent a basic styling change in 1968. The new body was longer and wider and featured a Chevelle-inspired semi-fastback roofline with wide, flaring sail panels. Another change was a reduction in base model offerings, with only two- and four-door sedans remaining. The four-cylinder engine remained available, but only slightly more than 1,000 were sold. The 230 cid engine was the base six and the 307 cid was the base V-8. Even the Turbo-Jet 396 high-performance V-8s was optional. So was a Super Sport equipment package. The Chevy II would stay with this basic body through 1974 and a just slightly modified one thereafter. However, the 1968 model is easy to spot by the positioning of the Chevy II name at the center of the upper grille surround. Other features included single headlamps set into square bezels; a full-width multiple bar grille; and the Chevelle-like rear end look. Standard equipment included all GM safety features; heater and defroster; front armrests; foot-operated emergency brake; ignition alarm system; concealed fuel filler; front and rear side marker lights; and 7.35 x 14 (four-ply rated) two-ply blackwall tires.

CHEVY II SERIES

Series Number	Body/Style Number	Body Type & Seating	Factory Price	Shipping Weight	Production Total
FOUR					
111	69	4-dr Sed-6P	2229	2790	Note 1
111	27	2-dr Sed-6P	2199	2760	Note 1
SIX					
113	69	4-dr Sed-6P	2291	2890	Note 2
113	27	2-dr Sed-6P	2261	2860	Note 2
V-8					
114	69	4-dr Sed-6P	2396	NA	Note 2
114	27	2-dr Sed-6P	2367	NA	Note 2

NOTE 1: 1,270 four-cylinder 1968 Chevy IIs built.
NOTE 2: Rounded-off totals include 146,300 sixes and 53,400 V-8s.

CAMARO — (SIX/V-8) — The Camaro was virtually unchanged as it entered its second model year, although close inspection would show the addition of the new front and rear side marker lights and ventless door glass. Standard equipment included all GM safety features; integrated front headlamps and parking lights; Strato-Bucket front seats; all-vinyl interior; carpeting; Astro Ventilation system; front shoulder belts; outside rearview mirror; the new side marker lights; heater and defroster; five 7.35 x 14 (two-ply) four-ply rated blackwall tires; and courtesy lights in the convertible.

CAMARO SERIES

Series Number	Body/Style Number	Body Type & Seating	Factory Price	Shipping Weight	Production Total
123/124	37	2-dr HT Spt Cpe-4P	2638/2727	3040/3050	214,711
123/124	67	2-dr Conv-4P	2852/2941	3160/3295	20,440

NOTE 1: Production included 50,937 sixes and 184,178 V-8s.
NOTE 2: 40,977 Camaros had the RS equipment package.
NOTE 3: 27,884 Camaros had the SS equipment package.
NOTE 4: 7,199 Camaros had the Z-28 option.
NOTE 5: 12,997 Camaros built for export.
NOTE 6: 54,948 three-speeds/47,572 four-speeds/132,631 automatics built.
NOTE 7: 35,866 with A/C; 115,280 cars with p/s 3,304 with p/w.
NOTE 8: Data above slash for six/below slash for V-8.

1968 Camaro, two-door SS-350 hardtop sports coupe, V-8 (AA)

CHEVROLET BASE ENGINES

CHEVY II ENGINES

INLINE: Four. Overhead valves. Cast iron block. Displacement: 153 cid. Bore and stroke: 3.875 x 3.25 inches. Compression ratio: 8.5:1. Brake hp: 90 at 4000 rpm. Five main bearings. Hydraulic valve lifters. Carburetor: Rochester one-barrel Model 7028009.

(CHEVELLE 300/CHEVY II NOVA/CAMARO) Inline Six: Overhead valve. Cast iron block. Displacement: 230 cid. Bore and stroke 3.875 x 3.25 inches. Compression ratio 8.5:1. Brake hp 140 at 4400 rpm. Seven main bearings. Hydraulic valve lifters. Carburetor; Rochester one-barrel Model 7028017.

(BISCAYNE/BEL AIR/IMPALA) Inline Six: Overhead valve. Cast iron block. Displacement: 250 cid. Bore and stroke: 3.875 x 3.53 inches. Compression ratio: 8.5:1. Brake hp: 155 at 4200 rpm. Seven main bearings. Hydraulic valve lifters. Carburetor: Carter one-barrel Model 3891593.

(BISCAYNE/BEL AIR/IMPALA/CHEVELLE/CHEVY II/CAPRICE) V-8: Overhead valves. Cast iron block. Displacement: 307 cid. Bore and stroke: 3.875 x 3.25 inches. Compression ratio: 10.0:1. Brake hp: 200 at 4600 rpm. Five main bearings. Carburetor: Rochester two-barrel Model 7028101.

(CAMARO) V-8: Overhead valves. Cast iron block. Displacement: 326.7 cid. Bore and stroke: 4.00 x 3.25 inches. Compression ratio: 8.75:1. Brake hp: 210 at 4000 rpm. Five main bearings. Hydraulic valve lifters. Carburetor: Rochester two-barrel. Model 7028101.

(CAPRICE) V-8: Overhead valves. Cast iron block. Displacement: 307 cid. Bore and stroke: 3.875 x 3.25 inches. Compression ratio: 10.0:1. Brake hp: 200 at 4600 rpm. Five main bearings. Carburetor: Rochester two-barrel Model 7028101.

(CHEVELLE SS-396) V-8: Overhead valves. Cast iron block. Displacement: 396 cid. Bore and stroke: 4.09 x 3.76 inches. Compression ratio: 10.25:1 Brake hp: 325 at 4800 rpm. Five main bearings. Hydraulic valve lifters. Carburetor: Rochester Quadra-Jet four-barrel.

CHASSIS FEATURES: Wheelbase: (Chevrolet) 119 inches; (Chevelle two-door) 112 inches; (Chevelle four-door) 116 inches; (Nova) 111 inches; (Camaro) 108 inches. Overall length: (Chevrolet wagon) 214 inches; (Chevrolet) 215 inches; (Chevelle wagon) 208 inches; (Chevelle four-door) 202 inches, (Chevelle two-door) 198 inches; (Nova) 190 inches; (Camaro) 185 inches. Front tread: (Chevrolet) 62.5 inches; (Chevelle) 59 inches; (Nova) 59 inches; (Camaro) 59 inches. Rear tread: (Chevrolet) 62.4 inches; (Chevelle) 59 inches; (Nova) 58.9 inches; (Camaro 58 inches. Various tire options.

CHEVROLET OPTIONS: Dual stage air cleaner, with six ($5.30). Four Season air conditioning, except with 425 hp V-8 ($368.65). Comfortron automatic temperature control air conditioning, except with 425 hp V-8 ($447.65). Posi-traction rear axle ($42.15). Station wagon load area carpeting ($52.70). Heavy-duty chassis equipment on Biscayne ($36.90). Electric clock, standard in Caprice ($15.80). Heavy-duty clutch ($10.55). Rear window defroster ($2 1. 10). Turbo-Fire 250 hp 3:27 cid V-8 ($63.20). Turbo-Fire 275 hp 327 cid V-8 ($92.70). Turbo-Jet 325 hp 396 cid V-8 ($158). Turbo-Jet 385 hp 427 cid V-8, included with SS-427 option ($263.30). Turbo-Jet 425 hp 427 cid V-8 ($447.65). Dual exhausts with 250, 275, Or 325 hp V-8 ($27.40). Tinted glass, windshield ($25.30); all windows ($39.50). Caprice retractable headlights ($79). Head rests with Strato bucket seats ($52.70); with bench seats ($42.15). Special instrumentation including ammeter, oil pressure, temperature gauges and tachometer, in Caprice ($79), in other models, including clock, ($94.80). Remote control left-hand OSRV mirror ($9.50). Station wagon rooftop luggage rack, fixed type ($44.25); adjustable type ($63.20). Power rear antenna ($28.45). Power drum brakes ($42.15). Power disc brakes, includes 15 inch hubcaps, wheels and tires ($121.15). Power door lock system, two-door ($44.80); four-door ($68.50). Six-Way power seat, except Biscaynes, cars with bucket seats or cars with four-speed manual transmission ($94.80). Four-Way power left-hand bucket seat ($69.55). Power steering ($94.80). Power tailgate window ($31.60). Power windows, except Biscayne and Styles 15511-611 ($100.10). Heavy-duty radiator ($13.70).Push-button AM radio with antenna ($61.10).Push-button AM/FM radio with front antenna ($133.80). AM/FM radio and stereo ($239.15). Rear manual antenna ($9.50). Rear speaker ($13.20). Stereo tape system with four speakers ($133.80). White or black vinyl roof for all hardtops ($89.55). Cloth Strato-Back seats ($105.35). Strato-Back seats, bucket style ($158). Superlift shock absorbers, standard type ($42.15); automatic level control type ($89.55). Cruise Master speed control ($92.70). Rear fender skirts, except station wagons and disc brakes ($26.35). Speed warning indicator ($10.55). Deluxe steering wheel ($4.25). Comfort-Tilt steering wheel ($42.15). Sport steering wheel ($31.60). Front and rear special purpose suspension ($21.10). Overdrive transmission ($115.90). Powerglide transmission, with six ($184.35); with V-8s, except '427' ($194.85). Close-Range four-speed manual transmission with '427' V-8 ($184.35). Heavy-duty Close-Range four-speed manual transmission with '427' V-8 only ($310.70). Wide-Range four-speed manual transmission, in all V-8 models ($184.35). Turbo-Hydramatic transmission ($226.45-$237). All-vinyl interior trim ($5.30-$10.55). Wheelcovers, standard 14 inch ($21.10), mag-style 14 inch — Caprice or Super Sport ($52.70); others ($73.75); simulated wire type — Caprice or Super Sport ($55.85); others ($73.75). Mag spoke 14 inch wheelcovers. Caprice or Super Sport ($52.70); others ($73.75). Rally wheels, on Caprice or SS-427 without disc brakes; ($21.10); others ($31.60); with discs ($10.55). Appearance Guard Group ($26.35-$49.55). Auxiliary Lighting Group ($2.65-$39). Convenience Operating Group ($9.50-46.40). Decor Group ($21.10-$72.80). RPO Z03 Impala Super Sport Option, includes special all-vinyl interior; Strato-Bucket seats; center console; SS wheelcovers and console shift with automatic or four-speed manual transmissions, on Impala Custom coupe, sport coupe or convertible ($179.05). RPO Z24 Impala SS 427 Option, includes all above, plus special hood; Red Stripe tires; ornamentation; special suspension features and 15 inch wheels, with RPO L36 Turbo-Jet 385 hp V-8 ($358.10); with RPO L72 TurboJet 425 hp V-8 ($542.45). Notes: V-8 engine option prices are in addition to cost of base V-8. Where a range of prices is indicated, retail varied according to model, trim level, body style or inclusion of other features. It was usually slightly less expensive to add some options to the topline models. Numerous tire options were provided for all 1968 Chevrolets.

CHEVELLE OPTIONS: Four-Season air conditioning ($360.20). Station wagon air deflector ($19). Positraction rear axle ($42.15). Economy or performance axle ($2.15). Heavy-duty battery ($7.40). Station wagon rooftop carrier ($44.25). Electric clock ($15.80). Heavy-duty clutch, with six ($5.30); with V-8 ($10.55). Center console, including electric clock and with bucket seats, gear shift lever is mounted in console/available with three-speed only in SS-396 ($50.60). Rear windshield defroster ($21.10). RPO L22/ 250 cid 155 hp six ($26.35). RPO L73/ 327 cid 250 hp V-8 ($63.20). RPO L30/ 327 cid 275 hp V-8 ($92.70). RPO L79/ 327 cid 325 hp V-8 ($198.05). RPO L34/ 396 cid 350 hp V-8. in SS-396 only ($105.35). RPO L78/396 cid 375 hp V-8. in SS-396 only ($237). Dual exhausts ($27.40). Temperature-controlled fan ($15.80). Tinted glass, all windows ($34.80); windshield only ($26.35). Special instrumentation, Malibu V-8s and SS-396 only ($94.80). Light monitoring system ($26.35). Remote-control left-hand outside rearview mirror ($9.50). Two-tone paint ($21.10). Power disc front brakes ($100.10). Power front drum brakes ($42.15). Power steering ($94.80). Power convertible top ($52.70). Power windows, in Concours/Malibu/SS396 only ($100.10). AM/FM radio with front antenna ($61.10). AM/FM radio with front antenna ($133.80). AM/FM radio with stereo and front antenna ($239.15). Rear seat speaker ($13.20). White or black vinyl top on hardtops ($84.30). Strato bucket seats in Malibu/SS396 ($110.60). Superlift shock absorbers ($42.15). Speed and Cruise Control, automatic transmission required ($52.70). Speed warning indicator ($10.55). Comfortilt steering wheel ($42.15). Sport style steering wheel ($31.60). SS-396 accent striping ($29.50). Four-speed manual transmissions: special close-ratio type for SS396 with 375 hp V-8 ($237); close-ratio for all models with 325-360-375 hp V-8s ($184.35); Wide-Range type ($184.35). Turbo-Hydramatic in SS-396 with 325-350 hp V-8s ($237). Three-speed manual transmission with floor-shift ($79). Powerglide transmission, with six ($184.35); with small V-8s ($194.85). Overdrive ($115.90). Vinyl interior trim, Malibu or 300s ($10.55). Wheelcovers, regular type ($6.35); mag style ($21.10); simulated wire/mag-spoke Rally styles, all ($73.75). Rally wheels with special hubcaps and trim rings ($31.60). Hidden windshield wipers ($19).

CHEVY II OPTIONS: All-Season air conditioning, except four-cylinders ($347.60). Rear positraction axle ($42.15). Console with floor mounted shift, except four-cylinders, (bucket seats required) not available on 295 or 325 hp engine with standard transmission ($50.60). Electric clock ($15.80). Heavy-duty clutch ($5.30). 155 hp, 250 six-cylinder ($26.35). 275 hp, 327 V-8 ($92.70). 325 hp, 327 V-8 ($198.05). Dual exhaust, V-8 models with standard or 275 hp engine only ($27.40). Tinted glass, all windows ($30.55); windshield only ($21.10). Special instrumentation, V-8 coupes with console ($94.80). Left-hand outside remote-control mirror ($9.50). Power brakes, all with drum-type brakes except four-cylinder ($42.15). Power brakes, all with disc-type brakes except four-cylinder ($100.10). Power steering, except four-cylinder ($84.30). Vinyl roof cover in white or black, all except four-cylinder ($73.75). Sport-styled steering wheel ($31.60). Stereo tape system ($133.80)' Powerglide, four and six-cylinder models ($163.70). Powerglide, with 200, 275, 295 and 325 hp engines ($174.25). Four-speed wide range, with 200, 275, 295 and 325 hp engines ($184.35). Four-speed close range, with 325 hp engines ($79.00). Simulated wire wheelcovers ($73.75). Mag-style wheelcovers ($73.75). Mag spoke wheelcovers ($31.60). Custom Exterior Group ($68.50). Exterior Decor Package. ($31.60). Nova SS Option includes: 295 hp Turbo-Fire 350 engine, special steering wheel, hood ornaments, black accented grille and rear deck plate, hood insulation, nameplate, deck emblems, SS grille, red stripe tires on six inch rims. Special Interior Group ($15.80).

CAMARO OPTIONS: Four-Season air conditioning ($360.20). Positraction rear axle ($42.15). Electric clock ($15.80). Rear window defroster ($21.10). 155 hp Turbo-Thrift, six-cylinder ($26.25). 275 hp, Turbo-Fire, V-8 ($92.70). Dual exhaust with deep tone mufflers, with 210 or 275 hp engines ($27.40). Dual exhaust, with 210 or 275 hp engines ($27.40): Tinted glass on all windows, with air conditioning ($26.35); windshield only ($30.55). Special instrumentation not available with 375 hp or 302 cid engine. Includes ammeter, temperature, oil pressure and fuel gauges mounted on console, electric clock and tachometer mounted in instrument panel, in V-8 models with console ($94.80). Light monitoring system ($26.35). Power drum brakes ($42.15). Power disc brakes ($100.10). Power steering ($84.30). Power top in white, black or blue on convertible ($52.70). Power windows ($100.10). Heavy-duty radiator, standard with air; not available with 302 or 396 cid engines ($13.70).Push-button AM radio ($61.10).Push-button AM /FM radio ($133.80).Push-button AM/FM stereo radio ($239.15). Manual rear antenna, not available with AM/FM or auxiliary panel and valance, ($9.50). Stereo tape system ($133.80). White or black vinyl roof cover, Sport Coupe ($73.75). Rear folding seat ($42.15). Strato-back front seat, Sport Coupe, not available with console ($32.65). Speed and Cruise-Control, V-8 only, Powerglide required ($52.70). Speed warning indicator ($10.55). Special rear springs. included rear bumper guards ($20.05). Special steering with quick response ($15.80). Comfort-Tilt steering wheel, automatic or floor-mounted transmission required ($42.15). Sport style steering wheel ($31.60). Accent striping ($13.70). Powerglide, six-cylinder ($184.35). Powerglide, with all 210, 275 and 295 hp V-8 ($194.85). Three-speed special with 295, 325, 350 and 375 hp engines ($79.00). Four-speed wide range, except with 375 hp engines ($184.35). Four-speed close ratio, with 350, 375 hp and 302 engines ($184.35). Four-speed heavy-duty close ratio, with 375 hp engine ($310.70). Turbo-Hydra-Matic, with 325 and 350 hp engines ($237.00). Rally wheels ($31.60). Bright metal wheelcovers (21.10). Simulated wire wheelcovers ($73.75). Mag-styled wheelcovers ($73.75). Mag spoke wheelcovers ($73.75). Appearance Guard Group ($40.10). Camaro SS Option includes: special hood, special red stripe tires, SS emblems, hood insulation, black accented grille, front accent band, engine accents, special suspension, V-8 engine, (dual exhausts, no charge) with 295 hp L48 V-8 ($210.65); with 325 hp L35 V-8 ($263.30); with 350 hp L34 V-8 ($368.65); with 375 hp L78 V-8 ($500.30). Rally Sport Group ($105.35).

HISTORICAL FOOTNOTES: Style Number 47, the Formal-Top (FT) coupe was called the Custom coupe. The Impala Super Sport option, RPO Z03 was available for styles 87, 47 and 67 at $179.05 extra. The Impala SS 427 package, RPO Z24 with 385 hp L36 Turbojet 427 V-8 was available for the same models at $358. 10 extra. The Impala SS 427 package, RPO Z24 with 425 hp L72 Turbo-Jet 427 V-8 was available for the same models at $542.45 extra. A total of 38,210 Impalas had one of these options installed. 105,858 Chevy IIs made for domestic sale had dual exhausts.

1969 CHEVROLET

BISCAYNE — (SIX/V-8) — SERIES 153/154 — Full-sized Chevrolets were completely redesigned. While wheelbase was unchanged, cars grew an inch in length; station wagons three inches. A new, integrated bumper/grille imparted a narrower look, although the width of 80 inches was the same as the previous year. The area around the front and rear wheel-housings was flared out, giving a more highly sculptured appearance. The lower body feature line kicked-up, between the flares, giving a 'pinched' bodyside effect. A straight, upper feature line ran between the wraparound ends of the front and back bumpers. The grille surround was a heavy chrome molding completely encircling headlamps and grille. The grille insert was a grid-patterened type, with bright, prominent cross-hatched moldings forming large, square openings which were filled with multiple, smaller blades. Parking lamps were set into the front gravel pan, which had a wide slot at the center allowing a portion of the grille to show through. Vertical, rectangular side markers were positioned at the extreme forward edge of front fenders. Taillights were of a round-cornered rectangular shape and set into the rear bumper. Twin lamps were seen on Biscaynes (triple lamps on upper series cars). Identification trim consisted of a Chevrolet insignia at the center of the grille; Chevrolet scripts on the left hood and right deck lid edges and a model script behind the front wheelwell at mid-fender height. New transmissions, some new engines, ventless side window glass; and an anti-theft steering column were promoted advances. New options included a headlight washing device and automatic liquid 'tire chain' dispensing system. Basic equipment on the Biscayne included all GM safety features; head restraints (as a mandatory option); door-actuated light switches; heater and defroster; cigarette lighter; locking glovebox; carpeting; armrests; center dome light; 8.25 x 14 two-ply (four-ply rated) black sidewall tires and either the 155 hp six or 235 hp V-8 as base powerplants. Standard equipment in Biscayne and all other full-size Chevrolet station wagons included all GM safety features: heater and defroster; front head restraints (mandatory option); all-vinyl trim; dual-speed electric wipers and washers; carpeting; Hide-Away windshield wipers; Astro Ventilation; dual-action tailgate; and ashtray light.

CHEVROLET I.D. NUMBERS: Serial Numbers on all Chevrolet products were now found on the top left-hand surface of the instrument panel. They were visible through the windshield. The Vehicle Identification Number had thirteen symbols. The first three symbols indicate make and series and appear as Series Number in first column of charts below. For example, first car listed has number 153 (1=Chevrolet; 53=Biscayne six) for six-cylinder series and 154 (1=Chevrolet; 54=Biscayne V-8) for eight-cylinder series. Fourth and fifth symbols indicate body type and appear as Body/Style Number in second column of charts below. Sixth symbol indicates model year, 9=1969. Seventh symbol identifies assembly plant: A=Atlanta, Ga.;

B=Baltimore, Md.; C=Southgate, Calif.; D=Doraville, Ga.; F=Flint, Mich.; G=Framingham, Mass.; J=Janesville, Wis.; K=Kansas City, Mo.; L=Los Angeles, Calif.; N=Norwood, Ohio; R=Arlington, Texas; S=St. Louis, Mo.; T=Tarrytown, NY; U=Lordstown, Ohio; W=Willow Run, Mich.; Y=Wilmington, Del.; Z=Fremont, Calif.; 2=Canada. Next six symbols are sequential production number. Body tag riveted to cowl indicates some of the same information, plus paint and trim codes. Engine numbers are stamped on right side of V-8 blocks and right side of six-cylinder blocks behind distributor. Consult factory or aftermarket sources for numerous Chevrolet engine codes.

BISCAYNE SERIES

Series Number	Body/Style Number	Body Type & Seating	Factory Price	Shipping Weight	Production Total
153/154	69	4-dr Sed-6P	2687/2793	3590/3725	Note 1
153/154	11	2-dr Sed-6P	2645/2751	3630/3670	Note 1
153/154	36	4-dr Sta Wag-6P	3064/3169	4045/4170	Note 1

NOTE 1: In rounded-off total, 68,700 Biscayne cars and wagons were built.
NOTE 2: Rounded-off total includes 27,400 sixes and 41,300 V-8s.
NOTE 3: Data above slash for six if offered/below slash; no slash is V-8 data.

BEL AIR — (SIX/V-8) — SERIES 155/156 — The Bel Air represented the next step up from Biscayne. Cars in this line featured a thin, horizontal molding along the full-length of the upper body feature line; Bel Air front fender side scripts; and twin taillamps. Interiors were slightly upgraded. Standard equipment included all items found on Biscaynes, plus side moldings; bright metal rear window, roof drip and windshield moldings; front and rear side marker lamps; and glovebox light. Base powerplants were the same as in Biscaynes, but the Bel Air level Townsman station wagon came only with the V-8 this season. Townsman (Bel Air) and Kingsman (Impala) station wagons also had courtesy lights; bodyside moldings and, on Kingswood only, Deluxe steering wheel; and extra thick front foam seat cushions.

BEL AIR SERIES

Series Number	Body/Style Number	Body Type & Seating	Factory Price	Shipping Weight	Production Total
155/156	69	4-dr Sed-6P	2787/2893	3590/3725	Note 1
155/156	11	2-dr Sed-6P	2745/285	3540/3670	Note 1
156	46	4-dr TwnMn Wag-9P	3345	4230	Note 1
156	36	4-dr TwnMn Wag-6P	3232	4175	Note 1

NOTE 1: In rounded-off total 155,700 Bel Air cars and wagons were built.
NOTE 2: Rounded-off total includes 16,000 sixes and 137,700 V-8s.
NOTE 3: Data above slash for six if offered/below slash; no slash is V-8 data.

IMPALA — (SIX/V-8) — SERIES 163/164 — The Impala, being a bit fancier than Biscayne/Bel Air models, came with the triple taillight arrangement. There were also wide, bright metal underscores along the lower portion of the body, between the wheel openings. Bodyside scripts bore the Impala name. The two-door sedan was not offered, but four other styles joined the four-door sedan in this line. Sportier models, such as the convertible and Custom Coupe with formal (blind rear quarter) roof came with V-8 power only. Other models, including two and four-door hardtops, offered buyers the choice of a six or V-8. Impala level Kingswood station wagons also came solely with V-8 engines. Standard equipment included everything used for Bel Airs, except that bright roof drip moldings were deleted from all the full-pillared models. In addition, all Impalas added a Deluxe steering wheel; door and window frame moldings; glovebox and luggage compartment lighting; and extra-thick front foam seat cushions. The Sport Coupe also had bright metal moldings below the doors combined with wheel lip moldings. The convertible had all of this, plus all-vinyl upholstery and carpeted lower door panels. Kingsman station wagons also had courtesy lights and bodyside moldings.

1969 Chevrolet, Impala two-door hardtop Custom Coupe, V-8

IMPALA SERIES

Series Number	Body/Style Number	Body Type & Seating	Factory Price	Shipping Weight	Production Total
163/164	69	4-dr Sed-6P	2911/3016	3640/3760	Note 1
163/164	39	4-dr HT Spt Sed-6P	2981/3086	3735/3855	Note 1
163/164	37	2-dr HT Spt Cpe-6P	2927/3033	3650/3775	Note 1
164	47	2-dr FT Cus Cpe-6P	3085	3800	Note 1
164	67	2-dr Conv-6P	3261	3835	Note 1/2
164	46	4-dr KgWd Wag-9P	3465	4285	Note 1
164	36	4-dr KgWd Wag-6P	3352	4225	Note 1

NOTE 1: In rounded-off total 777,000 Impalas and Kingwoods were built.
NOTE 2: Rounded-off total includes 8,700 sixes and 768,300 V-8s.
NOTE 3: 14,415 Chevrolet Impala convertibles in 1969 model year totals.
NOTE 4: 2,425 full-sized 1969 Chevrolets had the Super Sport option.
NOTE 5: Data above slash for six if offered/below slash; no slash is V-8 data.

CAPRICE — (V-8) — SERIES 166 — The Caprice was the top-rung offering in the Chevrolet full-sized lineup. Standard features included the complete assortment of Impala equipment, plus full wheelcovers; Caprice signature scripts; front fender marker lamps; distinctive side molding treatment; electric clock; and front seat with center armrest. The Caprice Sport Coupe also provided the Astro Ventilation system at its base price. The Caprice-level station wagon was the luxurious Kingswood Estate, which came with all items used on Impala-level Kingswood models, plus full wheelcovers; electric clock; glovebox light; window moldings; two-spoke steering wheel; sculptured wheel openings; Look-of-Wood side paneling; recessed step-in boarding type rear bumper; wheel lip moldings; and Kingswood Estate identification scripts on the rear fendersides. Passenger styles had rear fender skirts, but the Kingswood Estate wagons did not. Retractable headlights were optional on all Caprices. Variable-ratio power steering was a new extra-cost feature offered for Impala/Caprice models only.

CAPRICE SERIES

Series Number	Body/Style Number	Body Type & Seating	Factory Price	Shipping Weight	Production Total
166	39	4-dr HT Spt Sed-6P	3346	3895	Note 1
166	47	2-dr FT Cus Cpe-6P	3294	3815	Note 1
166	46	4-dr KgWd Est Wag-9P	3678	4300	Note 1
166	36	4-dr KgWd Est Wag-6P	3565	4245	Note 1

NOTE 1: Rounded-off total of 166,900 Caprices and Kingswood Estates built.

CHEVELLE 300 DELUXE — (SIX/V-8) — SERIES 133/134 — For 1969, the Chevrolet intermediate size car had new frontal styling. The forward edge of the hood and fenders was more beveled than 1968. The square-shaped housings containing the circular headlight lenses were changed from the former bright-finished appearance, with the new dull-finish look emphasizing negative space effects. This treatment was carried to the grille insert, which also had a dull-finish treatment that gave prominence to a bright, horizontal molding stretching, full-width, between the headlights. A Chevrolet insignia was placed at the center of this bar. A new front bumper with wider, horizontal slots on either side of the license plate area was seen. The parking lamps were set into the slots. At the rear, there were larger taillight lenses mounted in the body corners. The front side marker lamps, although still rectangular, grew smaller and were repositioned closer to the upper feature line. Different wheelbases once again appeared: 112 inches on two-door styles and 116 inches on four-doors. Standard equipment on Chevelle 300 Deluxe models included all GM safety features; head restraints (as a mandatory option); heater and defroster; front armrests; dual headlights; 7.35 x 14 four-ply rated blackwall tires; and either a 140 hp six or 200 hp V-8 as base powerplant. The low-level Chevelles were characterized by thin rocker panel moldings; bright metal windshield and rear window framing; bright metal roof drip moldings; and series identification badges on the front fenders behind the wheel opening. With all factors totaled, the Chevelle was a very handsome machine, even in its most basic forms. Chevelle wagons proliferated in 1969. Although non-Deluxe passenger cars were dropped, the comparable Nomad wagon was carried over as an economy model which listed with the 300 Deluxe line below. Extra station wagon features included all-vinyl interior trim; dual-speed electric wipers; and windshield washers. Nomad series coding is the same as that of 1968 Chevelle 300s. Some Chevelle wagons had a new "Dual-Action" tailgate (indicated on chart with symbols /D). The Greenbrier was the true Chevelle 300 Deluxe trim station wagon.

CHEVELLE 300 DELUXE SERIES

Series Number	Body/Style Number	Body Type & Seating	Factory Price	Shipping Weight	Production Total
133/134	69	4-dr Sed-6P	2488/2577	3100/3230	Note 1
133/134	37	2-dr HT Spt Cpe-6P	2521/2611	3075/3205	Note 1
133/134	27	2-dr Cpe-6P	2458/2548	3035/3165	Note 1
131/132	35	4-dr Nomad-6P	2668/2758	3390/3515	Note 3
131/132	36	4-dr Nomad/D-6P	2710/2800	NA/NA	Note 3
133/134	35	4-dr GrnBr Wag-6P	2779/2869	3445/2585	Note 3
133/134	36	4-dr GrnBr Wag	2821/2911	NA/NA	Note 3
134	46	4-dr GrnBr/D Sta Wag	3024	3740	Note 3

NOTE 1: In rounded-off total 42,000 Chevelle 300 passenger cars built 1969.
NOTE 2: Rounded-off total includes 21,000 sixes and 21,000 V-8 non-wagons.
NOTE 3: Rounded-off total of 45,900 Chevelle wagons built in all lines.
NOTE 4: Wagon total includes 7,400 sixe/38,500 V-8s, but no series breakouts
NOTE 5: Data above slash for six if offered/below slash; no slash is V-8 data.

1969 Chevelle, SS 396 2-dr hardtop sports coupe, V-8

CHEVELLE MALIBU — (SIX-V-8) — SERIES 135/136 — The Malibu was the mid-priced, mid-sized series and included all equipment found on the base line, plus Hide-Away two-speed wipers; Deluxe steering wheel; glovebox light; window moldings; and carpets. Specific identification features varied by body type and optional equipment packages that a buyer ordered. It was possible to order Chevelles and Malibus in over 300 different variations. Some that collectors look for are the Malibu four-door hardtop (Sports sedan) with the RPO Z16 Concours package or the Malibu two-door hardtop (Sports coupe) with Argent Silver lower bodyside treatment, both of which added greatly to a sporty appearance. Several pages of new or revised options packages were released by Chevrolet in May, 1969. A convertible was also available in Malibu trim and had all of the above standard equipment, plus courtesy lights. The SS-396 (Z-25) was still offered as an option package.

MALIBU SERIES

Series Number	Body/Style Number	Body Type & Seating	Factory Price	Shipping Weight	Production Total
135/136	69	4-dr Sed-6P	2567/2657	3130/3265	Note 1
135/136	39	4-dr HT Sed-6P	2672/2762	3205/3340	Note 1
135/136	37	2-dr HT Spt Cpe-6P	2601/2690	3095/3230	Note 1
135/136	67	2-dr Conv-6P	2800/2889	3175/3300	Note 5
136	46	4-dr Estate Wag-9P	3266	3730	Note 3
136	36	4-dr Estate Wag-6P	3153	3680	Note 3

NOTE 1: In rounded-off tota l367,100 Malibu passenger cars built in 1969.
NOTE 2: Rounded-off total includes 25,000 sixes and 343,600 V-8 non-wagons.
NOTE 3: Rounded-off total of 45,900 Chevelle wagons built in all lines.
NOTE 4: Wagon total includes 7,400 sixes/38,500 V-8s, but no series breakouts
NOTE 5: 8,927 cars in rounded-off total were Malibu or SS-396 convertibles.
NOTE 6: 86,307 cars in rounded-off totals had SS-396 option.
NOTE 7: Data above slash for six if offered/below slash; no slash is V-8 data.

1969 Chevrolet, Nova 2-dr sedan, V-8 (AA)

NOVA — (FOUR/SIX/V-8) — The Chevy II name was dropped from the 'senior' compact offerings, which were now simply called Novas. Due to this change, a Chevrolet emblem was placed on the center of the upper grille bar. Vertical louvers were optional on the side of the cowl, behind the front wheel opening. A Nova script was seen on the right-hand corner of the deck lid. The front side marker lights were enlarged and moved slightly closer to the body corner. A vast selection of options, including Super Sport equipment, could be ordered. Standard equipment included the corporate safety assortment; head restraints (mandatory option); heater and defroster; front armrests; concealed fuel filler; and 7.35 x 14 four-ply rated black sidewall tires. Base engines were the 90 hp four; 140 hp six or 200 hp V-8 from the Chevrolet power team lineup.

NOVA SERIES

Series Number	Body/Style Number	Body Type & Seating	Factory Price	Shipping Weight	Production Total
FOUR					
111	69	4-dr Sed-6P	2267	2810	Note 1
111	27	2-dr Cpe-6P	2237	2785	Note 1
SIX					
113	69	4-dr Sed-6P	2345	2920	Note 2
113	27	2-dr Cpe-6P	2315	2895	Note 2
V-8					
114	69	4-dr Sed-6P	2434,	NA	Note 3
114	27	2-dr Cpe-6P	2405	NA	Note 3

NOTE 1: 6,103 four-cylinder Novas were built; no body style breakouts.
NOTE 2: Rounded-off total of 157,400 six-cylinder Novas built in model year.
NOTE 3: Rounded-off total of 88,400 Nova V-8s were built during model year.
NOTE 4: 17,654 Novas included above were equipped with the Super Sport Option.

1969 Camaro, Z28 two-door hardtop sports coupe, V-8 (AA)

CAMARO — (SIX/V-B) — **SERIES 123/124** — A new body gave the 1969 Camaro a longer and lower appearance. Sport coupe and convertible styles were offered, with option package selections having a great effect on final appearance features. The formerly smooth-sided body was now more highly sculptured with a side feature line tracing the forward edge of the front wheelhousing and running straight from the top of the opening to the rear of the car. A second line traced the front of the rear wheel opening and blended into the main one. Simulated vertical air slots were positioned ahead of the rear wheel. The Rally Sport option offered a special black grille with concealed headlights, the retractable headlamp doors being decorated by a triple-slot design motif. A functional 'Super Scoop' hood was available with Z-28 or Super Sport (SS) packages. Standard equipment began at the safety-oriented level and included the mandatory headrest option plus, heater and defroster; integrated front headlight and parking light unit; Strato-Bucket front seats; all-vinyl interior; carpeting; Astro Ventilation system; front shoulder safety belts; left-hand OSRV mirror; side marker lights; E78 x 14 two-ply (four-ply rated) black sidewall tires; 140 hp six or 210 hp V-8 and, in convertibles, interior courtesy lights. In terms of power, the rare ZL-I Camaros became one of the year's hottest and most collectible cars. Optioned with a 427 cid V-8 featuring aluminum block construction and three two-barrel carburetors, these 425 hp jobs were built in limited numbers for factory experimental racing purposes. Production of only 69 units has been reported. Nearly as desirable to car collectors, although not quite as rare, is the Indianapolis Pace Car replica Camaro. According to several articles, about 100 original editions were built and provided as official cars for dignitaries and press personalities attending the 500 Mile Race. The actual Pace Car was an RS/SS-396 convertible and most of the replicas were SS-350 ragtops. A Pace Car replica package was issued to the general public on Feb. 4, 1969. This lead to the sale of 3,675 cars with the Z11 Indy Sport Convertible option. Also made for a few weeks was the Z10 Indy Sport Coupe option. About 200-300 cars in a special promotional run had this package.

1969 Chevrolet, Camaro RS two-door convertible, V-8

CAMARO SERIES

Series Number	Body/Style Number	Body Type & Seating	Factory Price	Shipping Weight	Production Total
123/124	37	2-dr HT Spt Cpe-4P	2638/2727	3040/3050	214,280
123/124	67	2-dr Conv-4P	2852/2941	3160/3295	16,519

ADDITIONAL NOTES: The figures above are for domestic market units only. Production included 65,008 sixes; 178,087 V-8s; 37,773 Rally Sports; 33,980 Super Sports (some cars had both Rally Sport and Super Sport packages); 19,014 cars with the Z-28 option; 72,395 cars with three-speed manual transmission; 50,128 cars with four-speed manual transmission; 120,572 cars with automatic transmission; 37,878 cars with air conditioning; 120,060 cars with power steering and 2,913 cars with power windows. A total of 12,316 Camaros were built for export.

BASE ENGINES

(NOVA) Inline: Four. Overhead valves. Cast iron block. Displacement: 153.3 cid. Bore and stroke: 3.875 x 3.25 in. Compression ratio: 8.5:1. Brake hp: 90 at 4000 rpm. Four main bearings. Hydraulic valve lifters. Carburetor: Rochester model 7028017 one-barrel.

(BISCAYNE/BEL AIR/IMPALA SIX) Inline Six: Overhead valves. Cast iron block. Displacement: 250 cid. Bore and stroke: 3.88 x 3.53 inches. Compression ratio: 8.5:1. Brake hp: 155 at 4200 rpm. Seven main bearings. Hydraulic valve lifters. Carburetor: Rochester one-barrel Model 7029017.

(BISCAYNE/BEL AIR/IMPALA/CAPRICE V-8) Overhead valves. Cast iron block. Displacement: 326.7 (327) cid. Bore and stroke: 4.00 x 3.25 inches. Compression ratio: 9.0:1. Brake hp: 235 at 4800 rpm. Five main bearings. Hydraulic valve lifters. Carburetor: Rochester two-barrel Model 7029127.

(CHEVELLE/MALIBU/NOVA/CAMARO SIX) Inline Six: Overhead valves. Cast iron block. Displacement 230 cid. Bore and stroke: 3.875 x 3.25 inches. Compression ratio: 8.5:1. Brake hp: 140 at 4400 rpm. Seven main bearings. Hydraulic valve lifters. Carburetor: Rochester one-barrel Model 7029017.

(CHEVELLE/MALIBU/NOVA V-8) Overhead valves. Cast iron block. Displacement: 306.6 (307) cid. Bore and stroke: 3.875 x 3.25 inches. Compression ratio: 9.0:1. Brake hp 200 at 4600 rpm. Five main bearings. Hydraulic valve lifters. Carburetor: Rochester two-barrel.

(CAMARO BASE V-8) Overhead valves. Cast iron block. Displacement: 326.7 (327) cid. Bore and stroke: 4.00 x 3.25 inches. Compression ratio: 9.0:1. Brake hp: 210 at 4600 rpm. Five main bearings. Hydraulic valve lifters. Carburetor: Rochester two-barrel.

(TURBO-JET SS-396) V-8: Overhead valves. Cast iron block. (Aluminum cylinder heads optional after midyear). Displacement: 396 cid. Bore and stroke: 4.09 x 3.76 inches. Compression ratio: 10.25:1. Brake hp: 325 at 4800 rpm. Hydraulic valve lifters. Five main bearings. Carburetor: Rochester four-barrel Quadra-Jet.

CHASSIS FEATURES: Wheelbase: (Chevrolet) 119 inches; (Chevelle two-door) 112 inches; (Chevelle four-door) 116 inches; (Nova) 111 inches; (Camaro) 108 inches. Overall length: (Chevrolet wagon) 217 inches; (Chevelle) 216 inches; (Chevelle two-door) 197 inches; (Chevelle wagon) 208 inches; (Chevelle four-door) 201 inches; (Nova) 190 inches; (Camaro) 186 inches. Front tread: (Chevrolet) 62.5 inches; (Chevelle/Nova/Camaro) 59 inches. Rear tread: (Chevrolet) 62.4 inches; (Chevelle) 59 inches; (Nova) 58.9 inches; (Camaro) 58 inches. Base tires: (Chevrolet) 8.25 x 14 cars; 8.55 x 14 wagons; (Chevelle/Nova) 7.35 x 14 cars; 7.75 x 14 wagons; (Camaro) E78 x 14-B.

OPTIONS: [Early 1969] Four-Season air conditioning ($363.40-$384.45). Comfortron air conditioning ($463.45). Station wagon rear deflector ($19). Custom Deluxe shoulder belts ($12.15-$16.90). Power drum brakes, except Nova Four ($42.15). Power front disc brakes, except Nova Four ($64.25). Special Camaro front bumper ($42.15). Load floor carpeting in Kingswood and Kingswood Estate ($52.70). Adjustable roof rack ($52.70). Electric clock ($15.80). Heavy-duty clutch ($47.50-$52 0). Console with courtesy light ($53.75). Electro-Clear rear defroster ($32.65). Power door locks, Chevrolet/Chevelle two-door ($44.80); four-door ($68.50). Retractable headlights, Caprice/Estate ($79). Headlight washer ($15.80). Special instrumentation; in Chevelle/Camaro ($94.80). Light monitoring system ($26.35). Two-tone paint, all except Camaro ($23.20); on Camaro, includes roof molding, ($31.60). AM push-button radio ($61.10). AM/FM push-button radio ($133.80). AM/FM radio and stereo ($239.10). Rear manual antenna ($9.50-$10.55). Vinyl roof ($79-$88.55). Camaro folding rear seat ($42.15). Six-Way power seat ($100.10). Strato Bucket seat, in Caprice, includes front center armrest and Custom knit black cloth trim ($115.90). Strato Bucket in Malibu coupe/convertible ($121.15); in Caprice, including console with shift if automatic or four-speed, plus center console ($168.55). Automatic level control. Chevrolets ($89.66). Rear fender skirts, Chevrolets with 14 inch wheels ($31.60). Speed and Cruise Control, V-8 and automatic required ($57.95). Power steering ($89.55-$105.35). Special steering with Quick-Response feature in Camaro, power steering required with air conditioner or 396 cid V-8, ($15.80). Comfort-Tilt steering column ($45.30). Sport styled steering wheel, except Nova ($34.80). Chevelle SS 396 fender accent striping ($26.35). Camaro front accent or Sport striping ($25.30). Liquid tire chain ($23.20). Power convertible top on Chevelle/Camaro ($52.70). Power trunk opener on Chevrolet ($14.75). Power tailgate window, standard in three seat wagon; in two-seat styles ($34.80). Hide-Away wipers as option ($19). Full wheelcovers ($21.10). Mag-spoke wheelcovers, Caprice and Kingswood Estate ($52.70); all others ($73.75). Simulated wire wheels, Caprice and Kingswood Estate ($55.85). Special wheelcovers and Caprice and Kingswood Estate ($57.95); on other full-sized Chevrolets ($79). [May 1, 1969 changes]: Adjustable wagon roof rack ($52.70). Electro-Clear rear defroster ($47.40). Special ducted hood for Camaro SS with performance package ($79). Front and rear spoiler, Camaro without performance package ($32.65). Special rear springs, on Camaro, includes rear bumper guards ($20.05). [Early 1969]: Turbo-Thrift '250' six, in Chevelle/Camaro/Nova

($26.35). Turbo-Fire '350' V-8 in Chevrolet/Camaro ($52.70); in Chevelle/Nova ($68.50). RPO L66/396 cid Turbo-Jet 265 hp V-8, in Chevrolets ($68.50). RPO L48/350 cid 300 hp V-8, in Chevrolet ($52.70); in Chevelle ($68.50). RPO L35/396 cid Turbo-Jet 325 hp V-8 in Camaro SS only ($63.20). RPO LS1/427 cid 355 hp V-8, in Chevrolets only ($163.25). RPO L34/396 cid Turbo-Jet 350 hp V-8, in Chevelle SS-396 ($121.15); in Camaro SS/Nova SS ($184.35). RPO L78/396 cid Turbo-Jet 375 hp V-8, in Chevelle SS-396 ($252.80); in Camaro SS/Nova SS ($316). RPO L78-89/375 hp Turbo-Jet V-8 with special aluminum cylinder heads, in Chevelle SS-396 ($647.75); in Camaro SS ($710.95). RPO L36/427 cid 390 hp Turbo-Jet V-8, in Chevrolet ($237). RPO L72/427 cid 425 hp Turbo-Jet V-8, in Chevrolet ($447.65); in Chevrolet with SS option ($183.35). Dual exhausts ($30.55). Wide-Range four-speed manual transmission, in Camaro ($195.40); in others ($184.80). Close-ratio four-speed manual transmission, in Camaro ($195.40); in others ($184.80). Heavy-duty four-speed manual transmission, in Nova ($312.55); in Camaro ($322.10); in Chevelle ($264); in Chevrolet ($313). Powerglide automatic transmission, with Nova V-8 ($158.40); with Nova four/six ($147.85); with other V-8s ($174.25); with other sixes ($163.70). Special three-speed manual transmission, standard with SS-427/SS-396 and Camaro SS/Nova SS; in others ($79). Torque-Drive, in Camaro/Nova six only ($68.65). Turbo-HydraMatic (M40 type), in Nova six ($174.25); in other six ($190.10); in all, except Nova, with 255/300 hp V-8 ($200.65); in Nova with 255/300 hp V-8 ($190.10); in all with 375/425 hp V-8 ($290.40); in all with other V-8s ($221.80). Floor-mounted shift lever, as optional equipment ($10.55). Posi-traction axle ($42.15). [May 1, 1969 changes]: PO L65/250 cid Turbo-Fire 250 hp V-8, in Chevelle/Nova/Camaro ($21.10); RPO LMI/350 cid Turbo-Fire 255 hp V-8, in Chevrolet and Camaro ($52.70); in Chevelle/Nova ($68.50). RPO NC8 dual chambered exhaust system, in Chevelle SS396/Z28/Camaro SS with 325/350/375 hp V-8 ($15.80).

OPTION PACKAGES

RPO Z27 Camaro SS-350 option includes: special hood; sport striping: hood insulation: F70 x 14 white-letter tires; 14 x 7 inch wheels; power disc brakes; special three-speed manual transmission; bright fender louvers; engine accents; emblems; and 300 hp '350' V-8 ($295.95); after May 1, 1969 ($311.75).

RPO Z16 Chevelle Concours sedan (hardtop) includes: luxury cloth seat and sidewall trim; steering wheel emblem; panel trim plate; black accented lower bodyside and wheel opening moldings; deck lid nameplate and; special insulation ($131.65).

RPO ZJ2 Nova Custom exterior package includes: simulated front fender louvers with bright accents; bodysill and rear fender moldings; black bodysill and lower rear fender trim panels; and accent striping. Coupe also had bright side window moldings and lower body accent band. Sedan also had bodyside molding with black vinyl insert, on coupe ($97.95); on sedan ($79).

RPO Z87 (Camaro)/ZJI (Nova with bench)/A51 (Nova with buckets) Custom interior trim. Included on Camaro: molded vinyl door panel with built-in armrest; assist grip; carpeted lower door panel; woodgrain panel accents; woodgrain steering wheel; bright pedal trim; glovebox light; insulation and baggage mat. Included, on Nova, luxury seats and sidewalls; bright accents; rear armrest ashtrays; carpets; Deluxe mirror; interior or light switches; baggage mat; insulation. Price for bucket seat Nova ($231.75); price for other ($110.60).

RPO Z24 Impala SS-427 option, on Custom Coupe, Sport Coupe or convertible includes: power disc brakes; special three-speed transmission; ornamentation; chassis and suspension features; 15 inch wheels; Red Stripe tires and 390 hp 427 cid V-8 ($422.35).

RPO Z26 Nova SS option package, on coupe only, includes simulated air intakes on hood; simulated front fender louvers; black accents; black accent grille and rear panel; SS emblems; Red Stripe F70 x 14 tires; 14 x 7 inch wheels; special suspension and three-speed gearbox; power disc brakes; bright engine accents; hood insulation; and 300 hp '350' V-8 ($280.20).

RPO Z22 Camaro Rally Sport (RS) option package includes special grille with concealed headlights; headlight washers; fender striping (except with SS); bright accents on simulated rear fender louvers; front and rear wheel lip moldings; black body sills; RS emblems; nameplates; accented tail and parking lights; back-up lights below bumper; steering wheel accents and coupe roof drip moldings ($131.65).

RPO Z35, Camaro SS 396 option includes special hood, ornamentation and suspension; Sport wheels; white letter tires (Wide-Oval); power disc brakes; special three-speed transmission; black accented grille and 325 hp '396' V-8 ($347.60).

RPO Z28, Camaro Special Performance Package includes dual exhaust with deep-toned muffler; special front and rear suspension; heavy-duty radiator and temperature controlled fan; quick-ratio steering; 15 x 7 inch Rally wheels; E70 x 15 white letter tires; 3.73 ratio axle; Rally stripes on hood and rear deck and special 302 cid V-8 (estimated hp rating 350). Four-speed manual transmission and power disc brake options were additional mandatory options (at regular price in addition to Z-28 retail). Posi-traction rear axle was also recommended. Cost ($458.15); after May 1, 1969 ($506.60). A total of 503 were equipped with disc brakes.

RPO Z11/RPO Z10 Camaro Indy Pace Car packages. Contact International Camaro Owners Association, 2001 Pittston Ave., Scranton, PA 18503 for full details.

HISTORICAL FOOTNOTES: The 1969 Chevrolet lineup was introduced Sept. 26, 1968. John Z. DeLorean was general manager of Chevrolet Div. Model year output figures included exactly 1,109,013 full-sized Chevrolets; 439,611 Chevelles; 269,988 Novas and 243,085 Camaros. Market penetration, including Corvettes and Corvairs, was an even 25 percent. The 1969 Camaro captured top honors in SCCA Trans-Am Championship racing for cars in the over 2.5 liter class. Mark Donahue and Roger Penske were the top Chevrolet drivers.

1970 CHEVROLET

NOTE: 1970 and later Chevrolet models cataloged by platform groupings.

FULL-SIZED CHEVROLET — (SIX/V-8) — ALL SERIES — The 'big' Chevrolets were the same in size as the previous models. There were changes front and rear. The front fenderline, hood and grille were redone, eliminating the encircling, integrated bumper/grille look. Round dual headlamps were set horizontally in square bezels flanking a finer-textured grille, although a crosshatched insert design was retained. The gravel pan was re-shaped to round the front body corners and incorporate slightly larger parking lamps as well as triple-slit side markers. At the rear, the taillights took a new vertical-slot shape and were recessed into the bumper. A base '350' V-8, optional regular-fuel '400' V-8 and transmission-controlled vacuum spark advance were technical refinements. Standard equipment for Biscaynes included all safety features; windshield antenna; Astro Ventilation; Hide-Away wipers; Delco-Eye battery; side-guard door beams; heater/defroster: cigarette lighter; locking glovebox; carpets; ashtray light; center dome lamp; F78-15 blackwalls; and either the '250' six or '350' V-8. The Bel Air was equipped likewise, plus having side and roof drip moldings and a glovebox light. The Impala had all above, plus foam seat cushions; fabric and vinyl trim (all-vinyl in convertible); Deluxe steering wheel; trunk light; door/window frame moldings; vinyl-insert bodyside moldings; and luggage lamps. The Impala Sport Coupe also had bright metal moldings below the doors and on its wheel lips. The Custom coupe had power front disc brakes and the convertible had courtesy lights and carpeted lower door panels. Tires were size F78-15 on sixes; G78-15 on V-8s. The Caprice was equipped with all of the above, plus power front disc brakes; distinctive side moldings; color-keyed wheelcovers; electric clock; G78-15/B bias-belted blackwalls; 250 hp base engine; and, in sedans, a center armrest seat. Station wagons had such items as vinyl trim; Dual-Action tailgates and glovebox light, plus all Biscayne passenger car equipment. The Kingswood wagon compared to the Impala trim level, with courtesy lights; bodyside moldings; and foam cushions included. The Kingswood Estate was the Caprice-level counterpart with a Deluxe steering wheel; clock and window moldings; and exterior woodgrain paneling. Base engine for all wagons was the '350' V-8 and H78-15/D tires were used. Power disc brakes were standard with Kingswood Estates.

1970 Chevrolet, Caprice two-door hardtop Custom Coupe, V-8

CHEVROLET I.D. NUMBERS: Serial Numbers on all Chevrolet products were now found on the top left-hand surface of the instrument panel. They were visible through the windshield. The Vehicle Identification Number had 13 symbols. The first three symbols indicate make and series and appear as Series Number in first column of charts below. For example, first car listed has number 153 (1=Chevrolet; 53=Biscayne six) for six-cylinder series and 154 (1=Chevrolet; 54=Biscayne V-8) for eight-cylinder series. Fourth and fifth symbols indicate body type and appear as Body/Style Number in second column of charts below. Sixth symbol indicates model year, 0=1970. Seventh symbol identifies assembly plant: A=Atlanta, Ga.; B=Baltimore, Md.; C=Southgate, Calif.; F=Flint, Mich.; G=Framingham, Mass.; I=Oshawa, Canada; J=Janesville, Wis.; K=Kansas City, Mo.; L=Los Angeles, Calif.; N=Norwood, Ohio; R=Arlington, Texas; S=St. Louis, Mo.; T=Tarrytown, NY; U=Lordstown, Ohio; W=Willow Run, Mich.; Y=Wilmington, Del.; Z=Fremont, Calif. Next six symbols are sequential production number. Body tag riveted to cowl indicates some of the same information, plus paint and trim codes. Engine numbers are stamped on right side of V-8 blocks and right side of six-cylinder blocks behind distributor. Consult factory or aftermarket sources for numerous Chevrolet engine codes.

1970 Chevrolet, Impala two-door convertible, V-8

FULL-SIZED CHEVROLET

Series Number	Body/Style Number	Body Type & Seating	Factory Price	Shipping Weight	Production Total
BISCAYNE SERIES (INCLUDES BROOKWOOD WAGON)					
153/154	69	4-dr Sed-6P	2787/2998	3600/3759	Note 1
154	36	4-dr Sta Wag-6P	3294	4204	Note 2
BEL AIR SERIES (INCLUDES TOWNSMAN WAGONS)					
155/156	69	4-dr Sed-6P	2887/2998	3604/3763	Note 3
156	46	4-dr Sta Wag-9P	3469	4263	Note 2
156	36	4-dr Sta Wag-6P	3357	4208	Note 2
IMPALA SERIES (INCLUDES KINGSWOOD WAGONS)					
163/164	69	4-dr Sed-6P	3021/3132	3655/3802	Note 4
163/164	37	2-dr HT Spt Cpe-6P	3038/3149	3641/3788	Note 4
164	39	4-dr HT Spt Sed-5P	3203	3871	Note 4
164	47	2-dr Cus Cpe-6P	3266	3801	Note 4
164	67	2-dr Conv-6P	3377	3843	Note 4/5
164	46	4-dr Sta Wag-9P	3589	4321	Note 2
164	36	4-dr Sta Wag-6P	3477	4269	Note 2
CAPRICE SERIES (INCLUDES KINGSWOOD ESTATE)					
166	39	4-dr HT Sed-6P	3527	3905	Note 7
166	47	2-dr HT Sed-6P	3474	3821	Note 7
166	46	4-dr Sta Wag-9P	3866	4361	Note 2
166	36	4-dr Sta Wag-6P	3753	4295	Note 2

FIGURES BELOW ARE ROUNDED-OFF (except Note 5):

NOTE 1: 35,400 Biscayne cars were built (12,300 sixes/343,600 V-8s).
NOTE 2: 162,800 full-size Chevrolet wagons built (all V-8s).
NOTE 3: 75,800 Bel Air cars were built (9,000 sixes/66,800 V-8s).
NOTE 4: 612,800 Impala cars built (6,500 sixes/606,300 V-8s).
NOTE 5: Exactly 9,562 Impala convertibles are included in Note 4.
NOTE 6: 86,307 cars in rounded-off totals had SS-396 option.
NOTE 7: 92,000 Caprice V-8s built.
NOTE 8: Data above slash for six if offered/below slash; no slash is V-8 data.

1970 Chevrolet, Monte Carlo 2-dr hardtop coupe, V-8

MONTE CARLO — (V-8) — SERIES 138 — The original Monte Carlo was said to combine action and elegance in a sporty, personal luxury package. Based on the same platform as the re-designed 1969 Pontiac Grand Prix, the Monte Carlo was bigger than the Chevelle and had a price tag in the Impala range. A long hood/short deck image and smart interior and exterior appointments were incorporated. Styling features included large, single headlamps mounted in square-shaped bright housings; a rectangular front opening with a grid-textured grille of thin bright horizontal moldings (with a center badge); and a profile emphasizing the popular 'venturi' shape, enhanced by a crisply sculptured upper feature line. Although mainly luxurious in overall character, the Monte Carlo turned out to be quite a fine high-performance machine. The potent, SS-454 version was capable of 0-to-60 mph in under eight seconds. This package was found to be extremely suitable to short track stock car racing. This was due to a combination of good power-to-weight distribution along with aerodynamic factors. The only available body style was a coupe. Standard equipment included all features found on Malibu, plus power front disc brakes; electric clock; assist straps; elm-burl dash panel inlays; G78-15-B bias-belted black sidewall tires; and a 350 cid V-8. Although commonly seen on most Monte Carlos, fender skirts were optional.

MONTE CARLO SERIES

Series Number	Body/Style Number	Body Type & Seating	Factory Price	Shipping Weight	Production Total
138	57	2-dr HT Cpe-5P	3123	3460	145,975

1970 Chevelle, SS-396 two-door hardtop sports coupe, V-8

MID-SIZED CHEVELLE — (SIX/V-8) — ALL SERIES — The more highly sculptured 1970 Chevelle featured a bold-looking frontal treatment with split grille and dual, blending headlights. A new slotless front bumper incorporated rectangular parking lamps directly below the headlamps. The swept-back front fender look was gone, replaced by a blunter image. An upper feature line ran from above the headlight level to the top of the back bumper, with a prominent dip at mid-waist height. Rear side markers and segmented look were seen. The Chevelle 300 Deluxe name was dropped. The Chevelle was the base model and the Malibu was one step up. A wide range of station wagons included the Nomad (comparable to the old standard 300 line); the Deluxe Greenbriers; Malibu-level Concours and the top-of-the-line Concours Estate Wagon (essentially with Monte Carlo-level appointments). Chevelle level standard equipment included the safety assortment: heater/defroster; locking glovebox; cigarette lighter; rubber floor mats; and a 155 hp 250 cid six or 200 hp 307 cid V-8. The blackwall tires were size E78-14-B on both sixes and V-8s. Malibu had all of the above features, plus hidden antenna; Astro Ventilation; side-guard door beam construction; Delco-Eye battery; Hide-Away wipers; and a glovebox light. The convertible also came with interior courtesy lights. Malibu six engines and tires were the same. On Malibu V-8s, larger F78-14-B rubber was used. All station wagons came with GM safety features; Dual-Action tailgates; in-the-windshield hidden antenna; Hide-Away wipers; side beam doors; heater/defroster; all-vinyl trim; and cigarette lighter. Concours also had courtesy lights. Concours Estates added carpeting; door edge moldings; and simulated woodgrain exterior paneling. Engines were the same used on passenger cars and V-8s had power front disc brakes. All station wagons had G78-14-B blackwalls.

INTERMEDIATE-SIZED SERIES

Series Number	Body/Style Number	Body Type & Seating	Factory Price	Shipping Weight	Production Total
NOMAD STATION WAGONS					
131/132	36	4-dr Sta Wag-6P	2835/2925	3615/3718	Note 1
CHEVELLE (GREENBRIER STATION WAGONS)					
133/134	69	4-dr Sed-6P	2537/2627	3196/3312	Note 2
133/134	37	2-dr Cpe-6P	2572/2662	3142/3260	Note 2
133/134	36	4-dr Sta Wag-6P	2946/3100	3644/3748	Note 1
134	46	4-dr Sta Wag-9P	3213	3794	Note 1

CHEVELLE MALIBU SERIES (CONCOURS STATION WAGON)

135/136	69	4-dr Sed-6P	2685/2775	3221/3330	Note 3
135/136	39	4-dr HT Sed-6P	2790/2881	3302/3409	Note 3
135/136	3	2-dr Spt Cpe-6P	2719/2809	3197/3307	Note 3
135/136	67	2-dr Conv-6P	2919/3009	3243/3352	Note 4
135/136	36	4-dr Sta Wag-6P	3056/3210	3687/3794	Note 1
136	46	4-dr Sta Wag-9P	3323	3836	Note 1

CONCOURS ESTATE STATION WAGON

138	46	4-dr Sta Wag-9P	3455	3880	Note 1
138	36	4-dr Sta Wag-6P	3342	3821	Note 1

FIGURES BELOW ARE ROUNDED-OFF (except Note 4):

NOTE 1: 40,600 Chevelle wagons (5,600 six/35,000 V-8) built in all series.
NOTE 2: 23,900 Base Chevelles built (10,700 sixes/13,200 V-8s).
NOTE 3: 375,800 Malibu built (21,100 sixes/354,700 V-8s).
NOTE 4: Exactly 7,511 Malibu/Malibu SS convertibles included in Note 3 total.
NOTE 5: Data above slash for six if offered/below slash; no slash is V-8 data.

1970 Chevrolet, Chevelle Malibu 4-dr hardtop Sport Sedan, V-8

1970 Chevrolet, Nova 2-dr sedan, V-8

NOVA — (FOUR/SIX/V-8) — SERIES 111/113/114 — The 1970 Nova had a grille insert with squarer openings than the previous model. The Chevrolet badge at the center of the upper grille molding was slightly fatter and not quite as wide as before. Options included simulated bright vertical cowside louvers; in-the-windshield radio antennas; and new variable-ratio power steering. The sporty Nova SS package included a hefty 300 hp '350' V-8. Regular equipment included GM safety hardware; front armrests; heater/defroster; Delco-Eye battery; and E78-14 black sidewall tires. Base engines were the 90 hp four-cylinder; 140 hp '230' six and the 307 cid V-8.

NOVA SERIES

Model Number	Body/Style Number	Body Type & Seating	Factory Price	Shipping Weight	Production Total
FOUR					
111	69	4-dr Sed-6P	2205	2843	Note 1
111	27	2-dr Cpe-6P	2176	2820	Note 1
SIX					
113	69	4-dr Sed-6P	2284	2942	Note 2
113	27	2-dr Cpe-6P	2254	2919	Note 2
V-8					
114	69	4-dr Sed-6P	2533	NA	Note 3
114	27	2-dr Sed-6P	2503	NA	Note 3

NOTE 1: Exactly 2,247 Nova fours were built for the 1970 model year.
NOTE 2: Exactly173, 632 Nova sixes were built for the 1970 model year.
NOTE 3: Exactly139,243 Nova V-8s were built for the 1970 model year.

1970 Camaro, two-door sports coupe, V-8

CAMARO SERIES — (SIX/V-8) — Due to slow sales of 1969 Camaros, no new design was introduced for this series at model introduction time in the fall of 1969. Chevrolet dealers continued to sell leftover units until supplies ran out. This may have led to some cars with 1969 specifications being sold and titled as 1970s. The true 1970 models (often called 1970-1/2 Camaros) did not go on sale until Feb. 26, 1970. They had completely new styling with high-intensity headlamps; a semi-fastback roofline; snout-styled grille (with eggcrate insert); and a much smoother-looking rear end. The only body style available was the sport coupe. Standard equipment included all GM safety features; Strato-Bucket front seats; all-vinyl interior; carpeting; Astro Ventilation; left-hand OSRV mirror; side marker lights; and E78-14-B bias-belted blackwall tires. The 155 hp six was base engine while the '307' V-8 was standard in the V-8 line. Desirable options were the SS, RS, and Z28 special-performance packages. The latter carried a retail price of $572.95 and featured the 360 hp 350 cid V-8.

CAMARO SERIES

Model Number	Body/Style Number	Body Type & Seating	Factory Price	Shipping Weight	Production Total
123/124	87	2-dr HT Spt Cpe-4P	2749/2839	3058/3172	117,604

NOTE 1: Figures above are for domestic market units only.
NOTE 2: Figures include 12,566 sixes; 112,323 V-8s.
NOTE 3: Figures include 27,135 RS/12,476 SS (some cars had both packages)
NOTE 4: Figures include 8,733 Z-28s.
NOTE 5: Transmissions: 14,859 3-speed; 18,678 4-speed; 91,352 cars automatic.
NOTE 6: 38,565 with A/C; 92,640 with power steering.
NOTE 7: 7,295 Camaros were exported.
NOTE 8: Data above slash for six if offered/below slash; no slash is V-8 data.

BASE ENGINES

(NOVA) Inline: Four. Overhead valves. Cast iron block. Displacement: 153.3 cid. Bore and stroke: 3.875 x 3.25 in. Compression ratio: 8.5:1. Brake hp: 90 at 4000 rpm. Four main bearings. Hydraulic valve lifters. Carburetor: Rochester model 7028017 one-barrel.

(CHEVROLET/CHEVELLE/NOVA/CAMARO SIX) Inline Six: Overhead valves. Cast iron block. Displacement: 250 cid. Bore and stroke: 3.875 x 3.53 inches. Compression ratio: 8.5:1. Brake hp: 155 at 4200 rpm. Seven main bearings. Hydraulic valve lifters. Carburetor: Rochester one-barrel.

(CHEVROLET/MONTE CARLO V-8) V-8: Overhead valves. Cast iron block. Displacement: 350 cid. Bore and stroke: 4.00 x 3.48 inches. Compression ratio: 9.0:1. Brake hp: 250 at 4500 rpm. Five main bearings. Hydraulic valve lifters. Carburetor: Rochester two-barrel.

(CHEVELLE/NOVA/CAMARO V-8) Overhead Valves: Cast iron block. Displacement: 307 cid. Bore and stroke: 3.875 x 3.53 inches. Compression ratio: 9.0:1. Brake hp: 200 at 4600 rpm. Five main bearings. Hydraulic valve lifters. Carburetor: Rochester two-barrel.

1970 Chevrolet, Monte Carlo two-door hardtop Sport Coupe, V-8

CHASSIS FEATURES: Wheelbase: (Chevrolet) 119 inches; (Chevelle two-door) 112 inches; (Chevelle four-door) 116 inches; (Monte Carlo) 116 inches; (Nova) 111 inches; (Camaro) 108 inches. Overall length: (Chevrolet wagon) 217 inches; (Chevrolet) 216 inches; (Chevelle wagon) 207 inches; (Chevelle two-door) 198 inches; (Chevelle four-door) 202 inches; (Monte Carlo) 206 inches; (Nova) 190 inches; (Camaro) 188 inches. Width: (Chevrolet) 80 inches; (Chevelle) 76 inches; (Monte Carlo) 76 inches; (Nova) 73 inches; (Camaro) 75 inches. Tires: Refer to text.

OPTIONS: Comfortron air conditioning ($463.45). Four Season air conditioning ($363.40-$384.15). Wagon defector ($19). Power drum brakes ($41.15-$43.05). Power front disc brakes ($64.25-$65.65). Carpeted load floor ($52.70). Monte Carlo console ($53.75). Console in Malibu/Nova with bucket seats ($53.75). Electro Clear rear defroster ($41.70). Standard rear defroster ($20.85-$29.20). Power door locks, two-door ($35.45); four-door ($54.12). Tinted glass ($24.83-$30). Headlight delay system ($18.36). Special instrumentation, includes tachometer, ammeter and temperature gauges. Malibu coupe/convertible ($84.30); Monte Carlo ($68.50); Camaro and Nova V-8 with console ($94.80). Vigilante light monitoring system, except Nova ($26.35). AM push-button radio ($61.10). AM/FM push-button radio ($133.80). AM/FM radio with FM stereo ($239.10). Stereo tape, with AM radio ($194.85); with AM/FM radio and FM stereo ($372.85). Black, blue, dark gold, green or white vinyl tops; on Monte Carlo ($126.40); on Chevrolet ($105.35); on Nova six/V-8 ($84.30); on Camaro sport coupe, including roof rail molding ($84.30); on Chevelle ($94.80). Six-Way power front seat ($100.10). Power Strato-Bucket seat ($121.15). Rear fender skirts; on Monte Carlo and Chevrolet, except wagons ($31.60). Power steering ($89.55-$105.35). Comfort-Tilt steering wheel ($46). Wheelcovers ($21). Monte Carlo color-keyed wheelcovers ($15.80). Special wheelcovers ($57.95-$80.70). Six 15 x 7JK wheels on Monte Carlo ($10.55). Rally styled wheels, on Caprice and Kingswood Estate ($21); others ($36). Nova Sport styled wheels ($79). Fingertip windshield wiper control ($19). Rear deck lid spoiler, on 1970-1/2 Camaro, standard with Z28 package ($32.65). Air conditioning, 1970-1/2 Camaro ($380.25). Console, including compartment, ashtray and automatic shift lever, in 1970-1/2 Camaro ($59). Vinyl roof on 1970-1/2 Camaro ($89.55). RPO L65/250 hp '350' V-8, in 1970-1/2 Camaro ($31.60); in base Chevelle ($21.10); in Malibu and Nova ($16.70). RPO L34/350 hp '396' V-8, in 1970-1/2 Camaro with RPO Z27 ($152.75). RPO L78/375 hp '396' V-8, in 1970-1/2 Camaro with RPO Z27, positraction required ($385.50). RPO L48/300 hp Turbo-Fire V-8, in 1970-1/2 Chevelles and Malibus ($68.50). RPO LS3/330 hp 400 cid Turbo-Jet V-8, in 1970-1/2 Chevelles ($162.20); in Malibu and Chevelle wagons ($128.32); in Monte Carlo ($111.67). RPO LS6/450 hp 454 cid Turbo-Jet V-8, in 1970-1/2 Chevelle with SS-454 Option package ($263.30). RPO LF6/265 hp Turbo-Fire 400 V-8 ($50). RPO LS4/345 hp 454 cid Turbo-Jet V-8, except Novas and Chevelles ($133.35). RPO Code L22/155 hp 250 cid Turbo-Thrift six, in Camaro and Nova ($20.85). Wide-range type four-speed manual transmission, in 1970-1/2 Camaro ($205.96); in 1970-1/2 Chevelle ($184.80): in Malibu/Nova/Monte Carlo ($184.80). Special close-ratio four-speed manual transmission in 1970-1/2 Chevelle ($221.80); in 1970-1/2 Camaro ($232.35). Regular close-ratio four-speed manual transmission in Malibu/Nova ($184.80), in 1970-1/2 Camaro ($205.95); in 1970-1/2 Chevelle ($184.80). Turbo-Hydramatic transmission, in 1910-1/2 Chevelle with 330/350/360 hp V-8s ($221.80); in same model with 450 hp V-8 ($290.40); in Nova six ($174.25); in other sixes ($190.10); in 200/250/300 hp V-8s, except Nova ($200.65); in Nova with 250/300 hp V-8 ($190.10); in all with 265/330/345/350/390 hp V-8 ($221.80); in all with 325/425 hp V-8. Torque-Drive transmission, in Nova four/six ($68.65). Powerglide transmission in sixes except Nova ($163.70); in V-8s except Nova ($174.25); in Nova six ($147.85); in Nova V-8 ($158.40). RPO ZL2 Chevelle cowl-induction hood, SS-396/SS-454 option required ($147.45). Posi-traction axle ($42.15). Heavy-duty battery ($15.80). Dual exhausts ($24.17). 63 ampere generator, without air conditioning ($21); with air conditioning ($4). Engine block heater ($10.55). Heavy-duty radiator ($15-$32, per size of car).

OPTION PACKAGES:

Nova Custom Exterior Package, includes simulated front fender louvers; bright accents; rear panel trim plate; body sill and rear fender moldings; black body sill and lower rear fender; accent striping on coupe; bright side window and lower body moldings; black lower accent band and black vinyl insert type side molding on sedan; on coupes ($97.95); on sedans ($79).

Nova Custom Interior Package, includes luxury seat and sidewall trim with bright accents; rear armrest ashtrays; carpeting; bright rearview mirror support, dome light bezel and pedal trim; right front hood light switch; glovebox light; trunk mat; and insulation.

RPO Z23 1970-1/2 Camaro interior accent group, includes additional instrument cluster lighting; woodgrain dash accents and steering wheel ($21.10) or included with Z28 package at no charge.

RPO Z27 1970-1/2 Super Sport (SS) package, includes 350 cid/300 hp V-8; bright engine accents; power brakes; special ornamentation; hood insulation; F70-14 white-letter tires; 17 x 7 inch wheels; black-painted grille; Hide-A-Way wipers with black arms; and SS emblems ($289.65).

RPO Z22 1970-1/2 Camaro RS (Rally Sport) package, includes black-painted grille with rubber-tipped vertical center bar and resilient body-color grille frame; independent left and right front bumpers; license plate bracket mounted below right front bumper; parking lights with bright accents molded on grille panel; Hide-A-Way wipers; bright window, hood panel and body sill moldings; body-colored door handle inserts; RS emblems; nameplate; bright accented taillamps and back-up lamps, F78-14 or E70-14 tires required ($188.35).

RPO Z28 1970-1/2 Camaro Special Performance Package, includes special 360 hp '350' V-8 with bright engine accents; heavy-duty radiator, dual exhausts; black painted grille; Z28 emblems; special performance suspension; heavy-duty front and rear springs; 15 x 7 inch wheels; special center caps and trim rings; hood insulation; F60-15B white-lettered tires; rear deck spoiler; and special paint stripes on hood and deck ($572.95).

RPO Z15. 1970-1/2 Chevelle SS-454 Package, includes bright engine accents; dual exhausts with bright tips; black-painted grille; wheel opening moldings; power front disc brakes; special rear suspension and rear bumper with black insert; special 'power bulge' hood; SS emblems; 454 cid/360 hp Turbo-Jet V-8; heavy-duty battery; F70-14 white letter tires; 14 x 7 wheels (sport type); deletion of body sill molding; and deletion of beltline molding, on Malibu V-8 Sport coupe or convertible, with M40 Turbo-Hydramatic or four-speed manual transmissions only ($503.45).

RPO Z20 Monte Carlo SS Package, includes 360 hp '454' V-8; Superlift with Automatic Level Control; dual exhausts; G70-15/B white letter tires; 15 x 7 wheels; 454 emblems on body sill moldings; and requires Turbo-Hydramatic ($420.25).

RPO Z26 Nova SS Package, includes 300 hp '350' V-8; dual exhausts: power front disc brakes; simulated air intake on hood; simulated front fender louvers; bright accents; black-finished grille and rear panel; 14-7 wheels; E70-14 White Stripe tires; hood insulation and SS emblems. Four-speed manual or Turbo-Hydramatic transmission required ($290.70).

RPO L34 Nova SS-396 package, includes same as above with 350 hp Turbo-Jet V-8 ($184.35 extra).

RPO L38 Nova SS-396 package, includes same as above with 375 hp Turbo-Jet V-8 ($316.00).

RPO Z25 Chevelle SS-396 package, includes 350 hp 396 cid Turbo-Jet V-8; power front disc brakes; dual exhausts with bright tips; black-painted grille; wheel opening moldings; special rear bumper with black inserts; 'power dome' hood; special suspension; 14 x 7 inch Sport style wheels; G70-14 white lettered tires; and SS emblems. Four-speed or Turbo-Hydramatic required ($445.55).

RPO Z25 with L78 Chevelle SS-396 with 375 hp V-8 and cast iron heads. Includes same as above, except engine ($210.65).

RPO Z25 with L78/L89 Chevelle SS-396, includes same as above with 375 hp V-8 and aluminum heads ($394.95).

HISTORICAL FOOTNOTES: The 1970-1/2 Camaro was not introduced until Feb. 26, 1970. The other new Chevrolet products hit the showrooms on Sept. 18, 1969. John Z. DeLorean was general manager of the Chevrolet Motor Div. this year. Calendar year production of models included in this section was as follows: (Chevrolet) 550,596; (Monte Carlo) 130,659; (Nova) 247,344; (Chevelle) 354,839; and Camaro (143,675). Model year output included 143,664 Camaros; 354,855 Chevelles; 130,657 Monte Carlos; 550,571 Chevrolets; and 254,242 Novas. A total of 53,599 Malibu SS models left the factory, including 3,733 with the 454 cid V-8. Also carrying SS equipment were 3,823 Monte Carlos and 19,558 Novas.

1971 CHEVROLET

1971 Chevrolet, Kingswood Estate four-door station wagon, V-8

FULL-SIZED CHEVROLET — (SIX/V-8) — ALL SERIES — All-new styling and increased size were characteristics of the big Chevrolets for 1971. All models grew, but the station wagon showed the largest gain in inches and was now on a longer wheelbase than passenger cars. The grille had an eggcrate look and was higher, but narrower. Parking lamps were resituated on the front body corners, where the large, ribbed, vertical lenses were set into fender extension caps. The dual horizontal headlamps were housed in square bezels. The hood panel bulged at the center and carried Chevrolet block lettering on its front edge. Bodyside contours were more rounded and straighter. The rear fenders kicked-up at the upper rear quarter region, then slanted back towards the tail. New taillight treatments were seen. Power disc brakes became standard on all full-sized models, as well as on Monte Carlos and Camaros. Standard equipment for Bel Airs included hidden (in-the-windshield) antenna; Astro-Ventilation, concealed wipers; side-guard beam doors; heater and defroster; cigarette lighter; locking glovebox; center dome light; armrests; 145 hp six or 245 hp V-8; inside hood release; and left-hand OSRV mirror. Bel Airs had all these features, plus glovebox light and cloth with vinyl trim interior. Impalas had the same equipment as Bel Airs, plus luggage compartment light; vinyl-trimmed pattern cloth upholstery; woodgrain accented dash; Deluxe steering wheel; foam front seat cushions; and, on convertibles, courtesy lights; lower door carpeting; and all-vinyl seats. Tires were F78 x 15 on Bel Air/Biscayne, G78 x 15 on Impala. The Caprice added ashtray and courtesy lights; electric clock; rear fender skirts; distinctive cloth and vinyl trim; color-keyed wheelcovers; and 225 hp V-8. It also used G78 x 15 tires. The Caprice sedan was equipped with a fold-down center armrest in the front seat. Features of full-sized station wagons were a concealed storage bin; cushioned-center steering wheel; flush and dry rocker panels; all-vinyl interior; power disc/drum brakes; Hide-Away wipers; Glide-Away tailgate with power window; Air-Flow rear contour; recessed dual headlights; flush-style curved side glass, Flow-through power ventilation; open rocker panels; inside hood release; forward-facing rear seat on nine-passenger; 245 hp '350' V-8; and L78 x 15 tires mounted on 15 x 6 inch wheels. Brookwoods added a map light. Townsman/Kingswood models added mirror map and glovebox lights and the Kingswood Estate also had ashtray, courtesy, glovebox and mirror map lights; door edge guards; electric clock; and woodgrained side and rear panels.

CHEVROLET I.D. NUMBERS: Serial Numbers on all Chevrolet products were now found on the top left-hand surface of the instrument panel. They were visible through the windshield. The Vehicle Identification Number had thirteen symbols. The first three symbols indicate make and series and appear as Series Number in first column of charts below. For example, first car listed has number 153 (1=Chevrolet; 53=Biscayne six) for six-cylinder series and 154 (1=Chevrolet; 54=Biscayne V-8) for eight-cylinder series. Fourth and fifth symbols indicate body type and appear as Body/Style Number in second column of charts below. Sixth symbol indicates model year, 1=1971. Seventh symbol identifies assembly plant: A=Atlanta, Ga.; B=Baltimore, Md.; C=Southgate, Calif.; F=Flint, Mich.; G=Framingham, Mass.; I=Oshawa, Canada; J=Janesville, Wis.; K=Kansas City, Mo.; L=Los Angeles, Calif.; N=Norwood, Ohio; R=Arlington, Texas; S=St. Louis, Mo.; T=Tarrytown, NY; U=Lordstown, Ohio; W=Willow Run, Mich.; Y=Wilmington, Del.; Z=Fremont, Calif. Next six symbols are sequential production number. Body tag riveted to cowl indicates some of the same information, plus paint and trim codes. Engine numbers are stamped on right side of V-8 blocks and right side of six-cylinder blocks behind distributor. Consult factory or aftermarket sources for numerous Chevrolet engine codes.

FULL-SIZED CHEVROLET SERIES

Series Number	Body/Style Number	Body Type & Seating	Factory Price	Shipping Weight	Production Total
BISCAYNE (BROOKWOOD STATION WAGON)					
153/154	69	4-dr Sed-6P	3096/3448	3732/3888	Note 1
154	35	4-dr Sta Wag-6P	3929	4542	Note 2
BEL AIR (TOWNSMAN STATION WAGON)					
155/156	69	4-dr Sed-6P	3232/3585	3732/3888	Note 3
156	45	4-dr Sta Wag-9P	4135	4598	Note 2
156	35	4-dr Sta Wag-6P	4020	4544	Note 2
IMPALA (KINGSWOOD STATION WAGON)					
163/164	69	4-dr Sed-6P	3391/3742	3760/3914	Note 4
163/164	57	2-dr HT Cpe-6P	3408/3759	3742/3896	Note 4
164	39	4-dr HT Sed-6P	3813	3978	Note 4
164	47	2-dr Cus Cpe-6P	3826	3912	Note 4
164	67	2-dr Conv-6P	4021	3960	Note 4/5
164	45	4-dr Sta Wag-9P	4227	4648	Note 2
164	35	4-dr Sta Wag-6P	4112	4588	Note 2
CAPRICE (KINGSWOOD ESTATE WAGON)					
166	39	4-dr HT Sed-6P	4134	4040	Note 6
166	47	2-dr Cus Cpe-6P	4081	3964	Note 6
166	45	4-dr Sta Wag-9P	4498	4738	Note 2
166	35	4-dr Sta Wag-6P	4384	4678	Note 2

FIGURES BELOW ARE ROUNDED-OFF (except Note 5):
NOTE 1: 37,600 Biscayne cars were built (2,900 sixes/34,700 V-8s).
NOTE 2: 91,300 full-size Chevrolet wagons built (all V-8s).
NOTE 3: 20,000 Bel Air cars were built (5,000 sixes/15,000 V-8s).
NOTE 4: 427,700 Impala cars built (2,300 sixes/425,400 V-8s).
NOTE 5: EXACTLY 4,576 Impala convertibles are included in Note 4.
NOTE 6: 91,300 Caprice V-8s built.
NOTE 7: Data above slash for six if offered/below slash; no slash is V-8 data.

1971 Chevrolet, Monte Carlo two-door hardtop coupe, V-8

MONTE CARLO — (V-8) — SERIES 138 — A new grille with a finer insert mesh appeared on 1971 Monte Carlos. A front bumper with rectangular parking lamps was used in this model's second year. Another change was a raised hood ornament. The original wheelbase was carried over, but overall length grew an inch. The headlight bezels were squarer. This was the last year for the Monte Carlo SS-454, of which only 1,919 examples were built in 1971. Standard Monte Carlo features included all safety equipment; power front disc brakes; power ventilation system; electric clock; sideguard door beam structure; assist straps; vinyl buried elm finish instrument panel; concealed wipers; 245 hp '350' V-8; glovebox light; and left-hand OSRV mirror. Size G78 x 15 tires were used.

MONTE CARLO SERIES

Series Number	Body/Style Number	Body Type & Seating	Factory Price	Shipping Weight	Production Total
138	57	2-dr HT Cpe-5P	3416	3488	112,599

NOTE 1: The production figure includes 1,919 cars with SS-454 equipment.

1971 Chevelle, Malibu two-door hardtop sports coupe, V-8

1971 Chevrolet, Chevelle Malibu two-door hardtop, V-8

INTERMEDIATE-SIZED CHEVELLE — (SIX/V-8) — ALL SERIES — The Chevelle models received changes to the front and rear for 1971. A new twin level grille was divided by a bright, horizontal bar with a Chevrolet 'bow tie' insignia at the middle. The grille inserts were of multiple, horizontal blades segmented by wide-spaced vertical dividers. Single headlamps in square bezels were used. Parking lamps were moved from the previous bumper location into the front fenders. There were two parking lamps lenses, set into individual rectangular housings that wrapped around the body corners. The upper lens was amber and the lower lens was white. At the rear, circular taillights were deeply recessed into the bumper. Standard equipment for base editions consisted of Astro-Ventilation; cigarette lighter; side-guard door beam structure; concealed wipers; and either the 145 hp '250' six or 200 hp '307' V-8. The Malibu convertible also had interior courtesy lamps, while all Malibus featured a glovebox light and left OSRV mirror. Equipment included on Nomad, Concours and Greenbriers was comprised of Dual-Action tailgate; concealed storage compartment; cushioned-center steering wheel; flush and dry rocker panels; all-vinyl interior; bias-belted G78 x 14 tires; carpeting; vinyl-coated textured metal cargo floor; and Guard-Beam side door construction. The Nomad came as a six or V-8, while the other wagons came

V-8 only. Concours and Concours Estates also had Hide-Away wipers; power front disc/rear drum brakes; and a glovebox light. The Estate also included door edge guards and woodgrained exterior paneling, with rear-facing third seats and power tailgate window in nine-passenger jobs.

INTERMEDIATE-SIZED CHEVELLE SERIES

Series Number	Body/Style Number	Body Type & Seating	Factory Price	Shipping Weight	Production Total
NOMAD STATION WAGONS					
131/132	36	4-dr Sta Wag-6P	2997/3097	3632/3746	Note 1

Model Number	Body/Style Number	Body Type & Seating	Factory Price	Shipping Weight	Production Total
CHEVELLE (GREENBRIER WAGONS)					
133/134	69	4-dr Sed-6P	2677/2773	3210/3338	Note 2
133/134	37	2-dr HT Cpe-6P	2712/2807	3166/3296	Note 2
134	46	4-dr Sta Wag-9P	3340	3882	Note 1
134	36	4-dr Sta Wag-6P	3228	3820	Note 1
CHEVELLE MALIBU (CONCOURS WAGON)					
135/136	69	4-dr Sed-6P	2851/2947	3250/3380	Note 3
135/136	37	2-dr HT Cpe-6P	2885/2980	3212/3342	Note 3
136	39	4-dr HT Sed-6P	3052	3450	Note 3
136	67	2-dr Conv-6P	3260	3390	Note 3/4
136	46	4-dr Sta Wag-9P	3450	3908	Note 1
136	36	4-dr Sta Wag-6P	3337	3864	Note 1
CONCOURS ESTATE WAGON					
138	46	4-dr Sta Wag-9P	3626	3944	Note 1
138	36	4-dr Sta Wag-6P	3514	3892	Note 1

GENERAL NOTE: All model year production figures given below are expressed to the nearest 100 units. No body style breakouts are available, except for convertibles.
NOTE 1: Some 43,200 Chevelle intermediate-sized station wagons were built during the 1971 model year. This includes 2,800 sixes (all Nomads) and 39,500 V-8s. This includes all Nomad, Greenbrier, Concours and Concours Estate wagons, with no additional breakout by series available at the current time.
NOTE 2: Some 35,600 base Chevelles were built during the 1971 model year. This included 11,500 sixes and 24,100 v-8s.
NOTE 3: Some 249,300 Chevelle Malibu were built during the 1971 model year. This included 9,100 sixes and 240,200 V-8s.
NOTE 4: Exactly 5,089 Chevelle Malibu convertibles were built during the 1971 model year. This breakout is included in the rounded-off totals in Note 3 above. All convertibles were V-8s. There is no additional breakout available as to the number of Super Sport convertibles built.
ADDITIONAL NOTE: In rounded-off figures, a total of some 80,000 Chevelles were sold with Super Sport equipment packages. Exactly 19,992 of these cars wer Chevelle SS 454s.

1971 Chevrolet, Nova two-door sedan, V-8

NOVA SERIES — (SIX/V-8) — SERIES 113/114 — The disappearance of the Nova four was one change for the 'senior' compact models. There was also a very slight amount of revision to the grille. It seemed to highlight the vertical elements more than the year before. A vertical molding was also seen in the front fender corner trim panels. Amber plastic parking lamp lenses were new. Simulated fenderside louvers were off the optional equipment list, but many new packages were added. The body was essentially the same design introduced in 1968. Standard features included front armrests; foot-operated brake; ignition key alarm system; anti-theft steering wheel column lock; heater and defroster; and either the '250' six or '307' V-8. The Nova wore E78 x 14 tires in standard trim.

1971 Chevrolet, Nova two-door sedan, V-8

NOVA SIX/V-8 SERIES

Series Number	Body/Style Number	Body Type & Seating	Factory Price	Shipping Weight	Production Total
111/113	69	4-dr Sed-6P	2205/2284	2843/2942	Note 1
111/113	27	2-dr Cpe-6P	2176/2254	2820/2919	Note 1

NOTE 1: 194,878 Novas were built (94,928 sixes/99,950 V-8s.)
NOTE 2: 7,015 Novas included in the total above had Super Sport option.

1971 Chevrolet, two-door Vega 2300 notchback sedan, 4-cyl

VEGA 2300 — (FOUR) — SERIES 2300 — The Vega was a completely new sub-compact car from Chevrolet. Three two-door models, notchback sedan, hatchback coupe and Kammback station wagon were offered. Single headlights, round parking lamps and a slightly 'veed' rectangular grille with eggcrate insert characterized the front of the car. A full-width, wraparound bumper ran across the grille. The rear panel had a slightly concave treatment, with twin rectangular taillamps at each side. Three sets of louvers were punched in the deck of the notchback and on the rear quarter of wagons. The hatchback had its louvers at the rear roof pillar. Power came from an aluminum four with overhead camshaft. A dome-shaped bulge was on the hood of all three styles. A nameplate was placed ahead of the forward hood seam, above the upper left-hand corner of the grille. It read 'Chevrolet Vega 2300.' Standard features included side marker lights and reflectors; functional vent louvers; flush and dry rocker panels; left OSRV mirror; front bucket seats; rear bucket-style bench seats; Flow-Through ventilation; three-speed manual transmission with floor shift control; windshield washers; dual speed wipers; ashtray; all-vinyl upholstery; exhaust emission control system; storage well in driver's door; and 80 hp four. The coupe also had hatchback rear deck construction; fold-down back seat; front area carpeting; passenger sliding seat adjustment; cargo area rubber mats; and concealed-under-floor storage area. Sedans and wagons had front manual disc brakes. The wagon included carpeting. All featured a three-point safety belt system. Size 6.00 x 13 tires were used as standard equipment.

1971 Chevrolet, Vega 2300 two-door Kammback Wagon, 4-cyl

VEGA 2300 SERIES

Series Number	Body/Style Number	Body Type & Seating	Factory Price	Shipping Weight	Production Total
141	11	2-dr Sed-4P	2090	2146	58,800
141	77	2-dr Cpe-4P	2196	2190	168,300
141	15	2-dr Sta Wag-4P	2328	2230	42,800

NOTE 1: 274,699 Vegas were built during the 1971 model year.
NOTE 2: Chart shows rounded-off totals for each passenger body style.
NOTE 3: Some 7,800 Vega panel wagons were also included in model year total.

CAMARO — (SIX/V-8) — SERIES 123/124 — There was hardly any change in the 1971 Camaro. As on other Chevrolets, the grille insert seemed to have a more vertical character, although the design elements remained basically unchanged. Trim details varied according to the options ordered for each car. New options were brown or blue vinyl top coverings. Power disc brakes were standard. So were side marker lights; reflectors; defroster; washers and dual speed wipers; inside day/nite mirror; outside rearview mirror; all-vinyl interior; bucket seats; rear bucket style seat cushions; front disc brakes; steel side guard rails; three-speed manual transmission with floor shift; cigarette lighter; carpeting; Astro-Ventilation; and either the '250' six or '307' V-8. Size E78 x 14 tires were standard equipment. The Camaro SS package included dual exhausts; power brakes; left-hand remote-control sport mirror; special ornamentation and hood insulation; F70-14 tires (white-lettered); 14 x 7 inch wheels; black-finished grille, Hide-Away wipers; and the 270 hp 350 cid V-8 with bright engine accents. Rally Sport equipment included special black-finished grille with rubber-tipped vertical center bar and resilient body-color grille frame; independent front left- and right-hand bumpers; license plate bracket below right bumper; parking lights with bright accents mounted on grille panel; Hide-Away wipers; bright roof drip, window and hood panel moldings; body-color insert on door handles; RS emblem on steering wheel; RS front fender nameplates; and bright accented taillights and back-up lamps (RS emblems were deleted when SS or Z/28 packages were ordered). The Z/28 package also included special 330 hp '350' V-8 with bright engine trim; remote-control left-hand OSRV mirror; special instrumentation; power brakes; 3.73:1 ratio positraction rear axle; heavy-duty cooling; dual exhausts; black accented grille; Z/28 front fender emblems; rear bumper guards; sport suspension; rear deck spoiler with Z/28 decal; special paint stripes on hood and rear deck (choice of black or white stripes except with vinyl top or roof with black or white paint finish); heavy-duty front and rear springs; 15 x 7 inch wheels with chrome lug nuts; special center hubcaps with trim rings; and F60-15/B bias-belted white-letter tires.

1971 Camaro SS 396, two-door sports coupe, V-8

CAMARO SERIES SIX/V-8

Series Number	Body/Style Number	Body Type & Seating	Factory Price	Shipping Weight	Production Total
123/124	87	2-dr HT Cpe-4P	2921/3016	3094/3218	107,496

NOTE 1: Production included 18,404 Rally Sports
NOTE 2: Production included 8,377 Super Sports.
NOTE 3: Production included 4,862 Z-28s.
NOTE 4: 103,452 had V-8s; 11,191 had sixes.
NOTE 5: Transmissions: 13,042 3-speed; 10,614 4-speed; 90,987 automatic.
NOTE 6: Options: 42,537 cars with A/C; 93,163 cars with power steering.
NOTE 7: 7,147 Camaros were built in the U.S. for export market sales.

BASE ENGINES

(ALL SIX-CYLINDER) Inline Six: Cast iron block. Displacement: 250 cid. Bore and stroke: 3.875 x 3.53 inches. Compression ratio: 8.5:1. Brake hp: 145 at 4200 rpm. Seven main bearings. Hydraulic valve lifters. Carburetor: Rochester one-barrel.

(V-8 BISCAYNE/BEL AIR/IMPALA/MONTE CARLO) V-8: Overhead valves. Cast iron block. Displacement: 350 cid. Bore and stroke: 4.00 x 3.48 inches. Compression ratio: 8.5:1. Brake hp 245 at 4800 rpm. Five main bearings. Hydraulic valve lifters. Carburetor: Rochester two-barrel.

(V-8 CAPRICE AND STATION WAGONS) V-8: Overhead valves. Cast iron block. Displacement: 400 cid. Bore and stroke: 4.125 x 3.75 inches. Compression ratio: 8.51:1. Brake hp: 255 at 4400 rpm. Five main bearings. Hydraulic valve lifters. Carburetor: Rochester two-barrel.

(CHEVELLE/MALIBU/NOVA/CAMARO) V-8: Overhead valves. Cast iron block. Displacement: 307 cid. Bore and stroke: 3.875 x 3.25 inches. Compression ratio: 8.5:1. Brake hp: 200 at 4600 rpm. Five main bearings. Hydraulic valve lifters. Carburetor: Rochester two-barrel.

(VEGA) Inline Ohc-four: Aluminum block. Displacement: 140 cid. Bore and stroke-. 3.501 x 3.625 inches. Compression ratio: 8.0:1. Brake hp: 90 at 46-4800 rpm. Hydraulic valve lifters. Carburetor: one-barrel.

CAMARO SERIES ENGINES

CHASSIS FEATURES: Wheelbase: (Chevrolet wagon) 125 inches; (Chevrolet) 121.5 inches-(Monte Carlo/Chevelle four-door) 116 inches; (Chevelle two-door) 112 inches; (Nova) 111 inches; (Camaro) 108 inches; (Vega) 97 inches. Overall length: (Chevrolet wagon) 224 inches; (Chevrolet) 217 inches; (Monte Carlo/Chevelle wagon) 207 inches; (Chevelle two-door) 198 inches; (Chevelle four-door) 202 inches; (Nova) 190 inches; (Camaro) 188 inches; (Vega) 170 inches. Width: (Chevrolet) 80 inches; (Monte Carlo/Chevelle) 76 inches; (Nova) 73 inches; (Camaro) 75 inches; (Vega) 66 inches. Tires: Refer to text.

OPTIONS: Vega power steering ($95). Vega air conditioning ($360). Nova vinyl top ($84). Nova power steering ($103). Nova air conditioning ($392). Chevelle vinyl top ($95). Monte Carlo/Camaro/Chevelle air conditioning ($408). Camaro vinyl top ($90). Monte Carlo vinyl top ($126). Chevrolet AM/FM stereo ($239). Chevrolet power windows ($127). Vega GT coupe package ($349). Nova SS package ($328). Chevelle SS package ($357). Malibu SS package ($357). Camaro SS package ($314). Monte Carlo SS-454 package ($485). Camaro RS package ($179). Three-speed manual transmission was standard. Automatic transmission. Special three-speed manual floor shift transmission. Four-speed manual floor shift transmission. Wide-ratio four-speed manual transmission with floor shift. Close-ratio four-speed manual transmission with floor shift. Vega Four 140 cid 110 hp two-barrel engine. Chevrolet V-8 400 cid 255 hp two-barrel engine. Chevrolet V-8 402 cid 300 hp four-barrel engine. Chevrolet V-8 454 cid 365 hp four-barrel engine. Monte Carlo/Corvette 402 cid 300 hp four-barrel engine. Monte Carlo/Chevelle V-8 454 cid 365 hp four-barrel engine. Chevelle V-8 350 cid 245 hp two-barrel engine. Chevelle V-8 350 cid 270 hp four-barrel engine. Nova V-8 350 cid 245 hp two-barrel engine. Camaro V-8 350 cid 245 hp two-barrel engine. Camaro V-8 350 cid 270 hp four-barrel engine. Camaro V-8 402 cid 300 hp four-barrel engine.

HISTORICAL FOOTNOTES: The full-sized Chevrolets were introduced on Sept. 29, 1970 and the Vega appeared in dealer showrooms Sept. 10. Calendar year production of 2,275,694 cars was recorded. John L. DeLorean was the chief executive officer of the company this year. In the high-performance car field, Chevrolet built some 80,000 Chevelle Super Sports; 7,015 Nova Super Sports; 1,919 Monte Carlo SS-454 models and 8,377 Camaro Super Sports. Only 19,292 Chevelle SS models had the 454 cid V-8 installed. Monte Carlos continued to compete and win on the NASCAR short tracks, even with horsepower reduced to 425 due to lower 9.0:1 compression ratio. This compared to 460 hp in the late 1970 LS6-equipped Chevelles. Most other Chevrolets were limited to an 8.5:1 maximum compression ratio to insure adaptability of the new motors to low-lead or no-lead fuel. However, the Camaro Z-28 was an exception. It came with a 9.0:1 compression 350 cid V-8 that produced 330 hp.

1972 CHEVROLET

FULL-SIZED CHEVROLET — (SIX/V-8) — ALL SERIES — Chevrolet's standard models continued to get bigger, with a slight increase in passenger car wheelbase as well. The front lip of the hood dipped deeper creating a slimmer grille above the full-width bumper. However, more of the grille showed through underneath. Parking lamps, while still in the fender extension caps, were smaller. The grille had a finer texture and a Chevrolet insignia was seen at the center of the hood. A lower body feature line was used on the bodysides and the upper rear fender edge was somewhat raised. Tires were size G78 x 15/B on Impala/Caprice; F78 x 15/B on Biscayne/Bel Air; and H78 x 5 on station wagons. Power brakes; power steering; and automatic transmission became standard in all full-sized lines. For this season only, engine horsepower ratings were expressed in both the traditional way and in the new SAE Net (nhp) format.

1972 Chevrolet, Caprice two-door hardtop coupe, V-8

CHEVROLET I.D. NUMBERS: Serial Numbers on all Chevrolet products were now found on the top left-hand surface of the instrument panel. They were visible through the windshield. The Vehicle Identification Number had 13 symbols. The first symbol indicate make 1=Chevrolet and the second symbol indicated car-line: B=Nomad; C=Chevelle/Greenbrier; D=Malibu/Concours; H=Monte Carlo/Concours Estate; K=Biscayne/Brookwood; L=Bel Air/Townsman; M=Impala/Kingswood; N=Caprice/Kingswood Estate; Q=-Camaro; V=Vega; X=Nova. (These appear in Series Number column of charts below). The third and fourth digits indicated body type and appear in Body/Style Number column of charts below. Fifth symbol indicates engine: B=140 cid four; D=250 cid six; F=307 cid V-8; H=350 cid V-8 2V; J=350 cid V-8 (L48); L=Camaro Z28 four-barrel 350 cid V-8 (high-output); R=400 cid V-8; S=402 cid (LS3) V-8 single exhaust; U=402 cid (LS3) V-8 dual exhaust; V=454 cid V-8 (LS5) single exhaust; W=454 cid V-8 4V (LS5) dual exhausts. Sixth symbol indicates model year 2=1972. Seventh symbol indicates assembly plant: A=Lakewood, Ga.; B=Baltimore, Md.; C=Southgate, Calif.; D=Doraville, Ga.; F=Flint, Mich.; J=Janesville, Wis.; K=Leeds, Mo.; L=Van Nuys, Calif.; N=Norwood, Ohio; R=Arlington, Texas; S=St. Louis, Mo.; T=Tarrytown, NY;U=Lordstown, Ohio; V=Pontiac, Mich.; W=Willow Run, Mich.; Y=Wilmington, Del.; Z=Fremont, Calif.; 1=Oshawa, Canada; 2=St. Therese, Quebec, Canada. Next six symbols are sequential production number. Body tag riveted to cowl indicates some of the same information, plus paint and trim codes. Engine numbers are stamped on right side of V-8 blocks and right side of six-cylinder blocks behind distributor. Consult factory or aftermarket sources for numerous Chevrolet engine serial numbers.

FULL-SIZED CHEVROLET SERIES K-L-M-N

Series Number	Body/Style Number	Body Type & Seating	Factory Price	Shipping Weight	Production Total
BISCAYNE (BROOKWOOD STATION WAGON)					
1K	69	4-dr Sed-6P	3074/3408	3857/4045	Note 1
1K	35	4-dr Sta Wag-6P	3882	4686	Note 2
BEL AIR (TOWNSMAN STATION WAGON)					
1L	69	4-dr Sed-6P	3204/3538	3854/4042	Note 3
1L	45	4-dr Sta Wag-9P	4078	4769	Note 2
1L	35	4-dr Sta Wag-6P	3969	4687	Note 2
IMPALA (KINGSWOOD STATION WAGONS)					
1M	69	4-dr Sed-6P	3369/3704	3928/4113	Note 4
1M	57	2-dr HT Cpe-6P	3385/3720	3864/4049	Note 4
1M	39	4-dr HT Sed-6P	3771	4150	Note 4
1M	47	2-dr Cus Cpe-6P	3787	4053	Note 4
1M	67	2-dr Conv-6P	3979	4125	Notes 4 /5
1M	45	4-dr Sta Wag-9P	4165	4817	Note 2
1M	35	4-dr Sta Wag-6P	4056	4734	Note 2
CAPRICE (KINGSWOOD ESTATE WAGON)					
1N	69	4-dr Sed-6P	4009	NA	Note 6
1N	47	2-dr Cus Cpe-6P	4026	4102	Note 6
1N	45	4-dr Sta Wag-9P	4423	4883	Note 2
1N	35	4-dr Sta Wag-6P	4314	4798	Note 2

FIGURES BELOW ARE ROUNDED-OFF (except Note 5):

NOTE 1: 20,500 Biscayne cars were built (1,500 sixes/19,000 V-8s).
NOTE 2: 171,700 full-size Chevrolet wagons built (all V-8s).
NOTE 3: 41,900 Bel Air cars were built (900 sixes/41,000 V-8s).
NOTE 4: 597,500 Impala cars built (1,500 sixes/596,000 V-8s).
NOTE 5: Exactly 6,456 Impala V-8 convertibles are included in Note 4.
NOTE 6: 178,500 Caprice V-8s built.
NOTE 7: Data above slash for six if offered/below slash; no slash is V-8 data.

1972 Chevrolet, Caprice four-door hardtop sedan, V-8

1972 Chevrolet, Impala two-door convertible, V-8

MONTE CARLO — (V-8) — SERIES 1H — The new Monte Carlo grille covered the entire area between the square-bezeled headlamps. It had horizontal blades divided by prominent vertical blades. Parking lamps were moved from the bumper and were vertically positioned at the outboard grille segments. It was the last season for the original Monte Carlo body style. Standard equipment tires were size G78 x 15/B blackwalls.

MONTE CARLO SERIES H

Series Number	Body/Style Number	Body Type & Seating	Factory Price	Shipping Weight	Production Total
1H	57	2-dr HT Cpe-6P	3362	3506	180,819

1972 Chevrolet, Impala Custom Coupe two-door hardtop, V-8

1972 Chevrolet, Caprice Estate four-door station wagon, V-8

INTERMEDIATE-SIZED CHEVELLE — (SIX/V-8) — ALL SERIES — Changes to the Chevelle were of a minor nature. The grille had a new texture and was divided horizontally by two even-spaced moldings giving a three-tier look. Parking lamps were still found in the fender cap, but now had a larger, one-piece plastic lens of square shape. It wrapped around the body corner, serving double duty as a side marker lamp. A new molding treatment with some trim

levels included a stainless steel spear at mid-body height running only between the front and rear wheel openings. Tires for base models were size E78 x 14/8 blackwalls. Station wagons had G78 x 14/B tires. Chevelle V-8s built for California sale were equipped with the 350 cid engine in 165 or 175 hp form. Federal cars had either the '250' six or the '307' two-barrel V-8.

1972 Chevelle, Malibu two-door hardtop sports coupe, V-8

INTERMEDIATE-SIZED CHEVELLE SERIES B-C-D-H

Series Number	Body/Style Number	Body Type & Seating	Factory Price	Shipping Weight	Production Total
NOMAD STATION WAGON					
1B	36	4-dr Sta Wag-6P	2926/3016	3605/3732	Note 1
CHEVELLE (GREENBRIER STATION WAGON)					
1C	69	4-dr Sed-6P	2636/2726	3204/3332	Note 2
1C	37	2-dr HT Cpe-6P	2669/2759	3172/3300	Note 2
1C	46	4-dr Sta Wag-9P	3247	3870	Note 1
1C	36	4-dr Sta Wag-6P	3140	3814	Note 1

Model Number	Body/Style Number	Body Type & Seating	Factory Price	Shipping Weight	Production Total
MALIBU (CONCOURS STATION WAGONS)					
1D	69	4-dr Sed-6P	2801/2891	3240/3371	Note 3
1D	39	4-dr HT Sed-6P	2991	3438	Note 3
1D	37	2-dr HT Cpe-6	2833/2923	3194/3327	Note 3
1D	67	2-dr Conv-6P	3187	3379	Notes 3/4
1D	46	4-dr Sta Wag-9P	3351	3909	Note 1
1D	36	4-dr Sta Wag-6P	3244	3857	Note 1
CONCOURS ESTATE WAGON					
1H	46	4-dr Sta Wag-9P	3588	3943	Note 1
1H	36	4-dr Sta Wag-6P	3431	3887	Note 1

FIGURES BELOW ARE ROUNDED-OFF (except Note 4):
NOTE 1: 54,400 Chevelle wagons built all series (3,000 sixes/51,400 V-8s).
NOTE 2: 49,400 base Chevelles built (13,800 sixes/35,600 V-8s).
NOTE 3: 290,100 Malibu built (8,400 sixes/281,700 V-8s).
NOTE 4: 4,853 Malibu/Malibu SS convertibles included in above total.
NOTE 5: 24,946 SS counted in Note 3 total (including 3,000 SS-454).
NOTE 6: Data above slash for six if offered/below slash; no slash is V-8 data.

1972 Chevrolet, Chevelle Malibu two-door sports coupe, V-8

NOVA — (SIX/V-8) — SERIES X — The Nova was carried over from 1971 without any obvious change, except for an indented license plate housing on the front bumper. If closely examined, a slight change in the bevel of the hood could be seen. There were numerous decor packages available to create anything from a hot rod to personal/luxury car look. However, true high-performance hardware was no longer provided. Base engines in all states were the '250' six or '307' V-8. A 245 hp '350' V-8 was optional. Regular tires were E78 x 14/8 blackwalls.

NOVA SERIES X

Series Number	Body/Style Number	Body Type & Seating	Factory Price	Shipping Weight	Production Total
1X	69	4-dr Sed-6P	2405/2501	2976/3108	Note 1
1X	27	2-dr Cpe-6P	2376/2471	2952/3084	Note 1

NOTE 1: 349,733 Novas built in model year (139,769 sixes and 209,964 V-8s).
NOTE 2: Above includes 12,309 cars sold with Nova SS equipment package.

VEGA 2300 — (FOUR) — SERIES 1V — The grille on the Vega was finished in a manner that made its vertical elements slightly less prominent. A model identification emblem was positioned on the side of the cowl. A change to A78 x 13 tires was made for standard equipment. Otherwise, there was very little difference from 1971.

1972 Chevrolet, Nova two-door sedan, V-8

1972 Chevrolet, Nova two-door sedan, V-8

1972 Chevrolet, Vega 2300 two-door coupe, 4-cyl

VEGA 2300 SERIES 1V

Series Number	Body/Style Number	Body Type & Seating	Factory Price	Shipping Weight	Production Total
1V	11	2-dr Sed-4P	2060	2158	55,800
1V	77	2-dr Cpe-4P	2160	2294	262,700
1V	15	2-dr Sta Wag-4P	2285	2333	72,000

NOTE 1: Model year production was 394,592 units.

NOTE 2: Model year production includes 4,114 panel express trucks.

NOTE 3: Chart shows body style production rounded-off to nearest 100 units.

1972 Chevrolet, Vega two-door coupe, 4-cyl

1972 Camaro SS, two-door sport coupe, V-8

CAMARO — (SIX/V-8) — SERIES Q — The Camaro, for 1972, had a slightly different grille mesh and new high-back bucket seats. The fate of the car was said to be in danger, since a strike at the Camaro assembly plant (Lordstown, Ohio) turned into a disaster. The walkout stranded thousands of bodies on the assembly line and, by the time it was over, these cars were unfit for sale under new federal safety standards. General Motors was forced to scrap the bodies and almost decided to do the same with the Camaro/Firebird program. Chevrolet engineer Alex Mair fought successfully for survival of the Camaro which went on to higher sales. Camaros wore E78 x 14 tires in standard trim and base engine selections were the same as in Chevelles, with different V-8s used for federal and California cars.

CAMARO SERIES Q

Series Number	Body/Style Number	Body Type & Seating	Factory Price	Shipping Weight	Production Total
1Q	87	2-dr HT Cpe-4P	2730/2820	3121/3248	68,656

NOTE 1: Production total includes 11,364 RS; 6,562 SS; 2,575 Camaro Z28s.

NOTE 2: 63,832 cars had V-8s; 4,824 cars had sixes.

NOTE 3: Transmission: 6,053 had 3-speed; 5,835 had 4-speed; 56,768 had THM.

NOTE 4: Options: 31,737 had A/C; 59,857 had power steering.

NOTE 5: 3,698 cars were built in U.S. for export sales.

1972 Chevrolet, Camaro two-door sports coupe, V-8

BASE ENGINES

(CHEVROLET/CHEVELLE/NOVA) Inline Six: Overhead valves. Cast iron block. Displacement: 250 cid. Bore and stroke: 3.875 x 3.53 inches. SAE Net hp: 110. Seven main bearings. Hydraulic valve lifters. Carburetor: one-barrel.

(V-8 BISCAYNE/BEL AIR/IMPALA/MONTE CARLO/CHEVELLE CALIF.) V-8: Overhead valves. Cast iron block. Displacement: 350 cid. Bore and stroke: 4.00 x 3.48 inches. SAE Net hp: 165. Five main bearings. Hydraulic valve lifters.

(V-8 CAPRICE/ALL STATION WAGONS) V-8: Overhead valves. Cast iron block. Displacement: 400 cid. Bore and stroke: 4.126 x 3.75 inches. SAE Net hp: 170. Five main bearings. Hydraulic valve lifters. Carburetor: two-barrel.

CAMARO FEDERAL V-8: See 1972 Nova Series V-8 engine data.

CAMARO CALIFORNIA V-8: See 1972 Chevrolet Series V-8 engine data.

(V-8 NOVA/CHEVELLE FEDERAL/CAMARO) V-8: Overhead valves. Cast iron block. Displacement: 307 cid. Bore and stroke: 3.875 x 3.25 inches. Brake hp: 200. Five main bearings. Hydraulic valve lifters. Carburetor: two-barrel.

(VEGA) Inline Four: Overhead valves. Cast aluminum block. Displacement: 140 cubic inches. Bore and stroke: 3.50 x 3.625 inches. Brake hp 80. Carburetor: one-barrel.

CHASSIS FEATURES: Wheelbase: (Chevrolet passenger) 122 inches, (all other models) same as 1971. Overall length: (Chevrolet wagon) 226 inches; (Chevrolet) 220 inches; (all other models) same as 1971. Tires: (all models) Refer to text.

OPTIONS: Vega power steering ($92). Vega air conditioning ($349). Nova vinyl top ($82). Nova power steering ($100). Nova air conditioning ($381). Nova Super Sport Package ($320). Chevelle vinyl top ($92). Monte Carlo/Chevelle air conditioning ($397). Chevelle SS Package ($350). Chevrolet/Monte Carlo/Chevelle AM/FM stereo ($233). Chevrolet/Monte Carlo/Chevelle AM/FM Stereo with tape ($363). Camaro vinyl top ($87). Camaro air conditioning ($397). Camaro SS package ($306). Camaro RS Package ($118). Monte Carlo vinyl top ($123). Monte Carlo Custom trim ($350). Chevrolet vinyl top ($106). Chevrolet air conditioning ($405). Chevrolet power windows ($113). Vega GT Package ($339). Camaro Z28 Special Performance option ($598). Three-speed manual transmission was standard on all sixes and non-full-sized lines. Automatic transmission was standard on full-sized V-8s. Overdrive transmission. Automatic transmission. Three-speed manual floor shift transmission. Four-speed manual floor shift transmission. Wide-ratio four-speed manual transmission with floor shift. Close-ratio four-speed manual transmission with floor shift. Vega four-cylinder 140 cid 90 hp two-barrel engine. Chevrolet V-8 350 cid 255 hp four-barrel engine ($168). Chevrolet V-8 400 cid 170 hp four-barrel engine. Chevrolet V-8 402 cid 210 hp four-barrel engine. Chevrolet V-8 454 cid 270 hp four-barrel engine. Monte Carlo V-8 350 cid 175 hp two-barrel dual-exhaust.

Monte Carlo V-8 402 cid 240 hp four-barrel engine ($142). Monte Carlo V-8 454 cid 270 hp four-barrel engine ($261). V-8 454 hp four-barrel engine. Chevelle V-8 350 cid 165 hp two-barrel engine. Chevelle V-8 350 cid 175 hp two-barrel dual exhaust. Chevelle V-8 402 cid 240 hp four-barrel engine ($168). Chevelle V-8 454 cid 270 hp four-barrel engine ($272). Nova V-8 350 cid 165 hp two-barrel engine. Camaro V-8 350 cid 165 hp two-barrel engine. Camaro V-8 350 cid 200 hp four-barrel engine. Camaro V-8 350 cid 255 hp high-output engine. Camaro V-8 402 cid 240 hp four-barrel engine.

HISTORICAL FOOTNOTES: The full-sized Chevrolets were introduced on Sept. 23, 1971 and the other models appeared in dealer showrooms at the same time. Calendar year production of 2,252,892 cars was recorded. Sales of models covered here, made by U.S. franchised dealers in calendar 1973, peaked at 2,300,812 cars. This figure excludes Corvettes and Sports Vans, which Chevrolet Motor Div. normally accounted with auto production. F. James McDonald was the chief executive officer of the company this year.

1973 CHEVROLET

FULL-SIZED CHEVROLET — (SIX/V-8) — ALL SERIES — New styling, front and rear, characterized 1973 Chevrolet model offerings made up of Bel Airs, Impalas, Caprice Classics and three station wagon lines. A wider, bolder grille design was featured. On Caprice Classics, the grille had an open grid texture and a Caprice medallion was placed at the center of the hood lip. Grilles on other Series had additional vertical bars and a Chevrolet 'bow tie' badge at the grille center, instead of the hood medallion. On all cars, the upper grille border was at a level even with the top of the headlamp surrounds. The front lamp treatment used dual, round lenses housed in side-by-side square bezels. Parking lamps were moved from the fender extension caps, into the bumper. which was a new hydraulically-cushioned, energy-absorbing type. The rear bumper panel slanted forward and housed rectangular lamps. Following the pattern established in 1958, the higher-priced models had triple taillamps, while Biscaynes and Bel Airs had a dual lens design. All station wagons had single-unit taillights in the fenders and Dual-Action tailgate construction. At the front of all models, the license plate housing was moved to the center of the bumper. instead of to one side. The only full-sized convertible remaining was in the Caprice Classic lineup. Power steering and power front disc brakes were standard equipment. All V-8 models included automatic transmission at base price. A new, 22 gallon fuel tank provided a longer cruising range. The first cars of the year were assembled August 7, 1972. With the discontinuance of the Biscayne, the Bel Air became the low-priced Chevrolet and the only model available with the 250 cid six. A 145 hp 350 cid V-8 was base powerplant in the Bel Air station wagon and all Impalas. The 400 cid V-8, now rated at 150 SAE Net hp, was standard in all Caprice Classics and Caprice Estate wagons. The station wagons no longer used distinctive nameplates, such as Brookwood or Kingswood. Standard sized tires were G78-15B on Bel Air: H78-15B on Bel Air station wagons and L78-15B on Impala coupes/Caprice/Estate and Impala station wagons.

1973 Chevrolet, Caprice two-door hardtop Custom Coupe, V-8

CHEVROLET I.D. NUMBERS: VIN top left side of dash, visible through windshield. First symbol 1=Chevrolet. Second symbol indicates car-line: C=Chevelle Deluxe; D=Malibu; E=Laguna; G=Malibu Estate; H=Monte Carlo/Laguna Estate; K=Bel Air; L=Impala; N=Caprice; Q=Camaro; S=Type LT; V=Vega; X=Nova; Y=Nova Custom. Third and fourth symbols indicate body type and appear in Body/Style Number column of charts below. Fifth symbol indicates engine: A=140 cid four one-barrel; B=140 cid four two-barrel; D=250 cid six; F=307 cid V-8 2V; H=350 cid V-8 2V; K=350 cid V-8 4V; T=350 cid V-8 (Z28); R=400 cid V-8 2V; X=454 cid V-8 (L54) single exhausts; Y=454 cid V-8 dual exhausts. Sixth symbol 3=1973. Seventh symbol indicates assembly plant: A=Lakewood; B=Baltimore; C=Southgate; D=Doraville; F=Flint; J=Janesville; K=Leeds; L=Van Nuys; N=Norwood; R=Arlington; S=St. Louis; T=Tarrytown; U=Lordstown; V=Pontiac; W=Willow Run; Y=Wilmington; Z=Fremont; 1=Oshawa; 2=St. Therese. Next six symbols are sequential production number. Body tag on right or left of firewall gives some of same information, plus plant production sequence, trim code, paint code and date code. Engine numbers stamped on right side of V-8 block and left side of four-cylinder and six-cylinder blocks behind distributor. Consult factory or aftermarket reference sources for numerous Chevrolet engine serial numbers.

1973 Chevrolet, Caprice Classic two-door convertible, V-8

FULL-SIZED CHEVROLET SERIES

Series Number	Body/Style Number	Body Type & Seating	Factory Price	Shipping Weight	Production Total
BEL AIR SERIES					
1K	69	4-dr Sed-6P	3247/3595	3895/4087	Note 1
1K	45	4-dr Sta Wag-9P	4136	4770	Note 1
1K	35	4-dr Sta Wag-6P	4022	4717	Note 1
IMPALA SERIES					
1L	69	4-dr Sed-6P	3752	4138	Note 1
1L	39	4-dr HT Sed-6P	3822	4162	Note 1
1L	57	2-dr Spt Cpe-6P	3769	4096	Note 1
1L	47	2-dr Cus Cpe-6P	3836	4110	Note 1
1L	45	4-dr Sta Wag-9P	4233	4807	Note 1
1L	35	4-dr Sta Wag-6P	4119	4742	Note 1
CAPRICE CLASSIC SERIES					
1N	69	4-dr Sed-6P	4064	4176	Note 1
1N	39	4-dr HT Sed-6P	4134	4208	Note 1
1N	47	2-dr Cus Cpe-6P	4082	4143	Note 1
1N	67	2-dr Conv-6P	4345	4191	Notes 1/2
1N	45	4-dr Sta Wag-9P	4496	4858	Note 1
1N	35	4-dr Sta Wag-6P	3282	.4779	Note 1

NOTE 1: Model year of all full-size Chevrolets totaled 941,104 units.
NOTE 2: 7,339 Caprice Classic convertibles included in above total.
NOTE 3: Bel Air sedan only available with a six; see data above slash/.

MONTE CARLO — (V-8) — SERIES 1H — The 1973 Monte Carlo saw extensive styling changes. It was four inches longer and had a heavily sculptured look with new rear quarter sheet metal. The upper grille border was lowered and the front lip of the hood extended down to meet it. Parking lamps were placed vertically in the front fender ends. The grille insert had a neat, cross-hatched texture. There was a badge at its center, plus a script on the left side of the hood. A wide, 'U' shaped guard was built into the new front bumper, which was re-engineered with federal standards. Headlights were round units set into circular housings, which blended in the rounded upper fender contour. The outer fender surface swooped in a radical curve, to the middle of the door. The rear fenderline had a prominent kick-up, with extra crisp sculpturing seen here as well. A V-shaped rear window was used and opera window treatments were optional. At the back, the fenders tapered to a crisply shaped tail, which was highlighted by a U-shaped panel. It curved upwards around the trapezoid-shaped taillamps, which were accented with multiple horizontal moldings. Back-up lights were incorporated into the bumper again. The Monte Carlo was now offered in three basic levels of trim with countless options packages available. There was the base Monte Carlo, the 'S' Series and the Landau. The latter model featured wide lower body accents and bright wheel lip moldings. Standard equipment included power disc front brakes, power steering and automatic transmission. The base engine was the same '350' V-8 used in Impalas. Regular tires were G78 x 15 blackwalls.

1973 Chevrolet, Monte Carlo two-door coupe, V-8

MONTE CARLO SERIES

Series Number	Body/Style Number	Body Type & Seating	Factory Price	Shipping Weight	Production Total
MONTE CARLO					
1H	57	2-dr HT Cpe-5P	3415	3713	Note 1
MONTE CARLO 'S'					
1H	57	2-dr HT Cpe-5P	3562	3720	Note 1
MONTE CARLO LANDAU					
1H	57	2-dr HT Cpe-5P	3806	3722	Note 1

NOTE 1: Exactly 233,689 Monte Carlos were built in the 1973 model year.

1973 Chevelle, two-door Laguna Colonnade coupe, V-8

CHEVELLE INTERMEDIATES — (SIX/V-S) — ALL SERIES — Totally new 'Colonnade hardtop' styling was seen on 1973 Chevelles. Primarily a safety advance engineered to meet new federal rollover standards, this innovative design consisted of a body with inner and outer shells; side guard door beam construction; and improved fuel tank isolation. Extremely heavy roof pillars and a side window treatment similar to that used in building limousines created a car that looked like a hardtop, but really was not. The Colonnade hardtop look was great on coupes and sedans, but seemed somewhat awkward for station wagons. General styling highlights included cross-hatched grilles with a very flat look that continued below the single headlights. They had extremely narrow extensions. Bodysides were quite plain, with Malibus wearing rocker panel moldings. All models carried their nameplates at the left of the grille and on the fenders in back of the front wheel opening. New energy-absorbing front bumpers incorporated rectangular parking lights at the outer ends. Taillamps were circular units, recessed into a back panel that was 'veed' horizontally along its centerline. The top-of-the-line entry was the Laguna, with a special die-cast grille accented with double horizontal moldings and circular rally lights. It had a racy European flavor. The Chevelle convertible was discontinued. Each of three series — Chevelle Deluxe, Malibu and Laguna — offered the Colonnade coupe, sedan and station wagons. Base power plants in the Deluxe and Malibu lines were the '250' six or the '307' V-8. Laguna offerings started with the '350' V-8 under the hood. The big-block '454' V-8 was down to a 245 nhp. Tire sizes varied by model; E78-14 on most passenger cars; G78-14 on most wagons and Lagunas; and H78-14 on the Laguna Estate.

CHEVELLE SERIES

Series Number	Body/Style Number	Body Type & Seating	Factory Price	Shipping Weight	Production Total
DELUXE SERIES					
1C	29	4-dr Col Sed-6P	2719/2835	3435/3585	Note 1
1C	37	2-dr Col Cpe-6P	2743/2860	3423/3580	Note 1
1C	35	4-dr Sta Wag-8P	3331	4054	Note 1
1C	35	4-dr Sta Wag-6P	3106/3198	3849/4006	Note 1
MALIBU SERIES					
1D	29	4-dr Col Sed-6P	2871/2987	3477/3627	Note 1
1D	37	2-dr Col Cpe-6P	2894/3010	3430/3580	Note 1
1D	35	4-dr Sta Wag-8P	3423	4075	Note 1
1D	35	4-dr Sta Wag-6P	3290	4027	Note 1
MALIBU ESTATE					
1G	35	4-dr Sta Wag-8P	3608	4080	Note 1
1G	35	4-dr Sta Wag-6P	3475	4032	Note 1
LAGUNA SERIES					
1E	29	4-dr Col Sed-6P	3179	3627	Note 1
1E	37	2-dr Col Cpe-6P	3203	3678	Note 1
1E	35	4-dr Sta Wag-8P	3616	4158	Note 1
1E	35	4-dr Sta Wag-6P	3483	4110	Note 1
LAGUNA ESTATE					
1H	35	4-dr Sta Wag-8P	3795	4189	Note 1
1H	35	4-dr Sta Wag-6P	3662	4141	Note 1

NOTE 1: 328.533 Chevelles were built in the 1973 model year.
NOTE 2: 28,647 Chevelle SS-396 option packages were installed on above cars.
NOTE 3: 2,500 Chevelle SS-454 option packages were installed on above cars.

NOVA — (SIX/V-8) — ALL SERIES — The Nova was 'customized' this season, but could still be purchased in standard trim, too. The new Nova Custom Series was simply a bit richer inside and out. General appearance changes were 'hatched' out of a program that emphasized refinements, instead of major revamps. One change, in fact, was a hatchback coupe with an easily lifted, counter-balanced panel that flipped-up to give rear compartment access. Side guard beam door construction; flow-through ventilation; improved sound deadening and a 21-gallon fuel tank were standard equipment revisions. A new grille design featured a more open crosshatch texture and built-in parking lights. Dual, rectangular taillight treatments were seen on each side at the rear. A heftier, safer bumper protected both ends of the car, with the rear unit having a new center dip and both using black vinyl impact strips. The Nova nameplate was above the left side of the grille. Attractive half-vinyl tops made the options list. Base engines were the '250' six or '307' V-8. Standard tires were E78-14 blackwalls.

1973 Chevrolet, Nova two-door hatchback coupe, V-8

NOVA SERIES

Series Number	Body/Style Number	Body Type & Seating	Factory Price	Shipping Weight	Production Total
NOVA					
1X	69	4-dr Sed-6P	2407/2497	3065/3194	Note 1
1X	27	2-dr Cpe-6P	2377/2467	3033/3162	Note 1
1X	17	2-dr Hatch-6P	2528/2618	3145/3274	Note 1
NOVA CUSTOM					
1Y	69	4-dr Sed-6P	2580/2671	3105/3234	Note 1
1Y	27	2-dr Cpe-6P	2551/2641	3073/3203	Note 1
1Y	17	2-dr Hatch-6P	2701/2791	3152/3281	Note 1

NOTE 1: 369,511 Novas were built in the 1973 model year.
NOTE 2: 35,542 Nova Super Sports were built for the 1973 model year.

1973 Chevrolet, Vega 2300 two-door sedan, 4-cyl

VEGA — FOUR — The 1973 Vega had a new front bumper with stronger mountings. It provided better protection for the carry over sheet metal. The nameplate was changed to read 'Vega by Chevrolet' with the 2300 engine size call-out being dropped. Unaccustomed to using cubic centimeter measurements for engine displacement, American buyers had trouble relating to the meaning of the original nomenclature. New Chevrolet-built three and four-speed transmissions, with improved shift linkages and a better emissions control system were featured in the third generation Vega. Using the new SAE system, the base, one-barrel four was rated at just 72 hp; the optional two-barrel engine at 85. The standard tire size was, again, A78-13. Vega's new grille had a handsome, eggcrate texture.

1973 Chevrolet, Vega two-door Kammback GT station wagon, 4-cyl

VEGA SERIES

Series Number	Body/Style Number	Body Type & Seating	Factory Price	Shipping Weight	Production Total
1V	11	2-dr Notch-4P	2087	2219	Note 1
1V	77	2-dr Hatch-4P	2192	2313	Note 1
1V	15	2-dr Sta Wag-4P	2323	2327	Note 1

NOTE 1: 395,792 Vegas were built; no breakout as to body style is available.

1973 Chevrolet, Camaro two-door sports coupe, V-8

CAMARO — (SIX/V-8) — SERIES 1Q — The 1973 Camaro had very few changes from the previous style. The texture of the grille insert was modified by using slightly heavier, deeper moldings and reducing the number of vertical moldings from 12 to seven. Those trim packages featuring a full-width front bumper bar had new, black rubber faced guards. They protruded both above and below the bumper, housing the license plate at the bottom, center. Fifteen new colors were available. a new soft-rim steering wheel with four spokes was used and the rear seats received a bit more foam padding. A new decor treatment was the 'luxuring touring' Camaro LT package, which included rocker panel accents; dual outside rearview mirrors; Hide-Away wipers; full instrumentation (with tachometer); 14 x 7 inch Rally wheel rims and extra sound-deadening insulation. A new option was a set of Turbine II wheels, for all models except those with the Z/28 package. Air conditioning was, however, available for the first time with Z/28 'special performance' equipment. Base Camaro engines were the '250' six or '307' V-8 and E78 x 14 tires were used. Standard in Z/28s was a hydraulic lifter '350' V-8 with a new low-restriction air cleaner and 245 nhp.

CAMARO SERIES

Series Number	Body/Style Number	Body Type & Seating	Factory Price	Shipping Weight	Production Total
BASE LEVEL					
1Q	87	2-dr Spt Cpe-4P	2781/2872	3119/3238	Note 1

LT LEVEL

1S	87	2-dr Spt Cpe-4P	3268	3349	Note 1

NOTE 1: 89,988 Camaros were built in the US.
NOTE 2: Total includes 16,133 RS; 11,574 Camaro Z/28s.
NOTE 3: Total includes 93,138 V-8s; 3,618 sixes.
NOTE 4: Transmissions: 5,964 had 3-speed; 11,388 had 4-speed; 79,404 had THM.
NOTE 5: Options: 49,504 with A/C; 96,752 power steering; 217 with power windows.
NOTE 6: 6,768 cars 'made in the U.S. for export markets.

1973 Camaro, two-door LT sports coupe, V-8

BASE ENGINES

(BEL AIR/CHEVELLE/NOVA/CAMARO SIX) Inline Six: Cast iron block. Displacement: 250 cid. Bore and stroke: 3.875 x 3.53 inches. Compression ratio: 8.25:1. SAE Net hp: 100 at 3600 rpm. Seven main bearings. Hydraulic valve lifters. Carburetor: one-barrel.

(V-8 BEL AIR/IMPALA/MONTE CARLO/LAGUNA) V-8: Overhead valves. Cast iron block. Displacement: 350 cid. Bore and stroke: 4.00 x 3.48 inches. Compression ratio: 8.5:1. SAE Net hp: 145 at 4000 rpm. Five main bearings. Hydraulic valve lifters. Carburetor: two-barrel.

(V-8 CAPRICE) V-8: Overhead valves. Cast iron block. Displacement: 400 cid. Bore and stroke: 4.126 x 3.75 inches. Compression ratio: 8.5:1. SAE Net hp: 150 at 3200 rpm. Five main bearings. Hydraulic valve lifters. Carburetor: two-barrel.

(V-8 CHEVELLE DELUXE/MALIBU/NOVA/CAMARO) V-8: Overhead valves. Cast iron block. Displacement: 307 cid. Bore and stroke: 3.87 x 3.25 inches. Compression ratio: 8.5:1. SAE Net hp: 115 at 3600 rpm. Five main bearings. Hydraulic valve lifters. Carburetor: two-barrel.

(VEGA) Inline Four: Overhead camshaft. Aluminum block. Displacement: 140 cid. Bore and stroke: 3.501 x 3.625 inches. Compression ratio: 8.0:1. Brake hp: 72 at 4400 rpm. Hydraulic valve lifters. Carburetor: one-barrel.

CHASSIS FEATURES: Wheelbase: (Chevrolet wagon) 125 inches; (Chevrolet) 121.5 inches; (Monte Carlo/Chevelle four-door) 116 inches; (Chevelle two-door) 112 inches; (Nova) 111 inches (Vega) 97 inches; (Camaro) 108 inches. Overall length: (Chevelle wagon) 229 inches; (Chevrolet) 223 inches; (Monte Carlo) 211 inches; (Chevelle four-door) 207 inches; (Chevelle two-door) 203 inches; (Chevelle wagon) 214 inches; (Nova) 195 inches; (Vega) 173 inches; (Camaro) 189 inches. Width: (Chevrolet) 80 inches; (Monte Carlo) 78 inches; (Chevelles) 77 inches; (Novas) 73 inches; (Vega) 66 inches; (Camaro) 75 inches. Tires: Refer to text.

POPULAR OPTIONS: Vega power steering ($92). Vega air conditioning ($349). Vega Estate Wagon package ($212). Vega hatchback GT package ($340). Vega station wagon GT package ($314). Vega Custom interior ($115). Nova vinyl top ($82). Nova air conditioning ($381). Nova Super Sport package ($123). Nova skyroof ($179). Chevelle / Camaro / Nova power brakes ($46). Nova power brakes with front discs ($68). Chevelle vinyl top ($92). Chevelle/Monte Carlo/Camaro AM/FM stereo ($233). Chevrolet/Monte Carlo/Chevelle AM/FM stereo with tape ($363). Chevelle Malibu SS package ($243). Monte Carlo vinyl top ($123). Chevelle/Monte Carlo skyroof ($325). Camaro vinyl top ($87). Monte Carlo/Camaro air conditioning ($397). Camaro LT Special Performance package ($502). Camaro Z/28 Special Performance package ($598). Chevrolet vinyl top ($106). Chevrolet power seats ($103). Chevrolet power windows ($124). Chevrolet air conditioning ($482). Nova power steering ($100). Three-speed manual transmission was standard in Vega / Nova / Chevrolet / Chevelle / Monte Carlo and Camaro with fours or sixes. Automatic transmission was standard in Chevrolet V-8s and Camaro LTs and was, also a no-cost option in the Z/28. Automatic transmission was optional, except in above models. Four-speed manual floor shift transmission was optional in Vega / Nova / Monte Carlo/Chevelle/Camaro. Vega four-cylinder 140 cid 85 hp two-barrel engine ($41*). Chevrolet V-8 350 cid 175 hp four-barrel engine. Chevrolet V-8 400 cid 150 hp two-barrel engine. Chevrolet V-8 454 cid 215 hp four-barrel engine ($231). Chevrolet V-8 454 cid 245 hp four-barrel dual-exhaust engine. Monte Carlo V-8 350 cid 175 hp four-barrel engine. Monte Carlo V-8 454 cid 245 hp four-barrel dual-exhaust engine ($209). Chevelle V-8 350 cid 145 hp two-barrel engine. Chevelle V-8 350 cid 175 hp four-barrel engine. Chevelle V-8 454 cid 24 hp four-barrel engine ($235). Camaro V-8 350 cid 145 hp two-barrel engine. Camaro V-8 350 cid 175 hp four-barrel engine. Camaro V-8 350 cid 245 hp Z/28 engine (*). Nova V-8 350 cid 145 hp two-barrel engine. Nova V-8 350 cid 175 hp four-barrel engine. Positive traction rear axle. NOTE: The Vega GT package included the two-barrel four. The Camaro Z/28 package included the 245 hp '350' V-8.

HISTORICAL FOOTNOTES: The 1973 Chevrolets were introduced on Sept. 21, 1972. Model year production peaked at 2,365,381 units. Calendar year sales of 2,434,890 cars were recorded. F. J. MacDonald was the chief executive officer of the company this year. Early (1971 and 1972) Vegas came with steel head gaskets which were easily 'done-in' by water and heat. The result was that dealers had to replace many motors under the original 12,000 miles engine warranty. The early motors earned such a bad reputation that the warranty was later extended to 50,000 miles to help prevent a too large drop in sales due to the problem.

1974 Chevrolet, Impala two-door hardtop coupe, V-8

FULL-SIZED CHEVROLET — (V-8) — ALL SERIES — Caprice Classics had a different appearance than Bel Airs and Impalas this year and all models were changed at the front and rear. A new grille on the low/medium-priced cars was completely above the bumper and the number of vertical bars was cut more than 50 percent. Their new front bumper had no parking light or grille reveal openings, but rubber-faced protective guards were standard. The license plate attachment was moved from the center to the left. On these Bel Airs and Impalas, the parking lamps were placed in the fender extension caps, outboard of the dual, square headlamp housings. A 'bow tie' insignia was at the center of the grille, with a Chevrolet inscription on the left side of the upper grille frame molding. A model identification script was seen behind the front wheel housings. Standard equipment for Bel Airs included all regulation safety features; body sill moldings; power steering; power brakes (with front disc and rear finned drums); inside day/nite mirror; foam seats; power ventilation system; glovebox light; cigar lighter; recessed wipers; inside hood release; left-hand OSRV mirror; windshield antenna; pattern cloth and vinyl interior; and Turbo-Hydramatic transmission on V-8s. Most sources indicate that all big Chevrolets were V-8 powered, but the Bel Air sedan was available with a six and three-speed manual gearbox, at least at the beginning of the year. There is no record of any such cars being built and sold. The Impalas had all of the above, plus bright bodyside moldings (with a black vinyl insert on the Custom coupe); triple taillights with silver accents; front and rear wheel lip moldings (on Custom coupe) and a luggage compartment mat. The base V-8 was the two-barrel 350 cid and regular tire were G78-15 blackwalls. All front end sheetmetal on the Caprice was distinctive and had a more swept back look with different fenders; hood; grille; header bar and lamps. The grille was more elaborate with 11 prominent bright moldings forming a dozen segments. Each segment was filled with multiple horizontal and vertical bars. A signature script was placed in the left-hand side of the grille and a Caprice crest was seen at the center of the wider, upper border bar. The Caprice parking lights were moved to a position between the headlights and the grille. The Custom Coupe had a form of Colonnade styling, in which over-sized opera windows were used at the upper rear roof quarters. Bodysides were decorated with a low, full length molding, which was extra-wide and carried color-keyed vinyl protective strips. A Caprice crest was placed on the coupes central roof pillar. The Caprice had the same equipment as Impalas, plus ashtray and courtesy lights, electric clock; rear fender skirts; distinctive cloth and vinyl interior; color-keyed wheelcovers; GT8-15/B tires and a 400 cid V-8. The sedan used a fold-down center armrest seat. Station wagons were equipped like their passenger car counterparts. plus hidden storage compartment; Glide-Away tailgate; all-vinyl upholstery; power taillight window. L78-15/B tires and forward-facing rear seat on nine passenger styles. The Caprice Estate also had a vertical bar grille; electric clock; ashtray and courtesy lights and 400 cid two-barrel V-8 engine. Woodgrained siding was optional.

CHEVROLET I.D. NUMBERS: VIN top left side of dash, visible through windshield. First symbol 1 = Chevrolet. Second symbol indicates car-line: C = Chevelle & Malibu; D = Malibu Classic; E = Laguna; G = Malibu Estate; H = Monte Carlo; K = Bel Air; N = Caprice Classic/Caprice Estate; L = Impala; Q = Camaro; S = Type LT; V = Vega; X = Nova Cyustom. Third and fourth symbols indicate body type and appear in Body/Style Number column of charts below. Fifth symbol indicates engine: A = 140 cid four one-barrel; B = 140 cid four two-barrel; D = 250 cid six; F = 307 cid V-8 2V; H = 350 cid V-8 2V; K = 350 cid V-8 4V; T = 350 cid V-8 (Z28); R = 400 cid V-8 2-V; X = 454 cid V-8 (L54) single exhausts; Y = 454 cid V-8 dual exhausts. Sixth symbol 4 = 1974. Seventh symbol indicates assembly plant: A = Lakewood; B = Baltimore; C = Southgate; D = Doraville; F = Flint; J = Janesville; K = Leeds; L = Van Nuys; N = Norwood; R = Arlington; S = St. Louis; T = Tarrytown; U = Lordstown; V = Pontiac; W = Willow Run; Y = Wilmington; Z = Fremont; 1 - Oshawa; 2 - St. Therese. Next six symbols are sequential production number. Body tag on right or left of firewall gives some information, plus plant production sequence, trim code, paint codt and date code. Engine numbers stamped on right side of V-8 block and left side of four-cylinder and six-cylinder blocks behind distributor. Consult factory or aftermarket reference sources for numerous Chevrolet engine serial numbers.

FULL-SIZED CHEVROLET SERIES

Series Number	Body/Style Number	Body Type & Seating	Factory Price	Shipping Weight	Production Total
BEL AIR SERIES					
1K	69	4-dr Sed-6P	3960	4148	Note 1
1K	45	4-dr Sta Wag-9P	4578	4884	Note 2
1K	35	4-dr Sta Wag-6P	4464	4829	Note 2
IMPALA SERIES					
1L	69	4-dr Sed-6P	4135	4205	Note 3
1L	39	4-dr HT Sed-6P	4215	4256	Note 3
1L	57	2-dr Spt Cpe-6P	4162	4167	Note 3
1L	47	2-dr Cus Cpe-6P	4229	4169	Note 3
1L	45	4-dr Sta Wag-9P	4675	4936	Note 2
1L	35	4-dr Sta Wag-6P	4561	4891	Note 2

CAPRICE CLASSIC

1N	69	4-dr Sed-6P	4465	4294	Note 4
1N	39	4-dr HT Sed-6P	4534	4344	Note 4
1N	47	2-dr Cus Cpe-6P	4483	4245	Note 4
1N	67	2-dr Conv-6P	4745	4308	Notes 4/5
1N	45	4-dr Sta Wag-9P	4914	5004	Note 2
1N	35	4-dr Sta Wag-6P	4800	4960	Note 2

1974 Chevrolet, Caprice Classic two-door Custom coupe, V-8

1974 Chevrolet, Caprice Estate four-door station wagon, V-8

1974 Chevrolet, Caprice Classic two-door convertible, V-8

GENERAL NOTE: Domestic model year production of full-sized Chevrolets totaled exactly 630,861 units. This total is again distorted, by the fact that production of some models for U.S. sales was quartered in Canada. The exact number of full-sized Chevrolets sold by dealers holding U.S. franchises was 565,376 cars. This means that some 65,485 Bel Airs, Impalas and Caprice Classics built in U.S. factories were shipped to Canada under the new trade agreements. A similar situation existed in other Chevrolet model lines. This should be kept in mind when using the series output figures given below.

NOTE 1: Exactly 34,095 Bel Air passenger cars were built for the 1974 model year. All were V-8s.
NOTE 2: Exactly 35,331 full-sized wagons were built for the 1974 model year. All were V-8s. This includes all station wagons with no further breakout. by series, available at this time.
NOTE 3: Exactly 405.286 Impala passenger cars were built for the 1974 model year- All were V-8s.
NOTE 4: Exactly 155.860 Caprice passenger cars were built for the 1974 Model year. All were V-8s.
NOTE 5: Exactly 4,670 Caprice Classic convertibles were built for the 1974 model year, All were V-8s.

ADDITIONAL NOTE: Though listed as available early in the year, standard reference sources do not indicate the price or weight of a Bel Air six and Chevrolet production records indicate that no such cars were built.

MONTE CARLO — (V-8) — SERIES 1H — The 1974 Monte Carlo received minor appearance changes, the most obvious a new eggcrate grille. Bodyside moldings used with some decor packages were of a new design that extended completely forward to hit the rear edge of the front wheelhousing. The front lip of the hood was decorated with a center medallion, instead of the former left side script. Landau or Monte Carlo 'S' packages replaced the mid-bodyside molding (described above) with wide. bright rocker panel accents having both front and rear extensions. At the rear. a new bumper was used. It incorporated two, full-width rubber impact strips and protruded out further, giving the cars three extra inches of length. Rubber faced rear bumper guards were also new. The back-up lights were moved, from the bumper. to a license-plate-flanking position on the deck latch panel. The design of the trunk lock was simplified and the multiple, short accent moldings were removed from the taillights. Crests and chrome signatures called-out the various levels of trim. Standard equipment included PowerBeam single-unit headlights; formal coupe roofline; rear quarter 'coach' style

windows. Hide-Away wipers; rear stabilizer; power front disc brakes; power steering; ignition key alarm; flow-thru power ventilation; electric clock, wood-burl dash and steering wheel accents; Delco-Eye battery; carpets; door map pockets; knit cloth and vinyl trim cigar lighter; inside hood release; GR70-15 radial tires and '350' V-8. The Landau also had a landau vinyl top; color-keyed rear window and belt moldings; fender accent stripes, body-color Sport mirrors (left remote-control), wheelcovers; visor/vanity mirror; 15 x 7 Turbine II wheels; radial tuned suspension; passenger assist grips and door map pockets.

1974 Chevrolet, Monte Carlo two-door sport coupe, V-8

MONTE CARLO SERIES

Series Number	Body/Style Number	Body Type & Seating	Factory Price	Shipping Weight	Production Total
MONTE CARLO 'S'					
1H	57	2-dr HT Cpe-5P	3885	3926	Note 1
MONTE CARLO LANDAU					
1H	57	2-dr HT Cpe-5P	4129	3950	Note 1

NOTE 1: Exactly 312,217 Monte Carlos were built for the 1974 Model year. All were V-8s. No additional breakouts per trim level are available. Monte Carlo sales by U.S dealers peaked at 284.867 cars. This indicates that over 25,000 U.S. built cars were shipped to Canada.

1974 Chevelle, Malibu Classic 4-dr station wagon, V-8

INTERMEDIATE-SIZED CHEVELLES — (SIX/V-8) — ALL SERIES — The Nomad and Chevelle Deluxe Series model were dropped in 1974 and the intermediate-sized Chevrolet products now came in Malibu, Malibu Classic, Malibu Classic Estate and Laguna decor levels. Basic styling changes were modest. They included a bumper without the flattened license plate attachment panel in the center; twin-slot side marker lamps and a radiator-style grille that looked like a Mercedes-Benz unit stretched-out sideways. Decor option packages, however. had a big effect on final appearances. Chevelles came in a variety of 'flavors' ranging from the 'unmarked police car' look to the race-ready image of the Laguna Type S-3 coupe. One way to spot a 1974 model for sure, was to eyeball the round-corner trapezoid shape of the large rear lamps. Early models had round taillights; later versions became more rectangular, so the 1974 types are very distinctive. A new, stand-up hood ornament decorated the Malibu Classic, which also had wide, lower body accent panels. Optional innovations included the canopy top or louvered rear 'coach' window treatments. Standard equipment on the base Malibu included regulation safety equipment; flow-through power ventilation system; double panel steel acoustical roof; inside hood release; manual front disc brakes; side marker lamps and reflectors; defroster; dual speed wipers with washers; inside day/nite mirror; left OSRV mirror; full foam rubber seats; color-keyed vinyl roof covering; cigar lighter; Hide-Away wipers; windshield radio antenna; Delcotron generator; E78-14/B tires and either the '250' six or '350' two-barrel V-8. Malibu V-8s wore G7814/B tires. The Malibu Classic came with all of the above, plus carpeting; glovebox light; mixed pattern cloth and vinyl interior; bodyside, roof drip and wheel opening moldings and Deluxe center armrest in front seat. The Laguna Colonnade Coupe came only in V-8 form. it featured, in addition to the above, patterned cloth and vinyl (or all-vinyl) interior; woodgrain vinyl accents on dash (with elm-burl center vinyl inlay); full wheelcovers; bright accented dual-unit taillights; wheel lips and scalp-moldings; GR70-15/B steel-belted radial tires and the two-barrel '350' V-8. The high-performance image Laguna type S-3 coupe added a custom eggcrate grille isolated within a body-color front end panel; bright grille crossbar with Square Rally lights at each end; nerf-bar bumper treatment; louvered 'coach' window styling; swivel bucket seats; variable-ratio power steering; heavy-duty Pliacell shock absorbers; radial-tuned suspension; Specific Type S-3 nameplates at grille center and behind front wheels; engine callout decals above side markers; lower body perimeter striping and black-accent treatment; body-color twin Sport mirrors (left remote-controlled); Red or white stripe radial tires; body color reveal moldings; full-instrumentation (with round-faced gauges); four-spoke steering wheel and 15 x 7 Turbine 11 wheels. Top power option was the detuned — SAE rated — 235 hp 454 cid V-8.

1974 Chevrolet, Chevelle Malibu Classic Colonnade coupe, V-8

1974 Chevrolet, Chevelle Laguna S-3 Colonnade coupe, V-8

CHEVELLE INTERMEDIATE SERIES

Series Number	Body/Style Number	Body Type & Seating	Factory Price	Shipping Weight	Production Total
MALIBU					
1C	29	4-dr Col Sed-6P	3049/3340	3638/3788	Note 1
1C	37	2-dr Col Cpe-6P	3054/3345	3573/3723	Note 1
1C	35	4-dr Sta Wag-8P	3834	4223	Note 2
1C	35	4-dr Sta Wag-6P	3701	4191	Note 2
MALIBU CLASSIC					
1D	29	4-dr Col Sed-6P	3304/3595	3695/3845	Note 3
1D	37	2-dr Col Cpe-6P	3307/3598	3609/3759	Note 3
1D	37	2-dr Lan Cpe-6P	3518/3800	NA/NA	Note 3
1D	35	4-dr Sta Wag-9P	4251	4315	Note 2
1D	35	4-dr Sta Wag-6P	4118	4283	Note 2
MALIBU CLASSIC ESTATE					
1G	35	4-dr Sta Wag-9P	4424	4338	Note 2
1G	35	4-dr Sta Wag-6P	4291	4306	Note 2
LAGUNA					
1E	37	2-dr Col Cpe-6P	3723	3951	Note 4
LAGUNA TYPE 5-3					
1E	37	2-dr Col Cpe-5P	4504	NA	Note 4

NOTE 1: Exactly 91,612 Malibu passenger cars were built for the 1974 Model year, including 27,188 sixes and 64,424 V-8s.
NOTE 2: Exactly 44,108 Chevelle intermediate-sized station wagons were built for the 1974 Model year. All were V-8s. This includes all Malibu, Malibu Classic and Malibu Classic Estate wagons, with no breakouts per trim level available at this time.
NOTE 3: Exactly 204,870 Malibu Classic passenger cars were built for the 1974 model year, including 8,940 sixes and 195,930 V-8s.
NOTE 4: Exactly 21,902 Lagunas were built for the 1974 model year. All were V-8s. No breakout per trim level is available at this time.

1974 Chevrolet, Nova two-door sedan with 'Spirit of America' option, V-8

NOVA — (SIX/V-8) — ALL SERIES — Never a car to change for the sake of change, the 1974 Nova was basically unaltered. A 'bow tie' badge was added at the center of the grille and the nameplate on the left-hand side of the hood lip read 'Nova by Chevrolet'. Rubber-faced front bumper guards were standard, now, and eleven new colors were available. Coupes or hatchbacks with Super Sport options received the black-out grille treatment with prominent horizontal moldings bridging the rectangular parking lamps top and bottom. Two-tone finish was available for Body Style Number 17. The designers also added new hubcaps, with a bright anodized look. Two-speed Powerglide automatic transmission was no longer offered. Standard equipment included color-keyed rubber floor coverings; flow-through ventilation

system; full-foam front seats; foam rear seats; dual-speed electric wipers; left OSRV mirror; cargo-guard luggage compartment (except hatchback) and '250' six. The hatch back added the swing-up rear deck and fold-down rear seat. The Nova Custom also had bright parking lights and liftgate accents; body sill and scalp moldings, Deluxe bumpers with black vinyl impact strips; carpets; inside day/nite mirror; glovebox light; right front door light switch; cigarette lighter and trunk mat. Standard tire were size E78-14/B blackwalls and the two-barrel '350' was base V-8.

NOVA SERIES

Series Number	Body/Style Number	Body Type & Seating	Factory Price	Shipping Weight	Production Total
NOVA					
1X	69	4-dr Sed-6P	2841/2949	3192/3330	Note 1
1X	27	2-dr Cpe-6P	2811/2919	3150/3288	Note 1
1X	17	2-dr Hatch-6P	2935/3043	3260/3398	Note 1
NOVA CUSTOM					
1Y	69	4-dr Sed-6P	3014/3123	3233/3371	Note 1
1Y	27	2-dr Cpe-6P	2985/3093	3206/3344	Note 1
1Y	17	2-dr Hatch-6P	3108/3217	3299/3437	Note 1

NOTE 1: Exactly 390,537 Novas were built during the 1974 model year, 171,430 sixes and 219,107 V-8s. No breakouts per body style or trim level are available at the current time.
NOTE 2: Included in the total given above were exactly 21,419 cars equipped with the Nova SS option package. No additional breakout per coupes and hatch back styles is available at the current time.

1974 Chevrolet, Vega two-door Estate wagon, 4-cyl

VEGA — (FOUR) — SERIES 1V — New for the Vega sub-compact was a shovel nosed look with a quad-level, air-slot style grille, divided into two halves with a vertical, body colored center divider strip. The headlamps were recessed into slanting, square-shaped housings finished in bright metal style. A much thicker, full-width wraparound bumper incorporated black rubber guards and vinyl black impact strips. Single-unit square taillamps (or vertical tender-mount lamps on wagons) were seen at the rear, where a more protrusive bumper — with vinyl impact strips, was used. A three-inch length increase resulted. Standard equipment included all regulation safety devices; side marker lights and reflectors; left OSRV mirror; back-up lights; bright hubcaps; foam-filled front bucket/rear bucket style seats, storage well in driver's door; glovebox; power vent system; folding seatback latches; steel side guard beams; inside windshield moldings; carpets; heater and defroster; windshield washer and electric wipers; inside hood release; manual front disc brakes; three-speed manual transmission with floor shift; OHC-Four engine and AT78-13 black sidewall tires. The hatch back added a fold-down rear seat and storage compartment. The station wagon (Kammback) also had a swing-up tailgate and folding rear seat. The Estate wagon featured Deluxe interior and exterior trim; full carpeting and concealed storage compartment.

VEGA SERIES

Series Number	Body/Style Number	Body Type & Seating	Factory Price	Shipping Weight	Production Total
1V	11	2-dr Cpe-4P	2087	2219	63,591
1V	77	2-dr Hatch-4P	2192	2313	271,682
1V	15	2-dr Sta Wag-4P	2323	2327	113,326
1HV	05	2-dr Panel-2P	2404	2402	4,289

NOTE 1: The production totals given in the chart above are the exact model year output figures per body style. The panel delivery is included to indicate Model Number, price and weight characteristics of this particular body style. The panel truck was marketed strictly as a commercial vehicle, although this model is very popular with many involved in the modified vehicles, segment of the old car hobby.

CAMARO — (SIX/V-8) — ALL SERIES — The Camaro got a major restyling for the 1974 model year. It followed the Vega's shovel nosed theme and included a soft urethane-cushioned front panel. The forward angled grille featured an eggcrate motif, with grille texture reveal below the new, widened front bumper. At the rear, a new appearance was also achieved. The four round taillamps from previous models gave way to large lenses that slid around the body corners to serve double-duty as side marker lights. The area between the lamps was flattened. The Z/28 option included a bolder graphics treatment with decals calling-out the model nomenclature within stripes that dominated the hood and deck lids. Parking lamps were now circular and located inside slanting, scooped-out square recesses between the grille and front fenders. Standard equipment included safety features; side markers and reflectors; rear markers; rocker moldings; Astro vents; day/nite inside mirror; double-panel roof; pull-type door handles; color-keyed carpets; front bumper guards; bucket seats; all-vinyl interior; dual wipers and washers; left OSRV mirror; rear bucket cushions; manual front disc brakes; three-speed with floor-shift; E78-14 tires and '250' six or '350' two-barrel V-8. The Camaro LT Coupe added electric clock; special instrumentation; OSRV Sport mirrors (left remote-controlled); Rally wheels and Hide-Away wipers; plus the base V-8 as standard equipment.

1974 Chevrolet, Camaro two-door sports coupe, V-8

CAMARO SERIES

Series Number	Body/Style Number	Body Type & Seating	Factory Price	Shipping Weight	Production Total
CAMARO LEVEL					
1Q	87	2-dr HT Cpe-4P	3162/3366	3309/3450	Note 1
CAMARO LT LEVEL					
1S	87	2-dr HT Cpe-4P	3713	3566	Note 1

NOTE 1: Exactly 146,595 Camaros were built for the U.S. market in the 1974 model year. Exactly 4,412 Camaros were built for export, bringing total output to 151,008 units. This included 13,802 Camaros with the Z/28 package; 128,810 V-8s; 22,198 sixes: 11,174 with three-speeds, 11,175 with four-speeds; 128,659 with automatic; 79,279 with air conditioning and 151,008 with power steering. No breakout is currently available as to the number of cars equipped in LT level trim.

BASE ENGINES

(V-8 BEL AIR/IMPALA/MONTE CARLO) V-8: Overhead valves. Cast iron block. Displacement: 350 cub c inches. Bore and stroke. 4 00 x 3.48 inches. Compression ratio: 8.5:1. SAE Net hp: 145 at 2400 R.P M. Five main bearings. Hydraulic valve lifters. Carburetor: two-barrel

(V-8 CAPRICE): V-8. Overhead values. Cast iron block Displacement: 400 cid. Bore and stroke: 4.126 x 3.75 inches. Compress on ratio: 8.5:1 SAE Net hp: 150 at 2400 rpm. Five main bearings. Hydraulic valve lifters. Carburetor: two-barrel.

CHEVELLE SERIES ENGINES

SIX: See 1973 Chevelle series six-cylinder engine data.

V-8: See 1974 Chevrolet series engine data.

NOVA ENGINES

SIX: See 1973 Chevelle series six-cylinder engine data.

V-8: See 1974 Chevelle series V-8 engine data.

VEGA ENGINE: See 1973 Vega series engine data. Specifications were basically unchanged, though a 75 hp rating was advertised in 1974.

CAMARO ENGINES

SIX: See 1973 Chevrolet series six-cylinder engine data.

V-8: See 1974 Chevrolet series V-8 engine data.

CHASSIS FEATURES: Wheelbase: (Chevrolet wagon) 125 inches; (Chevrolet) 121.5 inches; (Monte Carlo/Chevelle four-door) 116 inches; (Nova/Nova Custom) 111 inches; (Vega) 97 inches; (Camaro) 108 inches. Overall length: (Chevrolet wagon) 229 inches; (Chevrolet) 223 inches; (Monte Carlo) 214 inches; (Chevelle wagon) 216 inches; (Chevelle four-door) 211 inches; (Chevelle two-door) 207 inches; (Nova) 197 inches; (Nova Custom) 198 inches; (Vega) 176 inches; (Camaro) 196 inches. Width: Same as 1973 for all styles. Tires: Refer to text.

OPTIONS: Power brakes. Power steering. Monte Carlo / Camaro / Chevelle / Chevrolet AM/ FM stereo ($233). Monte Carlo / Chevelle / Chevrolet AM/FM stereo with tape ($363). Chevrolet power seats ($106). Chevrolet wagon luggage rack ($77). Impala 'Spirit of America' sport coupe package ($399). Vega vinyl top ($75). Vega power steering ($95). Vega air conditioning ($362). Vega GT package ($359). Nova air conditioning ($396). Nova SS package ($140). Chevelle vinyl top ($92). Monte Carlo/Chevelle sky roof ($325). Camaro vinyl top ($87). Camaro air conditioning ($412). Three-speed manual transmission standard in Chevelle/Nova/Camaro six. Automatic transmission was standard in Bel Air/Impala/Caprice. Automatic transmission optional in others. Three-speed manual floor shift transmission, standard in Vega. Four-speed manual floor shift transmission was optional in Nova/Camaro/ Vega. Vega four-cylinder 140 cid 85 hp two-barrel engine. Chevrolet V-8 350 cid 160 hp four-barrel engine. Chevrolet V8 400 cid 150 hp two-barrel engine. Chevrolet V-8 400 cid 180 hp four-barrel engine. Chevrolet V-8 454 cid 235 hp four-barrel engine. Monte Carlo V-8 350 cid 160 hp four-barrel engine. Monte Carlo V-8 400 cid 150 hp two-barrel engine. Monte Carlo V-8 400 cid 180 hp four-barrel engine. Monte Carlo 454 cid 235 hp four-barrel engine ($241). Chevelle V-8 400 cid 150 hp two-barrel engine. Chevelle V-8 400 cid 180 hp four-barrel engine. Chevelle V-8 454 cid 235 hp four-barrel engine ($293). Nova V-8 350 cid 160 hp four-barrel engine. Nova V-8 350 cid 185 hp four-barrel dual-exhaust engine. Camaro V-8 350 cid 160 hp four-barrel engine. Camaro V-8 350 cid 185 hp four-barrel dual-exhaust engine. Posi-traction rear axle.

1974 Camaro, two-door LT sports coupe, V-8

HISTORICAL FOOTNOTES: The 1974 Chevrolets were introduced Sept. 22, 1973. Model year production peaked at 2,396,284 units. Calendar year sales of 2.156,460 cars were recorded. Robert L. Lund was the chief executive officer of the company this year. Sales of Chevrolet's full-line of cars. Sport vans, and Vega panel express models dropped 12.3 percent from 1973 levels. Note: The model year production and calendar year sales figures given above cover only models included in this section, excluding Corvette and Sport van production and sales. Vega panel express models are, however, included in both totals.

1975 CHEVROLET

1975 Chevrolet, Caprice 4-dr hardtop sedan, V-8

FULL-SIZED CHEVROLET — (SIX/V-8) — ALL SERIES — Model year 1975 is best known as the season of the catalytic converter and the 'last' Chevrolet convertible. Additional innovations included introduction of the standard High-Energy ignition system and new Colonnade style rooflines for four-door sedans and Sport sedans (four-door hardtops). The Bel Air and Impala received a revised frontal treatment which was similar to that of the 1974 Caprice Classic. This brought changes including the placement of parking lamps between grille and headlamps; a bright signature script on the left-hand face of the grille and repositioning of the Chevrolet 'bow tie' near the center of the hood lip. Bel Airs had no side spears and stuck with a two-unit taillight design. Impalas were highlighted with three-quarter length bodyside moldings that ran from behind the front upper wheel lip to the rear of the car. Bright-accented, triple taillamps were used. The Caprice Classic had a distinctive vertical barred grille that was even with the upper headlamp borders and partially revealed through an opening below the front bumper. A bright signature script was placed on the left of the grille; a Caprice Crest was seen at the upper center and parking lamps were moved into the bumper, directly under the headlamps. Tires were HR78-15/B blackwalls on passenger cars and LR78-15/C size on station wagons. The standard V-8 in all models was the 145 hp job of 350 cid displacement. Other equipment features were comparable to those listed in 1974.

CHEVROLET I.D. NUMBERS: VIN top left side of dash, visible through windshield. First symbol 1=Chevrolet. Second symbol indicates car-line: C=Malibu; D=Malibu Classic; E=Laguna; G=Malibu Estate; H=Monte Carlo/Laguna Estate; K=Bel Air; M=Monza; N=Caprice Classic/Caprice Estate; L=Impala; Q=Camaro; R=Monza 2+2; S=Type LT; V=Vega; X=Nova; Y=Nova Custom. Third and fourth symbols indicate body type and appear in Body/Style Number column of charts below. Fifth symbol indicates engine: A=140 cid four one-barrel; B=140 cid four two-barrel; D=250 cid six; F=307 cid V-8 2V; G=262 cid 2V V-8; H=350 cid V-8 2V; K=350 cid V-8 4V; T=350 cid V-8 (Z28); R=400 cid V-8 2V; X=454 cid V-8 (L54) single exhausts; Y=454 cid V-8 dual exhausts. Sixth symbol 5=1975. Seventh symbol indicates assembly plant: A=Lakewood; B=Baltimore; C=Southgate; D=Doraville; F=Flint; J=Janesville; K=Leeds; L=Van Nuys; N=Norwood; R=Arlington; S=St. Louis; T=Tarrytown; U=Lordstown; V=Pontiac; W=Willow Run; Y=Wilmington; Z=Fremont; 1=Oshawa; 2=St. Therese. Next six symbols are sequential production number. Body tag on right or left of firewall gives some of same information, plus plant production sequence, trim code, paint code and date code. Engine numbers stamped on right side of V-8 block and left side of four-cylinder and six-cylinder blocks behind distributor. Consult factory or aftermarket reference sources for numerous Chevrolet engine serial numbers.

FULL-SIZED CHEVROLET

Series Number	Body/Style Number	Body Type & Seating	Factory Price	Shipping Weight	Production Total
BEL AIR					
1K	69	4-dr Sed-6P	4345	4179	Note 1
1K	45	4-dr Sta Wag-9P	4998	4913	Note 2
1K	35	4-dr Sta Wag-6P	4878	4856	Note 2

IMPALA

Series	Body/Style	Body Type & Seating	Factory Price	Shipping Weight	Production Total
1L	69	4-dr Sed-6P	4548	4218	Note 3
1L	39	4-dr HT Sed-6P	4631	4265	Note 3
1L	57	2-dr Spt Cpe-6P	4575	4207	Note 3
1L	47	2-dr Cus Cpe-6P	4626	4190	Note 3
1L	47	2-dr Lan Cpe-6P	4901	NA	Note 3
1L	45	4-dr Sta Wag-9P	5121	4959	Note 2
1L	35	4-dr Sta Wag-6P	5001	4910	Note 2

CAPRICE

Series	Body/Style	Body Type & Seating	Factory Price	Shipping Weight	Production Total
1N	69	4-dr Sed-6P	4819	4311	Note 4
1N	39	4-dr HT Sed-6P	4891	4360	Note 4
1N	47	2-dr Cus Cpe-6P	4837	4275	Note 4
1N	47	2-dr Lan Cpe-6P	5075	NA	Note 4
1N	67	2-dr Conv-6P	5113	4342	Note 4/5
1N	45	4-dr Sta Wag-9P	5351	5036	Note 2
1N	35	4-dr Sta Wag-6P	5231	4978	Note 2

NOTE 1: 13,168 Bel Air four-door sedans built in 1975 model run.
NOTE 2: 58,529 full-sized wagons built in 1975 model year (all series).
NOTE 3: 176,376 Impala cars built in 1975 model year; no body type breakouts.
NOTE 4: 103,944 Caprice Classics built in 1975; one body type breakout below.
NOTE 5: 8,349 Caprice Classic convertibles were built in the 1975 model year.

1975 Chevrolet, Monte Carlo two-door sport coupe, V-8

MONTE CARLO (V-8) SERIES H — Chevrolet's personal/luxury car was refined for model year 1975. A new grille treatment featured two rows of 14 chrome-framed squares, arranged horizontally above the bumper with an additional row revealed through a long, oval slot below. Each of the 42 square segments was highlighted with three, short vertical moldings. A shield-shaped medallion was placed at the center of the upper grille opening, with a Monte Carlo signature on the left-hand hood lip. Parking lamps were housed at the front fender corners, with a strip of body-colored sheet metal dividing the lens vertically. A new taillight treatment featured a stack of four horizontal slats that wrapped around the rear body edges. The Monte Carlo signature was removed from the right-hand trunk corner and dropped to the rear deck lid latch panel, directly below. Wheelcover design details were changed. Luxurious interiors featured new trim and fabrics and a choice of options such as 50/50 reclining passenger seats or swivel bucket seats. Standard engine was the '350' V-8 in its two-barrel form. Power front disc brakes were included.

MONTE CARLO

Series Number	Body/Style Number	Body Type & Seating	Factory Price	Shipping Weight	Production Total
MONTE CARLO 'S'					
1H	57	2-dr HT Cpe-5P	4249	3927	Note 1
MONTE CARLO LANDAU					
1H	57	2-dr HT Cpe-5P	4519	3950	Note 1

NOTE 1: 258,909 Monte Carlos built in the 1975 model year; no series breakout.

CHEVELLE — (SIX/V-8) — ALL SERIES — Appearance features of Chevelles were changed in small details from 1974. The grille was still of the "Mercedes-type" with a chromed radiator shell, but was modified with prominent division bars forming 10 vertical segments. Each segment had a screen-like texture within. On Malibu Classics, the screening was black-finished, making the bright metal elements standout with a look of increased elegance. The Classic models also featured stand-up hood ornaments. Taillamp designs were again based on a horizontal, rectangular-shaped lens. The lamps, however, were somewhat longer and narrower with nearly square back-up lights added at the inboard side. On Malibu Classics, the rectangular panel housing the taillights and center license plate indentation received a satin silver finish and held a model identifying signature script on the right side. It was midyear before the Laguna Type S-3 coupe was reintroduced, again featuring a unique styling treatment. Prime among its special touches was a sloping, urethane plastic front end with a grille opening that was divided both horizontally and vertically. This formed four large rectangular slots with screen-textured inserts. Also included were Rally wheels, louvered opera windows and radial tuned suspension. The S-3 came in a choice of six colors with specific body striping and half-vinyl roofs on its optional equipment list. Technical innovations for Chevelles were a more efficient six, High-Energy ignition and catalytic converter. Base V-8 was the '350' two-barrel and tire sizes were FR78-15/B on passenger cars; HR7815/B on wagons and special GR70-15/B wide profile type on Laguna Type S-3.

CHEVELLE SERIES

Series Number	Body/Style Number	Body Type & Seating	Factory Price	Shipping Weight	Production Total
MALIBU					
1C	29	4-dr Col Sed-6P	3402/3652	3713/3833	Note 1
1C	37	2-dr Col Cpe-6P	3407/3657	3642/3762	Note 1
1C	35	4-dr Sta Wag-6P	4463	NA	Note 2
1C	35	4-dr Sta Wag-6P	4318	4207	Note 2
MALIBUE CLASSIC					
1D	29	4-dr Col Sed-6P	3695/3945	3713/3898	Note 3
1D	37	2-dr Col Cpe-6P	3698/3948	3681/3801	Note 3
1D	37	2-dr Lan Cpe-6P	3930/4180	NA/NA	Note 3
1D	35	4-dr Sta Wag-9P	4701	NA	Note 2
1D	35	4-dr Sta Wag-6P	4556	4275	Note 2

MALIBU CLASSIC ESTATE

Series	Body/Style	Body Type & Seating	Factory Price	Shipping Weight	Production Total
1G	35	4-dr Sta Wag-9P	4893	NA	Note 2
1G	35	4-dr Sta Wag-6P	4748	4301	Note 2

LAGUNA TYPE S-3

Series	Body/Style	Body Type & Seating	Factory Price	Shipping Weight	Production Total
1E	37	2-dr Col Cpe-5P	4113	3908	Note 4

NOTE 1: 63,530 Malibus built in model year (21,804 sixes/41,726 V-8s.
NOTE 2: 45,582 Chevelle wagons (all types) built in 1975 model year. All V-8s.
NOTE 3: 131,455 Malibu Classics built in model year (3,844 sixes/127,611 V-8s.
NOTE 4: 6,714 Chevelle Laguna coupes built in 1975 model year. All were V-8s.
NOTE 5: Data above slash for six/below slash; no slash is V-8 data.

1975 Chevrolet, Nova LN two-door sedan, V-8

NOVA — (SIX/V-8) — ALL SERIES — The 'senior compact' Novas underwent the most change in the Chevrolet lineup with their first big revisions in eight years. Patterned after the German Mercedes-Benz, the body was squarer and more luxurious looking. Rooflines received the major share of attention with thinner pillars on all models and a slimmer roof increasing the total area of glass. The windshield was 15 percent larger. A functional louver treatment for venting stale air from the interior was featured on two-door Novas. Swing-out rear quarter windows were optional on coupes, while the hatchback had lift gate improvements. The new Nova grille was a simple, but elegant rectangle with two full-width bright accent moldings and a bright vertical center trim bar. Rectangular parking lamps stood up in the outboard ends of the grille and circular headlights were placed into large, square, bright-finished housings. Rectangular taillamps were seen. Available lines included the base models, Nova Customs with thin rocker moldings and luxurious LNs (with fancy fender medallions and lower perimeter moldings which accented the front and rear quarters and wheel lips, plus the area between the wheel openings and above the rock panel trim). The Nova LN also featured thick window reveal moldings and vertically grooved trim plates on the center body pillar. Technical innovations included either the improved six-cylinder engine or an all-new 262 cid (4.3 litre) V-8, except on cars certified for California sale. Three-speed manual transmission was standard (automatic with '350' V-8 in California cars); Turbo Hydramatic was optional and a 'Muncie' four-speed could be ordered for attachment with only the most powerful optional engine. The High-Energy electronic ignition system was standard equipment. Regular tire equipment was size E78 x 14 bias-belted blackwalls. The new Nova six had an EPA fuel economy rating of 16 city/23 highway miles per gallon.

NOVA SERIES

Series Number	Body/Style Number	Body Type & Seating	Factory Price	Shipping Weight	Production Total
NOVA 'S'					
1X	27	2-dr Cpe-5P	3099/3174	NA/NA	Note 1
NOVA					
1X	69	4-dr Sed-5P	3209/3284	3306/3408	Note 1
1X	27	2-dr Cpe-5P	3205/3280	3276/3378	Note 1
1X	17	2-dr Hatch-5P	3347/3422	3391/3493	Note 1
NOVA CUSTOM					
1Y	69	4-dr Sed-5P	3415/3490	3367/3469	Note 1
1Y	27	2-dr Cpe-5P	3402/3477	3335/3437	Note 1
1Y	17	2-dr Hatch-5P	3541/3616	3421/3523	Note 1
NOVA LN					
1Y	69	4-dr Sed-5P	3795/3870	NA/NA	Note 1
1Y	27	2-dr Cpe-5P	3782/3857	NA/NA	Note 1

NOTE 1: Exactly 272,982 Novas were built in the 1975 model year, including 138,879 sixes and 134,103 V-8s. No breakouts per body style or trim level are available at the current time. Exactly 9,067 Novas were sold with the Super Sport option.
NOTE 2: Adjusted on a new Cumulative model year basis, the above total increased slightly to 273,014 units for the 1975 model year. In cases where shipping weights are not available, the car listed was not a distinct model, but a decor package (or decor package deletion, in the case of the stripped-down Nova 'S').

1975 Chevrolet, Vega GT two-door hatchback coupe, 4-cyl

Standard Catalog of American Cars

VEGA — (FOUR) — SERIES V — While unchanged, in a basic sense when it appeared in the fall of 1974, the Vega built to 1975 specifications included a number of refinements ranging from a new catalytic converter and spark and carburetion improvements to redesigned front suspension equipment. Power brakes and a tilt steering wheel were optional for the first time. In the middle of the year, a special, limited-edition Cosworth Vega appeared on the scene (2,061 built). Its double overhead camshaft, 16 valve four-cylinder engine was designed by England's famed Cosworth Engineering, Ltd. (a renowned race car building firm) and underwent final development in the Chevrolet Engineering laboratories. A true, high-performance machine, the Cosworth Vega also featured a Bendix electronic fuel injection system; special pulse air injection hardware; Vega heavy-duty front suspension, Chevrolet torque-arm rear suspension; stainless steel exhaust headers, breakerless High-Energy ignition; on board Motorola computer; black vinyl interior with adjustable driver's seatback; black carpeting; padded Sport steering wheel; 8000 rpm. tachometer; electric clock; temperature gauges; volt meter; passenger grab bar; gold-colored cast aluminum wheels; black exterior finish with specific gold pin striping; dual Sport mirrors; black-finished wiper arms; blacked-out headlamp bezels and instrument panel 'Twin Cam' nameplate finished in gold and engraved with owner's name and car serial number. The Vega engine in the Cosworth was extensively modified so as to qualify as a virtually hand-crafted powerplant. The engines were, in fact, built by hand assembly methods at Chevrolet's Tonawanda, New York plant. They were then shipped to Lordstown, Ohio. where the installation took place in bodies constructed off-line, apart from the regular production models. Special components included shot-peened rods; forged and magna-fluxed crank shaft; the computer-controlled induction setup; 16-valve aluminum Cosworth cylinder head; deep-dished high-compression pistons; low-lift design performance cam shaft (for smooth idle); solid valve lifters and over-sized, oval-shaped exhaust ports connected to scavenging type steel tube headers and low-restriction pipes and mufflers. Engine displacement was actually reduced to 122 cid (2 liters) and specifications included 3.16 x 3.50 bore and stroke, 8.5:1 compression ratio and 120 hp at 5200 rpm. However, experimental racing versions prepared by Cosworth Engineering's Keith Duckworth, featured 11.5:1 compression and 270 hp at 8.750 rpm. The production version (which was originally scheduled for 1974-1/2 introduction, but failed to achieve government certification due to a burned exhaust valve in the test prototype) came with a close-ratio four-speed manual transmission and rode on six inch wide spoked wheels. The regular, single cam Vega, on the other hand, featured 78 hp in one-barrel carburetor/base engine form and had standard three-speed manual attachment and A78-13/B blackwall tires on conventional rims.

1975 Chevrolet, Vega Kammback GT 2-dr station wagon 4-cyl

VEGA SERIES

Series Number	Body/Style Number	Body Type & Seating	Factory Price	Shipping Weight	Production Total
VEGA					
1V	11	2-dr Cpe-4P	2786	2415	35,133
1V	77	2-dr Hatch-4P	2899	2478	112,912
1V	15	2-dr Sta Wag-4P	3016	2531	56,133
VEGA ESTATE					
1V		2-dr Sta Wag-4P	3255	NA	Note 1
VEGA 'LX'					
1V	11	2-dr Cpe-4P	3119	NA	Note 2
COSWORTH VEGA					
1V	77	2-dr Hatch-4P	5916	NA	2,061
VEGA PANEL EXPRESS					
1H	05	2-dr Panel-2P	2822	2401	1,525

NOTE 1: Included in two-door station wagon total. No breakout is available for number of wagons equipped with 'Estate' trim package.
NOTE 2: Included in two-door (notchback) coupe total. No breakout is available for number of coupes equipped with 'LX' decor package.

1975 Chevrolet, two-door Monza 2 + 2 hatchback, 4-cyl.

MONZA — (FOUR) — ALL SERIES — A popular Chevrolet nameplate of the past appeared again in the fall of 1974, on an all-new sub-compact with a sporty, European like body. Originally planned to be called the Chaparral, this fastback 2 + 2 coupe was built-off the Vega platform, but bore an uncanny resemblance to the Ferrari GTC-4. It was some four-inches longer and 180 pounds heavier than its Vega counterpart, which left enough room for a small block V-8 under the hood. Base engine, however, was the aluminum 2.3 liter four and the

same V-8s used for Novas were optional. Standard features included front bucket seats in leather-look vinyl; armrests; door map pockets; added Sport steering wheel; woodgrain dash inserts; three-speed manual floor-shift transmission; manual front disc/rear drum brakes; Firestone BR78 x 13 steel-belted radial tires on six inch wide rims; tight-sealing rear hatch panel; carpeting and fold down rear seatback. In April, 1975, to answer the threat of the new Mustang II Ghia coupe, the midyear Monza 'S' notchback was introduced as an addition to the line. This Style was 1.5 inches shorter and 135 pounds lighter than the 2 + 2 and had increased headroom. a new instrument panel and single, round headlights in place of the fastback's dual, rectangular type. It was classified as the 'Towne Coupe'.

MONZA SERIES

Series Number	Body/Style Number	Body Type & Seating	Factory Price	Shipping Weight	Production Total
MONZA 'S'					
1M	27	2-dr Twn Cpe-4P	3570	2675	Note 1
1M	07	2-dr Hatch-4P	3648	NA	Note 1
MONZA (2 + 2)					
1R	07	2-dr Hatch-4P	3953	2753	Note 1

NOTE: Exactly 66,615 Monzas were built during the 1975 model year, including 41,658 Fours and 24,957 V-8s. No breakouts by body style or trim level are available at the current time.

CAMARO — (SIX/V-8) — ALL SERIES — The Camaro featured a new, wraparound backlight for 1975. It provided a 10 percent increase in rear visibility. The Z/28 'Special Performance Package' was (temporarily) dropped, but the Rally Sport option was reissued to fill the gap. Standard equipment echoed that of the previous season, plus High-Energy ignition and the catalytic converter. The RS added Rally wheels; radial tuned suspension; specific ornamentation and graphics including black paint accents for the grille; hood; front fendertops; headlamp bezels; window reveal area; forward sail panels and roof header. Engine selections were down to just three EPA-era choices: improved 105 hp '140' six; RPO L65/145 hp two-barrel '350' V-8 (not available in cars for California sale) and the RPO LM 1 / 155 hp four-barrel '350' V-8 (in California and high-altitude counties only).

VEHICLE IDENTIFICATION NUMBERS: The numbering system and code locations were the same as for previous models with the first four symbols changed to Camaro nomenclature. Sequential unit production numbers on 1975 Camaros began with 500001 and up.

CAMARO SERIES

Series Number	Body/Style Number	Body Type & Seating	Factory Price	Shipping Weight	Production Total
CAMARO					
1Q	87	2-dr HT Cpe-4P	3540/3685	3421/3532	141,629
CAMARO TYPE LT					
1S	7	2-dr HT	Cpe-4P	4057/3616	Note 1

NOTE 1: Production of the Camaro LT is included in the total figure given for base Camaro in chart above. This represents domestic production for the U.S. market. An additional 4,160 cars were built for export. Of the full total, 29,359 were sixes and 116,430 were V-8s.
NOTE 2: The total above also included 8,688 cars with four speeds; 10,568 with three-speeds; 126,533 with automatics; 77,290 with air conditioning; 7,000 with Rally Sport equipment; 145,755 with power steering and 10,598 with power windows.

1975 Camaro, two-door sports coupe, V-8

BEL AIR/IMPALA/CAPRICE ENGINE: See 1974 Bel Air/Impala series engine data.

MONTE CARLO ENGINE: See 1974 Bel Air/Impala series engine data.

CHEVELLE SERIES ENGINES

SIX: See 1975 Nova series six-cylinder engine data.

V-8: See 1974 Bel Air/Impala V-8 engine data.

NOVA SERIES ENGINES

SIX:

INLINE, L-HEAD SIX: Cast iron block. Displacement: 250 cid. Bore and stroke: 3.875 x 3.53 inches. Compression ratio: 8.2:1. SAE Net hp: 105 at 1800 rpm. Seven main bearings. Hydraulic valve lifters. Carburetor: one-barrel.

'FEDERAL 'V-8: V-8. Overhead valves. Cast iron block. Displacement: 262 cid. Bore and stroke: 3.671 x 3.10 inches. Compression ratio: 8.5:1. SAE Net hp: 110 at 3600 rpm. Five main bearings. Hydraulic valve lifters. Carburetor: Rochester two-barrel.

'CALIFORNIA' V-8: V-8. Overhead valves. Cast iron block. Displacement: 350 cid. Bore and stroke: 4.00 x 3.48 inches. Compression ratio: 8.5:1. SAE Net hp: 155 at 3800 rpm. Five main bearings. Hydraulic valve lifters. Carburetor: four-barrel.

VEGA ENGINE: See 1974 Vega Series engine data. Brake hp for the 1975 one-barrel Four was 78 at 4200 rpm., but other specifications were unchanged. The two-barrel Four (87 hp at 4400 rpm.) was standard in cars built for California sale and was also included in Vega Estate and Monza LX packages. Refer to text for Cosworth Vega specifications.

MONZA ENGINES

FOUR: See 1974 and 1975 Vega series engine data.

V-8: See 1975 Nova Series engine data.

CHASSIS FEATURES: Wheelbase: (Chevrolet/Monte Carlo/Camaro/Nova/Vegas/Chevelle) same as 1974; (Monza) 97 inches. Overall length: (Chevrolets/Monte Carlo/Camaro/Nova/Vegas/Chevelle wagons) same as 1974; (Chevelles two-doors) 206 inches; (Chevelle four-doors) 210 inches; (Monza 2+2) 180 inches; (Monza Town Coupe) 179 inches. Width: (Monza) 66 inches; (all other models) same as 1974. Tires: Refer to text.

OPTIONS: Vega vinyl top ($79). Vega power steering ($111). Monza Vega air conditioning ($398). Monza / Vega AM/FM stereo ($213). Vega hatch back GT packages ($425). Monza 5.7 liter engine ($298). Camaro / Nova vinyl top ($87). Nova air conditioning ($435). Nova tape deck ($199). Nova AM/FM stereo ($223). Chevelle wagons 454 V-8 engines ($285). Chevelle 454 V-8 engine ($340). Chevelle vinyl top ($96). Chevrolet / Monte Carlo / Camaro / Chevelle AM/FM stereo ($233). Chevrolet / Monte Carlo / Camaro /

Chevelle AM/FM stereo with tape ($363). Monte Carlo / Chevelle sky roof ($350). Chevelle wagon luggage rack ($65). Chevrolet / Monte Carlo Chevelle power seats ($113). Camaro / Chevelle Rally wheels ($46). Monte Carlo Camaro power windows ($91). Monte Carlo vinyl top ($123). Monte Carlo 454 V-8 engine ($285). Chevrolet Group 454 V-8 engine ($315). Chevrolet wagon luggage rack ($77). Chevrolet Group wagons 454 V-8 engine ($172).

HISTORICAL FOOTNOTES: The full-sized Chevrolets were introduced in Sept., 1974 and the Cosworth Vega, Laguna Type S-3 and Monza Towne Coupe appeared in dealer showrooms during April, 1975. Model year production peaked at 1,600,878 units. Calendar year production of 1,639,490 cars were recorded. R.L. Lund was the Chief Executive Officer of the company this year. The Monza 2 + 2 coupe was selected as 1975 "Car of the Year" by MOTOR TREND magazine.

1956 Chevrolet, Bel Air Nomad two-door station wagon, V-8

1958 Chevrolet, Del Ray Yeoman four-door station wagon, 6-cyl

1956 Chevrolet, Bel Air four-door hardtop Sports Sedan, V-8

1959 Chevrolet, Impala two-door convertible, V-8

1957 Chevrolet, Bel Air two-door convertible, V-8

1967 Chevrolet, Impala two-door hardtop Sport Coupe, V-8

1957 Chevrolet, Bel Air Nomad two-door station wagon, V-8

1975 Chevrolet, Camaro two-door hardtop Sport Coupe, V-8

Standard Catalog of American Cars

STANDARD CATALOG OF
CORVAIR
1960-1969

The Chevrolet Corvair, introduced in the fall of 1959 as a 1960 model, is perhaps the most significant automobile of the postwar era. The controversy surrounding the handling qualities of the 1960-1963 Corvairs inspired Ralph Nader to write a best-selling book on "the designed-in dangers of the American automobile." Entitled UNSAFE AT ANY SPEED, that book ushered in a new era of zealous governmental regulation that continues to this day.

By Tony Hossain

The Corvair was a wholly unconventional automobile. It measured a tight 180 inches in overall length and it sat on a compact 108 inch wheelbase. An aluminum, air-cooled, horizontally-opposed six-cylinder engine was rear-mounted, as in the popular German Volkswagen. The fully independent suspension system used coil springs all around and swing axles in the rear. An oddly shaped trunk was up front, where the engine was on all other American cars. The Corvair's primary competition, the Ford Falcon and the Plymouth Valiant, were also introduced in the 1960 model year. But they were, basically, scaled down versions of bigger cars.

Auto enthusiasts loved the new Corvair. MOTOR TREND Magazine proclaimed it 'Car of the Year.' The buff books liked the quick handling qualities, the gutsy sounding rear engine and the European flavor of Chevy's new small car.

Unfortunately the public was unsure. The conventionally engineered Ford Falcon outsold the Corvair by a wide margin in 1960.

It was the Monza Club Coupe, introduced in April, 1960 that saved the day for the Corvair. By 1961 the Monza, with its luxurious appointments and sporty bucket seats, was outselling every other Corvair model. The Corvair had found its niche, not as a small family compact, but as an economical sporty car. Monza owners found out that four-speed transmissions and agile handling made driving a lot more fun.

In mid-1962 the Corvair station wagon, never very popular, was phased out. The Monza convertible took its place on the assembly line. Also making its debut in 1962 was the Monza Spyder option, with its handling suspension and turbocharged engine.

An all-new Corvair arrived in 1965. The lines were very smooth and would characterize GM styling for years to come. Once again, the Corvair was one of America's style leaders. A new rear suspension, Corvette-inspired, corrected some of the oversteering tendencies of the original design and in turbocharged form horsepower ratings went as high as 180. But it was too late. On April 17, 1964, Ford introduced the car that quickly took over the 'Monza market' that Chevy had discovered four years earlier. That car was the Mustang.

With the bad publicity stemming from Ralph Nader's book and the public's preference for the relatively unsophisticated, but brutally powerful V-8 Mustang, Corvair sales plummeted in 1966. Chevy introduced the Camaro in 1967, but the Corvair limped along as an afterthought in the division's model line for two more years. The last Corvair built, a gold Monza coupe, left the Willow Run, Mich. assembly line on May 14, 1969.

1960 CORVAIR

1960 Corvair, Series 500 four-door sedan, 6-cyl

CORVAIRS STANDARD — (SIX) — SERIES 500 — The first Corvair was publicly introduced on Oct. 2, 1959. Its lightweight air-cooled rear engine, unique suspension system and rear mounted transaxle drive setup were a radical departure from other American cars of the day. All of the compact Corvairs were just over four feet high and 15 feet in overall length. All were designed to seat six people. Unitized construction of frame and body was a technical advance for Corvair. The Series 500 models were the standard line. Equipment features included electric windshield wipers; left-hand sun visor; turn signals and five tubeless black sidewall tires. Other items found in all 1960 Corvairs were friction type ventipane latches; single key locking system; push-button outside door handles; dual horizontal headlamps; front ashtray; and center dome light with instrument panel switch. The sole model available at introduction time was the four-door sedan, but a standard 500 Series two-door coupe was a running addition to the line in January, 1960.

CORVAIR I.D. NUMBERS: The numbering system and code locations were the same as for Chevrolet models. Corvair Serial Numbers were located on the left center body pillar. Twelve numbers appeared. The first symbol designated the model year ('0' = 1960). The second and third symbols designated the series ('05' = 500; '07' = 700; '09' = 900 Monza). The fourth and fifth symbols designated the type of body (See last two digits in second column of charts below). The sixth symbol designated the assembly plant. The following group of symbols was the sequential unit production number. The Corvair production sequence began at 100001 and went up from there at each factory where Corvair production was quartered. Body Style Numbers were comprised of the two-digit series and body type codes and appeared, on the vehicle, with a two-digit model year prefix (for example: 60-0569, for a 1960 Corvair 500 four-door sedan). In this catalog, the main Body Style Number appears in the second column of charts; this prefix is not shown, but will always correspond to the year. The engine number for Corvairs is stamped on top of the block, ahead of the generator/oil filter adapter. It consists of six or seven symbols, the first identifying the point of manufacture; the next two indicating month of manufacture and the final one or two symbols identifying the horsepower and the type of transmission attachment.

STANDARD SERIES 500

Series Number	Body/Style Number	Body Type & Seating	Factory Price	Shipping Weight	Production Total
500	0569	4-dr Sed-6P	2038	2305	47,683
500	0527	2-dr Clb Cpe-6P	1984	2270	14,628

1960 Corvair, Series 700 four-door sedan, 6-cyl (AA)

CORVAIR Deluxe — (SIX) — SERIES 700 — Corvairs in the Series 700 line were Deluxe models. Standard equipment included everything found on Corvair 500s, plus right-hand sun visor; chrome exterior moldings; front armrest; cigarette lighter; and upgraded upholstery design. There were also dual horns; automatic front door dome light switches; luggage compartment mat; colored-keyed floor mats and a choice of three different interior trims. Like the standard models, the Corvair Deluxe 700 came only as a four-door sedan at first, but a two-door coupe was added to the line in January, 1960. As opposed to the four-door sedan's flat-top, overhanging roof styling, the two-door edition had a smooth, flowing roofline with large, curved glass backlight.

CORVAIR DELUXE SERIES 700

Series Number	Body/Style Number	Body Type & Seating	Factory Price	Shipping Weight	Production Total
700	0769	4-dr Sed-6P	2103	2315	139,208
700	0727	2-dr Clb Cpe-6P	2049	2290	36,562

CORVAIR MONZA — (SIX) — SERIES 900 — The sporty Corvair Monza two-door Club Coupe made its debut at the Chicago Auto Show, in February 1960, as a show car. It was a dressed up Deluxe 700 coupe with bucket seats and a sun roof. Public response prompted the release of a production model, bearing the same name, in May of the year. Standard equipment included bucket seats with chrome trim; stainless steel rocker sill moldings; special wheelcovers; bright metal seat and armrest moldings; leather-like vinyl upholstery; chrome simulated rear deck air vents; folding rear seat; rear ashtrays; dual sun visors and glovebox light, plus all other Series 700 features.

MONZA SERIES 900

Series Number	Body/Style Number	Body Type & Seating	Factory Price	Shipping Weight	Production Total
900	0927	2-dr Clb Cpe-5P	2238	2280	11,926

ENGINE: (ALL) Horizontally opposed six. Overhead valves. Aluminum block. Displacement: 140 (139.6) cid. Bore and stroke: 3.375 x 2.60 inches. Compression ratio: 8.0:1. Brake hp: 80 at 4400 rpm. Four main bearings. Hydraulic valve lifters. Carburetor: Two (2) Rochester one-barrels Model 7015311.

CHASSIS FEATURES: Wheelbase: (all models) 108 inches. Overall length: (all models) 180 inches. Front tread: (all models) 54 inches. Rear tread (all models) 54 inches. Tires: (all models) 6.50 x 13.

OPTIONS: Rear axle with 3.89:1 ratio gearing ($2). Heater ($74). Padded dash ($18). Manual radio ($54). Rear folding seat, standard in Monza ($32). Wheel trim rings ($11). Five (5) white sidewall tires, 6.50 x 13, four-ply ($21). Two-tone paint in selected schemes was offered as regular production option only. Undergear option was always black. Wheel paint was determined by color and tire equipment. Comfort and Convenience Group: including left outside rearview mirror, push-button windshield washers; back-up lights and glovebox light ($32). Deluxe Body Equipment Group: including cigarette lighter; right-hand sun visor; front armrests, for standard models only ($11). Three-speed manual transmission was standard, Automatic transmission ($146). Six-cylinder 140 cid 95 hp dual one-barrel engine ($27). Heavy-duty battery ($3). Available rear axle gear ratios: (standard) 3.55:1; (optional) 3.89:1.

HISTORICAL FOOTNOTES: The first Corvairs were introduced Oct. 2, 1959 and the Monza appeared in dealer showrooms during May. Model year production peaked at 250,007 units. Calendar year sales of 250,000 cars were recorded. Ed Cole was the chief executive officer of Chevrolet this year. Automatic transmission (Powerglide) was installed in 63.5 percent of all 1960 Corvairs. 39.8 percent had radios: 90.2 percent had heaters; 55 percent had whitewall tires; 42.6 percent windshield washers; 42.6 percent back-up lamps and only 0.6 percent had E-Z-Eye tinted windshields. Series production amounted to 62,300 Standards; 175,800 Deluxes and 11,900 Monzas.

1961 CORVAIR

1961 Corvair Greenbrier Sports Wagon, 6-cyl

CORVAIR — (SIX) — SERIES 500 — The Corvair line was expanded for 1961. New models included a station wagon, van type Sports Wagon and three half-ton trucks. On all models, the spare tire was relocated over the rear engine compartment. Corvairs were advertised and promoted as the lowest-priced Chevrolets. New styling features included a convex nose panel; Corvair lettering replaced Chevrolet lettering on the rear deck and there was a wider Chevrolet insignia housing on the front panel. Series nameplates on 500 models were repositioned to a point high on the sides of the front fenders, but below the belt molding, in the cowl region of the body. Standard equipment for the base series was comprised of directional signals: left-hand sun visor; dual electric windshield wipers; folding rear seat (in Lakewood station wagon) and five 6.50 x 13 black sidewall tubeless tires available except on Lakewood models which used 7.00 x 13 blackwall tubeless. Gray, green or blue interior trims, of slightly improved quality, were provided. With the rear seat folded, the new Lakewood station wagons provided 58 cubic feet of load space. The 500 Series Lakewood lasted only this one model year.

CORVAIR I.D. NUMBERS: The numbering system and code locations were the same as for previous models with the first symbol changed to a '1' to indicate 1961 model year. New Body Style Numbers identified the Lakewood station wagons.

CORVAIR SERIES 500

Series Number	Body/Style Number	Body Type & Seating	Factory Price	Shipping Weight	Production Total
500	0569	4-dr Sed-6P	1974	2355	18,752
500	0527	2-dr Clb Cpe-5P	1920	2320	16,857
500	0535	4-dr Sta Wag-6P	2266	2530	5,591

1961 Corvair, Series 700 two-door Club Coupe, 6-cyl

CORVAIR — (SIX) — SERIES 700 — Corvair's middle-priced models wore '700' nameplates on the cowl sides of the fenders. They had all equipment included on the base level cars, plus chrome exterior moldings; interiors with richer trims; dual horns; coat hooks and automatic light switches that were rigged to operate when the front door was opened.

CORVAIR Deluxe SERIES 700

Series Number	Body/Style Number	Body Type & Seating	Factory Price	Shipping Weight	Production Total
700	0769	4-dr Sed-6P	2039	2380	51,948
700	0727	2-dr Clb Cpe-5P	1985	2350	24,786
700	0735	4-dr Sta Wag-6P	2330	2555	20,451

1961 Corvair, Series 700 four-door Lakewood station wagon, 6-cyl

CORVAIR MONZA — (SIX) — SERIES 900 — Behind the front wheelwell of Monza models, a special ornament bearing the 900 Series designation could be seen. Wheelcovers were the same as used on 1961 Corvair 500 and 700 models. Standard were all features of 700 Series Corvairs, plus front bucket seats and carpeting. All-vinyl interior trim was standard on two-door Monzas only, while the four-door used a vinyl/cloth combination, front armrests; cigarette lighter; right-hand sun visor; back-up lights; Deluxe steering wheel; glovebox light; rear armrests (sedan) and folding rear seat. The Monza sedan was not available at fall introduction time, but became a running addition to the line soon-thereafter. Prices for both Monzas were identical. Interestingly, Chevrolet reduced the rated passenger capacity of all 1961 Club Coupes by one person. Thus, the coupes in the 500 and 700 Deluxe Series were rated as five-passenger models, while the Monza coupe — with bucket seats — was classified a four-place car.

CORVAIR MONZA SERIES 900

Series Number	Body/Style Number	Body Type & Seating	Factory Price	Shipping Weight	Production Total
900	0969	4-dr Sed-6P	2201	2420	33,745
900	0927	2-dr Clb Cpe-4P	2201	2395	109,945

CORVAIR ENGINE: Horizontally opposed six. Overhead valves. Aluminum block. Displacement: 145 (144.8) cid. Bore and stroke: 3.438 x 2.609 inches. Compression ratio: 8.0:1. Brake hp: 80 at 4400 rpm. Four main bearings. Hydraulic valve lifters. Carburetor: Two (2) Rochester one-barrel Model 7019101.

CHASSIS FEATURES: Wheelbase (all models) 108 inches. Overall length: (all models) 180 inches. Front tread: (all models) 54 inches. Rear tread: (all models) 54 inches. Tires: (Lakewood) 7.00 x 13; (all other models) 6.50 x 13.

OPTIONS: Wheelcovers, standard on Monza ($11). Rear door armrests for 500/700 four-door sedan ($10). Comfort and Convenience Group, 500/700 four-door sedan ($39). Comfort and Convenience Group, Monza ($28). Deluxe body equipment, 500/700 models ($11). Tinted glass, all windows ($27); windshield only ($13). Direct-air heater ($74). Gasoline operated heater ($92). Padded dash, all models ($18). Spare wheel lock ($5). Two-tone paint finish ($11). Manual radio ($54). Push-button radio ($62). Folding rear seat 500/700 coupes and sedans ($27). Heavy-duty shock absorbers ($8). Windshield washer ($11). Two-speed windshield wipers ($16). Three-speed manual transmission was standard. Powerglide automatic transmission ($157). Four-speed manual floor shift transmission ($650). Six-cylinder 145 cid 98 hp dual one-barrel engine ($27). Heavy-duty battery ($5). Special

crankcase vent ($4). Generator, 35-amp ($38). Available rear axle gear ratios: (standard) 3.27:1; (optional) 3.55.1, but standard in wagons; with air conditioning, or with automatic and 98 hp engine. 3.89:1 optional.

1961 Corvair, Series 700 four-door sedan, 6-cyl

HISTORICAL FOOTNOTES: The 1961 Corvairs were introduced Oct. 8, 1960 and the Monza sedan appeared in dealer showrooms at mid-season. Model year production peaked at 297,881 units. Calendar year sales of 316,028 cars were recorded. Semon E. 'Bunkie' Knudsen was the chief executive officer of the company this year. On a model year basis, 60.1 percent of 1961 Corvairs had automatic transmission installed; 49.2 percent had radios; 95.4 percent had heaters; 42.5 percent bucket seats; 69.6 percent whitewall tires; 48 percent windshield washers; 24.4 percent tinted glass; 50.9 percent back-up lights and one percent had a new, midyear option, air conditioning. An interesting comparison can be made between the entire 1961 model year and the first few months of 1962 model production to show how fast the popularity of bucket seats was growing. A total of 132,000 models built to 1961 specifications had this option, but by December of 1961, there had been 70,470 Corvairs (1962 models) already built with bucket seats.

1962 CORVAIR

1962 Corvair, Monza Spyder two-door convertible, 6-cyl (AA)

CORVAIR — SIX — SERIES 500 — There were no significant changes in the 1962 Corvair. After a year of strong sales, Chevrolet decided to leave well enough alone. Revision was seen in the front, side and rear trim; redesigned hubcaps and plusher interiors. A V-shaped ornament was placed at the center of the front panel. It was flanked by thin, horizontally divided, simulated air vents on either side. Model nameplates were still on the sides of the front fenders. Interiors on the 500 Series models were comparable to the previous Deluxe trims. They came in vinyl and cloth combinations (with a checkered pattern) in colors of aqua, red or fawn (tan). Standard equipment included directional signals; left-hand sun visor; electric windshield wipers; heater and defroster; rubber floor mats; front foam seat cushions and five 6.50 x 13 black sidewall tubeless tires. The Corvair 500 Lakewood station wagon was no longer on the market and the four-door sedan was gone too.

CORVAIR I.D. NUMBERS: The numbering system and code locations were the same as for previous models, with the first symbol changed to a '2' to indicate 1962 model year. A new convertible used Body Style Number '0967' the '09' designating Monza Series and the '67' designating the new body type.

CORVAIR SERIES 500

Model Number	Body/Style Number	Body Type & Seating	Factory Price	Shipping Weight	Production Total
500	0527	2-dr Clb Cpe-5P	1992	2350	16,245

CORVAIR — (SIX) SERIES 700 — The Corvair 700 Deluxe Series models had all equipment found on the basic line, plus extra chrome exterior moldings; dual horns; ungraded upholstery and, on station wagons, a folding rear seat and 7.00 x 13 black sidewall tires. The Lakewood was dropped in the middle of the model run, since it was in direct competition with the new Chevy II station wagon. The latter car was cheaper to build and easier to sell, due to its greater conventionality. Model nameplates on 700s were located ahead of the front wheelhousing. Another trim change was that the upper belt molding no longer ran entirely around the cars.

CORVAIR SERIES 700

Model Number	Body/Style Number	Body Type & Seating	Factory Price	Shipping Weight	Production Total
700	0769	4-dr Sed-6P	2111	2410	35,368
700	0727	2-dr Clb Cpe-5P	2057	2390	18,474
700	0735	4-dr Sta Wag-6P	2407	2590	3,716

1962 Corvair, Series 900 Monza two-door Club Coupe, 6-cyl

CORVAIR MONZA — (SIX) — SERIES 900 — The Monza was becoming the true star of the Corvair lineup, as Chevrolet's rear engined wonder caught on with the sports car crowd. These cars Included all Items found on lower lines, plus all-vinyl Interior trims standard in the coupe and convertible, while four-door Monzas and Monza wagons used cloth-vinyl upholstery as standard, carpets; rear armrests; cigarette lighter; right-hand sun visor; back-up lights; Deluxe steering wheel (with horn ring); glovebox light; bucket type front seats. Model nameplates on Monzas were of a special design, located behind the front wheelwell. Bright ribbed metal rocker panel moldings were used along the lower body sills. New models included an extra-sporty midyear Monza convertible, plus a short-lived Monza station wagon that was introduced in the fall and killed by the spring.

CORVAIR MONZA SERIES 900

Model Number	Body/Style Number	Body Type & Seating	Factory Price	Shipping Weight	Production Total
900	0969	4-dr Sed-6P	2273	2455	48,059
900	0927	2-dr Clb Cpe-4P	2273	2440	151,738
900	0967	2-dr Conv-4P	2483	2625	16,569
900	0935	4-dr Sta Wag-6P	2569	2590	2,362

CORVAIR MONZA SPYDER — (SIX) — SERIES 900 — About the same time that the new convertible appeared, a car called the Monza Spyder began receiving attention in the press. One such car was tested in POPULAR SCIENCE magazine, April, 1962 and MOTOR TREND magazine got its hands on another. Technically, Spyder equipment was an options package for the Monza convertible and coupe. At least that's the way it was cataloged in 1963, but most people thought of it as a new model. In either case, the package included a special 150 hp, turbocharged version of the Corvair engine, plus crossflags identification badges on the rear deck and a round "turbocharged" emblem on the rear deck. (A crossed flags emblem signified the optional 102 hp engine.) It was not available on cars with air conditioning or two-speed Powerglide automatic transmission.

CORVAIR MONZA SPYDER

Model Number	Body/Style Number	Body Type & Seating	Factory Price	Shipping Weight	Production Total
900	0927	2-dr Clb Cpe-4P	2569	2490	(6,894)
900	0967	2-dr Conv-4P	2779	2675	(2,574)

NOTE 1: Figure in parentheses indicate the number of each body style equipped with the turbocharged six. These figures are included in the Monza Series 900 body style production totals of coupes and convertibles.

CORVAIR ENGINES

(BASE SIX) Horizontally opposed six. Overhead valves. Aluminum block. Displacement: 145 cid. Bore and stroke: 3.43 x 2.60 inches. Compression ratio: 8.0:1. Brake hp: 80 at 4400 rpm. Four main bearings. Hydraulic valve lifters. Carburetor: Two (2) Rochester one-barrel Model 702101.

(MONZA POWERGLIDE SIX) An 84 hp (at 4400 rpm) engine was used with Powerglide equipped Monzas only. It came with a compression ratio of 9.0:1.

(MONZA SPYDER TURBO SIX) Horizontally opposed six. Overhead valves. Aluminum block. Displacement: 145 cid. Bore and stroke: 3.43 x 2.60 inches. Compression ratio: 8.0:1. Brake hp: 150 at 4400 rpm. Four main bearings. Hydraulic valve lifters. Induction: Carter one-barrel carburetor Model 3817245 with turbocharger.

CHASSIS FEATURES: Wheelbase:. (all models) 108 inches. Overall. length: (all models) 180 inches. Front tread (all models) 54.5 inches. Rear tread: (all models) 54.5 inches. Tires: (station wagons) 7.00 x 13; (passenger) 6.50 x 13.

OPTIONS: Air Conditioning ($350). Pair of front seat belts, all ($20). Comfort and Convenience Equipment in 500/700 ($39). Comfort and Convenience Equipment in 900 ($28). Tinted glass, all windows ($27); windshield only ($13). Padded instrument panel ($16). Two-tone paint, all models ($11). Manual radio ($48). Push-button radio ($57). Folding rear seat, for 500 Series and Styles 0727/0769 ($27). Front bucket seats for Monza Sedan, standard in 0927/0967 ($54). Heavy-duty suspension, all ($22). Whitewall tires, exchange ($29). Full wheelcovers, standard on Monzas ($11). Wire wheel design hubcaps, 500/700 ($38); Monzas ($27). Two-speed windshield wipers and washers ($16). Three-speed manual transmission was standard. Automatic transmission ($157). Four-speed manual floor shift transmission ($65). Six-cylinder 145 cid 102 hp 9.0:1 engine ($27). Six-cylinder 145 cid 84 hp Powerglide engine. Generator, 35-amp ($5). Available rear axle gear ratios: (standard) 3.27:1; and the 3.55:1 axle ratio was standard in wagons; with air conditioning; with Spyder equipment, and with the 102 hp engine and Powerglide.

HISTORICAL FOOTNOTES: The 1962 Corvairs were introduced Sept. 29, 1961 and the convertible and Spyder appeared in dealer showrooms around May, 1962. Model year production peaked at 306,023 units. Calendar year sales of 292,531 cars were recorded. S.E. Knudsen was the chief executive officer of the company this year. Series production, expressed in round figures for the model year included 16,300 Corvair 500s; 53,800 Corvair 700s; 216,400 Monza 900s and 19,500 station wagons. Of all Corvair passenger cars and station wagons built to 1962 model specifications, 48 percent had automatic transmissions; 38 percent four-speed gearboxes; tires; 55.1 percent radios; 64.6 percent bucket seats; 86.7 percent white sidewall tires; 55 percent windshield washers; 2.5 percent air conditioning and 5.9 percent limited-slip differentials.

1963 CORVAIR

CORVAIR — (SIX) — SERIES 500 — The pattern of minimum annual change continued for 1963 in the Corvair lineup. The trim on the front panel was changed once again. A strip of chrome was centered between the quad headlamps, running horizontally across the car. Its center section was finished in black paint. Amber colored front parking lamps were a new touch. So was a Corvair nameplate placed in the upper left-hand corner of the hood latch panel. On the side, model identification badges were placed above and ahead of the front wheel opening. Standard equipment included directional signals; electric windshield wipers; heater and defroster; front foam seat cushions; five 6.50 x 13 black sidewall tires and small hubcaps. There was little difference, in the interior, from 1962. The model lineup was unchanged. Standard power came from the rear-mounted, air-cooled six carried over from the previous season. It gave 80 hp with synchromesh transmission. Prices for the Corvair 500 coupe were unchanged from 1962.

CORVAIR I.D. NUMBERS: The numbering system and code locations were the same as for previous models with the first symbol changed to a '3' to indicate 1963 model year.

CORVAIR 500 SERIES

Series Number	Body/Style Number	Doors/Style Seating	Factory Price	Shipping Weight	Production Total
500	0527	2-dr Clb Cpe-5P	1992	2300	16,680

1963 Corvair, Monza four-door sedan, 6-cyl (AA)

CORVAIR (Deluxe) — (SIX) SERIES 700 — The Club Coupe and the four-door sedan remained available in the Corvair 700 Series. Prices for both models decreased one dollar. Weights were down, too, indicating the deletion of some formerly standard hardware. One way to spot a 700 was to look for an upper belt molding that followed the body feature line from the middle of the front door forward, around the front end and down to the middle of the opposite door. A Corvair 700 nameplate was seen ahead of the front wheel opening. And a rocker panel molding was used. Standard features began with everything found on lower priced models, plus the chrome exterior moldings; fancier interior upholstery; color-keyed vinyl rubber floor mats; dual horns; and automatic dome lamp switches. This was last run for the Corvair 700 Club Coupe.

CORVAIR 700 SERIES

Series Number	Body/Style Number	Doors/Style Seating	Factory Price	Shipping Weight	Production Total
700	0769	4-dr Sed-6P	2110	2385	20,684
700	0727	2-dr Clb Cpe-5P	2056	2355	12,378

CORVAIR MONZA — (SIX) — SERIES 900 — The Corvair Monza had all standard equipment found on other models and more. For example, all-vinyl interiors with a new tufted pattern were used on four-door models and convertibles only. Equipment included a cigarette lighter; back-up lights; Deluxe steering wheel; glovebox light; full wheelcovers; rocker panel

moldings; and distinct model identification badges on the lower front fender in back of the wheel openings. Bucket seats were standard in all models including the four-door sedan. Spyder equipment was optional on the coupe and convertible at an attractive price. Sintered metallic brakes were no longer included. What did come on Spyders was a round turbocharged emblem on the rear deck; crossed checkered racing flag emblems on the rear deck; tachometer; 120 mph speedometer; full instrumentation; special brushed metal dash insert panel; and turbocharged flat six. This engine included heavy-duty engine bearings; hardened crank; chromed upper piston rings; special valves; and heavy-duty clutch. Spyders had Carter YH single-barrel sidedraft carburetors.

1963 Corvair, Series 900 Monza two-door convertible, 6-cyl

CORVAIR 900 SERIES

Series Number	Body/Style Number	Doors/Style Seating	Factory Price	Shipping Weight	Production Total
MONZA					
900	0969	4-dr Sed-6P	2326	2450	31,120
900	0927	2-dr Clb Cpe-4P	2272	2415	117,917
900	0967	2-dr Conv-4P	2481	2525	36,693
MONZA WITH SPYDER OPTION					
900	0927	2-dr Clb Cpe-4P	2589	2440	11,627
900	0967	2-dr Conv-4P	2798	2550	7,472

ENGINES

(CORVAIR 500/700/900 SERIES ENGINE): Horizontally-opposed six. Overhead valves. Aluminum block. Displacement: 145 cid. Bore and stroke: 3.438 x 2.609 inches. Compression ratio: 8.0:1. Brake hp: 80 at 4400 rpm. Four main bearings. Hydraulic valve lifters. Carburetor: Two (2) Rochester one-barrel Model 7017360.

(MONZA SPYDER TURBO SIX): Horizontally opposed six. Overhead valves. Aluminum block. Displacement: 145 cid. Bore and stroke: 3.43 x 2.60 inches. Compression ratio: 8.0:1. Brake hp: 150 at 4400 rpm. Four main bearings. Hydraulic valve lifters. Induction: Carter one-barrel carburetor Model 3817245 with turbocharger.

CHASSIS FEATURES: Wheelbase: (all models) 108 inches. Overall length: (all models) 180 inches. Front tread: (all models) 54.5 inches. Rear tread: (all models) 54.5 inches. Tires: (all models) 6.50 x 13.

OPTIONS: Air conditioning ($350). Rear armrest, style 769 only ($10). Pair of front seat belts ($19). Comfort and Convenience equipment, Monza ($28); others ($39). Tinted glass, all windows ($27); windshield only ($13). Padded instrument panel ($16). Spare wheel lock ($5). Two-tone paint ($11). Manual radio ($48). Push-button radio ($57). Push-button radio and front and rear speaker, except convertible ($70). Folding rear seat, Styles 727, 769 and all 500s ($27). Four-ply white sidewall tires ($29). Power convertible top ($54). Full wheelcovers, standard on Monzas ($11). Wire design wheelcovers, 500/700 ($38); Monza ($27). Kelsey-Hayes wire wheels with knock-off hubs, all models ($404). Three-speed manual transmission was standard. Powerglide automatic transmission ($157). Four-speed manual floor shift transmission ($92). Six-cylinder 164 cid 110 hp 9.25:1 engine ($30). Six-cylinder 164 cid 150 hp turbocharged engine (*). Positive traction rear axle ($38). Heavy-duty air cleaner ($17). Heavy-duty clutch (*). Available rear axle gear ratios: 3.27:1; 3.55:1. Generator, 35-ampere ($38).

NOTE: Options marked (*) are included in Spyder equipment package at $317.45.

HISTORICAL FOOTNOTES: The 1963 Corvairs were introduced Sept. 28, 1962. Model year production peaked at 254,571 units. Calendar year production of 261,525 cars was recorded. S.E. Knudsen was the chief executive officer of the company this year. Optional equipment installation rates for Corvettes built to 1963 model specifications were as follows, automatic

transmission (44.3 percent); four-speed manual gearbox (44.3 percent); radio (55.9 percent); heater (99.4 percent); bucket seats (80.5 percent); seat belts (17.6 percent); whitewall tires (77.4 percent); windshield washers (58.6 percent); tinted windshield (39.4 percent); all tinted glass (8.6 percent); air conditioning (2.5 percent); limited-slip differential (7.7 percent) and full wheelcovers (92.0 percent).

NOTE: Percentages are based on a slightly higher model year output figure (266,564) that includes Greenbrier trucks. See Krause Publications *STANDARD CATALOG of AMERICAN LIGHT-DUTY TRUCKS* for information about Chevrolet and Corvair trucks.

1963 Corvair, Greenbrier Sports Wagon, 6-cyl

1964 CORVAIR

CORVAIR — (SIX) — SERIES 500 — Seven models in four series comprised Corvair offerings for 1964. Improved brakes and redesigned suspensions were highlights of the year. The base powerplant now gave 95 hp with manual transmission attachments. A thicker crossbar stretched between the headlights. Below it was a triangular Chevrolet badge. Corvair block letters trimmed the edge of the hood and deck. The circular taillamp bezels were redone. Standard equipment on the 500 Club Coupe was comprised of directional signals; electric wipers, heater and defroster; front foam seat cushions; rubber floor mats; locking glovebox; dual sun visors; cigarette lighter; front armrests; small hubcaps and five tubeless black sidewall tires. Model nameplates remained in their location ahead of front wheel cutouts. Interiors came in red, aqua and fawn (tan). They were slightly plainer in design this year. Many refinements made the 1964 Corvair truly the best of the early editions. It was a great machine for the money, which was less than $10 higher for most models.

CORVAIR I.D. NUMBERS: The numbering system and code locations were the same as for previous models with the first symbol changed to a '4' to indicate 1964 model year.

CORVAIR 500 SERIES

Series Number	Body/Style Number	Doors/Style Seating	Factory Price	Shipping Weight	Production Total
500	0527	2-dr Clb Cpe-5P	2000	2365	22,968

CORVAIR (DELUXE) — (SIX) — SERIES 700 — Only the four-door sedan was available in the Corvair 700 Series this season. It came with all features found on the base-level models, plus front fender model nameplates; chrome exterior moldings; upgraded interior and dual horns. A blue cloth and vinyl interior trim combination was offered and buyers could also select from these materials in the same colors available for Corvair 500s. The Series 700 Club Coupe was dropped due to lagging sales. There were three reasons for the dip in deliveries. First, the new Chevy II had more appeal to conservative buyers in the compact car market. Second, the Corvair hadn't changed much in five years and had lost much of its novelty. Its styling was growing too stale for the mass market, although not for the enthusiast buyer. Third, an unearned reputation for unsafe handling traits was beginning to gain publicity. The result of these three factors combined was that Corvair sales tapered off and also became concentrated in the sportier Monza Series. However, the introduction of the Ford Mustang, in mid-1964, began hurting even the enthusiast market sales. Meanwhile, Chevrolet kept reducing the availability of low trim level Corvairs.

CORVAIR 700 SERIES

Series Number	Body/Style Number	Doors/Style Seating	Factory Price	Shipping Weight	Production Total
700	0769	4-dr Sed-6P	2119	2415	16,295

1964 Corvair, Series 900 Monza Club Coupe, 6-cyl

CORVAIR MONZA — (SIX) — SERIES 900 — Corvair Monzas could be most easily identified by their wider rocker panel moldings; inverted-cross-shaped insignias mounted behind the front wheelhousing; stylish full wheelcovers; and trim moldings along the lips of both front and rear wheel cutouts. A new interior feature was map pockets on the front door panels. Standard equipment included everything found on Series 700 models, plus all-vinyl upholstery on four-door and convertible body styles; rear armrests; back-up lights; Deluxe steering wheel with chrome horn ring; glovebox light; and simulated vents below rear window. The Monza Spyder officially became part of a separate series this year. All Monzas also featured bucket seats.

CORVAIR MONZA 900 SERIES

Series Number	Body/Style Number	Doors/Style Seating	Factory Price	Shipping Weight	Production Total
900	0969	4-dr Sed-5P	2335	2470	21,926
900	0927	2-dr Clb Cpe-4P	2281	2445	88,440
900	0967	2-dr Conv-4P	2492	2555	31,045

1964 Corvair, Monza Spyder two-door convertible, 6-cyl (AA)

CORVAIR MONZA SPYDER — (SIX) — SERIES 600 — The Monza Spyder looked a great deal like the Series 900 Monza on the outside and inside. There was a Spyder signature below the Monza badges on the lower front fender and a round turbocharged emblem on the rear deck. Also, the full wheel covers had special Spyder center inserts. While displacement was up 19 cubic inches over the '63 engine, the 150 hp rating was the same (though the '64 developed it at 4000 rpm and the '63 did it at 4400 rpm). Like all 1964 Corvair powerplants, this one had redesigned hardware and gaskets to better seal oil leakage around the rocker arm covers, as this had been a common problem in the past. Also new were finned rear brakes and the addition of a transverse leaf spring to the rear suspension. With all these changes, the 1964 Corvairs were significantly improved automobiles and the Spyder was the best of the lot. Sales, however, dropped by nearly 50 percent.

CORVAIR MONZA/SPYDER SERIES 600

Series Number	Body/Style Number	Doors/Style Seating	Factory Price	Shipping Weight	Production Total
600	0627	2-dr Cpe-4P	2599	2470	6,480
600	0667	2-dr Conv-4P	2811	2580	4,761

ENGINES

(CORVAIR): Horizontally opposed six. Overhead valves. Aluminum block. Displacement: 164 (163.6) cid. Bore and stroke: 3.438 x 2.938 inches. Compression ratio: 8.25:1. Brake hp: 95 at 3600 rpm. Four main bearings. Hydraulic valve lifters. Carburetor: Two (2) Rochester one-barrel Model 7024023.

(MONZA SPYDER SERIES): Horizontally opposed six. Overhead valves. Aluminum block. Displacement: 164 cubic inches. Bore and stroke: 3.438 x 2.938 inches. Compression ratio: 8.25:1. Brake horsepower: 150 at 4000 rpm. Four main bearings. Hydraulic valve lifters. Carburetor: Rochester three-barrel.

CHASSIS FEATURES: Wheelbase: (all models) 108 inches. Overall length: (all models) 180 inches. Front tread: (all models) 54.5 inches. Rear tread: (all models) 54.5 inches. Tires: (all models) 6.50 x 14.

OPTIONS: Air conditioning ($350). Rear armrest, style 769 only ($10). Pair of front seat belts ($19). Comfort and Convenience equipment, Monza ($28); others ($39). Tinted glass, all windows ($27); windshield only ($13). Padded instrument panel ($16). Spare wheel lock ($5). Two-tone paint ($11). Manual radio ($48). Push-button radio ($57). Push-button radio and front and rear speaker, except convertible ($70). Folding rear seat, Styles 727, 769 and all 500s ($27). Four-ply white sidewall tires ($29). Power convertible top ($54). Full wheelcovers, standard on Monzas ($11). Wire design wheelcovers, 500/700 ($38); Monza ($27). Kelsey-Hayes wire wheels with knock-off hubs, all models ($404). Three-speed manual transmission was standard. Powerglide automatic transmission ($157). Four-speed manual floor shift transmission ($92). Six-cylinder 164 cid 110 hp 9.25:1 engine ($30). Six-cylinder 164 cid 150 hp

turbocharged engine (*). Positive traction rear axle ($38). Heavy-duty air cleaner ($17). Heavy-duty clutch (*). Available rear axle gear ratios: 3.27:1; 3.55:1. Generator, 35-ampere ($38).

Options marked (*) are available only as standard equipment on the Monza Spyder.

HISTORICAL FOOTNOTES: The 1964 Corvairs were introduced Sept. 26, 1963. Model year production peaked at 199,387 units. Calendar year production of 195,770 cars was recorded. S.E. Knudsen was the chief executive officer of the company this year. Optional equipment installation rates for Corvairs built to 1964 specifications (including Greenbriers) were as follows: automatic transmission (47 percent); four-speed manual transmission (39.5 percent); radio (92.8); heater (100 percent); bucket seats (79.5 percent); whitewall tires (75 percent); windshield washers (64.8 percent); tinted windshield only (40.5 percent); all tinted glass (7.3 percent); back-up lights (87.6 percent); air conditioning (3.1 percent); limited slip differential (6.8 percent); and wheelcovers (82.4 percent).

1965 CORVAIR

CORVAIR 500 — (SIX) — SERIES 101 — The Corvair had a completely new body for 1965 and it was beautiful. CAR and DRIVER magazine said, "It unabashedly borrows from the best of the already established foreign and domestic coachwork without losing any of its identity as a Corvair." The new styling was a direct adaptation of the Italian school of industrial design and highlighted smooth-flowing rounded lines; a 'venturi' shaped profile and a pillarless hardtop look on all closed body styles. The Corvair was also two inches wider than before, somewhat lower, and about three inches longer end-to-end. Curved side glass was another innovation. The base Corvair 500 Series included Sport Coupe and Sport Sedan. Trim consisted of a horizontal front panel molding, red in color, set directly below the feature line, with a Chevrolet badge at its center; Corvair script above the left-hand headlight housing; rectangular parking lamps set into a smooth bumper underpan; roof gutter rails painted roof colors; nameplates above and behind front wheel opening; Corvair script on right side of engine lid; and small center hubcaps. Standard equipment included directional signals; electric wipers; heater and defroster; all-vinyl interior; twin sun visors; front seat belts; front armrests; locking glovebox; cigar lighter; coat hooks and interior light.

CORVAIR I.D. NUMBERS: The numbering system and code locations were changed as follows: VIN was located on the top face of the left-hand frame side rail, behind the battery bolts. The engine number was on top of the block, behind the oil pressure sending unit. The VIN had 13 symbols. The first symbol '1' designated Chevrolet product. The second and third symbols designated car-line, as follows: '01' = Corvair 500; '05' = Corvair Monza and '07' = Corvair Corsa. The fourth and fifth symbols designated body style, as follows: '39' = four-door hardtop (Sport Sedan),' '37' = two-door hardtop (Sport Coupe); '67' = convertible. The sixth symbol designated the model year ('5' = 1965). The seventh symbol designated the Chevrolet assembly plant. The following group of symbols was the sequential unit production number, with series in mixed production at a specific plant. Body style numbers (also called model number) were used and correspond to those in second column of the specifications charts below. These numbers were located on the vehicle data plate, on which they were proceeded by a two-digit prefix indicating model year ('65' for 1965). The 1965 Corvair engine number contained a two letter code indicating equipment features as follows: 'RA' = manual transmission; 'RB' = base engine; 'RD' = high-performance; 'RE' = manual transmission/air conditioning; 'RF' = high-performance w/air conditioning; 'RG' = Powerglide; 'RH' = high-performance w/Powerglide; 'RJ' = Powerglide w/air-conditioning; 'RK' high-performance w/ Powerglide. RA manual transmission, 95 hp; RB base engine; 'RD' high-perf. manual transmission, 140 hp; RD opt. manual transmission, 110 hp; RE manual transmission, 95 hp and A/C; RF opt. manual transmission, 110 hp and A/C; RG automatic, 95 hp; RH opt. automatic, 110 hp; RJ automatic, 95 hp and A/C; RK opt automatic, 110 hp and A/C; RL opt. (Corsa only) manual, 180 hp; RM opt. (except Corsa) manual, 140 hp; RN opt. (except Corsa) automatic, 140 hp.

CORVAIR 500

Series Number	Body/Style Number	Doors/Style Seating	Factory Price	Shipping Weight	Production Total
101	10139	4-dr HT Spt Sed-6P	2096	2405	17,560
101	10137	2-dr HT Spt Cpe-4P	2022	2385	36,747

CORVAIR MONZA — (SIX) — SERIES 105 — Monzas now represented the mid-price Corvair models, as the Corvair 700 line was dropped. Standard equipment included all items found on the lower priced cars, plus full wheelcovers; rocker sill moldings; front bucket seats; carpeting; courtesy and glovebox lights; front armrests; rear armrests were not standard (nor available) on two-door coupe styles; back-up lights; and folding rear seats on Sport Coupes and Sport Sedan. As in the past, a Monza badge, consisting of a vertical bar passing through a V-shaped horizontal ornament, was seen on the lower front fenders behind the wheel opening. Whereas the Corvair 500 had only red, aqua or fawn interior color choices, the Monza had no aqua, but blue, black, saddle, slate, white available with aqua or black accents depending on exterior color. The rear panel, to which the engine lid latched, was outlined with a chrome molding. A convertible was also provided in this series and came standard with a manual top and top boot. A handsome new feature of all Corvairs was a slanted-back instrument panel with deep tunnels containing the gauges. On Series 500 and Monza models they housed a speedometer gas gauge, warning-lights and, if ordered, an optional electric clock.

CORVAIR MONZA

Series Number	Body/Style Number	Doors/Style Seating	Factory Price	Shipping Weight	Production Total
105	10539	4-dr HT Spt Sed-5P	2370	2465	37,157
105	10537	2-dr HT Spt Cpe-4P	2297	2440	88,954
105	10567	2-dr Conv-4P	2440	2675	26,466

1965 Corvair, Corsa two-door convertible, 6-cyl (AA).

CORVAIR CORSA — (SIX) — SERIES 107 — The Corvair Corsa models were the top line models in 1965. They carried Corsa lettering on the front fender cowlsides, below the main feature line (just under the new, square gas filler door). In addition a Corsa badge was placed just ahead of the rear wheel opening. It had an oval-shaped ornament with a 'C' in the middle, flanked by vertical bars running up and down. Standard equipment included all items featured with Monzas, plus electric clock; tachometer; oil pressure gauge; temperature gauge; Satin Silver special ornamentation; and special interior trim. There was also a difference in base motivation, the Corsa coming standard with a high-compression 164 cid flat six that put out 140 hp and inducted fuel and air through four single-barrel Rochester carburetors. An important advance on all 1965 Corvairs was a new, Corvette-like, fully independent rear suspension with upper axle half-shafts; lower equal-length trailing torque arms, rubber-bushed rods; and coil springs at each corner. It was complemented by an improved front suspension. Handling with this system was much better than in the past.

CORVAIR CORSA

Series Number	Body/Style Number	Doors/Style Seating	Factory Price	Shipping Weight	Production Total
107	10731	2-dr HT Spt Cpe-4P	2465	2475	20,291
107	10767	2-dr Conv-4P	2608	2710	8,353

ENGINES

(500/MONZA SIX) Horizontally opposed six. Overhead valves. Aluminum block. Displacement: 164 cid. Bore and stroke: 3.438 x 2.938 inches. Compression ratio: 8.25. Brake hp: 95 at 3600 rpm. Four main bearings. Hydraulic valve lifters. Carburetor: Two (2) Rochester one-barrel Model 7025023.

(CORSA SIX) Horizontally opposed six. Overhead valves. Aluminum block. Displacement: 164 cid. Bore and stroke: 3.438 x 2.938 inches. Compression ratio: 9.25:1. Brake hp: 140 at 5200 rpm. Four main bearings. Hydraulic valve lifters. Carburetor: Four (4) Rochester one-barrel Model 7025023 with progressive linkage.

CHASSIS FEATURES: Wheelbase (all models) 108 inches. Overall length: (all models) 183.3 inches. Front tread: (all models) 55 inches. Rear tread: (all models) 56.6 inches. Tires: (all models) 6.50 x 13.

OPTIONS: All-weather air conditioning, Series 500 or Monza, not with 140 hp six ($350). Rear antenna, in place of front mounted antenna (No Charge). Rear armrest, Style Number 139 ($10). Tinted glass, all windows ($27); windshield only ($13). Front or rear bumper guards ($10). Padded instrument panels ($16). Spare wheel lock, all ($5). Two-tone paint available on Model 139 only ($11). Manual radio with front antenna ($50). Push-button radio with front antenna ($59). AM/FM push-button radio with front antenna ($137). Seat belts with retractor ($8). Folding rear seat, as option ($27). Sport style steering wheel ($32). Telescopic steering shaft, includes Sport style wheel ($75). White sidewall tires, size 6.50 x 13, four-ply ($29). Power top for all convertibles ($54). Wheelcovers, on 500 series models ($11). Wire design covers, on 500 Series ($70); on Monza/Corsa ($59). Delete options for credit, heater/defroster ($72 credit); seat belts ($11 credit). 500 Series Convenience Group, includes; left OSRV mirror; non-glare inside mirror; two-speed wiper/washer; back-up and glovebox lights ($39). Monza/Corsa Comfort and Convenience Group, includes; all above, less back-up and glovebox lights which are standard. Comfort and Convenience Group 'B' includes; all above with left OSRV remote-control mirror, 500 Series ($48); others ($38). Three-speed manual transmission was standard. Powerglide automatic transmission, In 500 and Monza Series ($157). Four-speed manual floor shift transmission ($92). Monza and 500 six-cylinder 164 cid 110 hp Turbo-Air engine ($27). Monza and 500 six-cylinder 164 cid 140 hp Turbo-Air engine ($81). Corsa Series six-cylinder 164 cid 180 hp turbocharged engine ($161). Positive traction rear axle ($38). Heavy-duty air cleaner, 500 or Monza without air conditioning or 140 hp six ($32). Available rear axle gear ratios: 3.27:1 and 3.55:1. Heavy-duty 70 ampere battery ($8). Delcotron 47-ampere generator, standard with air conditioning; ($16) on others.

HISTORICAL FOOTNOTES: The 1965 Corvairs were introduced Sept. 24, 1964. Model year production peaked at 235,500 units. Calendar year sales of 204,007 cars were recorded. S. E. Knudsen was the chief executive officer of the company this year. Of all Corvairs built during the 1965 model year, 53.1 percent had automatic transmission; 33.6 percent four-speed gearboxes; 62.9 percent had radios: 99.2 percent had heaters; 76.9 percent bucket seats; 92.6 percent seat belts; 73.9 white sidewall tires; 69.2 percent windshield washers; 40.2 percent tinted windshields only; 9.6 percent all windows tinted; 86.8 percent back-up lights; 4.0 percent air conditioning; 3.7 percent telescopic steering shafts; 6.1 percent limited-slip differential and 80.7 percent wheelcovers. The turbocharged Corsair could move from 0 to 60 mph in under 11 seconds and cover the quarter-mile in around 18 seconds hitting 79 mph in the process. Top speed was over 113 mph.

1966 CORVAIR

CORVAIR 500 — (SIX) — SERIES 101 — Styling refinements including a new one-piece rear grille and taillights were featured in the Corvair for 1966. Slimmer moldings were used to accent the wheel openings front and rear. A front spoiler made the scene. The front panel trim bar was widened and had a blue painted center section. The V-shaped Chevrolet ornament in the center was not quite as large end-to-end, but a little fatter. The Corvair signature was

moved (from above the headlights) back onto the front panel, where it was positioned, on the left-hand side, at a rakish angle. The 500 models featured an expanded list of standard equipment, such as padded dash; padded sun visors; back-up lights; two-speed wipers; windshield washers; left outside rearview mirror; cigar lighter; coat hooks; locking glovebox; interior lamps; and rear seat belts. A more luxurious all-vinyl interior was seen. Technical advances included a fully-synchromesh three-speed transmission (with both manual gearboxes being highly refined); larger 7.00 x 13 standard tires; and the spoiler below the bumper, which improved both handling and gas mileage.

CORVAIR I.D. NUMBERS: The numbering system and code locations were the same as for previous models with the sixth symbol changed to a '6' to indicate 1966 model year. Several new engine number codes appeared as follows: 'RQ' = Special high-performance with exhaust emissions system; 'RR' = air conditioned; 'AT' = base engine with exhaust emissions system; 'RV' = Powerglide with exhausts emissions system; 'RW' = high-performance with exhaust emissions system and 'RY' = special high-performance with Powerglide and air conditioning. Codes 'RV' and 'RX', as used in 1965, were changed or deleted, while all other 1965 codes were applicable again. RQ opt. 140 hp, manual transmission, Air*; RR Corsa 140 hp, manual transmission, A/C; RS Std. 95 hp, manual transmission, Air*; RV Std. 95 hp, automatic transmission, Air*; RU opt. 110 hp, manual transmission, Air*; RY opt. 140 hp, automatic transmission, A/C; RW opt. 110 hp, automatic transmission, Air*; RT Corsa 140 hp, Air*.

*Air — air injection reactor (Emissions Control)

CORVAIR 500

Series Number	Body/Style Number	Body Type & Seating	Factory Price	Shipping Weight	Production Total
101	10139	4-dr HT Spt Sed-6P	2157	2445	8,779
101	10139	2-dr Spt HT Cpe-5P	2083	2400	24,045

1966 Corvair, Monza two-door hardtop Sports Coupe, 6-cyl (PH)

CORVAIR MONZA — (SIX) — SERIES 105 — The Monza was easy to spot. On the lower front fender, behind the wheel opening, was a badge that looked like a stylized airplane with delta wings flying straight downwards. The center of the badge was black-finished and carried the word Monza across its 'wings'. There were chrome outline moldings around the rear deck panel; thin rocker panel moldings; bright metal roof gutter trim and wheelcovers with the delta-winged logo in the center. Standard extras included front bucket seats; carpeting; luggage compartment mat; automatic dome and glovebox lights; fold-down rear seat on closed styles; front and rear ashtrays and rear foam seat cushions. Pleated upholstery with metal buttons was seen.

CORVAIR MONZA

Series Number	Body/Style Number	Body Type & Seating	Factory Price	Shipping Weight	Production Total
105	10539	4-dr HT Spt Sed-5P	2424	2495	12,497
105	10537	2-dr HT Spt Cpe-4P	2350	2445	37,605
105	10567	2-dr Conv-4P	2493	2675	10,345

CORVAIR CORSA (SIX) — SERIES 107 — In its last season, the sporty, high-performance Corsa still clung to a few visual distinctions to set it apart from more lowly models. Most evident was Corsa front fender lettering above and behind the wheel opening and below the body feature line. There were special Corsa ornaments ahead of the rear wheel openings; a Satin Silver finished engine lid latch panel; and an emblem that read "140" or Turbocharged, depending upon the engine ordered at the very center of the engine lid. The wheelcovers had special turbine style center inserts with the Corsa "C-inside-an-oval" badge at the middle. This badge was also seen on the special steering wheel hub insert. Standard equipment included everything found with Monzas, plus full instrumentation; tachometer; oil pressure gauge; temperature gauge. For 1966, three special colors Marina blue, Lemonwood yellow and Chateau slate came only on Monzas and Corsas.

CORVAIR CORSA

Series Number	Body/Style Number	Body Type & Seating	Factory Price	Shipping Weight	Production Total
107	10737	2-dr HT Spt Cpe-4P	2519	2485	7,330
107	10767	2-dr Conv-4P	2662	2720	3,142

ENGINES

(500/MONZA SIX) Horizontally opposed six. Overhead valves. Aluminum block. Displacement: 164 cid. Bore and stroke: 3.438 x 2.938 inches. Compression ratio: 8.25:1. Brake hp: 95 at 3600 rpm. Four main bearings. Hydraulic valve lifters. Carburetor: Two (2) Rochester one-barrel Model 7026023.

(CORSA SIX) Horizontally opposed six. overhead valves. Aluminum block. Displacement: 164 cid. Bore and stroke: 3.438 x 2.938 inches. Compression ratio: 9.25.1 Brake hp: 140 at 5200 rpm. Four main bearings, Hydraulic valve lifters. Carburetor: Four (4) Rochester one-barrel Model 7026023 with progressive linkage.

CHASSIS FEATURES: Wheelbase: (all models) 108 inches. Overall length: (all models) 184 inches. Front tread: (all models) 55 inches. Rear tread: (All models) 56.6 inches. Tires: (all models) 7.00 x 14.

OPTIONS: All-weather air conditioning, Series 500 or Monza, not with 140 hp six ($350). Rear antenna, in place of front mounted antenna (No Charge). Rear armrest, Style Number 139 ($10). Tinted glass, all windows ($27); windshield only ($13). Front or rear bumper guards ($10). Padded instrument panels ($16). Spare wheel lock, all ($5). Two-tone paint available on Model 139 only ($11). Manual radio with front antenna ($50). Push-button radio with front antenna ($59). AM/FM push-button radio with front antenna ($137). Seat belts with retractor

(\$8). Folding rear seat, as option (\$27). Sport style steering wheel (\$32). Telescopic steering shaft, includes Sport style wheel (\$75). White sidewall tires, size 6.50 x 13, four-ply (\$29). Power top for all convertibles (\$54). Wheelcovers, on 500 series models (\$11). Wire design covers, on 500 series (\$70); on Monza/Corsa (\$59). Delete options for credit, heater/defroster (\$72 credit); seat belts (\$11 credit). 500 Series Convenience Group, includes; left OSRV mirror; non-glare inside mirror; two-speed wiper/washer; back-up and glovebox lights (\$39). Monza/Corsa Comfort and Convenience Group, includes; all above, less back-up and glovebox lights which are standard. Comfort and Convenience Group 'B' includes; all above with left OSRV remote-control mirror, 500 Series (\$48); others (\$38). Three-speed manual transmission was standard. Powerglide automatic transmission, in 500 and Monza Series (\$157). Four-speed manual floor shift transmission (\$92). Monza and 500 six-cylinder 164 cid 110 hp Turbo-Air engine (\$27). Monza and 500 six-cylinder 164 cid 140 hp Turbo-Air engine (\$81). Corsa Series six-cylinder 164 cid 180 hp turbocharged engine (\$161). Positive traction rear axle (\$38). Heavy-duty air cleaner, 500 or Monza without air conditioning or 140 hp six (\$32). Available rear axle gear ratios: 3.27:1 and 3.55 to 1. Heavy-duty 70 ampere battery (\$8). Delcotron 47-ampere generator, standard with air conditioning; (\$16) on others.

HISTORICAL FOOTNOTES: The 1966 Corvairs were introduced Oct. 7, 1965. Model year production peaked at 103,743 units. Calendar year production of 73,30 cars was recorded. E.M. Estes was the chief executive officer of the company this year. For the 1966 Corvair model year, optional equipment percentage Installation rates were as follows (percentages in parenthesis): automatic transmission (57.2); four-speed manual transmission (26.7); radio (61.4); heater (99); telescopic steering shaft (2.2); bucket seats (68.4); whitewall tires (68); tinted windshield only (39.5); all glass tinted (8.4); air conditioning (4.6); limited-slip axle (6.8); wheelcovers (73.6); power antenna (0.4) and non-glare rearview mirror (4.9). At the end of the year Chevrolet announced plans for a major expansion of its Willow Run, Mich. assembly plant.

1967 CORVAIR

CORVAIR 500 — (SIX) — SERIES 101 — The high-priced Corvair Corsa Series was dropped for 1967, leaving only five models in hardtops and convertibles. New Strato bucket seats and oval shaped steering wheels were seen. A wider bezel was used on the taillamps from early 1966 on. Dash padding was heavier; the window handle knobs were color-keyed plastic covered and the Powerglide transmission was no longer operated via a T-handle. Now a more conventional knob was used. Otherwise, appearance aspects were about identical to 1966. An eight-track solid state stereo tape player was a brand new option. And 7.00 x 13 tires were used. Standard in Corvair 500 models were all federally mandated safety equipment (called "GM Safety Features"), closed positive crankcase ventilation; all-vinyl interior; cigarette lighter; interior light; foam-cushioned front seat; front door armrest; three-speed manual full-Synchromesh transmission and 95 hp 'Turbo-Air 164' six-cylinder engine.

CORVAIR I.D. NUMBERS: The numbering system and code locations were the same as for previous models with the sixth symbol changed to a '7' to indicate 1967 model year. No new 'R' engine codes were used, although several were dropped. There was however, a completely different group of codes, beginning with letter 'Q'. All of these included exhaust emission controls for California sale. They were as follows: 'QM' = manual transmission and air conditioning; 'QO' = Powerglide w/air conditioning; 'QP'= high-performance w/Powerglide and 'QS' = high-performance w/manual transmission and air-conditioning. QM 95 hp manual, A/C and Air; QO 95 hp automatic A/C and Air; QP 110 hp automatic, A/C and Air; QS 110 hp manual, A/C and Air.

*Air — air injection reactor (Emissions Control)

CORVAIR 500

Series Number	Body/Style Number	Doors/Style Seating	Factory Price	Shipping Weight	Production Total
101	10139	4-dr HT Spt Sed-6P	2194	2470	2,959
101	10137	2-dr HT Spt Cpe-5P	2128	2435	9,257

1967 Corvair, Monza four-door hardtop sedan, 6-cyl (AA)

CORVAIR MONZA — (SIX) — SERIES 105 — Appearance distinctions of the 1967 Monza were the same as seen the year before. They included full wheelcovers with Monza 'delta-wing' insignia; rocker panel moldings; 'delta-wing' fenderside badges, behind front wheel openings; bright metal roof gutter rail moldings; wheel opening moldings and rear panel outline trim. The Monza came with all equipment included on Corvair 500 models, plus dual headlamps; front lockable trunk; bucket seats; carpeting; luggage compartment mat; automatic dome and glovebox lights; fold-down rear seat (except convertibles); speedometer, odometer, fuel gauge, generator and temperature warning lights; front and rear ashtrays and rear foam seat cushions. The turbocharged engine was no longer available. The 140 hp option was deleted and, then, reinstated. New for this year was General Motor's first engine/drivetrain five-year warranty.

CORVAIR MONZA

Series Number	Body/Style Number	Doors/Style Seating	Factory Price	Shipping Weight	Production Total
105	10539	4-dr HT Spt Sed-5P	2464	2515	3,157
105	10537	2-dr HT Spt Cpe-4P	2398	2465	9,771
105	10567	2-dr Conv-4P	2540	2695	2,109

CORVAIR ENGINE: Horizontally opposed six. Overhead valves. Aluminum block. Displacement: 164 cid. Bore and stroke: 3.438 x 2.938 inches. Compression ratio: 8.25:1. Brake hp: 95 at 3600 rpm. Four main bearings. Hydraulic valve lifters. Carburetor: Two-(2) Rochester one-barrel Model 7026023.

CHASSIS FEATURES: Wheelbase: (all models) 108 inches. Overall length: (all models) 183 inches. Front tread: (all models) 55 inches. Rear tread: (all models) 56.6 inches. Tires: (all models) 7.00 x 13.

OPTIONS: All-Weather air conditioning (\$342). Rear manual antenna, substitution (No Charge). Center rear seat belt (\$6). Front and rear Custom Deluxe seat belts (\$6). Center rear seat belt, Custom Deluxe type (\$8). Custom Deluxe front shoulder belts, with Custom Deluxe Group (\$26). Standard front shoulder belt (\$23). Electric clock, all models (\$16). Door edge guards, four-door (\$6); two door (\$3), Tinted glass, all windows (\$31); windshield only. (\$21). Front or rear bumper guards (\$10). Available on model 139 only. Push-button radio; with front antenna (\$57); and rear speaker (\$71). AM/FM push-button radio, with front antenna and rear speaker (\$133). Eight-Track stereo-tape system, includes quad speakers (\$129). White, black or blue power convertible top (\$53). Deluxe steering wheel, 500 (\$7). Monza (\$4). telescoping type (\$42). Speed warning indicator (\$11). Special purpose (heavy-duty) front and rear suspension (\$11). Mag-style wheelcovers, 500 (\$73). Monza (\$63). Simulated wire wheelcovers, 500 (\$69). Monza (\$58). Whitewall tires (\$28). Folding rear seat, 500 Series (\$26). Appearance Guard Group (\$39-42). Auxiliary lighting Group (\$7-14). Three-speed manual transmission was standard. Four-speed manual floor shift transmission, with 95 hp only (\$90). Monza and 500 six-cylinder 164 cid 110 hp Turbo-Air engine (\$26). Monza six-cylinder 164 cid 140 hp Turbo-Air engine (\$79). Positive traction rear axle (\$42). Heavy-duty air cleaner (\$4). Available rear axle gear ratios: 3.27:1 and 3.55:1. air injection reactor, mandatory California cars (\$45). Heavy-Duty 70-ampere battery (\$7). Heavy-Duty 47-ampere Delcotron (\$16).

HISTORICAL FOOTNOTES: The 1967 Corvairs were introduced Sept. 29, 1966. Model year production peaked at 27,253 units. Calendar year production of 18,703 cars was recorded. E.M. Estes was the chief executive officer of the company this year. For the 1967 model year, optional equipment installation rates (percentages in brackets) were as follows: automatic (67.9); four-speed (14.8); AM radio (63.6); air conditioning (5.1); telescoping steering column (1.1); bucket seats (55.2); white sidewall tires (60.8); tinted windshield only (34.7; all tinted glass (7.5); limited-slip axle (4.8); wheelcovers (64.2); AM/FM radio (1.3); and electric clock (6.9).

1968 CORVAIR

CORVAIR 500 — (SIX) — SERIES 101 — Model availability for the Corvair dropped from five to three for the 1968 model year. The Monza Sport Sedan and the 500 Sport Sedan were discontinued. This eliminated all four-door styles from the lineup. Side marker lamps on the front and rear fenders are the easy way to spot a 1968 model from past editions. A look inside will reveal a dash with even more stuffings and padded windshield pillar posts. What else was new? A larger floor shift lever knob; restyled, padded armrests; new vinyl upholstery fabrics and on Jan. 1, 1968, shoulder safety belts became mandatory. The Corvair 500 coupe came with all GM Safety Features; cigarette lighter; heater and defroster (no longer deletable); 7.00 x 13 two-ply, four-ply rated blackwall tires and the 95 hp 'Turbo-Air' six. The four-carb 'Turbo-Air 140' job was still optional. Hubcaps were standard.

CORVAIR I.D. NUMBERS: The numbering system and code locations were the same as for previous models with the sixth symbol indicating 1968 model year. Engine/equipment combinations were down to eight choices, coded as follows: 'RS' = manual transmission; 'RM' = high-performance; 'RF' = high-performance with air conditioning; 'RW' = high-performance with Powerglide; 'RJ' = Powerglide with air conditioning!; 'RK' = high-performance with Powerglide and air conditioning; 'RE' = air conditioning and 'RV' = Powerglide. NOTE: Not explained is why engine codes with air conditioning are listed, although this particular factory option was dropped! RS 95 hp, manual transmission; RU 110 hp, manual transmission; RV 95 hp, automatic transmission; RW 110 hp, automatic transmission; RY 140 hp, manual transmission; RZ 140 hp automatic transmission.

CORVAIR 500

Series Number	Body/Style Number	Body Type & Seating	Factory Price	Shipping Weight	Production Total
101	10137	2-dr HT Spt Cpe-5P	2243	2470	7,206

CORVAIR 500: Horizontally opposed six. Overhead valves. Aluminum block. Displacement: 164 cubic inches. Bore and stroke: 3.438 x 2..938 inches. Compression ratio: 8.25:1. Brake horsepower: 95 at 3600 rpm. Four main bearings. Hydraulic valve lifters. Carburetor: Two (2) Rochester one-barrel Model 7028005.

1968 Corvair, Monza two-door hardtop Sports Coupe, 6 cyl (AA)

CORVAIR MONZA — (SIX) — SERIES 105 — The Monza had all features found on the Corvair 500, plus glovebox light; dual headlamps; front bucket seats; carpeting; courtesy lights (in convertible) and folding rear seat (in coupe). Appearance extras were full wheelcovers; chrome roof gutter strips; rocker panel moldings; rear panel outline trim strips and Monza inverted 'delta wing' badges behind the front wheel opening, plus wheel lip moldings and high-grade interior trimmings in blue, black or gold. The folding rear seat had an improved latching mechanism instead of the old, hard to operate, friction type.

CORVAIR MONZA

Series Number	Body/Style Number	Body Type & Seating	Factory Price	Shipping Weight	Production Total
105	10537	2-dr HT Spt Cpe-4P	2507	2500	6,807
105	10567	2-dr Conv-4P	2626	2725	1,386

CORVAIR ENGINE: Horizontally opposed six. Overhead valves. Aluminum block. Displacement: 164 cid. Bore and stroke: 3.438 x 2.938 inches. Compression ratio: 8.25:1. Brake hp: 95 at 3600 rpm. Four main bearings. Hydraulic valve lifters. Carburetor: Two (2) Rochester one-barrel Model 7028005.

CHASSIS FEATURES: Wheelbase: (all models) 108 inches. Overall length: (all models) 183 inches. Front tread: (all models) 55 inches. Rear tread: (all models) 56.6 inches. Tires: (all models) 700 x 13.

OPTIONS: Rear manual antenna, except with AM/FM ($10). Front and rear Custom Deluxe shoulder belts, with bucket seats ($8). Front and rear Custom Deluxe shoulder belts, with full-width seats ($10). Pair of front shoulder belts, standard type ($23); front and rear ($46). Custom Deluxe shoulder belts, front pair ($26); front and rear ($53). Electric clock ($16). Rear window defroster, except convertible ($21). Door edge guards, all ($4). Tinted glass, all windows ($31); windshield only ($21). Head restraints, pair, in 500 ($42); in Monza ($52). Spare wheel lock ($5). Twin front and rear floor mats, all ($11). Left OSRV remote control mirror, all ($10). Radios, push-button with front antenna ($61); same AM/FM ($134). Rear speaker, except with stereo ($13). Folding rear seat, 500 Series, standard in Monza coupe ($32). Speed warning indicator ($11). Adjustable steering column ($42). Deluxe steering wheel, 500 coupe ($7); Monzas ($4). Sport style steering wheel, all models ($32). Stereo tape system, includes quadraphonic ($134). Special purpose front and rear suspension ($11). Whitewall tires, 7.00 x 13-4 ply ($28). Power convertible top ($53). wheelcovers: standard in 500 ($21); mag-style, in 500 ($74); mag-style in Monza ($63); wire style in 500 ($69); wire style in Monza ($58). Appearance Guard Group ($34). Three-speed manual transmission was standard. Automatic transmission, all ($153). Four-speed manual floor shift transmission, all ($90). Turbo-Air six-cylinder 164 cid 110 hp 9.25:1 engine ($26). Turbo-Air six-cylinder 164 cid 140 hp four-carb engine ($79). Heavy-duty 70-ampere battery ($7). Positive traction rear axle ($42). Heavy-duty air cleaner ($6). Available rear axle gear ratios: availability depends on power teams.

HISTORICAL FOOTNOTES: The 1968 Corvairs were introduced Sept. 21, 1967. Model year production peaked at 15,400 units. Calendar year production 11,490 cars were recorded. John Z. DeLorean was the chief executive officer of the company this year. For the 1968 model year, optional equipment installation rates (percentages in brackets) were as follows: automatic (70); AM radio (66); telescoping steering wheel (1.5); bucket seats (53); whitewalls (58); tinted windshield only (23); all glass tinted (10); limited-slip axle (7); wheelcovers (63); AM/FM radio (4) and stereo tape system (0.5).

1969 CORVAIR

CORVAIR 500 — (SIX) — SERIES 101 — Aside from color choices, the 1969 interiors were identical to 1968. Two coupes and one convertible were offered in the last season of Corvair production. Appearance changes were very minor. They included a bigger rearview mirror and amber front side marker lens. The Corvair 500 came with front head rests as a mandatory option; cigarette lighter; heater and defroster; 7.00 x 13 four-ply rated blackwall tires and unchanged 95 hp Turbo-Air engine. Vinyl interiors now came in black, blue and medium green.

CORVAIR I.D. NUMBERS: The numbering system and code locations were the same as for previous models with the sixth symbol changed to a '9' to indicate 1969 model year. Engine identification codes were the same as in 1968.

CORVAIR 500

Series Number	Body/Style Number	Body Type & Seating	Factory Price	Shipping Weight	Production Total
101	10137	2-dr HT Cpe-5P	2258	2515	2,762

1969 Corvair, Series 105 Monza two-door convertible, 6-cyl

CORVAIR MONZA — (SIX) — SERIES 105 — The Monza came with all equipment found on the base-line coupes, plus glovebox light; dual headlamps; front bucket seats; courtesy lights (in convertible) and folding rear seat (in coupe). Appearance distinction was identical to those of the 1968 Monza. An Olympic gold Monza, serial number 105379W706000 was the last Corvair built and may be in the possession of General Motors today.

CORVAIR MONZA

Series Number	Body/Style Number	Body Type & Seating	Factory Price	Shipping Weight	Production Total
105	10537	2-dr HT Cpe-4P	2522	2545	2,717
‘05	10567	2-dr Conv-4P	2641	2770	521

1969 Corvair, Monza two-door hardtop Sports Coupe, 6-cyl

HISTORICAL FOOTNOTES: The 1969 Corvairs were introduced Sept. 26, 1968. Model year production peaked at 6,000 units. Calendar year sales of 3,103 cars were recorded. John Z. DeLorean was the chief executive officer of the company this year. For the 1969 model year, optional equipment installation rates (percentages in brackets) were as follows: Powerglide 2); four-speed gearbox (14); AM radio (80); AM/FM radio (3); bucket seats (54); whitewall tires (55); tinted windshield (0.1); all tinted glass (26); posi-traction (8); standard wheelcovers (54); optional wheelcovers (13); electric clock (11); telescoping steering wheel (2.5); In mid-May, 1969, Chevrolet offered Corvair buyers a $150 discount coupon to use in purchasing any new Chevrolet from then, until 1973. The idea was to compensate for any lost resale value experienced due to the discontinuance of the marque. Today, these cars hold a small premium in the collector market for being last year models.

CORVETTE
1953-1975

The 1953 Corvette was based on the 1952 EX-122 show car. It was one of the few Motorama dream cars to actually go into production with the styling virtually unchanged.

The Corvette was created as an economical sports car for young adults. It was also something that could be used as a performance-image builder while Chevrolet waited for its V-8. The car's fiberglass body was not only novel, but practical. It lowered the cost of production in limited numbers and expedited the Corvette's debut. Steel-bodied models were originally planned for later model years.

By Charles Webb

Sports car enthusiast and TV celebrity Dave Garroway heaped a lot of praise on the pretty new Corvette in the Chevrolet sales promotion film "Halls of Wonder." Yet, many of the sports car fans it was meant for snubbed it. They harbored a prejudice that nothing good could come out of Detroit and certainly not from Chevrolet. Remember, at the time, a "Chevy" was the car mothers drove to the A & P to pick up peanut butter and jelly for their childrens' lunch. The marque did not have a hot-car image yet. The fact that Corvettes used standard 'family car' mechanical components and came with a Powerglide automatic transmission were other points of criticism.

Most of the people who knocked the 'Vette never drove one. As ROAD & TRACK said of the 1954, "The outstanding characteristic of the Corvette is probably its deceptive performance."

The car looked the same in 1955, but the 265 cid V-8 made it much hotter. Unfortunately, like a beautiful debutante with a black belt in karate, its appearance belied its power. Sales were so bad Chevrolet management was on the verge of killing the Corvette. However, when Ford came out with its two-passenger Thunderbird, the company was forced, for competitive reasons, to continue production.

Sales shot up dramatically in 1956. One of the main reasons was the Corvette now had looks to match its performance. A manual transmission, roll-up side windows and lockable doors also added to its appeal. And several prestigious racing victories contributed to its performance image.

With the introduction of fuel-injection in 1957, advertising proclaimed, "For the first time in automotive history — one h.p. for every cubic inch." Chrysler 300 fans knew better, but it did make good copy and sales once again increased.

The clean, classic styling of 1956 and 1957 was jazzed-up in 1958. Although the basic design was attractive, the chrome-laden 1958 is generally considered the gaudiest Corvette. But, apparently, that's what the public wanted and sales climbed significantly over the previous year's model.

Some of the excess glitter was removed in 1959. In 1961, the Corvette received a new 'duck tail' rear end treatment. Two years later, in a major restyling, the 1963s were an immediate hit. Demand was so great many customers had to wait two months or more to take delivery of their new Sting Ray coupe or ragtop. By now, Corvette's reputation as a powerful sports car was firmly established on the track and street.

A four-passenger Corvette was considered for 1963. It might have been quite successful. Thunderbird sales soared when it went that route in 1958. However, the T-Bird never really claimed to be a true sports car; it was a 'sporty' personal car. Putting a back seat in the Corvette might have hurt its image.

The basic aerodynamic styling introduced in 1968 would remain until 1983. After the early 1970s, Corvettes became significantly tamer. Still, when you mention performance, the American car that comes first to most people's minds is Corvette.

1954 Corvette, two-door convertible, 6-cyl

1959 Corvette, two-door convertible with hardtop, V-8

1954 Corvette, two-door convertible, 6-cyl

1960 Corvette, two-door convertible, V-8

1956 Corvette, two-door convertible, V-8

1961 Corvette, two-door convertible, V-8

1958 Corvette, two-door convertible, V-8

Standard Catalog of American Cars

1963 Corvette, Sting Ray two-door convertible, V-8

1963 Corvette, Sting Ray two-door convertible, V-8

1964 Corvette, Sting Ray two-door convertible, V-8

1965 Corvette, Sting Ray two-door convertible, V-8

1966 Corvette, Sting Ray two-door convertible with hardtop, V-8

1968 Corvette, Stingray two-door convertible, V-8

1969 Corvette, Stingray two-door T-top coupe, V-8

1970 Corvette, Stingray two-door T-top coupe, V-8

1972 Corvette, Stingray two-door T-top coupe, V-8

1953 CORVETTE

CORVETTE — (6-CYL) — SERIES E2934 — The new 1953 Corvette had a fiberglass body chrome-framed grille with 13 heavy vertical chrome bars, rounded front fenders with recessed headlights, no side windows or outside door handles, a wraparound windshield and protruding, fender-integrated taillights. The interior featured a floor-mounted shifter, Power-glide automatic and a full array of gauges including a tachometer. Each 1953 Corvette was virtually hand-built and a lot of minor changes were made during the production run.

CORVETTE I.D. NUMBERS: The Corvette used the standard Chevrolet coding system. It consisted of a total of 10 symbols, except for V-8s, which in some years utilized 11 symbols. The first symbol was an 'E' for 1953-1957 models and a 'J' for 1958-1959 models. The second and third symbols designated model year. The fourth symbol desig-nated the manufacturing plant, as follows: F=Flint, Mich. and S=Saint Louis, Mo. The following group of numbers (usually six digits) was the sequential unit production number. Corvettes, for 1953, were numbered E53F001001 to E53F001300. The Serial number was located on the left front door hinge pillar post. Engine numbers were found on the right-hand side of the crankcase, behind the distributor. The engine numbers for 1953 models used the prefix 'LAY'. Since Corvette bodies were virtually handmade, they did not carry standard Fisher Body Style Numbers, as did other GM cars. The Corvette model number consisted of four symbols '2934', which also served as the body style number for the early production years.

1953 Corvette, two-door roadster convertible, 6-cyl (AA)

Model Number	Body/Style Number	Body Type & Seating	Factory Price	Shipping Weight	Production Total
2934	2934	2-dr Conv-2P	3498	2705	300

BASE ENGINE: Inline six. Overhead valves. Cast iron block. Displacement: 235.5 cid. Bore and stroke: 3.56 x 3.93 inches. Compression ratio: 8.0:1. Brake hp: 150 at 4200 rpm. Carbu-retor: Three (3) Carter Type YH one-barrels Model 2066S (early models); Model 2055S (late models).

CHASSIS FEATURES: Wheelbase: 102 inches. Overall length: 167 inches. Front tread: 57 inches. Rear tread: 59 inches. Tires: 6.70 x 15.

OPTIONS: Signal-seeking AM radio ($145.15). Heater ($91.40). White sidewall tires.

HISTORICAL FOOTNOTES: The first Corvette was built on June 30, 1953 at the Flint, Mich. assembly plant. Model year production peaked at 200 units. Calendar year sales of 300 cars were recorded. T.H. Keating was the Chief Executive Officer of Chevrolet this year. By early 1954, Chevrolet announced the 315 Corvettes had been built and that production of the model had been shifted to the assembly plant In St. Louis. Programming, at that point, called for production of 1,000 Corvettes per month by June, 1954. The company predicted that 10,000 per year could be built and sold.

1954 CORVETTE

CORVETTE SERIES — (6-CYL) — SERIES E2934 — For all practical purposes, the 1953 and 1954 Corvettes were the same. Minor changes were made to the window storage bag, air cleaners, starter and location of the fuel and brake lines. Unlike the previous year's model, 1954s were available in Pennant blue, Sportsman red and black in addition to Polo white. The softtop was now offered only in beige.

1954 Corvette, two-door roadster convertible, 6-cyl (AA)

CORVETTE I.D. NUMBERS: The numbering system and code locations were the same as for previous models. Serial Numbers were E54SO01001 to E54S004640. Engine numbers, for 1954, had the suffix 'YG'.

CORVETTE

Model Number	Body/Style Number	Body Type & Seating	Factory Price	Shipping Weight	Production Total
2934	2934	2-dr Conv-2P	3523	2705	3,640

BASE ENGINE: Inline Six. Overhead valves. Cast iron block. Displacement: 235.5 cid. Bore and stroke: 3.56 x 3.93 inches. Compression ratio: 8.00:1. Brake hp: 150 at 4200 rpm. Four main bearings. Solid valve lifters. Carburetor: Carter, three (3) one-barrel Type YH Model 2066SA.

NOTE: Later in the model year, a new camshaft upped horsepower to 155.

CHASSIS FEATURES: Wheelbase: 102 inches. Overall length: 167 inches. Front tread: 57 inches. Rear tread: 59 inches. Tires: 6.70 x 15. Signal-seeking AM radio ($145.15). Heater ($91.40). Windshield washer ($11.85). Parking brake alarm ($5.65). Powerglide transmission standard. Various rear axle ratios.

HISTORICAL FOOTNOTES: Approximately 80 percent of 1954 Corvettes were painted white. About 16 percent had a blue exterior. A 1954 Corvette could go from 0-60 mph in 11 seconds. From 0-100 in 41 seconds.

1955 CORVETTE

1955 Corvette, two-door roadster convertible, V-8

CORVETTE SERIES — (6-CYL) — SERIES E2934 — Styling remained the same as last year's model. The big news was the availability of a V-8 engine. An enlarged gold 'V' in the word Chevrolet, on the front fenders, was a quick way to tell V-8 powered (12-volt electrical system) cars from those with a six-cylinder engine (and 6-volt electrical system).

CORVETTE I.D. NUMBERS: The numbering system and code locations were the same as for previous models with the number symbols changed as follows: VE55SO01001 to VE55S001700.

NOTE: Cars equipped with a six-cylinder engine did not have a 'V' in their vehicle identification number. Motor Number suffixes used were 'YG' (six-cylinder); 'FG' (V-8 and automatic) and 'GR' (V-8 with manual transmission).

Model Number	Body/Style Number	Body Type & Seating	Factory Price	Shipping Weight	Production Total
2934	2934	2-dr Conv-2P	2934	2705	700

ENGINES

SIX. Inline Six-cylinder. Overhead valves. Cast iron block. Displacement: 235.5 cid. Bore and stroke: 3.56 x 3.93 inches. Compression ratio: 8.00:1. Brake hp 155 at 4200 rpm. Four main bearings. Solid valve lifters. Carburetor: Three (3) Carter one-barrel Model 3706989.

V-8: Overhead valves. Cast iron block. Displacement: 265 cid. Bore and stroke: 8.00:1. Brake hp: 195 at 5000 rpm. Five main bearings. Solid valve lifters. Carburetor: Rochester four-barrel Model 7008005.

CHASSIS FEATURES: Wheelbase: 102 inches. Overall length: 167 inches. Front tread: 57 inches. Rear tread: 59 inches. Tires: 6.70 x 15.

OPTIONS: Parking brake alarm ($5.65). Signal-seeking AM radio ($145.15). Windshield washer ($11.85). Heater ($91.40). Automatic transmission with floor shift was standard. Six-cylinder 235.5 cid 155 hp 'Tri-Carb' engine standard. V-8 265 cid 195 hp four-barrel engine ($135).

HISTORICAL FOOTNOTES: The overwhelming majority of 1955 Corvettes were V-8 powered, but at least a half-dozen six-cylinder models were reportedly produced. A V-8 powered 1955 Corvette could go from 0-60 mph in 8.7 seconds; from 0-100 mph in 24.7 seconds. Harvest gold exterior finish was introduced along with Gypsy red and Corvette copper. Tops now came in white, dark green, or beige. Red, yellow, light beige and dark beige Elascofab interiors were available.

1956 CORVETTE

CORVETTE SERIES — (V-8) — SERIES E2934 — A lot of people would have been perfectly content if Chevrolet had frozen Corvette styling with the 1956 model. Although the same basic grille was kept, there were new front fenders with chrome-rimmed headlights; external door handles; chrome-outlined concave side body coves and sloping, taillight-integrated rear fenders. The dash layout remained the same as in the past. Upholstery colors were limited to beige or red, but six nitro-cellulose lacquer body colors were available. They were Oxyx black, Polo white, Venetian red, Cascade green, Aztec copper and Arctic blue.

CORVETTE I.D. NUMBERS: were the same as for previous models with the number symbols changed as follows E56S001001 to E56S004467. Starting Engine Numbers were 0001001 and up at each assembly plant. with an 'F' = Flint, Mich. and 'T' = Tonawanda, N.Y. Suffixes were as follows: 'GV' for 265 cid V-8 with Synchromesh; 'GU' for 265 cid V-8 with two (2) four-barrel carburetors and high-lift camshaft; 'GR' for regular 265 cid dual four-barrel V-8; 'FK' for 265 cid V-8 with Powerglide and 'FG' for latter V-8 combinations with dual four-barrel carburetors.

1956 Corvette, two-door convertible, V-8 (AA)

CORVETTE

Model Number	Body/Style Number	Body Type & Seating	Factory Price	Shipping Weight	Production Total
2934	2934	2-dr Conv-2P	3120	2870	3,467

BASE ENGINE: V-8. Overhead valves. Cast iron block. Displacement: 265 cid. Bore and stroke: 3.75 x 3 inches. Compression ratio: 9.25:1. Brake hp: 210 at 5200 rpm. Five main bearings. Solid valve lifters. Carburetor: Carter Type WCFB four-barrel Model 2419S.

CHASSIS FEATURES: Wheelbase: 102 inches. Overall length: 168 inches. Front tread: 57 inches. Rear tread: 59 inches. Tires: 6.70 x 15.

OPTIONS: Power top ($100). Power windows ($60). Windshield washer ($11). Detachable hardtop ($200). Signal seeking AM radio ($185). Heater ($115). A close ratio three-speed manual floor shift transmission was standard. Automatic transmission ($175). V-8 265 cid 225 hp dual four-barrel carburetors, high-lift cam engine ($175). V-8 265 cid 240 hp dual four-barrel engine ($160). Available rear axle gear ratios: 3.27:1.

HISTORICAL FOOTNOTES: A 225 hp 1956 Corvette could go from 0-60 mph in 7.3 seconds; from 0-100 mph in 20.7 seconds.

1957 CORVETTE

CORVETTE SERIES — (V-8) — SERIES E2934 — The 1957 Corvette looked the same as last year's model. The big news was the availability of a 283 hp 283 cid fuel-injected V-8. Among the standard features were: dual exhaust; all-vinyl bucket seats; three-spoke competition style steering wheel; carpeting; outside rearview mirror; electric clock and tachometer. It was available in seven colors: Onyx black; Polo white; Aztec copper; Arctic blue; Cascade green; Venetian red or silver. White, silver, and beige were optional color choices for the cove.

CORVETTE I.D. NUMBERS: The numbering system and code locations were the same as for previous models with the numbers changed as follows: E57S100001 to E57S106339. Engine Number suffixes were: 'EF' four-barrel/synchromesh; 'EG' dual four-barrel high-lift

synchromesh; 'EH' dual four-barrel/synchromesh; 'EL' fuel-injection/high-lift; 'EN' fuel-injection/high-lift; 'FG' Powerglide dual four-barrel; 'FH' Powerglide and 'FK' Powerglide/fuel-injection.

1957 Corvette, two-door convertible, V-8 (AA)

CORVETTE

Model Number	Body/Style Number	Body Type & Seating	Factory Price	Shipping Weight	Production Total
2934	2934	2-dr Conv-2P	3465	2730	6,339

BASE ENGINE: V-8. Overhead valves. Cast iron block. Displacement: 283 cid. Bore and stroke: 3.87 x 3 inches. Compression ratio: 9.50:1. Brake hp: 220 at 4800 rpm. Five main bearings. Valve lifters: (see note). Carburetor: Carter four-barrel Model 3744925.

NOTE: A solid lifter camshaft was used with 'EL' and 'EG' engines; hydraulic lifters with others.

CHASSIS FEATURES: Wheelbase: 102 inches. Overall length: 168 inches. Front tread: 57 inches. Rear tread: 59 inches. Tires: 6.70 x 15.

OPTIONS: Special 15 x 5.5 inch wheels ($14). Signal-seeking AM radio ($185). Detachable hardtop ($215). Power top ($130). Courtesy lights ($8). Heater ($118). Windshield washer ($12). Parking brake alarm ($5). Whitewall tires ($32). Dual carbs ($151). Two-tone paint ($19). Motorola radio ($125). Electric windows ($55). Hydraulic power top ($99). Three-speed manual floor shift transmission was standard. Automatic transmission ($175). Four-speed manual floor shift transmission ($188). V8 283 cid 245 hp dual four-barrel carb. engine ($140). V-8 283 cid 270 hp dual four-barrel carb. engine ($170*). V-8 283 cid 250 hp fuel-injection engine ($450). V-8 283 cid 283 hp fuel-injection engine ($450*). "RPO 579E" V-8 283 cid 283 hp fuel-injection engine ($675**). Positive traction rear axle ($45). Heavy-duty racing suspension ($7 25). Available rear axle gear ratios 3.70:1, 4.11:1, 4.56:1. (*) With competition camshaft. (**) With cold-air induction system.

HISTORICAL FOOTNOTES: Only 1,040 of the 1957 Corvettes were fuel-injected. A 283 hp fuel-injection 1957 Corvette could go from 0-60 mph in 5.7 seconds. From 0-100 mph in 16.8 seconds. It had a top speed of 132 mph.

1958 CORVETTE

1958 Corvette, two-door convertible, V-8 (AA)

CORVETTE SERIES — (V-8) — SERIES J800 — Styling was jazzed up for 1958. There were now four chrome rimmed headlights with a fender length chrome strips running between each pair of lights. As if that weren't enough glitter, fake louvers were placed on the hood. The grille was similar to last year's, but had four fewer vertical bars. Three horizontal chrome strips were added to the new cove. A couple of vertical chrome bars decorated the trunk. They detracted from an otherwise graceful rear end treatment. The wraparound front and rear bumpers were larger. The interior changed dramatically. The gauges were clustered together, rather than spread across the dash as before. A center console and passenger assist (sissy) bar were added. Upholstery was available in red, charcoal, or blue-green. There were six acrylic lacquer exterior colors offered: charcoal, white, yellow, red, blue and turquoise. The cove could be painted silver or white.

CORVETTE I.D. NUMBERS: The numbering system and code locations were the same as for previous models with the numbers changed as follows: J58S100001 to J58S109168. Engine codes were: 'CQ' = manual transmission; 'CR' = manual and fuel injection; 'CS' = manual/high-lift cam and fuel injection; 'CT' = manual and dual four-barrels; 'CU' = manual/

high-lift and dual four-barrels; 'DG' = Powerglide transmission; 'DH' = Powerglide and dual injection and 'DJ' = Powerglide and dual four-barrel. Note: Both three and four-speed manual transmissions used same engine code suffixes.

CORVETTE

Series Number	Body/Style Number	Body Type & Seating	Factory Price	Shipping Weight	Production Total
J800	867	2-dr Conv-2P	3631	2781	9,168

BASE ENGINE: V-8. Overhead valves. Cast iron block. Displacement: 283 cid. Bore and stroke: 3.87 x 3 inches. Compression ratio: 9.50:1. Brake hp: 230 at 4800 rpm. Five main bearings. Hydraulic valve lifters. Carburetor: Carter Type WCFB four-barrel.

CHASSIS FEATURES: Wheelbase: 102 inches. Overall length: 177.2 inches. Front tread: 57 inches. Rear tread: 59 inches. Tires: 5.70 x 15.

OPTIONS: Heater ($97). Power top ($140). Additional cove color ($16.15). Detachable hardtop ($215). Signal-seeking AM radio ($144). Power windows ($59.20). Special 15 x 5.5 inch wheels (no cost). Windshield washer ($16). Whitewall tires ($31.55). Courtesy lights ($6.50). Parking brake alarm ($5.40). Three-speed manual floor shift transmission was standard. Automatic transmission ($188). Four-speed manual floor shift transmission ($215). V8 283 cid 245 hp dual four-barrel carb engine ($150). V-8 283 cid 270 hp dual four-barrel carb engine ($182.95). V-8 283 cid 250 hp fuel-injection engine ($484). V-8 283 cid 290 hp fuel-injection engine ($484). Positive traction rear axle ($48.45). Heavy-duty brakes and suspension ($780.10). Available rear axle gear ratios: 3.70:1; 4.11:1; 4.56:1.

HISTORICAL FOOTNOTES: Almost 11 percent of 1958 Corvettes were powered by the 290 hp 283 cid fuel-injected V-8. A 1958 Corvette with the standard 230 hp V-8 could go from 0-60 mph in 9.2 seconds. One with the 290 hp fuel-injected engine took only 6.9 seconds and got slightly better gas mileage.

1959 CORVETTE

CORVETTE SERIES — (V-8) — SERIES J800 — The 1959 Corvette was basically a cleaned-up 1958. The fake hood louvers and vertical chrome strips on the trunk were removed. Interior changes included redesigned bucket seats and door panels, a fiberglass package tray under the sissy bar and concave gauge lenses. A tachometer, outside rearview mirror, dual exhausts and electric clock were among the standard features. Seven exterior color choices were offered: black; white; cream, silver; red; blue and Crown Sapphire. The cove could be painted either silver or white. Blue, red, turquoise and (for the first time) black interiors were available.

CORVETTE I.D. NUMBERS: The numbering system and code locations were the same as for previous models with the numbers changed as follows J59S100001 to J59S109670. Engine Number suffixes were similar to those of 1958.

1959 Corvette, two-door convertible, V-8 (AA)

CORVETTE

Series Number	Body/Style Number	Body Type & Seating	Factory Price	Shipping Weight	Production Total
J800	867	2-dr Conv-2P	3875	2900	9,670

BASE ENGINE: V-8. Overhead valves. Cast iron block. Displacement: 283 cid. Bore and stroke: 3.87 x 3 inches. Compression ratio: 9.50:1. Brake hp: 230 at 4800 rpm. Five main bearings. Hydraulic valve lifters. Carburetor: Carter Type WCFB four-barrel Model 2816.

CHASSIS FEATURES: Wheelbase: 102 inches. Overall length: 177.2 inches. Front tread: 57 inches. Rear tread: 59 inches. Tires: 6.70 x 15.

OPTIONS: Power top ($139.90). Windshield washer ($16.15). Signal-seeking transistor radio ($149.80). Deluxe heater ($102.25). Two-tone paint ($16.15). Electric windows ($59.20). Courtesy light ($6.50). Parking brake alarm ($5.40). Sunshades ($10.80). Special 15 x 5.5 inch wheels (no cost). Detachable hardtop ($236.75). Three-speed manual floor shift transmission was standard. Automatic transmission ($199). Four-speed manual floor shift transmission ($188). V8 283 cid 245 hp dual four-barrel carb engine ($150.65). V-8 283 cid 270 hp dual four-barrel carb engine ($182.95). V-8 283 cid 250 hp fuel-injection engine ($484). V-8 283 cid 290 hp fuel-injection engine ($484). Metal brakes ($26.90). Positive traction rear axle ($48.45). Heavy-duty brakes and suspension ($425.05).

HISTORICAL FOOTNOTES: A 290 hp fuel-injected 1959 Corvette could go from 0-60 mph in 6.6 seconds; from 0-100 mph in 15.5 seconds. It had a top speed of 128 mph.

1960 CORVETTE

CORVETTE SERIES — (V-8) — SERIES 0800 — The 1960 Corvette looked much the same as last year's model. A new rear suspension sway-bar improved the car's handling. Aluminum heads and radiator were introduced, but later withdrawn. Standard equipment included: tachometer; sun visors; dual exhaust; carpeting; outside rearview mirror and electric clock. Buyers could choose from eight exterior finishes: black: white; turquoise; blue; silver; green; red; and maroon. The cove was available in silver or white. Three colors of convertible tops: black, white and blue, were offered.

CORVETTE I.D. NUMBERS: The numbering system and code locations were the same as for previous models with the numbers changed as follows: 00867S100001 to 00867S110261. The first symbol designated year. The second, third, fourth and fifth symbols designated Model Number ('0800') and Body Style, '67' = convertible; '63' = coupe. The sixth symbol designated manufacturing plant, 'S' St. Louis. The last six digits were the sequential production numbers.

1960 Corvette, two-door convertible, V-8 (AA)

CORVETTE

Series Number	Body/Style Number	Body Type & Seating	Factory Price	Shipping Weight	Production Total
0800	67	2-dr Conv-2p	3872	2840	10,261

BASE ENGINE: V-8. Overhead valves. Cast iron block. Displacement: 283 cid. Bore and stroke: 3.87 x 3 inches. Compression ratio: 9.25:1. Brake hp: 230 at 4800 rpm. Five main bearings. Hydraulic valve lifters. Carburetor: Carter Type WCFB four-barrel Model 3779178.

CHASSIS FEATURES: Wheelbase: 102 inches. Overall length: 177.2 inches. Front tread: 57 inches. Rear tread: 59 inches. Tires: 6.70 x 15.

OPTIONS: Power top ($139.90). Windshield washer ($16.15). Signal-seeking transistor radio ($137.75). Deluxe heater ($102.25). Detachable hardtop ($236.75). Two-tone paint ($16.15). Electric windows ($59.20). Whitewall tires ($31.55). Courtesy lights ($6.60). Parking brake alarm ($5.40). Sunshades ($10.80). Permanent anti-freeze ($5.00). Special 15 x 5.5 inch wheels (no cost). Three-speed manual floor shift transmission was standard. Automatic transmission ($199.10). Four-speed manual floor shift transmission ($188). V8 283 cid 245 hp dual four-barrel carb engine ($150.65). V-8 283 cid 270 hp dual four-barrel carb. engine ($182.95). V-8 283 cid 275 hp fuel-injection engine ($484). V-8 283 cid 315 hp fuel-injection engine ($484). Metallic brakes ($26.90). Positive traction rear axle ($43.05). Heavy-duty brakes and suspension ($333.60). Available rear axle gear ratios 3.70:1, 4.11:1, 4.56:1.

HISTORICAL FOOTNOTES: The majority of 1960 Corvettes, 50.1 percent, were sold with a detachable hardtop. Most 51.9 percent, also had a four-speed manual transmission.

1961 CORVETTE

CORVETTE SERIES — (V-8) — SERIES 0800 — A refined, thin vertical and horizontal bar grille and 'duck tail' rear end treatment with four cylindrical taillights quickly set the new 1961 Corvette apart from its predecessor. The exhaust now exited under the car, rather than through bumper ports. Standard equipment included: tachometer; seat belts; sun visors; dual exhaust; carpeting; electric clock; and an outside rearview mirror. Seven exterior colors were available: black; white; red; maroon; beige; blue and silver.

CORVETTE I.D. NUMBERS: The numbering system and code locations were the same as for previous models with the numbers changed as follows: 10867S100001 to 10867S110939.

CORVETTE

Series Number	Body/Style Number	Body Type & Seating	Factory Price	Shipping Weight	Production Total
0800	67	2-dr Conv-2P	3934	2905	10,939

1961 Corvette, two-door convertible, V-8 (AA)

BASE ENGINE: V-8. Overhead valves. Cast iron block. Displacement: 283 cid. Bore and stroke: 3.87 x 3 inches. Compression ratio: 9.5:1. Brake hp: 230 at 4800 rpm. Five main bearings. Hydraulic valve lifters. Carburetor: Carter Type WCFB four-barrel Model 3779178.

CHASSIS FEATURES: Wheelbase: 102 inches. Overall length: 177.2 inches. Front tread: 57 inches. Rear tread: 59 inches. Tires: 6.70 x 15.

OPTIONS: Power top ($161.40). Windshield washer ($16.15). Signal-seeking transistor radio ($137.75). Deluxe heater ($102.25). Detachable hardtop ($236.75). Two-tone paint ($16.15). Electric windows ($59.20). Whitewall tires ($31.55). Blackwall nylon tires ($5.40). Crankcase ventilating system $5.40. Oversize 24 gallon fuel tank ($161.40). Permanent anti-freeze ($5.00). Special 15 x 5.5 inch wheels (no cost). Three-speed manual floor shift transmission was standard. Automatic transmission ($199). Four-speed manual floor shift transmission ($188). V-8 283 cid 245 hp dual four-barrel carb engine ($150.65). V-8 283 cid 270 hp dual four-barrel carb. engine ($182.95). V-8 283 cid 275 hp fuel-injection engine ($484). V-8 283 cid 315 hp fuel-injection engine ($484). Metallic brakes ($37.70). Positive traction rear axle ($43.05). Heavy-duty brakes and suspension ($333.60).

HISTORICAL FOOTNOTES: Most 1961 Corvettes, 51.98 percent, came with a detachable hardtop and 64.1 percent had a four-speed manual transmission. This was the last year wide whitewall tires were available.

1962 CORVETTE

1962 Corvette, two-door convertible, V-8 (AA)

CORVETTE SERIES — (V-8) — SERIES 0800 — The most noticeable changes for 1962 were the removal of the side cove chrome, a blacked-out grille and ribbed chrome rocker panel molding. For the first time since 1955, Corvettes were offered in solid colors only. Standard features included: electric clock; dual exhaust; tachometer; heater and defroster; seat belts; outside rearview mirror; and windshield washer. The wheels were available in black, beige, red, silver or maroon. The last time buyers had a choice of wheel colors was in 1957. In following years, wheels would be offered in only a single color.

CORVETTE I.D. NUMBERS: The numbering system and code locations were the same as for previous models with the numbers changed as follows: 20867S100001 to 20867S114531.

CORVETTE

Series Number	Body/Style Number	Body Type & Seating	Factory Price	Shipping Weight	Production Total
0800	67	2-dr Conv-2P	4038	2905	14,531

BASE ENGINE: V-8. Overhead valves. Cast iron block. Displacement: 327 cid. Bore and stroke: 4 x 3.25 inches. Compression ratio: 10.5:1. Brake hp: 250 at 4400 rpm. Five main bearings. Hydraulic valve lifters. Carburetor: Carter Type WCFB four-barrel Model 3788246.

CHASSIS FEATURES: Wheelbase: 102 inches. Overall length: 177.2 inches. Front tread: 57 inches. Rear tread: 59 inches. Tires: 6.70 x15.

OPTIONS: Power top ($161.40). Detachable hardtop ($236.75). Signal-seeking transistor radio ($137.75). 24 gallon fuel tank ($118.40). Electric windows ($59.20). Whitewall tires ($31.55). Black wall nylon tires ($15.70). Crankcase ventilation system ($5.40). Heavy-duty brakes with metallic facings ($37.70). Permanent anti-freeze ($5.00). Special 15 x 5.5 inch wheels (no cost). Three-speed manual floor shift transmission was standard. Automatic transmission ($199). Four-speed manual floor shift transmission ($188). V8 326 cid 300 hp dual four-barrel carb engine ($53.80). V-8 327 cid 340 hp dual four-barrel carb engine ($107.60.

V-8 327 cid 360 hp fuel-injection engine ($484). Direct flow exhaust system (no cost). Metallic brakes ($37.70). Positive traction rear axle ($43.05). Heavy-duty brakes and suspension ($333.60).

HISTORICAL FOOTNOTES: A 360 hp fuel-injected 1962 Corvette could go from 0-60 mph in 5.9 seconds; from 0-100 mph in 14 seconds.

1963 CORVETTE

1963 Corvette, two-door Sting Ray coupe, V-8 (AA)

STING RAY SERIES — (V-8) — SERIES 0800 — The Corvette received major restyling in 1963. Although the rear deck treatment resembled that of the previous year's model, the rest of the car appeared totally new. The headlights were hidden in an electrically operated panel. This was more than a styling gimmick, as it added to the car's basic aerodynamic design. The recessed fake hood louvers were another matter. Front fenders louvers, vents on the roof side panels (of the fastback sport coupe) and ribbed rocker panel molding were styling features used on the sides of the new Corvette. The interior had circular gauges with black faces. There was storage space under the seats of early models. Among the standard equipment was; windshield washer; carpeting; outside rearview mirror; dual exhaust; tachometer; electric clock; heater and defroster; cigarette lighter; and safety belts. Seven exterior colors were offered: black; white; silver; silver-blue; Daytona blue; red; and tan. For the first time since 1957, a beige softtop was available.

CORVETTE I.D. NUMBERS: The numbering system and code locations were the same as for previous models with the numbers changed as follows: 30867S100001 to 30867S121513, or 30837S100001 to 30837S121513.

STING RAY

Series Number	Body/Style Number	Body Type & Seating	Factory Price	Shipping Weight	Production Total
0800	37	2-dr FsBk Cpe-2P	4257	2859	10,594
0800	67	2-dr Conv-2P	4037	2881	10,919

BASE ENGINE: V-8. Overhead valves. Cast iron block. Displacement: 327 cid. Bore and stroke: 4 x 3.25 inches. Compression ratio: 10:50:1. Brake hp: 250 at 4400 rpm. Five main bearings. Hydraulic valve lifters. Carburetor: Carter Type WCFB four-barrel Model 3501S.

CHASSIS FEATURES: Wheelbase: 98 inches. Overall length: 175.2 inches. Front tread: 56.8 inches. Rear tread: 57.6 inches. Tires: 6.70 x 15.

CONVENIENCE OPTIONS: Power brakes ($43.05). Power steering ($73.35). Air conditioning ($421.80). Detachable hardtop ($236.75). Signal-seeking transistor radio ($137.75). Electric windows ($59.20). Whitewall tires ($31.55). Blackwall nylon tires ($15.70). Heavy-duty brakes with metallic facings ($37.70). Sebring Silver paint ($80.70). Woodgrain plastic steering wheel ($16.15). Aluminum knock-off wheels ($322.80). AM-FM radio ($174). Tinted windshield ($10.80). Tinted glass ($16.15). Leather seat trim ($80.70). Three-speed manual floor-shift transmission was standard. Automatic transmission ($199.10). Four-speed manual floor shift transmission ($188). 'L75' V-8 327 cid 300 hp four-barrel engine ($53.80). 'L76' V-8 327 cid 340 hp four-barrel engine ($107.60). 'L84 'V-8 327 cid 360 hp fuel-injection engine ($430.40). Sintered metallic brakes ($37.70). Off-road exhaust system ($37.70). RPO Z06 Special performance package (coupe): metallic power brakes; heavy-duty shocks; stabilizers; knock-off type aluminum wheels; positraction rear axle; four-speed manual gear box; 360 hp fuel-injection V-8 ($1,818). Positive traction rear axle ($43.05). Available rear axle gear ratio: 4.11:1, 4.56:1, 3.08:1, 3.36:1, 3.55:1, 3.70:1.

HISTORICAL FOOTNOTES: A rare option in 1963 Corvettes is air conditioning. Only 1.3 percent were so-equipped. However, 83.5 percent came with four-speed manual transmission. An 'L84' powered Corvette could go from 0-60 mph in 5.9 seconds; from 0-100 mph in 16.5 seconds. The historic Corvette Grand Sport was constructed in 1963. A total of five were built before the program was canceled. They weighed 1,908 pounds, had 377 cid versions of the small block V-8 equipped with aluminum cylinder block and aluminum hemi-head cylinder heads with twin ignition and port fuel-injection.

1964 CORVETTE

STING RAY SERIES — (V-8) — SERIES 0800 — Styling was cleaned up a bit for 1964. The distinctive rear window divider was replaced by a solid piece of glass. The fake hood vents were eliminated and the roof vents were restyled. A three-speed fan was available in the coupe to aid in ventilation. Seven exterior colors were offered: black; white; tan; Daytona blue; silver-blue; silver; and red.

CORVETTE I.D. NUMBERS: The numbering system and code locations were the same as for previous models with the numbers changed as follows 40867S100001 to 40867S122229, or 40837S100001 to 40837S122229.

1964 Corvette, two-door Sting Ray coupe, V-8 (AA)

STING RAY

Series Number	Body/Style Number	Body Type & Seating	Factory Price	Shipping Weight	Production Total
0800	37	2-dr FsBk Cpe-2P	4252	2945	8,304
0800	67	2-dr Conv-2P	4037	2960	13,925

BASE ENGINE: V-8. Overhead valves. Cast iron block. Displacement: 327 cid. Bore and stroke: 4 x 3.25 inches. Compression ratio: 10.50:1. Brake hp: 250 at 4400 rpm. Carburetor Carter Type WCFB four-barrel Model 3846247.

CHASSIS FEATURES: Wheelbase: 98 inches. Overall length: 174.2 inches. Front tread: 56.8 inches. Rear tread: 57.6 inches. Tires: 6.70 x 15.

OPTIONS: Power brakes ($43.05). Power steering ($73.35). Air conditioning ($421.80). Leather seat trim ($80.70). Soft-ray tinted windows ($16.15). Softray tinted windshield ($10.80). Electric windows ($59.20). Detachable hardtop ($236.75). Sintered metallic power brakes ($53.80). Special 36 gallon fuel tank, coupe only ($202.30). Special cast aluminum knock-off wheels ($322.80). Blackwall nylon tires ($15.70). Whitewall rayon tires ($31.85). Back-up lights ($10.80). AM/FM radio ($176.50). Three-speed manual floor shift transmission was standard. Automatic transmission ($199.10). Four-speed manual floor shift transmission ($188). 'L75' V-8 327 cid 300 hp four-barrel carb engine ($53.80). 'L76' V-8 327 cubic 365 hp four-barrel carb engine ($107.60). 'L84' V-8 327 cid 375 hp fuel-injection engine ($538). Positive traction rear axle ($43.50). Off-road exhaust system ($37.70). Special front and rear suspension ($37.70). Transistor ignition system ($73.75). Special Sintered Metallic brakes package ($629.50). Available rear axle gear ratios: 4.11:1; 4.56:1; 3.08:1; 3.36:1; 3.55:1; 3.70:1.

HISTORICAL FOOTNOTES: Only 3.2 percent of 1964 Corvettes were sold with the standard three-speed manual transmission. Most, 85.7 percent were equipped with a four-speed manual transmission. An 'L84' powered 1964 Corvette could go from 0-60 mph in 6.3 seconds and from 0-100 mph in 14.7 seconds. It had a top speed of 138 mph.

1965 CORVETTE

1965 Corvette, two-door Sting Ray coupe, V-8 (AA)

STING RAY SERIES-(V-8)-SERIES 194 — Three functional, vertical front fender louvers; a blacked-out, horizontal bar grille and different rocker panel moldings were the main styling changes for 1965. Standard equipment included: tachometer; safety belts; heater and defroster; windshield washer; outside rearview mirror; dual exhaust; electric clock; carpeting; manually operated top (convertible); and sun visors. Eight exterior colors were available; black; white; yellow; red; blue; green; silver and maroon.

CORVETTE I.D. NUMBERS: The numbering system and code locations were the same as for previous models with the numbers changed as follows: 194675S00001 to 194675S123562 or 194375S100001 to 194375S123562. The first symbol designated make ('1' = Chevrolet). The second, third, fourth and fifth symbols designated Corvette Series and Body Style ('37' — coupe, '67' — convertible). The sixth symbol designated year. The last six digits were the sequential production numbers and started at 100,001.

STING RAY

Series Number	Body/Style Number	Body Type & Seating	Factory Price	Shipping Weight	Production Total
194	37	2-dr FsBk Cpe-2P	2947	3570	8,187
194	67	2-dr Conv-2P	3212	3645	15,377

BASE ENGINE: V-8. Overhead valves. Cast iron block. Displacement: 327 cid. Bore and stroke: 4 x 3.25 inches. Compression ratio: 10:50:1. Brake hp: 250 at 4400 rpm. Five main bearings. Hydraulic valve lifters. Carburetor. Carter Type WCFB four-barrel Model 3846247.

CHASSIS FEATURES: Wheelbase: 98 inches. Overall length: 175.2 inches. Front tread: 56.8 inches. Rear tread: 57.6 inches. Tires: 7.75 x 15.

OPTIONS: Power brakes ($43.05). Power steering ($96.85). Air conditioning ($421.80). Back-up lights and inside rearview mirror ($16.15). Heater and defroster ($100.00) Tinted glass (16.15) Tinted windshield ($10.80). Special 36-gallon fuel tank, coupe only ($202.30). Power windows ($59.20). AM/FM radio with power antenna ($203.00) Teakwood steering wheel ($48.15). Detachable hardtop ($236.75). Whitewall tires ($31.30). Goldwall tires ($51). Saddle trim leather seats ($80.70). Special 15 inch knock-off type wheels ($322,80). Telescopic steering column ($43.05). Three-speed manual transmission was standard. Automatic transmission ($199.10). Four-speed manual floor shift transmission ($188). Close-ratio four-speed manual transmission with floor shift ($237). 'L75' V-8 327 cid/300 hp dual four-barrel carb engine ($53.80). 'L79' V-8 327 cid/350 hp dual four-barrel carb engine ($107.60). "L76" V-8 327 cid/365 hp four-barrel carb engine ($129.15). "L84" V-8 327 cid/375 hp fuel-injection engine ($538). Special front and rear suspension ($37.70). Off-road exhaust system ($37.70) side-mount exhaust system ($134.50). Transistor ignition system ($75.35). Positive traction rear axle (43.05). Available rear axle gear ratios: 4.11:1, 4.56:1, 3.08:1, 3.36:1, 3.55:1, 3.70:1.

HISTORICAL FOOTNOTES: Most 1965 Corvettes (89.6 percent) were sold with a four-speed manual transmission, 8.6 percent had Powerglide automatic transmission; 69.5 percent tinted glass, 10.3 percent air conditioning and 13.7 percent power steering. An 'L78' powered 1965 Corvette could go from 0-60 mph in 5.7 seconds: from 0-100 mph in 13.4 seconds.

1966 CORVETTE

1966 Corvette, two-door Sting Ray coupe, V-8 (AA)

STING RAY SERIES-(V-8) — SERIES 194 — An eggcrate grille; ribbed rocker panel molding; chrome plated exhaust bezels; spoke style wheelcovers; vinyl covered headliner; and the elimination of roof vents helped set the 1966 Corvette apart from last year's model. Those equipped with the new 427 cid V-8 came with a power-bulge hood. The 10 lacquer exterior finishes offered included: black; white; Nassau blue; Laguna blue; Trophy blue; red; green; maroon; yellow and silver.

CORVETTE I.D. NUMBERS: The numbering system and code locations were the same as for previous models with the numbers changed as follows 194676S100001 to 194676S127720 or 194376S100001 to 194376S127720.

STING RAY

Series Number	Body/Style Number	Body Type & Seating	Factory Price	Shipping Weight	Production Total
194	37	2-dr FsBk Cpe-2P	4295	2985	9,958
194	67	2-dr Conv-2P	4084	3005	17,762

BASE ENGINE: V-8. Overhead valves. Cast iron block. Displacement: 327 cid. Bore and stroke: 4 x 3.25 inches. Compression ratio: 10.5:1. Brake hp: 300 at 5000 rpm. Five main bearings. Hydraulic valve lifters. Carburetor. Holley four-barrel Model 3884505.

CHASSIS FEATURES: Wheelbase: 98 inches. Overall length: 17.2 inches. Front tread: 56.8 inches. Rear tread: 57.6 inches. Tires: 7.75 x 15.

OPTIONS: Power brakes ($43.05). Power steering ($94.80). Air conditioning ($412.90). Leather seats ($79.00). Tinted windows ($15.80). Tinted windshield ($10.55). Electric windows ($59.20). Headrests ($42.15). Shoulder harness ($26.35). Detachable hardtop ($231.75). Special 36-gallon fuel tank ($198.05). Teakwood steering wheel ($48.45). Telescopic steering column ($42.15). Special cast aluminum knock-off wheels ($326.00). Whitewall tires ($31.30). Goldwall tires ($46.55). AM/FM radio ($199.10). Traffic-hazard lamp switch ($11.60). Three-speed manual transmission was standard. Automatic transmission ($194.85). Four-speed manual floor shift transmission ($184). Close-ratio four-speed manual transmission with floor shift ($184). Heavy-duty close-ratio four-speed manual transmission with floor shift ($237). 'L79' V-8 327 cid/350 hp four-barrel engine ($105). 'L39' V-8 427 cid/390 hp four-barrel engine ($181.20). 'L72' V-8 427 cid/425 hp four-barrel engine ($312). Positive traction rear axle ($42.15). Heavy-duty brakes ($342.30). Special front and rear suspension ($36.90). Transistor ignition system (73.75). Off-road exhaust system ($36.90). Side-mount exhaust system ($131.65). Available rear axle gear ratios: 3.08:1; 3.36:1; 3.55:1; 3.70:1; 4.11:1; 4.56:1.

HISTORICAL FOOTNOTES: Only two percent of all 1966 Corvettes had a three-speed manual transmission; 89.3 percent came with a four-speed manual gearbox; 13.2 percent had a tilting steering wheel and 20.2 percent had power steering.

1967 CORVETTE

1967 Corvette, two-door Sting Ray coupe, V-8 (AA)

STING RAY SERIES — (V-8) — SERIES 194 — Some consider the 1967 the best looking of the early Sting Rays. Its styling, although basically the same, was cleaner. Unlike the others, it had five functional front fender louvers. Minor changes were made to the interior. The most noticeable was the relocation of the parking brake from under the dash to the center console. Standard equipment included: rally wheels; odometer; clock; carpeting; wheel trim rings; tachometer; and all-vinyl foam-cushioned bucket seats in black, white, Teal blue, saddle, bright blue or green.

CORVETTE I.D. NUMBERS: The numbering system and code locations were the same as for previous models with the numbers changed as follows: 194677S100001 to 194677S122940 or 194377S100001 to 194377S122940.

STING RAY

Series Number	Body/Style Number	Body Type & Seating	Factory Price	Shipping Weight	Production Total
194	37	2-dr FsBk Cpe-2P	4353	3000	8,504
194	67	2-dr Conv-2P	4141	3020	14,436

BASE ENGINE: V-8. Overhead valves. Cast iron block. Displacement: 327 cid. Bore and stroke: 4 x 3.25 inches. Compression ratio: 10.00:1. Brake hp: 300 at 5000 rpm. Five main bearings. Hydraulic valve lifters. Carburetor: Holley four-barrel Model R3810A or R3814A.

CHASSIS FEATURES: Wheelbase: 98 inches. Overall length: 175.2 inches. Front tread: 56.8 inches. Rear tread: 57.6 inches. tires: 7.75 x 15.

OPTIONS: Power brakes ($42.15). Power steering ($94.80). Air conditioning ($412.90). Front shoulder belts ($26.35). Special 36-gallon fuel tank ($198.05). Tinted windows ($15.80). Tinted windshield ($10.55). Strato-ease driver and passenger headrests ($42.15). Heater defroster ($97.85). Power windows ($57.95). AM/FM radio with rear antenna ($172.75). Black vinyl roof cover ($52.70). Leather seats ($79). Speed warning indicator ($10.55). Telescope steering shaft ($42.15). Four-ply whitewall tires size 7.75 x 15 ($31.35). Four-ply red stripe nylon tires size 7.75 x 15 ($46.55). Detachable hardtop ($231.75). Headrests ($42.15). Cast aluminum bolt-on wheels ($263.30). Three-speed manual transmission was standard. Automatic transmission ($194.35). Heavy-duty close ratio four-speed manual floor shift transmission ($237). Wide-ratio four-speed manual transmission with floor shift ($184). Close-ratio four-speed manual transmission with floor shift ($184). 'L79' V-8 327 cid/350 hp four-barrel engine ($105). 'L36' V-8 427 cid/390 hp four-barrel engine ($200.15). 'L68' V-8 427 cid/400 hp Tri-Power engine ($305). 'L71' 427 cid/435 hp Tri-Power engine ($437). Aluminum cylinder heads for 'L71' V-8 ($368). 'L88' V-8 427 cid/430 hp V-8 (actual output around 530 hp; aluminum heads included, $947.90. (L-88 features: single Holley four-barrel; no radio; heater; no fan shroud. About 20 built). Special front and rear suspension ($36.90). Heavy-duty brakes ($342.30). Off-road exhaust system ($36.90). Transistor ignition system ($74.75). Side-mount exhaust system ($131.65). Available rear axle gear ratios: 3.08:1, 3.36:1, 3.5 5:1, 3.70:1, 4.11:1.

HISTORICAL FOOTNOTES: Eighty-eight percent of 1967 Corvettes came with four-speed manual transmission; 10.1 percent had Powerglide automatic transmission; 20.8 percent had power brakes; 16.5 percent had air-conditioning; 10.5 percent had a tilting steering wheel and 25.1 percent came with power steering. A 300 hp/327 cid V-8 powered Corvette of this vintage would go from 0-60 mph in 7.8 seconds; from 0-100 mph in 23.1 seconds.

1968 CORVETTE

CORVETTE SERIES — (V-8) — SERIES 194 — The first major restyling since 1963 occurred this year. As the sales brochure said, "Corvette '68. . . all different all over." The fastback was replaced by a tunneled-roof coupe. It featured a removable back window and a two-piece detachable roof section or T-Top. The convertible's optional hardtop had a glass rear window. The front end was more aerodynamic than those on previous Corvettes. As before, the headlights were hidden. Now they were vacuum-operated, rather than electrical. The wipers also disappeared when not in use. Except for the rocker panels, the sides were devoid of chrome. Conventional door handles were eliminated and in their place were push-buttons. The blunt rear deck contained four round taillights with the word Corvette printed in chrome in

the space between them. The wraparound, wing-like rear bumper and license plate holder treatment resembled that used on the 1967 models. Buyers had their choice of 10 exterior colors.

CORVETTE I.D. NUMBERS: The numbering system and code locations were the same as for previous models with the numbers changed as follows: 194678S100001 to 194678S128566 or 194379S100001 to 194378S128566.

1968 Corvette, two-door sports coupe, V-8 (AA)

CORVETTE

Series Number	Body/Style Number	Body Type & Seating	Factory Price	Shipping Weight	Production Total
194	37	2-dr Spt Cpe-2	4663	3055	9,936
194	67	2-dr Conv-2	4347	3070	18,630

BASE ENGINE: V-8. Overhead valves. Cast iron block. Displacement: 327 cid. Bore and stroke: 4 x 3.25 inches. Compression ratio: 10.00:1. Brake hp: 300 at 5000 rpm. Five main bearings. Hydraulic valve lifters. Carburetor: Rochester Type 4MV four-barrel Model 7028207.

CHASSIS FEATURES: Wheelbase: 98 inches. Overall length: 182.5 inches. Front tread: 58.7 inches. Rear tread: 59.4 inches. Tires: F70-15.

OPTIONS: Power brakes ($42.15). Power steering ($94.80). Air conditioning ($412.90). Custom Deluxe front shoulder belts ($26.35). Rear window defroster ($31.60). Tinted windows ($15.80). Tinted windshield ($10.55). Driver and passenger head restraints ($42.15). Heavy-duty power brakes ($384.45). Power windows ($57.95). AM/FM radio with fixed height antenna ($172.75). AM/FM stereo radio ($278.10). Black vinyl roof ($52.70). Leather seats ($79). Speed warning indicator ($10.55). Adjustable steering shaft ($42.15). Detachable hardtop ($231.75). Four wheelcovers ($57.95). Special red stripe F70-15 tires ($31.30). Special white stripe F70-15 tires ($31.30). Alarm system ($26.35). Three-speed manual transmission was standard. Automatic transmission ($226). Heavy-duty close ratio four-speed manual floor shift transmission ($263). Wide-ratio four-speed manual transmission with floor shift ($184). Close-ratio four-speed manual transmission with floor shift ($184). 'L79' V-8 327 cid/350 hp four-barrel engine ($105). 'L36' V-8 427 cid/390 hp four-barrel engine ($200.15). 'L68' V-8 427 cid/400 hp Tri-Power engine ($305). 'L71' V-8 427 cid/435 hp Tri-Power engine ($437.10). 'L71/89' V-8 427 cid/435 hp Tri-Power engine ($805.75). 'L88' V-8 427 cid/430 hp with actual output around 530 hp. [L-88 features; Aluminum heads included. Option price $947.90. Single Holley four-barrel. Production of 80 cars. Heater was standard as was a high-rise, fresh air, bubble hood.] Special front and rear suspension ($36.90). Heavy-duty brakes ($384.45). Off-road exhaust system ($36.90). Transistor ignition system ($73.75). Positive traction rear axle ($46.35). Available rear axle gear ratios: 2.73:1, 3.08:1, 3.36:1, 3.55:1, 4.11:1.

HISTORICAL FOOTNOTES: Just over 80 percent of 1968 Corvettes were equipped with four-speed manual transmission; 81 percent had tinted glass; 36.3 percent had power steering; 19.8 percent had air-conditioning and 33.7 percent had power brakes. The 'L-79' powered Corvette of this year could go from 0-60 mph in 7.7 seconds and from 0-100 mph in 20.7 seconds.

1969 CORVETTE

STINGRAY SERIES — (V-8) — SERIES 194 — After a year's absence, the Stingray name (now spelled as one word) re-appeared on the front fenders. The back-up lights were integrated into the center taillights. The ignition was now on the steering column and the door depression button used in 1968 was eliminated. (A key lock was put in its place.) Front and rear disc brakes; headlight washers; center console; wheel trim rings; carpeting; and all-vinyl upholstery were standard.

CORVETTE I.D. NUMBERS: The numbering system and code locations were the same as for previous models with the numbers changed as follows 194679S138762 or 194379S100001 to 194379S138762.

STINGRAY

Series Number	Body/Style Number	Body Type & Seating	Factory Price	Shipping Weight	Production Total
194	37	2-dr Spt Cpe-2P	4763	3091	22,129
194	67	2-dr Conv Cpe-2P	4420	3096	16,633

BASE ENGINE: V-8. Overhead valves. Cast iron block. Displacement: 350 cid. Bore and stroke: 4 x 3.48 inches. Compression ratio: 10.25:1. Brake hp: 300 at 4800 rpm. Five main bearings. Hydraulic valve lifters. Carburetor: Rochester four-barrel Model 7029203.

CHASSIS FEATURES: Wheelbase: 98 inches. Overall length: 182.5 inches. Front tread: 58.7 inches. Rear tread: 59.4 inches. Tires: F70 x 15.

OPTIONS: Power brakes ($42.15). Power steering ($105.35). Air conditioning ($428.70). Auto alarm system ($26.35). Custom Deluxe front shoulder belts ($42.15). Rear window defroster ($32.65). Tinted windows ($16.90). Front fender louver trim ($21.10). Heavy-duty power brakes ($384.45). Power windows ($63.20). AM/FM radio with fixed height antenna ($172.75). AM/FM push-button stereo radio ($278.10). Black vinyl roof cover ($57.95).

Leather seat trim ($79.00). Speed warning indicator ($11.60). Telescopic tilt steering wheel ($84.30). Special red stripe tires ($31.30). Special white stripe tires ($31.30). Detachable hardtop ($252.80). Four wheelcovers ($57.95). Three-speed manual transmission was standard. Automatic transmission ($221.80). Heavy-duty close-ratio four-speed manual floor shift transmission ($290). Wide-ratio four-speed manual transmission with floor shift ($184). Close ratio four-speed manual transmission with floor shift ($184). 'L46' V-8 350 cid/350 hp four-barrel engine ($131.65). 'L36' V-8 427 cid/390 hp four-barrel engine ($221.20). 'L68' V-8 427 cid/400 hp Tri-Power engine ($326). 'L71' V-8 427 cid/435 hp Tri-Power engine ($437.10). 'L88' engine option 427 cid, rated at 430 hp with actual output around 530 hp. Aluminum heads included. Option price $1,032.15. Single Holley four-barrel. Production of 116 cars. 'L88' 1967, '68, '69 Corvette engined models were targeted at road racers. The drivetrain was quite different from other 427 equipped Corvettes, with many heavy-duty parts and performance assembly techniques. There were no standard visual changes in the body (aside from the '68, '69 hood). A decal on the parking brake console warned of engine damage unless run on 103 octane gasoline. ZL1 427 cid ($3000). Only two were built. Special front and rear suspension ($36.90). Transistor ignition system ($81.10). Side-mount exhaust system ($147.45). Positive traction rear axle ($46.35). Available rear axle gear ratios: 2.73:1, 3.08:1, 3.36:1, 3.55:1, 3.70:1, 4.11:1, 4.56:1.

1969 Corvette, two-door Stingray coupe, V-8 (AA)

HISTORICAL FOOTNOTES: The majority of 1969 Corvettes, 59.2 percent, came with power steering, 78.4 percent had four-speed manual attachments and one-in-four had power windows. A 300 hp 350 cid V-8 was available this season. Cars with this powerplant and automatic transmission were capable of 0-60 speeds in the 8.4 second bracket and could move from 0-100 mph in approximately 21.7 seconds.

1970 CORVETTE

1970 Corvette, two-door Stingray convertible, V-8

STINGRAY SERIES — (V-8) — SERIES 194 — Refinements were made to the basic styling used since 1968. A new 'ice cube tray' design grille and side fender louvers; rectangular, amber front signal lights; fender flares and square exhaust exits were exterior changes. The bucket seats and safety belt retractor containers were also improved. Standard equipment included: front and rear disc brakes; headlight washers; wheel trim rings; carpeting; center console and all-vinyl upholstery (in either black, blue, green, saddle or red).

CORVETTE I.D. NUMBERS: The numbering system and code locations were the same as for previous models with the numbers changed as follows: 194670S100001 to 194670S117316 or 194370S100001 to 194370S117316.

STINGRAY

Series Number	Body/Style Number	Body Type & Seating	Factory Price	Shipping Weight	Production Total
194	37	2-dr Spt Cpe-2P	5469	3153	10,668
194	67	2-dr Conv-2P	5129	3167	6,648

BASE ENGINE: V-8. Overhead valves. Cast iron block. Displacement: 350 cid. Bore and stroke: 4 x 3.48 inches. Compression ratio: 10.25. Brake hp: 300 at 4800 rpm. Five main bearings. Hydraulic valve lifters. Carburetor: Rochester Type Quadra-Jet four-barrel Model 4MV.

CHASSIS FEATURES: Wheelbase: 98 inches. Overall length: 182.5 inches. Front tread: 58.7 inches. Rear tread: 59.4 inches. Tires: F70-15.

OPTIONS: Power brakes ($33.55). Power steering ($83.35). Air conditioning ($339.16). Audio alarm system ($20.85). Custom Deluxe front shoulder belts ($33.35). Rear window defroster ($25.83). Tinted windows ($13.38). Front fender louver trim ($16.70). Heavy-duty power brakes ($304.15). Power windows ($50). AM/FM radio with fixed height antenna ($136.67). AM/FM push-button stereo radio ($220.02). Black vinyl roof cover ($45.85). Genuine leather seat trim ($62.50). Speed warning indicator ($9.18). Telescopic tilt steering wheel ($66.70). Detachable hardtop ($200). Wheelcovers ($45.85). Automatic transmission (no cost). A wide-range four-speed manual floor shift transmission was standard. Close-ratio four-speed manual transmission with floor shift (no cost). Heavy-duty close ratio four-speed manual transmission with floor shift ($95). 'L56' V-8 350 cid/350 hp four-barrel engine ($158). 'LT1' V-8 350 cid/370 hp four-barrel engine ($447.60). 'LS5' V-8 454 cid/390 hp four-barrel engine ($289.65). 'LS7' V-8 454 cid/460 hp Tri-Power engine ($3,000). Side-mounted exhaust system ($116.65). Full transistor ignition system ($64.16). Special front and rear suspension ($29.20). Positive traction rear axle standard, but optional ratios cost $12. Heavy-duty clutch ($62.50). Available rear axle gear ratios: 2.73:1; 3.08:1; 3.36:1; 3.55:1; 4.11:1; 4.56:1.

HISTORICAL FOOTNOTES: Most 1970 Corvettes, 70.5 percent, came with four-speed manual transmission; 33.5 percent had tilting steering wheels; 27.9 percent power windows; 38.5 percent air-conditioning and 68.8 percent power steering. An L-70 powered 1970 Corvette would do 0-60 in seven seconds and go from 0-100 mph in 14 seconds.

1971 CORVETTE

1971 Corvette, two-door Stingray convertible with LT-1 package, V-8

STINGRAY SERIES (V-8) — SERIES 194 — If you liked the 1970 Corvette, you'd like the 1971. They were virtually the same car. A new resin process (that supposedly improved the body) and a different interior were the major changes. Under the hood, the compression ratios were dropped a bit to enable Corvette engines to run on lower octane fuel. Standard equipment included: all-vinyl upholstery; outside rearview mirror; carpeting; center console; wheel trim rings; electric clock; tachometer; heavy-duty battery; front and rear disc brakes with warning light; and tinted glass.

CORVETTE I.D. NUMBERS: The numbering system and code locations were the same as for previous models with the numbers changed as follows 194671S100001 to 194671S21801 or 194371S100001 to 194371S121801.

STINGRAY

Series Number	Body/Style Number	Body Type & Seating	Factory Price	Shipping Weight	Production Total
194	37	2-dr Spt Cpe-2P	5536	3153	14,680
194	67	2-dr Conv-2P	5299	3167	7,121

BASE ENGINE: V-8. Overhead valves. Cast iron block. Displacement: 350 cid. Bore and stroke: 4 x 3.48 inches. Compression ratio: 8.50:1. Brake hp: 270 at 4800 rpm. Five main bearings. Hydraulic valve lifters. Carburetor: Rochester Type QuadraJet four-barrel Model 4MV.

CHASSIS FEATURES: Wheelbase: 98 inches. Overall length: 182.5 inches. Front tread: 58.7 inches. Rear tread: 59.4 inches. Tires: F70 x 15.

OPTIONS: Power brakes ($47.40). Power steering ($115.90). Air conditioning ($464.50). Audio alarm system ($31.60). Heavy-duty battery ($15.80). Custom Deluxe shoulder belts ($42.15). Rear window defroster ($42.15). AM/FM push-button radio ($178). AM/FM stereo radio ($283.35). Black vinyl roof cover ($63.20). Telescopic tilt steering wheel ($84.30). White stripe tires ($30.35). White letter tires ($43.65). Custom trim ($158). Custom wheelcovers ($63.20). Power windows ($85.35). Automatic transmission (no cost with standard engine, $100 with others). Wide-range four-speed manual floor shift transmission was standard. Close-ratio four-speed manual transmission with floor shift (no cost). Heavy-duty close-ratio four-speed manual transmission with floor shift ($100). 'LT1' V-8 300 cid/350 hp four-barrel engine ($483). 'LS5' V-8 454 cid/365 hp four-barrel engine ($295). 'LS6' V-8 454 cid/425 hp four-barrel engine ($1,221). A 'ZR1' option package included heavy-duty brakes; close-ratio four-speed manual transmission; special front stabililizer bar; special springs and shock absorbers; fully-transistorized ignition system; and the 'LT-1' engine at a price of $1,010. A 'ZR2' option package included all features listed above, except that the 'LS6' power plant was substituted, at a price of $1,747. Available rear axle gear ratios: 2.73:1; 3.08:1; 3.36:1; 3.55:1; 4.11:1; 4.56:1.

HISTORICAL FOOTNOTES: Slightly over one-third of 1971 Corvettes had a tilting steering wheel; 53.9 percent had a four-speed manual; 82.1 percent had power steering; 52.7 percent had air conditioning and 28.4 percent had power windows.

1972 CORVETTE

1972 Corvette, two-door Stingray coupe, V-8

STINGRAY SERIES — (V-8) — SERIES Z — The 1972 Corvette was basically the same as the 1971. Among the standard equipment were: a positraction rear axle; outside rearview mirror; tinted glass; flo-thru ventilation system; front and rear disc brakes; electric clock; carpeting; wheel trim rings; all-vinyl upholstery; and anti-theft alarm system. Ten exterior colors were available. The convertible top could be ordered in white or black.

CORVETTE I.D. NUMBERS: The numbering system and code locations were changed as follows 1Z67K2S500001 to 1Z67K2S527004 or 1Z37K2S500001 to 1Z67K2S527004. The first symbol designated make ('1' = Chevrolet). The second symbol designated series ('Z' = Corvette). The third and fourth symbol designated Body Style ('37' = coupe; '67' = convertible) the fifth symbol designated engine ('K' = standard 350 V-8 in 1972; 'J' = standard 350 V-8 in 1973-1976; 'L' = LT-1; 'T' = L-82; 'Y' = 454 V-8). The seventh symbol designated manufacturing-assembly plant ('S' = Saint Louis). The last six digits were the sequential production numbers.

STINGRAY

Series Number	Body/Style Number	Body Type & Seating	Factory Price	Shipping Weight	Production Total
Z	37	2-dr Spt Cpe-2P	5472	3215	20,496
Z	67	2-dr Conv-2P	5246	3215	6,508

BASE ENGINE: V-8. Overhead valves. Cast iron block. Displacement: 350 cid. Bore and stroke: 4 x 3.48 inches. Compression ratio: 8.50:1. Brake hp: 200 at 4400 rpm. Five main bearings. Hydraulic valve lifters. Carburetor: Rochester Type QuadraJet four-barrel Model 4MV.

CHASSIS FEATURES: Wheelbase: 98 inches. Overall length: 182.5 inches. Front tread: 58.7 inches. Rear tread: 59.4 inches. Tires: F70 x 15.

OPTIONS: Power brakes ($47.40). Power steering ($115.90). Air conditioning ($464.50). Custom interior ($158). Electric power windows ($85.35). Custom shoulder belts ($26.35). Detachable hardtop ($273.85). Vinyl roof covering for detachable hardtop ($158). Telescopic tilt steering column ($84.30). Rear window defroster ($42). White stripe nylon tires ($30.35). White lettered nylon tires ($42.65). Heavy-duty battery ($15.80). Stereo AM-FM radio ($283). AM-FM radio ($178). Automatic transmission (no cost with standard engine, $97 with others). Wide range four-speed manual floor shift transmission was standard. Close-ratio four-speed manual transmission with floor shift (no cost). 'LT1' V-8 350 cid/255 hp engine ($483.45). 'ZR1' V-8 350 cid/255 hp engine ($1,010.05). 'LS5' 454 cid/270 hp engine ($294.90). Note: Only 30 ZR1-equipped cars were built.

HISTORICAL FOOTNOTES: Over one-third of 1972 Corvettes came with power windows; 46.1 percent had a four-speed manual; 88.1 percent had power steering; 63.8 percent had air conditioning; 48.1 percent had a tilting steering wheel and one percent were powered by the 'LT1' engine.

1973 CORVETTE

STINGRAY SERIES — CV-8) — SERIES Z — There were predictions in the automotive press that Chevrolet would introduce a mid-engine Corvette this year. However, nothing as radical as that came to be. Major changes for 1973 were a new domed hood, body-color urethane plastic front bumper and a fixed rear window (which added a little extra trunk space). Radial tires became standard and an effort was made to reduce noise. It was generally effective, but a ROAD & TRACK report found the 1973 to be louder than a 1971 in certain circumstances. Buyers who wanted a leather interior could select from black, medium saddle and dark saddle.

STINGRAY

Series Number	Body/Style Number	Body Type & Seating	Factory Price	Shipping Weight	Production Total
Z	37	2-dr Spt Cpe-2	5921	3407	25,520
Z	67	2-dr Conv-2P	5685	3407	4,943

1973 Corvette, two-door Stingray coupe, V-8

BASE ENGINE: V-8. Overhead valves. Cast iron block. Displacement: 350 cid. Bore and stroke: 4 x 3.48 inches. Compression ratio: 8.50:1. Brake hp: 190 at 4400 rpm. Five main bearings. Hydraulic valve lifters. Carburetor: Rochester. Type Quadra-Jet four-barrel Model 4MV.

CHASSIS FEATURES: Wheelbase: 98 inches. Overall length: 182.5 inches. Front tread: 58.7 inches. Rear tread: 59.4 inches. Tires: F70 x 15.

OPTIONS: Power brakes ($46). Power steering ($113). Air conditioning ($452). Custom interior ($154). Power windows ($83). Custom shoulder belts ($41). Detachable hardtop ($267). Vinyl roof covering for detachable hardtop ($62). Rear window defroster ($42). Telescopic tilt steering column ($82). Custom wheelcovers ($62). White stripe radial tires ($32) White letter radial tires ($45). Heavy-duty battery ($15). Stereo AM/FM radio ($276). AM/FM radio ($173) Cast aluminum wheels ($175). Automatic transmission (no cost). Four-speed manual floor shift transmission (was standard). Close-ratio four-speed manual transmission with floor shift (no cost). 'L82' V-8 350 cid/250 hp engine ($299). 'LS4' V-8 454 cid/275 hp engine ($250). Off-road suspension and brake package ($369).

HISTORICAL FOOTNOTES: The majority of 1973 Corvettes, 70.8 percent were sold with air conditioning; 41.2 percent had a four-speed manual transmission; 91.5 percent power steering; 79.3 percent power brakes and 46 percent power windows. A 1973 'L82' powered Corvette could go from 0-60 mph in 7.2 seconds and from 0-100 mph in 17.9 seconds.

1974 CORVETTE

1974 Corvette, two-door Stingray coupe, V-8

STINGRAY SERIES — (V-8) — SERIES Z — A re-styled sloping rear end and the elimination of the conventional rear bumper with a body-color urethane plastic bumper substitute were two noticeable changes for 1974. The power steering, seat belts and radiator were improved. The alarm system activator was relocated. Buyers once again had their choice of 10 exterior finishes: medium blue; gray; bright yellow; dark green; medium red; orange; white; dark brown; silver and Mille Miglia red.

CORVETTE I.D. NUMBERS: The numbering system and code locations were the same as for previous models with the numbers changed as follows 1Z67J4S400001 to 1Z67J4S437502 or 1Z37J4S400001 to 1Z37J4S437502.

STINGRAY

Series Number	Body/Style Number	Body Type & Seating	Factory Price	Shipping Weight	Production Total
Z	37	2-dr Spt Cpe-2P	6372	3532	32,029
Z	67	2-dr Conv-2P	6156	3532	5,472

BASE ENGINE: V-8. Overhead valves. Cast iron block. Displacement: 350 cid. Bore and stroke: 4 x 3.48 inches. Compression ratio: 9.0:1. Brake hp: 250 at 5200 rpm. Five main bearings. Hydraulic valve lifters. Carburetor: Rochester Type Quadra-Jet four-barrel Model 4MV.

CHASSIS FEATURES: Wheelbase: 98 inches. Overall length: 185.5 inches. Tires: GR70 x 15.

OPTIONS: Power brakes ($49). Power steering ($117). Air conditioning ($467). Custom interior ($154). Power windows ($83). Custom shoulder belts ($41). Detachable hardtop ($267). Vinyl covered detachable hardtop ($329). Rear window defogger ($41). Telescopic tilt steering column ($82). White stripe radial tires ($32). White letter radial tires ($45). Dual horns

($4). AM/FM stereo radio ($276). AM/FM radio ($173). Heavy-duty battery ($15). Map light ($5). Cast aluminum wheel trim ($175). Automatic transmission (no cost with standard engine, $97 with others). Four-speed manual floor shift transmission was standard. Close-ratio four-speed manual transmission with floor shift (no cost). 'L82' V-8 350 cid/250 hp engine ($299). 'LS4' V-8 454 cid/270 hp engine ($250). Off-road suspension and brake package ($400). Gymkhana suspension ($7).

HISTORICAL FOOTNOTES: Most 1974 Corvettes, 95.6 percent had power steering; 88.3 percent had power brakes; 63.1 percent had power windows; 72.9 percent had tilting steering wheel; 77.7 percent had air-conditioning and 33.7 percent had a four-speed manual transmission.

1975 CORVETTE

STINGRAY SERIES — (V-8) — SERIES Z — Most of the changes for 1975 were hidden. The bumpers were improved (but looked the same). Under the hood were a catalytic converter and a new High-Energy ignition. On the inside, the speedometer included kilometers-per-hour for the first time. This was the last year for the Corvette convertible.

CORVETTE I.D. NUMBERS: The numbering system and code locations were the same as for previous models with the numbers changed as follows 1Z67J5S400001 to 1Z67J5S438465 or 1Z37J5S400001 to 1Z37J5S438465.

CORVETTE

Series Number	Body/Style Number	Body Type & Seating	Factory Price	Shipping Weight	Production Total
Z	37	2-dr Spt Cpe-2P	7117	3532	33,836
Z	67	2-dr Conv-2P	6857	3532	4,629

BASE ENGINE: V-8. Overhead valves. Cast iron block. Displacement: 350 cid. Bore and stroke 4 x 3.48 inches. Compression ratio: 8.50. Brake hp: 165 at 3800 rpm. Five main bearings. Hydraulic valve lifters. Carburetor: Rochester Type Quadra-Jet four-barrel Model 4MV.

CHASSIS FEATURES: Wheelbase: 98 inches. Overall length: 185.5 inches. Tires: GR70 x 15.

1975 Corvette, two-door Stingray coupe, V-8

OPTIONS: Power brakes ($50). Power steering ($129). Air conditioning ($490). Custom interior ($154). Power windows ($93). Custom shoulder belts ($41). Detachable hardtop ($267). Vinyl covered detachable hardtop ($350). Rear window defroster ($46). Telescopic tilt steering column ($82). White stripe tires ($35). White letter tires ($48). Dual horns ($4). AM/FM stereo radio ($284). AM/FM radio ($178). Heavy-duty battery ($15). Map light ($5). Automatic transmission (no cost). Four-speed manual floor shift transmission was standard. Close-ratio four-speed manual transmission with floor shift (no cost). 'L82' V-8 350 cid/205 hp engine ($336). Off-road suspension and brake package ($403). Gymkhana suspension ($7).

HISTORICAL FOOTNOTES: The 454 cid Corvette engine was dropped this year, as was the convertible style. CAR AND DRIVER tested a 1975 model and covered the quarter-mile in 16.1 seconds. The magazine timed the car at 0-60 mph in 7.7 seconds and found it to have a top speed of 129 mph. Robert D. Lund became Chevrolet general manager. Zora Arkus-Duntov retired as the division's chief engineer. He was replaced by David R. McLellan.

CHRYSLER

1946-1975

Chrysler Corporation was heavily involved with war production even prior to the curtailment of automobile manufacturing in February, 1942. As the war drew to a close, both in Europe and the Pacific, plans were put into effect to resume the production of automobiles, based mainly on the designs of 1942.

By Sherwood Kahlenberg

Chrysler's start-up time for retooling, plus nationwide materials shortages, delayed the onset of the manufacturing until the end of 1945. The 1946 models were carried forward, virtually unchanged, through 1948. This was due to the unparalleled demand for vehicles in the immediate postwar period. This demand, coupled with the long lead time for complete model changeovers, prevented major styling advances until the 1949 model year.

The new Town & Country series showed one marked departure from earlier, prewar patterns. Formerly relegated only to station wagon models, the unique, wood-bodied line now adopted four-door sedan and convertible styles in place of station wagons. In addition, a small number of two-door hardtops were built off the convertible's body and one prototype two-door Brougham was built. A roadster design was contemplated, but never left the drawingboard.

The 1949 Chryslers, while all-new, did not move as far ahead, stylingwise, as the rest of the industry. As a result,

Chrysler remained 12th ranked in sales standings for the model year.

The same basic "25th Anniversary" type body was carried through 1954. The major advance, during 1949-1954, was introduction of the Firepower V-8 with hemispherical combustion chambers. The same year, 1951, the corporation pioneered popular acceptance of power steering. A minor facelift occurred in 1953, when the one-piece curved windshield was reintroduced. In midyear 1953, the fully-automatic PowerFlite transmission was introduced.

In 1955, Chrysler registered its Imperial as a separate division. Even so, the acceptance of a brand new, "100 Million Dollar Look," rendered by designer Virgil Exner, moved Chrysler Division to ninth rank on the industry's sales charts. The year 1955 also brought another important advance, introduction of the mighty Chrysler 300 Letter Car, which was immediately embraced by enthusiastic buyers. The Chrysler 300 earned championship titles in both NASCAR Grand National and AAA stock car racing.

In 1956, a turnabout took place and Chrysler sales plummeted to their lowest level in a decade. This happened in spite of slightly revised styling that brought with it a new, more tasteful finned look. The second Chrysler Letter Car, dubbed the 300B, was offered in two horsepower ratings. This helped it bring more fame to the company through repeated achievements on the nation's stock car racing tracks. The 300B broke

the world's passenger car speed record in competition at Daytona Beach, Fla., with an average of nearly 140 mph.

By 1957, a new direction in styling was unleashed by Exner and his talented staff. This new "Forward Look," with its graceful tailfins, took numerous styling awards. The major chassis development, which was to remain a Chrysler forte into the 1980s (on some models), was a torsion bar front suspension. MOTOR TREND magazine awarded the 1957 Chrysler its highest honor — the "Car of the Year" title. Its superb handling qualities and engineering characteristics were the main reasons for the award.

Model year 1958 brought a minor facelifting, from the standpoint of styling. At this time, the first-generation hemispherical (Hemi) engine was in its last year. An electronic fuel injection system, designed by Bendix, was briefly made available as an option on the latest 300D Letter Car. For the following season, 1959 styling was given another period of exposure, before another new look was introduced. There was, however, a brand-new Chrysler engine introduced this year, called the 'Golden Lion' V-8. It was larger in displacement than its predecessor and used a wedge-shaped combustion chamber design.

A new era for Chrysler began in 1960, as a switch to building unitized bodies was made. These "Uni-Body" cars were styled with the customary tailfins, although they were more rakish in overall design. A major engineering feat was introduction of ram-induction manifolding. On the corporate level, Lester L. Colbert replaced William C. Newberg as president of Chrysler around midyear.

The 1961 models were again slightly facelifted. The major degree of change was reflected in frontal appearance and at the rear, with alterations to the headlights and taillamps. Sales improved sufficiently to boost Chrysler Division to 11th position on industry sales charts.

By 1962, tailfins were no longer the order of the day. A new mid-priced 300 series was offered, along with the luxurious, high-performance Letter Car series 300.

Styling in 1963 was totally revamped. A clean, slab-sided look evolved. To the dismay of management, sales dropped and Chrysler remained America's 11th largest automaker. A five-year or 50,000 mile warranty on all drivetrain components became a marketing tool to boost confidence and spur extra sales. A slight styling revision was seen for 1964 and sales climbed over 30 percent. Unfortunately, the company remained at the number 11 slot.

Freshly styled 1965 models helped set a blistering, all-time sales record. National economic gains, combined with the extended warranty program, established an excellent business climate and generated a 65 percent sales gain. But, thereafter, styling stayed basically unchanged until the 1969 model year. And why not, since Chrysler had continued to break records, reaching more and more buyers every season. For the 1966 to 1968 period, the company placed ninth or 10th in sales each year.

The 1969 model year debuted with a popular, new 'fuselage look' and yet Chrysler dropped back to 11th position. A slight economic recession, in conjunction with only minor 1970 changes, caused Chrysler deliveries to nose-dive 30 percent. For the first time since the 1964 model year, the division marketed fewer than 200,000 cars.

John J. Riccardo was installed as Chrysler president in early 1970. The so-called fuselage look remained in vogue. It lasted until the announcement of 1974 models. Prior to its disappearance, a 1973 production model became the one-millionth car ever to bear the Chrysler nameplate.

A total redesign highlighted the introduction of the 1974 Chryslers. The new cars were shorter, wider and lower. Sales, however, fell-off drastically, mainly as a result of the Arab oil embargo against the United States. From that point on, all manufacturers de-emphasized styling changes, and Chrysler's designs remained somewhat static until 1975. According to reports of the day, the changing expectations caused by economic and political turmoil were soon to bring a major revamping of the Chrysler Corporation.

1946 Chrysler, New Yorker Town & Country, two-door hardtop, 8-cyl

1957 Chrysler, 300 C two-door convertible, V-8

1954 Chrysler, New Yorker two-door convertible, V-8

1974 Chrysler, New Yorker, four-door hardtop, V-8

1946 Chrysler, Royal four-door sedan, 6-cyl (AA)

ROYAL SERIES — (6-CYL) — The least expensive car of the postwar Chrysler family. Design based on the 1942 models. Refinements and advances included front fenders that flowed smoothly into newly-skinned front doors, beautifully detailed die-cast eggcrate style grille, new front and rear bumpers and different fender trim. Some year-to-year running changes occurred. The body-structure was all-steel, a longtime Chrysler hallmark. Separate chassis/frame construction was used. Body insulation included the interior structure of the body, roof, side panels, floor, cowl and trunk. Postwar developments were Safe Guard hydraulic brakes and a permanent Oilite fuel tank filter. Rust-proofing protected the interior body structure. Series identification was provided by nameplates found on the hoodsides. Standard equipment included armrests on both front doors; directional signals; entrance light; brake warning light; cigar lighter with illuminated ashtray; rubber floor covering in front compartment (except club coupe and 8-passenger sedans which are carpeted); dual outside front door locks; glovebox light and lock; pile fabric or broadcloth upholstery; luggage compartment light; assist straps and robe cords on sedans and broughams; dual two-speed electric wipers; plastic steering wheel; Automatic dome light; whitewall wheelcovers and interior door locks.

CHRYSLER I.D. NUMBERS: Serial numbers are found on the left front door hinge post. Motor numbers were located on the left side of the block below the cylinder head between first and second cylinders. Serial numbers 70,011,001 to 70,023,022 appeared on Royals and Royal motor numbers ran from C38-1001 up. Serial numbers 70,515,001 to 70,564,428 appeared on Windsors and 71,000,001 to 71,000,127 appeared on Windsor Town & Countrys. Windsor motor numbers ran from C38-1001 and up. Serial numbers 6,765,001 to 67665545 appeared on Saratogas and Saratoga motor numbers ran from C39-1001 and up. Serial numbers 7,025,001 to 7,037,248 appeared on New Yorkers. New Yorker Town & Country serial numbers ran from 7,400,001 to 7,402,036. New Yorker motor numbers ran from C39-1001 and up.

ROYAL SERIES

Model Number	Body/Style Number	Body Type & Seating	Factory Price	Shipping Weight	Production Total
(STANDARD WHEELBASE)					
C38S	n.a.	2-dr Cpe-3P	1415	3373	Note 1
C38S	n.a.	2-dr Clb Cpe-6P	1535	3443	Note 1
C38S	n.a.	2-dr Sed-6P	1510	3458	Note 1
C38S	n.a.	4-dr Sed-6P	1545	3523	Note 1
(LONG WHEELBASE)					
C38S	n.a.	4-dr Sed-8P	1925	3977	Note 1
C38S	n.a.	4-dr Limo-8P	2045	4022	Note 1

NOTE 1: 1946-1949 first-series production recorded as a single total, with no model year breakouts available. See the 1948 Chrysler section for these totals.

1946 Chrysler, Windsor two-door three-passenger coupe, 6-cyl

WINDSOR SERIES — (6-CYL) — This upgraded version of the Royal included all Royal features, plus two-tone wool broadcloth upholstery, carpeted front compartment, electric clock, rear seat folding armrest on sedans and exterior 'goose neck' mirror on convertibles only. The Windsor offered luxury on par with the New Yorker line, but was powered by the L-head six-cylinder engine. Windsors were identified by nameplates on both sides of the hood. An optional Highlander interior was available on both open and closed models. Wood-bodied

Town & Countrys were considered an integral part of the Windsor series, through serial numbers were not integrated. All Town & Country sedans, except for 100 eight-cylinder sedans built in late 1946, were powered by the six-cylinder L-head engine offered on all Windsors.

WINDSOR SERIES

Model Number	Body/Style Number	Body Type & Seating	Factory Price	Shipping Weight	Production Total
(STANDARD WHEELBASE)					
C38W	n.a.	2-dr Cpe-3P	1465	3383	Note 1
C38W	n.a.	2-dr Clb Cpe-6P	1585	3448	Note 1
C38W	n.a.	2-dr Conv-6P	1845	3693	Note 1
C38W	n.a.	2-dr Sed-6P	1575	3468	Note 1
C38W	n.a.	4-dr Sed-6P	1595	3528	Note 1
C38W	n.a.	4-dr T & C-6P	2366	3917	Note 1
(LONG WHEELBASE)					
C38W	n.a.	4-dr Sedan-8P	1975	3977	Note 1
C38W	n.a.	4-dr Sedan-8P	2095	4052	Note 1

NOTE 1: 1946-1949 first-series production recorded as a single total, with no model year breakouts available. See the 1948 Chrysler section for these totals.

SARATOGA SERIES — (8-CYL) — The Saratoga was an eight-cylinder equivalent to the six-cylinder Royal in appointments. The wheelbase was lengthened six inches, forward of the cowl, to accommodate the longer engine. Fluid Drive was standard, as well as hydraulic rear sway strut; electric clock; rear fold down armrests in sedan and two-door sedan (Brougham); wax-impregnated springs and gray pile fabric or broadcloth upholstery. Four choices of optional color leather upholstery were available at extra cost. Only the Club Coupe was offered with a carpeted front compartment. Only the three-passenger coupe used a rubber rear mat instead of carpeting. Saratoga nameplates were located on hoodsides.

SARATOGA SERIES

Model Number	Body/Style Number	Body Type & Seating	Factory Price	Shipping Weight	Production Total
C39K	n.a.	2-dr Cpe-3P	1735	3785	Note 1
C39K	n.a.	2-dr Clb Cpe-6P	1830	3892	Note 1
C39K	n.a.	2-dr Sed-6P	1838	3875	Note 1
C39K	n.a.	4-dr Sed-6P	1845	3972	Note 1

NOTE 1: 1946-1949 first-series production recorded as a single total, with no model year breakouts available. See the 1948 Chrysler section for these totals.

1946 Chrysler, Town & Country two-door convertible, 8-cyl

NEW YORKER SERIES — (8-CYL) — The high-line New Yorker models included all of the standard equipment found on the Saratoga and added such features as two-tone wool broadcloth upholstery, a carpeted front compartment and, on convertibles, a 'goose neck' style mirror. New Yorker production began in January, 1946. Model identification was found on nameplates mounted on the side of the hood near the cowl. Highlander plaid upholstery was an option available on the New Yorker. The cars so equipped wore a "Highlander" nameplate. Town & Country models were mounted on the New Yorker chassis and are included in New Yorker series. All motor numbers used same C39 prefix.

NEW YORKER SERIES

Model Number	Body/Style Number	Body Type & Seating	Factory Price	Shipping Weight	Production Total
C39N	n.a.	2-dr Cpe-3P	1825	3805	Note 1
C39N	n.a.	2-dr Clb Cpe-6P	1930	3897	Note 1
C39N	n.a.	2-dr Conv-6P	2175	4132	Note 1
C39N	n.a.	2-dr Sed-6P	1920	3932	Note 1
C39N	n.a.	4-dr Sed-6P	1945	3987	Note 1
C39N	n.a.	4-dr Sed T&C-6P	2718	4344	(100)
C39N	n.a.	2-dr Conv T&C	2725	4332	Note 1

NOTE 1: 1946-1949 first-series production recorded as a single total, with no model year breakouts available. See the 1948 Chrysler section for these totals.

ROYAL/WINDSOR ENGINE: L-head six-cylinder. Cast iron block. Displacement: 250.6 cid. Bore and stroke: 3.438 x 4.5 inches. Compression ratio: 6.6:1. Brake hp: 114 at 3600 rpm. Four main bearings. Solid lifters. Carburetors: (Fluid Drive and Vacumatic) B-B EV1-EV2 or E7L4; (Standard transmission) B-B EX1, EX2, EX3.

NEW SARATOGA/NEW YORKER ENGINE: L-head eight-cylinder. Cast iron block. Displacement: 323.5 cid. Bore and stroke: 3.25 x 4.875 inches. Compression ratio: 6.7:1. Brake hp: 135 at 3400 rpm. Five main bearings. Solid lifters. Carburetor: B-B E7AI.

CHASSIS FEATURES: (ROYAL/WINDSOR) Wheelbase: (Long wheelbase models) 139112 inches; (all others) 121-1/2 inches. Three-speed manual transmission standard with Fluid Drive and hydraulically operated M-5 transmission optional. Whitewalls not available in 1946. Tires: Short wheelbase cars used 6.50 x 15 and long wheelbase cars used 7.00 x 16. (SARATOGA/NEW YORKER): Wheelbase: 127.5 inches. Fluid Drive and hydraulically operated M-5 transmission standard.

OPTIONS: Highlander upholstery. All-Weather Air control system. Twin heaters with heat, defroster and fan control. Comfort Master Heater. Right-hand unit for All-Weather Air control system (fresh air intake optional). Deluxe heater mounted on dash with fan and defroster controls. Radios: Model 602 with six tubes and automatic tuning; Model 802 with eight tubes and automatic tuning. Three types of radio antennas, including a concealed cowl mounted

unit. Central bumper guard. Electric clock (Royal). Lifeguard tubes. Six-ply tires. Top luggage rack on eight-passenger models. MoPar locking gas cap. Spare tire valve extension. Refrigeration unit. Weatherproof ignition. MoPar Auto Compass. Exhaust extension. Underhood light. Spotlamp. Windshield washer and sun visor. Fog lamps. Spotlight(s).

1947 CHRYSLER

1947 Chrysler, Royal club coupe, 6-cyl.

ROYAL SERIES — (6-CYL) — There were virtually no changes in the 1947 Chrysler models. Whitewall tires became available after April 1, 1947, which necessitated a change to rear fenders with larger wheelhouse openings. The high-beam indicator was moved from above the speedometer on the 1946 model to the speedometer dial, replacing the left turn signal arrow light. The right arrow now became a signal flashing indicator light. Red taillamp buttons replaced the white buttons used on 1946 Chryslers. Also, door locks and lock covers were changed in design from earlier models. Prices were slightly changed and a small weight increase was noted in specification charts over the earlier model. Standard equipment remained as before.

CHRYSLER I.D. NUMBERS: Serial numbers are found on the left front door hinge post. Motor numbers were located on the left side of the block below the cylinder head between first and second cylinders. Serial numbers 70,023,023 to 70,029,673 appeared on Royals and Royal motor numbers ran from C38-1001 up. Serial numbers 70,564,429 to 70,633,016 appeared on Windsors and 71,000,128 to 71,002,879 appeared on Windsor Town & Countrys. Windsor motor numbers ran from C38-1001 and up. Serial numbers 6,766,546 to 6,768,485 appeared on Saratogas and Saratoga motor numbers ran from C39-1001 and up. Serial numbers 7,037,249 to 7,062,597 appeared on New Yorkers. New Yorker Town & Country serial numbers ran from 7,402,037 to 7,405,173. New Yorker motor numbers ran from C39-1001 and up.

ROYAL SERIES

Model Number	Body/Style Number	Body Type & Seating	Factory Price	Shipping Weight	Production Total
(STANDARD WHEELBASE)					
C38S	n.a.	2-dr Cpe-3P	1431	3378	Note 1
C38S	n.a.	2-dr Clb Cpe-6P	1551	3448	Note 1
C38S	n.a.	2-dr Sed-6P	1526	3458	Note 1
C38S	n.a.	4-dr Sed-6P	1561	3573	Note 1
(LONG WHEELBASE)					
C38S	n.a.	4-dr Sed-8P	1943	3917	Note 1
C38S	n.a.	4-dr Limo-8P	2063	4022	Note 1

NOTE 1: 1946-1949 first-series production recorded as a single total, with no model year breakouts available. See the 1948 Chrysler section for these totals.

WINDSOR SERIES — (6-CYL) — This upgraded version of the Royal included all Royal updates and features plus two-tone wool broadcloth upholstery; carpeted front compartment; electric clock; rear seat folding armrest on sedans and exterior 'goose neck' mirrors on convertibles only. The Windsor offered luxury on par with the New Yorker line. The Windsors were nearly indistinguishable from their 1946 counterparts, except as noted in the Royal series updates. Town & Country sedans were now produced with six-cylinder engines only. This policy lasted until the end of production of the first series 1949 models.

1947 Chrysler, Town & Country four-door sedan, 6-cyl (AA)

WINDSOR SERIES

Model Number	Body/Style Number	Body Type & Seating	Factory Price	Shipping Weight	Production Total
(STANDARD WHEELBASE)					
C38W	n.a.	2-dr Cpe-3P	1481	3383	Note 1
C38W	n.a.	2-dr Clb Cpe-6P	1601	3448	Note 1
C38W	n.a.	2-dr Conv-6P	1861	3693	Note 1
C38W	n.a.	2-dr Sed-6P	1591	3468	Note 1
C38W	n.a.	4-dr Sed-6P	1611	3523	Note 1
C38W	n.a.	4-dr Trav-6P	1846	3610	Note 1
C38W	n.a.	4-dr T&C-6P	2366	3917	Note 1
(LONG WHEELBASE)					
C38W	n.a.	4-dr Sed-8P	1993	3977	Note 1
C38W	n.a.	4-dr Limo-8P	2113	4052	Note 1

NOTE 1: 1946-1949 first-series production recorded as a single total, with no model year breakouts available. See the 1948 Chrysler section for these totals.

1947 Chrysler Windsor eight-passenger limousine, 6-cyl., JL

SARATOGA SERIES — (8-CYL) — There were virtually no changes in the 1947 Saratoga, except as outlined in the Royal series for 1947. Prices were up slightly from 1946 models and published specification charts indicate a slight weight increase (less than one percent). As noted earlier, whitewall tires were made available after April, 1947 as an option. Standard equipment remained unchanged.

SARATOGA SERIES

Model Number	Body/Style Number	Body Type & Seating	Factory Price	Shipping Weight	Production Total
C39K	n.a.	2-dr Cpe-3P	1753	3817	Note 1
C39K	n.a.	2-dr Clb Cpe-6P	1848	3892	Note 1
C39K	n.a.	2-dr Sed-6P	1838	3907	Note 1
C39K	n.a.	4-dr Sed-6P	1863	3972	Note 1

NOTE 1: 1946-1949 first-series production recorded as a single total, with no model year breakouts available. See the 1948 Chrysler section for these totals.

NEW YORKER SERIES — (8-CYL) — There were virtually no changes in the 1947 New Yorker series, except as outlined in the 1947 Royal series. Prices were up slightly from 1946 models and published specification charts indicate a slight weight increase over the earlier model. As noted earlier, whitewall tires became an option after April, 1947. Standard equipment remained unchanged. Town & Country models were now all built on the New Yorker chassis and all were convertibles.

NEW YORKER SERIES

Model Number	Body/Style Number	Body Type & Seating	Factory Price	Shipping Weight	Production Total
C39N	n.a.	2-dr Cpe-3P	1853	3837	Note 1
C39N	n.a.	2-dr Clb Cpe-6P	1948	3897	Note 1
C39N	n.a.	2-dr Conv-6P	2193	4132	Note 1
C39N	n.a.	2-dr Sed-6P	1938	3932	Note 1
C39N	n.a.	4-dr Sed-6P	1963	3987	Note 1
C39N	n.a.	2-dr Conv T&C	2998	4332	Note 1

NOTE 1: 1946-1949 first-series production recorded as a single total, with no model year breakouts available. See the 1948 Chrysler section for these totals.

ROYAL/WINDSOR ENGINE: L-head six-cylinder. Cast iron block. Displacement: 250.6 cid. Bore and stroke: 3.438 x 4.5 inches. Compression ratio: 6.6:1. Brake hp: 114 at 3600 rpm. Four main bearings. Solid lifters. Carburetors: (Fluid Drive and Vacumatic) B-B EV1-EV2 or E7L4; (Standard transmission) B-B EX1, EX2, EX3.

NEW SARATOGA/NEW YORKER ENGINE: L-head eight-cylinder. Cast iron block. Displacement: 323.5 cid. Bore and stroke: 3.25 x 4.875 inches. Compression ratio: 6.7:1. Brake hp: 135 at 3400 rpm. Five main bearings. Solid lifters. Carburetor: B-B E7AI.

ROYAL/WINDSOR CHASSIS FEATURES: Wheelbase: (Long wheelbase models) 139112 inches; (all others) 121-112 inches. Fluid Drive and hydraulically operated M-5 transmission optional. Whitewalls available after April, 1947. During model year tire size changed from 6.50 x 15 to 7.60 x 15 on Royal and Windsor short wheelbase cars.

NEW YORKER/SARATOGA CHASSIS FEATURES: Wheelbase: 127.5 inches. Fluid drive and hydraulically operated M-5 transmission standard. Whitewall tires available after April, 1947. Tire size changed during the model year to 8.20 x 15.

OPTIONS: Highlander upholstery. All-Weather Air control system. Twin heaters with heat, defroster and fan control. Comfort Master Heater. Right-hand unit for All-Weather Air control system (fresh-air intake optional). Deluxe Heater, mounted on dash with fan and defroster control. Radios: Model 602 with six tubes and automatic tuning; Model 802 with eight tubes and automatic tuning. Three types of antennas, including a concealed cowl mounted unit. Center bumper guard. Electric clock (Royal). Lifeguard tire tubes. Six-ply tires. Top luggage rack on eight-passenger models (Traveler rack standard). Mopar locking gas cap. Refrigeration unit. Weatherproof ignition. Mopar Auto Compass. Exhaust extension. Underhood light. Spotlamp. Windshield washer. Sun visor. Fog lamps.

1948 CHRYSLER

1948 Chrysler, Town & Country two-door convertible, 8-cyl

ROYAL SERIES — (6 CYL) — Minimal physical changes marked the Royal models built in the final production run, although rather steep price increases were recorded. Some additional colors became available during the model year. The larger, low-pressure tires adopted in 1947 became standard fare in 1948. Stainless steel trim rings became more common once whitewall tires were made optional again. Cars built after Dec. 1, 1948 were officially considered as First Series 1949 models.

CHRYSLER I.D. NUMBERS: Serial numbers are found on the left front door hinge post. Motor numbers were located on the left side of the block below the cylinder head between first and second cylinders. Serial numbers 70,029,674 to 70,037,180 appeared on Royals. Effective Dec. 1, 1948, Royals with serial number 70,037,181 to 70,038,791; were considered 1949 models for purposes of registration only. Royal motor numbers ran from C38-1001 up. Windsor serial numbers ranged from 70,633,017 to 70,702,442 and 70,702,443 to 70,717,748 for first-series 1949 models of Detroit manufacture. Los Angeles built cars had numbers 67,001,001 to 67,001.920 and 67,001,921 to 67,003.000 for first-series 1949s. Windsor Town & Countrys were all built in Detroit and were numbered 71,002,880 to 71,004,055. Saratoga serial numbers ran from 6,768,486 to 6,770,180 for 1948 designated models and from 6,770,181 to 6,770,612 for first-series 1949s. Saratoga motor numbers ran from C39-1001 and up. New Yorker serial numbers ran from 7,062,598 to 7,085,469 for the 1948 series. First-series 1949 numbers ran from 7,085,470 to 7,092,068. Motor numbers began with the C39 prefix and were located as on the Saratoga series. New Yorker Town & Country serial numbers ranged from 7,405,174 to 7,408,109 for 1948 and their first-series 1949 numbers ran from 7,408,110 to 7,408,483. New Yorker motor numbers ran from C39-1001 and up.

ROYAL SERIES

Model Number	Body/Style Number	Body Type & Seating	Factory Price	Shipping Weight	Production Total
(STANDARD WHEELBASE)					
C38S	n.a.	2-dr Cpe-3P	1839	3395	1,221
C38S	n.a.	2-dr Cpe-6P	1954	3473	4,318
C38S	n.a.	2-dr Sed-6P	1928	3498	1,117
C38S	n.a.	4-dr Sed-6P	1975	3533	24,279
C38S	n.a.	Chassis	—	—	1
(LONG WHEELBASE)					
C38S	n.a.	4-dr Sed-8P	2400	3925	626
C38S	n.a.	4-dr Limo-8P	2526	4022	169

NOTE 1: Production totals above cover all 1946-1949 Chrysler C38 and C39 models.

1948 Chrysler, four-door Traveler sedan, 6-cyl

1948 Chrysler, Windsor convertible, 6-cyl.

WINDSOR SERIES — (6 CYL) — This upgraded version of the Royal had virtually no changes. There was little to distinguish 1946-1947 Chrysler Windsor models from their 1948 and first-series 1949 counterparts. Low pressure tires were now standard for short wheelbase cars.

WINDSOR SERIES

Model Number	Body/Style Number	Body Type & Seating	Factory Price	Shipping Weight	Production Total
(STANDARD WHEELBASE)					
C38W	n.a.	2-dr Cpe-3P	1906	3393	1980
C38W	n.a.	2-dr Clb Cpe-6P	2020	3463	26,482
C38W	n.a.	2-dr Conv-6P	2434	3693	11,200
C38W	n.a.	2-dr Sed-6P	2009	3508	4,034
C38W	n.a.	4-dr Sed-6P	2041	3528	161,139
C38W	n.a.	4-dr Trav-6P	2183	3610	4,182
C38W	n.a.	4-dr T&C-6P	2880	3957	3994
C38W	n.a.	Chassis	—	—	1
(LONG WHEELBASE)					
C38W	n.a.	4-dr Sed-8P	2454	3935	4390
C38W	n.a.	4-dr Sed Limo-8P	2581	4035	1496

NOTE 1: Production totals above cover all 1946-1949 Chrysler C38 and C39 models.
NOTE 2: One chassis-only was built. It was apparently used to build a prototype two-door Town & Country Brougham.

SARATOGA SERIES — (8 CYL) — There were virtually no changes in the 1948 Saratoga as compared to the 1947 model. Prices were up substantially over earlier years.

SARATOGA SERIES

Model Number	Body/Style Number	Body Type & Seating	Factory Price	Shipping Weight	Production Totals
C39K	n.a.	2-dr Cpe-3P	2190	3817	74
C39K	n.a.	2-dr Clb Cpe-6P	2290	3930	765
C39K	n.a.	2-dr Sed-6P	2279	3900	155
C39K	n.a.	4-dr Sed-6P	2316	3972	4,611

NOTE 1: Production totals above cover all 1946-1949 Chrysler C38 and C39 models.

NEW YORKER SERIES — (8 CYL) — There were virtually no differences between the 1948 New Yorker and its 1947 counterpart. The change to larger, low-pressure tires and a change in rear fender design were the only significant changes.

NEW YORKER SERIES

Model Number	Body/Style Number	Body Type & Seating	Factory Price	Shipping Weight	Production Total
C39N	n.a.	2-dr Cpe-3P	2068	3837	699
C39N	n.a.	2-dr Clb Cpe-6P	2410	4037	10,735
C39N	n.a.	2-dr Conv-6P	2840	4132	3,000
C39N	n.a.	2-dr Sed-6P	2153	3932	545
C39N	n.a.	4-dr Sed-6P	2436	3987	52,036
C39N	n.a.	Chassis	—	—	2
C39N	n.a.	2-dr T&C HT	—	—	7
C39N	n.a.	2-dr Conv-6P	3420	4332	8,368

NOTE 1: Production totals above cover all 1946-1949 Chrysler C38 and C39 models.

ROYAL/WINDSOR ENGINE: L-head six-cylinder. Cast iron block. Displacement: 250.6 cid. Bore and stroke: 3.438 x 4.5 inches. Compression ratio: 6.6:1. Brake hp: 114 at 3600 rpm. Four main bearings. Solid lifters. Carburetors: (Fluid Drive and Vacumatic) B-B EV1-EV2 or E7L4; (Standard transmission) B-B EX1, EX2, EX3.

NEW SARATOGA/NEW YORKER ENGINE: L-head eight-cylinder. Cast iron block. Displacement: 323.5 cid. Bore and stroke: 3.25 x 4.875 inches. Compression ratio: 6.7:1. Brake hp: 135 at 3400 rpm. Five main bearings. Solid lifters. Carburetor: B-B E7AI. Stromberg AAUS-2 also used.

ROYAL/WINDSOR CHASSIS FEATURES: Wheelbase: (Long wheelbase models) 1391/2 inches; (all others) 121 1/2 inches. Short wheelbase cars used 7.60 x 15 tires. Fluid Drive and M-5 hydraulically operated transmission optional.

SARATOGA/NEW YORKER CHASSIS FEATURES: Wheelbase: 127.5 inches. Fluid Drive and hydraulically operated M-5 transmission standard. Tire size: 8.20 x 15. Separate body and frame. Box type frame with coil springs front and leaf springs at rear. Sway eliminator standard on all models.

OPTIONS: Highlander upholstery. All-Weather Air control system. Twin heaters with heat, defroster and fan control. Comfort Master Heater. Right-hand unit for All-Weather Air control system (fresh air intake optional). Deluxe heater, mounted on dash with fan and defroster controls. Radios: Model 620 with six tubes and automatic tuning; Model 802 with eight tubes and automatic tuning. Three types of antennas, including a concealed cowl mounted unit. Center bumper guard. Electric clock (Royal). Lifeguard tire tubes. Six-ply tires. Top luggage rack on eight-passenger models. Mopar locking gas cap. Spare tire valve extension. Refrigeration unit. Weatherproof ignition. Mopar Auto Compass. Exhaust extension. Underhood light. Spotlamp. Windshield washer. Sun visor. Fog lamps.

1949 CHRYSLER

1949 Chrysler, Royal four-door station wagon, 6-cyl

ROYAL SERIES — (6 CYL) — The first postwar all-new styling change welcomed Chrysler's 25th Anniversary model to the motoring public. The well-known eggcrate grille was simplified. Chair-high seats were a strong selling point and bodies appeared taller and boxier than previous models. Front and rear overhangs were shortened. Coupled with the bustle back rear styling, this gave the car a stubby look similar to the same year DeSoto, which shared the same body. A station wagon, the first for Chrysler since 1942, appeared in this series. It was given a look reminiscent of the wood-bodied Town & Country. The spare tire was mounted on the tailgate this year only. Wheelbase was stretched four inches, with all the increase due to moving the rear axle housing further aft. Price increases continued into the 1949 model year as a result of labor settlements of 1948.

CHRYSLER I.D. NUMBERS: Serial numbers were located on the left front door hinge post. Cars built in Detroit used number 70,041,001 to 70,572,284. Cars built in Los Angeles used number 65,002,001 to 65,003,000. Motor numbers were in the same position as on earlier models and began with C45-1001 and ended with C45-93419. Windsor serial numbers were 70,725,001 to 70,793,638 on Detroit built cars. Los Angeles numbers were 67,005,001 to 67,010,795. Windsor motor numbers were C45-1001 to C45-93419. Saratoga serial numbers ranged from 6,772,001 to 6,774,475. Saratoga motor numbers ran from C46-1001 to C46-28838. No code numbers were provided for positive identification of body/style type. New Yorker serial numbers ranged from 7,094,001 to 7,118,581. Town & Country models used serial numbers beginning with 7,410,001 and ending with 7,411,001. New Yorker/Town & Country motor numbers ran from C46-1001 to C46-28838.

ROYAL SERIES

Model Number	Body/Style Number	Body Type & Seating	Factory Price	Shipping Weight	Production Total
(STANDARD WHEELBASE)					
C45S	n.a.	2-dr Clb Cpe-6P	2002	3531	4,849
C45S	n.a.	4-dr Sed-6P	2021	3571	13,192
C45S	n.a.	4-dr Sta Wag-9P	2968	4060	850
(LONG WHEELBASE)					
C45S	n.a.	4-dr Sed-8P	2843	4200	185

1949 Chrysler, Windsor two-door convertible, 6-cyl

WINDSOR SERIES — (6 CYL) — This upgraded version of the Royal included Fluid Drive and Presto-matic transmission as standard fare. All 1949 dashboards were padded for safety. Key starting was now available across the board on all Chryslers. Windsor nomenclature was found on the rear part of the front fender, above the trim strip. Highlander plaid upholstery was an option. The gas filler was now located on the left rear fender. Production began late, due to a strike affecting tooling in 1948. Front and rear exterior door locks were standard on all eight-passenger sedans. Three-passenger coupes were dropped at end of the 1948 run.

WINDSOR SERIES

Model Number	Body/Style Number	Body Type & Seating	Factory Price	Shipping Weight	Production Total
(STANDARD WHEELBASE)					
C45W	n.a.	2-dr Clb Cpe-6P	2186	3631	1 7,732
C45W	n.a.	4-dr Sed-6P	2206	3681	55,879
C45W	n.a.	2-dr Conv-6P	2598	3845	3,234
LONG WHEELBASE					
C45W	n.a.	4-dr Sed-8P	3037	4290	373
C45W	n.a.	4-dr Sed Limo-8P	3164	4430	73

1949 Chrysler Windsor four-door sedan, 6-cyl.

SARATOGA — (8 CYL) — This low-line eight was available in only two body styles, Club Coupe and four-door Sedan. Fluid Drive and Presto-matic transmission standard. The Saratoga nameplate was located on the rear portion of the front fender, just above the horizontal trim molding. The chassis was lengthened four inches in the same manner as the six-cylinder cars of 1949. A padded dash was featured, with all gauges arranged in a round housing located directly in front of the driver. The dash chrome trim below the padding had a horizontal "combed" look. The radio was offset to the left of center for driver convenience. The heater controls were placed directly below the radio.

SARATOGA SERIES

Model Number	Body/Style Number	Body Type & Seating	Factory Price	Shipping Weight	Production Total
C46K	n.a.	2-dr Clb Cpe-6P	2448	4115	465
C46K	n.a.	4-dr Sed-6P	2473	4187	1,810

1949 Chrysler, New Yorker two-door club coupe, 8-cyl

NEW YORKER SERIES — (8 CYL) — This high-line version of the Saratoga had the same mechanical features, while interior appointments surpassed those offered in the low-line eights. The Town & Country was offered as a convertible only this year, although one prototype Town & Country hardtop was built and listed as available in some sales literature. The Town & Country was a part of the New Yorker series and was offered in eight-cylinder form only. Ash woodwork was used over an all-steel body. Dinoc inserts replaced the real mahogany panels used on early Town & Country models. Late production cars deleted the Dinoc and used body color painted panels. A weight increase on the T&C was more related to the across-the-board increases on all 1949s rather than to the heaviness of wood itself, as on the previous T&Cs. The advertising theme was, "Bigger on the inside, smaller on the outside." An interesting styling note is the wraparound rear bumper, which fit into a recess in the rear fender.

NEW YORKER SERIES

Model Number	Body/Style Number	Body Type & Seating	Factory Price	Shipping Weight	Production Total
C46N	n.a.	2-dr Clb Cpe-6P	2558	4115	4,524
C46N	n.a.	4-dr Sed-6P	2583	4187	18,779
C46N	n.a.	2-dr Conv-6P	3039	4277	1,137
C46N	n.a.	2-dr T&C Conv	3765	4610	993
C46N	n.a.	Chassis	—	—	1

ROYAL/WINDSOR ENGINE: L-head six cylinder. Cast iron block. Displacement: 250.6 cid. Bore and stroke: 3,438 x 4.5 inches. Compression ratio: 7.0:1. Brake hp: 116 at 3600 rpm. Four main bearings. Solid lifters. Carburetors: (Standard shift) Ball and Ball Model B-B EX1R or B-B EX2R; (Fluid Drive and M-6 transmission) Ball and Ball model B-B E7LI-L2.

SARATOGA/NEW YORKER ENGINE: L-head eight cylinder. Cast iron block. Displacement: 323.5 cid. Bore and Stroke: 3.25 x 4.875 inches. Compression ratio: 7.25:1. Brake hp: 135 at 3200 rpm. Torque: 270 foot-pounds at 1600 rpm.

CHASSIS FEATURES: [Royal and Windsor] Wheelbase: (Long wheelbase models) 139.5 inches; (All others) 125.5 inches. Tires: 7.60 x 15 and 8.20 x 15 for long wheelbase models and station wagon. Three-speed manual standard on Royals. Fluid Drive and M-6 optional on

Royals and standard on Windsors. [Saratoga and New Yorker] Wheelbase: 131.5 inches. Tire size: 8.20 x 15 for all eight-cylinder models. Presto-matic semi-automatic transmission standard on all eight-cylinder models. Chrysler Safe-Guard hydraulic brakes.

OPTIONS: White sidewall tires. Wing vent wind deflectors. Middle rear bumper guard. Exhaust deflector. Fog lights. Grille guard (dealer installed). Highlander plaid upholstery. Radio. Heater. Locking gas cap. Weatherproof ignition. Mopar auto compass. Underhood light. Spot lamp. Windshield washer. Spare tire valve extension.

1950 CHRYSLER

1950 Chrysler, Royal four-door station wagon, 6-cyl

ROYAL SERIES — (6-CYL) — This was the last year for the Royal nameplate. A minor facelift of the short-lived 1949 series centered around a bolder, heavier looking eggcrate grille treatment. Blade-like front and rear bumpers appeared. License plate location changed from the deck lid to the center of the rear bumper. The "Town & Country" wagon was not a part of the Town & Country series which was built on the New Yorker chassis. This wagon carried over 1949 styling, except for offering a different configuration for the rear spare tire embossed tailgate. No longer was the embossment visible from the exterior. Also continued was ash paneled trim, bolted onto the steel body. Later, a new all-steel station wagon body was introduced as a running addition to the line. A three-piece rear window was common on all sedans and club coupes. Royal nameplates were found on the front fender, behind the wheelhouse opening and below the horizontal trim molding.

CHRYSLER I.D. NUMBERS: Serial numbers were located, as in previous models, on the left door hinge post. Motor numbers were found on the left side of the block below the cylinder head between the first and second cylinders. [Royal] Detroit built serial numbers ran 70,058,001 to 70,079,351. Los Angeles built Royals used serial number 65,004,001 to 65,063,318. Motor numbers ran from C48-1001 to C48-133,824. [Windsor] Detroit production numbers ran from 70,794,001 to 70,889,370. Los Angeles serial numbers ranged 67,011,001 to 67,024,682. Motor numbers for all six-cylinder cars started at C48-1001 and ended with C48-133,824. [Saratoga] Saratogas were built only in Detroit. Serial numbers were 6,774,501 to 6,775,800. Motor numbers on the Eights ranged upward from C49-1001 to C49-43041. [New Yorker] Serial numbers ranged from 7,119,001 to 7,159,341. Town & Country numbers ran from 7,411,501 to 7,412,201. Motor numbers were C49-1001 to C49-43041.

ROYAL SERIES

Model Number	Body/Style Number	Body Type & Seating	Factory Price	Shipping Weight	Production Total
C48S	n.a.	2-dr Clb Cpe-6P	2114	3540	5900
C48S	n.a.	4-dr Sed-6P	2154	3610	17,713
(LONG WHEELBASE)					
C48S	n.a.	4-dr Sed-8P	2855	4190	375
C48S	n.a.	4-dr T&C Sta Wag	2735	3964	599
C48S	n.a.	4-dr Sta Wag-6P	3163	4055	100

1950 Chrysler Windsor club coupe, 6-cyl.

WINDSOR SERIES — (6-CYL) — Traditionally an upgraded Royal, the Windsor line now had a different selection of body styles to offer. No wagon was available. A Traveler sedan melded sedan styling with the utility of a station wagon. The floor extended from rear deck lid to the back of the front seat when the rear seat was folded forward. The Traveler, while not popular, included a Town & Country style roof rack. Big news this year was the Newport two-door hardtop, which featured a new roofline and wraparound three-piece rear window. Taillamps

were small and rectangular and set mid-height in the back portion of the rear fenders. Separate back-up lights were inset from the taillamps, on the main body panel, beside the rear deck lid. Presto-matic transmission was standard. Windsor nameplates were located on the front fender.

WINDSOR SERIES

Model Number	Body/Style Number	Body Type & Seating	Factory Price	Shipping Weight	Production Total
(STANDARD WHEELBASE)					
C48W	n.a.	2-dr Clb Cpe-6P	2308	3670	20,050
C48W	n.a.	4-dr Sed-6P	2329	3765	78,199
C48W	n.a.	2-dr Conv-6P	2741	3905	2,201
C48W	n.a.	2-dr Newport-6P	2637	3875	9,925
C48W	n.a.	4-dr Trav-6P	2560	3830	900
(LONG WHEELBASE)					
C48W	n.a.	4-dr Sed-8P	3050	4295	763
C48W	n.a.	4-dr Limo-8P	3176	4400	174

SARATOGA SERIES — (8-CYL) — The Saratoga followed the path of the other 1950 models with a minor facelifting of 1949 lines. Styling touches used to distinguish the Saratoga from its six-cylinder brethren included the longer hood and front fenders, necessitated by the longer eight cylinder engine, and stainless steel facia, surrounding the parking lamps beside the grille. Only two body styles were offered in this low-line Eight series.

SARATOGA SERIES

Model Number	Body/Style Number	Body Type & Seating	Factory Price	Shipping Weight	Production Total
C49K	n.a.	2-dr Clb Cpe-6P	2616	4110	300
C49K	n.a.	4-dr Sed-6P	2642	4170	1,000

1950 Chrysler, Town & Country two-door hardtop coupe, 8-cyl

NEW YORKER SERIES — (8-CYL) — This became the last year for the Chrysler inline eight that began production (in 1930) on the 1931 Series CD-8. The high-line New Yorker used all-wool carpeting and offered a larger selection of interior fabrics and colors than the comparable Saratoga. The Newport two-door hardtop was another first for Chrysler, although seven hardtops had been manufactured as Town & Country semi-customs in 1946. Body shells of the Newport were shared with the convertible. The Town & Country was now produced as a Newport only and 1950 was to be the last year of wood-trimmed cars from Chrysler. Bodies were all-steel, with wood trim added as in 1949. Taillamps were unlike other 1950 series Chryslers, but were more closely akin to the 1949 Town & Country. The rear bumper no longer wrapped around the rear fender as in 1949. The back-up light was now placed on Town & Country's rear deck and the license plate frame was now mounted to the rear bumper, as on other 1950 Chryslers. Rear fender trim was also mounted in a higher position than on other 1950 Chryslers. Panels between the ash-wood structure were painted body color.

NEW YORKER SERIES

Model Number	Body/Style Number	Body Type & Seating	Factory Price	Shipping Weight	Production Total
C49N	n.a.	2-dr Clb Cpe-6P	2732	4110	3,000
C49N	n.a.	4-dr Sed-6P	2758	4190	22,633
C49N	n.a.	2-dr Conv-6P	3238	4360	899
C49N	n.a.	2-dr Newport-6P	3133	4370	2,800
C49N	n.a.	4-dr Wood Wagon	—	—	1
C49N	n.a.	Chassis	—	—	2
C49N	n.a.	2-dr T&C Newport	4003	4670	700

ROYAL/WINDSOR ENGINE: L-head six-cylinder. Cast iron block. Displacement: 250.6 cid. Bore and stroke: 3.438 x 4.5 inches. Compression ratio: 7.0:1. Brake hp: 116 at 3600 rpm. Five main bearings.

SARATOGA/NEW YORKER ENGINE: L-head eight cylinder. Cast iron block. Displacement: 323.5 cid. Bore and stroke: 3.25 x 4.875 inches. Compression ratio: 7.25:1. Five main bearings. Brake hp: 135 at 3200 rpm.

CHASSIS FEATURES: Wheelbase: (New Yorker/Saratoga) 131.5 inches; (Royal/Windsor) 125.5 inches; (Long-wheelbase models) 139.5 inches. Overall length: (New Yorker/Saratoga) 214-1/8 inches; (Station wagons) 214-1/8 inches; (long-wheelbase models) 222-1/4 inches; (standard Royal/Windsor) 208-1/2 inches. Tires: (Station wagons and long wheelbase models) 8.20 x 15; (All other models) 7.60 x 15.

CONVENIENCE OPTIONS: White sidewall tires. Wing vent wind deflectors. Exhaust deflector. Radio. Heater. Locking gas cap. Weatherproof ignition. Mopar auto compass. Windshield washer. Spare tire valve extension. A brand new option, for Eights only, was electrically operated power window lifts.

HISTORICAL FOOTNOTES: Dealer introduction for 1950 Chrysler was January 5, 1950. The Town & Country Newport hardtop was added to the line May 23, 1950.

Standard Catalog of American Cars

1951 CHRYSLER

1951 Chrysler, Windsor two-door convertible, 6-cyl

WINDOR SERIES — (6-CYL) — The Royal line was dropped from the Chrysler fold and the Windsor became the low-priced series. A major sheetmetal revision of the 1950 Chrysler line was accomplished with relative ease. The grille lost the costly eggcrate styling look. Parking lamps were now located directly below the headlamps within the top grille molding. The top grille molding also wrapped completely around the front end and ran rearward to the middle of the front door. The three-piece rear window now wrapped around the rear roof area, emulating the style and theme of the 1950 Newport hardtop. Production of this series ran for two model years (18 months). Production figures are combined as a two-year total in the same fashion as the 1946-1948 Chrysler totals. Rear styling essentially duplicated the 1950 Chrysler, with the exception of a new bumper design. Windsor nameplates were located on the front fenders, above the trim moldings. Town & Country station wagons were a part of the Windsor Series.

CHRYSLER I.D. NUMBERS: Serial numbers located on the left front door hinge post. Motor numbers were located on the left side of the block below the cylinder head, between the first and second cylinders. Only serial numbers were used for identification purposes. [Windsor] Detroit built cars used numbers 70,081,001 to 70,094,148. Los Angeles cars used numbers 65,007,001 to 65,008,808. Motor numbers ranged from C51-1001 to C51-84487. [Windsor Deluxe] Detroit-built cars were numbered 70,891,001 to 70,952,163. Los Angeles built cars were numbered 67,026,001 to 67,033,209. Motor numbers used the same prefix as on Windsors. [Saratoga] Detroit built cars had numbers 76,500,001 to 76,511,983. Los Angeles built cars had numbers 66,500,001 to 66,501,672. Motor numbers began with C51-8-1001 and up. [New Yorker] Serial numbers for the New Yorkers ranged from 7,165,001 to 7,199,806. Motor numbers used the C51-8 prefix. New Yorkers were manufactured in Detroit only.

WINDSOR SERIES

Model Number	Body/Style Number	Body Type & Seating	Factory Price	Shipping Weight	Production Total
(STANDARD WHEELBASE)					
C51	n.a.	2-dr Clb Cpe-6P	2368	3570	Note 1
C51	n.a.	4-dr Sed-6P	2390	3627	Note 1
C51	n.a.	4-dr Sta Wag	3063	3965	Note 1
C51	n.a.	4-dr Ambulance	—	—	(153)
(LONG WHEELBASE)					
C51	n.a.	4-dr Sed-8P	3197	4145	Note 1

NOTE 1: Production totals for 1951-1952 combined; see 1952 chart.

1951 Chrysler, Windsor Deluxe club coupe, 6-cyl.

WINDSOR DELUXE SERIES — (6-CYL) — This top-of-the-line six was identified externally by the use of a Windsor Deluxe nameplate on the front fender, above the wheelhouse opening. Presto-matic transmission was standard on this model. This was the final year for the 250.6 cid six-cylinder engine. The Traveler model was continued, in this series, with the same features as the 1950 Traveler. However, the luggage rack now became an optional feature.

WINDSOR DELUXE SERIES

Model Number	Body/Style Number	Body Type & Seating	Factory Price	Shipping Weight	Production Total
(STANDARD WHEELBASE)					
C51-2	n.a.	2-dr Clb Cpe-6P	2585	3700	(8,365)
C51-2	n.a.	4-dr Sed-6P	2608	3775	Note 1
C51-2	n.a.	4-dr Trav-6P	2867	3890	(850)
C51-2	n.a.	2-dr Conv-6P	3071	3845	Note 1
C51-2	n.a.	2-dr Newport-6P	2953	3855	Note 1
(LONG WHEELBASE)					
C51-2	n.a.	4-dr Sed-8P	3416	4295	(720)
C51-2	n.a.	4-dr Limo-8P	3537	4415	(152)

NOTE 1: Production totals for 1951-1952 combined; see 1952 chart.

SARATOGA SERIES — (8-CYL) — The big news for 1951 was the introduction of the new Hemi engine. Combining a Windsor series chassis with the new V-8 engine resulted in an upgraded Saratoga. Its wheelbase was a full six inches shorter than the Hemi-engined New Yorker, while weight was about 250 lbs. less than for the longer series. The Saratoga was a late addition to the line and was introduced to the public more than three months after other 1951 Chryslers. Saratoga nameplates were located on the front fenders and a new 'V' ornament graced the hood and deck lid. Presto-matic semi-automatic transmission was standard equipment. A Town & Country wagon was a part of this series and was the first of this nameplate with a V-8 engine.

1951 Chrysler, Saratoga four-door sedan, V-8

SARATOGA SERIES

Model Number	Body/Style Number	Body Type & Seating	Factory Price	Shipping Weight	Production Total
(STANDARD WHEELBASE)					
C55	n.a.	2-dr Clb Cpe-6P	2989	3948	Note 1
C55	n.a.	4-dr Sed-6P	3016	4018	Note 1
C55	n.a.	4-dr T&C Wag-6P	3681	4310	Note 1
(LONG WHEELBASE)					
C55	n.a.	4-dr Sed-8P	3912	4465	Note 1
C55	n.a.	4-dr Limo-8P	4240	—	Note 2

NOTE 1: Production totals for 1951-1952 combined; see 1952 chart.
NOTE 2: Special order.

1951 Chrysler, New Yorker two-door hardtop coupe, V-8

NEW YORKER SERIES — (8-CYL) — This top-of-the-line Chrysler was the first New Yorker to use a V-8 engine. Wheelbase was longer than the Windsor or Saratoga models by six inches. Cars with V-8 power in the Chrysler lines were identified by large 'V' ornaments on the hood and deck lid. New Yorker nameplates were placed on the front fenders. The V-8 was called the 'Firepower' engine. Power steering was an industry first and Oriflow shock absorbers were now available. Styling changes were basically limited to the area in front of the cowl. Grille changes consisted of a heavily chromed look with a chromed center piece. There was new location for the parking lights, below the headlamps, and a chrome panel separated the two grille bars on each fender. Side trim on the rear fender began above the stone shield, then dipped abruptly before continuing, horizontally, to the rear. Town & Country rear fenders matched those of the Windsor and Saratoga in design. The dash panel continued its padded design and remained similar to the 1949 type.

1951 Chrysler, New Yorker four-door. sedan, V-8

NEW YORKER SERIES

Model Number	Body/Style Number	Body Type & Seating	Factory Price	Shipping Weight	Production Total
C52	n.a.	2-dr Clb Cpe-6P	3348	4145	(3,533)
C52	n.a.	4-dr Sed-6P	3378	4260	Note 1
C52	n.a.	2-dr Conv-6P	3916	4460	Note 1
C52	n.a.	2-dr Newport-6P	3798	4330	Note 1
C52	n.a.	4-dr T&C Wag-6P	4026	4455	251)

NOTE 1: Production totals for 1951 and 1952 models were recorded as a single total, with no model year breakout available except as shown for some 1951 models.

SIX-CYLINDER ENGINES: L-head six-cylinder. Cast iron block. Displacement: 250.6 cid. Bore and stroke: 3.438 x 4.5 inches. Compression ratio: 7.0:1. Brake hp: 116 at 3600 rpm. Five main bearings. Solid lifters. Carburetor: With Fluid Drive and M-6 transmission — BB E9AI.

HEMI V-8 ENGINE: V-8. Overhead valve. Displacement: 331.1 cid. Bore and stroke: 3.81 x 3.63 inches. Brake hp: 180 at 4000 rpm. Five main bearings. Hydraulic valve lifters. Compression ratio: 7.5:1. Carburetors: Early cars used Carter WCD 830S, 830SA, 830SB or 93 1 SC. Later cars used Carter WCD 931 S, 931 SA, 931 SB or 931 SC.

CHASSIS FEATURES: Wheelbase: (New Yorker) 131.5 inches; (Windsor, Windsor Deluxe and Saratoga) 125.5 inches. Long wheelbase models used a wheelbase of 139.5 inches. Tire sizes: 7.60 x 15 for Windsor and Windsor Deluxe short wheelbase and 8.20 x 15 for long wheelbase. Saratoga used 8.00 x 15 and 8.20 x 15 for long wheelbase. New Yorkers used 8.20 x 15. Windsor and Windsor Deluxe were 202.5 inches overall. Saratogas were 207.8 inches in overall length.

CONVENIENCE OPTIONS: White sidewall tires. Electric windows lifts. Sun visor. Radio. Heater. Power steering. Fluid-Torque Drive. Exhaust deflector. Locking gas cap. Windshield washer. Fog lamps. Outside rear view mirror. Vanity mirror.

HISTORICAL FOOTNOTES: Dealer introduction of 1951 Chryslers was scheduled for Feb. 9, 1951. On a calendar year basis total 1951 production was 165,000 units, of which 78,000 were six-cylinder powered and 87,000 had the new Firepower V-8 installed. Also on a calendar year basis for 1951, Chrysler manufactured approximately 4,000 convertibles: 14,460 two-door hardtops and 1,950 station wagons. (Note: It should be pointed out that calendar and model years were nearly concurrent at this time, as opposed to the system in use today).

1952 CHRYSLER

1952 Chrysler, Windsor four-door. sedan, 6-cyl.

WINDSOR SERIES — (6-CYL) — A continuation of the 1951 Windsor series carried forward with only a minor change in taillamp design. Back-up lamps were now integrated into the taillamp itself. The engine was modified with a longer stroke giving more torque and horsepower.

CHRYSLER I.D. NUMBERS: Serial numbers located on the left front door hinge post. Motor numbers were located on the left side of the block below the cylinder head, between the first and second cylinders. Only serial numbers were used for identification purposes. [Windsor] Detroit built cars had numbers from 70.094,301 to 70.103,232. Los Angeles built cars had numbers 65,008,901 to 65,009,895. Engine numbers continued with the C52 prefix.

[Windsor Deluxe] Detroit built cars used numbers 70,952,301 to 70,936,308 and Los Angeles built cars used numbers 67,033,301 to 67,036,059.

[Saratoga] Detroit built cars used numbers 76,512,101 to 76,593,089 and Los Angeles built cars used 66,501,801 to 66,505,363. Motor number prefix was C52-8. [New Yorker] 1952 production runs began with car number 7,199,901 and ended with car number 7,217,301. Motor number prefix was C52-8.

WINDSOR SERIES

Model Number	Body/Style Number	Body Type & Seating	Factory Price	Shipping Weight	Production Total
(STANDARD WHEELBASE)					
C51-1	n.a.	2-dr Clb Cpe-6P	2475	3550	6,735
C51-1	n.a.	4-dr Sed-6P	2498	3640	16,112
C51-1	n.a.	4-dr T&C Wag-6P	3200	4015	1,967
(LONG WHEELBASE)					
C51-1	n.a.	4-dr Sed-8P	3342	4145	633

NOTE 1: Production totals are combined 1951-1952 output, with no breakouts, except as shown in 1951 Windsor section.

WINDSOR DELUXE SERIES — (6-CYL) — The use of the larger six-cylinder engine and taillamp change paralleled the low-line 1952 Windsor series. For 1952 model year the Club Coupe was dropped as well as the Traveler and eight-passenger models in this series. Interior appointments were slightly upgraded over the Windsor series.

WINDSOR DELUXE SERIES

Model Number	Body/Style Number	Body Type & Seating	Factory Price	Shipping Weight	Production Total
C51-2	Note 1	4-dr Sed-6P	2727	3775	75,513
C51-2	n.a.	2-dr Cpe-6P	3210	3990	4,200
C51-2	n.a.	2-dr Newport-6P	3087	3855	10,2000
C51-2	n.a.	2-dr Conv-6P 3230 3945 4200			

NOTE 1: Production totals are combined 1951-1952 output, with no breakouts, except as shown in 1951 Windsor Deluxe section.

SARATOGA SERIES — (8-CYL) — This series continued with virtually no changes from the 1951 model. The taillamp design with integral back-up lamp was the major styling change.

SARATOGA SERIES

Model Number	Body/Style Number	Body Type & Seating	Factory Price	Shipping Weight	Production Total
(STANDARD WHEELBASE)					
C55	n.a.	2-dr Clb Cpe-6P	3187	3948	8,501
C55	n.a.	4-dr Sed-6P	3215	4010	35,516
C55	n.a.	4-dr T&C Wag-6P	3925	4345	1,299
C55	n.a.	4-dr Ambulance	—	—	1
(LONG WHEELBASE)					
C55	n.a.	4-dr Sed-8P	4172	4570	183

NOTE 1: Production totals are combined 1951-1952 output, with no breakouts, except as shown in 1951 Saratoga section.
NOTE 2: One hardtop with New Yorker body is included in the total for club coupe.

NEW YORKER SERIES — (8-CYL) — A continuation of the 1951 model with the only styling change paralleling other 1951-1952 changes in the taillamps. The club coupe and Town & Country bodies were dropped with the onset of 1952 production.

NEW YORKER SERIES

Model Number	Body/Style Number	Body Type & Seating	Factory Price	Shipping Weight	Production Total
C52	Note 1	4-dr Sed-6P	3530	4260	40,415
C52	n.a.	2-dr Conv-6P	4033	4460	2,200
C52	n.a.	2-dr Newport-6P	3969	4325	5,800
C52	n.a.	Chassis	—	—	1

NOTE 1: Production totals are combined 1951-1952 output, with no breakouts, except as shown in 1951 New Yorker section.

SIX-CYLINDER ENGINE: L-head. Six-cylinder. Cast iron block. Displacement: 264.5 cid. Bore and stroke: 3.438 x 4.75 inches. Compression ratio: 7.0:1. Brake hp: 119 at 3600 rpm. Five main bearings. Carburetors: (with Fluid Drive and M-6 transmission) B-B E9AI Carter or Stromberg 380349.

HEMI V-8 ENGINE: V-8. Overhead valves with hemispherical combustion chamber. Displacement: 331.1 cid. Bore and stroke: 3.81 x 3.63 inches. Brake hp: 180 at 4000 rpm. Five main bearings. Hydraulic valve lifters. Compression ratio: 7.5:1. Carburetors: Carter WCD 931S, 931SA, 931SB, or 931CS.

CHASSIS FEATURES: Wheelbase: (New Yorkers) 131.5 inches; (Windsor, Windsor Deluxe and Saratoga standard wheelbase) 125.5 inches, (Long wheelbase models) 139.5 inches. Tire size: (Windsor and Windsor Deluxe) 7.60 x 15 and 8.20 long wheelbase; (Saratoga) 8.00 x 15 standard wheelbase and 8.20 x 15 for long wheelbase cars; (New Yorkers) 8.20 x 15.

CONVENIENCE OPTIONS: White sidewall tires. Electric windows lifts. Sun visor. Radio. Heater. Power steering. Fluid-Torque Drive. Exhaust deflector. Spare tire valve extension. Locking gas cap. Windshield washer. Fog lamps. Outside rear view mirror. Vanity mirror. Solex glass, (1952 only). Power brakes.

HISTORICAL FOOTNOTES: The 1952 Chrysler line was introduced, in dealer showrooms, on Dec. 14, 1951. Chrysler received OPS (Office of Price Stability) permission to raise prices on Feb. 11, 1952, as was necessary in the Korean War era. Calendar year production was registered at 120,678 units. Model year production or sales totals for 1952 Chryslers were not reported as single year figures, but only as a combined total with cars sold as 1951 models. On a calendar year basis Chrysler is estimated to have turned out 8,337 two-door hardtops; 2,793 convertibles; and 1,942 station wagons built to 1952 model specifications. (Note: Model years and calendar years were nearly concurrent at this time). On a calendar year basis, Chrysler manufactured approximately 46,491 six-cylinder 1952 models and 70,206 cars carrying the new Firepower V-8 engine. (All figures above include Imperials, which are covered in the Imperial section of this catalog). Power steering was available on sixes this year.

212

1953 CHRYSLER

1953 Chrysler, Windsor Deluxe two-door convertible, 6-cyl

WINDSOR SERIES — (6-CYL) — A major change in most sheetmetal panels carried forward the styling of 1951-1952. The major changes were in the new sloping roofline, one-piece curved windshield (the first since the CW Airflow of 1934-1937), taillamps and the grille. The Club Coupe now became more sedan-like in style and all wagons and eight-passenger cars continued to use the 1951-1952 rear fenders including trim and taillamps. The gas filler was now located below the deck lid on the left side, except on those models using the earlier style fender. PowerFlite, a fully automatic two-speed transmission, debuted near the end of the model year. Chromed wire wheels made their debut after a hiatus of 20 years. The Windsor remained the low-price Chrysler offering.

CHRYSLER I.D. NUMBERS: The serial number was found on the left door hinge post and the six-cylinder motor number was on the left side of the block below the head between the first and second cylinders. Motor numbers on the V-8 were positioned on top of the engine block between the heads and under the water outlet elbow. [Windsor] Detroit built cars had numbers 70,110,001 to 70,140,156. Los Angeles cars had numbers 65,011,001 to 6,013,020. Motor numbers ranged from C53-1001 to C53-82918. [Windsor Deluxe] Detroit built cars used serial numbers 71,005,001 to 71,050,372 and Los Angeles cars used numbers 67,040,001 to 67,043,434. Motor numbers used the C53 prefix. [New Yorker] Serial numbers for Detroit built cars were from 76,540,001 to 76,585,872. Serial numbers for Los Angeles built cars were 66,506,001 to 66,509,462. Motor numbers were from C53-8-1001 to C53-8-86292. [New Yorker Deluxe] Detroit numbers were 7,222,001 to 7,245,465. Los Angeles car numbers were 69,001,001 to 69,003,868. Motor numbers used the C53-8 prefix as on the New Yorker.

WINDSOR SERIES

Model Number	Body/Style Number	Body Type & Seating	Factory Price	Shipping Weight	Production Total
(STANDARD WHEELBASE)					
C60-1	n.a.	2-dr Clb Cpe-6P	2555	3595	11,646
C60-1	n.a.	4-dr Sed-6P	2577	3655	18,879
C60-1	n.a.	4-dr T&C Wag-6P	3279	3955	1,242
(LONG WHEELBASE)					
C60-1	n.a.	4-dr Sed-8P	3279	3955	425

WINDSOR DELUXE SERIES — (6-CYL) — An upgraded version of the Windsor featured only three body styles. Styling was identical to the Windsor series. Parking lamps were located on a separate pod below the headlamps and between the upper and lower wraparound grille bars. Chrysler added a third grille bar to the New Yorker which encompassed the parking lamps. Windsor rear fender stone shields were noted for their stylized horizontal bumps. Rear taillamps used an integrated back-up lens with the upper red lens divided vertically.

WINDSOR DELUXE SERIES

Model Number	Body/Style Number	Body Type & Seating	Factory Price	Shipping Weight	Production Total
C60-2	n.a.	4-dr Sed-6P	2806	3770	45,385
C60-2	n.a.	2-dr Conv-6P	3290	4000	1,250
C60-2	n.a.	2-dr Newport-6P	3166	3770	5,642

1953 Chrysler, New Yorker two-door hardtop coupe, V-8

NEW YORKER SERIES — (8-CYL) — The third year for the Hemi engine continued with the same configuration of 331.1 cid and 180 bhp. Even the Buick surpassed the mighty Chrysler in the horsepower department. Major styling changes paralleled the Windsor changes, although there were additional model definition, grille, and rear fender splash shield differences. The Saratoga series was dropped and replaced by the New Yorker on the Windsor wheelbase of 125.5 inches. This was the first attempt by Chrysler to down-size during the postwar period. A reduction in weight of five percent was noted in the V-8 Chryslers for 1953. A common option was two-tone paint. The 'V' insignia was affixed to the hood and rear deck lid and denoted the Hemi engine. The eight-passenger and Town & Country models used the 1951-1952 style rear fenders and trim.

NEW YORKER SERIES

Model Number	Body/Style Number	Body Type & Seating	Factory Price	Shipping Weight	Production Total
(STANDARD BASE)					
C56-1	n.a.	2-dr Clb Cpe-6P	3336	3920	7,749
C56-1	n.a.	4-dr Sed-6P	3365	4000	37,540
C56-1	n.a.	2-dr Newport-6P	3782	4015	2,252
C56-1	n.a.	4-dr T&C Wag-6P	4077	4260	1,399
(LONG WHEELBASE)					
C56-1	n.a.	4-dr Sed-8P	4363	4510	100

NEW YORKER DELUXE SERIES — (8-CYL) — Top-of-the-line Chrysler used the same wheelbase as all other Chrysler series in 1953. The Deluxe offered an additional body style, the convertible coupe and deleted the eight-passenger sedan and Town & Country station wagon. The upholstery was upgraded notably. Air conditioning and wire wheels were the big option news in 1953. PowerFlite automatic transmission became standard equipment late in the model year replacing Fluid Drive or Fluid-Torque Drive transmissions. Nameplates were located on the front fender above the wheelhouse opening.

NEW YORKER DELUXE SERIES

Model Number	Body/Style Number	Body Type & Seating	Factory Price	Shipping Weight	Production Total
C56-2	n.a.	2-dr Clb Cpe-6P	3470	3920	1,934
C56-2	n.a.	4-dr Sed-6P	3526	4020	20,585
C56-2	n.a.	2-dr Conv-6P	4025	4290	950
C56-2	n.a.	2-dr Newport-6P	3493	4020	3,715
C56-2	n.a.	Chassis	—	—	1

WINDSOR SERIES ENGINES: L-head. Six-cylinder. Cast iron block. Displacement: 264.5 cid. Bore and stroke: 3.438 x 4.75 inches. Compression ratio: 7.0:1. Five main bearings. Carburetors: (Fluid Drive and M-6 transmission) Carter Ball and Ball E9AI; (Standard transmission) B-B E9C, E9C1.

NEW YORKER ENGINE: V-8. Overhead valves with hemispherical combustion chamber. Displacement: 331.1 cid. Bore and stroke: 3.81 x 3.63 inches. Brake hp: 180 at 4000 rpm. Five main bearings. Hydraulic valve lifters. Compression ratio: 7.5:1. Carburetors: Carter WCD 935S, 935SA.

CHASSIS FEATURES: All standard wheelbase cars used a 125.5 inch wheelbase. Long wheelbase cars used the 139.5 inch wheelbase. 6-cylinder cars used 7.60 x 15 tires. New Yorker V-8s used 8.00 x 15 tires. The long wheelbase cars used 8.20 x 15 tires. Overall length for standard wheelbase cars was 211 inches.

CONVENIENCE OPTIONS: Air conditioning. Power steering. Power brakes. Power windows. Radios. Heaters. Outside rear view mirrors. Two-tone paint. Wire wheels. Continental wheel kit. Locking gas cap. Fog lamps. Fluid-Torque Drive. PowerFlite (late in model year). Windshield washer. Solex glass. Exhaust deflector. Spare tire valve extension. Sun visor.

HISTORICAL FOOTNOTES: The 1953 Chrysler line was introduced, in dealer showrooms, on Oct. 30, 1952. A new Chrysler Custom Imperial Newport was added to the line March 18, 1953. Prices on most Chrysler models were lowered on March 25, 1953 by $27-274. Model year production was counted at 162,187 cars. Calendar year production totals included 78,814 sixes and 83,373 V-8s. PowerFlite transmission was introduced in June and over 35,000 had been installed in Chryslers by the end of the model year.

1954 CHRYSLER

1954 Chrysler, Windsor two-door convertible, 6-cyl

WINDSOR DELUXE SERIES — (6-CYL) — A minor facelift of the relatively popular Windsor series of 1953 personified the single series six-cylinder offering of 1954. Gone now was the low-line Windsor series, which was combined, in 1953, with a Windsor Deluxe Series. Only one Windsor was available in 1954 (the Windsor Deluxe). The face-lifting consisted of changes to the grille, trim and taillamps. The dash, while showing a resemblance to the earlier 1949-1953 Chryslers, was restyled. The front grille trim no longer wrapped around the fenders ala previous Imperial style. The Windsor Deluxe grille center bar was abbreviated at both

ends, which helped to differentiate it from the upscale New Yorker's. The flat six-cylinder was now in its last year in a Chrysler. The Club Coupe was also in its last year as a Chrysler body style.

CHRYSLER I.D. NUMBERS: Serial numbers were found on the left front hinge post. Engine numbers were located on the block behind the water pump. Only serial numbers were meant to be used for identification purposes. Cars built in Detroit were numbered 70,141,001 to 70,181,908. Los Angeles cars were numbered from 65,014,001 to 65,015,185. Motor numbers used a C54 prefix. [New Yorker] Cars built in Detroit used numbers 76,591,001 to 76,610,490. Los Angeles cars used numbers 66,510,001 to 66,510,937. Motor numbers began with C541-8-1001. [New Yorker Deluxe] Cars built in Detroit were numbered 7,249,001 to 7,279,807. Los Angeles built cars used numbers 69,005,001 to 69,007,248. Engine numbers began with C542-8-1001 and up.

WINDSOR DELUXE SERIES

Model Number	Body/Style Number	Body Type & Seating	Factory Price	Shipping Weight	Production Total
(STANDARD WHEELBASE)					
C62	Note 1	2-dr Club Cpe-6P	2541	3565	5,659
C62	Note 1	4-dr Sed-6P	2562	3655	33,563
C62	Note 1	2-dr Conv-6P	3046	3915	500
C62	Note 1	2-dr Newport-6P	2831	3685	3,655
C62	Note 1	4-dr T&C Wag-6P	3321	3955	650
(LONG WHEELBASE)					
C62	Note 1	4-dr Sed-8P	3492	4186	500

NOTE 1: Code numbers identifying body style were not used.

1954 Chrysler, New Yorker club coupe, V-8

NEW YORKER SERIES (8-CYL) — A slight facelift of the 1953 model paralleled the changes in the Windsor Deluxe Series as far as body and trim. Only New Yorker nameplates were seen on the rear fenders and the 'V' insignia on the hood and deck lid were means of outwardly identifying this Hemi-engined model. It was the last year for the long wheelbase 139.5 inch chassis. One-piece rear windows were now used on all body styles.

NEW YORKER SERIES

Model Number	Body/Style Number	Body Type & Seating	Factory Price	Shipping Weight	Production Total
(STANDARD WHEELBASE)					
C63-1	Note 1	2-dr Clb Cpe-6P	3202	3910	2,079
C63-1	Note 1	4-dr Sed-6P	3229	3970	15,788
C63-1	Note 1	2-dr Newport-6P	3503	4005	1,312
C63-1	Note 1	4-dr T&C Wag-6P	4023	4245	1,100
(LONG WHEELBASE)					
C63-1	Note 1	4-dr Sedan-8P	4368	4450	140

NOTE 1: Code numbers identifying body style were not used.

1954 Chrysler, New Yorker Deluxe 4-dr. sedan, V-8

NEW YORKER DELUXE — (8-CYL) — This top-of-the-line Chrysler used more trim than other series in 1954. The grille center bar was bow shaped and dipped at both ends to parallel the upper grille design. The front fender stone shield was unique to the New Yorker Deluxe. The rear fender stone shield had a horizontal trim piece in the middle, matching the trim on the front fender shield. Hubcap design was unique to the New Yorker Deluxe and consisted of a very flat, spinner-like design in gold color that matched the exterior insignia. The big news this year was the beginning of the horsepower race, as Chrysler raised the ante with new heads, four-barrel carburetors and dual exhausts. The division capped the top spot in the performance race with a rating of 235 hp. The 1954 Chrysler was advertised as "Anything less . . . Yesterday's Car!" Styling, however, was essentially six years old and sales plummeted more than 40 percent on all Chryslers, although the New Yorker Deluxe outsold its 1953 counterpart by nearly 25 percent. Performance, it seems, did sell cars in 1954.

NEW YORKER DELUXE SERIES

Model Number	Body/Style Number	Body Type & Seating	Factory Price	Shipping Weight	Production Total
C63-2	Note 1	2-dr Clb Cpe-6P	3406	4005	1,816
C63-2	Note 1	4-dr Sed-6P	3433	4065	26,907
C63-2	Note 1	2-dr Conv-6P	3938	4265	724
C63-2	Note 1	2-dr Newport-6P	3707	4095	4,814
C62-2	Note 1	Chassis	—	—	17

NOTE 1: Code numbers identifying body style were not used.

1954 Chrysler New Yorker Deluxe four-door V-8.

WINDSOR DELUXE ENGINE: L-head. Six cylinder. Cast iron block. Displacement: 264.5 cid. Bore and stroke: 3.438 x 4.75 inches. Compression ratio: 7.0:1. Brake hp: 119 at 3600 rpm. Five main bearings. Carburetors: (PowerFlite transmission) Carter, Ball and Ball, Model B-B E9B 1; (Standard transmission) B-B E9C, E9C1.

NEW YORKER SERIES ENGINE: V-8. Overhead valves with hemispherical-segment combustion chambers. Displacement: 331.1 cid. Bore and stroke: 3.81 x 3.63 inches. Brake hp: 195 at 4400 rpm. Five main bearings. Hydraulic valve lifters. Compression ratio: 7.5:1. Carburetor: Carter WCD 2039S, 2039SA.

NEW YORKER DELUXE ENGINE: V-8. Overhead valves with hemispherical combustion chamber. Displacement: 331.1 cid. Bore and stroke: 3.81 x 3.63 inches. Brake hp: 235 at 4400 rpm. Five main bearings. Hydraulic valve lifters. Dual exhaust system. Compression ratio: 7.5:1. Carburetor: WCFB Carter 2041 S.

CHASSIS FEATURES: A 125.5 inch wheelbase was used with all models, except for eight-passenger sedans. Tire size: 7.60 x 15 Windsor Deluxe; 8.00 x 15 New Yorker and New Yorker Deluxe; 8.20 x 15 long wheelbase cars. Coil springs, front; leaf springs, rear. Length 215.5 inches New Yorker and New Yorker Deluxe.

OPTIONS: PowerFlite on Windsor ($175). Power steering ($130). White sidewall tires. Power brakes. Radio ($101). Heater ($79). Air Temp air conditioning ($595). Solex tinted glass ($20). Fog lights. Wire wheels ($260). Continental kit. Rear seat radio speaker. Windshield washers. Spot lamps. Outside rearview mirror. Two-tone paint. Highlander trim ($63). New Yorker leather trim ($121). Power windows ($125).

HISTORICAL FOOTNOTES: Chrysler opened its Chelsea Proving Grounds in 1954 and Chrysler test drivers teamed with Tony Bettenhausen to complete a 24-hour endurance run of 2,836 miles averaging 118.18 mph.

1955 CHRYSLER

1955 Chrysler, Windsor Deluxe four-door sedan, V-8

WINDSOR DELUXE SERIES — (8-CYL) — The "100 Million Dollar Look" designed by Virgil Exner, brought Chrysler fans an all-new car from stem to stern. The six-cylinder engine was no longer available in any Chrysler series. The new powerplant was a 301 cid V-8. A pair of two-door hardtops were offered in the Windsor series. The low-line version was named the Nassau and the high-line was named the Newport. Later in the model year another Newport was offered, with slightly modified trim borrowed from the New Yorker St. Regis. Depending upon the color ordered, the late versions were named 'Green Falcon' or 'Blue Heron.' In addition, the sedan used the same trim package as the later Newports. Windsor Deluxe grilles were identical with the upgraded New Yorker, except the Windsor used round parking lamps while the New Yorker parking lamps were a part of the upper bumper guard. Lower grille areas

behind the bumper were also different on the Windsor Deluxe. Windshields were now of the wraparound style, as were the rear windows on the hardtop and sedan. Taillamps were integrated into a housing which began at the top of the rear fender and dropped toward the bumper. Back-up lamps were affixed to the panel beneath the deck lid. A new, highly touted feature was the dash-mounted shift lever for the PowerFlite automatic transmission.

CHRYSLER I.D. NUMBERS: Serial numbers were found on the left front hinge post. Engine numbers were located on the block behind the water pump. [Windsor Deluxe] Detroit built cars were numbered W55-1001 to W55-99194. Los Angeles built cars were numbered W55L-1001 to W55L-4777. Engine numbers were WE55-1001 and up. [New Yorker Deluxe] Detroit numbers were N55-1001 to N55-49395 and Los Angeles built cars had numbers N55L1001 to N55L-3560. Motor numbers began with NE55-1001 and up. [Chrysler 300] Detroit built cars numbered 3N55-1001 to 3N55-2724. Motor numbers ranged from 3NE55-1001 and up.

WINDSOR DELUXE SERIES

Model Number	Body/Style Number	Body Type & Seating	Factory Price	Shipping Weight	Production Total
C67	Note 1	4-dr Sed-6P	2660	3915	63,896
C67	Note 1	2-dr Nassau-6P	2703	3920	18,474
C67	Note 1	2-dr Newport-6P	2818	3915	13,126
C67	Note 1	2-dr Conv-6P	3090	4075	1,395
C67	Note 1	4-dr T&C Wag-6P	3331	4295	1,983

1955 Chrysler, Windsor Deluxe four-door station wagon, V-8

NOTE 1: Code numbers to provide positive identification of body type were not provided.
NOTE 2: Production totals for special hardtops and sedans are included in totals for standard offerings.

1955 Chrysler, Windsor four-door sedan, V-8

NEW YORKER DELUXE SERIES — (8-CYL) — This top-drawer Chrysler continued the use of the 331.1 cid Hemi engine, although horsepower increased. The two-door hardtop came as a standard Newport and an upgraded St. Regis, the latter noted for its unique two-tone styling. Later, a summer sales special used the St. Regis curved upper bodyside trim on the standard New Yorker Deluxe Newport, providing a rather unusual two-toning effect. The "Forward Look" made a successful debut with new styling and engineering changes. Minor lower grille and bumper alterations were seen in the front and a different rear bumper treatment set the New Yorker apart from its Windsor brethren. Insignia was placed at the rear of the bodyside color sweep on standard cars and to the rear, below the horizontal molding, on the St. Regis.

1955 Chrysler, New Yorker St. Regis two-door hardtop, V-8

NEW YORKER DELUXE SERIES

Model Number	Body/Style Number	Body Type & Seating	Factory Price	Shipping Weight	Production Total
C68	Note 1	4-dr Sed-6P	3494	4160	33,342
C68	Note 1	2-dr Newport-6P	3652	4140	5,777
C68	Note 1	2-dr St Reg-6P	3690	4125	11,076
C68	Note 1	2-dr Conv-6P	3924	4255	946
C68	Note 1	4-dr T&C Wag-6P	4208	4430	1,036
C68	Note 1	Chassis	—	—	1

NOTE 1: Code numbers to provide positive identification of body type were not provided.
NOTE 2: Production totals for midyear additions to the line are included in the totals for standard offerings.

1955 Chrysler, New Yorker four-door sedan, V-8

CHRYSLER 300 SERIES (8-CYL) — The most powerful automobile of the year sported a much modified Hemi-engine of 331.1 cid developing 300 brake horsepower. Two four-barrel carburetors, a full race camshaft and heavy-duty suspension, coupled with an Imperial grille and full leather interior, marked this car as something special. Performance and styling, combined in one package of such magnitude, created an aura that was to last for more than a decade.

300 SERIES

Model Number	Body/Style Number	Body Type & Seating	Factory Price	Shipping Weight	Production Total
C68-300	Note 1	2-dr HT Cpe	4109	4005	1,725

NOTE 1: Code numbers to provide positive identification of body type were not provided.

1955 Chrysler, C-300 two-door hardtop sport coupe, V-8

WINDSOR DELUXE ENGINE: V-8. Overhead valves. Cast iron block. Displacement: 301 cid. Bore and stroke: 3.625 x 3.625 inches. Compression ratio: 8:1. Brake hp: 188 at 4400 rpm. Hydraulic valve lifters. Carburetors: (Standard shift) Carter BBD 2180S, 2180SA, 2180SB. (PowerFlite) BBD 2162S, 2162SA, 2162SB.

NEW YORKER DELUXE ENGINE: V-8. Overhead valves with hemispherical combustion chambers. Displacement: 331.1 cid. Bore and stroke: 3.81 x 3.63 inches. Brake hp: 250 at 4600 rpm. Five main bearings. Hydraulic valve lifters. Dual exhaust system. Compression ratio: 8.5:1. Carburetor: Carter WCFB 2126S.

CHRYSLER 300 ENGINE: V-8. Overhead valves with hemispherical combustion chambers. Cast iron block. Displacement: 331.1 cid. Bore and stroke: 3.81 x 3.63 inches. Brake hp: 300 at 5200 rpm. Compression ratio: 8.5:1. Solid lifters with full-race camshaft. Two four-barrel carburetors.

CHASSIS FEATURES: Wheelbase: (All) 126 inches. Overall length: (Windsor Deluxe) 218.6 inches; (All other models) 218.8 inches. Tires: (Windsor) 7.60 x 15; (New Yorker) 8.00 x 15; (New Yorker and Town & Country with wire wheels) 8.20 x 15. Six-volt positive ground electrical system.

OPTIONS: PowerFlite transmission on Windsor Deluxe. Power steering. White sidewall tires. Chrome wire wheels. Air Temp air conditioning. Power brakes. Radio. Heater. Solex glass. Fog lights. Spot lamps. Rear seat radio speaker. Windshield washers. Outside rearview mirror. Two-tone paint. Power windows. Power front seat.

HISTORICAL FOOTNOTES: The Chrysler and Imperial lines for 1955 (including Nassau and St. Regis hardtops) were introduced Nov. 17, 1954. Chrysler Town & Country station wagons were added to the line Jan. 5, 1955. The Chrysler 300 was added to the line Feb. 10, 1955. Chrysler took second place in the high-priced sales field this season.

1956 CHRYSLER

WINDSOR SERIES — (8-CYL) — The "100 Million Dollar Look" was carried forward with a tasteful facelift centered around grille changes and integrated taillamps. The two-piece grille of 1955 was re-designed with a look reminiscent of the FliteSweep I show car. Three horizontal grille bars floated within a chrome surround. The new taillamps formed a natural extension of the uplifted outer rear bumper ends. The Windsor line had some further sub-series, which covered all body styles. A pillarless four-door hardtop was introduced and 12-volt electrical systems were adopted for all Chrysler models. Standard features included Oriflow shock absorbers, new safety door latches, independent parking brake, safety rim wheels and center plane brakes.

1956 Chrysler, Windsor two-door convertible, V-8 (AA)

CHRYSLER I.D. NUMBERS: Serial numbers were found on the left front hinge post. Engine numbers were located on the block behind the water pump. [Windsor] Detroit built cars were numbered W56-1001 to W56-75206. Los Angeles built cars were numbered W56L-1001 to W56L-7091. Engine numbers ranged from WE56-1001 to WE5681623. [New Yorker] Detroit built cars were numbered N56-1001 to N56-36162. Los Angeles built cars were numbered N56L-1001 to N56L-5197. Engine numbers ranged from NE56-1001 to NE56-40609. [300B] Production of Chrysler 300 Letter cars took place exclusively in Detroit, with numbers ranging from 3N56-1001 to 3N56-2150. Engine numbers were 3NE56-1001 to 3NE56-2174.

WINDSOR SERIES

Model Number	Body/Style Number	Body Type & Seating	Factory Price	Shipping Weight	Production Total
C71	Note 1	4-dr Sed-6P	2770	3900	53,119
C71	Note 1	2-dr Conv-6P	3235	4100	1,011
C71	Note 1	4-dr T&C Wag-6P	3498	4290	2,700
C71-1	Note 1	2-dr Nassau-6P	2804	3910	11,400
C71-2	Note 1	2-dr Newport-6P	2941	3920	10,800
C71-2	Note 1	4-dr Newport-6P	3028	3990	7,050

NOTE 1: Code numbers to provide positive identification of body were not used.

1956 Chrysler, New Yorker four-door sedan, V-8 (AA)

NEW YORKER — (8-CYL) — Tastefully restyled, the New Yorker used a finer detailed grille and different bumpers to set it apart from the Windsor. Additional moldings created unique two-tone paint combinations and a tri-tone combination in the St. Regis series. Big news this year was the first size increase for the Hemi engine, to 354 cid. This increased brake horsepower, in standard form, by more than 10 percent. A distinctive New Yorker styling touch was the appearance of eight chromed teeth on the rear fender, above the horizontal molding. This feature was to become a New Yorker hallmark for many years. Push-buttons at the left edge of the dash controlled all Chrysler automatic transmissions.

NEW YORKER SERIES

Model Number	Body/Style Number	Body Type & Seating	Factory Price	Shipping Weight	Production Total
C72	Note 1	4-dr Sed-6P	3673	4110	24,749
C72	Note 1	2-dr Conv-6P	4136	4360	921
C72	Note 1	4-dr T&C Wag-6P	4417	4460	1,070
C72-1	Note 1	2-dr Newport-6P	3845	4175	4,115
C72-1	Note 1	4-dr Newport-6P	3995	4220	3,599
C72-2	Note 1	2-dr St. Reg-6P	3889	4175	6,686

1956 Chrysler, 300B two-door, hardtop sport coupe, V-8

300B SERIES — (8-CYL) — The 300B's styling reflected the same unique flavor of the first Chrysler Letter Car introduced in 1955. Changes were essentially limited to taillamp alterations, in line with those appearing on other Chryslers. The push-button control for the Power-Flite cars (later cars had TorqueFlite transmission) was positioned to the left side of the dashboard. Technically a sub-series of the New Yorker, the 300B was available with automatic or standard shift transmissions and two high-performance Hemi engines. Leather upholstery was standard fare.

300B SERIES

Model Number	Body/Style Number	Body Type & Seating	Factory Price	Shipping Weight	Production Total
C72-300	Note 1	2-dr Spt Cpe-6P	4242	4360	1,102

NOTE 1: Code numbers to provide positive identification of body type were not used.

WINDSOR ENGINE: V-8. Overhead valves. Cast iron block. Displacement: 331.1 cid. Bore and stroke: 3.81 x 3.63 inches. Compression ratio: 8.5:1. Brake hp: 225 at 4400 rpm. (Optional engine with dual exhaust and single four-barrel carburetor produced 250 brake horsepower). Hydraulic valve lifters. Carburetors: (Standard Shift) Carter BBD 2312S; (PowerFlite) Carter 2313S; (Power package, with all transmissions) Carter WCFB 2367S or 2367SA.

NEW YORKER ENGINE: V-8. Overhead valves. Cast iron block. Displacement: 354 cid. Bore and stroke: 3.94 x 3.63 inches. Brake hp: 280 at 4600 rpm. Compression ratio: 9:1. Five main bearings. Hydraulic valve lifters. Carburetor: Carter WCFB 2314S or 2314SA.

300B ENGINE: V-8. Overhead valves. High-lift camshaft. Extra stiff valve springs. Cast iron block. Displacement: 354 cid. Bore and stroke: 3.94 x 3.63 inches. Brake hp: 340 at 5200 rpm. (With optional 10:1 compression ratio, brake horsepower became 355 at 5200 rpm.).

1956 Chrysler, 300B two-door hardtop sport coupe, V-8 (AA)

CHASSIS FEATURES: Three speed column mounted transmission standard on the Windsor (available on special order on 300B). PowerFlite transmission standard on New Yorker and 300B. Late 300Bs used three-speed TorqueFlite transmissions. Wheelbase: (all models) 126 inches. Overall length: (Windsor) 220.5 inches; (New Yorker) 221 inches; (New Yorker Town & Country) 221.2 inches; (Windsor Town & Country) 220.4 inches. Last year for front coil springs combined with rear leaf springs.

OPTIONS: Power steering. Power brakes. Power front seat. Highway Hi-Fi record player. Air Temp air conditioning. Electric window lifts. Power radio antenna. Hot water heater. Instant gas heater. Solex safety glass. Whitewall tires. Steering wheel mounted clock. Power package on Windsor (included dual exhaust and four-barrel carburetor).

HISTORICAL FOOTNOTES: The 300B, America's fastest and highest powered car in 1956, set the World Passenger Car Speed Record at Daytona Beach, averaging 139.9 mph.

1957 CHRYSLER

WINDSOR — (8-CYL) — The second edition of Chrysler's 'Forward Look' was widely acclaimed. Drawing the most attention were the sweeping rear fender fins. Dual headlights became standard equipment shortly after production commenced. The 1957 Chryslers had new bodies as well as new chassis features. Torsion bar suspension was one innovation this year. The long standing Newport name was no longer used for the pillarless body styles. Hardtop models had optional 'Flight Sweep' color panels on the rear fenders. Dual rear aerials were an interesting option.

CHRYSLER I.D. NUMBERS: Serial numbers were found on the left front door hinge post. Engine numbers were located on the block behind the water pump. [Windsor] Detroit built cars were numbered W57-1001 and up. Los Angeles built cars were numbered W57L-1001 and up. Engine numbers ranged from WE57-1001 to WE57-48864. [Saratoga] Detroit built cars were numbered L57-1001 and up. Los Angeles built cars were numbered L57L-1001 and up. Engine numbers ranged from LE57-1001 and up. [New Yorker] Detroit built cars were numbered N57-1001 and up. Los Angeles built cars were numbered N57L-1001 and up. Motor numbers ranged from NE57-1001 to NE57-35552. [300] Serial numbers were 3N57-1001 and up. Engine numbers ranged from 3NE57-1001 to 3NE57-3338. All production of Chrysler 300s was quartered in Detroit.

1957 Chrysler, Windsor four-door hardtop, V-8

WINDSOR SERIES

Model Number	Body/Style Number	Body Type & Seating	Factory Price	Shipping Weight	Production Total
C75-1	145	4-dr Sed-6P	3088	3995	17,639
C75-1	146	2-dr HT-6P	3153	3925	14,027
C75-1	149	4-dr HT-6P	3217	4030	14,354
C75-1	148	4-dr T&C Wag-6P	3574	4210	2,035

SARATOGA SERIES — (8-CYL) — The Saratoga name returned after an absence of five years. This mid-line Chrysler, based on Windsor components, featured upgraded upholstery, a higher horsepower engine with dual exhausts, back-up lamps and brake warning signals. TorqueFlite transmission, stainless steel wheelcovers and power steering were standard equipment. A single horizontal trim molding ran from front to rear, giving the car a long sweeping look that reflected Virgil Exner's design inspiration. Two-tone finish was optional and popular. The Saratoga insignia was located below the horizontal trim line, just aft of the front wheelhouse opening. The grille used a broad, horizontal motif. Early cars had single headlamps, with a dual system optionally available.

SARATOGA SERIES

Model Number	Body/Style Number	Body Type & Seating	Factory Price	Shipping Weight	Production Total
C75-2	255	4-dr Sed-6P	3718	4165	14,977
C75-2	256	2-dr HT-6P	3754	4075	10,633
C75-2	259	4-dr HT-6P	3832	4195	11,586

1957 Chrysler, New Yorker two-door hardtop, V-8

NEW YORKER SERIES — (8-CYL) — This top-of-the-line model featured the largest production car engine available in 1957. The Hemi engine's bore and stroke were increased. Displacement was raised nearly ten percent. A narrow, dart-like color sweep distinguished the sides of the New Yorker. Cars with two-tone finish had the roof color added to the side trim area. Advertised as, "The most glamorous cars in a generation," all body styles were included in this series. Dual rear antennas were a popular option that emphasized the sweep of the tailfins. Chrysler 'firsts' for 1957 included Torsion-Aire ride, completely concealed tailpipes, spool-like engine mounts and optional Captive-Aire tires on the New Yorker Town & Country station wagon (A spare tire wasn't provided on this model).

NEW YORKER SERIES

Model Number	Body/Style Number	Body Type & Seating	Factory Price	Shipping Weight	Production Total
C-76	165	4-dr Sed-6P	4173	4315	12,369
C-76	166	2-dr HT-6P	4202	4220	8,863
C-76	169	4-dr HT-6P	4259	4330	10,948
C-76	163	2-dr Conv-6P	4638	4365	1,049
C-76	168	4-dr T&C Wag-6P	4746	4490	1,391

300C SERIES — (8-CYL) — The third version of the 300 continued as the fastest and most powerful production car in the country. The 300 featured full leather interior trims and a new, masculine grille that was unlike any seen on previous Chrysler offerings. Exterior ornamentation was kept to a minimum with single spear-like moldings on the lower rear quarter panels. The round 300 medallion, with a red-white-blue background and model numbers and lettering made its debut. Two medallions were placed on the side spear, four on each hubcap, one each on the hood, deck lid, glovebox and another within the steering wheel center hub. Only the two on the spears carried both numbers and letters. The others had only the '300' designation. The colors of the emblem were claimed to be representative of the high-performance nature of the American car buying public. With smaller, 14 inch wheels being used, it was found necessary to provide for additional brake cooling on the Chrysler 300. This was accomplished by adding a rectangular opening below the headlamps which admitted air and guided it, via a duct, to the front brakes. Monotone colors were used exclusively on the 300 and the front did not have the short, narrow vertical bumper guards found on other 1957 Chryslers. The 300s were considered a part of the New Yorker series, but were actually a world apart from most other U.S. production automobiles of the day.

1957 Chrysler, 300C two-door hardtop sport coupe, V-8

300 SERIES

Model Number	Body/Style Number	Body Type & Seating	Factory Price	Shipping Weight	Production Total
C76-300	566	2-dr HT-6P	4929	4235	1,918
C76-300	563	2-dr Conv-6P	5359	4390	484

WINDSOR ENGINE: V-8. Overhead valves. Cast iron block. Displacement: 354 cid. Bore and stroke: 3.94 x 3.63 inches. Compression ratio: 9.25:1. Brake hp: 285 at 4600 rpm. Five main bearings. Hydraulic valve lifters. Carburetor: Carter two-barrel, Type BBD Model 2527S.

SARATOGA ENGINE: See 1957 Windsor Series basic engine data. Standard extras on Saratogas included a four-barrel carburetor, dual exhausts and full-flow oil filter. The Saratoga engine was rated at 295 brake horsepower. V-8. Overhead valves. Cast iron block. Displacement: 354 cid. Bore and stroke: 3.94 x 3.63 inches. Compression ratio: 9.25:1. Brake hp: 295 at 4600 rpm. Five main bearings. Hydraulic valve lifters. Carburetor: Carter WCFB-2589S four-barrel. (Dual exhausts.)

NEW YORKER ENGINE: V-8. Cast iron block. Overhead valves with hemispherical combustion chambers. Displacement: 392 cid. Bore and stroke: 4.00 x 3.9 inches. Compression ratio: 9.25:1. Brake hp: 325 at 4600 rpm. Five main bearings. Solid valve lifters. Single Carter WCFB model 2590S four-barrel carburetor. (Dual exhausts).

300C ENGINE: V-8. Cast iron block. Overhead valves with hemispherical combustion chambers. Displacement: 392 cid. Bore and stroke: 4.00 x 3.9 inches. Compression ratio: 9.25:1. Brake hp: 375 at 5200 rpm. Five main bearings. Carburetor: Two (2) Carter model WCFB-2334S four-barrels.

OPTIONAL 300C ENGINE: V-8. Cast iron block. Overhead valves with hemispherical combustion chambers. Displacement: 392 cid. Bore and stroke: 4.00 x 3.9 inches. Compression ratio: 9.25:1. Brake hp: 390 at 5400 rpm. Five main bearings. Carburetor: Two (2) Carter model WCFB-2334S four-barrels. This extra-cost solid lifter competition engine was intended mainly for acceleration trials and stock racing cars. It was available only with stick shift (adapted from a Dodge column-mounted three-speed) and no power options. It had a 10.0:1 compression ratio, four-bolt cast iron exhaust headers and a 2-1/2 inch low back-pressure exhaust system. Solid valve lifters and twin four-barrel carburetors were used.

CHASSIS FEATURES: Standard shift standard on Windsor. TorqueFlite optional on Windsor; standard on Saratoga, New Yorker and 300C. Wheelbase: 126 inches. Separate body and frame construction. Hotchkiss drive. Hypoid rear axle. Total-Contact brakes. Overall length: (Windsor, Saratoga, New Yorker and 300C) 219.2 inches; (Town & Country Wagon) 218.9. Safety wheel rims. Tires: (Windsor and Saratoga) 8.50 x 14; (New Yorker and 300C) 9.00 x 14. Front tread: (Windsor and Saratoga) 61 inches; (New Yorker) 61.2 inches. Rear tread: (Windsor and Saratoga) 59.7 inches; (New Yorker) 60 inches. Width: (all models) 78.8 inches. Torsion bar front suspension.

OPTIONS: Power steering on Windsor (standard on other series). Hand-brake warning signal option on Windsor. Back-up lights optional on Windsor. Dual headlamps (became standard on all lines shortly after production commenced). Air-Temp air conditioning. Power brakes. Power window lifts. Six-Way power seat. Whitewall tires. Nylon tires. Chrome stainless steel wheelcovers on Windsor. Radio with Music Master or Electro-Touch tuner. Dual rear antennas. Power front antenna. Rear seat speaker. Fresh air heater. Instant Air heater. Two-tone finish. Tinted glass. Rear window defroster. Windshield washer. Undercoating. Non-slip differential. Outside mirrors. Full-flow oil filter on Windsor. Captive Air tires on Town and Country station wagon. Hi-Way Hi-Fi phonograph.

HISTORICAL FOOTNOTES: The 1957 Chrysler models were introduced on Oct. 39, 1956. Output in 1957 was 156,679 cars of which 118,733 were Chryslers and 37,946 Imperials. Since 1926, when the first one was produced, Imperials had been built in the corporation's East Jefferson plant at Detroit, along with Chryslers. Beginning in 1955, the Imperial was given a distinctively different styling treatment and, by 1957, there no longer were any body parts interchangeable with Chrysler.

1958 CHRYSLER

WINDSOR SERIES — (8-CYL) — A Dodge chassis was now used under the Windsor's sheetmetal. The car had typical Chrysler styling motifs, with the major change being that the front end sheetmetal was capped-off with a chrome eyebrow running from side to side, above the headlamps. The 1958 style grille was tastefully adapted to the Dodge-like front end. Side trim on the standard offering was a single molding, at mid-level, running horizontally from the rear to just aft of the front wheelhouse opening. In the spring, a Dartline package was introduced which added some flair to the Windsor's styling. The Dartline package was an addition to the hardtop line. Besides additional trim on the front fender and a metal insert, this option included bright sill moldings, special roof trim and three slim moldings on each side of the rear deck license plate housing. The standard two-door hardtop used a sweep of color similar to the

1957 version, with the major difference being the sharper pointed front part of the sweep on the 1958. Introduced this year was Auto-Pilot speed control and a new three seat nine-passenger station wagon. The third seat faced to the rear.

CHRYSLER I.D. NUMBERS: Serial numbers were found on the left front hinge post. Engine numbers were located on the block behind the water pump. [Windsor] Detroit built cars were numbered LCI-1001 and up. Los Angeles built cars were numbered LCIL-1001 and up. Engine numbers ranged from 58W-1001 and up. [Saratoga] Detroit built cars used numbers LC2-1001 and up. Los Angeles built cars used numbers LC2L-1001 and up. Engine numbers ranged from 58S-1001 and up. [New Yorker] Detroit built cars were numbered LC3-1001 and up. Los Angeles cars were numbered L-1001 and up. Engine numbers ranged from 58N-1001 and up. [300D] All 300s were built in Detroit and serial numbers began with LC4-1001 and up. Engine numbers started at 58N3-1001 and up.

1958 Chrysler, Windsor, two-door hardtop coupe (Dartline), V-8

WINDSOR SERIES

Model Number	Body/Style Number	Body Type & Seating	Factory Price	Shipping Weight	Production Total
LC1-L	513	4-dr Sed-6P	3129	3895	12,861
LC1-L	512	2-dr HT-6P	3214	3860	6,205
LC1-L	514	4-dr HT-6P	3279	3915	6,254
LC1-L	571	4-dr T&C Wag-6P	3616	4155	862
LC1-L	572	4-dr T&C Wag-9P	3803	4245	791
LC1-L	515	2-dr Conv-6P	—	—	2

1958 Chrysler, Saratoga two-door hardtop sport coupe, V-8

SARATOGA SERIES — (8-CYL) — This series continued almost unchanged from 1957. Instrument panel background color changed, as did the metal background of the radio and heater control panels. The side trim began at the forward edge of the front door and continued rearward to the taillamp bezel. The Saratoga nameplate was placed to the rear of the front fender, directly in line with the side trim molding. A color spear was available at extra cost. On cars with this option the extra trim began at the middle of the front door and rose slightly, in a very gentle line, as it ran rearward. The taillamps were similar to the previous type, except that the lenses rose to a point only two-thirds the way up rather than running full height, as in 1957. The lenses were also narrower and revealed more of the housing itself. The grille continued its horizontal flair, with the topmost part of the bumper horizontally dividing the opening. Dual headlamps were a standard feature. The rearview mirror, as in all 1957 and 1958 models, was mounted on the dash rather than the windshield header.

SARATOGA SERIES

Model Number	Body/Style Number	Body Type & Seating	Factory Price	Shipping Weight	Production Total
LC2-M	533	4-dr Sed-6P	3818	4120	8,698
LC2-M	532	2-dr HT-6P	3878	4045	4,456
LC2-M	534	4-dr HT-6P	3955	4145	5,322

1958 Chrysler, New Yorker four-door hardtop

1958 Chrysler, New Yorker, four-door hardtop sedan, V-8

NEW YORKER SERIES — (8-CYL) — Little changed from 1957 as far as New Yorkers went. A facelift paralleled changes seen in the less expensive Chrysler models. The Saratoga-style mid-line body trim molding was seen, but a unique emblem, placed just rearward of the front door, set New Yorkers apart. A color spear of anodized aluminum graced the area between the two trim pieces and covered the rear portion of the car. While not as substantial or as long as the color sweep of 1957, it helped distinguish this model from its brethren. Auto-Pilot and remote-control outside rearview mirrors were new options. Interior fabric was 'Fountaineblau' Jacquard and metallic vinyl and was slightly richer than the 'Chainmail' fabric and metallic vinyl used on the Saratoga. (Windsors used 'Bahama' Jacquard and metallic vinyl trim combinations). The Town & Country station wagon now had a third seat option, with the seat facing the rear of the car. All hardtops sported the new domed windshield introduced on 1957 convertibles.

NEW YORKER SERIES

Model Number	Body/Style Number	Body Type & Seating	Factory Price	Shipping Weight	Production Total
LC3-H	553	4-dr Sed-6P	4295	4195	7,110
LC3-H	552	2-dr HT-6P	4347	4205	3,205
LC3-H	554	4-dr HT-6P	4404	4240	5,227
LC3-H	555	2-dr Conv Cpe-6P	4761	4350	666
LC3-H	575	4-dr T&C Wag-6P	4868	4435	775
LC3-H	576	4-dr T&C Wag-6P	5083	4445	428

300D SERIES — (8-CYL) — This super high-performance car was again a sub-series of the New Yorker. It carried forward the design motifs of 1957 with only minor alterations. The windshield on hardtops now conformed to the windshield style (domed) of the convertible. Hubcaps now had red finish, painted in the depressed outer areas of the wheelcovers. Instrument face backgrounds were identical to those of other 1958 Chryslers. Large red-white-blue rear quarter panel medallions returned for the second year, but the letter 'D' replaced the 'C' used in 1957. In all, there were 10 locations for the various size 300 medallions on the car: glovebox, grille, deck lid, steering hub, hubcaps and the aforementioned rear quarters. A limited number of 300Ds were built with an electronic fuel injection system called the Bendix Electrojector. This marked the first use of a computer in a Chrysler product. A recall program was instituted, in late summer 1958, and most of the EFI units were replaced by conventional carburetors in the dual four-barrel configuration that was standard on all 300s. It was also the last year for the 'Firepower' Hemi-engine.

300D SERIES

Model Number	Body/Style Number	Body Type & Seating	Factory Price	Shipping Weight	Production Total
LC3-S	592	2-dr HT-6P	5173	4305	618
LC3-S	595	2-dr Conv Cpe-6P	5603	4475	191

WINDSOR ENGINE: V-8. Overhead valves. Cast iron block. Displacement: 354 cid. Bore and stroke: 3.94 x 3.63 inches. Compression ratio: 10.0:1. Brake hp: 290 at 4600 rpm. Five main bearings. Hydraulic valve lifters. Carburetor: Carter Type BBD Model 2733S two-barrel.

SARATOGA ENGINE: V-8. Overhead valves. Cast iron block. Displacement: 354 cid. Bore and stroke: 3.94 x 3.63 inches. Compression ratio: 10.0:1. Brake hp: 310 at 4600 rpm. Five main bearings. Hydraulic valve lifters. Carburetor: Carter four-barrel.

NEW YORKER ENGINE: V-8. Cast iron block. Overhead valves with hemispherical combustion chambers. Displacement: 392 cid. Bore and stroke: 4.00 x 3.9 inches. Compression ratio: 10:1. Brake hp: 345 at 4600 rpm. Five main bearings. Hydraulic valve lifters. Carburetor: Carter Type AFB four-barrel Model 2651S. Dual exhausts.

300D LETTER CAR ENGINE: V-8. Cast iron block. Overhead valves with hemispherical combustion chambers. Adjustable valve lifters. Displacement: 392 cid. Bore and stroke: 4.00 x 3.9 inches. Compression ratio: 10:1. Brake hp: 380 at 5200 rpm. Dual Carter WCFB four-barrel carburetors.

EFI ENGINE: Optional fuel injected engine produced 390 brake horsepower at 5200 rpm. Low back pressure exhaust system available.

CHASSIS FEATURES: Standard shift standard on Windsor. TorqueFlite optional on Windsor and standard on Saratoga, New Yorker and 300D. Wheelbase: 122 inches on Windsor; 126 inches on all other series. Constant control power steering optional on Windsor and standard on other series. Torsion-Aire front suspension, sway bar and Oriflow shock absorbers standard on all models. 300D used larger diameter torsion bars. Windsor length was 218 inches (217.7 inches on Town and Country). Saratoga was 220 inches in length. New Yorkers were 220.2 inches (Town and Country was 219.9 inches). Tire sizes were 8.00 x 14 Windsor; 8.50 x 14 Saratoga and 9.00 x 14 for New Yorkers and 300D. Safety rim wheels standard all models.

OPTIONS: Power steering on Windsor. TorqueFlite on Windsor. Power brakes. Power windows. Power seat. Air-Temp air conditioning. White sidewall rayon tires (Nylon tubeless super soft cushion tires in black and white optional). Stainless wheelcovers on Windsor. Remote control mirror. Radios. Antennas including power antenna. Two-tone finish. Tinted glass. Heaters. Rear window defroster. Windshield washer. Undercoating. Non-slip differential. Hi-Fi Phonograph. Auto-Pilot.

HISTORICAL FOOTNOTES: Dealer introductions of 1958 Chryslers were held on Nov. 1, 1957. Production included 26,500 Windsors; 18,300 New Yorkers and 15,700 Saratogas. Emphasizing the Imperial as a separate line was a major step in the division's 1958 activities. Passenger car production for calendar 1958 was 63,186 units, including Imperial's share of 13,673 or 21.6 percent of the total. Installation rates of the leading equipment items continued high on 1958 models. Such accessories as automatic transmission, power steering, heater

and windshield washer, neared 100 percent for Chrysler. Auto-Pilot was Chrysler's unique driver assist option. First introduced in 1958, the device permits the driver to dial his speed and remove his foot from the accelerator while cruising.

1959 CHRYSLER

1959 Chrysler, Windsor two-door hardtop sport coupe, V-8

WINDSOR — (8-CYL) — The low line Windsor used the same basic body structure of the earlier finned versions, but the sheetmetal was craftily changed. Although continuing the dart-like shape of Virgil Exner's famous design theme, a new look was achieved. The grille carried forward its horizontal flair, but the lower section now wrapped around the fender and ran back to near the wheelhouse opening. Bumpers, front and rear, were noticeably different and the rear license plate was no longer embedded in the deck lid. It was now positioned at the center inset of the rear bumper. Taillamps came in a notched housing totally unlike previous designs. A unique feature was the 'outlined roof' treatment which, as an option, could be ordered in colors that matched the bodyside sweep inserts. A new, wedge-like combustion chamber "Golden Lion" V-8 engine was used on all 1959 Chryslers. This engine was a deriv-ative of the B-block introduced in 1958 for DeSoto, Dodge and Plymouth. The Town & Country name continued to identify the station wagons. All hardtops and convertibles used the dome-like windshield pioneered on 1957 convertibles. Interior upholstery came in 14 color and fabric choices using 'Times Square' metallic threaded cloth with pleated vinyl inserts. Swivel seats were available on all body styles, except the wagon, and were standard on Chrysler 300Es. The Windsor continued to be built on the Dodge chassis.

CHRYSLER I.D. NUMBERS: Serial numbers were found on the left front hinge post. Engine numbers were located on the boss behind the water pump. Chrysler instituted a new serial number coding system which consisted of 10 symbols. [Windsor] First symbol 'M' indicated 1959. The second digit '5' indicated Chrysler. The third digit '1' indicated Windsor and the fourth digit indicated the assembly plant, as follows: 1=Detroit; 4=Los Angeles. The last six symbols represented the production sequence number, beginning with 100001. Detroit built cars were numbered M511-100001 and up. Los Angeles built cars were numbered M514-100001 and up. Detroit built station wagons were numbered M571-100001 and up. Los Angeles built station wagons were numbered M574-100001 and up. [Saratoga] Detroit built cars used numbers M531-100001 and up. Los Angeles built cars used numbers M534-100001 and up. The coding system was the same used on all Chryslers. The third symbol, '2' indicated Saratoga. [New Yorker] Detroit built cars used numbers M551-100001 and up. Los Angeles built cars used numbers M554-100001 and up. Detroit built station wagons used serial numbers M571-100001. Los Angeles built station wagons used serial numbers M574-100001 and up. Third symbol '3' indicated New Yorker/300E. [300E] All cars were built in Detroit and numbered M591-100001 and up.

WINDSOR SERIES

Model Number	Body/Style Number	Body Type & Seating	Factory Price	Shipping Weight	Production Total
MC1-L	513	4-dr Sed-6P	3204	3800	19,910
MC1-L	512	2-dr HT Cpe-6P	3289	3735	6,775
MC1-L	514	4-dr HT Sed-6P	3353	3830	6,084
MC1-L	515	2-dr Conv-6P	3620	3950	961
MC1-L	576	4-dr T&C Wag-6P	3691	4045	992
MC1-L	577	4-dr T&C Wag-6P	3878	4070	751

1959 Chrysler, Saratoga four-door hardtop sedan, V-8

SARATOGA SERIES — (8-CYL) — The Saratoga used the long wheelbase chassis of 126 inches. From the cowl area back, the sheetmetal was identical to that of the Windsor. However, the front end sheetmetal was four inches longer. A new color sweep began at the lower rear quarter panel and arched upward, in a graceful manner, to a mid body location. It then ran forward to the tip of the front fender. Standard two-tone color combinations had the body and roof panel insert in the same color and contrasting finish on the color sweep, roof outline and C-pillar. A Saratoga nameplate was located just forward of the taillamp housing. A Golden Lion medallion was used in Chrysler's new promotional theme, "Chrysler 1959 — presenting the Lion-hearted Car that's every inch a New Adventure." An array of options included the unique swivel seat. Interiors were all vinyl. Optional were seat inserts made of Jacquard material called 'Mayfair.'

SARATOGA SERIES

Model Number	Body/Style Number	Body Type & Seating	Factory Price	Shipping Weight	Production Total
MC2-M	533	4-dr Sed-6P	3966	4010	8,783
MC2-M	532	2-dr HT Cpe-6P	4026	3970	3,753
MC2-M	534	4-dr HT Sed-6P	4104	4035	4,943

NEW YORKER SERIES — (8-CYL) — The B-series engine was used for the first time in a New Yorker. The Hemi-engine was no longer available. horsepower was up slightly, as was displacement. Engine weight, simplicity of design and lower manufacturing costs were the principal reasons for the change in powerplant. The New Yorker used a spear-like color sweep with horizontal top trim. The lower trim molding dipped and broadened, at the rear, running to bumper level height. An anodized insert ran from front to rear, within the color spear, and seven slash type strips were added at the rear. They continued the same pattern used on previous New Yorkers. The Golden Lion insignia was placed below the New Yorker script at the rear portion of the front fender. Upholstery options consisted of 22 combinations of vinyl and Jacquard fabric. The instrument panel and dashboard were relatively unchanged from the two previous years.

NEW YORKER SERIES

Model Number	Body/Style Number	Body Type & Seating	Factory Price	Shipping Weight	Production Total
MC3-H	553	4-dr Sed-6P	4424	4120	7,792
MC3-H	552	2-dr HT Cpe-6P	4476	4080	2,435
MC3-H	554	4-dr HT Sed-6P	4533	4165	4,805
MC3-H	555	2-dr Conv-6P	4890	4270	286
MC3-H	578	4-dr T&C Wag-6P	4997	4295	444
MC3-H	579	4-dr T&C Wag-9P	5212	4360	564
MC3-H	—	Chassis	—	—	2

1959 Chrysler, 300E two-door hardtop sports coupe, V-8

300E SERIES — (8-CYL) — Considered a part of the New Yorker series, the "Beautiful Brute" continued the tradition of luxurious, high-performance driving pleasure. Minor styling revisions and the use of a wedge-shaped combustion chamber engine were changes. The new engine was said to have performance equal to or slightly better than the Hemi engine, which left no doubt as to the car's heritage. A revised grille, on the familiar theme, eliminated the vertical bar look. A 300 insignia was placed on the driver's side of the hood, in line with the headlamps. Swivel bucket seats were available and the red-white-blue medallion was positioned in its usual place. The letter 'E' was added to the medallion to signify the new model as the 300E. This was the last year for separate body and frame design.

300E SERIES

Model Number	Body/Style Number	Body Type & Seating	Factory Price	Shipping Weight	Production Total
MC3-H	592	2-dr HT-6P	5319	4290	550
MC3-H	595	2-dr Conv-6P	5749	4350	140

WINDSOR ENGINE: V-8. Cast iron block. Displacement: 383 cid. Bore and stroke: 4.03 x 3.75 inches. Compression ratio: 10.1:1. Brake hp: 305 at 4600 rpm. Five main bearings. Hydraulic valve lifters. Carburetor: Carter Type BBD two-barrel Model 2872S.

SARATOGA ENGINE: V-8. Cast iron block. Displacement: 383 cid. Bore and stroke: 4.03 x 3.75 inches. Compression ratio: 10.1:1. Brake hp: 325 at 4600 rpm. Five main bearings. Hydraulic valve lifters. Carburetor: Carter Type AFB four-barrel Model 2797S.

NEW YORKER ENGINE: V-8. Cast iron block. Displacement: 413 cid. Bore and stroke: 4.18 x 3.75 inches. Compression ratio: 10.0:1. Brake hp: 350 at 4600 rpm. Five main bearings. Hydraulic valve lifters. Carburetor: Carter Type AFB four-barrel.

300E ENGINE: V-8. Cast iron block. Displacement: 413 cid. Bore and stroke: 4.18 x 3.75 inches. Compression ratio: 10.1:1. Brake hp: 380 at 5000 rpm. Five main bearings. Hydraulic valve lifters. Carburetors: Two (2) Carter four-barrels Type AFB Model 2798S.

CHASSIS FEATURES: Wheelbase: (Windsor) 122 inches, (Saratoga) 126 inches, (New Yorker) 126 inches, (300E) 126 inches. Overall length: (Windsor) 216.6 inches; (Saratoga) 220.6 inches; (New Yorker) 220.9 inches; (300E) 220.9 inches. Front tread: (Windsor) 60.9 inches; (Saratoga) 60.9 inches; (New Yorker) 61.2 inches; (300E) 61.2 inches. Rear tread: (Windsor) 59.8 inches; (Saratoga) 59.8 inches; (New Yorker) 60.0 inches; (300E) 60.0 inches. Tires: (Windsor) 8.00 x 14; (Saratoga) 8.50 x 14; (New Yorker) 9.00 x 14; (300E) 9.00 x 14.

OPTIONS: Power steering (Windsor). TorqueFlite (Windsor). Power brakes (Windsor). Power windows. Power seat. Swivel seats. Air-Temp air conditioning. Custom super soft cushion rayon tires. White sidewall tires. Nylon and Captive Air tires. Stainless steel wheelcovers on Windsor (standard on Windsor Town & Country). Remote control mirror. Radios. Antennas

(including power antenna). Two-tone finish. Solex glass. Heater. Rear window defroster. Auto-Pilot. Windshield washer. Undercoating. Non-slip differential. Hand-brake warning lights. Back-up light (Windsor). Sill moldings (Windsor).

HISTORICAL FOOTNOTES: First year for 'B' block engines. Last year for separate body and frame construction. Golden Lion was new advertising theme. The 1959 models were introduced Oct. 24, 1958.

1960 CHRYSLER

1960 Chrysler, Windsor two-door hardtop sport coupe, V-8

WINDSOR SERIES — (8-CYL) — An all new body style featured a 300-type grille and a modified fin look. The big news this year was Unibody construction. The Windsor series was again on the short wheelbase platform and was the least expensive Chrysler. The grille insert was a mesh-like affair with a golden lion medallion affixed to the center. Fins were rakish and set at an angle. They were emphasized by deep, rounded indentations at mid body height. Station wagons used a pillarless design giving a hardtop style look. Taillamps were set into a sharply arched housing mounted at the extreme end of the tailfin. Dual headlamps were standard fare. An optional Flitesweep deck lid was available at modest cost. Stone shields and sill moldings were a Windsor option.

CHRYSLER I.D. NUMBERS: Serial numbers were found on the left front hinge post. Engine numbers were located on the boss behind the water pump. [Windsor] Detroit built cars were numbered 8103-100001 and up. Los Angeles built cars were numbered 8105-100001 and up. Windsor wagons were numbered 8503-100001 and up. [Saratoga] Detroit built cars were numbered 8203-100001 and up. [New Yorker] Detroit built cars were numbered 8303-100001 and up. [300F] Serial numbers began with 8403-100001 and up. Engine numbers were identical to the New Yorker series. All 300s were built in Detroit. A new engine numbering system deciphered as follows: First symbol indicated year/series: PR=1960 Windsor; second symbol indicated displacement: 38=383 cid; third symbol indicated month (7=July) and day (1= first day of month, etc.). Thus, the code PR-387-5 indicates a Chrysler Windsor/Saratoga 383 V-8 built on July 5. The code for a New Yorker/300 engine built the same day would be: P-41-7-5, as P =1960 model year; 41=413 cid V-8; 7-5 = date of manufacture (July 5).

WINDSOR SERIES

Model Number	Body/Style Number	Body Type & Seating	Factory Price	Shipping Weight	Production Total
PC1-L	813	4-dr Sed-6P	3194	3815	25,152
PC1-L	812	2-dr HT Cpe-6P	3279	3850	6,496
PC1-L	814	4-dr HT Sed-6P	3343	3855	5,897
PC1-L	815	2-dr Conv-6P	3623	3855	1,467
PC1-L	858	4-dr T&C Wag-6P	3733	4235	1,120
PC1-L	859	4-dr T&C Wag-9P	3814	4390	1,026

1960 Chrysler, Saratoga two-door hardtop sport coupe, V-8

SARATOGA SERIES — (8-CYL) — The Saratoga was built on the long wheelbase chassis and included, as standard equipment, many features not found on the less expensive Windsor series. Front fender scripts were the basic means of identification, although the longer front sheetmetal was readily apparent to a sharp-eyed enthusiast. Interior fabrics were of better quality than in the Windsor series. Standard equipment included: TorqueFlite transmission; power steering and brakes; rear foam seats; electric clock; wheelcovers; Deluxe steering wheel; windshield washers; padded dash; back-up lights; parking brake lights; map lights; luggage lights; stone shields and sill moldings.

SARATOGA SERIES

Model Number	Body/Style Number	Body Type & Seating	Factory Price	Shipping Weight	Production Total
PC2-M	823	4-dr Sed-6P	3929	4010	8,463
PC2-M	822	2-dr HT Cpe-6P	3989	4030	2,963
PC2-M	824	4-dr HT Sed-6P	4067	4035	4,099

1960 Chrysler, New Yorker two-door hardtop sport coupe, V-8

NEW YORKER SERIES — (8-CYL) — The New Yorker was built on the long wheelbase chassis. The masculine 300-type grille was 'frenched'. A fine horizontal bar motif inset appeared within the grille outline. New Yorkers continued to use rear fender trim bars for the fifth consecutive year. For 1960 the number of bars was increased to nine. Exterior brightwork was kept to a minimum, with stone shields and sill moldings standard. The front bumper dipped in the center to match the lower contour of the grille opening.

NEW YORKER SERIES

Model Number	Body/Style Number	Body Type & Seating	Factory Price	Shipping Weight	Production Total
PC3-H	833	4-dr Sed-6P	4409	4145	9,079
PC3-H	832	2-dr HT Cpe-6P	4461	4175	2,835
PC3-H	834	4-dr HT Sed-6P	4518	4175	5,625
PC3-H	835	2-dr Conv-6P	4875	4185	556
PC3-H	878	4-dr T&C Wag-6P	5022	4515	624
PC3-H	879	4-dr T&C Wag-9P	5131	4535	671

1960 Chrysler, 300F two-door convertible, V-8

300F SERIES — (8-CYL) — The sixth edition of the letter series 300 continued its tradition as a high-performance vehicle. Besides the all-new styling and Unibody construction, big improvements in engineering were evident with the unveiling of a Ram-Tuned induction manifold option. Ram-tuning had long been a means of raising torque and horsepower for drag racing. Chrysler engineers adapted this idea with cross-over ram induction manifolds which placed one bank of cylinder's carburetor on the far side of the opposing bank of cylinder's carburetor. No longer were the carburetors placed inline, between the cylinder heads, as on previous dual carbureted 300s. Two horsepower versions were available in 1960 and a few cars (seven to 10, including at least one convertible) were built with the French Pont-A-Mousson four-speed gearbox. All New Yorker standard features were included on the 300F, plus power swivel seats. White sidewall Nylon tires were standard.

300 SERIES

Model Number	Body/Style Number	Body Type & Seating	Factory Price	Shipping Weight	Production Total
PC3-300	842	2-dr HT Cpe-4P	5411	4270	964
PC3-300	845	2-dr Conv-4P	5841	4310	248

WINDSOR ENGINE: V-8. Cast iron block. Displacement: 383 cid. Bore and stroke: 4.03 x 3.75 inches. Compression ratio: 10.0:1. Brake hp: 305 at 4600 rpm. Five main bearings. Hydraulic valve lifters. Carburetor: Carter Type BBD two-barrel Model.

SARATOGA ENGINE: V-8. Cast iron block. Displacement: 383 cid. Bore and stroke: 4.03 x 3.75 inches. Compression ratio: 10.0:1. Brake hp: 325 at 4600 rpm. Five main bearings. Hydraulic valve lifters. Carburetor: Carter AFB-2927S four-barrel.

NEW YORKER ENGINE: V-8. Cast iron block. Displacement: 413 cid. Bore and stroke: 4.188 x 3.75 inches. Compression ratio: 10.0:1. Brake hp: 350 at 4600 rpm. Five main bearings. Hydraulic valve lifters. Carburetor: Carter AFB-2903S four-barrel.

300 ENGINE: V-8. Cast iron block. Overhead valves. Displacement: 413 cid. Bore and stroke: 4.188 x 3.75 inches. Brake hp: 375 at 5000 rpm. (Optional engine: 400 at 5200 rpm). Compression ratio: 10.1:1. Hydraulic valve lifters. (Optional engine: solid valve lifters). Dual carburetion with 30 inch Ram Induction manifold (Optional engine: dual carburetion with 15 inch Ram Induction manifold).

CHASSIS FEATURES: Wheelbase: (Windsor) 122 inches; (Saratoga) 126 inches; (New Yorker and 300) 126 inches. Overall length: (Windsor) 215.5 inches; (Windsor Wagon) 216 inches; (Saratoga) 219.4 inches; (New Yorker) 219.6 inches; (New Yorker Wagon) 220 inches. Front tread: (Windsor and Saratoga) 61 inches; (New Yorker) 61.2 inches. Rear tread: (Windsor and Saratoga) 59.7 inches; (New Yorker) 60 inches. Tires: (Windsor) 8.00 x 14; (Windsor T&C and Saratoga) 8.50 x 14; (New Yorker and 300F) 9.00 x 14.

OPTIONS: Power steering, on Windsor ($108). TorqueFlite, on Windsor ($227). Power brakes on Windsor ($44). Power windows on Windsor and Saratoga ($108). Power seat ($102). Swivel seats, except two-seat station wagons and 300F. Air conditioning ($510). Dual air conditioning, all except convertible and 300F ($714). Heater ($102). Golden tone radio ($100). Golden tone with touch tuner ($124). Rear seat speaker ($17). Power antenna ($26). Auto-Pilot ($486). Automatic beam changer ($44). Flitesweep deck lid, all but 300F and station wagons ($43). Windsor fender ornament ($9). Rear window defogger ($21). Sure Grip differ-

ential ($52). Remote-control left hand outside mirror, standard in New Yorker ($18). Solex glass ($43). Two-tone paint, on New Yorker ($20); on Windsor and Saratoga ($40). Windshield washer on Windsor ($14). White sidewall tires: Size 8.00 x 14 rayon, on Windsor ($42); Nylon ($60). Size 8.50 x 14 rayon, on Windsor station wagon and Saratoga ($46); Nylon ($66). Size 9.00 x 14rayon, on New Yorkers ($51); nylon ($72); Captive Air, on station wagons; on Windsor ($89); on New Yorker ($94). Vacuum door locks, on two-doors ($37); on four-doors ($56).

HISTORICAL FOOTNOTES: The 300F continued traditions by winning the first six places in Flying Mile competition at Daytona with top speed of nearly 145 mph. William C. Newberg ascended to presidency of Chrysler Corp., but was forced to resign within months when conflict of interest with suppliers came to light. Lester L. (Tex) Colbert became president after Newberg's resignation. Chrysler sales improved more than 25 percent over 1959, but the division remained in 12th place in industry standings.

1961 CHRYSLER

1961 Chrysler, Newport four-door hardtop, V-8

NEWPORT SERIES — (8-CYL) — In an attempt to offer Chrysler automobiles to a larger segment of the marketplace, Chrysler management reintroduced the Newport name (formerly applied to a hardtop body style) to create a low line series. Using the previous year's Windsor wheelbase, Chrysler was able to slash its entry level prices by nearly seven percent. The same number of total series was retained, by discontinuing the Saratoga nameplate. The result was a tremendous price gap between the top and bottom priced Chryslers. Minor facelifting of the 1961s centered on the grille. It now had a fine horizontal bar motif, a straight bumper and slanted headlamps. Taillamps were relocated into the deck lid latch panel and the tailfins ended in chromed inserts with tiny back-up lamps. The rear fins looked similar to the 1960 style, although there were changes from the middle of the front door forward. This was the last year for Virgil Exner's fins. Lighter weights, coupled with the smallest engine offered in a Chrysler, helped the Newport win the 1961 Mobil Oil economy run.

CHRYSLER I.D. NUMBERS: Serial numbers were found on the left front hinge post. Engine numbers were located on the boss behind the water pump. [NEWPORT] Serial numbers began with 8113-100001 and up. Station wagons used numbers 8513-100001 and up. Engine numbers indicated the year, cid displacement and date of manufacture only. They were not used for identification purposes. [WINDSOR] Windsor series serial numbers began with 8213-100001 and up. [NEW YORKER] Serial numbers began with 8313-100001 and up. Station wagons began with 8713-100001 and up. [300G] Serial numbers for Detroit built cars began with 8413-100001 and up.

NEWPORT SERIES

Model Number	Body/Style Number	Body Type & Seating	Factory Price	Shipping Weight	Production Total
RC1-L	813	4-dr Sed-6P	2964	3710	34,370
RC1-L	812	2-dr HT Cpe-6P	3025	3690	9,405
RC1-L	814	4-dr HT Sed-6P	3104	3730	7,789
RC1-L	815	2-dr Conv-6P	3442	3760	2,135
RC1-L	858	4-dr T&C Wag-6P	3541	4070	1,832
RC1-L	859	4-dr T&C Wag-9P	3622	4155	1,571

WINDSOR SERIES — (8-CYL) — The Windsor was upgraded in status in comparison to the 1960 version. It shared the same three body styles used on the longer wheelbase Saratoga series which it effectively replaced. Styling features paralleled those found on the Newport, although additional standard features were available. They included a larger displacement engine, chrome drip rail moldings, seat side shields, full wheelcovers and chrome upper door covers on the sedan.

WINDSOR SERIES

Model Number	Body/Style Number	Body Type & Seating	Factory Price	Shipping Weight	Production Total
RC2-M	832	4-dr Sed-6P	3218	3730	10,239
RC2-M	822	2-dr HT Cpe-6P	3303	3710	2,941
RC2-M	824	4-dr HT Sed-6P	3367	3765	4,156

NEW YORKER SERIES — (8-CYL) — Minor facelifting on the New Yorker followed the same pattern as changes in the shorter wheelbase Newports and Windsors. Side trim was kept to a minimum. The rear front fender trim bars were now divided into two groups of five bars each. Side trim consisted of sill and wheelhouse moldings. Station wagons used the 1960 style rear quarter panels and taillamp design. The horizontal grille bars were divided by seven fine vertical bars in an unobtrusive manner. Many features were standard equipment on the New Yorker. Dual exhausts were optional except on the station wagons.

NEW YORKER SERIES

Model Number	Body/Style Number	Body Type & Seating	Factory Price	Shipping Weight	Production Total
RC3-H	833	4-dr Sed-6P	4133	4055	9,984
RC3-H	832	2-dr HT Cpe-6P	4175	4065	2,541
RC3-H	834	4-dr HT Sed-6P	4261	4100	5,862
RC3-H	835	2-dr Conv-6P	4592	4070	576
RC3-H	878	4-dr T&C Wag-6P	4764	4425	676
RC3-H	879	4-dr T&C Wag-9P	4871	4455	760

1961 Chrysler, 300G two-door hardtop sport coupe, V-8

300G SERIES — (8-CYL) — The 300G was still considered a part of the high-performance market by those who appreciated brute horsepower in a luxury automobile. Its styling mirrored the minor styling changes found in the other 1961 Chryslers. The grille insert was 300 through-and-through and the lower rear quarter panel molding and red-white-blue medallion continued for the fifth continuous model year. Ram manifolding (long type) continued as standard fare. A few cars were built with three-speed standard shift. Some cars were built with a special "short-ram" high-output engine. These short rams look virtually identical to long rams on the outside, as the shortening was done to the effective length of the inside of the tubes.

300 G SERIES

Model Number	Body/Style Number	Body Type & Seating	Factory Price	Shipping Weight	Production Total
RC4-P	842	2-dr HT Cpe-4P	5411	4260	1,280
RC4-P	845	2-dr Conv-4P	5841	4315	337

NEWPORT ENGINE: V-8. Cast iron block. Overhead valve. Displacement: 361 cid. Bore and stroke: 4.125 x 3.375 inches. Brake hp: 265 at 4400 rpm. Compression ratio: 9.0:1. Five main bearings. Hydraulic valve lifters. Carburetor: Stromberg WWC3-188 two-barrel.

WINDSOR ENGINE: V-8. Cast iron block. Overhead valves. Displacement: 383 cid. Bore and stroke: 4.25 x 3.375 inches. Compression ratio: 10.0:1. Brake hp: 305 at 4800 rpm. Five main bearings. Hydraulic valve lifters. Carburetor: Carter BBD2923SA two-barrel.

NEW YORKER ENGINE: V-8. Cast iron block. Overhead valves. Displacement: 413 cid. Bore and stroke: 4.188 x 3.75 inches. Brake hp: 350 at 4600 rpm. Compression ratio: 10.1:1. Carburetor: Carter AFB-3108S four-barrel.

300G ENGINE: V-8. Cast iron block. Overhead valves. Displacement: 413 cid. Bore and stroke: 4.188 x 3.75 inches. Brake hp: 375 at 5000 rpm. (400 at 5200 rpm. optional). Compression ratio: 10.1:1. Five main bearings. Hydraulic valve lifters. (Solid valve lifters on optional V-8). Carburetors: Two (2) Carter four-barrel Type AFB Model 2903S.

CHASSIS FEATURES: Wheelbase: (Newport and Windsor) 122 inches; (New Yorker and 300G) 126 inches. Overall length: (Newport and Windsor) 215 inches; (Newport wagon) 216.1 inches; (New Yorker and 300G) 219.8 inches; (New Yorker wagon) 220.1 inches. Tires: (Newport and Windsor) 8.00 x 14; (Newport wagon) 8.50 x 14; (New Yorker) 8.50 x 14; (New Yorker wagon) 9.00 x 14; (300G) 8.00 x 15.

OPTIONS: Power steering on Newport and Windsor ($108). TorqueFlite in Newport and Windsor ($227). Power brakes in Newport and Windsor ($44). Power windows, except standard in 300G ($108). Power seat ($102). Swivel seat in Newport convertible and New Yorkers except station wagons ($87). Heater ($102). Air conditioner, all except station wagons ($510). Air conditioner, in station wagons ($714). Golden Tone radio ($100). Golden Touch Tuner radio ($124). Power antenna ($26). Auto-Pilot, except in 300G ($86) Flitesweep deck lid, except station wagons and 300G ($21). Rear window defogger ($21). Sure grip differential ($52). Left-hand outside remote mirror, in all except New Yorker ($18). Tinted glass ($43). Undercoating, standard on 300G ($18). Dual exhausts. New Yorkers except station wagons ($27). Closed crankcase vent system ($5).

HISTORICAL FOOTNOTES: Last year for Virgil Exner's finned look. Newport wins Mobil Gas Economy Run with an average just below 20 mpg. Lester L. Colbert resumed position as Chairman of the Board and Lynn Townsend became Chrysler president. Elwood Engel, former Ford design chief, was appointed to replace fired Exner as Chrysler chief designer. First year for the low-block 383 cid engine in a Chrysler.

1962 CHRYSLER

NEWPORT SERIES — (V-8) — The volume low-priced Chrysler continued with the same body styles found in 1961. While mechanical details were similar to its predecessor a minor facelift gave the car a distinctly different look. Gone forever were the Exner inspired tailfins and the indented side body styling. The grille, headlamps, front bumper and parking lamps were essentially unchanged from their 1961 counterpart. The grille mesh was reminiscent of the 1960 Windsor and Saratoga series. Taillamps now wrapped over the de-finned, flattened rear fenders and a stainless steel trim piece ran from the front to the rear at mid-body height. A new aluminum cased TorqueFlite transmission was the last to use a parking brake at the rear of the case. Lighter weight and improved engine efficiency accounted for an increase of seven percent in claimed fuel economy. All 1962 models, except for the New Yorker, used the 122 inch wheelbase.

1962 Chrysler, Newport four-door sedan, V-8

CHRYSLER I.D. NUMBERS: Serial numbers were found on the left front hinge post. Engine numbers were located on the boss behind the water pump. [NEWPORT] Newport serial numbers began with 8123-100001 and up while station wagon numbers began with 8523-10001 and up. [300 SPORT SERIES] Serial numbers for the Detroit built cars began with 8223-100001 and up. The engine code began with the 'S' prefix, plus the two digit code signifying displacement and the date. [NEW YORKER] Detroit built serial numbers began with 8323-100001 and up. Station wagons began with 8723-100001 and up. [300H SERIES] Serial numbers began with 8423-100001 and up. Chrysler engine numbers were stamped with a letter denoting the year code, plus two numbers denoting cid: [Newport/Sport 300] 38=383 and additional symbols signify month/day. [New Yorker] The engine prefix was S41. [300H] The engine code began with S41, then the date, plus a horsepower code. The date was given in numerical form, such as 11-12 = November 12. Chrysler engines no longer had a true serial identification number.

NEWPORT SERIES

Model Number	Body/Style Number	Body Type & Seating	Factory Price	Shipping Weight	Production Total
SC1-L	813	4-dr Sed-6P	2964	3720	54,813
SC1-L	812	2-dr HT Cpe-6P	3027	3705	11,910
SC1-L	814	4-dr HT Sed-6P	3106	3735	8,712
SC1-L	815	2-dr Conv-6P	3399	3780	2,051
SC1-L	858	4-dr T&C Sta Wag-6-P	3478	4125	3,271
SC1-L	859	4-dr T&C Sta Wag-9P	3586	4185	2,363

1962 Chrysler, 300 two-door hardtop sport coupe, V-8

300 SERIES — (V-8) — The Windsor name was dropped to make room for a Sport Series 300 line. Confusion resulted from this marketing move as buyers associated the 300 name with high-performance and high cost. The exterior appearance of the hardtop (two-door) and the convertible were identical to the 300H Letter Car, except for hubcaps, tires and the lack of a tiny 'H' on the rear deck. A four-door hardtop had never been offered in the Chrysler 300 Letter Car line. Even the grille, medallions and side trim were indistinguishable, at first glance, from the higher-priced, performance oriented 300H. The Sport Series 300 interiors were upgraded versions of the low-line Newport series.

300 SERIES

Model Number	Body/Style Number	Body Type & Seating	Factory Price	Shipping Weight	Production Total
SC2-M	823	4-dr Sed-6P	3258	3780	1,801
SC2-M	822	2-dr HT Cpe-6P	3323	3765	11,776
SC2-M	824	4-dr HT Sed-6P	3400	3810	10,030
SC2-M	825	2-dr Conv-6P	3883	3880	1,971

NEW YORKER SERIES — (8-CYL) — The New Yorker continued to use the long wheelbase chassis, although it was available only in three body types, all with four doors. The New Yorker nameplate was found at the same location (near the parking lamp) as in 1961. The 10 bar rear fender trim continued on the rear quarters of New Yorkers, except the station wagon. The rear quarter panel on the wagon was styled differently than sedan or hardtop models. The grille used the crossbar look, formerly found on only the 300 series.

NEW YORKER SERIES

Model Number	Body/Style Number	Body Type & Seating	Factory Price	Shipping Weight	Production Total
SC3-H	833	4-dr Sed-6P	4125	3950	12,056
SC3-H	834	4-dr HT Sed-6P	4263	3970	6,646
SC3-H	878	4-dr T&C Wag-6P	4766	4325	728
SC3-H	879	4-dr T&C Wag-9P	4873	4385	793

1962 Chrysler 300-H convertible

300H SERIES — (V-8) — The true high-performance 300 used the same series designation as the Sport Series 300, but serial number identification was different. Tan leather upholstery was standard, although special order colors were available. Both interiors and exteriors came with special colors in earlier years. A variety of high-performance engine options were available, although the inline, dual carbureted engine was standard. The 300H chassis was no longer shared with the New Yorker Series, as with past models. Sales dropped dramatically for the Letter Cars this year, mostly due to the competition of the Sport 300 series, which offered nearly everything found on the 300H as standard or optional equipment.

1962 Chrysler, New Yorker four-door hardtop sedan, V-8

300H SERIES

Model Number	Body/Style Number	Body Type & Seating	Factory Price	Shipping Weight	Production Total
SC2-M	842	2-dr HT Cpe-4P	5090	4050	435
SC2-M	845	2-dr Conv-4P	5461	4105	123

NEWPORT ENGINE: V-8. Overhead valves. Cast iron block. Displacement: 361.8 cid. Bore and stroke: 4.125 x 3.375 inches. Compression ratio: 9.0:1. Brake hp: 265 at 4400 rpm. Five main bearings. Hydraulic valve lifters. Carburetor: Stromberg Type WWC3 two-barrel Model 201A.

300 SPORT ENGINE: V-8. Overhead valves. Cast iron block. Displacement: 383 cid. Bore and stroke: 4.25 x 3.375 inches. Compression ratio: 10.0:1. Brake hp: 305 at 4600 rpm. Five main bearings. Hydraulic valve lifters. Carburetor: Carter Type BBD two-barrel Model 3244S.

NEW YORKER ENGINE: V-8. Overhead valves. Cast iron block. Displacement: 413.3 cid. Bore and stroke: 4.188 x 3.75 inches. Compression ratio: 10.1:1. Brake hp: 340 at 4600 rpm. Five main bearings. Hydraulic valve lifters. Carburetor: Carter Type AFB four-barrel Model 3251S.

300H ENGINES: V-8. Overhead valves. Cast iron block. Displacement: 413.3 cid. Bore and stroke: 4.188 x 3.75 inches. Compression ratio: 10.1:1. Brake hp: 380 at 5200 rpm. Five main bearings. Solid valve lifters. Carburetor: Two Carter Type AFB four-barrels Models 3258S.

CHASSIS FEATURES: Wheelbase: (Newport, 300 Sport Series, 300H) 122 inches; (New Yorker) 126 inches. Overall length: (Newport, 300 Sport Series, 300H) 214.9 inches; (Newport station wagon) 216.4 inches; (New Yorker) 219.3 inches; (New Yorker station wagon) 220.4 inches. Tires: (Newport and Sport Series 300) 8.00 x 14; (Newport station wagon) 8.50 x 14; (New Yorker) 8.50 x 14; (New Yorker station wagon) 9.00 x 14; (300H) 7.60 x 15.

OPTIONS: Power brakes ($48). Power steering ($108). Air conditioning ($510); same with groups 304 or 306 ($409). Dual Deluxe air conditioning ($714). Power radio antenna ($26). Auto pilot ($86). Rear window defogger ($21). Vacuum door locks ($56). Custom Conditionaire heater ($102). Left outside remote control mirror ($18). Power door locks ($56). Front power seats ($102). Rear shelf radio speaker ($17). Golden Tone radio ($93). Golden Touch Tone radio ($129). Tinted windshield ($29). Tinted glass, all windows ($43). Shaded backlight ($74). Newport full wheelcovers ($19). Newport windshield washer ($14). Leather front bucket seats ($201). Vinyl trim in Newport ($121). Vinyl trim in New Yorker ($86). Vinyl trim in New Yorker four-door hardtop ($65). Variable speed windshield wipers ($6). Tailgate assist handle ($17). Padded steering wheel in Newport ($16). Electric clock in Newport and Sport 300 ($19). Undercoating ($18). Three-speed manual transmission with non-synchro first and floor shift was standard on Newport and Sport Series 300. Automatic transmission was standard with New Yorker and 300H. Optional automatic transmission ($227). V-8 413 cid 340 hp four-barrel engine ($162). V-8 413 cid 380 hp dual four-barrel engine ($486). V-8 413 cid 405 hp ram-induction engine. Positive traction rear axle ($52). Available rear axle gear ratios: 2.93:1; 3.23:1.

HISTORICAL FOOTNOTES: A 1962 Chrysler New Yorker won luxury class in the Mobil Gas Economy Run with slightly more than 18 mpg. No two-door model was offered in the Chrysler New Yorker series for first time since the New York Special of 1938. Chrysler sales rose slightly more than 10 percent, but industry position remained unchanged (11th place).

1963 CHRYSLER

NEWPORT SERIES — (V-8) — A major, tasteful restyling of the entire 1963 Chrysler line used a semi-slab side look with a minimal use of trim. Hood, fenders and rear deck had a flat, broad look that contributed to the overall integrated styling theme. For the first time since its inception in the 1961 model year, the closed crankcase venting system became standard equipment across the board. The Newport was built on the 122 inch wheelbase, as were all other Chryslers this year. Headlamps reverted back to a more normal horizontal style. The grille theme continued the 300 crossbar look pioneered in 1957. Thin horizontal bright bars were placed in front of a blacked-out thin vertical bar background giving the car a broader, lower frontal appearance. Rear taillamps were mounted on pods on each side of the rear end. Chrysler included a five-year, 50,000 miles warranty on all drivetrain parts. This policy helped Chrysler improve market penetration approximately 50 percent in a very short period of time.

1963 Chrysler, Newport four-door sedan, V-8 (IMS)

CHRYSLER I.D. NUMBERS: Serial numbers were found on the left front hinge post. Engine numbers were located on the boss behind the water pump. [NEWPORT SERIES] Serial numbers began with 813-100001 and up. Station wagons began with 8533-100001 and up. [300 SPORT SERIES]: Detroit-built cars began with serial number 8233-100001 and up. Engine prefix was the letter 'T'. [NEW YORKER SERIES] Detroit built cars began with serial number 8333-100001 and up. Station wagons used serial numbers 8733-100001 and up. Engine prefix began with T-41 and then the date code as on previous series engines. [300J SERIES] Numbers began with 8433-100001 and up. Engine prefix was C300J and then a month, day, year code (i.e. 11-10-62 — denoted November 10, 1962 build date).

NEWPORT SERIES

Model Number	Body/Style Number	Body Type & Seating	Factory Price	Shipping Weight	Production Total
TC1-L	813	4-dr Sed-6P	2964	3745	49,067
TC1-L	812	2-dr HT Cpe-6P	3027	3735	9,809
TC1-L	814	4-dr HT Sed-6P	3106	3775	8,437
TC1-L	815	2-dr Conv-6P	3399	3800	2,093
TC1-L	858	4-dr T&C Sta Wag-6P	3478	4175	3,618
TC1-L	859	4-dr T&C Sta Wag-9P	3586	4190	2,948

300 SPORT SERIES — (V-8) — The 300 Sport Series continued with the same body types as used in 1962. A later addition to the 300 lineup was the Pace Setter Series, introduced to commemorate the use of a 300 as the Pace Car for the Indianapolis 500 mile race. Pace Setter editions were identified by special interiors and a small checkered flag placed below the front fender 300 emblem. They had a square-shaped steering wheel, as opposed to the round steering wheel used in other Sport 300s. An option was full leather in cars with a bucket seat interior.

1963 Chrysler, 300 Sport Series two-door convertible, V-8 (MC)

300 SPORT SERIES

Model Number	Body/Style Number	Body Type & Seating	Factory Price	Shipping Weight	Production Total
TC2-M	822	2-dr HT Cpe-6P	3430	3765	9,423
TC2-M	823	4-dr Sed-6P	3765	3785	1,625
TC2-M	824	4-dr HT Sed-6P	3400	3790	9,915
TC2-M	825	2-dr Conv-6P	3790	3820	1,535
TC2-M	802	2-dr Pace Car HT	3769	3790	306
TC2-M	805	2-dr Pace Car Conv	4129	3840	1,861

NOTE 1: The four-door sedan referred to above was built as a Saratoga for the Canadian market, but counted in the plant as a 300.

NEW YORKER SERIES — (V-8) — The New Yorker displayed the crisp, new custom look emphasized in 1963 advertising. A thin beltline molding ran from front to rear and the unusual New Yorker trim bars were now found on the front fender, behind the wheel opening and below the New Yorker nameplate. The number of trim bars was reduced to six. Interiors featured deeply quilted, luxurious jacquard fabrics and soft durable vinyl trim. The custom look was divided into two halves and eggcrate style inserts, reminiscent of the earlier 1955 and 1956 Imperials, added to the custom look. Wheelbase this year matched the other less expensive lines wearing the Chrysler nameplates. A four-door hardtop Salon option was offered with a luxurious interior, vinyl roof and special side trim plus 'Salon' nameplates.

NEW YORKER SERIES

Model Number	Body/Style Number	Body Type & Seating	Factory Price	Shipping Weight	Production Total
TC3-H	833	4-dr Sed-6P	3981	3910	14,884
TC3-H	834	4-dr HT Sed-6P	4118	3950	10,289
TC3-H	884	4-dr Salon-6P	5344	4290	593
TC3-H	878	4-dr T&C Wag-6P	4708	4350	950
TC3-H	879	4-dr T&C Wag-9P	4815	4370	1,244

300J SERIES — (V-8) — Available in two-door hardtop form only, the 300J continued Chrysler's image of providing the motoring public with a high-performance luxury automobile so synonymous with previous 300s. Leather interiors were standard and special 'J' medallions distinguished this car from the more common Sports Series 300s. Heavy-duty torsion bars, shocks and springs, plus Ram-Tube induction manifolds were the main backbone of the 300J's image.

300J SERIES

Model Number	Body/Style Number	Body Type & Seating	Factory Price	Shipping Weight	Production Total
TC2-M	842	2-dr HT Cpe-6P	5260	4000	400

NEWPORT ENGINE: V-8. Overhead valves. Cast iron block. Displacement: 361 cid. Bore and stroke: 4.12 x 3.38 inches. Compression ratio: 9.0:1. Brake hp: 265 at 4400 rpm. Five main bearings. Hydraulic valve lifters. Carburetor: Stromberg Type WWC-3 two-barrel Model 221.

300 SPORT ENGINE: V-8. Overhead valves. Cast iron block. Displacement: 383 cid. Bore and stroke: 4.25 x 3.375 inches. Compression ratio: 10.0:1. Brake hp: 305 at 4600 rpm. Five main bearings. Hydraulic valve lifters. Carburetor: Carter Type BBD two-barrel Model 3476S.

NEW YORKER ENGINE: V-8. Overhead valves. Cast iron block. Displacement: 413.8 cid. Bore and stroke: 4.188 x 3.75 inches. Compression ratio: 10.0:1. Brake hp: 340 at 4600 rpm. Five main bearings. Hydraulic valve lifters. Carburetor: Carter Type AFB four-barrel Model 3256S.

300J ENGINE: V-8. Overhead valves. Cast iron block. Displacement: 413.8 cid. Bore and stroke: 4.188 x 3.75 inches. Compression ratio: 10.0:1. Brake hp: 390 at 4800 rpm. Five main bearings. Solid valve lifters. Carburetor: Two (2) Carter Type AFB four-barrels Model 3505S.

CHASSIS FEATURES: Wheelbase: (All Series) 122 inches. Overall length: (Newport station wagon) 219.4 inches; (New Yorker station wagon) 219.7 inches; (all other models) 215.3 inches. Front tread: (Newport and 300) 61 inches; (New Yorker) 59.7 inches. Rear tread: (Newport and 300) 59.7 inches; (New Yorker) 59.9 inches. Tires: (Newport and 300 Sport Series) 8.00 x 14; (New Yorker) 8.50 x 14; (300J) 7.60 x 15.

OPTIONS: Power brakes in Newport and Sport 300 ($48). Power steering in Newport and Sport 300 ($108). Dual air conditioning in Newport and Sport 300 ($612). Air conditioning with heater ($150). Power antenna, except station wagons ($26). Auto pilot ($86). Front console in 300 ($165). Rear window defogger ($21). Custom Conditionaire heater ($102). Left outside remote control mirror ($18). Station wagon two-tone paint ($20). Left or right power bucket seat ($93). Power door locks in four-door ($56). Power front bench seat ($101). Power windows ($108). Golden Tone radio ($93). Golden Touch Tune radio ($13). Rear speaker, except convertible and station wagon ($17). Pair of front seat belts ($24). Tailgate assist handle ($17). Tinted windshield ($29). All tinted glass ($43). Leather trim in 300 hardtop and convertible ($93). Undercoating ($18). Leather front bucket seats in 300 four-door hardtop ($201). Vinyl bucket seats in 300 four-door hardtop ($108). Vinyl bucket seats in New Yorker ($86). A three-speed manual transmission with non-synchro first and floor shift was standard on Newport and Sport 300s. Automatic transmission was standard on New Yorkers and 300Js. V-8 413 cid 360 hp twin four-barrel engine ($162). V-8 413 cid 365 hp twin four-barrel engine. V-8 426 cid 373 hp twin four-barrel engine. V-8 426 cid 415 hp short ram engine. V-8 426 cid 425 hp short ram engine. Positive traction rear axle ($52).

HISTORICAL FOOTNOTES: The 1963 Chryslers were introduced Sept. 26, 1962. Model year production peaked at 118,800 units. Calendar year sales of 116,040 cars were recorded. P.N. Buckminster was chief executive officer of the company this year. Chrysler held 11th rank in the auto industry this season. A Chrysler 300 'Pacesetter' convertible paced the 1963 Indianapolis 500 mile race.

1964 CHRYSLER

NEWPORT SERIES — (V-8) — A minor facelift greeted 1964 Chrysler buyers on new model announcement day. The grille now had brightwork with an emblem centered on each of three cross-bars. Side trim had a wider look with a gentle thickening towards the rear. Taillamps were located at the extreme side of the rear end, but were rectangular in nature, versus the round 1963 housings. Station wagons continued to use the four-door pillarless body style introduced in 1960. Prices remained relatively constant with prior years.

CHRYSLER I.D. NUMBERS: Serial numbers were found on the left front hinge post. Engine numbers were located on the boss behind the water pump. [NEWPORT SERIES] Motor numbers used a V36 prefix plus the date of build. Serial numbers began with 8143-100001 and up. Station wagons used 8543100001 and up. [300 SERIES] Serial numbers began with 8243-100001 and up. Prefix for the 300 began with V38 for the standard engines and V41 for the optional 413 cid engine. [NEW YORKER] Engine prefix was V41. Serial numbers began with 8343-100001 and up. Salons began with 8843-100001 and up while Town and Country station wagons used 8743-100001 and up. [300K SERIES] Serial numbers began with 8443-100001 and up. Engine numbers began with V41 and then the date code as before. 11-1 2 referred to November 12 production date. The letters HP were also stamped on the non-Ram-Tuned 300Ks. Ram-Tune inducted cars used a slightly different system. The prefix was C300K then the complete date followed (i.e. 11-1263).

NEWPORT SERIES

Model Number	Body/Style Number	Body Type & Seating	Factory Price	Shipping Weight	Production Total
VC1-L	813	4-dr Sed-6P	2901	3790	55,957
VC1-L	812	2-dr HT Cpe-6P	2962	3770	10,579
VC1-L	814	4-dr HT Sed-6P	3042	3810	9,710
VC1-L	815	2-dr Conv-6P	3334	3830	2,176
VC1-L	858	4-dr T&C Wag-6P	3414	4165	3,720
VC1-L	859	4-dr T&C Wag-9P	3521	4200	3,041

1964 Chrysler, 300 two-door hardtop sport coupe, V-8

CHRYSLER 300 SERIES — (V-8) — This series dropped the 'Sport' designation used in earlier years. Silver anodized side trim was unique to the 300. A special 300 was introduced as a spring option. It included a silver exterior finish and black vinyl roof with black leather/vinyl interior. A star-shaped insignia was placed at the C-pillar on hardtops and the rear part of the front fender on convertibles. The insignia matched the style of the grille insert used on all 300s.

300 SERIES

Model Number	Body/Style Number	Body Type & Seating	Factory Price	Shipping Weight	Production Total
VC2-M	822	2-dr HT Cpe-6P	3443	3850	13,401
VC2-M	824	4-dr HT Sed-6P	3521	3865	11,460
VC2-M	825	2-dr Conv-6P	3803	4120	2,026
VC2-M	823	4-dr Sed-6P	3371	3875	

1964 Chrysler, New Yorker four-door sedan, V-8.

NEW YORKER SERIES — (V-8) — The New Yorker facelift paralleled changes seen throughout the 1964 Chrysler lineup. The eggcrate grille halves were dropped and a very fine horizontal bar ensemble was placed within the cavity. The New Yorker Town & Country station wagon used the same side trim as the Newport Town and Country. The New Yorker Salon's base price made it the most expensive regular Chrysler model of the year. It carried virtually every available option, except dual unit air conditioning, adjustable steering wheel, Sure Grip differential and leather trim. The New Yorker script was placed low on the rear portion of the front fender, except on the Salon, where a Salon script was set slightly higher on the fender.

1964 Chrysler, New Yorker four-door hardtop sedan, V-8

NEW YORKER SERIES

Model Number	Body/Style Number	Body Type & Seating	Factory Price	Shipping Weight	Production Total
VC3-H	832	2-dr HT Cpe-6P	NA	NA	300
VC3-H	833	4-dr Sed-6P	3994	4015	15,443
VC3-H	834	4-dr HT Sed-6P	4131	4030	10,887
VC3-H	878	4-dr T&C Wag-6P	4721	4385	1,190
VC3-H	879	4-dr T&C Wag-9P	4828	4395	1,603
VC3-H	884	4-dr Salon-6P	5860	4280	1,621

NOTE 1: Some sources list production of four-door hardtop Salon as 1,748.

1964 Chrysler, 300K convertible, V-8

300K SERIES — (V-8) — The convertible returned to the Chrysler 300 Letter Car series lineup after a one year hiatus. Styling paralleled the regular 300 series, although interiors were more luxuriously detailed. A between-the-seat console was standard and leather trim was optional. A Ram-Tuned induction manifold setup was available as an option.

300K SERIES

Model Number	Body/Style Number	Body Type & Seating	Factory Price	Shipping Weight	Production Total
VC2-M300842		2-dr HT Cpe-4P	4056	3965	3,022
VC2-M300845		2-dr Conv-4P	4522	3990	625

NEWPORT ENGINE: V-8. Overhead valves. Cast iron block. Displacement: 360.8 cid. Bore and stroke: 4.125 x 3.375 inches. Compression ratio: 9.0:1. Brake hp: 265 at 4400 rpm. Five main bearings. Hydraulic valve lifters. Carburetor: Stromberg Type WWC-3 two-barrel Model 244.

300 ENGINES: V-8. Overhead valves. Cast iron block. Displacement: 383 cid. Bore and stroke: 4.25 x 3.375 inches. Compression ratio: 10.0:1. Brake hp: 305 at 4600 rpm. Five main bearings. Hydraulic valve lifters. Carburetor: Carter Type BBD two-barrel Model 3685S.

NEW YORKER ENGINE: V-8. Overhead valves. Cast iron block. Displacement: 413.8 cid. Bore and stroke: 4.188 x 3.75 inches. Compression ratio: 10.0:1. Brake hp: 340 at 4600 rpm. Five main bearings. Hydraulic valve lifters. Carburetor: Carter Type AFB four-barrel Model 36155.

300K ENGINE: V-8. Overhead valves. Cast iron block. Displacement: 413.8 cid. Bore and stroke: 4.188 x 3.75 inches. Compression ratio: 10.1:1. Brake hp 390 at 4800 rpm. Five main bearings. Solid valve lifters. Carburetor: Dual Carter Type AFB four-barrel Model 3614S.

CHASSIS FEATURES: Wheelbase: 122 inches. Overall length: (Newport and VC2-M 300) 215.3 inches; (Newport station wagon) 219.4 inches; (300J and New Yorker) 215.5 inches; (New Yorker station wagon) 219.7 inches. Tires: (Newport, 300, 300K) 8.00 x 14; (New Yorker) 8.50 x 14.

OPTIONS: Power steering in Newport and 300, standard in other ($108). Power brakes in Newport and 300, standard in others ($48). Power windows, all models ($108). Six-Way power seat in Newport and New Yorker ($102). Power door locks in four-door styles ($56). Heater and defroster, all models ($102). Air conditioning, all models ($510). Deluxe dual air conditioning, all except convertibles ($714). Golden Tone radio, all models ($93). AM/FM radio, all models ($157). Golden Touch Tuner radio, all models ($129). Center Console in all 300 models ($129). Leather trim in 300 and 300K ($94). Leather trim in New Yorker Salon ($72). Seat belts, all models ($7). Heavy-duty springs, shocks, sway bar and brakes ($36). Adjustable steering wheel, all models ($47). Undercoating, all models ($18). Tinted glass, all windows ($43). Three-speed manual floor mounted transmission with non-synchro first gear was standard on Newport and non-Letter Series Chrysler 300s. Automatic transmission was standard on New Yorker and 300K. Automatic transmission was optional on Newport and non-Letter 300 ($227). Close-ratio four-speed manual floor shift was optional ($227). V-8 413 cid 360 hp four-barrel engine on 300 and 300 J. ($43). V-8 413 cid 390 hp dual four-barrel Ram-Tuned induction engine ($375). Positive traction rear axle ($52). Available rear axle gear ratios: 3.23: 1; 3.91: 1; 2.76:1.

HISTORICAL FOOTNOTES: The 1964 Chryslers were introduced Sept. 20, 1963. Model year production peaked at 145,192 units. Calendar year production of 145,338 cars was recorded. This was the last year for the optional availability of the Ram-Tuned induction V-8. Chrysler sales rebounded by 11 percent, although the division remained the 11th ranked American automaker. Fifty experimental Chrysler gas turbine cars were provided to selected individuals for test driving and field evaluations under normal operating conditions. The majority of these unique automobiles were later destroyed, although several survive in private collections, museums and the Chrysler Historical Collection today.

1965 CHRYSLER

NEWPORT SERIES — (V-8) — A major retooling effort coupled with a base price of less than $3,000 helped Chrysler achieve a banner year with sales rising about 55 percent over those of the previous year. Nearly half of all Chrysler sales were in the Newport Series. Newports featured a boldly sculptured side panel that was outlined with stainless steel at the top beltline

and again at a level slightly above, wheel hub height. Both headlamps and taillights were inset from the outer edges of the fender line. The taillamps were set in a horizontally outlined panel above the rear bumper and below the deck lid. The dual headlamps nestled within the grille area which carried the same broad outlined look of the side panels. The grille insert was a fine, horizontal bar motif with a rectangular medallion set upright in the center. The new chassis used a two inch longer wheelbase than previous Newports. A new, larger displacement engine was now featured as was a six-window sedan which complemented the standard sedan. The common sedan outsold the new style by five-to-one.

1965 Chrysler, Newport four-door hardtop sedan, V-8

CHRYSLER I.D. NUMBERS: [NEWPORT SERIES] A new serial number format was introduced. The location of the serial numbers and engine numbers were unchanged from previous series. Detroit built cars used serial numbers with C153-100001 and up. Delaware built cars used serial numbers C156-100001 and up. Newport station wagons built in Detroit used numbers C553-100001 and up and those built in Delaware used serial numbers beginning with C556-100001 and up. The engine prefix was 'A' for 1965 models. The engine displacement code followed and preceeded codes depicting month and date. A-383-9-12 can be identified as a 1965 Newport with a 383 cid engine built on Sept. 12 (of 1964). [300 SERIES] Serial numbers for Detroit built cars began with C253-100001 and up. Delaware built cars began with C256-100001 and up. Chrysler 300s with the standard 383 cid V-8 had motor numbers with an A-383 prefix located on the front, right-hand side of the engine block. Chrysler 300s with the optional 413 cid V-8 had motor numbers with an A-413 prefix located on the top of the block, to the left of the water pump. [NEW YORKER] Detroit built cars began with serial number C353-100001 and up and Delaware cars began with C356-100001 and up. Station wagons built in Detroit used C753-100001 and up and those built in Delaware used C756-100001 and up. Engine prefix was A-413. [300K SERIES] Detroit built units began with C453-100001 and up while Delaware built cars began with C456-100001 and up. Engine prefix began with A-413 and then the date code. 300L's also had an 'HP' stamped on the block, alongside the date code.

NEWPORT SERIES

Model Number	Body/Style Number	Body Type & Seating	Factory Price	Shipping Weight	Production Total
AC1-L	C13	4-dr Sed-6P	2968	4025	61,054
AC1-L	C18	4-dr Twn Sed-6P	3100	4040	12,411
AC1-L	C-12	2-dr HT Cpe-6P	3028	3985	23,655
AC1-L	C14	4-dr HT Sed-6P	3582	4040	17,062
AC1-L	C15	2-dr Conv-6P	3192	4070	3,192
AC1-L	C56	4-dr T&C Sta Wag-6P	3470	4400	4,683
AC1-L	C57	4-dr T&C Sta Wag-9P	3576	4465	3,738

300 SERIES — (V-8) — A star-shaped emblem continued to be used on the blacked-out grille bars as on the previous Chrysler 300 Series. Headlamps were built into the outlined grille and were covered by a unique glass shield. Lower body trim differed from the Letter Car series 300. It had three uniquely stamped imprints at the forward edge of the trim, behind the wheelhouse opening. The interiors of the non-Letter Car 300s were upgraded over the Newport versions. The four-door sedan found in the 300 Series was the six-window version.

300 SERIES

Model Number	Body/Style Number	Body Type & Seating	Factory Price	Shipping Weight	Production Total
AC2-M	C22	2-dr HT Cpe-5P	3500	4115	11,621
AC2-M	C24	4-dr HT Sed-5P	3575	4210	12,452
AC2-M	C25	2-dr Conv-5P	3852	4185	1,418
AC2-M	C28	4-dr Sed-6P	3570	4160	2,187

1965 Chrysler, New Yorker two-door hardtop sports coupe, V-8

NEW YORKER SERIES — (V-8) — The all-new New Yorker featured glass covered headlamps like the 300 models. The grille had bold vertical and horizontal divisions, which gave the effect of rectangular spaces filled with finer bars. The grille was worthy of the New Yorker's status at the top-of-the-line. The station wagons now featured a center pillar like the sedans. The hardtop look in the station wagon was no longer available. Fender skirts were standard on all models in 1965. The New Yorker script was placed on the rear quarter panel. The New Yorker sedan was of the six-window Town sedan type.

NEW YORKER SERIES

Model Number	Body/Style Number	Body Type & Seating	Factory Price	Shipping Weight	Production Total
AC3-H	C38	4-dr Sed-6P	4173	4245	16,339
AC3-H	C32	2-dr HT Cpe-6P	4098	4190	9,357
AC3-H	C34	4-dr HT Sed-6P	4173	4245	21,110
AC3-H	C76	4-dr T&C Wag-6P	4751	4645	1,368
AC3-H	C77	4-dr T&C Wag-9P	4856	4710	1,697

1965 Chrysler, 300L two-door convertible, V-8 (MC)

300L SERIES — (V-8) — This was the last year for the Letter Series high-performance specialty car. It closely resembled the standard 300. The letter 'L' in the center of the grille cross-bar lit-up when the lights were turned on. The 300L used high-performance tires and suspension. Coupled with a high-output 413 cid single carb engine, this set it apart from the regular 300. Styling touches used to distinguish the Chrysler 300L were a painted insert in the upper body molding and a damascened insert between the rear taillamps. There were also special interior appointments and appropriate Letter Series medallions.

300L SERIES

Model Number	Body/Style Number	Body Type & Seating	Factory Price	Shipping Weight	Production Total
AC2-P	C42	2-dr HT Cpe-5P	4090	4225	2,405
AC2-P	C45	2-dr Conv-5P	4545	4155	440

NEWPORT ENGINE: V-8. Overhead valves. Cast iron block. Displacement: 383 cid. Bore and stroke: 4.25 x 3.375 inches. Compression ratio: 9.2:1. Brake hp: 270 at 4400 rpm Five main bearings. Hydraulic valve lifters. Carburetor: Carter Type BBD two-barrel Model 3849S.

300 ENGINES: V-8. Overhead valves. Cast iron block. Displacement: 383 cid. Bore and stroke: 4.25 x 3.375 inches. Compression ratio: 10.0:1. Brake hp: 315 at 4400 rpm. Five main bearings. Hydraulic valve lifters. Carburetor: Carter Type AFB four-barrel Model 3855S.

NEW YORKER ENGINE: V-8. Overhead valves. Cast iron block. Displacement: 413.8 cid. Bore and stroke: 4.188 x 3.75 inches. Compression ratio: 10.0:1. Brake hp: 340 at 4600 rpm. Five main bearings. Hydraulic valve lifters. Carburetor: Carter Type AFB four-barrel model 3858S.

300L ENGINE: V-8. Overhead valves. Cast iron block. Displacement: 413.8 cid. Bore and stroke: 4.188 x 3.75 inches. Compression ratio: 10.0:1. Brake hp: 360 at 4800 rpm. Five main bearings. Hydraulic valve lifters. Carburetor: Carter Type AFB four-barrel Model 3860S.

CHASSIS FEATURES: Wheelbase: (Newport, 300, New Yorker) 124 inches; (Town and Country station wagons) 121 inches. Overall length: (Newport, 300, New Yorker) 218.2 inches; (Town and Country station wagons) 218.4 inches. Tires: (Newport, 300) 8.25 x 14; (New Yorker, 300L, Town and Country) 8.55 x 14.

OPTIONS: Power steering (Newport, 300). Power brakes (Newport, 300). Power windows. Power seat. Reclining bucket seats. Power door locks. Heater and defroster. Air conditioner (dual air conditioning on all except convertible). Golden Tone radio. AM-FM radio. Golden Touch tuner. Rear seat speaker. Console (300). Seat belts. Heavy-duty springs, shocks, sway bar and brakes (300). Adjustable steering wheel. Undercoating. Tinted glass. Day/Night rearview mirror. Remote control mirror. Three-speed manual transmission was standard in Newport and non-letter 300. Automatic transmission was standard in New Yorker and 300L models. Automatic transmission was optional in Newport and non-letter 300s. Automatic transmission column shift controls replaced push-buttons this year. Four-speed manual floor shift transmission was optional in Newports, 300s and 300Ls. V-8 383 cid 315 hp four-barrel engine in Newports. V-8 413 cid 360 hp four-barrel engine in 300s and New Yorkers. Positive traction rear axle was optional in all models at extra cost.

HISTORICAL FOOTNOTES: Last year for Letter Series 300s. Chrysler built more than 200,000 cars for the first time ever. Last year for 413 engine.

1966 CHRYSLER

NEWPORT — (V-8) — The Newport, for 1966, continued as the Chrysler price leader with minimal styling changes. There were the usual cosmetic touches to the grille and rear deck area. The lower trim molding had a painted insert, which ran forward from the rear bumper to just ahead of the front door hinge post. From there a solid, non-painted trim piece continued further forward. Fender skirts were a standard item on all body styles. Nameplates were placed on the rear quarter panels. The six-window sedan was in its second and last year of production, as sales slid nearly 25 percent from 1965. The station wagon continued with its

sedan look, but used a shorter chassis. Overall, Chrysler sales rose more than 14 percent. A Cleaner Air Package was available for emission control and a shoulder harness was a new safety option.

1966 Chrysler, Newport two-door convertible, V-8

CHRYSLER I.D. NUMBERS: Serial numbers and engine numbers were located in the usual positions. Serial numbers now included a code that revealed the body styles, as follows: 23=two-door hardtop, 41=four-door sedan; 42=six-window four-door sedan; 27=convertible; 45=six-passenger station wagon and 46=nine-passenger station wagon. The type of engine was designated by an alphabetical code as follows: 'G' = 383 cid V-8; 'J' = 440 cid V-8. A '6' was the next symbol and designated the 1966 model year. Numerical codes designated the assembly plant, as follows: '3' = Detroit, Michigan and '6' = Delaware. The last six symbols were the sequential manufacturing number. Motor numbers had a 'B' prefix and then three numbers designating displacement as in previous years. [NEWPORT SERIES] Newports built in Detroit used serial numbers CL23G63-100001 and up and Delaware built cars used serial numbers CL23G66-100001 and up. [300 SERIES] 300 serial numbers were assigned in a similar fashion to the Newport series except that the prefix was 'CM' rather than 'CL'. CM23J66-100001 and up would identify a 1966 Chrysler 300 two-door hardtop with the 440 cid engine built in Delaware. [NEW YORKER] Detroit built serial numbers for sedans were CH42J63-100001 and up while Delaware built sedans began with CH42J66-100001 and up. Engine prefix was B-440 and then the date code as in previous years.

NEWPORT SERIES

Model Number	Body/Style Number	Body Type & Seating	Factory Price	Shipping Weight	Production Total
BC1-L	CL41	4-dr Sed-6P	3474	3875	74,964
BC1-L	CL42	4-dr Twn Sed-6P	3605	3910	9,432
BC1-L	CL23	2-dr HT Cpe-6P	3534	3845	37,622
BC1-L	CL43	4-dr HT Sed-6P	3612	4010	24,966
BC1-L	CL27	2-dr Conv-6P	3898	4020	3,085
BC1-L	CL45	4-dr T&C Wag-6P	4177	4370	9,035
BC1-L	CL46	4-dr T&C Wag-9P	4283	4550	8,567

1966 Chrysler, 300 two-door hardtop sport coupe, V-8

300 SERIES — (V-8) — The facelift of the design introduced in 1965 was limited to trim alterations, plus minor changes to the front and rear facades. The glass covered headlamps and the cross-bar grille motif were dropped in favor of a more contemporary look. Two decorative trim pieces were added to each front fender, behind the wheelhouse opening, as a styling flair. Bucket seats were standard on this model. The 300 offered an optional engine for the performance enthusiast.

300 SERIES

Model Number	Body/Style Number	Body Type & Seating	Factory Price	Shipping Weight	Production Total
BC2-M	CM23	2-dr HT Cpe-5P	4005	3940	24,103
BC2-M	CM43	4-dr HT Sed-5P	4081	4000	20,642
BC2-M	CM27	2-dr Conv-5P	4358	4015	2,500
BC2-M	CM41	4-dr Sed-6P	NA	NA	2,353

NOTE: Style CM41 probably built for Canadian market and called a Saratoga.

1966 Chrysler, New Yorker four-door hardtop sedan, V-8

NEW YORKER SERIES — (V-8) — The New Yorker continued as the high-line Chrysler series. An optional high-performance engine was available. New Yorker styling was a gentle facelift of 1965 Chrysler styling. New Yorker medallions were located just behind the front wheelhouse opening and above the lower trim molding. Headlamps were located at the outer edge of the grille cavity within a chromed, recessed bezel. This was the last year for the six-window Town Sedan.

NEW YORKER SERIES

Model Number	Body/Style Number	Body Type & Seating	Factory Price	Shipping Weight	Production Total
BC3-H	CH42	4-dr Sed-6P	4192	4110	13,025
BC3-H	CH23	2-dr HT Cpe-6P	4248	4095	7,955
BC3-H	C				

NEWPORT ENGINES: V-8. Overhead valves. Cast iron block. Displacement: 383 cid. Bore and stroke: 4.25 x 3.375 inches. Compression: 9.2:1. Brake hp: 270 at 4400 rpm. Five main bearings. Hydraulic valve lifters. Carburetion: Carter Type BBD two-barrel model 4125S.

300 ENGINE: V-8. Overhead valves. Cast iron block. Displacement: 383 cid. Bore and stroke: 4.25 x 3.375 inches. Compression ratio: 10.1:1. Brake hp: 325 at 4800 rpm. Five main bearings. Hydraulic valve lifters. Carburetor: Carter Type AFB four-barrel Model 4130S.

NEW YORKER ENGINE: V-8. Overhead valves. Cast iron block. Displacement: 440 cid. Bore and stroke: 4.326 x 3.75 inches. Compression ratio: 10.1:1. Brake hp: 350 at 4400 rpm. Five main bearings. Hydraulic valve lifters. Carburetor: Carter Type AFB four-barrel model 4131S.

CHASSIS FEATURES: Wheelbase: (passenger cars) 124 inches; (station wagons) 121 inches. Overall length: (passenger cars) 219 inches; (station wagons) 219.6 inches. Tires: (Newport) 8.25 x 14; (300, New Yorker, station wagons) 8.55 x 14.

OPTIONS: Power steering. Power brakes. Power windows. Power seat. Power door locks. Heater and defroster. Air conditioner (Dual air conditioning on all except convertible). Golden Tone radio. AM/FM radio. Golden Touch Tuner. Rear seat speaker. Console (300). Seat belts. Heavy-duty springs, shocks, sway bar and brakes. Adjustable steering wheel. Undercoating. Tinted glass. Day/night mirror. Remote control mirror. White sidewall tires. Front disc brakes. Three-speed manual transmission was standard in the Newport and 300 models. Automatic transmission was standard in New Yorker models. Automatic transmission was optional in the Newport and 300 models. Four-speed manual floor shift transmission was optional in 300 models. V-8 383 cid 325 hp four-barrel engine in Newport. V-8 440 cid 365 hp four-barrel engine in all models. Positive traction rear axle was optional in all models.

HISTORICAL FOOTNOTES: The variety of Chrysler offerings was reduced from 1965 model lineup. Sales rose more than 12 percent. Cleaner Air Package offered for emission control. Six-window sedan was only sedan available in the New Yorker series. First year for the 440 cid engine.

1967 CHRYSLER

NEWPORT SERIES — (V-8) — In 1967, the Newport Series was marketed in standard and slightly upgraded Custom trim. The low-line Newport had a major facelift consisting of the customary changes to the grille, rear deck and side body panels. The six-window Town Sedan was no longer provided. The two-door hardtop had a redesigned roof with a convertible-like look. Lower sill moldings were the only trim on the base Newport. This model had an exclusive taillamp treatment with a tiered effect. A thin, horizontal bar on the rear deck lid was the only vestigial indication of the side-to-side taillamp ensemble seen in previous years. Rear fender skirts were fitted. Standard equipment included all federal safety features plus carpeting, front and rear ashtrays; three-speed wipers; electric windshield washers; trip odometer; cigar lighter; glovebox with three-cup tray; secret compartment; center panel convenience drawer; brake warning system; front foam cushion with center folding armrest; heater and defroster; and 383 cid two-barrel V-8. The convertible had front and rear foam seat cushion and a glass rear window. Hardtop styles featured Flow-Thru ventilation and rear pillar interior courtesy lamps.

CHRYSLER I.D. NUMBERS: [Newport] The numbering system and code locations were the same as for previous models. The first four symbols designated the Body Style Number using the codes reflected in the second column of the charts below. The fifth symbol designated the engine and was 'G' for the '383' V-8. The sixth symbol designated the model year and was a '7' for 1967. The seventh symbol designated manufacturing plant: '3' = Detroit; '6' = Delaware. The following group of six symbols was the sequential unit production number beginning with 100001 at each assembly plant. [Newport Custom] The first two symbols were 'CL' to indicate Chrysler Newport Custom series. Additional coding was the same as on base Newports. The letter 'H' as the fifth symbol indicated the attachment of the optional high-performance '383' V-8 engine. [300] The first two symbols were to 'CM' to indicate Chrysler 300 Series. Additional coding used the same system utilized on Newports and Newport Customs. The letter 'K' as the fifth symbol indicated the attachment of the standard 440 cid/350 hp V-8; the letter 'L' indicated attachment of the optional 440 cid/375 hp V-8. [New Yorker] The first two symbols were 'CH' to indicate Chrysler New Yorker Series. Additional coding followed the

same system utilized on other series. The letter 'K' as the fifth symbol indicated attachment of the standard 440 cid/350 hp V-8; the letter 'L' indicated attachment of the optional 440 cid/375 hp V-8.

NEWPORT SERIES

Model Number	Body/Style Number	Body Type & Seating	Factory Price	Shipping Weight	Production Total
CC1-E	CE41	4-dr Sed-6P	3579	3950	48,945
CC1-E	CD23	2-dr HT Cpe-6P	3639	3925	26,583
CC1-E	CD43	4-dr HT Sed-6P	3716	3985	14,247
CC1-E	CE27	2-dr Conv-6P	4003	3975	2,891
CC1-E	CE45	4-dr T&C Wag-6P	4286	4500	7,183
CC1-E	CE46	4-dr T&C Wag-9P	4390	4555	7,520

1967 Chrysler, Newport Custom two-door hardtop sport coupe, V-8

NEWPORT CUSTOM SERIES — (V-8) — Upgraded upholstery options and a change in lower body moldings set the Newport Custom apart from its lower priced brethren. Fender skirts were standard equipment on the Newport Custom, as on all 1967 Chryslers. Only three body styles were offered in this series. Newport Customs came with all features found on or in base Newports, plus front bumper reveal moldings; front and rear foam seat cushions; closed crankcase ventilation system and, on the four-door sedan, bright upper door moldings and seat side shields.

NEWPORT CUSTOM SERIES

Model Number	Body/Style Number	Body Type & Seating	Factory Price	Shipping Weight	Production Total
CC1-L	CL41	4-dr Sed-6P	3767	3980	23,101
CC1-L	CL23	2-dr HT Cpe-6P	3827	3940	14,193
CC1-L	CL43	4-dr HT Sed-6P	3905	4000	12,728

1967 Chrysler, 300 two-door hardtop sport coupe, V-8

300 SERIES — (V-8) — The Chrysler 300 Series was further upgraded in comparison to the Newport Custom. Unique to the 300 was the rear end assembly, including deck lid, rear fender quarter panels and rear bumper. Taillamps were located at the extreme end of the rear fender and sloped from deck level down to bumper height. The back-up lamps were set into the bumper, below the taillamps, in a similar fashion. The effect was pleasing and smooth. The front grille was in the style of previous 300 Series models, with the usual crossbar division within the grille cavity. Hubcaps with small spinners were an added touch. Standard equipment on 300 models included all features found on Newport Custom, plus bright interior garnish moldings; TorqueFlite automatic transmission; bucket seats with center armrest; lower door trim carpet panels; carpeted bucket seatbacks; left-hand ashtray; Deluxe spinner wheel covers (as described above); 8.55 x 14 black sidewall tires and 440 cid four-barrel V-8 power-plant.

CHRYSLER 300 SERIES

Model Number	Body/Style Number	Body Type & Seating	Factory Price	Shipping Weight	Production Total
CC2-M	CM23	2-dr HT Cpe-5P	4134	4075	11,556
CC2-M	CM43	4-dr HT Sed-5P	4210	4140	8,744
CC2-M	CM27	2-dr Conv-5P	44-87	4110	1,594

1967 Chrysler, New Yorker four-door hardtop sedan, V-8

NEW YORKER SERIES — (V-8) — New Yorker Series bodies differed from Newports and 300s in the style of the rear taillamps and rear quarter panels. Safety features included reduced glare windshield wiper arms and blades, double ball joint mirror mount and cushioned instrument panels and visors. The instrument panel was symmetrical and anchored by air conditioner vents at the extreme ends. Lights, to indicate low brake hydraulic pressure, turn signals, coolant temperature, high beam operation, and oil pressure, were placed on a horizontal plane above the speedometer assembly and below the cushioned upper dash. The front fenders differed from the other series by using parking lamp housings, in line with the grille, at the extreme forward position. The rear taillamps wrapped around the rear fenders. Standard equipment included all items found on Chrysler 300s, plus power brakes; under-coating; hood pad; light package; clock; bright upper door and front bumper reveal moldings; walnut appliques; power steering; wraparound taillights; front and rear center armrests; cloth and vinyl bench seats; glovebox, twin ashtray, map, courtesy and trunk lights; carpeted trunk; fender mounted turn signals; and Deluxe steering wheel.

NEW YORKER SERIES

Model Number	Body/Style Number	Body Type & Seating	Factory Price	Shipping Weight	Production Total
CC3-H	CH41	4-dr Sed-6P	4299	4190	10,907
CC3-H	CH23	2-dr HT Cpe-6P	4355	4175	6,885
CC3-H	CH43	4-dr HT Sed-6P	4430	4245	21,665

NEWPORT/NEWPORT CUSTOM ENGINE: V-8. Overhead valves. Cast iron block. Displacement: 383 cid. Bore and stroke: 4.25 x 3.375 inches. Compression ratio: 9.2:1. Brake hp: 270 at 4400 rpm. Five main bearings. Hydraulic valve lifters. Carburetor: Carter Type BBD two-barrel Model 4296S.

CHRYSLER 300/NEW YORKER ENGINE: V-8. Overhead valves. Cast iron block. Displacement: 440.7 cid. Bore and stroke: 4.326 x 3.75 inches. Compression ratio: 10.1:1. Brake hp: 350 at 4400 rpm. Five main bearings. Hydraulic valve lifters. Carburetor: Holley four-barrel Model R-3667A.

CHASSIS FEATURES: Wheelbase: (passenger cars) 124 inches; (station wagons) 122 inches. Overall length: (Newport, Newport Custom, New Yorker) 219.3 inches; (Chrysler 300) 223.5 inches; (Town and Country) 220.3 inches. Tires: (Newport) 8.25 x 14; (Town and Country) 8.85 x 14; (Chrysler 300 and New Yorker) 8.55 x 14.

OPTIONS: Power brakes ($47). Power steering ($107). Air conditioning ($406). Dual Unit air conditioning ($605). Auto pilot ($84). Automatic headlamp dimmer ($45). Credit for vinyl bench seats in Chrysler 300 ($82). Disc brakes ($70). Leather bucket seats in Chrysler 300 ($129). Electric clock ($19). Rear window defogger ($21). Single head rests ($21). Town and Country roof luggage rack ($97). Two-tone paint ($26). Power antenna ($25). Power door locks, two-doors ($37). Power door locks, four-doors ($55). Six-Way power bench seat ($100). Six-Way left hand bucket or split-type seats ($91). Six-Way bucket or split-type seats, pair ($183). Power trunk release ($11). Power vent windows ($53). Power windows ($106). Golden Tone AM/FM radio ($154). Golden Tone radio ($91). Golden Touch Tuner AM/FM radio ($186). Rear reverberator speaker ($32). Right hand recliner seat in Newport and 300 ($32). All glass tinted ($42). Three-speed manual transmission was standard on Newport and Newport Custom. Automatic transmission was standard on other Chrysler models. Automatic transmission was optional on Newport and Newport Custom ($222). Newport V-8 383 cid 325 hp four-barrel engine ($34.50). Newport V-8 440 cid 375 hp four-barrel 'TNT' engine ($198.35). Town & Country V-8 440 cid 375 hp four-barrel 'TNT' engine ($164). New Yorker/300 V-8 440 cid 375 hp four-barrel 'TNT' engine ($79.40). Positive traction rear axle ($50.70). Heavy-duty positive traction rear axle for Chrysler 300 only ($140.65). Heavy-duty air cleaner ($25).

HISTORICAL FOOTNOTES: The 1967 Chryslers were introduced Sept. 29, 1966. Model year production peaked at 218,716 units. Calendar year sales of 206,974 cars were recorded. G.E. White was the chief executive officer of the company this year. Virgil Boyd was promoted to the presidency of Chrysler Corp. effective Jan. 1, 1967. Sales of Chrysler Div. models, excluding Imperial, slipped by 10.9 percent during calendar 1967. Options and accessories with low installation rates included: movable type steering column (4.8 percent); disc brakes (6.2 percent); power side windows (19.8 percent); power tailgate window (7.4 percent); dual exhausts (2.8 percent); limited slip differential (11.4 percent) and Auto Pilot (5.0 percent). Bucket seats were installed in 13.2 percent of all 1967 Chryslers.

1968 CHRYSLER

NEWPORT SERIES — (V-8) — Front bumpers, grilles and rear end treatments were restyled for 1968. The Newport had a V-shaped, mesh type grille insert with horizontal highlight moldings running between the four beam headlights. A vertical Chrysler badge was set into its center and Chrysler block lettering appeared at the edge of the hood. An indented, horizontal panel at the rear of the car stretched full-width, above the bumper, and housed a large taillamp at each end. Small, square, side marker lamps on the rear fenders were an all-new 1968 feature required by federal law. Standard equipment on base Newports included all Chrysler safety features; carpeting; dual front and rear ashtrays; trip odometer; cigar lighter; glovebox with three-cup tray and secret compartment; center panel convenience drawer with coin sorter; heater and defroster; cleaner air systems; exhaust emission controls; torsion air

suspension; 8.55 x 14 blackwall tires; and a 383 cid two-barrel V-8. Hardtops had rear pillar lamps and convertibles had all-vinyl bench seats with a front center armrest. Town & Country station wagons had all these features plus lighting group; bright upper door moldings and seat side shields; power brakes; power steering; foam seat cushions; three-speed wipers; Deluxe wheelcovers; TorqueFlite transmission; time delay ignition light switch; power tailgate window; all-vinyl bench seats with front center armrests; and simulated wood-grained exterior body paneling. Three-seat station wagons had a rear step/pad bumper guard. Two-seat station wagons had lockable hidden storage compartments. Buyers were offered a choice of 8.85 x 14 or 8.85 x 15 black sidewall tires. All Newports came with rear wheel opening skirts. Controls for the Auto Pilot speed control option were now integral with the turn signal lever, on cars so equipped. An attractive option, made available in the spring, was wood-grained exterior side body paneling for Newport convertibles and two-door hardtops. Chrysler's new styling was well received and sales climbed by nearly 10 percent over 1967.

1968 Chrysler, 300 two-door hardtop sport coupe, V-8

CHRYSLER 300 SERIES — (V-8) — The Chrysler 300 models were distinguished by special grille, front bumper and body decoration treatments. The grille featured blacked-out finish highlighted by a full-width horizontal bar design and incorporated hidden headlights. The front bumper had long, horizontal air slots on either side of the center license plate indentation. Bright body underscores ran between the wheel openings and had long, rear extensions. Five short, slanting slashes of chrome were placed behind the front wheel openings. Three-Hundred lettering appeared on the trailing sides of the rear fender, directly in front of circular side marker lamps. New, cast metal 'road wheels' were an option introduced for Chrysler 300s this season. Standard equipment included all items found on Newport Customs, plus a 70-amp. battery; TorqueFlite automatic transmission; Deluxe wheel covers; all-vinyl bucket seats with center cushion armrest; bright metal horn blow ring; and the previously mentioned hidden headlights. The base powerplant for Chrysler 300s was a 440 cid four-barrel V-8. The word Chrysler was placed on the right-hand front edge of the hood on 300 models, instead of at the center.

1968 Chrysler, Newport two-door hardtop, V-8 (with Sports Grain option)

CHRYSLER I.D. NUMBERS: Serial numbers were now located on a plate attached to the left side of the instrument panel and visible through the windshield. Serial numbers consisted of a seven symbol prefix, plus production sequence code. The first symbol 'C' = Chrysler Div. [NEWPORT] The second symbol indicated series and was an 'E' for base Newports. The third and fourth symbols indicated a Body Style code which corresponded to the numerical portion of the codes in the second column of the chart below. The fifth symbol was an engine code as follows: 'G' = 383 cid V-8; 'H' = high-performance 383 cid V-8; 'K' = 440 cid V-8; 'L' = high-performance 440 cid V-8 and 'M' = special order V-8. The sixth symbol was a '8' indicating 1968 model year. The seventh symbol indicated the assembly plant, as follows: 'C' = Detroit, Michigan and 'F' = Newark, N.J. (All station wagons and convertibles were assembled in Detroit at the Jefferson Avenue plant). The production sequence code followed and began with 100001 at each factory. Engine numbers were now stamped on the left rear portion of the block near the oil pump flange. They took the form PT44021870002 with this specific code designating a Trenton (engine) plant 440 cid V-8 built on July 24, 1967 and second sequentially. The symbols 'PT' are the factory code; the symbols '440' indicate 440 cid V-8 and the symbols 2187 are the day production code. [NEWPORT CUSTOM] The numbering system and code locations were the same as for base Newport models with the second symbol changed to an 'L' to indicate a Newport Custom model. The code 'G' 383 cid two-barrel V-8 was the standard engine for 1968 Chrysler Newport Customs. [CHRYSLER 300] The numbering system and code locations were the same as for previous models with the second symbol changed to an 'M' to indicate a Chrysler 300 model. The code 'K' 440 cid V-8 was the standard engine for 1968 Chrysler 300s. [NEW YORKER] The numbering system and code locations were the same as for previous models with the second symbol changed to an 'H' to indicate a Chrysler New Yorker. The code 'K' 440 cid V-8 was the base engine for 1968 New Yorkers.

CHRYSLER 300 SERIES

Model Number	Body/Style Number	Body Type & Seating	Factory Price	Shipping Weight	Production Total
DC2-M	CM23	2-dr HT Cpe-5P	4209	3985	16,953
DC2-M	CM43	4-dr HT Sed-5P	4285	4015	15,507
DC2-M	CM27	2-dr Conv-5P	4536	4050	2,161

1968 Chrysler, New Yorker two-door hardtop sport coupe, V-8

NEW YORKER SERIES — (V-8) — The New Yorker featured a third style of frontal design. The grille insert was V-shaped and had a grid type pattern highlighted by a horizontal center blade stretching between quad headlamps. New Yorker headlights, however, were housed in distinctive square bezels. The front bumper and hood lettering treatments were similar to the Newport style. Wide, bright metal panels underscored the rocker sill and extended to the fender skirts and lower rear quarter panels. The deck lid latch panel was beautified with a grid pattern rear grille that covered the recessed taillights. On the sedan, a New Yorker script was placed low on the front fenders, behind the wheel opening. Similar signatures appeared on the rear roof pillars of hardtops, in place of the front fender scripts. Standard equipment was of the Chrysler 300 level, with the following additions or variations: light group; electric clock; remote control left-hand OSRV mirror; power brakes; power steering; Deluxe steering wheel with horn bars; undercoating; hood insulation pad; three-speed wipers; time delay ignition switch light; pleated cloth and vinyl bench seats with center armrest; body accent stripes; fender top turn indicator lamps; textured vinyl roof pillar appliques on four-door hardtops; and bright upper door moldings on four-door sedans.

NEW YORKER SERIES

Model Number	Body/Style Number	Body Type & Seating	Factory Price	Shipping Weight	Production Total
DC3-H	CH41	4-dr Sed-6P	4459	4055	13,092
DC3-H	CH23	2-dr HT Cpe-6P	4516	4060	8,060
DC3-H	CH43	4-dr HT Sed-6P	4592	4090	26,991

NEWPORT SERIES

Model Number	Body/Style Number	Body Type & Seating	Factory Price	Shipping Weight	Production Total
DC1-E	CE41	4-dr Sed-6P	3727	3850	61,436
DC1-E	CE23	2-dr HT Cpe-6P	3787	3840	36,768
DC1-E	CE43	4-dr HT Sed-6P	3865	3865	20,191
DC1-E	CE27	2-dr Conv-6P	4125	3910	2,847
DC1-E	CE45	4-dr T&C Wag-6P	4286	4500	9,908
DC1-E	CE46	4-dr T&C Wag-9P	4390	4555	12,233

NEWPORT CUSTOM SERIES — (V-8) — The Newport Custom models were dressed-up versions of the base Newport offerings available in a more limited range of body styles. Standard equipment included all items found on base Newports, plus bright seat side shields; front and rear foam seat cushions; bench seats with front center armrest; and bright, upper door moldings on the Custom four-door sedan. As on base Newport models, the center section of the re-designed grille met the forward edge of the hood and then faded inward, as it approached the deeply inset four-beam headlamps. The rear deck lid panel ensemble for 1968 had the same styling motifs found on the front of the car. The horizontal, rectangular taillamps pointed towards the outer edge of the fenders, with a raised section of the taillamp outline continuing towards the center of the panel. Whereas the base models carried their identification script at the rear of the back fenders, the Custom editions wore script nameplates high on the front fenders, near the sides of the cowl. Newport Customs also had the federally required side marker lamps this season.

NEWPORT CUSTOM SERIES

Model Number	Body/Style Number	Body Type & Seating	Factory Price	Shipping Weight	Production Total
DC1-L	CL41	4-dr Sed-6P	3914	3865	16,915
DC1-L	CL23	2-dr HT Cpe-6P	3973	3860	10,341
DC1-L	CL43	4-dr HT Sed-6P	4052	3890	11,460

NEWPORT/NEWPORT CUSTOM ENGINE: V-8. Overhead valves. Cast iron block. Displacement: 383 cid. Bore and stroke: 4.25 x 3.375 inches. Compression ratio: 9.2:1. Brake hp: 290 at 4400 rpm. Five main bearings. Hydraulic valve lifters. Carburetor: Carter Type BBD two-barrel Model 4422S.

CHRYSLER 300/NEW YORKER ENGINE: V-8. Overhead valves. Cast iron block. Displacement: 440 cid. Bore and stroke: 4.326 x 3.75 inches. Compression ratio: 10.1:1. Brake hp: 350 at 4400 rpm. Five main bearings. Hydraulic four-barrel Model R-3918A.

Standard Catalog of American Cars

CHASSIS FEATURES: Wheelbase (station wagons) 122 inches; (passenger cars) 124 inches. Overall length: (nine-passenger station wagons) 220.3 inches; (six-passenger station wagons) 219.5 inches; (passenger cars) 219.2 inches. Front tread: (all models) 62 inches. Rear tread: (all models) 60 inches. Tires: (station wagons) 8.85 x 14; (station wagons) 8.85 x 15; (passenger cars) 8.55 x 14.

OPTIONS: Power brakes ($47). Power steering ($107). Air conditioning ($406). Dual air conditioning ($636). Automatic speed control, TorqueFlight and power brakes required ($67). Front and rear bumper guards ($34). Electric clock ($19). Console, on models with bucket seats ($127). Rear window defogger ($22). Tinted glass, all windows and windshield ($42). Left and right front head restraints ($44). Automatic headlamp dimmer ($47). Safeguard sentinel ($34). Station wagons rooftop luggage rack ($97). Two-tone paint on specific models ($28). Special buffed paint, all models ($22). Power radio antenna ($27). Remote control trunk release ($13). Power vent windows ($53). Power side windows ($106). Golden Tone AM radio with tape deck ($222). Golden Tone AM radio ($92). Golden Tone AM/FM Touch Tuner radio ($187). Golden Tone AM/FM Multiplex radio ($247). Three-in-one vinyl bench seat ($106). Three-in-one cloth and vinyl bench seat ($70). Vinyl bucket seats in Newports ($99-$158). Leather bucket seats in New Yorker/300 ($129-$189). Tilt-A-Scope steering wheel ($88). Vinyl roof, except station wagon ($109). Styled 14 inch road wheels for Newports ($99). Styled 14 inch road wheels for 300/New Yorker ($80). Deluxe 14 inch wheelcovers, Newports ($18). Deluxe 15 inch wheelcovers, Newports ($25). Sport wheelcovers, Chrysler 300 ($19). Deep dish 14 inch wheelcovers, Newports ($54). Deep dish 14 inch wheelcovers, other models ($35). Three-speed windshield wipers ($5). Station wagon window wiper and washer for tailgate ($39). Basic accessory group package ($211). Light group package ($23). Heavy-duty suspension package ($13). Disc brakes ($74). Rear seat heater, except station wagon ($62). Cornering lights ($36). Remote control left-hand OSRV mirror ($10). License plate frames ($7). Six-Way power bench seat ($100). Left and right power bucket or three-in-one seats ($183). Rear seat radio speaker ($17). Pair of shoulder belts ($27). Passenger side reclining front seat ($32). Vinyl bench seats in Chrysler 300, credit ($82). Cloth and vinyl bench seat in Chrysler 300, credit ($82). Sports Grain woodgrain applique side trim on Newport two-door hardtop, convertible and T&C station wagons. Three-speed manual transmission was standard in Newport/Newport Custom. Automatic transmission was optional in Newport/ Newport Custom, with the four-barrel 383 cid engine ($227); with the four-barrel 440 cid engine ($227); and with the two-barrel 383 cid engine ($222). Automatic transmission was standard in Chrysler 300s, Town & Country and New Yorker. The 330 hp four-barrel high-performance 383 cid engine was optional in Newport/Newport Custom and Town & Country ($68). The 350 hp four-barrel 440 cid V-8 with dual exhausts was optional in Town & Countrys ($164). The 375 hp four-barrel 440 cid 'TNT' engine was optional in Newport/Newport Custom with TorqueFlite automatic transmission ($198) and optional in all Chrysler 300s and New Yorkers ($79). Sure-Grip differential was optional in all models ($51). A 46-amp alternator was optional in all models ($11) and standard on cars with air conditioning. Numerous tire options also available.

HISTORICAL FOOTNOTES: The 1968 Chryslers were introduced in September, 1967. Model year production peaked at 264,863 units. Calendar year sales of 263,266 cars were recorded. Robert Anderson was the chief executive officer of the Chrysler-Plymouth Div. this year. The introduction of the Newport two-door hardtop coupe and convertible with wood-grained exterior paneling took place at the 1968 Chicago Automobile Show in February. A limited number of cars with this particular option were sold. Chrysler was America's 10th ranked auto manufacturer this season.

1969 CHRYSLER

NEWPORT SERIES — (V-8) — All-new styling greeted Newport buyers this year. It used smoother, arched side panels creating an airplane fuselage look. A massive front bumper structure housed a wide grille formed of many fine horizontal blades. The V-shaped look was continued, but was toned down with a flattened center section decorated with three, stacked star-type Chrysler emblems. Newports carried a Chrysler signature on the right-hand side of the grille insert. A molding ran from the front bumper to the rear bumper ends, angling slightly downward so that it passed through the front wheel opening, but above the unskirted rear wheel cutout. Standard Newport equipment included all Chrysler safety features; cleaner air system; odometer; tripometer; heater and defroster; carpeting; dual rear seat ashtrays; 8.55 x 15 black sidewall tires; the two-barrel 383 cid V-8; and, on convertibles, all-vinyl bench seats with a front center armrest. The Town & Country station wagons were no longer grouped with Newport models. Base Newport models carried a chrome signature type nameplate on the rear fender, above the rear tip of the side trim molding.

CHRYSLER I.D. NUMBERS: Serial numbers were now located on a plate attached to the left side of the instrument panel and visible through the windshield. Serial numbers consisted of a seven symbol prefix, plus production sequence code. The first symbol 'C' = Chrysler Div. The second symbol indicated series and was an 'E' for base Newports. The third and fourth symbols indicated a Body Style code which corresponded to the numerical portion of the codes in the second column of the chart below. The fifth symbol was an engine code as follows: 'G' = 383 cid V-8; 'H' = high-performance 383 cid V-8; 'K' = 440 cid V-8; 'L' = high performance 440 cid V-8 and 'M' = special order V-8. The sixth symbol was a '9 indicating 1969 model year. The seventh symbol indicated the assembly plant, as follows: 'C' = Detroit, Michigan and 'F' = Newark, N.J. (All station wagons and convertibles were assembled in Detroit at the Jefferson Avenue plant). [NEWPORT] Production sequence code followed same format and began with first two symbols 'CE.' The code 'G' engine was again the base power-plant. [NEWPORT CUSTOM] The numbering system and code locations were the same as for previous models with the second symbol changed to an 'L' to indicate Newport Custom. The code 'G' engine was standard equipment. [CHRYSLER 300] The numbering system and code locations were the same as for previous models with the second symbol changed to an 'M' to indicate Chrysler 300. The Code 'K' engine was standard equipment. [NEW YORKER] The numbering system and code locations were the same as for previous models with the second symbol changed to an 'H' to indicate Chrysler New Yorker. The code 'K' engine was standard equipment. [TOWN & COUNTRY] The numbering system and code locations were the same as for previous models with the second symbol changed to a 'P' to indicate Town & Country. The code 'G' engine was standard equipment.

NEWPORT SERIES

Model Number	Body/Style Number	Body Type & Seating	Factory Price	Shipping Weight	Production Total
EC-E	CE41	4-dr Sed-6P	4252	4001	55,083
EC-E	CE23	2-dr HT Cpe-6P	4323	3991	33,639
EC-E	CE43	4-dr HT Sed-6P	4387	4016	20,608
EC-E	CE27	2-dr Conv-6P	4661	4061	2,169

1969 Chrysler, Newport Custom four-door hardtop sedan, V-8

NEWPORT CUSTOM — (V-8) — The Newport Customs now came in all Newport body styles, except two-door convertibles, adding to each a slightly higher level of trim and standard equipment. An easy way to identify cars in this series was to look for the Newport Custom signature script on the front fender, above the side trim molding and ahead of the wheel opening. Another distinction was a horizontal rear deck beauty panel with a vertically segmented grille pattern that ran across the taillights. Newport Customs had all features found on base models, plus foam padded cloth and vinyl bench seats; pull-down front armrests; and full-length bodyside accent strips. When optional vinyl roof coverings were ordered, an elongated emblem was affixed at the rear roof pillar.

NEWPORT CUSTOM SERIES

Model Number	Body/Style Number	Body Type & Seating	Factory Price	Shipping Weight	Production Total
EC-L	CL41	4-dr Sed-6P	4418	4016	18,401
EC-L	CL23	2-dr HT Cpe-6P	4470	4021	10,955
EC-L	CL43	4-dr HT Sed-6P	4568	4051	15,981

1969 Chrysler, 300 two-door hardtop sport coupe, V-8

CHRYSLER 300 SERIES — (V-8) — The 300 Series had the same overall styling as lower priced Newports. The designation Three-Hundred was spelled out, with chrome block lifters, on the rear quarter panels. A grille with a variation of traditional Chrysler 300 themes was placed within the heavily chromed bumper/grille surround. It had a blacked-out insert, against which was set a cross-bar combination with a circular medallion in its center. Hidden headlights were featured again and the parking lamps were tucked in each corner. The rear deck featured a thin, horizontal panel with blacked-out finish, long horizontal taillamps and 300 lettering at its center. Standard equipment included the following additions or variations from Newport specifications: TorqueFlite automatic transmission; heavy-duty battery; turn signal indicator lights; power operated concealed headlamps: triple body accent stripes; front and rear foam seat cushions; bench seat with fold-down center armrest in hardtops; vinyl bucket seats with center cushion armrest in convertibles; and the 350 hp 440 cid four-barrel V-8.

CHRYSLER 300 SERIES

Model Number	Body/Style Number	Body Type & Seating	Factory Price	Shipping Weight	Production Total
EC-M	CM23	2-dr HT Cpe-6P	4714	4120	16,075
EC-M	CM43	4-dr HT Sed-6P	4793	4150	14,464
EC-M	CM27	2-dr Conv-5P	5060	4185	1,933

NEW YORKER SERIES — (V-8) — The New Yorker models were distinguished by special grille styling and decorative treatments. The grille was of the same general shape seen on Newports, but with a different insert pattern highlighted by horizontal division bars. The segments between these chrome bars were finished in blacked-out style. A vertical strip at the center of the grille was used as an emblem. The headlights were spaced slightly wider apart, than on Newports, and Chrysler lettering appeared on the hood center panel. Bright metal underscores highlighted the lower body sills. Equipment features, except the type of headlights, were based on the Chrysler 300 specifications, plus numerous extras. They included, exhaust system emissions control; power steering; power front disc brakes; glovebox; courtesy, trunk and front ashtray lights; electric clock; simulated walnut grained interior appliques; pleated cloth and vinyl bench seats (with front armrest in two-door styles; front and rear in four-doors); full horn blowing ring; carpeted lower door trim panels; fender mounted turn indicator lights; body accent stripes; undercoating; carpeted trunk; and rear cigar lighters in four-door models.

NEW YORKER SERIES

Model Number	Body/Style Number	Body Type & Seating	Factory Price	Shipping Weight	Production Total
EC-H	CH41	4-dr Sed-6P	5097	4185	12,253
EC-H	CH23	2-dr HT Cpe-6P	5149	4175	7,537
EC-H	CH43	4-dr HT Sed-6P	5225	4200	27,157

TOWN & COUNTRY SERIES — (V-8) — The Town & Country station wagons were now grouped as a separate series. They used the new, fuselage type body styling and featured New Yorker type grilles. Standard equipment included all Chrysler safety features; cleaner air system; exhaust emissions control system; Torque-Flite transmission; power steering; power front disc brakes; glovebox, map, courtesy and front and rear dome lamps; odometer; tripometer; power tailgate window; heater and defroster; simulated walnut dashboard appliques; vinyl bench seats with front center armrest; carpeting; wind deflector; simulated woodgrained body side paneling; stainless steel wheelcovers; dual-action tailgate; fender-mounted turn indicator lamps; 8.85 x 15 black sidewall tires; the code 'G' engine; and, on two-seat models, a lockable hidden storage compartment.

TOWN & COUNTRY SERIES

Model Number	Body/Style Number	Body Type & Seating	Factory Price	Shipping Weight	Production Total
EC-P	CP45	4-dr T&C Wag-6P	5193	4425	10,108
EC-P	CP46	4-dr T&C Wag-9P	5279	4495	14,480

NEWPORT/NEWPORT CUSTOM/T&C ENGINE: V-8. Overhead valves. Cast iron block. Displacement: 383 cid. Bore and stroke: 4.25 x 3.375 inches. Compression ratio: 9.2:1. Brake hp: 290 at 4400 rpm. Five main bearings. Hydraulic valve lifters. Carburetor: Carter Type BBD two-barrel Model 4422S.

CHRYSLER 300/NEW YORKER ENGINE: V-8. Overhead valves. Cast iron block. Displacement: 440 cid. Bore and stroke: 4.326 x 3.75 inches. Compression ratio: 10.1:1. Brake hp: 350 at 4400 rpm. Five main bearings. Hydraulic four-barrel Model R-3918A.

CHASSIS FEATURES: Wheelbase: (station wagons) 122 inches; (passenger cars) 124 inches. Overall length: (station wagons) 224.8 inches; (passenger cars) 224.7 inches. Front tread: (all models) 62.1 inches. Rear tread: (all models) 60.7 inches. Tires: (station wagons) 8.85 x 15; (passenger cars) 8.55 x 15.

OPTIONS: Power brakes ($47). Power steering ($112). Air conditioning ($406); with Auto Temp included ($481). Dual air conditioning ($636); with Auto Temp included ($713). Power door locks, two-doors ($46). Power door locks, four-doors ($67). Six-Way power bench seat ($103). Left and right power buckets or Three-in-One seats ($188). Remote control trunk release ($15). Power side windows ($112). Power vent windows ($54). Heavy-duty suspension ($18). Front disc brakes ($49). Electric clock ($19). Center console with bucket seats ($68). All windows tinted ($44). Automatic headlight beam changer ($49). Cornering lights ($37). Station wagon luggage rack ($64). Two-tone paint ($38). AM radio ($92). AM radio with stereo tape ($222). AM/FM radio ($187). AM/FM multiplex radio with tape ($301). Rear seat radio speaker ($17). Vinyl roof covering ($122). Automatic speed control ($67). Newport Sports Grain siding ($127). Tilt-A-Scope steering wheel ($91). Deep dish wheelcovers ($35). Undercoating and hood insulation pad ($21). Powertrain options were the same as for 1968 Chrysler models. Prices for optional engines were the same. Prices on optional transmissions were $6 higher this season, for comparable applications. Other powertrain options were priced similarly to the same features a year earlier.

HISTORICAL FOOTNOTES: The 1969 Chryslers were introduced in September, 1968. Model year production peaked at 260,771 units. Calendar year sales of 226,590 cars were recorded. Robert Anderson was the chief executive officer of the company this year. Chrysler Div. was ranked as America's 11th largest automaker. Sales for the calendar year declined by approximately 14 percent. The Automotive Conversion Corp., of Troy, Mich. produced an "Amblewagon" based on the 1969 Town & Country. This was essentially a factory approved, aftermarket type of inexpensive ambulance, constructed on the standard wheelbase Chrysler station wagon with a minimum of modifications.

1970 CHRYSLER

NEWPORT SERIES — (V-8) — A new grille for 1970 was formed of short, closely spaced, vertical blades that ran in three horizontal tiers. The rear deck panel was also restyled. It had a concave 'Cove' treatment, with oblong taillamps, banded in chrome, at each end. Standard equipment on Newports included all basic regulation safety features; cleaner air system; 5.9 amp. battery; silenced air cleaner; cloth and vinyl bench seats (all-vinyl on convertibles); carpeting; rear seat ashtrays; wheelcovers; H78-15 black sidewall tires and the 290 hp 383 cid V-8. A special order Cordoba model was made available. It came with gold exterior finish; gold vinyl roof; special vinyl interior trim (with Aztec eagle embossment) and Cordoba wheelcovers with a similar emblem. The Aztec eagle was also seen on the grille insert medallion. The Cordoba had dual horns; ventless side glass (on two-door hardtops); pedal dress-up package; special wheelcovers and trip odometer. Newport 440 was an upgraded Newport which used the 440 cid New Yorker engine. Standard equipment included vinyl side body moldings; vinyl roof; light group; and TorqueFlite automatic transmission. Aluminized mufflers and tailpipes were standard equipment on all models.

CHRYSLER I.D. NUMBERS: Serial numbers were now located on a plate attached to the left side of the instrument panel and visible through the windshield. Serial numbers consisted of a seven symbol prefix, plus production sequence code. The numbering system and code locations were the same for previous models with the sixth symbol changed to '0' to indicate 1970 model year. [NEWPORT] Base Newport models used serial numbers beginning with the symbols 'CE' to indicate Chrysler Newport. The code 'L' engine (290 hp 383 cid) was standard equipment. [NEWPORT CUSTOM] The numbering system and code locations were the same as for previous models with the second symbol changed to an 'L' to indicate Newport Custom. The code 'L' engine was standard equipment. [CHRYSLER 300] The numbering system and code locations were the same as for previous models with the second symbol changed to an 'M' to indicate Chrysler 300. The code 'T' engine was standard equipment. The numbering system and code locations were the same as for previous models with the second symbol changed to 'H' to indicate Chrysler New Yorker. The code 'T' engine was standard equipment. The numbering system and code locations were the same as for previous models with the second symbol changed to 'P' to indicate Town & Country. The code 'L' engine was standard equipment. Engine serial numbers were assigned codes as follows: (plant code) PT = Trenton; (displacement code) 440 = 440 cid; (calendar date/correlated number) 3079 = January 1, 1970 and a four-digit manufacturing sequence number. beginning with 1001, for each day's production. NOTE: New alphabetical engine identification codes used for 1970-1972 Chryslers, as follows: 'G' = 318 cid two-barrel V-8; 'J' = 360 cid four-barrel V-8; 'K' = 360 cid two-barrel V-8; 'L' = 383 cid two-barrel V-8; 'M' = 400 cid two-barrel V-8; 'N' = 400 cid four-barrel V-8 or 383 cid four-barrel V-8; 'P' = 400 cid V-8 (1975 type); 'T' = 440 cid standard four-barrel V-8 and 'U' = 440 cid high-performance four-barrel V-8.

NEWPORT SERIES

Model Number	Body/Style Number	Body Type & Seating	Factory Price	Shipping Weight	Production Total
EC-E	CE41	4-dr Sed-6P	4358	4050	39,285
EC-E	CE23	2-dr HT Cpe-6P	4433	3990	19,796
EC-E	CE23	2-dr Cor Cpe-6P	4613	4030	1,868
EC-E	CE43	4-dr Cor HT-6P	4676	4070	1,873
EC-E	CE43	4-dr HT Sed-6P	4496	4070	15,067
EC-E	CE27	2-dr Conv-6P	4769	4100	1,124
EC-E	CE23	2-dr 440 HT-6P	4885	NA	Note 1
EC-E	CE43	4-dr 440 HT-6P	4948	NA	Note 1

NOTE 1: The Newport 440 models were technically regular Newports with the 440 cid V-8 ($198.35) installed. This installation required automatic transmission and included dual exhausts. The production total for Newport 440s is included in the figures given for cars with similar Body Style Numbers (CE23 and CE43).

1970 Chrysler, Newport Custom four-door hardtop sedan, V-8

NEWPORT CUSTOM SERIES — (V-8) — The 1970 Newport Custom continued the custom of providing the basic Chrysler offering with an upgraded level of trim. While standard Newports carried a model identification script on the front fender (behind wheel opening), Customs had roof pillar scripts. Newport Customs had all equipment found on lower series Chryslers, plus pull-down center front armrest; front and rear foam padded seat cushions; carpeted lower door trim panels; upgraded interior upholstery materials; bright upper door moldings and roof drip rails.

NEWPORT CUSTOM SERIES

Model Number	Body/Style Number	Body Type & Seating	Factory Price	Shipping Weight	Production Total
FC-L	CL41	4-dr Sed-6P	4554	4065	13,767
FC-L	CL23	2-dr HT Cpe-6P	4625	4005	6,639
FC-L	CL43	4-dr HT Sed-6P	4705	4085	10,873

CHRYSLER 300 SERIES — (V-8) — The 300 facelift of the 1969 model paralleled the styling updates seen in the other 1970 Chryslers. Disappearing headlights were retained in the 300 Series. A 300 emblem was placed in the center of the grille, which had black vertical bars. Two thin rectangular moldings were placed on either side of the center of the grille and were painted in red with bright edges. Taillamp design treatments differed from other 1970 models. On 300s they ran unobstructed, across the rear indented area of the bumper. Standard equipment included body accent stripes, all-vinyl or cloth and vinyl bucket seats and Torque-Flite automatic transmission. This was the last year for the Chrysler convertible. The high-performance 300-H was a modified Chrysler 300 built by Hurst Performance Corp. It was offered with saddle color leather bucket seats; fiberglass power bulge hood (with functional air scoop); dual, depressed, rotary hood latches; fiberglass deck and rear end caps; special paint (Spinnaker white); Satin Tan color accents; special striping; and an integrated wing-type rear spoiler. Other standard features included: 440 TNT engine; heavy-duty suspension with sway bar; styled road wheels; and raised white letter tires. Other features found on all 1970 Chrysler 300s included heavy-duty battery; cleaner air system; turn signal indicator lamps; ash receiver lights; carpeting; front and rear foam padded seats; carpeted lower door trim panels; rear ashtrays; wraparound bumpers; and full wheelcovers. The Three-Hundred designation, in bright chrome block letters, appeared at the right-hand corner of the trunk lid.

1970 Chrysler, two-door 300-H (Hurst) sports coupe, V-8

CHRYSLER 300 SERIES

Model Number	Body/Style Number	Body Type & Seating	Factory Price	Shipping Weight	Production Total
FC-M	CM23	2-dr HT Cpe-5P	4849	4125	9,589
FC-M	CM43	4-dr HT Sed-6P	4625	4005	9,846
FC-M	CM27	2-dr Conv-5P	5195	4225	1,077
FC-M	CM23	2-dr Hurst-5P	5842	NA	485

CHRYSLER/HURST 300-H SERIES ENGINE: V-8. Overhead valves. Cast iron block. Displacement: 440 cid. Bore and stroke: 4.326 x 3.75 inches. Compression ratio: 9.7:1. Brake hp: 375 at 4600 rpm. Five main bearings. Hydraulic valve lifters. Carburetor: four-barrel.

NEW YORKER SERIES — (V-8) — Three body styles were offered in this series. They had a slight facelift of the fuselage shape design. The grille used the characteristic horizontal and vertical bars with fine horizontal bars placed within the outline. A broad trim molding ran from front to rear at a level even with the lower portion of the bumpers. The rear taillamp ensemble had a horizontal bar look. The center section of the rear latch panel 'grille' was shaped like the front grille. Standard equipment included power brakes; carpeted trunk; electric clock; light group; left-hand OSRV remote control mirror; power steering; undercoating; hood insulation; three-speed windshield washers; dome light; time delay ignition switch; fresh air heater and defroster; simulated walnut instrument panel applique; pleated cloth and vinyl bench seats with folding center armrests (front only in two-doors); rear cigar lighters; fender mounted turn signals; exhaust emission controls; J78-15 tires (black sidewall); and the 440 cid 350 hp code 'T' V-8 engine. New Yorker signature scripts appeared on the lower front fenders, behind the wheelhousings, and on the right-hand corner of the trunk lid.

NEW YORKER SERIES

Model Number	Body/Style Number	Body Type & Seating	Factory Price	Shipping Weight	Production Total
FC-H	CH41	4-dr Sed-6P	5241	4230	9,389
FC-H	CH23	2-dr HT Cpe-6P	5292	4155	4,917
FC-H	CH43	4-dr HT Sed-6P	5372	4265	19,903

TOWN & COUNTRY SERIES — (V-8) — Chrysler's Town & Country station wagon line was a separate series again this year. Advertised as a "Luxury Car Made Into a Wagon," the Town & Country was designed for work, for comfort and for pleasure. Simulated Brazilian Rosewood bodyside and tailgate appliques were standard. There was 109.2 cubic feet of storage space, including a lockable storage compartment, plus room for a 4 x 8 piece of plywood. Carrying capacity was a selling feature of the full-sized wagons. Front power disc brakes were standard equipment. Other features provided at base cost to all Chrysler station wagon buyers included cleaner air system; exhaust emission control; TorqueFlite automatic transmission; 59-amp/hour battery; power steering; light group package; time delay ignition switch; glovebox and dashboard simulated walnut appliques; vinyl bench seats with front center armrest; foam padded cushions; carpeting; carpeted lower door trim panels and cargo deck; wind deflector; stainless steel wheelcovers; dual action tailgate; fender mounted turn signals; J78-15 black sidewall tires; and 290 hp 383 cid V-8.

TOWN & COUNTRY SERIES

Model Number	Body/Style Number	Body Type & Seating	Factory Price	Shipping Weight	Production Total
FC-P	CP45	4-dr T&C Wag-6P	5349	4445	5,686
FC-P	CP46	4-dr T&C Wag-9P	5435	4505	9.583

NEWPORT/NEWPORT CUSTOM/T&C ENGINE: V-8. Overhead valves. Cast iron block. Displacement: 383 cid. Bore and stroke: 4.25 x 3.375 inches. Compression ratio: 8.7:1. Brake hp: 290 at 4400 rpm. Five main bearings. Hydraulic valve lifters. Carburetor: Carter Type BBD two-barrel Model 4894S.

CHRYSLER 300/NEW YORKER/ SERIES ENGINE: V-8. Overhead valves. Cast iron block. Displacement: 440 cid. Bore and stroke: 4.326 x 3.75 inches. Compression ratio: 9.7:1. Brake hp: 350 at 4400 rpm. Five main bearings. Hydraulic valve litters. Carburetor: four-barrel.

CHASSIS FEATURES: Wheelbase (station wagon) 122 inches; (passenger cars) 124 inches. Overall length: (station wagon) 224.8 inches; (passenger car) 224.7 inches. Front tread: (all models) 62.1 inches. Rear tread: (all models) 62 inches. Tires (Newport/Custom/300) H78-15; (New Yorker/station wagon) J78-15.

OPTIONS: Power brakes in Newport, Custom and 300 ($46.85). Door locks in two-door ($45.55); in four-door ($69.50). Power Six-Way bench seat ($102.80). Power buckets or three-in-one left and right seats ($188.05). Power steering in Newport, Custom, 300 ($117.20). Power vent windows ($54.25). Heavy-duty suspension ($17.50). Remote trunk release ($14.75). Power side windows ($111.55). Front disc brakes ($46.85). Electric clock ($19.05). Console ($67.95). Sure-Grip differential ($50.70). Tinted glass all windows ($44.80). Automatic headlight beam changer ($48.70). Cornering lights ($36.50). Time delay headlights ($18.40). Air conditioning ($405.85); with Auto Temp ($481.20). Dual air conditioning in station wagons ($635.80); with Auto Temp ($712.40). Luggage rack ($63.95). Two-tone paint ($43.05). Golden Tone AM radio ($92.30). Golden Tone AM radio with Stereo Tape Player and speakers ($222.25). Golden Tone AM/FM radio Search Tuner, ($186.90). Multiplex AM/FM radio with Stereo Type Player and speakers ($353.95). Rear seat speaker ($17.00). Vinyl roof covering ($124.55). Automatic speed control ($66.50). Tilt and Telescope with rim blow ($90.50). Undercoating and hood insulator pad ($20.50). Chrome styled road wheels, except station wagon and Cordoba ($98.50). Three-speed manual transmission was standard in Newport and Newport Custom. Automatic transmission was standard in all other Series. Automatic transmission in Newport/Custom with '383' ($229); with '440'($234). V-8 383 cid 335 hp four-barrel engine ($68). V-8 440 cid 350 hp station wagon engine ($164). V-8 440 cid 375 hp 'TNT' engine in Newports/Custom ($198); in New Yorker/300 ($79). Positive traction rear axle ($51).

HISTORICAL FOOTNOTES: This was the last year for the Chrysler convertible. Sales declined more than 30 percent for the year, but industry sales position climbed to 10th place. John J. Riccardo became Chrysler president.

1971 CHRYSLER

NEWPORT ROYAL SERIES — (V-8) — The Newport Royal was considered a sub-series of the Newport. The Royal nameplate returned after an absence of more than 20 years and signified, as before, the low end of the price spectrum. The fuselage shape, introduced in 1969, was retained with minimal changes to the grille and rear taillamp assembly. The 360 cid V-8 Chrysler engine made its debut in the Newport Royal series. The 360 engine was not available in any other 1970 Chrysler series. Optional engines, however, were available. Unique cloth and vinyl upholstery identified Royal interiors.

CHRYSLER I.D. NUMBERS: Serial numbers were now located on a plate attached to the left side of the instrument panel and visible through the windshield. Serial numbers consisted of a seven symbol prefix, plus production sequence code. The sixth symbol changed to '1' to indicate 1971 model year. [NEWPORT ROYAL] Serial numbers began with the Body Style Number. CE41K1C-100001 could be deciphered as a Series CE Chrysler Newport Royal Body Style Number 41 four-door sedan with standard 360 engine (K) made in Detroit (C) as the first car built sequentially (100001). [NEWPORT] Serial numbers and engine numbers were same as for Newport Royal Series, except the engine code for the standard 383 engine was L. [NEWPORT CUSTOM] CL23U1C-100001 could be deciphered as a Series CLL Newport Custom Body Style Number 23 two-door hardtop with optional high output 440 engine (U) for 1971 (1), made in Detroit (C) as the first car built sequentially (100001). [CHRYSLER 300] CS23T1C-I0000I could be deciphered as a Series CS Chrysler 300 Body Style Number 23 two-door hardtop with the standard 440 engine (T) for 1971 (1), made in Detroit as the first car built sequentially. [NEW YORKER] CH43U1C-100001 could be deciphered as a Series CH New Yorker Body Style Number 43 four-door hardtop with optional 440 'TNT' engine (U) for 1971 (1) made in Detroit (C) as the first car built sequentially (100001). [Town & Country] CP46U1C-100001 could be deciphered as a Series CP nine-passenger Chrysler Town & Country Body Style Number 46 station wagon with optional 440 'TNT' engine (U) for 1971 (1) made in Detroit (C) as the first car built sequentially (100001). Engine serial numbers contained a plant code PM (Mount Rd) displacement code 360 (360 cid) and a four-digit calendar date/correlated number 3444 (Jan. 1, 1971) followed by a four-digit sequential number for each day's production.

NEWPORT ROYAL SERIES

Model Number	Body/Style Number	Body Type & Seating	Factory Price	Shipping Weight	Production Total
GC-E	CE41	4-dr Sed-6P	4597	4060	19,662
GC-E	CE23	2-dr HT Cpe-6P	4672	4010	8,500
GC-E	CE43	4-dr HT Sed-6P	4735	4080	5,188

1971 Chrysler, Newport two-door hardtop coupe, V-8

NEWPORT SERIES — (V-8) — The Newport was identical to the Royal sub-series except for the addition of body side moldings; its own cloth and vinyl seat trim and a larger displacement base powerplant. The TNT optional engine was no longer available in the Newport Series as the performance era was waning. Newport side body trim ran from front to rear, unlike the Royal trim, which ran from rear to just forward of the front door.

NEWPORT SERIES

Model Number	Body/Style Number	Body Type & Seating	Factory Price	Shipping Weight	Production Total
GC-E	CE41	4-dr Sed-6P	4709	4120	24,834
GC-E	CE23	2-dr HT Cpe-6P	4784	4070	15,549
GC-E	CE43	4-dr HT Sed-6P	4847	4140	10,800

NEWPORT CUSTOM SERIES — (V-8) — The Newport Custom models included a number of features not found in the two lower priced Newports. A single front seat folding armrest; front and rear armrests; bodyside moldings with vinyl inserts; bright upper door frames on the sedan; front seat foam cushions; and upgraded cloth and vinyl upholstery were standard on this slightly restyled series. The Newport Custom grille matched that of the lower series Chrysler in design.

NEWPORT CUSTOM SERIES

Model Number	Body/Style Number	Body Type & Seating	Factory Price	Shipping Weight	Production Total
GC-L	CL41	4-dr Sed-6P	4838	4130	11,254
GC-L	CL23	2-dr HT Cpe-6P	4910	4075	5,527
GC-L	CL43	4-dr HT Sed-6P	4990	4160	10,207

300 SERIES — (V-8) — The Chrysler 300 series used its own distinctive grille (with hidden headlights) and full width taillamps. Color-coordinated vinyl side rub strips and unique hubcaps helped to distinguish the 300 from the other series. Only two body styles were offered this season as the 300 nameplate was in its last year.

300 SERIES

Model Number	Body/Style Number	Body Type & Seating	Factory Price	Shipping Weight	Production Total
GC-S	CS23	2-dr HT Cpe-6P	5126	4195	7,256
GC-S	CS43	4-dr HT Sed-6P	5205	4270	6,683

NEW YORKER SERIES — (V-8) — The New Yorker styling changes paralleled those of the other 1971 Chryslers. The grille texture was more detailed than that found on the Newport. Cairo cloth and vinyl upholstery was a standard New Yorker feature, as was full carpeting (including trunk); cigarette lighters; electric clock; light group; left-hand remote control mirror; rear fender skirts; wide lower side body moldings: front fender peak strips; paint accent stripes; wheelhouse opening moldings; undercoating; hood insulation; and three-speed windshield wipers.

NEW YORKER SERIES

Model Number	Body/Style Number	Body Type & Seating	Factory Price	Shipping Weight	Production Total
GC-H	CH41	4-dr Sed-6P	5555	4335	9,850
GC-H	CH23	2-dr HT Cpe-6P	5606	4250	4,485
GC-H	CH43	4-dr HT Sed-6P	5686	4355	20,633

TOWN & COUNTRY SERIES — (V-8) — The Town & Country had a minor facelift from 1970. The station wagons continued to use the Brazilian wood applique on the side and rear panels although this type of trim could be deleted without credit. Town & Country offered all New Yorker features, except the electric clock, mirror and undercoating. Standard features

included luggage compartment lock; all-vinyl front bench seat with center armrest; dual action tailgate; and aerodynamic rear roof wind deflector. Station wagon sales rose nearly 10 percent over 1970 totals.

TOWN & COUNTRY SERIES

Model Number	Body/Style Number	Body Type & Seating	Factory Price	Shipping Weight	Production Total
GC-P	CP45	4-dr Sta Wag-6P	5596	4525	5,697
GC-P	CP46	4-dr Sta Wag-9P	5682	4580	10,993

NEWPORT ROYAL ENGINE: V-8. Cast iron block. Displacement: 360 cid. Bore and stroke: 3.91 x 3.58 inches. Brake hp: 255. Compression ratio: 8.7:1. Five main bearings. Hydraulic valve lifters. Carburetion: two-barrel.

NEWPORT/NEWPORT CUSTOM/T&C ENGINE: V-8. Cast iron block. Displacement: 383 cid. Bore and stroke: 4.25 x 3.375 inches. Brake hp: 275. Compression ratio: 8.5:1. Five main bearings. Carburetion: two-barrel.

300/NEW YORKER ENGINE: V-8. Cast iron block. Displacement: 440 cid. Bore and stroke: 4.326 x 3.75 inches. Brake hp: 335. Compression ratio: 8.8:1. Five main bearings. Hydraulic valve lifters. Carburetion: four-barrel.

CHASSIS FEATURES: Wheelbase: (passenger cars) 124 inches; (station wagon) 122 inches. Overall length: (passenger cars) 224.6 inches-, (station wagon) 224.8 inches. Tires: (Newport Royal) G78 x 15; (300) H78 x 15; (New Yorker) J78 x 15; (Town & Country) L84 x 15.

OPTIONS: Power brakes in Newport ($76). Power steering in Newport ($125). Air conditioning ($426); with Automatic Temperature control ($501). Power door locks, in two-doors ($48). Power door locks, in four-doors ($73). Six-Way power bench seat ($106). Pair of Six-Way power bucket or 50/50 seats ($198). Power vent windows, New Yorker four-door hardtop ($67). Power windows ($133). Heavy-duty suspension ($18). Remote trunk release ($16). Electric clock, standard in New Yorker ($19). Center console ($71). All tinted glass ($54). Automatic headlamp dimmer ($51). Cornering lights ($38). Safeguard Sentinel ($37). Dual air conditioning, Town & Country ($656). Town & Country luggage rack ($69). Two-tone paint ($45). High-impact paint ($15). AM radio ($92). AM radio with stereo tape ($224). AM/FM Search-Tuner radio ($196). AM/FM stereo system ($243). AM/FM stereo with cassette tape ($407). Automatic speed control ($69). Rear seat speaker ($19). Tilt and Telescope steering ($91). Vinyl roof ($128). Sun roof ($598). Strato Ventilation, without air conditioning ($18). Road wheels ($102). Undercoating and hood insulation ($27). Three-speed manual transmission was standard on all early Newport models. Automatic transmission was optional on all early Newports ($241). It was made standard equipment, on these cars, later in the year. Newport Royal V-8 383 cid 275 hp two-barrel engine ($27). Newport Royal V-8 383 cid 300 hp four-barrel engine ($98). Newport V-8 383 cid 300 hp four-barrel engine ($71). Newport Custom V-8 383 cid 300 hp four-barrel engine ($71). Town & Country V-8 383 cid 300 hp four-barrel engine ($71). Town & Country V-8 440 cid 355 hp four-barrel engine ($125). Newport V-8 440 cid 335 hp four-barrel engine ($208). Newport Custom 440 cid 335 hp four-barrel engine ($208). Chrysler 300 V-8 440 cid 370 hp four-barrel 'TNT' engine ($83). Positive traction rear axle ($51).

HISTORICAL FOOTNOTES: Chrysler sales declined only three-percent from 1970 figures. It was the last year for the Chrysler 300 Series. Convertibles were no longer available in any Chrysler line. Around May, 1971, automatic transmission became standard equipment on all Chryslers and prices were increased to reflect the change.

1972 CHRYSLER

1972 Chrysler, Newport Royal two-door hardtop coupe, V-8

NEWPORT ROYAL SERIES — (V-8) — The Newport Royal Series, in 1972, combined the two low-end models (Newport Royal/Newport) of 1971. The basic fuselage shape was retained, but a clever restyling of all sheet metal bodyside panels, plus front and rear ends including the hood and deck, provided a fresh look. The heavily chrome front bumper/grille combination was retained, but was now divided in the center providing two grille inserts. The rear taillamps were located at the outer ends of the rear bumper, with the lower half inset to the bumper and the upper half inset to the fender. The taillamps were unique to the Newport Royal series. Newport Royals now included many standard features such as: power front disc brakes; color-keyed carpeting; electronic ignition; power steering; and automatic transmission.

CHRYSLER I.D. NUMBERS: Serial numbers and engine numbers were located in the usual positions. Serial numbers began with the Body Style code. [NEWPORT ROYAL] CL41K2C-100001 could be deciphered as a Newport Royal four-door sedan (CL41) with standard 360 engine (K) for 1972 (2) made in Detroit (C) as the first car built sequentially (100001). Engines were built at the Trenton plant and used the prefix PT. Codes revealed the displacement (360) and a four-digit calendar date/correlated code (3809 denoting Jan. 1, 1972 for example). A four-digit sequential number indicated each day's production. The code for the optional 440 cid Newport engine was 'T.' [NEWPORT CUSTOM] CM23M2C-100001 could be deciphered as a Chrysler Newport Custom two-door hardtop (CM23) with standard 400 engine (M) for 1972 (2) made in Detroit (C) as the first car built sequentially on the Newport Royal series. Engines were identified as on the Newport Royal series. [NEW YORKER] Serial numbers and engine numbers were located in the usual position. Serial numbers began with the usual Body Style code. CH43T2C-100001 could be deciphered as a New Yorker four-door hardtop (CH43) with 440 standard engine (T)

for 1972 (2) made in Detroit (C) as the first car built sequentially. Engine Numbers were assigned as on the Newport Royal series. [NEW YORKER BROUGHAM] CS41T2C-100001 could be deciphered as a Chrysler New Yorker Brougham four-door sedan (CS41) with 440 engine (T) for 1972 (2) made in Detroit (C) as the first car built sequentially (100001). Engine numbers were assigned as on previous series. [TOWN & COUNTRY] CP45T2C-100001 could be deciphered as a six-passenger Town & Country station wagon (CP45) with 440 engine (T) for 1972 (2) made in Detroit (C) as the first car built sequentially (100001). Engine Numbers were assigned as on previous models.

NEWPORT ROYAL SERIES

Model Number	Body/Style Number	Body Type & Seating	Factory Price	Shipping Weight	Production Total
HC-L	CL41	4-dr Sed-6P	4557	4197	47,437
HC-L	CL23	2-dr HT Cpe-6P	4630	4132	22,622
HC-L	CL43	4-dr HT Sed-6P	4692	4202	15,185

NEWPORT CUSTOM SERIES — (V-8) — The Newport Custom series was identical in style to the Newport Royal, but had an enriched interior with foam seat cushions; cloth and vinyl bench seat; front folding center armrest; and bright finished bases on the door armrests. The four-door sedan had bright upper door frames as standard equipment. The base engine for the Newport Custom was the all-new 400 cid V-8. All two-door hardtops used a new roof structure this year, in keeping with the other sheet metal changes outlined in the Newport Royal series.

NEWPORT CUSTOM SERIES

Model Number	Body/Style Number	Body Type & Seating	Factory Price	Shipping Weight	Production Total
HC-M	CM41	4-dr HT-6P	4793	4287	19,278
HC-M	CM23	2-dr HT Cpe-6P	4863	4232	10,326
HC-M	CM43	4-dr HT Sed-6P	4941	4297	15,457

NEW YORKER SERIES — (V-8) — The New Yorker series was split into two distinct parts this year to replace the 300 Series, which was no longer offered. The New Yorker had an interior that was considerably upgraded from the Newport Custom. It featured unique cloth and vinyl seats, with front and rear center folding armrests, and an electric clock. Trunk carpeting was also standard. along with the light group package; left-hand remote control outside rearview mirror; lower bodyside moldings; undercoating; hood insulation pad; and rear fender skirts. The same front bumper/grille combination used on Newports was seen, but the grille insert had a horizontal flair. The rear taillamp assembly was inset into the bumper, in narrow rectangular fashion, and was divided, in the center, by the back-up lamps.

NEW YORKER SERIES

Model Number	Body/Style Number	Body Type & Seating	Factory Price	Shipping Weight	Production Total
HC-H	CH41	4-dr Sed-6P	5502	4437	7,296
HC-H	CH23	2-dr HT Cpe-6P	5552	4372	5,567
HC-H	CH43	4-dr HT Sed-6P	5630	4467	10,013

1972 Chrysler, New Yorker Brougham four-door hardtop sedan, V-8

NEW YORKER BROUGHAM SERIES — (V-8) — The Brougham was the top-of-the-line Chrysler and included, as standard equipment, many features which were optional on other models. Console style front and rear armrests with wood-grained trim; fender mounted directional light indicators; front fender peak moldings; automatic seatback release (on two-door hardtops); special two-spoke steering wheel; and power windows were just a few of the Brougham's standard extras. Unique chrome 'Brougham' emblems graced the C-pillar and the rear deck lid.

NEW YORKER BROUGHAM SERIES

Model Number	Body/Style Number	Body Type & Seating	Factory Price	Shipping Weight	Production Total
HC-S	CS41	4-dr Sed-6P	5728	4437	5,971
HC-S	CS23	2-dr HT Cpe-6P	5777	4372	4,635
HC-S	CS43	4-dr HT Sed-9P	5856	4467	20,328

1972 Chrysler, Town & Country four-door station wagon, V-8

TOWN & COUNTRY SERIES — (V-8) — Styling changes seen on the Town & Country followed those of sedans and hardtops this year. The grille was identical to the New Yorker type. The loop-style front bumper had a center bar which split the grille. The simulated wood-grain applique was placed lower on the side body panels than in 1971. Sales increased more than 20 percent over the previous station wagons, with the nine-passenger model showing a substantial improvement. Standard equipment included electric clock; lockable luggage compartment; all-vinyl bench seats with folding center armrest; automatic locking tailgate; dual action tailgate; power-operated tailgate window; aerodynamic rear roof wind deflector; and bodyside and rear panel wood-grain appliques.

TOWN & COUNTRY SERIES

Model Number	Body/Style Number	Body Type & Seating	Factory Price	Shipping Weight	Production Total
HC-P	CP45	4-dr T&C Wag-6P	5692	4712	6,473
HC-P	CP46	4-dr T&C Wag-9P	5576	4767	14,116

NEWPORT ROYAL ENGINE: V-8. Cast iron block. Displacement: 360 cid. Bore and stroke: 4.00 x 3.58 inches. SAE Net hp: 175. Compression ratio: 8.8:1. Five main bearings. Hydraulic valve lifters. Carburetor: two-barrel.

NEWPORT CUSTOM/NEW YORKER BROUGHAM/T&C ENGINE: V-8. Cast iron block. Displacement: 400 cid. Bore and stroke: 4.34 x 3.375. SAE Net hp: 190. Compression ratio: 8.2:1. Five main bearings. Hydraulic valve lifters. Carburetion: two-barrel.

NEW YORKER ENGINE: V-8. Cast iron block. Displacement: 440 cid. Bore and stroke: 4.326 x 3.75 inches. SAE Net hp: 225 (245 with optional dual exhaust). Compression ratio: 8.2:1. Five main bearings. Hydraulic valve lifters. Carburetion: four-barrel.

CHASSIS FEATURES: Wheelbase (passenger cars) 124 inches; (station wagons) 122 inches. Overall length: (passenger cars) 224.1 inches; (station wagons) 224.8 inches. Tires: (Newport Royal and Custom) H78 x 15; (New Yorker and Brougham) J78 x 15; (station wagon) L84 x 15.

OPTIONS: Air conditioning ($416); with Automatic temperature control ($490). Dual air conditioning ($640); with Auto Temp ($714). Power door locks, two-door ($47). Power door locks, four-door ($72). Six-Way power bench seat ($104). Six-Way power buckets or 50/50 seat ($193). Power vent windows, New Yorker four-door hardtop ($65). Power windows ($131). Remote trunk release ($15). Electric clock ($19). All tinted glass ($42). Cornering lights ($38). Luggage rack and assist handles ($86). Two-tone paint ($44). New Yorker/Brougham paint stripe ($16). AM radio ($90). AM radio with 8-track stereo tape ($219). AM/FM Search Tuner radio ($192). AM/FM stereo ($237). AM/FM stereo with cassette ($398). Vinyl roof cover ($125). Station wagon vinyl roof cover ($141). Automatic speed control ($68). Chrome styled road wheels ($100). Sun roof ($585). Heavy-duty shock absorbers ($5). Automatic transmission was standard on all 1972 Chryslers. Dual exhausts were optional on all models combined with the 440 cid V-8 ($35). A 70-amp. battery was optional on all models, except standard with New Yorkers ($15). An engine block heater was optional on all models ($15). Electronic ignition was optional on all models ($34). An optional exhaust emission control system was available for all, mandatory with California sale ($28). V-8 440 cid 225 hp four-barrel engine, except standard in New Yorker ($122). Positive traction rear axle. Optional rear axle gear ratios included 2.76:1 ($13) and 3.23:1 ($13).

HISTORICAL FOOTNOTES: Last year for the Royal nameplate after a brief revival. Chrysler sales rose more than 16 percent over year earlier totals, reflecting the popularity of the new sheet metal restyling. A new 400 cid engine made its debut. Horsepower ratings for 1972 were expressed in SAE net horsepower and seemed much lower than before.

1973 CHRYSLER

1973 Chrysler, Newport Royal four-door hardtop sedan, V-8

NEWPORT SERIES — (V-8) — The Royal portion of the name was dropped this year and the low-line Chrysler was the Newport. A Newport sedan became the millionth car to bear the Chrysler nameplate. Styling refinements centered around the front bumper and grille area. The loop-type bumper was changed to a more conventional type, with the dual headlights and rectangular grille outlined in chrome above the bumper. The grille had a fine vertical/horizontal bar motif. The rear taillamps had a slight cosmetic change. An electronic ignition system became standard equipment along with power disc brakes; front and rear bumper guards; inside hood release; wheelhouse moldings; pedal dress-up kit; and tripodometer. A special 'Navajo' package was offered. It featured Navajo copper metallic paint; orange paint stripes; vinyl roof; and white bench seats with unique Navajo (Indian blanket) cloth inserts.

CHRYSLER I.D. NUMBERS: Serial numbers and engine numbers were located in the usual positions. Serial numbers began with the Body Style code. [NEWPORT] CL41M3C-100001 could be deciphered as a Newport four-door sedan (CL41) with standard 400 cid engine (M) for 1973 (3) made in Detroit (C) as the first car built sequentially. [NEWPORT CUSTOM] CM23T3C-100001 could be deciphered as a Newport Custom two-door hardtop (CM23) with optional 440 engine (T) for 1973 (3) made in Detroit (C) as the first car built sequentially (100001). [NEW YORKER] CH41U3C-100001 could be deciphered as a New Yorker four-door sedan (CH41) with optional 440 engine (U) for 1973 (3) made in Detroit (C) as the first

car built sequentially (100001). [NEW YORKER BROUGHAM] CS43T3C-100001 could be deciphered as a New Yorker Brougham four-door hardtop (CS43) with standard 440 engine (T) for 1973 (3) made in Detroit (C) as the first car built sequentially (100001). [TOWN & COUNTRY] CP46T3C-100001 could be deciphered as a nine-passenger station wagon (CP46) with standard 440 engine (T) for 1973 (3) made in Detroit (C) as first car built sequentially (100001). Engine Numbers were found on the right-hand side of the 400 cid V-8 and the left bank of cylinders, adjacent to the tappet rail, on the 440 cid V-8. Engine Numbers were assigned as on previous models.

NEWPORT SERIES

Model Number	Body/Style Number	Body Type & Seating	Factory Price	Shipping Weight	Production Total
3C-L	CL41	4-dr Sed-6P	4693	4305	54,147
3C-L	CL23	2-dr HT Cpe-6P	4766	4265	27,456
3C-L	CL43	4-dr HT Sed-6P	4828	4315	20,175

NEWPORT CUSTOM SERIES — (V-8) — This was an upgraded version of the Newport. Newport Custom nameplates were placed on the C-pillar, rather than on the front fender behind the wheelhouse molding. This series offered enriched interiors, with unique cloth and vinyl bench seats; bodyside moldings with vinyl inserts; bright upper door moldings on the sedan; single center folding front armrests; and bright finished bases on the front and rear door armrests.

NEWPORT CUSTOM SERIES

Model Number	Body/Style Number	Body Type & Seating	Factory Price	Shipping Weight	Production Total
3C-M	CM41	4-dr Sed-6P	4931	4305	20,092
3C-M	CM23	2-dr HT Cpe-6P	4996	4250	12,293
3C-M	CM43	4-dr HT Sed-6P	5079	4330	20,050

1973 Chrysler, New Yorker four-door sedan, V-8

NEW YORKER SERIES — (V-8) — The New Yorker was offered in only two body styles this year. They had a unique grille insert with a horizontal flair and a thinner upper grille surround. Taillamps were also unique to the New Yorker. They used a horizontal layout, structured within the rear bumper. The New Yorker's standard features included a larger battery; full carpeting (including trunk); electric clock; left-hand control OSRV mirror; wheelhouse opening moldings; rear fender skirts; undercoating; hood insulation; three-speed windshield wipers; and upgraded cloth and vinyl seats.

NEW YORKER SERIES

Model Number	Body/Style Number	Body Type & Seating	Factory Price	Shipping Weight	Production Total
3C-H	CH41	4-dr Sed-6P	5641	4460	7,991
3C-H	CH43	4-dr HT Sed-6P	5769	4480	7,619

NEW YORKER BROUGHAM SERIES — (V-8) — The New Yorker Brougham was the top-of-the-line Chrysler with many features as standard equipment. They included: rear folding armrests; bucket seats or three-in-one bench seat with folding armrests; light package; fender mounted directional signal indicators; front fender peak moldings; automatic seatback release (two-door hardtop); two-spoke rim-blow steering wheel, power windows; and concealed three-speed windshield wipers with coordinated washers. With the new styling, sales of this series increased more than 40 percent.

NEW YORKER BROUGHAM SERIES

Model Number	Body/Style Number	Body Type & Seating	Factory Price	Shipping Weight	Production Total
3C-S	CS41	4-dr Sed-6P	5876	4530	8,541
3C-S	CS23	2-dr HT Cpe-6P	5925	4440	9,190
3C-S	CS43	4-dr HT Sed-6P	6004	4545	26,635

TOWN & COUNTRY SERIES — (V-8) — Styling of the Town & Countrys reflected the changes of the other 1973 Chryslers. The New Yorker grille was seen and the wood-grain side and rear body panels continued to be used. Other standard features included an electric clock; luggage compartment lock; all-vinyl bench seats with front center armrest; automatic tailgate lock; dual action tailgate; power-operated tailgate window; and aerodynamic rear roof wind deflector. Station wagon sales, even with the new styling, fell 2.5 percent over the banner year of 1972.

TOWN & COUNTRY SERIES

Model Number	Body/Style Number	Body Type & Seating	Factory Price	Shipping Weight	Production Total
3C-P	CP45	4-dr T&C Wag-6P	5885	4775	5,353
3C-P	CP46	4-dr T&C Wag-9P	6010	4830	14,687

NEWPORT/NEWPORT CUSTOM ENGINE: V-8. Cast iron block. Displacement: 400 cid. Bore and stroke. 4.34 x 3.375. SAE Net hp: 185. Compression ratio: 8.2:1. Five main bearings. Hydraulic valve lifters. Carburetion: four-barrel.

NEW YORKER/NEW YORKER BROUGHAM/T&C ENGINE: V-8. Cast iron block. Displacement: 440 cid. Bore and stroke: 4.326 x 3.75 inches. SAE Net hp: 215. Compression ratio: 8.2:1. Five main bearings. Hydraulic valve lifters. Carburetion: four-barrel.

CHASSIS FEATURES: Wheelbase: (passenger cars) 124 inches; (station wagons) 122 inches. Overall length: (passenger cars) 230.1 inches; (station wagons) 229.6 inches; (New Yorker) 230.8 inches. front tread: 62.1 inches. Rear tread: 63.4 inches. Tires: (Newport and Newport Custom) H78 x 15; (New Yorker and New Yorker Brougham) J78 x 15; (station wagons) L84 x 15.

OPTIONS: Door locks, two-door ($47.40); four-door ($72.75). Power Six-Way bench seat ($105.30). Power Six-Way buckets or 50-50 seat ($195.75). Power vent windows in New Yorker. New Yorker Brougham ($66.00). Power windows, standard in Brougham ($132.20). (Remote control trunk release ($15.15). Electronic digital clock ($39.40). Electric clock ($19.15). Tinted glass ($53.00). Cornering lights ($38.00). Air conditioning ($420.85); with Auto Temp ($495.15). Dual air conditioning on wagons ($648.00); with Auto Temp ($722.60). Luggage rack and assist handles ($87.35). Two-tone paint ($44.40). Paint stripe (New Yorker and Brougham ($15.90). AM radio ($91.40). AM radio with Stereo Tape eight track ($221.55). AM/FM Search Tuner ($194.55). AM/FM Stereo ($240.35). AM/FM with Stereo Tape cassette ($402.80). AM/FM Stereo with eight track Stereo Tape ($376.80). Vinyl roof cover ($126.60). Automatic speed control ($68.70). Chromed styled road wheels ($101.35). Premier wheel-covers ($40.30). Sun roof ($592.00). Heavy-duty suspension (39.90). Security alarm system ($101,20). 440 engine (Newport and Custom) $123. 1 0. Sure Grip differential ($50.30).

HISTORICAL FOOTNOTES: The One-Millionth Chrysler was produced this year. It was also the last year for the fuselage body design introduced in 1969. Sales increased 15 percent over 1972 totals.

1974 CHRYSLER

1974 Chrysler, Newport two-door hardtop coupe, V-8

NEWPORT SERIES — (V-8) — An all-new Newport was introduced this year. It was distinctively sized: one inch lower, one inch wider, and five inches shorter than the 1973 model. The front grille had a heavy chrome outline and the grille insert was a richly designed affair with three tiers of squares, outlined with bold horizontal and vertical bars. The squares were filled-in with smaller vertical and horizontal bars giving a true luxury appearance. Sales declined drastically, because of the Arab oil embargo. Chrysler, for the first time ever, offered a small displacement engine option at no extra cost (360 cid V-8 instead of 400 cid V-8).

CHRYSLER I.D. NUMBERS: Serial numbers and engine numbers were located as on previous models. Serial numbers began with the Body Style code. [NEWPORT] CL41J4C100001 could be deciphered as a Newport four-door sedan (CL41) with optional 360 engine (J) for 1974 (4) made in Detroit (C) as the first car built sequentially (100001). [NEWPORT CUSTOM] CM23M4C-100001 could be deciphered as a Newport Custom two-door hardtop (CM23) with standard 400 engine (M) for 1974 (4) made In Detroit (C) as the first car built sequentially (100001). [NEW YORKER] CH43U4C-100001 could be deciphered as a New Yorker four-door hardtop (CH43) with optional 440 engine (U) for 1974 (4) made in Detroit (C) as the first car built sequentially (100001). [NEW YORKER BROUGHAM] CS43T4C-100001 could be deciphered as a New Yorker Brougham four-door hardtop (CS43) with standard 440 engine (T) for 1974 (4) made in Detroit (C) as the first car built sequentially (100001). [TOWN & COUNTRY] CP45T4D-100001 could be deciphered as a Town & Country six-passenger station wagon (CP45) with standard 440 engine (T) for 1974 (4) made in Belvidere (D) as the first car built sequentially. The 360 cid engine had the serial number on the left front of the block, below the cylinder head. 4M360R09100001 could be deciphered as 1974 Mound Road built powerplant (4M) of 360 cid displacement (360), designed for regular fuel and manufactured on September 10 (0910) as the first engine built that day (0001). Serial numbers on 400 cid motors were located on the right-hand side of the block, adjacent to the distributor. Serial numbers on 440 cid motors were located on the left-hand bank of cylinders, adjacent to the front tappet rail. The 400/440 cid engines used the following method of identification: 4F440R 8-222, which could be deciphered as 1974 Trenton plant (4T) 440 displacement regular fuel engine (R) built on Aug. 22 (8122) during the second shift (2).

NEWPORT SERIES

Model Number	Body/Style Number	Body Type & Seating	Factory Price	Shipping Weight	Production Total
4C-L	CL41	4-dr Sed-6P	5225	4530	26,944
4C-L	CL23	2-dr HT Cpe-6P	5300	4480	13,784
4C-L	CL43	4-dr HT Sed-6P	5364	4540	8,968

NEWPORT CUSTOM SERIES — (V-8) — The Newport Custom used the same distinctive grille and taillamps as the Newport. The Custom, however, added its own 50/50 bench front seat with folding center armrest and cloth and vinyl trim. Also included, as in previous years, were front and rear door armrests; vinyl bodyside inserts; and bright upper door moldings on the sedan. Like Newports, Customs offered, as standard equipment, electronic ignition; automatic transmission; inside hood release; power front disc brakes; wheelhouse moldings; and inside day/night mirrors. Newport Custom sales fell more than 45 percent, owing to the Arab oil embargo.

NEWPORT CUSTOM SERIES

Model Number	Body/Style Number	Body Type & Seating	Factory Price	Shipping Weight	Production Total
4C-M	CM41	4-dr Sed-6P	5586	4580	10,569
4C-M	CM23	2-dr HT Cpe-6P	5653	4530	7,206
4C-M	CM43	4-dr HT Sed-6P	5738	4600	9,892

1974 Chrysler, New Yorker four-door hardtop sedan, V-8

NEW YORKER SERIES — (V-8) — The New Yorker shared the styling changes of the Newport, except the grille insert retained its horizontal flair of previous years. The rear bumper and taillamp assembly was totally unique to the New Yorker. Taillamps retained the narrow, across-the-width look of previous years and the rear license plate was mounted in the center of the bumper, just above the lower edge. Only two four-door styles were available in this series. Sales fell more than 60 percent in comparison to year earlier totals, owing to the Arab oil embargo.

CHRYSLER NEW YORKER SERIES

Model Number	Body/Style Number	Body Type & Seating	Factory Price	Shipping Weight	Production Total
4C-H	CH41	4-dr Sed-6P	5554	4560	3,072
4C-H	CH43	4-dr HT Sed-6P	5686	4595	3,066

NEW YORKER BROUGHAM — (V-8) — The New Yorker Brougham was an upgraded version of the New Yorker and included such additional items as automatic seatback release; two-spoke rim-blow horn; power windows; light package; 50/50 divided bench seat; unique cloth and vinyl upholstery; and wood-grained console style front and rear door armrests. A special St. Regis package was available and included fixed formal open windows, body paint accent stripes and forward half-covered vinyl roof.

NEW YORKER BROUGHAM SERIES

Model Number	Body/Style Number	Body Type & Seating	Factory Price	Shipping Weight	Production Total
4C-S	CS41	4-dr Sed-6P	6479	4740	4,533
4C-S	CS23	2-dr HT Cpe-6P	6530	4640	7,980
4C-S	CS43	4-dr HT Sed-6P	6611	4755	13,165

TOWN & COUNTRY SERIES — (V-8) — Styling of the Town & Country followed the pattern of the New Yorker Series. Wood-grain appliques were standard on the body side and rear panels. Taillamps were unique to the wagon as they were placed horizontally on the tailgate and wrapped around the sides. A new hood ornament sat atop the broad, chromed hood outline as on the New Yorker Series. The emblem featured a mythological animal, the griffin, in profile. As in previous years, the Town & Country had, as standard equipment, an electric clock; luggage compartment lock; all-vinyl 50/50 bench seats with front center armrest; automatic locking tailgate; three-way action tailgate (with power operated window); and rear aerodynamic wind deflector. Town & Country sales declined more than 55 percent. All were built at the Belvidere assembly plant.

TOWN & COUNTRY SERIES

Model Number	Body/Style Number	Body Type & Seating	Factory Price	Shipping Weight	Production Total
4C-P	CP45	4-dr T&C Wag-6P	5767	4915	2,236
4C-P	CP46	4-dr T&C Wag-6P	5896	4970	5,958

NEWPORT/NEWPORT CUSTOM ENGINE: V-8. Cast iron block. Displacement: 400 cid. Bore and stroke: 4.34 x 3.375 inches. Brake hp: 185. Compression ratio: 8.2:1. Five main bearings. Hydraulic valve lifters. Carburetor: two-barrel.

NEW YORKER/NEW YORKER BROUGHAM/T&C ENGINE: V-8. Cast iron block. Displacement 440 cid. Bore and stroke: 4.326 x 3.75 inches. Brake hp: 230. Compression ratio: 8.2:1. Five main bearings. Hydraulic valve lifters. Carburetion: four-barrel.

CHASSIS FEATURES: Wheelbase: 124 inches. Overall length (passenger cars) 225.1 inches; (station wagons) 224.7 inches. Tires: (New port and Newport Custom) HR78 x 15; (New Yorker and New Yorker Brougham) JR78x 15; (Town & Country) LR78 x 15.

OPTIONS: Door locks, on two-door ($50.65); or four-door ($77.80). Power Six-Way bench seat ($112.60). Power Six-way 50/50 seat ($209.35). Power vent windows ($141.35). Remote control release ($16.60). Electronic digital clock ($42.10). Tinted glass ($56.65). Cornering lights ($40.60). Engine block heater ($16.60). Air conditioning ($50.20); with Auto Temp ($129.70). Locking gas cap ($4.55). AM radio ($97.75). AM/FM radio ($156.90). AM/FM Stereo Search Tune ($313.80). AM/FM Stereo with eight track stereo tape ($305.30). Vinyl roof cover ($135.40). Automatic speed control ($73.40). Heavy-duty suspension ($19.40). Manual vent windows on four-door models ($36.10). Chrome styled road wheels ($108.40). Premier wheelcovers ($43. 10). Security alarm system ($108.20). 400 cid four-barrel V-8 in Newport and Newport Custom (($39.75). 440 cid four-barrel V-8 in Newport and Newport Custom ($131.65). Sure Grip differential ($53.80). Automatic transmission, power steering and power disc brakes were standard. The 360 cid engine was a no-cost option for Newports.

HISTORICAL FOOTNOTES: The Arab oil embargo played havoc with the sale of large-sized automobiles. Chrysler sales fell almost 50 percent when compared to the 1973 model year totals. R.K. Brown was group vice-president of Chrysler-Plymouth Div. this year. Model year sales peaked at 107,059 units.

Standard Catalog of American Cars

1975 CHRYSLER

NEWPORT — (V-8) — The Newport remained relatively unchanged from its 1974 counterpart. A new front bumper with openings, plus a new grille insert accentuated with horizontal ribs, were styling highlights. A moulded fiberglass headliner was standard, as were front and rear bumper guards and steel-belted radial tires. A fuel pacer with fender-mounted light (using the same indicator as turn signal lights) was optional. Electronic ignition; power front disc brakes; power steering; and automatic transmission continued as standard equipment.

CHRYSLER I.D. NUMBERS: Serial numbers and engine numbers were located in the same positions as on previous models. Serial numbers began with the Body Style code. [NEWPORT] CL41K5-100001 could be deciphered as: a Newport four-door sedan (CL41) with 360 cid standard engine (K) for 1975 (5) made in Detroit (D) as the first car built sequentially (100001). [NEWPORT CUSTOM] CM23J5C-100001 could be deciphered as: a Newport Custom two-door hardtop (CM23) with optional 360 cid four-barrel engine (J) for 1975 (5) made in Detroit (C) as the first car built sequentially (100001). [NEW YORKER BROUGHAM] CS43T5C-10001 could be deciphered as a New Yorker Brougham four-door hardtop (CS43) with standard 440 engine (T) for 1975 (5) made in Detroit (C) as the first car built sequentially (100001). [TOWN & COUNTRY] CP46N5D-10001 could be deciphered as: a nine-passenger Town & Country wagon (CP46) with optional 400 cid engine (N) for 1975 (5) made in Belvidere (D) as the first car built sequentially. [CORDOBA] SS22G5R100001 could be deciphered as: a Cordoba specialty hardtop (SS22) with standard 318 cid engine (G) for 1975 (5) made in Windsor, Canada (R) as the first car built sequentially (100001). Engine Numbers were assigned as on previous series.

NEWPORT SERIES

Model Number	Body/Style Number	Body Type & Seating	Factory Price	Shipping Weight	Production Total
5C-I	CL41	4-dr Sed-6P	5428	4450	24,339
5C-L	CL23	2-dr HT Cpe-6P	5511	4405	10,485
5C-L	CL43	4-dr HT Sed-6P	5582	4485	6846

NEWPORT CUSTOM SERIES — (V-8) — The Custom series was identical to the Newport, except for the usual upgraded interior appointments. Special cloth and vinyl upholstery and 50/50 bench seats with folding front center armrests; bright upper door moldings on the sedan; front and rear door armrests; and bodyside vinyl insert moldings were standard items on the Newport Custom.

NEWPORT CUSTOM SERIES

Model Number	Body/Style Number	Body Type & Seating	Factory Price	Shipping Weight	Production Total
5C-M	CM41	4-dr Sed-6P	5828	4405	9,623
5C-M	CM23	2-dr HT Cpe-6P	5903	4455	5,831
5C-M	CM43	4-dr HT Sed-6P	5997	4525	11,626

1975 Chrysler, New Yorker Brougham four-door hardtop sedan, V-8

NEW YORKER BROUGHAM SERIES — (V-8) — The New Yorker Brougham was the only New Yorker offered in 1975. A new grille insert (divided into six rectangular sections by chrome moldings) was the major styling change. The 400 cid V-8 could be had in the Brougham, at no extra cost, as an economy option. The St. Regis package was available as an extra cost item. Broughams featured power windows; automatic seatback release (in two-doors); three-speed coordinated windshield wipers and washers; folding rear armrest on rear seats; and a light package as standard equipment.

NEW YORKER BROUGHAM SERIES

Model Number	Body/Style Number	Body Type & Seating	Factory Price	Shipping Weight	Production Total
5C-S	CS41	4-dr Sed-6P	7818	4660	5,698
5C-S	CS23	2-dr HT Cpe-6P	7875	4680	7,567
5C-S	CS43	4-dr HT Sed-6P	7965	4785	12,774

TOWN & COUNTRY SERIES — (V-8) — The Town & Country styling changes followed those of the New Yorker Brougham. A molded fiberglass headliner was standard and a new electrically heated rear tailgate window was available. Another option was the automatic vehicle ride height control system. The 400 engine was a no charge option, in lieu of the standard 440 powerplant.

TOWN & COUNTRY SERIES

Model Number	Body/Style Number	Body Type & Seating	Factory Price	Shipping Weight	Production Total
5C-P	CP45	4-dr T&C Wag-6P	7954	5080	1,891
5C-P	CP46	4-dr T&C Wag-9P	8099	5115	4,764

CORDOBA SERIES — (V-8) — A new specialty hardtop, the Cordoba, was built with luxury trim and appointments on a wheelbase of 115 inches. The front grille was mostly similar in appearance to the other Chryslers of 1975. However, there were two horizontal bars, which divided numerous fine vertical bars. Single headlamps were located in pods and smaller pods contained the parking lamps. The hood and deck lids were highly sculptured and vertical rectangular taillamps were suggestive of the Newport type. A Cordoba nameplate graced the front fenders and distinctive medallions were set into the taillamps and the stand-up hood ornament. Cordoba seats were upholstered in brocade trim. One optional interior was a combination of leather and vinyl. Opera windows were seen in the rear quarter roof pillars. The Cordoba sales picture was the only bright spot in the Chrysler fine for all of 1975.

CORDOBA SERIES

Model Number	Body/Style Number	Body Type & Seating	Factory Price	Shipping Weight	Production Total
5S-S	SS22	2-dr HT Cpe-6P	5581	4035	150,105

NEWPORT/NEWPORT CUSTOM ENGINE: V-8. Overhead valves. Cast iron block. Displacement: 400 cid. Bore and stroke: 4.34 x 3.38 inches. Compression ratio: 8.2:1. SAE NET hp: 175 at 4000 rpm. Five main bearings. Hydraulic valve lifters. Carburetor: two-barrel.

NEW YORKER BROUGHAM/T&C ENGINES: V-8. Cast iron block. displacement: 440 cid. Bore and stroke: 4.326 x 3.75 inches. Brake hp: 215 at 4000 rpm. Compression ratio 8.2:1. Five main bearings. Hydraulic valve lifters. Carburetion: four-barrel.

CORDOBA SERIES ENGINES: V-8. Cast iron block. Displacement: 318 cid. Bore and stroke: 3.91 c 3.31 inches. Brake hp: 150 at 4000 rpm. Compression ratio: 8.5:1. Five main bearings. Hydraulic valve lifters. Carburetion: two-barrel.

CHASSIS FEATURES: Wheelbase: (Chryslers) 124 inches; (Cordoba) 115 inches. Overall length: (Town & Country) 227.2; (Newport/Custom) 227.1; (New Yorker/Brougham) 226.6; (Cordoba) 215.3 inches. Front track: (Chrysler) 64 inches. (Cordoba) 61.9 inches. Rear track: (Chrysler) 63.4 inches. (Cordoba) 62 inches. Tires: (Newport/Newport Custom) HR78 x 15. (New Yorker/Brougham) JR78 x 15. (Town & Country) LR78 x 15. (Cordoba) GR78 x 15.

OPTIONS: Door locks (two-door), [$60.70]. (Cordoba) [$59.90]. Door locks (4-door), [$88.35]. Power bench seat (Newport), [$121.35]. Power 6-way 50/50 seat, (r&l), [$242.70]. Power bench (Cordoba), [$117.15]. Power bucket (left-Cordoba), [$117.15]. Remote trunk release, [$18.70]. Remote trunk release (Cordoba), [$18.45]. Sure Grip differential, [$54.55]. Sure Grip differential (Cordoba) [$49.95]. Tinted glass, [$63.35]. Tinted glass (Cordoba), [$50.70]. Air conditioning, [$475.15] (add $76.60 for Auto Temp). Air conditioning (Cordoba). [$436.90]. Locking gas cap, [$6.00]. Locking gas cap (Cordoba), [$5.95]. AM Radio, [$99.10] (std. on Cordoba). AM/FM Radio, [$159.05]. AM/FM Radio (Cordoba), [$76.85]. Heavy-duty suspension, [$26.70]. Heavy-duty suspension (Cordoba), [$23.70]. Sun roof, [$781.20]. Sun roof manual (Cordoba), [$296.10].

POWERTRAIN OPTIONS: 400 cid V-8 in Newport/Newport Custom ($40.30)., 440 cid V-8 in Newport/Newport Custom ($164.65). 400 cid V-8 in Cordoba ($73). Sure-Grip differential, in Cordoba ($49.95); in other Chryslers ($54.55).

HISTORICAL FOOTNOTES: Sales of large body cars such as Newport and New Yorkers fell another 12 percent in 1975. The only bright spot was the Cordoba which had 60 percent of all Chrysler sales. Chrysler sales were the best showing for the division since 1969's banner year.

STANDARD CATALOG OF
IMPERIAL
1946-1975

1958 Imperial, Crown Southampton four-door hardtop, V-8 (CHC)

The postwar Imperial began as an extra fancy Chrysler. Although larger and more luxurious, its styling was not particularly distinctive from the corporation's less expensive series.

By Charles Webb

There wasn't all that much reason to be different. From 1946 to mid-1953, automakers enjoyed a seller's market. As the Salesman's Data Book for 1946 Chryslers told dealers "you have a car that puts you in a perfect position to pick your owners... to select the type of person who appreciates a fine motor car... one whose prestige and pride of ownership will reflect credit on the car and on your organization."

Chrysler styling seemed to reflect this attitude. At a time when customers demanded flash and glamour, the Imperial was sedate. It had a rather clean, practical design that didn't change dramatically until 1955. Engineering and passenger comfort had priority over appearance.

Imperial became a separate brand of Chrysler Corp. in 1954. But, it wasn't until a year later that it started to develop its own personality. The swank 1955 and 1956 models, with their free-standing taillights, were a tremendous boost to Imperial's image. They also showed that a car could have style without looking like "a jukebox on wheels," as noted industrial designer Raymond Loewy put it.

"The flying saucers have landed at last!" That's what a bit character in an Elvis Presley movie exclaimed when he saw a 1967 Imperial convertible. It was easy to see why. Imperial styling this year was to the left of "Wow!" The public loved it. This would be the best sales year ever for the make.

Four years later, Imperial made an attempt to capture the beauty of the classic era by using free-standing headlights. Whether or not it succeeded is a matter of personal opinion. Yet, at least no one could accuse the company of not being innovative.

In 1964, Imperial styling reflected the influence of the handsome 1961-1963 Lincoln Continental. While not as original as the previous models, they were handsome. They seemed more in tune with the pre-1955 conservative designs (but a bit flashier).

Although luxurious and attractive, by 1957 the make was drifting back to its former 'fancy Chrysler' image. At a time when Ford was trying to make Mercurys resemble Lincolns and Chevrolets received Cadillac-inspired styling,

Imperial began to look more like the lower-cost Chryslers. However, other than the free-standing headlights and taillights, there wasn't really an 'Imperial look' that the corporation could bestow on its less expensive cars. And the fact just about everyone referred to the make as 'Chrysler-Imperial' didn't help matters.

The fuelage-styled Imperials, introduced in 1969, were the sleekest cars in their price class. They were also quite popular, at least initially. Sales dropped the next year to their lowest level since 1958.

From 1971 until 1975, Imperial was just a top-of-the-line

Chrysler. It was no surprise that the 1976 New Yorker looked virtually the same as the previous year's Imperial. Still, to a lot of people, there will always be something special about owning an Imperial.

1946 Chrysler Imperial, four-door limousine, 8-cyl

1952 Chrysler Imperial, four-door sedan, V-8

1947 Chrysler Imperial, Derham Custom Continental Coupe, 8-cyl

1953 Chrysler Imperial, four-door sedan, V-8

1948 Chrysler Imperial, two-door Derham Custom Coupe, 8-cyl

1953 Chrysler Imperial, Custom two-door Newport hardtop, V-8

1951 Chrysler Imperial, four-door sedan, V-8

1956 Imperial, Southampton four-door hardtop, V-8

Standard Catalog of American Cars

1957 Imperial, Crown two-door convertible, V-8

1960 Imperial, Crown two-door convertible, V-8

1961 Imperial, Southampton four-door hardtop, V-8

1964 Imperial, Crown two-door convertible, V-8

1968 Crown Imperial, two-door convertible, V-8

1968 Crown Imperial, Southampton four-door hardtop, V-8

1969 Crown Imperial, Southampton four-door hardtop, V-8

1970 Imperial, LeBaron four-door hardtop, V-8

238

1946 IMPERIAL

1946 Chrysler Crown Imperial, four-door limousine, 8-cyl (AA)

CROWN IMPERIAL SERIES — SERIES C40 — The 1946 Crown Imperial had a new criss-cross pattern grille with wraparound top, center and lower horizontal pieces. Yet, the basic 1942 styling remained. Because of the shortage of whitewall tires, white metal beauty rings were used.

IMPERIAL V.I.N.S: For 1946 models, the serial number on Chrysler-Imperials was located on the right-hand front door hinge post. Serial numbers ranged from 7810001 to 7810166. Motor numbers were located on the left side of the engine block, below cylinder head and between cylinders number 1 and number 2. Motor numbers for 1946 Crown Imperials were C40-1001 and up. Body Style numbers were not used.

CROWN IMPERIAL SERIES

Series Number	Body/Style Number	Body Type & Seating	Factory Price	Shipping Weight	Production Total
C40	Note 1	4-dr Limo-8P	3875	4814	Note 2

NOTE 1: Not available.

NOTE 2: A total of 750 Crown Imperial limousines were made from 1946 to 1948.

ENGINE: Inline. L-head 8. Cast iron block. Displacement: 323.5 cid. Bore and stroke: 3.25 x 4.87 inches. Compression ratio: 6.80:1. Brake hp: 135 at 3400 rpm. Five main bearings. Solid valve lifters. Carburetor: Stromberg two-barrel Model AAV-2.

CHASSIS FEATURES: Wheelbase: 145.5 inches. Overall length: 235 inches. Front tread: 58 inches. Rear tread: 62 inches. Tires: 7.50 x 15.

OPTIONS: Mopar heater and defroster. Mopar radio. Electric clock. Spot lights. Fog lights. Directional signals. Fluid Drive, four-speed hydraulic semi-automatic transmission. Heavy-duty air cleaner. Available rear axle gear ratios: 3.58:1.

HISTORICAL FOOTNOTES: The Chrysler Crown Imperial was introduced in March, 1946. Calendar year sales of 76,753 cars were recorded. Fluid Drive was standard equipment on Crown Imperials. A limited number of Derham Customs were built off the 1946 Chrysler Custom Imperial platform. A one-off 'Pullman' limousine was made for Post Brand cereal heiress Margery Merryweather. Also constructed off this chassis, for commercial emergency use, were a number of sedan ambulances made by McClintock, Co. of Lansing, Mich.

1947 IMPERIAL

1947 Chrysler Crown Imperial, four-door limousine, 8-cyl (AA)

CROWN IMPERIAL SERIES — SERIES C40 — Styling was virtually unchanged for 1947. The high-beam indicator was moved from the top of the speedometer into the speedometer dial, replacing the left turn signal arrow. Red taillamp buttons replaced the white ones used previously. The details of the door locks and lock covers were modified slightly. White sidewall tires were made optional after April 1, 1947. Most of these were running changes that took effect during the 1947 calendar year. However, all of the 1946-1948 models were in the same C-40 Series. Cars with serial numbers higher than 7810167 and assembled after Jan. 1, 1947 were registered as 1947 automobiles.

IMPERIAL I.D. NUMBERS: Serial number on plate on left front door hinge pillar post. Motor number on top front center of engine block. Serial numbers ranged from 7810167 to 7810907. Motor numbers were in the same series as in 1946 and continued through consecutively, with no record of the first number for the year.

CROWN IMPERIAL SERIES

Series Number	Body/Style Number	Body Type & Seating	Factory Price	Shipping Weight	Production Total
C40	Note 1	4-dr Sed-8P	4205	4865	Note 2
C40	Note 1	4-dr Limo-8P	4305	4875	Note 3

NOTE 1: Not available.

NOTE 2: A total of 650 Crown Imperial sedans were made from 1947 to 1948.

NOTE 3: See 1946 Productions.

ENGINE: Inline. L-head 8. Cast iron block. Displacement: 323.5 cid. Bore and stroke: 3.25 x 4.87 inches. Compression ratio: 6.80:1. Brake hp: 135 at 3400 rpm. Five main bearings. Solid valve lifters. Carburetor: Stromberg two-barrel Model AAV-2.

CHASSIS FEATURES: Wheelbase: 145.5 inches. Overall length: 235 inches. Front tread: 58 inches. Rear tread: 62 inches. Tires: 7.50 x 15.

OPTIONS: Mopar heater. Mopar defroster. Mopar radio. Electric clock. Spot lights. Fog lights. Directional signals. Fluid Drive, four-speed hydraulic semi-automatic transmission. Heavy-duty air cleaner. Available rear axle gear ratios: 3.58:1.

HISTORICAL FOOTNOTES: The 1947 Crown Imperials were introduced in January, 1947. First season for the non-limousine eight-passenger sedan. This model was the same size as the 'limo' and also had the same type of jump seats, but did not feature a division window between driver's compartment and rear passenger area. Cameramen at Paramount Studios crossed a Dodge pickup truck with an Imperial chassis and came up with an unique mobile camera rig.

1948 IMPERIAL

1948 Chrysler Crown Imperial, four-door limousine, 8-cyl

CROWN IMPERIAL SERIES — SERIES C40 — The new 1948 Crown Imperial looked the same as last year's model. It was still in the same C-40 Series, too. The major change was that larger, low-pressure tires were used. Two models were offered again this year. The limousine had a separate driver's compartment, with the front and rear sections split by a division window. The chauffeur's compartment was usually trimmed in leather, while the rear compartment was done in luxury cloth and had folding jump seats. Jump seats were also a feature of eight-passenger sedans, but division windows were not. The C-40 Series was actually carried into the next calendar year, with units assembled late in the run intended to be registered as 1949 cars. This fact sometimes causes confusion today.

IMPERIAL I.D. NUMBERS: Serial number on plate on left front door hinge pillar post. Motor number on top front center of engine block. Serial numbers 7810908 to 7811347 were used on 1948 Chrysler Crown Imperials. Effective Dec. 1, 1948 Crown Imperials bearing serial numbers 7811348 and higher were to be considered of the 1949 Series, for purposes of registration only. For evaluation purposes, then and now, these cars were comparable to 1948 models. Motor numbers were continued from 1947, with no record of the year's starting or ending numbers.

CROWN IMPERIAL SERIES

Series Number	Body/Style Number	Body Type & Seating	Factory Price	Shipping Weight	Production Total
C40	Note 1	4-dr Sed-8P	4712	4865	Note 2
C40	Note 1	4-dr Limo-8P	4817	4875	Note 3

NOTE 1: Not used.

NOTE 2: See 1947 Production Total.

NOTE 3: See 1946 Production Total.

ENGINE: Inline. L-head 8. Cast iron block. Displacement: 323.5 cid. Bore and stroke: 3.25 x 4.87 inches. Compression ratio: 6.80: 1. Brake hp: 135 at 3400 rpm. Five main bearings. Solid valve lifters. Carburetor: Stromberg two-barrel Model AAV-2.

CHASSIS FEATURES: Wheelbase: 145.5 inches. Overall length: 235 inches. Front tread: 58 inches. Rear tread: 62 inches. Tires: 8.90 x 15.

OPTIONS: Mopar heater. Mopar defroster. Mopar radio. Spot lights. Front and rear center bumper guard. Wheel trim rings. Left outside rearview mirror. Right outside rearview mirror. White sidewall tires. Also, see 1948 Chrysler options. Fluid Drive, four-speed hydraulic semi-automatic transmission. Heavy-duty air cleaner. Available rear axle gear ratios: 3.58:1.

HISTORICAL FOOTNOTES: The 1948 Chryslers were introduced Jan. 1, 1948 and were continued into the next calendar year as First Series 1949 models. Model year production is combined with 1946-1947 unit totals. Calendar year sales were part of the full Chrysler total. Derham Customs continued to be built on the 1948 Imperial chassis. Derham also converted one such unit into a four-door phaeton, under a commission from King Ibn Saud, of Saudi Arabia. It was used for gazelle hunting. Some of these custom built cars may be eligible for recognition as full Classics, upon owner application to the Classic Car Club of America.

1949 IMPERIAL

IMPERIAL SERIES — SERIES C46-2 — The new custom-built Imperial sedan was based on the New Yorker. It shared the same trim, but had a canvas-covered roof and leather and broadcloth Imperial upholstery. These features were installed, by Derham, on the all-new postwar Chrysler sheetmetal.

IMPERIAL I.D. NUMBERS: Serial number on plate on left front door hinge pillar post. Motor number on top front center of engine block. Imperial sedan and Deluxe sedan serial numbers were 7107801 to 7107850. Motor numbers C46-1001 to 28838 were used in mixed production with other Chrysler Eights. The first symbol 'C' designated Chrysler division. The second and third symbols designated consecutive series code. Body Style numbers were not used. Note: Production halted when the C-47 was introduced.

IMPERIAL SERIES [Early 1948-1/2]

Series Number	Body/Style Number	Body Type & Seating	Factory Price	Shipping Weight	Production Total
C46-2	Note 1	4-dr Sed-6P	4665	4300	50

NOTE 1: Not used.

ENGINE: Inline. L-head 8. Cast iron block. Displacement: 323.5 cid. Bore and stroke: 3.25 x 4.87 inches. Compression ratio: 7.25:1. Brake hp: 135 at 3400 rpm. Five main bearings. Solid valve lifters. Carburetor: Carter Type Ball & Ball two-barrel Model BB-E7J1-2.

1949 Chrysler Crown Imperial, four-door limousine, 8-cyl

CROWN IMPERIAL SERIES — SERIES C47 — Early 1949s were actually just leftover 1948s. The really new models didn't arrive until March of 1949. Their styling was sleeker than previous Imperials, yet conservative. Fewer, but heavier, bars were used in the crisscross pattern grille. The upper and center horizontal pieces wrapped around the front fenders. Rocker panel moldings, rear fender stone guards, full-length lower window trim and horizontal chrome strips on the rear fenders (and from the headlights to about half-way across the front doors) were used to decorate the side body.

IMPERIAL I.D. NUMBERS: Serial number on plate on left front door hinge pillar post. Motor number on top of engine block at front water outlet elbow. Chrysler Crown Imperials had serial numbers 7813001 to 7813088. Motor number C47-1001 to 1095 were used. These were distinct numbers for Custom Imperials. The first symbol 'C' designated Chrysler Div. The second and third symbol designated consecutive series code. Body Style numbers were not used.

CROWN IMPERIAL SERIES

Series Number	Body/Style Number	Body Type & Seating	Factory Price	Shipping Weight	Production Total
C47	Note 1	4-dr Sed-8P	5229	5250	40
C47	Note 1	4-dr Limo-8P	5334	5295	45

NOTE 1: Not used.

ENGINE: Inline. L-head 8. Cast iron block. Displacement: 323.5 cid. Bore and stroke: 3.25 x 4.87 inches. Compression ratio: 7.25:1. Brake hp: 135 at 3400 rpm. Five main bearings. Solid valve lifters. Carburetor: Carter Type Ball & Ball two-barrel Model BB-E7J1-2.

CHASSIS FEATURES: Wheelbase: (Imperial) 131.5 inches. (Crown Imperial) 145.5 inches. Overall length: (Imperial) 210 inches; (Crown Imperial) 234.75 inches. Front tread: (Imperial) 57 inches; (Crown Imperial) 57 inches. Rear tread: (Imperial) 58 inches; (Crown Imperial) 64 inches. Tires: (Imperial) 8.20 x 15; (Crown Imperial) 8.90 x 15.

OPTIONS: MoPar heater and defroster. MoPar radio. Electric clock. Spotlights. Fog lights. Whitewall tires. Wing vent deflectors. Middle bumper guards. Exhaust deflector. Grille guard. Weather proof ignition. Auto compass. Underhood light. Windshield washer. Spare tire valve extension. Prestomatic transmission and Fluid Drive were standard. Heavy-duty air cleaner. Available rear axle gear ratios: 3.90: 1; 4.0: 1.

HISTORICAL FOOTNOTES: The 1949 Imperials entered production in January, 1949 and the cars appeared in dealer showrooms by March. Model year production peaked at 145 units. Calendar year sales of 15,000 Chrysler Eights were recorded. D.A. Wallace was president of Chrysler Div. this year. Cycle bonded brake linings were used. Another Imperial-based mobile camera car was built by MGM studios this year. The Imperial Eight sedan carried Chrysler New Yorker nameplates and wheelcovers.

1950 IMPERIAL

IMPERIAL SERIES — SERIES C49N — The new Imperial was essentially a New Yorker with custom interior. It had a Cadillac-style grille treatment that included circular signal lights enclosed in a wraparound, ribbed chrome piece. Side trim was similar to last year's model, but the front fender strip ended at the front doors and the rear fender molding was at tire-top level and integrated into the stone guard.

IMPERIAL I.D. NUMBERS: Serial number on plate on left front door hinge pillar post. Motor number on top front center of engine block. Serial numbers 7146001 to 7156654 were used only on Series C49 Imperials. (Crown Imperial) Serial numbers 7813501 to 7813916 were used on Series C-50 Crown Imperials. Motor numbers on regular Imperials were shared with the other 1950 Chrysler Eights. They fell within the range C49-1001 to 43041. The motor numbers used on Crown Imperials were distinct and ranged from C50-1001 to 1433.

IMPERIAL SERIES

Series Number	Body/Style Number	Body Type & Seating	Factory Price	Shipping Weight	Production Total
C49-N	Note 1	4-dr Sed-6P	3055	4245	9,500
C49-N	Note 1	4-dr DeL Sed-6P	3176	4250	1,150

1950 Chrysler Crown Imperial, four-door limousine, 8-cyl (AA)

CROWN IMPERIAL SERIES — SERIES C50 — Unlike the standard Imperial, the Crown had a side trim treatment in which the rear fender molding and stone guard were separate. Body sill moldings were used on all Imperials, but were of a less massive type on the more massive Crown models. A special version of the limousine was available. It featured a unique leather interior and a leather-covered top that blacked out the rear quarter windows. Power windows were standard.

CROWN IMPERIAL SERIES

Series Number	Body/Style Number	Body Type & Seating	Factory Price	Shipping Weight	Production Total
C50	Note 1	4-dr Sed-8P	5229	5235	209
C50	Note 1	4-dr Limo-8P	5334	5305	205

ENGINE: Inline L-head 8. Cast iron block. Displacement: 323.5 cid. Bore and stroke: 3.25 x 4.87 inches. Compression ratio: 7.25:1. Brake hp: 135 at 3200 rpm. Five main bearings. Solid valve lifters. Carburetor: Carter one-barrel Model BB-E7J4.

CHASSIS FEATURES: Wheelbase: (Imperial) 131.5 inches; (Crown Imperial) 145.5 inches. Overall length: (Imperial) 214 inches; (Crown Imperial) 230.25 inches. Front tread: (Imperial) 57 inches; (Crown Imperial) 57 inches. Rear tread: (Imperial) 58 inches; (Crown Imperial) 64 inches. Tires: (Imperial) 8.20 x 15; (Crown Imperial) 8.90 x 15. The industry's first disc brakes were standard on Crown Imperials. Ausco-Lambert "self-energizing" disc brakes standard in Crown Imperial series.

OPTIONS: White sidewall tires. Wing vent deflectors. Exhaust deflector. MoPar radio. MoPar heater. Locking gas cap. Weather-proof ignition. MoPar auto compass. Windshield washer. Spare tire valve extension. A brand new option (also available on Chrysler Eights) was electrically operated power windows. Prestomatic transmission with Fluid Drive was standard. Heavy-Duty oil bath air cleaner. Vacuum booster fuel pump.

HISTORICAL FOOTNOTES: The 1950 Chrysler Imperial models were introduced in January, 1950. Model year production began in December, 1949. D.A. Wallace was president of the Chrysler Div. of Chrysler Corp., with offices at 12200 East Jefferson Avenue, Detroit, Mich. The Derham custom body company, of Rosemont, Pa., continued to create some beautiful vehicles on the Imperial chassis.

1951 IMPERIAL

IMPERIAL SERIES — SERIES C54 — In an unusual move for the 1950s, the Imperial had less chrome than the lower-priced New Yorker that it was based on. It had three horizontal grille bars (one across center); parking lights between the bars and a chrome vertical center

piece. Aside from its front fender nameplate, side body trim was limited to moldings below the windows; rocker panel moldings; bright metal stone shields and a heavy, horizontal molding strip running across the fender skirts.

IMPERIAL I.D. NUMBERS: Serial number on plate on left front door hinge pillar post. Motor number on top front center of engine block. Series C-51 Imperial Eights had serial numbers 7736501 to 7753512. Motor numbers used on these cars were in the same range of numbers (C51-8-1001 to 67967) used on other 1951 Chrysler Eights, with the engines in mixed production sequence. Series C-53 Crown Imperials had serial numbers 7814501-7815000. Motor numbers on these cars were also in the same range as for other Chrysler Eights.

1951 Chrysler Imperial, four-door sedan, V-8

IMPERIAL SERIES

Series Number	Body/Style Number	Body Type & Seating	Factory Price	Shipping Weight	Production Total
C54	Note 1	4-dr Sed-6P	3699	4350	21,711
C54	Note 1	2-dr Clb Cpe-6P	3687	4230	1,189
C54	Note 1	2 dr HT-6P	4067	4380	3,450
C54	Note 1	2-dr Conv-6P	4427	4570	650

NOTE 1: Not used.

NOTE 2: Production totals include 1952 models.

CROWN IMPERIAL SERIES — SERIES C53 — In addition to its size and increased passenger capacity, center-opening rear doors and a concealed gas filler cap were a couple of distinguishing features for the Crown Imperial. The hood ornament had a 'crown' medallion in the center of the 'V' on the car's nose. Imperial models did not have lower front fender belt moldings. Power steering and Fluid Torque Drive were standard in Crown Imperials.

CROWN IMPERIAL SERIES

Model Number	Body/Style Number	Body Type & Seating	Factory Price	Shipping Weight	Production Total
C53	Note 1	4-dr Sed-8P	6623	5360	360
C53	Note 1	4-dr Limo-8P	6740	5450	338

NOTE 1: Not used.

NOTE 2: Production total includes 1952 models.

ENGINE: V-8. Overhead valves. Cast iron block. Displacement: 331.1 cid. Bore and stroke: 3.81 x 3.62 inches. Compression ratio: 7.50:1. Brake hp: 180 at 4000 rpm. Five main bearings. Hydraulic valve lifters. Carburetor: Carter two-barrel Model WCD-830S.

CHASSIS FEATURES: Wheelbase: (Imperial) 131.5 inches; (Crown Imperial) 145.5 inches. Front tread: (Imperial) 56 inches; (Crown Imperial) 60 inches. Rear tread: (Imperial) 58 inches; (Crown Imperial) 66 inches. Tires: (Imperial) 8.20 x 15; (Crown Imperial) 8.90 x 15.

OPTIONS: Hydraguide power steering, in Imperial Eight ($226); standard in Crown Imperial Eight. Power brakes. Power disc brakes standard on Crown Imperial. Power steering. Air conditioning. All Weather Comfort System. Electric lift windows. MoPar Radio. White sidewall tires. External sun visor. Fog lights. Spotlights. Exhaust deflector. Outside rearview mirror.

HISTORICAL FOOTNOTES: The 1951 Chrysler line (including Imperials) was introduced to the public on Feb. 9, 1951. On May 28, 1951 the Economic Stabilization Agency permitted the company to change its prices, to cover increased costs of the new V-8s. The increases were $251.19 for New Yorkers and Imperial Eights and $261.38 for the Crown Imperials. New features of this year included the Firepower V-8 engine (with hemispherical-segment cylinder heads); Hydraguide power steering and Oriflow shock absorbers. Assemblies of 1951 models began in December 1950 and the model year ran until November, 1951. In this time span an estimated 156,000 units were built to 1951 specifications (Chrysler and Imperials together). A total of three special 'parade phaetons' were built off the Crown Imperial chassis and used by the cities of Los Angeles, New York and Detroit. These cars were later updated with mid-'50s styling. The 'Imperial Rose' was a special C51 Series show car custom-made by the factory this year.

1952 IMPERIAL

IMPERIAL SERIES — SERIES C54 — If you liked the 1951 Imperial, you'd feel the same way about the 1952 models, since they were practically identical. The best way to separate cars of both years is through reference to serial numbers. The convertible body style was dropped. Unlike the case with Chryslers, the Imperial's taillights were not changed. Power steering was standard.

IMPERIAL I.D. NUMBERS: Serial number on plate on left front door hinge pillar post. Motor number on top front center of engine block. Serial numbers for C-54 Imperials built as 1952 models were recorded as C-7753601 to 7763596. Motor numbers C52-8-1001 to 59631 were used in this series, as well as in other Chrysler Eights, with engines built in mixed production sequence. Crown Imperials had serial numbers 7815101 to 7815306. Motor numbers, however, were shared with Chrysler V-8s.

1952 Chrysler Imperial, four-door sedan, V-8

IMPERIAL SERIES

Series Number	Body/Style Number	Doors/Style Seating	Factory Price	Shipping Weight	Production Total
C54	Note 1	4-dr Sed-6P	3864	4350	Note 2
C54	Note 1	2-dr Clb Cpe-6P	3851	4230	Note 2
C54	Note 1	2-dr HT-6P	4249	4380	Note 2

NOTE 1: Not used.

NOTE 2: See 1951 Production Total.

CROWN IMPERIAL SERIES — SERIES C53 — The 'new' Crown Imperial was unchanged for 1952. Only 338 of these cars were made in the 1951-1952 model run and serial numbers indicate that 205 were registered as 1952 automobiles. A very minor change was a one inch reduction in front tread measurement.

CROWN IMPERIAL SERIES

Series Number	Body/Style Number	Doors/Style Seating	Factory Price	Shipping Weight	Production Total
C53	Note 1	4-dr Sed-8P	6922	5360	Note 2
C53	Note 1	4-dr Limo-8P	7044	5450	Note 2

NOTE 1: Not used.

NOTE 2: See 1951 Production Total.

ENGINE: V-8. Overhead valves. Cast iron block. Displacement: 331.1 cid. Bore and stroke: 3.81 x 3.62 inches. Compression ratio: 7.50:1. Brake hp: 180 at 4000 rpm. Five main bearings. Hydraulic valve lifters. Carburetor: Carter two-barrel Model WCD-884S.

CHASSIS FEATURES: Wheelbase: (Imperial) 131.5 inches; (Crown Imperial) 145.5 inches. Overall length: (Imperial) 213-1/8 inches; (Crown Imperial) 145-1/2 inches. Front tread: (Imperial) 57 inches; (Crown Imperial) 57 inches. Rear tread: (Imperial) 58 inches; (Crown Imperial) 66 inches. Tires: (Imperial) 8.20 x 15; (Crown Imperial) 8.90 x 15. Ausco-Lambert "self-energizing" disc brakes standard in Crown Imperial series.

OPTIONS: Power brakes. (Power disc brakes standard on Crown Imperial.) Power steering, on C-54 ($199); on C-53 (standard equipment). Air conditioning. Solex glass (new option). White sidewall tires. Electric window lifts. Sun visor. Radio. Heater and defroster. Exhaust deflector. Spare tire valve extension. Locking gas cap. Windshield washer. Fog lamps. Spotlights. Outside rearview mirror. Vanity mirror. Fluid-Torque drive was $167 extra on C-54 Imperials and standard equipment in C-53 Crown Imperials. Heavy-duty oil bath air cleaner. Vacuum booster fuel pump. Oil filter.

HISTORICAL FOOTNOTES: The 1952 Chrysler models, including Imperials, were introduced Dec. 14, 1951. The Office of Price Stabilization, which set pricing policies during the Korean War, allowed Chrysler to make an across-the-board increase in retails on Feb. 11, 1952. On August 23, the OPS abandoned the policy of placing ceilings on new car prices and Chrysler again boosted its tags from $18-$30. D.A. Wallace was president of the division again. Model year production for all Chryslers was estimated at 91,253 units. The Imperial convertible, introduced only one year earlier, was dropped and not replaced until 1957.

1953 IMPERIAL

1953 Chrysler Custom Imperial, two-door Newport hardtop, V-8

CUSTOM IMPERIAL SERIES — SERIES C-58 — Although the Custom Imperial resembled the New Yorker, it had a different wheelbase, taillights and side trim. Clean front fenders and a higher rear fender stone shield set it apart from the 'ordinary' Chryslers. This was the first year for the stylized eagle hood ornament. Power brakes. power windows, center folding armrests (front and rear) and a padded dash were standard. Parking lights on all Imperials were positioned between the top and center grille moldings, a variation from the design used on other Chrysler cars. The Custom Imperial six-passenger limousine had, as standard equipment, electric windows; electric division window: floor level courtesy lamps: rear compartment heater; fold-up footrests: seatback mounted clock and special, luxury cloth or leather interior trims. On March 18, 1953 the Custom Imperial Newport hardtop was added to the Imperial line at $325 over the price of the eight-passenger sedan. However, Chrysler instituted a general price cut on March 25, and the new model was then reduced $45. A week later, the delivery and handling charges for Imperials were raised $10, so the customer came out $35 ahead in the long run.

IMPERIAL I.D. NUMBERS: Serial number on plate on left front door hinge pillar post. Motor number on top of engine block at front water outlet elbow. Serial numbers C58-7765001 to 7773869 were used on 1953 Custom Imperials. Motor numbers fell in the range C53-8-1001 to 86292 which was shared with other Chrysler V-8 Series. Crown Imperials had serial numbers C597816001 to 7816162. Engine numbers were in the same range used for Custom Imperials, as well as other Chrysler V-8s.

CUSTOM IMPERIAL SERIES

Series Number	Body/Style Number	Body Type & Seating	Factory Price	Shipping Weight	Production Total
C58	Note 1	4-dr Sed-8P	4260	4305	7,793
C58	Note 1	4-dr Limo-6P	4797	4525	243
C58	Note 1	2-dr HT-6P	4560	4290	823

NOTE 1: Not used.

CROWN IMPERIAL SERIES — SERIES C-59 — The eagle hood ornament was about the only thing new on the 1953 Crown Imperial. The nameplate was changed slightly and the limousine featured moldings on top of rear fenders. It had a 12-volt electrical system (the Custom had a six-volt system). Power steering was standard and PowerFlite fully-automatic transmission was installed in a small number of late-in-the-year cars for testing and evaluation.

CROWN IMPERIAL SERIES

Series Number	Body/Style Number	Body Type & Seating	Factory Price	Shipping Weight	Production Total
C59	Note 1	4-dr Sed-8P	6922	5235	48
C59	Note 1	4-dr Limo-8P	7044	5275	111

NOTE 1: Not used.

ENGINE: V-8. Overhead valves. Cast iron block. Displacement: 331.1 cid. Bore and stroke: 3.81 x 3.62 inches. Compression ratio: 7.50:1. Brake hp 180 at 4000 rpm. Five main bearings. Hydraulic valve lifters. Carburetor: Carter WCD 935S.

CHASSIS FEATURES: Wheelbase: (Custom Imperial hardtop) 131.5 inches; (sedan and limousine) 133.5 inches; (Crown Imperial) 145.5 inches. Overall length: (Custom Imperial) 219 inches; (Crown Imperial) 229 inches. Front tread: (Custom Imperial) 57 inches; (Crown Imperial) 57 inches. Rear tread: (Custom Imperial) 57 inches, (Crown Imperial) 66 inches. Tires: (Custom Imperial) 8.20 x 15; (Crown Imperial) 8.90 x 15. Ausco-Lambert "self-energizing" disc brakes standard in Custom Imperial series.

OPTIONS: Power disc brakes were standard on C59 Crown Imperials. Power steering was optional on Custom Imperials ($177) and standard in Crown Imperials. Air conditioning. Power windows. At the start of the model year Fluid-Torque transmission was standard equipment on all Imperials. In June, 1953, PowerFlite fully-automatic transmission was selectively introduced and was subsequently made standard equipment in all 1954 Imperials.

HISTORICAL FOOTNOTES: The 1953 Chrysler line, including Imperials, was introduced Oct. 30, 1952. The Custom Imperial Newport hardtop was introduced on March 18, 1953. E.C. Quinn became president of Chrysler Div. this year. Chrysler Corp. unveiled its PowerFlite transmission early in the summer. At that time, it had been under "road test" by a number of specially-selected customers whose use of the fully-automatic transmission was monitored. By the time the production go-ahead was given, assembly of 1953 Imperials had ended. Thus, it is possible to find 1953 Imperials with PowerFlite, although the first general-sales installations were made in 1954 models. It was made standard in Imperials and optional in other Chrysler cars.

1954 IMPERIAL

1954 Chrysler Custom Imperial four-door sedan, V-8

CUSTOM IMPERIAL SERIES — SERIES C64 — The new Custom Imperial had a grille consisting of a heavy, wraparound horizontal center bar (with five ridges on top) and integrated circular signal lights. Its front fender nameplate was above a chrome strip, which ran the length of the front door to the front wheel opening. The rear fender stone guard was

larger than in 1953, but the rocker panel molding and rear fender chrome strip style were still the same. The back-up lights were now located directly below the taillights, rather than dividing the lights as in the previous year's model.

IMPERIAL I.D. NUMBERS: Serial number on plate on left front door hinge pillar post. Motor number on top of engine block at front water outlet elbow. Serial numbers C64-7775001 to 7780767 were found on Custom Imperials. Serial numbers C64-7817001 to 7817100 were used on 1954 Crown Imperials. The Motor numbers C542-8-1001 to C542-8-40478 were used on all 1954 Chrysler Eights.

CUSTOM IMPERIAL SERIES

Series Number	Body/Style Number	Body Type & Seating	Factory Price	Shipping Weight	Production Total
C64	Note 1	4-dr Sed-6P	4260	4355	4,324
C64	Note 1	2-dr HT-6P	4560	4345	1,249
C64	Note 1	4-dr Limo-6P	4797	4465	85

NOTE 1: Not used.

1954 Chrysler Crown Imperial, four-door limousine, V-8

CROWN IMPERIAL SERIES — SERIES C66 — The Crown shared basic styling with the Custom. However, it had center-opening rear doors and Cadillac-like rear fender taillights. Air conditioning was standard.

CROWN IMPERIAL SERIES

Series Number	Body/Style Number	Body Type & Seating	Factory Price	Shipping Weight	Production Total
C66	Note 1	4-dr Sed-8P	6922	5220	23
C66	Note 1	4-dr Limo-8P	7044	5295	77

NOTE 1: Not used.

ENGINE: V-8. Overhead valves. Cast iron block. Displacement: 331.1 cid. Bore and stroke: 3.81 x 3.62 inches. Compression ratio: 7.50:1. Brake hp: 235 at 4400 rpm. Five main bearings. Hydraulic valve lifters. Carburetor: Carter four-barrel Model WCFB-2041S.

CHASSIS FEATURES: Wheelbase: (Custom Imperial hardtop) 131.5 inches; (Custom Imperial sedan and hardtop) 133.5 inches; (Crown Imperial) 145.5 inches. Overall length: (C64 Newport) 221.75 inches; (C64) 223.75 inches, (C66) 236-3/8 inches. Tires: (Custom Imperial) 8.20 x 15. (Crown Imperial) 8.90 x 15. Ausco-Lambert "self-energizing" disc brakes standard in Crown Imperial series.

OPTIONS: Power disc brakes were standard on Crown Imperial. Power drum brakes optional on Custom Imperial. Power steering standard on Crown Imperial. Power steering optional on Custom Imperial. Air conditioning. Electric lift windows.

HISTORICAL FOOTNOTES: Derham Custom Body Co. built a special Custom Imperial Landau Victoria this year, with a Victoria-style half-roof and open driver's compartment. This Contessa show car was seen at the 1954 automobile shows. It was based on the Custom Imperial Newport hardtop with modifications including a vinyl-and-plexiglas roof; continental tire extension kit: chromed Kelsey-Hayes wire wheels and custom pink and white interior and exterior finish.

1955 IMPERIAL

1955 Imperial, Newport two-door hardtop, V-8

242

IMPERIAL SERIES — SERIES C69 — Imperial, like all Chrysler Corp. cars, was completely restyled for 1955. It had bumper-integrated signal lights. Each section of the two-piece split grille consisted of two large vertical bars, crossed by like-size horizontal ones. The Imperial eagle crest was placed between the sections. Side trim consisted of fender-to-fender mid-body molding and full length lower body trim. Unique to the make were free standing rear-fender-mounted taillights.

IMPERIAL I.D. NUMBERS: Serial number on plate on left front door hinge pillar post. Motor number on top of engine block at front water outlet elbow. Imperials and Crown Imperials were numbered C551,001 — C5,512,464. Motor numbers CE551001 to CE5512490 were used in mixed series production.

IMPERIAL SERIES

Series Number	Body/Style Number	Doors/Style Seating	Factory Price	Shipping Weight	Production Total
C69	Note 1	4-dr Sed-6P	4483	4565	7,840
C69	Note 1	2-dr HT-6P	4720	4490	3,418

NOTE 1: Not used.

CROWN IMPERIAL SERIES — SERIES C70 — The center-opening rear doors of previous Crown sedans and limousines were replaced by conventional ones in '55. It shared the same basic styling as the standard Imperial but had a different roof with a smaller, rectangular rear window. New features included power disc brakes and a 12-volt electrical system.

CROWN IMPERIAL SERIES

Series Number	Body/Style Number	Doors/Style Seating	Factory Price	Shipping Weight	Production Total
C70	Note 1	4-dr Sed-8P	7603	5145	45
C70	Note 1	4-dr Limo-8P	7737	5205	127

NOTE 1: Not used.

1955 Imperial two-door hardtop

ENGINE: V-8. Overhead valves. Cast iron block. Displacement: 331.1 cid. Bore and stroke: 3.81 x 3.62 inches. Compression ratio: 8.50:1. Brake hp: 250 at 4600 rpm. Carburetor: Carter four-barrel Model WCFB-2126S.

CHASSIS FEATURES: Wheelbase: (Imperial) 130 inches; (Crown Imperial) 149.5 inches.; Tires: (Imperial) 8.20 x 15: (Crown Imperial) 8.90 x 15.

OPTIONS: Power brakes and power steering were standard with all Imperials. A Four-Way power seat was standard in eight-passenger styles. Extra-cost options: Air conditioning. Power windows. Signal-seeking radio.

HISTORICAL FOOTNOTES: The Custom Imperial Town Limousine was dropped for 1955. Model year introductions were scheduled Nov. 17, 1954. E. C. Quinn was president of Chrysler Div. this year. Beginning this season, Chrysler considered the Imperial to be a separate 'marque' or 'make' and duly registered it as such with the U.S. Government. Therefore, Imperial production figures were broken out from the totals for the rest of the Chrysler line. Chrysler Div.'s New Yorker and Imperial Series climbed to second rank in the high-priced field, with 64,330 new car registrations in calendar 1955. This total included some 1954 "Chrysler-Imperials" and could be a misleading figure to some degree. The Imperial/New Yorker Div. competed with Cadillac, Lincoln and Packard and Packard was the only one of those companies the Imperial "outsold" by itself. (New Yorkers were targeted against senior Buicks). Genuine leather interior trims were offered in the front seat of Crown Imperial Limousines and eight-passenger sedans and in combinations for the Imperial Southhampton four-door. Al 1955 Imperial production was moved to the Jefferson Ave. plant in Detroit, Mich.

1956 IMPERIAL

IMPERIAL SERIES — SERIES C73 — Front end styling resembled last year's model, but the rear fenders were taller and the full-length mid-body side molding wrapped around them. The rear bumpers were attractively redesigned and seemed integrated into the rear fenders. Taillights were once again mounted on the fenders.

IMPERIAL I.D. NUMBERS: Serial number on plate on left front door hinge pillar post. Motor number on top of engine block at front water outlet elbow. Serial numbers for C-73 Series models were C56-1001 to 11715. Serial numbers for C70 models were C56-1001 to 9826. Engine numbers CE56-1001 to 11750 were used in cars of both series.

IMPERIAL SERIES

Series Number	Body/Style Number	Body Type & Seating	Factory Price	Shipping Weight	Production Total
C73	Note 1	4-dr Sed-6P	4832	4575	6,821
C73	Note 1	4-dr HT-6P	5225	4680	1,543
C73	Note 1	2-dr HT-6P	5094	4555	2,094

CROWN IMPERIAL SERIES — SERIES C70 — Styling changes were minimal. About the only difference between the 1956 and last year's Crown was the side trim. The new version had mid-body moldings that extended only from the tip of the front fender to slightly beyond the beginning of the rear fender. There were five slanted slashes and a chrome outline of the tailfin on the rear fenders.

CROWN IMPERIAL SERIES

Series Number	Body/Style Number	Body Type & Seating	Factory Price	Shipping Weight	Production Total
C70	Note 1	4-dr Sed-8P	7603	5145	51
C70	Note 1	4-dr Limo-8P	7737	5205	119

ENGINE: V-8. Overhead valves. Cast iron block. Displacement: 353:1 cid. Bore and stroke 3.94 x 3.63 inches. Compression ratio 9.00:1. Brake hp: 280 at 4600 rpm. Carburetor: Carter four-barrel Model WCFB-2314S.

1956 Imperial, four-door sedan, V-8

CHASSIS FEATURES: Wheelbase: (Imperial) 133 Inches: (Crown Imperial) 149.5 inches. Tires: (Imperial) 8.20 x 15; (Crown Imperial) 8.90 x 15.

OPTIONS: Power steering, power brakes and Four-Way power seats were standard equipment. Options included power windows and air conditioning. PowerFlite automatic transmission, now with push-button control, was standard in all Imperials when the model year started. A new three-speed TorqueFlite automatic transmission became available on all Imperials in the spring.

HISTORICAL FOOTNOTES: The 1956 Imperials were introduced Oct. 21, 1955. Model year production peaked at 10,685 cars. Calendar year production was counted as 12,130 units. This was the first calendar year that Imperial production records were recorded separate from Chrysler figures for the entire 12 months. E.C. Quinn was president of the Chrysler Div. this year. Imperial was emerging as a strong selling luxury car in this period. Separate production lines for Imperials were setup at Chrysler's Kercheval and Jefferson plants in Detroit. The 1956 Imperial could go from 0-60 mph in 12.8 seconds. It had a top speed of over 104 mph.

1957 IMPERIAL

IMPERIAL SERIES — SERIES IM-1 — Imperial styling moved further away from that of other Chrysler Corp. cars in 1957. Hardtop models featured a distinctive "overlapping" rear-section roof. The taillights were now integrated into the tips of the tailfins. Wraparound "eyebrow" trim above the headlights extended half the length of the front fenders. Mid-body chrome trim ran from the rear deck panel to the front tire well. The grille looked like a mesh of chrome pieces. Signal lights were sandwiched between the two horizontal bumpers. A simulated spare-tire-cover trunk lid was optional on all 1957 Imperials.

1957 Imperial, four-door hardtop sedan, V-8 (FK)

IMPERIAL I.D. NUMBERS: Serial number on plate on left front door hinge pillar post. Motor number on top of engine block at front water outlet elbow. Imperial, Imperial Crown, LeBaron and Crown Imperial serial numbers were C57-1001 — 36,890. Motor numbers were CE57-1001 to 36950.

IMPERIAL SERIES

Series Number	Body/Style Number	Body Type & Seating	Factory Price	Shipping Weight	Production Total
IM1-1	Note 1	4-dr Sed-6P	4838	4640	5,654
IM1-1	Note 1	4-dr HT-6P	4838	4780	7,527
IM1-1	Note 1	2-dr HT-6P	4736	4640	4,885

IMPERIAL CROWN SERIES — SERIES IM1-2 — Like all Imperial series, the Imperial Crown (not to be confused with the plusher Crown Imperial, of course) had recessed door handles. Exterior styling was basically the same as that used on the standard Imperial. However, Imperial Crowns had a tiny crown emblem above the second 'I' in the Imperial nameplate. A convertible was offered for the first time since 1951.

IMPERIAL CROWN SERIES

Series Number	Body/Style Number	Body Type & Seating	Factory Price	Shipping Weight	Production Total
IM1-2	Note 1	4-dr Sed-6P	5406	4740	3,642
IM1-2	Note 1	4-dr HT-6P	5406	4920	7,843
IM1-2	Note 1	2-dr HT-6P	5269	4755	4,199
IM1-2	Note 1	2-dr Conv-6P	5598	4830	1,167

NOTE 1: Not used.

IMPERIAL LeBARON SERIES — SERIES IM1-4 — A distinctive front-fender emblem in place of the Imperial signature was the easiest way to tell the plush LeBaron from other Imperials.

IMPERIAL LeBARON SERIES

Series Number	Body/Style Number	Body Type & Seating	Factory Price	Shipping Weight	Production Total
IM1-4	Note 1	4-dr Sed-6P	5743	4765	1,729
IM1-4	Note 1	4-dr HT-6P	5743	4900	911

NOTE 1: Not used.

CROWN IMPERIAL SERIES — The 1957 Crown Imperials were custom-built by Ghia in Turin, Italy. Several coats of blue, maroon, black. or green lacquer were applied to them for an unsurpassed finish. The Crown Imperials had 1958 style grilles and their doors extended into the roof. Carpeting, air conditioning and power windows were just a few of the standard features.

CROWN IMPERIAL SERIES

Series Number	Body/Style Number	Body Type & Seating	Factory Price	Shipping Weight	Production Total
Note 1	Note 2	4-dr Limo-8P	12,000	5960	36

NOTE 1: None.

NOTE 2: Not used.

ENGINE: V-8. Overhead valves. Cast iron block. Displacement: 392.7 cid. Bore and stroke: 4 x 3.9 inches. Compression ratio: 9.25:1. Brake hp: 325 at 4600 rpm. Carburetor: Carter Type four-barrel Model WCFB-2590S.

CHASSIS FEATURES: Wheelbase: (Imperial, Crown and LeBaron) 129 inches; (Crown Imperial) 149.5 inches. Tires: 9.50 x 14.

OPTIONS: Power brakes (standard). Power steering (standard). FourWay power seat. Air conditioning ($590). Radio ($176). Solex glass ($50). Power windows ($125). TorqueFlite automatic transmission with push-button shift control was standard equipment.

HISTORICAL FOOTNOTES: The new Imperials were introduced, with other Chryslers. on Oct. 30, 1956. The Ghia-built Crown Imperial limousine was announced on Jan. 2, 1957. Originally programmed for production of 75 units, the car sold less than half that amount. Model year output for Imperial peaked at 35,734 cars including, in rounded figures, 17,500 C57 Imperials; 16,000 Crown Imperials and 2,500 LeBarons. Calendar year production was recorded as 37,946 units. E.C. Quinn was president of Chrysler Div. again this year.

1958 IMPERIAL

IMPERIAL SERIES — SERIES LY1-L — "America's most distinctive fine car" is how advertisements described the new Imperial. Styling changes were confined primarily to the grille. The mesh pattern of '57 was replaced by four "stacks" of horizontal bars. The front bumper was now one solid piece with circular signal light pods extending from its lower section. Standard equipment included power brakes, power steering, back-up lights, windshield washer, and four headlights. A simulated spare-tire-cover trunk lid was optional on all 1958 Imperials.

IMPERIAL I.D. NUMBERS: Serial number on plate on left front door hinge pillar post. Motor number on top of engine block at front water outlet elbow. Serial numbers LY1-1001 to 17,325 for Imperial, Imperial Crown and Imperial LeBaron models. Motor numbers 58C-1001 and up were used in these series. Crown Imperial limousines were numbered C57-1001 and up and had motor numbers CE57-1001 and up.

IMPERIAL SERIES

Series Number	Body/Style Number	Doors/Style Seating	Factory Price	Shipping Weight	Production Total
LY1-L	Note 1	4-dr Sed-6P	4945	4950	1,926
LY1-L	Note 1	4-dr HT-6P	4839	4795	3,336
LY1-L	Note 1	2-dr HT-6P	4945	4640	1,901

NOTE 1: Not used.

1958 Crown Imperial, two-door convertible, V-8

IMPERIAL CROWN SERIES — SERIES LY1-M — A tiny crown emblem above the second "I" in the Imperial nameplate remained the easiest way to tell the Crown from the standard Imperial. It came with a Six-Way power seat, power windows, and an outside rearview mirror.

IMPERIAL CROWN SERIES

Series Number	Body/Style Number	Doors/Style Seating	Factory Price	Shipping Weight	Production Total
LY1-M	Note 1	4-dr Sed-6P	5632	4755	1,240
LY1-M	Note 1	4-dr HT-6P	5632	4915	4,146
LY1-M	Note 1	2-dr HT-6P	5388	4730	1,939
LY1-M	Note 1	2-dr Conv-6P	5759	4820	675

NOTE 1: Not used.

IMPERIAL LEBARON SERIES — SERIES LY1-H — LeBarons had a distinctive emblem on the front fenders, instead of the Imperial name in script.

IMPERIAL LEBARON SERIES

Series Number	Body/Style Number	Doors/Style Seating	Factory Price	Shipping Weight	Production Total
LY1-H	Note 1	4-dr Sed-6P	5969	4780	501
LY1-H	Note 1	4-dr HT-6P	5969	4940	538

NOTE 1: Not used.

1958 Crown Imperial, four-door limousine, V-8

CROWN IMPERIAL SERIES — Because of its late introduction in 1957, the "new" custom-built Crown Imperial was the same as last year's model. Great care was taken in the construction of this car. In fact, reportedly as much as 17 hours were spent on every auto just to make sure the doors fit perfectly. Carpeting, air conditioning, power steering, power windows and power brakes were only some of the many standard features.

CROWN IMPERIAL SERIES

Series Number	Body/Style Number	Doors/Style Seating	Factory Price	Shipping Weight	Production Total
Note 1	Note 2	4-dr Limo-8P	15,075	5960	31

NOTE 1: None.

NOTE 2: Not used.

ENGINE: V-8. Overhead valves. Cast iron block. Displacement: 392.7 cid. Bore and stroke: 4 x 3.9 inches. Compression ratio: 10.00:1. Brake hp: 345 at 4600 rpm. Carburetor: Carter four-barrel Model AFB-2651S.

CHASSIS FEATURES: Wheelbase: (Imperial, Crown, and LeBaron) 129 inches; (Crown Imperial) 149.5 inches; Tires: 9.50 x 14.

OPTIONS: Power brakes. Power steering. Air conditioning ($590.20). Rear window defogger ($21.45). Custom heater ($140.60). Instant heater ($177.50). Six-Way power seat ($118.30). Power windows ($1 25.00). Electric touch radio with rear speaker and power antenna ($76.00). Solex glass ($50.40). White sidewall rayon tires (9.50 x 14) ($55.10). Standard two-tone paint ($20.45). Auto pilot ($88.70). Electric door locks (two-door hardtops) with power windows ($40.70). Electric door locks (four-door models) with power windows ($65.80).

HISTORICAL FOOTNOTE: The 1958 Imperial line was introduced to the public Nov. 1, 1957. Most 1958 Imperials, 93.6 percent, had power seats; 92.9 percent had power windows; 86 percent had whitewall tires and 33.3 percent had air conditioning.

1959 IMPERIAL

IMPERIAL CUSTOM SERIES — SERIES MY1-L — The front-end treatment was jazzed up for '59. Chrome-encased headlight pods were linked together by a large, center grille bar with five curved vertical pieces. Side trim, roof designs and the protruding tailfin taillight resembled last year's models. A lower rear-quarter panel stone shield and the Imperial name printed on the front fenders were two other changes. Buyers had their choice of three optional hardtop roof treatments. The Landau had a simulated rear canopy. The Silvercrest featured a stainless steel section covering the front half of the roof. The Silvercrest Landau was a combination of the first two. All 1959 Imperials came with power brakes, power steering, dual exhaust, electric clock, windshield washer and undercoating.

1959 Imperial, Custom two-door hardtop, V-8

IMPERIAL I.D. NUMBERS: Serial number on plate on left front door hinge pillar post. Motor number stamped behind water pump on engine. Serial numbers took the form: M617100001 and up. The first symbol designated year ('M' = 1959). The second symbol designated make ('6' = Imperial). The third symbol designated Series ('1' = Custom, '3' = Crown, '5' = LeBaron). The fourth symbol designated manufacturing plant ('7' = Detroit, Mich.). The fifth to tenth symbols designated production numbers. Body number plates, located below the hood in various locations, indicate schedule date, body production number, and body series (see column 2 in charts below), plus trim, paint and accessories data.

IMPERIAL CUSTOM SERIES

Series Number	Body/Style Number	Body Type & Seating	Factory Price	Shipping Weight	Production Total
MY1-L	613	4-dr Sed-6P	5016	4735	2,071
MY1-L	614	4-dr HT-6P	5016	4745	3,984
MY1-L	612	2-dr HT-6P	4910	4675	1,743

1959 Imperial Crown, two-door hardtop coupe, V-8 (AA)

IMPERIAL CROWN SERIES — SERIES MY1-M — Crown emblems on the front fenders were about the only way to distinguish the exterior of a Crown from a Custom. Standard features included Six-Way power seat, power windows, outside rearview mirror, vanity mirror and license plate frame.

IMPERIAL CROWN SERIES

Series Number	Body/Style Number	Body Type & Seating	Factory Price	Shipping Weight	Production Total
MY1-M	633	4-dr Sed-6P	5647	4830	1,335
MY1-M	634	4-dr HT-6P	5647	4840	4,714
MY1-M	632	2-dr HT-6P	5403	4810	1,728
MY1-M	635	2-dr Conv-6P	5774	4850	555

IMPERIAL LE BARON SERIES — SERIES MY1-H — Its nameplate on the front fenders and special emblem on the chrome rear quarter panels were exterior features of the Le Baron. In addition to the standard equipment found on the other series, Le Barons had two-tone paint and whitewall tires.

IMPERIAL LE BARON SERIES

Series Number	Body/Style Number	Body Type & Seating	Factory Price	Shipping Weight	Production Total
MY1-H	653	4-dr Sed-6P	6103	4865	510
MY1-H	654	4-dr HT-6P	6103	4875	622

CROWN IMPERIAL SERIES — Custom built by Ghia of Italy, the Crown Imperial remained one of the finest custom-built luxury cars in the world. Basic styling was like that used on the standard Imperials. It came with air conditioning, power windows, carpeting, and many other features.

CROWN IMPERIAL SERIES

Series Number	Body/Style Number	Body Type & Seating	Factory Price	Shipping Weight	Production Total
Note 1	Note 2	4-dr Limo-8P	16,000	5,960	7

NOTE 1: None.

NOTE 2: Not used.

ENGINE: V-8. Overhead valves. Cast iron block. Displacement: 413.2 cid. Bore and stroke: 4.18 x 3.75 inches. Compression ratio: 10.10:1. Brake hp: 350 at 4600 rpm. Carburetor: Carter four-barrel Model AFB-2797S.

CHASSIS FEATURES: Wheelbase: (Custom, Crown and LeBaron) 129 inches; (Crown Imperial) 149.5 inches. Tires: (all models) 9.50 x 14.

OPTIONS: Power brakes, standard. Power steering. Air conditioning ($590.20). Air suspension ($156). Rear window defogger ($21.45). Custom conditioned heater ($136.30). Instant heater ($164.95). Six-Way power seat ($124.80). Power windows ($125). Electric Touch radio, plus speaker and power antenna ($168.80). Electric Touch radio, plus speaker and power antenna for convertibles ($153.40). Solex glass ($53.75). Whitewall Rayon tires ($55.10). Whitewall nylon tires ($76.55). Whitewall nylon ties on Le Baron ($27.50). Two-tone paint ($20.45). Landau two-tone paint ($31.20). Auto pilot ($96.80). Electric door locks on two-doors with power windows ($47.40). Electric door locks on four-doors with power windows ($72.10). Automatic beam changer ($54.90). Flitesweep deck lid ($55.45). Extra heavy-duty 40 amp generator ($42.60). Mirror-matic on Imperial Custom ($22.20); on Crown and Le Baron ($18.20). Outside remote control mirror on custom ($18.75); on Crown and Le Baron ($11.90). Outside manual mirror ($6.85). Power swivel seat on Custom ($226.15); on Crown and Le Baron ($101.35). Stainless steel roof, hardtops ($139.80). Sure-grip differential ($57.45). True-level ride ($159.90). Leather trim. Crown hardtops and convertible ($52.70).

HISTORICAL FOOTNOTES: The vast majority of 1959 Imperials, 97.1 percent had radios, 37.5 percent had air conditioning and 81.1 percent came with tinted glass.

1960 IMPERIAL

IMPERIAL CUSTOM SERIES — SERIES PY1-L — Imperials had new bodies for 1960. The headlights were somewhat recessed under the overhanging front fenders. The grille had a clean, fine vertical and horizontal pieces treatment. Circular signal light pods were mounted on the lower half of the stylized 'wing' bumpers. The Imperial name was written on the grille and front fenders. Side trim started above the headlights and ran at a slightly downward angle, almost to the end of the rear fender. Chrome trimmed taillights once again protruded from the tailfins. The roof had chrome trim pieces running from the rear quarter panel to the top of the windshield. This trim curved inward above the doors, giving the roof an overlapping effect. All 1960 Imperials had power steering; power brakes; dual exhaust; undercoating; electric clock; and windshield washers.

IMPERIAL I.D. NUMBERS: VIN on plate on left front door hinge pillar. First symbol: 9=Imperial. Second symbol: 1=Imperial Custom; 2=Imperial Crown; 3=Imperial LeBaron; 9=Crown Imperial limousine. Third symbol: 0=1960. Fourth symbol: 4=Imperial plant in Detroit, Mich. Last six symbols are sequential production number. Engine number stamped on boss behind water pump: P-41 indicates 413 cid/350 hp V-8. Body number plate on fender, cowl or radiator support under hood indicates (SO) schedule date; (NUMBER) body production number; (BDY) body series code [see second column in charts below], (TRM) trim code; and (PNT) paint code.

IMPERIAL CUSTOM SERIES

Series Number	Body/Style Number	Body Type & Seating	Factory Price	Shipping Weight	Production Total
PY1-L	913	4-dr Sed-6P	5029	4700	2,335
PY1-L	914	4-dr HT-6P	5029	4670	3,953
PY1-L	912	2-dr HT-6P	4923	4655	1,498

1960 Imperial Crown, two-door convertible, V-8 (AA)

IMPERIAL CROWN SERIES — SERIES PY1-M — The word Crown printed beneath the Imperial nameplate was the easiest way to distinguish the Imperial Crown from the lower-priced Custom. Like all 1960 Imperials, a simulated spare-tire-cover trunk lid was optional. A Six-Way power seat; license frame; vanity mirror and outside rearview mirror were standard.

IMPERIAL CROWN SERIES

Series Number	Body/Style Number	Body Type & Seating	Factory Price	Shipping Weight	Production Total
PY1-M	923	4-dr Sed-6P	5647	4770	1,594
PY1-M	924	4-dr HT-6P	5647	4765	4,510
PY1-M	922	2-dr HT-6P	5403	4720	1,504
PY1-M	925	2-dr Conv-6P	5774	4820	618

LeBARON SERIES — SERIES PY1-H — LeBarons had a distinctive rectangular (rather than wraparound) rear window. It added a limousine quality to the series styling. The model name was also written, in chrome, on the trunk lid and front fenders. Power windows and two-tone paint were among the standard features.

LeBARON SERIES

Series Number	Body/Style Number	Body Type & Seating	Factory Price	Shipping Weight	Production Total
PY1-H	933	4-dr Sed-6P	6318	4860	692
PY1-H	934	4-dr HT-6P	6318	4835	999

CROWN IMPERIAL SERIES — The 1960 Imperial styling looked good on the custom-built Crown Imperial. It came with such things as: automatic headlight dimmer; auto pilot; dual radios; power windows, speaker phone and three heaters. The standard exterior color was black, but other combinations were available. The interior could be had in beige or gray.

CROWN IMPERIAL SERIES

Series Number	Body/Style Number	Body Type & Seating	Factory Price	Shipping Weight	Production Total
Note 1	Note 2	4-dr Limo-8P	16,000	5960	16

NOTE 1: None.

NOTE 2: Not used.

ENGINE: V-8. Overhead valves. Cast iron block. Displacement: 413.2 cid. Bore and stroke: 4.18 x 3.75 inches. Compression ratio: 10.10:1. Brake hp: 350 at 4600 rpm. Carburetor: Carter four-barrel Model AFB-2927S.

CHASSIS FEATURES: Wheelbase: (Custom Imperial, Imperial Crown and LeBaron) 129 inches; (Crown Imperial) 149.5 inches. Tires: (Custom Imperial, Imperial Crown and LeBaron) 8.20 x 15; (Crown Imperial) 8.90 x 15.

OPTIONS: Air conditioning ($590.20). Auto pilot ($96.80). Automatic beam changer ($46.00). Rear window defogger ($21.45). Door guards: for two-doors ($4.40); for four-doors ($6.50). Electric door locks: for two-door hardtop and convertible with power windows ($47.40). Electric door locks: for four-door models with power windows ($72.10). Flitesweep deck lid ($55.45). Extra-heavy-duty 40 amp. generator ($42.60). Heater ($136.30). Custom rear license plate frame ($6.05). Mirrormatic, except on convertibles ($18.20). Outside, left remote-control mirror ($11.90). Outside, right-hand manual mirror ($6.85). Sill molding ($27.60). Standard two-tone paint ($20.45). Six-Way power front seat, in Custom ($124.80). Automatic power swivel seat ($121.00). Power vent windows ($76.60). Power windows in Custom ($125.00). Electric Touch-Tuner radio with power antenna and rear speaker ($168.80). Electric Touch-Tuner radio with power antenna, in convertible ($153.30). Solex glass ($53.75). Stainless steel roof, for Custom and Crown four-door models only ($62.40). Sure-Grip differential ($57.45). Whitewall Rayon tires ($55.10). Whitewall nylon tires ($76.55). Whitewall nylon tires on LeBaron ($27.50). Leather trim, in Crown four-door sedan and hardtop ($104.30).

HISTORICAL FOOTNOTES: Chrysler sales were up this year, but Imperial deliveries dropped around 19.7 percent. A total of 17,707 units were made during the model year. In rounded figures, that total included 7,800 Custom Imperials; 8,200 Crown Imperials and 1,700 LeBarons. On a calendar year basis, production was counted at 16,829 units or just 25 percent of the total American market. This year, as in 1959, the cars were built by the Chrysler-Imperial Div. of Chrysler Corp., headed by C.E. Briggs, as vice-president and general manager. Plans were made to begin transfer of Imperial production from the Warren Road factory, Dearborn, to the Jefferson-Detroit facility which had formerly housed Imperial assembly lines until August, 1958. Most 1960 Imperials, 84.6 percent had tinted glass, 44.7 percent air conditioning. and 92.9 percent power windows.

1961 IMPERIAL

IMPERIAL CUSTOM SERIES — SERIES RY1-L — A new horizontal bar grille and slightly recessed, free-standing headlights dramatically changed the front end appearance of the 1961 Imperial. The make's name was now printed on the top section of the grille. The tailfins were more prominent and came to a point. The taillight pods stuck out from the lower section of the fins. A highly stylized flying eagle was placed on the rear fender part of the slightly slanted mid-body molding. Wheelwell openings and rocker panels were also trimmed with chrome. The unusual overlapping styled roof treatment, used in 1960, was continued. Power steering and power brakes were standard.

IMPERIAL I.D. NUMBERS: VIN on plate on left front door hinge pillar. First symbol: 9=Imperial. Second symbol: 1=Imperial Custom; 2=Imperial Crown; 3=Imperial LeBaron; 10=Crown Imperial limousine. Third symbol: 1=1961. Fourth symbol: 4=Imperial plant in Detroit, Mich. Last six symbols are sequential production number. Engine number stamped on boss behind water pump: R-41 indicates 413 cid/350 hp V-8. Body number plate on fender, cowl or radiator support under hood indicates (SO) schedule date; (NUMBER) body production number; (BDY) body series code [see second column in charts below], (TRM) trim code; and (PNT) paint code.

IMPERIAL CUSTOM SERIES

Series Number	Body/Style Number	Body Type & Seating	Factory Price	Shipping Weight	Production Total
RY1-L	914	4-dr HT-6P	5111	4740	4,129
RY1-L	912	2-dr HT-6P	4925	4715	889

IMPERIAL CROWN SERIES — SERIES RY1-M — The Imperial Crown looked virtually the same as the Custom. It came with power seat; rear license plate frame; vanity mirror; carpeting; power windows; and outside rearview mirror.

1961 Crown Imperial, four-door hardtop sedan, V-8

IMPERIAL CROWN SERIES

Series Number	Body/Style Number	Body Type & Seating	Factory Price	Shipping Weight	Production Total
RY1-M	924	4-dr HT-6P	5649	4855	4,769
RY1-M	922	2-dr HT-6P	5405	4790	1,007
RY1-M	925	2-dr Conv-6P	5776	4865	429

IMPERIAL LeBARON SERIES — SERIES RY1-H — Its unique formal roof treatment set the LeBaron apart from the other series. Power vent windows, stone shield moldings and whitewall tires were among standard features.

IMPERIAL LeBARON SERIES

Series Number	Body/Style Number	Body Type & Seating	Factory Price	Shipping Weight	Production Total
RY1-H	934	4-dr HT-6P	6428	4875	1,026

CROWN IMPERIAL SERIES — The few Crown Imperials built in 1961 came with 1960 styling. Air conditioning; auto pilot; automatic headlight dimmer; three heaters; and power windows were just some of the many standard luxury features on this custom-built car.

Series Number	Body/Style Number	Body Type & Seating	Factory Price	Shipping Weight	Production Total
Note 1	Note 2	4-dr Limo-8P	16,000	5960	9

NOTE 1: None.

NOTE 2: Not used.

ENGINE: V-8. Overhead valves. Cast iron block. Displacement: 413.2 cid. Bore and stroke: 4.18 x 3.75 inches. Compression ratio: 10.10:1. Brake hp: 350 at 4600 rpm. Carburetor: Carter Type four-barrel Model AFB-3108S.

CHASSIS FEATURES: Wheelbase: (Imperial Custom, Imperial Crown and Imperial LeBaron) 129 inches; (Crown Imperial) 149.5 inches. Tires: (Imperial Custom, Imperial Crown and Imperial LeBaron) 8.20 x 15, (Crown Imperial) 8.90 x 15.

OPTIONS: Power brakes. Power steering. Air conditioning ($590.20). Auto pilot ($96.80). Automatic beam changer ($46). Crankcase ventilation system ($5.20). Rear window defogger ($21.45). Door guards two-doors ($4.40); four-doors ($6.50). Electric door locks two-doors with power windows ($47.40); four-doors with power windows ($72.10). Flitesweep deck lid ($55.45). Heater ($136.30). Rear license plate frame in Custom ($6.05). Outside, left remote-control mirror ($11.90); right remote-control mirror ($6.85). Wheelhouse, stone shields and sill molding ($39.60). Six-Way power front seat in Custom ($124.80). Power vent windows ($76.60). Power windows in Custom ($125). Electric Touch-Tuner radio with rear speaker and power antenna ($168.80). Electric Touch-Tuner radio with power antenna in convertibles ($153.30). Solex glass ($53.75). Stainless steel roof in Custom ($62.40). Sure-Grip differential ($57.45). Swivel seat, manual power seat required ($101.35). Whitewall rayon tires ($55.10). Leather trim in Crown ($104.30); in LeBaron ($69.70). Basic group two-doors ($396.60); four-doors ($398.70). Basic group includes: heater; radio with rear speaker and power antenna; door edge protectors; remote-control outside rear mirror on left, solex glass; rear window defogger. Convenience group: power seat; power windows; license plate frame in Custom ($255.85). Decor group: Flitesweep deck lid; stone shields; sill moldings; manual right outside rearview mirror, except LeBaron ($101.90).

HISTORICAL FOOTNOTES: The last gasp of the finned Imperials was heard this year. Some people christened them "Bat-mobiles." Chrysler's luxury line returned to body-on-frame construction. Just over half of all 1961 Imperials came equipped with air conditioning.

1962 IMPERIAL

IMPERIAL CUSTOM SERIES — SERIES SY1-L — The Custom Imperial featured a new hood ornament and a split, thin, horizontal bar grille. The recessed, free-standing headlights, introduced in 1961, were used again. Trim, starting at the headlight eyebrows, extended at a slight angle to the rear quarter panel. Wheelwell openings and rocker panel moldings also helped to decorate the sides. The taillights were mounted atop the rear fenders. Power brakes and power steering were standard.

IMPERIAL I.D. NUMBERS: VIN on plate on left front door hinge pillar. First symbol: 9=Imperial. Second symbol: 1=Imperial Custom; 2=Imperial Crown; 3=Imperial LeBaron. Third symbol: 2=1962. Fourth symbol: 3=Detroit, Mich. Last six symbols are sequential production number. Engine number stamped on boss behind water pump: S-41 indicates 413 cid/340 hp V-8. Body number plate on fender, cowl or radiator support under hood indicates (SO) schedule date; (NUMBER) body production number; (BDY) body series code [see second column in charts below], (TRM) trim code; and (PNT) paint code.

IMPERIAL CUSTOM SERIES

Series Number	Body/Style Number	Body Type & Seating	Factory Price	Shipping Weight	Production Total
SY1-L	914	4-dr HT-6P	5106	4620	3,587
SY1-L	912	2-dr HT-6P	4920	4540	826

1962 Imperial Crown, four-door hardtop sedan, V-8

CROWN IMPERIAL SERIES — SERIES SY1-M — With deletion of the custom-built Crown Imperial limousines, the cars formerly known as Imperial Crowns became Crown Imperials. The Crown name and emblem on the rear fenders, below the taillights, was one way to tell the high-dollar Imperial from the lower-priced series. It came with the same standard equipment as the Custom, plus hand-brake warning signal; electric clock; power windows; center armrest; and Six-Way power front seat.

CROWN IMPERIAL SERIES

Series Number	Body/Style Number	Body Type & Seating	Factory Price	Shipping Weight	Production Total
SY1-M	924	4-dr HT-6P	5644	4680	6,911
SY1-M	922	2-dr HT-6P	5400	4650	1,010
SY1-M	925	2-dr Conv-6P	5770	4765	554

IMPERIAL LeBARON SERIES — SERIES SY1-H — A distinctive rectangular rear window and formal roof were styling features of the top-of-the line LeBaron.

IMPERIAL LeBARON SERIES

Series Number	Body/Style Number	Body Type & Seating	Factory Price	Shipping Weight	Production Total
SY1-H	934	4-dr HT-6P	6422	4725	1,449

ENGINE: V-8. Overhead valves. Cast iron block. Displacement: 413.2 cid. Bore and stroke: 4.18 x 3.75 inches. Compression ratio: 10.10:1. Brake hp: 340 at 4600 rpm. Carburetor: Carter four-barrel Model AFB-3215S.

CHASSIS FEATURES: Wheelbase: (All) 129 inches. Tires: (All) 8.20 x 15.

OPTIONS: Power brakes. Power steering. Air conditioning ($590.20). Auto pilot ($98.80). Automatic beam changer ($46). Crankcase ventilation system ($5.20). Rear window defogger ($21.45). Door guards, two-doors ($4.40); four-doors ($6.50). Electric door locks, two-doors with power windows ($47.40); four-doors with power windows ($72.10). Heater ($136.30). Rear license plate frame, Custom, ($6.05). Rear license plate frame and door edge protectors, Custom and two-door hardtops ($10.45). Rear license plate frame and door edge protectors, Custom four-door hardtops ($12.55). Outside, left remote-control mirror ($11.90). Outside right manual mirror ($6.85). Wheelhouse, stone shields and sill molding ($40.90). Six-Way power front seat, Custom ($124.80). Power vent windows ($76.60). Electric Touch-Tuner radio with rear speaker and power antenna ($168.80). Electric Touch-Tuner radio with power antenna, convertible ($153.30). Tinted glass ($53.75). Sure-Grip differential ($57.45). Two front seat belts ($20.20). Whitewall Rayon tires ($55.10). Leather trim, Crown ($104.30); LeBaron ($69.70). Accessory Group: includes heater; radio with rear speaker and power antenna; door edge protectors; remote-control outside rearview mirror on left; tinted glass; power seat and power windows. Accessory Group on Custom two-door hardtop ($624.95); on Custom four-door hardtop ($627.05); on Crown two-door hardtop ($375.15); on Crown and LeBaron four-door hardtop ($377.25).

HISTORICAL FOOTNOTES: The 1962 Imperials were introduced Sept. 26, 1961, one year and two days after the 1961 models first appeared. Total model year production hit 14,337 units, including 613 cars built for export markets. In rounded figures, this total included 4,400 Custom Imperials; 8,500 Crown Imperials and 1,400 LeBarons. For the calendar year, 14,787 units bearing Imperial nameplates were produced. The car's maker was now called the Chrysler-Plymouth Div. of Chrysler Corp., which had been formed in 1961. C.E. Briggs remained vice-president and general manager. Imperial sales were up 17 percent over the previous year and were the highest since late 1957. Most 1962 Imperials. 60.3 percent, came with air conditioning, 64.4 percent had power seats and 95.1 percent had power windows. No Ghia-built Crown Imperial limousines were sold in 1962.

1963 IMPERIAL

IMPERIAL CUSTOM SERIES — SERIES TY1-L — The 1963 Custom Imperial had a new stacked horizontal bar grille, divided in the center by a rectangular section containing a stylized eagle emblem. Free-standing headlights were once again tucked under front fender 'eyebrows.' These were trimmed with a chrome piece that ran, at an angle, the entire length of the car and connected to the rear deck panel trim. The vertical taillights were now placed in the tailfins. Circular back-up lights were integrated into the rear bumpers. The roof design was less slanted than that of the previous year's models. Power steering, power brakes, and power windows were standard.

IMPERIAL I.D. NUMBERS: VIN on plate on left front door hinge pillar. First symbol: 9=Imperial. Second symbol: 1=Imperial Custom; 2=Imperial Crown; 3=Imperial LeBaron. Third symbol: 3=1963. Fourth symbol: 3=Jefferson Ave. plant, Detroit, Mich. Last six symbols are sequential production number. Engine number stamped on boss behind water pump: T-41 indicates 413 cid/340 hp V-8. Body number plate on fender, cowl or radiator support under hood indicates (SO) schedule date; (NUMBER) body production number; (BDY) body series code [see second column in charts below], (TRM) trim code; and (PNT) paint code.

IMPERIAL CUSTOM SERIES

Series Number	Body/Style Number	Body Type & Seating	Factory Price	Shipping Weight	Production Total
TY1-L	914	4-dr HT-6P	5243	4690	3,264
TY1-L	912	2-dr HT-6P	5058	4640	749

IMPERIAL CROWN SERIES — SERIES TY1-M — The Crown Imperial line returned, so the one-step-up cars became Imperial Crowns again. The Crown name and emblem was in a small rectangular trim piece on the upper rear fenders, next to the taillights. It was the easiest way to distinguish the Crown from other Imperials.

IMPERIAL CROWN SERIES

Series Number	Body/Style Number	Body Type & Seating	Factory Price	Shipping Weight	Production Total
TY1-M	924	4-dr HT-6P	5656	4740	6,960
TY1-M	922	2-dr HT-6P	5412	4720	1,067
TY1-M	925	2-dr Conv-6P	5782	4795	531

1963 Imperial Crown, four-door hardtop sedan, V-8

IMPERIAL LeBARON SERIES — SERIES TY1-H — The LeBaron crest on the roof quarter panels was subject to federal jewelry excise tax. It, and the unique rectangular rear window, were exclusive features of the top-of-the-line LeBaron.

IMPERIAL LeBARON SERIES

Series Number	Body/Style Number	Body Type & Seating	Factory Price	Shipping Weight	Production Total
TY1-H	934	4-dr HT-6P	6434	4830	1,537

CROWN IMPERIAL SERIES — The exclusive, custom-built Crown Imperial returned this year. Standard features included carpeting; air conditioning; three heaters; Auto Pilot: automatic headlight dimmer; power steering; power brakes; and power windows.

Series Number	Body/Style Number	Body Type & Seating	Factory Price	Shipping Weight	Production Total
Note 1	Note 2	4-dr Sed-8P	18,500	6000	1
Note 1	Note 2	4-dr Limo-8P	18,500	6100	12

NOTE 1: None available.

NOTE 2: Not used.

ENGINE: V-8. Overhead valves. Cast iron block. Displacement: 413.2 cid. Bore and stroke: 4.18 x 3.75 inches. Compression ratio: 10.10:1. Brake hp: 340 at 4600 rpm. Carburetor: Carter Type four-barrel Model AFB-3256S.

CHASSIS FEATURES: Wheelbase: (Custom Imperial, Imperial Crown and LeBaron) 129 inches; (Crown Imperial) 149.5 inches. Tires: 8.20 x 15.

OPTIONS: Power brakes. Power steering. Air conditioning ($590.20). Auto Pilot ($98.80). Automatic beam changer ($46). Flitesweep deck lid ($55.45). Rear window defogger ($21.45). Door guards two-doors ($4.40); four-doors ($6.50). Electric door locks two-doors ($47.40); four-doors ($72.10). Heater ($136.30). Rear license plate frame in Custom ($6.05). Rear license plate frame and door edge protectors in Custom two-door hardtop ($10.45); four-doors ($12.55). Outside right manual mirror ($6.85). Wheelhouse, stone shields and sill molding ($39.60). Six-Way power front seat in Custom ($124.80). Power vent windows ($76.60). Remote control power trunk lock ($53.15). Electric Touch-Tuner radio with rear speaker and power antenna ($168.80). Electric Touch-Tuner radio with power antenna in convertible ($153.30). Tinted glass ($53.75). Sure Grip differential ($57.45). Two front seat belts ($18.75). Whitewall Rayon tires ($55.10). Leather trim in Crown ($104.30); in LeBaron ($69.70). Accessory group includes: heater; radio and rear speaker and power antenna; door edge protectors; tinted glass and power seat. Accessory group in Custom two-door hardtop ($488.05); four-door ($490.15). Accessory group in Imperial Crown two-door hardtop ($363.25); in Imperial Crown and LeBaron four-door hardtop ($365.35).

HISTORICAL FOOTNOTES: The 1963 Imperials were introduced Sept. 26, 1962. Calendar year production was up to 33,717 units or .44 percent of industry sales. P.N. Buckminster became vice-president and general manager of Chrysler-Plymouth Div. The majority of 1963 Imperials, 64.3 percent, had air conditioning, and 91.9 percent had tinted glass.

1964 IMPERIAL

IMPERIAL CROWN SERIES — SERIES VY1-M — Imperial was attractively restyled for 1964. The model lineup was reduced to four cars in two series. Imperial Crown was now the base trim level. The free-standing headlights became chrome-ringed ones embedded in the slit, horizontal bar grille. Bodysides featured full-length, bumper-to-bumper upper body moldings and chrome-trimmed wheelwell openings and rocker panels. The taillights were integrated into the rear bumper and the trunk lid was designed with a simulated continental kit. The entire car seemed influenced by the crisp Lincoln-Continental styling. This was no doubt influenced by the fact that Chrysler had hired stylist Elwood Engle away from Ford two years earlier. Power steering, power windows and power brakes were standard.

IMPERIAL I.D. NUMBERS: VIN on plate on left front door hinge pillar. First symbol: 9=Imperial. Second symbol: 2=Imperial Crown; 3=Imperial LeBaron. Third symbol: 4=1964. Fourth symbol: 3=Jefferson Ave. plant, Detroit, Mich. Last six symbols are sequential production number. Engine number stamped on boss behind water pump: V-41 indicates 413 cid/340 hp V-8. Body number plate on fender, cowl or radiator support under hood indicates (SO) schedule date; (NUMBER) body production number; (BDY) body series code [see second column in charts below], (TRM) trim code; and (PNT) paint code.

1964 Imperial Crown, four-door hardtop sedan, V-8

IMPERIAL CROWN SERIES

Series Number	Body/Style Number	Doors/Style Seating	Factory Price	Shipping Weight	Production Total
VY1-M	Y24	4-dr HT-6P	5581	4970	14,181
VY1-M	Y22	2-dr HT-6P	5739	4950	5,233
VY1-M	Y25	2-dr Conv-6P	6003	5185	922

IMPERIAL LeBARON SERIES — SERIES VY1-H — The LeBaron name on the front fenders and roof quarter panels were the main exterior differences between this top-of-the-line series and the Imperial Crown.

IMPERIAL LeBARON SERIES

Series Number	Body/Style Number	Doors/Style Seating	Factory Price	Shipping Weight	Production Total
VY1-H	934	4-dr HT-6P	6455	5005	2,949

CROWN IMPERIAL SERIES — Imperial's new styling was very becoming on the custom-built Crown Imperial. It was available with either six windows or with blind rear quarter roof panels.

CROWN IMPERIAL SERIES

Series Number	Body/Style Number	Doors/Style Seating	Factory Price	Shipping Weight	Production Total
Note 1	Note 2	4-dr Limo-8P	18,500	6100	10

NOTE 1: Not available.

NOTE 2: Not used.

ENGINE: V-8. Overhead valves. Cast iron block. Displacement: 413.2 cid. Bore and stroke: 4.18 x 3.75 inches. Compression ratio: 10.10:1. Brake hp: 340 at 4600 rpm. Carburetor: Carter four-barrel Model AFB-3644S.

CHASSIS FEATURES: Wheelbase: (Crown and LeBaron) 129 inches; (Crown Imperial) 149.5 inches. Tires: 8.20 x 15.

OPTIONS: Power brakes and power steering standard. Air conditioning ($461.95). Dual air conditioning ($649.85). Auto pilot ($96.80). Automatic beam changer ($46.00). Rear window defogger ($21.45). Door guard, two-door ($4.40). Door guard, four-door ($6.50). Electric door locks, two-door ($47.40). Electric door locks, four-door ($72.10). Left and right headrest ($45.60). Outside right mirror ($6.85). Two-tone paint ($20.85). Six-Way power front seat, in Imperial Crown four-door hardtop ($124.80). Positive crankcase vent system ($5.10). Power trunk lock, remote control ($28.80). AM Touch Tuner radio with rear speaker and power antenna ($168.80). AM/FM radio with rear speaker and power antenna ($195.70). Rear reverberator speaker ($37.65). Two front retractable seat belts ($22.80). Adjustable steering wheel ($51.30). Sure-Grip differential ($57.45). Tinted glass ($53.75). Whitewall Rayon tires ($55.10). Leather trim ($104.30). Individual front seat trim, in Crown four-door hardtop ($506.10). Individual front seat trim, in LeBaron ($381.40). Vinyl roof, in Crown coupe ($91.20). Vinyl roof, in LeBaron and Crown four-door hardtop ($110.80).

HISTORICAL FOOTNOTES: Imperials built to 1964 specifications were introduced Sept. 25, 1963. Chrysler-Plymouth Div., with P.N. Buckminster at the helm, produced exactly 23,285 Imperials during the model year. Most 1964 Imperials, 95 percent, had tinted glass, 77.5 percent had air conditioning, 28.8 percent had a tilting steering wheel and 98.8 percent had a radio. The Imperial Custom series disappeared and the Imperial Crown car-line became the base series. Sales increased 65 percent over 1963 levels.

1965 IMPERIAL

IMPERIAL CROWN SERIES — SERIES AY1-M — The basic styling originated in 1964 was kept. However, a new mesh-pattern grille, divided by chrome into four sections, was used. The headlights were recessed behind glass panels. The simulated spare-tire 'bulge' rear deck treatment was continued. Power brakes; power windows; power steering; carpeting; electric clock; padded dash and remote-control outside rearview mirror were standard.

IMPERIAL I.D. NUMBERS: VIN on plate on left front door hinge pillar. First symbol: Y=Imperial. Second symbol: 2=Imperial Crown; 3=Imperial LeBaron. Third symbol: 5=1965. Fourth symbol: 3=Jefferson Ave. plant, Detroit, Mich. Last six symbols are sequential production number. Engine number stamped on boss behind water pump: A-413 indicates 413 cid/360 hp V-8. Body number plate on fender, cowl or radiator support under hood indicates (SO) schedule date; (NUMBER) body production number; (BDY) body series code [see second column in charts below], (TRM) trim code; and (PNT) paint code.

1965 Imperial Crown, two-door hardtop coupe, V-8

IMPERIAL CROWN SERIES

Series Number	Body/Style Number	Body Type & Seating	Factory Price	Shipping Weight	Production Total
AY1-M	Y24	4-dr HT-6P	5772	5015	11,628
AY1-M	Y22	2-dr HT-6P	5930	5075	3,974
AY1-M	Y25	2-dr Conv-6P	6194	5345	633

1965 Crown Imperial, four-door. hardtop sedan, V-8

IMPERIAL LeBARON SERIES — SERIES AY1-H — Aside from a fancier interior and its name written on the roof quarter panels, the LeBaron was the same basic car as the Imperial Crown. A Six-Way bench seat and whitewall tires were standard.

IMPERIAL LeBARON SERIES

Series Number	Body/Style Number	Body Type & Seating	Factory Price	Shipping Weight	Production Total
AY1-H	934	4-dr HT-6P	6596	5080	2,164

CROWN IMPERIAL SERIES — This was the last year for the custom-built Ghia Crown Imperials. As before, they were available with either six windows or a blind rear roof quarter panel.

CROWN IMPERIAL SERIES

Series Number	Body/Style Number	Body Type & Seating	Factory Price	Shipping Weight	Production Total
Note 1	Note 2	4-dr Limo-8P	16,000	Note 1	10

NOTE 1: None Used.

NOTE 2: None used.

ENGINE: V-8. Overhead valves. Cast iron block. Displacement: 413.2 cid. Bore and stroke: 4.18 x 3.75 inches. Compression ratio: 10.10:1. Brake hp: 340 at 4600 rpm. Carburetor: Carter four-barrel Model AFB-3871S.

CHASSIS FEATURES: Wheelbase: (Imperial Crown and LeBaron) 129 inches; (Crown Imperial) 149.5 inches. Tires: 8.20 x 15.

OPTIONS: Air conditioning ($461.95). Dual air conditioning ($649.85). Auto Pilot ($96.80). Automatic beam changer ($46). Rear window defogger ($21.45). Door guards, two-door ($4.40); four-door ($6.50). Electric door locks, two-door ($47.40); four-door ($72.10). Left and right headrests ($45.60). Outside right mirror ($6.85). Two-tone paint ($20.85). Six-Way power front seat, in Crown four-door hardtop ($124.80). Positive crankcase vent system ($5.10). Power trunk lock, remote-control ($28.80). AM Touch-Tuner radio with rear speaker and power antenna ($168.80). AM/FM radio with rear speaker and power antenna ($195.70). Rear reverberator speaker ($37.65). Two front retractable seat belts ($22.80). Adjustable steering wheel ($51.30). Sure-Grip differential ($57.45). Tinted glass ($53.75) Whitewall Rayon tires ($55.10). Leather trim ($104.30). Individual front seat trim, in Crown four-door hardtop ($506.10). Individual front seat trim, in LeBaron ($381.40). Vinyl roof on Crown coupe ($91.20). Vinyl roof on LeBaron and Crown four-door hardtops ($110.80).

HISTORICAL FOOTNOTES: Introduced on Sept. 30, 1964, the new Imperial line earned Robert Anderson's Chrysler-Plymouth Div. 18,399 assemblies for the model year. Calendar year production peaked at 16,422 units. Close to one in three 1965 Imperials came with a tilting steering wheel and 86.9 percent had air conditioning.

1966 IMPERIAL

CROWN IMPERIAL SERIES — SERIES BY1-M — Chrysler again changed the name of the less expensive "Crown" series to Crown Imperial, after dropping the line of custom-built Crown Imperial limousines for the second time. The 1966 Crown Imperial received a relatively minor facelift. It featured a new ice-cube-tray style grille with the four headlights recessed into chrome panels. The same rear deck treatment used the last two years was continued. All 1966 Imperials came with power brakes; power steering; power windows; electric clock; carpeting; undercoating; and vanity with mirror.

1966 Imperial Crown, four-door hardtop sedan, V-8

IMPERIAL I.D. NUMBERS: VIN on plate on left front door hinge pillar. First symbol: Y=Imperial. Second symbol: M= medium-price Crown Imperial; H=high-price Imperial LeBaron. Third and fourth symbols indicate body style: 23=two-door hardtop; 27=convertible; 43=four-door hardtop. Fifth symbol: J=440 cid V-8. Sixth symbol: 6=1966. Seventh symbol identifies assembly plant: 3=Jefferson Plant, Detroit, Mich. Last six symbols are sequential production number. Body number plate under hood gives (SO) schedule date; (NUMBER) body production sequence number; (BDY) body code (column two of charts below); (TRM) trim code; and (PNT) paint code. Engine number on left of block, front, near water pump. Engine code B-440 for 440 cid V-8.

CROWN IMPERIAL SERIES

Series Number	Body/Style Number	Body Type & Seating	Factory Price	Shipping Weight	Production Total
BY1-M	YM43	4-dr HT-6P	5733	4965	8,977
BY1-M	YM23	2-dr HT-6P	5887	5020	2,373
BY1-M	YM27	2-dr Conv-6P	6146	5295	514

IMPERIAL LeBARON SERIES — BY1-H — The LeBaron remained a slightly fancier version of the Crown. Except for its nameplate, exterior styling was the same. However, the LeBaron had a plusher interior, with standard Six-Way power seats.

IMPERIAL LeBARON SERIES

Series Number	Body/Style Number	Body Type & Seating	Factory Price	Shipping Weight	Production Total
BY1-H	YH43	4-dr HT-6P	6540	5065	1,878

ENGINE: V-8. Overhead valves. Cast iron block. Displacement: 440 cid. Bore and stroke: 4.32 x 3.75 inches. Compression ratio: 10.1:1. Brake hp: 350 at 4400 rpm. Carburetor: Carter four-barrel Model AFB-4131S.

CHASSIS FEATURES: Wheelbase: 129 inches. Tires: 9.15 x 15.

OPTIONS: Automatic transmission was standard. Air conditioning ($452.25). Dual unit air conditioner $636.15). Auto Pilot ($94.90). Automatic beam changer ($45.10). Cleaner air package ($25.00). Rear window defogger ($26.20). Door edge guards in Crown two-door ($4.35); in four-door ($6.40). Left and right headrest ($52.45). Rear seat heater with defroster ($63.30). Front license plate frame ($5.95). Outside right mirror ($6.75). Mobile Director, in Crown coupe ($597.40). Power door locks, in Crown two-door ($46.50). Power door locks, in four-doors ($70.70). Six-Way left power seat, in Crown four-door hardtop ($105.50). Six-Way power seat, for driver and passenger, in Crown four-door hardtop ($210.85). Six-Way power bench seat, in Crown four-door sedan ($122.35). Power trunk release ($28.25). Power vent windows ($71.75). AM Touch-Tuner radio with rear speaker and power antenna ($165.45). AM/FM Touch-Tuner radio with rear speaker and power antenna ($227.75). Reverberator rear speaker ($36.90). Safeguard sentinel lighting ($36.10). Front center passenger seat belt ($9.20). Rear center passenger seat belt ($9.20). Front left and right shoulder belts ($26.80). Tilt-a-scope steering wheel ($92.45). Sure-Grip differential ($56.35). Tinted glass ($52.70). White three-ring tires ($54.05). Split bench seats, with leather trim, in four-door hardtops ($102.25). Vinyl roof ($129.70).

HISTORICAL FOOTNOTES: Sept. 30, 1965 was the big day! The 1966 Imperials appeared in dealer showrooms. By the model year's end, 13,742 of them had left the factory. Calendar year production was recorded at 17,653 cars. Lynn Townsend was pulling the strings at Chrysler Corp., although Robert Anderson was vice-president and general manager of the Chrysler-Plymouth Div. Model year sales were 25.3 percent off previous levels, although total market share was just about the same. Air conditioning was in 92.5 percent of 1966 Imperials. Only 30.4 percent had a tilting steering wheel. Last year for body-on-frame construction, as Imperials went to unit-body construction in 1968. The 440 cid V-8 replaced the 413 cid V-8 in Imperials, providing the cars with 10 additional horsepower.

1967 IMPERIAL

IMPERIAL SERIES — SERIES CY1-M — Imperial had a new look this year. Its name was printed in a rectangular box in the center of the fine horizontal bar grille. Wraparound signal lights were another new feature. Full-length upper tire-level moldings decorated the sides. The rear fenders were integrated into the bumpers. Power disc brakes; power steering; carpeting; electric clock and power windows were among the standard equipment.

IMPERIAL I.D. NUMBERS: VIN on plate on left front door hinge pillar. First symbol: Y=Imperial. Second symbol: M=medium-price Crown Imperial; H=high-price Imperial LeBaron. Third and fourth symbols indicate body style: 23=two-door hardtop; 27=convertible; 41=four-door sedan; 43=four-door hardtop. Fifth symbol: L=440 cid V-8. Sixth symbol: 7=1967. Seventh symbol identifies assembly plant: 3=Jefferson Plant, Detroit, Mich. Last six symbols are sequential production number. Body number plate under hood gives (SO) schedule date; (NUMBER) body production sequence number; (BDY) body code (column two of charts below); (TRM) trim code; and (PNT) paint code. Engine number on left of block, front, near water pump. Engine code C-440 for 440 cid V-8.

IMPERIAL SERIES

Series Number	Body/Style Number	Body Type & Seating	Factory Price	Shipping Weight	Production Total
CY1-M	YM41	4-dr Sed-6P	5374	4830	2,193
CY1-M	YM27	2-dr Conv-6P	6244	4815	577

IMPERIAL CROWN SERIES — SERIES CY1-M — The Crown had an additional full-length side body trim, just below the door handles, to set it apart from the standard Imperial.

IMPERIAL CROWN SERIES

Series Number	Body/Style Number	Body Type & Seating	Factory Price	Shipping Weight	Production Total
CY1-M	YM43	4-dr HT-6P	5836	4860	9,415
CY1-M	YM23	2-dr HT-6P	6011	4780	3,235

1967 Imperial LeBaron, four-door hardtop sedan, V-8

IMPERIAL LeBARON SERIES — SERIES CY1-H — An easy way to identify the new LeBaron was to look at its sides. It featured distinctive upper tire level molding. It also came with sliding assist straps; reading lights; power vents; Six-Way power seats and whitewall tires.

IMPERIAL LeBARON SERIES

Series Number	Body/Style Number	Body Type & Seating	Factory Price	Shipping Weight	Production Total
CY1-H	YH43	4-dr HT-6P	6661	4970	2,194

ENGINE: V-8. Overhead valves. Cast iron block. Displacement: 440 cid. Bore and stroke: 4.32 x 3.75 inches. Compression ratio: 10.1:1. Brake hp: 350 at 4400 rpm. Carburetor: Holley four-barrel Model R-3667A.

CHASSIS FEATURES: Wheelbase: 127 inches. Tires: 9.15 x 15.

OPTIONS: TorqueFlite transmission was standard. Air conditioning ($452.25). Dual unit air conditioner ($636.15). Auto Pilot ($94.90). Automatic beam changer ($45.10). Clean-Air package ($25). Rear window defogger ($26.20). Door edge guards on two-doors ($4.35); on four-doors ($6.40). Left and right headrests ($52.45). Rear seat heater with defroster ($63.30). Front license plate frame ($5.95). Outside right mirror ($6.75). Mobile Director, in Crown coupe ($597.40). Power door locks, in Crown two-door ($46.50). Power door locks ($70.70). Six-Way left power seat, in Crown four-door hardtop ($105.50). Six-Way power seat, for driver and passenger, in Crown four-door hardtop ($210.85). Six-Way power bench seat, in Crown four-door sedan ($122.35). Power trunk release ($28.25). Power vent windows ($71.75). AM Touch-Tuner radio with rear speaker and power antenna ($165.45). AM/FM Touch-Tuner radio with rear speaker and power antenna ($227.75). Reverberator rear speaker ($36.90). Safeguard sentinel lighting ($36.10). Front center passenger seat belt ($9.20). Rear center passenger seat belt ($9.20). Front left and right shoulder belts ($26.80). Tilt-A-Scope steering wheel ($92.45). Sure-Grip differential ($56.35). Tinted glass ($52.70). White three-ring tires ($54.05). Split bench seats leather trim, in four-door hardtops ($102.25). Vinyl roof ($129.70).

HISTORICAL FOOTNOTES: Robert Anderson, Chrysler-Plymouth general manager picked Sept. 29, 1966, to introduce the 1967 Imperial models to the public. It was the start of a 17,614 car model run. That total included some 15,400 Crown models and 2,200 LeBarons. As you can see, the 1967 Chrysler luxury car was somewhat of a success. On a calendar year basis, the line on the sales graph peaked at the 15,506 unit level, a decline over 12 months before. AM/FM stereo multiplex radio was a first time option this year. Most 1967 Imperials, 98 percent, had tinted glass, 95.1 percent had air conditioning, 44.2 percent had vinyl roofs, 40.6 percent used speed control and 21.6 percent came with bucket seats.

1968 Imperial Crown, four-door hardtop sedan, V-8

CROWN IMPERIAL SERIES — SERIES AY1-M — Although the rear end looked much the same as last year, the Imperial received a new horizontal bar grille that wrapped around the front fenders. It was divided in the center by a vertical bar with a circular emblem. The headlights were recessed into the grille. The rectangular signal lights were located in the front bumpers. Full-length upper fender level trim and fender-to-fender tire level moldings were used on the sides. The Crown two-door hardtop came with vinyl covered quarter panels and rear roof. All 1968 Imperials came with power steering; power disc brakes; power windows; carpeting; energy-absorbing steering column; padded dash; undercoating; heater; electric clock and remote-control outside mirror.

IMPERIAL I.D. NUMBERS: VIN on plate on left front door hinge pillar. First symbol: Y=Imperial. Second symbol: M=medium-price Crown Imperial; H=high-price Imperial LeBaron. Third and fourth symbols indicate body style: 23=two-door hardtop; 27=convertible; 41=four-door sedan; 43=four-door hardtop. Fifth symbol: K=440 cid V-8; L=high-performance 440 cid V-8. Sixth symbol: 8=1968. Seventh symbol identifies assembly plant: 3=Jefferson Plant, Detroit, Mich. Last six symbols are sequential production number. Body number plate under hood gives (SO) schedule date; (NUMBER) body production sequence number; (BDY) body code (column two of charts below); (TRM) trim code; and (PNT) paint code. Engine number on left of block, front, near water pump. Engine code D-440 for 440 cid V-8.

CROWN IMPERIAL SERIES

Series Number	Body/Style Number	Body Type & Seating	Factory Price	Shipping Weight	Production Total
DY1-M	YM41	4-dr Sed-6P	5653	4770	1,887
DY1-M	YM43	4-dr HT-6P	6114	4775	8,492
DY1-M	YM23	2-dr HT-6P	5721	4740	2,656
DY1-M	YM27	2-dr Conv-6P	6522	4845	474

IMPERIAL LeBARON SERIES — SERIES AY1-H — The LeBaron had a distinctive roof with smaller back window than found on the Crown. It had all the standard features of the lower-priced series, plus sliding assist straps, Six-Way power seats, reading lamps and whitewall tires.

IMPERIAL LeBARON SERIES

Series Number	Body/Style Number	Body Type & Seating	Factory Price	Shipping Weight	Production Total
DY1-H	YH43	4-dr HT-6P	6939	4840	1,852

ENGINE: V-8. Overhead valves. Cast iron block. Displacement: 440 cid. Bore and stroke: 4.32 x 3.75 inches. Compression ratio: 10.1:1. Brake hp: 350 at 4400 rpm. Carburetor: Holley four-barrel Model R-3918A.

CHASSIS FEATURES: Wheelbase: 127 inches. Tires: 9.15 x 15.

OPTIONS: TorqueFlite transmission was standard. Power brakes. Power steering. Air conditioning ($493.45). Dual unit air conditioning ($771.40). Auto pilot ($94.90). Automatic beam changer ($50.15). Leather bucket seats, two-door hardtops ($351.40). Rear window defogger ($26.20). Door edge guards, two-doors ($5.00). Door edge guards, four-doors ($8.50). Dual 440, dual exhausts and air cleaner ($43.05). Right and left front head restraints ($52.45). Rear seat heater with defroster ($69.60). Front license plate frame ($5.95). Outside right manual mirror ($7.15). Mobile Director, Crown coupe ($317.60). Power door locks, two-doors ($46.50). Power door locks, four-doors ($70.70). Six-Way left power seat, Crown four-door hardtop ($105.50). Six-Way driver and passenger power seat ($210.85). Six-Way bench power seat ($122.35). Power trunk lid release ($29.60). Power vent windows ($71.75). AM Touch-Tuner radio with rear speaker and power antenna ($165.45). AM/FM Touch-Tuner radio with rear speaker and power antenna ($227.75). Multiplex AM/FM stereo with stereo speaker and power antenna ($294.85). Stereo tape player ($136.60). Safeguard Sentinel lighting ($36.10). Front, left and right shoulder belts ($26.80). Rear, left and right shoulder belts ($26.80). Front center passenger seat belt ($6.55). Rear center passenger seat belt ($6.55). Spare tire cover ($11.40). Tilt-A-Scope steering wheel ($92.45). Sure-Grip differential ($56.35). Tinted glass, all windows ($52.70). Trailer towing package, models without air conditioning ($63.85). Split bench seats with leather trim, four-door hardtops ($124.55). Vinyl roof, Crown coupe ($103.30). Vinyl roof, other models ($136.15). Trailer towing package, models with air conditioning ($53.55).

HISTORICAL FOOTNOTES: Over 80 percent of 1968 Imperials had a vinyl roof, 14.4 percent had bucket seats, 72.4 percent had tilting steering wheel, 64.8 percent had Cruise Control and 97.2 percent had air conditioning. Last year for convertible.

1969 Imperial Crown, four-door hardtop sedan, V-8

CROWN IMPERIAL SERIES — SERIES EY-M — The sharp, crisp lines of the last few years were replaced with 'fuselage' styling. Headlights were behind a grille consisting of fine vertical and horizontal pieces, with two larger bars in the center running from end to end. The grille and wraparound signal lights were framed in chrome. Upper signal light level full-length trim and three rectangular safety lights (between the front bumper and front wheel well openings) graced the sides. The rear bumper was integrated into the rear deck and contained the rectangular tail and back-up lights. Standard equipment included power front disc brakes; power steering; power windows; electric clock; carpeting and remote-control outside mirror.

IMPERIAL I.D. NUMBERS: VIN on plate on dash visible through windshield. First symbol: Y=Imperial. Second symbol: M=medium-price Crown Imperial; H=high-price Imperial LeBaron. Third and fourth symbols indicate body style: 23=two-door hardtop; 41=four-door sedan; 43=four-door hardtop. Fifth symbol: K=440 cid V-8; L=High-performance 440 cid V-8. Sixth symbol: 9=1969. Seventh symbol identifies assembly plant: C=Jefferson Plant, Detroit, Mich. Last six symbols are sequential production number. Body number plate under hood gives (SO) schedule date; (NUMBER) body production sequence number; (BDY) body code (column two of charts below); (TRM) trim code; and (PNT) paint code. Engine number on left of block, front, near water pump. Engine code 440 for 440 cid V-8.

CROWN IMPERIAL SERIES

Series Number	Body/Style Number	Body Type & Seating	Factory Price	Shipping Weight	Production Total
EY-M	YM41	4-dr Sed-6P	6411	4741	1,617
EY-M	YL43	4-dr HT-6P	6411	Note 1	823
EY-M	YL23	2-dr HT-6P	6233	Note 1	244

NOTE 1: Not available.

IMPERIAL LeBARON SERIES — SERIES EY-M — The LeBaron came with a vinyl covered roof formal rear window; cloth and leather bench seats and storage compartments in all doors.

IMPERIAL LeBARON SERIES

Series Number	Body/Style Number	Body Type & Seating	Factory Price	Shipping Weight	Production Total
EY-M	YM43	4-dr HT-6P	6772	4801	14,821
EY-M	YM23	2-dr HT-6P	6539	4795	4,572

ENGINE: V-8. Overhead valves. Cast iron block. Displacement: 440 cid. Bore and stroke: 4.32 x 3.75 inches. Compression ratio: 10.1:1. Brake hp: 350 at 4400 rpm. Carburetor: Holley Type four-barrel Model R-4166A.

CHASSIS FEATURES: Wheelbase: 127 inches. Tires: 9.15 x 15.

OPTIONS: Power brakes. Power steering. Air conditioning ($732.05). Automatic beam changer ($51.65). Automatic speed control ($91.75). Rear window defogger ($27). Door edge guards two-doors ($5.20); four-doors ($8.80). Right and left front head restraints ($26.40). Rear seat heater with defroster ($71.65). Front and rear license plate frame ($11.80). Carpet protection mats ($13.75). Outside right manual mirror ($7.35). Power door locks two-doors ($47.90); four-doors ($70.70). Six-Way left power seat ($108.55). Six-Way driver and passenger power seat ($217.10). Six-Way bench power seat ($122.35). Power trunk lid release ($30.50). Power vent windows ($73.85). AM Touch-Tuner radio with rear speaker and power antenna ($165.45). AM/FM Touch-Tuner radio with rear speaker and power antenna ($234.35). Multiplex AM/FM stereo tape with five speakers and power antenna ($350.70). Safeguard sentinel lighting ($36.10). Leather bucket seats ($361.60). Left and rear shoulder belts ($26.80). Spare tire cover ($11.70). Tilt and telescope steering wheel ($96.70). Sure-Grip differential ($58). Tinted glass, all windows ($54.25). Whitewall two-ring fiberglass-belted tires (9.15 x 15). Trailer towing package, models without air conditioning ($65.70). Split bench seats with leather trim ($137.65). Vinyl roof ($152.05). Trailer towing package, models with air conditioning ($55.10) TorqueFlite transmission was standard.

HISTORICAL FOOTNOTES: Only 12.3 percent of 1969 Imperials came with bucket seats, 99.7 percent had a radio, 96 percent had a vinyl roof and 61.3 percent had a tilting steering wheel.

1970 IMPERIAL

1971 IMPERIAL

CROWN IMPERIAL SERIES — SERIES FY-L — Styling changes for 1970 were mild. The four headlights were hidden behind a new, full-width grille of a grid pattern. A double pinstripe ran from upper signal light level to the rear bumper. There was a full-length lower body molding and a rectangular side marker light (located between the front bumper and front wheelwell opening). The rear side marker lights were incorporated into the bumpers and the taillights were decorated with thin chrome pieces. Standard equipment included power windows; trip odometer; electric clock; undercoating; and pile carpeting.

IMPERIAL I.D. NUMBERS: VIN on plate on dash visible through windshield. First symbol: Y=Imperial. Second symbol: M= medium-price Crown Imperial; H=high-price Imperial LeBaron. Third and fourth symbols indicate body style: 23=two-door hardtop; 43=four-door hardtop. Fifth symbol: T=440 cid V-8; U=High-performance 440 cid V-8. Sixth symbol: 0=1970. Seventh symbol identifies assembly plant: C=Jefferson Plant, Detroit, Mich. Last six symbols are sequential production number. Body number plate under hood gives (SO) schedule date; (NUMBER) body production sequence number; (BDY) body code (column two of charts below); (TRM) trim code; and (PNT) paint code. Engine number on left of block, front, near water pump. Engine code 440 for 440 cid V-8.

CROWN IMPERIAL SERIES

Series Number	Body/Style Number	Doors/Style Seating	Factory Price	Shipping Weight	Production Total
FY-L	YL43	4-dr HT-6P	5956	4775	1,333
FY-L	YL23	2-dr HT-6P	5779	4640	254

1970 Imperial LeBaron, two-door hardtop coupe, V-8

IMPERIAL LeBARON SERIES — SERIES FY-M — Outside of a standard vinyl roof, formal rear window and more luxurious cloth and leather interior, there was little difference between the Imperial LeBaron and Crown Imperial.

IMPERIAL LeBARON SERIES

Series Number	Body/Style Number	Doors/Style Seating	Factory Price	Shipping Weight	Production Total
FY-M	YM43	4-dr HT-6P	6328	4785	8,426
FY-M	YM23	2-dr HT-6P	6095	4665	1,803

ENGINE: V-8. Overhead valves. Cast iron block. Displacement: 440 cubic inches. Bore and stroke: 4.32 x 3.75 inches. Compression ratio: 9.70:1. Brake hp: 350 at 4400 rpm. Carburetor: four-barrel.

CHASSIS FEATURES: Wheelbase: 127 inches. Overall length: 229.7 inches. Tires: L78x15.

OPTIONS: Power brakes. Power steering. Air conditioning ($474.95). Dual Air conditioning ($713.53). Air conditioning with automatic temperature control ($493.45). Dual air conditioning with automatic temperature control ($732.05). Automatic beam changer ($51.65). Automatic speed control ($91.75). Rear-window defogger ($31.75). Door edge guards, two-doors ($5.20); four doors ($8.80). Evaporative emissions control ($38.35). Rear seat heater with defroster ($75.90). Front and rear license plate frame ($11.80). Accessory floor mats ($13.75). Outside right manual mirror ($7.35). Power door locks, in two-doors ($47.90); in four-doors ($70.70). Six-Way left power seat ($108.55). Six-Way driver and passenger power seat ($217.10). Six-Way bench power seat ($122.35). Power trunk lid release ($33.45). Power vent windows ($73.85). AM Touch-Tuner radio with floor tuning switch rear speaker and concealed antenna ($165.45). AM/FM Touch-Tuner with floor tuning switch, rear speaker and concealed antenna ($234.35). Multiplex AM/FM stereo type, with five speakers and concealed antenna ($403.75). Safeguard sentinel lighting ($36.10). Leather bucket seats ($361.60). Left and right rear shoulder belts ($26.80). Spare tire cover ($11.70). Tilt and telescope steering wheel ($96.70). Sure-Grip differential ($58.00). Tinted glass, all windows ($55.60). Whitewall L78-15 fiberglass-belted tires ($46.45). Trailer towing package ($56.35). Split bench seat with leather trim in LeBaron four-door hardtop ($137.65). Vinyl roof ($54.70). Vinyl bodyside protection moldings ($15.00). TorqueFlite transmission was standard.

HISTORICAL FOOTNOTES: The 1970 Imperials were introduced Sept. 23, 1969. Calendar year sales hit 10,555 units against a 12 month production total of 10,111 cars (.15 percent penetration rate). On a model year basis, 11,816 Imperials left the assembly line, a whopping increase from 1969. Of these, some 1,600 were Crowns and 10,200 LeBarons. Lynn A. Townsend remained at the helm of Chrysler Corp., while R.D. McLaughlin, who held the title of General Sales Manager, was the top-ranked executive at Chrysler-Plymouth Div. On a model year basis, 90 percent of Imperial Crowns and 97.5 percent of LeBarons had power seats in 1970.

1971 Imperial LeBaron, four-door hardtop sedan, V-8

IMPERIAL LeBARON SERIES — SERIES FY-L — Imperial was down to one series this year. Styling changes were minimal. There were rectangular headlight doors on the grille. The Imperial name was printed on the face of the hood. The front side marker lights were divided into a square amber section and a rectangular white section. Imperial was printed on the rear quarter panels, above full-length, upper tire-level moldings. The LeBaron name was written on the roof quarter panels. Among the standard features were cloth and leather individual adjustable seats (with passenger side recliner); switch-operated rear reading lights; door assist handles; buried walnut instrument panel; power windows; power steering; power disc brakes; fender skirts; vinyl roof and rim-blow steering wheel.

IMPERIAL I.D. NUMBERS: VIN on plate on left top of dash visible through windshield. First symbol: Y=Imperial. Second symbol: M=medium-price Imperial LeBaron. Third and fourth symbols indicate body style: 23=two-door hardtop; 43=four-door hardtop. Fifth symbol: T=440 cid V-8; U=High-performance 440 cid V-8. Sixth symbol: 1=1971. Seventh symbol identifies assembly plant: C=Jefferson Plant, Detroit, Mich. Last six symbols are sequential production number. Body number plate under hood gives schedule date, body production sequence number, body code (column two of chart below), trim and paint data. Engine number on left of block, front, near water pump. Engine code 440 for 440 cid V-8.

IMPERIAL LeBARON SERIES

Series Number	Body/Style Number	Body Type & Seating	Factory Price	Shipping Weight	Production Total
GY-M	YM43	4-dr HT-6P	6276	4855	10,116
GY-M	YM23	2-dr HT-6P	6044	4705	1,442

ENGINE: V-8. Overhead valves. Cast iron block. Displacement: 440 cid. Bore and stroke: 4.32 x 3.75 inches. Compression ratio: 8.80:1. Brake hp: 335 at 4400 rpm.

CHASSIS FEATURES: Wheelbase: 127 inches. Overall length: 229.5 inches. Front tread: 62.4 inches. Rear tread: 62 inches. Tries: J78 x 15.

OPTIONS: Air conditioning ($489.95). Dual air conditioning ($72&8.60). Air conditioning with automatic temperature controls ($508.45). Dual air conditioning with automatic temperature control ($747.10). Automatic beam changer ($51.70). Automatic speed control ($95.10). Rear window defogger ($31.80). Door edge protectors, on two-doors ($6.55); on four-doors ($11.80). Power door locks, on two-doors ($50.35); on four-doors ($74.30). Engine block heater ($15.75). Exhaust emission control ($13.10). Accessory floor mats ($15.95). Four wheel Sure-Brake ($351.50). Glass tinted all windows ($58.45). Rear seat heater and defroster ($79.75). Front and rear license plate frames ($11.30). Safeguard sentinel lighting ($38.00). Right manual mirror ($7.75). Microphone ($11.80). AM/FM search tuner radio ($250.20). AM/FM stereo radio ($308.20). AM/FM stereo with stereo tape cassette ($445.95). AM/FM stereo with 8-track ($419.70). Six-Way power bench seat, in two-doors ($122.45). Six-Way left-hand power 50/50 seat, in four-doors ($114.05). Six-Way power bucket seat or 50/50 left or right unit ($228.10). Rear shoulder belts ($26.85). Spare-tire cover ($12.35). Tilt and telescope steering wheel ($96.75). Power operated sun roof (two-doors) ($597.55). Sure-Grip differential ($58.05). Whitewall bias-belted tires L84 x 15 ($46.35). Trailer towing package ($59.20). Interior trim, two-door with leather bucket seats ($380.35). Interior trim, four-door with leather trim split bench seat ($157.40). Power trunk lid release ($33.45). Vent windows, in four-doors ($87.20). Headlamp washer and wipers ($29.65).

1972 IMPERIAL

IMPERIAL LeBARON SERIES — SERIES HY-M — The LeBaron received a new grille for 1972. The Imperial name was taken off the face of the hood and replaced by a small eagle emblem. The front side marker lights were raised a bit. They were now located above the full-length, upper tire level side molding. The rear end styling featured narrow, slanted, vertical rear fender integrated taillights. Among the standard equipment was a vinyl roof, carpeting, power steering, power brakes, air conditioning and power windows. Although engine compression was lowered and motors were de-tuned to meet new federal emissions standards, the 1972 Imperial did offer "anti-skid" brakes as a $250 option. Designed by Bendix, the system available on Imperials led U.S. makes into the "ABS" era.

IMPERIAL I.D. NUMBERS: VIN on plate on left top of dash visible through windshield. First symbol: Y=Imperial. Second symbol: M=medium-price Imperial LeBaron. Third and fourth symbols indicate body style: 23=two-door hardtop; 43=four-door hardtop. Fifth symbol: T=440 cid V-8; U=High-performance 440 cid V-8. Sixth symbol: 2=1972. Seventh symbol identifies assembly plant: C=Jefferson Plant, Detroit, Mich. Last six symbols are sequential production

number. Body number plate under hood gives schedule date, body production sequence number, body code (column two of chart below), trim and paint data. Engine number on left of block, front, near water pump. Engine code 440 for 440 cid V-8.

1972 Imperial LeBaron, two-door hardtop coupe, V-8

IMPERIAL LeBARON SERIES

Series Number	Body/Style Number	Body Type & Seating	Factory Price	Shipping Weight	Production Total
HY-M	YM43	4-dr HT-6P	6762	4955	13,472
HY-M	YM23	2-dr HT-6P	6534	4790	2,322

ENGINE: V-8. Overhead valves. Cast iron block. Displacement: 440 cid. Bore and stroke: 4.32 x 3.75 inches. Compression ratio: 8.20:1. Brake hp: 225 nhp at 4400 rpm. (Net horsepower rating system introduced). Carburetor: four-barrel.

CHASSIS FEATURES: Wheelbase: 127 inches. Overall length: 229.5 inches. Tires: L84 x 15.

OPTIONS: Power brakes, power steering, air conditioning and power windows were standard. Dual control air conditioner ($250.85). Automatic beam changer ($50.60). Automatic speed control ($93.10). Rear window defogger ($35.15). Power door locks, two-doors ($49.30). Four-doors ($72.70). Engine block heater ($15.40). Exhaust emission control system ($28.30). Rear seat heater and defroster ($78.10). Safeguard sentinel lighting ($37.20). AM radio with stereo tape cassette ($271.50). AM/FM radio with five speakers ($301.60). AM/FM stereo with stereo tape cassette ($436.40). AM/FM stereo with 8 track stereo tape ($410.75). AM/FM radio with rear speaker ($244.80). 6-way power bench seat two-doors ($119.80); four-doors ($111.60). 6-way power bucket or 50/50 bench seat ($223.20). Tilt and telescope steering wheel ($94.70). Power-operated sun roof ($584.75). Sure-Grip differential ($18). Four-wheel Sure brake system ($344). Heavy-duty suspension ($18). 2-stripe whitewall tires L84 x 15, bias belted ($45.35). Whitewall tires L84 x 15, steel belted ($79.70). Bench seats with leather trim four-doors ($154); two-doors ($372.20). Bucket seats with leather trim two-doors ($372.20). Power vent windows four-doors ($85.35). Accessory group includes accessory floor mats, carpeted spare tire, right manual outside mirror, door protection guards. Accessory group two-doors without H54 ($41.70); two-doors with H54 ($28.60); four-doors without H54 ($46.90); four-doors with H54 ($34.80). Trailer towing package ($71.70). Automatic transmission standard.

HISTORICAL FOOTNOTES: Most 1972 Imperials. 99.5 percent, were sold with a radio, 78.2 percent had an adjustable steering column, 83.8 percent had speed control, and 11 percent came with bucket seats.

1973 IMPERIAL

LeBARON SERIES — SERIES 3Y-M — The biggest styling changes for the 1973 were a new mesh-pattern grille and front bumper guards. Among the standard equipment were power steering; power brakes; air conditioning; power windows; carpeting and a vinyl roof.

IMPERIAL I.D. NUMBERS: VIN on plate on left top of dash visible through windshield. First symbol: Y=Imperial. Second symbol: M=medium-price Imperial LeBaron. Third and fourth symbols indicate body style: 23=two-door hardtop; 43=four-door hardtop. Fifth symbol: T=440 cid V-8; U=High-performance 440 cid V-8. Sixth symbol: 3=1973. Seventh symbol identifies assembly plant: C=Jefferson Plant, Detroit, Mich. Last six symbols are sequential production number. Body number plate under hood gives schedule date, body production sequence number, body code (column two of chart below), trim and paint data. Engine number on left of block, front, near water pump. Engine code 440 for 440 cid V-8.

IMPERIAL LeBARON SERIES

Series Number	Body/Style Number	Body Type & Seating	Factory Price	Shipping Weight	Production Total
3Y-M	YM43	4-dr HT-6P	7541	4940	14,166
3Y-M	YM23	2-dr HT-6P	7313	4775	2,563

1973 Imperial LeBaron, four-door hardtop sedan, V-8

ENGINE: V-8. Overhead valves. Cast iron block. Displacement: 440 cid. Bore and stroke: 4.32 x 3.75 inches. Compression ratio: 8.20:1. Brake hp: 215 nhp at 3600 rpm. Carburetor: four-barrel.

CHASSIS FEATURES: Wheelbase: 127 inches. Overall length: 229.6 inches. Tires: L84 x 15.

OPTIONS: Automatic transmission, power brakes, power steering, air conditioning were standard. Dual control air conditioner ($250.85). Automatic beam changer ($50.60). Automatic speed control ($93.10). Rear window defogger ($35.15). Power door locks, two-doors ($49.30); four-doors ($72.70). Engine block heater ($15.40). Exhaust emission control system ($28.30). Rear seat heater and defroster ($78.10). Safeguard sentinel lighting ($37.20). AM radio with stereo tape cassette ($271.50). AM/FM radio with five speakers ($301.60). AM/FM stereo with stereo tape cassette ($436.40). AM/FM stereo with 8-track stereo tape ($410.75). Six-Way power bucket or 50/50 bench seat ($223.20). Tilt, telescope steering wheel ($94.70). Power-operated sun roof ($584.75). Sure-Grip differential ($18). Four-wheel Sure Brake system ($344). Heavy-duty suspension ($18). Two-stripe whitewall tires L84 x 15, bias belted ($45.35). Whitewall tires L84 x 15, steel belted ($79.70). Bench seats with leather trim four-doors ($154); two-doors ($372.20). Power vent windows, four-doors ($85.53). Accessory Group includes; accessory floor mats, carpeted spare tire, right manual outside mirror, door protection guards. Accessory group two-doors without H54 ($41.70); Accessory Group, two-doors with H54 ($28.60); Accessory Group, four-doors without H54 ($46.90); Accessory Group, four-doors with H54 ($34.80). Trailer towing package ($71.70). Anti-Lock Brakes ($250).

HISTORICAL FOOTNOTES: Most 1973 Imperials, 97.5 percent had power seats, 99.9 percent had tinted glass and 83.7 percent had a tilting steering wheel.

1974 IMPERIAL

1974 Imperial LeBaron, four-door hardtop sedan, V-8

IMPERIAL LeBARON SERIES — SERIES 4Y-M — The 1974 LeBaron received a major restyling. (At least in the front.) Its narrow, slightly protruding 'waterfall' grille gave it a definite Lincoln-Continental look. The wraparound front signal lights also were similar to Lincoln styling. The vertical slanting taillights resembled, but were larger than, last year's. The circular Imperial emblem was raised from the rear deck panel to the trunk. Standard equipment included power steering; ribbed velour upholstery; windshield washer; four-wheel power disc brakes and power windows. The Crown Coupe, an option for the two-door hardtop, included opera windows and vinyl covering the front portion of the roof. It became available late in the year.

IMPERIAL I.D. NUMBERS: VIN on plate on left top of dash visible through windshield. First symbol: Y=Imperial. Second symbol: M=medium-price Imperial LeBaron. Third and fourth symbols indicate body style: 23=two-door hardtop; 43=four-door hardtop. Fifth symbol: T=440 cid V-8. Seventh symbol identifies assembly plant: C=Jefferson Plant, Detroit, Mich. Last six symbols are sequential production number. Body number plate under hood gives schedule date, body production sequence number, body code (column two of chart below), trim and paint data. Engine number on left of block, front, near water pump. Engine code 440 for 440 cid V-8.

Standard Catalog of American Cars

Model Number	Body/Style Number	Doors/Style Type Seating	Factory Price	Shipping Weight	Production Total
4Y-M	YM43	4-dr HT-6P	7230	4862	10,576
4Y-M	YM23	2-dr HT-6P	7793	4770	3,850
4Y-M	YM23	2-dr Crn Cpe-6P	7856	N/A	57

ENGINE: V-8. Overhead valves. Cast iron block. Displacement: 440 cid. Bore and stroke: 4.32 x 3.75 inches. Compression ratio: 8.20:1. Brake hp: 230 nhp at 4000 rpm. Carburetor: four-barrel.

CHASSIS FEATURES: Wheelbase: 124 inches. Overall length: 231.1 inches. Tires: LR78x15.

OPTIONS: Automatic transmission, power steering, power disc brakes, air conditioning and power windows were standard. Anti-Lock brakes ($250). Automatic beam changer ($53.20). Automatic speed control ($97.95). Rear window defogger ($32.75). Sure-Grip differential ($59.80). Power door locks two-doors ($51.85); four-doors ($76.45). Emission control testing system ($29.70). Engine block heater ($16.15). Locking gas cap ($4.95). Safeguard sentinel lighting ($39.10). AM/FM radio ($194.15). AM/FM search tuner with dual front and rear speakers ($332.80). AM/FM stereo with 8-track stereo tape four speakers ($432.50). Power bench seat, left 50/50 four-doors ($117.45). 50/50 Power bench or power bucket seat, left and right ($234.90). Tilt and telescope steering wheel ($99.60). Power sun roof ($615.65). Security alarm system ($105.20). Heavy-duty shock absorbers ($5.40). Heavy-duty suspension ($18.90). Whitewall steel-belted radial tires LR84 x 15 ($80.60). Leather trim bench seats, in four-doors ($162.10). Power release trunk deck ($34.35). Manual vent windows, in four-door ($35.10). Imperial accessory group: includes accessory floor mats; carpeted spare cover; mirror; right outside rearview mirror and door edge guards, in two-doors ($50.00); in four-doors ($55.55). Trailer towing package ($276.20).

HISTORICAL FOOTNOTES: Most 1974 Imperials, 97.4 percent, came with power seats and 84.1 percent had a tilting steering wheel.

1975 IMPERIAL

IMPERIAL LeBARON SERIES — SERIES 5Y-M — This was the 'last' Imperial... until 1981. Styling was basically the same as in 1974. Power steering; power disc brakes; power windows; air conditioning and tinted glass were among the many standard features. The 'final' Imperial built was a four-door hardtop, Serial Number YM43-T5C-182947.

IMPERIAL I.D. NUMBERS: VIN on plate on left top of dash visible through windshield. First symbol: Y=Imperial. Second symbol: M=medium-price Imperial LeBaron. Third and fourth symbols indicate body style: 23=two-door hardtop; 43=four-door hardtop. Fifth symbol: T=440 cid V-8. Sixth symbol: 5=1975. Seventh symbol identifies assembly plant: C=Jefferson Plant, Detroit, Mich. Last six symbols are sequential production number. Body number plate under hood gives schedule date, body production sequence number, body code (column two of chart below), trim and paint data. Engine number on left of block, front, near water pump. Engine code E-86 for 440 cid V-8.

Series Number	Body/Style Number	Body Type & Seating	Factory Price	Shipping Weight	Production Total
5Y-M	YM43	4-dr HT-6P	9046	5065	6,102
5Y-M	YM23	2-dr HT-6P	8900	4965	1087
5Y-M	YM23	2-dr Crn Cpe-6P	9277	5165	1641

ENGINE: V-8. Overhead valves. Cast iron Block. Displacement: 440 cid. Bore and stroke: 4.32 x 3.75 inches. Compression ratio: 8.20:1 Brake hp: 215 at 4000 rpm. Carburetor: four-barrel.

1975 Imperial LeBaron, two-door hardtop, V-8

CHASSIS FEATURES: Wheelbase: 124 inches. Overall length: 231.1 inches, tires: LR78 x 15.

OPTIONS: Automatic transmission standard. Automatic beam changer ($53.20). Automatic speed control ($97.95). Rear window defogger ($32.75). Sure-Grip differential ($59.80). Power door locks, in two-door ($51.85); in four-door ($76.45). Emission control testing system ($29.70). Engine block heater ($16.15). Locking gas cap ($4.45). Safeguard sentinel lighting ($39.10). AM/FM radio ($194.15). AM/FM search tuner with dual front and rear speakers ($332.80). AM/FM stereo with 8-track stereo tape and four speakers ($432.50). Power bench seat, left 50/50 seat in four-door ($117.45). 50/50 Power bench or power bucket seat, left and right ($234.90). Tilt-telescope steering wheel ($99.60). Power sun roof ($615.65). Security alarm system ($105.20). Heavy-duty shock absorbers ($5.40). Heavy-duty suspension ($18.90). Whitewall steel-belted radial tires LR84 x 15 ($80.60). Leather trim bench seats, in four-doors ($162.10). Power release trunk deck ($34.35). Manual vent windows, in four-door ($35.10). Imperial accessory group: includes accessory floor mats; carpeted spare tire cover; mirror; right outside rearview mirror; door edge guards on two-door ($50.00); on four-doors ($55.55).

HISTORICAL FOOTNOTES: This 'last' Imperial was introduced Oct. 1, 1974. For the 1975 model year, a total or exactly 8,830 Imperials were assembled. Calendar year production was a mere 1,930 units. R.B. McCurry, Jr. was group vice-president for U.S. automotive sales for Chrysler-Plymouth Div. this year. Imperial new car dealer sales, for 1975 models, were recorded as 6,957 units. Lack of sales was the official reason for Imperial's phase-out. Production halted June 12, 1975. The final unit was an Imperial LeBaron four-door hardtop with the serial number given above in the 1975 introduction.

STANDARD CATALOG OF
DESOTO
1946-1961

During the war, DeSoto was responsible for assemblies of fuselage sections for the Martin B-26 Marauder; the manufacture of parts for Bofors antiaircraft cannon; the building of Hell-Diver airplane wings sections and construction of B-29 aircraft nose sections (using parts supplied from Chrysler and Plymouth factory assembly lines). With the end of the war, plans to convert back to a civilian economy were frought with many difficulties. Materials shortages and labor problems. The actual work of converting plants also delayed 1946 model introductions. Finally, in March of that calendar year, the postwar DeSoto arrived.

By Sherwood Kahlenberg

Based on the same body as the short-lived 1942 offering, the latest DeSoto deviated, stylingwise, in a number of areas. There were new front fenders with conventional, exposed headlights; a redesigned grille; redone doors; new bumpers and updated ornamentation. The Suburban was a late addition to the line, arriving in November, 1946. The initial postwar series was carried forth for 1947 and 1948, plus into the first part of the next calendar year, as an early 1949 line.

The updated S-13 models were delayed in production, due to labor unrest in the tooling plants during 1948. Finally, they appeared as second-series 1949 models. These practical, newly-styled automobiles were advertised as, "The Car With

You In Mind." Essentially, this fresh, new postwar look would remain in production through the 1954 model year. There were, however, a number of styling refinements within this period, which paralleled those found in Chrysler counterparts.

The DeSoto FireDome V-8, with its free-breathing, hemispherical-segment shaped combustion chambers, was introduced in 1952. The following year marked the division's 25th Anniversary, which was suitably celebrated by creation of the Adventurer show car. This "dream car" was wrought by Italian coachbuilder Ghia, but based on a near-standard DeSoto FireDome chassis. A number of new options appeared the same season, including refrigerated air conditioning and authentic chrome wire spoke wheels. It was the first time this style of wheel rim had been seen on DeSotos in over 20 years!

For model year 1954, DeSoto sales declined dramatically, despite introduction of PowerFlite two-speed, fully-automatic transmission. This new gearbox, although a giant technical improvement, was priced $45 lower than the inconvenient, semi-automatic unit it replaced. The Adventurer II 'idea car,' with even sleeker design work by Ghia, was heralded as a "Car of the Future," when seen by the public at many new car shows.

A major turning point in the fortunes of the division occurred in 1955, as Chrysler's highly-promoted 'Forward Look' debuted and brought an 85 percent sales boost in

DeSotoLand. The all-modern styling erased the stodgy appearance of the past, replacing it with designs of a new, youthful flair. In some cases, three-tone paint treatments were added for extra buyer appeal. These 'Styled-For-Tomorrow' models helped lead the corporation to a banner sales year and it was hard to imagine that DeSoto had but six years to live.

In 1956, the Adventurer nameplate was seen on a production car for the first time. This was DeSoto's shot at the enthusiast market, shared with such magical MoPar models as the Chrysler 300, Dodge D-500 or Plymouth Fury sport coupe. Other offerings for the year were characterized by a slight styling facelift, front and rear, with a new emphasis placed on the height of tailfins.

The year 1957 saw the DeSoto redesigned again, with even more of an upwards tailfin sweep. Such styling, coupled with a lower bodyside color sweep panel, served to enhance the cars' length and beauty. Sales climbed over the previous season, but not to the same degree as the other Chrysler products' sales improved.

Disastrous sales were the 1958 trend for DeSotos, as production plunged more than 60 percent, to a level not seen since the dark days of 1938. These cars would also be the last company products to leave the famous Wyoming Avenue factory, in Detroit.

Separate body/frame construction was in its final year when the 1959 DeSoto line was introduced. Continuing to be marketed as a specialty model was the low-production Adventurer, which came only fully-equipped and custom finished in specific colors. Sales continued to decline, dropping yet another notch, while Chrysler went forward with plans to integrate DeSoto assemblies with those of the corporation's other automotive divisions. Already, some observers were predicting the demise of the marque and a close to DeSoto history.

Still, the DeSoto was carried into 1960, with production quartered alongside that of Chryslers in the Jefferson Avenue plant. The Unibody method of construction was the primary engineering advance of the year, but could not offset an additional 40 percent falloff over the low totals of 1959.

A 1961 model with restyled headlight, grille and taillight treatments was unveiled in mid-October, but on Nov. 30, 1960, production of the once popular DeSoto automobile came to its end. Noted always for solid value and regarded as a marque 'Built to Last,' the proud DeSoto nameplate had been affixed to a total of 2,024,629 since its inception in the summer of 1928. More than half of these cars were built in the postwar era.

1946 DeSoto, Custom two-door convertible, 6-cyl

1949 DeSoto, Custom four-door sedan, 6-cyl

1947 DeSoto, Custom four-door long wheelbase sedan, 6-cyl
Standard Catalog of American Cars

1949 DeSoto, Custom two-door Club Coupe, 6-cyl

1949 DeSoto, Custom two-door convertible, 6-cyl

1953 DeSoto, Firedome four-door long wheelbase sedan, V-8

1950 DeSoto, Custom four-door sedan, 6-cyl

1957 DeSoto, Firedome Sportsman two-door hardtop, V-8

1951 DeSoto, Custom two-door sedan, 6-cyl

1958 DeSoto, Fireflite Sportsman four-door hardtop, V-8

Standard Catalog of American Cars

1946 DESOTO

DELUXE SERIES — (6-CYL) — The first postwar models were based on the short lived 1942 line. Major changes included new hoods, grilles, wraparound bumpers, front fenders that blended into the doors and redesigned rear fenders. There were additional changes in exterior trim and interior design. Burl and grain garnish moldings, large full vision steering wheels and chrome trim and fine appointments were seen. The hidden headlamps of 1942 were not carried over. An interesting feature was a speedometer that changed colors in increments: green to 39 mph, amber to 50 mph and red at higher speeds. The body structure was all-steel, a longtime Chrysler Corporation characteristic. Separate chassis/frame construction was used. Body insulation included the interior structure of the body, roof, side panels, floor, cowl and trunk. Postwar developments were Safe Guard hydraulic brakes and a permanent Oilite fuel tank filter. Rustproofing now protected even the interior structure of the body. Identification of series was provided by nameplates found on the sides of the hood. Standard equipment on Deluxes included dual sun visors, dual two-speed electric wipers, directional signals with parking brake light, cigar lighter, illuminated glove box with lock, dual outside door locks, map light, counter balanced luggage compartment lid, illuminated luggage compartment, right and left front door armrests, interior door locks and bumper guards front and rear.

DESOTO SERIES I.D. NUMBERS: Early 1946 cars had serial number codes on right front door door hinge pillar post. After March 1, 1946 on left front door hinge pillar post. Letters shown in midsection of lines, before the serial numbers, identified the assembly plant as follows: D=Detroit, Mich.; LA=Los Angeles, Calif.; W=Windsor, Ontario, Canada. These letters were not part of the serial number. Serial numbers 6,154,001 to 6,172,862 appeared on Deluxes. Serial numbers 5,784,001 to 5,825,784 appeared on Customs. Serial numbers 5,102,501 to 5,105,413 appeared on taxis. Motor numbers were located on the left side of the block below cylinder head between first and second cylinders. Motor numbers ran from S111,001 up.

DELUXE SERIES

Model Number	Body/Style Number	Body Type & Seating	Factory Price	Shipping Weight	Production Total
S11S	Note 1	2-dr Cpe-3P	1315	3257	(1,950)
S11S	Note 1	2-dr Clb Cpe-6P	1435	3347	(8,580)
S11S	Note 1	2-dr Sed-6P	1410	3352	(12,751)
S11S	Note 1	4-dr Sed-6P	1445	3382	(32,213)

NOTE 1: Owners seeking parts were advised: "There is no way to positively identify the type of body. When in doubt specify vehicle serial number and vehicle body number in ordering parts."
NOTE 2: Production totals are in parenthesis because they are combined totals for 1946, 1947, 1948 and early (first series) 1949 models. DeSoto recorded these only as a combined total, with no model year breakouts.

ENGINE: L-head. Six-cylinder. Cast iron block. Displacement: 236.7 cid. Bore and stroke: 3.438 x 4.25 inches. Compression ratio: 6.6:1. Brake hp: 109 at 3600 rpm. Four main bearings. Solid valve lifters. Carburetors: (Taxicab) B-B EL1L or EX3R; (Fluid Drive and Vacumatic) B-B EV1 or B-B EV2 or E7L4; (Standard transmission) B-B EX1, B-B EX2 or B-B EX3.

1946 DeSoto, four-door nine-passenger Suburban, 6-cyl (AA)

CUSTOM SERIES — (6-CYL) — Custom models were clearly identified by the nameplates on the sides of the hood. The front compartment was equipped with tailored carpets and chrome plated window sashes. Front seat cushions included a foam rubber pad. The Custom represented an upgraded, high-line version of the Deluxe. A suburban was added to the Custom line in November, 1946. Delon plastic upholstery was featured. Standard equipment on Customs included white plastic trim rings (prior to introduction of white sidewall tires), plastic steering wheel, foam rubber seat cushions and tailored front carpets. Three colors of broadcloth upholstery were available: green, blue and tan. The convertible coupe had Bedford cord and leather in various colors.

CUSTOM SERIES

Model Number	Body Style Number	Body Type & Seating	Factory Price	Shipping Weight	Production Total
(Standard Wheelbase)					
S11C	Note 1	2-dr Clb Cpe-6P	1485	3337	(38,720)
S11C	Note 1	2-dr Conv Cpe-6P	1745	3575	(8,100)
S11C	Note 1	2-dr Sed-6P	1475	3377	(1,600)
S11C	Note 1	4-dr Sed-6P	1495	3390	(126,226)
(Long Wheelbase)					
S11C	Note 1	4-dr Sub-8P	2175	4000	(7,500)
S11C	Note 1	4-dr Sedan-8P	1875	3837	(3,530)
S11C	Note 1	4-dr Limo-8P	1995	3937	(120)

NOTE 1: See 1946 DeSoto Deluxe Series specifications chart. Eight-passenger models were on the long wheelbase chassis.
NOTE 2: Production totals are in parenthesis because they are combined totals for 1946, 1947, 1948 and early (first series) 1949 models. DeSoto recorded these only as a combined total, with no model year breakouts.

ENGINE: L-head. Six-cylinder. Cast iron block. Displacement: 236.7 cid. Bore and stroke: 3.438 x 4.25 inches. Compression ratio: 6.6: 1. Brake hp: 109 at 3600 rpm. Four main bearings. Solid valve lifters. Carburetors: (Fluid Drive and Vacumatic) B-B EV1 or B-B EV2 or E7L4; (Standard transmission) B-B EX1, B-B EX2 or B-B EX3.

CHASSIS FEATURES: Wheelbase: (Long wheelbase models) 139-1/2 inches; (All others) 121-1/2 inches. Tires: Long wheelbase cars used 6.50 x 16 tires until car number 5802797 and 7.00 x 15 tires thereafter. Short wheelbase cars used 6.50 x 16 tires. Whitewalls were not available in 1946. Three-speed manual transmission was standard in Deluxes. Gyrol Fluid Drive with Tip-Toe Shift four-speed was standard in customs and optional in Deluxes.

HISTORICAL FOOTNOTES: Calendar year production was 62,368 units, making DeSoto the 13th largest automaker in the U.S. The model year started on March 1, 1946 for DeSoto. The company produced only 2.8 percent of the nation's cars.

1947 DESOTO

1947 DeSoto, Deluxe three-passenger coupe, 6-cyl (AA)

DELUXE SERIES — (6-CYL) — There were virtually no changes in the 1947 DeSoto models. Prices for Deluxe editions were slightly changed and published specifications charts indicate that a weight increase of just a few pounds was registered. Whitewall tires were reintroduced, as an option, after April 1, 1947. Standard equipment features remained as before.

DESOTO I.D. NUMBERS: Serial number codes on left door hinge pillar post. Letters shown in midsection of lines, before the serial numbers, identified the assembly plant as follows: D=Detroit, Mich.; LA=Los Angeles, Calif.; W=Windsor, Ontario, Canada. These letters were not part of the serial number. Serial numbers 6,172,863 to 6,190,369 appeared on Deluxes. Serial numbers 5,825,785 to 5,885,815 appeared on Customs. Serial numbers 5,102,501 to 5,105,413 appeared on taxis. Motor numbers were located on the left side of the block below cylinder head between first and second cylinders. Motor numbers ran from S111,001 up.

DELUXE SERIES

Model Number	Body/Style Number	Body Type & Seating	Factory Price	Shipping Weight	Production Total
S11s	Note 1	2-dr Coupe-3P	1331	3303	(1,950)
S11S	Note 1	2-dr Clb Cpe-6P	1451	3393	(8,580)
S11S	Note 1	2-dr Sed-6P	1426	3398	(12,751)
S11S	Note 1	4-dr Sed-6P	1461	3428	(32,213)

NOTE 1: Owners were again advised that there was no way to positively identify the type of body by code numbers.
NOTE 2: Production totals are in parenthesis because they are combined totals for 1946, 1947, 1948 and early (first series) 1949 models. DeSoto recorded these only as a combined total, with no model year breakouts.

ENGINE: L-head. Six-cylinder. Cast iron block. Displacement: 236.6 cid. Bore and stroke: 3.438 x 4.25 inches. Compression ratio: 6.6: 1. Brake hp: 109 at 3600 rpm. Four main bearings. Solid valve lifters. Carburetors: (Taxicab) B-B EL1L or EX3R; (Fluid Drive and Vacumatic) B-B EV1 or B-B EV2 or E7L4; (Standard transmission) B-B EX1, B-B EX2 or B-B EX3.

1947 DeSoto, Custom four-door sedan, 6-cyl (AA)

CUSTOM SERIES — (6-CYL) — Custom models were indiscernible from their 1946 counterparts. Once again, prices and weights were slightly increased. Custom models were basically Deluxes with upgraded trim and appointments, except in the case of the long wheelbase models, which were totally distinctive offerings built off a stretched platform.

CUSTOM SERIES

Model Number	Body/Style Number	Body Type & Seating	Factory Price	Shipping Weight	Production Total
(Standard Wheelbase)					
S11C	Note 1	2-dr Clb Cpe-6P	1501	3378	(38,720)
S11C	Note 1	2-dr Conv Cpe-5P	1761	3618	(8,100)
S11C	Note 1	2-dr Sed-6P	1491	3423	(1,600)
S11C	Note 1	4-dr Sed-6P	1511	3433	(126,226)
(Long Wheelbase)					
S11C	Note 1	4-dr Sedan-7P	1893	3837	(3,530)
S11C	Note 1	4-dr Limo-7P	2013	3995	(120)
S11C	Note 1	4-dr Sub-9P	2193	4012	(7,500)

NOTE 1: Owners were again advised that there was no way to positively identify the type of body through code numbers.
NOTE 2: Production totals are in parenthesis because they are combined totals for 1946, 1947, 1948 and early (first series) 1949 models. DeSoto recorded these only as a combined total, with no model year breakouts.

ENGINE: L-head. Six-cylinder. Cast iron block. Displacement: 236.6 cid. Bore and stroke: 3.438 x 4.25 inches. Compression ratio: 6.6:1. Brake hp: 109 at 3600 rpm. Four main bearings. Solid valve lifters. Carburetors: (Fluid Drive and Vacumatic) B-B EV1 or B-B EV2 or E7L4; (Standard transmission) B-B EX1, B-B EX2 or B-B EX3.

CHASSIS FEATURES: Wheelbase: (Long wheelbase models) 139-1/2 inches; (All others) 121-1/2 inches. Tires: Long wheelbase cars now used 7.00 x 15 inch tires. Short wheelbase cars again used 6.50 x 16 inch tires, switching to 7.60 x 15 late in the year. Whitewalls became available (optionally) in mid-1947. Three-speed manual transmission was standard. Fluid Drive was optional. Fluid Drive with Tip-Toe shift was $121 extra.

HISTORICAL FOOTNOTES: Calendar year production of 82,232 cars put DeSoto in 14th rank in the auto industry. The DeSoto model year started Jan. 1, 1947 and corresponded with the calendar year. In April, 1947, white sidewall tires were returned to the optional equipment list.

1948 DESOTO

DELUXE SERIES — (6-CYL) — Minimal physical change marked the DeSoto S-11 models built in the final production run, although rather steep price increases and decreases in weights were recorded. They averaged $298 and 38 pounds. Low-pressure tires were adopted and stainless steel wheel beauty rings were seen, after the use of white plastic 'whitewalls' was dropped. Cars built after December 1, 1948 were officially considered as 1949 models, although the only difference from previous offerings was the serial numbers used.

DESOTO I.D. NUMBERS: Serial number codes on left door hinge pillar post. Letters shown in midsection of lines, before the serial numbers, identified the assembly plant as follows: D=Detroit, Mich.; LA=Los Angeles, Calif.; W=Windsor, Ontario. These letters were not part of the serial number. Serial numbers 6,190,370 to 6,209,494 appeared on Deluxes. Serial numbers 5,885,816 to 5,962,601 appeared on Customs made in Detroit; 62,001,001 to 62,001,894 on Customs made in Los Angeles. Effective Dec. 1, 1948 Detroit-built Deluxes with serial numbers 6205976 to 6209494 were considered 1949 models for purposes of registration only. Effective the same date, Customs with serial numbers 5,948,453 to 5,962,601 were considered 1949 models for purposes of registration only. Serial numbers 5,102,501 to 5,105,413 appeared on taxis. Motor numbers were located on the left side of the block below cylinder head between first and second cylinders. Motor numbers continued from 1946-1947.

DELUXE SERIES

Model Number	Body/Style Number	Body Type & Seating	Factory Price	Shipping Weight	Production Total
S11S	Note 1	2-dr Cpe-3P	1699	3285	(1,950)
S11S	Note 1	2-dr Clb Cpe-6P	1815	3385	(8,580)
S11S	Note 1	2-dr Sed-6P	1788	3375	(12,751)
S11S	Note 1	4-dr Sed-6P	1825	3435	(32,213)
S11S	Note 1	4-dr Cal. Taxi-6P	NA	NA	(11,600)

NOTE 1: Owners were again advised that there was no way to positively identify the type of body by code numbers.
NOTE 2: Production totals are in parenthesis because they are combined totals for 1946, 1947, 1948 and early (first series) 1949 models. DeSoto recorded these only as a combined total, with no model year breakouts.

ENGINE: L-head. Six-cylinder. Cast iron block. Displacement: 236.6 cid. Bore and stroke: 3.438 x 4.25 inches. Compression ratio: 6.6:1. Brake hp: 109 at 3600 rpm. Four main bearings. Solid valve lifters. Carburetors: (Taxicab) B-B EL1L or EX3R; (Fluid Drive and Vacumatic) B-B EV1 or B-B EV2 or E7L4; (Standard transmission) B-B EX1, B-B EX2 or B-B EX3.

1948 DeSoto, Custom two-door Club coupe, 6-cyl

CUSTOM SERIES — (6-CYL) — There were virtually no differences, externally, between 1946-1947 DeSoto Custom models and their 1948 counterparts. Low-pressure tires were adopted for standard wheelbase models.

CUSTOM SERIES

Model Number	Body/Style Number	Body Type & Seating	Factory Price	Shipping Weight	Production Total
(Standard Wheelbase)					
S11C	Note 1	4-dr Sed-6P	1892	3439	(126,226)
S11C	Note 1	2-dr Sed-6P	1860	3399	(1,600)
S11C	Note 1	2-dr Club-Cpe-6P	1874	3389	(38,720)
S11C	Note 1	2-dr Conv Cpe-6P	2296	3599	(8,100)
(Long Wheelbase)					
S11C	Note 1	4-dr Sedan-7P	2315	3819	(3,530)
S11C	Note 1	4-dr Limo-7P	2442	3995	(120)
S11C	Note 1	4-dr Sub-9P	2631	3974	(7,500)
S11C	Note 1	Chassis Only	NA	NA	(105)

NOTE 1: Owners were again advised that there was no way to positively identify the type of body by code numbers.
NOTE 2: Production totals are in parenthesis because they are combined totals for 1946, 1947, 1948 and early (first series) 1949 models. DeSoto recorded these only as a combined total, with no model year breakouts. Chassis only were supplied to professional car makers.

ENGINE: L-head. Six-cylinder. Cast iron block. Displacement: 236.6 cid. Bore and stroke: 3.438 x 4.25 inches. Compression ratio: 6.6:1. Brake hp: 109 at 3600 rpm. Four main bearings. Solid valve lifters. Carburetors: (Taxicab) B-B EL1L or EX3R; (Fluid Drive and Vacumatic) B-B EV1 or B-B EV2 or E7L4; (Standard transmission) B-B EX1, B-B EX2 or B-B EX3.

CHASSIS FEATURES: Wheelbase: (Long wheelbase models) 139-1/2 inches; (All others) 121-1/2 inches. Tires: Long wheelbase cars used 7.00 x 15 size tires; Short wheelbase cars used 7.60 x 15 size tires, which were adopted late in 1947. Three-speed manual transmission was standard. Fluid Drive with Tip-Toe shift transmission was available at $121 extra.

HISTORICAL FOOTNOTES: The model year started Jan. 1, 1948, corresponding directly with the calendar year. Calendar year production of 93,369 cars put DeSoto in 15th rank in the industry.

1949 DESOTO

DELUXE SERIES — (6-CYL) — The 1946-'48 models were carried over during the first part of the model year. Those built from Dec. 1, 1948 to about March 1, 1949 (when the new, redesigned models appeared) are known as first-series 1949s. The second series 1949 DeSoto line featured an all-new postwar body shell and was marketed as "The Car Designed With You In Mind." Styling was characterized by sheet metal panels with shorter overhangs front and rear. When coupled with the new, taller roof structure, this gave the second series 1949 models a short, stubby look. A tooth-like grille theme was adopted and had a noticeable peak in line with the front of the hood. Conventional bustleback contours were seen where the roofline ended at the deck lid. The rear license plate was mounted in a slightly recessed housing on the deck lid. Taillamps were set into long, narrow housings attached atop the rear fenders. A totally new style was called the Carry-All Sedan. It featured a modified. fold-down rear seat which, when folded, provided nearly eight-feet of storage space from the rear of the body to the rear of the front seatback. The station wagon was a new addition to the DeSoto line; the first body of this type seen since the Cantrell bodied chassis of the 1930s. It did not enter production until July. The wagon featured steel body construction with ash wood exterior framing. The convertible came with a full-width vinyl rear window.

DESOTO I.D. NUMBERS: Serial numbers were located on the left front door hinge pillar post. Letters shown in midsection of lines, identified the assembly plant as follows: D=Detroit, Mich.; LA=Los Angeles, Calif.; W=Windsor, Ontario, Canada. These letters were not part of the serial number. Deluxes built in Detroit used numbers 6212001 to 6232740; those built in Los Angeles used 60002001 to 600004755. Taxis were numbered 5115001 to 5115680. Customs built in Detroit used numbers 500001001 to 50061189; those built in Los Angeles used numbers 620004001 to 62011187. Motor numbers were located on the left side of the block below cylinder head between first and second cylinders. Motor numbers began with S13-1001 and ran through S13-93581.

DELUXE SERIES

Model Number	Body/Style Number	Body Type & Seating	Factory Price	Shipping Weight	Production Total
S13-1	Note 1	2-dr Clb Cpe-6P	1871	3455	6,807
S13-1	Note 1	4-dr Sed-6P	1881	3520	13,148
S13-1	Note 1	4-dr Carry-All-6P	2075	3455	2,690
S13-1	Note 1	4-dr Sta Wag 9P	2805	3915	850

NOTE 1: Owners were again advised that there was no way to positively identify the type of body by code number. The production figures include 680 taxicabs in the Deluxe line.

ENGINE: L-head. Six-cylinder. Cast iron block. Displacement: 236.7 cid. Bore and stroke: 3.438-x 4.25 inches. Compression ratio: 7.00:1. Brake hp: 112. Carburetor: (Standard shift) Ball and Ball model B-B EXLR or B-B EX2R; (Fluid Drive or M-6 transmission) Ball and Ball model B-B E7LI-L2.

CUSTOM SERIES — (6-CYL) — The new Custom line was externally identified by extra chrome trim. It consisted of two short strips mounted low on front fenders, behind the wheel opening. The interior was enriched, with a rear armrest as an option. Fluid Drive and Tip-Toe shift transmission were standard features. The Suburban had a roof mounted luggage rack as standard equipment. Production began late, due to a strike affecting tooling in 1948.

CUSTOM SERIES

Model Number	Body/Style Number	Body Type & Seating	Factory Price	Shipping Weight	Production Total
(Standard Wheelbase)					
S13-2	Note 1	2-dr Clb Cpe-6P	2042	3585	18,431
S13-2	Note 1	2-dr Conv Cpe-6P	2443	3785	3,385
S13-2	Note 1	4-dr Sed-6P	2059	3645	48,589
(Long Wheelbase)					
S13-2	Note 1	4-dr Sed-8P	2863	4200	342
S13-2	Note 1	4-dr Sub-9P	3179	4410	129

NOTE 1: Owners were again advised that there was no way to positively identity the type of body by code number.

ENGINE: L-head. Six-cylinder. Cast iron block. Displacement: 236.7 cid. Bore and stroke: 3.438-x 4.25 inches. Compression ratio: 7.00:1. Brake hp: 112. Carburetor: (Standard shift) Ball and Ball model B-B EXLR or B-B EX2R; (Fluid Drive or M-6 transmission) Ball and Ball model B-B E7LI-L2.

CHASSIS FEATURES: Wheelbase (Long wheelbase models) 139.5 inches; (All others) 125.5 inches. Tires: 7.60 x 15 for all standard wheelbase models; 8.20 x 15 for others. Three-speed manual transmission was standard on Deluxes. Tip-Toe Hydraulic shift with Gyrol Fluid Drive was standard equipment on Customs and $121 extra on Deluxes.

HISTORICAL FOOTNOTES: Calendar year production of 107,174 cars registered as 1949 models put DeSoto in 13th spot in the U.S. auto production race.

1950 DESOTO

DELUXE SERIES — (6-CYL) — A minor facelift on the previous year's model was advertised as the "New DeSoto" and referred to as a "car built for owner satisfaction." The rear fenders now had a peaked design, as the only change in the sheetmetal. Grille textures and ornamentation features were slightly revised. An easy way to spot cars built to 1950 specifications is to look for the body color vertical grille divider, which was unlike any previous or later DeSoto design. Series identification was carried on a plate at the top front of the front doors.

1950 DeSoto, Custom two-door club coupe, 6-cyl.

DESOTO I.D. NUMBERS: Serial numbers were located on the left front door hinge pillar post. Letters shown in midsection of lines, before the serial numbers, identified the assembly plant as follows: D=Detroit, Mich.; LA=Los Angeles, Calif.; W=Windsor, Ontario, Canada. These letters were not part of the serial number. Deluxes built in Detroit had serial numbers 6233501 to 6262653; those built in Los Angeles had serial numbers 60005001 to 60009175. Taxis were numbered 5116001 to 5118350. Customs built in Detroit had serial numbers 50062001 to 50148412. Cars built in Los Angeles had serial numbers 62011501 to 62023225. Motor numbers were located on the left side of the block below cylinder head between first and second cylinders. Motor numbers began with S13-1001 and ran through S13-93581.

DELUXE SERIES

Model Number	Body/Style Number	Body Type & Seating	Factory Price	Shipping Weight	Production Total
(Standard Wheelbase)					
S14-1	Note 1	2-dr Club Cpe-6P	1976	3450	10,703
S14-1	Note 1	4-dr Sed-6P	19860	3525	18,489
S14-1	Note 1	4-dr Carry-All-6P	2191	3600	3,900
(Long Wheel base)					
S14-1	Note 1	4-dr Sed-8P	2676	3995	235

NOTE 1: Code numbers identifying body style were not used.
NOTE 2: The production totals above include 2,350 taxicabs in the Deluxe series.

ENGINE: L-head. Six-cylinder. Cast iron block. Displacement 236.7 inches. Bore and stroke: 3.438 x 4.25 in. Compression ratio: 7.0:1. Brake hp: 112 at 3600 rpm. Carburetor: (Fluid Drive or M-6) B-B E7L3 or B-B E7L4; (Standard transmission) EX2R or EX3R.

1950 DeSoto, four-door Custom eight-passenger sedan, 6-cyl (AA)

CUSTOM SERIES — (6-CYL) — The Custom series reflected the same minor styling changes seen on 1950 Deluxe models. Identification could be made by spotting the word Custom on front doors of all styles, except the Suburban, which featured suitable identification letters. The word Sportsman appeared on this hardtop model. Factory literature showed the lettering under the vent window, although there are photos of cars with the name on the door. The Sportsman was an all-new, two-door pillarless coupe. Another innovation seen on the Suburban was all-steel panel construction. Whitewalls and full wheelcovers were standard on the Sportsman and the convertible coupe.

CUSTOM SERIES

Model Number	Body/Style Number	Body Type & Seating	Factory Price	Shipping Weight	Production Total
(Standard Wheelbase)					
S14-2	Note 1	4-dr Sed-6P	2174	3640	72,664
S14-2	Note 1	2-dr Clb Cpe-6P	2156	3575	6,100
S14-2	Note 1	2-dr SptMn HT-6P	2489	3735	4,600
S14-2	Note 1	2-dr Conv Cpe-6P	2578	3815	2,900
S14-2	Note 1	4-dr Sta Wag-6P	3093	4035	600
S14-2	Note 1	4-dr Stl Sta Wag-6P	2717	3900	100
(Long Wheelbase)					
S14-2	Note I	4-dr Sed-8P	2863	4115	734
S14-2	Note 1	4-dr Sub-8P	3179	4400	623

NOTE 1: Code numbers identifying body style were not used.

ENGINE: L-head. Six-cylinder. Cast iron block. Displacement 236.7 inches. Bore and stroke: 3.438 x 4.25 in. Compression ratio: 7.0:1. Brake hp: 112 at 3600 rpm. Carburetor: (Fluid Drive or M-6) B-B E7L3 or B-B E7L4; (Standard transmission) EX2R or EX3R.

CHASSIS FEATURES: Wheelbase (Long wheelbase models) 139.5 inches; (All others) 125.5 inches. Tires: 7.60 x 15 for all standard wheelbase models; 8.20 x 15 for others. Three-speed manual transmission was standard on Deluxes. Tip-Toe Hydraulic shift with Gyrol Fluid Drive was standard equipment on Customs and $121 extra on Deluxes.

OPTIONS: Tip-Toe Hydraulic Shift with Gyrol Fluid Drive on Deluxe models ($121): standard on Custom models. Radio. Heater. Chrome full wheelcovers. Directional signals (Del.). Back-up lights (Del.). Whitewalls. Electric clock. Lighted hood ornament. Two-tone paint.

HISTORICAL FOOTNOTES: DeSoto came in 14th in the production race with 127,430 assemblies for the 1950 calendar year.

1951 DESOTO

DELUXE SERIES — (6-CYL) — The 1951 DeSoto S15 lineup continued with the same models as the previous year. The most noticeable of several obvious, but not major, design changes was a re-shaped hood that sloped towards a flatter, broader looking grille. A more massive front bumper was adopted along with rounder front fender contours. Deluxe models lacked front door nomenclature and came standard with small hubcaps. Equipment highlights included Oriflow shock absorbers; high-compression motor; Floating Power engine mounts; 'Featherlight' steering; long wheelbase stance; chair-high seating; Hotchkiss drive; super rim wheels; Safety Cushion tires; Big 12-inch brakes: new parking brakes: heavy-duty generator; hypoid rear axle; removable bearings; full-length engine water jacket; Synchromesh silent gears; roller bearing universals; Oilite gas filter; oil bath air cleaner and automatic choke. A wood grained dashboard was standard on closed cars.

DESOTO I.D. NUMBERS: Serial numbers were located on the left front door hinge pillar post. Letters shown in midsection of lines, before the serial numbers, identified the assembly plant as follows: D=Detroit, Mich.; LA=Los Angeles, Calif.; W=Windsor, Ontario, Canada. These letters were not part of the serial number. Only serial numbers were to be used for identification purposes. Deluxe models built in Detroit had serial numbers 6269001 to 6283459. Deluxe models built in Los Angeles had serial numbers 600011001 to 60012889. Custom models built in Detroit has serial numbers 50155001 to 50230003. Custom models built in Los Angeles had serial numbers 62024001 to 62032486. Motor numbers were located on the left side of the block below cylinder head between first and second cylinders. Motor numbers were S15-1001 and up for models and series and were continued into 1952 without interruption.

DELUXE SERIES

Model Number	Body/Style Number	Body Type & Seating	Factory Price	Shipping Weight	Production Total
(Standard Wheelbase)					
S15-1	Note 1	4-dr Sed-6P	2227	3570	Note 2
S15-1	Note 1	2-dr Clb Cpe-6P	2215	3475	Note 2
S15-1	Note 1	4-dr Carry-All-6P	2457	3685	Note 2
(Long Wheelbase)					
S15-1	Note 1	4-dr Sed-8P	3001	4005	Note 2

NOTE 1: Body style code numbers were not provided.
NOTE 2: Production for 1951 and 1952 was lumped together, with no breakouts available for individual model year production. See Historical Footnotes for additional production data.

ENGINE: L-head. Six-cylinder. Cast iron block. Displacement: 250.6 cid. Bore and stroke: 3.438 x 4.5 in. Compression ratio: 7.0:1. Brake hp: 116 at 3600 rpm. Five main bearings. Carburetor: Stromberg 380359; (with M-6 transmission) Stromberg 380349 (also with M-6 transmission) Carter E9AI.

1951 DeSoto, Custom four-door sedan, 6-cyl

CUSTOM SERIES — (6-CYL) — Various models in the Custom series were distinguished by the words Custom, Sportsman, or Suburban on the front fenders. Body panel changes were the same seen on the Deluxes, as were most regular equipment features. These 1951 models were carried into the 1952 model year due to manufacturing sanctions imposed by involvement in the Korean War.

CUSTOM SERIES

Model Number	Body/Style Number	Body Type & Seating	Factory Price	Shipping Weight	Production Total
(Standard Wheelbase)					
S15-1	Note 1	4-dr Sed-6P	2438	3685	Note 2
S15-2	Note 1	2-dr Clb Cpe-6P	2418	3585	Note 2
S15-2	Note 1	2-dr SptMn HT-6P	2761	3760	Note 2
S15-2	Note 1	2-dr Conv Cpe-6P	2862	3840	Note 2
S15-2	Note 1	4-dr Sta Wag-6P	3047	3960	Note 2
(Long Wheelbase)					
S15-2	Note 1	4-dr Sed-8P	3211	4155	Note 2
S15-2	Note 1	4-dr Sub-9P	3566	4395	Note 2

NOTE 1: Body style code numbers were not provided.
NOTE 2: Production for 1951 and 1952 was lumped together, with no breakouts available for individual year production. See Historical Footnotes for additional production data.

ENGINE: L-head. Six-cylinder. Cast iron block. Displacement: 250.6 cid. Bore and stroke: 3.438 x 4.5 in. Compression ratio: 7.0:1. Brake hp: 116 at 3600 rpm. Five main bearings. Carburetor: Stromberg 380359; (with M-6 transmission) Stromberg 380349 (also with M-6 transmission) Carter E9AI.

CHASSIS FEATURES: Wheelbase (LWB) 139.5 in. (others) 125.5 in. Three-speed manual transmission was standard in Deluxe models. Tip-Toe Shift Fluid Drive (Prest-0-Matic) was optional on Deluxes and standard on Customs. As an option it was priced $132. The number of cars built with automatic transmission (semi-automatic in DeSotos) was governed by rules established by the National Price Administration. The permissible NPA attachment rates varied in relation to a car's sales price bracket. In the DeSoto price class, the limit was established at 65 percent. Tire sizes: (Short Wheelbase models) 7.60 x-15; (long wheelbase models) 8.20 x 15.

OPTIONS: Radio. Heater. Whitewall tires. Full wheelcovers. Lighted hood ornament. Directional signals. Back-up lights. Two-tone paint.

HISTORICAL FOOTNOTES: The 1951 DeSotos were introduced at showroom level on January 27, 1951. Due to the Korean War, production for the 1951 and 1952 model years was counted as a single total. However, industry sources record that 121,794 Desotos (2.28 percent of total industry output) were built in the 1951 model year. Of these, 3,910 were Custom convertibles; 6,775 were Custom hardtops and 1,637 were Custom station wagons. Calendar year production stood at 120,757 units, which put DeSoto 12th in the industry. On December 16, 1950 the Economic Stabilization Agency (ESA) froze prices of automobiles at the Dec. 1, level. This freeze lasted until March 1, 1951.

1952 DESOTO

DELUXE SERIES — (6-CYL) — The 1952 DeSotos were introduced to the public on Nov. 15, 1951. The DeSoto Firedome V-8 became an addition to the line on Valentine's Day, 1952. The cars available early in the season were basically a carryover series from the previous model run. Minor exterior changes included rear taillamp frames which tapered towards the top and had integral back-up lights. The name DeSoto was placed on the hood in block letters, a variation from the script style logo used in 1951. The hood medallion became taller and narrower than that used on earlier models. After the introduction of the Firedome V-8, Deluxe cars adopted a newly designed hood. It had an air scoop and a medallion similar to the 1951 style medallion. In all cases, the word Deluxe was seen on front fendersides. Features receiving promotional backing included Cyclebond brake linings; box-type frame construction; full waterproof ignition; narrow corner posts; electric windshield wipers; bolted-on fenders; air foam seat cushions; internal expanding positive action parking brake; Super Cushion tires; a new wider frame; tapered leaf rear springs; coil front springs; straddle mounted steering gear and fuel filter in gasoline tank. Other features promoted during 1951 appeared again, too.

DESOTO I.D. NUMBERS: Serial numbers were located on the left front door hinge pillar post. Letters shown in midsection of lines, before the serial numbers, identified the assembly plant as follows: D=Detroit, Mich.; LA=Los Angeles, Calif.; W=Windsor, Ontario, Canada. These letters were not part of the serial number. Only serial numbers were to be used for identification purposes. Deluxe models built in Detroit had serial numbers 6283601 to 6288250. Deluxe models built in Los Angeles had serial numbers 60013001 to 60013651. An important

phase of DeSoto operations was the manufacture of taxicabs built off the long wheelbase platform with body shell furnished to taxicab manufacturer's specifications. Taxis had serial numbers 5121401 to 5122684. Custom models built in Detroit has serial numbers 50203101 to 50261940. Custom models built in Los Angeles had serial numbers 62032601 to 62036371. Firedome models built in Detroit had serial numbers 5500001 to 55040155. Firedome models built in Los Angeles had serial numbers 64001001 to 64005899. Six-cylinder motor numbers were located on the left side of the block below cylinder head between first and second cylinders. These numbers were S15-145987 and up for Deluxes and Customs and continued into 1952 without interruption. On the V-8 the engine number was positioned atop the engine block under the water outlet elbow. Motor numbers S17-1001 to 46488 were used at both assembly plants.

Model Number	Body/Style Number	Body Type & Seating	Factory Price	Shipping Weight	Production Total
(Standard Wheelbase)					
S15-1	Note 1	4-dr Sed-6P	2333	3540	13,506
S15-1	Note 1	2-dr Clb Cpe-6P	2319	3435	6,100
S15-1	Note 1	4-dr Carry-All-6P	2572	3650	1,700
(Long Wheelbase)					
S15-1	Note 1	4-dr Taxi-6P	NA	NA	3550
S15-1	Note 1	4-dr Sed-8P	3142	4035	343

NOTE 1: Code numbers identifying body style were not used.
NOTE 2: Production totals are a combination of 1951 and 1952 output, with no breakouts per model year available. See Historical Footnotes in 1951 section for additional production data. Totals for Deluxe models include 3,550 California taxicabs. For the 1952 calendar year DeSoto produced 97,585 cars, including 5,325 hardtops, 1,319 station wagons and 1,150 convertibles. These body styles were available with Custom trim only.

ENGINES: L-head. Six-cylinder. Cast iron block. Displacement: 250.6 cid. Bore and stroke 3.438 x 4.5 inches. Compression ratio: 7.0:1. Brake hp: 116 at 3600 rpm. Five main bearings. Carburetor: Stromberg 380359: (With M-6 transmission) Stromberg 380349: or (Also with M-6 transmission) Carter E9AI.

1952 DeSoto, Custom two-door Sportsman hardtop coupe, 6-cyl

CUSTOM SERIES — (6-CYL) — The Custom six was also a carryover from 1951 with the same changes outlined in Deluxe models plus upgraded upholstery choices. The word Custom appeared on the front fenders. Late models used the Air-Vent type hood similar to the Firedome V-8. This hood was also slightly lower than the previous type.

CUSTOM SERIES

Model Number	Body/Style Number	Body Type & Seating	Factory Price	Shipping Weight	Production Total
(Standard Wheelbase)					
S15-2	Note 1	4-dr Sed-6P	2552	3660	88,491
S15-2	Note 1	2-dr Clb Cpe-6P	2531	3565	19,000
S15-2	Note 1	2-dr SptMn HT-6P	2890	3720	8,750
S15-2	Note 1	2-dr Conv Cpe-6P	2996	3865	3,950
S15-2	Note 1	4-dr Sta Wag-6P	3189	4020	1,440
Model Number	Body/Style Number	Body Type & Seating	Factory Price	Shipping Weight	Production Total
(Long Wheelbase)					
S15-2	Note 1	4-dr Sed-8P	3362	4155	769
S15-2	Note 1	4-dr Sub-9P	3734	4370	600

NOTE 1: Code numbers identifying the body style were not used.
NOTE 2: Production totals are a combination of 1951 and 1952 output, with no breakouts per model year available. See 1952 DeSoto Deluxe specifications chart notes for additional production data.

ENGINE: L-head. Six-cylinder. Cast iron block. Displacement: 250.6 cid. Bore and stroke 3.438 x 4.5 inches. Compression ratio: 7.0:1. Brake hp: 116 at 3600 rpm. Five main bearings. Carburetor: Stromberg 380359: (With M-6 transmission) Stromberg 380349: or (Also with M-6 transmission) Carter E9AI.

FIREDOME SERIES — (V-8) — The big news from DeSoto for 1952 was the introduction of the spherical segment combustion chamber engine in the DeSoto chassis. This is commonly referred to as the DeSoto Hemi V-8. It had been available in specific Chrysler models since 1951 and was the first eight-cylinder engine offered in a DeSoto since the inline eight of 1930-1931. Essentially, the Firedome models were Customs with suitable modifications to accommodate the new V-8. Nomenclature consisted of the name 'Firedome 8' placed on front fender sides and an '8' positioned on the deck lid. Shortly after introduction, the '8' emblems were replaced with a V-8 insignia for the deck.

1952 DeSoto, Firedome four-door sedan, V-8 (AA)

FIREDOME SERIES

Model Number	Body/Style Number	Body Type & Seating	Factory Price	Shipping Weight	Production Total
(Standard Wheelbase)					
S17	Note 1	4-dr Sed-6P	2740	3760	35,651
S17	Note 1	2-dr Clb Cpe-6P	27 18	3675	5,699
S17	Note 1	2-dr SptMn HT-6P	3078	3850	3.000
S17	Note1	2-dr Conv Cpe-6P	3183	3950	850
S17	Note 1	4-dr Sta Wag-6P	3377	4080	550
(Long Wheelbase)					
S17	Note1	4-dr Sed-8P	3547	4325	80

NOTE 1: Code numbers identifying the body style were not used. This series was offered exclusively in 1952 and production totals for Firedome models are for this model year only.

ENGINE: V-8. Overhead valves. Hemispherical combustion chambers. Displacement 276.1 cid. Bore and stroke: 3.626 x 3.344 inches. Compression ratio-. 7.0:1. Brake hp: 160 at 4400 rpm. Five main bearings. Hydraulic valve lifters. Carburetors: Carter WCD two-barrel models 884S, 884SA and 884SC. Also used were models 901S with Fluid Drive or Torque Convertor and M-6 transmission; 9055 with standard transmission-, 906S with standard transmission in combination with overdrive. Later Firedome V-8s used models 908S, 909S, and 910S, which carried over into 1953 production.

CHASSIS FEATURES: Wheelbase: (Long wheelbase — all lines) 139-1/2 inches; (Short wheelbase — all lines) 125-1/2 inches. Overall length — (Long wheelbase models) 224-3/8 inches; (Short wheelbase models) 208-3/8 inches. Front tread: (all) 56-5/16 inches. Rear tread: (all) 59-9/16 inches. Tires: (eight-passenger) 8.20 x 15; (all others) 7.60 x 15.

OPTIONS: Power steering ($199); Overdrive ($102); Tip-Toe Shift with Fluid Torque Drive ($257). Tip-Toe Shift with Fluid Drive ($132). Solex tinted glass. Electric window lifts. Radio. Heater. White sidewall tires. Power brakes. Two-tone paint.

HISTORICAL FOOTNOTES: Actual building of Firedome V-8s commenced Oct. 18, 1951. About 85 percent of DeSotos were built at the Wyoming Ave. assembly plant in Detroit. Engines were built at the Warren Ave. plant, a so-called 'push-button' facility. The transfermatic machinery in this factory had a capacity of 60 V-8 powerplants per hour. Calendar year output of 97,585 cars put DeSoto 12th in the industry.

1953 DESOTO

POWERMASTER SIX SERIES — (6-CYL) — A new series debuted with this 25th anniversary model. Gone were the Deluxe and Custom names. The 1953s had an appearance similar to the previous series, yet the design was a major sheetmetal revamp. The front fender line extended front to rear and the back fenders were now integral with the body structure. Only the station wagon continued with 1952 fender styling. The new Sportsman used the 1952 style roof structure and three-piece rear window treatment, while the eight-passenger sedan used the 1952 body with the new one-piece curved windshield, pioneered by Chrysler in 1934 on the CW Airflow. All other models featured curved, one-piece windshields and rear windows. The new 'grinning' grille added two more teeth, versus the nine on the 1952 DeSoto offerings. Side chrome was more evident, in addition, as Korean War demands abated. The roofline now faded into the rear deck in a more pleasing fashion. It was much improved over the abrupt styling of 1952. The Club Coupe was now more sedan-like than the previous year's counterpart. For identification purposes, the word Powermaster was on both front fenders, which had no additional chrome trim.

DESOTO I.D. NUMBERS: Serial numbers were located on the left front door hinge pillar post. Letters shown in midsection of lines, before the serial numbers, identified the assembly plant as follows: D=Detroit, Mich.; LA=Los Angeles, Calif.; W=Windsor, Ontario, Canada. These letters were not part of the serial number. Only serial numbers were to be used for identification purposes. Powermasters built in Detroit had serial numbers 50266001 to 50304981. Powermasters built in Los Angeles had serial numbers 6239001 to 62042345. Taxis were numbered 5124001 to 512571. Firedome models built in Detroit had serial numbers 55050001 to 55127622. Firedome models built in Los Angeles had serial numbers 64008001 to 64015691. Six-cylinder motor numbers were located on the left side of the block below cylinder head between first and second cylinders. These numbers were S18-1001 and up for Powermasters. On the V-8 the engine number was positioned atop the engine block under the water outlet above. Motor numbers S16-1001 and were used.

POWERMASTER SIX SERIES

Model Number	Body/Style Number	Body Type & Seating	Factory Price	Shipping Weight	Production Total
S18	Note 1	2-dr Clb Cpe-6P	2434	3495	8,063
S18	Note 1	4-dr Sed-6P	2456	3555	33,644
S18	Note 1	4-dr Sedan-8P	3266	4070	225
S18	Note 1	2-dr Sptmn HT-6P	2781	3596	1,470
S18	Note 1	4-dr Sta Wagon-6P	3093	3855	500

NOTE 1: Code numbers identifying body style were not used. Production totals include 1,700 California taxicabs. Eight-passenger models were on the long wheelbase chassis.

ENGINE: L-head. Six-cylinder. Cast iron block. Displacement: 250.6 cid. Bore and stroke: 3.438 x 4.5 inches. Compression ratio: 7.0:1. Brake hp: 116 at 3600 rpm. Five main bearings. Carburetor: Stromberg 380359 (with M-6 transmission) Stromberg 380349; or (also with M-6 transmission) Carter E9Al.

1953 DeSoto prototype, Firedome two-door Sportsman hardtop coupe, V-8 (AA)

FIREDOME SERIES — (V-8) — This was the second year for the V-8 models. They shared most features of the six-cylinder series and offered the same six body styles as seen in 1952. Highlights included brakes with 12-inch drums; Cyclebond brake linings; Oriflow shock absorbers; coil front springs; waterproof ignition; full-length water jackets; full-pressure lubrication; air vent hoods and an improved frame designed to resist twisting. Changes from 1952 included new combination tail, stop and back-up lights and a gas cap positioned below the deck lid on the left side. The words 'Fire Dome V-8' appeared on both front fenders and the word 'Eight' was affixed on the right side, below the deck lid. A chrome trim slash was seen on the front fenders of all models except the eight-passenger sedan and the station wagon.

1953 DeSoto, Firedome two-door club coupe

FIREDOME SERIES

Model Number	Body/Style Number	Body Type & Seating	Factory Price	Shipping Weight	Production Total
S16	Note 1	2-dr Clb Cpe-6P	2718	3640	14,591
S16	Note 1	4-dr Sed-6P	2740	3705	64,211
S16	Note 1	4-dr Sed-8P	3544	4290	200
S16	Note 1	2-dr Conv Cpe-6P	3172	3965	1,700
S16	Note 1	2-dr Sptmn HT-6P	3069	3675	4,700
S16	Note 1	4-dr Sta Wag-6P	3366	3990	1,100

NOTE 1: Code numbers identifying body style were not used. Eight passenger models were on the long wheelbase chassis.

ENGINE: V-8. Overhead valves. Hemispherical combustion chambers. Displacement: 276.1 cid. Bore and stroke 3.626 x 3.344 inches. Compression ratio: 7.0:1. Brake hp: 160 at 4400 rpm. Five main bearings. Hydraulic valve lifters. Carburetors: Same as 1952 late year models.

CHASSIS FEATURES: Wheelbase: (Long wheelbase — all lines) 139-1/2 inches; (Short wheelbase — all lines) 125-1/2 inches. Overall length: (Long wheelbase models) 224 inches; (Short wheelbase models) 213-3/8 inches; (station wagon) 212-3/4 inches. Front tread: (all) 56-5/16 inches. Rear tread: (all) 59-9/16 inches. Tires: (8-passenger) 8.20 x 15; (all others) 7.60 x 15.

OPTIONS: Overdrive ($98). Tip-Toe shift with Fluid Drive ($130); Tip-Toe Shift with Fluid Torque Drive ($237). Power steering ($177). Power brakes. Solex safety glass. Electric window lifts. White sidewall tires. Air conditioning. Continental tire kit. Wire spoke wheelcovers. Full wheelcovers. Radio. Heater.

HISTORICAL FOOTNOTES: Calendar year production of 129,959 units put DeSoto 12th in the industry this year. Chrysler purchased the Briggs Manufacturing Co. this year for $35,000,000. This was the 25th anniversary for DeSoto, but no special models were offered. The DeSoto Adventurer experimental show car was seen during 1953. The model year started in November, 1952. Air conditioning was introduced in January, which seems a bit odd.

1954 DESOTO

POWERMASTER SERIES — (6-CYL) — The annual model changeover this year brought a DeSoto with the same basic styling as the 1953 model. Exterior changes were limited to revisions for trim moldings, grille, bumpers and taillights. The grille reverted to a nine-tooth look with parking lamps floating inside the grille outline. The protector guards were redesigned and looked a bit more massive. New step down chrome moldings were seen on front fenders and doors. The rear fender side moldings now stretched completely to the rear of the cars and the gravel shields were redesigned. Headlight and taillight clusters were updated with decorative bezels on top. The word Powermaster was incorporated on front fender moldings and a Powermaster crest adorned the hood. A horizontal chrome handle dressed up the deck lid. Completely new interior styling was adopted with upholstery, instrument panel and all appointments color-keyed to better harmonize with exterior finish. Highlighted in advertisements were a number of technical features included No-Sway ride control; Oriflow shocks; Safe Guard hydraulic brakes; safety rim wheels: box type frame side rails; independent parking brake: waterproof ignition; rubber insulated body moldings; mountings; tapered leaf sply mounted rear springs and rubber insulated rear spring shackles. Compression ratios were raised and horsepower ratings also jumped. A new, fully automatic transmission with the industry's highest starting ratio and torque convertor multiplication ratio was optional. It was said to provide instant response with no lagging or lurching between shifts.

DESOTO I.D. NUMBERS: Serial numbers were located on the left front door hinge pillar post. Letters shown in midsection of lines, before the serial numbers, identified the assembly plant as follows: D=Detroit, Mich.; LA=Los Angeles, Calif.; W=Windsor, Ontario, Canada. These letters were not part of the serial number. Only serial numbers were to be used for identification purposes. Powermasters built in Detroit were numbered 50306001 to 50322514: in Los Angeles 62043001 to 62043897; taxicabs 5126001 to 5128005. Firedomes built in Detroit were numbered 55130001 to 55182504; in Los Angeles 64017001 to 64020704. Six-cylinder motor numbers were located on the left side of the block below cylinder head between first and second cylinders. These numbers were S20-1001 through S20-21082. On the V-8 the engine number was positioned atop the engine block under the water outlet elbow. Motor numbers S19-1001 to S19-57604 were used.

POWERMASTER SIX SERIES

Model Number	Body/Style Number	Body Type & Seating	Factory Price	Shipping Weight	Production Total
S20	Note 1	2-dr Clb Cpe-6P	2364	3525	3,499
S20	Note 1	4-dr Sed-6P	2386	3590	14,967
S20	Note 1	4-dr Sed-8P	3281	4120	263
S20	Note 1	2-dr Spl Clb Cpe-6P	2893	3815	250
S20	Note 1	4-dr Sta Wag-6P	3108	3855	225

NOTE 1: Code numbers identifying body style were not used. Powermaster production totals include 2005 taxicabs.
NOTE 2: Records show no Powermaster hardtops were sold in the U.S. They were sold in Canada only and were called Powermaster 6 Special Club Coupes (not Sportsman) although they were true pillarless hardtops.
NOTE 3: Eight-passenger sedan was on the long wheelbase chassis.

ENGINE: L-head. Six-cylinder. Displacement: 250.6 cid. Bore and stroke: 3.438 x 4.5 inches. Compression ratio: 7.0:1. Brake hp: 116 at 3600 rpm. Carburetor: Carter BBD two-barrel, (with standard transmission) Model 2067S; (with overdrive) Model 2068S; (with PowerFlite) Model 2070S.

1954 DeSoto, Firedome two-door Sportsman hardtop coupe, V-8 (AA)

FIREDOME SERIES — (V-8) — The word Firedome, incorporated between the step down front fender moldings, identified the V-8 models for 1954. There were also prominent V-8 emblems on the front of the hood and rear fender sides, plus a V-shaped insignia on the rear deck lid. Seven models appeared at introduction time and a luxury four-door Coronado sedan was added in the spring. Outside embellishments on this car included special rear fender signature logos and small medallions on the rear roof C-pillar. A one-piece rear window was seen on the Sportsman V-8.

FIREDOME SERIES

Model Number	Body/Style Number	Body Type & Seating	Factory Price	Shipping Weight	Production Total
S-19	Note 1	2-dr Clb Cpe-6P	2652	3685	5,762
S-19	Note 1	4-dr Sed-6P	2673	3750	45,095
S-19	Note 1	4-dr Sed-8P	3559	4275	165
S-19	Note 1	2-dr Conv Cpe-6P	3144	3995	1,025
S-19	Note 1	2-dr Sptmn HT-6P	2923	3775	4,382
S-19	Note 1	4-dr Sta Wag-6P	3361	4025	946

NOTE 1: Code numbers to provide positive identification of type of body were not provided.
NOTE 2: The eight-passenger sedan was on the long wheelbase platform.
NOTE 3: Six-passenger sedan total includes Coronado production.

ENGINE: V-8. Overhead valves. Cast iron block. Displacement: 276.1 cid. Bore and stroke 3.625 x 3.344 inches. Compression ratio: 7.5:1. Brake hp: 170 at 4400 rpm. Five main bearings. Hydraulic valve lifters. Carburetor: Carter BBD two-barrel model 2070S; (with standard transmission) models 2067S or 2129S; (with overdrive) models 2068S or 2130S. Carter models 2250S and 2131S also saw applications on PowerFlite equipped cars. Larger diameter valves were used in some Firedome V-8 models late in the year.

CHASSIS FEATURES: Three-speed manual column mounted transmission was standard. Overdrive manual transmission was optional at $98 extra. PowerFlite automatic transmission was optional at $189 extra. Wheelbase: (standard) 125-1/2 inches; (eight-passenger) 139-1/2 inches. Overall length: (standard) 214-1/2 inches; (eight-passenger) 223-7/8 inches. Front tread: (all) 56-5/16 inches; Rear tread: (all) 59-5/8 inches. Tires: (eight-passenger) 8.20 x 15; (all others) 7.60 x 15.

OPTIONS: Power steering ($140). Power brakes ($37). Power windows ($101). Radio ($101). Heater ($78). Air Temp air conditioning ($643). Electric clock ($33). Solex tinted glass ($33). Fog lights ($33). White sidewall tires ($33 exchange). Wire spoke wheel rims. Wheelcovers. Rear seat radio speaker. Windshield washers. Outside rearview mirror.

HISTORICAL FOOTNOTES: DeSoto ranked as the 12th largest volume manufacturer in the industry this year, based on calendar year production of 69,844 cars. Only 1.27 percent of American cars were DeSotos. The '54s were promoted as 'DeSoto Automatics,' to spotlight the new, fully-automatic PowerFlite transmission. The Coronado was a midyear spring model. Chrysler Corp. held elaborate dedication ceremonies for its new proving grounds, at Chelsea, Michigan, during 1954. The Ghia-built Adventurer II show car appeared this year.

1955 DESOTO

1955 DeSoto, Firedome two-door Sportsman hardtop coupe, V-8 (AA)

FIREDOME — (V-8) — Styling changes were evident as an all-new "Forward Look" made its debut. A six was no longer provided in DeSotos and the Firedome V-8 became the low rung line. New exterior sheet metal was highlighted by lower, longer, wider body contours. A wraparound windshield appeared. The redesigned seven-tooth grille featured intergrated bumper guards and floating parking lamps. Styling on the interior was of 'cockpit' inspiration with the radio and clock option centered in dash. The glove box, a series nameplate and the radio speaker graced the right-hand side of the dashboard. All gages and a dash-mounted automatic shift lever were to the left. Hood ornaments and taillamp clusters had fresh treatments. Cars in this line were identifiable by the Firedome name, in script, on front fenders. Bodyside decorations took the form of constant width chrome moldings running front to rear with a slight kickup above the rear wheel housing. There were nameplates and round medallions, mounted to the rear roof pillar, to help in picking out Sportsman models. Shortly after production began, FireFlite color sweep treatments became a Firedome option, as did sun cap visors. Standard equipment included five tubeless tires; waterproof ignition; adjustable speed electric windshield wipers; Oriflow shock absorbers and Safety Rim wheels.

1955 DeSoto, Firedome Sportsman two-door hardtop coupe, V-8

FIREDOME I.D. NUMBERS: Serial numbers and motor numbers were in the previous locations, only the former usable for identification. Cars built in Detroit were numbered 55185001 to 55256392; in Los Angeles 64022001 to 64026847; Taxicab numbers began at 5130001. Engine numbers were S22-1001 to 76620.

FIREDOME SERIES

Model Number	Body/Style Number	Body Type & Seating	Factory Price	Shipping Weight	Production Total
S22	Note 1	4-dr Sed-6P	2498	3870	46,388
S22	Note 1	2-dr Conv Cpe-6P	2824	4010	625
S22	Note 1	2-dr Sptmn HT	2654	3805	28,944
S22	Note 1	2-dr Spl Cpe-6P	2541	3810	(See Notes)
S22	Note 1	4-dr Sta Wag-6P	3125	4175	1,803

NOTE 1: Code numbers to provide positive identification of body type were not provided.
NOTE 2: Production totals include taxicabs. The production of FireFlite Special two-door hardtop coupes was counted in the figures for Sportsman hardtops. All DeSotos were on a common wheelbase this season.

1955 DeSoto, FireFlite four-door sedan, V-8

FIREFLITE SERIES — (V-8) — DeSoto's top line also offered new aircraft inspired Forward Look styling. Identification features included FireFlite front fender scripts; chrome fender top ornaments running back from headlamps; and rocker panel beauty trim. Four-door models had a single, flared, chrome side molding with slight kickup above rear wheel housing. Special side color sweep beauty panels were standard on FireFlite convertibles and hardtops, optional on other DeSoto models. The Coronado was an added springtime model. It was a sedan featuring a leather interior and three-tone exterior finish treatment. The fuel filler was now located behind a door on the right rear quarter panel. There were V-8 emblems on the rear quarter panel, set lower and forward inside the color sweep. On cars without color sweep styling treatments had the V-8 emblem slightly offset, forward of the gas filler and even with the taillamp centerline. A sun cap visor treatment was seen. Genuine leather trimmed upholstery was provided in the FireFlite Sportsman. Others had silky nylon upholstery and nylon carpeting, too. A 200 hp four-barrel V-8 with hemispherical segment combustion chambers was another FireFlite standard.

FIREFLITE I.D. NUMBERS: Code number locations same as previous. Detroit numbers 50330001 to 50364093; Los Angeles numbers 62045001 to 62047586. Motor numbers S210-1001 to 35660.

FIREFLITE SERIES

Model Number	Body/Style Number	Body Type & Seating	Factory Price	Shipping Weight	Production Total
S21	Note 1	4-dr Sed-6P	2727	3395	26,637
S21	Note 1	4-dr Coronado Sed-6P	NA	NA	(Note 2)
S21	Note 1	2-dr Conv Cpe-6P	3151	4090	775
S21	Note 1	2-dr Sptmn-6P	2939	3490	10,313

NOTE 1: Code numbers to provide positive identification of body type were not provided.
NOTE 2: Coronado Sedan production included in total for FireFlite four-door sedan.

ENGINES:

(FIREDOME) V-8: Overhead valves. Cast iron block. Displacement: 291 cid. Bore and stroke 3.72 x 3.344 inches. Compression ratio: 7.5:1. Brake hp: 200 at 4400 rpm. Five main bearings. Hydraulic valve lifters. Carburetors: (standard transmission) Carter BBD two-barrel model 2067S; (overdrive transmission) Carter BBD model 2177S-SA; (PowerFlite transmission) Carter BBD model 2178S-SA.

(FIREFLITE) V-8: Overhead valves. Cast iron block. Displacement: 291 cid. Bore and stroke 3.72 x 3.344 inches. Compression ratio: 7.5:1. Brake hp: 200 at 4400 rpm. Five main bearings. Hydraulic valve lifters. A Carter WCFB four-barrel carburetor model 2210S was employed.

CHASSIS FEATURES: Three-speed manual column mounted transmission was standard. Overdrive manual transmission was optional at $108 extra. PowerFlite automatic transmission with 'Flight Control' selector lever protruding from dashboard was $189 extra. Wheelbase: (all) 126 inches. Overall length: (station wagon) 218.6 inches; (all others) 217.9 inches. Front tread: (all) 60.2 inches. Rear tread: (all) 59.6 inches. Tires: Tubeless blackwalls of 7.60 x 15 size.

OPTIONS: Power steering ($113). Power brakes ($40). Power front seat ($70). Four-barrel power package for Firedome series ($90). Radios ($110 and $128). Heater ($92). Power windows ($102). Air conditioning ($567). Directional signals. White sidewall tires. Other standard accessories.

HISTORICAL FOOTNOTES: Dual exhausts were available on all models, but station wagons, at extra cost. Three famous Ghia built experimental show cars with DeSoto running gear appeared this year at auto shows. They were the Falcon roadster; Flight Sweep I convertible; and Flight Sweep II coupe.

1956 DESOTO

FIREDOME — (V-8) — A new perforated mesh grille with a large 'V' in the center dominated the 1956 DeSoto frontal revamping. Redesigned taillight clusters had three tiers of turret-shaped lenses and tailfin rear fenders appeared. Color sweep two-toning remained a feature, although the shape of the contrast panels was revised. New front bumper guards incorporated

park lamps. A large, V-shaped emblem dominated the rear deck. Cars in the Firedome series had suitable nameplates on front fenders, chrome plated headlamp hoods and plain top front fenders. Standard side trim was a plain, full-length molding of consistent width, while color sweep two-toning was optional on hardtop models. This option took a shape that was distinctive to the Firedome line, although another pattern was available for cars in the FireFlite series. Station wagons could be ordered with a third type of color sweep pattern and had chrome plated bolt-on type rear fins. Standard equipment included full-time power steering; independent parking brake; safety rim wheels; Oriflow shock absorbers; constant speed electric windshield wipers; new safety door latches; all-weather headlights; Super Highway taillamp clusters and center plane brakes. A 12-volt electrical system was adopted. Low-priced hardtops were designated as Sevilles and a four-door pillarless model was introduced.

1956 DeSoto, Firedome two-door Seville hardtop coupe, V-8

FIREDOME I.D. NUMBERS: Serial and motor numbers were in the usual locations. Use serial number only for identification purposes. Cars built in Detroit numbered 55258001 to 55329506; in Los Angeles 64028001 to 64034406. Motor numbers S231001 to 79267 were used.

FIREDOME SERIES

Model Number	Body/Style Number	Body Type & Seating	Factory Price	Shipping Weight	Production Total
S23	Note 1	2-dr SeV HT-6P	2684	3865	19,136
S23	Note 1	4-dr SeV HT-6P	2833	3940	4,030
S23	Note 1	2-dr SptMn-6P	2783	3910	4,589
S23	Note 1	4-dr SptMn-6P	2954	3920	1,645
S23	Note 1	4-dr Sed-6P	2805	3855	44,909
S23	Note 1	2-dr Conv Cpe-6P	3032	4230	646
S23	Note 1	4-dr Sta Wag-6P	3321	4230	2,950

NOTE 1: Code numbers to provide positive identification of body type were not used.

1956 DeSoto, Firedome four-door sedan, V-8

FIREFLITE — (V-8) — FireFlite models had suitable front fender nameplates and painted headlight hoods with chrome strips on top extending back along the peak of the front fenders. The upper arm of color sweep panels on FireFlites extended in a solid line from in back of headlights to the extreme tip of the tailfin. A double molding was used and grew wider at the front edge of the front door spreading to an even wider flare at the rear fender. On four-door sedans the side trim could be had in the color sweep format or an optional format that utilized the upper double molding only. FireFlite four-doors with the latter choice are considered very rare today. All FireFlite cars had PowerFlite automatic transmission as standard equipment. This transmission now incorporated push-button gear selection controls. On Jan. 11, 1956, DeSoto announced that a FireFlite convertible with heavy-duty underpinnings, but standard engine, would pace the Indianapolis 500 and that a limited-edition 'Pacesetter' convertible would be available to the public. These cars had the same special features and a heavy complement of power accessories, but were not lettered like the authentic pace car.

FIREFLITE I.D. NUMBERS: Serial and motor numbers were in the usual locations with serial numbers meant for identification purposes. Cars built in Detroit were numbered 50366001 to 50392114; in Los Angeles 62048001 to 62051424. Motor numbers S241001 to S29811 were used

FIREFLITE SERIES

Model Number	Body/Style Number	Body Type & Seating	Factory Price	Shipping Weight	Production Total
S24	Note 1	2-dr SptMn-6P	3256	4030	7,479
S24	Note 1	4-dr Sed-6P	3029	4005	18,207
S24	Note 1	4-dr SptMn-6P	3341	4015	3,350
S24	Note 1	2-dr Conv Cpe-6P	3454	4125	1,485
S24	Note 1	2-dr Conv Pace Car-6P	3565	4070	(Note 2)

NOTE 1: Code numbers to provide positive identification of body type were not used.
NOTE 2: Production of Pacesetter convertibles is included in base convertible totals.

1956 DeSoto, FireFlite four-door sedan, V-8 (AA)

ADVENTURER — (V-8) — The Adventurer two-door hardtop coupe was introduced as a limited-production, specialty car on Feb. 18, 1956. It was technically a FireFlite sub-series and was sometimes called the Golden Adventurer. It had a special high-performance engine, dual exhausts and custom appointments and finish. Standard equipment included power brakes, whitewall tires, dual tailpipe extensions, dual outside rearview mirrors, rear mounted manual radio antennas, padded instrument panel, power front seat, electric windows, windshield washers, electric clock and heavy-duty suspension.

ADVENTURER I.D. NUMBERS: Coding on Adventurers was the same as on Detroit built FireFlites in terms of serial numbers. Motor numbers S24A-1001 to S24A-29811 were used in Adventurers.

ADVENTURER SUB-SERIES

Model Number	Body/Style Number	Body Type & Seating	Factory Price	Shipping Weight	Production Total
S24A	Note 1	2-dr HT Cpe-6P	3678	3870	996

NOTE 1: Code numbers to provide positive identification of body type were not used.

ENGINES

(FIREDOME) V-8: Overhead valves. Cast iron block. Displacement: 330.4 cid. Bore and stroke: 3.72 x 3.80 inches. Compression ratio: 8.5:1. Brake hp: 230 at 4400 rpm. Five main bearings. Hydraulic valve lifters. Carburetors: Carter BBD two-barrel (with standard transmission) model 2308S; (overdrive transmission) model 2309S; (PowerFlite transmission) 2310S.

(FIREFLITE) V-8: Overhead valves. Cast iron block. Displacement 330.4 cid. Bore and stroke. 3.72 x 3.80 inches. Compression ratio: 8.5:l. Brake hp: 255 at 4400 rpm. Five main bearings. Hydraulic valve lifters. Carburetion: Carter WCFB four-barrel model 2311S (primary and secondary).

(ADVENTURER) V-8: Overhead valves with enlarged valve ports, high-lift camshaft, large diameter valves and stiffer valve springs. Cast iron block with modified slipper pistons, heavy-duty connecting rods and shot-peened crankshaft. Displacement: 341.4 cid. Bore and stroke: 3.78 x 3.80 inches. Compression ratio. 9.25:l. Brake hp: 320 at 5200 rpm. Five main bearings. Hydraulic valve lifters. Carburetion: Carter dual four-barrel WCFB type: (front) model 2476S: (rear) model 2445S.

CHASSIS FEATURES: Three-speed column mounted transmission was standard on Firedome and not normally available on FireFlite. Overdrive transmission $108 on Firedome and not normally available on FireFlite. PowerFlite automatic transmission was optional on Firedome for $189 extra and standard on FireFlite. Push-button PowerFlite controls were adopted. Wheelbase: (all) 126 inches. Overall length: (four-door sedan and Sportsman) 217.9 inches; (all two-doors) 220.9 inches: (station wagon) 218.6 inches. Front tread: (all) 60.4 inches. Rear tread: (all) 59.6 inches. Tires: 7.60 x 15.

OPTIONS: Power steering ($97). Power brakes ($40). Power front seat ($70). Highway Hi-Fi record player. Air Temp air conditioning. Electric window lifts. Power radio antenna. Hot water heater. Instant heat. Conditionair (operates on gasoline burner). Solex safety glass. Whitewall tires. Steering wheel mounted clock. Seat belts. Other standard accessories.

HISTORICAL FOOTNOTES: An Adventurer hardtop paced the 1956 Pike's Peak Hill Climb. Another Adventurer competed in Daytona SpeedWeeks.

1957 DESOTO

FIRESWEEP SERIES — (V-8) — All new styling and chassis engineering characterized 1957 DeSotos. Changes from 1956 included new bodies that were lower and longer; new side trim and color sweep treatments, a massive new bumper grille combination, new upswept rear fender tailfins and a new Firesweep series, which was essentially a 1957 Dodge under its skin and built by Dodge Division. Identification features for this line were Firesweep rear fender nameplates; a wide continuous metal band on tops and side of the headlamp hoods: optional dual color sweep moldings or a standard trim treatment that had a molding starting at the rear of the car and extending forward across two-thirds of the front door. Standard features now included Torsionaire torsion bar front suspension; Oriflow shocks; Safety-Lock door latches; Total Contact brakes; and Power-Tip spark plugs.

FIRESWEEP I.D. NUMBERS: Serial numbers and engine numbers were in their familiar locations. Cars built in Detroit were numbered 58001001 to 58038408; in Los Angeles 60014001 to 60017360. Motor numbers KDS-1001 to 287531 were used. Firesweep models were actually manufactured by Chrysler Corporation's Dodge Div.

Model Number	Body/Style Number	Body Type & Seating	Factory Price	Shipping Weight	Production Total
S-27	Note 1	2-dr SptMn-6P	2836	3645	13,333
S-27	Note 1	4-dr Sed-6P	2777	3675	17,300
S-27	Note 1	4-dr SptMn-6P	2912	3720	7,168
S-27	Note 1	4-dr Sta Wag-6P	3169	3965	2,270
S-27	Note 1	4-dr Sta Wag-9P	3310	3970	1,198

NOTE 1: Code numbers designating body style were not provided. The six-passenger wagon was called the 'Shopper'; the nine-passenger wagon was called the 'Explorer'.

1957 DeSoto, Firedome four-door sedan, V-8 (AA)

FIREDOME SERIES — (V-8) — The former low-priced DeSoto was the middle series for 1957. This was a true DeSoto in the sense it shared no parts with a Dodge though, of course, it did share the major body structure of all Chrysler products. The triple round taillamp theme was a carryover from 1956. The grille was now part of the bumper structure and the color sweep was located low on the body panels. Exhaust tips were integrated with the rear bumper and were of a flat oval or elliptical shape, suggestive of the styling used for the grille. Sedans had six windows and the license plate housing was recessed into the deck lid. Twin rear antennas and dual headlamps were available in this series. There were rear fender nameplates; a Firesweep-like standard molding treatment; and optional color sweep style side moldings.

FIREDOME I.D. NUMBERS: Serial numbers and motor numbers were in their familiar locations. Cars built in Detroit were numbered 55332001 to 55377868; in Los Angeles 64035001 and up. Motor numbers S25-1001 to 47060 were used.

Model Number	Body/Style Number	Body Type & Seating	Factory Price	Shipping Weight	Production Total
S25	Note 1	2-dr SptMn-6P	3085	3910	12,179
S25	Note 1	4-dr Sed-6P	2958	3955	23,339
S-25	Note 1	4-dr SptMn-6P	3142	3960	9,050
S-25	Note 1	2-dr Conv Cpe-6P	3361	4065	1,297

NOTE 1: Code numbers designating body style were not provided.

1957 DeSoto, FireFlite four-door hardtop, V-8 (AA)

FIREFLITE SERIES — (V-8) — For identification, models in the top line series had FireFlite rear fender nameplates. In addition, medallions were seen at the front fender side moldings. Headlights were positioned separate of the grille (as on Firedomes) with cutback notches in the sides of the hood. Dual color sweep moldings were standard on all models. The six passenger wagon was again referred to as the 'Shopper,' while the nine-passenger job was called the 'Explorer.' The convertible coupe used a distinctive, dome-like windshield, which became standard on all Sportsman models for 1958. Front fendertop chrome ornaments appeared in mixed applications on some FireFlite models. TorqueFlite automatic transmission; foam seat cushions; back-up lights; and full wheelcovers were standard.

FIREFLITE I.D. NUMBERS: Serial numbers and motor numbers were in their familiar locations. Cars built in Detroit were numbered 50396001 to 50426380; in Los Angeles 62053001 and up. Motor numbers S26-1001 to 29541 were used.

FIREFLITE SERIES

Model Number	Body/Style Number	Body Type & Seating	Factory Price	Shipping Weight	Production Total
S-26	Note 1	2-dr SptMn-6P	3614	4000	7,217
S-26	Note 1	4-dr Sed-6P	3487	4025	11,565
S-26	Note 1	4-dr SptMn-6P	3671	4125	6,726
S-26	Note 1	2-dr Conv Cpe-6P	3890	4085	1,151
S-26	Note 1	4-dr Sta Wag-6P	3982	4250	837
S-26	Note 1	4-dr Sta Wag-9P	4124	4290	934

NOTE 1: Code numbers designating body style were not used.

ADVENTURER SERIES — (V-8) — This was a high-powered, performance car line. The Adventurer hardtop coupe was introduced two months after regular DeSoto introductions on Oct. 30, 1956. An Adventurer convertible was marketed even later. Both models had special gold colored trim accents to carry forward the tradition begun in 1956. They also featured TorqueFlite automatic transmission; power brakes; dual exhausts; dual rear radio antenna; dual outside rearview mirrors; white sidewall tires; padded dashboards and special paint and trim as standard equipment. Distinctive nameplates appeared on the rear fender and bright metal strips graced the rear deck lid. Dual headlamps were seen and had now become accepted as legal equipment in all states. A special V-8 with dual four-barrel carburetors was installed. This motor provided one hp per cubic inch of displacement.

ADVENTURER I.D. NUMBERS: Serial numbers and engine numbers were in their familiar locations. All Adventurers were built at the Detroit factory, according to reference sources, with serial numbers 50396001 to 50426380 utilized. This range of numbers is the same listed for Detroit-built FireFlites which indicates the Adventurer was a sub-series of this line. Motor numbers also fell into the previously listed FireFlite sequence.

1957 DeSoto, Adventurer two-door hardtop coupe, V-8 (AA)

ADVENTURER SERIES

Model Number	Body/Style Number	Body Type & Seating	Factory Price	Shipping Weight	Production Total
S-26A	Note 1	2-dr HT Cpe-6P	3997	4040	1,650
S-26A	Note 1	2-dr Conv Cpe-6P	4272	4235	300

NOTE 1: Code numbers designating body style were not used.

ENGINES

(FIRESWEEP) V-8: Overhead valves. Cast iron block. Displacement: 325 cid. Bore and stroke: 3.69 x 3.80 inches. Compression ratio: 8.5:1. Brake hp: 245 at 4400 rpm. Five main bearings. Hydraulic valve lifters. Carburetor: Carter two-barrel model number 2532S.

(FIREDOME) V-8: Overhead valves. Cast iron block. Displacement: 341.4 cid. Bore and stroke: 3.78 x 3.80 inches. Compression ratio: 9.25:1. Brake hp: 270 at 4600 rpm. Five main bearings. Hydraulic valve lifters. Carburetor: Carter two-barrel model number 2522S.

(FIREFLITE) V-8: Overhead valves. Cast iron block. Displacement: 341.4 cid. Bore and stroke: 3.78 x 3.80 inches. Compression ratio: 9.25:1. Brake hp: 270 at 4600 rpm. Five main bearings. Hydraulic valve lifters. Carburetor: Carter model 2588S four-barrel.

(ADVENTURER) V-8: Overhead valves. Cast iron block. Displacement: 345 cid. Bore and stroke: 3.80 x 3.80 inches. Compression ratio: 9.25:1. Brake hp: 345 at 5200 rpm. Five main bearings. Hydraulic valve lifters. Carburetor: Carter dual-quad induction.

CHASSIS FEATURES: Automatic transmissions were now considered standard DeSoto equipment at slight additional cost for lower cost models; no extra cost for FireFlites and Adventurers. PowerFlite automatic transmission was offered only in Firesweep models at approximately $180 extra. TorqueFlite automatic transmission was offered in all lines at approximately $220 extra. Push-button gearshifting was featured with both transmissions. Three-speed manual transmission with column-mounted gearshifting was an infrequently ordered 'deduct option.' Wheelbase: (S-27) 122 inches; (all others) 126 inches. Overall length: (S-27 station wagon) 217.4 inches; (S-27 passenger cars) 215.8 inches; (Adventurer) 221 inches; (all other station wagons) 219.5 inches; (all passenger cars) 218 inches. Front tread: (S-27) 60.9 inches; (all others) 61 inches. Rear tread: (all) 59.7 inches. Tires: (S-26A) 9.00 x 14; (S-26 and S-25) 8.50 x 14; and (S-27) 8.00 x 14.

OPTIONS: Power brakes ($39). Power steering ($106). Power window lifts ($106). Six-way power seat ($101). Dual exhaust, except standard on Adventurer, ($34). Whitewalls, except standard on Adventurer ($42-45). Radio with antenna ($120). Electro Tune radio with antenna ($120). Dual rear antenna ($16). Rear seat speaker ($15). Single rear power antenna ($24). Fresh Air heater ($89). Instant Air heater ($157). Standard two-tone finish ($19). Special finish, solid or two-tone ($71). Tinted glass ($32). Electric clock ($18). Self-winding steering wheel clock ($30). Windshield washer ($12). Variable speed windshield wiper, except standard Firedome and FireFlite ($7). Air Foam seat cushions, except standard on FireFlite and Firedome ($11). Armrest on four-door and sport models ($27). Air Conditioning with Fresh Air heater ($493). Air conditioning group order ($404). Padded safety panel (dash), except standard on Adventurer ($21). Firesweep back-up lights ($12). Engine four-barrel power-pack, Firesweep only ($45). Undercoating ($14). Wheelcovers ($16). Front and rear carpets in Firesweep ($14). Rear window defogger ($21). Non-Slip differential ($50). Outside mirror ($6).

HISTORICAL FOOTNOTES: The 1957 DeSoto Adventurer was the first base model U.S. car to provide one horsepower per cubic inch of displacement, as the 345 hp engine was not considered optional equipment. The 1956 Chrysler 300-B and 1957 Chevrolet were also available with one hp per cubic inch V-8s as optional equipment. DeSoto earned 1.63 percent of total U.S. auto sales for 1957. It was the third best year in the division's history. The Firesweep line made DeSoto the only maker in the medium-low price field to achieve a gain in new car sales over the previous season. The offering of an overdrive transmission was discontinued this year. When equipped with the optional Power-Pack four-barrel V-8, the 1957 DeSoto Firesweep models were rated 260 hp at 4400 rpm, a gain of 15 hp over the base two-barrel engine.

1958 DESOTO

FIRESWEEP SERIES — (V-8) — This series continued to use the Dodge chassis. Styling was characterized by a minor facelift of the 1957 model. Changes included a honeycomb grille insert, a dip in the center of the middle grille bar and round parking lights at the outboard ends of the lower grille opening. Dual headlamps were seen on all models. Bodyside trim was redesigned so that the upper molding ran at an angle to the upper corner of the tailfin. There were Firesweep rear fender nameplates and a continuous band of metal again decorated the front lip of the hood and climbed over the headlamp hoods. Sportsman models had the dome-like windshield seen on 1957 convertibles, while sedans continued with a visored windshield

header. An upgraded interior, similar to that fitted inside Firedome models, was an available option. Electric windshield wipers were employed and a new V-8 engine with wedge-shaped combustion chambers and full-flow oil filter was standard.

1958 DeSoto, Firesweep four-door Explorer station wagon, V-8 (AA)

FIRESWEEP I.D. NUMBERS: Serial numbers and engine numbers were in the familiar locations. Cars built in Detroit had serial numbers LS1-1001 to 18900; in Los Angeles LS1L-1001. Motor numbers L350-1001 and up were used.

FIRESWEEP SERIES

Model Number	Body/Style Number	Body Type & Seating	Factory Price	Shipping Weight	Production Total
LS1-L	Note 1	2-dr SptMn-6P	2890	3660	5,635
LS1-L	Note 1	4-dr Sed-6P	2819	3660	7,646
LS1-L	Note 1	4-dr SptMn-6P	2953	3720	3,003
LS1-L	Note 1	2-dr Conv Cpe-6P	3219	3850	700
LS1-L	Note 1	4-dr Sta Wag-6P	3266	3955	1,305
LS1-L	Note 1	4-dr Sta Wag-9P	3408	3980	1,125

NOTE 1: Code numbers designating body style were not used. The six-passenger station wagon was the Shopper. The nine-passenger station wagon was the Explorer.

FIREDOME SERIES — (V-8) — Firedome nameplates on the rear fenders identified DeSoto's one step up line. Firedome models had the same side trim as Firesweeps, but not the same frontal molding treatment. Windsplit ornaments for tops of front fenders were optional. A richer interior was featured. Upholstery materials were defined as Frontier Homespun fabric in combination with grained vinyl, colored to harmonize with exterior finish. These same interiors could be had in selected Firesweep models at slight extra cost.

FIREDOME I.D. NUMBERS: Serial numbers and engine numbers were in the familiar locations. Cars built in Detroit had serial numbers LS2-1001 to 17409. Some reference sources indicate no Los Angeles production. Others indicate that Los Angeles numbers ran from LS2L-1001 and up. Motor numbers L360-1001 and up were used.

FIREDOME SERIES

Model Number	Body/Style Number	Body Type & Seating	Factory Price	Shipping Weight	Production Total
LS2-M	Note 1	4-dr Sed-6P	3085	3855	9,505
LS2-M	Note 1	2-dr SptMn-6P	3178	3825	4,325
LS2-M	Note 1	4-dr SptMn-6P	3235	3920	3,130
LS2-M	Note 1	2-dr Conv Cpe-6P	3489	4065	519

NOTE 1: Code numbers designating body style were not used.

1958 DeSoto, FireFlite Sportsman two-door hardtop coupe, V-8 (AA)

FIREFLITE SERIES — (V-8) — Identifiers for the top rung series included specific rear fender nameplates and a distinctive upper bodyside molding which extended the full length of the car and incorporated special medallions on sides of front fenders. Windsplit fendertop ornaments were standard equipment. Color sweep trim was standard on hardtops and convertibles. Eighty-six two-tone and 14 solid color schemes were offered for DeSotos. The FireFlites used the same new V-8 which featured a rigid, deep skirt block; inline overhead valves employing a single shaft in each cylinder head; a reduced weight of 640 pounds; and wedge-shaped combustion chambers. A springtime trim package was released as an option for all models, except Adventurers. It featured two groups of four vertical bright metal deck lid slashes, with one group affixed to each side of the recessed license plate housing. New exterior colors were announced about the same time. FireFlite interiors were done in metallic Damask and vinyl and incorporated integrated armrests with aluminum finish recesses above them.

FIREFLITE I.D. NUMBERS: Serial numbers and engine numbers were in their familiar locations. Reference sources give Detroit numbers only. They run from LS3-1001 to 13552. Motor numbers were L360-1001 and up.

Model Number	Body/Style Number	Body Type & Seating	Factory Price	Shipping Weight	Production Total
LS3-H	Note 1	4-dr Sed-6P	3583	3990	4,192
LS3-H	Note 1	2-dr SptMn-6P	3675	3920	3,284
LS3-H	Note 1	4-dr SptMn-6P	3731	3980	3,243
LS3-H	Note 1	2-dr Conv Cpe-6P	3972	4105	474
LS3-H	Note 1	4-dr Sta Wag-6P	4030	4225	318
LS3-H	Note 1	4-dr Sta Wag-9P	4172	4295	609

NOTE 1: Code numbers designating body style were not used. The six-passenger station wagon was the Shopper; the nine-passenger station wagon was the Explorer.

1958 DeSoto, Adventurer two-door hardtop coupe, V-8 (AA)

ADVENTURER SERIES — (V-8) — The Adventurer models again represented a sub-series. Like the FireFlites that they were based on, these high-performance cars came standard with TorqueFlite transmission, back-up lamps and full wheelcovers. But there were some other extras, too, such as power brakes, dual exhausts, dual rear radio antennas, dual outside rearview mirrors, white sidewall tires, dashboard safety panel and special paint and trim. The latter included gold highlights, twin groupings of four deck lid bars, triangular rear side sweep inserts and special upholstery. This specialty series was announced at the 1958 Chicago Auto Show on January 4 of the year. Other DeSoto models had been introduced Nov. 1, 1957. A new option was an electronic fuel injection system manufactured by Bendix. Cars so-equipped wore special nameplates above the front fender medallions and were later recalled to the factory for reconversion into 'standard,' dual-quad carburetor form.

ADVENTURER SERIES I.D. NUMBERS: As a FireFlite sub-series the Adventurers used corresponding serial and engine numbers.

ADVENTURER SERIES

Model Number	Body/Style Number	Body Type & Seating	Factory Price	Shipping Weight	Production Total
LS3-S	Note 1	2-dr HT Cpe-6P	4071	4000	350
LS3-S	Note 1	2-dr Conv Cpe-6P	4369	4180	82

ENGINES

(FIRESWEEP) V-8: Overhead valves. Cast iron block. Displacement: 350 cid. Bore and stroke: 4.06 x 3.38 inches. Compression ratio: 10.0:1. Brake hp: 280 at 4600 rpm. Five main bearings. Hydraulic valve lifters. Carburetor: Carter two-barrel part number 1855633.

(FIREDOME) V-8: Overhead valves. Cast iron block. Displacement: 361 cid. Bore and stroke: 4.12 x 3.38 inches. Compression ratio: 10.0:1. Brake hp: 295 at 4600 rpm. Five main bearings. Hydraulic valve lifters. Carburetor: Carter two-barrel part number 1855633.

(FIREFLITE) V-8: Overhead valves. Cast iron block. Displacement: 361 cid. Bore and stroke: 4.12 x 3.38 inches. Compression ratio: 10.0:1. Brake hp: 305 at 4600 rpm. Five main bearings. Hydraulic valve lifters. Carburetor: Carter number 1822053.

(ADVENTURER) V-8: Overhead valves. Cast iron block. Displacement: 361 cid. Bore and stroke: 4.12 x 3.38 inches. Compression ratio: 10.25:1. Brake hp: 345 at 5000 rpm. Five main bearings. Hydraulic valve lifters. Carburetor: two (2) four-barrel Carter carburetors (front carburetor part number 1826081; rear carburetor part number 1826082).

CHASSIS FEATURES: Automatic transmission was still considered "standard" DeSoto equipment, but again cost extra on Firesweep and Firedome models. There was no charge for automatic transmission in FireFlite and Adventurer models. PowerFlite two-speed automatic transmission was available only in Firesweeps at $180 extra. TorqueFlite three-speed automatic transmission was offered in all lines and cost $220 extra in Firesweeps and Firedomes. Push-button gearshifting was used again, too. Three-speed manual transmission with column mounted controls was an infrequently ordered 'deduct option.' The Bendix-built EFI (fuel-injection) system was $637.20 option in Adventurers only. It was installed in a very limited number of 1958 Adventurers, Chrysler 300-Ds, Dodge D-500s and Plymouth Furys. These cars were originally built with dual-quad carburetors and were then converted to fuel-injection at the DeSoto factory. Adventurers so-equipped were rated 355 hp at 5000 rpm. As previously noted, these cars were factory recalled for reconversion to 'standard' carburetion systems, although some may have escaped the call-back. Wheelbase: (LS1-L) 122 inches; (all others) 126 inches. Overall length: (LS1-L station wagon) 218.1 inches; (LS1-L passenger cars) 216.5 inches; (Adventurer) 221 inches; (all other station wagons) 220.2 inches; (all passenger cars) 218.6 inches. Front tread: (LS1-L) 60.9 inches; (all others) 61 inches. Rear tread: (all) 59.7 inches. Tires: (Adventurer) 9.00 x 14; (LS1-L and LS2-M) 8.50 x 14; and (LS3-H) 8.00 x 14. Several sources indicate that 9.00 x 14 tires were used on 1957 and 1958 Adventurers and that 6-ply 8.50 x 14 tires were used on Explorer station wagons. Other references do not confirm this information, however.

OPTIONS: Power brakes ($39). Power steering ($106). Power window lifts ($106). Six-way power seat ($101). Dual exhaust, except standard on Adventurer, ($34). Whitewalls, except standard on Adventurer ($42-45). Radio with antenna ($120). Electro Tune radio with antenna ($120). Dual rear antenna ($16). Rear seat speaker ($15). Single rear power antenna ($24). Fresh Air heater ($89). Instant Air heater ($157). Standard two-tone finish ($19). Special finish, solid or two-tone ($71). Tinted glass ($32). Electric clock ($18). Self-winding steering wheel clock ($30). Windshield washer ($12). Variable speed windshield wiper, except standard Firedome and FireFlite ($7). Air foam seat cushions, except standard on FireFlite and Firedome ($1 1). Armrest on four-door and sport models ($27). Air Conditioning with Fresh Air heater ($493). Air conditioning group order ($404). Padded safety panel (dash), except standard on Adventurer ($21). Firesweep back-up lights ($12). Engine four-barrel

power-pack, Firesweep only ($45). Undercoating ($14). Wheelcovers ($16). Front and rear carpets in Firesweep ($14). Rear window defogger ($21). Non-Slip differential ($50). Outside mirror ($6). EFI fuel-injection ($637.20).

1959 DESOTO

1959 DeSoto, Firesweep four-door sedan, V-8 (AA)

FIRESWEEP — (V-8) — Air scoops were 'in' for 1959. DeSotos had three and they were built right into the bi-level front bumper. At the bottom was a full-width scoop. Above it, on either side of the license plate indentation (in the lower grille bar), were two more. A rectangular cross-hatched grille insert, where the parking lights were placed, stretched between the headlights. On the sides of the body's full-length sweep spears were narrower and redesigned. They took a dip behind the rear wheel openings and, then, curved upwards towards the tips of tall tailfins. Tri-cluster, turret-shaped taillight lenses were seen again. Also characterizing the rear end styling was a large double bumper, with beauty panels between the top and bottom members. There were no series nameplates on Firesweeps and silver colored inserts along the sides were optional. The four-door sedan had painted side window trim. At the start of the season, four body styles appeared in this line, but two Seville hardtops were introduced as mid-run additions. Standard equipment included front foam cushions, dual exhausts on the convertible, four black nylon Captive Air tires on three-seat station wagons and front and rear carpets (except on the six-passenger station wagon and four-door sedan).

FIRESWEEP I.D. NUMBERS: Serial numbers and engine numbers were in their familiar locations. Cars built in Detroit were numbered M412-100001 and up; in Los Angeles M414-100001 and up. Station wagons were numbered M471-100001 and up and were all assembled in Detroit.

1959 DeSoto, Firedome two-door Sportsman hardtop, V-8

FIRESWEEP SERIES MS1-L

Model Number	Body/Style Number	Body Type & Seating	Factory Price	Shipping Weight	Production Total
413	41	4-dr Sed-6P	2904	3670	9,649
414	43	4-dr SptMn-6P	3038	3700	2,875
412	23	2-dr SptMn-6P	2967	3625	5,481
415	27	2-dr Conv Cpe-6P	3315	3840	596
476	45A	4-dr Sta Wag-6P	3366	3950	1,054
477	45B	4-dr Sta Wag-9P	3508	3980	1,179

NOTES: Two-digit body model (style) numbers were now provided. Two and four-door Seville hardtops were midyear models included in production figures for two-door and four-door Sportsmen. The six-passenger four-door station wagon was the Shopper; the nine-passenger four-door station wagon was the Explorer.

FIREDOME — (V-8) — For identification a series nameplate was affixed to front fenders. Silver color sweeps were optional. Side window trim on four-door sedans was of bright metal. Standard equipment was the same as in Firesweeps, plus back-up lights, padded dash panel, rear foam cushions, front and rear carpets, wheelcovers, special steering wheel and vari-speed windshield wipers.

FIREDOME I.D. NUMBERS: Serial numbers and engine numbers were in their familiar locations. Cars built in Detroit were numbered M43-10001 and up. No California production is noted in standard reference sources.

FIREDOME SERIES MS2-M

Model Number	Body/Style Number	Body Type & Seating	Factory Price	Shipping Weight	Production Total
433	41	4-dr Sed-6P	3234	3840	9,171
434	43	4-dr SptMn-6P	3398	3895	2,862
432	23	2-dr SptMn-6P	3341	3795	2,744
435	27	2-dr Conv Cpe-6P	3653	4015	299

NOTE 1: Seville two and four-door hardtops added at midyear are included in Sportsman production figures.

1959 DeSoto, FireFlite two-door hardtop coupe, V-8 (AA)

FIREFLITE SERIES — (V-8) — FireFlites looked very similar to Firedomes, but could be distinguished by a different series nameplate on front fenders and by large medallions above the dip in the side trim on the rear fenders. Standard equipment matched all found on Firedomes, plus TorqueFlite transmission; front and rear bumper guards; electric clock; hand brake warning light; color sweep molding; roof molding package; molding package number 2; windshield washer; and 8.50 x 14 tires. Three-seat station wagons came with a power tailgate and four-ply black nylon Captive Air tires as regular features.

FIREFLITE I.D. NUMBERS: Serial numbers and engine numbers were in their familiar locations. All cars were built in Detroit and were numbered M451-100001 and up.

FIREFLITE SERIES M54-M

Model Number	Body/Style Number	Body Type & Seating	Factory Price	Shipping Weight	Production Total
453	41	4-dr Sed-6P	3763	3920	4,480
454	43	4-dr SptMn-6P	3888	3950	2,364
452	23	2-dr SptMn-6P	3831	3910	1,393
455	27	2-dr Conv Cpe-6P	4152	4105	186
478	45A	4-dr Sta Wag-6P	4216	4170	271
479	45B	4-dr Sta Wag-9P	4358	4205	433

NOTES: The six-passenger station wagon was the Shopper; the nine-passenger station wagon was the Explorer.

ADVENTURER SERIES — (V-8) — Cars in this line had Adventurer nameplates on their front fenders. Gold color sweep inserts were affixed and the grille was also finished in gold. A narrow vertical medallion was placed at the dip in the side trim on rear fenders. Wheel cutout moldings were used. The two-door hardtop had simulated Scotch-grain leather finish for the roof. Standard equipment was the same as for FireFlites, plus power steering; power brakes; dual exhausts; dual rear radio antennas; dual outside rearview mirrors; white sidewall tires constructed of Rayon (size 8.50 x 14); brushed aluminum sweep insert; deck lid moldings; swivel front driver's seat; and high-performance Adventurer dual four-barrel carburetor V-8 with high-lift camshaft.

ADVENTURER I.D. NUMBERS: Serial numbers and engine numbers were in their familiar locations. Adventurers were assembled in Detroit and had serial numbers M491100001 and up.

ADVENTURER SERIES MS3-H

Model Number	Body/Style Number	Body Type & Seating	Factory Price	Shipping Weight	Production Total
492	23	2-dr SptMn-6P	4427	3980	590
495	27	2-dr Conv Cpe-6P	4749	4120	97

ENGINES

(FIRESWEEP) V-8: Overhead valves. Cast iron block. Displacement: 361 cid. Bore and stroke: 4.12 x 3.38 inches. Compression ratio: 10.0:1. Brake hp: 295 at 4600 rpm. Five main bearings. Hydraulic valve lifters. Carburetor: Carter BBD two-barrel, model number 2870S.

(FIREDOME) V-8: Overhead valves. Cast iron block. Displacement: 383 cid. Bore and stroke: 4.25 x 3.38 inches. Compression ratio: 10.1:1. Brake hp: 305 at 4600 rpm. Five main bearings. Hydraulic valve lifters. Carburetor: Carter BBD two-barrel, model number 2871S.

(FIREFLITE) V-8: Overhead valves. Cast iron block. Displacement: 383 cid. Bore and stroke: 4.25 x 3.38 inches. Compression ratio: 10.1:1. Brake hp: 325 at 4600 rpm. Five main bearings. Hydraulic valve lifters. Carburetor: Carter BBD four-barrel, model number 2794.

(ADVENTURER) V-8: Overhead valves. Cast iron block. Displacement: 383 cid. Bore and stroke: 4.25 x 3.38 inches. Compression ratio: 10.1:1. Brake hp: 350 at 5000 rpm. Five main bearings. Hydraulic valve lifters. Carburetors: Two (2) Carter AFB four-barrels, model number 2794.

CHASSIS FEATURES: Three-speed manual transmission was the base price attachment on Firesweep and Firedome models, although automatic transmission was often referred to as standard equipment. TorqueFlite automatic transmission was included in the price of FireFlite and Adventurer models. Wheelbase: (Firesweep) 122 inches; (all others) 126 inches. Overall length: (MSI-L passenger cars) 217.1 inches; (MSI-L station wagons) 216.1 inches; (MS3-H station wagons) 220.1 inches; (all other passenger cars) 221.1 inches. Tires: (Firesweep) 8.00 x 14; (all others) 8.50 x 14.

OPTIONS: TorqueFlite transmission as option ($227). PowerFlite transmission ($189). Power steering ($106). Power brakes ($43). Power window lifts ($106). Six-way seat ($101). Firedome/FireFlite power front swivel seat ($187). Adventurer power swivel passenger seat ($101). Manual swivel seat ($86). Note: Swivel seats not available on Firedome four-door sedan and FireFlite wagon; available in Firesweep Sportsman. Dual exhaust as option ($34). Whitewall 8.00 x 14 four-ply Rayon tires on all, but Explorer ($42). Whitewall 8.50 x 14 four-ply Rayon tires on all, but Explorer ($46). Whitewall 9.80 x 14 four-ply Rayon tires on Explorer ($147). Radio with antenna ($94). Electric Tuner radio with antenna ($94). Rear seat speaker ($17). Manual dual rear antenna ($16). Hot water heater ($98). Instantaneous heater ($135). Standard two-tone paint ($21). Special solid or two-tone paint ($71). Color sweep trim ($21). Solex tinted glass ($43). Electric clock ($18). Windshield washer ($12). Variable speed windshield wiper ($7). Air foam cushion as option ($11). Air conditioning with hot water heater ($501). Air conditioning with accessory groups ($404). Dual air conditioning with hot water

heater for station wagons ($710). Padded dash as option ($21). Firesweep back-up lights ($12). Undercoating ($14). Full wheelcovers ($18). Firesweep front and rear carpets ($14). Rear window defogger ($21). Sure Grip differential ($50). Outside rearview mirror ($6). Remote control outside rearview mirror on Adventurer ($11); on others ($18). Photo electric tilt rearview mirror ($23). Power tailgate on six-passenger wagon ($40). Rear air suspension ($140). Aluminum sweep insert ($21). Automatic headlamp beam changer ($50). Front bumper guards ($12). Front and rear bumper guards ($24). Adventurer dual four-barrel V-8 for Firesweep ($142); for Firedome ($122); for FireFlite ($108). Station wagon luggage locker ($31). Adventurer deck lid molding ($11). Sill and lower deck molding package ($27). Number 1 roof molding package for four-door sedans and station wagons ($14). Number 2 roof molding package for Firesweep and Firedome Sportsman ($38). Special plastic steering wheel ($10). Panoramic rear window ($24). Air suspension (rear only).

HISTORICAL FOOTNOTES: Special appointments, including plaid upholstery, padded dash and custom steering wheel were added to the Firedome standard equipment list in the spring. Last season for DeSoto convertibles and station wagons. Final year for separate frame and body construction.

1960 DESOTO

FIREFLITE — (V-8) — Formerly a high-priced line, this series was relegated to low rung status for 1960, while cheaper nameplates were dropped altogether. New styling was actually a pleasant departure from the past few seasons, with cleaner renditions of the same general dart-shaped theme. Chrysler Corp.'s new unitized body construction was used. The DeSotos, in fact, were very Chrysler-like in appearance. Plain, full-length moldings adorned the bodysides and no sweep spear inserts were seen. The frontal treatment was dominated by a drop-center bumper, a flat, but distinctively shaped, grille and horizontal dual headlamps. Fins on the rear fenders were canted outward and ended with boomerang-shaped notches that housed the taillamp lenses. There were no convertibles or station wagons and the Sportsman designation for pillarless styles was dropped. Standard equipment was comprised of turn signals, front foam seat cushions and five 8.00 x 14 Rayon black tires.

FIREFLITE I.D. NUMBERS: Vehicle numbers were on the left front door hinge pillar post. Motor numbers were found on top of the engine, below the water outlet elbow. FireFlite vehicle numbers were 7103-100001 and up.

FIREFLITE SERIES PS1-L

Model Number	Body/Style Number	Body Type & Seating	Factory Price	Shipping Weight	Production Total
713	41	4-dr Sed-6	3017	3865	9,032
712	23	2-dr HT Cpe-6P	3102	3885	3,494
714	43	4-dr HT Sed-6P	3167	3865	1,958

1960 DeSoto, Adventurer two-door hardtop coupe, V-8 (AA)

ADVENTURER (V-8) — While FireFlites had no signature scripts for identification, three models in a new Adventurer series did. Such nameplates were affixed to the tailfins. Two-tone paint treatments were limited to roofs finished in contrasting color. The only big news of the year — and the only throwback to previous high-performance Adventurer models — was the use of Ram-Tuned induction with dual four-barrel carburetors. Standard equipment included all features found on FireFlites, plus padded dash panel; variable speed windshield wipers; full wheelcovers; special steering wheel; roof molding package; rear stone deflectors; bumper guards; back-up lamps; rear foam seat cushions and TorqueFlite automatic transmission with push-button controls.

ADVENTURER I.D. NUMBERS: Vehicle numbers and motor numbers were positioned as on FireFlites. Adventurer numbers began at 7203-100001 and up. All production was at one assembly point.

ADVENTURER SERIES PS3-M

Model Number	Body/Style Number	Body Type & Seating	Factory Price	Shipping Weight	Production Total
722	23	2-dr HT Cpe-6P	3663	3945	3,092
723	41	4-dr Sed-6P	3579	3895	5,746
724	43	4-dr HT Sed-6P	3727	3940	2,759

ENGINES

(FIREFLITE) V-8: Overhead valves. Cast iron block. Displacement: 361 cid. Bore and stroke: 4.12 x 3.38 inches. Compression ratio: 10.0:1. Brake hp: 295 at 4600 rpm. Five main bearings. Hydraulic valve lifters. Carburetor: Carter BBD two-barrel, model number 2923S.

(ADVENTURER) V-8: Overhead valves. Cast iron block. Displacement: 383 cid. Bore and stroke: 4.25 x 3.38 inches. Compression ratio: 10.0:1. Brake hp: 305 at 4600 rpm. Five main bearings. Hydraulic valve lifters. Carburetor: BBD two-barrel, model number 2923S.

CHASSIS FEATURES: Three-speed manual transmission was regular cost equipment on FireFlite models. TorqueFlite automatic transmission was standard in Adventurer. Wheelbase: (all) 122 inches. Overall length: (FireFlite) 215.4 inches; (Adventurer) 217 inches. Tires: 8.00 x 14.

OPTIONS: Four-barrel 383 cubic inch V-8, with dual exhausts and TorqueFlite required, in FireFlites ($85). Same engine for Adventurer ($54). Ram-induction 383 cubic inch dual four-barrel V-8 with dual exhausts and 12 inch brakes in Adventurer only ($283). Rear foam seat cushion as option ($11). Heater ($98). License plate frame ($4). Safe-T-Matic door lock in two-door model ($36); in four-door model ($43). Back-up lights for FireFlite ($12). Parking brake light ($4). Left outside rearview mirror ($6). Left remote control outside mirror ($18). Right outside rearview mirror ($6). Three-way Prismatic mirror ($5). Vanity mirror ($2). Front fender ornament ($9). Two-tone paint ($21). Power brakes with automatic only ($43). Six-way power seat ($101). Power steering. Automatic transmission required ($106). Power windows ($106). Push-button radio ($89). Radio with rear seat speaker ($106). Rear speaker with accessory groups ($17). RCA Automatic Record Player, radio required ($52). FireFlite four-door roof molding ($14). FireFlite two-door roof molding package ($38). Padded instrument panel in FireFlites ($21). Solex glass ($43). Easy Grip steering wheel ($10). Rear stone deflectors on FireFlites ($8). Sure-Grip differential ($50). Automatic swivel seats ($106). Five 8.00 x 14 Rayon whitewall tires ($42). Five 8.00 x 14 nylon whitewall tires ($59). Five 8.50 x 14 nylon whitewall tires ($83). PowerFlite transmission with 383 cubic inch V-8 in FireFlites only ($189). TorqueFlite transmission in FireFlites ($227). Undercoating with fiberglass pad ($15). Wheelcovers on FireFlites ($19). Windshield washers ($12). Variable speed wipers in FireFlites ($7). Same with washers in FireFlites ($18).

HISTORICAL FOOTNOTES: Next-to-last year for DeSotos. The Ram-Tuned induction Adventurer V-8 produced 330 hp at 4800 rpm. The FireFlite V-8 was again called a Turbo-Flash engine. The four-barrel Adventurer V-8 was called the Mark I powerplant. The ram inducted dual-quad V-8 was called the Ramcharger option. Manual transmission was considered a special order feature and automatic transmission was referred to as standard equipment, although it cost extra in FireFlites. Air suspension was dropped from the option list.

1961 DESOTO

DESOTO — (V-8) — DeSoto's long and illustrious history came to an end on Nov. 30, 1960, just 47 days after models built to 1961 specifications were introduced. New styling had reflected a minor facelift of the 1960 Adventurer series, with Chrysler-like themes. Rear taillamp design was altered, as were features of the bodyside trim. The fins were modified just ever so slightly, but not enough to draw extra sales. Canted headlamps had been adopted as part of the annual change and were integrated into an unusual double-tiered grille. Horizontal front bumpers were used. Series nomenclature disappeared for all practical purposes. The two available models were based on the former FireFlites, but referred to only as DeSotos. The end of production marked a sad close to 32 years of DeSotos and untold miles of practical use by millions of owners.

DESOTO I.D. NUMBERS: Serial numbers and motor numbers were found in the previous locations. Vehicle numbers 6113-100001 and up were used.

1961 DeSoto, Adventurer four-door hardtop sedan, V-8 (AA)

DESOTO SERIES RS1-L

Model Number	Body/Style Number	Body Type & Seating	Factory Price	Shipping Weight	Production Total
612	23	2-dr HT Sed-6P	3102	3760	911
614	43	4-dr HT Sed-6P	3166	3820	2,123

ENGINE: V-8: Overhead valves. Cast iron block. Displacement: 361 cid. Bore and stroke: 4.12 x 3.38 inches. Compression ratio: 9.0:1. Brake hp: 265 at 4400 rpm. Five main bearings. Hydraulic valve lifters. Carburetor: Stromberg WWC two-barrel, model number 3-188.

CHASSIS FEATURES: TorqueFlite automatic transmission was considered standard. Manual transmission was a deduct option. Wheelbase: 122 inches. Overall length: 215.6 inches. Tires: 8.00 x 14.

OPTIONS: Air conditioning including heater ($501). Air conditioning with Basic Group ($403). Permanent anti-freeze ($5). Crankcase vent system ($5). Heater ($98). Back-up lights ($12). Left-hand remote control outside rearview mirror ($18). Three-way Prismatic rearview mirror ($5). Two-tone paint ($21). Power brakes ($43). Six-way power seat ($101). Power steering ($106). Power windows ($106). Push-button radio ($89). RCA Automatic Record Player, radio required ($52). Four-door roof molding package ($14). Two-door roof molding package ($38). Padded instrument panel ($21). Solex glass ($43). Easy Grip steering wheel ($10). Sure-Grip differential ($50). Five 8.00 x 14 Rayon whitewall tires ($50). Five 8.00 x 14 Rayon whitewall tires ($42). TorqueFlite transmission ($227). Undercoating with fiberglass pad ($14). Full wheelcovers ($19). Windshield washers and variable speed windshield wipers ($19). Basic Group, including heater; radio; power steering; power brakes; windshield washer; variable speed windshield wipers; electric clock; and wheelcovers ($390). Deluxe Group, including left-hand remote control outside rearview mirror; rear foam seat cushion; rear bumper guards; padded instrument panel; sill and wheelhouse moldings and stone deflectors ($93). Light package, including glove box, trunk, map, backup, parking brake lights ($23).

HISTORICAL FOOTNOTES: Good-bye DeSoto.

DODGE
1946-1975

After World War II, Dodge re-entered the auto market with face-lifted prewar models. Like other Chrysler cars, they changed little, until 1949, when new midyear models appeared as a 'Second Series.' Introduced was a boxy exterior look. Deluxe and Custom names gave way to those like Coronet or Meadowbrook. Especially interesting, were Wayfarer coupes and Sportabout roadsters. An all-steel Sierra station wagon was introduced for 1950 and Sportabouts and eight-passenger sedans were dropped in 1951.

By John R. Smith

Despite model cutting, 1951 was a good year. Dodge operated at its highest, level. W.C. Newberg, president of the Hamtramck, Mich. based firm, ruled over Chrysler's largest plant, known as 'Dodge Main.' While most popular with Easterners, many Dodges were made in the huge San Leandro, Calif. plant or another in Los Angeles.

A Meadowbrook Special Series replaced the Wayfarer in 1952. The big news of 1953 was a 'Red Ram' V-8 in some series. In 1954, Dodge brought out the Firearrow show car and PowerFlite fully-automatic transmission for production models. With 10 extra horses, the 1954 Dodge V-8 set 196 speed records at Bonneville Salt Flats.

All-new 1955s came in three series with longer, lower, wider bodies; new hardtops; three-tone paint and more up-market trims. Some economy models disappeared, but luxurious Custom Royals were added. The styling program clicked, as Dodge sales jumped 160.3 percent. Even more cars could have been sold, except Dodge and Plymouth shared the same V-8 plant. This created a production jam-up, but Dodge still made 237,000 V-8s in a 273,000 unit year!

Restyling was seen at the tail of 1956s. Back fenders grew into fins. An innovative, push-button transmission, was introduced. The D-500 was introduced for performance buffs. Unfortunately, there was no magic push-button to help sales, which tumbled 22.4 percent. M.C. Patterson became President of Dodge in 1957 and new swept-wing styling appeared. Anticipating an improved market, renovations began at the home plant and led to 42 percent higher sales.

On Oct. 27, 1957, over 65,000 Dodge employee families attended Family Day, at Dodge Main, to preview 1958 models. They retained the swept-wing look and added a super-powerful B-block engine package. (A handful of electronic fuel-injected 1958s were built and later recalled.) Unfortunately, sales by the end of the year amounted to just over two cars for every 'Dodge boy' at the party. Dodge dropped to 3.1 percent of industry, after holding 4.5 percent the year before. Then, 1959 got off to a worse start. Labor problems, in 1958, resulted in a late production start. Potential buyers had to wait weeks for delivery, since showroom units were needed for display. What a way to begin the 45th year of Dodge history!

Aimed at competition with the Big Three was Dodge's expanded 1960 line of 118 inch wheelbase Darts, plus full-size Polaras and Monacos. Unitized bodies and a host of convenience options were new. Buyer reaction to the multi-size program was great and Dodge nearly caught Plymouth, after moving less than half as many cars in 1959!

Dodge entered the compact field in 1961. Under the direction of a new General Manager, B.J. Nichols, the Dodge Lancer appeared. It was a Plymouth Valiant with a slightly altered look. The Polara, on the 'big' chassis, had new medium prices. The Matador was dropped. Americans went on a big car buying binge and Dodge felt a substantial 2.15 percent drop in market share.

1962 Darts had a Lancer-inspired image. Wheelbase was down to 116 inches for a leaner size. Big Dodges were dropped, but returned at midyear as the Custom 880s. The 1962 Lancer, with a brighter grille and bucket seat GT, was a hit in an otherwise bad run. For 1963, the 111 inch wheelbase Dart replaced Lancer as a 'family-sized' compact. Polaras got a 119 inch wheelbase, abandoning 1962's 'lean-bred' theme. Flatter rooflines, squared-off decks and bolder grilles contributed to a high-performance image and helped output soar.

Dodge had a very successful year in 1964. Darts were changed little. Full-size Dodges had more glass area, larger doors and 'Golden Anniversary' styling updates. Aluminum grilles and downward tapering roof pillars were new appearance accents. The 880 and Custom 880 models gave buyers a big-car option from 1962 through 1964. Performance V-8s ranged from 265 to 425 hp. The 1965 Dodge was offered in 17 models, including a plush, new Monaco with front and rear bucket seats. Coronets were resized and poised for performance. The option list provided '426' Hemi V-8s, floor shifts, bucket seats and consoles. Model year output of 550,795 units eclipsed 1964's record 475,672 cars.

The 1966 Dodge Charger was a fastback show car brought to life. It was based on the new Coronet and both models combined high-performance and luxury. New Dart options included improved power steering and front disc brakes. Polaras came in seven varieties, ranging from economy sedan to sporty hardtop. Tilt & Telescope steering wheels and front disc brakes were optional. Advertised as Dodge's 'Rebellion,' the sales battle registered a gain, with a 6.6 percent market share. Model year output, however, tumbled to its first decline since 1962.

R.B. McCurry, Jr. became vice-president and general manager of Dodge in 1967, when Darts and Polaras were restyled. America's largest compact had a new unit body, curved side glass and delta-shaped taillamps. Polara was 6.3 inches

larger and innovated a new, blind quarter hardtop roofline. The face lifted Charger/Coronet received a new R/T option package for the performance crowd. But, again, Dodge popularity declined.

Moderate styling changes were seen on the smallest and largest 1968 Dodges, while Coronet/Chargers adopted a slim, rounded, 'Coke-bottle' theme. No longer slope-backed, the Charger had conventional hardtop styling on a Coronet body tipped by a unique wind-splitting nose. It came V-8 powered only, up to the hefty Hemi Charger. The popular 1968 lineup gave Dodge its fifth sales record in six years.

Hailed as 'Dodge Fever,' the brand's popularity saw only a small decline for 1969, which was still the second best year in Dodge history. The division hit a strong 6.8 percent market share. Big styling changes were reserved for the Polara/Monaco full-sized models, which took on the Chrysler 'fuselage' look with smooth, convex bodysides and curved, ventless side window glass.

As the 1970s dawned, Dodge continued to emphasize sportiness and performance, but the market began to change rapidly with governmental regulation and oil embargoes. The sporty, all-new Challenger, introduced in 1970 as a companion to Plymouth's Barracuda, was too late to find large success in the waning days of the muscle car era. It survived only through 1974, although the name was reintroduced later for a Japanese model imported by Dodge.

As gas mileage became more of a sales factor, the large cars gradually lost ground, and model offerings were pared down as a consequence. Restyled for 1971, the mid-range was split between the Charger two-door sport models and the Coronet sedans and wagons, all of which were reasonably successful through the styling cycle, which ran through 1974.

There was more buyer interest in the Dart line, which in response expanded to include additional luxury sedans and sporty, performance coupes with names like Demon and Swinger. Dodge imported its entries for the sub-compact market, the Colt line.

The full-size Polara and Monaco lines were restyled in 1974. When Coronets received a major face-lift in 1975, hardtop coupes were again included. The Charger nameplate went onto a personal luxury model based on the new Chrysler Cordoba's body shell. High-performance engines were gradually toned down, while options and luxury appointments were expanded.

Calendar year builds placed Dodge in seventh place for 1970, 1971, 1972, 1973 and 1975. In 1974, however, Dodge was able to pass Buick in annual production.

1946 Dodge, Custom two-door convertible, 6-cyl

1949 Dodge, Coronet four-door sedan, 6-cyl (OCW)

1950 Dodge, Meadowbrook two-door convertible, 6-cyl

1970 Dodge, Coronet Super Bee 440 Six-Pack two-door hardtop, V-8

1959 Dodge, Custom Royal Lancer four-door hardtop, V-8

1970 Dodge, Challenger T/A 340 Six-Pack, two-door hardtop, V-8

1966 Dodge, Charger two-door fastback coupe, V-8

1971 Dodge, Charger SE two-door hardtop, V-8

1968 Dodge, Coronet R/T two-door convertible, V-8

Standard Catalog of American Cars

1975 Dodge, Charger SE two-door hardtop coupe, V-8

1946 DODGE

1946 Dodge three-passenger Business Coupe, 6-cyl. JL

DELUXE SERIES — (SIX-CYLINDER) — The Deluxe was the base trim level and the least expensive of the 1946 Dodges. Postwar Dodges used the bodies and mechanical parts from 1942 models, with very slight restyling. A new checkerboard pattern grille replaced the 1942 grille and the parking lights were mounted low on the fenders, directly below the headlights. Several new mechanical innovations were included in the 1946 models. Among them were the introduction of the famous Fluid-Drive, a push-button starter system, Micronic filtration of the oil, twin-cylinder front wheel brakes and Oilite fuel filters. All Dodges built between 1946 and 1948 were classified as Series D-24 models, regardless of the particular body style.

DELUXE SERIES I.D. NUMBERS: All Dodges, if assembled in Detroit, began at 30645001 and went up to 30799737 and if assembled in Los Angeles began at 45000001 and went up to 45002145. The Deluxe models were identified by the suffix 'S' after the D-24 model designation.

1946 Dodge, two-door sedan, 6-cyl.

DELUXE SERIES

Model Number	Body/Style Number	Body Type & Seating	Factory Price	Shipping Weight	Production Total
D24S	Note 1	4-dr Sed-6P	1339	3256	Note 2
D24S	Note 1	2-dr Sed-6P	1299	3236	Note 2
D24S	Note 1	2-dr Cpe-3P	1229	3146	Note 2

NOTE 1: Owners seeking parts were advised, "There is no way to positively identify type of body. When in doubt, specify vehicle serial number and vehicle body number in ordering parts."
NOTE 2: No model year breakdown of production figures was available from Chrysler. Figures shown for 1948 Dodge represent total production of 1946, 1947, 1948 and first series 1949 models.

CUSTOM SERIES — (SIX-CYLINDER) — Dodge Custom Series models looked identical to the base offerings at first glance. Standard extras included Air Foam front seat cushions, dual electric windshield wipers and a chrome bead around the outside windows. Interiors were of a slightly richer trim. The Town Sedan had four doors, all of which opened from the rear.

CUSTOM SERIES I.D. NUMBERS: All Dodges, if assembled in Detroit, began at 30645001 and went up to 30799737 and if assembled in Calif., began at 45000001 and went up to 45002145. The Custom models were identified by the suffix 'C' after the D-24 model designation.

CUSTOM SERIES

Model Number	Body/Style Number	Body Type & Seating	Factory Price,	Shipping Weight	Production Total
D24C	Note 1	4-dr Sed-6P	1389	3281	Note 2
D24C	Note 1	4-dr Twn Sed-6P	1444	3331	Note 2
D24C	Note 1	4-dr Sed-7P	1743	3757	Note 2
D24C	Note 1	2-dr Clb Cpe-6P	1384	3241	Note 2
D24C	Note 1	2-dr Conv-5P	1649	3461	Note 2

NOTE 1: Owners seeking parts were advised, "There is no way to positively identify type of body. When in doubt, specify vehicle serial number and vehicle body number in ordering parts."
NOTE 2: No model year breakdown of production figures was available from Chrysler. Figures shown for 1948 Dodge represent total production of 1946, 1947, 1948 and first series 1949 models.

PRODUCTION NOTE: Total series output was 170,986 Deluxe models and 479,013 Custom models. Included in the Custom production totals are two (2) limousines and 302 chassis.

1946 ENGINES: L-head. Inline. Six-cylinder. Cast iron block. Displacement: 230 cid. Bore and stroke: 3.25 x 4.38 inches. Compression ratio: 6.6:1. Brake hp: 102. Four main bearings. Solid valve lifters. Carburetion: Stromberg BXV-2 single-barrel.

CHASSIS FEATURES: Wheelbase: (seven-passenger sedan) 137.5 inches; (others) 119.5 inches. Overall length: (seven-passenger sedan) 222.5 inches; (others) 204.5 inches. Tires: 6.00 x 16 tube-type black sidewall (white sidewall tires were not available in 1946). Three-speed manual transmissions were standard, with the Fluid-Drive as an option. Fluid-Drive "provides fluid transfer to the drive line with no metal-to-metal contact between the power source and drive."

CONVENIENCE OPTIONS: Electric clock. Turn signals. Radio. Heater. White wheel trim rings. Back-up lights.

HISTORICAL FOOTNOTES: The five millionth Dodge ever made was constructed this season, a year in which model year output peaked at 156,148 units. That left Dodge with a 7.4 percent share of the U.S. market. L.L. "Tex" Colbert was the president of Dodge.

1947 DODGE

1947 Dodge, four-door sedan, 6-cyl

DELUXE SERIES — (SIX-CYLINDER) — 1947 Dodges were identical to the 1946 models. The only change in the entire car was that the Ram ornament on the hood became slightly more detailed than the previous year. Dodge made a running change to 15-inch wheels during the year.

DELUXE SERIES I.D. NUMBERS: All Dodges, if assembled in Detroit, began at 30799738 and went up to 31011765 and if assembled in Los Angeles began at 45002146 and went up to 45022452. The Deluxe models were identified by the suffix 'S' after the D-24 model designation.

DELUXE SERIES

Model Number	Body/Style Number	Body Type & Seating	Factory Price	Shipping Weight	Production Total
D24S	Note 1	4-dr Sed-6P	1457	3256	Note 2
D24S	Note 1	2-dr Sed-6P	1417	3236	Note 2
D24S	Note 1	2-dr Cpe-3P	1347	3147	Note 2

NOTE 1: Owners seeking parts were advised, "There is no way to positively identify type of body. When in doubt, specify vehicle serial number and vehicle body number in ordering parts."
NOTE 2: Production figures given for 1948 represent total production for 1946, 1947, 1948 models and first series 1949 models. No model year breakouts were available from Chrysler. See 1948 for totals.

CUSTOM SERIES — (SIX-CYLINDER) — The Custom line Dodges continued to be just a little richer than Deluxes on close inspection. Dual electric wipers, pencil-stripe seats and rear fender moldings were the primary differentiation points. Dodge made a running change to 15-inch wheels during the year.

CUSTOM SERIES I.D. NUMBERS: All Dodges, if assembled in Detroit, began at 30799738 and went up to 31011765 and if assembled in Los Angeles began at 45002146 and went up to 45022452. The Custom models were identified by the suffix 'C' after the D-24 model designation.

CUSTOM SERIES

Model Number	Body/Style Number	Body Type & Seating	Factory Price	Shipping Weight	Production Total
D24C	Note 1	4-dr Sed-6P	1507	3281	Note 2
D24C	Note 1	4-dr Twn Sed-6P	1577	3331	Note 2
D24C	Note 1	4-dr Sed-7P	1861	3757	Note 2
D24C	Note 1	2-dr Clb Cpe-6P	1502	3241	Note 2
D24C	Note 1	2-dr Conv-5P	1871	3461	Note 2

NOTE 1: Owners seeking parts were advised. "There is no way to positively identify type of body. When in doubt, specify vehicle serial number and vehicle body number in ordering parts."
NOTE 2: Production figures given for 1948 represent total production for 1946, 1947, 1948 and first series 1949 models. No model year breakouts were available from Chrysler. See 1948 for totals.

ENGINES: Inline. L-head. Six-cylinder. Cast iron block. Displacement: 230 cid. Bore and stroke: 3.25 x 4.38 inches. Compression ratio: 6.6:1. Brake hp: 102 at 3800 rpm. Four main bearings. Solid valve lifters. Carburetion: Stromberg one-barrel Model BXV-3.

DODGE CHASSIS FEATURES: Wheelbase: (seven-passenger sedan) 137.5 inches; (other models) 119.5 inches. Overall length: (seven-passenger sedan) 222.5 inches; (other models) 204.5 inches. Tires: 6.00 x 16 tube-type black sidewall (7.10 x 15 after Ser. No. 30993973). Three-speed manual transmissions were standard, with Fluid Drive as an option (See 1946 chassis features).

CONVENIENCE OPTIONS: Electric clock. Turn signals. Radio. Heater. Goodyear Super Cushion low-pressure tires. White wheel trim rings. Back-up lights.

HISTORICAL FOOTNOTES: Dodge Div. of Chrysler Corp. was America's fifth ranked automaker this year. Calendar year production was recorded as 232,472 units for a 6.52 percent share of the total domestic market. State registration agencies totaled 209,552 registrations for the Dodge nameplate this year. This was also a record sales year for Dodge trucks. See Krause Publication's *STANDARD CATALOG of LIGHT-DUTY AMERICAN TRUCKS* for more information about Dodge trucks up to one-ton.

1948 DODGE

1948 Dodge, four-door Town sedan, 6-cyl

DELUXE SERIES — (SIX CYLINDER) — 1948 Dodges were identical to the 1947 models, with a price increase being the only change.

DELUXE SERIES I.D. NUMBERS: All Dodges, if assembled in Detroit began at 31011766 and went up to 31242628 and if assembled in Los Angeles began at 41022453 and went up to 45045426. The Deluxe models were identified by the suffix 'S' after the D-24 model designation.

DELUXE SERIES

Model Number	Body/Style Number	Body Type & Seating	Factory Price	Shipping Weight	Production Total
D24S	Note 1	4-dr Sed-6P	1718	3256	61.987
D24S	Note 1	2-dr Sed-6P	1676	3236	81,399
D24S	Note 1	2-dr Cpe-3P	1587	3146	27,600

NOTE 1: Owners were once again advised that there was no way to positively identify the type of body by code numbers (See Note 1, 1947).
NOTE 2: Production figures are totals for 1946, 1947, 1948 and first series 1949 models.

CUSTOM SERIES — (SIX CYLINDER) — If you learned to tell apart 1946 and 1947 Deluxes and Customs, you knew how to spot the 1948 (and first-series 1949) editions. They were identical.

CUSTOM SERIES I.D. NUMBERS: All Dodges, if assembled in Detroit, began at 31011766 and went up to 37058328 and if assembled in Los Angeles began at 41022453 and went up to 45045426. The Custom models were identified by the suffix 'C' after the D-24 model designation.

CUSTOM SERIES

Model Number	Body/Style Number	Body Type & Seating	Factory Price	Shipping Weight	Production Total
D24C	Note 1	4-dr Sed-6P	1788	3281	333,911
D24C	Note 1	4-dr Twn Sed-6P	1872	3331	27,800
D24C	Note 1	4-dr Sed-7P	2179	3757	3,698
D24C	Note 1	2-dr Clb Cpe-6P	1774	3241	103,800
D24C	Note 1	2-dr Conv-5P	2189	3461	9,500

NOTE 1: Owners were once again advised that there was no way to positively identify the type of body by code numbers (See Note 1. 1947).
NOTE 2: Production figures are totals for 1946, 1947, 1948 and first series 1949 models.

PRODUCTION NOTE: Total series output was 170,986 Deluxe models and 479,013 Custom models. Included in the Custom production totals are two limousines and 302 chassis.

ENGINES: Inline. L-head. Six-cylinder. Cast iron block. Displacement: 230 cid. Bore and stroke: 3.25 x 4.38 inches. Compression ratio: 6.6:1. Brake hp: 102 at 3600 rpm Four main bearings. Solid valve lifters. Carburetion: Stromberg one-barrel Model BXV-3.

CHASSIS FEATURES: Wheelbase: (seven-passenger sedan) 137.5 inches; (other models) 119.5 inches. Overall length: (seven-passenger sedan) 222.5 inches; (other models) 204.5 inches. Tires: 7.10 x 15 tube-type black sidewall. Three-speed manual transmissions were standard with Fluid-Drive as an option (See 1946 Chassis Features).

CONVENIENCE OPTIONS: Electric clock. Turn signals. Radio. Heater. White sidewall tires. Back-up lights.

HISTORICAL FOOTNOTES: Effective Dec. 1, 1948 all Dodges being assembled were considered 1949 series models for registration purposes. This included units with Serial numbers 31201087 built at Dodge Main, in Hamtramck, Mich., plus units with serial numbers 45041546 to 45045426 built at the Los Angeles, Calif. assembly plant. Dodge built 378,048 cars during calendar 1948, earning a 6.12 percent share of market in the process.

1949 DODGE

1949 Dodge, Wayfarer two-door coupe, 6-cyl (TVB)

WAYFARER SERIES — (SIX-CYLINDER) — February, 1949 saw the introduction of the first new body styles since the war. New model names were adopted for the all-new sheetmetal, with the Wayfarer making up the base trim level. The new Wayfarers featured longer and lower bodies than the previous year. Front fenders flared into the body easily and rear fenders continued to be bolted on. The checkerboard grille had a more pronounced peak in the center. Round parking lights were located below the headlights on the front fenders. The base Wayfarer line also included an all-new roadster. It was introduced with detachable windows, but Dodge later substituted vent wings and roll-up windows during the model run. Fluid-Drive became standard for 1949, with the new Gyro-Matic semi-automatic transmission being the optional transmission.

WAYFARER SERIES I.D. NUMBERS: Wayfarer models, if assembled in Detroit, began at 37000101 and went up to 37058328; if assembled in San Leandro began at 48000101 and went up to 48003813; if assembled in Los Angeles began at 48,500,101 and went up to 48501977.

WAYFARER SERIES

Model Number	Body/Style Number	Body Type & Seating	Factory Price	Shipping Weight	Production Total
D29	Note 1	2-dr Sed-6P	1738	3180	49,054
D29	Note 1	2-dr Cpe-3P	1611	3065	9,342
D29	Note 1	2-dr Rds-3P	1727	3145	5,420

NOTE 1: See Note 1, 1947 Deluxe models.

MEADOWBROOK SERIES — (SIX-CYLINDER) — The Meadowbrook Series was the base trim level four-door sedan, and the series was offered only in the four-door sedan configuration.

MEADOWBROOK SERIES I.D. NUMBERS: Meadowbrook Series sedans, if assembled in Detroit, began at 312450001 and went up to 31417330; if assembled in San Leandro began at 45050001 and went up to 45063676; if assembled in Los Angeles began at 45500101 and went up to 45504688.

MEADOWBROOK SERIES

Model Number	Body/Style Number	Body Type & Seating	Factory Price	Shipping Weight	Production Total
D30	Note 1	4-dr Sed-6P	1848	3355	Note 2

NOTE 1: See Note 1, 1947 Deluxe models.
NOTE 2: Total Meadowbrook and Coronet four-door sedan production was 144,390.

CORONET SERIES — (SIX-CYLINDER) — The Coronet series was the top trim level 1949 Dodge. The Coronet and Meadowbrook models differed only in interior appointments and minor exterior trim differences. Both differed from Wayfarers in having taillights housed in chrome fin-like appendages atop the fenders. The brake light was incorporated into the license housing/trunk handle ensemble in the center of the deck lid. The Town Sedan had an upgraded interior.

1949 Dodge, Coronet four-door Suburban, 6-cyl (TVB)

CORONET SERIES I.D. NUMBERS: Coronets if assembled in Detroit, began at 312450001 and went up to 31417330; if assembled in San Leandro began at 45050001 and went up to 45063676; if assembled in Los Angeles began at 45500101 and went up to 45504688.

CORONET SERIES

Model Number	Body/Style Number	Body Type & Seating	Factory Price	Shipping Weight	Production Total
D30	Note 1	4-dr Sed-6P	1927	3380	Note 2
D30	Note 1	4-dr Twn Sed-6P	2030	3390	Note 2
D30	Note 1	2-dr Clb Cpe-6P	1914	3325	45,435
D30	Note 1	2-dr Conv-5P	2329	3570	2,411
D30	Note 1	2-dr Sta Wag-6P	2865	3830	800
D30	Note 1	4-dr Sed-8P	2635	4070	NA

NOTE 1: See Note 1, 1947 Deluxe models.
NOTE 2: There was no breakout of four-door sedan production between the Meadowbrook, and Coronet Series. There were 144,390 four-doors produced in both series.

ENGINES: Inline. L-head. Six-cylinder. Cast iron block. Displacement: 230 cid. Bore and stroke: 3.25 x 4.38 inches. Compression ratio: 7.1:1. Brake hp: 103 at 3600 rpm. Four main bearings. Solid valve lifters. Carburetion: Stromberg Type BXVD one-barrel Model 3-93A.

CHASSIS FEATURES: Wheelbase: (Wayfarer) 115 inches; (Meadowbrook and Coronet) 123.5 inches, (8-passenger) 137.5 inches. Overall length. (Wayfarer roadster) 194.38 inches: (Wayfarer sedan) 196.3 inches. Tires: (Wayfarer) 6.70 x 15 tube-type black sidewall; (Meadowbrook and Coronet) 7.10 x 15 tube-type black sidewall. Three-speed standard transmissions with Fluid-Drive were standard in all 1949 models.

CONVENIENCE OPTIONS: Electric clock. Turn signals. Radio. Heater. Gyromatic semiautomatic transmission (Coronets). White sidewall tires.

HISTORICAL FOOTNOTES: The regular 1949 Dodges were introduced in April, 1949 and the roadster and suburban appeared in dealer showrooms somewhat later. Model year production peaked at 260,000 units. Calendar year sales of 298,399 cars were recorded. L.L. "Tex" Colbert was the president of the division this year. Dodge was the number two maker in the medium-price class. Dodge had an 18.9 percent share of medium-price auto sales and a 5.82 percent share of America's total new car market. The company was ranked number six for the industry as a whole. Dodge registrations totaled 273,350.

1950 DODGE

1950 Dodge, Wayfarer two-door roadster, 6-cyl (AA)

WAYFARER SERIES — (SIX-CYLINDER) — The 1950 Dodges utilized the same body introduced in 1949, with minor restyling of trim and a completely new grille. The grille consisted of three heavy horizontal bars, with the upper bar curving down at the ends. The second and third bars formed a long oval with round parking lights incorporated at the ends. A large chrome center plaque contained the Dodge crest. A single horizontal chrome strip was located on each front and rear fender. The model name was located below the chrome strip, on the front fenders. As in 1949, the Wayfarer was the base trim level. The model name Wayfarer was located on the front fenders.

WAYFARER SERIES I.D. NUMBERS: Wayfarer numbers were: (Detroit) 37060001 to 37129622; (San Leandro) 48004001 to 48007069; (Los Angeles) 48502001 to 48504748.

WAYFARER SERIES

Model Number	Body/Style Number	Body Type & Seating	Factory Price	Shipping Weight	Production Total
D33	Note 1	2-dr Sed-6P	1738	3200	65,000
D33	Note 1	2-dr Cpe-3P	1611	3095	7,500
D33	Note 1	2-dr Rds-3P	1727	3190	2,903

NOTE 1: See Note 1, 1947 Deluxe models.

MEADOWBROOK SERIES — (SIX-CYLINDER) — The Meadowbrook was the base trim level four-door sedan and the series was offered only in this configuration.

MEADOWBROOK SERIES I.D. NUMBERS: Meadowbrook numbers were: (Detroit) 31420001 to 31660411; (San Leandro) 45064001 to 45077531; (Los Angeles) 45505001 to 45515652 and went up. Motor numbers began at D34-1001 and went to 341043.

1950 Dodge, Meadowbrook four-door sedan, 6-cyl

MEADOWBROOK SERIES

Model Number	Body/Style Number	Body Type & Seating	Factory Price	Shipping Weight	Production Total
D34	Note 1	4-dr Sed-6P	1848	3395	Note 2

NOTE 1: See Note 1, 1947 Deluxe models.
NOTE 2: Total Meadowbrook and Coronet four-door sedan production was 221,791.

1950 Dodge, Coronet four-door sedan, 6-cyl.

CORONET SERIES — (SIX-CYLINDER) — The Coronet Series continued as the top trim level for 1950 and included all the features of the Meadowbrook, plus chrome trim rings on the wheels, rear fender gravel guards and the Coronet name on the front fenders. New for 1950 was the Diplomat two-door hardtop, added in June 1950. The Town Sedan with the upgraded interior was dropped in Feb. 1950

CORONET SERIES I.D. NUMBERS: Coronet numbers were: (Detroit) 31420001 to 31660411; (San Leandro) 45064001 to 45077531; (Los Angeles) 45505001 to 45515652 and went up. Motor numbers began at D34-1001 and went to 341043.

CORONET SERIES

Model Number	Body/Style Number	Body Type & Seating	Factory Price	Shipping Weight	Production Total
D34	Note 1	4-dr Sed-6P	1927	3405	Note 2
D34	Note 1	4-dr Twn Sed-6P	2030	3410	Note 2
D34	Note 1	2-dr Clb Cpe-6P	2012	3410	38,502
D34	Note 1	2-dr HT Cpe-6P	2223	3515	3,600
D34	Note 1	2-dr Conv-6P	2329	3590	1,800
D34	Note 1	4-dr Sta Wag-6P	2865	3850	600
D34	Note 1	4-dr Mtl Wag-6P	2865	3726	100
D34	Note 1	4-dr Sed-8P	2617	4045	1,300

NOTE 1: See Note 1, 1947 Deluxe Series.
NOTE 2: There was no breakout of four-door sedan production between the Meadowbrook and the Coronet Series. Total production in both series was 221,791.
NOTE 3: The four-door metal station wagon was called the Sierra.

ENGINES: Inline. L-head. Six-cylinder. Cast iron block. Displacement: 230 cid. Bore and stroke: 3.25 x 4.38 inches. Compression ratio: 7.1:1. Brake hp: 103 at 3600 rpm. Four main bearings. Solid valve lifters. Carburetion: Stromberg BXVD-3-93.

CHASSIS FEATURES: Wheelbase: (Wayfarer) 115 inches; (Meadowbrook and Coronet) 123.5 inches, (8-passenger) 137.5 inches. Overall length. (Wayfarer roadster) 194.38 inches: (Wayfarer sedan) 196.3 inches. (Meadowbrook and Coronet) 202.9 inches. Tires: (Wayfarer) 6.70 x 15 tube-type black sidewall; (Meadowbrook and Cornonet) 7.10 x 15 tube-type black sidewall. Three-speed manual with Fluid-Drive was once again the standard transmission in 1950.

CONVENIENCE OPTIONS: Electric clock. Turn signals. Radio. Heater. Gyromatic semiautomatic transmission. White sidewall tires.

HISTORICAL FOOTNOTES: The standard Dodge line was introduced Jan. 4, 1950 and the Diplomat appeared in dealer showrooms June 11, 1950. Model year production peaked at 350,000 units. Calendar year sales of 332,782 cars were recorded. L.L. "Tex" Colbert was again president of the Dodge Div. this year. W.C. Newberg became the divisional vice-president, a role he would fill through 1951. Dodge held a 4.99 percent total market share.

1951 DODGE

WAYFARER SERIES — (SIX-CYLINDER) — Considered by many to be the nicest looking car produced by the Dodge Div. up to that point, the 1951 models were derived from the 1949-1950 models with new hood, grille and bumper styling. The hood sloped smoothly to the grille, which was dominated by a bold horizontal bar extending around the parking lights at both ends. Bumpers had a rounded cross-section. The Dodge crest was located in the center of the redesigned hood, directly above the Dodge name, in block letters. A single chrome strip appeared on both the front and rear fenders and the Wayfarer name appeared on the front fenders below the chrome strip and behind the front wheelwell.

WAYFARER SERIES I.D. NUMBERS: Wayfarer numbers were: (Detroit) 37135001 to 37174914; (San Leandro) 48008001 to 48009814; (Los Angeles) 48506001 to 48507517. Motor numbers began at D42-1001 and went up.

WAYFARER SERIES

Model Number	Body/Style Number	Body Type & Seating	Factory Price	Shipping Weight	Production Total
D41	Note 1	2-dr Sed-6P	1895	3210	70,700
D41	Note 1	2-dr Cpe-3P	1757	3125	6,702
D41	Note 1	2-dr Rds-3P	1884	3175	1,002

NOTE 1: See Note 1, 1947 Deluxe models.
NOTE 2: Production figures are totals for 1951 and 1952 model years.

MEADOWBROOK SERIES — (SIX-CYLINDER) — As in the past, the Meadowbrook was the base trim level four-door sedan, and the series was offered only in this configuration.

MEADOWBROOK SERIES I.D. NUMBERS: Meadowbrook numbers were: (Detroit) 31663001 to 31867688; (San Leandro) 45079001 to 45090488; (Los Angeles) 45518001 to 45527385. Motor numbers began at D42-1001 and went up.

MEADOWBROOK SERIES

Model Number	Body/Style Number	Body Type & Seating	Factory Price	Shipping Weight	Production Total
D42	Note 1	4-dr Sed-6P	2016	3415	Note 2

NOTE 1: See Note 1, 1947 Deluxe models.
NOTE 2: Total Meadowbrook and Coronet four-door sedan production was 329,202. This figure is the total for 1951 and 1952 model years.

1951 Dodge, Coronet four-door sedan, 6-cyl

CORONET SERIES — (SIX-CYLINDER) — The Coronet Series continued as the top trim level for 1951 and included all the features of the Meadowbrook, plus chrome trim rings on the wheels and the name Coronet on the front fenders.

CORONET SERIES I.D. NUMBERS: Coronet numbers were: (Detroit) 31663001 to 31867688; (San Leandro) 45079001 to 45090488; (Los Angeles) 45518001 to 45527385. Motor numbers began at D42-1001 and went up. See Meadowbrook Series.

CORONET SERIES

Model Number	Body/Style Number	Body Type & Seating	Factory Price	Shipping Weight	Production Total
D42	Note 1	4-dr Sed-6P	2103	3415	Note 2
D42	Note 1	2-dr Clb Cpe-6P	2088	3320	56,103
D42	Note 1	2-dr HT Cpe-6P	2426	3515	21,600
D42	Note 1	2-dr Conv-6P	2514	3575	5,550
D42	Note 1	4-dr Mtl Sta Wag-6P	2710	3750	4,000
D42	Note 1		2855	3935	1,150

NOTE 1: See Note 1, 1947 Deluxe Series.
NOTE 2: There was no breakout of four-door sedan production between the Meadowbrook and Coronet Series. Total production in both series was 329,202.
NOTE 3: Production figures are totals for 1951 and 1952 model years.
NOTE 4: The two-door hardtop is the Diplomat. The metal station wagon is the Sierra.

ENGINES: Inline. L-head. Six-cylinder. Cast iron block. Displacement: 230 cid. Bore and stroke: 3.25 x 4.38 inches. Compression ratio: 7.1:1. Brake hp: 103 at 3600 rpm. Four main bearings. Solid valve lifters. Carburetion: Stromberg Type BXVD one-barrel Model 3-93.

CHASSIS FEATURES: Wheelbase: (Wayfarers) 115 inches; (Meadowbrook and Coronet) 123.5 inches; (Eight-passenger) 137.5 inches. Overall length: (Wayfarer roadster) 194.38 inches; (Wayfarer sedan) 196.3 inches; (Meadowbrook and Coronet) 202.9 inches; (Eight-passenger) 222.9 inches. Front tread: (all models) 56 inches. Rear tread: (all models) 59 inches. Tires: (Wayfarer) 6.70 x 15; (Meadowbrook and Coronet) 7.10 x 15; (Sierra) 7.60 x 15; (Eight-passenger) 8.20 x 15.

POWERTRAIN OPTIONS: Fluid-Drive was standard. Gyromatic transmission ($95). Heavy-duty air cleaner. Available rear axle gear ratios: 3.73: 1; 3.90: 1; 4.0:1.

CONVENIENCE OPTIONS: Electric clock. Turn signals. MoPar radio. Heater (called the "All Weather Comfort System"). Chrome wheel trim rings (standard on Coronet). Back-up lights. Gyromatic semi-automatic transmission (with Sprint-Away passing gear). Whitewall tires.

HISTORICAL FOOTNOTES: The 1951 Dodges were introduced Jan. 20, 1951. Model year production peaked at 292,000 units. Calendar year sales of 325,694 cars were recorded. W.C. Newberg became president of Dodge Div. this year. Dodge earned a 6.10 percent share of total market. The Sierra all-steel station wagon and eight-passenger sedans were discontinued late in the calendar year, when production of models built to 1952 specifications commenced (Nov., 1951). Nearly 90 percent of Dodge Div. output was quartered at their Hamtramck, Michigan plant, which was called 'Dodge Main'. This large factory offered 5,480,312 square feet of floor space. Preparations began, late in the season, for production of an all-new Dodge V-8.

1952 DODGE

WAYFARER SERIES — (6-CYL) — While 1951 and 1952 Dodges are very nearly identical, there are some very minor revisions in the later year. Dodge was involved heavily in the massive war effort during the Korean conflict and was so busy with the construction of military vehicles, that the passenger car line was continued nearly the same. Some of the very subtle changes included a painted lower grille louver; red reflector dot below the taillight lenses; minor hubcap restyling; a new trunk handle; interior trim and the finish of the dashboard. Also, the rear fender moldings and taillight bezels were no longer connected. It was the last year for the low trim level, short wheelbase Wayfarer series, which was identified by the Wayfarer name on the front fenders. The Wayfarer roadster was dropped.

WAYFARER SERIES I.D. NUMBERS: Wayfarer models, if assembled in Detroit, began at 37175001 and went to 37207644. If assembled in San Leandro, Calif., began at 48009901 and went to 48011259 and, if assembled in Los Angeles, began at 48507601 and went to 48508754. Motor numbers continued where 1951 models left off and went up to D42-419735.

WAYFARER SERIES

Model Number	Body/Style Number	Body Type & Seating	Factory Price	Shipping Weight	Production Total
D41	Note 1	2-dr Sed-6P	2034	3140	Note 2
D41	Note 1	2-dr Cpe-3P	1886	3050	Note 2
D41	Note 1	2-dr Rds-3P	1924	3100	Note 2

NOTE 1: See Note 1, 1947 Deluxe models.
NOTE 2: Production figures were not separated between 1951 and 1952 models. Therefore, production figures shown for 1951 models represented totals for both 1951 and 1952 model years.

MEADOWBROOK SERIES — (6-CYL) — As in the past, the Meadowbrook was the base trim level four-door sedan and the series was offered only in the particular configuration.

MEADOWBROOK SERIES I.D. NUMBERS: Meadowbrook Series sedans, if assembled in Detroit, began at 31867801 and went to 32038822. If assembled in San Leandro, Calif., began at 45090601 and went to 45100113. If assembled in Los Angeles, began at 45527501 and went to 45534770. Motor numbers continued where 1951 models left off and went up to D42-419735.

MEADOWBROOK SERIES

Model Number	Body/Style Number	Body Type & Seating	Factory Price	Shipping Weight	Production Total
D41	Note 1	4-dr Sed-6P	2164	3355	Note 2

NOTE 1: See Note 1, 1947 Deluxe models.
NOTE 2: See Note 2, 1952 Wayfarer Series.

1952 Dodge, Coronet two-door convertible, 6-cyl (AA)

CORONET SERIES — (6-CYL) — The Coronet Series continued as the top trim level for 1952 and included all the features of the Meadowbrook, plus chrome trim rings on the wheels and the Coronet name on the front fenders. The eight-passenger sedan was dropped late in 1951.

CORONET SERIES I.D. NUMBERS: Coronets, if assembled in Detroit, began at 31867801 and went to 32038822. If assembled in San Leandro, Calif., began at 45090601 and went to 45100113. If assembled in Los Angeles, began at 45527501 and went to 45534770. Motor numbers continued where 1951 models left off and went up to D42-419735.

CORONET SERIES

Model Number	Body/Style Number	Body Type & Seating	Factory Price	Shipping Weight	Production Total
D41	Note 1	4-dr Sed-6P	2256	3385	Note 2
D42	Note 1	2-dr Clb Cpe-6P	2240	3290	Note 2
D42	Note 1	2-dr Diplomat-6P	2602	3475	Note 2
D42	Note 1	2-dr Conv-6P	2698	3520	Note 2
D42	Note 1	4-dr Sierra Wag-6P	2908	3735	Note 2
D42	Note 1	4-dr Sed-8P	3064	3935	Note 2

NOTE 1: See Note 1, 1947 Deluxe Series.
NOTE 2: See Note 2, 1952 Wayfarer Series.

ENGINES: Inline. L-head. Six-cylinder. Cast iron block. Displacement: 230 cid. Bore and store: 3.25 x 4.265 inches. Compression ratio: 7.0:1. Brake hp: 103 at 3600 rpm. Four main bearings. Solid valve lifters. Carburetion: Stromberg Type BXVD one-barrel Model 3-93.

CHASSIS FEATURES

Wheelbase: (Wayfarers) 115 inches; (Meadowbrook and Coronet) 123.5 inches; (eight-passenger sedan) 137.5 inches. Overall length: (Wayfarer roadster) 194.38 inches; (Wayfarer sedan) 196.3 inches; (Meadowbrook and Coronet) 202.9 inches; (eight-passenger sedan) 222.5 inches. Tires: (Wayfarers) 6.70 x 5 tube-type black sidewall; (Meadowbrook and Coronet) 7.10 x 15 tube-type black sidewall; (Sierra station wagon) 7.60 x 15 tube-type black sidewall; (eight-passenger sedan) 8.20 x 15 tube-type black sidewall. A three-speed manual with Fluid-Drive continued to be the standard transmission, with Gyromatic semi-automatic as an option on all models except the Wayfarer roadster.

CONVENIENCE OPTIONS: Electric clock. Turn signals. MoPar radio. Heater (called the 'All Weather Comfort System'). Chrome wheel trim rings (standard on Coronet). Back-up lights. Gyromatic semi-automatic transmission (with Sprint-Away passing gear). Dodge safety tint glass. White sidewall tires.

HISTORICAL FOOTNOTES: The 1952 Dodges were introduced Nov. 10, 1951. Model year production peaked at 206,000 units. Calendar year sales of 259,519 cars were recorded. W.C. Newberg was the president of Dodge Div. this year. The Meadowbrook Special Series was introduced late in the calendar year, as was a new 'Red Ram' Dodge V-8. Dodge was America's sixth largest automaker. The company reported that the number of Dodges licensed to operate on the roads this year was approximately 2.5 million cars. On a calendar year basis, Dodge made an estimated 15,613 hardtop coupes; 25,504 convertibles and 58,546 station wagons during 1952.

1953 DODGE

MEADOWBROOK SERIES — (6-CYL) — 1953 was a very significant year for Dodge for several reasons. Among them was the totally restyled body, the introduction of a fully automatic transmission and the introduction of the famous 241 cid 'Hemi' V-8 engine. In the styling department, the 1953 Dodge grille evolved from that of the 1950-52 models, now featuring two horizontal bars with five vertical dividing bars. On V-8 powered models, the hood featured a 'Jet Flow' scoop around the V-8 emblem. Also new for 1953 was the large, one-piece curved windshield. The new doors opened wider and the top featured a larger, wraparound rear window, one-piece on sedans and three-piece on the Diplomat hardtop. The new doors also featured pull-type handles. Oval taillights were used and the fuel filler was relocated to the lower left side of the escutcheon panel. The Meadowbrook Special was the base trim level for 1953 and was included primarily as a salesman's car. The Specials were devoid of any chrome side trim and had rubber windshield and rear window moldings. The interiors were as stark as possible. There was also a standard Meadowbrook Series. Meadowbrooks featured a Dodge crest on the hood, chrome windshield and rear window moldings and chrome side strips (which began low on the body, behind the front wheelwell, and ran horizontally back and swept up over the rear wheel opening). The Meadowbrook name was located at the tip of the front fenders.

MEADOWBROOK SERIES I.D. NUMBERS: Meadowbrook Series, if assembled in Detroit, began at 32042001 and went to 32152851 and, if assembled in San Leandro, began at 45102001 and went to 45105772. If assembled in Los Angeles, began at 45536001 and went to 45538622. Motor numbers began at D46-1001 and went to 134677.

MEADOWBROOK SERIES

Model Number	Body/Style Number	Body Type & Seating	Factory Price	Shipping Weight	Production Total
D46	Note 1	4-dr Spl Sed-6P	2000	3195	84,158
D46	Note 1	2-dr Spl Sed-6P	1958	3100	36,766
D46	Note 1	4-dr Sed-6P	2000	3175	Note 2
D46	Note 1	2-dr Sed-6P	1958	3085	Note 2
D47	Note 1	2-dr Sub-6P	2176	3190	15,751

NOTE 1: See Note 1, 1947 Deluxe models.
NOTE 2: There is no breakout between Meadowbrook Special models and standard Meadowbrook models. Therefore, figures given represent total Meadowbrook production for each of the body styles.

1953 Dodge, Coronet four-door sedan, V-8 (AA)

CORONET SERIES — (ALL ENGINES) — The Coronet was the top trim level for 1953 and included all the Meadowbrook Series features, plus an air scoop with the nomenclature "Dodge V-8" located beneath the Ram hood ornament, chrome gravel deflector and the Coronet name, in script, on the sides of the front fenders. The two-door hardtop was once again called the Coronet Diplomat. Six-cylinder sedans appeared in March.

CORONET SERIES I.D. NUMBERS: Coronet models powered by six-cylinder engines used the same serial number sequence as the Meadowbrook Series and V-8 powered 'Coronets. If assembled in Detroit, numbers began at 345001 and went to 34635734. If assembled in San Leandro, began at 4250001 and went to 42507899 and, if assembled in Los Angeles, began at 41500001 and went to 41504467. Motor numbers began at D44-1001 and went to 176412.

CORONET SERIES

Model Number	Body/Style Number	Body Type & Seating	Factory Price	Shipping Weight	Production Total
D46/44	Note 1	4-dr Sed-6P	211112220	3220/3385	Note 2
D46/44	Note 1	2-dr Sed-6P	2084/2198	3155/3325	Note 2
D48	Note 1	2-dr Diplomat-6P	2361	3310	17,334
D48	Note 1	2-dr Conv-6P	2494	3480	4,100
D48	Note 1	2-dr Sierra Wag-6P	2503	3425	5,400

NOTE 1: See Note 1, 1947 Deluxe models.
NOTE 2: See Note 2, 1953 Meadowbrook Series. The note also applies to Coronet two-door and four-door sedans equipped with six-cylinder engines.
NOTE 3: The V-8 was considered a separate series, not an option. Factory prices and weights, on charts, give data for six-cylinder cars above slash and V-8 data below slash.

ENGINES: Inline. L-head. Six-cylinder. Cast iron block. Displacement: 230 cid. Bore and stroke: 3.25 x 4.625 inches. Compression ratio: 7.1:1. Brake hp: 103 at 3600 rpm. Four main bearings. Solid valve lifters. Carburetion: Carter one-barrel Model D6H2.

Hemi head overhead valve V-8. Cast iron block. Displacement: 241 cid. Bore and stroke: 3.44 x 3.25 inches. Compression ratio: 7.0:1. Brake hp: 140 at 4400 rpm. Five main bearings. Hydraulic valve lifters. Carburetion: Stromberg two-barrel Model WW3-108.

CHASSIS FEATURES: Wheelbase: (Diplomat hardtop, convertible, Suburban station wagon) 114 inches; (Sedan and club coupe) 119 inches. Overall length: (Suburban and Sierra station wagons) 189.6 inches; (Convertible and Diplomat) 191.3 inches; (four-door sedans and club coupes) 201.4 inches. Tires: (Meadowbrook) 6.70 x 15 tube-type black sidewall; (Coronet) 7.10 x 15 tube-type blackwall. Three-speed manual transmission was once again the standard transmission, with Overdrive, Fluid-Drive and GyroTorque automatic as the optional transmissions.

CONVENIENCE OPTIONS: Electric clock. Turn signals. MoPar radio. Heater. Windshield washers. Back-up lights. Solex tinted glass. Wheelcovers. Overdrive. Gyro-Matic drive (Fluid-Drive). Gyro-Torque automatic drive. White sidewall tires. Bright wheel opening trim. Chrome wire wheels. Continental spare wheel kit.

HISTORICAL FOOTNOTES: The 1953 Dodges were introduced Oct. 23, 1952 and the Coronet Six appeared in dealer showrooms March 18, 1953. Model year production peaked at 304,000 units. Calendar year sales of 293,714 cars were recorded. W.C. Newberg was the president of Dodge Div. this year. The Meadowbrook Special Series was introduced late in the calendar year, as was a new 'Red Ram' Dodge V-8. On Jan. 15, 1953 the 100,000th Dodge built to 1953 specifications left the factory. A general price cut took effect March 25, 1953. Sales of a new option, air-conditioning, began April 6, 1953, during the same month the Meadowbrook Special was discontinued and the Coronet Six was announced for mid-March availability. Dodge topped all other American Eights in the Mobilgas Economy Run. In September 1953, a 1954 Dodge set 196 AAA stock car speed records at the Bonneville Salt Flats in Utah. On Nov. 12, 1953 the Dodge Firearrow, a futuristic sports roadster, was put on display at leading U.S. auto shows. NASCAR drivers liked the powerful Dodges and drove them to six wins in 1953, the first such victories for Dodge.

1954 DODGE

MEADOWBROOK SERIES — (ALL ENGINES) — For 1954, Dodges utilized the same body introduced in 1953, with minor changes. The new grille featured a prominent horizontal bar with a distinctive vertical post in the middle. The taillight clusters were redesigned and chrome stone shields were used on the rear fenders of the top trim levels. Rubber stone shields were used on the base trim level Meadowbrook Series. The Meadowbrooks also included rubber windshield and rear window moldings: the Dodge crest in the center of the hood; the Meadowbrook name, in script, on the rear fenders and a short chrome strip along the sides of the front fenders and part of the front door.

MEADOWBROOK SERIES I.D. NUMBERS: Meadowbrook Series, if assembled in Detroit, began at 32152901 and went to 32189926; if assembled in San Leandro, began at 45105801 and went to 45110883. Motor numbers began at D51-1001 and went to 1877 and D51A-1001 and went to 1877.

MEADOWBROOK SERIES

Model Number	Body/Style Number	Body Type & Seating	Factory Price	Shipping Weight	Production Total
D50/51	Note 1	4-dr Sed-6P	2000/2151	3195/3390	11,193
D50/51	Note 1	2-dr Clb Cpe-6P	1958/2129	3120/3335	4,251

NOTE 1: See Note 1, 1947 Deluxe models.
NOTE 2: The figures to the left of the slant bars represent six-cylinder models and the figures to the right of the slant bars represent V-8 powered models.

CORONET SERIES — (ALL ENGINES) — The Coronet was now the intermediate trim level Dodge and included all the Meadowbrook features, plus chrome windshield and rear window moldings; a full length chrome strip along the middle of the body (which dipped down behind the front door to near the top of the rear wheelwell) and chrome rear fender stone shields. The Coronet name, in script, appeared on the sides of the rear fenders.

CORONET SERIES I.D. NUMBERS: Coronet models powered by six-cylinder engines and assembled in Detroit, began at 32160001 and went up to 32189926; if assembled in San Leandro, began at 45110001 and went to 45110883. V-8 engines and assembled in Detroit, began at 34642001 and went up to 34739536 and, if assembled in San Leandro, began at 42510001 and went up to 42516879. Six-cylinder motor numbers began at DI-1001 and went to 35830. V-8 motor numbers began at D502-1001 and went up to 110857.

276

CORONET SERIES

Model Number	Body/Style Number	Body Type & Seating	Factory Price	Shipping Weight	Production Total
D50/51	Note 1	4-dr Sed-6P	2111/2220	3235/3405	50,963
D50/51	Note 1	2-dr Clb Cpe-6P	2084/2198	3165/3345	12,499
D52/53	Note 1	2-dr Sub-6P	2204/2492	3185/3400	9,489
D52/53	Note 1	4-dr Sierra-6P	2694/2935	3430/3605	1,300
D53-2	Note 1	2-dr HT Cpe-6P	2355	3310	100
D53-2	Note 1	2-dr Conv-6P	2489	3505	50

NOTE 1: See Note 1, 1947 Deluxe model.
NOTE 2: The figures to the left of the slant bars represent six-cylinder models and the figures to the right of the slant bars represent V-8 powered models. Those models with only one set of figures were available only with V-8 power.

1954 Dodge, Royal four-door sedan, V-8 (AA)

ROYAL SERIES — (V-8) — The Royal Series was the new top trim level for 1954 and was available only with the 241 cid 'Hemi' engine. The Royal models included all the Coronet features, plus chrome rocker panel moldings; V-8 emblem; 'Jet Flow' scoop on the front of the hood and chrome fins along the tops of the rear fenders.

ROYAL SERIES I.D. NUMBERS: Royal models assembled in Detroit, began at 34642001 and went up to 34799536 and those assembled in San Leandro began at 42510001 and went up to 42516879. Motor numbers began at D502-1001 and went up to 110857.

ROYAL SERIES

Model Number	Body/Style Number	Body Type & Seating	Factory Price	Shipping Weight	Production Total
D50-3	Note 1	4-dr Sed-6P	2348	3425	50,050
D50-3	Note 1	2-dr Clb Cpe-6P	2324	3365	8,900
D53-3	Note 1	2-dr HT Cpe-6P	2478	3355	3,852
D53-3	Note 1	2-dr Conv-6P	2607	3575	2,000

NOTE 1: See Note 1, 1947 Deluxe models.

ENGINES

Inline. L-head. Six-cylinder. Cast iron block. Displacement: 230 cid. Bore and stroke: 3.25 x 4.625 inches. Compression ratio: 7.25:1. Brake hp: 110 at 3600 rpm. Four main bearings. Solid valve lifters. Carburetion: Carter Model D6U1 one-barrel.

Hemi-head overhead valve V-8. Cast iron block. Displacement: 241 cid. Bore and stroke: 3.312 x 3.25 inches. Compression ratio: 7.5:1. (7.1:1 on Meadowbrook models). Brake hp: 150 at 4400 rpm (140 at 4400 rpm on Meadowbrook models). Five main bearings. Solid valve lifters. Carburetion: Stromberg two-barrel Model WW-3-108.

CHASSIS FEATURES: Wheelbase; (Hardtop, convertible and two-door station wagon models) 114 inches: (other models) 119 inches. Overall length: (short-wheelbase models) 196 inches; (long-wheelbase models) 205.5 inches. Tires: (Meadowbrook and six-cylinder equipped Suburbans) 6.70 x 15 tube-type black sidewall; (other models) 7.10 x 15 tube-type black sidewall. Three-speed manual transmission was once again the standard transmission, with Overdrive ($98); Fluid-Drive ($20) and PowerFlite automatic transmission ($189) being the optional transmissions. Gyro-Matic Drive was also available ($130).

1954 Dodge, Royal 500 convertible, V-8 (IMS)

CONVENIENCE OPTIONS: Electric clock. Turn signals, MoPar Radio. Power steering ($134). Back-up lights. Solex tinted glass. Airtemp air conditioning ($643). White sidewall tires ($30). Windshield washers. Power brakes ($37). Chrome wire wheels. Wire wheelcovers. Continental spare tire kit.

HISTORICAL FOOTNOTES: The full-sized Dodge and Royal models were introduced Oct. 8, 1953 and the four-door Dodge Sierra wagon appeared in dealer showrooms Dec. 8, 1953. Model year production peaked at 150,930 units. Calendar year sales of 151,766 cars were recorded. W.C. Newberg was president of Dodge Div. Dodge Div. earned a 2.75 percent share of the total U.S. market this year. In Jan., 1954, Dodge Div. initiated a heavy radio and television advertising campaign. On Feb. 7, 1954, an advertising contest to celebrate Dodge's 40th anniversary as a car maker was launched. On Feb. 20, the Firearrow dream car was exhibited at the Chicago Auto Show. A new range of special spring paint colors was announced March 22, 1954. On April 8, a Dodge equipped with overdrive transmission won out over all other low-medium priced U.S. cars in the Mobilgas Economy Run. It averaged 25.3873 mpg for the complete 1,335 mile course. On May 31, 1954 a specially-trimmed Dodge convertible paced the Indianapolis 500-Mile Race, and 701 Royal 500 pace car replica convertibles were produced; the figure is included in Royal convertible production totals. Pace car engines were equipped with four-barrel carburetors and dual exhausts. On June 16, 1954 the Firearrow proved itself to be a functional dream car, as it was used to establish a woman's world speed record of 143.44 mph for 4.7 miles at the Chrysler proving Grounds, in Chelsea, Mich. There was only a single Dodge win in NASCAR racing this year.

1955 DODGE

1955 Dodge, Coronet four-door sedan, 6-cyl (AA)

CORONET SERIES (ALL ENGINES) — All Dodge models were totally restyled once again for 1955. They were more than six inches longer than the 1954 models. They were also lower and wider and were powered by a larger and more powerful V-8 engine. The six-cylinder engine was also boosted, to 123 hp, as the great performance race of the mid-'50s began. Dodge's advertising people called the new styling 'Flair-Fashion.' This styling was set off by the use of tri-color paint schemes. The new grille was divided into two separate openings. Each opening housed a single horizontal bar that wrapped around the fender and incorporated the parking light. All models featured a simulated hood scoop. The windshield was a wraparound affair, which Dodge referred to as a 'new horizon' windshield. The new taillights were emphasized by a chrome trim piece and the higher trim levels featured dual lenses on each side (the lower of which was often replaced with back-up lights). Six-cylinder equipped models featured the large Dodge crest in the center of the hood and trunk lid. Those models with V-8 power featured the Dodge crest over a large "V". The Coronet was the base trim level for 1955 and featured chrome windshield and rear window moldings; chrome trim around the simulated hood scoop; chrome headlight doors and a single horizontal chrome strip running from the front fender to the rear of the front door. The Coronet name appeared in script, along the side of the front fenders on cars with Lancer trim and just ahead of the taillights on those with standard trim. Late in the year, Lancer trim was made available on sedans and station wagons.

CORONET SERIES I.D. NUMBERS: Six-cylinder powered Coronets assembled in Detroit began at 32192001 and went to 32225514 and those assembled in Los Angeles began at 48016001 and went to 48016299. V-8 powered models assembled in Detroit began with 34740001 and went to 34970679 and those assembled in Los Angeles began at 42518001 and went to 42526800. Six-cylinder motor numbers began at D56-1001 and went up to D56-34905. V-8 motor numbers began at D551-1001 and went up to D551-149857.

CORONET SERIES

Model Number	Body/Style Number	Body Type & Seating	Factory Price	Shipping Weight	Production Total
D55/56	Note 1	4-dr Sed-6P	2068/2171	3295/3395	46,074
D55/56	Note 1	2-dr Sed-6P	1988/2091	3235/3360	24,104
D55-1	Note 1	2-dr Lancer HT-6P	2256	3375	26,727
655/56	Note 1	2-dr Sub-6P	2324/2427	3410/3550	8,115
D55/56	Note 1	4-dr Sierra Wag-6P	2438/2541	3480/3590	5,952
D55/56	Note 1	4-dr Sierra Wag-8P	2540/2643	3595/3695	Note 2

NOTE 1: See Note 1, 1947 Deluxe models.
NOTE 2: There is no breakout per six and eight-passenger Sierra station wagon models. Production figures given under the six-passenger model represent the cumulative total for both styles.
NOTE 3: The figures to the left of the slant bars represent six-cylinder models and the figures to the right of the slant bars represent V-8 models. Those without a slant bar came only as V-8s.

ROYAL SERIES — (V-8) — The Royal was the intermediate trim level for 1955 and included all the Coronet features plus exterior, chrome headlight doors and the Royal name, in script, on the front or rear fenders. Lancer trim, standard on Lancers (as hardtops and convertibles were named in all lines), became optional on most or all other models. Narrow chrome strips trailed back from the hood scoop, dipped at the C-pillar, then continued high on the rear fenders to the taillight housings.

ROYAL SERIES I.D. NUMBERS: Royal V-8 powered models assembled in Detroit began with 34740001 and went to 34970679 and those assembled in Los Angeles began at 42518001 and went to 42526800. V-8 motor numbers began at D551-1001 and went up to D551-149857.

1955 Dodge, Royal Sierra four-door station wagon, V-8 (AA)

ROYAL SERIES

Model Number	Body/Style Number	Body Type & Seating	Factory Price	Shipping Weight	Production Total
D55-2	Note 1	4-dr Sed-6P	2285	3425	45,323
D55-2	Note 1	2-dr Lancer HT-6P	2370	3425	25,831
D55-2	Note 1	4-dr Sierra Wag-6P	2634	3655	5,506
D55-2	Note 1	4-dr Sierra Wag-8P	2736	3730	Note 2

NOTE 1: See Note 1, 1947 Deluxe models.
NOTE 2: See Note 2, 1955 Coronet models.
NOTE 3: The figures to the left of the slant bars represent six-cylinder models and the figures to the right of the slant bars represent V-8 models. Those without a slant bar came only as V-8s.

CUSTOM ROYAL SERIES — (V-8) — The Custom Royal was the top trim level for 1955 and included all the Royal features, plus the Royal name and medallion on the rear fenders of the sedans with standard side trim and on the front fenders of models with Lancer sweepspear trim. The Lancer hardtop and convertible models featured chrome fins on the tops of the rear fenders. In April, a a Royal Lancer four-door sedan appeared as an answer to the new four-door hardtops from General Motors. It had Lancer side trim. There was a midyear LaFemme option for the two-door Lancer.

CUSTOM ROYAL SERIES I.D. NUMBERS: Custom Royal V-8 powered models assembled in Detroit began with 34740001 and went to 34970679 and those assembled in Los Angeles began at 42518001 and went to 42526800. V-8 motor numbers began at D551-1001 and went up to D551-149857.

1955 Dodge, Royal Lancer two-door hardtop coupe, V-8 (AA)

CUSTOM ROYAL SERIES

Model Number	Body/Style Number	Body Type & Seating	Factory Price	Shipping Weight	Production Total
D55-3	Note 1	4-dr Sed-6P	2448	3485	55,503
D55-3	Note 1	2-dr Lancer HT-6P	2518	3480	30,499
D55-3	Note 1	2-dr Lancer Conv-6P	2723	3610	3,302
D55-3	Note 1	4-dr Lancer Sed-6P	NA	NA	NA

NOTE 1: See Note 1, 1947 Deluxe models.

ENGINES

Inline. L-head. Six-cylinder. Cast iron block. Displacement: 230 cid. Bore and stroke: 3.25 x 4.625 inches. Compression ratio: 7.4:1. Brake hp: 123 at 3600 rpm. Four main bearings. Solid valve lifters. Carburetion: Stromberg two-barrel Model WW3-124.

Red Ram V-8. Overhead valves. Polysphere combustion chambers. Cast iron block. Displacement: 270 cid. Bore and stroke: 3.63 x 3.26 inches. Compression ratio: 7.6:1. Brake hp: 175 at 4400 rpm. Five main bearings. Hydraulic valve lifters. Carburetion: Stromberg two-barrel Model WW3-131.

Super Red Ram V-8: Overhead valves. Hemispherical combustion chambers. Cast iron block. Displacement: 270 cid. Bore and stroke: 3.63 x 3.26 inches. Compression ratio: 7.6:1. Brake hp (std.) 183 at 4400 rpm; (opt.) 193 at 4400 rpm. Five main bearings. Hydraulic valve lifters. Carburetion: (std.) Stromberg two-barrel; (opt.) Carter four-barrel.

CHASSIS FEATURES: Wheelbase: 120 inches. Overall length: 212.1 inches. Tires: (Coronet Six) 6.70 x 15 tube-type black sidewall; (V-8 powered models) 7.10 x 15 black sidewall. Three-speed manual transmission was the standard transmission, with PowerFlite being the two-speed fully automatic optional transmission ($178). Overdrive was an option on standard transmission equipped models ($108).

CONVENIENCE OPTIONS: Electric clock. Turn signals. MoPar radio ($110). Power steering ($113). Power brakes ($38). Power seats ($70). Power windows ($102). Heater. Airtemp air conditioning ($567). Windshield washers. White sidewall tires. Engine power package ($48). Spinner wheelcovers. Chrome wire wheels. Tinted glass. Continental spare tire kit. Lancer trim offered a natural break for 16 two-tone and 16 three-tone color combinations.

HISTORICAL FOOTNOTES: The full-size Dodges were introduced Nov. 17, 1954 and the Coronet Sierra wagon and Royal Lancer appeared in dealer showrooms, Dec. 17, 1954. The Custom Royal four-door Lancer debuted in April. Another midyear trim option, called La Femme, was the industry's first appeal to women with special Heather Rose and Sapphire White color combinations and matching cape, boots, umbrella, shoulder bag and floral upholstery fabrics. Model year production peaked at 273,286 units. Calendar year sales of 313,038 cars were recorded. W.C. Newberg was president of Dodge Div. this year. The capacity of the Dodge V-8 plant was greatly increased during the final months of calendar 1955, when the Plymouth V-8 plant opened. MOTOR TREND magazine found its Custom Royal V-8 (with PowerFlite) capable of moving from 0 to 60 mph in 16.2 seconds and calculated a top speed of 101.8 mph for this model.

1956 DODGE

1956 Dodge, Custom Sierra four-door station wagon, V-8

CORONET SERIES — (ALL ENGINES) — Following a year of outstanding sales, Dodge chose wisely not to restyle their cars drastically for 1956. While the front end was very nearly identical to the previous year, the side trim and taillights were altered slightly. Also, the rear fenders grew fins, as was the current rage in Detroit. A four-door hardtop was offered for the first time in all three series. Electrical systems changed from six-volt to 12-volt. This was the year of the great horsepower race of the '50s and Dodge was right in the thick of things. The division had V-8 engines all the way up to 295 hp. The year ushered in one of Chrysler's most famous trademarks; the push-button selector for the automatic transmission. Carried over unchanged from 1955 were some of the customizer's most sought after items: the beautiful Dodge Lancer wheelcovers. No chopped and channeled custom of the '50s worth its weight in lug nuts would be caught dead without a set of the Lancer spinners. The Coronet was the base trim level for 1956 and included chrome windshield and rear window moldings; chrome trim around the simulated hood scoop; chrome headlight doors; 'SaddleSweep' chrome side trim and the Coronet name, in script, along the rear fenders.

CORONET SERIES I.D. NUMBERS: Six-cylinder powered Coronets assembled in Detroit began at 432227001 and went to 32254093 and those assembled in Los Angeles began at 48016501 and went to 48016723. V-8 powered models assembled in Detroit began at 34972001 and went to 35167854 and those assembled in Los Angeles began at 42608001 and went to 42618518. Motor numbers began at D62-1001 and went up, for six-cylinder engines and D63-1-1001 and up on V-8 engines.

CORONET SERIES

Model Number	Body/Style Number	Body Type & Seating	Factory Price	Shipping Weight	Production Total
D62/63	Note 1	4-dr Sed-6P	2232/2340	3295/3435	Note 2
D62/63	Note 1	2-dr Clb Sed-6P	2159/2267	3250/3380	Note 2
D63	Note 1	4-dr Lancer HT-6P	2517	3560	Note 2
D63	Note 1	2-dr Lancer HT-6P	2403	3430	Note 2
D63	Note 1	2-dr Conv-6P	2643	3600	Note 2
D62/63	Note 1	2-dr Sub-6P	2456/2564	3455/3605	Note 2
D63	Note 1	4-dr Sierra Wag-6p	2681	3600	Note 2
D63	Note 1	4-dr Sierra Wag-8P	2787	3715	Note 2

NOTE 1: See Note 1, 1947 Deluxe models.
NOTE 2: Production figures were not given for individual models and body styles. Dodge produced a total of 220,208 cars during calendar year 1956, included 142,613 Coronets. Model year production amounted to some 241,000 cars in all series.
NOTE 3: Prices and weights to left of slant bars are for sixes; on right of slant bars for V-8s.

1956 Dodge, Coronet Lancer two-door hardtop coupe, V-8

ROYAL SERIES — (V-8) — The Royal was once again the intermediate trim level and included all the Coronet features, plus six chrome 'fins' on the top of the center bar in the grille, chrome rain gutters and smooth taillight and back-up light housings. The Royal name appeared in script on the rear fenders, along with the V-8 emblem.

ROYAL SERIES I.D. NUMBERS: V-8 powered models assembled in Detroit began at 34972001 and went to 35167854 and those assembled in Los Angeles began at 42608001 and went to 42618518. Motor numbers began at D63-1-1001 and up on V-8 engines.

ROYAL SERIES

Model Number	Body/Style Number	Body Type & Seating	Factory Price	Shipping Weight	Production Total
D63-2	Note 1	4-dr Sed-6P	2478	3475	Note 2
D63-2	Note 1	4-dr Lancer HT-6P	2662	3625	Note 2
D63-2	Note 1	2-dr Lancer HT-6P	2548	3505	Note 2
D63-2	Note 1	2-dr Cus Sub-6P		2694	3620Note 2
D63-2	Note 1	4-dr Cus Sierra-6P	2834	3710	Note 2
D63-2	Note 1	4-dr Cus Sierra-8P	2939	3800	Note 2

NOTE 1: See Note 1, 1947 Deluxe models.
NOTE 2: See Note 2, 1956 Coronet models. A total of 48,780 Royal models were built.

1956 Dodge, Custom Royal Lancer two-door hardtop, V-8

CUSTOM ROYAL SERIES — (V-8) — The Custom Royal was once again the top trim level Dodge and included all the Royal features, plus hooded and painted headlight doors; grooved back-up and taillight housings; a strip of the lower body color extending up the rear edge of the rear fenders and the Custom Royal name, in script, on the rear fenders, along with the V-8 emblem. Midyear saw LaFemme and Golden Lancer options for the Lancer two-door hardtop.

CUSTOM ROYAL SERIES I.D. NUMBERS: V-8 powered models assembled in Detroit began at 34972001 and went to 35167854 and those assembled in Los Angeles began at 42608001 and went to 42618518. Motor numbers began at D63-1-1001 and up on V-8 engines.

CUSTOM ROYAL SERIES

Model Number	Body/Style Number	Body Type & Seating	Factory Price	Shipping Weight	Production Total
D63-3	Note 1	4-dr Sed-6P	2588	3520	Note 2
D63-3	Note 1	4-dr Lancer HT-6P	2772	3675	Note 2
D63-3	Note 1	2-dr Lancer HT-6P	2658	3505	Note 2
D63-3	Note 1	2-dr Conv-6P	2878	3630	Note 2

NOTE 1: See Note 1, 1947 Deluxe models.
NOTE 2: See Note 2, 1956 Coronet models. A total of 49,293 Custom Royal models were built.

ENGINES

Inline. L-head. Six-cylinder. Cast iron block. Displacement: 230 cid. Bore and stroke: 3.25 x 4.625 inches. Compression ratio: 7.6:1. Brake hp: 131 at 3600 rpm. Four main bearings. Solid valve lifters. Carburetion: Stromberg two-barrel Model WW3-124.

Red Ram V-8. Overhead valves. Polysphere combustion chambers. Cast iron block. Displacement: 270 cid. Bore and stroke: 3.63 x 3.26 inches. Compression ratio: 7.6:1. Brake hp: 189 at 4400 rpm. Five main bearings. Hydraulic valve lifters. Carburetion: Stromberg two-barrel Model WW3-135.

Super Red Ram V-8. Overhead valves. Polysphere combustion chambers. Cast iron block. Displacement: 315 cid. Bore and stroke: 3.63 x 3.80 inches. Compression ratio: 8.0:1. Brake hp: 218 at 4400 rpm. Five main bearings. Hydraulic valve lifters. Carburetion: Stromberg two-barrel Model WW3-148.

Super Red Ram V-8. Overhead valves. Polysphere combustion chambers. Cast Iron block. Displacement 315 cid. Bore and stroke: 3.63 x 3.80 Inches. Compression ratio: 8.0:1. Brake hp: 230 at 4400 rpm. Hydraulic valve lifters. Carburetion: Carter four-barrel Model WCFB.

D-500 V-8. Overhead valves. Hemispherical combustion chambers. Cast Iron block. Displacement: 315 cid. Bore and stroke: 3.63 x 3.80 Inches. Compression ratio: 9.25:1. Brake hp: 260 at 4400 rpm. Five main bearings. Solid valve lifters. Carburetion: Carter four-barrel Type WCFB. D-500-1 engine: same as above, but with dual Carter WCFB four-barrel carburetors and manual transmission. Brake hp: 295 at 4400 rpm. (These were midyear options.)

CHASSIS FEATURES: Wheelbase: 120 inches. Overall length: 212.0 inches. Tires (six-cylinder Coronets and Suburbans) 6.70 x 15 tubeless black sidewall; (Royals, Coronets, and V-8 station wagons) 7.10 x 15 tubeless black sidewall; (Custom Royals) 7.60 x 15. Three-speed manual continued to be the standard transmission, with Overdrive ($102) and Power-Flite fully-automatic ($184) being the optional transmissions.

CONVENIENCE OPTIONS: Electric clock. Turn signals. MoPar radio. Power steering ($92). Power brakes ($38). Power seats. Power windows. Heater. Airtemp air conditioning. Highway Hi-Fi automatic record player. Windshield washers. White sidewall tires.

HISTORICAL FOOTNOTES: The 1956 Dodge line was introduced on Oct. 7, 1955. Model year production peaked at exactly 233,686 units, giving the company a 3.7 percent share of the total market. Of this total (again on a model year basis) 1,687 had optional air conditioning. On a calendar year basis (Jan. '56 to Jan. '57), Dodge built 40,100 two-door hardtops; 10,900 four-door hardtops; 4,100 convertibles and 16,100 station wagons. These rounded off totals include 1957 models built in the fall of 1956, but 1956 models built in the fall of 1955 are not included, so this gives only a rough idea of how many of each particular body style were made. Calendar year production for Dodge totaled 205,727 cars. This was a decline of 22.4 percent over 1955. During 1956, Dodge installed automatic transmissions in 90.3 percent of all its cars. 94.8 percent had heaters; 62.6 percent had back-up lights; 60.2 percent had whitewalls; 17.3 percent had power brakes and 24.3 percent had power steering. M.C. Patterson became president and chief executive officer of Dodge Div. this season. The company's address was at 7900 Joseph Campau Avenue in Detroit, 31, Mich. Some mention must be made of two special options introduced midyear in the Custom Royal series. The "La Femme" featured a lavender and white paint job and matching interior with gold flecks. It came with a matching umbrella, cap and purse hook. The Golden Lancer featured a Sapphire white body and top with Gallant Saddle Gold exterior and interior trim. In Sept. 1955, a 1956 Dodge Custom Royal four-door sedan was driven 31,224 miles in 14 days at the Bonneville Salt Flats, Utah, and set 306 speed records. Dodges won 11 NASCAR races, a figure that wouldn't be topped until 1964.

1957 DODGE

CORONET SERIES — (ALL ENGINES) — The new Dodges were totally restyled from the previous year and were very much a part of the 'Forward Look' being promoted by Chrysler. They rode on longer wheelbases than any previous year since 1933 (except long wheelbase models) and were longer, lower and wider than any previous Dodge. Helping provide a low silhouette was a switch to 14-inch wheels. Front torsion bar suspension was also new. The headlights were now deeply recessed below large headlight 'brows' and the grille featured a gull-wing shaped horizontal bar, which dipped in the center and surrounded a large Dodge crest. All models used a single horizontal chrome strip along the bodyside and chrome trim along the base of the large rear fender fins. Chrome trim surrounded the headlights and grille opening. The Dodge name, in block letters, was spaced along the front and the grille, directly below the chrome jet-styled hood ornament. Among the more interesting features of the 1957 Dodges (and all 1957 Chrysler products) was the instrument panel-mounted inside rearview mirror. With two passengers in the car, rear vision was partially obstructed. With four or more passengers, there was virtually no rear vision. Yet, this mirror location lasted for several years, before returning to the conventional windshield mounting. While the new Dodges were beautiful to look at, quality control problems abounded and Dodge sales suffered for the next few years. The Coronet was the base line Dodge for 1957 and included chrome windshield and rear window moldings; chrome side trim; chrome trim along the fins and grille opening; wheelcovers and the Coronet name on the front fenders above the chrome strip.

1957 Dodge, Coronet four-door sedan, V-8

CORONET SERIES I.D. NUMBERS: Six-cylinder Coronets assembled in Detroit began at 32255061 and went to 32292657. V-8 Coronets assembled in Detroit began at 35172001 and went to 35303713 and those assembled in Los Angeles began at 42620001 and went to 45547041. Six-cylinder motor numbers began at D72-1001 and went to 9600. After Jan. 10, 1957 motor numbers began at KDS-6-9601 and went up to 18892. V-8 motor numbers began at KDS-1001 and went to 287536.

CORONET SERIES

Model Number	Body/Style Number	Body Type & Seating	Factory Price	Shipping Weight	Production Total
D66/72	Note 1	4-dr Sed-6P	2416/2524	3470/3620	Note 2
D66/72	Note 1	2-dr Clb Sed-6P	2335/2443	3400/3530	Note 2
D66	Note 1	4-dr Lancer HT-6P	2630	3665	Note 2
D66	Note 1	2-dr Lancer HT-6P	2545	3570	Note 2
D66	Note 1	2-dr Conv-6P	2807	3815	Note 2

NOTE 1: See Note 1. 1947 Deluxe models.
NOTE 2: Production figures were not given for individual models and body styles. Dodge produced a total of 257,488 cars during calendar year 1957, including 160,979 Coronets. Coronet model year output, in round figures, was 160,500 cars.
NOTE 3: Prices and weights to left of slant bars are for sixes; on right of slant bars for V-8s.

ROYAL SERIES — (V-8) — The Royal was once again the intermediate trim level and included all the Coronet features, plus chrome headlight doors and a 'V' medallion on the rear deck lid. The Royal name appeared on the front fender above the chrome trim strip.

ROYAL SERIES I.D. NUMBERS: Royal models assembled in Detroit began at 37240001 and went to 37321614 and those assembled in Los Angeles began at 45540001 and went to 42631610. V-8 motor numbers began at KDS-1001 and went to 287536.

ROYAL SERIES

Model Number	Body/Style Number	Body Type & Seating	Factory Price	Shipping Weight	Production Total
D67-1	Note 1	4-dr Sed-6P	2677	3620	Note 2
D67-1	Note 1	4-dr Lancer HT-6P	2783	3690	Note 2
D67-1	Note 1	2-dr Lancer HT-6P	2734	3585	Note 2
D67-1	Note 2	2-dr Lancer Conv 6P	2996	3830	Note 2

NOTE 1: See Note 1, 1947 Deluxe models.

NOTE 2: Production figures were not given for individual models and body styles. Dodge produced a total of 257,488 cars during calendar year 1957. A total of 40,999 Royal models were built on a calendar year basis. Royal Series model year output, in rounded off figures, was 41,000 cars.

1957 Dodge, Custom Royal Lancer two-door hardtop coupe, V-8 (AA)

CUSTOM ROYAL SERIES — (V-8) — The Custom Royal was once again the top trim level Dodge and included all the Royal features, plus six vertical bumper bars between the bumper and the horizontal grille bar, the Dodge name, in gold, on the hood and the trunk lid and the Custom Royal name on the sides of the front fenders, above the chrome trim strip.

CUSTOM ROYAL SERIES I.D. NUMBERS: Custom Royal models assembled in Detroit began at 37240001 and went to 37321614 and those assembled in Los Angeles began at 45540001 and went to 42631610. V-8 motor numbers began at KDS-1001 and went to 287536.

CUSTOM ROYAL SERIES

Model Number	Body/Style Number	Body Type & Seating	Factory Price	Shipping Weight	Production Total
D67-2	Note 1	4-dr Sed-6P	2846	3690	Note 2
D67-2	Note 1	4-dr Lancer HT-6P	2956	3750	Note 2
D67-2	Note 1	2-dr Lancer HT-6P	2885	3670	Note 2
D67-2	Note 1	2-dr Conv-6P	3111	3810	Note 2

NOTE 1: See Note 1, 1947 Deluxe models.
NOTE 2: See Note 2, 1957 Coronet models. A total of 55,149 Custom Royal models were built on a calendar year basis. Custom Royal Series output, on a model year basis, in round figures, was 47,000 cars.

STATION WAGON SERIES — (V-8) — For the first time, station wagons were included in their own series. The two-door Suburban and four-door Sierra models were the base trim level and compared to the Coronet Series of conventional cars. The Custom Sierra was the top trim level and compared to the Royal Series of conventional cars. An interesting feature of the 1957 Dodge station wagons was the location of the spare tire. It was mounted behind the right rear wheel and was accessible from a removable fender skirt located behind the rear wheelwell.

STATION WAGON SERIES I.D. NUMBERS: Station wagon models were assembled only in Detroit and began at 38001001 and went to 38022513 for the Suburban and Sierra models, or began at 38535001 and went to 38542217 for the Custom Sierra. motor numbers corresponded to Royal Series of conventional cars.

STATION WAGON SERIES

Model Number	Body/Style Number	Body Type & Seating	Factory Price	Shipping Weight	Production Total
D70	Note 1	2-dr Sub-6P	2826	3830	Note 2
D70	Note 1	4-dr Sierra-6P	2911	3930	Note 2
D70	Note 1	4-dr Sierra-9P	3038	4015	Note 2
D71	Note 1	4-dr Cus Sierra-6P	3052	3960	Note 2
D71	Note 1	4-dr Cus Sierra-6P	3180	4030	Note 2

NOTE 1: See Note 1, 1947 Deluxe models.
NOTE 2: See Note 2, 1957 Coronet models. A total of 30,481 station wagons were built on a calendar year basis. Station wagon model year output, in round figures, was 32,000 units.

D-500 SERIES — (V-8) — The D-500 was actually a high-performance engine option for all series. However, in this edition, we are listing it in series format, because of its importance to collectors. The representative prices and weights shown are based on adding the option to a pair of Custom Royal models. Dodge D-500s included all features of the base series models, plus the high-performance 285, 310 or 340 hp V-8 engines.

D500 SERIES I.D. NUMBERS: See Dodge V-8 model I.D. numbers above. Motor numbers began at KD-501-1001 and went to 1102.

D500 SERIES

Model Number	Body/Style Number	Body Type & Seating	Factory Price	Shipping Weight	Production Total
D501	Note 1	2-dr Clb Sed-6P	3279	3885	Note 2
D501	Note 1	2-dr Conv-6P	3635	3975	Note 2

NOTE 1: See Note 1, 1947 Deluxe models.
NOTE 2: Production of 500 Dodge D-500s was scheduled. Approximately 101 cars were fitted with D-501 engines.

ENGINES

Inline. L-head. Six-cylinder. Cast iron block. Displacement: 230 cid. Bore and stroke: 3.25 x 4.625 inches. Compression ratio: 8.0:1. Brake hp: 138 at 4000 rpm. Four main bearings. Solid valve lifter. Carburetion: Stromberg one-barrel Model WW3-159.

Red Ram V-8: Overhead valves. Cast iron block. Displacement 325 cid. Bore and stroke: 3.69 x 3.80 inches. Compression ratio: 8.5:1. Brake hp: 245 at 4400 rpm. in Coronet and Royal Series, 260 at 4400 rpm in Custom Royal Series. Five main bearings. Hydraulic valve lifters. Carburetion: (245 hp) Stromberg two-barrel Model WW3-149; (260 hp) Carter WCFB-2532S.

D-500 V-8: Overhead valves. Cast iron block. Displacement: 325 cid. Bore and stroke: 3.69 x 3.80 Inches. Compression ratio: 10.0:1. Hemispherical heads. Brake hp: 285 at 5200 rpm. Solid valve lifters. Carburetion: Carter four-barrel Type WCFB. Super D-500 engine: same as above but with dual Carter WCFB four-barrel carburetors. Brake hp: 310.

D-501 V-8: Overhead valves. Cast iron block. Displacement: 354 cid. Bore and stroke: 3.94 x 3.63 inches. Compression ratio: 10.0:1. Hemispherical heads. Brake horsepower: 340 at 5200 rpm. Hydraulic valve lifters. Carburetion: Two Carter WCFB four-barrels. (Midyear offering).

CHASSIS FEATURES: Wheelbase: 122 inches. Overall length: (station wagon) 214.4 inches; (other models) 212.2 inches. Tires: (Coronet) 7.50 x 14 tubeless black sidewall; (D500) 7.60 x 15 tubeless black sidewall; (Royal, Custom Royal, station wagons and convertibles) 8.00 x 14 tubeless black sidewall.

CONVENIENCE OPTIONS: Electric clock. Turn signals. MoPar radio. PowerFlite or Torque-Flite automatic transmissions. Power steering. Power brakes. Power windows. Power seats. Heater. Airtemp air conditioning. Highway Hi-Fi automatic record player. Windshield washers. White sidewall tires.

HISTORICAL FOOTNOTES: This year saw the introduction of the famous torsion bar front suspension, which Chrysler has used from 1957 to this date. The 1957 Dodge lineup was introduced Oct. 30, 1956, the same day that all other Chrysler products debuted that season. The division's total model year production peaked at 281,359 cars, which gave Dodge a 4.5 percent market share. On a 1957 calendar year basis, Dodge manufactured 82,220 two-door hardtops; 6,960 two-door convertibles; 8,100 two-door station wagons and 34,210 four-door station wagons. This does not include 1957 models built in the fall of 1956, but it does include 1958 models built in calendar 1957. Therefore, it can only be used as an indication of body style popularity in calendar 1957. On a model year basis, 96.5 percent of all 1957 Dodges had automatic transmissions; 25.9 percent had power brakes; 2.2 percent power seats; 2.1 percent power windows; 53.7 percent radios; 15.1 percent dual exhausts and 93.4 percent V-8 engines. M.C. Patterson was president of the division again this year.

1958 DODGE

CORONET SERIES — (ALL ENGINES) — The 1958 Dodges continued to use the 1957 body shell with only very minor restyling. The major change was a completely revised grille and quad headlights. The grille had abbreviated horizontal center bars, which housed the parking lights at their inside edge. A major concentration at Dodge in 1958 was power. All engines were of the "wedge" single rocker head design. The ultimate, an electronically fuel-injected 361 cid version, put out 333 hp. The Coronet was the base trim level for 1958 and included chrome windshield and rear window moldings; chrome trim around the grille opening and headlights; a single chrome strip along the bodyside and base of the rear fender fins and the Coronet name, in script, along the back of the side chrome strip. The Dodge name, in block letters, was spaced along the front edge of the hood.

CORONET SERIES I.D. NUMBERS: Six-cylinder Coronets assembled in Detroit began at LD1-1001 and up. Those assembled in Newark began at LD1N-1001 and up. V-8 Coronets assembled in Detroit began at LD2-1001 and up. Those assembled in Los Angeles began at LD2L-1001 and up. Those assembled at Newark began at LD2N-1001 and up. Motor numbers began at L230-1001 and up for sixes and L325-1001 and up for V-8s.

1958 Dodge, Coronet two-door sedan, V-8

CORONET SERIES

Model Number	Body/Style Number	Body Type & Seating	Factory Price	Shipping Weight	Production Total
LDI/2	Note 1	4-dr Sed-6P	2495/2602	3410/3555	Note 2
LDI/2	Note 1	2-dr Sed-6P	2414/2521	3360/3505	Note 2
LD2-L1	Note 1	4-dr Lancer HT-6P	2729	3605	Note 2
LD2-L1	Note 1	2-dr Lancer HT-6P	2644	3540	Note 2
LD2-L1	Note 1	2-dr Conv-6P	2907	3725	Note 2

NOTE 1: See Note 1, 1947 Deluxe models.
NOTE 2: Production figures were not given for individual models and body styles. Dodge produced a total of 135,505 cars during calendar year 1958, including 77,388 Coronets. Dodge model year output peaked at 133,953 units. In rounded figures, 77,000 of these cars were Coronets.
NOTE 3: Prices and weights to left of slant bars are for sixes; on right of slant bars for V-8s.

Standard Catalog of American Cars

1958 Dodge, Royal four-door hardtop sedan, V-8

ROYAL SERIES — (V-8) — The Royal was once again the intermediate trim level and included all the Coronet features. On this Series, the chrome trim at the base of the rear fender fin flared out to a pointed dip, before angling up to the top of the fin. Twin chrome hood ornaments were another distinction.

ROYAL SERIES I.D. NUMBERS: V-8 Royals assembled in Detroit began at LD2-1001 and up. Those assembled in Los Angeles began at LD2L-1001 and up. Those assembled at Newark began at LD2N-1001 and up. Motor numbers began at L325-1001 and up.

ROYAL SERIES

Model Number	Body/Style Number	Body Type & Seating	Factory Price	Shipping Weight	Production Total
LD2M	Note 1	4-dr Sed-6P	2757	3570	Note 2
LD2M	Note 1	4-dr Lancer HT-6P	2875	3640	Note 2
LD2M	Note 1	2-dr Lancer HT-6P	2814	3565	Note 2

NOTE 1: See Note 1, 1947 Deluxe models.
NOTE 2: A total of 15,165 Royal models were built on a calendar year basis. On a model year basis, using rounded off figures, Coronet output was counted as 15,500 units.

CUSTOM ROYAL SERIES — (V-8) — The Custom Royal was once again the top trim level Dodge and included all the Royal features, plus 'knight's head' emblems on the front fenders, a gold Dodge name on the hood and trunk and chrome rain gutter moldings. The Regal Lancer was a midyear two-door hardtop introduced in early 1958.

CUSTOM ROYAL SERIES I.D. NUMBERS: Custom Royal models assembled in Detroit began at LD3-1001 and went up. Those assembled in Los Angeles began at LD3L-1001 and went up. Those assembled in Newark began at LD3N-1001 and went up. Motor numbers began at L350-1001 and went up.

CUSTOM ROYAL SERIES

Model Number	Body/Style Number	Body Type & Seating	Factory Price	Shipping Weight	Production Total
LD3H	Note 1	4-dr Sed-6P	2985	3640	Note 2
LD3H	Note 1	4-dr Lancer HT-6P	3097	3670	Note 2
LD3H	Note 1	2-dr Lancer HT-6P	3026	3610	Note 2
LD3H	Note 1	2-dr Conv-6P	3253	3785	Note 2
LD3H	Note 1	2-dr Reg Lan-6P	3200	3655	Note 2

NOTE 1: See Note 1, 1947 Deluxe models.
NOTE 2: A total of 23,949 Custom Royal models were built on a calendar year basis. On a model year basis, Custom Royal output was 21,000 units in rounded off figures.

STATION WAGON SERIES — (V-8) — For 1958, station wagons continued to be in their own series. As in 1957, the two-door Suburban was the base trim level and compared to the Coronet Series of conventional cars. The Sierra was the intermediate trim level station wagon and compared to the Royal model of conventional cars. The Custom Sierra was the top trim level and compared to the Custom Royal Series of conventional cars.

STATION WAGON SERIES I.D. NUMBERS: Station wagon models used the same serial number sequence as the Custom Royal Series.

1958 Dodge, Custom Sierra four-door station wagon, V-8

STATION WAGON SERIES

Model Number	Body/Style Number	Body Type & Seating	Factory Price	Shipping Weight	Production Total
LD3L	Note 1	2-dr Sub-6P	2930	3875	Note 2
LD3L	Note 1	4-dr Sierra-6P	2995	3930	Note 2
LD3L	Note 1	4-dr Sierra-9P	3137	3990	Note 2
LD3H	Note 1	4-dr Cus Sierra-6P	3172	3955	Note 2
LD3H	Note 1	4-dr Cus Sierra-9P	3314	4035	Note 2

NOTE 1: See Note 1, 1947 Deluxe models.
NOTE 2: A total of 30,481 station wagons were built in the calendar year. On a model year basis, 20,000 station wagons were built (rounded off figures).

ENGINES

Inline. L-head. Six-cylinder. Cast iron block. Displacement: 230 cid. Bore and stroke: 3.25 x 4.625 inches. Compression ratio: 8.01. Brake hp: 138 at 4000 rpm. Four main bearings. Solid valve lifters. Carburetion: Stromberg one-barrel Model WW3-159.

Red Ram V-8. Overhead valves. Cast iron block. Displacement: 325 cid. Bore and stroke: 3.69 x 3.80 inches. Compression ratio: 8.0:1. Brake hp: 245 at 4400 rpm. (265 at 4600 rpm in Royal models). Five main bearings. Hydraulic valve lifters. Carburetion: (Coronet V-8) Stromberg Model WW3-163 two-barrel; (Royal V-8) Carter WCFB-2660S two-barrel.

Ram Fire V-8. Overhead valves. Cast iron block. Displacement 350 cid. Bore and stroke: 4.06 x 3.38 Inches. Compression ratio: 10.0:1. Brake hp 295 at 4600 rpm. Five main bearings. Hydraulic valve lifters. Carburetion: Carter four-barrel.

D-500 V-8. Overhead valves. Cast iron block. Displacement: 361 cid. Bore and stroke: 4.12 x 3.38 inches. Compression ratio: 10.0:1. Brake hp: 305 at 4600 rpm. Five main bearings. Hydraulic valve lifters. Carburetion: Carter four-barrel Model WCFB.

Super D-500 V-8. Overhead valves. Cast iron block. Displacement: 361 cid. Bore and stroke: 4.12 x 3.38 inches. Compression ratio: 10.0:1. Brake hp: 320 at 4600 rpm with dual Carter four-barrel Model WCFB carburetors.

Electronic Fuel-Injection V-8. Overhead valves. Cast iron block. Displacement: 361 cid. Bore and stroke: 4.12 x 3.38 inches. Compression ratio: 10.0:1. Brake hp: 333 at 4800 rpm. Five main bearings. Hydraulic valve lifters. Fuel system: Bendix electronic fuel injection.

CHASSIS FEATURES: Wheelbase: 122 inches. Overall length: (station wagons) 214.4 inches; (other models) 212.2 inches. Tires: (Coronets) 7.50 x 14; (Royals, Custom Royals and station wagons) 8.00 x 14 tubeless black sidewall.

CONVENIENCE OPTIONS: Electric clock. Turn signals. MoPar radio. PowerFlite ($180). TorqueFlite ($220). Power steering ($92). Power brakes ($38). Power windows. Power seats. Heater. Airtemp air conditioning ($381). Highway Hi-Fi automatic record player. Windshield washer. White sidewall tires. Seat belts.

HISTORICAL FOOTNOTES: The 1958 Dodges were introduced Nov. 1, 1957. Model year production peaked at 133,953 units. Calendar year sales of 114,206 cars were recorded. M.C. Patterson was president of the division this year. The demand for Dodge sixes increased during 1958, rising from 4.6 percent to 9.7 percent. On a model year basis, 96.4 percent of all Dodges had automatic transmission; 62.5 percent had power steering; 34 percent had power brakes; 2.5 percent had power windows; 44.7 percent had radios; 23.4 percent had tinted glass; 4.4 percent had air conditioning and 7.2 percent had dual exhausts. The 1958 Regal Lancer was a limited edition two-door hardtop with special paint trim and interior. It came only in bronze finish, combined with either black or white. Approximately 12 Dodges were built with the new Bendix EFI (electronic-fuel-injection) system. This option was later deleted and these cars were recalled for conversion to normal carburetion.

1959 DODGE

CORONET SERIES — (ALL ENGINES) — The new Dodges were easily recognizable as Dodges, even though the styling of the 1957-1958 models was simply exaggerated. The fins were more rakish, the brows over the headlights were much larger and the entire car was longer, lower and wider than in previous years. The grille was a modification of the split bumper grille bar theme backed by an aluminum mesh. The great horsepower race of the '50s was over, but Dodge continued to build high-performance cars. This year's offering in the high horsepower category was the first of the famous 383 cid V-8 engines, which Chrysler used for more than a decade. The 383 boasted 345 hp in its Super D-500 format. Also new, for 1959, was the Swivel-Seat option. A simple motion of the lever, at the side of the seat, and the unit swung out to meet the occupant. Dodge experimented with self-leveling rear air suspension, called LevelFlite, as an option. The Coronet continued to be the base trim level and included chrome windshield and rear window moldings, a single horizontal chrome strip along the bodyside and chrome trim at the lower edge of the fender fin. The Dodge name, in block letters, appeared on the trunk lid (directly below a combination Dodge crest and trunk handle). The Coronet name, in script, appeared on the front fender. At midyear, a "Silver Challenger" option was available on the two-door sedan.

1959 Dodge, Coronet two-door Club Sedan, V-8

CORONET SERIES I.D. NUMBERS: Six-cylinder Coronets assembled in Detroit began at M302100001 and up. Those assembled in Newark began at M305100001 and went up. V-8 powered models assembled in Detroit began at M312100001 and went up. Those assembled in Newark began at M315100001 and went up. V-8 models assembled in Calif. began at M314100001 and went up.

CORONET SERIES

Model Number	Body/Style Number	Body Type & Seating	Factory Price	Shipping Weight	Production Total
MD1/2L	41	4-dr Sed-6P	2537/2657	3425/3615	8103
MD1/2L	21	2-dr Clb Sed-6P	2466/2586	3375/3565	5432
MD1/2L	23	2-dr Lancer HT-6P	2594/2714	3395/3590	2151
MD2L	43	4-dr Lancer HT-6P	2792	3620	8946
MD2L	27	2-dr Conv-6P	3039	3775	1840

NOTE 1: A total of 96,782 Coronet models were produced during calendar 1959. Exactly 151,851 Dodges were built for the 1960 model year. In slightly rounded off figures, the model year output of Coronets was counted at 96,900 units.
NOTE 2: Prices and weights to left of slant bars are for sixes; on right of slant bars for V-8s.

ROYAL SERIES — (V-8) — The Royal continued to be the intermediate trim level and included all Coronet features, plus a long horizontal chrome strip (from the front wheelwell to the rear of the car) which is wider than the trim used on the Coronet. Royals also featured horizontal scoring on this strip. A stylized V-8 emblem appeared on the front fenders and the Royal name appeared on a wide molding at the front of the rear fender fins.

ROYAL SERIES I.D. NUMBERS: Royal models assembled in Detroit began at M332100001 and went up. Those assembled in Newark began at M335100001 and went up and those assembled in Calif. began at M334100001 and went up.

ROYAL SERIES

Model Number	Body/Style Number	Body Type & Seating	Factory Price	Shipping Weight	Production Total
MD3M	41	4-dr Sed-6P	2884	3640	8389
MD3M	43	4-dr Lancer HT-6P	3019	3690	2935
MD3M	23	2-dr Lancer HT-6P	2940	3625	3483

NOTE 1: A total of 14,807 Royal models were produced during calendar 1959. In slightly rounded off figures, the model year output of Royals was counted at 14,900 units.

1959 Dodge, Custom Royal Lancer four-door hardtop, V-8

CUSTOM ROYALS SERIES — (V-8) — The Custom Royal continued to be the top trim level and included all the Royal features, plus the Custom Royal name on the wide molding at the front of the rear fender fins.

CUSTOM ROYAL SERIES I.D. NUMBERS: Custom Royal models assembled in Detroit began at M352100001 and went up. Those assembled in Newark began at M355100001 and went up and those assembled in Calif. began at M354100001 and went up.

CUSTOM ROYAL SERIES

Model Number	Body/Style Number	Body Type & Seating	Factory Price	Shipping Weight	Production Total
MD3H	41	4-dr Sed-6P	3095	3660	8925
MD3H	43	4-dr Lancer HT-6P	3229	3745	5019
MD3H	23	2-dr Lancer HT-6P	3151	3675	6278
MD3H	27	2-dr Conv-6P	3372	3820	984

NOTE 1: A total of 21,206 Custom Royal models were produced during calendar 1959. In slightly rounded off figures, the model year output of Custom Royals was counted at 16,500 units.

STATION WAGON SERIES — (V-8) — Station wagons continued to be their own series for 1959. The two-door Suburban was dropped, and the four-door Sierra replaced the suburban as the base trim level. The Custom Sierra continued in the top trim level, equaling the Royal Series of conventional cars in trim.

STATION WAGON SERIES I.D. NUMBERS: Station wagon models assembled in Detroit began at 372100001 and went up. Those assembled in Newark began at 375100001 and went up and those assembled in Calif. began at 374100001 and went up.

STATION WAGON SERIES

Model Number	Body/Style Number	Body Type & Seating	Factory Price	Shipping Weight	Production Total
MD3-L	45A	4-dr Sierra-6P	3053	3940	11,069
MD3-L	45B	4-dr Sierra-9P	3174	4015	6650
MD3-H	45A	4-dr Cus Sierra-6P	3268	3980	2434
MD3-H	45B	4-dr Cus Sierra-9P	3389	4020	3437

NOTE 1: A total of 23,590 station wagons were produced during calendar 1959. In slightly rounded off figures, the model year output of Dodge station wagons was 23,500.

ENGINES

L-head. Inline. Six-cylinder. Cast iron block. Displacement: 230 cid. Bore and stroke: 3.25 x 4.38 inches. Compression ratio: 8.0:1. Brake hp: 135 at 3600 rpm. Four main bearings. Solid valve lifters. Carburetion: Stromberg one-barrel.

Red Ram V-8. Overhead valves. Cast iron block. Displacement: 326 cid. Bore and stroke: 3.95 x 3.31 inches. Compression ratio: 9.2:1. Brake hp: 255 at 4400 rpm. Five main bearings. Hydraulic valve lifters. Carburetion: Carter two-barrel.

Ram Fire V-8. Overhead valves. Cast iron block. Displacement: 361 cid. Bore and stroke: 4.12 x 3.38 inches. Compression ratio: 10.1:1. Brake hp: 295 at 4600 rpm on Royal and Sierra models, 305 at 4600 rpm on Custom Royal and Custom Sierra models. Five main bearings. Hydraulic valve lifters. Carburetion; (295hp) Carter two-barrel; (305-hp) Carter four-barrel.

D500 V-8. Overhead valves. Cast iron block. Displacement: 383 cid. Bore and stroke: 4.25 x 3.38 inches. Compression ratio: 10.1:1. Brake hp: 320 at 4600 rpm. Five main bearings. Hydraulic valve lifters. Carburetion: Carter four-barrel.

Super D-500 V-8: Overhead valves. Cast iron block. Displacement: 383 cid. Bore and stroke: 4.25 x 3.38 inches. Compression ratio: 10.0:1. Brake horsepower: 345 at 5000 rpm. Five main bearings. Hydraulic valve lifters. Carburetion: Two Carter four-barrels.

CHASSIS FEATURES: Wheelbase: 122 inches. Overall length: 217.4 inches. (216.4 inches on station wagons). Tires: 7.50 x 14 on Coronet models; 8.00 x 14 tubeless black sidewalls on all others.

CONVENIENCE OPTIONS: TorqueFlite transmission, all V-8 models ($226.90). PowerFlite transmission, Coronet and Royal ($189.10). Power steering, V-8 only ($92.15). Power brakes ($42.60). Power window lifts ($102.30). Power tailgate windows, two-seat wagons ($34.10). Six-Way power seat ($95.70). Dual exhaust ($30.90). Push-button radio ($86.50). Rear speaker ($14.95). Radio with dual antennas ($14.05). Heater and defroster ($93.55). Tires: white sidewall 7.50 x 14, Coronet except convertible ($33.35); 8.00 x 14, other models ($41.75). Two-tone paint, standard colors ($18.55); Deluxe colors ($34.10). Solex glass ($42.60); windshield only ($18.55). Back-up lights ($10.70). Wheelcovers ($14.30); Deluxe ($30.50). Electric clock ($15.95). Windshield washer ($11.80). Variable speed windshield wipers ($6.60). Windshield washer and Vari-speed wipers ($18.25). Front and rear Air Foam seat ($10.70). Undercoating ($12.85). Air conditioning with heater, V-8s only ($468.55); wagons ($662.95). Carpets ($11.80). Rear window defroster ($20.60). Sure-Grip differential, all except convertible ($49.70). Padded instrument panel ($20.00). Padded sun visors ($8.00). Automatic headlight beam changer ($49.70). Heavy-duty 70-amp battery ($8.60). Custom trim package, Coronet except convertible ($56.00). D500, 320 hp, 383 cid four-barrel carb engine with dual exhaust and TorqueFlite transmission, Coronet convertible ($368.00); Coronet V-8 except convertible ($398.90); Royal and Sierra wagons ($328.10); Custom Royal convertible ($273.35); Custom Royal and Custom wagons ($304.15). Super D500, 345 hp engine, Coronet V-8 except convertible ($540.45); Coronet convertible ($509.60); Royal and Sierra wagons ($469.65); Custom Royal convertible ($414.95); Custom Royal and Custom wagons ($445.75). LevelFlite, V-8s only ($127.55). Outside rearview mirror ($6.45). Remote control left outside rearview mirror ($17.75); right ($8.60). CoPilot speed warning device ($12.85). Stowage compartment with lock, two-seat wagons ($28.20). Swivel seat ($70.95).

HISTORICAL FOOTNOTES: The 1959 Dodges were introduced on Oct. 10, 1958. Model year production peaked at 151,851 units, of which approximately 15,600 were sixes and 136,200 were V-8 powered. Dodge assembled 13,515 two-door sedans; 65,752 four-door sedans; 29,610 two-door hardtops; 16,704 four-door hardtops; 2,733 convertibles; 13,515 four-door two-seat station wagons and 10,022 four-door three-seat station wagons in the 1959 model year. Dodge Div.'s calendar year output was 192,798 units this year, accounting for a 3.44 percent share of the total market. M.C. Patterson continued as president and general manager of Dodge Div. this season. For the model run, about 94 percent of all Dodges had automatic transmissions; 68.9 percent had power steering; 27.4 percent had power brakes; 23.2 percent had windshield washers; 84.7 percent had back-up lights; 4.5 percent had air conditioning and only 0.7 percent had the rare air suspension, an option that did not last very long.

1960 DODGE

DART SENECA — SERIES PD3/PD4 — (ALL ENGINES) — The year 1960 was a very significant one for Dodge. In addition to the full-sized Dodges, a line of slightly smaller cars was introduced. This new Dart Series rode on a smaller 118 inch wheelbase and was four inches shorter, overall, than the larger Dodge. Like all new Dodges, the Dart Seneca had unitized body/chassis construction for the first time. While standard Dodges used the 361 cid V-8 engine as base equipment, the new Dart was offered with the 225 cid 'Slant Six.' This engine was slanted toward the passenger side of the car to allow easier maintenance on the carburetor and spark plugs. This also allowed the use of longer intake manifold runners, which added considerably to power output. Styling of the new Darts left little doubt that they were products of Dodge Div., but the general appearance was more subdued than in 1959. The headlight 'eyebrows' were replaced by more conventional chrome bezels and the height of the fins was reduced substantially. The side styling was very simple, with a single horizontal chrome strip beginning at the rear of the front wheelwell and going back to the rear bumper. The taillamps were enclosed in a chrome bezel, which bore an interesting resemblance to the air intake scoop of an F-86 Sabre Jet. The Dodge name, in script, appeared on the lower right side of the trunk lid. At the front, the grille featured a vertical bar theme with five dividers, which was complemented by a split front bumper. A new Dodge crest, more contemporary than in previous years, was located on the front of the hood. The Seneca Series was the base trim level Dart and included chrome windshield and rear window moldings; a single chrome strip along the bodyside; chrome trim along the back edge of the fin; chrome license plate frame recessed into the trunk lid; front armrests; electric windshield wipers; sun visors; turn signals and the Seneca name, in script, along the side of the rear fender, just in front of the taillights.

SENECA SERIES I.D. NUMBERS — (ALL ENGINES) — Serial numbers are stamped/embossed on plate on left front door pillar and use the form 411()100001 and up. The first symbol indicates car-line/engine: 4=Dart 6-cyl.; 5=Dart V-8; 6=Dodge V-8. The second symbol indicates series: 1=Seneca/Matador; 2=Pioneer; 3=Phoenix/Polara; 5=Seneca/Matador wagon; 6=Pioneer wagon; 7=Polara wagon; 8=Taxicab and 9=Police Special. The third symbol indicates model year 0=1960. The fourth symbol indicates assembly plant: 1=Lynch Rd.; 2=Dodge Main; 3=Detroit (Jefferson); 5=Los Angeles, Calif.; 6=Newark, Del.; 7=St. Louis, Mo. and 8=Clairpointe, Mo. The last six symbols are the sequential production number starting at 100001 for each series at each factory. Body number plates are located under the hood on fenders, cowl or radiator crossmember. They carry symbols that tell the production schedule dates, body production number, body series and trim, paint and accessory codes. A three-digit body number identifies each model and appears in the Model Number column of the charts below, replacing series codes that appeared in earlier editions of this catalog. Model codes with alpha prefixes are also employed, as follows: L=low-priced; M=medium-priced; H=high-priced; P=premium-priced and S=specially-priced. These appear in charts below in the Body/Style Number column. Engine codes were stamped on the right side of most engines and the left side of 318 cid V-8s, as follows: P-22 on 225 cid Slant Six; P-318 on 318 cid V-8; P-36 on 361 cid V-8 and P-38 on 383 cid V-8.

SENECA SERIES

Model Number	Body/Style Number	Body Type & Seating	Factory Price	Shipping Weight	Production Total
413/513	L41	4-dr Sed-6P	2330/2449	3420/3600	Note 1 & 2
411/511	L21	2-dr Sed-6P	2278/2397	3385/3530	Note 1 & 2
456/556	L45	4-dr Sta Wag-6P	2695/2815	3805/3975	Note 1 & 2

NOTE 1: Exactly 306,603 Dodge Darts were built during the 1960 model year. In rounded off figures, this included 111,600 Dodge Dart Seneca passenger cars and an undetermined number of Seneca station wagons. (Station wagons were a separate series. A total of some 51,600 station wagons were built in all lines).
NOTE 2: During model year 1960, Dodge built exactly 44,719 two-door sedans; 162,420 four-door sedans; 54,345 two-door hardtops; 20,216 four-door hardtops; 8,817 convertibles; 38,275 four-door station wagons with two-seats and 13,379 station wagons with three seats.

Unfortunately, no breakouts are currently available as to how many of each body style were built in specific series or car-lines.

NOTE 3: Prices and weights to left of slant bars are for sixes; on right of slant bars for V-8s.

DART PIONEER — PD3/PD4 SERIES — (ALL ENGINES) — The Pioneer was the intermediate trim level Dart. It included all Seneca features, plus rear armrests; front foam cushions and cigarette lighter. Nine-passenger station wagons also included power tailgate windows.

PIONEER SERIES I.D. NUMBERS: See Seneca I.D. Number section above.

PIONEER SERIES

Model Number	Body/Style Number	Body Type & Seating	Factory Price	Shipping Weight	Production Total
423/523	M41	4-dr Sed-6P	2459/2578	3430/3610	Note 1
421/521	M21	2-dr Sed-6P	2410/2530	3375/3540	Note 1
422/522	M23	2-dr HT Cpe-6P	2488/2607	3410/3610	Note 1
466/566	M45A	4-dr Sta Wag-6P	2787/2906	3820/4000	Note 1
467/567	M45B	4-dr Sta Wag-9P	2892/3011	3875/4065	Note 1

NOTE 1: Exactly 306,603 Dodge Darts were built during the 1960 model year. In rounded off figures, this included 80,000 Pioneer passenger cars and an undetermined number of Pioneer station wagons. (Station wagons were in a separate series. A total of some 51,600 station wagons were built in all lines.)

NOTE 2: Body style production of 1960 Dodges is available in terms of total output only and cannot be broken-out by series or car-line at the current time. See Seneca Series Note 2 above.

NOTE 3: Prices and weights above slant bar are for Six/below slant bar for V-8.

1960 Dodge, Dart Phoenix four-door hardtop sedan, V-8

PHOENIX SERIES — (ALL ENGINES) — The Phoenix was the top trim level Dart for 1960 and included all the Pioneer features, plus exterior moldings; Custom upholstery; Custom interior trimmings and back-up lights.

PHOENIX SERIES I.D. NUMBERS: See Seneca ID Number section above.

PHOENIX SERIES

Model Number	Body/Style Number	Body Type & Seating	Factory Price	Shipping Weight	Production Total
433/533	H41	4-dr Sed-6P	2595/2715	3420/3610	Note 1
434/534	H43	4-dr HT Sed-6P	2677/2796	3460/3655	Note 1
432/532	H23	2-dr HT Cpe-6P	2618/2737	3410/3605	Note 1
435/535	H27	2-dr Conv-6P	2868/2988	3460/3690	Note 1

NOTE 1: Exactly 306,603 Dodge Darts were built during the 1960 model year. In rounded off figures, this included 70,700 Dodge Dart Phoenix passenger cars. (No station wagons were built in the Phoenix car line.)

NOTE 2: Body style production of 1960 Dodges is available in terms of total output only and cannot be broken-out by series or car line at the current time. See Seneca Series Note 2 above.

NOTE 3: Prices and weights above slash are for Six/below slash for V-8.

DODGE MATADOR — SERIES PD1L -(V-8) — The Matador was the base trim Dodge for 1960. Like all full-size Dodges, it featured styling very similar to the smaller Dart models, but with slightly exaggerated fins and more deeply tunneled taillights. The fin ended three-quarters of the way down the rear fender. It was capped with chrome rear trim and a reflector. A single horizontal chrome strip ran the entire length of the bodyside. The Matador name, in script, was located on the front fender, just behind the wheelwell. A highly stylized star was located on the side of the tailfin.

MATADOR SERIES I.D. NUMBERS: See Seneca ID Number section above.

MATADOR SERIES

Model Number	Body/Style Number	Body Type & Seating	Factory Price	Shipping Weight	Production Total
643	41	4-dr Sed-6P	2930	3725	Note 1
644	43	4-dr HT Sed-6P	3075	3820	Note 1
642	23	2-dr HT Cpe-6P	2996	3705	Note 1
678	45A	4-dr Sta Wag-6P	3239	4045	Note 1
679	45B	4-dr Sta Wag-9P	3354	4120	Note 1

NOTE 1: Exactly 42,517 Dodges (Matador/Polara) were built during the 1960 model year. In figures rounded off to the nearest 100, this included 23,600 Matador passenger cars and an undetermined number of Matador station wagons. (Station wagons were in a separate series. A total of some 51,600 station wagons were built in all car lines.)

NOTE 2: Body style production of 1960 Dodges is available in terms of total output only and cannot be broken-out by series or car line at the current time. See Seneca Series Note 2 above.

1960 Dodge, Polara two-door convertible, V-8

DODGE POLARA — SERIES PD2H — (V-8) — The Polara was the top trim level Dodge for 1960 and included all Matador features, plus dual exhausts; Deluxe interior appointments; rear fender aluminum stone shields; front fender ornaments and the Polara name, in script on the front fender, just behind the front wheelwell. The Polara station wagon featured pillarless hardtop styling. It was one of the nicest looking station wagons to come out of the Chrysler Corp. assembly plants.

POLARA SERIES I.D. NUMBERS: See Seneca ID Number section above.

POLARA SERIES

Model Number	Body/Style Number	Body Type & Seating	Factory Price	Shipping Weight	Production Total
543	41	4-dr Sed-6P	3141	3735	Note 1
544	43	4-dr HT Sed-6P	3275	3815	Note 1
542	23	2-dr HT Cpe-6P	3196	3740	Note 1
578	46A	4-dr Sta Wag-6P	3506	4085	Note 1
579	46B	4-dr Sta Wag-9P	3621	4220	Note 1
545	27	2-dr Conv-6P	3416	3765	Note 1

NOTE 1: Exactly 42,517 Dodges (Matador/Polara) were built during the 1960 model year. In figures rounded off to the nearest 100, this included 11,600 Polara passenger cars and an undetermined number of Polara station wagons. (Station wagons were in a separate series. A total of some 51,600 station wagons were built in all car lines.)

NOTE 2: Body style production of 1960 Dodges is available in terms of total output only and cannot be broken-out by series or car line at the current time. See Seneca Series Note 2 above.

1960 ENGINES

Slant Six. Overhead valves. Cast iron block. Displacement: 225 cid. Bore and stroke: 3.41 x 4.13 inches. Compression ratio: 8.5:1. Brake hp: 145 at 4000 rpm. Four main bearings. Solid valve lifters. Carburetion: Carter BBS-2985S one-barrel.

V-8. Overhead valves. Cast iron block. Displacement: 318 cid. Bore and stroke: 3.91 x 3.31 inches. Compression ratio: 9.0:1. Brake hp: 230 at 4400 rpm. Five main bearings. Hydraulic valve lifters. Carburetion: Carter BBD-2921S two-barrel. Another available version of this engine had a four-barrel carburetor and produced 255 hp.

Super Red Ram V-8: Overhead valves. Cast iron block. Displacement 361 cid. Bore and stroke: 4.12 x 3.38 inches. Compression ratio: 10.0:1. Brake hp 295 at 4600 rpm. Five main bearings. Hydraulic valve lifters. Carburetion: Stromberg WWC-3-188 two-barrel.

Ram Fire V-8, Overhead valves. Cast iron block. Displacement: 383 cid. Bore and stroke: 4.25 x 3.38 inches. Compression ratio: 10.0:1. Brake hp: 325 at 4600 rpm. Five main bearings. Hydraulic valve lifters. Carburetion: Holley R-1971-A four-barrel.

D-500 V-8. Ram Induction (Dart models). Overhead valves. Cast iron block. Displacement: 361 cid. Bore and stroke: 4.12 x 3.38 inches. Compression ratio: 10.0:1. Brake hp: 320 at 4800 rpm. Five main bearings. Hydraulic valve lifters. Carburetion: Two Carter four-barrels on 30-inch "cross ram induction" manifolds.

1960 DODGE CHASSIS FEATURES

DART: Wheelbase: 118 inches; (122 inches on station wagons). Overall length: 208.6 inches; (214.8 inches on station wagons). Tires: 7.50 x 14 tubeless black sidewall on sedans; (8.00 x 14 on station wagons).

DODGE: Wheelbase: 122 inches. Overall length: 212.6 inches; (214.8 inches on station wagons). Tires: 8.00 x 14 tubeless black sidewall.

CONVENIENCE OPTIONS: Electric clock ($15). Music Master radio ($59). PowerFlite ($189). TorqueFlite ($211). Power steering ($77). Power brakes ($43). Power seats ($96). Power windows ($102). Airtemp air conditioning ($446). Deluxe dual station wagon air conditioning ($640). Windshield washer ($12). Remote-control side mirror ($18). Swivel seats ($87). D500 engine in Polara ($359); in Matador ($379) and in Dart Phoenix ($418). White sidewall tires on Darts ($33); on Dodges ($58).

HISTORICAL FOOTNOTES: In 1960, a modified Dart Phoenix driven by Norm Thatcher set three world records at Bonneville in the B-Supercharged Gas Coupe class. The supercharged 383 cid V-8 powered hardtop achieved a speed of 191.8 mph over the measured course.

1961 DODGE

DART SENECA — SERIES RD3/RD4 — (ALL ENGINES) — The year 1961 saw the introduction of a major facelift for the Dart. The most unusual feature of the 1961 models was reverse-slanting fins. They appeared to grow out of the fenders, at the base of the roof 'C' pillar and then tapered toward the rear of the car. They then wrapped around and formed a chrome-trimmed feature line, which moved forward, to the back of the rear door. The front end was shaped like a single large air intake. The large grille opening contained grillework with a concave grid pattern, with the quad headlights set at either end. The Dodge name, in block letters, was located across the front of the hood and across the trunk lid, directly above the recessed license plate. The Seneca was the base level Dart and included chrome windshield and a rear window moldings; a single chrome strip along the top of the fin (that wrapped around the bodyside); front armrests; electric windshield wipers; sun visors; turn signals and the Seneca name, in script, directly below the fins.

1961 Dodge, Dart Phoenix four-door hardtop sedan, V-8

DART SENECA SERIES I.D. NUMBERS — (ALL ENGINES) — Serial numbers are stamped/embossed on plate on left front door pillar and use the form 411()100001 and up. The first symbol indicates car-line/engine: 4=Dart 6-cyl.; 5=Dodge V-8; 7=Lancer 6-cyl. The second symbol indicates series: 1=Seneca/Lancer 170; 2=Pioneer; 3=Phoenix/Lancer 770; 4=Polara; 5=Seneca/Lancer 170 wagon; 6=Pioneer wagon; 7=Polara wagon; 8=Taxicab; 9=Police Special; 0=Fleet car. The third symbol indicates model year 1=1961. The fourth symbol indicates assembly plant: 2=Dodge Main; 3=Detroit (Jefferson); 5=Los Angeles, Calif.; 6=Newark, Del.; 7=St. Louis, Mo. The last six symbols are the sequential production number starting at 100001 for each series at each factory. Body number plates are located under the hood on fenders, cowl or radiator crossmember. They carry symbols that tell the production schedule dates, body production number, body series and trim, paint and accessory codes. A three-digit body number identifies each model and appears in the Model Number column of the charts below, replacing series codes that appeared in earlier editions of this catalog. Model codes with alpha prefixes are also employed, as follows: L=low-priced; M=medium-priced; H=high-priced; P=premium-priced and S=specially-priced. These appear in charts below in the Body/Style Number column. Engine codes were stamped on the right side of most engines and the left side of 318 cid V-8s, as follows: R-17 on 170 cid Slant Six; R-22 on 225 cid Slant Six; R-318 on 318 cid V-8; R-36 on 361 cid V-8; R-38 on 383 cid V-8; R-41 on 413 cid V-8.

SENECA SERIES

Model Number	Body/Style Number	Body Type & Seating	Factory Price	Shipping Weight	Production Total
413/513	L41	4-dr Sed-6P	2330/2449	3335/3515	Note 1
411/511	L21	2-dr Sed-6P	2278/2397	3290/3470	Note 1
456/556	L45	4-dr Sta Wag-6P	2695/2815	3740/3920	Note 1

NOTE 1: A total of 66,100 Seneca passenger cars were built during the model year. During the 1961 model year, Dodge built 20,625 two-door sedans; 97,201 four-door sedans; 22.156 two-door hardtops; 9,665 four-door hardtops; 4,361 convertibles; 20,697 six-passenger station wagons and 7,005 nine-passenger station wagons. There are no available breakouts, per series; only by body style.
NOTE 2: Data above slashes for six-cylinder/below slash for V-8.

DART PIONEER — RD3/RD4 SERIES — (ALL ENGINES) — The Pioneer was the intermediate trim level Dart and included all Seneca features, plus armrests, front foam cushion and cigarette lighter. Nine-passenger station wagons also included power tailgate windows. The "Pioneer" name appeared in script at the rear of the rear fender fins.

PIONEER SERIES I.D. NUMBERS: See 1961 Seneca I.D. number listing. All models began at 100001 and went up in the unit number sequence.

PIONEER SERIES

Model Number	Body/Style Number	Body Type & Seating	Factory Price	Shipping Weight	Production Total
423/523	M41	4-dr Sed-6P	2459/2478	3335/3510	Note 1
421/521	M21	2-dr Sed-6P	2410/2530	3290/3460	Note 1
422/522	M23	2-dr HT Cpe-6P	2488/2607	3335/3500	Note 1
466/566	M45A	4-dr Sta Wag-6P	2787/2906	3740/3940	Note 1
467/567	M54B	4-dr Sta Wag-9P	2892/3011	3825/4005	Note 1

NOTE 1: A total of 38,600 Pioneer passenger cars were built during model year 1961. No production breakout is provided for individual body styles in each series. See Seneca Series for total production of each body style during 1961.
NOTE 2: Data above slashes for six-cylinder/below slash for V-8.

DART PHOENIX — RD3/RD4 SERIES — (ALL ENGINES) — The Phoenix was the top trim level Dart for 1961 and included all Pioneer features, plus exterior moldings; Custom interior upholstery and trim; and back-up lights.

PHOENIX SERIES I.D. NUMBERS: See 1961 Seneca Series I.D. Number listing. All models began at 100001 and went up in the unit number sequence.

PHOENIX SERIES

Model Number	Body/Style Number	Body Type & Seating	Factory Price	Shipping Weight	Production Total
433/533	H41	4-dr Sed-6P	2595/2715	3350/3535	Note 1
434/534	H43	4-dr HT Sed-6P	2677/2796	3385/3555	Note 1
432/532	H23	2-dr HT Cpe-6P	2618/2737	3325/3520	Note 1
435/535	H27	2-dr Conv-6P	2988	3580	Note 1

NOTE 1: A total of 37,300 Phoenixes were built during calendar year 1961. No production breakout is provided for individual body styles in each series. See Seneca Series for total production of each body style during 1961.
NOTE 2: Data above slashes are for six-cylinder/below slash for V-8. The Phoenix convertible came only with V-8 power.

DODGE POLARA — RD1 SERIES — (V-8) — The Polara was the only full-size Dodge offered in 1961. All Polaras utilized the 361 cid V-8 engine as standard equipment. The 383 cid V-8 was optional. Polara models featured chrome windshield and rear window moldings. A split chrome strip, with an aluminum insert changed back into a single strip behind the front door, then ran to the rear of the car, sweeping up, over the tailfin. Taillights recessed into bezels like jet airplane exhausts were contained in the wraparound sweep of the tailfins. Polaras used Dart grilles, with a crossbar ornament in the center. The Polara name, in script, was located on the front fender ahead of the wheelwell.

1961 Dodge, Polara four-door hardtop station wagon, V-8

POLARA SERIES I.D. NUMBERS: See I.D. Number listing. All models began at 100001 and went up in the unit number sequence.

POLARA SERIES

Model Number	Body/Style Number	Body Type & Seating	Factory Price	Shipping Weight	Production Total
543	L41	4-dr Sed-6P	2966	3700	Note 1
544	L43	4-dr HT Sed-6P	3110	3740	Note 1
542	L23	2-dr HT Cpe-6P	3032	3690	Note 1
545	L27	2-dr Conv-6P	3252	3765	Note 1
578	L46A	4-dr Sta Wag-6P	3294	4115	Note 1
579	L46B	4-dr Sta Wag-9P	3409	4125	Note 1

NOTE 1: A total of 14,032 Polaras were built during model year 1961. No production breakout is provided for individual body styles in each series. See Seneca Series for total production of each body style during 1961.

1961 Dodge, Lancer 770 four-door station wagon, 6-cyl

LANCER 170 — RW1 SERIES — (SIX-CYLINDER) — The big news for 1961 was the introduction of the compact Lancer Series. An offshoot of the Plymouth Valiant, the Lancer was nearly two feet shorter and 700 pounds lighter than a standard Dodge. The Lancer used the basic Valiant body shell, but with more attractive trim and much finer interior appointments. Powering the new Lancer was a smaller, 170 cid version of the Slant Six engine. The Lancer 170 was the base trim level and included chrome windshield and rear window moldings; a short chrome strip on the rear fender feature line (terminating at the taillights) and the Lancer name, in block letters, on the side of the front door (below the feature line). A Dodge crest was located on the front of the hood above the horizontal bar grille. The Dodge name, also in block letters, was located on the trunk lid. A grille of thin horizontal bars ran full width and incorporated quad headlights. Concave, round taillights were set into the rear fender fins.

LANCER 170 SERIES I.D. NUMBERS: See I.D. Number listing. All models began at 100001 and went up in the unit number sequence.

LANCER 170 SERIES

Model Number	Body/Style Number	Body Type & Seating	Factory Price	Shipping Weight	Production Total
711	L41	4-dr Sed-6P	2069	2595	Note 1
713	L21	2-dr Sed-6P	2007	2585	Note 1
756	L45	4-dr Sta Wag-6P	2382	2760	Note 1

NOTE 1: The exact model year output of Dodge Lancers was 74,773 units. In rounded figures, this included 20,800 Lancer 170 passenger cars; 44,300 Lancer 770 passenger cars and 9,700 Lancer station wagons (both Series).
NOTE 2: The model year output of 74,733 units included 12,637 two-door sedans; 44,864 four-door sedans; 7,552 two-door hardtops and 9,720 two-seat four-door station wagons. There is no further breakout by series.

LANCER 770 — RW1 SERIES — (SIX-CYLINDER) — The 770 Series was the top trim level Lancer for 1961 and included all the 170 Series trim, plus more exterior bright trim and more plush interior appointments.

LANCER 770 SERIES I.D. NUMBERS: See I.D. Number listing. All models began at 100001 and went up in the unit number sequence.

LANCER 770 SERIES

Model Number	Body/Style Number	Body Type & Seating	Factory Price	Shipping Weight	Production Total
733	H41	4-dr Sed-6P	2154	2605	Note 1
732	H23	2-dr HT Cpe-6P	2181	2595	Note 1
731	NA	2-dr Spt Cpe-6P	2092	NA	Note 1
776	H45	4-dr Sta Wag-6P	2466	2775	Note 1

NOTE 1: See Note 1 and Additional Notes under 1961 Dodge Lancer '170' listing.

1961 ENGINES

170 Slant Six. Overhead valves. Cast iron block. Displacement: 170 cid. Bore and stroke: 3.40 x 3.13 inches. Compression ratio: 8.2:1. Brake hp: 101 at 4400 rpm. Four main bearings. Solid valve lifters. Carburetion: Carter BBS-3093S one-barrel.

225 Slant Six. Overhead valves. Cast iron block. (Some 225 engines were built with aluminum blocks.) Displacement: 225 cid. Bore and stroke: 3.41 x 4.13 inches. Compression ratio: 8.2:1. Brake hp: 145 at 4000 rpm. Four main bearings. Solid valve lifters. Carburetor: Carter BBS-3098S one-barrel.

Hyper-Pak 225 Slant Six. Overhead valves. Cast iron block (See Historical footnotes). Displacement: 225 cid. Bore and stroke: 3.41 x 4.13 inches. Compression ratio: 8.2:1. Brake hp: 195 at 5200 rpm. Four main bearings. Solid valve lifters. Carburetion: Carter AFB 3083S four-barrel. Tuned exhaust headers leading to tuned exhaust system.

V-8. Overhead valves. Cast iron block. Displacement: 318 cid. Bore and stroke: 3.91 x 3.31 inches. Compression ratio: 9.0:1. Brake hp: 230 at 4400 rpm. Five main bearings. Hydraulic valve lifters. Carburetion: Stromberg WW-1543 two-barrel.

Polara V-8. Overhead valve. Cast iron block. Displacement: 361 cid. Bore and stroke: 4.12 x 3.38 inches. Compression ratio: 9.0:1. Brake hp: 265 at 4400 rpm. Five main bearings. Hydraulic valve lifters. Carburetion: Stromberg WWC-3-188 two-barrel.

Dart D-500 V-8. Overhead valve. Cast iron block. Displacement: 361 cid. Bore and stroke: 4.12 x 3.38 inches. Compression ratio: 9.0:1. Brake hp: 305 at 4800 rpm. Five main bearings. Hydraulic valve lifters. Carburetion: Carter AFB-3105S four-barrel.

Polara D-500 V-8. Overhead valve. Cast iron block. Displacement: 383 cid. Bore and stroke: 4.25 x 3.38 inches. Compression ratio: 10.0:1. Brake hp: 325 at 4800 rpm. Five main bearings. Hydraulic valve lifters. Carburetion: Carter AFB-2903S four-barrel.

Polara Ram-Induction D-500 V-8. Overhead valve. Cast iron block. Displacement: 383 cid. Bore and stroke: 4.25 x 3.38 inches. Compression ratio: 10.0:1. Brake hp. 330 at 5000 rpm. Five main bearings. Hydraulic valve lifters. Carburetion: Two Carter AFB-3084S four-barrels.

Super D-500 V-8. Overhead valve. Cast iron block. Displacement: 413 cid. Bore and stroke: 4.19 x 3.75 inches. Compression ratio: 10.0:1. Brake hp: 350 at 4800 rpm. Five main bearings. Hydraulic valve lifters. Carburetion: Carter AFB-3108S four-barrel. (Option added at midyear.)

Super Ram-Tuned D-500 V-8. Overhead valves. Cast iron block. Displacement: 413 cid. Bore and stroke: 4.19 x 3.75 inches. Compression ratio: 10.0:1. Brake hp: 375 at 5000 rpm. Five main bearings. Hydraulic valve lifters. Carburetion: Two Carter AFB-3084S four-barrels. (Option added at midyear; includes "short" ram-tuned induction system.)

1961 DODGE CHASSIS FEATURES

LANCER: Wheelbase: 106.5 inches. Overall length: 188.8 inches. Tires: 6.50 x 13 tubeless black sidewall. Three-speed manual transmission was standard on all Lancers, with the three-speed TorqueFlite automatic transmission optional.

DART: Wheelbase: 118 inches; (122 on station wagons). Overall length: 209.4 inches; (214.8 inches on station wagons). Tires: 7.00 x 14 tubeless black sidewall on sedans; 8.00 x 14 on station wagons. Three-speed manual transmission was standard on all Darts, with the three-speed TorqueFlite automatic transmission optional.

POLARA: Wheelbase: 122 inches. Overall length: 212.5 inches; (214.8 inches on station wagons). Tires: 8.00 x 14 tubeless black sidewall. Three-speed manual transmission was standard on all Polaras with three-speed TorqueFlite automatic transmission optional.

CONVENIENCE OPTIONS: Electric clock ($16). Music Master radio ($59). TorqueFlite automatic transmission ($211). Power steering ($77). Power brakes ($43). Power seats ($96). Power windows ($102). Airtemp air conditioning ($446); dual unit used in station wagons ($640). Windshield washer ($12). Remote-control outside mirror ($18). Tinted glass ($43). Ram-induction D500 V-8 ($313). White sidewall tires on Darts ($33); on Polaras ($64).

HISTORICAL FOOTNOTES: Beginning in mid-1961 the 225 cid Slant Six engine was produced with an aluminum engine block. Exact production dates are unavailable. There is no record of the number of these blocks produced. A special Hyper-Pak was available for the Slant Six. A competition engine, the Hyper-Pak featured a much more radical cam; a Carter AFB four-barrel carburetor mounted on an intake manifold with long ram passages; steel tubing exhaust headers; higher compression pistons and a special tuned exhaust system. Advertised at 195 hp, Hyper-Pak engines actually put out in excess of 275 bhp. They were the rulers of the lower stock classes at the drag races. The Hyper-Pak was available as a dealer-installed option. The D-500 and Super D-500 V-8 engines featured a very unusual intake system, with two Carter AFB four-barrel carburetors mounted on 30-inch long intake manifolds. The carburetor mounted over the right valve cover actually fed the left bank of the engine and vice versa. These extremely long manifolds produced incredible low-end torque.

1962 DODGE

DART SERIES — (ALL ENGINES) — Completely restyled for 1962, the Dart was new from the ground up. Riding on a two-inch shorter, 116 inch wheelbase, the new 202 inch overall length was 10 inches shorter than in 1961. The redesigned grille featured an unusual headlight arrangement. The inboard lights were mounted higher than the outer ones. An oval grille featured vertical bars, with five larger division bars spaced across the insert. Taillamps continued the angular theme of the front and, again, the inboard lenses were positioned higher than the outer ones. Very heavy feature lines characterized the bodysides. They originated as a 'brow' over the headlights and flared around the side of the fender. From there, they continued along the side, to the trailing edge of the front door. Another heavy feature line began immediately in front of the rear wheelwell. It swept up, along the wheel opening, and angled back to a point even with the inboard rear taillamp elevation. A chrome strip highlighted each feature line and continued across the trunk lid, between the uppermost taillights. The Dodge name, in block letters, was spaced along the edge of the hood. A Dodge crest was located above the chrome strip, on the trunk lid. The Dart was the base trim model and featured chrome windshield and rear window moldings; chrome headlight doors; turn signals; electric windshield wipers; driver's side inside sun visor and front armrests. The Dart name, in script, appeared on the front door edge.

DART SERIES I.D. NUMBERS — (ALL ENGINES) — Serial numbers are stamped/embossed on plate on left front door pillar and use the form 412()100001 and up. The first symbol indicates car-line/engine: 4=Dart 6-cyl.; 5=Dart V-8/Polara; 6=Dodge Custom 880 V-8; 7=Lancer 170/770/GT. The second symbol indicates series: 1=Lancer 170/Dart/880; 2=Dart 330; 3=Lancer 770/Dart 440; 5=Lancer 170/Dart Custom wagon; 6=Dart 330 wagon; 7=Lancer 770/Dart 440 wagon; 8=Taxicab; 9=Police Special; 10=Fleet car. The third symbol indicates model year 2=1962. The fourth symbol indicates assembly plant: 2=Dodge Main; 3=Detroit (Jefferson); 5=Los Angeles, Calif.; 6=Newark, Del.; 7=St. Louis, Mo. The last six symbols are the sequential production number starting at 100001 for each series at each factory. Body number plates are located under the hood on fenders, cowl or radiator cross-

member. They carry symbols that tell the production schedule dates, body production number, body series and trim, paint and accessory codes. A three-digit body number identifies each model and appears in the Body/Style Number column of the charts below. Engine codes were stamped on the right side of most engines and the left side of 318 cid V-8s, as follows: S-17 on 170 cid Slant Six; S-22 on 225 cid Slant Six; S-318 on 318 cid V-8; S-36 on 361 cid V-8; S-38 on 383 cid V-8; S-41 on 413 cid V-8.

DART SERIES

Model Number	Body/Style Number	Body Type & Seating	Factory Price	Shipping Weight	Production Total
SD1/2	413/513	4-dr Sed-6P	2297/2404	3000/3170	Note 1
SD1/2	411/511	2-dr Sed-6P	2241/2348	2970/3435	Note 1
SD1/2	456/556	4-dr Sta Wag-6P	2644/2751	3270/3435	Note 1

NOTE 1: The exact model year output of full-size Dodges was 165,861 units. In rounded totals, this included 48,200 Darts; 25,500 Darts 330s; 37,800 Dart 440s; 12,500 Polara 500s; 24,400 Dart station wagons; 15,400 Custom 880s and 2,100 Custom 880 station wagons.

NOTE 2: The exact model year production total given above included 13,500 two-door sedans; 85,163 four-door sedans; 21,499 two-door hardtops; 13,130 four-door hardtops; 6,024 convertibles; 19,124 four-door two-seat station wagons and 7,421 four-door three-seat station wagons. Unfortunately, there is no way to break out these individual body style totals, per series, at the present time.

NOTE 3: Data above slashes for six-cylinder/below slash for V-8.

NOTE 4: In rounded off totals, the series production figures in Note 1 include 35,500 Dart sixes; 8,800 Dart 330 sixes; 3,200 Dart 440 sixes and 5,300 six-cylinder Dart station wagons. All other Darts (some 95,600) were V-8 powered. All Polara 500s and Custom 880s had standard V-8 power.

1962 Dodge, Dart 330 two-door hardtop coupe, V-8

DART 330 SERIES — (ALL ENGINES) — The Dart 330 was the intermediate trim level Dart and included all the features of the Dart Series, plus a cigarette lighter; front foam cushion; rear armrests; and a power tailgate window (on nine-passenger station wagons).

DART 330 SERIES I.D. NUMBERS: See I.D. Number listing. All models began at 100001 and went up in the unit number sequence.

DART 330 SERIES

Model Number	Body/Style Number	Body Type & Seating	Factory Price	Shipping Weight	Production Total
SD1/2M	423/523	4-dr Sed-6P	2432/2540	3000/3170	Note 1
SD1/2M	421/521	2-dr Sed-6P	2375/2482	2965/3135	Note 1
SD1/2M	422/522	2-dr HT Cpe-6P	2463/2570	2985/3155	Note 1
SD1/2M	466/566	4-dr Sta Wag-6P	2739/2848	3275/3435	Note 1
SD2M	567	4-dr Sta Wag-9P	2949	3500	Note 1

NOTE 1: See all notes under 1962 Dodge Dart Series listing.

1962 Dodge, Dart 440 four-door hardtop sedan, V-8

DART 440 SERIES — (ALL ENGINES) — The Dart 440 was the top trim level Dart for 1962 and included all the Dart 330 features, plus back-up lights; Custom interior upholstery and trim; exterior moldings and a power tailgate window on nine-passenger station wagons.

DART 440 SERIES I.D. NUMBERS: See I.D. Number listing. All models began at 100001 and went up in the unit number sequence.

DART 440 SERIES

Model Number	Body/Style Number	Body Type & Seating	Factory Price	Shipping Weight	Production Total
SD1H/2H	433/533	4-dr Sed-6P	2584/2691	3045/3205	Note 1
SD1H/2H	432/532	2 dr HT Cpe-6P	2606/2731	3025/3185	Note 1
SD2H	534	4-dr HT Sed-6P	2763	3260	Note 1
SD2H	535	2-dr Conv-6P	2945	3285	Note 1
SD2H	576	4-dr Sta Wag-6P	2989	3460	Note 1
SD2H	477	4-dr Sta Wag-9P	3092	3530	Note 1

NOTE 1: See all notes under 1962 Dodge Dart Series listing.

POLARA 500 SERIES — (V-8) — The Polara 500 was the top trim level Dodge for 1962. It shared body and chassis components with the Dart Series and included all the features of the Dart 440, plus bucket seats; carpeting; dual exhausts; 361 cid V-8 engine; padded instrument panel; Deluxe steering wheel; wheelcovers; outside rearview mirror on the left door and the Polara name, in script, where the 'Dart' name appeared on Darts. Special exterior trim, in contrasting colors, was also a part of the Polara 500 package. The four-door hardtop was added on Nov. 5, 1961.

POLARA 500 SERIES I.D. NUMBERS: See I.D. Number listing. All models began at 100001 and went up in the unit number sequence.

POLARA 500 SERIES

Model Number	Body/Style Number	Body Type & Seating	Factory Price	Shipping Weight	Production Total
SD2P	544	4-dr HT Sed-6P	2960	3360	Note 1
SD2P	542	2-dr HT Cpe-6P	3019	3315	Note 1
SD2P	545	2-dr Conv-6P	3268	3430	Note 1

NOTE 1: See all notes under 1962 Dodge Dart Series listing. All Polara 500s were V-8 powered.

1962 Dodge Custom 880, four-door hardtop station wagon, 6-pass., V-8

CUSTOM 880 SERIES — (V-8) — The Custom 880 was the luxury Dodge offering for 1962. It was introduced on Jan. 21, 1962 to flush out the line with a 'big' Dodge and to plug the gap left with the demise of the DeSoto. Dodge combined the 1962 Chrysler body with the front end of a 1961 Dodge, creating a very attractive combination. Offering a full line of body styles, the Custom 880 also included a beautifully styled hardtop station wagon. The Custom 880 was, undoubtedly, the best looking of the 1962 Dodges. All Custom 880s were V-8 powered.

CUSTOM 880 SERIES I.D. NUMBERS: See I.D. Number listing. All models began at 100001 and went up in the unit number sequence.

CUSTOM 880 SERIES

Model Number	Body/Style Number	Body Type & Seating	Factory Price	Shipping Weight	Production Total
SD3L	613	4-dr Sed-6P	2964	3655	11,141
SD3L	614	4-dr HT Sed-6P	31009	3680	1855
SD3L	612	2-dr HT Cpe-6P	3030	3615	1761
SD3L	615	2-dr Conv-6P	3251	3705	684
SD3L	658	4-dr Sta Wag-6P	3292	4025	1174
SD3L	659	4-dr Sta Wag-9P	3407	4055	890

NOTE 1: See all notes under 1962 Dodge Dart Series listings. All Custom 880s were V-8 powered.

1962 Dodge, Lancer GT two-door hardtop coupe, 6-cyl

LANCER 170 SERIES — (SIX) — The year 1962 was the last for the Lancer name on Dodge's compact line. Styling was virtually the same as 1961, with some very minor trim updating. The convex grille featured a combination of vertical and horizontal bars in place of the horizontal bars used 1961. The taillights were slightly re-trimmed. The Lancer 170 continued to be the base trim level and included chrome windshield and rear window moldings; a short chrome strip on the rear fender feature line (terminating at the taillights) and the Lancer name, in block letters, on the side of the front door below the front feature line. A Dodge crest was located on the front of the hood, above the grille. The Dodge name, also in block letters, was located on the trunk lid.

LANCER 170 SERIES I.D. NUMBERS: See I.D. Number listing. All models began at 100001 and went up in the unit number sequence.

LANCER 170 SERIES

Model Number	Body/Style Number	Body Type & Seating	Factory Price	Shipping Weight	Production Total
SL1L	713	4-dr Sed-6P	2011	2525	Note 1
SL1L	711	2-dr Sed-6P	1951	2495	Note 1
SL1L	756	2-dr Sta Wag-6P	2306	2685	Note 1

NOTE 1: The exact model year output of Dodge Lancers was 64,271 units. In rounded off figures, this included 17,100 Lancer 170s; 26,100 Lancer 770s; 14,100 GT hardtops and 7,000 Lancer station wagons with two-seats.

NOTE 2: The exact model year production total given above included 14,333 two-door sedans; 28,793 four-door sedans; 14,140 hardtops and 7,005 four-door two-seat station wagons. Unfortunately, there is no further breakout of these individual body style totals, per series, currently available.

ADDITIONAL NOTE: All 1962 Dodge Lancers were six-cylinder powered.

LANCER 770 SERIES — (SIX) — The 770 Series was the top trim level Lancer for 1962 and included all the 170 Series trim, plus extra exterior trim and plusher interior appointments. A sport version of the 770 Series, called the 'GT,' was offered in two-door hardtop configuration only. It featured the larger 225 cid Slant Six engine.

LANCER 770 SERIES I.D. NUMBERS: See I.D. Number listing. All models began at 100001 and went up in the sequence unit numbers.

LANCER 770 SERIES

Model Number	Body/Style Number	Body Type & Seating	Factory Price	Shipping Weight	Production Total
SL1H	733	4-dr Sed-6P	2114	2540	Note 1
SL1H	731	2-dr Sed-6P	2052	2520	Note 1
SL1H	776	4-dr Sta Wag-8P	2408	2705	Note 1
SL1P	742	2-dr GT/HT Cpe-5P	2257	2560	(14,140)

NOTE 1: Except in one case (figure in parenthesis), it is currently impossible to break out individual body style production between the Lancer 170 and Lancer 770 Series. See all notes under 1962 Dodge Lancer 170 Series.

1962 ENGINES

170 Slant Six. Overhead valves. Aluminum block. Displacement: 170 cid. Bore and stroke: 3.40 x 3.13 inches. Compression ratio: 8.2:1. Brake hp: 101 at 4400 rpm. Four main bearings. Solid valve lifters. Carburetion: Carter BBS-3229S one-barrel.

225 Slant Six. Overhead valves. Aluminum block. Displacement: 225 cid. Bore and stroke: 3.41 x 4.13 inches. Compression ratio: 8.2:1. Brake hp: 145 at 4000 rpm. Four main bearings. Solid valve lifters. Carburetion: Carter BBS-3231S one-barrel.

Hyper-Pak 225 Slant Six. Overhead valves. Cast iron block. Displacement: 225 cid. Bore and stroke: 3.41 x 4.13 inches. Compression ratio: 8.2:1. Brake hp: 195 at 5200 rpm. Four main bearings. Solid valve lifters. Carburetion: Carter AFB 3083S four-barrel. Tuned exhaust headers leading to tuned exhaust system. (Available as a dealer-installed option. Installations at dealer level may have included kits left over from 1961.)

Dart V-8. Overhead valves. Cast iron block. Displacement: 318 cid. Bore and stroke: 3.91 x 3.31 inches. Compression ratio: 9.0:1. Brake hp: 230 at 4400 rpm. Five main bearings. Hydraulic valve lifters. Carburetion: Carter BBD-3240S two-barrel.

Dart V-8. Overhead valves. Cast iron block. Displacement: 318 cid. Bore and stroke: 3.91 x 3.31 inches. Compression ratio: 9.0:1. Brake hp: 260 at 4400 rpm. Five main bearings. Hydraulic valve lifters. Carburetion: Carter AFB four-barrel.

Polara V-8. Overhead valves. Cast iron block. Displacement: 361 cid. Bore and stroke: 4.12 x 3.38 inches. Compression ratio: 9.0:1. Brake hp: 305 at 4800 rpm. Five main bearings. Hydraulic valve lifters. Carburetion: Carter AFB 3252S four-barrel.

Ram-Charger "Max Wedge" 413 V-8. Overhead valves. Cast iron block. Displacement: 413 cid. Bore and stroke: 4.19 x 3.75 inches. Compression ratio: 11.0:1. Brake hp: 410 at 5400 rpm. Five main bearings. Solid valve lifters. Carburetion: Two Carter AFB 3084S four-barrels. (Midyear option)

Ram-Charger "Max Wedge" 413 V-8. Overhead valves. Cast iron block. Displacement: 413 cid. Bore and stroke: 4.19 x 3.75 inches. Compression ratio 13.5:1. Brake hp: 420 at 5400 rpm. Five main bearings. Solid valve lifters. Carburetion: Two Carter AFB 3084S four-barrels. (Midyear option)

1962 DODGE CHASSIS FEATURES

LANCER: Wheelbase: 106.5 inches. Overall length: 188.8 inches. Tires: 6.50 x 13 tubeless black sidewall. Three-speed manual transmission was standard on all Lancers, with the three-speed TorqueFlite automatic transmission optional.

DART AND POLARA: Wheelbase: 116 inches. Overall length: 202 inches; (210 inches on station wagons). Tires: 6.50 x 14 tubeless black sidewall (7.00 x 14 on Polaras and station wagons). Three-speed manual transmission was standard on all Darts and Polaras, with the three-speed TorqueFlite automatic transmission optional.

CUSTOM 880: Wheelbase: 122 inches. Overall length: 213.5 inches; (215 inches on station wagons). Tires: 8.00 x 14 tubeless black sidewall. Three-speed manual transmission was standard on all Custom 880s, with the three-speed TorqueFlite automatic optional.

CONVENIENCE OPTIONS: Electric clock ($16). Music Master radio ($58). TorqueFlite automatic transmission on six-cylinders ($192); on V-8s ($211). Power steering ($77). Power brakes ($43). Power seats ($96). Power windows ($102). Airtemp air conditioning ($445). Windshield washer ($12). 413 cid Ramcharger V-8 engine ($400). Four-speed manual transmission ($146). White sidewall tires ($33-$48).

HISTORICAL FOOTNOTES: The 1962 Dodge/Dart/Polara line was introduced on Sept. 28, 1961. The Custom 880 arrived in Jan., 1962. Model year production hit exactly 165,861 units. Calendar year output included 35,564 Lancers and 216,158 Dodges. Lancer production was discontinued in August, 1962. The new, 'senior-compact' sized Dodge Dart would replace the Lancer in 1963, the company's official Golden Anniversary. C.E. Briggs was the vice president and general manager of Dodge Div. While the Ram-Tuned engines of 1961 were extremely powerful, with their huge intake manifolds, they were mechanic's nightmares. Chrysler Corp. solved this problem with the midyear introduction of the famous Ram-Charger 413 engine, which utilized ram passages only 15 inches long. As the name implied, this motor represented the maximum performance state of tune for the 413 cid V-8. The intake and exhaust ports were 25 percent larger than in 1961 and there were dozens of other performance features, such as mechanical valve lifters and a cast-aluminum ram-induction manifold. Dodges proved themselves to be the car to beat on the dragstrip in 1962. Four NHRA records were taken by Ram-Charger 413 Dodges. In SS/S class, Dick Landy did the quarter-mile in 12.71 seconds. In SS/SA class, Bill "Maverick" Golden hit 12.50 seconds. The Golden Lancer, owned by Dode Martin and Jim Nelson, featured the 413 in a compact Lancer. Running in A/FX class, it made a record 12.26 second run. In the even wilder AA/D class, Nelson registered 8.59 seconds with another car. Once again, Norm Thatcher drove a specially-prepared Dart, equipped with a modified Ram-Charger V-8, to a Class B Production record of 167.3 mph in the Flying Mile.

1963 DODGE

DART 170 SERIES — (SIX-CYLINDER) — The Dart Series was the new compact in the Dodge lineup and was slightly larger than the Lancer it replaced. Overall, it was 4-1/2 inches longer than the previous models. For the first time, the Dart was offered with a convertible, both in the top line GT and the intermediate 270 Series. Styling was very smooth. A concave grille, featuring a vertical theme, was located between the single headlights. A Dodge crest was located on the hood and a single body feature line ran horizontally at the belt. A smaller feature line ran horizontally at the lower side of the body, swept up over the rear wheelwell and continued horizontally back to the rear bumper. The single round taillights were housed in a small chrome bezel and the Dodge name, in block letters, appeared on the vertical section of the trunk lid. The Dart 170 was the base trim level and included chrome windshield and rear window moldings; chrome headlight doors; a Dart emblem on the roof 'C' pillar; turn signals; electric windshield wipers; sun visors; dual horns; saddle moldings; cigar lighter; front armrests and the Dart name, in script, along the bodyside, at the back of the rear fender.

DODGE I.D. NUMBERS — (ALL ENGINES) — Serial numbers are stamped/embossed on plate on left front door pillar and use the form 713( )100001 and up. The first symbol indicates car-line/engine: 4=Dart 6-cyl.; 5=Dodge 880 V-8; 6=Dodge V-8; 7=Dart 170/270/GT. The second symbol indicates series: 1=170/330/Custom 880; 2=440; 3=270/Polara; 4=Dart GT/Polara 500; 5=170/330/880/Custom wagon; 6=440 wagon; 7=Polara 270 wagon; 8=Taxicab; 9=Police Special; 10=880/fleet. The third symbol indicates model year 3=1963. The fourth symbol indicates assembly plant: 2=Dodge Main; 3=Detroit (Jefferson); 5=Los Angeles, Calif.; 6=Newark, Del.; 7=St. Louis, Mo. The last six symbols are the sequential production number starting at 100001 for each series at each factory. Body number plates are located under the hood on fenders, cowl or radiator crossmember. They carry symbols that tell the production schedule dates, body production number, body series and trim, paint and accessory codes. A three-digit body number identifies each model and appears in the Body/Style Number column of the charts below. Engine codes were stamped on the right side of most engines and the left side of 318 cid V-8s, as follows: T-170 on 170 cid Slant Six; T-22 on 225 cid Slant Six; T-318 on 318 cid V-8; T-38 on 383 cid V-8; T-41 on 413 V-8 and T-42 on 426 Max Wedge V-8.

DART 170 SERIES

Model Number	Body/Style Number	Body Type & Seating	Factory Price	Shipping Weight	Production Total
TL1L	713	4-dr Sed-6P	2041	2634	Note 1
TL1L	711	2-dr Sed-6P	1983	2614	Note 1
TL1L	756	4-dr Sta Wag-6P	2309	2735	Note 1

NOTE 1: A total of 51,300 Dart 170s were built during model year 1963, all six-cylinder powered. In addition, a total of 13,000 station wagons were built in all of the Dart lines. All were sixes. There is no breakout of station wagon production by series, so this total includes both 170 and 270 station wagons. (All figures rounded off to the nearest 100 units).

DART 270 SERIES — (SIX-CYLINDER) — The Dart 270 was the intermediate trim level and included all the 170 features, plus carpeting, special upholstery and trim.

DART 270 SERIES I.D. NUMBERS: See I.D. Number listing. All models began at 100001 and went up in the unit number sequence.

DART 270 SERIES

Model Number	Body/Style Number	Body Type & Seating	Factory Price	Shipping Weight	Production Total
TL1H	733	4-dr Sed-6P	2135	2644	Note 1
TL1H	731	2-dr Sed-6P	2079	2624	Note 1
TL1H	735	2-dr Conv-6P	2385	2710	Note 1
TL1H	776	4-dr Sta Wag-6P	2433	2745	Note 1

NOTE 1: A total of 55,300 Dart 270 passenger cars were built during model year 1963, all six-cylinder powered. (Figures rounded off to nearest 100 units).

NOTE 2: Dart 270 station wagon production totals are included with Dart 170 station wagon production totals. See Dart 170 Series Note 1 above.

1963 Dodge, Dart GT two-door hardtop coupe, 6-cyl

DART GT SERIES — (SIX-CYLINDER) — The GT was the top trim level Dart for 1963 and included all the 270 features, plus padded instrument panel, wheelcovers and bucket seats.

DART GT SERIES I.D. NUMBERS: See I.D. Number listing. All models began at 100001 and went up in the unit number sequence.

DART GT SERIES

Model Number	Body/Style Number	Body Type & Seating	Factory Price	Shipping Weight	Production Total
TL1P	742	2-dr HT Cpe-5P	2290	2661	Note 1
TL1P	745	2-dr Conv-5P	2512	2740	Note 1

NOTE 1: A total of 34,300 Dart GTs were built during model year 1963, all six-cylinder powered. (Figures rounded off to nearest 100 units).

DODGE 330 SERIES — (ALL ENGINES) — The full-size Dodge was once again totally restyled for 1963 and rode a wheelbase stretched three inches to 119 inches. This season represented the end of the 'ugly' Dodge era. The rear end styling was very attractive and the front was just slightly less so. In the case of the Dodge, a massive full-width grille, featuring a vertical theme and convex styling, contained the inboard headlights. These were located lower than the outboard units, exactly the opposite of the 1962 styles. A nearly horizontal feature

line angled back from the front fenders, to the rear of the car, and dropped down to just in front of the taillights. Large rectangular taillights were used and a three-pointed stylized star, located on the trunk lid, housed the trunk lock. The license plate was recessed in the escutcheon panel. The 1963 Dodges were the absolute terror of the country's dragstrips during 1963. When powered by the new 426 cid Ram-Charger "Max Wedge" V-8, almost no other cars could catch them. The Dodge 330 was the base trim level Dodge for 1963 and included chrome windshield and rear window moldings; turn signals; electric windshield wipers; sun visors; PCV system; power tailgate windows on nine-passenger station wagons and the Dodge name, in block letters, on the right side of the trunk lid. The '330' model designation was carried on the roof 'C' pillars.

DODGE 330 SERIES I.D. NUMBERS: See I.D. Number listing. All models began at 100001 and went up in the sequence unit numbers.

DODGE 330 SERIES

Model Number	Body/Style Number	Body Type & Seating	Factory Price	Shipping Weight	Production Total
TD1L/2L	413/613	4-dr Sed-6P	2301/2408	3064/3253	Note 1
TD1L/SL	411/611	2-dr Sed-6P	2245/2352	3029/3218	Note 1
TD1L/2L	456/656	4-dr Sta Wag-6P	2648/2756	3293/3478	Note 1
TD1L/2L	457/657	4-dr Sta Wag-9P	2749/2857	3358/3543	Note 1

NOTE 1: A total of 64,100 Dodge 330 passenger cars were built during model year 1963. Of these, 40,100 were sixes and 24,000 were V-8s. In addition, a total of 26,100 station wagons were built in the Dodge 330 and 440 lines. This included 5,400 station wagons with sixes and 20,700 with V-8s. There is no breakout of station wagon production by series, except in the case of the Dodge 880 Series. The total includes both Dodge 330 and 440 station wagons. (Figures rounded off to the nearest 100 units).

DODGE 440 SERIES — (ALL ENGINES) — The Dodge 440 was the intermediate trim level Dodge and included all the features of the 330 models, plus front foam cushions, carpeting and power tailgate window on nine-passenger station wagons. The '440' model designation was carried on the roof 'C' pillars.

DODGE 440 SERIES I.D. NUMBERS: See I.D. Number listing. All models began at 100001 and went up in the unit number sequence.

DODGE 440 SERIES

Model Number	Body/Style Number	Body Type & Seating	Factory Price	Shipping Weight	Production Total
TD1M/2M	423/623	4-dr Sed-6P	2438/2546	3068/3262	Note 1
TD1M/2M	421/621	2-dr Sed-6P	2381/2489	3038/3232	Note 1
TD1M/2M	422/622	2-dr HT Cpe-6P	2470/2477	3053/3242	Note 1
TD2M	666	4-dr Sta Wag-6P	2854	3487	Note 1
TD2M	667	4-dr Sta Wag-9P	2956	3552	Note 1

NOTE 1: A total of 44,300 Dodge 440 passenger cars were built during model year 1963. Of these, 10,000 were sixes and 34,300 were V-8s. (Figures rounded off to the nearest 100).

NOTE 2: Dodge 440 station wagon production totals are included with Dodge 330 station wagon production totals. See Dodge 330 Series Note 1 above.

1963 Dodge, Polara two-door convertible, V-8 (AA)

POLARA SERIES — (ALL ENGINES) — The Polara was, once again, the top trim level Dodge. It included all the features of the 440, plus back-up lights; Custom interior and upholstery trim; exterior moldings and a power top on the convertible. The Polara designation was carried on the roof 'C' pillars. A special high-performance sport model, called the Polara 500, was also available. It included all the features of the Polara, plus bucket seats; rear foam cushions; padded instrument panel; Deluxe steering wheel; special wheelcovers and the 265 hp 383 cid V-8 engine. Polara 500 models also included special exterior trim on the rear quarter panels behind the rear wheelwell.

POLARA AND POLARA 500 SERIES I.D. NUMBERS: See I.D. Number listing. All models began at 100001 and went up in the unit number sequence.

POLARA SERIES

Model Number	Body/Style Number	Body Type & Seating	Factory Price	Shipping Weight	Production Total
TD1H/2H	433/633	4-dr Sed-6P	2602/2709	3096/3262	Note 1
TD1H/2H	432/632	2-dr HT Cpe-6P	2624/2732	3071/3280	Note 1
TD2H	634	4-dr HT Sed-6P	2781	3370	Note 1
TD2H	635	2-dr Conv-6P	2963	3380	Note 1

POLARA 500

Model Number	Body/Style Number	Body Type & Seating	Factory Price	Shipping Weight	Production Total
TD2P	642	2-dr HT Cpe-6P	2965	3426	Note 1
TD2P	645	2-dr Conv-6P	3196	3546	Note 1

NOTE 1: A total of 39,800 Polaras were built during model year 1963. Of these, 2,200 were sixes and 37,600 were V-8s. A total of 7,300 Polara 500s were built during model year 1963, all V-8s. (Figures rounded off to the nearest 100 units).

880 AND CUSTOM 880 SERIES — (V-8) — The 880 was the top trim level in conventional Dodges for 1963. While continuing to utilize the Chrysler body from the windshield back, a completely new front end was styled for 1963. This gave the car an identity all its own. The full-width grille was made up of very fine convex vertical bars. The Dodge name, in block letters, was located in the center of the hood. It also appeared in script, on the front fenders behind the headlights. Rear end styling featured new circular taillights and chrome housings. The Custom 880 was identical to the 880, with the addition of a few minor trim pieces. The 265 hp 361 cid V-8 engine was standard in all 880s and Custom 880s.

1963 Dodge Custom 880 four-door Sedan, V-8

880 AND CUSTOM 880 SERIES I.D. NUMBERS: See I.D. Number listing. All models began at 100001 and went up in the unit number sequence.

880 AND CUSTOM 880 SERIES

Model Number	Body/Style Number	Body Type & Seating	Factory Price	Shipping Weight	Production Total
880 LINE					
TA3E	503	4-d Sed-6P	2813	3790	7197
TA3E	556	4-dr Sta Wag-6P	3142	4135	1727
TA3E	557	4-dr Sta Wag-9P	3257	4185	907
CUSTOM 880 LINE					
TA3L	513	4-dr Sed-6P	2964	3730	9233
TA3L	514	4-dr HT Sed-6P	3109	3745	2564
TA3L	512	2-dr HT Cpe-6P	3030	3705	2804
TA3L	515	2-dr Conv-6P	3251	3770	822
TA3L	558	4-dr Sta Wag-6P	3292	4110	1647
TA3L	559	4-dr Sta Wag-9P	3407	4165	1365

NOTE 1: A total of 7,200 Dodge 880 and 15,400 Custom 880 passenger cars were built during model year 1963. In addition, some 5,600 station wagons (all V-8s) were built in both series, combined, during model year 1963. (Figures rounded off to the nearest 100 units).

1963 ENGINES

170 Slant Six. Overhead valves. Cast iron block. Displacement: 170 cid. Bore and stroke: 3.40 x 3.13 inches. Compression ratio: 8.2:1. Brake hp: 101 at 4400 rpm. Four main bearings. Solid valve lifters. Carburetion: Carter BBS-3462S one-barrel.

225 Slant Six. Overhead valves. Cast iron block. Displacement: 225 cid. Bore and stroke: 3.41 x 4.13 inches. Compression ratio: 8.2:1. Brake hp: 145 at 4000 rpm. Four main bearings. Solid valve lifters. Carburetion: Holley R2418A one-barrel.

V-8. Overhead valves. Cast iron block. Displacement: 318 cid. Bore and stroke: 3.91 x 3.31 inches. Compression ratio: 9.0:1. Brake hp: 230 at 4400 rpm. Five main bearings. Hydraulic valve lifters. Carburetion: Stromberg 3-222A two-barrel.

Polara V-8. Overhead valves. Cast iron block. Displacement 360.8 cid. Bore and stroke: 4.13 x 3.38 inches. Compression ratio: 9.0:1. Brake hp: 265 at 4400 rpm. Five main bearings. Hydraulic valve lifters. Carburetion: Carter BBD34763 two-barrel.

Polara four-barrel V-8. Overhead valves. Cast iron block. Displacement 383 cid. Bore and stroke: 4.25 x 3.38 inches. Compression ratio: 10.1:1. Brake hp 330 at 4600 rpm. Five main bearings. Hydraulic valve lifters. Carburetion: Carter BBD-3684-S four-barrel.

413 V-8. Overhead valves. Cast iron block. Displacement: 413.2 cid. Bore and stroke: 4.188 x 3.75 inches. Compression ratio: 10.0:1. Brake hp: 340 at 4800 rpm. Five main bearings. Hydraulic valve lifters. Carburetion: Carter AFB four-barrel.

413 V-8. Overhead valves. Cast iron block. Displacement: 413.2 cid. Bore and stroke: 4.188 x 3.75 inches. Compression ratio: 10.1:1. Brake hp: 360 at 4800 rpm. Five main bearings. Hydraulic valve lifters. Carburetion: Carter AFB four-barrel.

413 V-8. Overhead valves. Cast iron block. Displacement: 413.2 cid. Bore and stroke: 4.188 x 3.75 inches. Compression ratio: 10.1:1. Brake hp 390 at 4800 rpm. Five main bearings. Hydraulic valve lifters. Carburetion: Dual Carter AFB four-barrels.

(NOTE: The Ram-Charger 413 "Max Wedge" engine was not available in 1963)

426 "Max Wedge Stage II" Ramcharger V-8. Overhead valves. Cast iron block. Displacement: 426 cid. Bore and stroke: 4.25 x 3.75 inches. Compression ratio: 11.0:1. Brake hp: 415 at 5600 rpm. Five main bearings. Solid valve lifters. Carburetion: Dual Carter four-barrels.

426 "Max Wedge Stage II" Ramcharger V-8. Overhead valves. Cast iron block. Displacement: 426 cid. Bore and stroke: 4.25 x 3.75 inches. Compression ratio: 13.5:1. Brake hp: 425 at 5600 rpm. Five main bearings. Solid valve lifters. Carburetion: Dual Carter four-barrels.

(NOTE: Dodge changed the spelling of "Ram-Charger" to "Ramcharger" for identification of Chrysler's new 426 cid Max Wedge Stage II engine. This was an all-out racing mill. The Plymouth version had a black 7-blade fan, while Dodge's had a chrome fan in sales literature.)

1963 DODGE CHASSIS FEATURES

DART: Wheelbase: 111 inches; (106 inches on station wagons). Overall length: 195.9 inches; (190.2 inches on station wagons). Tires: 6.50 x 13 tubeless black sidewall. Three-speed manual transmission was standard on all Darts, with the three-speed TorqueFlite automatic transmission optional.

DODGE: Wheelbase: 119 inches; (116 inches on station wagons). Overall length: 208.1 inches; (210.7 inches on station wagons). Tires: 7.00 x 14 tubeless black sidewall. Three-speed manual transmission was standard on all Dodges, with the three-speed TorqueFlite automatic transmission optional.

880 AND CUSTOM 880: Wheelbase: 122 inches. Overall length: 214.8 inches; (216.3 inches on station wagons). Tires: 8.00 x 14 tubeless black sidewall. Three-speed manual transmission was standard on all 880s and Custom 880s, with the three-speed TorqueFlite automatic transmission optional.

DART CONVENIENCE OPTIONS: AM radio, on 170 and 270 Series ($169); on GT Series ($153). Carpets in 170s ($17). 225 cid aluminum Slant Six engine ($47). Tinted glass ($14). Heater and defroster ($74). Back-up lights ($11). Luggage rack on station wagons ($48). Outside rearview mirror on left front fender ($5). Padded instrument panel ($16). Two-tone paint ($16). Power steering ($73). Power tailgate window on station wagons ($33). Front seat belts ($19). TorqueFlite automatic transmission ($172). Wheelcovers ($16). Windshield washers ($12). White sidewall tires ($29).

DODGE CONVENIENCE OPTIONS: Electric clock ($16). Music Master radio ($58). TorqueFlite automatic transmission, with six-cylinders ($192); with V-8s ($211). Power steering ($77). Power brakes ($43). Power seats ($96). Power windows ($102). Airtemp air conditioning ($45). Windshield washer ($12). 426 cid Ramcharger V-8 engine ($445). Four-speed manual transmission ($146). White sidewall tires ($33-$48).

HISTORICAL FOOTNOTES: During calendar year 1963, Dodge built exactly 33,708 Dart two-door sedans; 67,265 Dart four-door sedans; 28,475 Dart two-door hardtops; 11,390 Dart convertibles and 13,083 Dart two-seat station wagons. These figures include Dart 170, Dart 270 and Dart GT models, with no series breakouts available at the current time. The company also built 18,339 full-sized Dodge two-door sedans; 118,135 Dodge four-door sedans; 24,406 Dodge two-door hardtops; 11,832 Dodge four-door hardtops; 5,358 Dodge convertibles; 20,794 Dodge six-passenger station wagons and 10,977 Dodge nine-passenger station wagons. These figures include Dodge 330, 440, Polara, 880 and Custom 880 models, with no series breakouts available at the current time. Dodge discontinued the aluminum engine block for the 225 Slant Six engine because buyer demand did not warrant the extra cost involved in producing the lighter alloy block. Dodge also continued to be the brand to catch on the dragstrips of America. Teams like the Ramchargers, of Michigan, competed in several different classes with their 426 cid powered sedans and station wagons. The popular team painted their cars white with red stripes running along the top surfaces of the cars. The manual transmission equipped cars were called 'Candysticks' and the automatic transmission equipped cars were called 'Candymatics.' At least one of these cars has been restored to original racing condition as an outgrowth of the current boom in nostalgic drag racing. The later 426 single four-barrel engine was primarily for stock car racing and street use, while the two Ramcharger dual four-barrel engines were used for drag racing. Dodge re-launched its NASCAR racing program in 1963, but no wins were registered this year.

1964 DODGE

DART 170 SERIES — (ALL ENGINES) — The Dart received a new grille and other minor trim changes, but, overall was the same car offered in 1963. The big news for 1964 was the addition of the new 273 cid V-8 engine to the powertrain options. Joining the 170 and 225 cid Sixes, the 180 hp V-8 proved to be a very reliable and powerful engine in the light car. The Dart 170 once again was the base trim level and included chrome windshield and rear window moldings; chrome headlight doors; a Dart emblem on the roof 'C' pillar; turn signals; electric windshield wipers; sun visors; dual horns; chrome trim around the simulated scoop on the hood; a revised grille; the Dodge name in block letters, dividing the grille horizontally; cigar lighter; front armrests and the Dart name, in block letters, on a front fender tip emblem.

DART 170 SERIES I.D. NUMBERS: See 1960 Seneca Series I.D. Number listing. All models began at 100001 and went up in the unit number sequence.

DART 170 SERIES

Model Number	Body/Style Number	Body Type & Seating	Factory Price	Shipping Weight	Production Total
VL1L/2L	713	4-dr Sed-6P	2053/2161	2620/2800	Note 1
VL1L/2L	711	2-dr Sed-6P	1988/2096	2585/2765	Note 1
VL1L/2L	756	4-dr Sta Wag-6P	2315/2423	2730/2910	Note 1

NOTE 1: A total of 70,200 Dart 170s were built during model year 1964. Of these, 68,000 were sixes and 2,200 were V-8s. In addition, a total of 14,000 station wagons were built in all of the Dart Series. This included 12,900 station wagons with sixes and 1,100 with V-8s. There is no breakout of station wagon production by series, so this total includes both 170 and 270 station wagons. (Figures rounded off to the nearest 100 units).

DART 270 SERIES — (ALL ENGINES) — The Dart 270 was, once again, the intermediate trim level. It included all the 170 features, plus carpeting, special upholstery and extra trim.

DART 270 SERIES I.D. NUMBERS: See 1963 Dodge I.D. Number listing. All models began at 100001 and went up in the unit number sequence.

DART 270 SERIES

Model Number	Body/Style Number	Body Type & Seating	Factory Price	Shipping Weight	Production Total
VL1H/2H	733	4-dr Sed-6P	2160/2268	2630/2810	Note 1
VL1H/2H	731	2-dr Sed-6P	2094/2202	2595/2775	Note 1
VL1H/2H	742	2-dr HT Cpe-6P	2182/2290	2640/2820	Note 1
VL1H/2H	776	2-dr Sta Wag-6P	2414/2522	2740/2920	Note 1
VLIH/2H	735	2-dr Conv-6P	2389/2497	2710/2890	Note 1

NOTE 1: A total of 60,400 Dart 270s were built during model year 1964. Of these, 53,700 were sixes and 6,700 were V-8s. (Figures rounded off to the nearest 100 units).

ADDITIONAL NOTE: Dart 270 station wagon production totals are included with Dart 170 station wagon production totals. See Dart 170 Series Note 1 above.

1964 Dodge, Dart GT two-door hardtop, 6-cyl (PH)

Standard Catalog of American Cars

DART GT SERIES — (ALL ENGINES) — The GT was the top trim level Dart for 1964 and included all the 270 features, plus padded instrument panel, wheelcovers and bucket seats.

DART GT SERIES I.D. NUMBERS: See 1963 Dodge I.D. Number listing. All models began at 100001 and went up in the unit number sequence.

DART GT SERIES

Model Number	Body/Style Number	Body Type & Seating	Factory Price	Shipping Weight	Production Total
VL1P/2P	742	2-dr HT-6P	2318/2426	2650/2830	Note 1
VL1P/2P	745	2-dr Conv-6P	2536/2644	2740/2920	Note 1

NOTE 1: A total of 50,700 Dart GTs were built during model year 1964. Of these, 38,200 were sixes and 12,500 were V-8s. (Figures rounded to the nearest 100 units).

DODGE 330 SERIES — (ALL ENGINES) — For 1964, Dodges were totally restyled once again. Many Dodge enthusiasts consider the 1964 models to be one of the most attractive ever built. Smooth styling was the keynote and every line seemed to flow into the next line. The grille was the epitome of simplicity. It began as small chrome moldings around the outboard headlights, narrowed slightly at the inboard headlights and featured a vertical bar theme. The Dodge name, in block letters, was spaced equally across the front of the hood. From the windshield back, the 1964 Dodges shared bodies with the previous models, except at the 'C' pillar of two-door hardtops, which was wider at the top than at the bottom. The basic 1963 body shell, combined with the new front end, produced a very attractive car, indeed. The 330 was the base trim level Dodge and included chrome windshield and rear window moldings; turn signals; electric windshield wipers; sun visors; PCV system; power tailgate window on nine-passenger station wagon and the Dodge name, in block letters, on the right side of the trunk lid. The '330' model designation was carried on the roof 'C' pillars.

DODGE 330 SERIES I.D. NUMBERS: See 1960 Seneca Series I.D. Number listing. All models began at 100001 and went up in the unit number sequence.

DODGE 330 SERIES

Model Number	Body/Style Number	Body Type & Seating	Factory Price	Shipping Weight	Production Total
VD1L/2L	413/613	4-dr Sed-6P	2317/2424	3105/3300	Note 1
VD1L/2L	411/611	2-dr Sed-6P	2264/2372	3075/3270	Note 1
VD1L/2L	456/656	4-dr Sta Wag-6P	2654/2762	3375/3555	Note 1
VD1L/2L	457/657	4-dr Sta Wag-9P	2755/2862	3445/3560	Note 1

NOTE 1: A total of 76,400 Dodge 330s were built during model year 1964. Of these, 44.800 were sixes and 31,600 were V-8s. In addition, a total of 30,300 full-sized Dodge station wagons were built in the 330 and 440 Series. This included 5,700 station wagons with sixes and 24,600 with V-8s. There is no breakout of station wagon production by series, so this total includes both 330 and 440 station wagons. (Figures rounded off to the nearest 100 units).

DODGE 440 SERIES — (ALL ENGINES) — The Dodge 440 was the intermediate trim level Dodge and included all the features of the Dodge 330 models, plus front foam cushions, carpeting and the '440' model designation on the roof 'C' pillars.

DODGE 440 SERIES I.D. NUMBERS: See 1963 Dodge I.D. Number listing. All models began at 100001 and went up in the unit number sequence.

DODGE 440 SERIES

Model Number	Body/Style Number	Body Type & Seating	Factory Price	Shipping Weight	Production Total
VD1M/2M	423/623	4-dr Sed-6P	2454/2562	3115/3310	Note 1
VD1M/2M	421/621	2-dr Sed-6P	2401/2508	3085/3280	Note 1
VD1M/2M	422/622	2-dr HT Cpe-6P	2483/2590	3090/3285	Note 1
VD2M	666	4-dr Sta Wag-6P	2861	3615	Note 1
VD2M	667	4-dr Sta Wag-9P	2962	3620	Note 1

NOTE 1: A total of 58,700 Dodge 440s were built during model year 1964. Of these, 10,200 were sixes and 48,500 were V-8s. (Figures rounded off to nearest 100).

ADDITIONAL NOTE: Dodge 440 station wagon production totals are included with Dodge 330 station wagon production totals. See Dodge 330 Series Note 1.

1964 Dodge, Polara two-door hardtop coupe, V-8 (PH)

POLARA SERIES — (ALL ENGINES) — The Polara was, once again, the top trim level Dodge. It included all the features of the Dodge 440, plus back-up lights; Custom interior and upholstery trim, special exterior moldings and a power top on the convertible. The Polara model designation was carried on the roof 'C' pillar. The Polara convertible and two-door hardtop were also offered with the special Polara 500 trim package, which consisted of bucket seats, a console, padded instrument panel; Deluxe wheelcovers and a console mounted shifter. Special Polara 500 identification badges and swirl-finish side trim moldings were also included.

POLARA SERIES

Model Number	Body/Style Number	Body Type & Seating	Factory Price	Shipping Weight	Production Total
VD1H/2H	433/633	4-dr Sed-6P	2615/2722	3150/3310	Note 1
VD1H/2H	432/632	2-dr HT Cpe-6P	2637/2745	3115/3310	Note 1
VD2H	634	4-dr HT Sed-6P	2794	3390	Note 1
VD2H	635	2-dr Conv-6P	2976	3415	Note 1

NOTE 1: A total of 64,900 Polaras were built during model year 1964. Of these, 2,200 were sixes and 62,700 were V-8s. In addition, a total of 18,400 Polara 500s were built during model year 1964. All of these were V-8s (Figures rounded off to the nearest 100 units).

1964 Dodge, Custom 880 two-door convertible, V-8 (PH)

880 AND CUSTOM 880 SERIES — (V-8) — The 880 and Custom 880 lines on the 122-inch wheelbase chassis continued with the same body as 1963. Rear quarter panels and taillights and a revised grille gave them a more modern look. The grille was concave and featured a central horizontal divider in the same shell as used in 1963. A single horizontal trim strip, at belt level, highlighted the smooth sides. It dipped down to form a front molding for the large, wraparound taillights. A polished aluminum rocker panel molding was used on the Custom 880 models. They also featured slightly more posh interiors than the standard 880 models. The Dodge name appeared, in block letters, on the center of the hood and along the rear fender. It also appeared, in script, along the right side of the trunk lid. A grooved aluminum panel was located between the taillights and highlighted the rear of the beautiful 880 models.

880 AND CUSTOM 880 SERIES I.D. NUMBERS: See 1963 Seneca Series I.D. Number listing. All models began at 100001 and went up in the unit number sequence.

880 AND CUSTOM 880 SERIES

Model Number	Body/Style Number	Body Type & Seating	Factory Price	Shipping Weight	Production Total
VA3E	503	4-dr Sed-6P	2826	3790	7536
VA3E	556	4-dr Sta Wag-6P	3155	4135	1908
VA3E	557	4-dr Sta Wag-9P	3270	4185	1082
CUSTOM 880 LINE					
VA3L	513	4-dr Sed-6P	2977	3800	9309
VA3L	514	4-dr HT Sed-6P	3122	3820	3634
VA3L	512	2-dr HT Cpe-6P	3043	3785	3798
VA3L	515	2-dr Conv-6P	3264	3845	1058
VA3L	558	4-dr Sta Wag-6P	3305	4135	1639
VA3L	559	4-dr Sta Wag-9P	3420	4230	1796

NOTE 1: A total of 7,500 Dodge 880s and 17,800 Custom 880s were built during model year 1964. In addition, 6,500 Dodge 880 and Custom 880 station wagons were built during model year 1964, all V-8s.

1964 ENGINES

170 Slant-Six. Overhead valves. Cast iron block. Displacement: 170 cid. Bore and stroke: 3.40 x 3.13 inches. Compression ratio: 8.2:1. Brake hp: 101 at 4000 rpm Four main bearings. Solid valve lifters. Carburetion: Carter BBS-3675S one-barrel.

225 Slant-Six. Overhead valves. Cast iron block. Displacement: 225 cid. Bore and stroke: 3.41 x 4.13 inches. Compression ratio: 8.4:1. Brake hp: 145 at 4000 rpm Four main bearings. Solid valve lifters. Carburetion: Carter BBS-3679S one-barrel.

V-8. Overhead valves. Cast iron block. Displacement: 273 cid. Bore and stroke: 3.63 x 3.31 inches. Compression ratio: 8.8:1. Brake hp: 180 at 4200 rpm. Five main bearings. Hydraulic valve lifters. Carburetion: Carter BBD-3843S two-barrel.

318 V-8. Overhead valves. Cast iron block. Displacement: 318 cid. Bore and stroke: 3.91 x 3.31 inches. Compression ratio: 9.0:1. Brake hp: 230 at 4400 rpm. Five main bearings. Hydraulic valve lifters. Carburetion: Carter BBD-3682S two-barrel.

361 V-8. Overhead valves. Cast iron block. Displacement: 361 cid. Bore and stroke: 4.13 x 3.38 inches. Compression ratio: 9.0:1. Brake hp: 265 at 4400 rpm. Five main bearings. Hydraulic valve lifters. Carburetion: Stromberg WWC-3-244 two-barrel.

383 V-8. Overhead valves. Cast iron block. Displacement: 383 cid. Bore and stroke: 4.25 x 3.38 inches. Compression ratio: 10.0:1. Brake hp: 305 at 4600 rpm. Five main bearings. Hydraulic valve lifters. Carburetion: Carter BBD-34763 two-barrel.

383 Four-Barrel V-8. Overhead valves. Cast iron block. Displacement: 383 cid. Bore and stroke: 4.25 x 3.38 inches. Compression ratio: 10.0:1. Brake hp: 330 at 6400 rpm. Five main bearings. Hydraulic valve lifters. Carburetion: Carter BBD-3684S four-barrel.

Ramcharger V-8. Overhead valves. Cast iron block. Displacement 426 cid. Bore and stroke: 4.25 x 3.75 inches. Compression ratio 10.3:1. Brake hp: 415 at 5600 rpm. Five main bearings. Solid valve lifters. Carburetion: Carter AFB-3859S four-barrel.

Ramcharger 'Eight-Barrel' Overhead valve. Cast iron block. Displacement: 426 cid. Bore and stroke: 4.25 x 3.75 inches. Compression ratio 11.0:1 (12.5:1 also available). Brake hp: 425 at 5600 rpm. Five main bearings. Solid valve lifters. Carburetion: Two Carter AFB-3084S four-barrels.

Hemi-charger (NASCAR) V-8. Overhead valves with hemispherical segment combustion chambers. Cast iron block. Displacement: 426 cid. Bore and stroke: 4.25 x 3.75 inches. Compression ratio 12.5:1. Brake hp: 400 at 5600 rpm. Five main bearings. solid valve lifters. Carburetion: Holley four-barrels.

Hemi-Charger V-8. Overhead valves with hemispherical-segment combustion chambers. Cast iron block. Displacement: 426 cid. Bore and stroke: 4.25 x 3.75 inches. Compression ratio: 11.0:1. Brake hp: 415 at 5600 rpm. Five main bearings. Solid valve lifters. Carburetion: Two Carter AFB-3859S four-barrels.

Hemi-Charger 'Eight Barrel' V-8. Overhead valves with hemispherical-segment combustion chambers. Cast iron block. Displacement: 426 cid. Bore and stroke: 4.25 x 3.75 inches. Compression ratio 12.5:1. Brake hp: 425 at 5600 rpm. Five main bearings. Solid valve lifters. Carburetion: Two Carter AFB-3084S four-barrels.

1964 DODGE CHASSIS FEATURES

DART: Wheelbase: 111 inches. (106 inches station wagons). Overall length: 195.9 inches. (190.2 inches on station wagons). Tires: 6.50 x 13 tubeless black sidewall. Three-speed manual transmission was standard on all Darts, with the three-speed TorqueFlite automatic transmission optional.

DODGE: Wheelbase: 119 inches; (116 inches on station wagons). Overall length: 209.8 inches; (212.3 inches on station wagons). Tires: 7.00 x 14 tubeless black sidewall; (7.50 x 14 on station wagons). Three-speed manual transmission was standard on all Dodges, with the three-speed TorqueFlite automatic transmission optional.

880 AND CUSTOM 880: Wheelbase: 122 inches. Overall length: 214.8 inches; (216.3 inches on station wagons). Tires: 8.00 x 14 tubeless black sidewall. Three-speed manual transmission was standard on all Dodge 880s and Custom 880s, with three-speed TorqueFlite automatic transmission optional.

DART CONVENIENCE OPTIONS: AM radio group on 170 and 270 Series ($169); on GT Series ($153). Carpets in 170s ($17). 225 cid six-cylinder engine ($47). 273 cid V-8 engine. Tinted glass ($14). Heater and defroster ($74). Back-up lights ($11). Luggage rack on station wagons ($48). Outside rearview mirror on left front fender ($5). Padded instrument panel ($16). Two-tone paint ($16). Power steering ($73). Power tailgate window on station wagon ($33). Front seat belts ($19). TorqueFlite automatic transmission ($172). Wheelcovers ($16). Windshield washers ($12). White sidewall tires ($29).

DODGE CONVENIENCE OPTIONS: Electric clock ($16). Music Master radio ($58). Torque-Flite automatic transmission on six-cylinder ($192); on V-8s ($211). Power steering ($77). Power brakes ($43). Power seats ($96). Power windows ($102). Airtemp air conditioning ($445). Windshield washers ($12). 426 cid Ramcharger V-8 engine ($445). Four-speed manual transmission ($146). White sidewall tires ($33-$48).

HISTORICAL FOOTNOTES: The year 1964 was significant for Dodge for several reasons, mainly for the reputation the marque was gaining in the performance market. The awesome Ramcharger was setting records on the nation's dragstrips. Roger Lindamood, driving the incredible 'Color Me Gone' Dodge 330 two-door sedan took the NHRA Top Eliminator title at the Winter Nationals Drag Races that year. Ramcharger powered Dodges also garnered the top four positions at the Super Stock Invitationals in York, Pa., and a Ramcharger equipped rail dragster set a new national NHRA record for AA/D (unlimited displacement rail dragsters) of 190.26 mph at East Hudson, Conn. drag strip. While the Ramcharger was tearing up the opposition on the drag strips, it was not doing as well on the NASCAR ovals and Chrysler decided to reintroduce the hemispherical-segment heads for the Ramcharger. This resulted in the 'Hemicharger' available for competition use only, in Dodges and Plymouths. The 'Hemi' immediately replaced the Ramcharger as the engine to beat. Conservatively rated at 410 hp with a four-barrel (or 425 hp with two-barrels) actual output was more in the neighborhood of 500 or 550 hp respectively. A pair of Dodge 330 two-door sedans powered by supercharged Hemi engines were used for exhibition runs during the summer of 1964. The Dodge 'Chargers' turned standing start quarter mile speeds in the 135 mile per hour range and were the fore-runners of today's Funny Cars.

1965 DODGE

DART SERIES — (ALL ENGINES) — Continuing to use the same body as in the previous two years, the 1965 Dart nonetheless looked much different than before. A new grille was a flat grid design. At the rear, new oval taillights were used in place of the former round type. Minor trim changes rounded out the new Dart styling for 1965. As in the past, the Dart 170 was the base trim level and included chrome windshield and rear window moldings; a Dodge crest on the hood; a single horizontal chrome strip along the center of the bodyside; the Dodge name, in block letters, at the back of the rear fender chrome strip; heater and defroster; front seat belts; electric windshield wipers and the 170 cid Slant-Six engine.

DART 170 SERIES I.D. NUMBERS: See 1960 Seneca Series I.D. Number listing. All models began at 100001 and went up in the unit number sequence.

DART 170 SERIES

Model Number	Body/Style Number	Body Type & Seating	Factory Price	Shipping Weight	Production Total
AL1L/2L	L13	4-dr Sed-6P	2112/2208	2660/2840	Note 1
AL1L/2L	L11	2-dr Sed-6P	2049/2145	2645/2825	Note 1
AL1L/2L	L56	4-dr Sta Wag-6P	2375/2471	2770/2950	Note 1

NOTE 1: A total of some 73,800 Dart 170 passenger cars were built during model year 1965. Of these, 70,900 were sixes and 2,900 were V-8s. In addition, a total of 29,400 station wagons were built in all of the Dart Series. This included 23,400 station wagons with sixes and 6,000 with V-8s. There is no breakout of station wagon production by series, so this includes both Dart 170 and Dart 270 station wagons. (Figures rounded off to the nearest 100 units).

DART 270 SERIES — (ALL ENGINES) — The Dart 270 was, once again, the intermediate trim level. It included all the 170 features, plus carpeting; Deluxe two-spoke steering wheel; full horn ring and vinyl trim on the convertible.

DART 270 SERIES I.D. NUMBERS: See 1963 Dodge I.D. Number listing. All models began at 100001 and went up in the unit number sequence.

DART 270 SERIES

Model Number	Body/Style Number	Body Type & Seating	Factory Price	Shipping Weight	Production Total
AL1/H/2H	L33	4-dr Sed-6P	2218/2314	2670/2850	Note 1
AL1H/2H	L31	2-dr Sed-6P	2153/2249	2650/2830	Note 1
AL1H/2H	L32	2-dr HT-6P	2245/2341	2675/2855	Note 1
AL1H/2H	L35	2-dr Conv-6P	2447/2543	2765/2945	Note 1
AL1H/2H	L76	4-dr Sta Wag-6P	2472/2568	2770/2950	Note 1

NOTE 1: A total of some 62,800 Dart 270 passenger cars were built during model year 1965. Of these, 52,900 were sixes and 9,900 were V-8s (Figures rounded off to the nearest 100 units).

ADDITIONAL NOTE: Dart 270 station wagon production totals are included with Dart 170 station wagon production totals. See Dart 170 Series Note 1 above.

1965 Dodge, Dart GT two-door hardtop coupe, V-8 (PH)

DART SERIES — (ALL ENGINES) — The GT was the top trim level Dart for 1965. It included all the 270 features, plus padded instrument panel; wheelcovers and bucket seats. In addition, the GTs had a special emblem on the roof 'C' pillar, three chrome louvers behind the front wheel opening and stone shields on the rear fenders.

DART GT SERIES I.D. NUMBERS: See 1963 Dodge I.D. Number listing. All models began at 100001 and went up in the unit number sequence.

DART GT SERIES

Model Number	Body/Style Number	Body Type & Seating	Factory Price	Shipping Weight	Production Total
ALIP/2P	L42	2-dr HT-5P	2372/2468	2715/2895	Note 1
ALIP/2P	L45	2-dr Conv-5P	2591/2687	2795/2975	Note 1

NOTE 1: A total of some 40,700 Dodge Dart GTs were built during model year 1965. All were passenger car models, as no station wagons were offered in this series. Of the total, 22,700 were sixes and 18,000 were V-8s. (Figures rounded off to the nearest 100 units).

CORONET SERIES — (ALL ENGINES) — The Coronet name last used by Dodge in 1959 was revised for the intermediate-sized Dodge models for 1965. While larger than Ford's Fairlane and Chevrolet's Chevelle, it was nevertheless smaller than full-sized Polara models. It was built on a 117-inch wheelbase platform, two inches shorter than the 1964 Polara / 440 / 330 models. Styling was very simple. The grille and rear end treatments were quite flat. There was a slab-sided look with only a belt-level feature line. Vertical bars patterned the grille and the taillights were also vertically positioned. The plain Coronet (330 call-out no longer used) was the base trim level. It included the 225 cid six-cylinder engine; 7.35 x 14 tubeless tires; heater and defroster; electric windshield wipers; front seat belts; the Dodge name, in block letters, across the front of the hood (and on the right side of the trunk lid) and the Coronet name, in script, on the front fender tip.

CORONET SERIES I.D. NUMBERS: See 1960 Seneca Series I.D. Number listing. All models began at 100001 and went up in the unit number sequence.

CORONET SERIES

Model Number	Body/Style Number	Body Type & Seating	Factory Price	Shipping Weight	Production Total
AW1L/2L	W13	4-dr Sed-6P	2267/2361	3140/3210	Note 1
AW1L/2L	W11	2-dr Sed-6P	2228/2322	3090/3160	Note 1
AW1L/2L	W56	4-dr Sta Wag-6P	2556/2650	3390/3470	Note 1

NOTE 1: A total of some 63,100 Coronet passenger cars were built during model year 1965. Of these, 37,100 were sixes and 26,000 were V-8s. In addition, a total of some 25,600 inter-mediate-sized Dodge station wagons were built in the Coronet and Coronet 440 Series. This included 3,800 sixes and 21,800 V-8s. There is no breakout of station wagon production by series, so these figures includes both Coronet and Coronet 440 station wagons. (Figures rounded off to the nearest 100 units).

1965 Dodge, Coronet 440 four-door sedan, V-8

CORONET 440 SERIES — (ALL ENGINES) — The Coronet 440 was the intermediate trim level of the new Coronet Series. It included all the features of the base Coronet Series, plus back-up lights; air foam front seats; carpeting in all models; power top and vinyl interior on the convertible and, in the nine-passenger station wagon, the 273 cid V-8 engine and a power tailgate window as standard equipment.

CORONET 440 SERIES I.D. NUMBERS: See 1963 Dodge I.D. Number listing. All models began at 100001 and went up in the unit number sequence.

CORONET 440 SERIES

Model Number	Body/Style Number	Body Type & Seating	Factory Price	Shipping Weight	Production Total
AW1/2H	W33	4-dr Sed-6P	2346/2440	3125/3230	Note 1
AW1/2H	W32	2-dr HT-6P	2371/2465	3100/3180	Note 1
AW1/2H	W35	2-dr Conv-6P	2586/2680	3230/3295	Note 1
AW1/2H	W76	4-dr Sta Wag-6P	2637/2731	3395/3490	Note 1
AW1/2H	W77	4-dr Sta Wag-9P	2827	3560	Note 1

NOTE 1: A total of some 87,500 Coronet 440 passenger cars were built during model year 1965. Of these, 11,900 were sixes and 75,600 were V-8s. (Figures rounded off to the nearest 100).

ADDITIONAL NOTE: Dodge Coronet 440 station wagon production totals are included with Dodge Coronet station wagon totals. See Dodge Coronet Note 1 above.

CORONET 500 SERIES — (ALL ENGINES) — The Cornet 500 was the top trim level of the Coronet Series and included all the 440 features plus padded instrument panel; console and bucket seats; wheelcovers; 273 cid V-8 engine; a single horizontal chrome strip at the beltline and the Coronet 500 name, in script, at the rear of the wheelwell on the front fenders.

CORONET 500 SERIES I.D. NUMBERS: See 1963 Dodge I.D. Number listing. All models began at 100001 and went up in the unit number sequence.

CORONET 500 SERIES

Model Number	Body/Style Number	Body Type & Seating	Factory Price	Shipping Weight	Production Total
AW2P	W42	2-dr HT-6P	2637	3255	Note 1
AW2P	W45	2-dr Conv-6P	2852	3340	Note 1

NOTE 1: A total of some 33,300 Coronet 500 passenger cars were built during model year 1965, all V-8s.

POLARA SERIES — (V-8) — The Polara for 1965 filled the position formerly held by the Dodge 880 in the completely restyled full-sized car line. the 121 inch wheelbase of the Polara, Custom 880 and Monaco models was an inch shorter than the 1964 Custom 880. The Polara included chrome windshield and rear window moldings; the Dodge name, in block letters, across the center of the hood face (directly above the butle-shaped grille and across the rear escutcheon panel). Also included were the 270 hp 383 cid V-8 engine; heater and defroster; front seat belts; power convertible top and 8.25 x 14 tubeless tires. All station wagons included a vinyl interior and the nine-passenger station wagon also had a power tailgate window and rear bumper guards with step pads.

POLARA SERIES I.D. NUMBERS: See 1960 Seneca Series I.D. Number listing. All models began at 100001 and went up in the unit number sequence.

POLARA SERIES

Model Number	Body/Style Number	Body Type & Seating	Factory Price	Shipping Weight	Production Total
AD2L	D13	4-dr Sed-6P	2770	3905	Note 1
AD2L	D14	4-dr HT-6P	2874	3965	Note 1
AD2L	D12	2-dr HT-6P	2800	3850	Note 1
AD2L	D15	2-dr Conv-6P	3088	3940	Note 1
AD2L	D56	4-dr Sta Wag-6P	3110	4220	Note 1
AD2L	D57	4-dr Sta Wag-9P	3214	4255	Note 1

NOTE 1: A total of some 75,100 Polara passenger cars were built during model year 1965, all V-8s. In addition, a total of 22,800 station wagons (all V-8s) were built in the Polara and Custom 880 Series combined. There is no breakout of station wagon production by series, so this figure included both Polara and Custom 880 station wagons. (All figures rounded off to the nearest 100 units).

1965 Dodge Custom 880 convertible, V-8,

CUSTOM 880 SERIES — (V-8) — The Custom 880 was a higher trim level than the Polara Series and included all the features of the Polara, plus air foam front seats and stainless steel window frames on station wagons and four-doors sedans. The hardtops had vinyl interior trim.

CUSTOM 880 SERIES I.D. NUMBERS: See 1963 Dodge I.D. Number listing. All models began at 100001 and went up in the unit number sequence.

CUSTOM 880 SERIES

Model Number	Body/Style Number	Body Type & Seating	Factory Price	Shipping Weight	Production Total
AD2H	D38	4-dr Sed-6P	2970	3915	9380
AD2H	D34	4-dr HT-6P	3107	4155	7966
AD2H	D32	2-dr HT-6P	3043	3945	4850
AD2H	D35.	2-dr Conv-6P	3288	3965	1416
AD2H	D76	4-dr Sta Wag-6P	3373	4270	4499
AD2H	D77	4-dr Sta Wag-9	3476	4335	5923

NOTE 1: A total of some 23,700 Custom 880 passenger cars were built during model year 1965, all V-8s. (Figures rounded off to the nearest 100 units).

ADDITIONAL NOTE: Dodge Custom 880 station wagon production totals are included with Dodge Polara station wagon production totals. See 1965 Dodge Polara Series Note 1 above.

1965 Dodge, Monaco two-door hardtop sports coupe, V-8

MONACO SERIES — (V-8) — The Monaco was the specialty coupe built by Dodge to compete directly with Pontiac's Grand Prix. Monacos were available only in the two-door hardtop configuration and were beautiful cars. Elegant simplicity is a term that describes the looks of the original edition for 1965. The Monaco featured all the standard equipment offered

on the custom 880, plus a 315 hp 383 cid V-8 engine; front and rear foam seats; electric clock; remote-control outside rearview mirror; console; inside glare-proof mirror; padded instrument panel; three-spoke steering wheel; special wheelcovers with spinners) and the Monaco name, in script, on the front fenders just behind the wheelwells.

MONACO SERIES I.D. NUMBERS: See 1963 Dodge I.D. Number listing. All models began at 100001 and went up in the unit number sequence.

MONACO SERIES

Model Number	Body/Style Number	Body Type & Seating	Factory Price	Shipping Weight	Production Total
AD2P	D42	2-dr HT-6P	3308	4000	13,200

1965 ENGINES

170 Slant-Six. Overhead valves. Cast iron block. Displacement: 170 cid. Bore and stroke: 3.41 x 3.13 inches. Compression ratio: 8.4:1. Brake hp: 101 at 4400 rpm. Four main bearings. Solid valve lifters. Carburetion: Carter BBS-3833S single-barrel.

225 Slant-Six. Overhead valves. Cast iron block. Displacement: 225 cid. Bore and stroke: 3.41 x 4.13 inches. Compression ratio: 8.4:1. Brake hp: 145 at 4000 rpm. Four main bearings. Solid valve lifters. Carburetion: Carter BBS-3839S single-barrel.

V-8. Overhead valves. Cast iron block. Displacement: 273 cid. Bore and stroke: 3.63 x 3.31 inches. Compression ratio: 8.8:1. Brake hp: 180 at 4200 rpm. Five main bearings. Hydraulic valve lifters. Carburetion: Carter BBD-3943S two-barrel.

318 V-8. Overhead valves. Cast iron block. Displacement: 318 cid. Bore and stroke: 3.91 x 3.31 inches. Compression ratio: 9.0:1. Brake hp: 230 at 4400 rpm. Five main bearings. Hydraulic valve lifters. Carburetion: Carter BBD-3947S two-barrel.

361 V-8. Overhead valves. Cast iron block. Displacement: 361 cid. Bore and stroke: 4.13 x 3.38 inches. Compression ratio: 9.0:1. Brake hp: 265 at 4400 rpm. Five main bearings. Hydraulic valve lifters. Carburetion: Carter BBD-3849S two-barrel.

383 V-8. Overhead valves. Cast iron block. Displacement: 383 cid. Bore and stroke: 4.25 x 3.38 inches. Compression ratio: 10.0:1. Brake hp: 330 at 4400 rpm (330 hp with dual exhausts). Five main bearings. Hydraulic valve lifters. Carburetion: Carter AFB 3855S four-barrels.

413 V-8. Overhead valves. Cast iron block. Displacement: 413 cid. Bore and stroke: 4.19 x 3.7 5 inches. Compression ratio: 10.1:1. Brake hp: 340 at 4600 rpm. Five main bearings. Hydraulic valve lifters. Carburetion: Carter AFB-3858S four-barrels.

426 V-8. Overhead valves. Cast iron block. Displacement: 426 cid. Bore and stroke: 4.25 x 3.75 inches. Compression ratio: 10.1:1. Brake hp: 365 at 4800 rpm. Five main bearings. Hydraulic valve lifters. Carburetion: Carter AFB-3959S four-barrels.

426 'Hemi' V-8. Overhead valves with hemispherical combustion chambers. Cast iron block. Displacement: 426 cid. Bore and stroke: 4.25 x 3.75 inches. Compression ratio: 11.0:1. Brake hp: 415 at 5600 rpm. Five main bearings. Solid valve lifters. Carburetion: Carter AFB-3859S four-barrel.

426 'Hemi-Eight Barrel' V-8. Overhead valves with hemispherical combustion chambers. Cast iron block. Displacement: 426 cid. Bore and stroke: 4.25 x 3.75 inches. Compression ratio: 12.0:1. Brake hp: 425 at 5600 rpm. Five main bearings. Solid valve lifters. Carburetion: Two (2) Carter AFB-3084S four-barrels.

1965 DODGE CHASSIS FEATURES

DART: Wheelbase: 111 inches: (106 on station wagons). Overall length: 195.9 inches; (190.2 inches on station wagons). Tires: 6.50 x 13 tubeless black sidewall. Three-speed manual transmission was standard on all Darts, with the three-speed TorqueFlite automatic and four-speed transmission optional.

CORONET: Wheelbase: 117 inches. Overall length: 204.2 inches; (209.3 inches on station wagons). Tires: 7.35 x 14 tubeless black sidewall; (7.75 x 14 on station wagons). Three-speed manual transmission was standard on all Coronets, with the three-speed TorqueFlite automatic and four-speed manual transmissions optional.

POLAR/CUSTOM 880 AND MONACO: Wheelbase: 121 inches. Overall length: 212.3 inches: (217.1 inches on station wagons). Tires: 7.35 x 14 tubeless black sidewall on Polaras; 8.25 x 14 tubeless blackwall on custom 880s and Monacos; 8.55 x 14 tubeless black sidewall on station wagons. Three-speed manual transmission was standard on all Polaras, Custom 880s and Monacos, with the three-speed TorqueFlite automatic and four-speed manual transmission optional.

DART CONVENIENCE OPTIONS: AM radio group ($79); on GTs ($67). Carpets in 170s ($13). Slant-Six, 225 cid engine ($39). 273 cid V-8 ($81). Four-speed manual transmission with Slant-Six ($152); with V-8 ($146). TorqueFlite automatic transmission with Slant-Six ($140); with V-8 ($148). Power convertible top ($42). Tinted glass ($22). Back-up lights ($8). Luggage rack on station wagons ($37). Left-hand outside rearview mirror ($4). Padded instrument panel, on GT (standard equipment); on others ($13). Two-tone paint ($12). Power steering ($67). Power tailgate window in station wagon ($25). Wheelcovers ($12). Windshield washers and variable speed wipers ($13). White sidewall tires ($23-25).

DODGE CONVENIENCE OPTIONS: Music Master AM radio ($45). Astrophonic AM radio ($69). AM/FM radio ($103). Rear speaker with reverberation ($28-$41 depending on model). Polara 500 Sport package for Polara two-door hardtops and convertibles (bucket seats. console, identification badges and deluxe spinner wheelcovers ($171). Air conditioning ($282-$315). Dual air conditioning in station wagon ($481). Auto Pilot ($66). Power steering ($67-$74). Power brakes ($33). Electric clock ($12). Rear window defogger ($16). Sure-Grip differential ($39). Power door locks ($43). Tinted glass ($31). Two-tone paint ($13). Power bench seats ($74). Power bucket seats, in Monaco ($61-$121). Tachometer ($39). TorqueFlite automatic transmission ($165-$181). Four-speed manual transmission ($146-$180). 230 hp V-8 engine ($25). 270 hp V-8 engine ($73). 316 hp V-8 engine ($86). 363 hp V-8 engine ($341-$444). 425 hp 'Hemi' V-8 engine (approximately $1,800).

HISTORICAL FOOTNOTES: The 1965 Dodge line was introduced Sept. 25, 1964. The company's exact model year production was 550,795 cars for a 6.2 percent share of the total U.S. market. This included 206,631 Dodge Darts; 209,393 Coronets and 134,771 Polara/Custom/Monaco models (See charts above, per series, for breakouts. Figures rounded off to the nearest 100 units). The 426 cid 'Hemi-Charger' powered Dodges continued to dominate the action on the drag strips across the country. A few Hemis were produced for street use and were sold 'as is', meaning Chrysler Corp. was not responsible for their use and all warranty provisions, normally associated with a new car, did not apply to the Hemi-Dodges.

1966 DODGE

DART SERIES — (ALL ENGINES) — Continuing to use the same body as in the past three years, the new Dart featured a restyled anodized aluminum grille and large, oval taillights as the styling changes for 1966. As in the past, the Dart was the base trim level, and included chrome windshield and rear window moldings, no side chrome and the Dodge name, in block letters, across the vertical section of the trunk lid and on the front of the hood. Also included was the heater and defroster, electric windshield wipers, the 170 cid Slant-Six engine, and manual transmission. Newly enacted Federal Safety Standards dictated that the new Darts also be equipped with back-up lights and emergency flashers as standard equipment, as well as the outside rearview mirror becoming standard.

DART I.D. NUMBERS: Chrysler Corp. changed the numbering system and code locations for 1966 and they can be broken down as follows: The first symbol was a letter designating the car line: "D" = Polara and Monaco, "W" = Coronet and Charger, "J" = Challenger (1971), and "L" = Dart. The second symbol designated the price class: "E" = Economy, "M" = Middle, "H" = High, "S" = Special and "P" = Premium. The third and fourth symbols indicated Body Style, as indicated in the chart below. The fifth symbol, a letter, designated the type and displacement of the engine: "A" = 170 cid Slant-Six, "B" = 225 cid Slant-Six, "C" = Special 225 cid Slant-Six, "E" = Special Order, "G" = 318 cid V-8, "H" = 273 cid four-barrel V-8, "J" = 340 cid V-8, "K" = 360 cid V-8, "L" = 383 cid V-8, "M" = 400 cid V-8, "N" = 383 cid four-barrel V-8, "P" = 400 cid V-8, "R" = 426 cid V-8, "T" = 440 cid V-8, "U" = 440 cid V-8, "V" = 440 cid V-8, "Z" = Special Order. The sixth represented the year produced ("6" = 1966, etc.) and the remaining six digits were the sequential unit number. Assembly plants were identified as follows: "A" = Lynch Road, "B" = Hamtramck, "C" = Jefferson, "D" = Belvedere, "F" = Newark, "G" = St. Louis, "R" Windsor.

DART 170 SERIES

Model Number	Body/Style Number	Body Type & Seating	Factory Price	Shipping Weight	Production Total
BL1L/2L	41	4-dr Sed-6P	2158/2286	2695/2895	Note 1
BL1L/2L	21	2-dr Sed-6P	2094/2222	2670/2860	Note 1
BL1L/2L	45	4-dr Sta Wag-6P	2436/2564	2780/2990	Note 1

NOTE 1: A total of 29,800 Darts were built during calendar year 1966. Of these, 28,400 were sixes and 1,400 were V-8s. A total of 29,300 station wagons were built that year. Of these, 20,900 were sixes and 8,400 were V-8s. No breakout is provided for individual models and the production figure represents total station wagon production.

DART 270 SERIES — (ALL ENGINES) — The Dart 270 was, once again, the intermediate trim level and included all the Dart features, plus carpeting, Deluxe two-spoke steering wheel, full horn ring and vinyl trim on the convertible.

DART 270 SERIES I.D. NUMBERS: See Dart Series I.D. Number listing. All models began at 100001 and went up in the unit number sequence.

DART 270 SERIES

Model Number	Body/Style Number	Body Type & Seating	Factory Price	Shipping Weight	Production Total
BL1/2H	41	4-dr Sed-6P	2280/2408	2680/2895	Note 1
BL1/2H	21	2-dr Sed-6P	2214/2342	2665/2860	Note 1
BL1/2H	23	2-dr HT-6P	2307/2435	2720/2890	Note 1
BL1/2H	27	2-dr Conv-6P	2570/2698	2805/2995	Note 1
BL1/2H	45	4-dr Sta Wag-6P	2533/2661	2795/3020	Note 1

NOTE 1: A total of 35,100 Dart 270s were built during calendar year 1966. Of these, 28,500 were sixes and 6,600 were V-8s.

1966 Dodge, Dart GT two-door convertible, V-8 (PH)

DART GT SERIES — (ALL ENGINES) — The GT was the top trim level Dart for 1966 and included all the 270 features, plus padded instrument panel, wheelcovers and bucket seats. In addition, the GTs had a special emblem on the roof 'C' pillar and chrome rocker panel trim.

DART GT SERIES I.D. NUMBERS: See Dart Series I.D. Number listing. All models began at 100001 and went up in the unit number sequence.

DART GT SERIES

Model Number	Body/Style Number	Body Type & Seating	Factory Price	Shipping Weight	Production Total
BL1P/2P	23	2-dr HT-6P	2417/2545	2735/2915	Note 1
BL1P/2P	27	2-dr Conv-6P	2700/2828	2830/2995	Note 1

NOTE 1: A total of 18,700 GTs were built during calendar year 1966. Of these, 8,700 were sixes and 10,000 were V-8s.

DART CONVENIENCE OPTIONS: Prices and availability were similar to 1965.

CORONET/CORONET DELUXE SERIES — (ALL ENGINES) — The Coronet continued as the intermediate size model for 1966. Completely restyled for the new year, the Coronet was to become one of the most attractive of that model ever to be produced. The 1966 models were nearly an inch shorter than the previous year and wider. They featured a mesh grille with the parking lights at the extreme ends and larger rectangular taillights which blended in nicely with the overall styling of the rear of the Coronet models. The Coronet was the base trim level and included the 225 cid six-cylinder engine, 7.35 x 14 tubeless tires, heater and defroster. electric windshield wipers, chrome windshield and rear window moldings, a single horizontal chrome strip along the bodyside and the Dodge name, in block letters, across the center of the front of the hood and the vertical section of the trunk lid.

CORONET SERIES I.D. NUMBERS: See Dart Series I.D. Number listing. All models began at 100001 and went up in the unit number sequence.

CORONET DELUXE SERIES

Model Number	Body/Style Number	Body Type & Seating	Factory Price	Shipping Weight	Production Total
BW1/2L	41	4-dr Sed-6P	2302/2396	3075/3240	Note 1
BW1/2L	21	2-dr Sed-6P	2264/2358	3050/3215	Note 1
BW1/2L	41	4-dr DeL Sed-6P	2341/2435	3075/3240	Note 1
BW1/2L	21	2-dr DeL Sed-6P	2303/2397	3050/3215	Note 1
BW1/2L	45	4-dr DeL Wag-6P	2631/2725	3480/3595	Note 1

NOTE 1: A total of 10,700 Coronets were built during calendar year 1966. Of these, 7,700 were sixes and 3,000 were V-8s. A total of 46,200 Coronet Deluxe models were built during that year. Of these, 25,600 were sixes and 20,600 were V-8s. A total of 27,700 station wagons were built during that year. Of these, 3,100 were sixes and 24,600 were V-8s. No breakout is provided for individual models, and the production figure represents total station wagon production.

CORONET 440 SERIES — (ALL ENGINES) — The Coronet 440 was the intermediate trim level of the Coronet Series and included all the features of the base Coronet Series, plus air foam front seat, power top and vinyl interior on the convertible, carpets and the nine-passenger station wagons had the 273 cid V-8 engine and power tailgate window as standard equipment.

CORONET 440 SERIES I.D. NUMBERS: See Dart Series I.D. Number listing. All models began at 100001 and went up in the unit number sequence.

CORONET 440 SERIES

Model Number	Body/Style Number	Body Type & Seating	Factory Price	Shipping Weight	Production Total
BW1/2H	41	4-dr Sed-6P	2432/2526	3095/3220	Note 1
BW1/2H	23	2-dr HT-6P	2457/2551	3075/3235	Note 1
BW1/2H	27	2-dr Conv-6P	2672/2766	3185/3310	Note 1
BW1/2H	45	4-dr Sta Wag-6P	2722/2816	3515/3585	Note 1
BW2H	46	4-dr Sta Wag-9P	2926	3680	Note 1

NOTE 1: A total of 110,600 440s were built during calendar year 1966. Of these, 14,000 were sixes and 96,600 were V-8s. See Coronet Series, Note 1, for station wagon production.

1966 Dodge, Coronet 500 two-door hardtop sports coupe, V-8

CORONET 500 SERIES — (ALL ENGINES) — The Coronet 500 was the top trim level Coronet for 1966 and included all the 440 features, plus, padded instrument panel, console and bucket seats, wheelcovers, 225 cid Slant-Six in the four-door sedan and 273 cid V-8 engine in all others, four vertical chrome louvers on the rear fenders just ahead of the rear wheelwell and the Coronet 500 name, in script at the front of the front fenders.

CORONET 500 SERIES I.D. NUMBERS: See Dart Series I.D. Number listing. All models began at 100001 and went up in the unit number sequence.

CORONET 500 SERIES

Model Number	Body/Style Number	Body Type & Seating	Factory Price	Shipping Weight	Production Total
BW1P/2P	41	4-dr Sed-6P	2586/2680	3120/3280	Note 1
BW2P	23	2-dr HT-6P	2705	3275	Note 1
BW2P	27	2-dr Conv-6P	2921	3345	Note 1

NOTE 1: A total of 55,700 500s were built during calendar year 1966. Of these, 500 were sixes and 55,200 were V-8s.

CHARGER SERIES — (V-8) — The Charger was Dodge's entry into the current 'fastback' craze. The Charger used Coronet chassis and running gear components, but the body was completely different. The Coronet grille opening was filled with a convex grille with fine vertical bars and a round Charger crest in the center. The rear end used a single, full-width taillight with the Charger name, in block letters spaced evenly across the entire length. Hidden headlights were becoming the rage and the Charger featured these items along with the full-width taillights. Two fine feature lines were used along the bodyside and the fastback too terminated at the rear end of the car. Inside, the Charger's rear bucket seats folded individually to provide a very spacious luggage compartment and the instrument panel was unique to the Charger. Four larger round pods contained all the instruments and located them directly in front of the driver. The floor shift (standard or automatic) was located in a full-length console which divided both front and rear seats.

CHARGER SERIES I.D. NUMBERS: See Dart Series I.D. Number listing. All models began at 100001 and went up in the unit number sequence.

CHARGER SERIES

Model Number	Body/Style Number	Body Type & Seating	Factory Price	Shipping Weight	Production Total
BX2P	29	2-dr HT-4P	3122	3499	37,300

POLARA SERIES — (V-8) — The Polara continued as the base trim level full-size Dodge. A slightly revised grille and large, delta shaped taillights highlighted the minor restyling for 1966. The Polara had chrome windshield and rear window moldings. The Dodge name, in block letters, across the center of the hood, directly above the hourglass-shaped grille. Also included were the 270 hp, 383 cid V-8 engine, heater and defroster, power top on convertibles, 8.25 x 14 tubeless tires. The station wagons also included a vinyl interior and the nine-passenger station wagons also included power tailgate window and rear bumper guards with step pads. A sporty version of the Polara, called the Polara 500 was also offered and was intended to complete directly with the Chevrolet Impala SS and the Ford Galaxie 500XL models. The Polara 500s featured all the standard Polara items, plus bucket seats and console with floor shift. Small round '500' emblems on the front fenders identified the 500s from the standard Polaras.

1966 Dodge, Charger two-door hardtop sports coupe, V-8

POLARA SERIES I.D. NUMBERS: See Dart Series I.D. Number listing. All models began at 100001 and went up in the unit number sequence.

POLARA SERIES

Model Number	Body/Style Number	Body Type & Seating	Factory Price	Shipping Weight	Production Total
BD21	41	4-dr Sed-6P	2838	3765	Note 1
BD2L	43	4-dr HT-6P	2948	3880	Note 1
BD2L	23	2-dr HT-6P	2874	3820	Note 1
BD2L	27	2-dr Conv-6P	3161	3885	Note 1
DB2L	45	4-dr Sta Wag-6P	3183	4265	Note 1
BD2L	46	4-dr Sta Wag-9P	3286	4295	Note 1

NOTE 1: A total of 75,400 Polaras were built during calendar year 1966, including 12,400 low-priced "Polara 318" economy models. All Polaras were V-8 powered. A total of 29,300 station wagons were produced during that year, although no breakout is provided for six and nine-passenger models.

MONACO SERIES — (V-8) — The Monaco line was expanded during 1966 to include four separate models. The position held by the 1965 Monaco was filled by a new, more luxurious Monaco 500 version of the Monaco. For 1966, the Monaco shared the Polara body and was merely a more highly trimmed Polara and shared drivetrain features with the Polara. The Monaco 500 was powered by the 325 hp four-barrel version of the 383 cid V-8 engine. All Monacos featured air foam front seats, stainless steel window frames on station wagons and four-door sedans. The hardtops had vinyl interior trim. The Monaco 500 featured all the Monaco standard equipment plus special exterior trim, bucket seats and a center console, wheelcovers with spinners and the Monaco name, in script, on the left side of the trunk lid.

MONACO SERIES I.D. NUMBERS: See Dart Series I.D. Number listing. All models began at 100001 and went up in the unit number sequence.

1966 Dodge, Monaco 500 two-door hardtop sports coupe, V-8

MONACO SERIES

Model Number	Body/Style Number	Body Type & Seating	Factory Price	Shipping Weight	Production Total
BD2H	41	4-dr Sed-6P	3033	3890	Note 1
BD2H	43	4-dr HT-6P	3170	3835	Note 1
BD2H	23	2-dr HT-6P	3107	3855	Note 1
BD2H	45	4-dr Sta Wag-6P	3183	4265	Note 1
BD2H	46	4-dr Sta Wag-9P	3539	4315	Note 1
BD2P	23	2-dr 500 HT-6P	3604	4270	Note 1

NOTE 1: A total of 30,600 Monacos and 7,300 Monaco 500s were built during calendar year 1966, all V-8s. See Note 1, Polara Series for station wagon production.

CORONETS/POLARAS/MONACOS CONVENIENCE OPTIONS: Specific data was not available at the time of publication of the Standard Catalog of American Cars 1946-1975. Prices and availability were similar to 1965.

1966 ENGINES

170 Slant-Six. Overhead valves. Cast iron block. Displacement: 170 cid. Bore and stroke: 3.41 x 3.13 inches. Compression ratio: 8.5:1. Brake hp: 101 at 4400 rpm. Four main bearings. Solid valve lifters. Carburetion: Carter BBS-4099S single-barrel.

225 Slant-Six. Overhead valves. Cast iron block. Displacement: 225 cid. Bore and stroke: 3.41 x 4.13 inches. Compression ratio: 8.4:1. Brake hp: 145 at 4000 rpm. Four main bearings. Solid valve lifters. Carburetion: Holley R-3271-A single-barrel.

273 V-8. Overhead valves. Cast iron block. Displacement: 273 cid. Bore and stroke: 3.63 x 3.31 inches. Compression ratio: 8.8:1. Brake hp: 180 at 4200 rpm. Five main bearings. Hydraulic valve lifters. Carburetion: Carter BBD-4113S two-barrel.

High-Performance 273 V-8. Overhead valves. Cast iron block. Displacement: 273 cid. Bore and stroke: 3.63 x 3.31 inches. Compression ratio: 10.5:1. Brake hp: 235 at 5200 rpm. Five main bearings. Hydraulic valve lifters. Carburetion: Carter AFB 3855S four-barrel.

318 V-8. Overhead valves. Cast iron block. Displacement: 318 cid. Bore and stroke: 3.91 x 3.31 inches. Compression ratio: 9.0:1. Brake hp: 230 at 4400 rpm. Five main bearings. Hydraulic valve lifters. Carburetion: Stromberg WW3-258 two-barrel.

361 V-8. Overhead valves. Cast iron block. Displacement: 361 cid. Bore and stroke: 4.13 x 3.38 inches. Compression ratio: 9.0:1. Brake hp: 265 at 4400 rpm. Five main bearings. Hydraulic valve lifters. Carburetion: Carter BBD-3849S two-barrel.

383 V-8. Overhead valves. Cast iron block. Displacement: 383 cid. Bore and stroke: 4.25 x 3.38 inches. Compression ratio: 9.2:1. Brake hp: 270 at 4400 rpm. Five main bearings. Hydraulic valve lifters. Carburetion: Carter BBD-4125S two-barrel.

383 'Four-barrel' V-8. Overhead valves. Cast iron block. Displacement: 383 cid. Bore and stroke: 4.24 x 3.38 inches. Compression ratio: 10.0:1. Brake hp: 325 at 4800 rpm. Five main bearings. Hydraulic valve lifters. Carburetion: Carter AFB 3855S four-barrel.

426 'Hemi' V-8. Overhead valves with hemispherical combustion chambers. Cast iron block. Displacement: 426 cid. Bore and stroke: 4.25 x 3.75 inches. Compression ratio: 12.0:1. Brake hp: 425 at 5600 rpm. Five main bearings. Solid valve lifters. Carburetion: Two Carter AFB-3084S four-barrels.

426 'Street Hemi' 'Eight Barrel' V-8. Same as 'Race Hemi' except hydraulic valve lifters and 10.25:1 compression ratio.

440 Wedge; Cast iron block. Displacement: 440 cid. Bore and stroke: 4.32 x 3.75. Compression ratio: 10.1. Brake hp: 365 at 4400 rpm. Five main bearings. Hydraulic valve lifters. Carburetion; Single Carter AFB-4130-S.

1966 DODGE CHASSIS FEATURES

DART: Wheelbase: 111 inches; (106 inches on station wagons). Overall length: 195.9 inches; (190.2 inches on station wagons). Tires: 6.50 x 13 tubeless black sidewall (7.00 x 13 on V-8s). Three-speed manual transmission was standard on all Darts, with the three-speed TorqueFlite automatic and four-speed manual transmissions optional.

CORONET: Wheelbase: 117 inches. Overall length: 203 inches; (207.9 inches on station wagons). Tires: 7.35 x 14 tubeless black sidewall on sixes; 7.75 x 14 on V-8s and 8.25 x 14 on station wagons). Three-speed manual transmission was standard on all Coronets, with the three-speed TorqueFlite and four-speed manual transmissions optional.

POLARA/MONACO/MONACO 500: Wheelbase: 121 inches. Overall length: 213.3 inches; (217.1 inches on six-passenger station wagons and 218.4 inches on nine-passenger station wagons). Tires: 8.25 x 14 tubeless black sidewall on Monaco 500s and 8.55 x 14 tubeless black sidewall on all others. Three-speed manual transmission was standard on all Polara, Monaco and Monaco 500 models, with three-speed TorqueFlite and four-speed manual transmissions optional.

1967 DODGE

DART SERIES — (ALL ENGINES) — The 1967 Darts all featured completely new styling from the ground up. Riding on the same chassis as in 1966, the new Darts looked larger than their predecessors, even though they were, in fact, half an inch shorter. The full-width grille housed single headlights and featured a vertical bar arrangement with a large vertical dividing bar in the center of the concave grille. The side profile was slightly more rounded than in previous years and carried basically the same lines as in the past. The rear end treatment featured large, nearly square taillights and a vertical section on the trunk lid which was as wide as the taillights were high. The Dart was the base trim level and included chrome windshield and rear window moldings, no side chrome, and the Dart name, in block letters, along the side of the rear fenders. The Dodge name, also in block letters, appeared on the front of the hood and across the vertical section of the trunk lid. Also included was a heater and defroster, electric windshield wipers, the 170 cid Slant-Six engine and manual three-speed transmission.

DART I.D. NUMBERS: See 1966 Dart I.D. Number listing.

DART SERIES

Model Number	Body/Style Number	Body Type & Seating	Factory Price	Shipping Weight	Production Total
CL1L/2L	41	4-dr Sed-6P	2224/2352	2725/2910	Note 1
CL1L/2L	21	2-dr Sed-6P	2187/2315	2710/2895	Note 1

NOTE 1: In figures rounded off to the nearest 100 units, a total of 53,100 Dodge Darts were built during model year 1967. Of these, 50,900 were sixes and 2,200 were V-8s. No additional breakouts by body style are available at this time.

NOTE 2: For all 1967 Dodge specifications listings in this catalog, model numbers, prices and weights above slash are for sixes/below slash for V-8s.

DART 270 SERIES — (ALL ENGINES) — The Dart 270 continued as the intermediate trim level and included all the Dart features, plus carpeting; Deluxe two-spoke steering wheel; full horn ring and vinyl interior trim.

DART 270 SERIES I.D. NUMBERS: See 1966 Dart Series I.D. Number listing. All models began at 100001 and went up in the unit number sequence.

DART 270 SERIES

Model Number	Body/Style Number	Body Type & Seating	Factory Price	Shipping Weight	Production Total
CLIH/2H	41	4-dr Sed-6P	2362/2490	2735/2915	Note 1
CLIH/2H	23	2-dr HT Cpe-6P	2388/2516	2725/2910	Note 1

NOTE 1: In figures rounded off to the nearest 100 units, a total of 63,200 Dodge Dart 270s were built during model year 1967. Of these, 49,700 were sixes and 13,500 were V-8s. No additional breakouts by body style are available at this time.

1967 Dodge, Dart GT two-door hardtop coupe, V-8

DART GT SERIES — (ALL ENGINES) — The GT was the top trim level Dart for 1967 and included all the Dodge Dart 270 features, plus padded instrument panel, wheelcovers and bucket seats. In addition, the GTs had a special emblem on the roof 'C' pillar and chrome rocker panel trim.

DART GT SERIES I.D. NUMBERS: See 1966 Dart Series I.D. Number listing. All models began at 100001 and went up in the unit number sequence.

DART GT SERIES

Model Number	Body/Style Number	Body Type & Seating	Factory Price	Shipping Weight	Production Total
CL1P/2P	23	2-dr HT Cpe-6P	2499/2627	2750/2930	Note 1
CL1P/2P	27	2-dr Conv-6P	2732/2860	2850/3030	Note 1

NOTE 1: In figures rounded off to the nearest 100 units, a total of 38,200 Dodge Dart GTs were built during the model year 1967. Of these. 16,600 were sixes and 21,600 were V-8s. No additional breakouts by body style are available at this time.

CORONET DELUXE SERIES — (ALL ENGINES) — The Coronet Deluxe was the intermediate size model for 1967. Using the 1966 body shell, the new Coronets adopted the Charger grille and featured a very slightly revised rear end treatment. The Coronet was the base trim level and featured chrome windshield and rear window moldings and the Coronet name, in block letters, along the sides of the rear fenders. The Dodge name, also in block letters, was seen across the front of the grille and on the vertical section of the trunk lid. Standard equipment included front and rear seat belts; windshield washer; 7.75 x 14 tubeless black sidewall tires (8.25 x 14 on V-8s); heater and defroster; two-speed electric wipers; right outside rearview mirror; dual parking system and warning light; padded instrument panel and sun visors; emergency warning flashers; left outside rearview mirror and prismatic inside mirror; 225 cid Slant Six engine; back-up lights and black rubber floor mats.

CORONET DELUXE I.D. NUMBERS: See 1966 Dart Series I.D. Number listing. All models began at 100001 and went up in the unit number sequence.

CORONET DELUXE SERIES

Model Number	Body/Style Number	Body Type & Seating	Factory Price	Shipping Weight	Production Total
CW1/2L	41	4-dr Sed-6P	2397/2491	3070/3235	Note 1
CW1/2L	21	2-dr Sed-6P	2359/2453	3045/3210	Note 1
CW1/2L	45	4-dr Sta Wag-6P	2693/2787	3495/3625	Note 2

NOTE 1: In figures rounded off to the nearest 100 units, a total of 27,800 Dodge Coronet Deluxe passenger cars were built during model year 1967. Of these, 14,100 were sixes and 13,700 were V-8s.

NOTE 2: Production of all Coronet-bodied station wagons, including those in both Deluxe and 440 trim lines, was counted as a lumped sum. In figures rounded off to the nearest 100 units, this production total was 24,200 units, including 3,300 sixes and 20,900 V-8s.

CORONET 440 SERIES — (ALL ENGINES) — The Coronet 440 continued as the intermediate trim level of the Coronet Series and included all features of the standard Coronet, plus carpeting; foam front seats and vinyl interiors on convertibles, hardtops and station wagons. Station wagons also included power tailgate windows and, on nine-passenger styles, a 273 cid V-8; rear bumper guards; step pads and cargo light were standard.

CORONET 440 SERIES I.D. NUMBERS: See 1966 Dart Series I.D. Number listing. All models began at 100001 and went up in the unit number sequence.

CORONET 440 SERIES

Model Number	Body/Style Number	Body Type & Seating	Factory Price	Shipping Weight	Production Total
CW1/2H	41	4-dr Sed-6P	2475/2569	3060/3225	Note 1
CW1/2H	23	2-dr HT Cpe-6P	2500/2594	3065/3235	Note 1
CW1/2H	27	2-dr Conv-6P	2740/2834	3140/3305	Note 1
CW1/2H	45	4-dr Sta Wag-6P	2771/2865	3495/3605	Note 2
CW2H	46	4-dr Sta Wag-9P	2975	3705	Note 2

NOTE 1: In figures rounded off to the nearest 100 units, a total of 92,500 Dodge Coronet 440 passenger cars were built in model year 1967. Of these, 8,600 were sixes and 83,900 were V-8s. This does not include station wagons. No additional body style breakouts are available at this time.

NOTE 2: See 1967 Dodge Coronet Deluxe Series Note 2.

CORONET 500 SERIES — (ALL ENGINES) — The Coronet 500 was the top trim level for 1967 and included all the 440 features, plus wheelcovers; console; bucket seats and vinyl interior. The Coronet 500 name, in block letters, appeared on the sides of the rear fenders.

CORONET 500 SERIES I.D. NUMBERS: See 1966 Dart Series I.D. Number listing. All models began at 100001 and went up in the unit number sequence.

CORONET 500 SERIES

Model Number	Body/Style Number	Body Type & Seating	Factory Price	Shipping Weight	Production Total
CW1/2P	41	4-dr Sed-6P	2654/2748	3075/3235	Note 1
CW1/2P	23	2-dr HT Cpe-6P	2679/2773	3115/3280	Note 1
CW1/2P	27	2-dr Conv-6P	2919/3013	3190/3355	Note 1

NOTE 1: In figures rounded off to the nearest 100 units, a total of 29,300 Dodge Coronet 500 passenger cars were built during model year 1967. This includes 400 sixes and 28,900 V-8s. No additional breakouts by body style are available at the current time.

CORONET R/T SERIES — (V-8) — The Coronet R/T was the high-performance model of the Coronet Series and included all Coronet 500 features, plus the 440 cid Magnum V-8 engine (with four-barrel carburetor and dual exhausts); TorqueFlite automatic transmission; a special paint stripe; 7.75 x 14 Red Streak nylon tires; heavy-duty shock absorbers and torsion bars; special hood (with scoops); 70 amp/hour battery and heavy-duty brakes. The convertible also included map and courtesy lights.

1967 Dodge, Coronet 500 two-door hardtop sports coupe, V-8

CORONET R/T SERIES I.D. NUMBERS: See 1966 Dart Series I.D. Number listing. All models began at 100001 and went up in the unit number sequence.

CORONET R/T SERIES

Model Number	Body/Style Number	Body Type & Seating	Factory Price	Shipping Weight	Production Total
CW2P	23	2-dr HT Cpe-6P	3199	3565	Note 1
CW2P	27	2-dr Conv-6P	3438	3640	Note 1

NOTE 1: A total of 10, 181 Dodge Coronet R/T passenger cars were built in model year 1967. All were V-8s. 628 R/T convertibles were made of this total.

1967 Dodge, Charger two-door hardtop sports coupe, V-8

CHARGER SERIES — (V-8) — The 1967 Charger utilized the same body introduced in 1966, with front fender mounted turn signal indicators and a few new chrome pieces added. The Chargers, being mounted on the Coronet chassis, included all the features found in Coronet 500 models, plus paint stripes; map and courtesy lights; front and rear bucket seats; rear center armrests; cigar lighter; 318 cid V-8 engine; tinted rear window; oil pressure gauge; tachometer and rear pillar interior lights.

CHARGER SERIES I.D. NUMBERS: See 1966 Dart Series I.D. Number listing. All Chargers began at 100001 and went up in the unit number sequence.

CHARGER SERIES

Model Number	Body/Style Number	Body Type & Seating	Factory Price	Shipping Weight	Production Total
CW2P	29	2-dr Spt HT-6P	3128	3480	15,788

NOTE: The production total above is an exact model year output figure. All Chargers were V-8 powered.

1967 Dodge Polara convertible, V-8

POLARA SERIES — (V-8) — Completely restyled for 1967, the new full-size Polara Series featured longer, lower and wider bodies than its 1966 counterpart. Large, delta-shaped plastic taillights were featured and this shape was duplicated, to a much lesser extent, in the grille.

Top styling of four-door models was the same as 1965 and 1966 models, while two-door hardtops had a new semi-fastback roof style with a reverse slant to the rear quarter window opening. Two feature lines were used on the bodysides, one at the belt-level and the other on the lower bodyside, which flared out slightly just in front of the rear wheel opening. The Polara was the base trim level and included chrome windshield and rear window moldings; 383 cid V-8 engine (318 engine in Polara '318' models); 8.25 x 14 tubeless black sidewall tires (8.55 x 14 on station wagons); outside left rearview mirror; two-speed wipers; rear bumper guards with step pads on nine-passenger station wagons; carpeting; right outside rearview mirror on station wagon; dual braking system and warning light; padded instrument panel and sun visors; emergency flasher system; vinyl interior on convertibles and station wagons; front and rear seat belts and back-up lights. The Polara name, in block letters, was located along the sides of the rear fenders and the Dodge name, in block letters, appeared on the front of the hood and across the vertical section of the trunk lid. A Polara 500 trim option including bucket seats and center console was available in two-door hardtop and convertible styles.

POLARA SERIES I.D. NUMBERS: See 1966 Dart Series I.D. Number listing. All models began at 100001 and went up in the unit number sequence.

POLARA SERIES

Model Number	Body/Style Number	Body Type & Seating	Factory Price	Shipping Weight	Production Total
CD2L	41	4-dr '318'Sed-6P	2843	3765	Note 1
CD2L	41	4-dr Sed-6P	2918	3885	Note 1
CD2L	43	4-dr HT Sed-6P	3028	3920	Note 1
CD2L	23	2-dr HT Cpe-6P	2953	3870	Note 1
CD2L	27	2-dr Conv-6P	3241	3930	Note 1
CD2L	45	4-dr Sta Wag-6P	3265	4400	Note 2
CD2L	46	4-dr Sta Wag-9P	3368	4450	Note 2

NOTE 1: In figures rounded off to the nearest 100 units, a total of 24,000 Polaras; 5,600 Polara 318s and 3,200 Polara 500 passenger cars were built during model year 1967. No additional body style breakouts are available at the current time.
NOTE 2: In addition to the totals in Note 1, some 8,900 full-sized Dodge (Polara and Monaco) station wagons were built during the 1967 model run, with no additional breakout as to trim level or passenger/seating configurations.

MONACO SERIES — (V-8) — The Monaco line adopted the Polara body and was considered the top trim level of that line. Monacos included all Polara features, plus glovebox light; ashtray light; map and courtesy lights; parking brake light; foam front seat cushions and wheelcovers. Hardtops and station wagons had vinyl trim and the nine-passenger wagon had a power tailgate window. The top line Monaco 500 had all the Monaco features plus console; paint stripes; electric clock; three-spoke Deluxe steering wheel; four-barrel carburetion; TorqueFlite or four-speed manual transmission; front bucket seats and a brushed stainless steel rocker panel molding.

1967 Dodge, Monaco four-door hardtop sedan, V-8

The Monaco or Monaco 500 name appeared, in block letters, across the sides of the rear fenders.

MONACO SERIES I.D. NUMBERS: See 1966 Dart Series I.D. Number listing. All models began at 100001 and went up in the unit number sequence.

MONACO AND MONACO 500 SERIES

Model Number	Body/Style Number	Body Type & Seating	Factory Price	Shipping Weight	Production Total
MONACO					
CD2H	41	4-dr Sed-6P	3138	3895	Note 1
CD2H	43	4-dr HT Sed-6P	3275	3945	Note 1
CD2H	23	2-dr HT Cpe-6P	3213	3885	Note 1
CD2H	45	4-dr Sta Wag-6P	3542	4425	Note 2
CD2H	45	4-dr Sta Wag-9P	3646	4475	Note 2
MONACO 500					
CD2P	23	2-dr HT Cpe-6P	3712	3970	Note 1

NOTE 1: In figures rounded off to the nearest 100 units, a total of 11,400 Monacos and 2,500 Monaco 500 passenger cars were built during the 1967 model year. All were V-8s. No additional breakouts are available at this time.
NOTE 2: The production of 1967 Monaco and Polara station wagons was expressed as a lumped sum only. See 1967 Polara Series Note 2 for the combined total. No additional breakout by trim level or passenger/seating configuration is available at this time.

1967 ENGINES

170 'Slant-Six'. Overhead valves. Cast iron block. Displacement: 170 cid. Bore and stroke: 3.41 x 3.13 inches. Compression ratio: 8.5:1. Brake hp: 101 at 4400 rpm. Four main bearings. Solid valve lifters. Carburetion: Carter BBS-4099S single-barrel.

225 Slant-Six. Overhead valves. Cast iron block. Displacement: 225 cid. Bore and stroke: 3.41 x 4.13 inches. Compression ratio: 8.4:1. Brake hp: 145 at 4000 rpm. Four main bearings. Solid valve lifters. Carburetion: Holley R-3271-A single-barrel.

273 V-8. Overhead valves. Cast iron block. Displacement: 273 cid. Bore and stroke: 3.63 x 3.31 inches. Compression ratio: 8.6:1. Brake hp: 180 at 4200 rpm. Five main bearings. Hydraulic valve lifters. Carburetion: Carter BBD-4113S two-barrel.

High-Performance 273 V-8. Overhead valves. Cast iron block. Displacement: 273 cid. Bore and stroke: 3.63 x 3.31 inches. Compression ratio: 10.5:1. Brake hp: 235 at 5200 rpm. Five main bearings. Hydraulic valve lifters. Carburetion: Carter AFB 3855S four-barrel.

318 V-8. Overhead valves. Cast iron block. Displacement: 318 cid. Bore and stroke: 3.91 x 3.31 inches. Compression ratio: 9.0:1. Brake hp: 230 at 4400 rpm. Five main bearings. Hydraulic valve lifters. Carburetion: Stromberg WW3-258 two-barrel.

383 V-8. Overhead valves. Cast iron block. Displacement: 383 cid. Bore and stroke: 4.25 x 3.38 inches. Compression ratio: 9.2:1. Brake hp: 270 at 4400 rpm. Five main bearings. Hydraulic valve lifters. Carburetion: Carter BBD-4125S two-barrel.

383 'Four-barrel' V-8. Overhead valves. Cast iron block. Displacement: 383 cid. Bore and stroke: 4.24 x 3.38 inches. Compression ratio: 10.0:1. Brake hp: 325 at 4800 rpm. Five main bearings. Hydraulic valve lifters. Carburetion: Carter AFB 3855S four-barrel.

426 'Street Hemi' V-8. Overhead valves with hemispherical combustion chambers. Cast iron block. Displacement: 426 cid. Bore and stroke: 4.25 x 3.75 inches. Compression ratio: 10.25:1. Brake hp: 425 at 5600 rpm. Five main bearings. Solid valve lifters. Carburetion: two Carter AFB-3084S four-barrels.

440 V-8. Wedge. Cast iron block. Displacement: 440 cid. Bore and stroke: 4.32 x 3.75 inches. Compression ratio: 10.1. Brake hp: 375 at 4400 rpm. Five main bearings. Hydraulic valve lifters. Carburetion: Single Carter AFB-4130-S.

440 Magnum V-8. Cast iron block. Displacement: 440 cid. Bore and stroke: 4.32 x 3.75 inches. Compression ratio: 10.1. Brake hp: 375 at 4400 rpm. Five main bearings. Hydraulic valve lifters. Carburetion: single Carter AFB-4130-S.

1967 DODGE CHASSIS FEATURES

DART: Wheelbase: 111 inches. Overall length: 195.4 inches. Tires: 6.50 x 13 tubeless black sidewall on sixes and 7.00 x 13 tubeless black sidewall on V-8. Three-speed manual transmission was standard on all Darts, with the three-speed TorqueFlite automatic or four-speed manual transmission optional.

CORONET: Wheelbase: 117 inches. Overall length: 203 inches (207.9 inches on station wagons). Tires: 7.35 x 14 tubeless black sidewall on six-cylinder sedans; 7.75 x 14 on six-cylinder station wagons; 7.35 x 14 on V-8 sedans and 8.25 x 14 on V-8 station wagons. Three-speed manual transmission was standard on all Coronets except the R/T, with the three-speed TorqueFlite and four-speed manual transmissions optional (TorqueFlite standard on R/T).

POLARA/MONACO/MONACO 500: Wheelbase: 122 inches. Overall length: 219.6 inches (221.3 inches on nine-passenger station wagon). Tires: 8.25 x 14 black sidewall on 318 sedans; 8.45 x 14 on all others. Three-speed manual transmission was standard on all Polara and Monaco models, with the three-speed TorqueFlite and four-speed standard on Monaco 500 models and optional on all others.

1967 ENGINE: Same as 1966. See 1966 Dodge engine specifications.

DART CONVENIENCE OPTIONS: 225 cid Slant Six engine ($38). 273 cid V-8 engine ($79). TorqueFlite automatic transmission for sixes ($139); for V-8s ($147). Four-speed manual transmission ($145). Power steering ($65). Power brakes ($32). Power front disc brakes ($54). Console on GTs ($38). Tinted glass ($22). Headrests for bucket seats ($32). Buffed paint on 270s and GTs ($18). Two-tone paint ($15). Music Master AM radio ($44). Rallye suspension ($11). Tachometer on GTs with Console ($38). Vinyl top ($58). Wheelcovers, on 13 inch wheels ($14); on 14 inch wheels ($16). Simulated 'Mag' wheelcovers on GTs ($43); on 270s ($57). White sidewall tires ($34).

CORONET/POLARA/MONACO CONVENIENCE OPTIONS: 318 cid V-8 engine ($24). 383 cid V-8 engine, in Charger ($56); in others ($81). 383 cid four-barrel V-8 engine, in Polara ($28); in Charger ($97); in other models ($121). 440 cid V-8 engine, in Monaco 500 ($69); in Monaco ($97); in Polaras and Monaco station wagons ($133). 426 cid 'Hemi' V-8, in Coronet R/T ($457); in Dodge Charger ($712). TorqueFlite automatic transmission, on six-cylinders ($153); depending on engine with V-8s ($163-$176). Four-speed manual transmission ($145-$175). Air conditioning on Coronets and Chargers ($274); on Polaras and Monacos ($311). Auto Pilot cruise control ($64). Power steering ($73). Power brakes ($16). Power front disc brakes ($54). Electric clock ($11). Console ($20). Sure-Grip differential ($29-$37). Heavy-duty differential ($107). Power door locks ($42). Dual exhausts ($24). Buffed paint ($16). Music Master AM radio on Coronets and Chargers ($44); on Polaras and Monacos ($47). Tilt & Telescope steering wheel ($67). Woodgrained steering wheel on Coronets and R/T ($20); on Chargers ($16); on Polaras and Monacos ($12). Tachometer ($38). Vinyl top on four-door sedans ($58); on hardtops ($70). Bucket seats ($75). Wheelcovers ($14-$22). Simulated 'Mag' wheelcovers ($41-$57). Road wheels ($59-$75). Three-speed windshield wipers ($4).

1968 DODGE

DART SERIES — (ALL ENGINES) — The 1968 Darts continued to use the same body as introduced in 1967 with only very minor trim updating. The Dart continued as the base trim level and included chrome windshield and rear window moldings, no side chrome and the Dart name, in block letters, along the side of the rear fenders. The Dodge name, also in block letters, appeared on the front of the hood and across the vertical section of the trunk lid. Also included in the standard Dart package, was the federally mandated Cleaner Air System; heater and defroster; 170 cid Slant six engine and three-speed manual transmission.

DART SERIES I.D. NUMBERS: See 1966 Dart Series I.D. Numbers listing.

DART SERIES

Model Number	Body/Style Number	Body Type & Seating	Factory Price	Shipping Weight	Production Total
CL1L/2L	41	4-dr Sed-6P	2334/2462	2725/2910	Note 1
CL1L/2L	21	2-dr Sed-6P	2297/2425	2710/2895	Note 1

NOTE 1: Some 60,300 Darts were built during model year 1968. Of those, 56,900 were sixes and 3,400 were V-8s.

ADDITIONAL NOTES: For all 1968 Dodge listings: Model numbers, prices and weights above slash are for sixes/below slash for V-8s. All 1968 Dodge model year production totals given in this catalog are expressed in figures rounded off to the nearest 100 units, unless otherwise noted.

DART 270 SERIES — (ALL ENGINES) — The Dart 270 was the intermediate trim level once again and included all the Dart features, plus carpeting; cigar lighter; half horn ring and dual horns. Hardtops also included a full-width all-vinyl bench seat.

DART 270 SERIES I.D. NUMBERS: See 1966 Dart Series I.D. Number listing. All models began at 10001 and went up in the unit number sequence.

DART 270 SERIES

Model Number	Body/Style Number	Body Type & Seating	Factory Price	Shipping Weight	Production Total
CL1H/2H	41	4-dr Sed-6P	2473/2601	2735/2915	Note 1
CL1H/2H	23	2-dr HT Cpe-6P	2499/2627	2725/2910	Note 1

NOTE 1: Some 76,500 Dart 270s were built during model year 1968. Of those, 55,200 were sixes and 21,300 were V-8s.

1968 Dodge, Dart 'GTS' two-door hardtop sports coupe, V-8

DART GT SERIES — (ALL ENGINES) — The GT was the top trim level Dart for 1968 and included all the 270 features, plus 14 or 15 inch wheels and tires with Deluxe wheelcovers. The hardtops had bucket seats and the convertibles had power tops and full-width all-vinyl bench seats. The GTS was a special, high-performance version of the GT and was equipped with the new 340 cid V-8 engine; hub caps; firm-ride shock absorbers; Rallye suspension; E70 x 14 Red Stread Wide Oval tires; TorqueFlite three-speed automatic (or four-speed manual transmission); Bumblebee stripes across the sides of the rear fenders and trunk lid and an engine dress-up kit (consisting of black, crinkle-finished aluminum valve covers and a special black, crinkle-finished aluminum air cleaner). The GTs and GTS models included the appropriate model designation on the sides of the front fenders, just behind the front wheel openings.

DART GT SERIES I.D. NUMBERS: See 1966 Dart Series I.D. Number listing. All models began at 100001 and went up in the unit number sequence.

DART GT SERIES

Model Number	Body/Style Number	Body Type & Seating	Factory Price	Shipping Weight	Production Total
DART GT					
CL1P/2P	23	2-dr HT Cpe-5P	2611/2739	2750/2930	Note 1
CL1P/2P	27	2-dr Conv-6P	2831/2959	2850/3030	Note 1
DART GTS					
CL2	23	2-dr HT Cpe-5P	3163	3038	Note 1
CL2	27	2-dr Conv-6P	3383	3310	Note 1

NOTE 1: Some 35,000 Dart GT and GTS models were built during model year 1968. Of those, 10,900 were sixes and 24,100 were V-8s. All GTS models were V-8 powered.

CORONET SERIES — (ALL ENGINES) — Completely restyled for 1968, the new Coronets presented a smoother, more rounded profile than in the previous year. To many they are one of the most attractive Coronets ever produced. A full-width grille housed the quad headlights and its insert design was a very fine, eggcrate arrangement. The taillights were housed in a full-width, concave escutcheon panel. The Coronet was the base trim level and featured chrome windshield and rear window moldings; the Coronet name, in block letters, along the sides of the rear fenders and the Dodge name, also in block lifters, on the vertical section of the escutcheon panel. Also included in the base Coronet were all federally mandated safety equipment; ashtray light; cigarette lighter; heater and defroster; window sill moldings; color-keyed rubber floor mats; rear armrests and ashtrays; the 225 cid Slant Six (or 273 cid V-8) engine and double-acting tailgate on station wagons.

CORONET SERIES I.D. NUMBERS: See 1966 Dart Series I.D. Number listing. All models began at 100001 and went up in the unit number sequence.

CORONET SERIES

Model Number	Body/Style Number	Body Type & Seating	Factory Price	Shipping Weight	Production Total
WL	41	4-dr Sed-6P	2499/2593	3070/3235	Note 1
WL	21	2-dr Cpe-6P	2461/2555	3045/3210	Note 1

NOTE 1: Some 45,000 Coronet passenger cars were built during model year 1968. Of those, 19,300 were sixes and 25,700 were V-8s. Also included in Coronet passenger car production were 4,844 police and taxi six-cylinder units and 2,206 police and taxi V-8 units. A total of 33,100 intermediate-sized Dodge station wagons were built during that year. Of those, 2,600 were six-cylinder and 30,500 were V-8s. No breakout is provided for individual lines and the production figure represents total production of all Coronet station wagons.

ADDITIONAL NOTE: Exact production of all Coronet models for model year 1968 was 196,242 units.

1968 Dodge, Coronet Super Bee two-door coupe, V-8

CORONET 440 SERIES — (ALL ENGINES) — The Coronet 440 continued as the intermediate trim level of the Coronet Series and included all the features of the Coronet, plus carpeting; dual horns; steering wheel with horn ring and padded hub. The hardtops and station wagons had all-vinyl bench seats and the hardtops and sedans had window sill moldings. Four-door sedans and station wagons included drip rail moldings and station wagons included wheel lip moldings. Nine-passenger station wagons included power tailgate window.

CORONET 440 SERIES I.D. NUMBERS: See 1966 Dart Series I.D. Number listing. All models began at 100001 and went up in the unit number sequence.

CORONET 440 SERIES

Model Number	Body/Style Number	Body Type & Seating	Factory Price	Shipping Weight	Production Total
WH	41	4-dr Sed-6P	2577/2683	3060/3225	Note 1
WH	23	2-dr HT Cpe-6P	2601/2707	3065/3235	Note 1
WH	45	4-dr Sta Wag-6P	2898/3004	3495/3605	Note 1
WH	46	4-dr Sta Wag-9P	3114	3705	Note 1

NOTE 1: Some 103,500 Coronet 440 passenger cars were built during model year 1968. Of those, 8,200 were sixes and 95,300 were V-8s. See Note 1, Coronet Series for station wagon production data.

CORONET 500 SERIES — (ALL ENGINES) — The Coronet 500 was the top trim level for 1968 and included all the Coronet 440 features, plus front air foam seats; all-vinyl bench seats; power top on convertible; all-vinyl bench seats and simulated woodgrain on the bodyside and tailgate panels of station wagons. All-vinyl front bucket seats were featured in sedans and hardtops. Sedans had an alternate choice of front bucket seats with cloth inserts. Bench seat models had foam padded rear seat cushions. Four-door sedans and station wagons had drip rail moldings and rear door automatic lamp switch with upper door frame moldings and quarter window moldings on station wagons. Sedans also included a fold-down center front armrest. The standard engine in the Coronet 500 was the 318 cid V-8.

CORONET 500 SERIES I.D. NUMBERS: See 1966 Dart Series I.D. Number listing. All models began at 100001 and went up in the unit number sequence.

CORONET 500 SERIES

Model Number	Body/Style Number	Body Type & Seating	Factory Price	Shipping Weight	Production Total
WP	41	4-dr Sed-6P	2886	3235	Note 1
WP	23	2-dr HT Cpe-6P	2836	3280	Note 1
WP	27	2-dr Conv-6P	3036	3355	Note 1
WP	45	4-dr Sta Wag-6P	3186	3615	Note 1
WP	46	4-dr Sta Wag-9P	3296	3715	Note 1

NOTE 1: Some 30,100 Coronet 500 passenger cars were built during model year 1968. All V-8s. See Note 1, Coronet Series for station wagon production data.

CORONET R/T SERIES — (V-8) — The Coronet R/T continued as the high-performance model of the Coronet Series. It included all Coronet 500 features plus the 440 cid Magnum V-8 engine with four-barrel carburetor and dual exhausts; ashtray light; front all-vinyl bucket seats; carpeting; cigarette lighter; drip rail, hub and window sill moldings; 150 mph speedometer; steering wheel with padded hub and horn ring; bodyside or Bumblebee stripes; TorqueFlite three-speed automatic transmission; R/T emblems in the grille; fender and rear latch panel medallions; 70 ampere/hour battery; heavy-duty drum brakes; dual horns; rear armrests and ashtrays; firm-ride shock absorbers; Rallye Suspension and F70 x 14 wide-tread black sidewall tires. The convertible also included power top, map and courtesy lights.

CORONET R/T SERIES I.D. NUMBERS: See 1966 Dart Series I.D. Numbers listing. All models began at 100001 and went up in the unit number sequence.

CORONET R/T SERIES

Model Number	Body/Style Number	Body Type & Seating	Factory Price	Shipping Weight	Production Total
WS	23	2-dr HT Cpe-5P	3353	3565	Note 1
WS	27	2-dr Conv-5P	3613	3640	Note 1

NOTE 1: Some 10,900 Coronet R/Ts were built during model year 1968, all V-8 powered. No breakout is provided for individual body styles, therefore, production figures represent total R/T production.

1968 Dodge, Charger two-door hardtop sports coupe, V-8 (AA)

CHARGER SERIES — (ALL ENGINES) — Completely restyled for 1968, the new Chargers went from a fastback body style to a semi-fastback style, which produced one of the best looking Dodge models ever built. A full-width grille was featured and a very smooth, slightly rounded 'coke-bottle' shape was used. At the rear end, two round taillights on each side were located in a flat-black finished escutcheon panel. The Charger was the base trim level and included all federally mandated safety features, plus all-vinyl front bucket seats; carpeting; three-spoke steering wheel with padded hub and partial horn ring; heater and defroster; electric clock; cigarette lighter; ashtray light; heavy-duty suspension (including sway bar); heavy-duty rear springs and torsion bars; front and rear bumper guards; wheel opening moldings; concealed headlights; quick-fill gasoline cap; the 318 cid V-8 engine and 7.35 x 14 tubeless black sidewall tires. The Charger R/T was the high-performance version of the Charger and included all the standard Charger features, plus the 440 cid Magnum V-8 engine; TorqueFlite three-speed automatic transmission; dual exhausts (with chrome tips); heavy-duty brakes; R/T handling package; racing stripes and F70 x 14 Red Streak or white sidewall tires.

CHARGER SERIES I.D. NUMBERS: See 1966 Dart Series I.D. Number listing. All models began at 100001 and went up in the unit number sequence.

CHARGER AND CHARGER R/T SERIES

Model Number	Body/Style Number	Body Type & Seating	Factory Price	Shipping Weight	Production Total
XP	29	2-dr HT Cpe-5P	3014	3500	Note 1
XS	29	2-dr R/T HT-5P	3480	3650	Note 1

NOTE 1: Some 96,100 Chargers and R/Ts were built during model year 1968; all V-8s. No breakout is provided for individual model, therefore, production figures represent total Charger production.

1968 Dodge, Polara four-door hardtop sedan, V-8

POLARA SERIES — (ALL ENGINES) — Only slightly restyled for 1968, the new Polara relied on trim updating to complete the changes for the year. The Polara was the base trim level and included chrome windshield and rear window moldings; 318 cid V-8 engine; heater and defroster; carpeting; cigar lighter; rear seat cushion foam pad; all-vinyl interior on station wagons and convertibles, plus power top on convertibles. The nine-passenger station wagons also had seat belts on the third seat; power tailgate window and rear bumper guards. The Polara name, in block letters, appeared on the sides of the front fenders and the Dodge name, also in block letters, appeared on the right side of the trunk lid. The Polara 500 was the top trim level of the Polara Series and included all the standard Polara features, plus Deluxe wheelcovers; window sill and wheel lip moldings and front air foam vinyl bucket seats (with center folding armrests). A console was optional at no extra charge.

MONACO SERIES — (ALL ENGINES) — The Monaco was the base trim level of the Monaco Series, which utilized the Polara body and chassis. Standard Monacos included all the Polara features, plus the Polara Light Package: 383 cid two-barrel V-8 engine, wheel lip and window sill moldings; air foam front seats and Deluxe wheelcovers. Four door sedans also had upper door frame moldings and station wagons also included upper door and quarter window moldings; power tailgate window; rear bumper guards and rear compartment lock. The Monaco 500 was the top trim level of the Monaco Series and included all the standard Monaco features, plus front foam vinyl-bucket seats (with center folding armrests), electric clock and TorqueFlite three-speed automatic transmission. A console was optional at no extra charge.

POLARA/SERIES I.D. NUMBERS: See 1966 Dart Series I.D. Number listing. All models began at 100001 and went up in the unit number sequence.

POLARA SERIES

Model Number	Body/Style Number	Body Type & Seating	Factory Price	Shipping Weight	Production Total
POLARA					
DL	41	4-dr Sed-6P	3001	3765	Note 1
DL	43	4-dr HT Sed-6P	3074	3920	Note 1
DL	23	2-dr HT Cpe-6P	3001	3870	Note 1
DL	27	2-dr Conv-6P	3288	3930	Note 1
DL	45	4-dr Sta Wag-6P	3212	4400	Note 1
DL	46	4-dr Sta Wag-9P	3676	4450	Note 1
POLARA 500					
DM	23	2-dr HT Cpe-5P	3200	3875	Note 1
DM	27	2-dr Conv-5P	3487	3935	Note 1

MONACO SERIES I.D. NUMBERS: See 1966 Dart Series I.D. Number listing. All models began at 100001 and went up in the unit number sequence.

MONACO SERIES

Model Number	Body/Style Number	Body Type & Seating	Factory Price	Shipping Weight	Production Total
DH	41	4-dr Sed-6P	3268	3895	Note 1
DH	43	4-dr HT Sed-6P	3406	3945	Note 1
DH	23	2-dr HT Cpe-6P	3343	3885	Note 1
DH	45	4-dr Sta Wag-6P	3676	4425	Note 1
DH	46	4-dr Sta Wag-9P	3809	4475	Note 1
MONACO 500					
DP	23	2-dr HT Cpe-5P	3843	3970	Note 1

NOTE 1: Some 70,100 Polara passenger cars were built during model year 1968, all V-8s. This figure includes 2,206 special Polara '318' units used in police and taxi operation. A total of 4,000 Polara 500s were built during the year, also all V-8s. A total of 21,100 Monacos and 3,400 Monaco 500 passenger cars were built during model year 1968, all V-8s. A total of 16,900 Polara and Monaco station wagons were also built during that year, although no breakout by series is provided for station wagons. Therefore, the total represents production of all station wagons in the full-size lineup.

ADDITIONAL NOTE: Exact production of all full-size Dodges was 138,933 units.

1968 Dodge, Monaco 500 two-door hardtop sports coupe, V-8

CHASSIS FEATURES: Wheelbase: (Dart) 111 inches; (Coronet/Charger) 117 inches;

(Polara/Monaco) 122 inches. Overall length: (Dart) 196 inches; (Coronet wagon) 210 inches; (Coronet) 207 inches; (Charger) 208 inches; (Polara/Monaco wagon) 220 inches; (Polara/Monaco) 219 inches. Width: (Dart) 70 inches; (Coronet/Charger) 77 inches. Tires: (Base Dart) 6.50 x 13; (Dart V-8/convertible) 7.00 x 13; (Dart GTS) E70-14; (Coronet/Charger) 7.35 x 14; (Coronet wagon) 8.25 x 14; (Coronet/Charger R/T) F70 x 14; (Polara/Monaco) 8.25 x 14; (Polara/Monaco wagon) 8.55 x 14.

1968 ENGINES: Same as 1967, with the addition of:

V-8. Overhead values. Cast iron block. Displacement: 340 cid. Bore and stroke: 4.04 x 3.31 inches. Compression ratio: 10.5:1. Brake hp: 275 at 5000 rpm. Five main bearings. Hydraulic value lifters. Carburetor: Carter Thermo-Quad four barrel.

383 V-8 Two-barrel was now rated at 290 hp with the same specifications. 383 V-8 Four-barrel was now rated at 300 hp with the specifications.

DART CONVENIENCE OPTIONS: Power brakes ($16). Power Steering ($80). Air conditioning ($335). 273 cid V-8 ($128). TorqueFlite transmission, with Six ($172); with V-8 ($181). Four-speed transmission ($179). Music Master AM radio ($44). Tachometer ($38). 'Mag' styled wheelcovers ($55).

CORONETS/CHARGERS/POLARAS/MONOCOS CONVENIENCE OPTIONS: 318 cid V-8 engine ($24). 383 cid V-8 engine ($56-$81). 383 cid four-barrel V-8 engine ($97-$121). 383 cid four-barrel V-8 in Polaras ($28). 440 cid Magnum V-8 engine ($68-$133). 426 cid 'Hemi' V-8 engine ($457-$712). TorqueFlite automatic transmission on six-cylinders ($153); on V-8s ($163-$176). Four-speed manual transmission ($145-$175). Air conditioning on Coronets and Chargers ($274); on Polaras and Monacos ($311). Auto Pilot cruise control ($64). Power steering ($73). Power brakes ($16). Power front disc brakes ($54). Electric clock ($11). Console ($20). Sure-Grip differential ($29-$37). Heavy-duty differential ($107). Power door locks ($42). Dual exhausts ($24). Buffed paint ($16). Music Master AM radio on Coronets and Chargers ($44); on Polaras and Monacos ($47). Tilt & Telescope steering wheel ($67). Woodgrained steering wheel on Coronets and R/Ts ($20); on Chargers ($16); on Polaras and Monacos ($12). Tachometer ($38). Vinyl top on four-door sedans ($58); hardtops ($70). Simulated 'Mag' wheelcovers ($41-$57). Road wheels ($59-$75). Three-speed windshield wipers ($4).

HISTORICAL FOOTNOTES: Dodges for 1968, were advertised under the high-performance 'Scat Pack' theme. At Daytona, the 'Coke Bottle' shaped Coronets were capable of lapping the NASCAR oval at speeds up to 185 mph. A low priced performance model, the Super Bee, with basic appointments and a 335-hp 383 as the base engine, was introduced in the spring. Five checkered flags were captured by Dodges, on the Grand National stock car racing circuit. Available this season was the 'Hemi' Dart, a stripped edition with special, lightweight body parts, that qualified for Super Stock drag racing classes.

1969 DODGE

DART SERIES — (ALL ENGINES) — The 1969 Darts featured new grilles; headlights; taillights and other exterior trim mounted on the same basic body shell as used in 1968. Dodge Dart was the base trim level for 1969 and included chrome windshield and rear window moldings and the Dodge name, in block letters, across the vertical section of the trunk lid and on the left front corner of the hood. Also included were all the mandatory safety equipment; heater and defroster; 6.50 x 13 black sidewall tubeless tires on six-cylinder equipped cars and 7.00 x 13 tubeless black sidewall on V-8s.

DART SERIES I.D. NUMBERS: See 1966 Dart Series I.D. Number listing. All models began at 100001 and went up in the unit number sequence.

DART SERIES

Model Number	Body/Style Number	Body Type & Seating	Factory Price	Shipping Weight	Production Total
DART					
LL41	N/A	4-dr Sed-6P	2413/2524	2726/2894	Note 1
SWINGER					
LL23	N/A	2-dr Cpe-6P	2400/2511	2711/2879	Note 1

GENERAL NOTE: All 1969 Dodge model year production figures listed in this catalog are series production totals expressed to the nearest 100 units. No additional breakouts by trim level, model or body style are currently available. In all of the specifications charts the prices and weights above slash are for six/below slash for V-8.

NOTE 1: Some 86,400 Dodge Dart passenger cars were built during calendar year 1969. Of these, 61,800 were sixes and 24,600 were V-8s.

1969 Dodge, Dart Swinger two-door hardtop sports coupe, V-8

DART SWINGER SERIES — (V-8) — The Swinger was a new economy sports/performance two-door hardtop in the Dart line. Standard Swingers could be equipped with any of the engines from the basic six to the 383 Magnum V-8. A special package called the Swinger 340 featured the 340 cid V-8 engine: Rallye Suspension: Firm Ride Shocks; 'Power Bulge' hood; Bumblebee stripes: chrome dual exhaust outlets: D70 x 14 wide-oval tires; Four-speed manual transmission (or TorqueFlite automatic) and carpeting.

DART SWINGER SERIES

Model Number	Body/Style Number	Body Type & Seating	Factory Price	Shipping Weight	Production Total
LM23	N/A	2-dr HT Cpe-6P	2836	3097	20,000

DART CUSTOM SERIES — (ALL ENGINES) — The Custom was the intermediate trim level Dart for 1969 and included all the Dart series features, plus cigarette lighter; carpeting and three-spoke steering wheel. The hardtop also had vinyl bench seats and the sedan had cloth and vinyl seats. A single horizontal chrome strip was used along the bodyside and ran the entire length of the car.

DART CUSTOM SERIES I.D. NUMBERS: See 1966 Dart Series I.D. Number listing. All models began at 100001 and went up in the unit number sequence.

DART CUSTOM

Model Number	Body/Style Number	Body Type & Seating	Factory Price	Shipping Weight	Production Total
LH41	N/A	4-dr Sed-6P	2550/2661	2726/2894	Note 1
LH23	N/A	2-dr Ht Cpe-6P	2577/2688	2711/2879	Note 1

NOTE 1: Some 63,700 Dodge Dart Custom passenger cars were built during model year 1969. Of these, 41,600 were sixes and 22,100 were V-8s.

DART GT AND GTS SERIES — (ALL ENGINES) — The GT continued as the top trim level Dodge Dart for 1969 and included all Dart Series features plus a special blacked-out grille with center horizontal divider bar and the Dart GT name, in block letters, on the side of the rear fenders just in front of the rear wheelwells. The GTS version of the GT included all the GT features plus E70 x 14 Red Line tires; 340 cid V-8 engine; TorqueFlite automatic transmission; three-spoke steering wheel; dual exhausts; carpeting; and engine dress-up kit. All GTS models also included the Bumblebee stripe across the trunk lid and down the sides of the body.

DART GT AND GTS SERIES I.D. NUMBERS: See 1966 Dart Series I.D. Number listing. All models began at 100001 and went up in the unit number sequence.

DART HIGH-PERFORMANCE SERIES

Model Number	Body/Style Number	Body Type & Seating	Factory Price	Shipping Weight	Production Total
Dart GT					
LP23	N/A	2-dr HT Cpe-6P	2672/2783	2716/2884	Note 1
LP27	N/A	2-dr Conv-6P	2865/2976	2821/2979	Note 1
Dart GTS					
LS23	N/A	2-dr HT Cpe-6P	3226	3105	Note 1
LS27	N/A	2-dr Conv-6P	3419	3210	Note 1

NOTE 1: Some 20,900 Dodge Dart GT passenger cars were built during model year 1969. Of these, 5,600 were sixes and 15,300 were V-8s. A total of some 6,700 GTS hardtops and convertibles were built during the model year, all V-8 powered.

CORONET SERIES — (ALL ENGINES) — New grilles and taillights adorned the Coronet for 1969 and presented an attractive package to the buyer. The grille continued Dodge's trend to delta shapes, while the taillights had long oval-shaped lenses. A new high-performance model, the Super Bee, was added to the base Coronet line. It offered outstanding performance without a high price tag. The Coronet was the base trim level and included a 225 cid Slant Six engine; heater and defroster; 7.35 x 14 tubeless black sidewall tires on sixes and 7.75 x 14 tires on V-8 models. Station wagons also included dual-action tailgates and automatic rear door interior lamp switches. The nine-passenger station wagon also included the 318 cid V-8 engine as standard equipment. The Super Bee had all the standard Coronet passenger car features plus the 383 cid engine (modified with 440 heads and a stronger cam), heavy-duty 11 inch drum brakes; Rallye Suspension with sway bar, Firm Ride shock absorbers; 'Power Bulge' hood; Bumblebee stripes; F70 x 14 Red Line wide-oval tires and four-speed manual transmission.

CORONET SERIES I.D. NUMBERS: See 1966 Dart Series I.D. Number listings. All models began at 100001 and went up in the unit number sequence.

CORONET SERIES

Model Number	Body/Style Number	Body Type & Seating	Factory Price	Shipping Weight	Production Total
Coronet					
WL41	N/A	4-dr Sed-6P	2589/2692	3018/3176	Note 1
WL21	N/A	2-dr Cpe-6P	2554/2657	2988/3146	Note 1
WL45	N/A	4-dr Sta Wag-6P	3025	3606	Note 1
Super Bee					
WM21	N/A	2-dr Cpe-6P	3076	3440	Note 1
WM23	N/A	2-dr HT Cpe-6P	3138	3470	Note 1

NOTE 1: Some 30,400 standard Coronet passenger cars and station wagons were built during model year 1969. Of these, 12,500 were sixes and 17,900 were V-8s. Some 27,800 Super Bees were built during the model year, all V-8 powered.

CORONET 440 SERIES — (ALL ENGINES) — The Coronet 440 was the intermediate trim level Coronet for 1969 and included all the Coronet features, plus carpeting and polished aluminum wheel lip moldings. A brushed aluminum escutcheon panel was located on the trunk lid (between the taillights) and the Coronet 440 name, in block letters, was located behind the front wheel cutouts.

CORONET 440 SERIES I.D. NUMBERS: See 1966 Dart Series I.D. Number listing. All models began at 100001 and went up in the unit number sequence.

1969 Dodge, Coronet Super Bee two-door hardtop coupe, V-8 (AA)

CORONET 440 SERIES

Model Number	Body/Style Number	Body Type & Seating	Factory Price	Shipping Weight	Production Total
WH41	N/A	4-dr Sed-6P	2670/2773	3023/3181	Note 1
WH21	N/A	2-dr Cpe-6P	2630/2733	2983/3151	Note 1
WH23	N/A	2-dr HT Cpe-6P	2692/2795	3018/3176	Note 1
WH45	N/A	4-dr Sta Wag-6P	3033/3136	3503/3606	Note 1
WH46	N/A	4-dr Sta Wag-9P	3246	3676	Note 1

NOTE 1: Some 105,900 Dodge Coronet 440 passenger cars and station wagons were built during model year 1969. Of these, some 4,700 were sixes and 101,200 V-8s.

CORONET 500 SERIES — (ALL ENGINES) — The Coronet 500 was the top trim level and included all the 440 Series features, plus the 318 cid V-8 engine; simulated woodgrain applique on instrument panel; extra thick foam seat cushions; map, ashtray and glovebox lights; wheel lip moldings; pedal dress-up kit; power top on convertible and bucket seats. Sedans and stations wagons also have rear door automatic interior lamp switches. The station wagon also had simulated woodgrained body appliques.

CORONET 500 SERIES I.D. NUMBERS: See 1966 Dart Series I.D. Number listing. All models began at 100001 and went up in the unit number sequence.

CORONET 500 SERIES

Model Number	Body/Style Number	Body Type & Seating	Factory Price	Shipping Weight	Production Total
WP41	N/A	4-dr Sed-6P	2963	3206	Note 1
WP23	N/A	2-dr HT Cpe-6P	2929	3171	Note 1
WP27	N/A	2-dr Conv-6P	3069	3306	Note 1
WP45	N/A	4-dr Sta Wag-6P	3280	3611	Note 1
WP46	N/A	4-dr Sta Wag-9P	3392	3676	Note 1

NOTE 1: Some 32,100 Dodge Coronet 500 passenger cars and station wagons were built during model year 1969. All were V-8 powered.

CORONET R/T SERIES — (V-8) — The Coronet R/T continued as the high-performance model in the Coronet Series and included all the features of the Coronet 500 plus the Magnum 440 cid V-8 engine; TorqueFlite automatic transmission; light group; sill moldings and 'R/T' nomenclature (in the Bumblebee stripe) across the trunk lid and down the fendersides. Two simulated scoops were also located on the rear fenders, just ahead of the rear wheelwell openings on each side.

CORONET R/T SERIES I.D. NUMBERS: See 1966 Dart Series I.D. Number listing. All models began at 100001 and went up in the unit number sequence.

CORONET R/T SERIES

Model Number	Body/Style Number	Body Type & Seating	Factory Price	Shipping Weight	Production Total
WS23	N/A	2-dr HT Cpe-6P	3442	3601	Note 1
WS27	N/A	2-dr Conv-6P	3660	3721	Note 1

NOTE 1: Some 7,200 Dodge Coronet R/T hardtops and convertibles were built during model year 1969, all V-8 powered.

CHARGER SERIES — (ALL ENGINES) — The 1969 Charger continued to use the beautifully styled body introduced with the 1968 model. The main changes in the two years were the new divided grille for the 1969 models and a new taillight treatment. Even though a mere 500 were built, the base engine for the Charger was the 225 cid Slant Six, with the 318 cid V-8 a much more popular 'base' power-plant for the performance-oriented Chargers. The R/T was the high-performance model in the Charger and Coronet lines. R/Ts featured all standard Charger trim, plus the Magnum '440' four-barrel V-8; dual exhausts with chrome tips; TorqueFlite automatic transmission; heavy-duty, manually-adjusted brakes; F70 x 14 Red Line tires; R/T handling package and Bumblebee stripes. The Charger SE was the sports/luxury model and included all the standard Charger features plus leather and vinyl front bucket seats; simulated woodgrained steering wheel; deep-dished wheelcovers; hood-mounted turn signal indicators; simulated woodgrain instrument panel trim and the light group. A limited number of super high-performance Charger 500s were built to fulfill a requirement for NASCAR stock car racing. The 500s were based on standard Chargers with a flush-mounted grille (not recessed into the oval grille opening), fixed headlights and a flush-mounted rear window glass for lower wind resistance.

CHARGER SERIES I.D. NUMBERS: See 1966 Dart Series I.D. Number listing. All models began at 100001 and went up in the unit number sequence.

CHARGER SERIES

Model Number	Body/Style Number	Body Type & Seating	Factory Price	Shipping Weight	Production Total
Base Line					
XP29	N/A	2-dr HT Cpe-6P	3020/3126	3103/3256	Note 1
R/T Line					
XS29	N/A	2-dr HT Cpe-6P	3592	3646	Note 1
SE/500 Line					
XX29	N/A	2-dr S/E HT Cpe-6P	3860	3671	Note 1
XX29	N/A	2-dr HT Cpe-6P	3860	3860	Note 1

NOTE 1: Some 69,100 Dodge Chargers and 20,100 Charger R/Ts were built during model year 1969. Of these, some 500 standard Chargers were sixes and 68,600 were V-8s. All R/Ts were V-8 powered.

1969 Dodge, Charger 500 two-door hardtop sports coupe, V-8

POLARA/MONACO — (V-8) — Completely restyled once again for 1969, the new Polaras featured what Chrysler advertising people called 'fuselage styling.' Smoother and more rounded than in the past, the new models were a very large, 18V4-plus feet overall. The Polara was the base trim level and included all the federally mandated safety features, plus the 318 cid V-8 engine; concealed windshield wipers; carpeting heater and defroster; rear seat foam cushion; 8.25 x 15 tubeless black sidewall tires; cloth and vinyl trim in the hardtops and sedans and all-vinyl trim in convertibles. The station wagons also included rear-mounted air deflector and dual action tailgate, plus larger, 8.85 x 15 tubeless black sidewall tires. The Polara 500 was the intermediate trim level and included all features found in the Polara plus, front bucket seats (with center folding armrest) and Deluxe wheelcovers. The Monaco was the top trim level of the Polara Series. It included all Polara features plus the light group and front and rear seat cushion pads. Sedans had cloth and vinyl interior trim. Two and four-door hardtops had all-vinyl interior trim. Station wagons had cloth and vinyl interior trim, power tailgate windows and, on the nine-passenger station wagon, a lockable third seat well.

POLARA SERIES I.D. NUMBERS: See 1966 Dart Series I.D. Number listing. All models began at 100001 and went up in the unit number sequence.

1969 Dodge, Polara four-door station wagon, V-8

POLARA SERIES

Model Number	Body/Style Number	Body Type & Seating	Factory Price	Shipping Weight	Production Total
Base Line					
DL41	N/A	4-dr Sed-6P	3095	3701	Note 1
DL43	N/A	4-dr HT Sed-6P	3188	3731	Note 1
DL23	N/A	2-dr HT Cpe-6P	3117	3646	Note 1
DL27	N/A	2-dr Conv-6P	3377	3791	Note 1
DL45	N/A	4-dr Sta Wag-6P	3522	4161	Note 1
DL46	N/A	4-dr Sta Wag-9P	3629	4211	Note 1
500 Line					
DM23	N/A	2-dr HT Cpe-6P	3629	3681	Note 1
DM27	N/A	2-dr Conv-5P	3576	3801	Note 1
Monaco Line					
DH41	N/A	4-dr Sed-6P	3452	3846	Note 1
DH43	N/A	4-dr HT Sed-6P	3591	3891	Note 1
DH23	N/A	2-dr HT Cpe-6P	3528	3811	Note 1
DH46	N/A	4-dr Sta Wag-6P	3917	4306	Note 1
DH46	N/A	4-dr Sta Wag-9P	4046	4361	Note 1

NOTE 1: Some 117,152 Polara and Monaco passenger cars and station wagons were built during model year 1969. All were V-8-powered. No additional breakouts by model, body style or trim level are available at the current time.

1969 DODGE CHASSIS FEATURES:

DART: Wheelbase: 111 inches. Overall length: 195.4 inches. Tires: 6.50 x 13 tubeless black sidewall on sixes and sedans, 6.95 x 14 on V-8 sedans and 7.00 x 13 on six cylinder convertibles. Three-speed manual transmission was standard on all Darts, with the three-speed TorqueFlite automatic or four-speed manual transmission optional.

CORONET AND CHARGER: Wheelbase: 117 inches. Overall length: 206.6 inches on Coronet sedans, 207.9 inches on station wagons. Tires: 7.75 x 14 tubeless black sidewall on Coronet sedans, 8.25 x 14 on station wagons, F70 x 14 on Coronet Super Bee, Charger, Charger R/T and Charger 500. Three-speed manual transmission was the standard transmission on all models unless noted, with the TorqueFlite three-speed automatic and four-speed manual transmission optional.

POLARA AND MONACO: Wheelbase: 112 inches. Overall length: 220.4 inches on station wagons and 220.8 inches on sedans. Tires: 8.25 x 15 tubeless black sidewall on sedans, 8.85 x 15 on station wagons. Three-speed manual transmission was standard on all models unless noted, with the three-speed TorqueFlite automatic and four-speed manual transmission optional.

1969 ENGINES: Same as 1967 with these changes: 170 slant six 115 hp; 383 Magnum V-8. Overhead valves. Cast iron block. Displacement: 383 cid. Bore and stroke 4.25 x 3.38 inches. Compression ratio: 10.0:1. Brake hp: 335 at 5200 rpm. Five main bearings. Hydraulic valve lifters. Carburetion: one four-barrel.

CONVENIENCE OPTIONS FOR DARTS: 225 cid Slant Six engine ($46). 273 cid V-8 engine ($79). TorqueFlite automatic transmission ($176 with Slant Six; $191 with small V-8s; $28 with 383 cid V-8). Four-speed manual transmission ($188). Power steering ($85). Power brakes ($43). Console ($53 — GT and GTS models only). Tinted glass ($33). Air conditioning ($361). Two-tone paint ($23). Music Master AM radio ($62). AM/FM radio ($135). AM/FM 8-Track stereo ($196). Custom steering wheel with full horn ring ($15). Simulated woodgrained Sport steering wheel ($32). White sidewall tires ($34).

CONVENIENCE OPTIONS FOR CORONET/CHARGER/POLARA/MONACO: '383' two-barrel V-8 ($70). '383' four-barrel V-8 ($68-$138). 440 cid 'Magnum' V-8 ($268). 426 cid 'Hemi' V-8 engine in Coronet Super Bee ($831); in Coronet R/T ($718); in Charger R/T ($648). TorqueFlite automatic transmission ($39-$206). Four-speed manual transmission ($197-no charge on R/T models). Air conditioning on Coronets and Chargers ($358); on Polaras and Monacos ($395). Power steering on Coronets and Chargers ($100); on Polaras and Monacos ($106). Power brakes ($43). Power front disc brakes ($49). Power seats ($100). Power windows, on Coronets and Chargers ($105); on Polaras and Monacos ($109). Electric clock on Coronets ($18); on Polaras and Monacos ($16). Console ($54). Sure-Grip differential on Coronets and Chargers ($42); on Polaras and Monacos ($48). Super light in Polaras and Monacos ($50). Two-tone paint on Coronets ($23); on Polaras and Monacos ($28). Music Master AM radio on Coronets and Chargers ($62); on Polaras and Monacos ($68). AM /FM radio on Coronets ($135). AM/FM Multiplex stereo radio, on Polara and Monaco ($184). AM/ 8-track stereo, in Coronets and Chargers ($196); in Polaras and Monacos ($200). Automatic speed control on Coronets and Chargers with 383 V-8 engines ($58); on Polaras and Monacos ($61). Sun roof on Chargers with vinyl top ($461). Rallye suspension, on Coronets and Chargers ($23); on Polaras and Monacos ($14). Woodgrained steering wheels, on Coronets and Chargers ($27); on Polara ($32). Tilt steering wheel on Polaras ($47). Vinyl top, on Coronets ($89); on Chargers ($94) and on Polaras and Monacos ($104). Chrome stamped 14 inch wheels, on Coronets and Chargers ($86); on Charger SE and Charger 500 ($48). White sidewall tires ($34).

HISTORICAL FOOTNOTES: With the factories backing NASCAR entries, a no-holds war for speedway supremacy was taking place. Aerodynamics became more important than in the past. Dodge Div. found that even the smoothed-over Charger 500 models were not aerodynamic enough to make for a clear-cut advantage over the super-powerful Fords. As a solution, the Daytona Charger was introduced. With an elongated fiberglass nose piece covering the standard grille opening and a huge, roof-high spoiler mounted on the trunk, these wild looking creations could navigate the super speedways at nearly 200 mph, with their big 'Hemi' engines. Bobby Issac won the Daytona 500 in Feb., 1969 with one of the Hemi-powered Daytona Chargers. To meet NASCAR's rules for homologation, approximately 1,000 Daytona Chargers were built during 1969, for sale to the general public for street use. While not particularly important from a historically significant point of view, the most widely recognized Dodge in the world today is the 'General Lee,' a 1969 Dodge Charger used in the TV series 'Dukes of Hazzard'. The little Dart Swinger 340s proved to be very popular to the economy minded performance enthusiast. While devoid of conventional creature comforts, such as carpeting, what 340s lacked in luxuries, they made up for with outstanding performance. The 340 remains, to this day, one high point of the '60s Supercar Era. 1969 also saw the introduction of the famous 'Six-Pak' option on the 340 and 440 cid V-8 engines. Three Holley two-barrel carburetors mounted on an Edelbrock aluminum intake manifold provided a 15-hp boost in power. The result was a very strong, fairly economical (when driven on the center carburetor only) engine. 1969 also saw the introduction of the novel 'Super-Light' option for Polaras and Monacos. A single, quartz-halogen light (mounted in the driver's side of the grille) threw out a broad, flat beam of bluish light, which provided much more illumination for the driver, without blinding oncoming traffic. This option was continued for the 1969 and 1970, but was discontinued after only two years. The idea was several years ahead of its time and also met with limited acceptance from law enforcement officials; in some states they were illegal.

1970 DODGE

DART SERIES — (ALL ENGINES) — While new Dodge Darts continued to use the same basic body, restyling of the front and rear made it look completely new. The styling was more rakish, with a grille that sloped forward at the top and was divided in the center. The rear had a lower sloped-back look and the taillights were inserted in the very simple rear bumper. With introduction of the sporty Challenger, the compact line was cut to five versions. The standard Dart was the base trim level of the line and included chrome windshield and rear window moldings; the Dodge name, in script, on the right side of the trunk lid and a similar signature in the center of the hood. The Dart name, in block letters appeared at the rear of the front fenders, just behind the front wheelwell. Also included was all federally mandated safety equipment; heater and defroster and 6.50 x 13 tubeless black sidewall tires on six-cylinder equipped cars (7.00 x 13 tubeless black sidewall tires on V-8s). The Dart Swinger 340 was the high-performance version of the Swinger two-door hardtop model and included all standard Dart features, plus 340 cid V-8 engine; three-speed manual transmission; 3.23 rear axle ratio; front disc brakes; Firm Ride shock absorbers; Rallye Suspension; E79 x 14 blackwall fiberglass tires and Dart 340 nameplates on the front fenders, just behind the front wheelwells.

DODGE I.D. NUMBERS: VIN located on plate attached to left-hand side of dashboard, visible through windshield. The VIN has 13 symbols. (The first four symbols, together, are the Model Number in second column of charts below.) The first symbol identifies the car-line or marque: D=Dodge; J=Challenger; L=Dart; W=Coronet and X=Charger. The second symbol indicates trim/price level as follows: E=Economy; H=High; K=Police; L=Low; M=Medium; P=Premium; T=Taxi; S=Special. The next two symbols identify the body style, as follows: 21=two-door sedan; 23=two-door hardtop; 27=convertible; 29=two-door Sports hardtop; 41=four-door sedan; 43=four-door hardtop; 45=six-passenger station wagon; 46=nine-passenger station wagon. The fifth symbol denotes the engine as follows: (6-cyl.) B=198 cid; C=225 cid; E=special order; (V-8) G=318 cid 2V; H=340 cid 4V (high-performance); J=340 cid 3x2V (high-performance); K=360 cid 2V; L=383 cid 2V; N=383 cid 4V (high-performance); R=426 cid "Street Hemi" 2x4V; T=440 cid 4V; V=440 cid 4V (high-performance); Z=special order. The sixth symbol denotes the model year as follows: 0=1970. The seventh symbol denotes the assembly plant, as follows: A=Lynch Rd. (Detroit); B=Hamtramck, Mich.; C=Jefferson Ave. (Detroit); D=Belvedere, Ill.; E=Los Angeles, Calif.; F=Newark, Del.; G=St. Louis, Mo.; R=Windsor, Ont. (Canada). The last six symbols are the sequential production number starting at 100001 for each series at each plant. Body code plate located under hood, on left (fender shield, wheelhousing or radiator support) includes S.O. number and trim/paint codes too numerous to list.

1970 Dodge, Dart Swinger two-door hardtop sports coupe, V-8

DART SERIES

Model Number	Body/Style Number	Body Type & Seating	Factory Price	Shipping Weight	Production Total
LL41	41	4-dr Sed-6P	2485/2595	2843/2963	35,449
LL23	23	2-dr Swinger HT-6P	2468/2579	2261/2461	119,883
LL23	23	2-dr 340 HT-6P	2808	3179	13,785

NOTE 1: Exactly 191,986 Dodge Dart/Dart Custom/Dart Swinger and Dart Swinger 340 passenger cars were built during model year 1970. In rounded off totals, this included only 3,900 units built in the United States. The additional cars, some 188,100, were manufactured in Canada for the U.S. market. Six-cylinder engines were installed in 69.7 percent of these cars and the rest were V-8s.
NOTE 2: Data above slash for six/below slash for V-8.

DART-CUSTOM SERIES — (ALL ENGINES) — The Custom was the top trim level Dart for 1970 and included all standard Dart features, plus dual horns; wheel lip moldings (on hardtop); bodyside moldings on sedan; steering wheel with partial horn ring; pile carpeting and, in sedans, cloth and vinyl bench seats. The Dart Custom name, in block letters, was located on the sides of the front fender, just behind the front wheelwell.

DART CUSTOM SERIES I.D. NUMBERS: See 1970 Dodge I.D. Number listing. All models began at 100001 and went up in the unit number sequence.

DART CUSTOM SERIES

Model Number	Body/Style Number	Body Type & Seating	Factory Price	Shipping Weight	Production Total
LH42	42	4-dr Sed-6P	2650/2761	2833/2955	23,779
LH23	23	2-dr HT-6P	2677/2788	2843/2965	17,208

NOTE 1: Data above slash for six/below slash for V-8.

CORONET SERIES — (ALL ENGINES) — The new Coronet was face-lifted with the addition of a new grille. The front bumper consisted of a very heavy molding around the grille, which had two, large, oval openings. The rear received an updating also, with the addition of large, delta-shaped taillights. The Coronet Deluxe was the base trim level and included all the federally mandated safety features; the 225 cid Slant Six engine or the 318 cid V-8 engine; all-vinyl front bench seat; color-keyed floor mats; heater and cigarette lighter; and F78 x 14 fiberglass belted black sidewall tires. The Dodge name, in block letters, appeared in the center of the rear escutcheon panel and beside the left high-beam headlight, in the grille. No model designation appeared on the outside of the cars. The Coronet Super Bee continued as the high-performance, intermediate-sized counterpart to the Dart Swinger 340s. Super Bees included all the Coronet Deluxe features, plus a special 383 cid Magnum V-8 engine; three-speed manual transmission with floor-mounted shifter; heavy-duty, automatic adjusting drum brakes; dual horns; heavy-duty front shock absorbers; Rallye Suspension with sway bar (or extra-heavy-duty suspension); three-speed windshield wipers; carpeting; F70 x 14 fiberglass belted white sidewall or black sidewall tires with raised white letters; and a three-spoke steering wheel with partial horn ring.

CORONET SERIES I.D. NUMBERS: See 1970 Dodge I.D. Number listing. All models began at 100001 and went up in the unit number sequence.

CORONET SERIES

Model Number	Body/Style Number	Body Type & Seating	Factory Price	Shipping Weight	Production Total
WL41	41	4-dr Sed-6P	2704/2806	3113/3268	7,894
WL21	21	2-dr Cpe-6P	2669/2771	3068/3238	2,978
WL45	45	4-dr Sta Wag-6P	3048/3150	3628/3728	3,694
WM21	21	2-dr Sup Bee Cpe	3012	3425	3,966
WM23	23	2-dr Sup Bee HT	3074	3390	11,540

NOTE 1: Data above slash for six/below slash for V-8.

CORONET 440 SERIES — (ALL ENGINES) — The Coronet 440 was the intermediate trim level Coronet for 1970 and included all the Coronet Deluxe features, plus cloth and vinyl front bench seats on sedans; carpeting; three-spoke steering wheel with partial horn ring; and the Coronet 440 name, in block letters, on the leading corners of front fenders.
NOTE 2: Data above slash for six/below slash for V-8.

CORONET 440 SERIES I.D. NUMBERS: See Dodge I.D. Number listing. All models began at 100001 and went up in the sequence unit numbers.

CORONET 440 SERIES

Model Number	Body/Style Number	Body Type & Seating	Factory Price	Shipping Weight	Production Total
WH41	41	4-dr Sed-6P	2783/2885	3108/3263	33,258
WH21	21	2-dr Cpe-6P	2743/2845	3088/3243	1,236
WH23	23	2-dr HT-6P	2805/2907	3108/3263	24,341
WH45	45	4-dr Sta Wag-6P	3156/3258	3623/3778	3,964
WH46	46	4-dr Sta Wag-9P	3368	3803	3,772

ADDITIONAL NOTE: In figures rounded off to the nearest 100 units, some 58,800 Dodge Coronet 440 passenger cars were built during the 1970 model year, including 2,000 sixes and 56,800 V-8s.

NOTE 1: Data above slash for six/below slash for V-8.

1970 Dodge, Coronet R/T two-door convertible, V-8

CORONET 500/RT SERIES — (ALL ENGINES) — The Coronet 500 was the top trim level Coronet and included all the 440 features, plus belt moldings on hardtops and convertibles; pedal dress-up kit; deluxe 14 inch wheelcovers; all-vinyl front bucket seats; G78 x 14 fiberglass belted tires and the Coronet 500 model designation, in block letters, on the front fender. The R/T continued to be the high-performance version of the Coronet 500 Series and included all the 500 features, plus the 440 cid Magnum V-8 engine; TorqueFlite automatic transmission; heavy-duty 70 ampere/hour battery; heavy-duty automatic adjusting drum brakes; heavy-duty front and rear shock absorbers; extra-heavy-duty suspension; three-speed windshield wipers; all-vinyl front bucket seat; carpeting; cigar lighter; F70 x 14 fiberglass belted white sidewall tires or black sidewall tires with raised white letters. Also included were two hood scoops near the outside edges of the hood. R/T model designations were carried on the simulated hood scoops (located on the rear quarter panels) and in the center of the rear escutcheon panel, below the Dodge name. All R/T models included blacked-out escutcheon panels and bumblebee stripes across the trunk lid and down the rear fendersides.

CORONET 500 AND R/T SERIES I.D. NUMBERS: See 1970 Dodge I.D. Number listing. All models began at 100001 and went up in the unit number sequence.

CORONET 500 AND R/T SERIES

Model Number	Body/Style Number	Body Type & Seating	Factory Price	Shipping Weight	Production Total
CORONET 500 SERIES					
WP41	41	4-dr Sed-5P	3082	3283	2,890
WP23	23	2-dr HT-5P	3048	3263	8,247
WP27	27	2-dr Conv-5P	3188	3373	924
WP45	45	4-dr Sta Wag-5P	3404	3743	1,657
WP46	46	4-dr Sta Wag-8P	3514	3813	1,779
R/T SERIES					
WS23	23	2-dr R/T HT-5P	3569	3573	2,319
WS27	27	2-dr R/T Conv-5P	3785	3638	296

1970 Dodge, Charger R/T two-door hardtop sports coupe, V-8

CHARGER SERIES — (ALL ENGINES) — The 1970 Charger continued to use the same body as in 1969, with very minor trim changes. A new, high-performance version of the Charger was introduced for 1970. Called the Charger R/T, it was powered by the 440 cid Magnum V-8 and was a very strong performer. A special interior and exterior trim package, called the Special Edition (S/E), was offered for both Charger 500s and Charger R/Ts. It included deep-dish wheelcovers; hood-mounted turn signal indicators; leather bucket seats and woodgrained steering wheel and instrument panel trim. The standard Charger was the base trim level and included all federally mandated safety features; the 225 cid Slant Six engine or 318 cid V-8 engine; vinyl front bench seat; carpeting; three-spoke steering wheel (with partial horn ring); heater and defroster; cigar lighter; heavy-duty suspension; heavy-duty front sway bar; rear bumper guards; concealed headlights; and F78 x 14 fiberglass belted black sidewall tires on sixes (G78 x 14 on V-8s). The Charger 500 was the intermediate

Charger trim level and included all the standard Charger trim, plus vinyl front bucket seats, electric clock and wheel lip moldings. The Charger R/T was the high-performance entry in the Charger lineup and included (in addition to the 440 cid V-8 engine), heavy-duty 70 ampere/hour battery; heavy-duty automatic adjusting drum brakes; front and rear heavy-duty shock absorbers; front and rear Rally Suspension with sway bar; TorqueFlite automatic transmission; three-speed windshield wipers; dual exhausts; R/T handling package; bumblebee racing stripe or longitudinal tape stripe; F70 x 14 fiberglass belted white or black sidewall tires (with raised white letters) and special R/T identification on the left side of the grille and on the simulated bodyside scoops.

CHARGER SERIES I.D. NUMBERS: See 1970 Dodge I.D. Number listing. All models began at 100001 and went up in the unit number sequence.

CHARGER SERIES

Model Number	Body/Style Number	Body Type & Seating	Factory Price	Shipping Weight	Production Total
CHARGER					
XH29	NA	2-dr HT-6P	3001/3108	3228/3363	Note 1
CHARGER 500					
XP29	NA	2-dr HT-5P	3139/3246	3228/3362	Note 1
CHARGER R/T					
XS29	NA	2-dr HT-5P	3711	3638	10,337

NOTE 1: The combined production of Models XH29 and XP29 was recorded as 39,431 units. No further breakout between the two models is available at the current time.
NOTE 2: In figures rounded off to the nearest 100 units, some 49,800 Dodge Chargers were built during model year 1970, including 300 sixes and 49,500 V-8s. (Only 7.4 percent of these cars had four-speed manual transmission attachment and 38.1 percent had an optional V-8.) The base V-8 was installed in 61.4 percent of the remaining Chargers, while another 0.5 percent were the scarce, but not highly collectible, six-cylinder cars).
NOTE 3: Data above slash for six/below slash for V-8.

1970 Dodge, Monaco four-door hardtop sedan, V-8

POLARA SERIES — (ALL ENGINES) — Slightly restyled for 1970, the new full-sized Dodge series was completely reshuffled. A massive grille molding formed the front bumper on the Polara models and the very large, oblong taillights were housed in a new rear bumper. The Polara Special was the base trim level for 1970 and included all federally mandated safety features, plus chrome windshield and rear window moldings and the Dodge name, in block letters, spaced across the front of the trunk. Dodge nameplates were also seen on the right side of the trunk. Midyear Polara Specials were used primarily for fleet, taxis and police duty. These were introduced on March 17 and represented an economy model with a 225 cid/145 hp six standard in the sedan, while the 318 cid V-8 was standard in station wagons. The Polara was the intermediate trim level in the series and included all the Special features; plus the 318 cid V-8 engine; cloth and vinyl interior trim in hardtop and sedan models; vinyl interiors in the convertible and station wagon models; color-keyed vinyl bodyside moldings; concealed wipers; pile carpeting; three-spoke steering wheel with padded hub; heater and defroster; cigarette lighter; glovebox lock; sway bar; thick padded front seat; and rear seat foam cushions. The convertible also had a power top and station wagons had roof-mounted air deflectors and dual action tailgate. Two-door hardtops and four-door sedans had G78 x 15 fiberglass belted tires; four-door hardtops and convertibles had H78 x 15 fiberglass belted tires and station wagons had J78 x 15 fiberglass belted black sidewall tires. The Polara Custom was the top trim level and included all the Polara features; Deluxe wheelcovers; 290 hp V-8 engine; wide sill moldings on four-door models; belt molding on hardtops; steering wheel with partial horn ring; H78 x 15 fiberglass belted black sidewall tires and the interior light group. The Monaco was the luxury version of the Polara Series and included all the Polara Custom features (except side moldings); simulated walnut instrument panel trim and door inserts; pedal dress-up kit; two-door hardtop and station wagon all-vinyl interiors (with split front bench seat and center armrests); and four-door sedan and hardtop vinyl and cloth interiors (with front center armrests). Station wagons also had J78 x 15 fiberglass belted black sidewall tires; cargo compartment carpeting and the nine-passenger station wagons had a lockable third seat well.

POLARA SERIES I.D. NUMBERS: See 1970 Dodge I.D. Number listing. All models began at 100001 and went up in the unit number sequence.

POLARA SERIES

Modal Number	Body/Style Number	Body Type & Seating	Factory Price	Shipping Weight	Production Total
POLARA					
DE41	41	4-dr Sed-6P	2960/3065	3745/3805	Note 1
DE45	45	4-dr Sta Wag-6P	3513	4180	Note 1
DE46	46	4-dr Sta Wag-9P	3621	4325	Note 1
POLARA 500					
DL41	41	4-dr 500 Sed-6P	3222	3828	18,740
DL43	43	4-dr 500 HT-6P	3316	3873	19,223
DL23	23	2-dr 500 HT-6P	3244	3973	15,243
DL27	27	2-dr 500 Conv-6P	3527	3853	842
DL45	45	4-dr 500 Sta Wag-6P	3670	4203	3,074
DL46	46	4-dr 500 Sta Wag-9P	3778	4258	3,546

Model Number	Body/Style Number	Body Type & Seating	Factory Price	Shipping Weight	Production Total
MONACO					
DM41	41	4-dr Custom Sed-6P	3426	3998	Note 1
DM43	43	4-dr Custom HT-6P	3528	4028	Note 1
DM23	23	2-dr Custom HT-6P	3458	3948	Note 1
MONACO 500					
DH41	41	4-dr Monaco Sed-6P	3604	4033	4,721
DH43	43	4-dr Monaco HT-6P	3743	4068	10,974
DH23	23	2-dr Monaco HT-6P	3679	3973	3,522
DH45	45	4-dr Sta Wag-6P	4110	4443	2,211
DH46	46	4-dr Sta Wag-9P	4242	4498	3,264

NOTE 1: Production of similar body styles in all Polara Series was recorded as a lumped sum, which is listed under the Polara 500 Series grouping in the chart above. The only additional breakouts available are by passenger car line and engine. They were recorded (in figures rounded off to the nearest 100 units) as follows: Polara Deluxe: A total of 50,400 passenger cars including 132 sixes and 50,268 V-8s. Polara 500: A total of 9,300 passenger cars, all V-8s. Polara station wagon totals cannot be segregated in this manner, since they were combined with totals for Monaco station wagons.
NOTE 2: Data above slash for six/below slash for V-8.

1970 Dodge, Challenger R/T two-door convertible, V-8

CHALLENGER SERIES — (ALL ENGINES) — The Challenger was Dodge's answer to the Mustang and Camaro and was offered in two body styles, a two-door hardtop and convertible. Challengers featured a low profile with a full-width, scoop-like grille opening. Bodysides had the familiar 'Coke-bottle' profile, with raised rear fenders tapering down at the taillights. Two large, rectangular taillights nearly filled the rear escutcheon panel, with a small, license-plate-width aluminum panel left to hold the Dodge name, in block letters. The Challenger Special Edition was the luxury version of the line and included a padded vinyl roof with a small rear window, luxurious interior appointments and special exterior ornamentation. The R/T was the high-performance version of the Challenger and included all the standard Challenger features plus electric clock; 383 cid four-barrel V-8 engine; instrument panel Rallye cluster; front and rear Rallye Suspension with sway bar; heavy-duty drum brakes; F70 x 14 fiberglass belted black sidewall tires (with raised white letters); longitudinal tape or bumblebee stripes and special R/T exterior ornamentation. On Jan. 8, 1970, the Challenger T/A two-door hardtop was announced to legalize the model for SCCA Trans-Am racing. It had a 340 cid "Six-Pack" V-8 with three two-barrel carbs. It listed for $4,056 and a production run of 2,500 units (one for each dealer) was planned. On March 17, 1970, a lower-priced Challenger called "The Deputy" was announced. It came with a 198 cid six-cylinder engine with a single-barrel carburetor and listed for $2,724. A 318 cid/230 hp engine was also available in this model. Among its economy features were fixed rear quarter windows.

CHALLENGER SERIES I.D. NUMBERS: See 1970 Dodge I.D. Number listing. All models began at 100001 and went up in the unit number sequence.

CHALLENGER SERIES

Model Number	Body/Style Number	Body Type & Seating	Factory Price	Shipping Weight	Production Total
JH23	23	2-dr HT-4P	2851/2953	3026/3118	53.337
JH29	29	2-dr SE Fml HT-4P	3083/3185	3026/3148	6,584
JH27	27	2-dr Conv-4P	3120/3198	3535/3470	3,173
LH23	23	2-dr HT-4P	2724/2803	NA	NA
R/T SERIES					
JS23	23	2-dr HT-4P	3266	3402	14,889
JS29	29	2-dr SE Fml HT-4P	3498	3437	3,979
JS27	27	2-dr Conv-4P	3535	3467	1070
T/A SERIES					
SS23	23	2-dr HT-4P	4056	NA	1000+

NOTE 1: The combined model year output of Challenger and Challenger R/T models was 83,032 cars. Of this total, 13.4 percent were sixes; 60 percent had the standard V-8 and 26.6 percent had optional V-8 installations. In addition, 12.7 percent had four-speed manual transmission; 36.2 percent had styled steel wheels; 63.2 percent wore vinyl tops; 94.3 percent had front bucket seats and 36.5 percent had dual exhausts.
NOTE 2: Data above slash for six/below slash for V-8.

1970 ENGINES

Slant Six. Overhead valves. Cast iron block. Displacement: 198 cid. Bore and stroke: 3.40 x 3.64 inches. Compression ratio: 8.4:1. Brake hp: 125 at 4400 rpm. Four main bearings. Solid valve lifters. Carburetion: one-barrel.

225 Slant Six. Overhead valves. Cast iron block. Displacement: 225 cid. Bore and stroke: 3.41 x 4.13 inches. Compression ratio: 8.4:1. Brake hp: 145 at 4000 rpm. Four main bearings. Solid valve lifters. Carburetion: one-barrel.

318 V-8. Overhead valves. Cast iron block. Displacement: 318 cid. Bore and stroke: 3.91 x 3.31 inches. Compression ratio: 9.0:1. Brake hp: 230 at 4400 rpm. Five main bearings. Hydraulic valve lifters. Carburetion: two-barrel.

340 V-8. Overhead valves. Cast iron block. Displacement: 340 cid. Bore and stroke: 4.04 x 3.31 inches. Compression ratio: 10.0:1. Brake hp: 275 at 5600 rpm. Five main bearings. Hydraulic valve lifters. Carburetion: Carter 'Thermo-Quad' four-barrel.

340 'Six-Pack' V-8. Overhead valves. Cast iron block. Displacement: 340 cid. Bore and stroke: 4.04 x 3.31 inches. Compression ratio: 10.0:1. Brake hp: 290 at 4400 rpm. Five main bearings. Hydraulic valve lifters. Carburetion: three Holley two-barrels.

383 two-barrel V-8: Overhead valves. Cast iron block. Displacement: 383 cid. Bore and stroke: 4.25 x 3.38 inches. Compression ratio: 9.2:1. Brake hp: 290 at 4400 rpm. Five main bearings. Hydraulic valve lifters. Carburetion: Carter BBD two-barrel.

383 four-barrel V-8. Overhead valves. Cast iron block. Displacement: 383 cid. Bore and stroke: 4.25 x 3.38 inches. Compression ratio: 10.0:1. Brake hp: 330 at 5200 rpm. Five main bearings. Hydraulic valve lifters. Carburetion: four-barrel.

383 four-barrel V-8. Overhead valves. Cast iron block. Displacement: 383 cid. Bore and stroke: 4.25 x 3.38 inches. Compression ratio: 10.0:1. Brake hp: 335 at 5000 rpm. Five main bearings. Hydraulic valve lifters. Carburetion: Carter BBD four-barrel.

440 Magnum V-8. Overhead valves. Cast iron block. Displacement: 440 cid. Bore and stroke: 4.32 x 3.75 inches. Compression ratio: 10.0:1. Brake hp: 350 at 4000 rpm. Five main bearings. Hydraulic valve lifters. Carburetion: Carter AVS four-barrel.

440 Magnum V-8. Overhead valves. Cast iron block. Displacement: 440 cid. Bore and stroke: 4.32 x 3.75 inches. Compression ratio: 10.0:1. Brake hp: 375 at 4000 rpm. Five main bearings. Hydraulic valve lifters. Carburetion: Carter AVS four-barrel.

440 'Six-Pack' V-8. Overhead valves. Cast iron block. Displacement: 440 cid. Bore and stroke: 4.32 x 3.75 inches. Compression ratio: 10.1:1. Brake hp: 390 at 4700 rpm. Five main bearings. Hydraulic valve lifters. Carburetion: three Holley two-barrels.

426 'Street Hemi' V-8. Overhead valves with hemispherical combustion chamber. Cast iron block. Displacement: 426 cid. Bore and stroke: 4.25 x 3.75 inches. Compression ratio: 10.25:1. Brake hp: 425 at 5000 rpm. Five main bearings. Hydraulic valve lifters. Carburetion: two (2) Carter AFB four-barrels.

DART/DODGE/CHARGER/CHALLENGER POWERTRAIN OPTIONS: Dart '225'Slant Six ($46). Dart '318' V-8 ($79). TorqueFlite in Dart with Slant Six ($175); with V-8 ($191). Dart four-speed manual transmission ($188). Dodge/Charger/Challenger '383'/290 hp V-8 ($70). High-performance 350 hp/ '383' V-8, in R/T and Super Bee (standard); in other Challenger/ Coronet models ($138). Magnum 440 V8/375 hp, in Challenger R/T ($131). Magnum 440 V-8/350 hp in Challenger R/T, base Coronet and Super Bee ($250); same in Coronet R/T, Polara Custom and Monaco ($119); same in base Polara ($189). Street Hemi 426 cid 425 hp V-8, in Challenger ($779); in Charger R/T ($648); in Coronet Super Bee ($848); in Coronet R/T ($718).

DART/DODGE/CHARGER/CHALLENGER CONVENIENCE OPTIONS: Power steering ($85). Power brakes ($43). Tinted glass ($33). Air conditioning ($361). Two-tone paint ($23). Music Master AM radio ($62). AM/FM radio ($135). AM radio with 8-track tape ($196). Simulated woodgrained Sport steering wheel ($32). White sidewall tires ($34).

1970 DODGE CHASSIS FEATURES

DART: Wheelbase: 111 inches. Overall length: 197 inches. Tires: D78 x 14 fiberglass belted black sidewalls (E70 x 14 on Swinger 340). Three-speed manual transmission was standard on all Darts, with the three-speed TorqueFlite automatic or four-speed manual transmission optional.

CORONET AND CHARGER: Wheelbase: 117 inches. Overall length: 210 inches on coronet sedans; 212 on Coronet station wagons and 208 inches on Chargers. Tires: F78 x 14 on Coronets and Charger V-8s, G78 x 14 on Coronet station wagons and F70 x 14 fiberglass belted black sidewall on Coronet and Charger R/T. Three-speed manual transmission was standard on all models unless noted, with TorqueFlite three-speed automatic and four-speed manual transmissions optional.

POLARA AND MONACO: Wheelbase: 122 inches. Overall length: 220 inches on sedans and 224 inches on station wagons. Tires: H78 x 15 fiberglass belted black sidewall on all sedans, J78 x 15 on all station wagons. Three-speed manual transmission was standard on all models unless noted, with TorqueFlite three-speed automatic and four-speed manual transmissions optional.

HISTORICAL FOOTNOTES: 1970 was a significant year for Dodge for several reasons. It was the last time a convertible would be offered in either the Coronet line or the Polara line. The SuperLite optional driving light for Polara and Monaco models was also discontinued because of less-than-enthusiastic public and official acceptance. Dodge introduced all the new 1970 models on Sept. 23, 1969 and a total of 503,392 Dodges were produced during that year, which was 7.07 percent of the market in 1970. The little Dart Swinger 340s continued to be very popular, in spite of the introduction of the sexy looking Challengers. The 340 Swingers were very quick cars and carried considerably lower insurance premiums than the 'pony cars' like Challengers. With the popularity of Trans American sedan racing during 1970, Dodge jumped on the bandwagon with the introduction of the Challenger T/A. This special version of the Challenger included the 340 cid V-8 engine and four-speed manual transmission as standard equipment, as well as special T/A exterior ornamentation. Unfortunately, this was meant to be a limited-production model and little more than 1,000 of the T/As were built. Chrysler built 1,543 "Street Hemi" engines for Dodges and Plymouths this year. Of these, 462 were used in Dodge models, as follows: (Coronet Super Bee hardtop) 21 four-speed and 11 TorqueFlite; (Coronet Super Bee coupe) four-speeds and no TorqueFlite; (Coronet R/T hardtop) four-speed and nine TorqueFlite; (Coroner R/T convertible) one with four-speed; (Charger R/T) 42 with no transmission break-out; (Challenger R/T hardtop) 137 four-speed and 150 TorqueFlite; (Challenger R/T convertible) Five four-speed and four TorqueFlite; (Challenger R/T SE hardtop) 23 four-speed and 37 TorqueFlite).

1971 DODGE

DEMON SERIES — (ALL ENGINES) — Given only slight grille and trim restyling for 1971, the Dart sedan and hardtop continued as popular Dodge products. A new coupe version of the Dart, utilizing Plymouth's Duster body, was also introduced. Dubbed the Demon, this model rode on a chassis with a three inch shorter wheelbase and overall length was reduced about four inches. The Demon was the base 'value package' version of the Dart series and included all the federally mandated safety features: pivoting rear quarter windows; 198 cid Slant Six engine; black rubber floor mats; and 6.45 x 14 polyester black sidewall tires. On cars with V-8 power, 6.95 x 14 black sidewall tires were substituted. Demon nameplates were located on the right side of the rear escutcheon panel and on the front fenders, just behind the front wheelwells. A special, high-performance Demon 340 was powered by 340 cid V-8 engine with three-speed manual transmission as standard equipment. Also included in the 340 package were E70 x 14 belted black sidewall tires; performance bodyside and rear deck panel tape stripes; front and rear Rallye Suspension (with sway bar); and floor-mounted transmission shifter. A Demon "Sizzler" was introduced Feb. 9, 1971 as a package for the base Demon. Its price of $141 ($131 V-8) included side hood stripes; rallye wheels; racing mirrors; and a special steering wheel among 13 extras. Later, an optional hood was announced for the Demon 340 featuring dual air scoops and a pair of tie-down pins.

1971 Dodge, Demon '340' two-door coupe, V-8

DODGE I.D. NUMBERS: VIN located on plate attached to left-hand side of dashboard, visible through windshield. The VIN has 13 symbols. (The first four symbols, together, are the Model Number in second column of charts below.) The first symbol identifies the car-line or marque: D=Dodge; J=Challenger; L=Dart; W=Coronet and X=Charger. The second symbol indicates trim/price level as follows: E=Economy; H=High; K=Police; L=Low; M=Medium; P=Premium; T=Taxi; S=Special. The next two symbols identify the body style, as follows: 21=two-door sedan; 23=two-door hardtop; 27=convertible; 29=two-door Sports hardtop; 41=four-door sedan; 43=four-door hardtop; 45=six-passenger station wagon; 46=nine-passenger station wagon. The fifth symbol denotes the engine as follows: (6-cyl.) B=198 cid; C=225 cid; E=special order (V-8); G=318 cid 2V; H=340 cid 4V (high-performance); J=340 cid 3x2V (high-performance); K=360 cid 2V; L=383 cid 2V; N=383 cid 4V (high-performance); R=426 cid "Street Hemi" 2x4V; T=440 cid 4V; U=440 cid 4V (high-performance); V=440 3x2V (high-performance); Z=special order. The sixth symbol denotes the model year as follows: 1=1971. The seventh symbol denotes the assembly plant, as follows: A=Lynch Rd. (Detroit); B=Hamtramck, Mich.; C=Jefferson Ave. (Detroit); D=Belvedere, Ill.; E=Los Angeles, Calif.; F=Newark, Del.; G=St. Louis, Mo.; R=Windsor, Ont. (Canada). The last six symbols are the sequential production number starting at 100001 for each series at each plant. Body code plate located under hood, on left (fender shield, wheelhousing or radiator support) includes S.O. number and trim/paint codes too numerous to list.

DEMON SERIES

Model Number	Body/Style Number	Body Type & Seating	Factory Price	Shipping Weight	Production Total
LL29	29	2-dr Cpe-6P	2343/2476	2845/2995	69,861
LM29	29	2-dr 340 Cpe-6P	2721	3165	10,098

NOTE 1: Data above slash for six/below slash for V-8.

DART SERIES — (ALL ENGINES) — Dart was the base trim level in the Dart sedan and hardtop lineup and included all federally mandated safety and pollution systems; front and rear armrests; ashtrays; cigarette lighter; concealed spare tire; rubber floor mats; glovebox with rotary latch; heater and defroster; dome light; parking brake and brake system warning lights; all-vinyl bench seats; three-spoke steering wheel with padded horn button; two-speed electric windshield wipers; 198 cid Slant Six (or 318 cid V-8) and vent wings. Dart Swinger and Custom models also included dual note horns; drip rail and wheel lip moldings; three-spoke steering wheel (with padded hub and horn tabs) and carpeting. Custom trim added bodyside moldings and ventless side windows. Each entry carried model identification on the front sides just behind the front wheel openings. A lower priced Swinger Special two-door hardtop was announced in Oct. 1970.

DART SERIES I.D. NUMBERS: See 1971 Dodge I.D. Number listing. All models began at 100001 and went up in the unit number sequence.

DART/SWINGER/CUSTOM SERIES

Model Number	Body/Style Number	Body Type & Seating	Factory Price	Shipping Weight	Production Total
DART SERIES					
LL41	41	4-dr Sed-6P	2450/2600	2900/3050	32,711
LL23	23	2-dr Spec HT-6P	2402/2552	2900/3050	13,485
SWINGER SERIES					
LH23	23	2-dr HT-6P	2561/2601	2900/3050	102,480
CUSTOM SERIES					
LH41	41	4-dr Sed-6P	2609/2759	2900/3050	21,785

NOTE 1: Data above slash for six/below slash for V-8.

CORONET SERIES — (ALL ENGINES) — In an effort to further segregate the Coronet from the Charger, 1971 saw the introduction of an all-new Coronet which was mounted on a chassis with a wheelbase of 118 inches. Styling was slightly more rounded than in the previous year. A full-width grille opening was accented by a large surround, which served as the front bumper. Horizontal grille bars were highlighted by the triangular Dodge symbol, first introduced in 1964. A subtle 'Coke bottle' profile lead to a simply styled rear end with two large, rectangular taillights (plus the license holder) housed in the rear bumper. For 1971, Coronet intermediate-sized Dodges were offered only in four-door sedan and station wagon models. The Coronet was the base trim level and included all federally mandated safety and pollution equipment; 225 cid Slant Six or 318 cid V-8 engine; color-keyed rubber floor mats; a single horn and no exterior moldings (except on windshield and rear window). Also included were a three-spoke steering wheel; rear ashtray and extra-thick foam seat cushions. Station wagons added heavy-duty brakes; drip rail moldings and three-way tailgate. The Coronet model designation was carried, in script, on the front fenders, just behind the wheelwell.

CORONET SERIES I.D. NUMBERS: See 1971 Dodge I.D. Number listing. All models began at 100001 and went up in the unit number sequence.

CORONET SERIES

Model Number	Body/Style Number	Body Type & Seating	Factory Price	Shipping Weight	Production Total
WL41	41	4-dr Sed-6P	2777/2872	3245/3360	11,794
WL45	45	4-dr Sta Wag-6P	3101/3196	3745/3810	5,470

NOTE 1: Data above slash for six/below slash for V-8.

CORONET CUSTOM SERIES — (ALL ENGINES) — The Custom was the intermediate trim level in the Coronet Series and included all the standard Coronet features, plus color-keyed carpeting; dual note horns; wheel opening, bodyside and drip rail moldings; and three-spoke steering wheel (with padded horn bars).

CORONET CUSTOM SERIES I.D. NUMBERS: See 1971 Dodge I.D. Number listing. All models began at 100001 and went up in the unit number sequence.

CORONET CUSTOM SERIES

Model Number	Body/Style Number	Body Type & Seating	Factory Price	Shipping Weight	Production Total
WH41	41	4-dr Sed-6P	2951/3046	3250/3365	37,817
WH45	45	4-dr Sta Wag-6P	3278/3373	3750/3815	5,365
WH46	46	4-dr Sta Wag-9P	3454	3890	5,717

NOTE 1: Data above slash for six/below slash for V-8.

1971 Dodge, Coronet Brougham four-door sedan, V8

BROUGHAM/CRESTWOOD SERIES — (ALL ENGINES) — The Brougham was the top trim level sedan and the Crestwood was the top trim level station wagon in the Coronet Series. These cars included all Custom features. The Brougham sedan added folding front seat center armrest; ashtray; glovebox light; ignition with time delay lamp; map and courtesy lights; pedal dress-up kit; upper door frame moldings; rear door automatic entrance light; and deluxe wheelcovers. The Crestwood station wagon also included wheel opening moldings; bright upper door frame and quarter window moldings; woodgrained side panels (with bright moldings) and, in its nine-passenger form, a tailgate inside safety latch.

BROUGHAM/CRESTWOOD SERIES I.D. NUMBERS: See 1971 Dodge I.D. Number listing. All models began at 100001 and went up in the unit number sequence.

BROUGHAM/CRESTWOOD SERIES

Model Number	Body/Style Number	Body Type & Seating	Factory Price	Shipping Weight	Production Total
WP41	41	4-dr Sed-6P	3332	3375	4,700
WP45	45	4-dr Sta Wag-6P	3601	3845	2,884
WP46	46	4-dr Sta Wag-6P	3682	3900	3,981

1971 Dodge, Charger Super Bee two-door hardtop sports coupe, V-8

CHARGER SERIES — (ALL ENGINES) — The Charger was completely restyled for 1971 to further segregate it from the Coronet Series. Chargers rode on a new 115 inch wheelbase chassis and were expanded to six coupes and hardtops in three series. All models were semi-fastback coupes featuring rear quarter window styling which swept up from the fender to meet the sloping upper window frame. The full-width bumper/grille shell was split by a large vertical divider on all Chargers and the rear end featured a small trunk lip spoiler and six square taillights located in the oval rear bumper. The standard Charger was the base trim level and included all federally mandated safety and pollution equipment; 225 cid Slant Six (or 318 V-8); cigarette lighter, dual horns; color-keyed carpeting; inside day/night mirror; roof drip rail and wheelwell moldings and two-speed windshield wipers. The Charger 500 was the intermediate trim level Charger and included all the standard Charger features, plus ashtray lights; glovebox, map and courtesy light; pedal dress-up kit; sail moldings; bucket seats; deluxe wheelcovers; and '500' exterior badges. The Charger Super Bee was patterned after the Coronet Super Bee to offer the buyer a low-cost, high-performance package. In addition to the standard Charger features, Super Bees included a 59 ampere/hour battery; heavy-duty brakes; heavy-duty shock absorbers; Rallye Suspension; Rallye instrument cluster; floor-mounted three-speed manual transmission; and 383 cid V-8 engine. The R/T was the more luxurious high-performance version of the Charger and included all the features of the charger 500, plus 70 ampere/hour battery; heavy-duty brakes and shock absorbers; pedal dress-up kit; extra heavy-duty Rallye suspension; TorqueFlite automatic transmission or four-speed manual transmission; 440 cid Magnum V-8 engine; and the R/T designation on the exterior of the body.

CHARGER SERIES I.D. NUMBERS: See 1971 Dodge I.D. Number listing. All models began at 100001 and went up in the unit number sequence.

CHARGER SERIES

Model Number	Body/Style Number	Body Type & Seating	Factory Price	Shipping Weight	Production Total
WL21	21	2-dr Cpe-6P	2707/2802	3215/3325	Note 1
WH23	23	2-dr HT-6P	2975/3070	3240/3350	Note 1
500 SERIES					
WP23	23	2-dr HT-5P	3223	3350	11,948
WP23	23	2-dr Sup Bee HT	3271	3640	5,054
WP29	29	2-dr SE HT-5P	3422	3375	15,811
R/T SERIES					
WS23	23	2-dr HT-5P	3777	3685	3,118

NOTE 1: Production of styles WL21 and WH23 was recorded as a single total: 46,183 units. Since Dodge combined rounded off totals of Coronets and Chargers this season, it is impossible to determine how many Chargers were equipped with sixes or V-8s.
NOTE 2: Data above slash for six/below slash for V-8.

1971 Dodge, Monaco two-door hardtop sports coupe, V-8

POLARA/MONACO SERIES — (ALL ENGINES) — Continuing to use the same body as introduced in 1969, the 1971 Polara featured slight trim updating to separate it from previous year models. A new grille, featuring horizontal bars with two wider center bars, ran the full width of the car. The rear end treatment consisted of tail and back-up lights housed behind a horizontal slotted bar arrangement which was raised slightly, at the center of the bottom bar, to house the license plate. Polara was the base trim level and included all federally mandated safety and pollution equipment; air control system; front and rear armrests; front and rear ashtrays; 46 ampere/hour battery; cigarette lighter; color-keyed carpeting; dual horns; dome and parking brake system warning lights; inside day/night mirror; outside left manual mirror; three-spoke steering wheel (with padded hub); electric windshield washers and wipers; and the '225' Six or '318' V-8. The Dodge name, in block letters, was spaced evenly across the front of the hood and trunk lid and the Polara model designation was located directly below the rear fender marker lights on each side. Polara Custom was the intermediate trim level in the Polara Series and included all Polara features; plus bodyside moldings with a vinyl insert; wheel opening moldings; foam rubber seat cushions; and the Custom model designation on the rear fenders. The base Polara four-door hardtop was a midyear model announced on Jan. 20, 1971. Brougham was the top trim level of the Polara Series and included all features of the Custom, plus folding front center armrest; 59 ampere/hour battery; ashtray, glovebox and trunk lights; headlight-on warning signal; front bumper surround moldings; pedal dress-up kit; upper door sill moldings; rear door automatic entrance light switches; deluxe wheelcovers; and 383 cid two-barrel V-8 engine. Monaco was the luxury model of the Polara line and included all Brougham features; plus nylon carpeting; cornering lights; dome/map lights; upper door frame moldings on four-door models; and a steering wheel with padded hub and horn tabs. Monacos featured a grille of die-cast zinc, in a rectangular slot pattern, which was duplicated at the rear and featured side-to-side taillights. The Monaco name appeared, in script, directly above the bodyside feature line and on the right side of the trunk lid.

POLARA/MONACO SERIES I.D. NUMBERS: See 1971 Dodge I.D. Number listing. All models began at 100001 and went up in the unit number sequence.

POLARA/MONACO SERIES

Model Number	Body/Style Number	Body Type & Seating	Factory Price	Shipping Weight	Production Total
POLARA SERIES					
DE41	41	4-dr Sed-6P	3298/3409	3755/3820	21,578
DE23	23	2-dr HT-6P	3319/3430	3715/3795	11,535
DE43	N43	4-dr HT-6P	3497	3875	2,487
DL41	41	4-dr Cus Sed-6P	3593	3835	13,860
DL43	43	4-dr Cus HT-6P	3681	3875	17,458
DL23	23	2-dr Cus HT-6P	3614	3805	9,682
DL45	45	4-dr Cus Wag-6P	3992	3280	Note 1
DL46	46	4-dr Cus Wag-9P	4098	4335	Note 1
DM43	43	4-dr Brghm HT-6P	3884	4035	2570
DM23	23	2-dr Brghm HT-6P	3818	3965	2024
MONACO SERIES					
DH41	41	4-dr Sed-6P	4223	4050	Note 2
DH43	43	4-dr HT-6P	4362	4080	Note 2
DH23	23	2-dr HT-6P	4298	4000	3,195
DH45	45	4-dr Wag-6P	4689	4525	Note 3
DH46	46	4-dr Wag-9P	4821	458	Note 3

NOTE 1: Total production of Polara Custom station wagons was 9,682 units, which included both DL45 and DL46 models.
NOTE 2: In figures rounded off to the nearest 100 units, 16,900 Monaco four-door passenger cars were built during the 1971 model year. All were V-8 powered. No breakout between Monaco four-door sedans and four-door hardtops is available at the current time.
NOTE 3: An exact total of 5,449 units for combined production of both DH45 and DH46 models is given in Dodge records. However, rounded off totals provided in industry statistics show a slightly higher figure, which varies by 1,480 units. This may be due to inclusion of station wagons built in Canada or, perhaps, station wagons built for police, taxi, emergency and other professional-use purposes.
NOTE 4: Data above slash for six/below slash for V-8.
NOTE 5: The totals given in the chart above for Models DE23 and DL41 are estimates, based on calculations from known records and should be considered 'ballpark' figures only. The total given for Model DE41 includes 308 taxicabs and 6,826 police cars.

1971 Dodge, Challenger R/T two-door hardtop sports coupe, Hemi V-8.

CHALLENGER SERIES — (ALL ENGINES) — The Challenger continued to use the same body as originally introduced back in 1970 with very minor trim changes, namely a slightly revised grille and slightly revised taillight treatments. The Challenger was the base trim level and included all the federally mandated safety and pollution equipment; 225 cid Slant Six (198 Slant Six on coupe) or 318 cid V-8 engine; front and rear side armrests and ashtrays; cigarette lighter (except coupe); color-keyed carpeting; ventless side windows; glovebox with rotary latch (locking on convertible); heater and defroster; dual horns (except coupe); dome and parking brake/brake system warning lights; outside left manual mirror; inside day/night mirror (except coupe); bucket seats; front foam seat cushion; three-spoke steering wheel with simulated woodgrain and padded hub; electric windshield washer and concealed two-speed wipers. The Challenger R/T continued as the high-performance model in the Challenger lineup and included all the base line Challenger equipment plus, heavy-duty drum brakes; chrome exhaust tips; Rallye instrument cluster with simulated woodgrain trim; Rallye suspension; bodyside tape stripe; variable speed wipers and 383 cid four-barrel V-8 engine. The convertible also had front courtesy and pocket panel lights and a collapsible spare tire.

CHALLENGER SERIES I.D. NUMBERS: See 1971 Dodge I.D. Number listing. All models began at 100001 and went up in the unit number sequence.

CHALLENGER SERIES

Model Number	Body/Style Number	Body Type & Seating	Factory Price	Shipping Weight	Production Total
CHALLENGER					
JL23	23	2-dr Cpe-4P	2727/2853	3020/3080	Note 1
JH23	23	2-dr HT-4P	2848/2950	3065/3120	Note 1
JH27	27	2-dr Conv-4P	3105/3207	3150/3210	2,165
R/T SERIES					
JS23	23	2-dr HT-4P	3273	3495	4,630

NOTE 1: A total of 23,088 units was recorded for Models JL23 and JH23, with no additional breakout, between the two models, available at the current time.
NOTE 2: In figures rounded off to the nearest 100 units, Challenger output included 2,000 sixes and 27,900 V-8s. Of the grand total of 29,883 Challengers built during 1971, only 5.3 percent had four-speed manual gearboxes; 6.7 percent were sixes; 76.5 percent featured standard V-8 power; and 16.8 percent were equipped with optional V-8 engines.
NOTE 3: Data above slash for six/below slash for V-8.

COLT SERIES — (1-4) — The Colt was Dodge's offering into the new sub-compact field shared by the Ford Pinto, Chevy Vega and AMC's Gremlin. Manufactured in Japan by Mitsubishi Motors Corp., and sold by Dodge dealers in this country, the Colt became the first of the 'Captive Imports' which, along with the Plymouth Cricket, was produced by Chrysler U.K. (formerly Rootes). It was sold overseas as the Hillman Avenger. Pleasantly styled, these little cars bore a resemblance to the Toyota Corolla models and Datsun 510 models from that era. The 97.5 cid engine (1600 cubic centimeters), was the only engine available with the Colt. Since the Colt was not a true American-built automobile, it will not be covered further in the following sections of this catalog devoted to Dodge.

COLT SERIES I.D. NUMBERS: See 1971 Dodge I.D. Number listing. All models began at 100001 and went up in the unit number sequence.

COLT SERIES

Model Number	Body/Style Number	Body Type & Seating	Factory Price	Shipping Weight	Production Total
6H41	41	4-dr Sed-4P	1995	2020	Note 1
6L21	21	2-dr Sed-4P	1924	2045	Note 1
6H23	23	2-dr HT-4P	2074	2055	Note 1
6H45	45	2-dr Sta Wag-4P	2225	2120	Note 1

NOTE 1: Sales of the Colt for 1971 were 28,381 units.

ENGINES

Colt four-cylinder. Overhead valves. Cast iron block. Displacement: 97.5 cid (1600 cubic centimeters). Bore and stroke: 3.03 x 3.39 inches. Brake hp: 100. Five main bearings. Hydraulic valve lifters.

198 Slant Six. Overhead valves. Cast iron block. Displacement: 198 cid. Bore and stroke: 3.40 x 3.64 inches. Compression ratio: 8.4:1. Brake hp: 125 at 4W rpm. Four main bearings. Solid valve lifters. Carburetion: one-barrel.

225 Slant Six. Overhead valves. Cast iron block. Displacement: 225 cid. Bore and stroke: 3.41 x 4.13 inches. Compression ratio: 8.4:1. Brake hp: 145 at 4000 rpm. Four main bearings. Solid valve lifters. Carburetion: one-barrel

318 V-8. Overhead valves. Cast iron block. Displacement: 318 cid. Bore and stroke: 3.91 x 3.31 inches. Compression ratio: 9.0:1. Brake hp: 230 at 4400 rpm. Five main bearings. Hydraulic valve lifters. Carburetion: two-barrel.

340 V-8. Overhead valves. Cast iron block. Displacement: 340 cid. Bore and stroke: 4.04 x 3.31 inches. Compression ratio: 10.0:1. Brake hp: 275 at 5600 rpm. Five main bearings. Hydraulic valve lifters. Carburetion: Carter 'Thermo-Quad' four-barrel.

360 V-8. Overhead valves. Cast iron block. Displacement: 360 cid. Bore and stroke: 4.00 x 3.58 inches. Compression ratio: 8.7:1. Brake hp: 255 at 4000 rpm. Five main bearings. Hydraulic valve lifters. Carburetion: two-barrel.

383 two-barrel V-8: Overhead valves. Cast iron block. Displacement: 383 cid. Bore and stroke: 4.25 x 3.38 inches. Compression ratio: 9.2:1. Brake hp: 275 at 4400 rpm. Five main bearings. Hydraulic valve lifters. Carburetion: two-barrel.

383 four-barrel V-8. Overhead valves. Cast iron block. Displacement: 383 cid. Bore and stroke: 4.25 x 3.38 inches. Compression ratio: 9.5:1. Brake hp: 300 at 4800 rpm. Five main bearings. Hydraulic valve lifters. Carburetion: four-barrels.

440 Magnum V-8. Overhead valves. Cast iron block. Displacement: 440 cid. Bore and stroke: 4.32 x 3.75 inches. Compression ratio: 9.7:1. Brake hp: 370 at 4800 rpm. Five main bearings. Hydraulic valve lifters. Carburetion: four-barrels.

440 'Six-Pack' V-8. Overhead valves. Cast iron block. Displacement: 440 cid. Bore and stroke: 4.32 x 3.75 inches. Compression ratio: 10.5:1. Brake hp: 385 at 5200 rpm. Five main bearings. Hydraulic valve lifters. Carburetion: three Holley two-barrels.

426 'Street Hemi' V-8. Overhead valves with hemispherical combustion chamber. Cast iron block. Displacement: 426 cid. Bore and stroke: 4.25 x 3.75 inches. Compression ratio: 10.25:1. Brake hp: 425 at 5600 rpm. Five main bearings. Hydraulic valve lifters. Carburetion: two Carter AFB four-barrels.

1971 DODGE CHASSIS FEATURES

(COLT) Wheelbase: 95.3 inches. Overall length: 164 inches (165 inches on station wagon). Tires: 6.00 x 13 tubeless black sidewall. Four-speed manual transmission was standard on all Colts with the three-speed automatic optional. (DEMON) Wheelbase: 108 inches. Overall length: 192.5 inches. Tires: 6.45 x 14 tubeless black sidewall (E70 x 14 belted black sidewall with raised white letters on Demon 340 models). Three-speed manual transmission was standard on all Demons, with the TorqueFlite automatic or four-speed manual transmission optional. (DART) Wheelbase: 111 inches. Overall length: 197 inches. Tires: D78 x 14 belted black sidewall. Three-speed manual transmission was standard on all Darts, with the TorqueFlite automatic or four-speed manual transmission optional. (CHALLENGER) Wheelbase: 110 inches. Overall length: 192 inches. Tires: 7.35 x 14 tubeless black sidewall (F70 x 14 belted black sidewall with raised white letters on R/T models). Three-speed manual transmission was standard on all Challengers unless otherwise noted, with the TorqueFlite automatic or four-speed manual transmissions optional.

(CHARGER) Wheelbase: 115 inches. Overall length: 206 inches. Tires: E78 x 14 belted black sidewall (F70 x 14 belted black sidewall with raised white letters on Super Bee and R/T models). Three-speed manual transmission was standard on all Chargers unless otherwise noted, with the TorqueFlite automatic or four-speed manual transmissions optional. (CORONET) Wheelbase: 118 inches. Overall length: 207 inches on sedans and 214 inches on station wagons. Tires: E78 x 14 belted black sidewalls on sedans and H78 x 14 belted black sidewall on station wagons. Three-speed manual transmission was standard on all Coronets, with the TorqueFlite automatic and four-speed manual transmissions optional. (POLARA/MONACO) Wheelbase: 122 inches. Overall length: 221 inches on sedans and 224 inches on station wagons. Tires: H78 x 15 on sedans and J78 x 15 on station wagons. All tires were belted black sidewalls. TorqueFlite automatic transmission was standard on all Polara and Monaco models.

CONVENIENCE OPTIONS: (Average prices) Power brakes ($45). Power disc brakes ($66). Challenger '340' four-barrel V-8 ($253). Dart/Demon/Challenger '225' Slant Six ($39). Challenger/Coronet/Super Bee '383' V-8 ($71). Challenger/Coronet/Super Bee '383' four-barrel V-8 ($145). Polara/Monaco '383' two-barrel V-8 ($73). Polara/Monaco '383' four-barrel V-8 ($145). Polara/Monaco '440' four-barrel V-8 ($198). Coronet 'Track Pack' ($138). Coronet 'Super Track-Pack' ($202). Monaco Brougham option ($220). Air conditioning, in Monaco/Polara ($423); in other models ($380). Hemi '426' V-8 in Super Bee ($837); in Charger R/T ($707); in Challenger ($790). (COLT) Automatic transmission. Full wheelcovers. Air conditioning. White sidewall tires.

HISTORICAL FOOTNOTES: Dodge offered many convenience options for the 1971 models. New items ranged from slightly wider rearview mirrors to cassette tape players. An optional 'lock door' and 'low fuel' warning light were also featured. Flow-through ventilation for the upper level of the car was a very popular option. The top-line station wagons featured a translucent woodgrain film that allowed the color of the main body to 'bleed' through, creating a very unusual effect. When its winged 1969 Daytona was effectively outlawed by NASCAR, Dodge cut back heavily on factory backing of stock car racing. After 22 Grand National wins in 1969 and 17 in 1970, there were only eight in 1971. Unfortunately, 1971 was also the last time the famous and awesome 'Hemi' V-8 engine was offered to the public, either as the Street version, or in the Race form. Insurance premiums were astronomical on high-performance cars and, beginning in 1972, all cars had to be able to run on regular gasoline. Rather than compromise the incredible 'Hemi', Chrysler wisely decided to retire it as a winner. Dodge installed a mere 156 of the engines in three 1971 models, as follows: (Charger Super Bee) Nine four-speed and 13 TorqueFlite; (Charger R/T) 30 four-speed and 33 TorqueFlite; (Challenger R/T hardtop) 59 four-speed and 12 TorqueFlite. During 1992, Chrysler announced that it would start making 426 cid Hemi engines again, for sale to racers and restorers through its Chrysler Performance (formerly Direct Connection) high-performance parts division.

1972 DODGE

DEMON SERIES — (ALL ENGINES) — Basically unchanged for 1972, the new Darts received only revised grilles and updated interiors to separate them from the previous year's models. Continuing to be the base 'value package' of the Dart lineup, the Demon was unchanged from the previous year, excepting a new grille and updated interior. Demons included all the federally mandated safety and pollution equipment, pivoting rear quarter windows, the 198 cid Slant Six engine, black rubber floor mats, 6.45 x 14 black sidewall tires on six-cylinder models and 6.95 x 14 black sidewall tires on V-8 models. The Demon model designation was once again carried on the right side of the rear escutcheon panel and on the front fenders. The Demon 340 continued as the high-performance version of the Demon and included all the standard Demon features, plus the 340 cid V-8 engine with three-speed manual transmission; E70 x 14 belted black sidewall tires; performance bodyside and rear deck panel tape stripes; front and rear Rally Suspension with sway bar; and floor-mounted shifter.

DODGE I.D. NUMBERS: VIN located on plate attached to left-hand side of dashboard, visible through windshield. The VIN has 13 symbols. (The first four symbols, together, are the Model Number in second column of charts below.) The first symbol identifies the car-line or marque: D=Dodge; J=Challenger; L=Dart; W=Coronet and X=Charger. The second symbol indicates trim/price level as follows: G= Dodge Taxi; H=High; K=Police; L=Low; M=Medium; P=Premium; T=Taxi; S=Special. The next two symbols identify the body style, as follows: 21=two-door sedan; 23=two-door hardtop; 29=two-door Sports hardtop; 41=four-door sedan; 43=four-door hardtop; 45=six-passenger station wagon; 46=nine-passenger station wagon. The fifth symbol denotes the engine as follows: (6-cyl.) B=198 cid; C=225 cid; E=special order (V-8); G=318 cid 2V; H=340 cid 4V (high-performance); K=360 cid 2V; M=400 cid 2V; P=400 cid 4V (high-performance); T=440 cid 4V; U=440 cid 4V (high-performance); V=440 3x2V (high-performance); Z=special order. The sixth symbol denotes the model year as follows:

2=1972. The seventh symbol denotes the assembly plant, as follows: A=Lynch Rd. (Detroit); B=Hamtramck, Mich.; C=Jefferson Ave. (Detroit); D=Belvedere, Ill.; F=Newark, Del.; G=St. Louis, Mo.; R=Windsor, Ont. (Canada). The last six symbols are the sequential production number starting at 100001 for each series at each plant. Body code plate located under hood, on left (fender shield, wheelhousing or radiator support) includes S.O. number and trim/paint codes too numerous to list.

DEMON SERIES

Model Number	Body/Style Number	Body Type & Seating	Factory Price	Shipping Weight	Production Total
LL29	29	2-dr Cpe-6P	2316/2449	2800/2995	39,880
LM29	29	2-dr 340 Cpe-6P	2759	3125	8,700

NOTE 1: The production total for Model LM29 is based on rounded off model year records that include only U.S. built cars. The production total for Model LL29 appears to be an exact model year record covering all cars built in the U.S. and Canada, for the U.S. market.
NOTE 2: Data above slash for six/below slash for V-8.

1972 Dodge, Dart Swinger two-door hardtop sports coupe, 6-cyl

DART SERIES — (ALL ENGINES) — The Dart was the standard base trim level in the Dart model lineup and included all federally mandated safety and pollution systems; front and rear armrests; ashtrays; cigarette lighter; concealed spare tire; rubber floor mats; glovebox with rotary latch; heater and defroster; dome light; parking brake and brake system warning lights; all-vinyl bench seats; three-spoke steering wheel (with padded horn button); two-speed electric windshield wipers; '198' Slant Six (or '318' V-8 engines); and vent wings. Dart Swinger and Custom models also included dual note horns; drip rail and wheel lip moldings; three-spoke steering wheel (with padded hub and horn tabs) and carpeting. The Custom models also included bodyside moldings and ventless side windows. Each model carried identification on the front fendersides just behind the front wheel openings.

DART/SWINGER/CUSTOM I.D. NUMBERS: See 1972 Dodge I.D. Number listing. All models began at 100001 and went up in the unit number sequence.

DART/SWINGER/CUSTOM SERIES

Model Number	Body/Style Number	Body Type & Seating	Factory Price	Shipping Weight	Production Total
LL41	41	4-dr Sed-6P	2420/2570	2855/3005	26,019
LL23	23	2-dr Spec HT-6P	2373/2523	2845/2995	19,210
LH23	23	2-dr Swinger HT-6P	2528/2678	2835/2985	119,618
LH41	41	4-dr Cus Sed-6P	2574/2724	2855/3005	49,941

NOTE 1: Data above slash for six/below slash for V-8.

CORONET SERIES — (ALL ENGINES) — Simplification was the key word in the Coronet lineup for 1972. Minor restyling, in the form of new grilles and taillights, highlighted the new Coronets. As in 1971, all Coronets were four-door models, either sedans or station wagons. The Coronet was the base trim level and included all federally mandated safety and pollution equipment; '225' Slant Six or '318' V-8 engine; color-keyed rubber floor mats; a single horn; and no exterior moldings, except windshield and rear window moldings. Also included was the three-spoke steering wheel; rear ashtray and extra-thick foam seat cushions. Station wagons added heavy-duty brakes; drip rail moldings; and three-way tailgates. The Coronet model designation was carried, in block letters, on the front fenders behind, the wheelwell. The Coronet Custom was the top trim level in the Coronet Series and included all standard Coronet features, plus color-keyed carpeting; dual note horns; wheel opening, bodyside and drip rail moldings; and a three-spoke steering wheel (with padded horn bar). Also included were upper door frame moldings, rear door automatic entrance light and Deluxe wheelcovers. The Crestwood station wagon added wheelwell moldings; bright upper door frame and quarter window moldings; woodgrain side panels and, on the nine-passenger Crestwood, an inside tailgate safety latch. Three Coronet and "Topper" trim packages were made available as a midyear option for the Custom four-door sedan.

CORONET SERIES I.D. NUMBERS: See 1972 Dodge I.D. Number listing. All models began at 100001 and went up in the unit number sequence.

CORONET SERIES

Model Number	Body/Style Number	Body Type & Seating	Factory Price	Shipping Weight	Production Total
WL41	NA	4-dr Sed-6P	2721/2828	3350/3375	11,293
WL45	NA	4-dr Sta Wag-6P	3209	3795	Note 1
WH41	NA	4-dr Cus Sed-6P	2891/2998	3310/3370	43,132
WH45	NA	4-dr Cus Wag-6P	3382	3800	Note 1
WH46	NA	4-dr Cus Wag-9P	3460	3840	Note 1
WP45	NA	4-dr Crstwd-6P	3604	3810	Note 2
WP46	NA	4-dr Crstwd-9P	3683	3850	Note 2

NOTE 1: Data above slash for six/below slash for V-8.

1972 Dodge, Coronet Custom four-door sedan, V-8

NOTE 2: The production of Model WL45 was counted as a lumped sum, together with production of Models WH45 and WH46. The total for all three was 5,452 units.

NOTE 3: The production of Models WP45 and WP46 was counted as a lumped sum of 6,471 units.

CHARGER SERIES — (ALL ENGINES) — As in 1971, all intermediate models were considered Chargers. The Charger lineup was simplified like the Coronet's, with three models replacing the six offered in 1971. The R/T Super Bee and 500 models were dropped and a new Rallye models was added. The standard Charger continued as the base trim level and included all federally mandated safety and Pollution equipment; '225' Slant Six or '318' V-8 engine; cigarette lighter; dual horns, color-keyed carpeting; Inside day/night mirror; roof drip rail and wheelwell moldings; and two-speed windshield wipers. The Charger Rallye option included all standard Charger features, plus front and rear sway bars; F70 x 14 white sidewall tires; special instrumentation; louvered taillights; and various types of exterior performance ornamentation. The Charger SE continued as the top trim level and included all the standard Charger features, plus a landau vinyl top and hidden headlights. The 440 cid 'Six Pack' engine continued to be offered, but only in the Rallye optioned Charger. Three midyear Topper trim packages were released for Charger hardtops.

CHARGER SERIES

Model Number	Body/Style Number	Body Type & Seating	Factory Price	Shipping Weight	Production Total
WL21	21	2-dr Cpe-6P	2652/2759	3245/3310	7,803
WL23	23	2-dr HT-6P	2913/3020	3260/3325	45,361
WH23	23	2-dr SE HT-6P	3249	3325	22,430

NOTE: Data above slash for six/below slash for V-8.

1972 Dodge, Polara Custom four-door hardtop sedan, V-8

POLARA AND MONACO SERIES — (ALL ENGINES) — 1972 was a year for a major facelift in the Polara lineup. A more formal appearance was evident, with the addition of new rooflines to the two- and four-door hardtops. Both grille and headlights were housed in a more massive, full-width bumper. The rear bumper was also redesigned and contained the large rectangular taillights. The Polara was the base trim level full-size Dodge and included all federally mandated safety and pollution equipment; air control system; front and rear armrests; front and rear ashtrays; 46 amp/hr battery; cigarette lighter; color-keyed carpeting; dual horns; dome and parking brake system warning lights; inside day/night mirror; outside left manual mirror; three-spoke steering wheel (with padded hub); electric windshield washers and two-speed wipers; and the 318 cid V-8 engine. The 225 cid six was available in Polaras made for fleet use. The Dodge name, in block letters, was spaced evenly across the front of the hood and across the center of the rear bumper. The Polara model designation, in script, was located on the rear fenders, just above the side marker lights. The Polara Custom was the intermediate trim level and included all the Polara features, plus bodyside moldings (with a vinyl insert); wheel opening moldings; and foam rubber seat cushions. The Custom model designation was located on the rear fenders. A greater attempt was made to segregate the Monaco from the Polara for 1972. Concealed headlights and special front and rear end treatments made the two models appear completely different. The Monaco included all Polara Custom features, plus folding front center armrest; 59 amp/hr battery; ashtray, glovebox and trunk lights; headlight-on warning light; pedal dress-up trim; upper door and sill moldings; rear door automatic entrance light switches; deluxe wheelcovers; 360 cid V-8 engine; nylon carpeting; cornering lamps; dome/map lights; and the Monaco name, in script, on the rear fenders (just above the side marker lights).

POLARA AND MONACO SERIES I.D. NUMBERS: See 1972 Dodge I.D. Number listing. All models began at 100001 and went up in the unit number sequence.

POLARA AND MONACO SERIES

Model Number	Body/Style Number	Body Type & Seating	Factory Price	Shipping Weight	Production Total
POLARA SERIES					
DL41	41	4-dr Sed-6P	3618	3835	25,187
D143	43	4-dr HT-6P	3709	3875	8,212
DL23	23	2-dr HT-6P	3641	3800	7,022
DM41	41	4-dr Cus Sed-6P	3808	3845	19,739
DM43	43	4-dr Cus HT-6P	3898	3890	22,505
DM23	23	2-dr Cus HT-6P	3830	3815	15,039

POLARA AND MONACO SERIES

Model Number	Body/Style Number	Body Type & Seating	Factory Price	Shipping Weight	Production Total
POLARA SERIES					
DM45	45	4-dr Cus Wag-6P	4262	4320	3,497
DM46	46	4-dr Cus Wag-9P	4371	4370	7,660
MONACO SERIES					
DP41	41	4-dr Sed-6P	4095	3980	6,474
DP43	43	4-dr HT-6P	4216	4030	15,039
DP23	23	2-dr HT-6P	4153	3960	7,786
DP45	45	4-dr Wag-6P	4627	4445	2,569
DP46	46	4-dr Wag-9P	4756	4490	5,145

NOTE 1: The production total listed for Model DL23 is an estimate of model year production for this model, excluding shipments to Canada. This should be considered a 'ballpark' figure only. All other totals above are exact model year records, including Canadian shipments.
NOTE 2: Data above slash for six/below slash for V-8.

1972 Dodge, Challenger two-door hardtop sports coupe, V-8

CHALLENGER SERIES — (ALL ENGINES) — The Challenger redesign for 1972 had a few cosmetic changes. Only two body styles were offered in 1972, with the beautiful convertible deleted. This was significant in that the Challenger was the last Dodge convertible to be produced until 10 years later. The Challenger was the base trim level hardtop and included all federally mandated safety and pollution equipment '225' Slant Six engine; front and rear side armrests; front ashtray; cigarette lighter; color-keyed carpeting; ventless side windows; glovebox with rotary latch: heater and defroster; dual horns; dome and parking brake/brake system warning lights; outside left manual mirror; inside day/night mirror-bucket seats; front foam seat cushion; three-spoke steering; wheel (with simulated woodgrain padded hub); electric windshield washer; and concealed two-speed wipers. The Challenger Rallye was the high-performance option for the series and included all the standard Challenger features, plus the 318 cid V-8 engine; a side scoop behind the front wheels; and strobe-type tape stripes that ran the full length of the car.

CHALLENGER SERIES I.D. NUMBERS: See 1972 Dodge I.D. Number listing. All models began at 100001 and went up in the unit number sequence.

CHALLENGER SERIES

Model Number	Body/Style Number	Body Type & Seating	Factory Price	Shipping Weight	Production Total
JH23	23	2-dr HT-4P	2790/2902	3070/3125	18,535
JS23	23	2-dr Rallye HT-4P	3082	3225	8,123

NOTE: Data above slash for six/below for V-8.

ENGINES

Slant Six. Overhead valves. Cast iron block. Displacement: 198 cid. Bore and stroke: 3.40 x 3.64 inches. Compression ratio: 8.4:1. Net hp: 100 at 4400 rpm. Four main bearings. Solid valve lifters. Carburetion: one-barrel.

Slant Six. Overhead valves. Cast iron block. Displacement: 225 cid. Bore and stroke: 3.41 x 4.13 inches. Compression ratio: 8.4:1. Net hp: 110 at 4000 rpm. Four main bearings. Solid valve lifters. Carburetion: one-barrel.

V-8. Overhead valves. Cast iron block. Displacement: 318 cid. Bore and stroke: 3.91 x 3.31 inches. Compression ratio: 8.6:1. Net hp: 150 at 4000 rpm. Four main bearings. Hydraulic valve lifters. Carburetion: two-barrel.

V-8. Overhead valves. Cast iron block. Displacement: 340 cid. Bore and stroke: 4.04 x 3.31 inches. Compression ratio: 8.5:1. Net hp: 240 at 4800 rpm. Five main bearings. Hydraulic valve lifters. Carburetion: Carter ThermoQuad four-barrel.

V-8. Overhead valves. Cast iron block. Displacement: 360 cid. Bore and stroke: 4.00 x 3.58 inches. Compression ratio: 8.8:1. Net hp: 175 at 40000 rpm. Five main bearings. Hydraulic valve lifters. Carburetion: two-barrel.

V-8. Overhead valves. Cast iron block. Displacement: 400 cid. Bore and stroke: 4.34 x 3.38 inches. Compression ratio: 8.2:1. Net hp: 190 at 4400 rpm. Five main bearings. Hydraulic valve lifters. Carburetion: two-barrel.

V-8. Overhead valves. Cast iron block. Displacement: 400 cid. Bore and stroke: 4.34 x 3.38 inches. Compression ratio: 8.2:1. Net hp: 255 at 4400 rpm. Five main bearings. Hydraulic valve lifters. Carburetion: four-barrel.

Magnum V-8. Overhead valves. Cast iron block. Displacement: 440 cid. Bore and stroke: 4.32 x 3.75 inches. Compression ratio: 8.2:1: Net hp: 280. Five main bearings. Hydraulic valve lifters. Carburetion: four-barrel.

'Six-Pack' V-8. Overhead valves. Cast iron block. Displacement: 440 cid. Bore and stroke: 4.32 x 3.75 inches. Compression ratio: 10.3:1. Net hp: 330 at 4800 rpm. Five main bearings. Hydraulic valve lifters. Carburetion: three Holley two-barrels.

1972 DODGE CHASSIS FEATURES:

(DEMON) Wheelbase: 108 inches. Overall length: 192.5 inches. Tires: 6.45 x 14 tubeless black sidewall (E70 x 14 belted black sidewall with raised white letters on Demon 340 models). Three-speed manual transmission was standard on all Demons, with the TorqueFlite automatic options. (DART) Wheelbase: 111 inches. Overall length: 197 inches. Tires: D78 x 14 belted black sidewall. Three-speed manual transmission was standard on all Darts, with the TorqueFlite automatic or four-speed manual transmissions optional. (CHALLENGER) Wheelbase: 110 inches. Overall length: 192 inches. Tires: 7.35 x 14 tubeless black sidewall on standard Challenger, F70 x 14 belted black sidewall on Rallye models. Three-speed manual transmission was standard on all Challengers unless otherwise noted, with the TorqueFlite automatic or four-speed manual transmission optional. (CORONET) Wheelbase: 118 inches. Overall length: 207 inches on sedans and 214 inches on station wagons. Tires: E78 x 14 belted black sidewall on sedans and H78 x 14 belted black sidewall on station wagons. Three-speed manual transmission was standard on all Coronets, with the Torque-Flite automatic and four-speed manual transmission optional. (CHARGER) Wheelbase: 115 inches. Overall length: 206 inches. Tires: E78 x 14 belted black sidewall (F70 x 14 belted black sidewall with raised white letters on Rallye models). Three-speed manual transmission was standard on all Chargers unless otherwise noted, with the TorqueFlite automatic or four-speed manual transmissions optional. (POLARA AND MONACO) Wheelbase: 122 inches. Overall length: 220 inches on sedans and 223 inches on station Wagons. Tires: F78 x 15 belted black sidewall on Polara sedans, G78 x 15 belted black sidewall on Monaco sedans, and J78 x 15 belted black sidewall on Polara six-passenger station wagons and L84 x 15 belted black sidewall on Polara nine-passenger station wagons. TorqueFlite automatic transmission was standard on all Polara and Monaco models.

CONVENIENCE OPTIONS FOR DEMON/DART/CHALLENGER: 225 cid Slant Six engine in Demons ($37.85). TorqueFlite automatic transmission ($177.75-$208.40). Four-speed manual transmission ($184.50). Power steering ($92.25). Power brakes, drum type ($40.45); disc type ($62.30). All tinted glass ($35.85); windshield only ($24.35). Air conditioning ($354). Two-tone paint ($30.40). Music Master AM radio ($59.40). AM/FM radio ($124.55). AM/8-track stereo ($196.25). Simulated woodgrained sport steering wheel ($18.40-$28.00).

CONVENIENCE OPTIONS FOR CORONET/CHARGER/POLARA/MONACO: 340 cid V-8 engine in Chargers ($209.70). 440 cid Six-Pack V-8 engine in Charger Rallyes ($306.45). 440 cid V-8 in Polaras and Monacos ($193.35-$148.60). TorqueFlite automatic transmission ($203.45-$231.65). Power steering ($102.65$113.70). Power brakes, disc only, required on wagons ($68.05). Power seats ($90.95-102.65). Power windows ($125). Power front disc brakes ($68.05). Air conditioning, single type ($364.80-$412.95). AM radio ($64.90). AM/FM radio ($209). AM/FM stereo radio with 8-track tape player ($358). Four-speed manual transmission ($201.85). Heavy-duty suspension ($13-$14). Deep Dish wheelcovers ($31.15$57.85). Deluxe wheelcovers ($26.75). Wire wheelcovers ($41.95-$68.50). Rallye Road wheels ($28.35-$57.85). Limited-slip differential ($44.75-$47.65). Vinyl top ($94).

HISTORICAL FOOTNOTES: 1972 was a significant year for several reasons in the mechanical aspect of the Dodges. A new federal law required that all automobiles produced that year have the ability to run on low lead or no lead gasoline, requiring that the compression ratio on the high-performance engines be lowered. Also, all engines were rated at SAE net horsepower, rather than brake horsepower, as in previous years. This is the theoretical horse-power with all accessories in place. Richard Petty switched from racing a Plymouth to a Dodge Charger midway through the 1972 NASCAR Grand National season. He would run these cars into 1978. Dodge won five events that year.

1973 DODGE

1973 DART SPORT SERIES — (ALL ENGINES) — Continuing to use the same body as in the previous few years, the new Darts were separated from their predecessors by an entirely new front end arrangement. It featured a new hood, with a ridge in the middle. An all-new grille protruded forward at the center. This was the first year for the new, federally mandated, safety bumpers on the front ends of cars. The Dart's new bumper carried the theme initiated by the grille. All new Chrysler products featured electronic ignition for 1973. The Demon nomenclature was dropped for the 'value package' Dart and the new name was Dart Sport. Dart Sports included all safety and pollution equipment; pivoting rear quarter windows; 198 cid Slant Six engine; black rubber floor mats; and 6.95 x 14 tubeless black sidewall tires. The Dart Sport designation was carried, in block letters, on the front fenders, behind the front wheelwells. The Dodge name, also in block letters, was carried on the right side of the rear escutcheon panel. The Dart Sport 340 continued as the high-performance version of the standard Dart Sport. It included all the standard Dart Sport features, plus the 340 cid V-8 engine with three-speed manual transmission; E70 x 14 belted black sidewall tires; 'performance' bodyside tape stripes; front and rear Rallye Suspension (with sway bar); and floor-mounted shift lever. A Rallye package for the base Dart Sport was available, at midyear, as was a "Topper" trim option.

DODGE I.D. NUMBERS: VIN located on plate attached to left-hand side of dashboard, visible through windshield. The VIN has 13 symbols. (The first four symbols, together, are the Model Number in second column of charts below.) The first symbol identifies the car-line or marque: D=Dodge; J=Challenger; L=Dart; W=Coronet and X=Charger. The second symbol indicates trim/price level as follows: G=New York Taxi; H=High; L=Low; M=Medium; P=Premium; S=Special. The next two symbols identify the body style, as follows: 21=two-door coupe; 23=two-door hardtop; 29=two-door Sports hardtop; 41=sedan; 43=hardtop sedan; 45=six-passenger station wagon; 46=nine-passenger station wagon. The fifth symbol denotes the engine as follows: (6-cyl.) B=198 cid; C=225 cid; E=special order (V-8); G=318 cid 2V; H=340 cid 4V (high-performance); K=360 cid 2V; M=400 cid 2V; P=400 cid 4V (high-performance); T=440 cid 4V; U=440 cid 4V (high-performance). The sixth symbol denotes the model year as follows: 3=1973. The seventh symbol denotes the assembly plant, as follows: A=Lynch Rd. (Detroit); B=Hamtramck, Mich.; C=Jefferson Ave. (Detroit); D=Belvedere, Ill.; F=Newark, Del.; G=St. Louis, Mo.; H=New Stanton, RI; R=Windsor, Ont. (Canada). The last six symbols are the sequential production number starting at 100001 for each series at each plant. Body code plate located under hood, on left (fender shield, wheelhousing or radiator support) includes S.O. number and trim/paint codes too numerous to list.

1973 Dodge Dart Sport two-door coupe

DART SPORT SERIES

Model Number	Body/Style Number	Body Type & Seating	Factory Price	Shipping Weight	Production Total
LL	29	2-dr Cpe-6P	2424/2557	2850/3045	68,113
LM	29	2-dr'340'Cpe-6P	2853	3205	11,315

NOTE 1: Data above slash for six/below slash for V-8s.

NOTE 2: Exact model year production totals are given for all models, except where otherwise noted.

DART SERIES — (ALL ENGINES) — The Dart was the standard base trim level in the Dart model lineup and included all federally mandated safety and pollution equipment; front and rear armrests; ashtrays; cigarette lighter; concealed spare tire; rubber floor mats; glovebox with rotary latch; heater and defroster; dome light; parking brake and brake system warning lights; all-vinyl bench seats; three-spoke steering wheel (with padded horn button); two-speed electric windshield wipers; 198 cid Slant Six engine (or 318 cid V-8 engine); and vent wings. Dart Swinger and Custom models also included dual note horns; drip rail and wheel lip moldings; three-spoke steering wheel (with padded hub and horn tabs); and carpeting. The Custom models also included bodyside moldings and ventless side windows. Each model carried the model designation on the front fender sides, behind the front wheel opening.

DART, SWINGER AND CUSTOM SERIES I.D. NUMBERS: See 1973 Dodge I.D. Number listing. All models began at 100001 and went up in the unit number sequence.

DART/SWINGER/CUSTOM SERIES

Model Number	Body/Style Number	Body Type & Seating	Factory Price	Shipping Weight	Production Total
DART					
LL	41	4-dr Sed-6P	2504/2654	2910/3060	21,539
LL	23	2-dr HT Cpe-6P	2462/2612	2895/3045	17,480
SWINGER					
LH	23	2-dr HT Cpe-6P	2617/2767	2890/3040	107,619
CUSTOM					
LH	41	4-dr Sed-6P	2658/2808	2910/3060	62,626

NOTE 1: Data above slash for six/below slash for V-8s.

1973 Dodge, Coronet Custom four-door sedan, V-8

CORONET SERIES — (ALL ENGINES) — Even though they continued to use the same body as in previous years, the new Coronets were much more pleasant cars due to the concentration on comfort and ride during 1973. More sound deadeners and insulation materials were added and the suspension contained redesigned components which contributed to a smoother ride. Again offered only in four-door sedan and station wagon configuration, the new Coronets featured slightly restyled taillights and grilles. They used new colors and updated interiors, too. The Coronet was the base trim level and included all federally mandated safety and pollution equipment; the 225 cid Slant Six (or 318 cid V-8 engine); color-keyed rubber floor mats; a single horn; and no exterior moldings (except on windshield and rear windows). Also included was the three-spoke steering wheel; rear ashtray; and extra thick foam seat cushion. Station wagons also included heavy-duty brakes; drip rail moldings and three-way tailgates. The Coronet model designation was carried, in block letters, on the front fenders behind the front wheelwell. The Coronet Custom was the top trim level in the Coronet Series and included all the standard Coronet features, plus color-keyed carpeting; dual note horns; wheel opening, bodyside and drip rail moldings; and three-spoke steering wheel with padded horn bars. Also included were upper door frame moldings, rear door automatic entrance light and deluxe wheelcovers. The Crestwood station wagons also included wheelwell moldings; bright upper door frame moldings and quarter window moldings; woodgrain side panels and, on the nine-passenger Crestwood, tailgate inside safety latch.

CORONET SERIES I.D. NUMBERS: See 1973 Dodge I.D. Number listing. All models began at 100001 and went up in the unit number sequence.

CORONET SERIES

Model Number	Body/Style Number	Body Type & Seating	Factory Price	Shipping Weight	Production Total
CORONET					
WL	41	4-dr Sed-6P	2867/2979	3440/3505	14,395
WL	45	4-dr Sta Wag-6P	3314	3955	4,874
CORONET CUSTOM					
WH	41	4-dr Sed 6P	3017/3129	3430/3495	46,491
WH	45	4-dr Sta Wag-6P	3442	3955	Note 1
WH	46	4-dr Sta Wag-9P	3560	4000	Note 1
CRESTWOOD					
WP	45	4-dr Sta Wag-6P	3671	3970	Note 2
WP	46	4-dr Sta Wag-9P	3791	4005	Note 2

NOTE 1: Exactly 13,018 Coronet Custom station wagons were built, included both six and nine-passenger styles.

NOTE 2: Exactly 8,755 Coronet Crestwood station wagons were built, including both six and nine-passenger styles.

NOTE 3: Data above slash for six/below slash for V-8s.

CHARGER SERIES — (ALL ENGINES) — Continuing the policy of the past two years, all two-door intermediate models were considered Chargers. The grille was revised slightly from the previous models, but the most noticeable change was in the new roofline, around the quarter windows. The new window line was more conservative than in the past, but was also more pleasing to many. New taillights, featuring 22 individual lenses, were used for 1973. The standard Charger continued as the base trim level and included all federally mandated safety and pollution equipment; 225 cid Slant Six (or 318 cid V-8) engine; cigarette lighter; dual horns; color-keyed carpeting; inside day/night mirror; roof drip rail and wheelwell moldings; and two-speed windshield wipers. The Charger Rallye option included all the standard Charger features, plus front and rear sway bars; F70 x 14 raised white-letter black sidewall tires; power bulge hood; Rallye instrument cluster; body tape stripes; hood pins; and special exterior ornamentation. The Charger SE continued as the top trim level and included all the standard Charger features, plus a landau vinyl top with three-section opera windows, replacing the quarter windows. The 440 cid Magnum V-8 engine continued as the largest engine option, but was offered only on the Rallye.

1973 Dodge, Charger SE two-door coupe, V-8

CHARGER SERIES I.D. NUMBERS: See 1973 Dodge I.D. Numbers listing. All models began at 100001 and went up in the unit number sequence.

CHARGER SERIES

Model Number	Body/Style Number	Body Type & Seating	Factory Price	Shipping Weight	Production Total
CHARGER COUPE					
WL	21	2-dr Cpe-6P	2810/2922	3395/3460	11,995
CHARGER HARDTOP					
WH	23	2-dr HT Cpe-6P	3060/3171	3450/3480	45,415
CHARGER SPECIAL EDITION					
WP	29	2-dr HT Cpe-6P	3375	3540	61,908

1973 Dodge, Monaco two-door hardtop sports coupe, V-8

POLARA/MONACO SERIES — (ALL ENGINES) — The new Polara was only slightly updated from the previous year. The new frontal treatment featured a rectangular grille with a rectangular grid pattern insert. Quad headlights and a new bumper were now separate from the grille. Taillights made up of multiple rectangular sections were set into the rear bumper.

The Polara was the base trim level full-size Dodge and included all federally mandated safety and pollution equipment; air control system; front and rear armrests; front and rear ashtrays; 46 ampere/hour battery; cigarette lighter; color-keyed carpeting; dual horns; dome and parking brake system warning lights; inside day/night mirror; outside left manual mirror; three-spoke steering wheel (with padded hub); electric windshield washers; two-speed wipers; and the 318 cid V-8 engine. The Dodge name, in block letters, was spaced evenly across the top of the grille surround trim and on the right side of the trunk lid. The Polara Custom was the intermediate trim level and included all the Polara features, plus bodyside moldings with a vinyl insert; wheel opening moldings, foam seat cushions and the Custom model designation located on the rear fenders. Continuing as the top trim level was the Monaco Series. As in the previous year, the Monaco was somewhat segregated from the basic Polara Series with a completely different front end. A revised grille insert and a new rear bumper and taillights distinguished the 1973 models from the 1972s. The six-cylinder base Polara for fleet use was still offered.

POLARA/MONACO SERIES I.D. NUMBERS: See 1973 Dodge I.D. Number listing. All models began at 100001 and went up in the unit number sequence.

POLARA/MONACO SERIES

Model Number	Body/Style Number	Body Type & Seating	Factory Price	Shipping Weight	Production Total
STANDARD POLARA					
DL	41	4-dr Sed-6P	NA/3729	NA/3865	15,015
DL	23	2-dr HT Cpe-6P	NA/3752	NA/3835	6,432
DL	45	4-dr Sta Wag-6P	4186	4420	3,327
POLARA CUSTOM					
DM	41	4-dr Sed-6P	3911	3870	23,939
DM	43	4-dr HT Sed-6P	4001	3905	29,341
DM	23	2-dr HT Cpe-6P	3928	3835	17,406
DM	45	4-dr Sta Wag-6P	4370	4440	3,702
DM	46	4-dr Sta Wag-9P	4494	4485	8,839
MONACO					
DP	41	4-dr Sed-6P	4218	4020	6,316
DP	43	4-dr HT Sed-6P	4339	4060	9,031
DP	23	2-dr HT Cpe-6P	4276	3985	6,133
DP	45	4-dr Sta Wag-6P	4730	4470	2,337
DP	46	4-dr Sta Wag-9P	4859	4515	5,579

NOTE 1: A Brougham option package for the Monaco four-door passenger cars included special nameplates; lower body moldings with front and rear extensions; 50/50 type split-back front center armrest (reclining passenger seatback); rear seat center armrests; carpeted trunk compartment; spare tire cover and cornering lamps. This package was installed on 4,200 sedans and 1,564 four-door hardtop sedans.
NOTE 2: Data above slash for six/below slash for V-8s.

1973 Dodge, Challenger Rallye two-door hardtop sports coupe, V-8

CHALLENGER SERIES — (ALL ENGINES) — The only change in the Challenger from the 1972 version was a revised grille insert and big rubber bumper guards to meet safety bumper regulations. The Challenger was the base trim level hardtop and included all the federally mandated safety and pollution equipment; 318 cid V-8 engine; front and rear side armrests; front ashtrays; cigarette lighter; color-keyed carpeting; ventless side windows; glovebox with rotary latch; heater and defroster; dual horns; dome and parking brake/brake system warning lights; outside left manual mirror; inside day/night mirror; bucket seats; front foam seat cushion; three-spoke steering wheel (with simulated woodgrain and padded hub); electric windshield washer; and concealed two-speed wipers. The Challenger Rallye option also included a side scoop (located behind the front wheels) and strobe-type tape stripes that ran the full length of the car.

CHALLENGER SERIES I.D. NUMBERS: See 1973 Dodge I.D. Number listing. All models began at 100001 and went up in the unit number sequence.

CHALLENGER SERIES

Model Number	Body/Style Number	Body Type & Seating	Factory Price	Shipping Weight	Production Total
JH	23	2-dr HT Cpe-4P	3011	3155	32,596

ENGINES

Slant Six. Overhead valves. Cast iron block. Displacement: 198 cid. Bore and stroke: 3.40 x 3.64 inches. Compression ratio: 8.4:1. Net hp: 95 at 4400 rpm. Four main bearings. Solid valve lifters. Carburetion: one-barrel.

Slant Six. Overhead valves. Cast iron block. Displacement: 225 cid. Bore and stroke: 3.41 x 4.13 inches. Compression ratio: 8.4:1. Net hp: 105 at 4000 rpm. Four main bearings. Solid valve lifters. Carburetion: one-barrel.

V-8. Overhead valves. Cast iron block. Displacement: 318 cid. Bore and stroke: 3.91 x 3.31 inches. Compression ratio: 8.6:1. Net hp: 150 at 4000 rpm. Four main bearings. Hydraulic valve lifters. Carburetion: two-barrel.

V-8. Overhead valves. Cast iron block. Displacement: 340 cid. Bore and stroke: 4.04 x 3.31 inches. Compression ratio: 8.5:1. Net hp: 240 at 4800 rpm. Five main bearings. Hydraulic valve lifters. Carburetion: Carter ThermoQuad four-barrel.

V-8. Overhead valves. Cast iron block. Displacement: 360 cid. Bore and stroke: 4.00 x 3.58 inches. Compression ratio: 8.4:1. Net hp: 170 at 40000 rpm. Five main bearings. Hydraulic valve lifters. Carburetion: two-barrel.

V-8. Overhead valves. Cast iron block. Displacement: 400 cid. Bore and stroke: 4.34 x 3.38 inches. Compression ratio: 8.2:1. Net hp: 175 at 4400 rpm. Five main bearings. Hydraulic valve lifters. Carburetion: two-barrel.

V-8. Overhead valves. Cast iron block. Displacement: 400 cid. Bore and stroke: 4.34 x 3.38 inches. Compression ratio: 8.2:1. Net hp: 260 at 4400 rpm. Five main bearings. Hydraulic valve lifters. Carburetion: four-barrel.

Magnum V-8. Overhead valves. Cast iron block. Displacement: 440 cid. Bore and stroke: 4.32 x 3.75 inches. Compression ratio: 8.2:1: Net hp: 280. Five main bearings. Hydraulic valve lifters. Carburetion: four-barrel.

CHASSIS FEATURES: Wheelbase: (Dart Coupe) 108 inches; (Dart hardtop/sedan) 111 inches; (Challenger) 110 inches; (all Coronets) 118 inches; (Charger) 115 inches; (Polara/Monaco) 122 inches. Overall length: (Dart Coupe) 200 inches; (Dart hardtop/sedan) 204 inches; (Challenger) 199 inches; (Coronet wagon) 218 inches; (Coronet/Charger) 213 inches; (Polara wagon) 228 inches; (Monaco wagon) 231 inches; (Polara) 227 inches; (Monaco) 229 inches. Width: (Dart Coupe) 72 inches; (Dart hardtop/sedan) 70 inches; (Challenger) 77 inches; (Charger) 77 inches; (Coronet wagon) 79 inches; (Coronet) 78 inches; (Polara/Monaco) 80 inches. Tires: (Dart '340') E70 x 14, (all other Darts) 6.95 x 14; (Challenger) 7.35 x 14; (Coronet/Charger) E78-14; (Coronet wagon) H78-14; (Polara/Monaco three-seat wagon) L84-15; (Polara/Monaco two-seat wagon) J78-15; (Polara passenger) G78-15; (Monaco passenger) H78-15.

POWERTRAIN OPTIONS: Four-barrel 340 cid V-8 engine in Coronet, Charger and Crestwood station wagon ($209). Four-barrel 340 cid V-8 engine, in Challenger ($181). Four-barrel 400 cid engine, in Coronet, Charger and Crestwood station wagon ($176). Automatic transmission standard in Polara, Polara Custom and Monaco. Two-barrel 318 cid V-8 engine in Dodge Dart ($143).

POPULAR CONVENIENCE OPTIONS: Vinyl top, on Dart ($61). Air conditioning, in Dart ($358). Vinyl top. on Coronet ($95). Coronet/Charger AM/FM stereo ($211). Coronet/Charger AM/FM stereo with tape deck ($362). Regular vinyl top on Charger, standard on Special Edition models; on other models ($115). Sunroof and canopy top, on Charger ($251). Sunroof with full-vinyl top, on Charger ($286). Sunroof with formal style vinyl roof, on Charger ($171). Vinyl top, on Challenger ($81). AM/FM stereo, in Challenger ($194). Challenger Rallye Package ($182). Air conditioning, in Challenger ($369). Vinyl top, on Monaco/Polara ($108). Monaco Brougham Package ($319). AM/FM stereo in Monaco/Polara ($212). AM/FM stereo with tape in Monaco/Polara ($363). Power windows, in Monaco/Polara ($126).

HISTORICAL FOOTNOTES: The full-sized Dodges were introduced in Sept., 1972 and the Dodge Darts appeared in dealer showrooms the same time. Model year production peaked at 675,161 units. Richard Petty accounted for six of eight Dodge wins in NASCAR Grand National stock car races in 1973, driving a Charger.

1974 DODGE

1974 DART SPORT SERIES — (ALL ENGINES) — Once again sporting the same body as in the past three years, the 1974 Darts were updated only with new taillight, rear bumper and rear valance treatments. The balance of the car remained unchanged. The Dart Sport continued as the base trim level and included all federally mandated safety and pollution equipment; pivoting rear quarter windows; the 198 cid Slant Six engine; black rubber floor mats; 6.95 x 14 black sidewall tubeless tires; and the Dart Sport designation, in block letters, on the front fenders (just behind the wheelwells). The Dodge name, also in block letters, was carried on the right side of the rear escutcheon panel. With a large displacement motor replacing last year's '340,' the Dart Sport 360 was the high-performance version of the Sport lineup and included all Dart Sport features, plus the 360 cid two-barrel V-8 engine; ventless side windows; E70 x 14 black sidewall tires; grille surround moldings; front and rear bumper guards; power front disc brakes; heavy-duty suspension and shock absorbers; wheelcovers; tape stripes; three-speed manual transmission with floor mounted shifter; electronic ignition; and cigar lighter. Special 360 exterior identification was also included in the 360 package. A "Hang Ten" option package was available, after midyear, for Dart Sport Coupes. A special striped interior and exterior were part of the surfing-oriented package. A "Topper" trim package was available, midyear, for the base Dart Sport Coupe.

DODGE I.D. NUMBERS: VIN located on plate attached to left-hand side of dashboard, visible through windshield. The VIN has 13 symbols. (The first four symbols, together, are the Model Number in second column of charts below.) The first symbol identifies the car-line or marque: D=Dodge; J=Challenger; L=Dart; W=Coronet/Charger. The second symbol indicates trim/price level as follows: G=Grand; H=High; L=Low; M=Medium; P=Premium; S=Special. The next two symbols identify the body style, as follows: 21=two-door coupe; 23=two-door hardtop; 29=two-door Special hardtop; 41=sedan; 43=hardtop sedan; 45=six-passenger station wagon; 46=nine-passenger station wagon. The fifth symbol denotes the engine as follows: (6-cyl.) B=198 cid; C=225 cid; E=special order (V-8); G=318 cid 2V; H=340 cid 4V (high-performance); J= 360 cid 4V; K=360 cid 2V; L=360 cid 4V (high-performance); M=400 cid 2V; N=400 cid 4V; P=400 cid 4V (high-performance); T=440 cid 4V; U=440 cid 4V (high-performance). The sixth symbol denotes the model year as follows: 4=1974. The seventh symbol denotes the assembly plant, as follows: A=Lynch Rd. (Detroit); B=Hamtramck, Mich.; C=Jefferson Ave. (Detroit); D=Belvedere, Ill.; F=Newark, Del.; G=St. Louis, Mo. The last six symbols are the sequential production number starting at 100001 for each series at each plant. Body code plate located under hood, on left (fender shield, wheelhousing or radiator support) includes S.O. number and trim/paint codes too numerous to list.

DART SPORT SERIES

Model Number	Body/Style Number	Body Type & Seating	Factory Price	Shipping Weight	Production Total
DART SPORT					
LL	29	2-dr Cpe-6P	2878/3029	2990/3140	Note 1
DART SPORT '360'					
LM	29	2-dr Cpe-6P	3320	3330	Note 1

NOTE 1: Some 63,518 Dart Sports were built during model year 1974. Of those, 40,293 were sixes and 23.225 were V-8s. Some 3.951 Dart Sport 360s were built during the year, all V-8s.
NOTE 2: Exact model year production totals are not available for 1974 Dodges. Figures given in the footnotes are model year totals for cars built in the U.S. for domestic sales and are expressed in exact amounts. Cars built in Canada for the domestic market are not included.

NOTE 3: Data above slash for six/below slash for V-8.

DART SERIES — (ALL ENGINES) — The Dart was the standard base trim level in the Dart model lineup and included all federally mandated safety and pollution equipment; front and rear armrests; ashtrays; cigarette lighter; concealed spare tire; rubber floor mats; glovebox

with rotary latch; heater and defroster; dome light; parking brake and brake system warning lights; all-vinyl bench seats; three-spoke steering wheel (with padded horn button); two-speed windshield wipers; 198 cid Slant Six (or 318 V-8 engine); and vent wings. Dart Swingers included all the standard Dart features plus, dual note horns; deluxe steering wheel; carpeting; and drip rail and door edge moldings. The Custom included all the Swinger features, plus cloth and vinyl seats. The Special Edition was a new, luxury version Dart model and included all the Customs features plus, padded vinyl top, brocade cloth seating surfaces and color-keyed deluxe wheelcovers. The Special Edition was released Jan. 13, 1974, as a midyear addition to the lineup.

1974 Dodge, Dart Swinger two-door hardtop sports coupe, V-8

DART / SWINGER / CUSTOM / SPECIAL EDITION SERIES I.D. NUMBERS: See 1974 Dodge I.D. Number listing. All models began at 100001 and went up in the unit number sequence.

DART(SWINGER/CUSTOM/SPECIAL EDITION SERIES

Mode Number	Body/Style Number	Body Type & Seating	Factory Price	Shipping Weight	Production Total
BASE/SPECIAL					
LL	41	4-dr Sed-6P	2961/3112	3055/3205	Note 1
LL	23	2-dr Spl HT Cpe-6P	2918/3069	3035/3185	Note 1
SWINGE CUSTOM					
LH	23	2-dr Swinger-6P	3077/3228	3030/3180	Note 1
LH	41	4-dr Cus Sed-6P	3119/3270	3055/3205	Note 1
SPECIAL EDITION					
LP	41	4-dr Sed-6P	3837/3988	3641/3791	Note 1
LP	23	2-dr HT Cpe-6P	3794/3945	3599/3749	Note 1

NOTE 1: Some 16,155 Swinger Specials were built during model year 1974. Of those, 14,211 were sixes and 1,944 were V-8s. Some 89,24 Swingers were built during that year. Of those, 56,126 were sixes and 33,116 were V-8s. During model year 1974 some 78,216 Customs were built. Of those. 50,047 were sixes and 28,16 were V-8s. Some 12,385 Special Editions were built during that year. Of those, 3,111 were sixes and 9,274 were V-8s.
NOTE 2: Data above slash for six/below slash for V-8.

1974 Dodge, Coronet Custom four-door sedan, V-8

CORONET SERIES — (ALL ENGINES) — Coronets received a front end restyling, changed rear bumper and new taillights for 1974. The full-width grille enclosed the quad headlights and the grille was an eggcrate design with rectangular openings. The Dodge name, in block letters, was spaced across the center of the hood and also appeared on the right side of the trunk lid. The Coronet was the base trim level and included all federally mandated safety and pollution equipment; the 225 cid Slant Six (or 318 cid V-8) engine; color-keyed rubber floor mats; vinyl bench seats; front and rear bumper guards; day/night inside mirror; foam cushion rear seat; three-spoke steering wheel; front and rear ashtrays and armrests; dome light; chrome hubcaps; cigarette lighter; glovebox lock; dual horns; sill moldings; and E78 x 14 black sidewall tubeless tires. The Coronet Custom was the next trim level in the Coronet Series and included all the Coronet trim plus, carpeting; roof drip rail moldings; wheel lip opening and bodyside moldings; dual note horns; and deluxe steering wheel. The Crestwood was the top trim level station wagon and included all the standard station wagon features, plus roof mounted air deflectors; deluxe wheelcovers; map and glovebox lights; cargo area carpeting; woodgrain bodyside panels; bright upper door frame and quarter widow moldings; and H78 x 14 black sidewall tires.

CORONET SERIES I.D. NUMBERS: See 1974 Dart Series I. D. Number listing. All models began at 100001 and went up in the unit number sequence.

CORONET SERIES

Model Number	Body/Style Number	Body Type & Seating	Factory Price	Shipping Weight	Production Total
CORONET					
WL	41	4-dr Sta Wag-6P	3271/3386	3510/3585	Note 1
WL	45	4-dr Sta Wag-6P	3699	4085	Note 1

CORONET CUSTOM

WH	41	4-dr Sed-6P	3374/3489	3500/3575	Note 1
WH	45	4-dr Sta Wag-6P	3882	4090	Note 1
WH	46	4-dr Sta Wag-9P	4196	4130	Note 1
CRESTWOOD					
WP	45	4-dr Sta Wag-6P	4117	4100	Note 1
WP	46	4-dr Sta Wag-9P	4433	4135	Note 1

NOTE1: Some 6,013 Coronets and Chargers were built during model year 1974. Of those, 3,315 were sixes and 2,698 were V-8s. Some 55,599 Customs were built during the year. Of those, 2,252 were sixes and 53,347 were V-8s. Some 30,957 Charger SEs were built during model year 1974, all V-8s.

1974 Dodge, Challenger two-door hardtop sports coupe V-8

CHARGER SERIES — (ALL ENGINES) — Featuring only slight changes in the grille and taillights, the 1974 Chargers continued to be very popular with the public. The standard Charger continued as the base trim level and included all federally mandated safety and pollution equipment; 225 cid Slant Six (or 318 cid V-8) engine; cigarette lighter; dual horns; color-keyed carpeting; inside day/night mirror; roof drip rail and wheelwell moldings; and two-speed windshield wipers. The Charger Rallye option included all the standard Charger features, plus front and rear sway bars; F70 x 14 raised white-letter black sidewall tires; power-bulge hood; Rally instrument cluster; body tape stripes; hood pins; and special exterior ornamentation. The Charger SE continued as the top trim level and included all the standard Charger features; landau vinyl top with filled quarter windows and six opera windows; electric clock; concealed headlights; inside hood release; belt and rear hood moldings; front stone shield molding; deluxe wheelcovers; front bench seat with folding center armrests; Light Group; Rallye instrument cluster; and F78 x 14 black sidewall tires.

CHARGER SERIES I.D. NUMBERS: See 1974 Dodge I.D. Numbers listing. All models began at 100001 and went up in the unit number sequence.

CHARGER SERIES

Model Number	Body/Style Number	Body Type & Seating	Factory Price	Shipping Weight	Production Total
WL	21	2-dr Cpe-6P	3212/3327	3470/3550	Note 1
WL	23	2-dr HT Cpe-6P	3412/3526	3490/3565	Note 1
WP	29	2-dr SE HT-6P	3742	3625	Note 1

NOTE 1: See Note 1 Coronet Series.
NOTE 2: Data above slash for six/below slash for V-8.

1974 Dodge, Monaco four-door station wagon, V-8

MONACO SERIES — (ALL ENGINES) — For the first time since 1960, the Polara name was not included in the full-size lineup. All full-size 1974 models were called Monacos. Completely restyled for the year, the new Monacos were, perhaps, the most pleasant looking of all 1974 Dodges. The rounded look of the previous few years was replaced by a leaner and less bulky body style. The grille was similar to the Buicks of that era and, when combined with the squarer sides, more angular rooflines and very conservative use of chrome trim, produced a very nice-looking car. The Monaco was the base trim level and included all federally mandated safety and pollution equipment; front ashtrays and armrests; cigar lighter; carpeting; dual headlights and horns; dome and parking brake/brake system warning lights; inside day/night mirror; concealed wipers; air control system; power steering; TorqueFlite automatic transmission; power front disc brakes; front and rear bumper guards; front seatback latches; trunk compartment rubber mats; 360 cid V-8 engine; and G78 x 15 tubeless black sidewall tires. Monaco station wagons also had a power tailgate window; 400 cid V-8 engine; and J78 x 15 tubeless black sidewall tires. The Custom was the intermediate trim level Monaco and included all the standard Monaco features, plus a glovebox lock; adjustable front seat; rear armrests with ashtrays; ignition switch light; front and rear foam padded seats; wheel lip moldings; trunk mat; and dome light. The two-door hardtop also included a rear pillar interior courtesy light. Four-doors added upper door frame moldings and Custom station wagons also included a cargo area dome light and heavy-duty brakes. The Brougham was the top trim level Monaco and included all the Custom features, plus nylon carpeting; cornering lights; electric clock; all-vinyl bench seats (with fold-down center armrest); headlights-on reminder; deluxe wheelcovers; and HR78 x 15 radial black sidewall tires. Brougham wagons added rear

compartment lock; bright upper door frame and quarter window moldings; rear door automatic entrance switches; deluxe wheelcovers; woodgrained side panels with surround moldings; and cargo compartment carpeting. The 400 cid V-8 engine was also standard on all Brougham models.

MONACO SERIES I.D. NUMBERS: See 1974 Dodge I.D. Number listing. All models began at 100001 and went up in the unit number sequence.

MONACO SERIES

Model Number	Body/Style Number	Body Type & Seating	Factory Price	Shipping Weight	Production Total
MONACO					
DM	41	4-dr Sed-6P	4259	4170	Note 1
DM	23	2-dr HT Cpe-6P	4283	4150	Note 1
DM	45	4-dr Sta Wag-6P	4706	4760	Note 1
MONACO CUSTOM					
DH	41	4-dr Sed-6P	4446	4175	Note 1
DH	43	4-dr HT Sed-6P	4539	4205	Note 1
DH	23	2-dr HT Cpe-6P	4464	4155	Note 1
DH	45	4-dr Sta Wag-6P	4839	4770	Note 1
DH	46	4-dr Sta Wag-9P	4956	4815	Note 1
MONACO BROUGHAM					
DP	41	4-dr Sed-6P	4891	4410	Note 1
DP	43	4-dr HT Sed-6P	4999	4445	Note 1
DP	23	2-dr HT Cpe-6P	4951	4370	Note 1
DP	45	4-dr Sta Wag-6P	5360	4860	Note 1
DP	46	4-dr Sta Wag-9P	5477	4905	Note 1

NOTE 1: Some 20,810 Monacos, 4,874 Monaco Specials (police and taxi), 34,414 Customs and 18,226 Broughams were built during model year 1974, all V-8s.

1974 Dodge, Charger two-door hardtop sports coupe, V-8

CHALLENGER SERIES — (ALL ENGINES) — Appearing for the last time in this configuration (the name would be revived for a Japanese-built Dodge sport compact), the 1974 Challenger was unchanged from the 1973 models. The Challenger continued to be the base trim level and included all federally mandated safety and pollution equipment, vinyl bucket seats; front foam seat cushions; concealed wipers; three-speed manual transmission with floor-mounted shifter; the 318 cid V-8 engine: 7.35 x 14 tubeless black sidewall tires; three-spoke steering wheel; front and rear bumper guards; heavy-duty suspension; ventless side windows; roof drip rail and wheel lip guards; heavy-duty suspension; ventless windows; roof drip rail and wheel lip moldings; cigar lighter; carpeting; day/night inside mirror; and electronic ignition. The Challenger Rallye option added a side scoop, behind the front wheels, with strobe-type tape stripes that ran the full-length of the car, plus two hood scoops and special cast wheels with trim rings and F70 x 14 raised white-letter tires.

CHALLENGER SERIES I.D. NUMBERS: See 1974 Dodge I.D. Number listing. All models began at 100001 and went up in the unit number sequence.

CHALLENGER SERIES

Model Number	Body/Style Number	Body Type & Seating	Factory Price	Shipping Weight	Production Total
JH	23	2-dr HT Cpe-4P	3143	3225	16,437

ENGINES

Slant Six. Overhead valves. Cast iron block. Displacement: 198 cid. Bore and stroke: 3.40 x 3.64 inches. Compression ratio: 8.4:1. Net hp: 95 at 4400 rpm. Four main bearings. Solid valve lifters. Carburetion: one-barrel.

Slant Six. Overhead valves. Cast iron block. Displacement: 225 cid. Bore and stroke: 3.41 x 4.13 inches. Compression ratio: 8.4:1. Net hp: 105 at 4000 rpm. Four main bearings. Solid valve lifters. Carburetion: one-barrel.

V-8. Overhead valves. Cast iron block. Displacement: 318 cid. Bore and stroke: 3.91 x 3.31 inches. Compression ratio: 8.6:1. Net hp: 150 at 4000 rpm. Four main bearings. Hydraulic valve lifters. Carburetion: two-barrel.

V-8. Overhead valves. Cast iron block. Displacement: 360 cid. Bore and stroke: 4.00 x 3.58 inches. Compression ratio: 8.4:1. Net hp: 200 at 40000 rpm. Five main bearings. Hydraulic valve lifters. Carburetion: two-barrel.

V-8. Overhead valves. Cast iron block. Displacement: 360 cid. Bore and stroke: 4.00 x 3.58 inches. Compression ratio: 8.4:1. Net hp: 245 at 40000 rpm. Five main bearings. Hydraulic valve lifters. Carburetion: four-barrel.

V-8. Overhead valves. Cast iron block. Displacement: 400 cid. Bore and stroke: 4.34 x 3.38 inches. Compression ratio: 8.2:1. Net hp: 205 at 4400 rpm. Five main bearings. Hydraulic valve lifters. Carburetion: four-barrel.

V-8. Overhead valves. Cast iron block. Displacement: 400 cid. Bore and stroke: 4.34 x 3.38 inches. Compression ratio: 8.2:1. Net hp: 250 at 4400 rpm. Five main bearings. Hydraulic valve lifters. Carburetion: four-barrel.

V-8. Overhead valves. Cast iron block. Displacement: 440 cid. Bore and stroke: 4.32 x 3.75 inches. Compression ratio: 8.2:1. Net hp: 230. Five main bearings. Hydraulic valve lifters. Carburetion: four-barrel.

Magnum V-8. Overhead valves. Cast iron block. Displacement: 440 cid. Bore and stroke: 4.32 x 3.75 inches. Compression ratio: 8.2:1. Net hp: 275. Five main bearings. Hydraulic valve lifters. Carburetion: four-barrel.

CHASSIS FEATURES: Wheelbase: (Dart Coupe) 108 inches; (Dart hardtop/sedan) 111 inches; (Challenger) 110 inches; (all Coronets) 118 inches; (Charger) 115 inches; (Monaco) 121.5 inches. Overall length: (Dart Coupe) 204 inches; (Dart hardtop/sedan) 204 inches; (Challenger) 199 inches; (Coronet wagon) 218 inches; (Coronet/Charger) 213 inches; (Polara wagon) 228 inches; (Monaco wagon) 231 inches; (Polara) 227 inches; (Monaco Sedan) 224 inches; (Monaco Custom) 226 inches; (Monaco wagon) 227 inches; (Brougham wagon) 229 inches. Width: (Dart Coupe) 72 inches; (Dart hardtop/sedan) 70 inches; (Challenger) 77 inches; (Charger) 77 inches; (Coronet wagon) 79 inches; (Coronet) 78 inches; (Polara/Monaco) 80 inches. Tires: G78 x 15 tubeless black sidewall on sedans; J78 x 15 on Broughams and LR78 x 15B radial black sidewall on station wagons. TorqueFlite automatic transmission was standard on all Monaco models.

POWERTRAIN OPTIONS: Automatic transmission was standard on Monaco, Monaco Custom and Monaco Brougham. Charger '360' V-8 engine ($222). Challenger '360' V-8 engine ($259). Charger '400' V-8 engine ($188). Dart '318' V-8 engine ($151).

CONVENIENCE OPTIONS: Vinyl top, on Dart ($88). Air conditioning, on Dart ($384). Sun roof, on Dart ($154). Vinyl top, on Coronet ($103). AM/FM stereo, in Coronet/Charger ($230). Regular vinyl top, on Charger Special Edition (standard equipment); on all other Chargers ($125). Sun roof with vinyl canopy top, on Charger ($261). Vinyl top, on Monaco ($117). AM/FM stereo, in Monaco ($254). AM/FM stereo with tape, in Monaco ($397). Power windows, in Monaco ($137). Sun roof, in Monaco ($521). RV7 Package, on Monaco ($400). Vinyl top, on Challenger ($84). AM/FM stereo, in Challenger ($202). Rally Package, on Challenger ($190). Sun roof with vinyl canopy top, on Challenger ($261).

HISTORICAL FOOTNOTES: The full-sized Dodges were introduced on Sept. 25, 1973 and the Darts appeared in dealer showrooms at the same time. As in the past several years, the production of certain models was quartered at specific factories in the United States and Canada. The series production totals listed in this Catalog are exact figures, but cover only cars built inside the United States. Cars built in Canada for the U.S. market will not be reflected in these records. Therefore, such totals should be considered only a guide to how many cars of a certain type were manufactured. For some Series, the number of units actually sold by U.S. franchised dealers could be much larger. Dodge marked its 60th year as an automaker during 1974. Dodge NASCAR drivers won 10 NASCAR Grand National races, of which six went to Richard Petty. It was the company's best racing year since 1970.

1975 DODGE

DART SPORT SERIES — (ALL ENGINES) — Continuing to use the basic body introduced in 1970, the new Darts received a slightly revised grille. A 'trademark' of the mid-1970s automobile — the spring-loaded hood ornament — was a new sight on Darts. The base Dart Sport models featured redesigned roof tape stripe treatments and lower escutcheon panel appliques. Integrated taillight bezels were also adopted. The remainder of the car stayed generally the same as before. Dart Sports included all federally mandated safety and pollution equipment; pivoting rear quarter windows; the 225 cid Slant Six (or 318 cid V-8); black rubber floor mats and 6.95 x 14B tubeless black sidewall tires. The designation Dart Sport appeared, in block letters, on the front fendersides. The Dart Sport '360' continued as the high-performance entry in this series. It included all base features, plus the 360 cid V-8; ventless side windows; E78 x 14 black sidewall tires; grille surround moldings; front and rear bumper guards; power front disc brakes; heavy-duty suspension and shock absorbers; wheelcovers; tape stripes; three-speed manual transmission with floor-mounted shifter; electronic ignition; cigar lighter; and special '360' exterior identification.

DODGE I.D. NUMBERS: VIN located on plate attached to left-hand side of dashboard, visible through windshield. The VIN has 13 symbols. (The first four symbols, together, are the Model Number in second column of charts below.) The first symbol identifies the car-line or marque: D=Monaco; L=Dart; W=Coronet; X=Charger. The second symbol indicates trim/price level as follows: D=Dodge Taxi; T=Taxi; S=Special; G=Grand; H=High; L=Low; M=Medium; P=Premium; S=Special. The next two symbols identify the body style, as follows: 21/22=two-door coupe; 23=two-door hardtop; 29=two-door Special hardtop; 41=sedan; 43=hardtop sedan; 45=six-passenger station wagon; 46=nine-passenger station wagon. The fifth symbol denotes the engine as follows: (6-cyl.) C=225 cid; E=special order six. (V-8); G=318 cid 2V; J= 360 cid 4V; K=360 cid 2V; L=360 cid 4V (high-performance); M=400 cid 2V; N=400 cid 4V; P=400 cid 4V (high-performance); T=440 cid 4V; T=440 cid 4V (high-performance); Z=Special Order V-8. The sixth symbol denotes the model year as follows: 5=1975. The seventh symbol denotes the assembly plant, as follows: A=Lynch Rd. (Detroit); B=Hamtramck, Mich.; C=Jefferson Ave. (Detroit); D=Belvedere, Ill.; F=Newark, Del.; G=St. Louis, Mo.; R=Canada; 5/9 = Japan (Cricket). The last six symbols are the sequential production number starting at 100001 for each series at each plant. Body code plate located under hood, on left (fender shield, wheelhousing or radiator support) includes S.O. number and trim/paint codes too numerous to list.

DART SPORT SERIES

Model Number	Body/Style Number	Body Type & Seating	Factory Price	Shipping Weight	Production Total
SPORT					
LL	29	2-dr Cpe-6P	3297/3447	2980/3130	Note 1
SPORT '360'					
LM	29	2-dr Cpe-6P	4014	3335	Note 1

NOTE 1: Some 37,192 Dart Sports were built during model year 1975. Of those, 28,391 were sixes and 8,801 were V-8s.
NOTE 2: The production totals given in the charts are exact figures for cars produced in the U.S. with breakouts by model year and series. No body style breakouts are available at the current time. Cars built in Canada for the U.S. market are not included. Therefore, these totals should serve only as 'ballpark' guidelines in determining the number of units produced for domestic sales.
NOTE 3: Data above slash for six/below slash for V-8.

Standard Catalog of American Cars

1975 Dodge, Dart SE two-door hardtop sports coupe, V-8

DART SERIES — (ALL ENGINES) — A grille with a more formal look and matching parking light arrangement highlighted exterior changes in the standard Dart models for 1975. Base trim level features included all federally mandated safety and pollution equipment; front and rear ashtrays; armrests; cigarette lighter; concealed spare tire; rubber floor mats; glovebox with rotary latch; heater and defroster; dome light; parking brake (and warning system); all-vinyl bench seats; three-spoke steering wheel (with padded horn button); two-speed windshield wipers; and vent wings. Power was supplied by either the '225' Slant Six or '318' cid V-8. Dart Swingers added dual horns; deluxe steering wheel; carpeting and drip rail and door edge moldings. The Dart Custom models also included plush cloth and vinyl seats. The top trim level was the Dart Special Edition, which included all Dart Custom equipment, plus a padded vinyl top, velour interior seating surfaces and color-keyed wheelcovers. A Dart Swinger Decorator package called the Spring Special debuted at midyear, featuring a special interior.

STANDARD DART SERIES

Model Number	Body/Style Number	Body Type & Seating	Factory Price	Shipping Weight	Production Total
DART					
LL	41	4-dr Sed-6P	3269/3419	3060/3210	Note 1
LL	23	2-dr Spl HT Cpe-6P	3341/3491	3045/3195	Note 1
DART CUSTOM					
LH	23	2-dr Swinger HT-6P	3518/3668	3035/3185	Note 1
LH	41	4-dr Cus Sed-6P	3444/3594	3060/3210	Note 1
DART SPECIAL EDITION					
LP	41	4-dr Sed-6P	4159/4309	3280/3430	Note 1
LP	23	2-dr HT Cpe-6P	4232/4382	3260/3410	Note 1

NOTE 1: Some 19,349 Darts were built during model year 1975. Of those. 17,600 were sixes and 1,749 were V-8s. Some 7,028 Swinger Specials were built during model year 1975. of those, 6.705 were sixes and 323 were V-8s. Some 93.557 Swingers and Dart Customs were built during model year 1975. Of those, 75,105 were sixes and 18,452 were V-8s. Some 13,971 Dart Special Editions were built during model year 1975. Of those, 7,393 were sixes and 6,598 were V-8s.
NOTE 2: Model year U.S. dealer sales of 1975 Dodge Darts (all Series) totaled exactly 164,434 cars. Calendar year registrations of Darts hit exactly 163,639 cars. The variations between production and sales, totals is due to the splitting of production between the U.S. and Canada.
NOTE 3: Data above slash for six/below slash for V-8.

1975 Dodge, Coronet Brougham two-door hardtop sports coupe, V-8

CORONET SERIES — (ALL ENGINES) — Once again offering a two-door model, the new Coronet line featured a restyled grille. It was characterized by a horizontal theme and divided in the center. The new, single unit headlights were housed in rectangular doors. Sharply sculptured feature lines accepted the revived hardtops, which were further highlighted by vertical taillights and a full-width bumper that housed the back-up lamps. Coronet was the base trim level and incorporated all federal equipment; the '225' Slant Six (or '318' V-8); color-keyed rubber floor mats; vinyl bench seats; front and rear bumper guards; inside day/nite mirrors; foam rear seat cushion; three-spoke steering wheel; front and rear ashtrays and armrests; dome light; chrome hubcaps; cigarette lighter; glovebox lock; dual horns; sill moldings; and E78 x 14 black sidewall tubeless tires. Coronet Customs added carpeting; roof drip rail, wheel lip and bodyside moldings; dual note horns and deluxe steering wheel. The Coronet Brougham was the top trim level, incorporating all Custom features, plus special bodyside moldings (with vinyl inserts); stand-up hood ornament; special exterior rearview mirrors; padded vinyl top; and turbine styled wheelcovers. The Crestwood was the high-level station wagon and included all standard station wagon features, plus roof mounted air deflector; deluxe wheelcovers; map and glovebox lights; cargo area carpeting; woodgrain bodyside paneling; bright upper door frame and quarter window moldings and H78 x 14 tubeless black sidewall tires.

CORONET SERIES I.D. NUMBERS: See 1975 Dodge I.D. Number listing. All models began at 100001 and went up in the unit number sequence.

CORONET SERIES

Model Number	Body/Style Number	Body Type & Seating	Factory Price	Shipping Weight	Production Total
STANDARD CORONET					
WL	41	4-dr Sed-6P	3641/3769	3595/3710	Note 1
WL	21	2-dr HT Cpe-6P	3591/3719	3565/3675	Note 1
WL	45	4-dr Sta Wag-6P	4358	4185	Note 2
CORONET CUSTOM					
WH	41	4-dr Sed-6P	3754/3883	3635/3750	Note 1
WH	23	2-dr HT Cpe-6P	3777/3904	3645/3760	Note 1
WH	45	4-dr Sta Wag-6P	4560	4240	Note 2
WH	46	4-dr Sta Wag-9P	4674	4290	Note 2
BROUGHAM/CRESTWOOD STATION WAGON					
WP	23	2-dr HT Cpe-6P	4154	3800	Note 1
WP	45	4-dr Sta Wag-6P	4826	4230	Note 2
WP	46	4-dr Sta Wag-9P	4918	4290	Note 2

NOTE 1: Some 11,608 Coronet passenger cars were built during model year 1974, included 1,697 sixes and 9,911 V-8s. Some 41,893 Custom Coronet passenger cars were built during model year 1975, including 2,854 sixes and 39,039 V-8s. Some 9,975 Coronet Brougham passenger cars were built during model year 1975, all V-8s.
NOTE 2: Some 8,019 intermediate-sized Dodge station wagons were built during model year 1975. This included all Coronet/Coronet Custom and Crestwood station wagons, with no further breakout by line. All station wagons were V-8 powered.
NOTE 3: Data above slash for six/below slash for V-8.

1975 Dodge, Charger SE two-door coupe, V-8

CHARGER SE SERIES — (ALL ENGINES) — Introduced to compete in the popular specialty car market occupied by the Chevrolet Monte Carlo and Ford Elite, the new Charger SE utilized very formal styling and was available only in a two-door coupe configuration. It used a popular long hood/short rear deck styling approach and the padded top featured opera windows with six horizontal louvers for accent. The front end treatment was highlighted by a large rectangular grille opening featuring three horizontal dividers bars and single headlights housed in round, chrome bezels. Double horizontal taillights gave a traditional Dodge look to the highly sculptured rear. The license plate was recessed in the center of the rear end, directly below the trunk lid. The dipped beltline provided a low-appearing silhouette. The Charger SE featured more standard equipment than any intermediate size Dodge previously offered. As well as the federally mandated safety and pollution equipment, all Charger SEs included the 360 cid two-barrel V-8 engine; TorqueFlite automatic transmission; power steering; power front disc brakes; electronic digital clock; radial white sidewall tires; dual horns; inside hood release and front and rear sway bars. On March 4, 1975 a Daytona option package was announced for the Charger SE. It came in three color combinations and featured two-tone exterior paint with Daytona lettering. The package, for $132, featured vinyl bucket seats. It was the first use of the Daytona name since the 1969 winged version. Ironically, for 1975, Dodge drivers in NASCAR avoided the 1975 SE and drove 1974 Chargers, which accounted for 14 Grand National wins.

CHARGER SE SERIES I.D. NUMBERS: See 1975 Dodge I.D. Number listing. All models began at 100001 and went up in the unit number sequence.

CHARGER SE SERIES

Model Number	Body/Style Number	Body Type & Seating	Factory Price	Shipping Weight	Production Total
XS	22	2-dr HT Cpe-5P	4903	3950	Note 1

NOTE 1: Production of the Charger SE was included with that of the Dodge Coronet lines, since cars in both series were built off the same platform.
NOTE 2: A total of exactly 30,812 Charger SE hardtops were sold by U.S. automobile dealers during the 1975 model year. Such sales figures do not conform exactly to production totals, but fall in the same general 'ballpark'.
NOTE 3: Data above slash for six/below slash for V-8.

MONACO SERIES — (ALL ENGINES) — Utilizing the same body as in 1974, the new models seemed different, if for no other reason than a massive change in model nomenclature. The base trim level Monaco continued to use the same name as in 1974 and included all federally mandated safety and pollution equipment; front ashtrays and armrests; cigar lighter; carpeting; dual headlights and horns; dome and parking brake/brake system warning lights; inside day/nite mirror; concealed wipers; air control system; power steering; power front disc brakes; front and rear bumper guards; front seatback latches; trunk compartment rubber mats; 360 cid V-8 engine; and G78 x 15 tubeless black sidewall tires. Monaco station wagons also included power tailgate window, 400 cid V-8 engine and J78 x 15 tubeless black sidewall tires. The 1974 Monaco Custom became the Royal Monaco for 1975. It included all the standard Monaco features, plus a glovebox lock; adjustable front radiator; rear armrests ashtrays; ignition switch light; front and rear foam padded seat; wheel lip moldings; trunk mat and dome light. The two-door hardtop also included a rear pillar courtesy light. Four-door models also included upper door frame moldings. Royal station wagons also included a cargo area dome light and heavy-duty features. The top trim level 1974 Monaco Brougham became the luxurious Royal Monaco Brougham for 1975 and included all the Royal Monaco features, plus nylon carpeting; cornering lights; electric clock; all-vinyl bench seats (with fold-down center armrest); deluxe wheelcovers; and HR78 x 15 radial black sidewall tires. Royal Monaco Brougham station wagons also included rear compartment lock; bright upper door frames and quarter window moldings; rear door automatic entrance switches; deluxe wheelcovers; woodgrained side panels with

surround moldings; and cargo compartment carpeting. A special, ultra-luxurious trim package was available for Royal Monaco Brougham two-door hardtops. Called the Diplomat, the package consisted of a wide, brushed aluminum trim band which crossed the roof. It was similar to the Ford Crown Victoria. The Diplomat also featured side opera windows, padded landau roof, special velour interior trim and distinctive exterior ornamentation. Royal Monacos and Royal Monaco Brougham models utilized the 400 cid V-8 engine as standard equipment. A Diplomat formal roof option was announced Dec. 13, 1974 for the Royal Monaco Brougham two-door hardtop. It featured a stainless steel band over the top of the roof at the door post.

MONACO SERIES I.D. NUMBERS: See 1975 Dodge I.D. Number listing. All models began at 100001 and went up in the unit number sequence.

MONACO SERIES

Model Number	Body/Style Number	Body Type & Seating	Factory Price	Shipping Weight	Production Total
BASE MONACO					
DM	41	4-dr Sed-6P	4605	4280	Note 1
DM	23	2-dr HT Cpe-6P	4631	4225	Note 1
DM	45	4-dr Sta Wag-6P	5109	4885	Note 2
ROYAL MONACO					
DH	41	4-dr Sed-6P	4848	4285	Note 1
DH	43	4-dr HT Sed-6P	4951	4310	Note 1
DH	23	2-dr HT Cpe-6P	4868	4240	Note 1
DH	45	4-dr Sta Wag-6P	5292	4905	Note 2
DH	46	4-dr Sta Wag-9P	5415	4945	Note 2
ROYAL MONACO BROUGHAM					
DP	41	4-dr Sed-6P	5262	4455	Note 1
DP	43	4-dr HT Sed-6P	5382	4485	Note 1
DP	29	2-dr FT Cpe-6P	5460	4370	Note 1
DP	45	4-dr Sta Wag-6P	5779	4980	Note 1
DP	46	4-dr Sta Wag-9P	5905	5025	Note 1

NOTE 1: Some 34,802 Monaco/Royal Monaco passenger cars (combined Series) were built during the 1975 model year. Some 22,218 Monaco Brougham passenger cars were built during the 1975 model year. All Monacos were V-8 powered.
NOTE 2: Some 8,019 full-sized Dodge station wagons were built during the 1975 model year. This included all Monaco/Royal Monaco and Monaco Brougham wagons, with no further breakouts by line available at the current time. All station wagons were V-8 powered.
NOTE 3: Data above slash for six/below slash for V-8.

1975 ENGINES

Inline Six. Overhead valves. Cast iron block. Displacement: 225 cid. Bore and stroke: 3.4 x 4.12 inches. Compression ratio: 8.4:1. SAE Net hp: 95 at 3600 rpm. Four main bearings. Solid valve lifters. Carburetor: one-barrel.

V-8. Overhead valves. Cast iron block. Displacement: 318 cid. Bore and stroke: 3.91 x 3.31 inches. Compression ratio: 8.5:1. SAE Net hp: 145 at 4000 rpm. Five main bearings. Hydraulic valve lifters. Carburetor: two-barrel.

V-8. Overhead valves. Cast iron block. Displacement: 360 cid. Bore and stroke: 4.00 x 3.58 inches. Compression ratio: 8.4:1. SAE Net hp: 180 at 4000 rpm. Five main bearings. Hydraulic valve lifters. Carburetor: two-barrel.

V-8. Overhead valves. Cast iron block. Displacement: 360 cid. Bore and stroke: 4.00 x 358 inches. Compression ratio; 8.4:1 SAE Net hp; 200 at 4400 rpm. Five main bearings. Hydraulic valve lifters. Carburetor: four-barrel.

V-8. Overhead valves. Cast iron block. Displacement: 400 cid. Bore and stroke: 4.34 x 3.38 inches. Compression ratio: 8.2:1. SAE Net hp: 175 at 4000 rpm. Five main bearings. Hydraulic valve lifters. Carburetor: two-barrel.

V-8. Overhead valves. Cast iron block. Displacement: 400 cid. Bore and stroke: 4.34 x 3.38 inches. Compression ratio: 8.2:1. SAE Net hp: 190 at 4200 rpm. Five main bearings. Hydraulic valve lifters. Carburetor: four-barrel.

V-8. Overhead valves. Cast iron block. Displacement: 440 cid. Bore and stroke: 4.32 x 3.75 inches. Compression ratio: 8.2:1. SAE Net hp: 215 at 4000 rpm. Five main bearings. Hydraulic valve lifters. Carburetor: four-barrel.

NOTE: When equipped with dual exhaust the two-barrel '400' V-8 was rated 185 hp and the four-barrel '400' V-8 was rated 235 hp.

CHASSIS FEATURES: Wheelbase: (Dart sedans and hardtops) 111 inches; (Dart coupes) 108 inches; (Coronet/Charger hardtops) 115 inches; (other Coronet models) 117.5 inches; (Monaco station wagon) 124 inches; (Monaco passenger cars) 121.5 inches. Overall length: (Dodge Dart sedans and hardtops) 204 inches; (Dart coupes) 201 inches; (Coronet hardtop) 214 inches, (Coronet station wagon) 226 inches; (other Coronets) 218 inches; (Charger hardtop) 216 inches; (all Monaco station wagons) 229 inches; (Monaco Royal/Brougham) 226 inches; (Monaco) 224 inches. Width: (Dart sedans and hardtops) 70 inches; (Dart coupes) 72 inches; (Coronet station wagon) 79 inches; (other Coronets) 78 inches; (Charger) 78 inches; (all Monacos) 80 inches. Tires: Refer to descriptive text above.

POWERTRAIN OPTIONS: Automatic transmission was standard in Dart '360' Sport/Dart Special Edition/Charger SE/Crestwood/Monaco. Automatic transmission was also standard with V-8s. Three-speed manual transmission standard with all six-cylinder attachments. Two-barrel '360' V-8 in Coronet ($89). Four-barrel '360' V-8 in Charger SE ($153). Four-barrel '360' V-8 in Coronet ($202). Four-barrel '400' in Coronet ($122). Four-barrel '400' V-8 in Charger SE ($73). Two-barrel '318' V-8 in Dart ($151).

CONVENIENCE OPTIONS: Bucket seats, in Dart ($133). Power disc brakes, in Dart ($65). Fold-down seats, in Dart ($99). Vinyl top, on Dart SE (standard); on other Darts ($88). Air conditioning, in Dart ($407). Sun roof, on Dart ($178). Dart Rallye Package ($594). Dart 'Sport Topper' roof treatment ($251). Dart 'Hang Ten' Package ($254). Coronet/Charger/Monaco AM/FM stereo ($254); same with tape deck ($397). Coronet station wagon luggage rack ($67). Coronet power windows ($139). Coronet power seats ($119). Easy Order Option Package, on Coronet/Charger SE ($812). Coronet Rallye Package ($225). Coronet/Charger SE sun roof ($296). Coronet/Charger Road Wheels ($109). Charger SE power seat ($117). Charger SE power windows ($97). Vinyl top, on Charger ($109). Vinyl top, on Monaco Brougham (standard); on Monaco ($117). Monaco sunroof ($634). Monaco station wagon luggage rack ($79). Easy Order Option Package, Monaco station wagons ($460); Royal Monaco ($435). Electric rear defroster, in Monacos ($73). Cornering lights, on Monacos ($41). Burglar alarm system, in Monaco ($112). Reclining passenger seat, includes special interior trim, for Monacos ($151).

NOTE: Power steering was standard on Special Edition/Charger SE/Monaco Series. Power brakes were standard on Dart '360' Sport/Charger SE/Crestwood/Monaco Series.

HISTORICAL FOOTNOTES: The full-sized Dodges were introduced Oct. 1, 1974 and the compact Dart Series appeared in showrooms on the same day. Model year production through Aug. 31, 1975 included 160,568 Darts; 70,351 Coronet/Charger models; 38,455 Charger SE models and 45,647 Monacos. (NOTE: In this footnote only, the Dart and Charger SE production figures include cars built in Canada for the U.S. market). Model year sales by U.S. franchised dealers peaked at the following levels: Colt — 59,865 units; Dart — 164,434 units; Coronet — 68,191 units; Charger SE — 30,812 units and Monaco — 42,511 units. R.K. Brown, Group Vice-President for U.S. Auto Sales, was chief executive officer of Dodge Div. this year.

STANDARD CATALOG OF
EDSEL
1958-1960

As early as 1948, Ford Motor Co., under the direction of Henry Ford II, realized that its coverage of the automotive sales spectrum was lacking. At General Motors, the one-step-up buyer could move from Chevrolet to Pontiac, then on to Oldsmobile and Buick, before topping out at Cadillac. Even MoPar buyers had three steps between Plymouth and Imperial. At Ford, it was Ford, Mercury, then Lincoln. Many one-step-up sales were being lost to the competition.

Data compiled by Dale Rapp
Introduction by Phil Skinner

So, this was the seed for the Edsel. Active planning was shelved in the early 1950s due to the Korean Conflict, but in late 1954 the marketing planners were once again looking toward a new make for FoMoCo. In 1955, a Special Products Div. was formed under which this new car would be developed.

An entire new branch of FoMoCo was to produce this vehicle. One that would be neither Ford, nor Mercury, but might share some basic components with both. Selected by FoMoCo chief stylist George Walker to head up the project was designer Roy Brown. His goal was to create a car that looked like no other, and would be immediately recognizable a block away.

Developed under the code name "E-car," ("E" meant "experimental") it featured a classic-inspired vertical center grille flanked by two horizontal side grilles and high-mounted headlights.

A graceful gull-wing effect represented the rear view and three distinct color areas — body, roof and scallops, were incorporated into the side views.

Under the leadership of R.E. Krafve, the Special Products Div. developed the E-car, with release dates pushed back several times before the fall of 1957 was decided on. Heading up the sales department was J.C. "Larry" Doyle, who was general sales and marketing manager. He organized 24 sales districts and signed up nearly 1,200 dealerships by opening day.

Just to select this new car's name was to prove a challenge. Under the direction of the Foote, Cone & Belding advertising agency, the division's account executive Dave Jenkins compiled a list of 18,000 possible names. Edsel was not among them!

On Nov. 19, 1956, after much negotiating with the Ford family, the name Edsel was decided on. From the initial list, the top four selections of Citation, Corsair, Pacer and Ranger, were used to name each of the Edsel series.

Shortly after the naming of the Edsel, the model lineup was announced. There were to be 18 models in four basic series, including five station wagons. Ranger was the price leader,

followed by Pacer. Both of these cars were mounted on the Ford Fairlane 118 inch wheelbase. The Corsair and Citation models were based on the 1957-1958 Mercury chassis with a special 124 inch wheelbase. A two-door Roundup station wagon, along with the four-door Villager wagons, were trimmed on a par with the Ranger, while the wood-trimmed upscale Bermuda wagon shared many of the Pacer's touches.

Production started on July 15, 1957 in four assembly plants. Producing the Ford-based models were Mahwah, N.J., Louisville, Ken., and San Jose, Calif. facilities. Producing the senior cars at the beginning was the Somerville, Mass factory. By Aug. 19, 1957, both the Wayne, Mich. and Los Angeles, Calif. plants were brought on-line.

In late August, 1957, the media was given a grand showing of the Edsel in Dearborn, Mich., at Ford Motor Co.'s expense. There were rare reviews of the cars and some 75 editors from across the country drove specially-prepared Pacers back to their hometowns.

On Sept. 4, 1957, the Edsel — billed as "The Newest Thing on Wheels," was released to the general public. Nearly 4,000 sales were reported that first day, which sounded great. However, sales soon plummeted and, within a month, the writing on the wall was already showing.

The junior Edsels were powered by the "E-400" V-8, with 361 cid and a 303 hp rating. It was part of the F-E series of Ford engines introduced in 1958. For the senior Corsair and Citation models, the "E-475" with 410 cid and 345 horses kept them moving. There were no optional power plants for 1958 Edsels.

On senior cars, Edsel's exclusive Teletouch push-button transmission was standard. This same unit was optional on junior cars and was installed in about 90 percent of those models, where the automatic transmission was actually based on the three-speed Ford-O-Matic. Proposed was a counterpart to the new Ford Cruise-O-Matic, but outside of a few prototypes, none were ever produced.

What went wrong with the Edsel? In C. Gayle Warnock's book THE EDSEL AFFAIR, he cites production problems. All Edsels were built at either Ford or Mercury plants and, at a ratio of 10-to-1 in some cases. Assembly line workers didn't like the odd changes required on Edsels and plant managers looked upon the car as a production problem for their divisions. This led to poor production quality in delivered cars.

By October, 1957, the sales picture started to look dismal. An economic recession had a lot of purse strings tied shut and, at that time of year, many dealers were offering great deals on the 1957 clearance models.

In early January, 1958, the Edsel Div. was involved in a reorganization and it was then placed in the new Mercury-Edsel-Lincoln Div. of Ford Motor Co.

Disenchanted dealers were dropping like flies. Prior to the Edsel's release, many established Ford and Mercury dealers couldn't get Edsel franchises. Now, they didn't want them! Only 63,110 of the 1958 Edsels were produced, a far cry from the 200,000 predicted by R.E. Krafve in January 1957.

The Edsel lineup was drastically cut-back for 1959. It was down to 10 models. Only the Ranger, Villager and Corsair nameplates remained. This year, both models were based on the Ford Fairlane. The Villager was based on Ford wagons and was available in both six- and nine-passenger forms.

Styling was toned-down a bit from the 1958 look, but was still distinctively Edsel. Cost-cutting in the design was seen by incorporating the 1958 Continental taillights and back-up lights into the 1959 Edsel units, thereby saving tooling costs on two plastic molds.

Edsel production in 1959 was limited to the Louisville, Ken. plant and quality was considered pretty good. While the marketing goal of the 1958 Edsel had been to fit into the medium-priced car range, for the 1959 model year, the aim was to stay just a smidgen above the "low-priced three." Released on Halloween day, Edsel's slogan this year was "Makes History by Making Sense."

Standard power for the Ranger series was now the 292 cid Y-block V-8 available in Fords since 1955. Standard in the Villager wagons and Corsair series was the 332 cid V-8, also identical to that used in Fords. As a delete-option, a 223 cid six-cylinder motor could be ordered for both the Ranger and Villager. An extra-cost option was the 361 cid V-8, which was held over from 1958.

Despite a more conventional car, the name Edsel seemed already tainted and just 44,861 of the 1959 models were built.

On Oct. 15, 1959, the 1960 Edsels were put on sale. Now limited officially to just seven models, there were five Rangers and two Villagers. Basically, the 1960 models were little more than face-lifted Fords. Using a more elaborate chrome-plated die-cast grille than Fords, the Edsel resembled the 1959 Pontiac in side trim and grille treatment.

Standard power for all 1960 models was the 292 cid V-8, with the six as a delete-option in all models except the convertible. The 300 hp version of the Ford 352 cid V-8 was available as an extra-cost option in all models.

On Nov. 19, 1959, Ford Motor Co. announced the end of the Edsel line. They stated that poor sales and steel shortages caused the decision, but there may have been deeper reasons within the corporation that caused the cut. As late as September, 1959, a new compact car, the Comet, was being readied for marketing as an Edsel.

The 1960 Edsel was not a bad car and AUTOMOTIVE NEWS selected it as the "Best Buy" for 1960 domestic cars. Unfortunately, this article was published in December, after the Edsel had ceased to exist.

So close to the 1960 Ford is the 1960 Edsel, that counterfeits have been produced. In considering the purchase of such a car, great care should be taken to research the sale.

In 1968, the Edsel Owners Club was formed to preserve these maligned orphans from Ford. A year later, the International Edsel Club was founded with similar goals. Both clubs have outlived the cars they honor and still exist today.

1958 Edsel, Ranger four-door sedan, V-8

1959 Edsel, Corsair, four-door hardtop, V-8

1958 EDSEL

1958 Edsel, Ranger two-door sedan, V-8 (AA)

RANGER — (V-8) — SERIES A — The all-new 1958 Edsel, said to be the product of nine years of planning, was publicly launched on Sept. 4, 1957, as a product of the Edsel Div. of Ford Motor Co. Although obviously based on contemporary Fords and Mercurys, the Edsel was described as being, "Entirely new to the industry." It was aimed at the medium-priced car field and came in four different lines with prices from $2,484 to a high of $3,796. The two lower-priced series, Ranger and Pacer, were built off the 118 inch wheelbase platform that 1958 Fords utilized. The two higher-priced lines, Corsair and Citation, were on a 124 inch wheelbase and had what was, essentially, a stretched Mercury chassis and sheet metal. Station wagons shared the 116 inch Ford wheelbase used on Ford wagons and Custom models. When compared to Ford and Mercury counterparts, on a model-for-model basis, the Edsels offered more power, more luxury, more standard equipment and more radical styling. They were intended to enter the sales battle against cars like Buick, Oldsmobile and Chrysler New Yorker, which Ford previously had no distinct product to compete with. In trying to make the Edsel into a car that buyers would view as something really different Ford went to the trouble of establishing a separate Edsel Div., with headquarters in Ecorse Township, Mich. It was the first time in automotive history that any major manufacturer had set up a large dealer organization (1,200 to 1,400 outlets) prior to the introduction and marketing of a completely new line of automobiles. Also, the Edsel's radical styling was part of the effort to give the new model its own personality. The frontal treatment was conceived as a modern interpretation of a classic Packard's tall, vertical center grille. There were smaller grilles at each side. Unfortunately, the public thought that the center grille looked like horse collar and that's what it was soon being called. The "horse collar" grille split the center of the car and was flanked by twin rectangular openings having horizontal grille bars and parking lamps at the outboard ends. Both the grille and the lamps wrapped around the front body corners. The front bumper was also split and had a concave indention that took on a projectile-like contour. The center of the hood had a broad peak or bulge which protruded to meet the horse collar. The name Edsel, in bright block letters, ran vertically down the center of the grille, inside a horse collar-shaped inner molding. The top of the hood was decorated with a stand-up hood ornament. Two headlamps were placed in each fender, being horizontally positioned and set into oval-shaped openings. Bodyside styling had a sort of reverse-angled, fin-shaped feature line running along the front fender and door. At the rear, was a sporty-looking indentation, usually referred to as a 'cove.' It was outlined with a thin chrome molding and had large, block letters inside. They spelled out the new car's name. Body panels and rooflines on the smaller models had a Ford look, while those on the big Edsels came straight from the Mercury studio. The rear end reverted to a more radical theme with a split-styled bumper, boomerang-shaped horizontal taillamps and the deck lid depressed below the level of the flat, rounded fendertops. Station wagons of all types had certain styling distinctions, which are described in the outline of the station wagon series given below. The Ranger was the base trim-level Edsel. Rangers could be identified by suitable model signature scripts placed above and ahead of the front wheel openings; lack of front fender and rocker panel trim; lack of upper body edge reveal moldings; and a slightly plainer appearance in general. Ranger sedans were equipped with front and rear armrests; three ashtrays; two coat hooks; black rubber floor mats and White vinyl headliners. Trims available for these cars were Code A (green cloth); Code B (blue cloth) and Code C (gray and black cloth). Ranger hardtops were equipped the same as sedans, except for the type of upholstery. Trims available for both two and four-door pillarless styles were Code K (white vinyl and green cloth); Code M (white vinyl and blue cloth) and Code N (White vinyl and black cloth). Three-speed manual transmission with column controls, a 361 cid/303 hp V-8 with four-barrel carburetion and 8.00 x 14 four-ply tires were featured as well.

EDSEL I.D. NUMBERS: Encoded information designating engine, model year, assembly plant, body style and consecutive unit production number was found on the upper line of the data plate, affixed to the left-hand front door post of all 1958 Edsels. The first symbol was a letter designating the type of engine, as follows: W = 361 cid V-8 or X = 410 cid V-8. The second symbol indicated model year: 8 = 1958. The third symbol was another letter, designating assembly plant, as follows: U = Louisville, Ken.; R = San Jose, Calif.; S = Somerville, Mass.; E = Mahwah, N.J.; W = Wayne, Mich. and J = Los Angeles, Calif. The fourth symbol was another letter, which designated the style of the body, as follows: C = Ranger two-door sedan; F = Ranger/Pacer four-door sedan; G = Ranger/Pacer two-door hardtop; H = Ranger/Pacer four-door hardtop; R = Pacer two-door convertible; S = Roundup wagon; T = six-passenger Villager/Bermuda wagon; V = Villager/Bermuda wagon; W = Corsair/Citation two-door hardtop; X = Corsair/Citation four-door hardtop; Y = Citation two-door convertible. The following symbols (six numbers) were the consecutive unit production number. Consecutive numbers at each plant began at 700001 and up. Additional encoded information designating body type, exterior color, interior trim, date of assembly, transmission type and rear axle was listed on the lower part of the data plate. The body type codes consisted of two numbers followed by a single letter, as shown in the second column of the specifications charts below. The exterior color code consisted of three letters, the first indicating main body color; the second indicating top color and the third indicating the color that the cove (or scallop) was painted. The codes and colors were as follows: A = Jet black; B = silver-grey metallic; C = Ember red; D = turquoise (n.a. Ranger/Villager/Roundup); E = Snow white (Pacer/Ranger wagons only) or E = Frost white (Corsair/Citation only); F = Powder blue; H = Royal blue metallic; J = Ice green; K = Spring green; L = Spruce green; M = Charcoal brown metallic; N = Driftwood (Pacer/Ranger wagons only); Q = Jonquil yellow; R =Unset coral (Pacer/Ranger wagons only); T = Chalk pink (Corsair/Citation only); U = Copper metallic (Corsair/Citation only); X = Gold metallic (Corsair/Citation only). The interior trim code was a single letter, as described in text covering each model. The date code consisted of one or two numbers and a letter. The numbers designated the day of the month that the car was built. The letter indicated the month of production: G = July 1957; H = August 1957; J = September 1957; K = October 1957; L = November 1957; M = December 1957; A = January 1958 (*); B = February 1957; C = March 1958; D = April 1958; E = May 1958; F = June 1958; U = July 1958; V = August 1958. (* Note: A few cars have been found with a month code of N. This represented Jan. 1958 as does the letter A). Transmission codes were numerical, as follows: 1 = standard manual; 2 = overdrive; 3 = column-lever automatic; and 4 = Teletouch push-button automatic. A letter was used to designate different rear axles, as follows: A = 2.91:1; B = 3.32:1; C = 3.70:1 and D = 3.89:1.

RANGER SERIES

Model Number	Body/Style Number	Body Type & Seating	Factory Price	Shipping Weight	Production Total
A	64A	2-dr Sed-6P	2484	3729	4,615
A	58A	4-dr Sed-6P	2557	3805	6,576
A	63A	2-dr HT Cpe-6P	2558	3724	5,546
A	57A	4-dr HT Sed-6P	2643	3796	3,077

1958 Edsel, Pacer two-door hardtop sport coupe, V-8

PACER — (V-8) — SERIES B — The Pacer represented the second step up in the Edsel product lineup. It used the same body as Rangers, with slightly more trim, extra equipment and fancier upholstery fittings. Pacers could be externally identified by the Pacer front fender scripts and the use of a slightly curved, fin-shaped molding on the sides of front fenders and doors. Available body styles were similar to those in the Ranger Series, except that the two-door sedan wasn't available. A two-door convertible was. Pacer sedans were equipped with four built-in armrests; two ashtrays; cigarette lighter; two coat hooks; chromed inside rearview mirror; one-third/two-thirds design front seat; color-keyed rubber floor mats; and a white vinyl headliner. Trims available in the sedan were: D = brown cloth; E = green cloth and F = blue cloth. Pacer hardtops carried the same equipment as sedans, but different trims were used. They were, as follows: R = white vinyl and brown cloth; S = white vinyl and coral cloth; AX = white vinyl and red cloth; AY = white vinyl and turquoise cloth; T = green cloth and vinyl and V = blue cloth and vinyl. Pacer convertibles came with four built-in armrests; three ashtrays; cigarette lighter; courtesy lights under instrument panel; rear armrest lights; and chrome inside rearview mirror. They also had one-third/two-third seat designs, color-keyed rubber floor mats, and vinyl-coated convertible tops in a choice of black, white, turquoise or coral. Convertible interior trims were, as follows: AJ = white and coral vinyl; AN = white and black vinyl; AV = white and turquoise vinyl; AZ = white and red vinyl.

PACER SERIES B

Model Number	Body/Style Number	Body Type & Seating	Factory Price	Shipping Weight	Production Total
B	58B	4-dr Sed-6P	2700	3826	6,083
B	63B	2-dr HT Cpe-6P	2770	3773	6,139
B	57B	4-dr HT Sed-6P	2828	3857	4,959
B	76B	2-dr Conv-6P	3766	4311	1,876

CORSAIR — (V-8) — SERIES A — The third step up in the 1958 Edsel lineup was the Corsair Series, which was comprised of two- and four-door hardtops on the 124 inch wheelbase. Cars in this line had the look of contemporary Mercurys with greater overall length and a roof styled with an overhanging rear edge and wraparound backlight. For identification, there were Corsair front fender scripts; fin-shaped side moldings across the upper mid-section of front fenders and doors; chrome outline moldings on the rear fender cove; bright Edsel block lettering within the rear fender cove; Edsel block lettering positioned vertically within the horse collar center grille; rocker panel moldings; and heavy chrome trim along the edge of the roof and rear body pillars. Vertical guards were optional on each of the front bumpers, being positioned quite close to the horse collar grille. The Corsair and Citation shared many chassis and inner body components with the 1958 Mercury, but little with Fords. Therefore, only a few components from the Ranger/Pacer series would interchange with the Corsair/Citation Series. Examples of parts that were common between the two types included the hood ornaments; center and side grilles; front bumpers; and starter. Standard equipment on Corsair hardtops included built-in front and rear armrests; ashtrays; cigarette lighter; two coat hooks; courtesy lights on the instrument panel; chromed inside rearview mirror; one-third/two-third design front seat; white vinyl headliner; and color-keyed floor carpeting. Trim codes available for Corsairs were: B = blue cloth and vinyl; C = white vinyl and turquoise cloth; D = green cloth and vinyl; E = white vinyl and gold cloth; X = gray vinyl and red cloth; and Y = white vinyl and copper cloth).

CORSAIR SERIES A

Model Number	Body/Style Number	Body Type & Seating	Factory Price	Shipping Weight	Production Total
A	63A	2-dr HT Cpe-6P	3311	4134	3,312
A	57A	4-dr HT Sed-6P	3390	4235	5,880

1958 Edsel, Citation four-door hardtop sedan, V-8 (HFM)

CITATION — (V-S) — SERIES B — The Citation was the top-of-the-line Edsel offering. It shared the Corsair body, but came with more DeLuxe interiors and trim. There were Citation front fender scripts; model medallions on the rear roof pillar; and a special decorative arrangement within the coves on the rear fendersides. Inside the cove an additional projectile-shaped beauty panel was formed by chrome outline moldings. Also, a large medallion was placed directly below the upper inner molding towards the rear. On most cars, the inner beauty panel was finished in one color and the cove was done in another, which often matched the color of the roof. It was then possible to select a third color for the main body itself. A wide variety of two-tone or three-tone combinations could be achieved with the 161 colors available for the big Edsels. Standard equipment on Citation hardtops included all items found on Corsairs, plus padded dashboard; electric clock and glove compartment light. Interior trims available in Citation hardtops were: AA = black vinyl and gray cloth; H = blue cloth and vinyl; J = white vinyl and turquoise cloth; K = green cloth and vinyl; L = white vinyl and gold cloth; Z = pink vinyl and brown cloth; AB = white vinyl and copper cloth. The Citation convertible came with the same equipment as hardtops, plus dual exhausts and vinyl-coated convertible tops available in black, white, turquoise and copper. Convertible color schemes were, as follows: AC = brown and pink vinyl; AD = red and white vinyl; AE = copper and white vinyl; S = turquoise and white vinyl; T = gold and white vinyl.

CITATION SERIES A

Model Number	Body/Style Number	Body Type & Seating	Factory Price	Shipping Weight	Production Total
B	63B	2-dr HT Cpe-6P	3500	4136	2,535
B	57B	4-dr HT Sed-6P	3580	4230	5,112
B	76B	2-dr Conv-6P	3766	4311	930

STATION WAGONS — (V-8) — MIXED SERIES CODING — The 1958 Edsel station wagons were all built off the 116 inch wheelbase Ford station wagon platform and utilized the basic sheet metal of two- or four-door Ford station wagons. Front end sheet metal was shared with the Edsel Ranger/Pacer series. The wagons had completely different (Ford) rear fenders and vertical taillights housed in chrome, boomerang-shaped bezels. Three models were available. The Roundup was a two-door station wagon with seating for six. A Roundup script was placed at the front fender tip and a projectile-shaped contrast panel was formed by a chrome outline molding. The projectile went from the rear of the car to the middle of the front door. All wagons were equipped with four armrests; ashtrays; cigarette lighter; two coat hooks; dome and courtesy lights and White vinyl headliner. The Roundup came with black rubber floor mats and a conventional split front seat (as used in Ford two-door sedans). The Villager station wagon was a four-door model, which came with six- or nine-passenger seating. It had all items that were standard on the Roundup, plus a solid front bench seat. Trim codes available for both wagons discussed above were: BA = white and green vinyl; BB = white and blue vinyl; BC = black vinyl and gold saran; BD = red vinyl with gold saran. The Bermuda was the top-line station wagon. It had four-doors and either six- or nine-passenger seating. Bermudas had simulated woodgrain exterior paneling; color-keyed rubber floor mats; one-third/two-third design front seats; and chromed inside rearview mirror. Trim included: AT = two-tone blue vinyl; AJ = white and coral vinyl; AS = two-tone green vinyl; AU = driftwood vinyl and brown saran and AV = white and turquoise vinyl.

STATION WAGON SERIES

Model Number	Body/Style Number	Body Type & Seating	Factory Price	Shipping Weight	Production Total
ROUNDUP					
NA	59A	2-dr Sta Wag-6P	2841	3761	924
VILLAGER					
NA	79C	4-dr Sta Wag-6P	2898	3827	2,054
NA	79A	4-dr Sta Wag-9P	2955	3900	1,735
BERMUDA					
NA	79D	4-dr Sta Wag-6P	3155	3853	892

BASE ENGINES

(RANGER/PACER/STATION WAGON SERIES) V-8. Overhead valves. Cast iron block. Displacement: 361 cid. Bore and stroke: 4.05 x 3.50. Compression ratio: 10. 5:1. Brake hp: 303 at 4600 rpm. Five main bearings. Hydraulic valve lifters. Carburetor: four-barrel Model B8E-9510A. Note: This engine was the 352 cid Ford V-8 with a slight overbore. The block and heads were painted yellow. The air cleaner and valve covers were painted white. There were red 'E 400' markings on the valve covers to designate torque (not horsepower).

(CORSAIR/CITATION SERIES) V-8. Overhead valves. Cast iron block. Displacement: 410 cid. Bore and stroke: 4.20 x 3.70 inches. Compression ratio: 10.5:1. Brake hp: 345 at 4600 rpm. Five main bearings. Hydraulic valve lifters. Carburetor: four-barrel Model EDH9510-A.

CHASSIS FEATURES: Wheelbase: (Ranger/Pacer) 118 inches; (all station wagons) 116 inches; (Corsair/Citation) 124 inches. Overall length: (Ranger/Pacer) 213.1 inches; (all station wagons) 205.4 inches; (Citation/Corsair) 218.8 inches. Front tread: (Ranger/Pacer) 59.44 inches; (station wagons) 58.97 inches; (Corsair/Citation) 59.38 inches. Rear tread: (Ranger/Pacer) 59 inches; (station wagons) 56.40 inches;(Corsair/Citation) 59 inches. Tires: (Citation/Corsair) 8.50 x 14; (all others) 8.00 x 14.

OPTIONS: Power steering ($84.95). Power brakes ($38.25). Power windows ($100.95). Four-Way power seats ($76.45). Dial-A-Temp heater and defroster ($92.45). Dial-A-Temp air conditioning with heater, on Ranger/Pacer ($417.70); on Corsair/Citation ($460.15). Push-button radio with manual antenna ($95.25). Station-seeking radio with electric antenna ($143.90). Rear seat speaker ($16). Tachometer ($14.95). Electric clock, standard in Citation ($15.94). Compass. Push-button chassis lubricator, on Corsair/Citation only ($42.50). Padded instrument panel ($22.65). Front seat belts. Windshield washer ($11.50). Tinted glass ($34). Back-up lights ($8.50). Full wheelcovers ($12.75). Full wheelcovers with appliques and spinner. Front bumper guards. Rear bumper guards. Engine compartment light. Glove compartment light. Luggage compartment light. Inside non-glare rearview mirror. Rocker panel moldings. Hooded outside mirror. Foam front seat cushion, standard in Corsair/Citation ($21.25). Foam rear seat cushion. Carpeting, standard in Corsair/Citation ($12.30). License plate frames. Courtesy lights. Oil filter, standard with Corsair/Citation ($9.15). Paper air cleaner. Two-tone paint on top or scallop or top and scallop ($17). Tri-tone paint. Size 8.00 x 14 whitewall tires, Rambler/Pacer ($40.35); Corsair/Citation ($44.25). Size 8.50 x 14 whitewall tires. Undercoating. Vacuum-booster windshield wipers ($11.70). Electric windshield wipers. Rear-mounted antennas, single or dual. Excess speed warning light. Parking brake warning light. Fuel level warning light. Oil level warning light. Open door warning light. Padded sun visors (included in padded dash safety package). Exhaust deflectors single or dual. Seat covers. Contour floor mats, front and rear. Locking fuel tank cap. Curb signals. Traffic light reflector. Standard-style outside mirror left and right. Spot light, left and right. Electric luggage compartment opener. Rear door safety locks, four-doors only. Fuel and vacuum booster pump. Extra-cooling radiator and fan. Three-speed manual transmission with column lever control was standard in Rangers, Pacers and all station wagons. Three-speed automatic transmission with push-button Teletouch Drive was standard and mandatory in Corsair/Citation. Overdrive transmission in Ford-based models only ($127.45). Three-speed automatic with column lever control ($217.70). Three-speed automatic transmission with Teletouch control in Ford-based models ($231.40). Dual exhausts, on Citation convertible (standard equipment); on other models ($23.45).

HISTORICAL FOOTNOTES: The Edsel received one of the best and longest lasting new car build-ups in automotive history. As early as Aug. 7, 1956, Ford announced that is Special Products Div. was in the process of establishing five regional sales offices through which to market an all-new car called the Edsel. The following October 15, the company appointed 24 district sales managers to oversee Edsel sales in major cities. On Jan. 11, 1957, Ford informed the world that the Edsel would be far more radical than any of its other products and that equally radical sales techniques would be adopted to marketing of the car. Ten days later, corporate officials predicted 200,000 sales in the first year and set their sights accordingly. After having named the car publicly on Nov. 19, 1956, Ford released the names and characteristics of each Edsel series on Feb. 5, 1957. To build even more interest, a March 10, 1957 press release identified five factories where Edsels were to be assembled, adding that a sixth factory, on the West Coast, would be added soon. Edsel production began in July, 1957, under the direction of R.E. Krafve, a Ford Motor Co. vice-president who was named general manager of the Edsel Div. The new division built 3,729 units in July; 19,876 units in August; 18,815 units in September; 7,566 units in October; 2,483 units in November and 2,138 units in December for a total of 54,607 cars in calendar 1957. Model year output was recorded as 63,110 cars for only 1.5 percent of the total U.S. market. Of this figure, 4,900 cars were built at Wayne, Mich.; 6,400 at Mahwah, N.J.; 33,300 at Louisville, Ken.; 5,600 at San Jose, Calif.; 11,400 at Somerville, Mass.; and 1,500 at Los Angeles, Calif. In mid-January, 1958, Ford combined the operations of Edsel, Mercury, Lincoln and English Ford to create a new Mercury-Edsel-Lincoln Div. Of all Edsels built in 1958, 91.9 percent had automatic transmission; 48.7 percent had power steering; 43.3 percent had power brakes; 7.6 percent had power seats; 5.6 percent had power windows; 80.3 percent had radios; 89.4 percent had a heater; 73.2 percent had white sidewall tires; 32.9 percent had tinted glass; 61.4 percent had windshield washers; 43.3 percent had back-up lights; 28.4 percent had dual exhausts; 1.6 percent had air conditioning; two percent had overdrive and all had V-8 engines. Although universally recognized as a failure in the area of sales, it is interesting to note that, in its first year, the Edsel set an all-time record for deliveries of a brand new medium-priced automobile.

1959 EDSEL

1959 Edsel, Ranger four-door sedan, V-8

RANGER — (V-8) — The Edsel Marketing Div. had expected to sell 200,000 cars during 1958, but soon admitted that there was a problem. The company went on record as saying that the Edsel had an "identity crisis." Since the first models covered such a wide market spectrum, buyers were unable to determine exactly where the Edsel fit in. Consequently, the Pacer and Citation Series were discontinued for 1959. More emphasis was placed on slotting the remaining models into the top end of the low-priced field. As previously indicated, the Edsel line joined Lincolns, Mercurys and English Fords in the new M-E-L marketing division. Upon instituting this regrouping, Henry Ford II, the president of the corporation, said, "Unified direction of the organizations responsible for the five M-E-L Division product lines (which included English Anglia, Prefect, Consul, Zephyr and Zodiac cars and Thames Van trucks) will strengthen the profit potential of our dealers and assist in increasing the company's efficiency." J.J. Nance was named general manager of M-E-L at its formation, but on Sept. 4, 1959, Ben D. Mills was appointed to the same post. Edsel launched its new 1959 program with the theme of "a new kind of car." Economy was stressed more than before. The Ranger was built off a new 120 inch wheelbase platform, with a 292 cid V-8 engine as base powerplant. It shared some common sheet metal with the 1959 Ford. Overall styling changes were quite obvious, although the original theme was not totally disregarded either. The horse collar grille was retained in a modified form. It was now filled with horizontal blades and an Edsel badge at the top. The stand-up hood ornament disappeared and the parking lamps were moved into

the split front bumpers. The side grilles each had three stacks of short prominent, moldings. There were also less noticeable moldings in between. They ran from the grille to the dual, horizontal headlamps. The hood still had a broad peak above the top of the grille. The front of the body was flatter and more shelf-like and the concave cove at the rear was nearly gone. A different type of sweepspear treatment was used. It had a distinct scallop shape for each car-line. On Rangers, it consisted of a full-length upper molding, combined with a lower molding that ran to the door, then dipped in a curved 'V' and continued in a taper to the rear, where it rejoined the top molding. The area between the moldings was often painted in a color other than that on the main body. It often matched the roof's color. The two-tone paint combinations consisted of a contrasting color being placed in the side scallop and on the roof. Widely-spaced block letters spelled out Edsel in chrome, with a few letters on each side of the front door break line. A Ranger script was placed near the rear body corner, under the sweep spear. The rear end still had a wing-like image, but no longer with the taillights in the wings. They were now placed into the rear deck latch panel, slightly above the horizontal centerline. The taillights consisted of three circular lenses placed horizontally against chrome grille panels housed in wedge-shaped chrome surrounds. A massive one-piece bumper (with a dip below the license plate) ran fully across the rear of the cars. The deck lid still had a wide, center depression with a simulated chrome air vent at the rear. Roof treatments looked like those on the big 1958 Edsels, with a rear overhang and a large, wraparound backlight with angular-looking edges. A grooved aluminum trim plate was used on the rear roof pillar. Standard equipment on all models included an air cleaner; positive action windshield wipers; front foam seat cushions; electric clock; cigarette lighter; and carpeting (except wagons). Rangers were also equipped with four armrests; front and rear ashtrays; two coat hooks; color-keyed vinyl headliner; and a conventional split front seatback. Trim codes on this series were: 23 = two-tone green vinyl and signet cloth; 24 = two-tone blue vinyl and signet cloth; 25 = white and buff vinyl and gold puff cloth; 50 = silver and black vinyl with black surf cloth (Surf cloth was leftover 1958 Edsel material). Around January, 1959, a four-pointed star cloth, originally made for 1957 Mercurys, was introduced. In March 1959, the trim code was changed to 501. In May, 1959, the cloth used in this option was changed to black Signet cloth.

EDSEL I.D. NUMBERS: The numbering system and code locations were basically the same as on 1958 Edsels. The first symbol in the top row of codes on the data plate designated engine type, as follows: A = six; C = 292 cid V-8: B = 332 cid V-8; W = 361 cid V-8. The second symbol indicated model year: 9 = 1959. Third symbols were the same for each Ford factory, but Edsels were now built only at Louisville, Ken. (Code U). Body style and consecutive numbering systems were unchanged, although less codes were used in 1959. On the lower row of codes, body type designations were as listed in the specification charts below. Exterior color codes were as follows: A = Jet black; B = Moonrise gray; C = gold metallic; D = Redwood metallic; E = Snow white; F = President red; G = Talisman red; H = Desert tan; J = Velvet maroon; K = Platinum gray metallic; L = Star blue metallic; M = Jet Stream blue; N = Light aqua; P = blue aqua; Q = Petal yellow; R = Mist green; S = Jadeglint green metallic. Interior trim codes are explained in the text. Date codes were as before, except that only the letters of normal progression are used. Transmission codes were the same as before, although few types were available. Axle codes were changed as follows: 1 = 3.10:1; 2 = 3.56:1; 3 = 3.70:1; 4 = 3.89:1; 5 = 2.91:1 and 6 = 2.69:1.

RANGER SERIES V-8

Model Number	Body/Style Number	Body Type & Seating	Factory Price	Shipping Weight	Production Total
NA	64C	2-dr Sed-6P	2629	3545	7,778
NA	58D	4-dr Sed-6P	2684	3775	12,814
NA	63F	2-dr HT Cpe-6P	2691	3690	5,474
NA	57F	4-dr HT Sed-6P	2756	3680	2,352

NOTE 1: The prices and weights given above are for Ranger V-8s.
NOTE 2: For sixes: subtract $84/deduct 99 pounds.

1959 Edsel, Corsair four-door hardtop sedan, V-8

CORSAIR — (V-8) — The Corsair was now nothing more than a Ranger with a bigger motor and longer list of standard features. Both series were built off the same platform. The biggest external difference between the two lines was the placement of side trim and variations in the body styles offered. The upper sweep spear molding on Corsairs actually started as a front hood lip accent, moved around the edge of the front fender, then began a long, subtle curve to the taillights. Upon hitting the taillight, it moved back across the quarter panel, then curved upwards and tapered to a point of the front fender tip. The area between the two moldings, at the rear, was filled with a scallop-shaped contrast panel, also outlined in chrome. A medallion was positioned at the forward tip of the 'scallop'. There was also a series identification script on the lower rear quarter panel, under the trim. Standard equipment on closed body styles included all Ranger items, except a one-third/two-thirds type seat design was used. Trim combinations included all of the following: 38 = aqua vinyl and Reception cloth; 39 = Redwood vinyl and Reception cloth; 40 = gold vinyl and black Reception cloth; 51 = black vinyl and black mesh cloth; 53 = green vinyl and green Reception cloth and 54 = blue vinyl and Reception cloth. Code 39 Redwood vinyl and Reception cloth was an alternate choice. Standard equipment on the Corsair convertible was the same as for closed cars, plus dual exhausts and a vinyl-coated top with vinyl boot. The ragtops featured all-vinyl interior trims in the following combinations: 41 = gold and white; 42 = black, white and silver; 43 = turquoise and white; 44 = black and red.

CORSAIR SERIES V-8

Model Number	Body/Style Number	Body Type & Seating	Factory Price	Shipping Weight	Production Total
NA	58B	4-dr Sed-6P	2812	3695	3,301
NA	63B	2-dr HT Cpe-6P	2819	3780	2,315
NA	57B	4-dr HT Sed-6P	2885	3710	1,694
NA	76E	2-dr Conv-6P	3072	3790	1,343

STATION WAGONS — (V-8 VILLAGER SERIES) — Only the Villager station wagon survived into 1959. It shared frontal treatments and side trim with the Ranger line of passenger models. Distinct styling was seen at the rear. The taillights consisted of two circular lenses set against a chrome grillework that was housed in a short, horizontal oval, which was banded in chrome. At the lower portion of the rear body, a full-width, oval-shaped beauty panel stretched across the Villager. It contained Edsel block lettering at its center and backup lights at each outboard end. The panel was usually (or always) painted a contrasting color, matching the sweep spear insert. A chrome outline molding encircled the panel and incorporated a rectangular nameplate at the top center. It carried the Villager name in block letters against a color field. Directly above this ornament, a combination lock button and handle was positioned. Villager rear fender tops formed a small, crisp tailfin and the bumper was a distinctive type, which was reshaped at the center to hold the license plate. Only the four-door wagon was available and it came with either six or nine-passenger seating. Standard equipment included four armrests; two ashtrays; cigarette lighter; color-keyed rubber floor mats; printed cardboard headliner with chrome bows and a solid-back bench seat. Available interior trims were: 30 = two-tone green vinyl and Gold puff cloth; 31 = white and red vinyl and gold puff cloth; 32 = buff and white vinyl and straw vinyl; 52 = two-tone blue vinyl with gold puff cloth.

VILLAGER SERIES

Model Number	Body/Style Number	Body Type & Seating	Factory Price	Shipping Weight	Production Total
NA	71E	4-dr Sta Wag-6P	2971	3840	5,687
NA	71F	4-dr Sta Wag-9P	3055	3930	2,133

NOTE 1: The prices and weights given above are for Villager V-8s.
NOTE 2: For sixes: subtract $84/deduct 99 pounds.

BASE ENGINES

(RANGER SERIES) V-8. Overhead valves. Cast iron block. Displacement: 292 cid. Bore and stroke: 3.75 x 3.30 inches. Compression ratio: 8.8:1. Brake hp: 200 at 4400 rpm. Five main bearings. Hydraulic valve lifters. Carburetor: two-barrel Model B9A9510-A. Note: This engine was available, as standard equipment in Rangers only. It came with the cylinder block and heads painted black; the air cleaner and valve covers painted gold.

(OPTIONAL RANGER SIX) Inline overhead valve Six. Cast iron block. Displacement: 223 cid. Bore and stroke: 3.62 x 3.60 inches. Compression ratio: 8.4:1. Brake hp: 145 at 4000 rpm. Four main bearings. Hydraulic valve lifters. Carburetor: one-barrel Model B9A9510-F. Note: This engine was available, as a delete option, only in the Ranger Series. It came with the cylinder block and heads painted black; air cleaner and valve covers painted red.

(CORSAIR SERIES) V-8. Overhead valves. Cast iron block. Displacement: 332 cid. Bore and stroke: 4.00 x 3.30 inches. Compression ratio: 8.9:1. Brake hp: 225 at 4400 rpm. Five main bearings. Hydraulic valve lifters. Carburetor: two-barrel Model PB9E9510-8.

CHASSIS FEATURES: Wheelbase: (Villager) 118 inches; (all others) 120 inches. Overall length: (Villager) 210.1 inches; (all others) 210.9 inches. Front tread: (all models) 59 inches. Rear tread: (all models) 56.4 inches. Tires: (Ranger with standard shift) 7.50 x 14 four-ply; (all others) 8.00 x 14 four-ply.

OPTIONS: Power brakes ($42.25). Four-Way power seat ($70.20). Power steering ($81.80). Power windows ($102.05). Lever-Temp heater ($74.45). Polar-Aire air conditioning with Dial-Temp heater/defroster ($431.20). Dial-Temp heater/defroster ($90.10). Back-up lights ($9.42). Eight-tube push-button radio ($64.95). Signal-Seeking radio ($89.20). Rear seat radio speaker ($10.70). Safety Package, including padded windshield header and dashboard ($20.60). Wheelcovers ($16.60). Wheelcovers with applique ($28). Windshield washer ($13.95). Tinted glass ($37.90). Two-tone top paint ($21.55). Electric windshield wipers ($8.40). Size 8.00 x 14 four-ply white sidewall tire ($35.68). Rocker panel molding ($17). Heavy-duty rear springs ($4.86). Heavy-duty front springs ($6.50). Heavy-duty shock absorbers ($14.60). Seat belts. Single or dual rear-mounted radio antenna. Continental tire carrier. Engine compartment light. Luggage compartment light. Courtesy lights. Contour floor mats. Fuel tank lock. Curb signals. Inside non-glare rearview mirror. License plate frames. Traffic light reflectors. Standard type outside rearview mirror. Hooded type outside rearview mirror. Single or dual spotlights. Seat covers. Rear door safety locks. Parking brake warning light. Station wagon rooftop carrier. Compass. Tissue dispenser. Litter container. Remote-control outside rearview mirror. Also available was the Visibility Group option package including back-up lights; windshield washer; hooded outside rearview mirror; courtesy and glovebox lights and non-glare inside rearview mirror ($35.40). A three-speed manual transmission with column control was standard equipment with the 233, 292 and 332 cid engines. Two-speed Mile-O-Matic transmission was optional on all models with any engine, but was rarely used in attachment with the 361 cid Super Express V-8 ($189.60). Three-speed Dual Drive automatic transmission was optional only with the Super Express V-8 ($230.80). Overdrive transmission was not officially listed as a factory option for 1959 Edsels. However, at least three 1959 models are known to have been specially ordered and factory-built with such attachments. In such cases, the space on the data plate for the transmission code is left blank. (Note: One of three six-cylinder cars is a Ranger driven on a daily basis by contributor Dale Rapp. It still delivers 20-22 mpg fuel economy today). Dual exhausts, on convertible (standard equipment); on other V-8 models ($31.90). Heavy-duty clutch ($17).

HISTORICAL FOOTNOTES: The 1959 Edsel lineup was publicly introduced on Oct. 31, 1958. Model year output peaked at 44,891 units, for 0.8 percent market penetration. Calendar year production hit 29,677 units. Ben D. Mills was the general manager of the Mercury-Edsel-Lincoln Div. All Edsels made to 1959 specifications were assembled at the Louisville, Ken. assembly plant. On a model year basis, 80.5 percent of all Edsels had automatic transmissions; 30.5 percent power steering; 18.9 percent power brakes: 2.3 percent power seats; 1.5 percent power windows; 75.5 percent radios; 95 percent heater/defrosters; 72.1 percent white sidewall tires; 8.2 percent tinted glass; 19.8 percent windshield washers; 12.2 percent electric windshield wipers; 31.7 percent backup lights; 2.9 percent dual exhausts; 2.2 percent air conditioning; 77.6 percent V-8 engines and 22.4 percent six-cylinder engines. Production during calendar year 1959 included 5,880 cars in January; 3,819 in February; 4,035 in March; 4,031 in April; 2,959 in May; 2,575 in June; 1.971 in July and 1,561 in August.

1960 EDSEL

EDSEL RANGER — (V-8) — In February, 1959, Henry Ford II attempted to dispel the rumors circulating in the auto industry about the Edsel's forthcoming demise. Ford Motor Co.'s president assured the world that the Edsel was to be a permanent member of the Ford family of cars. He said that he was certain the Edsel would prove successful and profitable in the long run and also revealed that the introduction date for 1960 models had already been set. These cars made their debut in October and featured a completely new body with numerous engineering improvements. Features included a lower silhouette, longer overall length and

greater body width. Offered only in Ranger and Villager configurations, the 1960 Edsel provided engines ranging from the 145 hp six to a 300 hp V-8. The horse collar grille was abandoned and, in its place, was an attractive design with dual headlamps 'floating' against a chrome grid. The grille was split at the center by a pinch-waist panel. A one-piece front bumper appeared on Edsels for the first time and incorporated a license plate housing at the center. The front parking lamps were integrated into the fenders in projectile-shaped housings. The new Edsel profile was straight from the Ford studios, with the exception of trim and decorations. A thin chrome molding swept from behind the upper front wheel cutout to the extreme lower corner of the rear body. Edsel block letters were placed above the molding at the trailing edge of the rear fender, while Ranger or Villager scripts appeared on the cowlside. At the rear, there was a wide, horizontal deck latch panel with a concave indentation and Edsel block lettering spaced across the center portion. Twin, vertical taillamps were positioned at each end of the car. They were somewhat oval-shaped, with the top portion rising higher than the upper edge of the deck. The deck lid and rear fendertop surfaces were formed into two narrow bulges on each side, which mated with the taillamps. The rear bumper was a one-piece unit, with a center license plate indentation and vertical side ribs directly below the vertical taillamp lenses. Standard equipment on all models included an electric clock; air cleaner; front foam cushion; oil filter; positive-action windshield wipers; cigarette lighter; turn signals; and carpets (except on station wagons). In addition, the Ranger convertible featured a DeLuxe trim package and standard dual exhausts. Also found inside all Rangers were four armrests; front and rear ashtrays; two coat hooks; and vinyl color-keyed headlinings. Standard trims available in Ranger sedans and hardtops were: 20 = silver vinyl and black pebble cloth; 22 = blue vinyl and black pebble cloth; 23 = green vinyl and brown pebble cloth; 24 = gold vinyl and brown pebble cloth; 25 = red vinyl and black pebble cloth. Also available in these styles were DeLuxe combinations including: 11 = silver vinyl and gray Champagne cloth; 15 = red vinyl and gray Champagne cloth; and 17 = turquoise vinyl and Champagne cloth. The DeLuxe combinations used in Ranger convertibles were: 54 = two-tone Gold vinyl; 55 = red and silver vinyl; 56 = black vinyl; 57 = two-tone turquoise vinyl.

1960 Edsel, Ranger, two-door convertible, V-8

EDSEL I.D. NUMBERS: Code locations were basically the same as on previous models. The first symbol indicated model year: 0 = 1960. The second symbol indicated the assembly plant: U = Louisville, Ken. The third and fourth symbols indicated body style: 11 = two-door sedan; 12 = four-door sedan; 13 = two-door hardtop; 14 = four-door hardtop; 15 = convertible; 17 = six-passenger station wagon; 18 = nine-passenger station wagon. The fifth symbol indicated the engine: V = 223 cid six; W = 292 cid V-8; Y = 352 cid V-8. The following numbers were the sequential production number starting at 700001 and ending at 703197. On the lower row of codes, Body Type designations were as listed in the second column of the specifications charts below. Exterior color codes were: A = black velvet; C = turquoise; E = Cadet blue metallic; F = Hawaiian blue; H = Alaskan gold metallic; J = Regal red; K = turquoise metallic; M = Polar white; N = Sahara beige; Q = Lilac metallic; R = Buttercup yellow; T = Sherwood green metallic; U = Bronze rose metallic; W = Sea Foam green; Z = Cloud silver metallic. Interior trim codes are explained in the text. Date codes were as in 1959 (Actually, all production took place during 1959). Transmission codes were unchanged. Axle codes were as follows: 1 = 3.56:1; 2 = 3.89:1; 3 = 3.10:1; 6 = 2.91:1; A = 3.56:1; with Equa-Lock; B = 3.89:1 with Equa-Lock and C = 3.10:1 with Equa-Lock.

RANGER SERIES V-8

Model Number	Body/Style Number	Body Type & Seating	Factory Price	Shipping Weight	Production Total
NA	64A	2-dr Sed-6P	2643	3601	777
NA	58A	4-dr Std Sed-6P	2697	3700	1,126
NA	58B	4-dr Del Sed-6P	2736	3700	162
NA	63A	2-dr Std HT-6P	2705	3641	243
NA	63B	2-dr Del HT-6P	2743	3641	52
NA	57A	4-dr Std HT-6P	2770	3718	104
NA	57B	4-dr Del HT-6P	2809	3718	31
NA	76B	2-dr Conv-6P	3000	3836	76

NOTE 1: Style Number suffix A = standard trim.
NOTE 2: Style number suffix B = DeLuxe interior trim.
NOTE 3: Prices shown for Deluxes are standard retail + Deluxe option price.
NOTE 4: Prices/weights are for V-8s; six-cylinder engine was delete option.
NOTE 5: For sixes: subtract $97/deduct 99 pounds.

STATION WAGON — (V-8) — VILLAGER SERIES — The Edsel station wagon for 1960 had the same general styling seen on the passenger cars. As usual, however, there were slight changes at the rear to accommodate the wagon body structure. This amounted to the upper rear fender feature line running straight across, above the taillamps, and then sweeping back to intersect the top of the concave lower panel. There was Edsel block lettering within the center of the lower panel, a Villager script directly above (on the tailgate) and, at the top of the gate, a chrome ornament that served as a handle containing the lock and latch mechanisms. As in the past, the wagon continued to offer an access arrangement with the upper liftgate and lower drop-down tailgate. The 1960 Villager came only in four-door styles, with a choice of six or nine-passenger seating configurations. Villagers had the same standard equipment as other lines, except that color-keyed rubber floor mats and printed cardboard headliners were utilized. Interior trims included: 32 = blue vinyl and ivy-stripe rib cloth; 33 = green vinyl and ivy-stripe rib cloth; 35 = red vinyl and ivy-stripe rib cloth; 50 = silver and black vinyl.

VILLAGER SERIES

Model Number	Body/Style Number	Body Type & Seating	Factory Price	Shipping Weight	Production Total
NA	71F	4-dr Sta Wag-6P	2989	4029	216
NA	71E	4-dr Sta Wag-9P	3072	4046	59

NOTE 1: Prices/weights are for V-8s; six-cylinder engine was delete option.
NOTE 2: For sixes: subtract $97/deduct 99 pounds.

BASE ENGINES

(RANGER SERIES) V-8. Overhead valves. Cast iron block. Displacement: 292 cid. Bore and stroke: 3.75 x 3.30 inches. Compression ratio: 8.8:1. Five main bearings. Hydraulic valve lifters. Carburetor: two-barrel Model B9A-9510-A. Note: The cylinder block and heads were painted black. The valve covers and air cleaner were painted red.

(OPTIONAL RANGER SIX) Inline overhead valve six. Cast iron block. Displacement: 223 cid. Bore and stroke: 3.62 x 3.60 inches. Compression ratio: 8.4:1. Brake hp: 145 at 4000 rpm. Four main bearings. Hydraulic valve lifters. Carburetor: one-barrel Model B9A9510-F. Note: This engine was available, as a delete option, only in the Ranger Series. It came With the cylinder block and heads painted black; air cleaner and valve covers painted red.

CHASSIS FEATURES: Wheelbase: (all models) 120 inches. Overall length: (Ranger) 216 inches; (Villager) 214.8 inches. Front tread: 61 inches. Rear tread: 60 inches. Tires: (Villager) 8.00 x 14; (Ranger) 7.50 x 14.

OPTIONS: Power steering ($81.80). Power brakes ($43.25). Power windows ($102.05). Four-Way power seat ($70.20). Lever-Temp heater and defroster ($74.45). Lever-Temp air conditioning with tinted glass and heater ($403.80). Polar-Air air conditioner. Back-up lights ($9.50). Push-button radio ($64.95). Rear seat speaker, except convertibles ($10.70). Single or dual rear-mounted antenna. Rocker panel moldings, except Villager ($17). Tinted glass ($37.90). Two-tone paint ($17). Full wheelcover ($16.60). Wheelcovers with applique and spinner ($30.10). Windshield washer ($8.40). Whitewall tires ($35.70). Inside non-glare rear view mirror. Standard outside mirror. Hooded outside mirror. Single spotlight with mirror. Remote-control outside mirror. Padded instrument panel. Padded sun visors. Courtesy lights. Glovebox light. Luggage compartment light. Parking brake warning light. Equa-lock differential. Seat belts. Heavy-duty cooling system. Fender skirts. Tissue dispenser. Litter bag. Locking fuel cap. Remote-control deck lid opener. Luggage rack, Villager. License plate frames. Rubber floor mats, front and rear. Rear door safety locks, four-door. A three-speed manual transmission was standard on all base models, but cars with the optional 352 cid 'Super Express' V-8 included automatic transmission as a mandatory option. Two-speed Mile-O-Matic automatic transmission, available in any model ($189.60). Three-speed Dual-Power Drive automatic transmission, available with the Super Express V-8 only ($230.80). The 362 cid 300 hp Super Express V-8, available as optional equipment over the base V-8 ($58). Note: Dual exhausts were standard equipment with the Super. Express V-8. This engine was painted black, with the valve covers and air cleaner finished in Turquoise Green. [OPTION PACKAGES]: DeLuxe trim package ($38.60). Visibility Group, includes back-up lights; windshield washer; inside non-glare mirror; outside hooded mirror ($30.90). Convenience Group A, includes heater and defroster; radio; Mile-O-Matic Drive; two-tone paint and full wheelcovers ($362.60). Convenience Group B, includes heater and defroster; radio; Dual-Power drive; two-tone paint; wheelcovers with applique and white sidewall tires ($453).

HISTORICAL FOOTNOTES: The 1960 Edsels were introduced on Oct. 15, 1959. The Edsel was discontinued on Nov. 19, 1959. Model year output amounted to 2,846 cars all of which were built in calendar 1959. Of these, 889 were made in September; 1,767 were made in October and 190 were built in November. All assemblies were made at the Louisville, Kentucky factory. Since the first Edsel was built, in 1957, a total of 110,847 were made. After Nov. 19, 1959, Ben D. Mills became general manager of Ford Motor Co.'s new Lincoln-Mercury Div. The much heralded — and now famous — Edsel was no more.

1960 Edsel, Corsair two-door convertible, V-8

1960 Edsel, Villager four-door station wagon, V-8

As was the case with the other major automakers, Ford entered the postwar market with a slightly restyled version of its 1942 models. The car-hungry market responded as if it were a completely new design and public demand dictated that the car remain nearly the same from 1946 through 1948.

By John Smith

When Henry Ford died in 1947, the wheels at Ford Motor Co. began to turn more smoothly and development of the all-new 1949 models began. Gone were the obsolete transverse rear springs and torque tube driveshaft. The new body was much lower, although shorter, than the previous year's models. Once again, the buying public flocked to the Ford showrooms eager to buy the slab-sided offering from Dearborn. Ford wisely decided to continue the same cars with very minor trim changes into the 1950 model year. The basic body style was used again in 1951, only this time the trim changes were more apparent. Model year 1951 also hailed the introduction of one of the most beautifully proportioned cars ever to come off of the Dearborn assembly lines, the 1951 Ford Victoria. Going hand in hand with the introduction of the hardtop Victoria was the introduction of the first fully automatic Ford-O-Matic transmission.

Ford continued to be "the car" to have if you were a performance enthusiast. Even though the old flathead V-8 was out-performed by the new overhead valve offerings from General Motors, many more speed parts were available for the flathead and that was as much a reason for their popularity as anything.

Continuing with a strong second place position in the low-priced field in the early '5Os, Ford sales hovered near the one million mark for the first three years of the decade. A very significant change, in 1954, was introduction of the first overhead valve V-8 in Ford's history. Another innovation was the company's first ball joint front end. Perhaps the most significant event of the year, however, was the late summer introduction of the Thunderbird. The beautiful little two-seater challenged both the European sports cars the GIs had fallen in love with during the war and also, the new Chevrolet Corvette.

Model year 1955 brought the introduction of a beautiful line of new Fairlanes, named after Henry Ford's mansion in Dearborn, Mich. Even though these mid-century Fords were warmly greeted by the public — and sold better than any models built since the war — the year's highlight event was taking place across town, with introduction of the ubiquitous small-block Chevrolet V-8.

For 1956, Ford once again decided to leave well enough alone in the styling department and offered a beautiful 1956 lineup to the public. Even though they looked similar to 1955s, the new models were flashier — a very important factor for the '50s. Ford introduced the sporty two-door station wagon the "Parklane" to compete with Chevrolet's Nomad. The great horsepower race of the '50s was in full swing by 1956 and all manufacturers were offering "power pack" options normally consisting of a four-barrel carburetor, slightly stronger cam, and, of course, dual exhausts. Ford offered its version for a new 312 cid V-8.

1964 saw a continued emphasis by Ford toward total performance. The big Galaxies, Fairlanes and Falcons continued to offer almost identical product lines and performance options carried over from the '63 1/2s. Falcons received the biggest styling changes in spite of the midyear introduction of the revolutionary Mustang. (Mustangs are covered in their own section of this book.)

A high-water mark in the horsepower race, for all manufacturers including Ford, was 1957. Chevrolet introduced the famous fuel-injected 283 cid V-8 engine and, in answer, Ford offered the supercharged "312" V-8. Conservatively rated at 300 hp, these supercharged motors were strong enough to handle any competition. The NASCAR versions, which put out in excess of 340 hp, absolutely dominated the stock car tracks during that year. If the supercharged version of the 312 was a little too wild for your tastes, you could order the engine in several different configurations, including two with twin four-barrel carburetion. Chevrolet was experiencing moderate success with its sport station wagon, the Nomad. To continue its answer to that challenge, Ford offered the Del Rio Ranch Wagon. In essence, Del Rios were base two-door Ranch Wagons sporting Custom 300 side trim and a fancy interior. Even though they did not enjoy the success or subsequent following of the Nomad, they were one-the-less very pleasant cars to look at. The fancier Parklane was discontinued after one year.

Mechanical innovations highlighted Ford model year 1958, while styling changes were made in the trim department. Even though 1957 and 1958 models look considerably different, they are still basically the same car. New for 1958 was the famous "FE" series of 332 and 352 cid V-8s, which grew into the "390" and the awesome "427." Also new for 1958, and offered for the first time in a Ford Division product, was the three-speed Cruise-O-Matic transmission. A novel suspension called Level-Aire-Ride, was offered this year only. Quality problems plagued the 1958 models and, as a consequence, only one million were made, the lowest production figure since 1952.

The following season witnessed introduction of a car that many consider to be the most beautiful Ford ever built, the 1959 Galaxie. Ford stylists took a Fairlane 500 two-door hardtop and added a Thunderbird inspired roof. The combination was so attractive that it was awarded the Gold Medal for Exceptional Styling at the Brussels World's Fair. With engines of up to 300 hp, they were spirited performers, also.

Even though they are not particularly well liked by many, the 1960 Fords were among the smoothest and most aerodynamic cars to come out of Dearborn. With other manufacturers producing engines well into the mid-300 hp range, Ford was being left behind and, in response, offered the 360 hp 352 cid V-8. While the other automakers were offering four-speed manual transmissions, Ford continued to offer only a three-speed manual with overdrive, which undoubtedly helped mileage, but hurt performance. The biggest news for 1960, however, was introduction of the compact Falcon. The most successful of the compact offerings from the big three auto makers, the Falcon was extremely simple and straightforward, both in styling and mechanical features.

Throughout the early '60s, Ford continued on a steady-as-she-goes course, offering the intermediate size Fairlane in 1962. Model year 1963 will be remembered as a high-water mark in the performance books at Ford. Not only was a new V-8 offered in the compact Falcon, but NASCAR and drag racing competition dictated the development and introduction of the most powerful engine ever to come from Dearborn, the incredible 427. These engines were used as race-only offerings, although some did find their way onto the streets. They produced 410 hp with one four-barrel carburetor and 425 hp with two. Fords absolutely dominated NASCAR racing with the "427" for the next four years and the record number of wins that they established in those seasons still stands as the most NASCAR victories for any one marque. Another highlight was the introduction of a car which many consider to be the most beautiful car of the '60s, the 1963-1/2 Galaxie 500 fastback. The body style was designed in answer to the demands of the NASCAR people who had nothing more aerodynamic to drive than the standard notchback Galaxie hardtops.

The 1965 season witnessed introduction of another significant contribution to the low-priced field, the luxurious LTD. This plush entry was embraced by luxury-hungry consumers on a tight budget. More than 100,000 were sold during the first year of production. The Fairlane was redesigned in 1965 and the Falcon continued to use the same basic body style first introduced in 1964.

The next year saw a slight redesigning in the full-size Ford lineup and, also, the introduction of the limited-Production seven-liter Galaxie models. These two-door hardtops and convertibles featured the new 428 cid V-8 engine, Cruise-O-Matic automatic transmission or four-speed manual transmission and power front disc brakes as standard equipment. With only 8,705 of the hardtops and 2,368 of the convertibles being produced, they are highly sought after collector's items today. The big news in 1966 was the complete redesigning of the intermediate Fairlane Series, which was made large enough to accommodate big-block Ford V-8s.

The full-size Galaxies were restyled for 1967 and presented a very attractive package to the buying public. Fairlanes continued to use the same body as in 1966 with only minor restyling. For 1967, NASCAR allowed the use of the intermediate size bodies in Grand National racing. The Fairlanes took the place of the Galaxies on the high banks, with Ford continuing to dominate the big races.

For 1968, the entire lineup received only minor restyling, with the exception of the intermediate Fairlane. Midyear introduction time witnessed the introduction of one of the strongest engines ever to come from the Dearborn drawing-boards, the incredible Cobra Jet 428. Very conservatively rated at 335 hp, actual output was more in the area of 400 hp.

As in the late '5Os, another great horsepower race was in full swing during the late '60s, with each manufacturer trying to out-power the other. Ford was right in the swing of things with the 428 CJ Mustang and Fairlane.

Engine and drivetrain options continued unchanged for 1970 but, in 1971, manufacturers produced the most awesome cars ever introduced to the general public. Ford produced the Boss 351 Mustang, the 429 SCJ Torino Cobras and the 429 SCJ Mustangs. Insurance companies were tightening the noose on "Supercar" owners by that time and

1971 is recognized as the last year for most true high-performance products from Ford until the '80s.

Ford made a significant contribution in the economy car field for 1971. In answer to the growing import threat and new sub-compacts from AMC and Chevrolet, Ford introduced its successful, but now infamous, Pinto. While competitors, like the Vega, were plagued with quality control and engineering problems, the simple Pinto continued to be a strong seller until it was finally withdrawn from the market in 1980 — to make room for the Escort.

The balance of the years from 1971 through 1975 are not attracting a great deal of enthusiast interest as yet, although several specific models have future potential. Those 1972 LTD and 1973 Mustang convertibles will undoubtedly gain popularity with collectors in the next few years.

Ford has long produced a car which appealed to the masses. Even though the marque was outsold by giant Chevrolet for most years since the war (except 1957 and 1959) many Fords continue to generate appeal with collectors. Fords of the '50s were among the best looking cars; the Fords of the '60s were among the fastest; and Fords of the '70s may someday be acclaimed as the most dependable and comfortable ever built.

1946 Ford, Super Deluxe Sportsman two-door convertible, V-8

1954 Ford, Crestline Sunliner two-door convertible, V-8

1950 Ford, Custom Deluxe two-door convertible, V-8

1957 Ford, Fairlane 500 Skyliner two-door retractable, V-8

1954 Ford, Crestline Sunliner two-door convertible, V-8

1957 Ford, Fairlane 500 Club Victoria two-door hardtop, V-8

Standard Catalog of American Cars

1959 Ford, Galaxie 500 two-door convertible, V-8

1966 Ford, Fairlane GTA two-door convertible, V-8

1967 Ford, Thunderbird two-door Landau, V-8

1968 Ford, Thunderbird, two-door hardtop coupe, V-8

1969 Ford, Fairlane Torino GTA two-door hardtop, V-8

1969 Ford, Thunderbird, four-door Landau, V-8

1971 Ford, Torino GT two-door hardtop, V-8

1972 Ford, LTD two-door hardtop coupe, V-8

1973 Ford, Grand Torino Sport, two-door hardtop, V-8

Standard Catalog of American Cars

1946 FORD

1946 FORDS — OVERVIEW — All 1946 Fords were, in essence, restyled 1942 models, utilizing the same drivetrain as the prewar models. The grille was restyled with horizontal bars on the outside of the rectangular opening, instead of the flush-mounted grille of the 1942 model. The remainder of the body was virtually the same as the prewar model.

DELUXE SERIES — (ALL ENGINES) — The Deluxe series was the base trim level for 1946 and included rubber moldings around all window openings, a horn button instead of a ring, one sun visor and armrests only on the driver's door.

DELUXE SIX-CYLINDER I.D. NUMBERS: Deluxe six-cylinder models began with the designation, "6GA", with production numbers beginning at 227524 and going to 326417.

DELUXE SIX-CYLINDER

Model Number	Body/Style Number	Body Type & Seating	Factory Price	Shipping Weight	Production Total
6GA	73A	4-dr Sed-6P	1198	3187	Note 1
6GA	70A	2-dr Sed-6P	1136	3157	Note 1
6GA	77A	2-dr Cpe-3P	1074	3007	Note 1

NOTE 1: See Deluxe V-8 Series listing. Production was counted by series and body style only, with no breakouts by engine type.

DELUXE V-8 SERIES I.D. NUMBERS: Deluxe V-8 powered models began with the designation, "69A", with production numbers beginning at 650280 and going to 1412707.

DELUXE V-8

Model Number	Body/Style Number	Body Type & Seating	Factory Price	Shipping Weight	Production Total
69A	73A	4-dr Sed-6P	1248	3220	9,246
69A	70A	2-dr Sed-6P	1185	3190	74,954
69A	77A	2-dr Cpe-3P	1123	3040	10,670

PRODUCTION NOTE: Total series output was 94,870 units. In addition, there were 84 chassis produced with closed drive front end, two chassis produced with open drive front end. Ford does not indicate the number of each model produced with sixes and V-8s. Therefore, all figures given above show total production of each body style with both types of engines.

1946 Ford, Super Deluxe four-door sedan, V-8 (AA)

SUPER DELUXE SERIES — (ALL ENGINES) — The Super Deluxe Series was the top trim level for 1946 and included chrome moldings around all windows, a horn ring, two sun visors, armrests on all doors, passenger assist straps on the interior "B" pillars for easier rear seat egress, horizontal chrome trim on the body and leather interior on the convertible models.

SUPER DELUXE SIX-CYLINDER I.D. NUMBERS: Super Deluxe six-cylinder models began with the same "6GA" designation and used the same production numbers as the Deluxe models.

SUPER DELUXE SIX-CYLINDER

Model Number	Body/Style Number	Body Type & Seating	Factory Price	Shipping Weight	Production Total
6GA	73B	4-dr Sed-6P	1273	3207	Note 1
6GA	70B	2-dr Sed-6P	1211	3157	Note 1
6GA	72B	2-dr Cpe Sed-6P	1257	3107	Note 1
6GA	77B	2-dr Cpe-3P	1148	3007	Note 1
6GA	79B	4-dr Sta Wag-8P	1504	3457	Note 1

NOTE 1: See Super Deluxe V-8 series listing. Production was counted by series and body style only, with no breakouts by engine type.

SUPER DELUXE V-8 SERIES I.D. NUMBERS: Super Deluxe V-8 models began with the same "69A" designation and used the same production numbers as the Deluxe models.

SUPER DELUXE V-8

Model Number	Body/Style Number	Body Type & Seating	Factory Price	Shipping Weight	Production Total
69A	73B	4-dr Sed-6P	1322	3240	92,056
69A	70B	2-dr Sed-P	1260	3190	163,370
69A	72B	2-dr Cpe Sed-6P	1307	3140	70,826
69A	77B	2-dr Cpe-3P	1197	3040	12,249
69A	76	2-dr Conv-6P	1488	3240	16,359
69A	71	2-dr SM Conv-6P	1982	3340	723
69A	79B	4-dr Sta Wag-8P	1553	3490	16,960

NOTE 1: Total series output was 372,543 units. In addition, there were 26 chassis produced with closed drive front end, three chassis produced with open drive front end and eight chassis-only produced. Ford does not indicate the number of each model produced with sixes or V-8s. Therefore, all figures given above show total production of each body style. With both types of engines, except in the case of convertibles, which come only with V-8 power.

SIX-CYLINDER: L-head. Cast iron block. Displacement: 226 cid. Bore & stroke: 3.30 x 4.40 inches. Compression ratio: 6.8:1. Brake hp: 90 at 3300 rpm. Carburetor: Holley single-barrel model 847F. Four main bearings.

V-8: L-head. Cast iron block. Displacement: 239 cid. Bore and stroke: 3.19 x 3.75 inches. Compression ratio: 6.8:1. Brake hp: 100 at 3800 rpm. Carburetor: Holley two-barrel model 94. Three main bearings.

CHASSIS FEATURES: Wheelbase: 114 inches. Overall length: 198.2 inches. Tires: 6.00 x 16.

1947 FORD

1947 FORDS — OVERVIEW — 1947 Fords were very slightly changed from the previous year. For example, the red tracer paint on the grille was dropped. A hood mounted emblem was seen up front. Circular parking lights looked attractive.

DELUXE SERIES — (ALL ENGINES) — The Deluxe series was the base trim level for the 1947 and included rubber moldings around all window openings, a horn button instead of a ring, one sun visor and armrests only on the driver's door.

DELUXE SIX-CYLINDER SERIES I.D. NUMBERS: Began with the designation, "7GA". Production numbers were 71GA-326418 to 71GA-414366; also (beginning 10/3/47) 77HA-0512 to 77HA-9038.

DELUXE SIX

Model Number	Body/Style Number	Body Type & Seating	Factory Price	Shipping Weight	Production Total
7GA	73A	4-dr Sed-6P	1270	3213	Note 1
7GA	70A	2-dr Sed-6P	1212	3183	Note 1
7GA	77A	2-dr Cpe-3P	1154	3033	Note 1

NOTE 1: See Deluxe V-8 Series listing. Production was counted by series and body style only, with no breakouts by engine type.

DELUXE V-8 SERIES I.D. NUMBERS: Deluxe V-8 models began with the designation, "79A", with the production numbers beginning at 799A-1412708 and going to 799A2071231.

DELUXE V-8

Model Number	Body/Style Number	Body Type & Seating	Factory Price	Shipping Weight	Production Total
79A	73A	4-dr Sed-6P	1346	3246	44,563
79A	70A	2-dr Sed-6P	1288	3216	44,523
79A	77A	2-dr Cpe-3P	1230	3066	10,872

NOTE 1: Total series output was 99,958 units. In addition, there were 23 chassis produced with closed drive front ends. Ford does not indicate the number of each model produced with sixes of V-8 engines. Therefore, all production figures given above show total production of each body style with both types of engines.

1947 Ford Sportsman convertible

SUPER DELUXE SERIES — (ALL ENGINES) — The Super Deluxe series was the top trim level for 1947 and included chrome moldings around all windows, a horn ring, two sun visors, armrests on all doors, passenger assist straps on the interior "B" pillars for easier rear seat egress, horizontal chrome trim on body and leather interior on the convertible models.

SUPER DELUXE SIX-CYLINDER I.D. NUMBERS: Super Deluxe six-cylinder models began with the designation, "7GA" and used the same production numbers as the Deluxe models.

SUPER DELUXE SIX

Model Number	Body/Style Number	Body Type & Seating	Factory Price	Shipping Weight	Production Total
7GA	73B	4-dr Sed-6P	1372	3233	Note 1
7GA	70B	2-dr Sed-6P	1309	3183	Note 1
7GA	72B	2-dr Cpe Sed-6P	1330	3133	Note 1
7GA	77B	2-dr Cpe-3P	1251	3033	Note 1
7GA	79B	4-dr Sta Wag-8P	1893	3487	Note 1

NOTE 1: See Super Deluxe V-8 series listing. Production was counted by series and body style only, with no breakouts by engine type.

SUPER DELUXE V-8 SERIES I.D. NUMBERS: Super Deluxe V-8 models began with the same "79A" designation and used the same production numbers as the Deluxe models.

SUPER DELUXE V-8

Model Number	Body/Style Number	Body Type & Seating	Factory Price	Shipping Weight	Production Total
79A	73B	4-dr Sed-6P	1440	3266	116,744
79A	70B	2-dr Sed-6P	1382	3216	132,126
79A	72B	2-dr Cpe Sed-6P	1409	3166	80,830
79A	77B	2-dr Cpe-3P	1330	3066	10,872
79A	76B	2-dr Conv-6P 1740	3266		22,159
79A	71B	2-dr SM Conv-6P 2282	3366		2,274
79A	79B	4-dr Sta Wag-8P 1972	3520		16,104

NOTE 1: Total series output was 385,109 units. In addition, there were 23 chassis produced with closed drive front ends. Ford does not indicate the number of each model produced with sixes or V-8s. Therefore, all figures given above show total production of each body style with both types of engines, except in the case of convertibles, which came only with V-8 power.

1947 ENGINES

SIX-CYLINDER: L-head. Cast iron block. Displacement: 226 cid. Bore & stroke: 3.30 x 4.40 inches. Compression ratio: 6.8:1. Brake hp: 90 at 3300 rpm. Carburetor: Holley single-barrel model 847F. Four main bearings.

V-8: L-head. Cast iron block. Displacement: 239 cid. Bore and stroke: 3.19 x 3.75 inches. Compression ratio: 6.8:1. Brake hp: 100 at 3800 rpm. Carburetor: Holley two-barrel model 94. Three main bearings.

CHASSIS FEATURES: Wheelbase: 114 inches. Overall length 198.2 inches. Tires: 6.00 x 16.

1948 FORD

1948 FORDS — OVERVIEW — 1948 Fords continued to share the 1946-1947 bodies with only slight trim changes. The parking lights were moved below the headlights from the former location between them. They were now round, instead of rectangular.

DELUXE SERIES — (ALL ENGINES) — The Deluxe series was the base trim level for 1948 and included rubber moldings around window openings, a horn button instead of horn ring, one sun visor and one armrest only on the driver's door.

DELUXE SIX-CYLINDER I.D. NUMBERS: Deluxe six-cylinder models began with the designation, "87HA," with production numbers beginning at 0536 and going to 73901.

DELUXE SIX

Model Number	Body/Style Number	Body Type & Seating	Factory Price	Shipping Weight	Production Total
87HA	73A	4-dr Sed-6P	1270	3213	Note 1
87HA	70A	2-dr Sed-6P	1212	3183	Note 1
87HA	77A	2-dr Cpe-3P	1154	3033	Note 1

NOTE 1: See Deluxe V-8 Series listing. Production was counted by series and body style only, with no breakout by engine type.

DELUXE V-8 I.D. NUMBERS: Deluxe V-8 powered models began with the designations "89A," with production numbers beginning with 899A-1984859 and going to 899A2381447.

DELUXE SIX

Model Number	Body/Style Number	Body Type & Seating	Factory Price	Shipping Weight	Production Total
89A	73A	4-dr Sed-6P	1346	3246	NA
89A	70A	2-dr Sed-6P	1288	3216	23,356
89A	77A	2-dr Cpe-3P	1230	3066	5,048

NOTE 1: Total series output was 28,404 units (not including the four-door sedan, for which production figures are not available). Ford does not indicate the number of each model produced with sixes or V-8s. Therefore, all production figures given above show total production of each body style with both types of engines.

SUPER DELUXE SERIES — (ALL ENGINES) — The Super Deluxe series was the top trim level for 1948 and included chrome moldings around the windows, horn ring, two sun visors, armrests on all doors, passenger assist straps on the interior "B" pillar for easier rear seat egress, horizontal chrome trim on the body and leather interior on the convertible models.

1948 Ford, Super Deluxe four-door sedan, V-8 (AA)

SUPER DELUXE SIX-CYLINDER I.D. NUMBERS: B began with the same "87HA" designation and used the same production numbers as the Deluxe models.

SUPER DELUXE SIX

Model Number	Body/Style Number	Body Type & Seating	Factory Price	Shipping Weight	Production Total
87HA	73B	4-dr Sed-6P	1372	3233	Note 1
87HA	70B	2-dr Sed-6P	1309	3183	Note 1
87HA	72B	2-dr Cpe Sed-6P	1330	3133	Note 1
87HA	77B	2-dr Cpe-3P	1251	3033	Note 1
87HA	79B	4-dr Sta Wag-8P	1893	3487	Note 1

NOTE 1: See Super Deluxe V-8 series listing. Production was counted by series and body style only, with no breakouts by engine type.

SUPER DELUXE I.D. NUMBERS: Super Deluxe V-8 powered models began with the same "89A" designation and used the same production numbers as the Deluxe models.

SUPER DELUXE V-8

Model Number	Body/Style Number	Body Type & Seating	Factory Price	Shipping Weight	Production Total
89A	73B	4-dr Sed-6P	1440	3266	71,358
89A	70B	2-dr Sed-6P	1382	3216	82,161
89A	72B	2-dr Cpe Sed-6P	1409	3166	44,828
89A	778	2-dr Cpe-3P	1330	3066	
89A	76B	2-dr Conv-6P	1740	3266	12,033
89A	71B	2-dr SM Conv-6P	2282	3366	28
89A	79B	4-dr Sta Wag-8P	1972	3520	8,912

NOTE 1: Total series output was 219,320 units (not including the two-door Coupe, for which production figures are not available). Ford does not indicate the number of each model produced with sixes or V-8 engines. Therefore, all figures given show total production of each body style with both types of engines. except in the case of convertibles, which came only with V-8 power.

1948 ENGINES

SIX-CYLINDER: L-head. Cast iron block. Displacement: 226 cid. Bore & stroke: 3.30 x 4.40 inches. Compression ratio: 6.8:1. Brake hp: 95 at 3300 rpm. Carburetion: Holley single-barrel model 847F. Four main bearings.

V-8: L-head. Cast iron block. Displacement: 239 cid. Bore & stroke: 3.19 x 3.75 inches. Compression ratio: 6.8:1. Brake hp: 100 at 3800 rpm. Carburetion: Holley two-barrel model 94. Three main bearings.

CHASSIS FEATURES: Wheelbase: 114 inches. Overall length: 198.2 inches. Tires: 6.00 x 16.

1949 FORD

1949 FORDS — OVERVIEW — 1949 represented the first totally new automobile produced by Ford since the end of World War II. The chassis was the wishbone type, with longitudinal rear springs replacing the transverse springs used on earlier models. Styling featured a heavy chrome molding curving from the top of the grille down to the gravel deflector, with 'FORD' in large block letters mounted above the grille molding. There was a horizontal chrome bar in the center of the grille, extending the full width of the opening, with parking lamps mounted on the ends of the bar. In the center of the bar was a large spinner, with either a '6' or '8' designation, indicating engine choice. The body was slab-sided, eliminating the rear fender bulge altogether. A chrome strip near the bottom of the body extended from the front fender openings back to the gas cap. Models for 1949 included the base Ford series, and the top line Custom series.

FORD SERIES — (ALL ENGINES) — The Ford series was the base trim level for 1949 and included rubber window moldings, a horn button instead of horn ring, one sun visor and an armrest only on the driver's door.

FORD SIX SERIES I.D. NUMBERS: Ford six-cylinder models began with the designation, "98HA", with production numbers beginning at 101 and going to 173310.

FORD SIX SERIES

Model Number	Body/Style Number	Body Type & Seating	Factory Price	Shipping Weight	Production Total
98HA	73A	4-dr Sed-6P	1472	2990	Note 1
98HA	70A	2-dr Sed-6P	1425	2945	Note 1
98HA	72A	2-dr Clb Cpe-6P	1415	2925	Note 1
98HA	72C	2-dr Bus Cpe-3P	1333	2871	Note 1

NOTE 1: See Ford V-8 Series listing. Production was counted by series and body style only, with no breakout per engine type.

FORD V-8 SERIES I.D. NUMBERS: Ford V-8 models began with the designation, "98BA", with production numbers beginning at 101 and going to 948236.

FORD V-8 SERIES

Model Number	Body/Style Number	Body Type & Seating	Factory Price	Shipping Weight	Production Total
98BA	73A	4-dr Sed-6P	1546	3030	44,563
98BA	70A	2-dr Sed-6P	1499	2985	126,770
98BA	72A	2-dr Clb Cpe-6P	1523	2965	4,170
98BA	72C	2-dr Bus Cpe-3P	1420	2911	28,946

NOTE 1: Total series output was 204,449 units. Ford does not indicate the number of each model produced with sixes or V-8s. Therefore, all production figures given show total production of each body style.

1949 Ford, Custom two-door sedan, V-8 (AA)

CUSTOM SERIES — (ALL ENGINES) — The Custom series was the top trim level for 1949 and included chrome window moldings, a horn ring, two sun visors, passenger assist straps on the interior B pillars for easier rear seat egress and horizontal chrome trim along the lower half of the body.

CUSTOM SIX SERIES I.D. NUMBERS: Custom six-cylinder models began with the same "98HA" designation and used the same production numbers as the Ford series.

CUSTOM SIX SERIES

Model Number	Body/Style Number	Body Type & Seating	Factory Price	Shipping Weight	Production Total
98HA	73B	4-dr Sed-6P	1559	2993	Note 1
98HA	70B	2-dr Sed-6P	1511	2948	Note 1
98HA	72B	2-dr Clb Cpe-6P	1511	2928	Note 1
98HA	76	2-dr Conv-6P	1886	3234	Note 1
98HA	79	2-dr Sta Wag-8P	2119	3523	Note 1

NOTE 1: See Custom V-8 Series listing. Production was counted by series and body style only with no breakout per engine type.

CUSTOM V-8 SERIES I.D. NUMBERS: Custom V-8 models began with the same "98HA" designation and used the same production numbers as the Ford series.

CUSTOM V-8 SERIES

Model Number	Body/Style Number	Body Type & Seating	Factory Price	Shipping Weight	Production Total
98BA	73B	4-dr Sed-6P	1638	3033	248,176
98BA	708	2-dr Sed-6P	1590	2988	433,316
98BA	72B	2-dr Clb Cpe-6P	1596	2968	150,254
98BA	76	2-dr Conv-6P	1949	3274	51,133
98BA	79	2-dr Sta Wag-8P	2264	3563	31,412

NOTE 1: Total series output was 914,291 units. Ford does not indicate the number of each model produced with sixes or V-8s. Therefore, all production figures given above show total production of each body style.

1949 ENGINES

SIX-CYLINDER: L-head. Cast iron block. Displacement: 226 cid. Bore and stroke: 3.30 x 4.40 inches. Compression ratio: 6.8:1. Brake hp: 95 at 3300 rpm. Carburetor: Holley one-barrel model 847FS. Four main bearings. Serial number code "H".

V-8: L-head. Cast iron block. Displacement: 239 cid. Bore and stroke: 3.19 x 3.75 inches. Compression ratio: 6.8:1. Brake hp: 100 at 3600 rpm. Carburetor: Holley two-barrel model AA 1. Three main bearings. Serial number code "B".

CHASSIS FEATURES: Three-speed manual transmission with a semi-centrifugal type clutch; three speed helical gears and synchronizers for second and third gears was standard equipment. Three-speed with automatic overdrive was optional. The automatic overdrive function cut in at 27 mph and cut out at 21 mph. Approximate drive ratio was 0.70:1. Wheelbase: 114 inches. Overall length: (Passenger cars) 196.8 inches; (Station wagons) 208 inches. Overall width: 72.8 inches. Rear axle gear ratios with standard transmission: (Passenger car) 3.73:1; (Station wagon) 3.92:1. Rear axle gear ratio with automatic overdrive: (Passenger car) 4.10:1; (Station wagon) 4.27:1. Tires: (Passenger car) 6.00 x 16; (Station wagon) 7.10 x 15.

1950 FORD

1950 FORDS — OVERVIEW — The 1950 Fords seemed identical to 1949 models, but were said to include "50 improvements for '50." Some of these improvements were, recessed gas filler neck, redesigned hood ornaments, flat-top horn ring, three-bladed cooling fan and push-button handles on exterior doors. An assembly plant designation was used in the serial numbers for the first time. (See NOTE 1).

DELUXE SERIES — (ALL ENGINES) — The Deluxe series was the base trim level for 1950, and included rubber window moldings, a horn button instead of horn ring, one sun visor, and an armrest only on the driver's door.

DELUXE SIX SERIES I.D. NUMBERS: (Ford factory codes) Assembly plant designations were as follows: AT = Atlanta; BF = Buffalo; CS = Chester; CH = Chicago; DL = Dallas; DA = Dearborn; EG = Edgewater; HM = Highland Park; KC = Kansas City; LB = Long Beach; LU = Louisville; MP = Memphis; NR = Norfolk; RH = Richmond; SP = Somerville; SR = Twin City (St. Paul). Deluxe six-cylinder models began with the designation, "OHA" followed by an assembly plant code and, finally, the unit's production number according to the final assembly plant. (See NOTE 1). Each plant began at 100001 and went up.

DELUXE SIX SERIES

Model Number	Body/Style Number	Body Type & Seating	Factory Price	Shipping Weight	Production Total
OHA	D73	4-dr Sed-6P	1472	3050	Note 1
OHA	D70	2-dr Sed-6P	1424	2988	Note 1
OHA	D72C	2-dr Bus Cpe-3P	1333	2933	Note 1

NOTE 1: See Deluxe V-8 Series listing. Production was counted by series and body style only, with no breakout per engine type.

DELUXE V-8 SERIES I.D. NUMBERS: Deluxe V-8 models began with the designation, "OBA" followed by an assembly plant code and, finally, the unit's production number according to the final assembly location. (See NOTE 1). Each plant began at 100001 and went up.

DELUXE V-8 SERIES

Model Number	Body/Style Number	Body Type & Seating	Factory Price	Shipping Weight	Production Total
OBA	D73	4-dr Sed-6P	1545	3078	77,888
OBA	D70	2-dr Sed-6P	1498	3026	275,360
OBA	D72C	2-dr Bus Cpe-3P	1419	2965	35,120

NOTE 1: Total series output was 388,368 units. Ford does not indicate the number of each model produced with sixes or V-8s. Therefore, all production figures given above show total production of each body style.

1950 Ford, Custom club coupe, V-8 (AA)

CUSTOM DELUXE SERIES — (ALL ENGINES) — The Custom Deluxe series was the top trim level and included chrome window moldings. chrome horn ring, two sun visors, armrests on all doors, passenger assist strap on the interior "B" pillars for easier rear seat egress and chrome strips along the lower half of the body, with the model identification at the front edge of the chrome strip.

CUSTOM DELUXE SERIES SIX I.D. NUMBERS: Custom Deluxe six-cylinder models began with the same "OHA" designation and used the same production numbers as Deluxe models.

CUSTOM DELUXE SIX SERIES

Model Number	Body/Style Number	Body Type & Seating	Factory Price	Shipping Weight	Production Total
OHA	C73	4-dr Sed-6P	1558	3062	Note 1
OHA	C70	2-dr Sed-6P	1511	2999	Note 1
OHA	C72	2-dr Clb Cpe-6P	1511	2959	Note 1
OHA	C79	4-dr Sta Wag-6P	2028	3491	Note 1

NOTE 1: See Deluxe V-8 Series listing. Production was counted by series and body style only, with no breakout per engine type.

CUSTOM DELUXE V-8 I.D. NUMBERS: Custom Deluxe V-8 models began with the same "OBA" designation and used the same production numbers as the Deluxe models.

1950 Ford, Custom Deluxe Crestliner two-door sedan, V-8 (AA)

CUSTOM DELUXE V-8 SERIES

Model Number	Body/Style Number	Body Type & Seating	Factory Price	Shipping Weight	Production Total
OBA	C73	4-dr Sed-6P	1637	3093	247,181
OBA	C73	2-dr Sed-6P	1590	3031	398,060
OBA	C70C	2-dr Crestliner	1711	3050	8,703
OBA	C72	2-dr Clb Cpe-6P	1595	3003	85,111
OBA	C76	2-dr Conv-6P	1948	3263	50,299
OBA	C79	2-dr Sta Wag-6P	2107	3531	29,017

NOTE 1: Total series output was 818,371 units. Ford does not indicate the number of each model produced with sixes or V-8s. Therefore, all production figures given above show total production of each body style with both types of engines, except in the case of Crestliners and convertibles, which came only with V-8 power.

1950 ENGINES

SIX-CYLINDER: L-head. Cast iron block. Displacement: 226 cid. Bore and stroke: 3.30 x 4.40 inches. Compression ratio: 6.8:1. Brake hp: 95 at 3300 rpm. Carburetor: Holley one-barrel model 847F5. Four main bearings. Serial number code "H."

V-8: L-head. Cast iron block. Displacement: 239 cid. Bore and stroke: 3.19 x 3.75 inches. Compression ratio: 6.8:1. Brake hp: 100 at 3600 rpm. Carburetor: Holley two-barrel model AA-1. Three main bearings. Serial number code "B."

CHASSIS FEATURES: The standard Ford transmission was a three-speed manual type with semi-centrifugal type clutch; three-speed helical gearset and synchronizers for second and third gears. A three-speed manual gearbox with automatic overdrive was optional. Specifications were similar to 1949. Wheelbase: (all models) 114 inches. Overall length: (Passenger cars) 196.8 inches; (Station wagons) 208 inches. Overall width: (all models) 72.8 inches. Tires: (standard) 6.00 x 16; (optional) 6.70 x 15; (Station wagon) 7.10 x 15. Rear axle gear ratios with standard transmission: (Passenger car) 3.73:l: (Station wagon) 3.92:1. Rear axle gear ratio with automatic overdrive: (Passenger car) 4.10:1; (Station wagon) 4.17:1.

HISTORICAL FOOTNOTES: The two-door sedan with short top was the Club Coupe. The two-door station wagon was the Country Squire. The Crestliner was a special two-door sedan with vinyl top covering; extra chrome; special steering wheel; special paint and full wheelcovers.

1951 FORD

1951 Ford, Deluxe two-door sedan, V-8 (AA)

1951 FORDS — OVERVIEW — While the 1951 Fords shared body components with the 1949-1950 models, a few trim changes made a substantial difference in looks. The horizontal bar in the grille had the single large spinner replaced by two smaller spinners, which were mounted at the ends of the bar. The taillight lenses were redesigned slightly and the license plate cover was reshaped. Inside, a completely different instrument panel was used and all instruments were grouped in front of the driver.

DELUXE SERIES — (ALL ENGINES) — The Deluxe series was the base trim level for 1951 and included rubber window moldings, a horn button instead of horn ring, one sun visor and an armrest only on the driver's door.

DELUXE SIX SERIES I.D. NUMBERS: Deluxe six-cylinder model numbers began with the designation "1HA" followed by an assembly plant code (See 195) and, finally, the unit's production numbers according to the final assembly location. (See NOTE 1). All plants began with 100001 and went up.

DELUXE SIX SERIES

Model Number	Body/Style Number	Body Type & Seating	Factory Price	Shipping Weight	Production Total
1HA	73	4-dr Sed-6P	1465	3089	Note 1
1HA	70	2-dr Sed-6P	1417	3023	Note 1
1HA	72C	2-dr Bus Cpe-3P	1324	2960	Note 1

NOTE: See Deluxe V-8 series listing. Production was counted by Series and body style only with no breakout per engine type.

DELUXE V-8 SERIES I.D. NUMBERS: Deluxe V-8 models began with the designation, "1BA", assembly code and, finally, the unit's production numbers, according to the final assembly location. (See NOTE 1). All plants began with 100001 and went up.

DELUXE V-8 SERIES

Model Number	Body/Style Number	Body Type & Seating	Factory Price	Shipping Weight	Production Total
1BA	73	4-dr Sed-6P	1540	3114	54,265
1BA	70	2-dr Sed-6P	1492	3062	146,010
1BA	72C	2-dr Bus Cpe-3P	1411	2997	20,343

NOTE 1: Total series output was 220,618 units. Ford does not indicate the number of each model produced with sixes or V-8s. Therefore, all production figures given above show total production of each body style.

1951 Ford, Custom Deluxe Victoria two-door hardtop, V-8 (AA)

CUSTOM DELUXE SERIES — (ALL ENGINES) — The Custom Deluxe series was the top trim level for 1951 and included chrome window moldings, chrome horn ring, two sun visors, armrests on all doors, passenger assist straps on interior "B" pillars for easier rear seat egress and horizontal chrome strips on the body exterior.

CUSTOM DELUXE SIX I.D. NUMBERS: Custom Deluxe, six-cylinder models began with the same "1HA" designation and used the same production numbers as the Deluxe models.

CUSTOM DELUXE SIX SERIES

Model Number	Body/Style Number	Body Type & Seating	Factory Price	Shipping Weight	Production Total
1HA	73	4-dr Sed-6P	1553	3089	Note 1
1HA	70	2-dr Sed-6P	1505	3023	Note 1
1HA	728	2-dr Clb Cpe-6P	1505	2995	Note 1
1HA	79	2-dr Sta Wag-8P	2029	3510	Note 1

NOTE 1: See Custom Deluxe V-8 Series. Production was counted by series and body style only with no breakouts per engine type.

CUSTOM DELUXE V-8 I.D. NUMBERS: Custom Deluxe V-8 models began with the same "1BA" designation and used the same production numbers as the Deluxe models. (See NOTE 1).

CUSTOM DELUXE V-8 SERIES

Model Number	Body/Style Number	Body Type & Seating	Factory Price	Shipping Weight	Production Total
1BA	73B	4-dr Sed-6P	1633	3114	232,691
1BA	70B	2-dr Sed-6P	1585	3062	317,869
1BA	70C	2-dr Crestliner	1595	3065	8,703
1BA	72C	2-dr Clb Cpe-6P	1590	3034	53,263
1BA	60	2-dr Vic HT-6P	1925	3188	110,286
1BA	76	2-dr Conv-6P	1949	3268	40,934
1BA	79	2-dr Sta Wag-8P	2110	3550	29,617

NOTE 1: Total series output was 792,763 units. Ford does not indicate the number of each model produced with sixes or V-8's. Therefore, all production figures given above are total production of each body style with both engines. except in the case of Crestliners, Victorias and Convertibles, which came only with V-8 power.

1951 ENGINES

SIX-CYLINDER: L-head. Cast iron block. Displacement: 226 cid. Bore and stroke: 3.30 x 4.40 inches. Compression ratio: 6.8:1. Brake hp: 95 at 3600 rpm. Carburetor: Holley one-barrel model. 847FS. Four main bearings. Serial number code "H."

V-8: L-head. Cast iron block. Displacement: 239 cid. Bore and stroke: 3.19 x 3.75 inches. Compression ratio: 6.8:1. Brake hp: 100 at 3600 rpm. Carburetor: Ford two-barrel model 8BA. Three main bearings. Serial number code "B."

CHASSIS FEATURES: The standard Ford transmission was a three-speed manual type with semi-centrifugal clutch, three-speed helical gearset and synchronizers for second and third gears. Three-speed transmission with automatic overdrive (see 1949 specifications) was optional at $92 extra. Two-speed Ford-O-Matic transmission was optional at $159 extra. This was a torque converter type transmission with three-speed (automatic intermediate gear for starting) automatic planetary geartrain and single stage, three element, hydraulic torque converter. Wheelbase: (all models) 114 inches. Overall length: (Passenger cars) 196.4 inches; (Station wagons) 208 inches. Overall width: (all models) 72.9 inches. Rear axle gear ratios with manual transmission: (standard) 3.73:1; (optional) 4.10:1. Rear axle gear ratio with automatic overdrive: 4.10:1. Rear axle ratio with Ford-O-Matic: 3.31:1. Tires: (standard) 6.00 x 16; (optional) 6.70 x 15 and (station wagon) 7.10 x 15.

HISTORICAL FOOTNOTES: The two-door sedan with short top was the Club Coupe. The two-door station wagon was the Country Squire. The Crestliner was a special two-door sedan with vinyl roof covering; extra chrome; special steering wheel; special paint and full wheelcovers. The Victoria was a new pillarless two-door hardtop.

1952 FORD

1952 — FORDS OVERVIEW — 1952 represented the first totally new body for Ford since 1949. The new models featured a one-piece curved windshield, full-width rear window, protruding round parking lights, round three-bladed spinner in the center of the grille bar, simulated scoop on the rear quarter panels, gas filler pipe and neck concealed behind the license plate, redesigned instrument panel and suspended clutch and brake pedals.

MAINLINE SERIES — (ALL ENGINES) — The Mainline series was the base trim level for 1952 and included rubber window moldings, a horn button instead of horn ring, one sun visor and an armrest only on the driver's door.

MAINLINE SIX SERIES I.D. NUMBERS: Mainline, six-cylinder models began with the designation, "A2", assembly plant code and finally the unit's production numbers according to the final assembly location. (See NOTE 1). Each plant began at 100001 and went up.

1952 Ford, Mainline Ranch Wagon (station wagon), V-8 (AA)

MAINLINE SIX SERIES

Model Number	Body/Style Number	Body Type & Seating	Factory Price	Shipping Weight	Production Total
A2	73A	4-dr Sed-6P	1530	3173	Note 1
As	70A	2-dr Sed-6P	1485	3070	Note 1
A2	72C	2-dr Bus Cpe-3P	1389	2984	Note 1
A2	59A	2-dr Sta Wag-6P	1832	3377	Note 1

NOTE 1: See Mainline V-8 Series listing. Production was counted by series and body style only, with no breakout per engine type.

MAINLINE V-8 SERIES I.D. NUMBERS: Mainline V-8 models began with the designation, "B2", assembly plant code and, finally, the unit's production numbers, according to the final assembly location (See NOTE 1). Each plant began at 100001 and went up.

MAINLINE V-8 SERIES

Model Number	Body/Style Number	Body Type & Seating	Factory Price	Shipping Weight	Production Total
B2	73A	4-dr Sed-6P	1600	3207	41,277
B2	70A	2-dr Sed-6P	1555	3151	79,931
B2	72C	2-dr Bus Cpe-3P	1459	3085	10,137
B2	59A	2-dr Sta Wag-6P	1902	3406	32,566

NOTE 1: Total series output was 163.911 units. Ford does not indicate the number of each model produced with sixes or V-8s. Therefore, all production figures given above show total production of each body style.

CUSTOMLINE SERIES — (ALL ENGINES) — The Customline series was the intermediate trim level for 1952 and included chrome window moldings, chrome horn ring, two sun visors, armrests on all doors, passenger assist straps on interior "B" pillars for easier rear seat egress, a horizontal chrome strip on the front fenders and a chrome opening on the rear quarter panel scoop.

CUSTOMLINE SIX SERIES I.D. NUMBERS: Customline, six-cylinder models began with the same "A2" designation and used the same production numbers as the Mainline models. (See NOTE 1).

CUSTOMLINE SIX SERIES

Model Number	Body/Style Number	Body Type & Seating	Factory Price	Shipping Weight	Production Total
A2	73B	4-dr Sed-6P	1615	3173	Note 1
A2	70B	2-dr Sed-6P	1570	3070	Note 1
A2	72B	2-dr Clb Cpe-6P	1579	3079	Note 1

NOTE 1: Customline V-8 Series listing. Production was counted by series and body style only with no breakout per engine type.

CUSTOMLINE V-8 SERIES I.D. NUMBERS: Customline V-8 models began with the same "B2" designation and used the same production numbers as the Mainline models. (See NOTE 1).

CUSTOMLINE V-8 SERIES

Model Number	Body/Style Number	Body Type & Seating	Factory Price	Shipping Weight	Production Total
B2	73B	4-dr Sed-6P	1685	3207	188,303
B2	708	2-dr Sed-6P	1640	3151	175,762
B2	72B	2-dr Clb Cpe-6P	1649	3153	26,550
B2	79C	4-dr Sta Wag-6P	2060	3617	11,927

NOTE 1: Total series output was 402,542 units. Ford does not indicate the number of each model produced with sixes and V-8s. Therefore, all production figures are total production of each body style.

1952 Ford, Crestline Victoria two-door hardtop, V-8 (AA)

CRESTLINE SERIES: The Crestline series was the top trim level for 1952 and was offered only with V-8 engines. This series included all trim in the Customline series, plus wheelcovers and additional chrome trim along the bottom of the side windows.

CRESTLINE SERIES I.D. NUMBERS: (V-8 only) Crestline models began with the same "B2" designation and used the same production numbers as the Mainline and Customline V-8 models.

CRESTLINESERIES

Model Number	Body/Style Number	Body Type & Seating	Factory Price	Shipping Weight	Production Total
B2	60B	2-dr Vic HT-6P	1925	3274	77,320
B2	76B	2-dr SL Conv-6P	2027	3339	22,534
B2	79B	4-dr Sta Wag-8P	2186	3640	5,426

1952 ENGINES:

SIX-CYLINDER: Overhead valves. Cast iron block. Displacement: 215 cid. Bore and stroke: 3.56 x 3.60 inches. Compression ratio: 7.0:1. Brake hp: 101 at 3500 rpm. Carburetion: Holley one-barrel model 847FS. Four main bearings. Serial number code "A."

V-8: L-head. Cast iron block. Displacement 239 cid. bore and stroke: 3:19 x 3.75 inches. Compression ratio: 7.2:1. Brake hp: 110 at 3800 rpm. Carburetion: Ford two-barrel model 8BA. Three main bearings. Serial number code "B."

CHASSIS FEATURES: The standard transmission was a three-speed manual type of the usual design. Three-speed manual with automatic overdrive (see 1949 specifications) was a $102 option. Ford-O-Matic transmission was a $170 option. Ford-O-Matic featured a torque converter transmission with automatic planetary geartrain; single stage three-element hydraulic torque converter; hydraulic mechanical automatic controls with no electrical or vacuum connections; forced air cooling; and power flow through the fluid member at all times. Wheelbase: (all models) 115 inches. Overall length: (all models) 197.8 inches. Overall width: (all models) 73.2 inches. Rear axle gear ratios: (manual transmission) 3.90:1; (overdrive) 4.10:1; (optional overdrive) 3.15:1; (Ford-0-Matic) 3.31:1; (optional with Ford-O-Matic) 3.54:1. Tires: (standard) 6.00 x 16; (optional) 6.70 x 15.

CONVENIENCE OPTIONS: A completely new line of custom accessories was brought out by the Ford Motor Company to match 1952 styling. Several interesting additions on the list were a speed governor; turn indicators; illuminated vanity mirror; engine compartment light; five-tube Deluxe radio; seven-tube Custom radio; spring wound clock; electric clock; color keyed rubber floor mats; wheel discs; wheel trim rings; rear fender skirts; rocker panel trim strips; hand brake signal lamp and Magic Air heater and defroster.

HISTORICAL FOOTNOTES: The Crestline Victoria was a two-door pillarless hardtop. The Sunliner in the same series was a two-door convertible. The four-door all-metal station wagon in the Crestline series was called the Country Squire. It came with woodgrained side trim appliques. The Mainline two-door station wagon was called the Ranch Wagon. The Customline four-door station wagon was called the Country Sedan. First year for overhead valve six-cylinder engine. The 1952 Fords were introduced to the public Feb. 1, 1952. Over 32 percent of cars built this year had Ford-O-Matic gear shifting. Over 20 percent of cars built with manual transmissions had the overdrive option. The Ford station wagon led the industry with 30.9 percent of the output for this body style. Of total production for the 1952 calendar year (617,725 units) it was estimated that a full 621,783 Fords were built with V-8 engines!

1953 FORD

1953 FORDS OVERVIEW — 1953 Fords utilized 1952 bodies with moderate trim updating. The grille incorporated a larger horizontal bar with three vertical stripes on either side of a large spinner. The length of this bar was increased and wrapped around the front edges of the fenders. Parking lights were rectangular instead of round. The Ford crest appeared in the center of the steering wheel hub and contained the words, "50th Anniversary 1903-1953."

MAINLINE SERIES — (ALL ENGINES) — The Mainline series was the base trim level for 1953 and included rubber window moldings, horn button instead of horn ring, one sun visor and an armrest only on the driver's door.

FORD I.D. NUMBERS: Beginning in 1953, Ford adopted a new coding system for serial numbers, which can be broken down as follows: The first symbol designates the engine type: (A) 215 cid six-cylinder; (B) 239 cid V-8; (P) 255 cid Law Enforcement V-8. The second symbol designates the model year: '3' for 1953; '4' for 1954 '5' for 1955, etc. The third symbol designates the final assembly plant, as follows: A = Atlanta; B = Buffalo; C = Chester; G = Chicago; F= Dearborn; E = Edgewater; E = Mawah; H = Highland Park; K = Kansas City; L = Long Beach; M Memphis, N = Norfolk; R = Richmond; R = San Jose; S = Somerville; P = Twin City (St. Paul). The fourth symbol designates body type, as follows: C = Sunliner; A = Customline Ranch Wagon; W = Mainline Ranch Wagon; X = Country Sedan; V = Victoria; T = Crestline four-door sedan: S =Sedan Delivery; G = Mainline and Customline two-door sedan, two-door coupe and four-door sedan. The fifth through tenth digits indicate the number of the unit built

at each assembly plant. beginning with 100001. Mainline six-cylinder models began with the designation, "A3". followed by assembly plant code, body type and, finally, the unit's production number. Each plant began at 100001 and went up.

1953 Ford, Mainline two-door sedan, 6-cyl

MAINLINE SIX SERIES

Model Number	Body/Style Number	Body Type & Seating	Factory Price	Shipping Weight	Production Total
A3	73B	4-dr Sed-6P	1783	3115	Note 1
A3	70B	2-dr Sed-6P	1734	3067	Note 1
A3	72B	2-dr Clb Cpe-6P	1743	3046	Note 1

NOTE 1: See Mainline V-8 Series listing. Production was counted by series and body style only, with no breakout per engine type.

MAINLINE V-8 SERIES I.D. NUMBERS: Mainline V-8 models began with the designation, "B3". assembly plant code, body type code, and, finally, the unit's production number according to the final assembly location. (See Ford serial numbers above.) Each plant began at 100001 and went up.

MAINLINE V-8 SERIES

Model Number	Body/Style Number	Body Type & Seating	Factory Price	Shipping Weight	Production Total
B23	73A	4-dr Sed-6P	1766	3181	66,463
B3	70A	2-dr Sed-6P	1717	3136	152,995
B3	72C	2-dr Bus Cpe-3P	1614	3068	16,280
B3	59A	2-dr Sta Wag-6P	2095	3408	66,976

NOTE 1: Total series output was 302,714 units. Ford does not indicate the number of each model produced with sixes or V-8s. Therefore, all production figures given above are total production of each body style with both engines.

CUSTOMLINE SERIES — (ALL ENGINES) — The Customline series was the intermediate trim level for 1953 and included chrome window moldings, chrome horn half-ring, two sun visors, armrests on all doors, passenger assist straps on interior "B" pillars for easier rear seat egress. A horizontal chrome strip on the front fenders and a chrome opening on the rear quarter panel scoop. There was another horizontal chrome strip from the scoop opening to the back of the body.

CUSTOMLINE SIX SERIES I.D. NUMBERS: Customline six-cylinder models began with the same "A3" designation and used the same production numbers as the Mainline models.

1953 Ford, Customline four-door sedan, V-8 (AA)

CUSTOMLINE SIX SERIES

Model Number	Body/Style Number	Body Type & Seating	Factory Price	Shipping Weight	Production Total
A3	73B	4-dr Sed-6P	1783	3115	Note 1
A3	70B	2-dr Sed-6P	1734	3067	Note 1
A3	72B	2-dr Clb Cpe-6P	1743	3046	Note 1

NOTE 1: See Customline V-8 Series listing. Production was counted by series and body style only, with no breakout per engine type.

CUSTOMLINE V-8 SERIES I.D. NUMBERS: Customline, V-8 models began with the same "B3" designation and used the same production numbers as the Mainline models.

CUSTOMLINE V-8 SERIES

Model Number	Body/Style Number	Body Type & Seating	Factory Price	Shipping Weight	Production Total
B3	73B	4-dr Sed-6P	1858	3193	374,487
B3	70B	2-dr Sed-6P	1809	3133	305,433
B3	72B	2-dr Clb Cpe-6P	1820	3121	43,999
B3	79B	4-dr Sta Wag-6P	2267	3539	37,743

NOTE 1: Total series output was 761,662 units. Ford does not indicate the number of each model produced with sixes or V-8s. Therefore, all production figures given above are total production of each body style with both engines, except for station wagons (Country Sedan), which came only with V-8 power.

CRESTLINE SERIES — The Crestline series was the top trim level for 1953 and was offered only with V-8 engines. This series included all trim in the Customline series, plus wheelcovers and additional chrome trim along the bottom of the side widows.

CRESTLINE I.D. NUMBERS: Crestline models began with the same "B3" designation and used the same production numbers as the Mainline and Customline V-8 models.

CRESTLINE SERIES

Model Number	Body/Style Number	Body Type & Seating	Factory Price	Shipping Weight	Production Total
B3	60B	2-dr Vic HT-6P	2120	3250	128,302
B3	76B	2-dr SL Conv-6P	2230	3334	40,861
B3	79C	4-dr Sta Wag-6P	2403	3609	11,001

1953 ENGINES

SIX-CYLINDER: Overhead valves. Cast iron block. Displacement: 215 cides. Bore and stroke: 3.56 x 3.60 inches. Compression ratio: 7.0:1 Brake hp: 101 at 3500 rpm. Carburetion: Holley one-barrel model 1904F. Four main bearings. Serial number code "A."

V-8: L-head. Cast iron block. Displacement: 239 cid. Bore and stroke: 3.19 x 3.75 inches. Compression ratio: 7.2:1. Brake hp: 110 at 3800 rpm. Carburetion: Holley two-barrel model 2100. Three main bearings. Serial number code "B."

CHASSIS FEATURES: Three-speed manual transmission was standard. This unit featured a semi-centrifugal type clutch; three-speed helical gears with synchronizers for second and third gears. Three-speed manual transmission with automatic overdrive was a $108 option. Specifications were the same above with automatic overdrive function cutting in 27 mph, cutting out at 21 mph. Approximate drive ratio was: 0.70:1. Manual control was provided below the instrument panel. Ford-O-Matic automatic transmission was a $184 option. This was a torque converter type transmission with automatic planetary geartrain; single stage, three-element hydraulic torque converter; hydraulic-mechanical automatic controls and no electrical or vacuum connections. Power was transmitted through the fluid member at all times. Wheelbase: 115 inches. Overall length: 197.8 inches. Overall width: 74.3 inches. Tires: 6.70 x 15 (standard) 7.10 x 15 (station wagon). Rear axle gear ratios: (standard transmission) 3.90:1; (optional) 4.10:1; (automatic overdrive) 4.10:1; (Ford-O-Matic) 3.31:1.

CONVENIENCE OPTIONS: Power steering ($125). Power brakes ($35). Ford-O-Matic transmission ($184). Overdrive ($108). Six-tube Deluxe radio ($88). Eight-tube Custom radio ($100). Recirculation type heater ($44). Deluxe heater ($71). Electric clock ($15). Directional signals ($15). Windshield washer ($10). Tinted glass ($23). White sidewall tires ($27).

HISTORICAL FOOTNOTES: The Mainline two-door all-metal station wagon was called the Ranch Wagon. The Customline four-door all-metal station wagon was called the Country Sedan. The Crestline four-door all-metal station wagon with woodgrain applique side trim was called the Country Squire. The Victoria was a pillarless two-door hardtop. The Sunliner was a two-door convertible. Introduction of 1953 models took place Dec. 12, 1953. On a model year basis 1,240,000 cars were built, of which total 876,300 were estimated to be V-8 powered units. Ford opened a new Technical Service Laboratory at Livonia, Mich. this year. A specially trimmed Sunliner convertible paced the 1953 Indianapolis 500-Mile Race. Master Guide power steering was introduced June 16, 1953.

1954 FORD

1954 Ford, Mainline two-door business coupe, 6-Cyl (AA)

1954 FORDS — OVERVIEW — 1954 Fords utilized the 1952-1953 bodies with moderate trim updating. The grille incorporated a large horizontal bar with large slots on either side of a centrally located spinner. Round parking lights were located at either end of the horizontal bar. Many new convenience options were added for 1954. Among them, were power windows, four-way power seats and power brakes. Ball joints replaced king pins in the front suspension. The big news from Ford Div. in 1954, however, was a new V-8 engine, with overhead valves. This new engine was rated at 130 hp, or nearly 25 percent more than the 1953 flathead. Even the introduction of the new V-8 overshadowed by the biggest news of all; the Feb. 20, 1954 announcement of an all new personal luxury car called the Thunderbird to be introduced in the 1955 model year.

MAINLINE SERIES — (ALL ENGINES) — The Mainline series was the base trim level for 1954 and included rubber window moldings, horn button instead of horn ring, one sun visor and an armrest only on the driver's door.

MAINLINE SIX SERIES I.D. NUMBERS: Mainline six-cylinder models began with the designation, "A4," followed by assembly plant code. body type code and, finally, the unit's production number according to the final assembly location. (See 1953 Ford serial numbers.) Each plant began at 100001 and went up.

MAINLINE SIX SERIES

Model Number	Body/Style Number	Body Type & Seating	Factory Price	Shipping Weight	Production Total
A4	73A	4-dr Sed-6P	1701	3142	Note 1
A4	70A	2-dr Sed-6P	1651	3086	Note 1
A4	72C	2-dr Bus Cpe-3P	1548	3021	Note 1
A4	59A	2-dr Sta Wag-6P	2029	3338	Note 1

NOTE 1: See Mainline V-8 Series listing. Production was counted by series and body style only, with no breakout per engine type.

MAINLINE V-8 SERIES I.D. NUMBERS: Mainline, V-8 models began with the designation, "U4", assembly plant code, body type and, finally, the unit's production number according to the final assembly location. Each plant began at 100001 and went up.

MAINLINE V-8 SERIES

Model Number	Body/Style Number	Body Type & Seating	Factory Price	Shipping Weight	Production Total
U4	73A	4-dr Sed-6p	1777	3263	55,371
U4	70A	2-dr Sed-6P	1728	3207	123,329
U4	72C	2-dr Bus Cpe-3P	1625	3142	10,665
U4	59A	2-dr Sta Wag-6P	2106	3459	44,315

NOTE 1: Total series output was 233, 680 units. Ford does not indicate the number of each model produced with sixes and V-8s. Therefore, all production figures given above are total production of each body style with both engines.

1954 Ford, Country Sedan four-door station wagon, V-8 (AA)

CUSTOMLINE SERIES — (ALL ENGINES) — The Customline series was the intermediate trim level for 1954 and included chrome window moldings, chrome half-horn ring, two sun visors, armrests on all doors, passenger assist straps on interior "B" pillars for easier rear seat egress, a horizontal chrome strip along the entire length of the body and a chrome stone shield near the bottom of the rear quarter panels.

CUSTOMLINE SIX SERIES I.D. NUMBERS: Customline six-cylinder models began with the same "A4" designation and used the same production numbers as the Mainline series.

CUSTOMLINE SIX SERIES

Model Number	Body/style Number	Body Type & Seating	Factory Price	Shipping Weight	Production Total
A4	73B	4-dr Sed-6P	1793	3155	Note 1
A4	70B	2-dr Sed-6P	1744	3099	Note 1
A4	72B	2-dr Clb Cpe-6P	1753	3080	Note 1
A4	59B	2-dr Sta Wag-6P	2122	3344	Note 1
A4	79B	4-dr Sta Wag-6P	2202	3513	Note 1

NOTE 1: Customline V-8 Series listing. Production was counted by series and body style only with no breakout per engine type.

CUSTOMLINE V-8 SERIES I.D. NUMBERS: Customline. V-8 models began with the same "U4" designation, and used the same production numbers as the Mainline series.

CUSTOMLINE V-8 SERIES

Model Number	Body/Style Number	Body Type & Seating	Factory Price	Shipping Weight	Production Total
U4	73B	4-dr Sed-6P	1870	3276	262,499
U4	70B	2-dr Sed-6P	1820	3220	293,375
U4	72B	2-dr Clb Cpe-6P	1830	3201	33,95
U4	59B	2-dr Sta Wag-6P	2198	3465	36,086
U4	79B	4-dr Sta Wag-6P	2279	3634	48,384

NOTE 1: Total series output was 674,295 units. Ford does not indicate the number of each model produced with sixes or V-8s. Therefore, all production figures given above are total production of each body style with both engines.

1954 Ford Crestline Skyliner two-door hardtop (glass roof), V-8

CRESTLINE SERIES — (ALL ENGINES) — The Crestline series was the top trim level for 1954, and included a six-cylinder engine for the first time since the series began in 1950. This series included all the Customline trim, plus three chrome hash marks behind the quarter panel stone shields, chrome "A" pillar moldings, additional chrome trim along the bottom of the side windows and wheelcovers.

CRESTLINE SIX I.D. SERIES NUMBERS: Crestline, six-cylinder models began with the same "A4" designation and used the same production numbers as the Mainline and Customline models.

CRESTLINE SIX SERIES

Model Number	Body/Style Number	Body Type & Seating	Factory Price	Shipping Weight	Production Total
A4	73C	4-dr Sed-6P	1898	3159	Note 1
A4	60B	2-dr Vic HT-6P	2055	3184	Note 1
A4	60F	2-dr Sky HT-6P	2164	3204	Note 1
A4	76B	2-dr SL Conv-6P	2164	3231	Note 1
A4	79C	4-dr Sta Wag-8P	2339	3563	Note 1

NOTE 1: See Mainline V-8 Series listing. Production was counted by series and body style only, with no breakout per engine type.

CRESTLINE V-8 SERIES I.D. NUMBERS: Crestline, V-8 models began with the same "U4" designation and used the same production numbers as the Mainline and Crestline V-8 models.

CRESTLINE V-8 SERIES

Model Number	Body/Style Number	Body Type & Seating	Factory Price	Shipping Weight	Production Total
U4	73C	4-dr Sed-6P	1975	3280	99,677
U4	60B	2-dr Vic HT-6P	2131	3305	95,464
U4	60F	2-dr Sky HT-6P	2241	3325	13,144
U4	76B	2-dr SL Conv-6P	2241	3352	33,685
U4	76C	4-dr Sta Wag-8P	2415	3684	12,797

NOTE 1: Total series output was 254,7687 units. Ford does not indicate the number of each model produced with sixes or V-8s. Therefore, all production figures are total production of each body style with both engines.

CHASSIS FEATURES: Wheelbase: 115 inches. Overall length: (passenger cars) 198.3 inches. (station wagons) 198.1 inches. Overall width: 73.5 inches. Tires: (standard) 6.70 x 15; (station wagon) 7.10 x 15.

1954 ENGINES

SIX-CYLINDER: Overhead valves. Cast iron block. Displacement: 223 cid. Bore and stroke: 3.62 x 3.60 inches. Compression ratio: 7.2:1. Brake hp: 115 at 3900 rpm. Carburetion: Holley one-barrel model 1904F. Four main bearings. Serial number code "A."

V-8: Overhead valves. Cast iron block. Displacement: 239 cid. Bore and stroke: 3.50 x 3.10 inches. Compression ratio: 7.2:1. Brake hp: 130 at 4200 rpm. Carburetion: Holley two-barrel model AA-1. Five main bearings. Serial number code "U."

LAW ENFORCEMENT V-8: Overhead valves. Displacement: 256 cid. Bore and stroke: 3.62 x 3.10 inches. Compression ratio: 7.5:1. Brake hp: 160 at 4400 rpm. Carburetion: Holley four-barrel. Five main bearings. Serial number code "P."

POWERTRAIN OPTIONS: Three-speed manual transmission was standard equipment. It featured a semi-centrifugal type clutch; three-speed helical gears and synchronizers for second and third gears. Three-speed with automatic overdrive was optional. Specifications were the same as above with automatic overdrive function cutting in at 27 mph, cutting out at 21 mph. Approximate drive ratio: 0.70:1. Manual control was mounted below the instrument panel. Ford-O-Matic automatic transmission was optional. This was a torque converter type transmission with automatic planetary geartrain; single stage, three-element hydraulic torque converter; hydraulic-mechanical automatic controls with no electrical or vacuum connections and power flow through the fluid member at all times. Rear axle gear ratios: (Ford) 3.90:1; (Ford with overdrive) 4.10:1; (Ford with Ford-O-Matic) 3.31:1;

CONVENIENCE OPTIONS: Automatic overdrive ($110). Ford-O-Matic transmission ($184). Power steering ($134). Power brakes ($41). Radio ($88-99). Heater and defroster ($44-71). Power windows ($102). Power seat ($64). White sidewall tires ($27 exchange). Note: Power windows available on Customline and Crestline only.

HISTORICAL FOOTNOTES: Public presentation of the original 1954 Ford line was made Jan. 6, 1954. Three new models, Crestline Skyliner, Crestline Sunliner and Ranch Wagon were introduced. The Ranch Wagon was a two-door station wagon in the Mainline series, but now had Customline appearance features. The Customline two-door sedan with short top was the Club Coupe. The Customline four-door station wagon was the Country Sedan. The Crestline four-door station wagon with wood grained trim was the Country Squire. The Victoria was a Crestline two-door pillarless hardtop. The Skyliner was a Crestline two-door pillarless hardtop with green tinted plastic insert in roof over front seat. The Sunliner was the Crestline convertible. Of the total 1,165,942 Fords built in the 1954 calendar year, industry sources estimate that 863,096 had V-8 engines installed. The 1,000,000th car of the 1954 production run was turned out Aug. 24, 1954. Slow motion production of cars built to 1955 specifications began Oct. 25, 1954.

1955 FORD

1955 FORDS — OVERVIEW — 1955 Fords were totally redesigned, inside and out, from the 1954 version. The bodies were longer, lower and wider. Even though the 1955 models used the same backlighted speedometer, first introduced in 1954, the rest of the instrument panel was new. A new Fairlane series replaced the Crestline as the top trim level. At the front, large, round parking lights were mounted in a concave grille underneath the headlights. The Ford crest was mounted above the word Fairlane, in script, on the front of the hood, and again, on the doors above the chrome Fairlane stripe. This stripe began at the tops of the front fenders, moved back along the tops of the fenders, over the side of the doors, into a dip and then to the rear of the car. The Fairlane series also featured chrome eyebrows on the headlight doors. The contemporary interest in horsepower and speed was reflected in two new, larger, overhead valve V-8 engines. Perhaps some of the most exciting news was the introduction on Oct. 22, 1954 of the all-new '55 two-passenger Thunderbird. The announced base price was $2,695.

MAINLINE SERIES — (ALL ENGINES) — The Mainline series was the base trim level for 1955 and included rubber window moldings, a horn button instead of chrome horn ring, one sun visor and an armrest only on the driver's door.

MAINLINE SIX I.D. NUMBERS: Mainline, six-cylinder models began with the designation, "A5" followed by assembly plant code, body type code and, finally, the unit's production number, according to the final assembly location. Each plant began at 100001 and went up. (See 1953 Ford serial numbers.)

MAINLINE SIX SERIES

Model Number	Body/Style Number	Body Type & Seating	Factory Price	Shipping Weight	Production Total
A5	73A	4-dr Sed-6P	1753	3106	Note 1
A5	70A	2-dr Sed-6P	1707	3064	Note 1
A5	70D	2-dr Bus Cpe-3P	1606	3026	Note 1

NOTE 1: See Mainline V-8 Series listing. Production was counted by series and body style only, with no breakout per engine type.

MAINLINE V-8 I.D. NUMBERS: Mainline, V-8 models began with the designation, "U5" (272 cid V-8) or "P5" (292 cid V-8), followed by assembly plant code, body type code and, finally, the unit's production number according to final assembly location. Each plant began at 100001 and went up.

MAINLINE SERIES V-8

Model Number	Body/Style Number	Body Type & Seating	Factory Price	Shipping Weight	Production Total
U5/P5	73A	4-dr Sed-6P	1853	3216	41,794
U5/P5	70A	2-dr Sed-6P	1807	3174	76,698
U5/P5	70D	2-dr Bus Cpe-3P	1706	3136	8,809

NOTE 1: Total series output was 127,301 units. Ford does not indicate the number of each model produced with sixes or V-8s. Therefore, all production figures given above are total production of each body style with both engines.

1955 Ford, Customline two-door sedan, V-8 (AA)

CUSTOMLINE SERIES — (ALL ENGINES) — The Customline series was the intermediate trim level for 1955 and included chrome window moldings, chrome horn half-ring, two sun visors, armrests on all doors, passenger assist straps on two-door interior "B" pillars for easier rear seat egress, a horizontal chrome strip along the entire length of the body and Customline in script on the rear fenders.

CUSTOMLINE SIX I.D. NUMBERS: Customline six-cylinder models began with the same "A5" designation and used the same production numbers as the Mainline series.

CUSTOMLINE SIX SERIES

Model Number	Body/Style Number	Body Type & Seating	Factory Price	Shipping Weight	Production Total
A5	73B	4-dr Sed-6P	1845	3126	Note 1
A5	70B	2-dr Sed-6P	1801	3084	Note 1

NOTE 1: See Customline V-8 Series listing. Production was counted by series and body style only, with no breakout per engine type.

CUSTOMLINE V-8 I.D. NUMBERS: Customline V-8 models began with the same "U5" or "P5" designation and used the same production numbers as the Mainline series.

CUSTOMLINE SIX SERIES

Model Number	Body/Style Number	Body Type & Seating	Factory Price	Shipping Weight	Production Total
U5/P5	73B	4-dr Sed-6P	1945	3236	235,417
U5/P5	70B	2-dr Sed-6P	1901	3194	236,575

NOTE 1: Total series output was 471,992 units. Ford does not indicate the number of each model produced with sixes and V-8s. Therefore, all production figures are total production of each body style with both engines.

FAIRLANE SERIES — (ALL ENGINES) — The Fairlane series was the top trim level for 1955 and included chrome window and "A" pillar moldings (hardtops and Sunliner), chrome eyebrows on the headlight doors and a chrome side sweep molding, plus all Customline trim (except the side chrome).

FAIRLANE SIX I.D. NUMBERS: Fairlane six-cylinder models began with the same "A5" designation and used the same production numbers as the Mainline and Customline Series.

1955 Ford, Fairlane Skyliner Crown Victoria two-door hardtop V-8

FAIRLANE SIX SERIES

Model Number	Body/Style Number	Body Type & Seating	Factory Price	Shipping Weight	Production Total
A4	73C	4-dr Twn Sed-6P	1960	3134	Note 1
A4	70C	2-dr Clb Sed-6P	1914	3088	Note 1
A4	60B	2-dr Vic HT-6P	2095	3184	Note 1
A4	64A	2-dr Crn Vic-6P	2202	3246	Note 1
A4	64B	2-dr Crn Vic Sky	2272	3264	Note 1
A4	76B	2-dr SL Conv-6P	2224	3248	Note 1

NOTE 1: See Fairlane V-8 Series listing. Production was counted by series and body style only, with no breakout per engine type.

FAIRLANE V-8 I.D. NUMBERS: Fairlane, V-8 models began with the same "U5" or "P5" designation and used the same production numbers as the Mainline and Customline Series.

1955 Ford Fairlane Club sedan, two-door sedan, V-8

FAIRLANE V-8 SERIES

Model Number	Body/Style Number	Body Type & Seating	Factory Price	Shipping Weight	Production Total
U5/P5	73C	4-dr Twn Sed-6P	2060	3268	254,437
U5/P5	70C	2-dr Clb Sed-6P	2014	3222	173,311
U5/P5	60B	2-dr Vic HT-6P	2195	3318	113,372
U5/P5	64A	2-dr Crn Vic-6P	2302	3380	33,165
U5/P5	64B	2-dr Crn Vic Sky	2372	3388	1,999
U5/P5	76B	2-dr SL Conv-6P	2324	3382	49,966

NOTE 1: Total series output was 626.250 units. Ford does not indicate the number of each model produced with sixes or V-8s. Therefore, all production figures given above are total production of each body style with both engines.

STATION WAGON SERIES — (ALL ENGINES) — Station wagons were, for the first time, included in their own series. The Ranch Wagon was the base trim level two-door wagon. Six and 8-passenger Country Sedans were the intermediate level and the Country Squire was the top level wagon. The level of trim equipment paralleled the Mainline, Customline and Fairlane series of passenger cars.

STATION WAGON SIX I.D. NUMBERS: Station wagon, six-cylinder models began with the same "A5" designation and used the same production numbers as the conventional cars.

STATION WAGON SIX SERIES

Model Number	Body/Style Number	Body Type & Seating	Factory Price	Shipping Weight	Production Total
A5	59A	2-dr Ranch Wag-6P	2043	3309	Note 1
A5	59B	2-dr Cus Ranch Wag	2109	3327	Note 1
A5	79B	4-dr Cty Sed-6P	2156	3393	Note 1
A5	798	4-dr Cty Sed-8P	2287	3469	Note 1
A5	79C	4-dr Cty Squire	2392	3471	Note 1

NOTE 1: See Station wagon V-8 Series listing. Production was counted by series and body style only, with no breakout per engine type.

STATION WAGON V-8 SERIES I.D. NUMBERS: Station Wagon V-8 models began with the same "U5" or "P5" designation and used the same production numbers as the conventional cars.

STATION WAGON V-8 SERIES

Model Number	Body/Style Number	Body Type & Seating	Factory Price	Shipping Weight	Production Total
U5/P5	59A	2-dr Ranch Wag-6P	2143	3443	40,493
U5/P5	59B	2-dr Cus Ranch Wag	2209	3461	43,671
U5/P5	79D	4-dr Cty Sed-6P	2256	3527	53,075
U5/P5	79B	4-dr Cty Sed-8P	2387	3603	53,209
U5/P5	79C	4-dr Cty Squire-8P	2492	3605	19,011

NOTE 1: Total series output was 209,459 units. Ford does not indicate the number of each model produced with sixes or V-8s. Therefore, all production figures given above are total production of each body style.

THUNDERBIRD (V-8) — SERIES 40A — A bright, high-spirited car, the Thunderbird was equipped with the new overhead valve V-8 engine, boosted to higher horsepower with the additional of a four-barrel carburetor and dual exhausts. A host of power-assist options including steering, windows, seat and brakes were available. The three-speed manual transmission was standard equipment, but overdrive and Ford-O-Matic automatic transmissions were optional accessories. Road clearance was only 5-1/2 inches, far less than the conventional Ford cars of the same year. The Thunderbird, with its two-seater personal car appeal, came from the factory with a fiberglass hardtop. A rayon convertible top was an extra-cost option priced $290. Full-scale production began during the week of Sept. 5, 1954. The 292 cid engine came with two compression ratios, 8.1 (193 hp) and 8.5 (198 hp). The lower ratio was used with the manual transmission only. The Thunderbird production line operated until Sept. 16, 1955. In addition to being started before the '54 model run was completed, it continued after the '56 model year began on Sept. 6, 1955. Only Thunderbirds were being assembled at the start and finish of the '55 model year run. This means that the first 1500 and the last 500 serial numbers from the series 100001 through 260557 were assigned only to Thunderbirds. The intervening numbers were assigned to the mixed production of Thunderbirds and the regular passenger car lines.

THUNDERBIRD SERIES I.D. NUMBERS: (V-8 only) Thunderbirds began with the prefix "P5FH" followed by the serial number starting at 100001.

1955 Ford, two-door Thunderbird convertible, V-8 (AA)

THUNDERBIRD SERIES

Model Number	Body/Style Number	Body Type & Seating	Factory Price	Shipping Weight	Production Total
P5	40	2-dr Conv-2P	2944	2980	16,155

1955 ENGINES

SIX-CYLINDER: Overhead valves. Cast iron block. Displacement: 223 cid. Bore and stroke: 3.62 x 3.60 inches. Compression ratio: 7.5:1. Brake hp: 120 at 4000 rpm. Carburetion: Holley single-barrel. Four main bearings. Serial number code "A."

V-8: Overhead valves. Cast iron block. Displacement: 272 cid. Bore and stroke: 3.62 x 3.30 inches. Compression ratio: 7.6:1. Brake hp: 162 at 4400 rpm. (182 at 4400 rpm. with the four-barrel "Power Pack"). Carburetion: Holley two-barrel. Five main bearings. Serial number code "U."

THUNDERBIRD V-8: Overhead valves. Cast iron block. Displacement: 292 cid. Bore and stroke: 3.75 x 3.30 inches. Compression ratio: 8.1:1 (8.5:1 with Ford-0Matic). Brake hp: 193 at 4400 rpm. (198 at 4400 rpm. with Ford-0-Matic). Carburetion: Holley four-barrel. Five main bearings. Serial number code "P."

FORD CHASSIS FEATURES: Wheelbase: (Passenger car) 115.5 inches; (Station wagon) 115.5 inches; (Thunderbird) 102 inches. Overall length: (Passenger cars) 198.5 inches; (Station wagon) 197.6 inches; (Thunderbird) 175.3 inches. Overall width: (Ford) 75.9 inches. (Thunderbird) 70.3 inches. Tires: (Station wagons) 7.10 x 15 tubeless; (All other cars) 6.70 x 15 tubeless. Front tread: (Ford) 58 inches; (Thunderbird) 56 inches. Rear tread: (Ford) 56 inches; (Thunderbird) 56 inches.

THUNDERBIRD CHASSIS FEATURES: Wheelbase: 102 inches. Overall length: 175.3 inches. Overall width: 70.3 inches. Tires: 6.70 x 15 tubeless.

FORD/THUNDERBIRD OPTIONS: Overdrive transmission ($110). Ford-O-Matic automatic transmission ($178). Radio ($99). Heater ($71). Power brakes ($32). Power seat ($64). Power windows ($102). White sidewall tires ($27 exchange). Soft-top for Thunderbird, in addition to hardtop ($290). Soft-top for Thunderbird, as substitute for hardtop ($75). Power steering ($91). Other standard factory and dealer-installed type options and accessories. Three-speed manual was standard equipment. It featured a Semi-centrifugal type clutch; three-speed helical gears and synchronizers for second and third gears. Three-speed with automatic overdrive was optional at $110. Specifications were the same as above with automatic overdrive function cutting in at 27 mph and cutting out at 21 mph. Approximate drive ratio: 0.70:1. Manual control below instrument panel.

HISTORICAL FOOTNOTES: The Town Sedan is a Deluxe Fairlane four-door sedan. The Club Sedan is a Deluxe Fairlane two-door sedan. The Victoria is a Fairlane two-door pillarless hardtop. The Crown Victoria is a Fairlane two-door, pillared hardtop with "basket handle" roof trim. The Crown Victoria Skyliner is a similar model with forward half of top constructed from transparent green plexiglass. The Sunliner is the two-door Fairlane convertible. The Ranch Wagon has Mainline level trim; the Custom Ranch Wagon has Customline trim; the Country Sedan is a four-door station wagon with Customline trim and the Country Squire is a Fairlane trim level station wagon with woodgrained side appliques. Production of 1955 Fords began Oct. 25, 1954 and ended August 30, 1955. The 1955 Ford was introduced to the public Nov. 12, 1954. Production of 1955 Thunderbirds began Sept. 7, 1954 and ended Sept. 16, 1955. The 1955 Thunderbird was introduced to the public Oct. 22, 1954. Of the total 1,435,002 cars built from October 1954 to September 1955, the majority were V-8s. During the 1955 calendar year 1,546,762 Ford V-8s and 217,762 sixes were manufactured. Also on a calendar year basis, 230,000 Fords had power steering; 31,800 had power brakes; 22,575 (of all FoMoCo products) had air-conditioning; 197,215 cars had overdrive and 1,014.500 cars had automatic transmissions. The 1955 run was the second best in Ford Motor Co. history, behind 1923 when Model Ts dominated the industry. A new factory in Mahwah, N.J. opened this year, to replace one in Edgewater, N.J. A new factory in San Jose, Calif. replaced a one-third as big West Coast plant in Richmond, Calif. A new factory was also opened in Louisville, Ken., replacing a smaller facility in the same city. Robert S. McNamara was vice-president and general manager of Ford Div.; J.0. Wright was assistant general sales manager; C.R.

Beacham was general sales manager; Holmes Brown was public relations director and G.C. Eldredge was advertising manager. Ford Motor Co. engineering had a experimental turbine-powered vehicle this year. It featured a modified 1955 body shell with an altered grille and exhaust system. This car was actually built in 1954 and had a "4" designation in the prefix code to the assigned serial number. The serial number was from the 1954 production serial number series. The car was scrapped after testing was completed.

1956 FORD

1956 FORDS — OVERVIEW — Ford reused the 1955 body again, with the exception of differences in the top configuration two-door hardtops of each year. New models were the Fairlane level Parklane two-door Sport wagon and a Customline Victoria two-door hardtop. Oval parking lights replaced the round units used on the 1955 models and the chrome trim was revised moderately from the previous year. The 1956 models used larger taillights with chrome rings around the lenses. Inside, the 1956 models were completely new. Safety was a very popular theme in 1956 and new Fords featured a completely redesigned instrument panel with optional padding and padded sun visors. Also, the steering wheel featured a 2-1/2 inch recessed hub, supposedly designed to lessen injury to the driver in the event of an accident. Seat belts were also offered for the first time in 1956.

MAINLINE SERIES — (ALL ENGINES) — The Mainline series was the base trim level for 1956 and included rubber window moldings, a horn button instead of horn ring, one sun visor and an armrest on the driver's door only.

MAINLINE SIX SERIES I.D. NUMBERS: Mainline six-cylinder models began with the designation, "A6", followed by assembly plant code, body type code and finally, the unit's production number, according to the final assembly location. (See production note). Each plant began at 100001 and went up.

MAINLINE SIX SERIES

Model Number	Body/Style Number	Body Type & Seating	Factory Price	Shipping Weight	Production Total
A6	73A	4-dr Sed-6P	1895	3127	Note 1
A6	70A	2-dr Sed-6P	1850	3087	Note 1
A6	70D	2-dr Bus Sed-3P	1748	3032	Note 1

NOTE 1: Total series output was 164,442 units. Ford does not indicate the number of each model produced with sixes or V-8s. See Mainline V-8 chart below.

MAINLINE V-8 SERIES I.D. NUMBERS: Mainline V-8 models began with the designation, "U6" (272 cid V-8), "M6" (292 cid V-8), or "P6" (312 cid V-8), followed by assembly plant code, body type code and finally, the unit's production number, according to the final assembly location. (See production note). Each plant began with 100001 and went up.

MAINLINE V-8 SERIES

Model Number	Body/Style Number	Body Type & Seating	Factory Price	Shipping Weight	Production Total
U/M/P-6	73A	4-dr Sed-6P	1995	3238	49,448
U/M/P-6	70A	2-dr Sed-6P	1950	3198	106,974
U/M/P-6	70D	2-dr Bus Sed-3P	1848	3143	8,020

NOTE 1: Total series output was 164,442 units. Ford does not indicate the number of each model produced with sixes or V-8s. Therefore, all production figures given above are total production of each body style with both engines.

CUSTOMLINE SERIES — (ALL ENGINES) — The Customline series was the intermediate trim level for 1956 and included chrome window moldings, horn ring, two sun visors, armrests on all doors, passenger assist straps on two-door interior "B" pillars, for easier rear seat egress; a chrome strip along the entire length of the body with the series identification just above, and forward of the rear wheel opening. Trunk lid identification consists of a Ford crest with horizontal chrome bars on either side of the crest.

CUSTOMLINE SIX SERIES I.D. NUMBERS: Customline, six-cylinder models began with the same "A6" designation and used the same production numbers as the Mainline series. (See production note).

CUSTOMLINE SIX SERIES

Model Number	Body/Style Number	Type & Seating	Factory Price	Shipping Weight	Production Total
A6	73B	4-dr Sed-6P	1985	3147	Note 1
A6	70B	2-dr Sed-6P	1939	3107	Note 1
A6	64D	2-dr Vic-6P	2093	3202	Note 1

1956 Ford, Customline four-door sedan, 6-cyl (AA)

NOTE 1: See Customline V-8 Series listing. Production was counted by series and body style only, with no breakout per engine type.

CUSTOMLINE V-8 SERIES I.D. NUMBERS: Customline V-8 models began with the same "U6", "M6". or "P6" designation and used the same production numbers as the Mainline series.

CUSTOMLINE V-8 SERIES

Model Number	Body/Style Number	Body Type & Seating	Factory Price	Shipping Weight	Production Total
U/M/P-6	73B	4-dr Sed-6P	2086	3258	170,695
U/M/P-6	70B	2-dr Sed-6P	2040	3218	164,828
U/M/P-6	64D	2-dr Vic-6P	2193	3345	33,130

PRODUCTION NOTE: Total series output was 368,653 units. Ford does not indicate the number of each model produced with sixes or V-8s. Therefore, all production figures given above are total production of each body style with both engines.

FAIRLANE SERIES — (ALL ENGINES) — The Fairlane series was the top trim level for 1956 and included chrome window moldings, chrome "A" pillar moldings on Sunliners, chrome side sweep moldings with simulated exhaust outlets at the back of the trim, Fairlane script below the Ford crest on the hood and a large, V-shaped insignia on the trunk lid. Also, V-8 equipped Fairlanes had rear bumpers with slots in each end for passage of the dual exhausts, which were standard with either V-8 engine.

FAIRLANE SIX-CYLINDER I.D. NUMBERS: Fairlane six-cylinder models began with the same "A6" designation and used the same production numbers as the Mainline and Customline series.

FAIRLANE SIX-CYLINDER SERIES

Model Number	Body/Style Number	Body Type & Seating	Factory Price	Shipping Weight	Production Total
A6	73C	4-dr Twn Sed-6P	2093	3147	Note 1
A6	70C	2-dr Clb Sed-6P	2047	3107	Note 1
A6	57A	4-dr Twn Vic-6P	2249	3297	Note 1
A6	64C	2-dr Clb Vic-6P	2194	3202	Note 1
A6	64A	2-dr Crn Vic-6P	2337	3217	Note 1
A6	64B	2-dr Crn Vic Sky-6P	2407	3227	Note 1
A6	76B	2-dr SL Conv-6P	2359	3312	Note 1

NOTE 1: See Fairlane V-8 Series listing. Production was counted by series and body style only, with no breakout per engine type.

FAIRLANE V-8 SERIES I.D. NUMBERS: Fairlane, V-8 models began with the same "U6". "M6", or "P6" designations and used the same production numbers as the Mainline and Customline series.

FAIRLANE V-8 SERIES

Model Number	Body/Style Number	Body Type Seating	Factory Price	Shipping Weight	Production Total
U/M/P-6	73C	4-dr Twn Sed-6P	2194	3290	244,872
U/M/P-6	70C	2-dr Clb Sed-6P	2147	3250	142,629
U/M/P-6	57A	4-dr Twn Vic-6P	2349	3440	32,111
U/M/P-6	64C	2-dr Clb Vic-6P	2294	3345	177,735
U/M/P-6	64A	2-dr Crn Vic-6P	2438	3360	9,209
U/M/P-6	64B	2-dr Crn Vic Sky-6P	2507	3370	603
U/M/P-6	76B	2-dr SL Conv-6P	2459	3455	58,147

PRODUCTION NOTE: Total series output was 645,306 units. Ford does not indicate the number of each model produced with sixes and V-8s. Therefore, all production figures given above are total production of each body style with both engines.

1956 Ford, Country Squire four-door station wagon, V-8 (AA)

STATION WAGON SERIES — (ALL ENGINES) — Station wagons continued as their own series for 1956. The Ranch Wagon was the base trim level two-door wagon; Country Sedans were the intermediate trim level and Country Squires were the top trim level with simulated woodgrain exterior paneling. The level of equipment paralleled the Mainline, Customline and Fairlane series of passenger cars.

STATION WAGON SIX-CYLINDER I.D. NUMBERS: Station wagon, six-cylinder models began with the same "A6" designation, and used the same production numbers as the conventional cars.

STATION WAGON SIX-CYLINDER SERIES

Model Number	Body/Style Number	Body Type & Seating	Factory Price	Shipping Weight	Production Total
A6	59A	2-dr Ranch Wag-6P	2185	3330	Note 1
A6	59B	2-dr Cus Ranch Wag	2249	3345	Note 1
A6	59C	2-dr Parklane Wag	2428	3360	Note 1
A6	79D	4-dr Cty Sed-6P	2297	3420	Note 1
A6	79B	4-dr Cty Sed-8P	2428	3485	Note 1
A6	79C	4-dr Cty Sq-8P	2533	3495	Note 1

NOTE 1: See Station wagon V-8 Series listing. Production was counted by series and body style only, with no breakout per engine type.

STATION WAGON V-8 SERIES I.D. NUMBERS: Station wagon V-8 models began with the same "U6", "M6" or "P6" designation and used the same production numbers as the passenger cars.

STATION WAGON V-8 SERIES

Model Number	Body/Style Number	Body Type & Seating	Factory Price	Shipping Weight	Production Total
U/M/P-6	59A	2-dr Ranch Wag-6P	2285	3473	48,348
U/M/P-6	59B	2-dr Cus Ranch Wag	2350	3488	42,317
U/M/P-6	59C	2-dr Parklane Wag	2528	3503	15,186
U/M/P-6	79D	4-dr Cty Sed-6P	2397	3536	—
U/M/P-6	79B	4-dr Cty Sed-8P	2528	3628	85,374
U/M/P-6	79C	4-dr Cty Sq-8P	2633	3638	23,221

PRODUCTION NOTE: Total series output was 214,446 units (not including six passenger Country Sedans, for which figures were unavailable). Ford does not indicate the number of each model produced with sixes or V-8 engines. Therefore, all production figures given above are total production of each body style with both engines.

THUNDERBIRD SERIES — (V-S) — Although the 1956 Thunderbird shared the same body as the 1955, there were a few significant changes which make the 1956 model very unique. Probably the most visible change is the outside location of the spare tire, which gave much more room in the trunk and, unfortunately, put so much weight behind the rear wheels that handling and steering were adversely affected. Also, the 1956 Thunderbird included wind wings on the windshield, cowl vents on each fender and a different rear bumper configuration with the simplified exhausts routed out the ends of the bumper.

1956 Ford, Thunderbird two-door convertible, V-8 HFM

THUNDERBIRD V-8 I.D. NUMBERS: Thunderbird models began with the designation "P6", assembly plant code "F" (Dearborn), body type code "H" (Thunderbird) and, finally, the production number beginning at 100001 and going up. Since 1956 Thunderbird production began over a month after the production of other 1956 Fords, the first Thunderbird serial number was later in the sequence.

THUNDERBIRD SERIES

Model Number	Body/Style Number	Body Type & Seating	Factory Price	Shipping Weight	Production Total
M6/P6	40A	2-dr Conv-2P	3151	3088	15,631

FORD/THUNDERBIRD ENGINES

SIX-CYLINDER: Overhead valves. Cast iron block. Displacement: 223 cid. Bore and stroke: 3.62 x 3.60 inches. Compression ratio: 8.0:1. Brake hp: 137 at 4200 rpm. Carburetion Holley one-barrel. Four main bearings. Serial number code "A."

V-8: Overhead valves. Cast iron block. Displacement: 272 cid. Bore and stroke: 3.62 x 3.30 inches. Compression ratio: 8.0:1. Brake hp: 173 at 4400 rpm. (176 at 4400 rpm. with Ford-O-Matic). Carburetion: Holley two-barrel. Five main bearings. Serial number code "U."

THUNDERBIRD V-8: Overhead valves. Cast iron block. Displacement: 292 cid. Bore and stroke: 3.75 x 3.30 inches. Compression ratio: 8.4:1. Brake hp: 200 at 4600 rpm. (202 at 4600 rpm with Ford-O-Matic). Carburetion: Holley four-barrel. Five main bearings. Serial number code "M."

THUNDERBIRD SPECIAL V-8: Overhead valves. Cast iron block. Displacement: 312 cid. Bore and stroke: 3.80 x 3.44 inches. Compression ratio: 8.4:1. Brake hp 215 at 4600 rpm. (225 at 4600 rpm. with Ford-O-Matic). Carburetion: Holley four-barrel. Five main bearings. Serial number code "P."

FORD CHASSIS FEATURES: Wheelbase: 115.5 inches. Overall length: 198.5 inches (197.6 inches on station wagons). Overall width: 75.9 inches. Tires: 6.70 x 15 4-ply tubeless, 7.10 x 15 4-ply tubeless on Victorias with Ford-O-Matic and on Ranch wagons, 7.10 x 15 6-ply tubeless on Country Sedans and Country Squire wagons.

THUNDERBIRD CHASSIS FEATURES: Wheelbase: 102 inches. Overall length: 175.3 inches (185 inches including continental kit). Overall width: 70.3 inches. Tires: 6.70 x 15 4-ply tubeless.

FORD/THUNDERBIRD OPTIONS: Automatic overdrive transmission ($110-$148). Ford-O-Matic transmission ($178-215). Power Steering for Mainline models ($91). Power steering for other models ($51-64). Power seat ($64). Radio ($100). Heater ($85). Power brakes ($32). Thunderbird V-8 for Fairlane models ($123). Thunderbird Special V-8 for Thunderbirds ($123). Power brakes ($40). Windshield washers ($10). Wire wheelcovers ($35). Power windows ($70). Chrome engine dress-up kit ($25). Rear fender shields. Full wheel discs. White sidewall tires. Continental tire kit. Tinted windshield. Tinted glass. Life-Guard safety equipment. Two-tone paint finish. Front and rear bumper guards. Grille guard package. Rear guard package. Rear mount radio antenna. Three-speed manual transmission with a semi-centrifugal type clutch, three-speed helical gears, and synchronizers for second and third gears standard equipment. Three-speed with automatic overdrive was optional (specifications same as above with automatic overdrive function cutting in at 27 mph, cutting out at 21 mph. Approximate drive ratio: 0.70:1. Manual control below instrument panel.) Ford-O-Matic automatic transmission was optional. This was a torque converter transmission with automatic planetary gear train; single stage, three-element hydraulic torque converter; hydro-mechanical automatic controls with no electric or vacuum connections and power flow through fluid member at all times. Six-cylinder rear axle ratios: (Ford-O-Matic) 3.22:1; (manual transmission) 3.89:1 and (overdrive) 3.89:1. V-8 rear axle ratios: (Ford-O-Matic) 3.22:1; (manual 3.78:1) and (overdrive) 3.89:1.

HISTORICAL FOOTNOTES: Production of 1956 Fords started Sept. 6, 1955 and the '56 Thunderbird began production on Oct. 17, 1955. The Parklane station wagon was a Deluxe Fairlane trim level two-door Ranch Wagon. The Crown Victoria Skyliner featured a plexiglass tinted transparent forward roof, the last year for this type construction. The Sunliner was a two-door convertible. The new Y-block Thunderbird V-8 came with double twin-jet carburetion; integrated automatic choke; dual exhausts; turbowedge shaped combustion chambers and

automatic Power Pilot. A 12-volt electrical system and 18-mm anti-fouling spark plugs were adopted this season. Model year sales peaked at 1,392,847 units. Calendar year production hit 1,373,542 vehicles. (Both figures include Thunderbird sales and production.)

1957 FORD

1957 FORDS — OVERVIEW — 1957 Fords were completely restyled and bore only a slight resemblance to earlier models. The new Fairlane series (including Fairlane and Fairlane 500 models) was five inches lower; had a two and one-half inch longer wheelbase and measured more than nine inches longer overall compared to 1956 models. The Custom series (including Custom and Custom 300 models) was three inches longer overall and had a one-half inch longer wheelbase than the 1956 models. As an aid in lowering the cars, all models had 14 inch wheels for the first time. Other design changes included a rear-opening hood, streamlined wheel openings and the use of windshield posts that sloped rearward at the bottom. Also, all 1957 Fords sported the latest styling craze, tailfins. Ford referred to these as "high-canted fenders." The big news for the year was the introduction of the Skyliner; the only true hardtop convertible in the world. At the touch of a button, an automatic folding mechanism retracted the top into the trunk, creating a true convertible.

CUSTOM SERIES — (ALL ENGINES) — The Custom series was the base trim level for 1957 and included chrome window moldings, a horn button instead of a horn ring, one sun visor and an armrest on the driver's door only. An abbreviated version of the 1955 Fairlane sweep type chrome trim began behind the front door and went back along the bodysides.

CUSTOM SIX SERIES I.D. NUMBERS: Custom, six-cylinder models began with the designation, "A7," followed by assembly plant code, body type code and, finally, the unit's production numbers according to the final assembly location. Each plant began at 100001 and went up.

CUSTOM SIX SERIES

Model Number	Body/Style Number	Body Type & Seating	Factory Price	Shipping Weight	Production Total
A7	73A	4-dr Sed-6P	2042	3197	Note 1
A7	70A	2-dr Sed-6P	1991	3154	Note 1
A7	70D	2-dr Bus Cpe-3P	1889	3145	Note 1

NOTE 1: See Custom V-8 Series listing. Production was counted by series and body style only, with no breakout per engine type.

CUSTOM V-8 I.D. NUMBERS: Custom V-8 models began with the engine designation code, followed by assembly plant code, body type code and, finally, the unit's production numbers, according to the final assembly location. Each plant began at 100001 and went up.

CUSTOM V-8 SERIES

Model Number	Body/Style Number	Body Type & Seating	Factory Price	Shipping Weight	Production Total
NA	73A	4-dr Sed-6P	2142	3319	68,924
NA	70A	2-dr Sed-6P	2091	3276	116,963
NA	70D	2-dr Bus Cpe-3P	1979	3267	6,888

PRODUCTION NOTE: Total series output was 192,775 units. Ford does not indicate the number of each model produced with sixes and V-8s. Therefore, all production figures given above are total production of each body style with both engines. "Model numbers" were now equivalent to V-8 engine code designations, which varied with specific powerplant attachments.

1957 Ford, Custom 300 four-door sedan, V-8

CUSTOM 300 MODELS — (ALL ENGINES) — The Custom 300 was the top trim level in the short wheelbase Custom series and included chrome window moldings; chrome horn ring; two sun visors; armrests on all doors and a slightly modified version of the new Fairlane sweep, featuring a gold anodized insert between two chrome strips. The word 'FORD' was spelled out in block letters above the grille and a small Ford crest appeared on the trunk lid.

CUSTOM 300 SIX SERIES I.D. NUMBERS: Custom 300 six-cylinder models began with the same "A7" designation and used the same production numbers as the Custom models.

CUSTOM 300 SIX SERIES

Model Number	Body/Style Number	Body Type & Seating	Factory Price	Shipping Weight	Production Total
A7	73B	4-dr Sed-6P	2157	3212	Note 1
A7	70B	2-dr Sed-6P	2105	3167	Note 1

NOTE 1: See Custom 300 V-8 Series listing. Production was counted by series and body style only, with no breakouts per engine type.

CUSTOM 300 V-8 SERIES I.D. NUMBERS: Custom 300 V-8 models began with the same engine designations and used the same production numbers as the Custom models.

CUSTOM 300 V-8 SERIES

Model Number	Body/Style Number	Body Type & Seating	Factory Price	Shipping Weight	Production Total
NA	73B	4-dr Sed-6P	2257	3334	194,877
NA	70B	2-dr Sed-6P	2205	3289	160,360

PRODUCTION NOTE: Total series output was 355,237 units. Ford does not indicate the number of each model produced with sixes or V-8s. Therefore, all production figures given above are total production of each body style with both engines. "Model Numbers" were equivalent to V-8 engine code designations, which varied with specific powerplant attachments.

1957 Ford, Fairlane Town Sedan, V-8 AA

FAIRLANE SERIES — (ALL ENGINES) — The Fairlane model was the base trim level for the longer wheelbase Fairlane series and included chrome window moldings with slightly less chrome around the "C" pillar than the Fairlane 500 model and a considerably different side stripe than the higher-priced model. The Fairlane side chrome began just behind the front door. It then followed the fin forward to its source, dropped over the side and swept back, at a 45-degree angle, to a point just above the wheel opening. From there it ran straight back to the rear bumper. The word Fairlane appeared in script, on the side of the front fenders, and above the grille. A large V-shaped Fairlane crest appeared on the trunk lid.

FAIRLANE SIX SERIES I.D. NUMBERS: Fairlane, six-cylinder models began with the same "A7" designation and used the same production numbers as the Custom series.

FAIRLANE SIX SERIES

Model Number	Body/Style Number	Body Type & Seating	Factory Price	Shipping Weight	Production Total
A7	58A	4-dr Twn Sed-6P	2286	3315	Note 1
A7	64A	2-dr Clb Sed-6P	2235	3270	Note 1
A7	57B	4-dr Twn Vic-6P	2357	3350	Note 1
A7	638	2-dr Clb Vic-6P	2293	3305	Note 1

NOTE 1: See Fairlane V-8 Series listing. Production was counted by series and body style only, with no breakouts per engine type.

FAIRLANE V-8 SERIES I.D. NUMBERS: Fairlane V-8 models began with the same engine designations and used the same production numbers as the Custom series.

FAIRLANE V-8 SERIES

Model Number	Body/Style Number	Body Type & Seating	Factory Price	Shipping Weight	Production Total
NA	58A	4-dr Twn Sed-6P	2386	3437	52,060
NA	64A	2-dr Clb Sed-6P	2335	3392	39,843
NA	578	4-dr Twn Vic-6P	2457	3471	12,695
NA	63B	2-dr Clb Vic-6P	2393	3427	44,127

PRODUCTION NOTE: Total series output was 148,725 units. Ford does not indicate the number of each model produced with sixes and V-8s. Therefore, all production figures given above are total production of each body style with both engines. "Model Numbers" were now equivalent to V-8 engine code designations, which varied with specific power plant attachments.

1957 Ford, Fairlane 500 two-door Sunliner convertible, V-8

FAIRLANE 500 MODELS — (ALL ENGINES) — The Fairlane 500 was the top trim level in the Fairlane series and included all the trim used on the Fairlane models plus slightly more chrome on the "C" pillars and different side trim. The side trim was a modified version of the Fairlane sweep which included a gold anodized insert between two chrome strips. It began on the sides of the front fenders, dipping near the back of the front doors, merging into a strip and following the crest of the fins to the rear of the body.

FAIRLANE 500 SIX SERIES I.D. NUMBERS: Fairlane 500 six-cylinder models began with the same "A7" designation and used the same production numbers as the Fairlane models and Custom series.

FAIRLANE 500 SIX SERIES

Model Number	Body/Style Number	Body Type & Seating	Factory Price	Shipping Weight	Production Total
A7	58B	4-dr Twn Sed-6P	2333	3300	Note 1
A7	64B	2-dr Clb Sed-6P	2281	3285	Note 1
A7	57A	4-dr Twn Vic-6P	2404	3365	Note 1
A7	63A	2-dr Clb Vic-6P	2339	3320	Note 1
A7	76B	2-dr SL Conv-6P	2505	3475	Note 1

NOTE 1: See Fairlane 500 V-8 Series listing. Production was counted by series and body style, with no breakouts per engine size.

FAIRLANE 500 V-8 SERIES I.D. NUMBERS: Fairlane 500 V-8 models began with the same engine designations and used the same production numbers as the Fairlane models and the Custom series.

FAIRLANE 500 V-8 SERIES

Model Number	Body/Style Number	Body Type & Seating	Factory Price	Shipping Weight	Production Total
NA	58B	4-dr Twn Sed-6P	2433	3452	193,162
NA	64B	2-dr Clb Sed-6P	2381	3407	93,753
NA	57A	4-dr Twn Vic-6P	2504	3487	68,550
NA	63A	2-dr Clb Vic-6P	2439	3442	183,202
NA	63A	2-dr Clb Vic-6P	2439	3442	183,202
NA	76B	2-dr SL Conv-6P	2605	3497	77,728
NA	51A	2-dr Sky Conv-6P	2942	3916	20,766

PRODUCTION NOTE: Total series output was 637,161 units. Ford does not indicate the number of each model produced with sixes and V-8s. Therefore, all production figures given above are total production of each body style. "Model Numbers" were now equivalent to V-8 engine code designations, which varied with specific powerplant attachments. All convertibles are two-door styles; all Skyliner retractable convertibles are V-8 powered.

STATION WAGON SERIES — (ALL ENGINES) — The Ranch Wagon was the base trim level two-door station wagon for 1957. Country Sedans were the intermediate level with four-door styling. Country Squires were the top trim level, also with four-door styling. The level of equipment paralleled Custom, Custom 300 and Fairlane 500 models of passenger cars.

STATION WAGON SIX SERIES I.D. NUMBERS: Station wagon six-cylinder models began with the same "A7" designation and used the same production numbers as the passenger cars.

STATION WAGON SIX SERIES

Model Number	Body/Style Number	Body Type & Seating	Factory Price	Shipping Weight	Production Total
A7	59A	2-dr Ranch Wag-6P	2301	3398	Note 1
A7	59B	2-dr Del Rio-6P	2397	3405	Note 1
A7	79D	4-dr Cty Sed-6P	2451	3468	Note 1
A7	79C	4-dr Cty Sed-9P	2556	3557	Note 1
A7	79E	4-dr Cty Sq-8P	2684	3571	Note 1

NOTE 1: See Station wagon V-8 Series listing. Production was counted by series and body style, with no breakouts per engine size.

STATION WAGON V-8 SERIES I.D. NUMBERS: Station wagon V-8 models began with the same engine designations and used the same production numbers as the passenger cars.

STATION WAGON V-8 SERIES

Model Number	Body/Style Number	Body Type & Seating	Factory Price	Shipping Weight	Production Total
NA	59A	2-dr Ranch Wag-6P	2401	3520	60,486
NA	59B	2-dr Del Rio-6P	2497	3527	46,105
NA	79D	4-dr Cty Sed-6P	2551	3590	135,251
NA	79C	4-dr Cty Sed-9P	2656	3679	49,638
NA	79E	4-dr Cty Sq-8P	2784	3693	27,690

PRODUCTION NOTE: Total series output was 319,170 units. Ford does not indicate the number of each model produced with sixes and V-8s. Therefore, all production figures given above are total production of each body style with both engines. "Model Numbers" were now equivalent to V-8 engine code designations, which varied with specific powerplant attachments. The Country Squire had simulated woodgrained exterior paneling.

1957 Ford, Thunderbird two-door convertible (with hardtop), V-8 (AA)

THUNDERBIRD V-8 SERIES — The 1957 model represented the first significant restyling since the T-Bird was first introduced. A longer rear section provided improved storage space. Riding and handling qualities were greatly enhanced by relocating the spare tire in the trunk. As with the large Fords, 1957 Thunderbirds featured fins on the rear fenders. Inside, the 1957 model used the instrument panel from full-sized 1956 Fords, with an engine-turned insert dressing-up the panel.

THUNDERBIRD V-8 SERIES I.D. NUMBERS: Thunderbird models began with the engine designation, "C7," "D7," "E7," or "F7" (depending on engine choice). The "F7" indicated the supercharged V-8. The assembly plant code was "F" for Dearborn. The body type code was "H" for Thunderbird. The production number was in series, beginning at 100001 and going up.

THUNDERBIRD V-8 SERIES

Model Number	Body/Style Number	Body Type & Seating	Factory Price	Shipping Weight	Production Total
C7/D7/E7	40	2-dr Conv-2P	3408	3134	21,380

1957 ENGINES

SIX-CYLINDER: Overhead valves. Cast iron block. Displacement: 223 cid. Bore and stroke: 3.62 x 3.60 inches. Compression ratio: 8.6:1. Brake hp: 144 at 4200 rpm. Carburetion: Holley one-barrel. Four main bearings. Serial number code "A."

V-8: Overhead valves. Cast iron block. Displacement: 272 cid. Bore and stroke: 3.62 x 3.30 inches. Compression ratio: 8.6:1. Brake hp: 190 at 4500 rpm. Carburetion: Holley two-barrel. Five main bearings. Serial number code "B."

THUNDERBIRD V-8: Overhead valves. Cast iron block. Displacement: 292 cid. Bore and stroke: 3.75 x 3.30 inches. Compression ratio: 9.1:1. Brake hp: 212 at 4500 rpm. Carburetion: Holley four-barrel. Five main bearings. Serial number code number code "D."

THUNDERBIRD SPECIAL V-8: Overhead valves. Cast iron block. Displacement: 312 cid. Bore and stroke: 3.80 x 3.44 inches. Compression ratio: 9.7:1. Brake hp: 245 at 4500 rpm. Carburetion: Holley four-barrel. Five main bearings. Serial number code "D."

THUNDERBIRD SPECIAL (8V) V-8: Overhead valves. Cast iron block. Displacement: 312 cid. Bore and stroke: 3.80 x 3.44 inches. Compression ratio: 9.7:1 (10.00:1 with Racing Kit). Brake hp: 270 at 4800 rpm. (285 at 5000 rpm with Racing Kit). Carburetion: two Holley four-barrels. Five main bearings. Serial number code "E."

THUNDERBIRD SPECIAL SUPERCHARGED V-8: Overhead valves. Cast iron block. Displacement: 312 cid. Bore and stroke: 3.80 x 3.44 inches. Compression ratio: 8.5:1. Brake hp: 300 at 4800 rpm. (340 at 5300 rpm — NASCAR version). Carburetion: Holley four-barrel with Paxton centrifugal supercharger. Five main bearings. Serial number code "E."

CHASSIS FEATURES: Wheelbase: (Custom, Custom 300 and station wagon Series) 116 inches; (Fairlane, Fairlane 500) 118 inches; (Thunderbird) 102 inches. Overall length: (Custom, Custom 300) 201.6 inches; (Fairlane 500 Skyliner V-8 Retractable) 210.8 inches. (All other Fairlane and Fairlane 500) 207.7 inches; (station wagons) 203.5 inches; (Thunderbird) 181.4 inches. Tires: (Custom, Custom 300) 7.50 x 14 four-ply tubeless; (Fairlane, Fairlane 500) 7.50 x 14 four-ply tubeless; (Country Sedans and Squires) 8.00 x 14; (Thunderbird) 7.50 x 14 four-ply tubeless.

FORD/THUNDERBIRD OPTIONS: Custom engine option, 292 cid V-8, ($439). Ford-O-Matic for Ford ($188): same for Thunderbird ($215). Automatic overdrive transmission for Ford ($108); same for Thunderbird ($146). Power steering ($68). Radio ($100). Heater and defroster ($85). Thunderbird windshield washers ($10). Power windows, Thunderbird ($70). Engine chrome dress-up kit, Thunderbird ($25). Power brakes ($38). Fairlane/station wagon 312 cid V-8 engine option. ($43). Rear fender shields (skirts). Two-tone paint. Back-up lamps. Large wheelcovers (standard on Fairlane 500). White sidewall tires. Continental tire extension kit. Outside rearview mirror. Lifeguard safety equipment package. Oversized tires. Radio antenna. Non-glare mirror. Three-speed manual transmission (with semi-centrifugal type clutch; three-speed helical gears and synchronizers for second and third gears) standard. Three-speed with automatic overdrive was optional. Specifications were the same as above with automatic overdrive function cutting in at 27 mph, cutting out at 21 mph. Approximate drive ratio: 0.70:1. Manual control below instrument panel. Ford-O-Matic automatic transmission was optional. This was a torque convertor transmission with automatic planetary gear train; single-stage, three-element hydraulic torque converter; hydro-mechanical automatic controls with no electric or vacuum connections and power flow through fluid member at all times. Six-cylinder rear axle ratios: (Ford-O-Matic) 3.22:l; (manual transmission) 3.89:1 and (automatic overdrive) 4.11:1. V-8 rear axle ratios: (Ford-O-Matic) 3.10:1; (manual transmission) 3.56:1 and (automatic overdrive) 3.70:1.

HISTORICAL FOOTNOTES: Introduction of 1957 Fords and Thunderbirds took place in October 1956. The Fairlane 500 Skyliner retractable-hardtop convertible was introduced as a midyear addition to the line. Overdrive or Ford-O-Matic could now be ordered for any car with any engine. Model year production was 1,655,068 vehicles. Calendar year sales amounted to 1,522,406 Fords and Thunderbirds. Ford out-produced Chevrolet this season, to become America's number one automaker of 1957 (model year basis). The Town Victoria was a four-door pillarless hardtop. The Del Rio was a Deluxe two-door Ranch Wagon in Fairlane level trim. The Club Victoria was a two-door pillarless hardtop coupe. The Sunliner was a conventional two-door convertible.

1958 FORD

1958 FORDS — OVERVIEW — Even though 1958 Fords shared the same basic body with 1957 models, there were many new styling ideas. A simulated air scoop hood and honeycomb grille were borrowed from Thunderbird stylists. A sculptured rear deck lid, plus dual headlamps, created a much more futuristic looking car than the previous model. Cruise-O-Matic three-speed automatic transmission was offered for the first time in 1958, as were 332 cid and 352 cid V-8s. Also new for 1958 (and offered only in 1958) was the Ford-Aire suspension system for use in Fairlane series cars and station wagons.

CUSTOM 300 SERIES — ALL ENGINES — The Custom 300 series was the base trim level for 1958 and included chrome window moldings, a horn button instead of a horn ring, one sun visor, an armrest on the drivers door only and a single chrome strip on the bodyside. This molding began on the side of the front fender, continued horizontally to the back of the front door, then turned down and joined a horizontal chrome strip which continued to the back of the body. A "Styletone" trim option duplicated this side trim, except the lower horizontal strip was a double strip with a gold anodized insert.

CUSTOM 300 SIX SERIES I.D. NUMBERS: Custom 300 six-cylinder models began with the designation, "A8," followed by assembly plant code, body type code, and finally, the unit's production numbers. according to the final assembly location. Each plant began at 100001 and went up.

1958 Ford, Custom two-door sedan, 6-cyl

1958 Ford, Fairlane 500 Skyliner two-door retractable hardtop, V-8

CUSTOM SIX SERIES

Model Number	Body/Style Number	Body Type & Seating	Factory Price	Shipping Weight	Production Total
A8	73A	4-dr Sed-6P	2119	3227	Note 1
A8	70A	2-dr Sed-6P	2065	3197	Note 1
A8	70D	2-dr Bus Cpe-3P	1977	3174	Note 1

NOTE 1: See Custom V-8 Series listing. Production was counted by series and body style only, with no breakout per engine type.

CUSTOM 300 I.D. NUMBERS: Custom 300, V-8 models began with the engine designation code, assembly plant code, body type code, and, finally, the unit's production numbers, according to the final assembly location. Each plant began at 100001 and went up.

CUSTOM V-8 SERIES

Model Number	Body/Style Number	Body Type & Seating	Factory Price	Shipping Weight	Production Total
NA	73A	4-dr Sed-6P	2256	3319	163,368
NA	70A	2-dr Sed-6P	2202	3289	173,441
NA	70D	2-dr Bus Cpe-3P	2114	3266	4,062

PRODUCTION NOTE: Total series output was 340,871 units. Ford does not indicate the number of each model produced with sixes or V-8s. Therefore, all production figures given above are total production of each body style with both engines. Individual "model numbers" not available, see 1957 Ford V-8 note.

FAIRLANE MODELS — ALL ENGINES — The Fairlane model was the base trim level for the longer wheelbase Fairlane series. It included chrome window moldings, with slightly less chrome around the "C" pillar than Fairlane 500 models. Also a considerably different side stripe was used compared to the higher-priced model. The base Fairlane side chrome had two strips. The lower molding began at the rear of the front wheel opening, then went straight to the back of the front door. From there it began to gradually curve upward. The upper strip began at the front of the fender and went straight back, to the back of the front door. It then began to curve gradually downward, merging with the lower strip directly over the rear wheel opening. A Fairlane script appeared on the rear fenders and directly above the front grille opening. Midyear Fairlanes came with an additional sweep spear of anodized aluminum trim centered in the panel created by the before mentioned trim. In addition midyear Fairlanes featured three porthole trim pieces on the rear where the Fairlane script would appear.

FAIRLANE SIX SERIES I.D. NUMBERS: Fairlane six-cylinder models began with the same "A8" designation and used the same production numbers as the Custom 300 series.

FAIRLANE SIX SERIES

Model Number	Body/Style Number	Body Type & Seating	Factory Price	Shipping Weight	Production Total
A8	58A	4-dr Twn Sed-6P	2250	3376	Note 1
A8	64A	2-dr Clb Sed-6P	2196	3307	Note 1
A8	57B	4-dr Twn Vic-6P	2394	3407	Note 1
A8	63B	2-dr Clb Vic-6P	2329	3328	Note 1

NOTE 1: See Fairlane V-8 Series listing. Production was counted by series and body style only, with no breakout per engine type.

FAIRLANE SIX SERIES I.D. NUMBERS: Fairlane V-8 models began with the same engine designations and used the same production numbers as the Custom 300 series.

FAIRLANE V-8 SERIES

Model Number	Body/Style Number	Body Type & Seating	Factory Price	Shipping Weight	Production Total
NA	58A	4-dr Twn Sed-6P	2374	3468	57,490
NA	64A	2-dr Clb Sed-6P	2320	3399	38,366
NA	57B	4-dr Twn Vic-6P	2517	3499	5,868
NA	63B	2-dr Clb Vic-6P	2453	3420	16,416

PRODUCTION NOTE: Total series output was 118,140 units. Ford does not indicate the number of each model produced with sixes or V-8s. Therefore, all production figures given above are total production of each body style with both engines.

FAIRLANE 500 MODELS — ALL ENGINES — The Fairlane 500 models had the top trim level in the Fairlane series. It included all the trim used in the Fairlane models plus slightly more chrome on the "C" pillars and different side trim. The side trim was a double runner chrome strip with a gold anodized insert. The top chrome strip began on the side of the front fender, sloped slightly, and terminated at the top of the rear bumper. The lower molding split from the upper strip where the front door began, dropped in a modified Fairlane sweep and merged with the upper strip at the rear bumper. Fairlane scripts appeared above the grille and on the trunk lid and the Fairlane 500 script appeared on the rear fenders, above the chrome side trim.

FAIRLANE 500 SIX SERIES I.D. NUMBERS: Fairlane 500 six-cylinder models began with the same "A8" designation and used the same production numbers as the Fairlane models and Custom series.

FAIRLANE 500 SIX SERIES

Model Number	Body/Style Number	Body Type & Seating	Factory Price	Shipping Weight	Production Total
A8	58B	4-dr Twn Sed-6P	2403	3380	Note 1
A8	64B	4-dr Clb Sed-6P	2349	3313	Note 1
A8	57A	4-dr Twn Vic-6P	2474	3419	Note 1
A8	63A	2-dr Clb Vic-6P	2410	3316	Note 1
A8	76B	2-dr SL Conv-6P	2625	3478	,Note 1

NOTE 1: See Fairlane 500 V-8 Series listing. Production was counted by series and body style, with no breakouts per engine type.

FAIRLANE 500 V-8 SERIES I.D. NUMBERS: Fairlane 500 V-8 models began with the same engine designation and used the same production numbers as the Fairlane models and Custom series.

FAIRLANE 500 V-8 SERIES

Model Number	Body/Style Number	Body Type & Seating	Factory Price	Shipping Weight	Production Total
NA	58B	4-dr Twn Sed-6P	2527	3510	105,698
NA	64B	2-dr Clb Sed-6P	2473	3443	34,041
NA	57A	4-dr Twn Vic-6P	2598	3549	36,059
NA	63A	2-dr Clb Vic-6P	2534	3446	80,439
NA	76B	2-dr SL Conv-6P	2749	3637	35,029
NA	51A	2-dr Sky Conv-6P	3138	4094	14,713

PRODUCTION NOTE: Total series output was 306,429 units. Ford does not indicate the number of each model produced with sixes and V-8s. Therefore, all production figures given above are total production of each body style with both engines. All convertibles are two-door styles; all Skyliner retractable convertibles are V-8 powered.

STATION WAGON SERIES — ALL ENGINES — The Ranch Wagon was the base trim level two-door and four-door station wagons for 1958. Country Sedans were intermediate level station wagons and Country Squires were the top trim level. The level of equipment paralleled Custom, Custom 300 and Fairlane 500 models of passenger cars.

STATION WAGON SIX SERIES I.D. NUMBERS: Station wagon six-cylinder models began with the same "A8" designation, and used the same production numbers as the passenger cars.

STATION WAGON SIX SERIES

Model Number	Body/Style Number	Body Type & Seating	Factory Price	Shipping Weight	Production Total
A8	59A	2-dr Ranch Wag-6P	2372	3480	Note 1
A8	79A	4-dr Ranch Wag-6P	2426	3543	Note 1
A8	59B	2-dr Del Rio-6P	2478	3504	Note 1
A8	79D	4-dr Cty Sed-6P	2532	3555	Note 1
A8	79C	4-dr Cty Sed-9P	2639	3625	Note 1
A8	79E	4-dr Cty Sq-9P	2769	3672	Note 1

NOTE 1: See Station wagon V-8 Series listing. Production was counted by series and body style, with no breakouts per engine type.

STATION WAGON V-8 SERIES I.D. NUMBERS: Station Wagon V-8 models began with the same engine designations, and used the same production numbers as the passenger cars.

STATION WAGON V-8 SERIES

Model Number	Body/Style Number	Body Type & Seating	Factory Price	Shipping Weight	Production Total
NA	59A	2-dr Ranch Wag-6P	2479	3607	34,578
NA	79A	4-dr Ranch Wag-6P	2533	3670	32,854
NA	59B	2-dr Del Rio-6P	2585	3631	12,687
NA	79D	4-dr Cty Sed-6P	2639	3682	68,772
NA	79C	4-dr Cty Sed-9P	2746	3752	20,702
NA	79E	4-dr Cty Sq-9P	2876	3799	15,020

PRODUCTION NOTE: Total series output was 184,613 units. Ford does not indicate the number of each model produced with sixes and V-8s. Therefore, all production figures given above are total production of each body style with both engines. The Country Squire station wagon has simulated woodgrained exterior paneling.

Standard Catalog of American Cars

1958 Ford, Thunderbird Tudor hardtop coupe, V-8 (AA)

THUNDERBIRD SERIES — V-8 — 1958 was the first year for the 4-passenger "Square Birds." The hardtop was introduced on Jan. 13, 1958 with the convertible not showing up until June of 1958. The new personal Thunderbirds were over 18 inches longer and 1,000 pounds heavier than their 1957 counterparts. The new T-Bird featured an extended top with squared-off "C" pillar. It had chrome trim along the base of the top and a small Thunderbird crest directly above the trim. A massive, one-piece bumper surrounded a honeycomb grille. The honeycomb look was duplicated in stamped and painted steel around the four circular taillights. A Thunderbird script appeared on the front fenders and five heavy, cast stripes appeared on the door, at the feature line. Inside, bucket seats and a vinyl covered console were used for the first time in a Thunderbird. Also for the first time, Thunderbirds were offered as either a hardtop or convertible, each being a separate model.

THUNDERBIRD V-8 SERIES I.D. NUMBERS: Thunderbird models began with the engine designation, "H8", assembly plant code "Y" (Wixom), body type code "H" (Thunderbird), and, finally, the unit's production number, beginning at 100001 and going up.

THUNDERBIRD V-8 SERIES

Model Number	Body/Style Number	Body Type & Seating	Factory Price	Shipping Weight	Production Total
H8	63A	2-dr HT-4P	3630	3708	35,758
H8	76A	2-dr Conv-4P	3914	3903	2,134

FORD/THUNDERBIRD ENGINES

SIX-CYLINDER: Overhead valves. Cast iron block. Displacement: 223 cid. Bore and stroke: 3.62 x 3.60 inches. Compression ratio: 8.6:1. Brake hp: 145 at 4200 rpm. Carburetion: Holley one-barrel. Four main bearings. Serial number code "A."

V-8: Overhead valves. Cast iron block. Displacement: 292 cid. Bore & stroke: 3.75 x 3.30 inches. Compression ratio: 9.1:1. Brake hp: 205 at 4500 rpm. Carburetion: Holley two-barrel. Five main bearings. Serial number code "C."

INTERCEPTOR V-8: Overhead valves. Cast iron block. Displacement: 332 cid. Bore and stroke: 4.00 x 3.30 inches. Compression ratio: 9.5:1. Brake hp: 240 at 4600 rpm. Carburetion: Holley two-barrel. Five main bearings. Serial number code "B."

INTERCEPTOR SPECIAL V-8: Overhead valves. Cast iron block. Displacement: 332 cid. Bore and stroke: 4.00 x 3.30 inches. Compression ratio: 9.5:1. Brake hp: 265 at 4600 rpm. Carburetion: Holley four-barrel. Five main bearings. Serial number code "G."

INTERCEPTOR 352 SPECIAL V-8: Overhead valves. Cast iron block. Displacement: 352 cid. Bore and stroke: 4.00 x 3.50 inches. Compression ratio: 10.2:1. Brake hp: 300 at 4600 rpm. Carburetion: Holley four-barrel. Serial number code "H."

CHASSIS FEATURES: Wheelbase: (Custom 300 and station wagons) 116.03 inches; (Fairlane, Fairlane 500) 118.04; (Thunderbird) 113 inches. Overall length: (Custom 300) 202 inches; (station wagons) 202.7 inches; (Skyliner retractable) 211 inches; (other Fairlane, Fairlane 500) 207 inches; (Thunderbird) 205.4 inches. Overall width: (all Fords) 78 inches; (Thunderbirds) 77 inches. Tires: (9-passenger wagons) 8.00 x 14; (Skyliner retractable) 8.00 x 14; (all other Fords) 7.50 x 14; (Thunderbirds) 8.00 x 14.

CONVENIENCE OPTIONS: Ford-O-Matic drive ($180). Cruise-O-Matic ($197). Ford-Aire suspension ($156). Overdrive ($108). Power brakes ($37). Power steering ($69). Front power windows ($50); on Custom 300 'business' two-door ($64). Front and rear power windows ($101). Manual four-way adjustable seat ($17). Four-way power adjustable seat ($64). Six-tube radio and antenna ($77). Nine-tube Signal-Seeking radio and antenna ($99). White sidewall tires, four-ply, size 7.50 x 14 ($33). White sidewall tires, four-ply, size 8.00 x 14 ($50). wheelcovers ($19 and standard on Fairlane 500). Styletone two-tone paint ($22). Tinted glass ($20). Back-up lights ($10). Custom 300 Deluxe interior trim ($24). Electric clock ($15 and standard on Fairlane 500). Windshield washer ($12). Positive action windshield wiper ($11). Lifeguard safety package with padded instrument panel and sun visors ($19). Lifeguard safety package, as above, plus two front seat belts ($33). Polar Air Conditioner includes tinted glass ($271). Select Air Conditioner includes tinted glass ($395). Interceptor 265 hp V-8 in Custom 300 ($196); in Fairlane ($183). Interceptor Special 300 hp V-8 in Fairlane 500 ($159); in station wagon ($150). Note: Interceptor engine prices are in place of base six-cylinder prices. Automatic overdrive ($108). Heater and defroster ($80). Base Interceptor 332 cid V-8 in Custom 300 models ($59). Interceptor Special V-8 in Fairlanes and station wagons ($54). Heater and defroster in Fairlanes and station wagons ($85). Power steering, Thunderbird ($69). Heater and defroster, Thunderbird ($95). Whitewall tires, Thunderbird ($36 exchange). Leather Interior, Thunderbird ($106). Three-speed manual transmission was standard equipment. If featured semi-centrifugal type clutch; three-speed helical gears, with synchronizers for second and third gears. Three-speed with automatic overdrive was optional. Specifications were the same as above with automatic overdrive function cutting in at 27 mph, cutting out at 21 mph. Approximate drive ratio: 0.70:1. Manual control below instrument panel. Ford-O-Matic automatic transmission was optional. This was a torque converter transmission with automatic planetary gear train; single-stage, three element hydraulic torque converter; hydro-mechanical automatic controls with no electrical or vacuum connections and power flow through fluid member at all times. Cruise-O-Matic automatic transmission was also optional. This unit was the same as Ford-O-Matic, except for having three-speeds forward. It was a high-performance automatic transmission with two selective drive ranges for smooth 1-2-3 full-power starts, or 2-3 gradual acceleration and axle ratio of 2.69:1 for fuel economy. Six-cylinder rear axle ratios: (Ford-O-Matic) 3.22:1; (manual transmission) 3.89:1 and (automatic overdrive) 4.11:1. V-8 rear axle ratios: (Cruise-O-Matic 2.69:1; (Ford-O-Matic) 3.10: 1; (manual transmission) 3.56:1 and (automatic overdrive) 3.70:1.

HISTORICAL FOOTNOTES: Dealer introductions for 1958 Fords were held Nov. 7, 1957. Dealer introductions for 1958 Thunderbirds were held Feb. 13, 1958. Production at three factories — Memphis, Buffalo and Somerville — was phased out this season. In June, 1958, a new plant, having capacity equal to all three above, was opened at Loraine, Ohio. On a model year basis, 74.4 percent of all Fords built in the 1958 run had V-8 power. Sixty-eight percent of these cars had automatic transmission. Model year production of Fords and Thunderbirds totaled 987,945 cars. Calendar year sales of Fords and Thunderbirds peaked at 1,038,560 units. The Thunderbird was, along with the Rambler, one of only two U.S. marques to see sales increases for 1958, a recession year in the U.S. The Town Victoria was a four-door pillarless hardtop style. The Club Victoria was a two-door pillarless hardtop style. The Custom 300 two-door sedan was also called the business sedan. The Sunliner was a conventional two-door convertible. The Skyliner was a retractable hardtop-convertible.

1959 FORD

1959 FORDS — OVERVIEW — 1959 Fords are considered by many to be the most beautifully styled Fords ever built. They were, in fact, awarded the Gold Medal for Exceptional Styling at the Brussels World Fair. With elegance and understated class, the car showed remarkable good taste and restraint. At a time when other car manufacturers were attempting to make their cars look like they were capable of inter-stellar travel or supersonic speeds, Ford excised restraint. Ford designers merely swept the rear fenders feature lines to the back of the car, formed a housing for the back-up lights and curved the lower portion around an oversized taillight for a startling effect. At the front end, the fenders were flattened across the top and housed the dual headlights. They had a sculptured effect at the sides, where they rolled over the side trim. The 1959 Fords were long, low and had an exceptionally flat hood. There was relatively little chrome trim. Bright colors were used for incredible effects. A new 430 cid/350 hp V-8 engine was optional in Thunderbirds and a wider grille extended from side to side. The parking lights were recessed into the bumper and, late in 1958, a new series called the Galaxie was introduced as the top line model. Galaxie stylists had adapted the roofline of the Thunderbird to the standard Fairlane 500 body and produced truly beautiful results. The Custom line was dropped, making the Custom 300 the base trim level for 1959.

CUSTOM 300 SERIES — (ALL ENGINES) — The Custom 300 series was the base trim level for 1959 and included chrome window moldings, a horn button instead of horn ring, one sun visor, an armrest only on the driver's door and a single chrome strip on the bodyside. The chrome strip followed the lines of the Fairlane sweep, but used only a single strip.

CUSTOM 300 SIX SERIES I.D. NUMBERS: Custom 300, six-cylinder models began with the designation, "A9" followed by assembly plant code, body type code, and finally, the unit's production numbers according to the final assembly location. Each plant began at 100001 and went up.

CUSTOM 300 SIX SERIES

Model Number	Body/Style Number	Body Type & Seating	Factory Price	Shipping Weight	Production Total
A9	58E	4-dr Sed-6P	2273	3385	Note 1
A9	64F	2-dr Sed-6P	2219	3310	Note 1
A9	64G	2-dr Bus Cpe-3P	2132	3283	Note 1

NOTE 1: See Custom 300 V-8 Series listing. Production was counted by series and body style only, with no breakout per engine type.

CUSTOM 300 V-8 SERIES I.D. NUMBERS: Custom 300 V-8 models began with the engine designation code, assembly plant code, body type code, and finally, the unit's production numbers according to the final assembly location. Each plant began at 100001 and went up.

CUSTOM 300 V-8 SERIES

Model Number	Body/Style Number	Body Type & Seating	Factory Price	Shipping Weight	Production Total
NA	58E	4-dr Sed-6P	2391	3486	249,553
NA	64F	2-dr Sed-6P	2337	3411	228,573

PRODUCTION NOTE: Total series output was 482,210 units. Ford does not indicate the number of each model produced with sixes or V-8s. Therefore, all production figures given above are total production of each body style with both engines.

FAIRLANE MODELS — (ALL ENGINES) — The Fairlane model was the intermediate trim level for 1959 and included chrome window moldings, a horn ring, two sun visors, armrests on all doors and a more complicated side trim than the Custom series. The trim was a two-piece design, which could feature an optional silver anodized insert between the two pieces forming the 1959 version of the Fairlane sweep.

FAIRLANE SIX SERIES I.D. NUMBERS: Fairlane, six-cylinder models began with the same "A9" designation and used the same production numbers as the Custom 300 series.

FAIRLANE SIX SERIES

Model Number	Body/Style Number	Body Type & Seating	Factory Price	Shipping Weight	Production Total
A9	58A	4-dr Twn Sed-6P	2411	3415	Note 1
A9	64A	2-dr Clb Sed-6P	2357	3332	Note 1

NOTE 1: See Fairlane V-8 Series listing. Production was counted by series and body style, with no breakouts per engine type.

FAIRLANE V-8 SERIES I.D. NUMBERS: Fairlane, V-8 models began with the same engine designations, and used the same production numbers as the Custom 300 series.

FAIRLANE V-8 SERIES

Model Number	Body/Style Number	Body Type & Seating	Factory Price	Shipping Weight	Production Total
NA	58A	4-dr Twn Sed-6P	2529	3516	64,663
NA	64A	2-dr Clb Sed-6P	2475	3433	35,126

PRODUCTION NOTE: Total series output was 97,789 units. Ford does not indicate the number of each model produced with sixes or V-8s. Therefore, all production figures given above are total production of each body style with both engines.

1959 Ford, Fairlane 500 Galaxie Town Victoria four-door hardtop, V-8

1959 Ford, Fairlane 500 Club Victoria two-door hardtop, V-8 AA

FAIRLANE 500 SERIES — (ALL ENGINES) — Prior to the introduction of the Galaxie, the Fairlane 500 was the top trim level for 1959, and included all the trim used in the Fairlane series, including the optional insert. In addition a large aluminum panel surrounded the rear wheel opening and ran to the rear bumper. Optional stainless steel fender skirts could be ordered to expand the large expanse of bright metal trim.

FAIRLANE 500 SIX SERIES I.D. NUMBERS: Fairlane 500, six-cylinder models began with the same "A9" designation and used the same production numbers as the Fairlane models and Custom models.

FAIRLANE 500 SIX SERIES

Model Number	Body/Style Number	Body Type & Seating	Factory Price	Shipping Weight	Production Total
A9	58B	4-dr Twn Sed-6P	2530	3417	Note 1
A9	64B	2-dr Clb Sed-6P	2476	3338	Note 1
A9	57A	4-dr Twn Vic-6P	2602	3451	Note 1
A9	63A	2-dr Clb Vic-6P	2537	3365	Note 1

NOTE 1: See Fairlane 500 V-8 listing. Production was counted by series and body style, with no breakout per engine type.

FAIRLANE 500 V-8 SERIES I.D. NUMBERS: Fairlane 500 V-8 models began with the same engine designation, and used the same production numbers as the Fairlane models and Custom models.

FAIRLANE 500 V-8 SERIES

Model Number	Body/Style Number	Body Type & Seating	Factory Price	Shipping Weight	Production Total
NA	58B	4-dr Twn Sed-6P	2648	3518	35,670
NA	64B	2-dr Clb Sed-6P	2594	3439	10,141
NA	57A	4-dr Twn Vic-6P	2720	3552	9,308
NA	63A	2-dr Clb Vic-6P	2655	3466	23,892

PRODUCTION NOTE: Total series output was 79,011 units. Ford does not indicate the number of each model produced with sixes or V-8s. Therefore, all production figures given above are total production of each body style with both engines.

GALAXIE SERIES — (ALL ENGINES) — The Galaxie was the new top line series for 1959. The only difference between the Galaxie and the Fairlane 500 was the styling of the top. Galaxies used the standard top with a Thunderbird style "C" pillar. The combination created one of the best looking cars ever to come out of Dearborn.

GALAXIE SIX SERIES I.D. NUMBERS: Galaxie six-cylinder models used the same "A9" designation and used the same production numbers as the Custom, Fairlane and Fairlane 500 models.

GALAXIE SIX SERIES

Model Number	Body/Style Number	Body Type & Seating	Factory Price	Shipping Weight	Production Total
A9	54A	4-dr Twn Sed-6P	2582	3405	Note 1
A9	64H	2-dr Clb Sed-6P	2528	3377	Note 1
A9	75A	4-dr Twn Vic-6P	2654	3494	Note 1
A9	65A	2-dr Clb Vic-6P	2589	3338	Note 1
A9	76B	2-dr SL Conv-6P	2839	3527	Note 1

NOTE 1: See Galaxie V-8 Series listing. Production was counted by series and body style, with no breakouts per engine type.

GALAXIE V-8 SERIES I.D. NUMBERS: Galaxie, V-8 models began with the same engine designation, and used the same production numbers as the Custom, Fairlane, and Fairlane 500 models.

GALAXIE V-8 SERIES

Model Number	Body/Style Number	Body Type & Seating	Factory Price	Shipping Weight	Production Total
NA	54A	4-dr Twn Sed-6P	2700	3506	183,108
NA	64H	2-dr Clb Sed-6P	2646	3478	52,848
NA	75A	4-dr Twn Vic-6P	2772	3595	47,728
NA	65A	2-dr Clb Vic-6P	2707	3439	121,869
NA	51A	2-dr Sky Conv-6P	3346	4064	12,915
NA	76B	2-dr SL Conv-6P	2957	3628	45,868

PRODUCTION NOTE: Total series output was 464,336 units. Ford does not indicate the number of each model produced with sixes or V-8s. Therefore, all production figures given above are total production of each body style for both engines. The Sunliner is a conventional two-door convertible. The Skyliner is a retractable hardtop convertible and came only with V-8 power.

STATION WAGON SERIES — (ALL ENGINES) — The Ranch Wagons were the base trim level two-door and four-door station wagons for 1959. Country Sedans were the intermediate trim level. Country Squires were the top trim level. The level of equipment paralleled Custom, Fairlane and Galaxie models of passenger cars.

STATION WAGON SIX SERIES I.D. NUMBERS: Station wagon, six-cylinder models began with the same "A9" designation and used the same production numbers as the conventional cars.

STATION WAGON SIX SERIES

Model Number	Body/Style Number	Body Type & Seating	Factory Price	Shipping Weight	Production Total
A9	59C	2-dr Ranch Wag-6P	2567	3590	Note 1
A9	71F	4-dr Ranch Wag-6P	2634	3685	Note 1
A9	59D	2-dr Cty Sed-6P	2678	3613	Note 1
A9	71F	4-dr Cty Sed-6P	2745	3718	Note 1
A9	71E	4-dr Cty Sed-9P	2829	3767	Note 1
A9	71G	4-dr Cty Sq-9P	2958	3758	Note 1

NOTE 1: See Station wagon V-8 Series listing. Production was counted by series and body style, with no breakout per engine.

STATION WAGON V-8 SERIES I.D. NUMBERS: Station wagon V-8 models began with the same engine designations and used the same production numbers as the conventional cars.

STATION WAGON V-8 SERIES

Model Number	Body/Style Number	Body Type & Seating	Factory Price	Shipping Weight	Production Total
NA	59C	2-dr Ranch Wag-6P	2685	3691	45,558
NA	71H	4-dr Ranch Wag-6P	2752	3786	67,339
NA	59D	2-dr Cty Sed-6P	2796	3714	8,663
NA	71F	4-dr Cty Sed-6P	2863	3819	94,601
NA	71E	4-dr Cty Sed-9P	2947	3868	28,881
NA	71G	4-dr Cty Sq-9P	3076	3859	24,336

PRODUCTION NOTE: Total series output was 269,378 units. Ford does not indicate the number of each model produced with sixes or V-8. Therefore, all production figures given above are total production of each body style with both engines.

1959 Ford, Thunderbird Tudor hardtop coupe, V-8 (AA)

THUNDERBIRD — V-8 SERIES — Thunderbird for 1959 saw only a few cosmetic changes to the basis 1958 body style. The honeycomb grille was replaced by a horizontal bar grille and the new look was duplicated in the small grilles behind the taillights. The four side stripes used on the 1958 model were removed and a chrome arrow took their place on the side. The instrument panel dial faces were white for 1959, instead of the black used in previous years.

THUNDERBIRD V-8 SERIES I.D. NUMBERS: Thunderbird models began with the engine designation, "H9", assembly plant code "Y" (Wixom), body type code and, finally. the units production number, beginning at 100001 and going up.

THUNDERBIRD V-8 SERIES

Model Number	Body/Style Number	Body Type & Seating	Factory Price	Shipping Weight	Production Total
H9	63A	2-dr HT-4P	3696	3813	57,195
H9	76A	2-dr Conv-4P	3979	3903	10,261

1959 ENGINES

SIX-CYLINDER: Overhead valves. Cast iron block. Displacement: 223 cid. Bore and stroke: 3.62 x 3.60 inches. Compression ratio: 8.6:1. Brake hp: 145 at 4000 rpm. Carburetion: Holley one-barrel. Four main bearings. Serial number code "A."

V-8: Overhead valves. Cast iron block. Displacement: 292 cid. Bore & stroke: 3.75 x 3.30 inches. Compression ratio: 8.8:1. Brake hp: 200 at 4400 rpm. Carburetion: Holley two-barrel. Five main bearings. Serial number code "C."

THUNDERBIRD 332 SPECIAL V-8: Overhead valves. Cast iron block. Displacement: 332 cid. Bore and stroke: 4.00 x 3.30 inches. Compression ratio: 8.9:1. Brake hp: 225 at 4400 rpm. Carburetion: Holley two-barrel. Five main bearings. Serial number code "B."

THUNDERBIRD 352 SPECIAL V-8: Overhead valves. Cast iron block. Displacement: 352 cid. Bore and stroke: 4.00 x 3.50 inches. Compression ratio: 9.6:1. Brake hp: 300 at 4600 rpm. Carburetion: Holley four-barrel. Five main bearings. Serial number code "H."

THUNDERBIRD 430 SPECIAL V-8: (Available only in Thunderbird and with Cruise-O-Matic transmission only) Overhead valves. Cast iron block. Displacement: 430 cid. Bore and stroke: 4.30 x 4.70 inches. Compression ratio: 10.0:1. Brake hp: 350 at 4400 rpm. Carburetion: Holly four-barrel. Serial number code "J."

FORD/THUNDERBIRD CHASSIS FEATURES: Wheelbase: (all Fords) 118 inches; (Thunderbird) 113 inches. Overall length: (Skyliner) 208.1 inches; (all other models) 208 inches. Overall width: (Ford) 76.6 inches; (Thunderbird) 77 inches. Tires: (Thunderbirds, Skyliners, 9-passenger station wagons and Sunliners with automatic transmission) 8.00 x 14 four-ply tubeless; (all other models) 7.50 x 14 four-ply tubeless.

FORD OPTIONS: Ford-O-Matic Drive ($190). Cruise-O-Matic ($231). Automatic overdrive ($108). Power brakes ($43). Power steering ($75). Front and rear power window ($102). Four-Way power seat ($64). Radio and push-button antenna ($59). Signal seeking radio and antenna ($83). Fresh Air heater and defroster ($75). Recirculating heater and defroster ($48). White sidewall tires, four-ply, 7.50 x 14 ($33); 8.00 x 14 ($50). Wheelcovers as option ($17). Styleton two-tone paint ($26). Tinted glass ($26). Back-up lights ($10). Custom 300 and Ranch Wagon Deluxe ornamentation package ($32). Electric clock ($15). Windshield washer ($14). Two-speed windshield wipers ($5). Lifeguard safety package including padded instrument panel and sun visor ($19); plus pair front seat safety belts ($21). Polar Aire Conditioner with tinted glass ($271). Select Aire Conditioner with tinted glass ($404). Heavy-duty 70amp battery ($8). Equa-Lock differential ($39). Four-way manual seat ($l7). Fairlane side molding ($11). Fairlane 500 rocker panel molding. Thunderbird special 225 hp 332 cid V-8 ($141 over base six). Thunderbird Special 300 hp 352 cid V-8 ($167 over base six). Standard 292 cid two-barrel V-8, all except Skyliner ($118). Three-speed manual transmission was standard. It featured a semi-centrifugal type clutch; three-speed helical gears and synchronizers for second and third gears. Three-speed with automatic overdrive was optional. Specifications were the same as above with automatic overdrive function cutting in at 27 mph, cutting out at 21 mph. Approximate drive ratio: 0.70:1. Manual control below instrument panel. Ford-O-Matic transmission was also optional. This was a torque converter transmission with automatic planetary gear ratio; single-stage, three-element hydraulic torque converter; hydromechanical controls with no electric or vacuum connections and power flow through fluid member at all times. Six-cylinder rear axle gear ratios: (Ford-O-Matic) 3.56:1; (manual transmission) 3.56:1; (optional with automatic overdrive) 3.56:1. V-8 rear axle gear ratios: (Ford-O-Matic with 292 V-8) 3.10:1; (Ford-O-Matic with 332/352 V-8) 2.91:1; (Cruise-O-Matic with 292 V-8) 3.10:1; (Cruise-O-Matic with 332 V-8) 2.91:1; Cruise-O-Matic with 352 V-8) 2.69:1; (manual transmission) 3.56:1. Equa-Lockrear axle gear ratios: 3.70:1 or 3.10:1.

THUNDERBIRD OPTIONS: Dual-Range Cruise-O-Matic transmission ($242). Overdrive ($145). Power brakes ($43). Power steering ($75). Four-way power driver's seat ($86). Front and rear power windows ($102). Heavy-duty 70-amp battery ($8). Fresh Air heater/defroster ($83). Push-button radio and antenna ($105). Select Air Conditioner ($446). Front seat belts ($23). back-up lights ($110). Tinted glass ($38). Wondershield washer ($14). Outside rearview mirror ($5). Conventional two-tone paint ($26). Full wheelcovers ($17). Rear fender shields ($27). Five 8.00 x 14 four-ply rayon white sidewall tubeless tires ($36 exchange). Undercoating ($13). Thunderbird Special 350 hp V-8 ($177); leather interior ($106) and other standard dealer installed accessories.

HISTORICAL FOOTNOTES: Dealer introduction for the 1959 Ford line was held Oct. 17, 1958. Thunderbirds were introduced to the public 10 days later. Model year production of Fords and Thunderbird was 1,462,140 units, while calendar year sales peaked at 1,528,592 cars. Special model nomenclature was similar to previous years. In March, 1958, Ford reported it had reduced the cost of making an automobile by $94 per unit between 1954 and 1958. On a model year basis, 78.1 percent of all 1959 Fords had V-8 power and 71.7 percent featured automatic transmission.

1960 FORD

1960 FORDS — OVERVIEW — Fords were totally redesigned from the ground up for 1960. They shared nothing with the previous models except engines and drivelines. While 1960 styling was considered controversial by many, it remains one of the smoothest designs ever to come from the Dearborn drawingboards. The new models were longer, lower and wider than their predecessors and were very restrained, especially when compared to some of their contemporaries. All 1960 Fords featured a single chrome strip from the top of the front bumper, sweeping up to the top of the front fender, then back, horizontally along the beltline, to the back of the car. There it turned inward and capped the small horizontal fin. Large semi-circular taillights were housed in an aluminum escutcheon panel below the fins and directly above a large chrome bumper. At the front end, a large, recessed mesh grille housed the dual headlights. The Fairlane series contained the word Ford spaced along the recessed section of the full-width hood and used four cast stripes along the rear quarter panel for trim. The Fairlane script was on the sides of the front fenders. The Galaxie series used a Ford crest, in script, on the deck lid and on the front fenders. A single chrome strip began near the center of the front door and continued back to the taillights on the side, with a ribbed, aluminum stone shield behind the rear wheel opening. This season also saw the introduction of the Falcon. Ford's entrant into the compact car race was a pleasingly styled, uncomplicated little car available in two-door and four-door sedans and station wagons. The styling left little doubt that they were Ford products, but was remarkably simple and attractive.

VIN NUMBERS: The serial number code can be broken down as follows: First symbol: indicates year 0 — 1960, 1 — 1961, etc.; Second symbol: assembly plant Third and fourth symbols: body type. Fifth symbol: engine choice (See engine section). The last six digits are the unit's production number, beginning with 100001 and going up, at each of the assembly plants, which were coded as follows: A = Atlanta; C = Chester; D = Dallas; E = Mawhah; F = Dearborn; P = Twin Cities; G = Chicago; L = Lorain; J = Los Angeles; K = Kansas City; N=Norfolk; Z = St. Louis; R = San Jose; S = Pilot Plant; T = Metuchen; U = Louisville and Y = Lincoln (Wixom).

1960 Ford, Fairlane 500 four-door sedan, 6-cyl

FAIRLANE SERIES — (ALL ENGINES) — The Fairlane series was the base trim level for 1960 and included chrome moldings around windshield and rear windows, two sun visors, armrests on all doors and no extra chrome side trim.

FAIRLANE 6-CYL SERIES I.D. NUMBERS: Fairlane six-cylinder models began with the number 0, followed by the assembly plant code, body type code, engine designation and, finally, the unit's production number, according to the final assembly location.

FAIRLANE 6-CYL SERIES

Model Number	Body/Style Number	Body Type & Seating	Factory Price	Shipping Weight	Production Total
V	32	4-dr Sed-6P	2311	3605	Note 1
V	31	2-dr Sed-6P	2257	3531	Note 1
V	32	2-dr Bus Cpe-3P	2170	3504	Note 1

NOTE 1: See Fairlane V-8 Series listing. Production was counted by series and body style only, with no breakout per engine type.

FAIRLANE V-8 SERIES I.D. NUMBERS: Fairlane V-8 models began with the number 'O', followed by assembly plant code, body type code, engine designation code and, finally, the unit's production number.

FAIRLANE V-8 SERIES

Model Number	Body/Style Number	Body Type & Seating	Factory Price	Shipping Weight	Production Total
NA	32	4-dr Sed-6P	2424	3706	110,373
NA	31	2-dr Sed-6P	2370	3632	93,561
NA	33	2-dr Bus Cpe-3P	2283	3605	1,733

PRODUCTION NOTE: Total series output was 205,667 units. This figure included 572 Custom 300 four-door sedans and 302 Custom 300 two-door sedans which were used in fleets (taxis, police cruisers, etc.). Ford does not indicate the number of each model produced with sixes and V-8s. Therefore, all production figures given above are total production of each body style with both engines.

FAIRLANE 500 SERIES — (ALL ENGINES) — The Fairlane 500 was the intermediate trim level and included all the Fairlane trim, plus four chrome stripes on the rear fenders and the Fairlane crest on the hood.

FAIRLANE 500 6-CYL SERIES I.D. NUMBERS: Fairlane 500 six-cylinder models used the same serial number sequence as the Fairlane models.

FAIRLANE 500 6-CYL SERIES

Model Number	Body/Style Number	Body Type & Seating	Factory Price	Shipping Weight	Production Total
V	42	4-dr Twn Sed-6P	2388	3609	Note 1
V	41	2-dr Clb Sed-6P	2334	3535	Note 1

NOTE 1: See Fairlane 500 V-8 Series listing. Production 'was counted by series and body style only, with no breakout per engine type.

FAIRLANE 500 V-8 I.D. NUMBERS: Fairlane 500 V-8 models used the same serial number sequence as the Fairlane models.

FAIRLANE 500 V-8 SERIES

Model Number	Body/Style Number	Body Type & Seating	Factory Price	Shipping Weight	Production Total
NA	41	4-dr Twn Sed-6P	2501	3710	153,234
NA	41	2-dr Clb Sed-6P	244	3636	91,041

PRODUCTION NOTE: Total series output was 224,275 units. Ford does not indicate the number of each model produced with sixes or V-8s. Therefore, all production figures given above are total production of each body style with both engines.

1960 Ford, Galaxie Starliner two-door hardtop coupe, V-8

GALAXIE AND GALAXIE SPECIAL SERIES — (ALL ENGINES) — The Galaxie and Galaxie Special series were the top trim level for 1960 and included chrome A pillar moldings, chrome window moldings, horizontal chrome strip on the side of the body, ribbed aluminum stone shields behind the rear wheels, Galaxie script on the front fenders and the Ford crest on the hood. The Galaxie Special series included the Starliner and Sunliner with all the high-level trim, except that the Galaxie script on the trunk lid was replaced with either the Sunliner or Starliner script.

Standard Catalog of American Cars

GALAXIE AND GALAXIE SPECIAL 6-CYL SERIES I.D. NUMBERS: Galaxie and Galaxie special, six cylinder models used the same serial number sequence as the Fairlane series.

GALAXIE AND GALAXIE SPECIAL 6-CYL SERIES

Model Number	Body/Style Number	Body Type & Seating	Factory Price	Shipping Weight	Production Total
V	52	4-dr Twn Sed-6P	2603	3633	Note 1
V	51	2-dr Clb Sed-6P	2549	3552	Note 1
V	54	4-dr Twn Vic-6P	2788	3752	Note 1
V	53	2-dr Star HT-6P	2610	3566	Note 1
V	55	2-dr SL Conv-6P	2860	3750	Note 1

NOTE 1: See Galaxie and Galaxie Special V-8 Series listing. Production was counted by series and body style only, with no breakout per engine type.

GALAXIE AND GALAXIE SPECIAL SERIES I.D. NUMBERS: Galaxie and Galaxie special V-8 models used the same serial number sequence as the Fairlane series.

GALAXIE AND GALAXIE SPECIAL V-8 SERIES

Model Number	Body/Style Number	Body Type & Seating	Factory Price	Shipping Weight	Production Total
NA	52	4-dr Twn Sed-6P	2716	3734	103,784
NA	51	2-dr Clb Sed-6P	2662	3653	31,866
NA	54	4-dr Twn Sed-6P	2716	3734	104,784
NA	53	2-dr Star HT-6P	2723	3667	68,641
NA	55	2-dr SL Conv-6P	2973	3841	44,762

PRODUCTION NOTE: Total series output was 289,268 units. Ford does not indicate the number of each model produced with sixes or V-8s. Therefore, all production figures given above are total production of each body style with both engines.

STATION WAGON SERIES — (ALL ENGINES) — The Ranch Wagon was the base trim level station wagon, Country Sedans were the intermediate level of equipment and Country Squires were the top trim level. The level of equipment paralleled Fairlane, Fairlane 500 and Galaxie models of conventional cars.

STATION WAGON 6-CYL SERIES I.D. NUMBERS: Station wagon, six-cylinder models used the same serial number sequence as Fairlane and Galaxie models of conventional cars.

STATION WAGONS 6-CYL SERIES

Model Number	Body/Style Number	Body Type & Seating	Factory Price	Shipping Weight	Production Total
V	61	2-dr Ranch Wag-6P	2586	3830	Note 1
V	62	4-dr Ranch Wag-6P	2656	3947	Note 1
V	64	4-dr Cty Sed-6P	2752	3961	Note 1
V	66	4-dr Cty Sed-6P	2837	4007	Note 1
V	68	4-dr Cty Sq-9P	2967	4021	Note 1

STATION WAGON 6-CYL SERIES I.D. NUMBERS: Station wagons, V-8 models used the same serial number sequence as Fairlane and Galaxie models of conventional cars.

STATION WAGON V-8 SERIES

Model Number	Body/Style Number	Body Type & Seating	Factory Price	Shipping Weight	Production Total
NA	61	2-dr Ranch Wag-6P	2699	3931	27,136
NA	62	4-dr Ranch Wag-6P	2769	4048	43,872
NA	64	4-dr Cty Sed-6P	2865	4062	59,302
NA	66	4-dr Cty Sed-9P	2950	4108	19,277
NA	68	4-dr Cty Sq-9P	3080	4122	22,237

PRODUCTION NOTE: Total series output was 171,824 units. Ford does not indicate the number of each model produced with sixes or V-8s. Therefore, all production figures given above are total production of each body style with both engines.

FALCON 6-CYL SERIES — The Falcon was Ford's contribution to the compact car field. While being nearly three feet shorter overall than the full-size Fords, the Falcon offered an interior spacious enough for occupants more than six-feet tall. The compact station wagon offered more than enough cargo space for the majority of buyers. Falcon styling was very simple and ultra-conservative. The body was slab-sided, with just a slightly recessed feature line. Two single headlights were mounted inside the grille opening and the grille itself was an aluminum stamping consisting of horizontal and vertical bars. The name Ford appeared on the hood, in front of the power bulge type simulated scoop. At the rear, the word Falcon, in block letters, appeared between the two round taillights. Power was supplied by a 144 cid six-cylinder engine. Transmission choices included the standard three-speed synchromesh manual transmission or optional two-speed Ford-O-Matic automatic transmission.

1960 Ford, Falcon Deluxe two-door station wagon, 6-cyl

FALCON 6-CYL SERIES I.D. NUMBERS: Falcon models used the same serial number sequence as the full-size Fords, except the engine code was "S."

FALCON 6-CYL SERIES

Model Number	Body/Style Number	Body Type & Seating	Factory Price	Shipping Weight	Production Total
S	58A	4-dr Sed-6P	1974	2317	167,896,
S	64A	2-dr Sed-6P	1912	2282	193,470
S	71A	4-dr Sta Wag-6P	2287	2575	46,758
S	59A	2-dr Sta Wag-6P	2225	2540	27,552

PRODUCTION NOTE: Total series output was 435,676 units.

1960 Ford Thunderbird Tudor hardtop coupe with sun roof option, V-8.

THUNDERBIRD V-8 SERIES: The 1960 Thunderbird used the same body as the previous two years, with only trim updating. This was the last of the 'Square Birds,' with the highly sculptured fender and body lines. The grille was the same pattern of small squares used in 1957 and was located behind a large horizontal chrome bar with three vertical dividers. The grille pattern was duplicated behind the taillights. Three taillights were used per side, instead of two, as in previous years. The Thunderbird script appeared on the door. Script was unique to 1960. Script in other years was sometimes shared ('63-'64). The 430 V-8 was again an option available only with automatic transmission. The most significant change for 1960 was the addition of a manually-operated sun roof and 2,536 cars were produced with this option.

THUNDERBIRD V-8 SERIES I.D. NUMBERS: Thunderbird models began with the number 'O' assembly plant code 'Y' (Wixom), body type code, engine type code 'Y' or 'J' and, finally, the unit's production number beginning at l00001 and going up.

THUNDERBIRD V-8 SERIES

Model Number	Body/Style Number	Body Type & Seating	Factory Price	Shipping Weight	Production Total
Y/J	71	2-dr HT Cpe-4P	3755	3799	80,938
Y/J	73	2-dr Conv-4P	4222	3897	11,860

FALCON/FORD/THUNDERBIRD ENGINES

FALCON SIX-CYLINDER: Overhead valves. Cast iron block. Displacement: 144 cid. Bore and stroke: 3.50 x 2.50 inches. Compression ratio: 8.7:1. Brake hp: 85 at 4200 rpm. Carburetion: Holley one-barrel. Four main bearings. Serial number code S (D code on export models).

FORD SIX-CYLINDER: Overhead valves. Cast iron block. Displacement: 223 cid. Bore and stroke: 3.62 x 3.60 inches. Compression ratio: 8.4:1. Brake hp: 145 at 4000 rpm. Carburetion: Holley single barrel. Four main bearings. Serial number code "V."

V-8: Overhead valves. Cast iron block. Displacement: 292 cid. Bore and stroke: 3.75 x 3.30 inches. Compression ratio: 8.8:1. Brake hp: 185 at 4200 rpm. Carburetion: Holley two-barrel. Five main bearings. Serial number code "W."

INTERCEPTOR V-8: Overhead valves. Cast iron block. Displacement: 352 cid. Bore and stroke: 4.00 x 3.50 inches. Compression ratio: 8.9:1. Brake hp: 235 at 4400 rpm. Carburetion: Holley two-barrel. Five main bearings. Serial number code "X" (Code G on export models).

INTERCEPTOR V-8: Overhead valves. Cast iron block. Displacement: 352 cid. Bore and stroke: 4.00 x 3.50 inches. Compression ratio: 9.6:1. Brake hp: 300 at 4600 rpm. Carburetion: Holley four-barrel. Five main bearings. Serial number code "Y."

INTERCEPTOR SPECIAL V-8: Overhead valves. Cast iron block. Displacement: 352 cid. Bore and stroke: 4.00 x 3.50 inches. Compression ratio: 10.6:1. Brake hp: 360 at 6000 rpm. Carburetion: Holley four-barrel. Five main bearings. Serial number code "R."

THUNDERBIRD SPECIAL V-8: Overhead valves. Cast iron block. Displacement: 430 cid. Bore and stroke: 4.30 x 3.50 inches. Compression ratio: 10. 2:1. Brake hp: 350 at 4400 rpm. Carburetion: Holley four-barrel. Five main bearings. Serial number code "J."

CHASSIS FEATURES: Wheelbase: (All Fords and Thunderbirds) 119 inches; (Falcons) 109.5 inches. Overall length: (All Fords) 213.7 inches; (Thunderbirds) 205.32 inches; (Falcon passenger cars) 181.2 inches; (Falcon station wagons) 189 inches. Overall width: (Fords) 81.5 inches; (Thunderbirds) 77 inches; (Falcons) 70 inches. Overall height, sedan: (Fords) 55 inches; (Thunderbirds) 52.5 inches; (Falcons) 54.5 inches. Tires: (Ford passenger cars-closed body) 7.50 x 14; (Ford convertibles and station wagons and Thunderbird) 8.00 x 14; (Falcon passenger cars) 6.00 x 13; (Falcon station wagon) 6.50 x 13.

FORD OPTIONS: Standard 185 hp V-8 engine ($113). Two-barrel 235 hp V-8 ($147.80). Four-barrel 300 hp V-8 ($177.40). Polar air-conditioning including Tinted Glass and V-8 ($27 1). Select-Air air-conditioning including Tinted Glass and V-8 ($404). Back-up lights ($11). Heavy-duty 70-amp battery ($8). Equa-Lock differential ($39). Electric Clock ($15). Fresh Air heater/defroster ($75). Recirculating heater/defroster ($47). Four-way manual seat ($11). Rocker, panel molding ($14). Padded dash and visors ($25). Two-tone paint ($19). Power brakes ($43). Power seat ($64). Power steering ($77). Front and rear power windows ($102). Push-button radio and antenna ($59). Front seat belts ($21). Tinted glass ($43). Cruise-O-Matic ($211). Ford-O-Matic with 6-cylinder ($180). Ford-O-Matic with V-8 ($190). Overdrive ($108). Wheelcovers ($17). Windshield washer 9$14). Two-speed windshield wipers ($10). Tires — Ford offered numerous tire options such as white sidewall and oversized models.

FALCON OPTIONS: Heavy-duty battery ($8). Deluxe trim package ($66). Fresh Air heater/defroster ($68). Two-tone paint ($17). Manual radio and antenna ($54). Safety equipment: padded dash and visors ($19). Front seat safety belts ($21). Whitewall tires ($29). Automatic transmission ($159). wheelcovers ($16). Windshield washer ($13). Electric windshield wiper ($10).

THUNDERBIRD OPTIONS: Cruise-O-Matic ($242). Overdrive ($145). Radio and antenna ($113). Fresh Air heater ($83). Air conditioner ($466). Tinted glass ($38). White sidewall tires, rayon, size 8.00 x 14 ($36). White sidewall tires, nylon, size 8.00 x 14 ($64). Engine, V-8, 350 hp ($177). Power steering ($75). Power windows ($102). Power brakes ($43). Four-Way

power driver's seat ($92). Outside, left or right mirror ($5). Back-up lights ($10). Windshield washers ($14). Rear fender shield ($27). Front seat belts ($23). Leather interior ($106). Heavy-duty 70-amp battery, standard on convertible, on other models: ($8). Two-Tone Paint ($26). Underseal ($14). Sliding roof for hardtop ($212).

HISTORICAL FOOTNOTES: All three lines of 1960 Fords were introduced to the public on Oct. 8, 1959. Falcon station wagons were added to the new compact series in March, 1960. Although Ford did not provide production breakouts by engine type, trade publications recorded that 67.5 percent of all Fords (excluding Thunderbirds and Falcons) had V-8 engines installed. All Falcons were sixes and all Thunderbirds were V-8 powered. Automatic transmissions were installed in 67.1 percent of all Fords, 44.5 percent of all Falcons and 97.9 percent of all Thunderbirds built during the model run. Ford's share of the overall automobile market dropped to 22.55 percent this year, compared to 27.33 percent in 1959. Model year production peaked at 911,034 Fords, 435,676 Falcons and 92,843 Thunderbirds. Model year series production was as follows: (Custom 300) 900; (Fairlane) 204,700; (Fairlane 500) 244,300; (Galaxie) 289,200; (station wagon) 171,800; (Thunderbird) 92,800. Just 297,400 six-cylinder Fords were produced for the model year.

1961 FORD

1961 FORDS — OVERVIEW — 1961 saw the third major restyling of the full-sized Ford line in as many years. From the beltline down, the 1961 Fords were completely new. The upper body structure was retained from the 1960 lineup. A full-width concave grille with a horizontal dividing bar highlighted front end styling. The Ford name, in block letters, replaced the crest used in previous years on Fairlane models and the series designation appeared on the front fenders, behind the headlights. The horizontal full-length fin, used in 1960, was replaced with a smaller canted fin, nearly identical in size and shape to the fin used on 1957-1958 Custom series cars. Large, round taillights were used once again. A horizontal chrome strip, very similar to one used on 1960 models, was used once again. It was complemented by a ribbed, aluminum stone guard on the Galaxie series. 1961 saw the beginning of the great horsepower race of the 1960s and Ford cracked the magic 400 barrier with a new engine; the 390 cid/401 hp V-8. The Falcon continued virtually unchanged from 1960, with an updated convex grille in place of the concave unit used the previous year. A 170 cid six-cylinder engine became optional throughout the line. The biggest styling changes for 1961 took place in the Thunderbird series. Replacing the 1958-1960 Square Bird, was a much longer, more rounded Thunderbird. A massive front bumper surrounded the grille, which was stamped aluminum and carried a horizontal grid pattern. A single chrome strip began at the top of the front bumpers, swept up and back and outlined the small, canted fins back to the taillights. Four cast stripes were stacked on the side, immediately in front of the taillights. A smooth deck lid replaced the heavily sculptured lid used during the previous three years. Two large, round taillights replaced the six lights used in 1960. Beginning in 1961, Cruise-O-Matic transmission, power steering and power brakes became standard equipment on all Thunderbirds.

1961 Ford, Fairlane Town Sedan four-door sedan, 6-cyl

FAIRLANE SERIES — (ALL ENGINES) — The Fairlane series was the base trim level for 1961 and included chrome moldings around the windshield and rear window, two sun visors, a horn button instead of horn ring, armrest on all doors and no extra side chrome.

FAIRLANE 6-CYL I.D. NUMBERS: Fairlane, six-cylinder models began with the number '1,' followed by the assembly plant code, body type code, engine designation 'V' and, finally, the unit's production number according to the final assembly location. Each plant began at 100001 and went up.

FAIRLANE 6-CYL SERIES

Model Number	Body/Style Number	Body Type & Seating	Factory Price	Shipping Weight	Production Total
V	32	4-dr Twn Sed-6P	2315	3585	Note 1
V	31	4-dr Clb Sed-6P	2261	3487	Note 1

NOTE 1: See Fairlane V-8 Series listing. Production was counted by series and body style only, with no breakouts per engine type.

FAIRLANE V-8 SERIES I.D. NUMBERS: Fairlane V-8 models began with the number '1,' followed by assembly plant code, body type code, engine designation code and, finally, the unit's production number according to final assembly location. Each plant began at 100001 and went up.

FAIRLANE V-8 SERIES

Model Number	Body/Style Number	Body Type & Seating	Factory Price	Shipping Weight	Production Total
NA	32	4-dr Twn Sed-6P	2431	3683	66,924
NA	31	2-dr Clb Sed-6P	2377	2685	97,208

PRODUCTION NOTE: Total series output was 164,132 units. This figure includes 303 Custom 300 four-door sedans and 49 Custom 300 two-door sedans which were used in fleet service (Taxis, Police cruisers, etc.). Ford does not indicate the number of each model produced with sixes or V-8s. Therefore, all production figures given above are total production of each body style with both engines.

FAIRLANE 500 SERIES — (ALL ENGINES) — The Fairlane 500 was the intermediate trim level and included all the Fairlane trim plus a chrome horn ring and a single horizontal chrome strip running from the back of the front wheelwell to the rear bumper.

FAIRLANE 500 V-8 SERIES I.D. NUMBERS: Fairlane 500 V-8 models used the same serial number sequence as the Fairlane models.

FAIRLANE 500 6-CYL SERIES

Model Number	Body/Style Number	Body Type & Seating	Factory Price	Shipping Weight	Production Total
V	42	4-dr Twn Sed-6P	2430	3593	Note 1
V	41	2-dr Clb Sed-6P	2376	3502	Note 1

NOTE 1: See Fairlane 500 V-8 Series listing. Production was counted by series and body style, with no breakouts per engine type.

FAIRLANE 500 6-CYL I.D. NUMBERS: Fairlane 500, six-cylinder models used the same serial number sequence as the Fairlane models.

FAIRLANE 500 V-8 SERIES

Model Number	Body/Style Number	Body Type & Seating	Factory Price	Shipping Weight	Production Total
NA	42	4-dr Twn Sed-6P	2546	3691	98,917
NA	41	4-dr Clb Sed-6P	2492	3600	42,468

PRODUCTION NOTE: Total series output was 141,385 units. Ford does not indicate the number of each model produced with sixes or V-8s. Therefore, all production figures given above are total production of each body style with both engines.

1961 Ford, Galaxie Sunliner two-door convertible, 6-cyl

GALAXIE V-8 SERIES I.D. NUMBERS: Galaxie, V-8 models used the same serial number sequence as the Fairlane series.

GALAXIE V-8 SERIES

Model Number	Body/Style Number	Body Type & Seating	Factory Price	Shipping Weight	Production Total
NA	52	4-dr Twn Sed-6P	2706	3668	141,823
NA	51	2-dr Clb Sed-6P	2652	3586	27,780
NA	54	4-dr Twn Vic-6P	2778	3686	30,342
NA	57	2-dr Clb Vic-6P	2713	3643	75,437
NA	53	2-dr Star HT-6P	2713	3615	29,669
NA	55	2-dr SL Conv-6P	2963	3792	44,614

PRODUCTION NOTE: Total series output was 349,665 units. Ford does not indicate the number of each model produced with sixes or V-8s. Therefore, all production figures are total production of each body style with each engine.

STATION WAGON SERIES — (ALL ENGINES) — The Ranch Wagon was the base trim level station wagon, Country Sedans were the intermediate level and Country Squire were the top time level. The level of equipment paralleled Fairlane. Fairlane 500 and Galaxie models of passenger cars.

STATION WAGON 6-CYL I.D. NUMBERS: Station wagon six-cylinder models used the same serial number sequence as Galaxie and Fairlane series conventional cars.

STATION WAGON 6-CYL SERIES

Model Number	Body/Style Number	Body Type & Seating	Factory Price	Shipping Weight	Production Total
V	61	2-dr Ranch Wag-6P	2586	3816	Note 1
V	62	4-dr Ranch Wag-6P	2656	3911	Note 1
V	64	4-dr Cty Sed-6P	2752	3934	Note 1
V	66	4-dr Cty Sed-9P	2856	3962	Note 1
V	67	4-dr Cty Sq	2941	3930	Note 1
V	68	4-dr Cty Sq	3011	3966	Note 1

NOTE 1: See Station wagon V-8 Series listing. Production was counted by series and body style, with no breakouts per engine type.

STATION WAGON V-8 SERIES I.D. NUMBERS: Station Wagon, V-8 models. used the same serial number sequence as Fairlane and Galaxie models of passenger cars.

STATION WAGON V-8 SERIES

Model Number	Body/Style Number	Body Type & Seating	Factory Price	Shipping Weight	Production Total
NA	61	2-dr Ranch Wag-6P	2702	3914	12,042
NA	62	4-dr Ranch Wag-6P	2772	4009	30,292
NA	64	4-dr Cty Sed-6P	2868	4032	46,311
NA	66	4-dr Cty Sed-9P	2972	4060	16,356
NA	67	4-dr Cty Sq	3057	4036	16,961
NA	68	4-dr Cty Sq	3127	4064	14,657

PRODUCTION NOTE: Total series output was 136,619 units. Ford does not indicate the number of each model produced with sixes or V-8s. Therefore, all production figures given above are total production of each body style with both engines.

FALCON 6-CYL SERIES — The Falcon continued unchanged from 1961, with the exception of a new convex grille. A new 170 cid six-cylinder was added to the lineup and the Futura two-door sedan was added to give a sporty flair to the compact car line. The Futura was the same body shell, equipped with a bucket seat interior and a center console.

OVER 550,000

1961 Ford, Falcon Deluxe four-door, 6-cyl

FALCON I.D. NUMBERS: Falcon model used the same serial number sequence as the full-size Fords, except the engine code was either 'S' or 'U.'

FALCON 6-CYL SERIES

Model Number	Body/Style Number	Body Type & Seating	Factory Price	Shipping Weight	Production Total
S/U	12	4-dr Sed-6P	1974	2289	159,761
S/U	11	2-dr Sed-6P	1912	2254	149,982
S/U	17	2-dr Futura Sed-5P	2160	2322	44,470
S/U	22	4-dr Sta Wag-6P	2268	2558	87,933
S/U	21	2-dr Sta Wag-6P	2225	2525	32,045

PRODUCTION NOTE: Total series output was 474,191 units.

1961 Ford, Thunderbird two-door convertible, V-8

THUNDERBIRD V-8 SERIES — The 1961 Thunderbirds were totally new cars. They were longer, lower, wider and heavier than the previous years. Cruise-O-Matic automatic transmission, power steering, power brakes and the new 390 cid V-8 engine were standard equipment on all Thunderbirds for 1961.

THUNDERBIRD V-8 SERIES I.D. NUMBERS: Thunderbird models began with the number '1,' assembly plant code 'Y' (Wixom), body type code, engine type code 'Z' and, finally, the unit's production number beginning at 100001 and going up.

THUNDERBIRD V-8 SERIES

Model Number	Body/Style Number	Body Type & Seating	Factory Price	Shipping Weight	Production Total
Z	71	2-dr HT Cpe-4P	4170	3958	62,535
Z	73	2-dr Conv-4P	4637	4130	10,516

1961 ENGINES

FALCON SIX-CYLINDER: Overhead valves. Cast iron block. Displacement: 144 cid. Bore and stroke: 3.50 x 2.50 inches. Compression ratio: 8.7:1. Brake hp: 85 at 4200 rpm. Carburetion: Holley one-barrel. Four main bearings. Serial numbers code "S" (D code on export units).

FALCON 170 SIX-CYLINDER: Overhead valves. Cast iron block. Displacement: 170 cid. Bore and stroke: 3.50 x 2.94 inches. Compression ratio: 8.7:1. Brake hp: 101 at 4400 rpm. Carburetion: Holley one-barrel. Four main bearings. Serial number code "U."

FORD SIX-CYLINDER: Overhead valves. Cast iron block. Displacement: 223 cid. Bore and stroke: 3.62 x 3.60 inches. Compression ratio: 8.4:1. Brake hp: 135 at 4000 rpm. Carburetion: Holley one-barrel. Four main bearings. Serial number code "V."

V-8: Overhead valves. Cast iron block. Displacement: 292 cid. Bore and stroke: 3.75 x 3.30 inches. Compression ratio: 8.8:1. Brake hp: 175 at 4200 rpm. Carburetion: Holley two-barrel. Five main bearings. Serial number code "W" (Code T on export units).

INTERCEPTOR V-8: Overhead valves. Cast iron block. Displacement: 352 cid. Bore and stroke: 4.00 x 3.50 inches. Compression ratio: 8.9:1. Brake hp: 220 at 4400 rpm. Carburetion: Holley two-barrel. Five main bearings. Serial number code "X."

THUNDERBIRD V-8: Overhead valves. Cast iron block. Displacement: 390 cid. Bore and stroke: 4.05 x 3.78 inches. Compression ratio: 9.6:1. Brake hp: 300 at 4600 rpm. Carburetion: Holley four-barrel. Five main bearings. Serial number code "Z."

THUNDERBIRD SPECIAL V-8: Overhead valves. Cast iron block. Displacement: 390 cid. Bore and stroke: 4.05 x 3.78 inches. Compression ratio: 10.6:1. Brake hp: 375 at 6000 rpm. Carburetion: Holley four-barrel. Five main bearings. Serial number code "Z" and "Q" (Code R on export units).

THUNDERBIRD SPECIAL (6V) V-8: Overhead valves. Cast iron block. Displacement: 390 cid. Bore and stroke: 4.05 x 3.78 inches. Compression ratio: 10.6:1. Brake hp: 401 at 6000 rpm. Carburetion: three Holley two-barrels. Five main bearings. Serial number code "Z."

CHASSIS FEATURES: Wheelbase: (Thunderbird) 113 inches; (Falcon) 109.5 inches; (all other models) 119 inches. Overall length: (Thunderbird) 205 inches; (Falcon station wagons) 189 inches; (other Falcons) 181.2 inches; (all other models) 209.9 inches. Front tread: (Thunderbird and Ford) 61 inches; (Falcon) 55 inches. Rear tread: (Thunderbird and Ford) 60 inches; (Falcon) 54.5 inches. Tires: (Thunderbird and Ford station wagons) 8.00 x 14; (Fords) 7.50 x 14; (Falcon station wagon) 6.50 x 13; (other Falcons) 6.00 x 13.

FALCON OPTIONS: Back-up lights ($11). Heavy-duty battery ($8). Crankcase vent system ($6). Deluxe trim package ($78). Engine, 170 cid; 101 hp ($37). Fresh Air heater/defroster ($73). Station Wagon luggage rack ($35). Two-tone paint ($19). Manual radio and antenna ($54). Safety Equipment including padded dash and visors ($22); plus front seat belts ($21). Electric tailgate windows for station wagons ($30). Automatic transmission ($163). Wheelcovers ($16). Windshield washer ($14). Electric windshield wiper ($10). Numerous oversize and white sidewall tire options.

FORD CONVENIENCE OPTIONS: Standard 175 hp V-8 Engine ($116). Two barrel, 220 hp V-8 ($148). Four-barrel, 300 hp V-8 ($197). Polar air-conditioner, including tinted glass ($271). Select air-conditioner, including tinted glass ($436). Back-up lights ($11). Heavy-duty, 70-amp battery ($8). Crankcase vent system ($6). Equa-Lock differential ($39). Electric clock ($15). Magic Aire heater/defroster ($75). Recirculating heater/defroster ($47). Four-way manual seat ($17). Rocker panel molding ($16). Padded dash and visors ($24). Two-tone paint ($22). Power brakes ($43). Power seat ($64). Power steering ($82). Power tailgate window ($32). Front and rear power windows ($102). Push-button radio and antenna ($59). Front seat belts ($21). Tinted glass ($43). Cruise-O-Matic transmission ($212). Ford-O-Matic transmission with six-cylinder engine ($180); Ford-O-Matic transmission with eight-cylinder engine ($190); Overdrive transmission ($108). Wheelcovers ($19). Windshield washer ($14). Two-speed windshield wipers ($12). Plus numerous oversize and white sidewall tire options with price variations by style, engine and use of air conditioning.

THUNDERBIRD CONVENIENCE OPTIONS: Radio and antenna ($113). Fresh Air heater ($83), Select Aire air-conditioner ($463). Tinted glass ($43). White sidewall tires, rayon 8.00 x 14 ($42); nylon ($70). Power windows ($106). Four-way driver's power seat ($92). Outside, left- or right-hand mirror ($5). Windshield washers ($14). Rear fender shields ($27). Front seat belts ($23). Leather interior ($106). Heavy-duty, 70-amp battery ($8). Two-tone paint ($26). Equa-Lock differential ($39). Movable steering control ($25) Note: Crankcase ventilation system standard on California cars only.

HISTORICAL FOOTNOTES: Lee A. Iacocca was in his second season at the Ford helm this year. Calendar year output totaled 1,362,186 cars. Market penetration was up to 24 percent as model year production peaked at 163,600 Fairlanes; 141,500 Fairlane 500s; 349,700 Galaxies; 136,600 station wagons; 73,000 Thunderbirds; 129,700 standard Falcons; 224,500 Deluxe Falcons and 135,100 Falcon station wagons. Dealer introduction dates were September 29 for Fords and Falcons, Nov. 12 for Thunderbirds. The full-size line production totals included 201,700 six-cylinder cars, while all Falcons were sixes and all Thunderbirds were V-8s.

1962 FORD

1962 FORDS — OVERVIEW — In 1962, Ford continued it's policy of making major styling changes in least one line. The 1962 Galaxies and full-size line were restyled and the end result is recognized as one of the cleaner designs to come from Dearborn. Except for one horizontal feature line at the beltline, the body was slab-sided. The model designation was carried in script along the rear fender. Ford continued the tradition of large round taillights throughout the entire line, with the taillights on Galaxies being separated by a stamped aluminum escutcheon panel. The model designation was spelled out in block letters across the trunk lid. At the front end, a full-width grille carried a horizontal grid pattern and was capped on each end by the dual headlights. The Ford crest was centered at the front of the hood throughout the full-size line. The Falcon line continued unchanged from the previous year, except for the addition of an updated grille. The convex grille bars carried a vertical pattern. Also, a woodgrained version of the Falcon four-door station wagon was added to the Deluxe series and was known as the Falcon Squire. A bucket seat two-door sedan sport model was added to the line as the Futura. Like the Falcon line, the 1962 Thunderbirds received only minor cosmetic changes for the new year. The new T-Birds had a smooth hood without the two ridges characteristic only of 1961 models. The 1962 taillights were also slightly different than the previous year, with a chrome ring around the center of the lens. The big news for 1962 was the introduction of the intermediate size Fairlane. The new model was nearly 12 inches shorter than the full-size Galaxie, yet was nearly eight inches longer than the compact Falcon. At the time of their introduction, the Fairlanes were compared to the 1949-1950 Fords in length and width. They were nearly identical, but were considerably lower. No one would ever guess the Fairlane was anything, but a Ford. They utilized the characteristic round taillights, 'high-canted' fenders and a grille which was nearly identical to the Galaxie line. This year saw a continuation of the great '60s horsepower race and to do combat with the GM and Chrysler offerings, Ford introduced the famous 406 cid V-8. It produced 405 hp. The re-sizing of the Fairlane also brought the introduction of a completely new line of small V-8 engines. At 221 cid, the new base V-8 was the same displacement as the first Ford flathead V-8. It was of thin-wall casting design and was the first in a series of lightweight V-8s.

GALAXIE SERIES — (ALL ENGINES) — The Galaxie series was the base trim level for 1962 and included chrome moldings around the windshield and rear window, two sun visors, a chrome horn ring, armrests on all doors and a single horizontal chrome strip at the beltline.

GALAXIE 6-CYL I.D. NUMBERS: Galaxie six-cylinder models began with the number '2', followed by the assembly plant code, body type code, engine designation 'V' and, finally, the unit's production number according to the final assembly location. Each plant began at 100001 and went up.

GALAXIE 6-CYL SERIES

Model Number	Body/Style Number	Body Type & Seating	Factory Price	Shipping Weight	Production Total
V	52	4-dr Sed-6P	2507	3583	Note 1
V	51	2-dr Sed-6P	2453	3478	Note 1

NOTE 1: See Galaxie V-8 Series listing. Production was counted by series and body style only, with no breakouts per engine type.

GALAXIE V-8 I.D. NUMBERS: Galaxie V-8 models began with the number '2,' followed by the assembly plant code, body type code, engine designation code and, finally, the unit's production number according to the final assembly location. Each plant began at 100001 and went up.

GALAXIE V-8 SERIES

Model Number	Body/Style Number	Body Type & Seating	Factory Price	Shipping Weight	Production Total
NA	52	4-dr Sed-6P	2616	3684	115,594
NA	51	2-dr Sed-6P	2562	3589	54,930

PRODUCTION NOTE: Total series output was 170.524 units. Ford does not indicate the number of each model produced with sixes or V-8s. Therefore, all production figures given above are total production of each body style with both engines.

1962 Ford Galaxie 500 two-door hardtop, V-8

GALAXIE 500 SERIES — (ALL ENGINES) — The Galaxie 500 Series was the top trim level for 1962 and included chrome 'A' pillar moldings, chrome window moldings, a color-keyed horizontal chrome strip at the beltline, chrome rocker panel moldings, quarter panel moldings and a chrome trim strip with a Ford crest at the base of the 'C' pillar, on the top.

GALAXIE 500 6-CYL I.D. NUMBERS: Galaxie 500 six-cylinder models used the same serial number sequence as the Galaxie series.

GALAXIE 5500 6-CYL SERIES

Model Number	Body/Style Number	Body Type & Seating	Factory Price	Shipping Weight	Production Total
V	62	4-dr Twn Sed-6P	2667	3568	Note 1
V	61	2-dr Clb Sed-6P	2613	3476	Note 1
V	64	4-dr Twn Vic-6P	2739	3577	Note 1
V	63	2-dr Clb Vic-6P	2674	3505	Note 1

NOTE 1: See Galaxie 500 V-8 Series listing. Production was counted by series and body style with no breakouts per engine type.

GALAXIE 500 V-8 SERIES I.D. NUMBERS: Galaxie 500 V-8 models used the same serial number sequence as the Galaxie series.

GALAXIE 500 V-8 SERIES

Model Number	Body/Style Number	Body Type & Seating	Factory Price	Shipping Weight	Production Total
NA	62	4-dr Twn Sed-6P	2776	3679	174,195
NA	61	2-dr Clb Sed-6P	2722	3587	27,824
NA	64	4-dr Twn Vic-6P	2848	3688	30,778
NA	63	2-dr Clb Vic-6P	2783	3616	87,562
NA	65	2-dr SL Conv-6P	3033	3782	42,646

PRODUCTION NOTE: Total series output was 404,600 units. Ford does not indicate the number of each model produced with sixes or V-8s. Therefore, all production figures are total production of each body style with each engine.

GALAXIE 500XL SERIES — (V-8) — The Galaxie 500XL series was new for 1962, and was the sporty series of the Galaxie line. The "XLs" included all the trim of the Galaxie 500 models, but offered bucket seats and a floor-mounted shift lever, as well as an engine-turned insert in the instrument panel and on the side stripe.

GALAXIE 500XL I.D. NUMBERS: Galaxie 500XL models used the same serial number sequence as the Galaxie and Galaxie 500 series.

GALAXIE 500XL SERIES V-8

Model Number	Body/Style Number	Body Type & Seating	Factory Price	Shipping Weight	Production Total
NA	63A	2-dr Clb Vic-5P	3108	3625	28,412
NA	76B	2-dr SL Conv-5P	3358	3804	13,183

PRODUCTION NOTE: Total series output was 41,595 units.

STATION WAGON SERIES — (ALL ENGINES) — The Ranch Wagon was the base trim level Station Wagon, Country Sedans were the intermediate level and Country Squires were the top trim level. The level of equipment paralleled Galaxie, Galaxie 500 and Galaxie 500XL models of passenger cars.

STATION WAGON 6-CYL I.D. NUMBERS: Station wagon six-cylinder models used the same serial number sequence as Galaxie series of passenger cars.

STATION WAGON 6-CYL SERIES

Model Number	Body/Style Number	Body Type & Seating	Factory Price	Shipping Weight	Production Total
V	17	4-dr Ranch Wag-6P	2733	3905	Note 1
V	72	4-dr Cty Sed-6P	2829	2829	Note 1
V	74	4-dr Cty Sed-9P	2933	3946	Note 1
V	76	4-dr Cty Sq-6P	3018	3942	Note 1
V	78	4-dr Cty Sq-9P	3088	3959	Note 1

NOTE 1: See Station wagon V-8 Series listing. Production was counted by series and body style, with no breakouts per engine type.

STATION WAGON V-8 SERIES I.D. NUMBERS: Station wagon V-8 models used the same serial number sequence as Galaxie series of passenger cars.

STATION WAGON V-8 SERIES

Model Number	Body/Style Number	Body Type & Seating	Factory Price	Shipping Weight	Production Total
NA	71	4-dr Ranch Wag-6P	2842	4016	33,674
NA	72	4-dr Cty Sed-6P	2938	4039	47,635
NA	74	4-dr Cty Sed-9P	3042	4057	16,562
NA	78	4-dr Cty Sq-9P	3197	4057	15,666

PRODUCTION NOTE: Total series output was 129,651 units. Ford does not indicate the number of each model produced with sixes or V-8s. Therefore, all production figures given above are total production of each body style with both engines.

FAIRLANE SERIES — (ALL ENGINES) — The Fairlane was the new intermediate size line of Fords for 1962. With styling very similar to the 1961 full-size Fords, there was no doubt of the Fairlane's heritage. The Fairlane line included the base Fairlane models and the top Fairlane 500 models. The new models also introduced the famous 221 series small-block Ford V-8, with the new thin-wall casting technique, producing the lightest complete V-8 engine of the time.

FAIRLANE SERIES — (ALL ENGINES) — The Fairlane was the base trim level of the line and included chrome windshield and rear window moldings, a horn button instead of horn ring, armrests on all doors, a single horizontal Fairlane sweep type strip (which followed the belt level feature line), the Ford crest on the hood and the word Ford, in block letters, on the trunk lid.

FAIRLANE SIX SERIES I.D. NUMBERS: Fairlane six-cylinder models began with the number "2," followed by the assembly plant code, body type code, engine designation 'U' and, finally the unit's production number according to the final assembly location. Each plant began at 100001 and went up.

FAIRLANE SIX SERIES

Model Number	Body/Style Number	Body Type & Seating	Factory Price	Shipping Weight	Production Total
U	32	4-dr Sed-6P	2216	2791	Note 1
U	31	2-dr Sed-6P	2154	2757	Note 1

NOTE 1: See Fairlane V-8 Series listing. Production was counted by series and body style only, with no breakouts per engine type.

FAIRLANE V-8 SERIES I.D. NUMBERS: Fairlane V-8 models began with the number '2,' followed by the assembly plant code, body type code, engine designation code 'L' and, finally the unit's production number according to final assembly location. Each plant began at 100001 and went up.

FAIRLANE V-8 SERIES

Model Number	Body/Style Number	Body Type Seating	Factory Price	Shipping Weight	Production Total
L	32	4-dr Sed-6P	2319	2949	45,342
L	31	2-dr Sed-6P	2257	2915	34,264

PRODUCTION NOTE: Total series output was 79,606 units. Ford does not indicate the number of each model produced with sixes or V-8s. Therefore, all production figures given above are total production of each body style.

1962 Ford Fairlane 500 two-door Sports Coupe, V-8

FAIRLANE 500 SERIES — (ALL ENGINES) — The Fairlane 500 models were the top trim level of the line and included chrome window moldings, a chrome horn ring, armrests on all doors, simulated chrome inserts on the door upholstery, a two-piece chrome Fairlane sweep with a ribbed aluminum insert and two sun visors. The Sport Coupe two-door sedan included bucket seats and special identification was introduced midyear.

FAIRLANE 500 SIX I.D. NUMBERS: Fairlane 500 six-cylinder models used the same serial numbers sequence as the Fairlane models.

FAIRLANE 500 SIX SERIES

Model Number	Body/Style Number	Body Type & Seating	Factory Price	Shipping Weight	Production Total
U	42	4-dr Sed-6P	2507	2808	Note 1
U	41	2-dr Sed-6P	2304	2774	Note 1
U	47	2-dr Spt Cpe-5P	2504	2870	Note 1

NOTE 1: See Fairlane 500 V-8 Series listing. Production was counted by series and body style, with no breakouts per engine type.

FAIRLANE 500 V-8 SERIES I.D. NUMBERS: Fairlane 500 V-8 models used the same serial number sequence as the Fairlane models.

FAIRLANE 500 V-8 SERIES

Model Number	Body/Style Number	Body Type & Seating	Factory Price	Shipping Weight	Production Total
L	42	4-dr Sed-6P	2407	2966	129,258
L	41	2-dr Sed-6P	2345	2932	68,624
L	47	2-dr Spt Cpe-5P	2607	3002	19,628

PRODUCTION NOTE: Total series output was 217,510 units. Ford does not indicate the number of each model produced with sixes or V-8s. Therefore, all production figures given above are total production of each body style.

Standard Catalog of American Cars

1962 Ford, Falcon Squire four-door station wagon, 6-cyl

FALCON SERIES — 6-CYL — The Falcon continued unchanged from 1961, with the exception of a new convex grille with vertical bars and a new Galaxie style top configuration. There were two separate Falcon lines for 1962; the standard and deluxe series, rather than the deluxe trim package, which was optional on all 1960 and 1961 Falcons. Also new was the Falcon Squire station wagon.

STANDARD FALCON I.D. NUMBERS: The standard series Falcon used the same serial number sequence as the full-size Fords, except the engine code was either 'S' or 'U.'

STANDARD SERIES FALCON

Model Number	Body/Style Number	Body Type & Seating	Factory Price	Shipping Weight	Production Total
S/U	12	4-dr Sed-6P	2047	2299	Note 1
S/U	11	2-dr Sed-6P	1985	2262	Note 1
S/U	22	4-dr Sta Wag-6P	2341	2595	Note 1
S/U	21	2-dr Sta Wag-6P	2298	2559	Note 1

NOTE 1: See Deluxe Falcon listing. Production was counted by body style, with no breakouts per level of trim.

DELUXE FALCON I.D. NUMBERS: Deluxe Falcon models, used the same serial number sequence as the full-size Fords, except the engine code was either 'S' or 'U.'

DELUXE SERIES FALCON

Model Number	Body/style Number	Body Type & Seating	Factory Price	Shipping Weight	Production Total
S/U	12	4-dr Sed-6P	2133	2319	126,041
S/U	11	2-dr Sed-6P	2071	2282	143,650
S/U	17	2-dr Futura Sed-5P	2232	2347	17,011
S/U	22	4-dr Sta Wag-6P	2427	2621	66,819
S/U	21	2-dr Sta Wag-6P	2384	2584	Note 1
S/U	26	4-dr Sq Wag-6P	2603	2633	22,583

PRODUCTION NOTE: Total series output was 396,129 units. Ford does not indicate the total number of standard models and Deluxe models produced. Therefore, all production figures are total production of each body style with both level of trim.

1962 Ford Thunderbird two-door Sports Roadster, V-8 (AA)

THUNDERBIRD SERIES — (V-8) — Except for minor exterior trim changes. the 1962 Thunderbirds were identical to their 1961 counterparts. The new Landau hardtop featured a vinyl top as standard equipment. It was the first time such a top was offered on the Thunderbird line. Also new for 1962, was the Sports Roadster. In an attempt to bring back the sporty appearance of the old two-seat T-Birds, Ford offered the Thunderbird convertible with a fiberglass tonneau cover for the back seats. The cover included two streamlined headrests, which contributed to a very sleek looking car when the top was down. The 390 cid "M" series engine was a new option for '62.

THUNDERBIRD I.D. NUMBERS: Thunderbird models began with the number '2,' assembly plant code 'Y' (Wixom), body type code, engine type code 'Z' and, finally, the unit's production number beginning at 100001 and going up.

THUNDERBIRD SERIES

Model Number	Body/Style Number	Body Type & Seating	Factory Price	Shipping Weight	Production Total
Z	83	2-dr HT Cpe-6P	4321	4132	68,127
Z	83	2-dr Lan HT Cpe-4P	4398	4144	Note 1
Z	85	2-dr Conv-4P	4788	4370	9,844
Z	85	2-dr Spt Rds Conv	5439	4471	Note 1

NOTE 1: Total series output was 78,011 units. Ford does not indicate the number of Landau hardtops and Sports Roadsters produced, separate from the standard hardtops and convertibles. Therefore, all production figures are total production of each.

NOTE 2: The Body/Style Number for the Sports Roadster was "85" for the first 558 units at which time it was changed to "89" for the balance of that model year production. The change to "89" took place with serial number 2Y 89 Z 127027. The last "85" Sports Roadster serial number was 2Y 85 Z 114640.

1962 ENGINES

FALCON SIX-CYLINDER: Overhead valves. Cast iron block. Displacement: 144 cid. Bore and stroke: 3.50 x 2.50 inches. Compression ratio: 8.7:1. Brake hp: 85 at 4200 rpm. Carburetion: Holley one-barrel. Seven main bearings. Serial number code "S."

FALCON 170 SIX-CYLINDER: Overhead valves. Cast iron block. Displacement: 170 cid. Bore and stroke: 3.50 x 2.94 inches. Compression ratio: 8.7:1. Brake hp: 101 at 4400 rpm. Carburetor: Holley one-barrel. Seven main bearings. Serial number code "U."

FORD SIX-CYLINDER: Overhead valves. Cast iron block. Displacement: 223 cid. Bore and stroke: 3.62 x 3.60 inches. Compression ratio: 8.4:1. Brake hp: 138 at 4200 rpm. Carburetion: Holley one-barrel. Four main bearings. Serial number code "V."

FAIRLANE V-8: Overhead valves. Cast iron block. Displacement: 221 cid. Bore and stroke: 3.50 x 2.87 inches. Compression ratio: 8.7:1. Brake hp: 145 at 4400 rpm. Carburetion: Holley two-barrel. Five main bearings. Serial number code "L."

FORD V-8: Overhead valves. Cast iron block. Displacement: 292 cid. Bore and stroke: 3.75 x 3.30 inches. Compression ratio: 8.8:1. Brake hp: 170 at 4200 rpm. Carburetion: Holley two-barrel. Five main bearings. Serial number code "W."

INTERCEPTOR V-8: Overhead valves. Cast Iron block. Displacement: 352 cid. Bore and stroke: 4.00 x 3.50 inches. Compression ratio: 8.9:1. Brake hp: 220 at 4300 rpm. Carburetion: Holley two-barrel. Five main bearings. Serial number code "X."

INTERCEPTOR 390 V-8: Overhead valves. Cast iron block. Displacement: 390 cid. Bore and stroke: 4.05 x 3.78 inches. Compression ratio: 9.6:1. Brake hp: 300 at 4600 rpm. Carburetion: Holley four-barrel. Five main bearings. Serial number code "Z."

THUNDERBIRD 390 V-8: Overhead valves. Cast iron block. Displacement: 390 cid. Bore and stroke: 4.05 x 3.78 inches. Compression ratio: 10.5:1. Brake hp: 340 at 5000 rpm. Carburetion: Three Holley two-barrels. Five main bearings. Serial number code "M."

THUNDERBIRD 406 V-8: Overhead valves. Cast iron block. Displacement: 406 cid. Bore and stroke: 4.13 x 3.78 inches. Compression ratio: 11.4:1. Brake hp: 385 at 5800 rpm. Carburetion: Holley four-barrel. Five main bearings. Serial number code "B."

THUNDERBIRD SPECIAL 406 V-8: Overhead valves. Cast iron block. Displacement: 406 cid. Bore and stroke: 4.13 x 3.78 inches. Compression ratio: 11.3:1. Brake hp: 405 at 4800 rpm. Carburetion: Three Holley two-barrels. Five main bearings. Serial number code "G."

CHASSIS FEATURES: Wheelbase: (Falcon) 109.5 inches; (Fairlane) 115.5 inches; (Thunderbird) 113 inches; (all others) 119 inches. Overall length: (Falcon station wagons) 189 inches; (other Falcons) 181.1 inches; (Fairlanes) 197.6 inches; (all Fords) 209.3 inches; (Thunderbird) 205 inches. Tires: (Fairlane Six and Falcon station wagons) 6.50 x 13; (Falcons) 6.00 x 13; (Fairlane V-8) 7.00 x 14; (Fairlane '260' V-8) 7.00 x 13; (Ford station wagons) 8.00 x 14; (other Fords) 7.50 x 14.

FALCON CONVENIENCE OPTIONS: Back-up lights ($11). Heavy-duty battery ($8). Squire bucket seats and console ($120). Crankcase ventilation system ($6). Deluxe trim package ($87). Engine, 170 cid 101 hp ($38). Tinted glass ($27). Windshield tinted glass ($13). Station wagons luggage rack ($39). Two-tone paint ($19). Push-button radio and antenna ($59). Safety Equipment, including padded dash and front visors ($22). Seat safety belts ($21). Electric tailgate windows ($30). Automatic transmission ($163). Vinyl trim for sedan (Deluxe trim package required) ($25). Wheelcovers ($16). Windshield washer ($14). Electric windshield wiper ($10).

FORD CONVENIENCE OPTIONS: Polar Aire air-conditioning with eight-cylinder ($271). Select Aire air-conditioning with eight-cylinder ($360). Back-up lights, standard Galaxie 500 ($11). Heavy-duty battery, 70-amp. ($8). Crankcase ventilation system ($6). Equa-Lock differential ($39). Electric clock, standard Galaxie 500 ($15). Re-circulating heater and defroster ($28 deduct option). Chrome luggage rack ($39). Four-way manual seat ($17). Rocker panel molding ($16). Padded dash and visors ($24). Two-tone paint ($22). Power brakes ($43). Power seat ($64). Power steering ($82). Power tailgate window ($32). Front and rear power windows ($102). Push-button radio and antenna ($59). Front seat belts ($21). Tinted glass ($40). Tinted windshield ($22). Cruise-O-Matic transmission ($212). Ford-O-Matic with six-cylinder ($180). Ford-O-Matic with V-8 ($190). Overdrive transmission ($108). Four-speed manual transmission 375 hp or 401 hp V-8 required ($188). Vinyl trim, Galaxie 500 except convertible ($26). Deluxe wheelcovers ($26). Wheelcovers ($19). Windshield washer and wipers, two-speed ($20).

THUNDERBIRD CONVENIENCE OPTIONS: Radio and antenna ($113). Engine, 340 hp Tri-carb V-8 ($242). Select Air air-conditioning ($415). Tinted glass ($43). Rayon white sidewall tires, 8.00 x 14 ($42). Nylon white sidewall tires, 8.00 x 14 ($70). Power windows ($106). Four-way power seat, driver or passenger ($92). Outside rearview mirror, ($14). Windshield washers ($14). Rear fender shields ($27). Front seat belts ($23). Seat bolsters and inserts, leather ($106). Heavy-duty battery, 70-amp ($8). Two-tone paint ($26). Chrome wire wheels ($373).

HISTORICAL FOOTNOTES: The 1962 Falcon was introduced Sept. 29, 1961. The 1962 Galaxie and station wagon lines appeared the same day. The new Thunderbirds were introduced Oct. 12, 1961. The Fairlane series did not debut until Nov. 16, 1961. Ford announced the introduction of the first transistorized ignition system, for production cars, in March, 1962. A total of 30,216 Fairlanes had the 260 cid V-8 installed. A total of 722,647 Galaxies, 386,192 Fairlanes, 381,559 Falcons and 75,536 Thunderbirds were built this year, second only to the record production since 1955. Midyear models included the Galaxie 500/XL hardtop and convertible, the Fairlane 500 Sports Sedan and the Falcon Sports Futura. Lee A. Iacocca was vice president and general manager of the Ford Div. again this year. In a historic move, Ford built 10 Galaxie "factory lightweight" drag racing cars late in model year 1962.

1963 FORD

1963 FORDS — OVERVIEW — In 1963, for the fifth year in a row, the full-size Ford line was completely restyled. As in 1962, the sides were devoid of any sculpture lines, except for the beltline feature line. The model designation was carried in script on the fender immediately behind the front wheel opening. Once again, the taillights were large round units mounted at the top of the rear fenders, with a stamped aluminum escutcheon panel being used on the Galaxie 500 series. The model designation was spelled out in block letters across the trunk lid. The grille was a full width aluminum stamping, again carrying a horizontal grid, and featuring a large Ford crest in the center, which was actually the hood release. The word FORD was spelled out in block letters across the front of the hood. For 1963, the famous

small-block 260 cid and 289 cid engines replaced the old 292 cid Y-block, which had been in continuous production since 1956 as the standard V-8. Also, with the other car makers continuing to escalate the horsepower race, Ford introduced the most powerful engines in its history; the 410 hp and 425 hp 427 cid big-blocks.

FORD 300 SERIES — (ALL ENGINES) — The Ford 300 was the base trim level for 1963 and included chrome moldings around the windshield and rear window, two sun visors, a chrome horn ring, armrests on all doors, and no chrome side trim.

FORD 300 SIX I.D. NUMBERS: Ford 300, six-cylinder models began with the number '3,' followed by the assembly plant code, engine designation 'V' and, finally, the unit's production number, according to the final assembly location. Each plant began at 100001 and went up.

FORD 300 SIX SERIES

Model Number	Body/Style Number	Body Type & Seating	Factory Price	Shipping Weight	Production Total
V	54	4-dr Sed-6P	2378	3645	Note 1
V	53	2-dr Sed-6P	2324	3565	Note 1

NOTE 1: See Ford 300 V-8 Series listing. Production was counted by series and body only. No engine breakouts.

FORD 300 V-8 SERIES I.D. NUMBERS: Ford 300 V-8 models began with the number '3,' followed by the assembly plant code, body type code, engine designation code and, finally, the unit's production number, according to the final assembly location. Each plant began at 100001 and went up.

FORD 300 SERIES

Model Number	Body/Style Number	Body Type & Seating	Factory Price	Shipping Weight	Production Total
NA	54	4-dr Sed-6P	2387	3640	44,142
NA	53	2-dr Sed-6P	2433	3560	26,010

PRODUCTION NOTE: Total series output was 70,152 units. Ford does not indicate the number of each model produced with sixes or V-8s. Therefore, all production figures given above are total production of each body style with both engines.

GALAXIE SERIES — (ALL ENGINES) — The Galaxie was the intermediate trim level for 1963 and included all the 300 series trim, plus a single chrome strip running horizontally along the lower bodysides and two chrome fender ornaments on the front fenders.

GALAXIE SIX SERIES I.D. NUMBERS: Galaxie, six-cylinder models used the same serial number sequence as the '300' series.

GALAXIE SIX SERIES

Model Number	Body/Style Number	Body Type & Seating	Factory Price	Shipping Weight	Production Total
V	52	4-dr Sed-6P	2507	3665	Note 1
V	51	2-dr Sed-6P	2453	3575	Note 1

NOTE 1: See Galaxie V-8 Series listing. Production was counted by series and body only. No engine breakouts.

GALAXIE V-8 SERIES I.D. NUMBERS: Galaxie V-8 models used the same serial number sequence as the '300' series.

GALAXIE V-8 SERIES

Model Number	Body/Style Number	Body Type & Seating	Factory Price	Shipping Weight	Production Total
NA	52	4-dr Sed-6P	2616	3660	82,419
NA	51	2-dr Sed-6P	2562	3850	30,335

PRODUCTION NOTE: Total series output was 112,754 units. Ford does not indicate the number of each model produced with sixes or V-8s. Therefore, all production figures given above are total production of each body style with both engines.

GALAXIE 500 SERIES — (ALL ENGINES) — The Galaxie 500 Series was the top trim level for 1963, and included chrome 'A' pillar moldings, chrome window moldings, two horizontal chrome strips on the side: one at the feature line and another, shorter one, beginning at the front of the front door and going to the back of the car, where it swept up and merged with the upper strip. Between the two chrome pieces, just in front of the taillights, were six cast 'hash marks.'

GALAXIE 500 SIX SERIES I.D. NUMBERS: Galaxie 500, six-cylinder models used the same serial number sequence as the '300' and Galaxie Series.

GALAXIE 500 SIX SERIES

Model Number	Body/Style Number	Body Type & Seating	Factory Price	Shipping Weight	Production Total
V	62	4-dr Twn Sed-6P	2667	3685	Note 1
V	61	2-dr Clb Sed-6P	2613	3605	Note 1
V	64	4-dr Twn Vic-6P	2739	3700	Note 1
V	63	2-dr Clb Vic-6P	2674	3620	Note 1
V	66	2-dr FsBk Cpe-6P	2674	3620	Note 1
V	65	2-dr SL Conv-6P	2924	3775	Note 1

NOTE 1: See Galaxie 500 V-8 Series listing. Production was counted by series and body only. No engine breakouts.

GALAXIE 500 V-8 I.D. NUMBERS: Galaxie 500, V-8 models used the same serial number sequence as the '300' and Galaxie series.

GALAXIE 500 V-8 SERIES

Model Number	Body/Style Number	Body Type & Seating	Factory Price	Shipping Weight	Production Total
NA	62	4-dr Twn Sed-6P 2776		3680	205,722
NA	61	2-dr Clb Sed-6P 2722		3600	21,137
NA	64	4-dr Twn Vic-6P	2848	3695	26,558
NA	63	2-dr Clb Vic-6P	2783	3615	49,733
NA	66	2-dr FsBk Cpe-6P	2783	3615	100,500
NA	65	2-dr SL Conv-6P	3033	3770	36,876

PRODUCTION NOTE: Total series output was 440,526 units. Ford does not indicate the number of each model produced with sixes or V-8s. Therefore, all production figures given above are total production of each body style with both engines.

1963 Ford, Galaxie XL two-door convertible, V-8 (AA)

GALAXIE 500XL SERIES — (V-8) — Galaxie 500XL models used the same serial number sequence as the Galaxie and Galaxie 500 Series.

GALAXIE 500XL V-8 SERIES

Model Number	Body/style Number	Body Type & Seating	Factory Price	Shipping Weight	Production Total
NA	62	4-dr Twn Vic-5P	3333	3750	12,596
NA	67	2-dr Clb Vic-5P	3628	3670	29,713
NA	68	2-dr FsBk Cpe-5P	3268	3670	33,870
NA	69	2-dr SL Conv-5P	3518	3820	18,551

PRODUCTION NOTE: Total series output was 94,730 units.

STATION WAGON SERIES — (ALL ENGINES) — The Country Sedans were the base trim level station wagons for 1963, with the Country Squires being the top trim level. The trim paralleled the Galaxie and Galaxie 500 models of conventional cars.

STATION WAGON SIX SERIES I.D. NUMBERS: Station wagon six-cylinder models used the same serial number sequence as Galaxie and Galaxie 500 series of conventional cars.

STATION WAGON SIX SERIES

Model Number	Body/Style Number	Body Type & Seating	Factory Price	Shipping Weight	Production Total
V	72	4-dr Cty Sed-6P	2829	3990	Note 1
V	74	4-dr Cty Sed-9P	2933	4005	Note 1
V	76	4-dr Cty Sq-6P	3018	4005	Note 1
V	78	4-dr Cty Sq-9P	2933	4015	Note 1

NOTE 1: See Station wagon V-8 series listing. Production was counted by series and body only. No engine breakouts.

STATION WAGON V-8 SERIES I.D. NUMBERS: Station wagon V-8 models used the same serial number sequence as Galaxie and Galaxie 500 models of conventional cars.

STATION WAGON V-8 SERIES

Model Number	Body/Style Number	Body Type & Seating	Factory Price	Shipping Weight	Production Total
NA	72	4-dr Cty Sed-6P	2938	3985	64,954
NA	74	4-dr Cty Sed-9P	3042	4000	22,250
NA	76	4-dr Cty Sq-9P	3127	4000	19,922
NA	78	4-dr Cty Sq-9P	3197	4010	19,246

PRODUCTION NOTE: Total series output was 126,372 units. Ford does not indicate the number of each model produced with sixes or V-8s. Therefore, all production figures given above are total production of each body style with both engines.

1963 FAIRLANES — OVERVIEW — The Fairlane was a carryover from 1962, with some minor trim changes. Two new models were added to the lineup, however. They were the Fairlane 500 two-door hardtop and the Fairlane 500 Sport Coupe. With their pillarless styling, they added a sporty look to the otherwise conservative Fairlane lineup.

FAIRLANE SERIES — (ALL ENGINES) — The 1963 carried over from the 1962 model year, with very few changes in chrome trim. The addition of two-door hardtop models added a sporty touch to the conservative Fairlane lineup.

FAIRLANE SIX SERIES I.D. NUMBERS: Fairlane, six-cylinder models began with the number '3,' followed by the assembly plant code, body type code, engine designation "U" and, finally, the unit's production number, according to the final assembly location. Each plant began at 100001 and went up.

FAIRLANE SIX SERIES

Model Number	Body/Style Number	Body Type & Seating	Factory Price	Shipping Weight	Production Total
U	32	4-dr Sed-6P	2216	2855	Note 1
U	31	2-dr Sed-6P	2154	2815	Note 1
U	38	4-dr Ranch Wag-6P	2525	3195	Note 1

NOTE 1: See Fairlane V-8 Series listing. Production was counted by series and body only. No engine breakouts.

FAIRLANE V-8 SERIES I.D. NUMBERS: Fairlane, V-8 models began with the number '3', followed by the assembly plant code, body type code, engine designation code and, finally, the unit's production number, according to the final assembly location. Each plant began at 100001 and went up.

FAIRLANE V-8 SERIES

Model Number	Body/Style Number	Body Type & Seating	Factory Price	Shipping Weight	Production Total
NA	32	4-dr Sed-6P	2319	2987	44,454
NA	31	2-dr Sed-6P	2257	2924	28,984
NA	38	4-dr Ranch Wag-6P	2628	3327	24,006

PRODUCTION NOTE: Total series output was 97,444 units. Ford does not indicate the number of each model produced with sixes or V-8s. Therefore, all production figures given above are total production of each body style with both engines.

1963 Ford, Fairlane 500 four-door station wagon, V-8

FAIRLANE 500 SERIES — (ALL ENGINES) — The Fairlane 500 models were the top trim level of the line and included chrome window moldings, a chrome horn ring, armrests on all doors, a version of the 'Fairlane sweep' which very strongly resembled the chrome used on 1959 full-size Fairlane 500s, three chrome exhaust ports located on the rear fenders, just ahead of the taillights, and a stamped aluminum escutcheon panel between the taillights, with the Ford crest situated in the center, on the gasoline filler cap.

FAIRLANE 500 SIX SERIES I.D. NUMBERS: Fairlane 500, six-cylinder models used the same serial number sequence as the Fairlane models.

FAIRLANE 500 SIX I.D. NUMBERS: Fairlane 500, six-cylinder models used the same serial number sequence as the Fairlane models.

FAIRLANE 500 SIX SERIES

Model Number	Body/Style Number	Body Type & Seating	Factory Price	Shipping Weight	Production Total
U	42	4-dr Sed-6P	2304	2870	Note 1
U	41	2-dr Sed-6P	2242	2830	Note 1
U	43	2-dr HT Cpe-6P	2324	2850	Note 1
U	47	2-dr Spt Cpe-5P	2504	2870	Note 1
U	48	4-dr Ranch Wag-6P	2613	3210	Note 1
U	49	4-dr Squire-6P	2781	3220	Note 1

NOTE 1: See Fairlane V-8 Series listing. Production was counted by series and body only. No engine breakouts.

FAIRLANE 500 I.D. NUMBERS: Fairlane 500 V-8 models used the same serial number sequence as the Fairlane models.

FAIRLANE 500 SERIES

Model Number	Body/Style Number	Body Type & Seating	Factory Price	Shipping Weight	Production Total
NA	42	4-dr Sed-6P	2407	3002	103,175
NA	41	2-dr Sed-6P	2345	2962	34,764
NA	43	2-dr HT Cpe-6P	2427	2982	41,641
NA	47	2-dr Spt Cpe-5P	2607	3002	28,268
NA	48	4-dr Ranch Wag-6P	2716	3342	29,612
NA	49	4-dr Squire-6P 2884	3352	7,983	8,983

PRODUCTION NOTE: Total series output was 246,443 units, including 277 Fairlane Squires with optional bucket seat interiors. Ford does not indicate the number of each model produced with sixes or V-8s. Therefore, all production figures given above are total production of each body style with both engines.

1963 FALCONS — OVERVIEW — The Falcon line continued to use the body shell introduced in 1960, but was updated with a new convex grille featuring a horizontal grid, and more bold use of chrome. The big news in the Falcon line was the addition of the two-door hardtop and the sporty convertible. These two body styles were available in the Futura series and the new high-powered Sprint series. A team of specially prepared 1963 Falcon Sprint hardtops terrorized the European rally circuit, with some very un-Falconlike performances.

FALCON SERIES — (ALL ENGINES) — The Falcon continued to use the same body as in previous years and had a new convex grille with a horizontal grid pattern, chrome side trim, and slightly revised taillight lenses, with additional chrome around the inside of the lens. The Deluxe models of 1962 were replaced by the Futura models for 1963 and included the addition of a two-door hardtop and a convertible. They offered V-8 power for the first time in the series' history.

STANDARD SERIES — (ALL ENGINES) — Falcon standard series cars were the base trim level for 1963 and included chrome windshield and rear window moldings, two horns, two sun visors, armrests on the front doors only and a push button instead of a chrome horn ring.

STANDARD SERIES I.D. NUMBERS: Falcon standard series cars used the same serial number sequence as the full-size Fords and the Fairlane

STANDARD FALCON SERIES

Model Number	Body/Style Number	Body Type & Seating	Factory Price	Shipping Weight	Production Total
NA	02	4-dr Sed-6P	2047	2345	62,365
NA	01	2-dr Sed-6P	1985	2305	70,630

1963 Ford, Falcon Futura two-door convertible, 6-cyl (AA)

FUTURA SERIES — (ALL ENGINES) — The Futura series was the top trim level for 1963 and included a chrome horn ring; rear armrests and ashtrays; two horns; Futura wheelcovers instead of hubcaps; the round 'Futura' symbol on the top 'C' pillar; chrome side window moldings; chrome windshield and rear window moldings; a horizontal chrome strip between the taillights; and a horizontal arrow style chrome strip on the bodyside. The Sport Coupe and Sprint versions also included wire wheelcovers and bucket seats.

FUTURA I.D. NUMBERS: Futura models used the same serial number sequence as the full size Fords, Fairlane models and standard series Falcons.

FUTURA SERIES

Model Number	Body/Style Number	Body Type & Seating	Factory Price	Shipping Weight	Production Total
NA	16	4-dr Sed-6P	2165	2355	31,736
NA	19	2-dr Sed-6P	2116	2315	16,674
NA	17	2-dr Sed-5P	2237	2350	10,344
NA	18	2-dr HT Cpe-6P	2198	2455	17,524
NA	18	2-dr Spt HT-5P	2319	2490	10,972
NA	18	2-dr Sprint-5P	2603	2875	10,479
NA	15	2-dr Conv-6P	2470	2655	18,942
NA	15	2-dr Spt Conv-5P	2591	2690	12,250
NA	15	2-dr Sprint Conv-4P	2837	2998	4,602

PRODUCTION NOTE: Total series output was 265,518 units. Ford does not indicate the number of each model produced with sixes or V-8s. Therefore, all production figures given above are total production of each body style with both engines.

1963 THUNDERBIRDS — OVERVIEW — While using the same body as the 1961-1962 T-Birds, the 1963 model is the most easily recognizable of the entire series. The major difference in the 1963 model was a mid-body feature line which moves back, horizontally, from the front of the car and then dips down near the back of the front door. Three sets of five cast 'hash marks' are used on the side of the door, just ahead of the feature line dip. In January, 1963, a Limited Edition Thunderbird Landau was introduced and was available only with Maroon exterior color, white top, white steering wheel and white leather interior. This model is often referred to as the Monaco Edition, as it was introduced in Monaco, Morocco.

1963 Ford, Thunderbird two-door hardtop coupe, V-8

THUNDERBIRD SERIES — (V-8) — The 1963 Thunderbird continued to use the same body as the past two years. However, the new side feature stripe makes it the most easily recognizable of the three-year body style. A single exhaust system was included as standard equipment for the first and only time and a 390 cid/340 hp V-8 was again an option. It featured three two-barrel carburetors.

THUNDERBIRD I.D. NUMBERS: Thunderbird models began with number '3,' assembly plant code 'Y' (Wixom), body type code, engine type code 'M' or 'Y,' and, finally, the unit's production number, beginning at 100001 and going up.

THUNDERBIRD SERIES

Model Number	Body/Style Number	Body Type & Seating	Factory Price	Shipping Weight	Production Total
Y/M	83	2-dr HT Cpe-4P	4445	4195	42,806
Y/M	87	2-dr Lan HT-4P	4548	4320	14,139
Y/M	85	2-dr Conv-4P	4912	4205	5,913
Y/M	89	2-dr Spt Rds-4P	5563	4395	455

PRODUCTION NOTE: Total series output was 63,313 units.

1963 ENGINES

FALCON SIX-CYLINDER: Overhead valves. Cast iron block. Displacement: 144 cid. Bore and stroke: 3.50 x 2.50 Inches. Compression ratio: 8.7:1. Brake hp: 85 at 4200 rpm Carburetion: Holley single barrel. Seven main bearings. Serial number code S (export code 2).

FALCON/FAIRLANE 170 SIX-CYLINDER: Overhead valves. Cast iron block. Displacement: 170 cid. Bore and stroke: 3.50 x 2.94 inches. Compression ratio: 8.7:1. Brake hp: 101 at 4400 rpm. Carburetion: Holley one-barrel. Seven main bearings. Serial number code "U."(export code 4).

FORD SIX-CYLINDER: Overhead valves. Cast iron block. Displacement: 200 cid. Bore and stroke: 3.68 x 3.13 inches. Compression ratio: 8.7:1. Brake hp: 116 at 4400 rpm. Carburetion: one-barrel. Four main bearings. Serial number code "T."

FORD SIX-CYLINDER: Overhead valves. Cast iron block. Displacement: 223 cid. Bore and stroke: 3.62 x 3.60 inches. Compression ratio: 8.4:1. Brake hp: 138 at 4200 rpm. Carburetion: Holley one-barrel. Four main bearings. Serial number code "V." (export code 5; taxi code E.)

FAIRLANE V-8: Overhead valves. Cast iron block. Displacement: 221 cid. Bore and stroke: 3.75 x 330 inches. Compression ratio: 8.8:1. Brake hp: 145 at 4400 rpm. Carburetion: Holley two-barrel. Five main bearings. Serial number code "L." (export code 3).

CHALLENGER 260 V-8: Overhead valves. Cast iron block. Displacement: 260 cid. Bore and stroke: 3.80 x 2.87 inches. Compression ratio: 8.7:1. Brake hp: 164 at 4400 rpm. Carburetion: Holley two-barrel. Five main bearings. Serial number code "F." (export code 8).

CHALLENGER 289 V-8: Overhead valves. Cast iron block. Displacement: 289 cid. Bore and stroke: 3.00 x 2.87 inches. Compression ratio: 8.6:1. Brake hp: 195 at 4400 rpm. Carburetion: Holley two-barrel. Five main bearings. Serial number code "C."

HIGH PERFORMANCE CHALLENGER 289 V-8: Overhead valves. Cast iron block. Displacement: 289 cid. Bore and stroke: 3.00 x 2.87 inches. Compression ratio: 10.5:1. Brake hp: 271 at 6000 rpm. Carburetion: Holley four-barrel. Five main bearings. Serial number code "K."

INTERCEPTOR V-8: Overhead valves. Cast iron block. Displacement: 352 cid. Bore and stroke: 4.00 x 3.50 inches. Compression ratio: 8.9:1. Brake hp: 220 at 4300 rpm. Carburetion: Holley two-barrel. Five main bearings. Serial number code "X."

THUNDERBIRD V-8: Overhead valves. Cast iron block. Displacement: 390 cid. Bore and stroke: 4.05 x 3.78 inches. Compression ratio: 9.6:1. Brake hp: 300 at 4600 rpm. Carburetion: Holley four-barrel. Five main bearings. Serial number code "P." (export code 9)

THUNDERBIRD V-8: Overhead valves. Cast iron block. Displacement: 390 cid. Bore and stroke: 4.05 x 3.78 inches. Compression ratio: 9.6:1. Brake hp: 330 at 5000 rpm. Carburetion: Holley four-barrel. Five main bearings. Serial number code "Z."

THUNDERBIRD SPECIAL "SIX-BARREL" V-8: Overhead valves. Cast iron block. Displacement: 390 cid. Bore and stroke: 4.05 x 3.78 inches. Compression ratio: 10.5:1. Brake hp: 340 at 5000 rpm. Carburetion: three Holley two-barrels. Five main bearings. Serial number code "M."

THUNDERBIRD 406 V-8: Overhead valves. Cast iron block. Displacement: 406 cid. Bore and stroke: 4.13 x 3.78 inches. Compression ratio: 11.4:1. Brake hp: 385 at 5800 rpm. Carburetion: Holley four-barrel. Five main bearings. Serial number code "B."

THUNDERBIRD SPECIAL "SIX-BARREL" V-8: Overhead valves. Cast iron block. Displacement: 406 cid. Bore and stroke: 4.13 x 3.78 inches. Compression ratio: 11.4:1. Brake hp: 405 at 5800 rpm. Carburetion: three Holley two-barrels. Five main bearings. Serial number code "G."

THUNDERBIRD HIGH-PERFORMANCE V-8: Overhead valves. Cast iron block. Displacement: 427 cid. Bore and stroke: 4.23 x 3.78 inches. Compression ratio: 11.5:1. Brake hp: 410 at 5600 rpm. Carburetion: Holley four-barrel. Five main bearings. Serial number code "Q."

THUNDERBIRD HIGH-PERFORMANCE 8V V-8: Overhead valves. Cast iron block. Displacement: 427 cid. Bore and stroke: 4.23 x 3.78 inches. Compression ratio: 11.5:1. Brake hp: 425 at 6000 rpm. Carburetion: two Holley four-barrels. Five main bearings. Serial number code "R."

NOTE: Export engines have lower compression and less hp.

FORD CHASSIS FEATURES: Wheelbase: 119 inches. Overall length 209.0 inches. Tires: 7.50 x 14 four-ply tubeless blackwalls (8.00 x 14 four-ply tubeless blackwalls on station wagons).

FAIRLANE CHASSIS FEATURES: Wheelbase: 115.5 inches. Overall length: 197.6 inches (201.8 inches on station wagons). Tires: 6.50 x 13 four-ply blackwall tubeless (7.00 x 14 four-ply blackwall tubeless on station wagons).

FALCON CHASSIS FEATURES: Wheelbase: 109.5 inches. Overall length: 181.1 inches. Tires: 6.00 x 13 four-ply tubeless blackwall (6.50 x 13 four-ply tubeless on station wagons and convertibles).

THUNDERBIRD CHASSIS FEATURES: Wheelbase: 113 inches. Overall length: 205 inches. Tires: 8.00 x 14 four-ply tubeless whitewalls.

FORD OPTIONS: Popular '300' and Galaxie series option included the 289 cid V-8 engine ($109). Cruise-O-Matic automatic transmission ($212). Power steering ($81). Power brakes ($43). White sidewall tires ($33). Popular Galaxie 500 and Galaxie 500XL options included the 390 cid V-8 engine ($246). Cruise-0-Matic automatic transmission ($212). Four-speed manual transmission ($188). Power steering ($81). Power brakes ($43). Two-tone paint ($22). White sidewall tires ($33). Windshield washers ($20). Back-up lights ($10). Electric clock ($14). Radio ($58). AM/FM radio ($129). Popular station wagon options included power tailgate window ($32). Luggage rack ($45). Electric clock ($14). There were 758 Country Squires produced with the optional bucket seat interior at $141 extra. Popular Fairlane and Fairlane 500 options included the 260 cid engines ($103 or $154). Ford-O-Matic automatic transmission ($189). Four-speed manual transmission with V-8s ($188). AM radio ($58). Power steering ($81). Power tailgate window on station wagons ($32). Luggage rack on station wagons ($45). Two-tone paint ($22). White sidewall tires ($34). Padded dashboard and sun visors ($24). Popular Falcon options included the 170 cid six-cylinder engine ($437). The 260 cid V-8s ($158 or $196). Ford-O-Matic automatic transmission ($163). Four-speed manual transmission ($90 with six-cylinder or $188 with V-8). Power tailgate window on station wagons ($29). Two-tone paint ($19). AM radio ($58). White sidewall tires ($29). Back-up lights ($10). Deluxe trim package for sedans ($37). Popular Thunderbird options included power windows ($106). Power seats ($92). Passenger power seats ($92). AM/FM radio ($83). Tinted glass ($43). Windshield washers ($13). Wire wheels ($343).

HISTORICAL FOOTNOTES: The "Fairlane 500 Sports Coupe" was a two-door pillarless hardtop. The "Falcon Sprint" was a compact, high-performance V-8 powered Falcon. The "Galaxie Fastback" was a full-size two-door hardtop with more gently sloping roofline than conventional hardtop, to produce less wind resistance. Ford built 50 Galaxie "factory lightweight" race cars this year.

1964 FORD

1964 FORDS — OVERVIEW — As is the case in the previous six years, the 1964 Fords were totally restyled. This year it wasn't just the regular Ford which came under the stylist's brush, but the entire line from the compact Falcon to the prestigious Thunderbird. Engine choices remained virtually unchanged for 1964.

FORD CUSTOM SERIES — (ALL ENGINES) — Full-size Fords were completely revamped for 1964. They were recognizable as Ford products only because of their traditional large, round taillights. The grille carried a horizontal grid highlighted with three vertical ribs. The Ford name, in block letters, was seen on all models, but side trim differed considerably. A sheetmetal feature line began on the front fender at beltline level. It continued horizontally, to the rear of the car, and dipped down. A lower sheetmetal feature line began behind the front wheels and continued, horizontally, toward the rear of the car. There it swept upward and merged with the upper feature line. All models using optional, large displacement V-8s, carried the engine designation symbol on the lower front fender. The Custom series was the base trim level. It included chrome windshield and rear window moldings; two sun visors, a chrome horn ring, armrests on all doors and three cast 'stripes' on the front fenders, just behind the headlights.

CUSTOM SIX SERIES I.D. NUMBERS: Custom six-cylinder models began with the numbers '4,' followed by the assembly plant code, engine designation 'V' and, finally, the unit's production number, according to the final assembly location. Each plant began at 100001 and went up.

CUSTOM SIX SERIES

Model Number	Body/Style Number	Body Type & Seating	Factory Price	Shipping Weight	Production Total
V	54	4-dr Sed-6P	2404	3621	Note 1
V	53	2-dr Sed-6P	2350	3521	Note 1

NOTE 1: See production note below.

CUSTOM V-8 SERIES I.D. NUMBERS: Custom V-8 models began with the number '4,' followed by the assembly plant code, body type code. engine designation code and, finally, the unit's production number, according to the final assembly location. Each plant began at 100001 and went up.

CUSTOM V-8 SERIES

Model Number	Body/Style Number	Body Type & Seating	Factory Price	Shipping Weight	Production Total
NA	54	4-dr Sed-6P	2513	3617	57,964
NA	53	2-dr Sed-6p	2459	3527	41,359

PRODUCTION NOTE: Total series output was 99,323 units. Ford does not indicate the number of each model produced with sixes or V-8s. Therefore, all production figures given above are total production of each body style with both engines.

CUSTOM 500 SERIES — (ALL ENGINES) — The Custom 500 was the upper trim level of the base-line Custom Series and included chrome windshield and rear window moldings; nylon carpeting (instead of the rubber mats used in the Custom models); armrests with ashtrays on all doors; two sun visors and all trim used in the Custom models, plus a single horizontal chrome strip on the exterior bodyside.

CUSTOM 500 SIX SERIES I.D. NUMBERS: Custom 500, six-cylinder models used the same serial number sequence as the Custom models.

CUSTOM 500 SERIES

Model Number	Body/Style Number	Body Type & Seating	Factory Price	Shipping Weight	Production Total
V	52	4-dr Sed-6P	2507	3661	Note 1
V	51	2-dr Sed-6P	2453	3561	Note 1

NOTE 1: See production note below.

CUSTOM 500 V-8 SERIES I.D. NUMBERS: Custom 500, V-8 models used the same serial number sequence as the Custom models

CUSTOM 500 V-8 SERIES

Model Number	Body/Style Number	Body Type & Seating	Factory Price	Shipping Weight	Production Total
NA	52	4-dr Sed-6P	2616	3657	68,828
NA	51	2-dr Sed-6P	2562	3557	20,619

PRODUCTION NOTE: Total series output was 89,447 units. Ford does not indicate the number of each model produced with sixes or V-8s. Therefore, all production figures given above are total production of each body style with both engines.

GALAXIE 500 SERIES — (ALL ENGINES) — The Galaxie 500 was the intermediate trim level for 1964 and included all Custom trim, plus chrome fendertop ornamentation, chrome window frames, the Ford crest on the roof 'C' pillar and a full-length chrome strip (which split at the rear of the front doors and included an aluminum insert forward of that point). 'Galaxie 500', in script, was included in the aluminum insert, at the front of the stripe. A stamped aluminum insert also highlighted the rear treatment and included 'Galaxie 500' in script, on the right side of the insert. Two-tone vinyl trim was used on the side of the doors and on the seats.

GALAXIE 500 SIX SERIES I.D. NUMBERS: Galaxie 500, six-cylinder models used the same serial number sequence as the Custom series

GALAXIE SIX SERIES

Model Number	Body/Style Number	Body Type & Seating	Factory Price	Shipping Weight	Production Total
V	62	4-dr Twn Sed-6P	2667	3676	Note 1
V	61	2-dr Clb Sed-6P	2613	3576	Note 1
V	64	4-dr Twn Vic-6P	2739	3691	Note 1
V	66	2-dr Clb Vic-6P	2674	3586	Note 1
V	65	2-dr SL Conv-6P	2936	3761	Note 1

NOTE 1: See production note below.

GALAXIE 500 V-8 SERIES I.D. NUMBERS: Galaxie 500, V-8 models used the same serial number sequence as the Custom series

GALAXIE 500 V-8 SERIES

Model Number	Body/Style Number	Body Type & Seating	Factory Price	Shipping Weight	Production Total
NA	62	4-dr Twn Sed-6P	2776	3672	198,805
NA	61	2-dr Clb Sed-6P	2722	3572	13,041
NA	64	4-dr Twn Vic-6P	2848	3687	49,242
NA	66	2-dr Clb Vic-5P	2783	3582	206,998
NA	65	2-dr SL Conv-5P	3045	3757	37,311

PRODUCTION NOTE: Total series output was 505,397 units. Ford does not indicate the number of each model produced with sixes or V-8s. Therefore, all production figures given above are total production of each body style with both engines.

GALAXIE 500XL SERIES — (V-8) — Galaxie 500XL was the top trim level for 1964 and included all the trim features of the Galaxie models, plus bucket seats and floor-mounted transmission shifter; polished door trim panels; dual-lens courtesy/warning lights in the doors; rear reading lights in hardtops and Galaxie 500XL badges on the body exterior. The 289 cid, 195 hp V-8 engine was standard on all 'XLs.'

GALAXIE 500 XL I.D. NUMBERS: Galaxie 500 XLs used the same serial number sequence as the Custom and Galaxie series

GALAXIE SERIES

Model Number	Body/Style Number	Body Type & Seating	Factory Price	Shipping Weight	Production Total
NA	60	4-dr Twn Vic-5P	3287	3722	14,661
NA	68	2-dr Clb Vic-5P	3222	3622	58,306
NA	69	2-dr Conv-5P	3484	3787	15,169

PRODUCTION NOTE: Total series output was 88,136 units.

1964 Ford, Country Squire, four-door station wagon, V-8

STATION WAGON SERIES — (ALL ENGINES) — The Country Sedans were the base trim level station wagons for 1964, with the Country Squires being the top trim level. The trim paralleled the Galaxie 500 and Galaxie 500XL models of conventional cars.

STATION WAGON SIX SERIES I.D. NUMBERS: Station wagon, six-cylinder models used the same serial number sequence as Custom and Galaxie 500 series of conventional cars.

STATION WAGON SIX SERIES

Model Number	Body/Style Number	Body Type & Seating	Factory Price	Shipping Weight	Production Total
V	72	4-dr Cty Sed-6P	2829	3975	Note 1
V	74	4-dr Cty Sed-9P	2933	3985	Note 1
V	76	4-dr Cty Sq-6P	3018	3990	Note 1
V	78	4-dr Cty Sq-9P	3088	4000	Note 1

NOTE 1: See production note below.

STATION WAGON V-8 SERIES I.D. NUMBERS: Station Wagon, V-8 models used the same serial number sequence as Custom and Galaxie 500 models of conventional cars.

STATION WAGON V-8 SERIES

Model Number	Body/Style Number	Body Type & Seating	Factory Price	Shipping Weight	Production Total
NA	72	4-dr Cty Sed-6P	2938	3971	68,578
NA	74	4-dr Cty Sed-9P	3042	3981	25,661
NA	76	4-dr Cty Sq-6P	3127	3986	23,570
NA	78	4-dr Cty Sq-9P	3197	3996	23,120

PRODUCTION NOTE: Total series output was 140,929 units. Ford does not indicate the number of each model produced with sixes or V-8s. Therefore, all production figures given above are total production of each body style with both engines.

FAIRLANE SERIES — (ALL ENGINES) — The 1964 Fairlane styling featured new sheetmetal for the bodysides and rear, which seemed to add to the Fairlane's 'Total Performance' image. The rear fenders featured a smoother top than 1963, with a complete absence of fins. The sides were sculptured into a convex shape, which flowed forward from the sides of the taillights and terminated in a chrome scoop. The grille carried the familiar horizontal grid with thin vertical dividers.

FAIRLANE V-8 SERIES I.D. NUMBERS: Fairlane V-8 models began with number '4,' followed by the assembly plant code, body type code, engine designation code and. finally, the unit's production number, according to the final assembly location. Each plant began at 100001 and went up.

FAIRLANE SIX SERIES

Model Number	Body/Style Number	Body Type & Seating	Factory Price	Shipping Weight	Production Total
U/T	32	4-dr Sed-6P	2224	2828	Note 1
U/T	31	2-dr Sed-6P	2183	2788	Note 1
U/T	38	2-dr Sta Wag-6P	2520	3223	Note 1

NOTE 1: See production note below.

NOTE 2: The station wagon was called the Ranch wagon.

FAIRLANE SIX SERIES I.D. NUMBERS: Fairlane, six-cylinder models began with the number '4,' followed by the assembly plant code, body type code, engine designation 'U' or 'T' and, finally, the unit's production number, according to the final assembly location. Each plant began at 100001 and went up.

FAIRLANE V-8 SERIES

Model Number	Body/Style Number	Body Type & Seating	Factory Price	Shipping Weight	Production Total
NA	32	4-dr Sed-6P	2324	2962	36,693
NA	31	2-dr Sed-6P	2283	2922	20,421
NA	38	2-dr Sta Wag-6P	2620	3357	20,980

PRODUCTION NOTE: Total series output was 78,094 units. Ford does not indicate the number of each model produced with sixes or V-8s. Therefore, all production figures given above are total production of each body style with both engines.

1964 Ford Fairlane 500 two-door hardtop Sports Coupe, V-8

FAIRLANE 500 SERIES — (ALL ENGINES) — The Fairlane 500 models were the top trim level of the line and included chrome window moldings; a chrome horn ring; armrests on all doors; a twin-spear side molding running the full length of the body, (with an accent color of red, black or white, between the spears). In addition, chrome, fendertop ornaments and the Ford crest appeared on the 'C' pillar of the more Deluxe model of the series. Fairlane 500 models also had carpeting.

FAIRLANE 500 SIX SERIES I.D. NUMBERS: Fairlane 500, six-cylinder models used the same serial number sequence as the Fairlane models

FAIRLANE 500 SIX SERIES

Model Number	Body/Style Number	Body Type & Seating	Factory Price	Shipping Weight	Production Total
U/T	42	4-dr Twn Sed-6P	2306	2843	Note 1
U/T	41	2-dr Clb Sed-6P	2265	2813	Note 1
U/T	43	2-dr HT Cpe-6P	2330	2858	Note 1
U/T	47	2-dr HT Spt Cpe-5P	2491	2878	Note 1
U/T	48	4-dr Cus Sta Wag	2601	3243	Note 1

NOTE 1: See production note below.

FAIRLANE 500 V-8 SERIES I.D. NUMBERS: Fairlane 500, V-8 models used the same serial number sequence as the Fairlane models

FAIRLANE 500 V-8 SERIES

Model Number	Body/Style Number	Body Type & Seating	Factory Price	Shipping Weight	Production Total
NA	42	4-dr Twn Sed-6P	2406	297	86,919
NA	41	2-dr Clb Sed-6P	2365	2913	23,477
NA	43	2-dr HT Cpe-6P	2430	2992	42,733
NA	47	2-dr HT Spt Cpe-5P	2591	3012	12,431
NA	48	4-dr Cus Sta Wag	2701	3377	24,962

PRODUCTION NOTE: Total series output was 199,522 units. Ford does not indicate the number of each model produced with sixes or V-8s. Therefore, all production figures given above are total production of each body style with both engines.

1964 Ford, Falcon Sprint two-door hardtop coupe, V-8

FALCON SERIES — (ALL ENGINES) — The 1964 Falcons reflected the 'Total Performance' image in their new styling. A more aggressive. angled grille lead a completely restyled body. As in 1963, the base trim level was the standard series, and the top trim level was the Futura. The highly styled sculptured bodysides gave the 1964 Falcons a racy appearance and added rigidity to the sheetmetal. A convex feature line began on the front fenders, but sloped slightly and increased in width gradually, until it met the taillights. The word Ford was spelled out across the hood in block letters and Falcon was spelled out in block letters between the taillights. The new grille featured a rectangular design that was angularly recessed and complemented the side profile. As in past years, the Falcons continued to use single headlamps. Standard Falcon cars were the base trim level for 1964. They included chrome windshield and rear window moldings, twin horns, two sun visors, armrests on the front doors only and a horn button instead of a chrome horn ring.

STANDARD FALCONS SERIES I.D. NUMBERS — (ALL ENGINES) — Standard series Falcons used the same serial number sequence as the full-size Fords and the Fairlane line.

STANDARD FALCON SERIES

Model Number	Body/Style Number	Body Type & Seating	Factory Price	Shipping Weight	Production Total
NA	02	4-dr Sed-6P	2040	2400	28,411
NA	01	2-dr Sed-6P	1985	2365	36,441

FALCON FUTURA SERIES — (ALL ENGINES) — The Futura series was the top trim level for 1964 and included a chrome horn ring; rear armrests with ashtrays; twin horns; Futura wheelcovers (instead of hubcaps); chrome hood ornament; Futura symbol on the front fender; chrome side window moldings: chrome windshield and rear window moldings; two horizontal sloping chrome strips on the bodyside and four cast hash marks on the rear fender in front of the taillights. The Sprint versions of the Futura hardtop and convertible also featured a V-8 engine, bucket seats and wire wheelcovers.

FALCON FUTURA I.D. NUMBERS: Futura models used the same serial number sequence as the full-size Fords, Fairlanes and standard series Falcons

Standard Catalog of American Cars

FALCON FUTURA SERIES

Model Number	Body/Style Number	Body Type & Seating	Factory Price	Shipping Weight	Production Total
NA	16	4-dr Sed-6P	2165	2410	38,032
NA	19	2-dr Sed-6P	2116	2375	16,261
NA	17	2-dr Sed-6P	2237	2350	212
NA	17	2-dr HT Cpe-6P	2198	2515	32,608
NA	11	2-dr Spt HT-5P	2314	2545	8,322
NA	15	2-dr Conv-6P	2470	2710	13,220
NA	12	2-dr Spt Conv-5P	2586	2735	2,980
NA	13	2-dr Sprint HT-5P	2425	2813	13,830
NA	14	2-dr Sprint Conv-5P	2660	3008	4,278

PRODUCTION NOTE: Total series output was 130,103 units. This figure includes 285 Sprint hardtops built without consoles, 626 Sprint convertibles built with bench seats. Ford does not indicate the number of each model produced with sixes or V-8s. Therefore, all production figures given above are total production of each body style with both engines. The Sprint models came only with V-8 engines and 5-passenger (bucket) seating.

FALCON STATION WAGON SERIES — (ALL ENGINES) — Falcon station wagons became a separate series for the first time in 1964 and included the base standard series, the intermediate Deluxe series and the top-line Squire wagon.

FALCON STATION WAGON I.D. NUMBERS: Falcon station wagons used the same serial number sequence as the full-size Fords, Fairlanes and Falcon sedans.

FALCON STATION WAGON SERIES

Model Number	Body/Style Number	Body Type & Seating	Factory Price	Shipping Weight	Production Total
NA	22	4-dr Sta Wag-6P	2349	2695	17,779
NA	21	2-dr Sta Wag-6P	2315	2660	6,034
NA	24	4-dr DeL Sta Wag	2435	2715	20,697
NA	26	4-dr Sq Wag-6P	2611	2720	6,766

PRODUCTION NOTE: Total series output was 51,276 units. Ford does not indicate the number of each model produced with sixes or V-8s. Therefore, all production figures given above are total production of each body style with both engines.

1964 Ford, Thunderbird two-door convertible

THUNDERBIRD SERIES — (V-8) — The 1964 Thunderbirds were also completely restyled and featured longer hoods and shorter roof lines than previous offerings. The side panels were highly sculptured. They had mirror-image feature lines at the beltline and lower bodyside. The front end was more aggressive and featured a larger power dome (scoop) on the hood. The headlights were spaced farther apart than in previous years. The rear of the 1964 T-Bird featured rectangular taillights set within a massive bumper. The Thunderbird name, in script, was located just behind the front wheels on the front fenders and Thunderbird, in block letters, was spaced along the front of the hood. The factory-built Sports Roadster was dropped, but dealers continued to add this kit, as an option, on a few 1964 Thunderbirds.

THUNDERBIRD I.D. NUMBERS: Thunderbird models began with the number '4', assembly plant code 'Y' (Wixom), body type code. engine type code 'Z' and, finally, the unit's production number, beginning at 100001 and going up.

THUNDERBIRD SERIES

Model Number	Body/Style Number	Body Type & Seating	Factory Price	Shipping Weight	Production Total
Z	83	2-dr HT Cpe-4P	4486	4431	60,552
Z	87	2-dr Landau-4P	4589	4586	22,715
Z	85	2-dr Conv-4P	4853	4441	9,198

PRODUCTION NOTE: Total series output was 92,465 units.

1964 ENGINES

FALCON SIX-CYLINDER: Overhead valves. Cast iron block. Displacement: 144 cid. Bore and stroke: 3.50 x 2.50 inches. Compression ratio: 8.7:1. Brake hp: 85 at 4200 rpm. Carburetion: Holley one-barrel. Seven main bearings. Serial number code "S."

FALCON/FAIRLANE/MUSTANG SIX-CYLINDER: Overhead valves. Cast iron block. Displacement: 170 cid. Bore and stroke: 3.50 x 2.94 inches. Compression ratio: 8.7:1. Brake hp: 101 at 4400 rpm. Carburetion: Holley one-barrel. Seven main bearings. Serial number code "U."

MUSTANG SIX-CYLINDER: Overhead valves. Cast iron block. Displacement: 200 cid. Bore and stroke: 3.68 x 3.13 inches. Compression ratio: 8.7:1. Brake hp: 116 at 4400 rpm. Carburetion: Holley one-barrel. Seven main bearings. Serial number code "T."

FORD SIX-CYLINDER: Overhead valves. Cast iron block. Displacement: 223 cid. Bore and stroke: 3.62 x 3.60 inches. Compression ratio: 8.4:1. Brake hp: 138 at 4200 rpm. Carburetion: Holley one-barrel. Four main bearings. Serial number code "V."

V-8: Overhead valves. Cast iron block. Displacement: 260 cid. Bore and stroke: 3.80 x 2.87 inches. Compression ratio: 8.8:1. Brake hp: 164 at 4400 rpm. Carburetion: Holley two-barrel. Five main bearings. Serial number code "F."

CHALLENGER 289 V-8: Overhead valves. Cast iron block. Displacement: 289 cid. Bore and stroke: 4.00 x 2.87 inches. Compression ratio: 9.0:1. Brake hp: 195 at 4400 rpm. Carburetion: Holley two-barrel. Five main bearings. Serial number code "C."

CHALLENGER 289 FOUR-BARREL V-8: Overhead valves. Cast iron block. Displacement: 289 cid. Bore and stroke: 4.00 x 2.87 inches. Compression ratio: 9.8:1. Brake hp: 225 at 4800 rpm. Carburetion: Holley four-barrel. Five main bearings. Serial number code "A."

HIGH-PERFORMANCE CHALLENGER 289 V-8: Overhead valves. Cast iron block. Displacement: 289 cid. Bore and stroke: 4.00 x 2.87 inches. Compression ratio: 10.5:1. Brake hp: 271 at 6000 rpm. Carburetion: Holley four-barrel. Five main bearings. Serial number code "K."

INTERCEPTOR V-8: Overhead valves. Cast iron block. Displacement: 352 cid. Bore and stroke: 4.00 x 3.50 inches. Compression ratio: 9.3:1. Brake hp: 250 at 4400 rpm. Carburetion: Holley four-barrel. Five main bearings. Serial number code "X."

THUNDERBIRD V-8: Overhead valves. Cast iron block. Displacement: 390 cid. Bore and stroke: 3.05 x 3.78 inches. Compression ratio: 10.0:1. Brake hp: 300 at 4600 rpm. Carburetion: Holley four-barrel, Five main bearings. Serial number code "Z."

THUNDERBIRD POLICE SPECIAL V-8: Overhead valves. Cast iron block. Displacement: 390 cid. Bore and stroke: 4.05 x 3.78 inches. Compression ratio: 10.0:1. Brake hp: 330 at 5000 rpm. Carburetion: Holley four-barrel. Five main bearings. Serial number code "P."

THUNDERBIRD HIGH PERFORMANCE V-8: Overhead valves. Cast iron block. Displacement: 427 cid. Bore and stroke: 4.23 x 3.78 inches. Compression ratio: 11.5:1. Brake hp: 410 at 5600 rpm. Carburetion: Holley four-barrel. Five main bearings. Serial number code "Q."

THUNDERBIRD SUPER HIGH-PERFORMANCE V-8: Overhead valves. Cast iron block. Displacement: 427 cid. Bore and stroke: 4.23 x 3.78 inches. Compression ratio: 11.5:1. Brake hp: 425 at 6000 rpm. Carburetion: Two Holley four-barrels. Five main bearings. Serial number code "R."

CHASSIS FEATURES: Wheelbase: (Full-size Fords) 119 inches; (Fairlanes) 115.5 inches; (Falcons) 109.5 inches; (Thunderbirds) 113.2 inches. Overall length: (Full-size Fords) 209.9 inches; (Fairlane passenger models) 197.6 inches; (Fairlane station wagons) 201.8 inches; (Falcon Sprints) 181.1 inches; (Falcon passenger cars) 181.6 inches; (Falcon station wagons) 189 inches; (Thunderbirds) 205.4 inches. Tires: (Ford Custom) 7.00 x 14; (Ford station wagons) 8.00 x 14; (all other Fords) 7.50 x 14; (Fairlane passenger cars) 6.50 x 14); (Fairlane station wagons) 7.00 x 14; (Falcon Sprint) 6.50 x 13; (Falcon convertibles) 6.50 x 13; (Falcon station wagons) 6. 50 x 13; (regular Falcons) 6.00 x 13; (Thunderbird) 8.15 x 15.

FORD OPTIONS: Popular Custom and Galaxie series options included 288 cid V-8 engine ($109). 390 cid V-8 engine ($246). Cruise-O-Matic automatic transmission ($189 or $212). Four-speed manual transmission ($188). Power steering ($86). Power brakes ($43). Power windows ($102). Tinted windshield ($21). AM radio ($58). Vinyl roof on two-door Victorias ($75). Wheelcovers ($45). White sidewall tires ($33). Popular station wagon options included the 390 cid V-8 engine ($246). Cruise-O-Matic automatic transmission ($212). Power steering ($86). Power brakes ($43). Power tailgate window ($32). Luggage rack ($45). White sidewall tires ($33). Electric clock ($14). Radio ($58 for AM, $129 for AM/FM).

FAIRLANE OPTIONS: 260 cid V-8 engine ($100). The 289 cid V-8 engine ($145). 390 cid V-8. 427 cid V-8. Ford-0-Matic automatic transmission ($189). Cruise-0-Matic automatic transmission ($189). Four-speed manual transmissions with V-8 engines ($188). AM radio ($58). Power steering ($86). Power tailgate window on station wagons ($32). Luggage rack on station wagons ($45). Two-tone paint ($22). White sidewall tires ($33). Wheelcovers ($18). Vinyl roof on two-door hardtops ($75).

FALCON OPTIONS: 170 cid six-cylinder engine ($17). The 260 cid V-8 engine ($170). Ford-O-Matic automatic transmission ($177). Four-speed manual transmission: ($92 with six-cylinder; $188 with V-8). AM radio ($58). Two-tone paint ($19). White sidewall tires ($30). Back-up lights ($10). Deluxe trim package for standard sedans ($43). Popular Falcon station wagon options included all those for sedans, plus power tailgate window ($30).

THUNDERBIRD OPTIONS: Air conditioning ($415). Tinted windows ($43). Leather seats ($106). Power seats ($184). Power windows ($106). AM/FM radio ($83). White sidewall tires ($42). Fiberglass tonneau cover for convertibles ($269). Deluxe wheelcovers ($16).

HISTORICAL FOOTNOTES: The full-size Fords, Fairlanes and Falcons were introduced Sept. 27, 1963 and the Mustang appeared in dealer showrooms during April, 1964. Model year production peaked at 1,015,697 units. Calendar year production of 1,787,535 cars was recorded. Lee A. Iacocca was the chief executive officer of the company this year. Note also that Ford introduced the famous Fairlane Thunderbolt drag cars and also the single-overhead cam hemi-engine that Ford tried to use for NASCAR racing. It was disallowed due to insufficient number produced for homogolation.

1965 FORD

1965 FORDS — OVERVIEW — As well as several of the lines being completely restyled once again for 1965, the new 'Total Performance' Ford lineup represented five full car-lines, with 44 models, the widest choice of models in Ford Div.'s history. The 1965 full-size Fords were billed as the "Newest since 1949." Luxury and comfort were featured with the big Fords, which used rear coil springs for the first time, new interior styling. 'Silent Flow' ventilation systems were standard on four-door hardtops. In keeping with the new luxury image, the Galaxie 500 LTD interior trim option was offered for the first time, for two- and four-door hardtops. Completely restyled once again, the full-size Fords possessed incredibly clean styling with very sharp, square lines, and almost no curves. The new grille featured thin horizontal bars which followed the leading edge contour of the hood and were framed by the new vertical dual headlights. From the side, a single, horizontal feature line divided the less prominent beltline and lower body lines. As in 1964, all full-size Fords carried the engine designation symbol on the front fender behind the front wheel, for the larger, optional V-8 engines.

FORD CUSTOM SERIES — (ALL ENGINES) — The Custom series was the base trim level full-size Ford for 1965, and included chrome windshield and rear window moldings, two sun visors, a chrome horn ring, armrests on all doors, and the "Custom" name on the front fender. The taillights were round lenses in a rectangular housing. The Ford name appeared in block letters across the front of the hood and on the vertical section of the trunk lid.

CUSTOM I.D. NUMBERS: (Six-cylinder models) Custom, six-cylinder models began with the number "5," followed by the assembly plant code, engine designation code "V," and finally, the unit's production number, according to the final assembly location. Each plant began at 100001 and went up.

CUSTOM SIX SERIES

Model Number	Body/Style Number	Body Type & Seating	Factory Price	Shipping Weight	Production Total
V	54	4-dr Sed-6P	2366	3350	Note 1
V	62	2-dr Sed-6P	2313	3278	Note 1

NOTE 1: See Deluxe Series V-8 listing.

CUSTOM I.D. NUMBERS: (V-8 models) Custom, V-8 model began with the number "5," followed by the assembly plant code, body type code, engine designation code, and finally, the unit's production number, according to the final assembly location. Each plant began at 100001 and went up.

CUSTOM EIGHT SERIES

Model Number	Body/Style Number	Body Type & Seating	Factory Price	Shipping Weight	Production Total
NA	54	4-dr Sed-6P	2472	3400	96,393
NA	62	2-dr Sed-6P	2420	3328	49,034

PRODUCTION NOTE: Total series output was 145,427 units. Ford does not indicate the number of each model produced with six and V-8 engines. Therefore, all production figures are total production of each body style.

CUSTOM 500 SERIES — (ALL ENGINES) — The Custom 500 was the upper trim level of the base-line Custom series, and included chrome windshield and rear window moldings, nylon carpeting instead of the rubber mats used in the Custom models, armrests, with ashtrays, on a doors, two sun visors, and all the trim used in the Custom models, plus a short horizontal chrome strip along the front fender and front door.

CUSTOM 500 I.D. NUMBERS: (Six-cylinder models) Custom 500, six-cylinder model used the same serial number sequence as the Custom models.

CUSTOM 500 SIX SERIES

Model Number	Body/Style Number	Body Type & Seating	Factory Price	Shipping Weight	Production Total
V	54B	4-dr Sed-6P	2467	3380	Note 1
V	62B	2-dr Sed-6P	2414	3308	Note 1

NOTE 1: See Custom 500 V-8 listing.

CUSTOM 500 I.D. NUMBERS: (V-8 models) Custom 500, V-8 models used the same serial number sequence as the Custom models.

CUSTOM 500 V-8 SERIES

Model Number	Body/Style Number	Body Type & Seating	Factory Price	Shipping Weight	Production Total
NA	54B	4-dr Sed-6P	2573	3430	71,727
NA	62B	2-dr Sed-6P	2520	3358	19,603

PRODUCTION NOTE: Total series output was 91,330 units. Ford does not indicate the number of each model produced with six and V-8 engines. Therefore, all production figures are total production of each body style.

GALAXIE 500 SERIES (ALL ENGINES) — The Galaxie 500 was the intermediate trim level for 1965, and included all the Custom trim, plus a chrome hood ornament, Ford crest in the center of the trunk lid, chrome window frames, the Ford crest on the roof "C" pillar, 'Galaxie 500,' in block letters at the front of the front fenders, chrome rocker panel trim, hexagonal taillights with chrome 'cross-hairs' trim and back-up lights. Two-tone vinyl trim was used on the insides of the doors and on the seats.

GALAXIE 500 I.D. NUMBERS: (Six-cylinder models) Galaxie 500, Six-cylinder models used the same serial number sequence as the Custom series.

1965 Ford, Galaxie 500 four-door sedan, V-8

GALAXIE 500 6-CYL SERIES

Model Number	Body/Style Number	Body Type & Seating	Factory Price	Shipping Weight	Production Total
V	54A	4-dr Sed-6P	2623	3412	Note 1
V	57B	4-dr HT-6P	2708	3452	Note 1
V	638	2-dr HT-6P	2630	3352	Note 1
V	76A	2-dr Conv-6P	2889	3556	Note 1

NOTE 1: See Galaxie 500 V-8 Series listing.

GALAXIE 500 I.D. NUMBERS: (V-8 models) Galaxie 500, V-8 models used the same serial number sequence as the Custom series.

GALAXIE 500 V-8 SERIES

Model Number	Body/Style Number	Body Type & Seating	Factory Price	Shipping Weight	Production Total
NA	54A	4-dr Sed-6P	2730	3462	181,183
NA	57B	4-dr HT-6P	2815	3502	49,982
NA	63B	2-dr HT-6P	2737	3402	157,284
NA	76A	2-dr Conv-6P	2996	3616	31,930

PRODUCTION NOTE: Total series output was 420,379 units. Ford does not indicate the number of each model produced with six and V-8 engines. Therefore, all production figures are total production of each body style.

GALAXIE 500XL SERIES — (V-8) — Galaxie 500XL was the sport trim version of the Galaxie 500 two-door hardtop and two-door convertible, and included all Galaxie 500 trim, plus bucket seats, and floor-mounted shift lever, polished door trim panels with carpeting on the lower portion of the doors, dual-lens courtesy/warning lights in the door panels, rear reading lights in hardtops and Galaxie 500XL badges on the body exterior. The 200 hp, 289 cid V-8 engine and Cruise-O-Matic automatic transmission were standard in both XL body styles.

GALAXIE 500XL I.D. NUMBERS: Galaxie 500XLs used the same serial number sequence as the Custom and Galaxie series.

GALAXIE 500XL V-8 SERIES

Model Number	Body/Style Number	Body Type & Seating	Factory Price	Shipping Weight	Production Total
NA	63C	2-dr HT-5P	3167	3507	28,141
NA	76B	2-dr Conv-5P	3426	3675	9,849

PRODUCTION NOTE: Total series output was 37,900 units.

GALAXIE 500 LTD SERIES — (V-8) — The Galaxie 500 LTD was the new top trim level for 1965, and included all the Galaxie 500 trim plus, 289 cid/200 hp V-8 engine and Cruise-O-Matic automatic transmission as standard equipment. Also included were thickly padded seats, with 'pinseal' upholstery, simulated walnut appliques on the lower edge of the instrument panel, Gabardine finish headlining and sun visors, front and rear door courtesy/warning lights, courtesy lights in the rear roof pillars on the interior and under the instrument panel, glovebox and ashtray lights, and a self regulating clock.

GALAXIE 500 LTD I.D. NUMBERS: Galaxie 500 LTD used the same serial number sequence as the Custom and Galaxie 500 series.

GALAXIE 500 LTD V-8 SERIES

Model Number	Body/Style Number	Body Type & Seating	Factory Price	Shipping Weight	Production Total
NA	57F	4-dr HT-6P	3245	3588	68,038
NA	63F	2-dr HT-6P	3167	3496	37,691

PRODUCTION NOTE: Total series output was 105,729 units.

STATION WAGONS SERIES — (ALL ENGINES) — The Ranch Wagon was once again the base trim level station wagon for 1965, with the Country Sedans being the intermediate level and the Country Squires being the top trim level. The trim paralleled the Custom 500, Galaxie 500 and Galaxie 500 LTD models of conventional cars.

STATION WAGON I.D. NUMBERS: (Six-cylinder models) station wagon, six-cylinder models used the same serial number sequence as Custom, and Galaxie 500 series of conventional cars.

STATION WAGON SERIES SIX

Model Number	Body/Style Number	Body Type & Seating	Factory Price	Shipping Weight	Production Total
V	71D	4-dr Ranch Wag-6P	2707	3841	Note 1
V	71B	4-dr Cty Sed-6P	2797	3851	Note 1
V	71C	4-dr Cty Sed-10P	2899	3865	Note 1
V	71E	4-dr Cty Sq-6P	3041	3895	Note 1
V	71A	4-dr Cty Sq-10P	3109	3909	Note 1

NOTE 1: See Station wagon V-8 Series listing.

STATION WAGON I.D. NUMBERS: (V-8 models) Station Wagon, V-8 models used the same serial number sequence as Custom, and Galaxie 500 model of conventional cars.

STATION WAGON V-8 SERIES

Model Number	Body/Style Number	Body Type & Seating	Factory Price	Shipping Weight	Production Total
NA	71D	4-dr Ranch Wag-6P	2813	3891	30,817
NA	71B	4-dr Cty Sed-6P	2904	3901	59,693
NA	71C	4-dr Cty Sed-10P	3005	3915	32,344
NA	71E	4-dr Cty Sq-6P	3147	3945	24,308
NA	71A	4-dr Cty Sq-10P	3216	3959	30,502

PRODUCTION NOTE: Total series output was 177,664 units. Ford does not indicate the number of each model produced with six and V-8 engines. Therefore, all production figures are total production of each body style.

1965 FORD FAIRLANE — OVERVIEW — The 1965 Fairlane featured new sheet metal below the beltline. for new front, rear and side appearance. Overall length and width were increased, resulting in the first total restyling of the line since it's introduction in 1962. The front end featured a wide horizontal grille and horizontal dual head lights. The hood incorporated a small peak in the center that swept forward over the leading edge and met a similar accent line in the grille. Overall profile was changed with a higher fender line that carried farther back, for a more massive look. For the first time since introduction, Fairlane taillights were not round, but, rather, rectangular and accented with chrome 'cross-hairs' accents across the lens face. The optional back-up lights were mounted in the center of the lens.

FAIRLANE MODELS — (ALL ENGINES) — The Fairlane was the base trim level for the line and included chrome windshield and rear window moldings, chrome horn ring, front and rear armrests, cigarette lighter, vinyl coated rubber floor mats, and the Fairlane name in block letters at the front of the front fenders.

FAIRLANE I.D. NUMBERS: (Six-cylinder models) Fairlane, six-cylinder models began with the number "5," followed by the assembly plant code, body type code, engine designation "T," and finally, it's production number, according to the final assembly location. Each plant began at 100001 and went up.

FAIRLANE SIX SERIES

Model Number	Body/Style Number	Body Type & Seating	Factory Price	Shipping Weight	Production Total
T	54A	4-dr Sed-6P	2223	2858	Note 1
T	62A	2-dr Sed-6P	2183	2806	Note 1
T	71D	4-dr Sta Wag-6P	2512	3183	Note 1

NOTE 1: See Fairlane V-8 Series listing.

FAIRLANE I.D. NUMBERS: (V-8 models) Fairlane, V-8 models began with the number "5," followed by the assembly plant code, body type code, engine designation code, and finally, the unit's production number, according to the final assembly location. Each plant began at 100001 and went up.

FAIRLANE V-8 SERIES

Model Number	Body/Style Number	Body Type & Seating	Factory Price	Shipping Weight	Production Total
NA	54A	4-dr Sed-6P	2329	3055	25,378
NA	62A	2-dr Sed-6P	2288	2998	13,685
NA	71D	4-dr Sta Wag-6P	2618	3375	13,911

PRODUCTION NOTE: Total series output was 52,974 units. Ford does not indicate the number of each model produced with six and V-8 engines. Therefore, all production figures are total production of each body style.

FAIRLANE 500 SERIES — (ALL ENGINES) — The Fairlane 500 models were the top trim level of the line. and included chrome window moldings, a chrome horn ring, front and rear armrest. A Ford crest on the roof "C" pillar, a chrome hood ornament and a single horizontal chrome strip with an aluminum insert. Ford appeared, in block letters, across the rear escutcheon panel, with two chrome strips between the taillights and a Ford crest in the center of the panel. The Fairlane 500 models also used carpet instead of the vinyl floor mats found in Fairlane models.

FAIRLANE 500 I.D. NUMBERS: (Six-cylinder models) Fairlane 500, six-cylinder models used the same serial number sequence as the Fairlane models.

1965 Ford Fairlane 500 two-door hardtop Sports Coupe, V-8

FAIRLANE 500 SIX SERIES

Model Number	Body/Style Number	Body Type & Seating	Factory Price	Shipping Weight	Production Total
T	548	4-dr Sed-6P	2303	2863	Note 1
T	62B	2-dr Sed-6P	2263	2806	Note 1
T	65A	2-dr HT-6P	2327	2877	Note 1
T	65B	2-dr Spt Cpe-5P	2484	2888	Note 1
T	71B	4-dr Sta Wag-6P	2592	3220	Note 1

NOTE 1: See Fairlane 500 V-8 Series listing.

FAIRLANE 500 I.D. NUMBERS: (V-8 models) Fairlane 500, V-8 models used the same serial number sequence as the Fairlane models.

FAIRLANE 500 V-8 SERIES

Model Number	Body/Style Number	Body Type & Seating	Factory Price	Shipping Weight	Production Total
NA	548	4-dr Sed-6P	2409	3055	77,836
NA	62B	2-dr Sed-6P	2369	2997	16,092
NA	65A	2-dr HT-6P	2432	3069	41,405
NA	65B	2-dr Spt Cpe-5P	2590	3080	15,141
NA	71B	4-dr Sta Wag-6P	2697	3412	20,506

PRODUCTION NOTE: Total series output was 170,980 units. Ford does not indicate the number of each model produced with six and V-8 engines. Therefore, all production figures are total production of each body style.

1965 Ford, Falcon Futura two-door convertible, V-8

1965 FALCONS — OVERVIEW — While continuing to use the 1964 body shell, trim changes made the 1965 Falcon look considerably different than the previous year. The grille was a thin horizontal bar design, which was divided into two sections by a wider vertical bar at the center. A vertical, three-colored crest was used on the center divider. The round taillights utilized chrome 'cross-hairs' for accent, and the optional back-up lights were mounted in the center of the lens.

FALCON SERIES — (ALL ENGINES) — Falcons were the base trim level for 1965, and included chrome windshield and rear window moldings, two horns, two sun visors, armrests on the front doors only, and a horn button instead of a chrome horn ring. A new Falcon emblem with black, paint-filled Falcon letters was attached to the front fender behind the wheel opening.

FALCON I.D. NUMBERS: — (ALL ENGINES) — Falcons used the same serial number sequence as the full-size Fords and the Fairlane line.

FALCON SERIES

Model Number	Body/Style Number	Body Type & Seating	Factory Price	Shipping Weight	Production Total
NA	54A	4-dr Sed-6P	2038	2410	30,186
NA	62A	2-dr Sed-6P	1977	2370	35,858

FUTURA SERIES — (ALL ENGINES) — The Futura series was the top Falcon trim level for 1965, and included a chrome horn ring, armrests front and rear, with ashtrays, two horns, Futura wheelcovers (instead of hubcaps), a chrome hood ornament, Futura symbol on the front fender behind the wheelwell, chrome windshield and rear window moldings and side window moldings, a full-length, spear-type chrome-molding, with either red, white or black painted insert.

FUTURA I.D. NUMBERS: — (ALL ENGINES) — Futura models used the same serial number sequence as the full-size Fords, Fairlanes, and Falcons.

FUTURA SERIES

Model Number	Body/Style Number	Body Type & Seating	Factory Price	Shipping Weight	Production Total
NA	54B	4-dr Sed-6P	2146	2410	33,985
NA	62B	2-dr Sed-6P	2099	2375	11,670
NA	63B	2-dr HT-6P	2179	2395	24,451
NA	63B	2-dr HT-5P	2226	2380	1,303
NA	76A	2-dr Conv-6P	2428	2675	6,191
NA	768	2-dr Conv-5P	2481	2660	124
NA	63D	2-dr Sprint HT-5P	2425	2813	2,806
NA	76D	2-dr Sprint Conv-5P	2660	3008	300

PRODUCTION NOTE: Total series output was 171,442 units, including 13,824 four-door sedans, and 13,850 two-door sedans with the Deluxe trim option in the Falcon model line. Ford does not indicate the number of each model with six and V-8 engines. Therefore, all production figures are total production of each body style.

NOTE 2: Models 638 and 768 have bucket seats.

FALCON STATION WAGON SERIES — (ALL ENGINES) — Falcon station wagons included the Falcon as the base trim level, Futura Wagon as the intermediate level and Squire as the top trim level.

STATION WAGON I.D. NUMBERS: — (ALL ENGINES) — Falcon station wagons used the same serial number sequence as the full-size Fords, Fairlanes and Falcon sedans.

FALCON STATION WAGON SERIES

Model Number	Body/Style Number	Body Type & Seating	Factory Price	Shipping Weight	Production Total
NA	71A	4-dr Sta Wag-6p	2317	2680	14,911
NA	59A	2-dr Sta Wag-6P	2284	2640	4,891
NA	71B	4-dr Futura Wag-6p	2453	2670	12,548
NA	71C	4-dr Sq Wag-6P	2608	2695	6,703

PRODUCTION NOTE: Total series output was 39,053 units. Ford does not indicate the number of each model produced with six and V-8 engines. Therefore. all production figures are total production of each body style.

1965 Ford, Thunderbird two-door convertible, V-8

1965 THUNDERBIRD OVERVIEW — Except for minor trim changes, the 1965 Thunderbird was the same as the 1964 model. Disc brakes and sequential turn signals were added to the 1965 list of features, as well as reversible keys and keyless locking system. Also available were vacuum-operated, power door locks (introduced as part of an optional safety group in 1964), and a remote trunk release. A simulated chrome scoop was incorporated in the front fenders, immediately to the rear of the front wheel openings. A new Thunderbird crest replaced the Thunderbird name across the front of the hood. A restyled Thunderbird emblem was used on the roof "C" pillar and new wheelcovers were used. The new horizontal grille featured six vertical bars and eight horizontal bars.

THUNDERBIRD SERIES — With a few trim changes, the 1965 Thunderbird continued to use the same body as introduced in 1964. A new grille was used within the existing shell, and a Thunderbird emblem replaced the block letters on the front of the hood. A die-cast front fender ornament, in the form of a forward-canted exhaust outlet was located directly behind the front wheelwell. A Thunderbird emblem was used on the roof "C" pillar and new wheelcovers were used.

THUNDERBIRD I.D. NUMBERS: Thunderbird models began with the number "5," assembly plant code "Y" (Wixom), body type code, engine type code "Z," and finally, the unit's production number, beginning at 100001 and going up.

THUNDERBIRD SERIES

Model Number	Body/Style Number	Body Type & Seating	Factory Price	Shipping Weight	Production Total
A	63B	2-dr HT-4P	4394	4470	42,652
Z	63B	2-dr Landau-4P	4495	4478	25,474
Z	76A	2-dr Conv-4P	4851	4588	6,846

PRODUCTION NOTE: Total series output was 74,972 units.

Standard Catalog of American Cars

1965 ENGINES

FALCON/FAIRLANE/MUSTANG 6-CYLINDER: Overhead valves. Cast iron block. Displacement: 170 cid. Bore and stroke: 3.50 x 2.94 inches. Compression ratio: 9.1:1. Brake hp: 105 at 4400 rpm. Carburetion: Holley single-barrel. Seven main bearings. Serial number code "U."

FALCON/FAIRLANE/MUSTANG 6-CYLINDER: Overhead valves. Cast iron block. Displacement: 200 cid. Bore and stroke: 3.68 x 3.13 inches. Compression ratio: 9.2:1. Brake hp: 120 at 4400 rpm. Carburetion: Holley single-barrel. Seven main bearings. Serial number code "T."

FORD 6-CYLINDER: Overhead valves. Cast iron block. Displacement: 240 cid. Bore and stroke: 4.00 x 3.18 inches. Compression ratio: 9.2:1. Brake hp: 150 at 4000 rpm. Carburetion: Holley one-barrel. Seven main bearings. Serial number code "V."

CHALLENGER 289 V-8: Overhead valves. Cast iron block. Displacement: 289 cid. Bore and stroke: 4.00 x 2.87 inches. Compression ratio: 9.3:1. Brake hp: 200 at 4400 rpm. Carburetion: Holley two-barrel. Five main bearings. Serial number code "C."

CHALLENGER 289 4V V-8: Overhead valves. Cast iron block. Displacement: 289 cid. Bore and stroke: 4.00 x 2.87 inches. Compression ratio: 10.0:1. Brake hp: 225 at 4800 rpm. Carburetion: Holley four-barrel. Five main bearings. Serial number code "A."

HIGH PERFORMANCE 289 V-8: Overhead valves. Cast iron block. Displacement: 289 cid. Bore and stroke: 4.00 x 2.87 inches. Compression ratio: 10.5:1. Brake hp: 271 at 6000 rpm. Carburetion: Holley four-barrel. Five main bearings. Serial number code "K."

INTERCEPTOR V-8: Overhead valves. Cast iron block. Displacement: 352 cid. Bore and stroke: 4.00 x 3.50 inches. Compression ratio: 9.3:1. Brake hp: 250 at 4400 rpm. Carburetion: Holley four-barrel. Five main bearings. Serial number code "X."

THUNDERBIRD V-8: Overhead valves. Cast iron block. Displacement: 390 cid. Bore and stroke: 4.05 x 3.78 inches. Compression ratio: 10.0:1. Brake hp: 300 at 4600 rpm. Carburetion: Holley four-barrel. Five main bearings. Serial number code "Z."

THUNDERBIRD INTERCEPTOR SPECIAL V-8: Overhead valves. Cast iron block. Displacement: 390 cid. Bore and stroke: 4.05 x 3.78 inches. Compression ratio: 10.0:1. Brake hp: 330 at 5000 rpm. Carburetion: Holley four-barrel. Five main bearings. Serial number code "P."

THUNDERBIRD SUPER HIGH-PERFORMANCE V-8: Overhead valves. Cast iron block. Displacement: 427 cid. Bore and stroke: 4.23 x 3.78 inches. Compression ratio: 11.5:1. Brake hp: 425 at 6000 rpm. Carburetion: Two Holley four-barrels. Five main bearings. Serial number code "R."

"SOHC 427" 427 4V V8: Hemispherical combustion chambers with overhead valves and overhead camshafts for each engine bank. Cast iron block and cylinder heads. Displacement: 427 cid. Bore and stroke: 4.23 x 3.78. Compression ratio: 12. 1:1. Brake hp: 616 @ 7000 rpm. Carburetion: Holley four-barrel. Five main bearings. (Code L: $2,500).

"SOHC 427" BV V8: Hemispherical combustion chambers with overhead valves and overhead camshafts for each engine bank. Cast iron block and cylinder heads. Displacement: 427 cid. Bore and stroke: 4.23 x 3.78. Compression ratio: 12.1:1. Brake hp: 657 @ 7500 rpm. Carburetion: Two Holley four-barrels. Five main bearings. Code "M."

FORD CHASSIS FEATURES: Wheelbase: 119 inches. Overall length: 210 inches. Tires: 7.35 x 15 4-ply tubeless blackwall (8.15 x 15 4-ply tubeless blackwall on station wagons).

FAIRLANE CHASSIS FEATURES: Wheelbase: 116 inches. Overall length: 198.4 inches, (203.2 inches on station wagons). Tires: 6.94 x 14 4-ply tubeless blackwall (7.35 x 14 4-ply tubeless on station wagons).

FALCON CHASSIS FEATURES: Wheelbase: 109.5 inches. Overall length: 181.6 inches (190 on Station Wagons). Tires: 6.50 x 13 (7.00 x 13 on station wagons). All tires were 4-ply tubeless blackwall.

THUNDERBIRD CHASSIS FEATURES: Wheelbase: 113.2 inches. Overall length: 205.4 inches. Tires: 8.15 x 15 4-ply tubeless blackwall.

FORD OPTIONS: Popular Custom and Custom 500 model options included the 289 cid V-8 engine ($109). Cruise-O-Matic automatic transmission ($189). Power steering ($97). AM radio ($58). Wheelcovers ($25). White side wall tires ($34). Popular Galaxie 500 and Galaxie 550 XL options included the 390 cid V-8 engine ($246). Cruise-O-Matic automatic transmission ($190); four-speed manual transmission ($188 — no charge on XLs). Power steering ($97). Power brakes ($43). Power windows ($102). Tinted windshield ($40). Air conditioning ($36). AM radio ($58). Vinyl roof ($76). Wheelcovers ($26). White sidewall tires ($34). Popular LTD options included the 390 cid V-8 engine ($137). Power steering ($97). Power brakes ($43). Power windows ($102). Tinted windshield ($40). Air conditioning ($364). AM radio ($72); AM/FM radio ($142). Vinyl roof ($76). White sidewall tires ($34). Popular station wagon options included the 390 cid V-8 engine ($246). Cruise-O-Matic automatic transmission ($190). Power steering ($97). Power brakes ($43). Tinted windows ($40). Power tailgate window ($32). Luggage rack ($45). AM radio ($58). White sidewall tires ($34). Wheelcovers ($25). A Borg-Warner T-10 four-speed transmission was replaced, for 1965, with the Ford produced T&C "top-loader" four-speed.

FAIRLANE OPTIONS: 289 cid V-8 engine ($108), or high-performance 289 cid V-8 ($430). Cruise-O-Matic automatic transmission ($190); four-speed manual transmission ($188). AM radio ($58). Power steering ($86). Power tailgate window on station wagons ($32). Luggage rack on station wagons ($45). Two-tone paint ($22). White sidewall tires ($34). Wheelcovers ($22). Vinyl roof on two-door hardtops ($76).

FALCON OPTIONS: 200 cid 6-cylinder engine ($45), or the 289 cid V-8 engine ($153). Cruise-O-Matic automatic transmission ($182 or $172 with 6-cylinder). Front bucket seats ($69). AM radio ($58). Two-tone paint ($19). White sidewall tires ($30). Sprint package ($222, 273 on convertibles.) Popular Falcon station wagon options included all those of the sedans, plus the following: Power tailgate window ($30). Luggage rack ($45).

THUNDERBIRD OPTIONS: Air conditioning ($425). Tinted windows ($43). Leather seats ($106). Power seats ($184). Power windows ($106). AM/FM radio ($84). White sidewall tires ($44). Vacuum trunk release ($13). Deluxe wheelcovers ($16).

HISTORICAL FOOTNOTES: Model names were dropped for 1965, in favor of designating the car by it's actual body style, i.e., "Club Victoria" became "two-door hardtop," and "Sunliner" became "two-door convertible", etc. The 427 cid single-overhead cam engine was installed In the Fairlane Thunderbolt drag cars.

1966 FORD

1966 FORDS — OVERVIEW — For 1966, Ford continued its policy of major restyling in several of the model lines. While 1965 and 1966 full-size Fords bear a resemblance to each other, they are quite different cars. The hood is the only interchangeable exterior body component. The 1966 models featured more rounded lines than the previous year, even though the feature lines were in the same location.

FORD CUSTOM SERIES — (ALL ENGINES) — The Custom series was the base trim level full-size Ford for 1966 and included chrome windshield and rear window moldings; two sun visors; a chrome horn ring; armrests on all doors; and the Custom name, in script, on the rear fender. The taillights had square lenses, with centrally-mounted back-up lights surrounded by a chrome bezel. The Ford name appeared, in block letters, across the front of the hood and across the vertical section of the trunk lid.

CUSTOM SIX SERIES IDENTIFICATION NUMBERS: Custom six-cylinder models began with the number '6,' followed by the assembly plant code, engine designation code 'V' and, finally, the unit's production number according to the final assembly location. Each plant began at 100001 and went up.

CUSTOM SIX SERIES

Model Number	Body/Style Number	Body Type & Seating	Factory Price	Shipping Weight	Production Total
V	54B	4-dr Sed-6P	2415	3433	Note 1
V	62B	2-dr Sed-6P	2363	3333	Note 1

NOTE 1: See Custom V-8 production note below.

CUSTOM V-8 SERIES IDENTIFICATION NUMBERS: Custom V-8 models began with the number '6,' followed by the assembly plant code, body type code, engine designation code and, finally, the unit's production number according to the final assembly location. Each plant began at 100001 and went up.

CUSTOM V-8 SERIES

Model Number	Body/Style Number	Body Type & Seating	Factory Price	Shipping Weight	Production Total
NA	54B	4-dr Sed-6P	2539	3477	72,245
NA	62B	2-dr Sed-6P	2487	3377	32,292

PRODUCTION NOTE: Total series output was 138,238 units. Ford does not indicate the number of each model produced with sixes or V-8s. Therefore, all production figures given above are total production of each body style with both engines.

CUSTOM 500 SERIES — (ALL ENGINES) — The Custom 500 was the upper trim level of the base-line Custom series and included chrome windshield and rear window moldings; nylon carpeting instead of the rubber mats used in the Custom models; armrests (with ashtrays) on all doors; two sun visors and; all trim used in the Custom models. There was also a horizontal chrome strip along the side feature line and the designation '500,' in a die-cast block with black-painted background, in front of the Custom script. A small Ford crest was located in the chrome side strip, on the front of the front fenders.

CUSTOM 500 SIX SERIES IDENTIFICATION NUMBERS: Custom 500 six-cylinder models used the same serial number sequence as the Custom models.

CUSTOM 500 SIX SERIES

Model Number	Body/Style Number	Body Type & Seating	Factory Price	Shipping Weight	Production Total
V	548	4-dr Sed-6P	2514	3444	Note 1
V	628	2-dr Sed-6P	2464	3375	Note 1

NOTE 1: See Custom 500 V-8 production note below.

CUSTOM 500 V-8 SERIES IDENTIFICATION NUMBERS: Custom 500 V-8 models used the same serial number sequence as the Custom models.

CUSTOM 500 V-8 SERIES

NA	54B	4-dr Sed-6P	2639	3488	109,449
NA	62B	2-dr Sed-6P	2588	3419	28,789

PRODUCTION NOTE: Total series output was 138,238 units. Ford does not indicate the number of each model produced with sixes or V-8s. Therefore, all production given above figures are total production of each body style with both engines.

GALAXIE 500 SERIES — (ALL ENGINES) — The Galaxie 500 was the intermediate trim level for 1966 and included all the Custom trim, plus a chrome hood ornament; Ford crest in the feature line on the front fender; stamped aluminum rocker panel moldings; and a stamped aluminum insert, between two chrome strips on the vertical section of the trunk lid, with Ford, in block letters, spaced evenly across. Two-tone vinyl trim was used on the inside of the doors and on the seats. Simulated wood appliques were used on the instrument panel trim pieces.

GALAXIE 500 SIX SERIES IDENTIFICATION NUMBERS: Galaxie 500 six-cylinder models used the same serial number sequence as the Custom and Custom 500 models.

GALAXIE 500 SIX SERIES

Model Number	Body/Style Number	Body Type & Seating	Factory Price	Shipping Weight	Production Total
V	54A	4-dr Sed-6P	2658	3456	Note 1
V	57B	4-dr FsBk Sed-6P	2743	3526	Note 1
V	63B	2-dr FsBk Cpe-6P	2685	3437	Note 1
V	76A	2-dr Conv-6P	2914	3633	Note 1

NOTE 1: See V-8 series production note below.

GALAXIE 500 V-8 SERIES IDENTIFICATION NUMBERS: Galaxie 500 V-8 models used the same serial number sequence as the Custom and Custom 500 series.

GALAXIE 500 V-8 SERIES

Model Number	Body/Style Number	Body Type & Seating	Factory Price.	Shipping Weight	Production Total
NA	54A	4-dr Sed-6P	2784	3500	171,886
NA	57B	4-dr FsBk Sed-6P	2869	3570	54,886
NA	63B	2-dr FsBk Cpe-6P	2791	3481	198,532
NA	76A	2-dr Conv-6P	3041	3677	27,454

PRODUCTION NOTE: Total series output was 452,758 units. Ford does not indicate the number of each model produced with sixes or V-8s. Therefore, all production figures given above are total production of each body style with both engines.

GALAXIE 500XL SERIES — (V-8) — Galaxie 500XL was the sport trim version of the Galaxie 500 two-door hardtop and two-door convertible and included all Galaxie 500 trim, plus bucket seats and floor-mounted shift lever; polished door trim panels with carpeting on the lower portion of the doors; dual-lens courtesy/warning lights in the door panels; rear reading lights (in hardtops) and Galaxie 500XL badges on the body exterior. The 200 hp, 289 cid V-8 engine and Cruise-O-Matic automatic transmission were standard in both 'XL' body styles.

GALAXIE 500XL IDENTIFICATION NUMBERS: Galaxie 500XLs used the same serial number sequence as the Custom and Galaxie series.

GALAXIE 500XL SERIES

Model Number	Body/Style Number	Body Type & Seating	Factory Price	Shipping Weight	Production Total
NA	63C	2-dr FsBk-5P	3208	3616	25,715
NA	76B	2-dr Conv-5P	3456	3761	6,360

PRODUCTION NOTE: Total series output was 32,075 units.

1966 Ford, Galaxie 500 '7-Litre' two-door hardtop sports coupe, V-8

GALAXIE 500 7-LITRE SERIES — The '7-Litre' was the high-performance version of the Galaxie 500XL and was equipped with the 345 hp, 428 cid V-8 engine as standard equipment, along with the Cruise-O-Matic automatic transmission. The four-speed manual transmission was available as a no-cost option for those who chose to be even more sporting. Along with the 428 engine, standard equipment also included a sport steering wheel (of simulated English walnut); bucket seats; floor shift; low restriction dual exhausts; and a non-silenced air cleaner system. Also standard were power disc brakes.

GALAXIE 500 7-LITRE IDENTIFICATION NUMBERS: Galaxie 500 7-Litres used the same serial number sequence as the Custom and Galaxie series.

GALAXIE 500 7-LITRE SERIES

Model Number	Body/Style Number	Body Type & Seating	Factory Price	Shipping Weight	Production Total
Q	63D	2-dr FsBk-5P	3596	3914	8,705
Q	76D	2-dr Conv-5P	3844	4059	2,368

PRODUCTION NOTE: Total series output was 11,073 units.

GALAXIE 500 LTD SERIES — (V-8) — The Galaxie 500 LTD was the top trim level for 1966 and included all the Galaxie 500 trim, plus the 200 hp, 289 cid (V-8) engine; Cruise-O-Matic automatic transmission; thickly padded seats (with 'pinseal' upholstery); simulated walnut appliques on the lower edge of the instrument panel (and in the door inserts); Gabardine finish headliner and sun visors; front and rear door courtesy/warning lights; courtesy lights on the rear interior roof pillars and under the instrument panel; glovebox and ashtray lights; and a self-regulating clock.

GALAXIE 500 LTD IDENTIFICATION NUMBERS: Galaxie 500 LTDs used the same serial number sequence as the Custom and Galaxie 500 series.

Model Number	Body/Style Number	Body Type & Seating	Factory Price	Shipping Weight	Production Total
NA	57F	4-dr HT Sed-6P	3278	3649	69,400
NA	63F	2-dr FsBk Cpe-6P	3201	3601	31,696

PRODUCTION NOTE: Total series output was 101,096 units.

STATION WAGON SERIES — (ALL ENGINES) — The Ranch Wagon was the base trim level station wagon for 1966. The Country Sedans were the intermediate level and the Country Squires were the top trim level. The trim paralleled the Custom 500, Galaxie 500 and Galaxie 500 LTD models of conventional cars.

STATION WAGON SIX SERIES IDENTIFICATION NUMBERS: Station wagon six-cylinder models used the same serial number sequence as Custom and Galaxie 500 series of conventional cars.

STATION WAGON SIX SERIES

Model Number	Body/Style Number	Body Type & Seating	Factory Price	Shipping Weight	Production Total
V	71D	4-dr Ranch Wag-6P	2793	3919	Note 1
V	71B	4-dr Cty Sed-6P	2882	3934	Note 1
V	71C	4-dr Cty Sed-9P	2999	3975	Note 1
V	71E	4-dr Cty Sq-6P	3182	4004	Note 1
V	71A	4-dr Cty Sq-9P	3265	4018	Note 1

NOTE 1: See V-8 series production note below.

STATION WAGON V-8 SERIES IDENTIFICATION NUMBERS: Station Wagon V-8 models used the same serial number sequence as Custom and Galaxie 500 models of conventional cars.

Model Number	Body/Style Number	Body Type & Seating	Factory Price	Shipping Weight	Production Total
NA	71 D	4-dr Ranch Wag-6P	2900	3963	33,306
NA	71B	4-dr Cty Sed-6P	2989	3978	55,616
NA	71C	4-dr Cty Sed-9P	3105	4019	36,633
NA	71E	4-dr Cty Sq-6P	3289	4048	27,645
NA	71A	4-dr Cty Sq-9P	3372	4062	47,953

PRODUCTION NOTE: Total series output was 195,153 units. Ford does not indicate the number of each model produced with sixes and V-8s. Therefore. all production figures given above are total production of each body style with both engines.

1966 FAIRLANE — OVERVIEW — Major restyling was given to the Fairlane lineup, which included 13 different models. They were longer, lower and wider, and featured new suspensions both front and rear. The full-width grille featured a horizontal grid with a large divider bar and the Fairlane crest in the center of the grille. The headlights were vertically stacked and angled back, at the bottom, for a more aggressive look. A full-length horizontal feature line was used for emphasis and the model designation, in block letters, was located on the rear fender. The taillights were rectangular and featured a chrome ring around the outside and around the centrally located back-up lights. Engine choices ranged from the 200 cid, 120 hp six-cylinder engine, up to the mighty, 335 hp, 390 cid 'GT' V-8 engine. For the first time, three convertibles were added to the lineup of hardtops and sedans. There was a total of 13 different models.

FAIRLANE MODELS — (ALL ENGINES) — The Fairlane was the base trim level for the 1966 and included chrome windshield and rear window moldings; chrome rain gutter molding; chrome horn ring; front and rear armrests; cigarette lighter; vinyl coated rubber floor mats; and the Fairlane name, in block letters, on the front fenders.

FAIRLANE SIX SERIES IDENTIFICATION NUMBERS: Fairlane six-cylinder models began with the number '6,' followed by the assembly plant code, body type code, engine designation 'T' and, finally, the unit's production number according to the final assembly location. Each plant began at 100001 and went up.

FAIRLANE SIX SERIES

Model Number	Body/Style Number	Body Type & Seating	Factory Price	Shipping Weight	Production Total
T	54	4-dr Sed-6P	2280	2792	Note 1
T	62	2-dr Sed-6P	2240	2747	Note 1
T	71	4-dr Sta Wag-6P	2589	3182	Note 1

NOTE 1: See V-8 series production note below.

FAIRLANE V-8 SERIES IDENTIFICATION NUMBERS: Fairlane V-8 models began with the number '6,' followed by the assembly plant code, body type code, engine designation code and, finally, the unit's production number according to the final assembly location. Each plant began at 100001 and went up.

FAIRLANE V-8 SERIES

Model Number	Body/Style Number	Body Type & Seating	Factory Price	Shipping Weight	Production Total
NA	54A	4-dr Sed-6P	2386	2961	26,170
NA	62A	2-dr Sed-6P	2345	2916	13,498
NA	71D	4-dr Sta Wag-6P	2694	3351	12,379

PRODUCTION NOTE: Total series output was 52,047 units. Ford does not indicate the number of each model produced with sixes or V-8s. Therefore, all production figures given above are total production of each body style with both engines.

1966 Ford, Fairlane GT two-door convertible, V-8

FAIRLANE 500 SERIES — (ALL ENGINES) — The Fairlane 500 was the intermediate trim level for 1966 and included all the Fairlane trim, plus polished aluminum rocker panel moldings; a Fairlane crest in the center of the grille; color-keyed carpets (front and rear); and Fairlane 500 identification, in block letters, on the rear fenders. A Fairlane crest and Fairlane script also appeared on the right-hand vertical section of the trunk lid.

FAIRLANE 500 SIX SERIES IDENTIFICATION NUMBERS: Fairlane 500 six-cylinder models used the same serial number sequence as the Fairlane models.

FAIRLANE 500 SIX SERIES

Model Number	Body/Style Number	Body Type & Seating	Factory Price	Shipping Weight	Production Total
T	54B	4-dr Sed-6P	2357	2798	Note 1
T	62B	2-dr Sed-6P	2317	2754	Note 1
T	63B	2-dr HT Cpe-6P	2378	2856	Note 1
T	76B	2-dr Conv-6P	2603	3084	Note 1
T	71B	4-dr Sta Wag-6P	2665	3192	Note 1
T	71E	4-dr Sq Wag-6P	2796	3200	Note 1

NOTE 1: See V-8 series production note below.

FAIRLANE 500 V-8 SERIES IDENTIFICATION NUMBERS: Fairlane 500 V-8 models used the same serial number sequence as the Fairlane models.

FAIRLANE 500 V-8 SERIES

	Body/Style Number	Body Type & Seating	Factory Price	Shipping Weight	Production Total
NA	54B	4-dr Sed-6P	2463	2967	68,635
NA	62B	2-dr Sed-6P	2423	2923	14,118
NA	63A	2-dr HT Cpe-6P	2484	3025	75,947
NA	76B	2-dr Conv-6P	2709	3253	9,299
NA	71B	4-dr Sta Wag-6P	2770	3361	19,826
NA	71E	4-dr Sq Wag-6P	2901	3369	11,558

PRODUCTION NOTE: Total series output was 199,383 units. Ford does not indicate the number of each model produced with sixes or V-8s. Therefore, all production figures given above are total production of each body style with both engines.

FAIRLANE 500XL SERIES — (ALL ENGINES) — The Fairlane 500XL was the sporty version of the Fairlane 500 series and included all the Fairlane 500 features, plus bucket seats and console; special name plaques and exterior trim; Deluxe wheelcovers; red safety lights and white courtesy lights in the door armrests.

FAIRLANE 500XL SIX SERIES IDENTIFICATION NUMBER: Fairlane 500XL six-cylinder models used the same serial number sequence as the Fairlane and Fairlane 500 models.

Model Number	Body/Style Number	Body Type & Seating	Factory Price	Shipping Weight	Production Total
T	63C	2-dr HT Cpe-5P	2543	2884	Note 1
T	76C	2-dr Conv-5P	2768	3099	Note 1

NOTE 1: See V-8 series production note below.

FAIRLANE 500XL V-8 SERIES IDENTIFICATION NUMBERS: Fairlane 500XL V-8 models used the same serial number sequence as the Fairlane and Fairlane 500 models.

FAIRLANE 500XL V-8 SERIES

Model Number	Body/Style Number	Body Type & Seating	Factory Price	Shipping Weight	Production Total
NA	63C	2-dr HT Cpe-5P	2649	3053	23,942
NA	76C	2-dr Conv-5P	2874	3268	4,560
NA	63D	2-dr GT HT-5P	2843	3493	33,015
NA	76D	2-dr GT Conv-5P	3068	3070	4,327

PRODUCTION NOTE: Total series output was 65,844 units. Ford does not indicate the number of each model produced with sixes or V-8s. Therefore. all production figures given above are total production of each body style with both engines.

NOTE 2: The Fairlane GT models came only with the 390 cid V-8 engine.

1966 Ford, Falcon Futura two-door coupe, V-8

1966 FALCONS — OVERVIEW — The Falcon series also received a total restyling for 1966, with a longer hood, shorter trunk and rounder lines than in 1965. The beautiful two-door hardtops were discontinued for 1966, with the Futura sport coupe carrying the sporty image for the year.

FALCON SERIES — (ALL ENGINES) — The Falcons were the base trim level of the compact Falcon line for 1966 and included chrome windshield. rear window and rain gutter moldings; twin horns and sun visors, armrests on the front doors only and a horn button, instead of a chrome horn ring. The Falcon script was located behind the front wheelwell, on the front fender, and Ford was spelled out, in block letters, across the front of the hood. Falcon was spelled out, in block letters, across the vertical section of the trunk lid.

FALCON IDENTIFICATION NUMBERS: (ALL ENGINES) — Falcons used the same serial number sequence as the full-size Ford and the Fairlane line.

FALCON SERIES

Model Number	Body/Style Number	Body Type & Seating	Factory Price	Shipping Weight	Production Total
NA	54A	4-dr Sed-6P	2114	2559	34,685
NA	62A	2-dr Sed-6P	2060	2519	41,432
NA	71A	4-dr Sta Wag-6P	2442	3037	16,653

PRODUCTION NOTE: Total series output was 92,770 units. Ford does not indicate the number of each model produced with sixes or V-8s. Therefore, all production figures given above are total production of each body style with both engines.

FUTURA SERIES — (ALL ENGINES) — The Futura series was the top trim level for 1966 and included all the standard Falcon features, plus a cigarette lighter; rear armrests and ashtrays; chrome horn ring; nylon carpeting; special Futura moldings, trim, emblems and nameplates; and chrome side window frames. In addition, the sports coupe also featured the 120 hp, 200 cid six-cylinder engine; bucket seats in front, special nameplates and special wheelcovers.

FUTURA IDENTIFICATION NUMBERS: (ALL ENGINES) — Futura models used the same serial number sequence as the full-size Fords, Fairlanes and Falcons.

FALCON FUTURA SERIES

Model Number	Body/Style Number	Body Type & Seating	Factory Price	Shipping Weight	Production Total
NA	54B	4-dr Sed-6P	2237	2567	34,039
NA	62B	2-dr Clb Cpe-6P	2183	2527	21,997
NA	62C	2-dr Spt Cpe-5P	2328	2597	20,289
NA	71B	4-dr Sq Wag-6P	2553	3045	13,574

PRODUCTION NOTE: Total series output was 89,899 units. Ford does not indicate the number of each model produced with sixes and V-8s. Therefore, all production figures are total production of each body style with both engines.

1966 Ford, Thunderbird two-door Landau sports coupe, V-8

THUNDERBIRD SERIES — (OVERVIEW) — Even though it used the body shell of the previous two years, the 1966 Thunderbird looked completely new. The grille was more sharply angled back and featured an eggcrate backing for a massive Thunderbird emblem which appeared to float in the grille. At the rear, a single, massive taillight stretched from side to side, with a single back-up light being part of the Thunderbird emblem in the center of the lens. The name Thunderbird appeared, in script, just ahead of the taillights on the rear fender. Another Thunderbird emblem appeared on the roof 'C' pillar. More horsepower was available in the form of the optional 345 hp, 428 cid V-8 engine.

THUNDERBIRD IDENTIFICATION NUMBERS: Thunderbird models began with the number '6,' assembly plant code 'Y' (Wixom), body type code, engine type codes 'Z' or 'Q' and, finally, the unit's production number, beginning at 100001 and going up.

Model Number	Body/Style Number	Body Type & Seating	Factory Price	Shipping Weight	Production Total
Z/Q	63A	2-dr HT Cpe-4P	4395	4386	13,389
Z/Q	63B	2-dr HT Twn Sed-4P	4451	4359	15,633
Z/Q	63D	2-dr Landau-4P	4552	4367	35,105
Z/Q	76A	2-dr Conv-4P	4845	4496	5,049

PRODUCTION NOTE: Total series output was 69,176 units.

ENGINES

FALCON/FAIRLANE SIX-CYLINDER: Overhead valves. Cast iron block. Displacement: 170 cid. Bore and stroke: 3.50 x 2.94 inches. Compression ratio: 9.1:1. Brake hp: 105 at 4400 rpm. Carburetion: Holley one-barrel. Seven main bearings. Serial number code "4."

FALCON/FAIRLANE/MUSTANG SIX-CYLINDER: Overhead valves. Cast iron block. Displacement: 200 cid. Bore and stroke: 3.68 x 3.13 inches. Compression ratio: 9.2:1. Brake hp: 120 at 4400 rpm. Carburetion: Holley one-barrel. Seven main bearings. Serial number code '"U."

FORD SIX-CYLINDER: Overhead valves. Cast iron block. Displacement: 240 cid. Bore and stroke: 4.00 x 3.18 inches. Compression ratio: 9.2:1. Brake hp: 150 at 4000 rpm. Carburetion: Holley one-barrel. Seven main bearings. Serial number code "V." (Police code B; taxi code E)

CHALLENGER 289 V-8: Overhead valves. Cast iron block. Displacement: 289 cid. Bore and stroke: 4.00 x 2.87 inches. Compression ratio: 9.3:1. Brake hp: 200 at 4400 rpm. Carburetion: Holley two-barrel. Five main bearings. Serial number code "C."

CHALLENGER 289 V-8: Overhead valves. Cast iron block. Displacement: 289 cid. Bore and stroke: 4.00 x 2.87 inches. Compression ratio: 10.0:1. Brake hp: 225 at 4800 rpm. Carburetion: Holley four-barrel. Five main bearings. Serial number code "A."

HIGH-PERFORMANCE 289 V-8: Overhead valves: Cast iron block. Displacement: 289 cid. Bore and stroke: 4.00 x 2.87 inches. Compression ratio: 10.5:1. Brake hp: 271 at 6000 rpm. Carburetion: Holley four-barrel. Five main bearings. Serial number code "K."

INTERCEPTOR V-8: Overhead valves. Cast iron block. Displacement: 352 cid. Bore and stroke: 4.00 x 3.50 inches. Compression ratio: 9.3:1. Brake hp: 250 at 4400 rpm. Carburetion: Holley four-barrel. Five main bearings. Serial number code "X."

THUNDERBIRD V-8: Overhead valves. Cast iron block. Displacement: 390 cid. Bore and stroke: 4.05 x 3.78 inches. Compression ratio: 9.5:1. Brake hp: 275 at 4400 rpm. Carburetion: Holley two-barrel. Five main bearings. Serial number codes 'Y' or (Special) "H."

THUNDERBIRD FOUR-BARREL V-8: Overhead valves. Cast iron block. Displacement: 390 cid. Bore and stroke: 4.05 x 3.78 inches. Compression ratio: 10.5:1. Brake hp: 315 at 4600 rpm. Carburetion: Holley four-barrel. Five main bearings. Serial number code "Z."

GT 390 V-8: Overhead valves. Cast iron block. Displacement: 390 cid. Bore and stroke: 4.05 x 3.78 inches. Compression ratio: 11.0:1. Brake hp: 335 at 4800 rpm. Carburetion: Holley four-barrel. Five main bearings. Serial number code "S."

THUNDERBIRD HIGH-PERFORMANCE V-8: Overhead valves. Cast iron block. Displacement: 427 cid. Bore and stroke: 4.23 x 3.78 inches. Compression ratio: 11.0:1. Brake hp: 410 15 5600 rpm. Carburetion: Holley four-barrel. Five main bearings. Serial number code "W."

THUNDERBIRD SUPER HIGH-PERFORMANCE V-8: Overhead valves. Cast iron block. Displacement: 427 cid. Bore and stroke: 4.23 x 3.78 inches. Compression ratio: 11.5:1. Brake hp: 425 at 6000 rpm. Carburetion: Two (2) Holley four-barrels. Five main bearings. Serial number code "R."

THUNDERBIRD SPECIAL V-8: Overhead valves. Cast iron block. Displacement: 428 cid. Bore and stroke: 4.13 x 3.98 inches. Compression ratio: 10.5:1. Brake hp: 345 at 4600 rpm. Carburetion: Holley four-barrel. Five main bearings. Serial number code "Q."

"SOHC 427" 4V V8: Hemispherical combustion chambers with overhead valves and overhead camshafts for each engine bank. Cast iron block and cylinder heads. Displacement: 427 cid. Bore and stroke: 4.23 x 3.78. Compression ratio: 12.1:1. Brake hp: 616 @ 7000 rpm. Carburetion: Holley four-barrel. Five main bearings. Engine was only available "over the counter" for $2500.

"SOHC 427" 8V V8: Hemispherical combustion chambers with overhead valves and overhead camshafts for each engine bank. Cast iron block and cylinder heads. Displacement: 427 cid. Bore and stroke: 4.23 x 3.78. Compression ratio: 12.1:1. Brake hp: 657 @ 7500 rpm. Carburetion: Two Holley four-barrels. Five main bearings. Availability as 4V version.

POLICE INTERCEPTOR V-8: Overhead valves. Cast iron block. Displacement: 428 cid. Bore and stroke: 4.13 x 3.98 inches. Compression ratio: 10.5:1. Brake hp: 360 at 5400 rpm. Carburetion: Holley four-barrel. Five main bearings. Serial number code 'P.'

FORD CHASSIS FEATURES: Wheelbase: 119 inches. Overall length: 210 inches (210.9 inches on station wagons). Tires: 7.35 x 15 four-ply tubeless blackwell (8.45 x 15 four-ply tubeless blackwell on station wagons).

FAIRLANE CHASSIS FEATURES: Wheelbase: 116 inches (113 inches on station wagons). Overall length: 197 inches (199.8 inches on station wagons). Tires: 6.95 x 14 four-ply tubeless blackwall (7.75 x 14 four-ply tubeless blackwall on station wagons).

FALCON CHASSIS FEATURES: Wheelbase: 110.9 inches (113 inches on station wagons). Overall length: 184.3 inches (198.7 inches on station wagons). Tires: 6.50 x 13 four-ply tubeless blackwalls (7.75 x 14 four-ply tubeless blackwall on station wagons).

THUNDERBIRD CHASSIS FEATURES: Wheelbase: 113.2 inches. Overall length: 205.4 inches. Tires: 8.15 x 15 four-ply tubeless blackwall.

FORD OPTIONS: Popular Custom and Custom 500 options included the 289 cid V-8 engine ($106). Cruise-O-Matic automatic transmission ($184). Power steering ($94). AM radio ($57). Wheelcovers ($22). White sidewall tires ($33). Popular Galaxie 500/Galaxie 500XL/Galaxie 500 7-Litre and Galaxie 500 LTD options included the 390 cid V-8 engine ($101 for two-barrel engine; $153 for four-barrel engine and not available in 7-Litre models). Power steering ($94). Power brakes ($42). Power windows ($99). Tinted windshield ($21). Air conditioning $353). AM radio ($57). AM/FM radio ($133). Vinyl roof on two-door hardtops ($74); on four-door hardtops ($83). White sidewall tires ($33). Popular station wagon options included all those in the Galaxie 500 models plus, power tailgate window ($31). Luggage rack ($44). Third passenger seat ($29).

FAIRLANE/FAIRLANE 500 OPTIONS: 289 cid V-8 engine ($105 and not available on GT). 390 cid V-8 engine ($206 and standard on GT). Cruise-O-Matic automatic transmission ($184 with 289 V-8; $214 with 390 V-8). Four-speed manual transmission ($183). AM radio ($57). Power steering ($84). Power tailgate window on station wagons ($31). Luggage rack on station wagons ($44). Two-tone paint ($21). White sidewall tires ($33). Wheelcovers ($21). Vinyl roof on two-door hardtops ($76).

FALCON OPTIONS: 200 cid six-cylinder engine ($26). The 289 cid V-8 engine ($131). Cruise-O-Matic automatic transmission ($167 with six-cylinder engine; $156 with 289 V-8). Power Steering ($84). Power tailgate on station wagons ($44). AM radio ($57). Vinyl roof on two-door models ($74). Wheelcovers ($21). White sidewall tires ($32).

THUNDERBIRD OPTIONS: Air conditioning ($413). The 428 cid V-8 engine ($64). Six-Way power seats ($193). Power windows ($103). Cruise control ($129). AM/FM radio ($82). Two-tone paint ($25). White sidewall tires with red stripe ($43).

HISTORICAL FOOTNOTES: The full-sized Fords were introduced Oct. 1, 1966 and all the Ford lines appeared in dealer showrooms the same day. Model year production peaked at 2,093,832 units. Calendar year sales of 2,038,415 cars were recorded. Donald N. Frey was the chief executive officer of the company this year. On a calendar year sales basis. Ford was the number two maker in America this year and held a 23.71 percent share of total market. Only 237 Ford Motor Co. products, of all types, had 427 cid V-8s installed during the 1966 calendar year.

1967 FORD

1967 FORDS — OVERVIEW — As in the previous 10 years, Ford continued to restyle at least one of the model lines. The 1967 full-size Fords were completely restyled from the previous year, sharing only drivetrains with the 1966 models. The new models were more rounded, with rounder tops and fenders. At the front end, stacked quad headlights were used once again, but the grille was all new. It was a double-stamped aluminum piece, featuring horizontal bars, divided by five vertical bars. The center portion of the grille projected forward and this point was duplicated in the forward edge of the hood and in the bumper configuration. The bodyside feature lines were in the same location as the 1966 models, but were somewhat less pronounced. The taillights were vertically situated rectangular units with chrome moldings and chrome cross-hairs surrounding the standard equipment back-up lights. All 1967 Fords are easily recognizable by the Energy-Absorbing steering wheels used in every model. A very large, deeply padded hub predominates the wheel. Also, all 1967 Fords were equipped with a dual brake master cylinder for the first time.

FORD CUSTOM SERIES — (ALL ENGINES) — The Custom Series was the base trim level Ford for 1967 and included chrome windshield and rear window moldings; a chrome horn ring; nylon carpeting, the Custom name in script on the front fenders and the Ford name, in block letters, spaced across the front of the hood and across the vertical section of the trunk lid.

CUSTOM SIX-CYLINDER I.D. NUMBERS: Custom six-cylinder models began with the number '7,' followed by the assembly plant code, engine designation code 'V' and, finally, the unit's production number, according to the final assembly location. Each plant began at 100001 and went up.

CUSTOM SIX SERIES

Model Number	Body/Style Number	Body Type & Seating	Factory Price	Shipping Weight	Production Total
V	54E	4-dr Sed-6P	2496	3469	Note 1
V	62E	2-dr Sed-6P	2441	3411	Note 1

CUSTOM V-8 SERIES I.D. NUMBERS: Custom V-8 models began with the number '7,' followed by the assembly plant code, body type code, engine designation code, and, finally, the unit's production number, according to the final assembly location. Each plant began at 100001 and went up.

CUSTOM V-8 SERIES

Model Number	Body/Style Number	Body Type & Seating	Factory Price	Shipping Weight	Production Total
NA	62E	4-dr Sed-6P	2602	3507	41,417
NA	62E	2-dr Sed-6P	2548	3449	18,107

PRODUCTION NOTE: Total series output was 59,524 units. Ford does not indicate the number of each model produced with sixes and V-8s. Therefore, all production figures given above are total production of each body style with both engines.

CUSTOM 500 SERIES — (ALL ENGINES) — The Custom 500 was the upper trim level of the base-line Custom Series and included all the Custom trim, plus special Custom 500 exterior trim and choices of four different upholsteries on the interior.

CUSTOM 500 SIX-CYLINDER SERIES I.D. NUMBERS: Custom 500 six-cylinder models used the same serial number sequence as the Custom models.

CUSTOM 500 SIX SERIES

Model Number	Body/Style Number	Body Type & Seating	Factory Price	Shipping Weight	Production Total
V	54B	4-dr Sed-6P	2551	3471	Note 1
V	62B	2-dr Sed-6P	2595	3513	Note 1

NOTE 1: See Custom 500 V-8 series listing. Production was counted by series and body style only, with no breakout per engine type.

CUSTOM 500 V-8 SERIES I.D. NUMBERS: Custom 500, V-8 models used the same serial number sequence as the Custom models.

CUSTOM 500 V-8 SERIES

Model Number	Body/Style Number	Body Type & Seating	Factory Price	Shipping Weight	Production Total
NA	54B	4-dr Sed-6P	2701	3509	83,260
NA	62B	2-dr Sed-6P	2659	3451	18,146

PRODUCTION NOTE: Total series output was 101,406 units. Ford does not indicate the number of each model produced with sixes and V-8s. Therefore, all production figures given above are total production of each body style with both engines.

GALAXIE 500 SERIES — (ALL ENGINES) — The Galaxie 500 was the intermediate trim level for 1967 and included all the Custom Series trim, plus stamped aluminum lower bodyside moldings; chrome side window moldings; simulated woodgrain appliques on the instrument panel and inner door panels and a stamped aluminum trim panel on the vertical section of the trunk lid. The name, Galaxie 500, in block letters, was located on the rear fenders and the Ford crest was located on the trunk lid above the aluminum trim panel.

GALAXIE 500 SIX-CYLINDER SERIES I.D. NUMBERS: Galaxie 500 six-cylinder models used the same serial number sequence as the custom Series.

GALAXIE 500 SIX SERIES

Model Number	Body/Style Number	Body Type & Seating	Factory Price	Shipping Weight	Production Total
V	54A	4-dr Sed-6P	2732	3481	Note 1
V	57B	4-dr FsBk Sed-6P	2808	3552	Note 1
V	63B	2-dr FsBk Cpe-6P	2755	3484	Note 1
V	76A	2-dr Conv-6P	3003	3660	Note 1

NOTE 1: See Galaxie 500 V-8 Series listing. Production was counted by series and body style only, with no breakout per engine type.

GALAXIE 500 V-8 SERIES I.D. NUMBERS: Galaxie 500, V-8 models used the same serial number sequence as the Custom and Custom 500 models.

GALAXIE 500 V-8 SERIES

Model Number	Body/Style Number	Body Type & Seating	Factory Price	Shipping Weight	Production Total
NA	54A	4-dr Sed-6P	2838	3519	130,063
N	57B	4-dr FsBk Sed-6P	2743	3526	57,087
NA	63B	2-dr FSBK Cpe-6P	2861	3522	197,388
NA	76A	2-dr Conv-6P	3110	3704	19,068

PRODUCTION NOTE: Total series output was 403,606 units. Ford does not indicate the number of each model produced with sixes and V-8s. Therefore, all production figures given above are total production of each body style with both engines.

GALAXIE 500XL V-8 SERIES — (ALL ENGINES) — The Galaxie 500XL was the sport trim version of the two-door fastback and two-door convertible and included the 200 hp '289' V-8 engine and SelectShift Cruise-O-Matic automatic transmission as standard equipment. Also, the model line included bucket seats and front console; all Galaxie 500 trim; special ornamentation; automatic courtesy and warning lights in the door panels; and chrome trim on the foot pedals.

GALAXIE 500XL V-8 SERIES I.D. NUMBERS: Galaxie 500XLs used the same serial number sequence as the Custom and Galaxie Series.

GALAXIE 500XL V-8 SERIES

Model Number	Body/Style Number	Body Type & Seating	Factory Price	Shipping Weight	Production Total
NA	63C	2-dr FsBk Cpe-5P	3243	3594	18,174
NA	76B	2-dr Conv-5P	3493	3704	5,161

PRODUCTION NOTE: Total series output was 23,335 units.

1967 Ford, LTD two-door hardtop sports coupe, V-8

LTD V-8 SERIES — (ALL ENGINES) — The LTD was the top trim level full-size Ford for 1967 and was considered its own series for the first time since introduced in 1965. LTDs included all the Galaxie 500 trim, plus the 200 hp 289 V-8 engine and SelectShift Cruise-O-Matic automatic transmission as standard equipment. Other regular features were flow-through ventilation system; distinctive LTD trim and ornamentation; special wheelcovers; simulated woodgrain on the instrument panel and door panels; automatic courtesy and warning lights in the doors; deep-foam cushioning in the seating surfaces; pull-down armrests front and rear; color-keyed steering wheel; and vinyl top on two-door hardtops.

LTD V-8 SERIES I.D. NUMBERS: LTDs used the serial number sequence as the Custom and Galaxie Series.

LTD V-8 SERIES

Model Number	Body/Style Number	Body Type & Seating	Factory Price	Shipping Weight	Production Total
NA	54F	4-dr Sed-6P	3298	3795	12,491
NA	57F	4-dr HT Sed-6P	3363	3676	51,978
NA	63F	2-dr HT Cpe-6P	3362	3626	46,036

PRODUCTION NOTE: Total series output was 110,505 units.

STATION WAGON SERIES — (ALL ENGINES) — The Ranch Wagon was the base trim level station wagon for 1967, with the Country Sedans being the intermediate level and the Country Squires being the top trim level. The trim paralleled the Custom 500, Galaxie 500 and LTD models of conventional cars.

STATION WAGON SIX-CYLINDER SERIES I.D. NUMBERS: Station wagon six-cylinder models used the same serial number sequence as Custom and Galaxie 500 Series of conventional cars.

STATION WAGON SIX SERIES

Model Number	Body/Style Number	Body Type & Seating	Factory Price	Shipping Weight	Production Total
V	71D	4-dr Ranch Wag-6P	2836	3911	Note 1
V	71B	4-dr Cty Sed-6P	2935	3924	Note 1
V	71C	4-dr Cty Sed-9P	3061	4004	Note 1
V	71E	4-dr Cty Squire-6P	3234	3971	Note 1
V	71A	4-dr Cty Squire-9P	3359	4011	Note 1

NOTE 1: See station wagon V-8 series listing. Production was counted by series and body style only, with no breakout per engine type.

STATION WAGON V-8 SERIES I.D. NUMBERS: Station wagon V-8 models used the same serial number sequence as the Custom and Galaxie 500 Series of conventional cars.

STATION WAGON V-8 SERIES

Model Number	Body/Style Number	Body Type & Seating	Factory Price	Shipping Weight	Production Total
NA	71D	4-dr Ranch Wag-6P	2943	3949	23,932
NA	71B	4-dr Cty Sed-6P	2042	3962	50,818
NA	71C	4-dr Cty Sed-9P	3168	4042	34,377
NA	71E	4-dr Cty Sq-9P	3340	4009	25,600
NA	71A	4-dr Cty Sq-9P	3466	4049	44,024

PRODUCTION NOTE: Total series output was 178,751 units. Ford does not indicate the number of each model produced with sixes and V-8s. Therefore, all production figures given above are total production of each body style with both engines.

1967 FAIRLANES OVERVIEW — The Fairlane continued to use the body introduced in 1966 with minor trim changes. The new grille was a single aluminum stamping instead of the two grilles used in the previous model and the taillights were divided horizontally by the back-up light, instead of vertically as in 1966.

FAIRLANE MODELS — (ALL ENGINES) — The Fairlane was the base trim level for 1967 and included chrome windshield and rear window moldings; chrome rain gutter moldings; a chrome horn ring; front and rear armrests; cigarette lighter; vinyl coated rubber floor mats; and a single horizontal chrome trim strip along the bodyside, with the Fairlane name, in block letters, at the forward end.

FAIRLANE SIX-CYLINDER SERIES I.D. NUMBERS: Fairlane six-cylinder models began with the number '7,' followed by the assembly plant code, body type code, engine designation 'T' and, finally, the unit's production number, according to the final assembly location. Each plant began at 100001 and went up.

FAIRLANE SIX-CYLINDER SERIES

Model Number	Body/Style Number	Body Type & Seating	Factory Price	Shipping Weight	Production Total
T	54	4-dr Sed-6P	2339	2782	Note 1
T	62	2-dr Sed-6P	2297	2747	Note 1
T	71	4-dr Sta Wag-6P	2643	3198	Note 1

NOTE 1: See Fairlane V-8 Series listing. Production was counted by series and body style only, with no breakout per engine type.

FAIRLANE V-8 SERIES I.D. NUMBERS: Fairlane V-8 models began with the number '7,' followed by the assembly plant code. body type code, engine designation code and, finally, the unit's production number, according to the final assembly location. Each plant began at 100001 and went up.

FAIRLANE V-8 SERIES

Model Number	Body/Style Number	Body Type & Seating	Factory Price	Shipping Weight	Production Total
NA	54A	4-dr Sed-6P	2445	2951	19,740
NA	62A	2-dr Sed-6P	2402	2916	10,628
NA	71D	4-dr Sta Wag-6P	2748	3367	10,881

PRODUCTION NOTE: Total series output was 41,249 units. Ford does not indicate the number of each model produced with sixes and V-8s. Therefore, all production figures given above are total production of each body style with both engines.

1967 Ford, Fairlane 500 four-door sedan, V-8

FAIRLANE 500 SERIES — (ALL ENGINES) — The Fairlane 500 was the intermediate trim level for 1967 and included all the Fairlane trim, plus special Fairlane 500 trim and moldings; color-keyed carpet front and rear and a choice of four nylon and vinyl upholsteries. Also included was a stamped aluminum lower bodyside molding which contained the Fairlane name, in block letters, at the forward edge and another aluminum stamping containing the Ford name, in block letters, located on the vertical section of the trunk lid.

FAIRLANE 500 SIX-CYLINDER SERIES I.D. NUMBERS: Fairlane 500, six-cylinder models used the same serial number sequence as the Fairlane models.

FAIRLANE 500 SIX SERIES

Model Number	Body/Style Number	Body Type & Seating	Factory Price	Shipping Weight	Production Total
T	54B	4-dr Sed-6P	2417	2802	Note 1
T	62B	2-dr Sed-6P	2377	2755	Note 1
T	63B	2-dr HT Cpe-6P	2439	2842	Note 1
T	76B	2-dr Conv-6P	2664	3159	Note 1
T	71B	4-dr Sta Wag-6P	2718	3206	Note 1
T	71E	4-dr Sq Wag-6P	2902	3217	Note 1

NOTE 1: See Fairlane 500 V-8 Series listing. Production was counted by series and body style only. with no breakout per engine type.

FAIRLANE 500 V-8 SERIES I.D. NUMBERS: Fairlane 500 V-8 models used the same serial number sequence as the Fairlane models.

FAIRLANE 500 V-8 SERIES

Model Number	Body/Style Number	Body Type & Seating	Factory Price	Shipping Weight	Production Total
NA	54B	4-dr Sed-6P	2522	2971	52,552
NA	628	2-dr Sed-6P	2482	2924	8,473
NA	NA	2-dr HT Cpe-6P	2545	3011	70,135
NA	76B	2-dr Conv-6P	2770	3328	5,428
NA	71B	4-dr Sta Wag-6P	2824	3375	15,902
NA	71E	4-dr Sq Wag-6P	3007	3386	8,348

PRODUCTION NOTE: Total series output was 159,838 units. Ford does not indicate the number of each model produced with sixes and V-8s. Therefore, all production figures given above are total production of each body style with both engines.

FAIRLANE 500XL SERIES — (ALL ENGINES) — The Fairlane 500XL was the sporty version of the Fairlane 500 Series and included all the Fairlane 500 features, plus bucket seats and console; special name plaques and exterior trim; Deluxe wheelcovers; and red safety lights and white courtesy lights in the lower interior door panels

FAIRLANE 500XL SIX-CYLINDER SERIES I.D. NUMBERS: Fairlane 500XL six-cylinder models used the same serial number sequence as the Fairlane and Fairlane 500 models.

FAIRLANE 500XL SIX SERIES

Model Number	Body/Style Number	Body Type & Seating	Factory Price	Shipping Weight	Production Total
T	63C	2-dr HT Cpe-5P	2619	2870	Note 1
T	76C	2-dr Conv-5P	2843	3187	Note 1

NOTE 1: See Fairlane 500XL V-8 series listing, with no breakout per engine style only.

FAIRLANE 500XL V-8 SERIES I.D. NUMBERS: Fairlane 500XL V-8 models used the same serial number sequence as the Fairlane and Fairlane 500 models.

FAIRLANE 500XL V-8 SERIES

Model Number	Body/Style Number	Body Type & Seating	Factory Price	Shipping Weight	Production Total
NA	63C	2-dr HT Cpe-5P	2724	3039	14,871
NA	76C	2-dr Conv-5P	2950	3356	1,943
NA	63D	2-dr GT HT Cpe-5P	2839	3301	18,670
NA	76D	2-dr GT Conv-5P	3064	3607	2,117

PRODUCTION NOTE: Total series output was 37,601 units. Ford does not indicate the number of each model produced with sixes and V-8s. Therefore, all production figures given above are total production of each body style with both engines.

1967 Ford, Falcon Futura two-door sedan, V-8

1967 FALCON — OVERVIEW — Like the Fairlane lineup, the 1967 Falcons continued to use the body introduced in 1966, with only minor trim changes. The most noticeable change in the two years, was the scoop-like indentations behind the front wheel openings, on the front fenders. The grille was nearly identical, with a horizontal and vertical dividing bar being the only difference.

FALCON SERIES — (ALL ENGINES) — The Falcons were the base trim level of the compact Falcon line for 1967 and included chrome windshield, rear window and rain gutter moldings, armrests on the front doors only and a horn button, instead of the chrome horn ring found on Futura models. The Falcon name, in script, was located on the rear fender, just ahead of the taillights and, in block letters, across the vertical section of the trunk lid.

FALCON SERIES I.D. NUMBERS — (ALL ENGINES) — Falcons used the same serial number sequence as the full-size Ford and Fairlane lines.

FALCON SERIES

Model Number	Body/Style Number	Body Type & Seating	Factory Price	Shipping Weight	Production Total
NA	54A	4-dr Sed-6P	2167	2551	13,554
NA	62A	2-dr Sed-6P	2118	2520	16,082
NA	71A	4-dr Sta Wag-6P	2497	3030	5,553

PRODUCTION NOTE: Total series output was 35,198 units. Ford does not indicate the number of each model produced with sixes and V-8s. Therefore, all production figures given above are total production of each body style with both engines.

FUTURA SERIES — (ALL ENGINES) — The Futura Series was the top trim level for 1967 and included all the standard Falcon features, plus a cigarette lighter, armrests and ashtrays on all doors; a chrome horn ring; nylon carpeting; special Futura moldings; trim, emblems and nameplates; and chrome side window frames. In addition, the sports coupe offered front bucket seats, special nameplates, a map light, ashtray, glovebox and trunk lights, 7.35 x 14 tires, a 'side accent stripe,' remote-control outside driver's mirror and Deluxe seat belts.

FUTURA SERIES I.D. NUMBERS: Futura models used the same serial number sequence as the full-size Fords. Fairlanes and Falcons.

FUTURA SERIES

Model Number	Body/Style Number	Body Type & Seating	Factory Price	Shipping Weight	Production Total
NA	54B	4-dr Sed-6P	2322	2559	11,254
NA	62B	2-dr Sed-6P	2280	2528	6,287
NA	62C	2-dr HT Spt Cpe-5P	2437	3062	7,053
NA	718	4-dr Sq Wag-6P	2609	2556	4,552

PRODUCTION NOTE: Total series output was 29,146 units. Ford does not indicate the number of each model produced with sixes and V-8s. Therefore, all production figures given above are total production of each body style with both engines.

THUNDERBIRD SERIES — (ALL ENGINES) — The 1967 Thunderbirds were totally restyled once again. The front end featured a full-width grille with hidden headlights and a large Thunderbird emblem floating in the center of the grille. As in 1966, the rear end featured a large, single taillight lens with a horizontal trim strip in the center. In addition, there were back-up lights, in the center of the strip, giving the impression of a large round taillight. For the first time in the Thunderbird's history, a four-door sedan, called the 'Landau Sedan,' was offered. This Landau was different than the sedans in that the rear doors opened to the front, giving the nickname 'suicide doors.'

1967 Ford, Thunderbird four-door Landau Sedan, V-8 (AA)

THUNDERBIRD SERIES I.D. NUMBERS — (ALL ENGINES) — Thunderbird models began with the number '7,' assembly plant code 'Y' (Wixom), body type code, engine type code 'Z' or 'Q' and, finally, the unit's production number, beginning at 100001 and going up.

THUNDERBIRD SERIES

Model Number	Body/Style Number	Body Type & Seating	Factory Price	Shipping Weight	Production Total
Z/Q	65A	2-dr HT-4P	4603	4348	15,567
Z/Q	65B	2-dr Landau-4P	4704	4256	37,422
Z/Q	57B	4-dr Landau-4P	4825	4348	24,967

PRODUCTION NOTE: Total series output was 77,956 units.

ENGINES

FALCON/FAIRLANE SIX-CYLINDER: Overhead valves. Cast iron block. Displacement: 170 cid. Bore and stroke: 3.50 x 2.94 inches. Compression ratio: 9.1:1. Brake hp: 105 at 4400 rpm. Carburetion: Holley one-barrel. Seven main bearings. Serial number code '4.'

FALCON/FAIRLANE/MUSTANG SIX-CYLINDER: Overhead valves. Cast iron block. Displacement: 200 cid. Bore and stroke: 3.68 x 3.13 inches. Compression ratio: 9.2:1. Brake hp: 120 at 4400 rpm. Carburetion: Holley one-barrel. Seven main bearings. Serial number code 'U.'

FORD SIX-CYLINDER: Overhead valves. Cast iron block. Displacement: 240 cid. Bore and stroke: 4.00 x 3.18 inches. Compression ratio: 9.2:1. Brake hp: 150 at 4000 rpm. Carburetion: Holley one-barrel. Seven main bearings. Serial number code 'V.' (Police code B; taxi code E)

CHALLENGER 289 V-8: Overhead valves. Cast iron block. Displacement: 289 cid. Bore and stroke: 4.00 x 2.87 inches. Compression ratio: 9.3:1. Brake hp: 200 at 4400 rpm. Carburetion: Holley two-barrel. Five main bearings. Serial number code 'C.'

CHALLENGER 289 V-8: Overhead valves. Cast iron block. Displacement: 289 cid. Bore and stroke: 4.00 x 2.87 inches. Compression ratio: 10.0:1. Brake hp: 225 at 4800 rpm. Carburetion: Holley four-barrel. Five main bearings. Serial number code 'A.'

HIGH-PERFORMANCE 289 V-8: Overhead valves: Cast iron block. Displacement: 289 cid. Bore and stroke: 4.00 x 2.87 inches. Compression ratio: 10.5:1. Brake hp: 271 at 6000 rpm. Carburetion: Holley four-barrel. Five main bearings. Serial number code 'K.'

INTERCEPTOR V-8: Overhead valves. Cast iron block. Displacement: 352 cid. Bore and stroke: 4.00 x 3.50 inches. Compression ratio: 9.3:1. Brake hp: 250 at 4400 rpm. Carburetion: Holley four-barrel. Five main bearings. Serial number code 'X.'

THUNDERBIRD V-8: Overhead valves. Cast iron block. Displacement: 390 cid. Bore and stroke: 4.05 x 3.78 inches. Compression ratio: 9.5:1. Brake hp: 275 at 4400 rpm. Carburetion: Holley two-barrel. Five main bearings. Serial number codes 'Y' or (Special) 'H.'

THUNDERBIRD FOUR-BARREL V-8: Overhead valves. Cast iron block. Displacement: 390 cid. Bore and stroke: 4.05 x 3.78 inches. Compression ratio: 10.5:1. Brake hp: 315 at 4600 rpm. Carburetion: Holley four-barrel. Five main bearings. Serial number code "Z."

GT 390 V-8: Overhead valves. Cast iron block. Displacement: 390 cid. Bore and stroke: 4.05 x 3.78 inches. Compression ratio: 11.0:1. Brake hp: 335 at 4800 rpm. Carburetion: Holley four-barrel. Five main bearings. Serial number code "S."

THUNDERBIRD HIGH-PERFORMANCE V-8: Overhead valves. Cast iron block. Displacement: 427 cid. Bore and stroke: 4.23 x 3.78 inches. Compression ratio: 11.0:1. Brake hp: 410 15 5600 rpm. Carburetion: Holley four-barrel. Five main bearings. Serial number code "W."

THUNDERBIRD SUPER HIGH-PERFORMANCE V-8: Overhead valves. Cast iron block. Displacement: 427 cid. Bore and stroke: 4.23 x 3.78 inches. Compression ratio: 11.5:1. Brake hp: 425 at 6000 rpm. Carburetion: Two (2) Holley four-barrels. Five main bearings. Serial number code "R."

THUNDERBIRD SPECIAL V-8: Overhead valves. Cast iron block. Displacement: 428 cid. Bore and stroke: 4.13 x 3.98 inches. Compression ratio: 10.5:1. Brake hp: 345 at 4600 rpm. Carburetion: Holley four-barrel. Five main bearings. Serial number code "Q."

"SOHC 427" 4V V8: Hemispherical combustion chambers with overhead valves and overhead camshafts for each engine bank. Cast iron block and cylinder heads. Displacement: 427 cid. Bore and stroke: 4.23 x 3.78. Compression ratio: 12.1:1. Brake hp: 616 @ 7000 rpm. Carburetion: Holley four-barrel. Five main bearings. Engine was only available "over the counter" for $2500.

"SOHC 427" 8V V8: Hemispherical combustion chambers with overhead valves and overhead camshafts for each engine bank. Cast iron block and cylinder heads. Displacement: 427 cid. Bore and stroke: 4.23 x 3.78. Compression ratio: 12.1:1. Brake hp: 657 @ 7500 rpm. Carburetion: Two Holley four-barrels. Five main bearings. Availability as 4V version.

POLICE INTERCEPTOR V-8: Overhead valves. Cast iron block. Displacement: 428 cid. Bore and stroke: 4.13 x 3.98 inches. Compression ratio: 10.5:1. Brake hp: 360 at 5400 rpm. Carburetion: Holley four-barrel. Five main bearings. Serial number code 'P.'

NOTE: A tunnel-port 427 was available as an over-the-counter kit, with tunnel-port intake on special cylinder heads and special intake manifold.

FORD CHASSIS FEATURES: Wheelbase: 119 inches. Overall length: (station wagons) 213.9 inches; (other models) 213 inches. Tires: (sedans) 7.75 x 15 four-ply tubeless blackwall; (hardtops) 8.15 x 15 four-ply tubeless blackwall; (station wagons) 8.45 x 15 four-ply tubeless blackwall.

FAIRLANE CHASSIS FEATURES: Wheelbase: (station wagons) 113 inches; (other models) 116 inches. Overall length: (station wagons) 199.8 inches; (other models) 197 inches. Tires: (hardtops and station wagons) 7.15 x 14 four-ply tubeless blackwall, (other models) 6.95 x 14 four-ply tubeless blackwall.

FALCON CHASSIS FEATURES: Wheelbase: (station wagons) 113 inches: (other models) 110.9 inches. Overall length: (station wagons) 19.7 inches; (other models) 184.3 inches. Tires: (sport coupe) 7.35 x 14 four-ply tubeless blackwall; (station wagons) 7.75 x 14 four-ply tubeless blackwall; (other models) 6.50 x 13 four-ply tubeless blackwall.

THUNDERBIRD SERIES CHASSIS FEATURES: Wheelbase: (four-door Landau) 117 inches; (other models) 115 inches. Overall length: (four-door Landau) 209.9 inches; (other models) 206.9 inches. Tires: 8.15 x 15 four-ply tubeless blackwall.

FORD OPTIONS: 200 hp/289 cid V-8 engine ($107). 275 hp/ 390 cid V-8 engine ($78 in XLs and LTDS; $184 in all others). 315 hp/390 cid V-8 engine ($158 in XLs and LTDS; $265 in all others). Cruise-O-Matic automatic transmission ($188 to $220 depending on engine choice). Four-speed manual transmission ($184). Power steering ($95). Power brakes ($42). Tinted windshield ($21). Air conditioning ($356). AM radio ($57). AM/FM radio ($134). Vinyl roof on two-door hardtops ($74); on four-door hardtops ($83). White sidewall tires ($35).

STATION WAGON OPTIONS: Included all those in the Custom and Galaxie 500 models, plus power tailgate window ($32). Luggage rack ($44). Deluxe adjustable luggage rack ($63).

FAIRLANE OPTIONS: Included the 200 hp/289 cid V-8 engine ($106, standard on GT models). 390 cid V-8 engines ($184 for two-barrel version, $264 for four-barrel version). Cruise-O-Matic automatic transmission ($188 to $220). Four-speed manual transmission ($184). AM radio ($57). Power steering ($84). Power tailgate window in station wagons ($32). Luggage rack on station wagons ($44). Two-tone paint ($22). White sidewall tires ($34). Wheelcovers ($41). Vinyl roofs on two-door hardtops ($74).

FALCON OPTIONS: Included the 200 cid six-cylinder engine ($26). 289 cid V-8 engine ($132). Four-barrel 289 cid V-8 engine ($183). Cruise-O-Matic automatic transmission ($187). Four-speed manual transmission ($184). Power steering ($84). Power tailgate window on station wagons ($32). Tinted windshield ($21). Luggage rack on station wagons ($44). AM radio ($57). Eight-track stereo tape ($128). Two-tone paint ($19). Vinyl roof on two-door sedans ($74). Wheelcovers ($21). White sidewall tires ($32).

THUNDERBIRD OPTIONS: Included the 345 hp, 428 cid V-8 engine ($91). Six-way power seats ($98 — driver's seat only). Power windows ($104). Cruise Control ($130). Air conditioning ($421). AM/8-track stereo radio ($128). AM/FM radio ($90). AM/FM multiplex stereo radio ($164). Two-tone paint ($25). White sidewall tires with red band ($52).

HISTORICAL FOOTNOTES: The 1967 Fords were introduced Sept. 30, 1966. The grand total of assemblies for the 1967 model year was 1,742,311 units. This included, 877,128 Fords; 238,688 Fairlanes; 76,500 Falcons; 472,121 Mustangs; and 77,956 Thunderbirds. Calendar year production for all the above lines peaked at 240,712 units. As far as sales and production, it was a good year for America's number two automaker. However, vice president and general manager M.S. McLaughlin did have other things to deal with, such as a 57 day United Auto Worker's strike. It was the longest lasting labor dispute in Ford history and culminated in a three-year contract agreement that included unprecedented wage and benefits packages. A positive note was the performance of the Ford GT-40 in the European Grand Prix racing circuit. A trio of these cars, running at LeMans, finished first, second and third. It was the first time American entries had ever captured the championship honors in the prestigious race.

1968 FORD

1968 FORDS — OVERVIEW — For the first time in 10 years, only one of the Ford lines received major restyling. The remainder of the model lineup stayed basically the same as in 1967. The 1968 full-size Fords were basically 1967 body shells with updated front ends. The two years look completely different. to be sure, but there is very little that changed behind the

windshield. The new grillework was less protruding than the 1967 version and offered hidden headlights on the upper lines. It was a honeycomb grille with a single, centrally located vertical dividing bar. The Ford name, in block letters, and the Ford crest, in a small emblem on the driver's side headlight door, appeared. The rooflines were a little more formal than the previous year and the taillights, although retaining the same shape, were divided horizontally by the back-up lights, rather than vertically. The large, padded hub used on the steering wheels of all 1967 Fords, was replaced by a more conventional pad covering the entire center spoke. More federally mandated safety regulations appeared in the form of front and rear fender marker lights. Power-wise, the mighty 427 cid V-8 engine was detuned to 390 hp by limiting carburetion to a single four-barrel and replacing the wild, solid-lifter camshaft with a more timid hydraulic lifter cam. At midyear, the 427 was discontinued and replaced by the equally famous and powerful Cobra Jet 428 and Super Cobra Jet 428 V-8s. These engines dominated the Super Stock classes at the drag races in 1968, when installed in the light Mustang bodies. Also, the new lightweight '385' series engines, displacing 429 cid, became the top power option in the big Thunderbirds.

FORD CUSTOM SERIES — (ALL ENGINES) — The Custom Series was the base trim level Ford for 1968 and included chrome windshield and rear window moldings; a chrome horn ring: nylon carpeting; the Custom name, in script, on the rear fenders; and Ford, in block letters, across the front of the hood.

CUSTOM SIX-CYLINDER SERIES I.D. NUMBERS: Custom six-cylinder models began with the number '8,' followed by the assembly plant code, engine designation 'V' and, finally, the unit's production number, according to the final assembly location. Each plant began at 100001 and went up.

CUSTOM SIX SERIES

Model Number	Body/Style Number	Body Type & Seating	Factory Price	Shipping Weight	Production Total
V	54E	4-dr Sed-6P	2642	3478	Note 1
V	62E	2-dr Sed-6P	2584	3451	Note 1

NOTE 1: See Custom V-8 Series listing. Production was counted by series and body style only, with no breakout per engine type.

CUSTOM V-8 SERIES I.D. NUMBERS: Custom V-8 models began with the number '8,' followed by the assembly plant code, body type code, engine designation code and, finally, the unit's production number, according to the final assembly location. Each plant began at 100001 and went up.

CUSTOM V-8 SERIES

Model Number	Body/Style Number	Body Type & Seating	Factory Price	Shipping Weight	Production Total
NA	54E	4-dr Sed-6P	2749	3518	45,980
NA	62E	2-dr Sed-6P	2691	3491	18,485

PRODUCTION NOTE: Total series output was 64,465 units. Ford does not indicate the number of each model produced with sixes or V-8s. Therefore, all production figures given above are total production of each body style with both engines.

CUSTOM 500 SERIES — (ALL ENGINES) — The Custom 500 was the upper trim level of the base-line Custom Series and included all the Custom trim, plus special Custom 500 exterior trim, a single horizontal chrome strip along the bodyside feature line and choices of four different upholsteries on the interior.

CUSTOM 500 SIX-CYLINDER SERIES I.D. NUMBERS: Custom 500 six-cylinder models used the same serial number sequence as the Custom models.

CUSTOM 500 SIX SERIES

Model Number	Body/Style Number	Body Type & Seating	Factory Price	Shipping Weight	Production Total
V	54B	4-dr Sed-6P	2741	3491	Note 1
V	62B	2-dr Sed-6P	2699	3440	Note 1

NOTE 1: See Custom 500 V-8 Series listing. Production was counted by series and body style only, with no breakout per engine type.

CUSTOM 500 V-8 SERIES I.D. NUMBERS: Custom 500 V-8 models used the same serial number sequence as the Custom models.

CUSTOM 500 V-8 SERIES

Model Number	Body/Style Number	Body Type & Seating	Factory Price	Shipping Weight	Production Total
NA	54B	4-dr Sed-6P	2848	3531	49,398
NA	62B	2-dr Sed-6P	2806	3480	8,938

PRODUCTION NOTE: Total series output was 58,336 units Ford does not indicate the number of each model produced with sixes and V-8s. Therefore, all production figures given above are total production of each body style with both engines.

1968 Ford, Galaxie 500 two-door convertible, V-8

GALAXIE 500 SERIES — (ALL ENGINES) — The Galaxie 500 was the intermediate trim level for 1968 and included all the Custom Series trim, plus stamped aluminum rocker panel moldings; simulated woodgrain appliques on the instrument panel and inner door panels and a stamped aluminum trim panel on the vertical section of the trunk lid. The name Ford, in block letters, was located on the vertical section of the trunk, on the passenger side of the car. The name Galaxie 500, in script, was located on the rear fenders, just in front of the taillights.

GALAXIE 500 SIX-CYLINDER SERIES I.D. NUMBERS: Galaxie 500 six-cylinder models used the same serial number sequence as the Custom Series.

GALAXIE 500 SIX SERIES

Model Number	Body/Style Number	Body Type & Seating	Factory Price	Shipping Weight	Production Total
V	54A	4-dr Sed-6P	2864	3496	Note 1
V	578	4-dr HT Sed-6P	2936	3542	Note 1
V	638	2-dr FsBk Cpe-6P	2881	3514	Note 1
V	65C	2-dr HT Cpe-6P	2916	3520	Note 1
V	76A	2-dr Conv-6P	3108	3659	Note 1

NOTE 1: See Galaxie 500 V-8 Series listing. Production was counted by series and body style only, with no breakout per engine type.

GALAXIE 500 V-8 SERIES I.D. NUMBERS: Galaxie 500 V-8 models used the same serial number sequence as the Custom Series.

GALAXIE 500 V-8 SERIES

Model Number	Body/Style Number	Body Type & Seating	Factory Price	Shipping Weight	Production Total
NA	54A	4-dr Sed-6P	2971	3536	117,877
NA	57B	4-dr HT Sed-6P	3043	3582	55,461
NA	63B	2-dr FsBk Cpe-6P	2988	3554	69,760
NA	65C	2-dr HT Cpe-6P	3023	3560	84,332
NA	76A	2-dr Conv-6P	3215	3699	11,832

PRODUCTION NOTE: Total series output was 339,262 units. Ford does not indicate the number of each model produced with sixes and V-8s. Therefore, all production figures given above are total production of each body style with both engines.

GALAXIE 500XL V-8 SERIES — (ALL ENGINES) — The Galaxie 500XL was the sport trim version of the Galaxie 500 two-door fastback and two-door convertible and included the 210 hp, 302 cid V-8 engine and SelectShift Cruise-O-Matic automatic transmission as standard equipment. Also, the model line included bucket seats and front console; hidden headlights; special 'XL' crest in the center of the hood; automatic courtesy; and warning lights in the door panels and chrome trim on the foot pedals.

GALAXIE 500XL V-8 SERIES I.D. NUMBERS: Galaxie 500XLs used the same serial number sequence as the Custom Series and standard Galaxie 500 models.

GALAXIE 500XL V-8 SERIES

Model Number	Body/Style Number	Body Type & Seating	Factory Price	Shipping Weight	Production Total
NA	63C	2-dr FsBk Cpe-5P	3092	3608	50.048
NA	76B	2-dr Conv-5P	3321	3765	6,066

PRODUCTION NOTE: Total series output was 56,114 units.

LTD V-8 SERIES — (ALL ENGINES) — The LTD was the top trim level full-size Ford for 1968 and included all the Galaxie 500 trim, plus the 210 hp, 302 cid V-8 engine and Select-Shift Cruise-O-Matic automatic transmission as standard equipment. Also included in the LTD package was flow-through ventilation; distinctive LTD trim and ornamentation; special wheelcovers; simulated woodgrain appliques on the instrument panel and inner door panels; automatic courtesy and warning lights in the doors; deep-foam cushioning in the seating surfaces; pull-down armrests, front and rear; color-keyed steering wheel; and vinyl top on two-door hardtops.

LTD V-8 SERIES I.D. NUMBERS: LTDs used the same serial number sequence as the Custom and Galaxie Series.

LTD V-8 SERIES

Model Number	Body/Style Number	Body Type & Seating	Factory Price	Shipping Weight	Production Total
NA	54C	4-dr Sed-6P	3135	3596	22.834
NA	57F	4-dr HT Sed-6P	3206	3642	61.755
NA	65A	2-dr HT Cpe-6P	3153	3679	54.163

PRODUCTION NOTE: Total series output was 138,752 units.

STATION WAGON SERIES — (ALL ENGINES) — The Ranch Wagon was the base trim level station wagon for 1968, with the Custom Ranch Wagons and the Country Sedans being the intermediate trim level and the Country Squires being the top trim level. The trim paralleled the Custom, Custom 500, Galaxie 500 and LTD models of conventional cars.

STATION WAGON SIX-CYLINDER SERIES I.D. NUMBERS: Station wagon six-cylinder models used the same serial number sequence as Custom and Galaxie 500 Series of conventional cars.

STATION WAGON SIX SERIES

Model Number	Body/Style Number	Body Type & Seating	Factory Price	Shipping Weight	Production Total
V	71D	4-dr Ranch Wag-6P	3000	3905	Note 1
V	71H	4-dr Cus Wag-6P	3063	3915	Note 1
V	71J	4-dr Cus Wag-9P	3176	3961	Note 1
V	71B	4-dr Cty Sed-6P	3181	3924	Note 1
V	71C	4-dr Cty Sed-9P	3295	3981	Note 1

NOTE 1: See station wagon V-8 Series listing. Production was counted by series and body style only, with no breakout per engine type.

STATION WAGON V-8 SERIES I.D. NUMBERS: Station wagon V-8 models used the same serial number sequence as the Custom and Galaxie 500 Series of conventional cars.

STATION WAGON V-8 SERIES

Model Number	Body/Style Number	Body Type & Seating	Factory Price	Shipping Weight	Production Total
NA	71D	4-dr Ranch Wag-6P	3107	3945	18,237
NA	71H	4-dr Cus Wag-6P	3170	3955	18,181
NA	71J	4-dr Cus Wag-9P	3283	4001	13,421
NA	71B	4-dr Cty Sed-6P	3288	3964	39,335
NA	71C	4-dr Cty Sed-9P	3402	4021	29,374
NA	71E	4-dr Cty Sq-6P	3539	4013	33,994
NA	71A	4-dr Cty Sq-9P	3619	4059	57,776

PRODUCTION NOTE: Total series output was 210,318 units. Ford does not indicate the number of each model produced with sixes and V-8s. Therefore, all production figures given above are total production of each body with both engines. It was during 1968 that Ford gained the title: 'Wagon Master,' because of the outstanding sales record of that particular body style in all the lines.

1968 FAIRLANE — OVERVIEW — The Fairlane line was the one chosen for major restyling for the new year. It was undoubtedly one of the nicest looking Fairlanes ever to come out of Detroit. It had a full-width grille, containing horizontally mounted quad headlights, and smooth sides with a single horizontal feature line running front to rear. The taillights were vertically

situated, rectangular units, with a centrally located back-up light. The word Ford was spaced evenly across the trunk lid, in block letters. The top-line Fairlane models for 1968 were called Torino, with the Fairlane 500 being demoted to intermediate trim level.

FAIRLANE MODELS — (ALL ENGINES) — The Fairlane was the base trim level for 1968 and included chrome windshield and rear window moldings; chrome rain gutters and side window frames; a chrome horn ring; front and rear armrests; cigarette lighter; vinyl-coated rubber floor mats; and the Fairlane name, in script, on the side of the rear fender. The Ford name was spelled out, in block letters, across the front of the hood and across the vertical section of the trunk lid.

FAIRLANE SIX-CYLINDER SERIES I.D. NUMBERS: Fairlane six-cylinder models began with the number '8,' followed by the assembly plant code, body type code, engine designation 'T', and, finally, the unit's production number, according to the final assembly location. Each plant began at 100001 and went up.

FAIRLANE SIX-CYLINDER SERIES

Model Number	Body/Style Number	Body Type & Seating	Factory Price	Shipping Weight	Production Total
T	54A	4-dr Sed-6P	2464	2889	Note 1
T	65A	2-dr HT Cpe-6P	2456	2931	Note 1
T	71B	4-dr Sta Wag-6P	2770	3244	Note 1

NOTE 1: See Fairlane V-8 Series listing. Production was counted by series and body style only, with no breakouts per engine type.

FAIRLANE V-8 SERIES I.D. NUMBERS: Fairlane V-8 models began with the number '8,' followed by the assembly plant code, body type code, engine designation code and, finally, the unit's production number, according to the final assembly location. Each plant began at 100001 and went up.

FAIRLANE V-8 SERIES

Model Number	Body/Style Number	Body Type & Seating	Factory Price	Shipping Weight	Production Total
NA	54A	4-dr Sed-6P	2551	3083	18,146
NA	65A	2-dr HT Cpe-6P	2544	3125	44,683
NA	71B	4-dr Sta Wag-6P	2858	3422	14,800

PRODUCTION NOTE: Total series output was 77,629 units. Ford does not indicate the number of each model produced with sixes and V-8s. Therefore, all production figures given above are total production of each body style with both engines.

FAIRLANE 500 SERIES — (ALL ENGINES) — The Fairlane 500 was the intermediate trim level for 1967 and included all the Fairlane trim, plus special Fairlane 500 trim and moldings: color-keyed carpeting, front and rear and a choice of four nylon and vinyl upholsteries. Also included was an aluminum dividing bar, in the center of the vertical portion of the trunk lid, and a horizontal dividing bar, in the center of the grille. The Fairlane 500 name, in script, appeared on the rear fender, just ahead of the taillights.

FAIRLANE 500 SIX-CYLINDER SERIES I.D. NUMBERS: Fairlane 500, six-cylinder models used the same serial number sequence as the Fairlane models.

FAIRLANE 500 SIX SERIES

Model Number	Body/Style Number	Body Type & Seating	Factory Price	Shipping Weight	Production Total
T	54B	4-dr Sed-6P	2520	2932	Note 1
T	63B	2-dr FsBk Cpe-6P	2543	2994	Note 1
T	65B	2-dr HT Cpe-6P	2568	2982	Note 1
T	76B	2-dr Conv-6P	2822	3136	Note 1
T	71D	4-dr Sta Wag-6P	2857	3274	Note 1

NOTE 1: See Fairlane 500 V-8 Series listing. Production was counted by series and body style only with no breakout per engine type.

FAIRLANE 500 V-8 SERIES I.D. NUMBERS: Fairlane 500 V-8 models used the same serial number sequence as the Fairlane models.

FAIRLANE 500 V-8 SERIES

Model Number	Body/Style Number	Body Type & Seating	Factory Price	Shipping Weight	Production Total
NA	54B	4-dr Sed-6P	2631	3121	42,390
NA	63B	2-dr FsBk Cpe-6P	2653	3177	32,452
NA	65B	2-dr HT Cpe-6P	2679	3136	33,282
NA	768	2-dr Conv-6P	2910	3323	3,761
NA	71D	4-dr Sta Wag-6P	2968	3466	10,190

PRODUCTION NOTE: Total series output was 122,075 units. Ford does not indicate the number of each model produced with sixes and V-8s. Therefore, all production figures given above are total production of each body style with both engines.

1968 Ford, Fairlane Torino GT two-door hardtop sports coupe, V-8

FAIRLANE GT SERIES — (ALL ENGINES) — The Fairlane GT was the sporty version of the Fairlane 500 Series and included all the Fairlane 500 features, plus the 210 hp, 302 cid V-8 engine, bucket seats and console, special name plaques and exterior trim, Deluxe wheelcovers and red safety and white courtesy lights on the interior door panels, as standard equipment.

FAIRLANE GT V-8 SERIES I.D. NUMBERS: Fairlane GT V-8 models used the same serial number sequence as the Fairlane and Fairlane 500 models.

FAIRLANE GT V-8 SERIES

Model Number	Body/Style Number	Body Type & Seating	Factory Price	Shipping Weight	Production Total
NA	63D	2-dr FsBk Cpe-5P	2747	3208	74,135
NA	65D	2-dr HT Cpe-5P	2772	3194	23,939
NA	76D	2-dr Conv-5P	3001	3352	5,310

PRODUCTION NOTE: Total series output was 103,384 units.

FAIRLANE TORINO SERIES — (ALL ENGINES) — The Fairlane Torino was the top trim level for 1968 and included all the Fairlane 500 trim, plus a lower bodyside molding, special emblems and trim inside and out and a Torino crest on the 'C' pillars of the two-door hardtop and four-door sedan.

FAIRLANE TORINO SIX-CYLINDER SERIES I.D. NUMBERS: Fairlane Torino six-cylinder models used the same serial number sequence as the Fairlane and Fairlane 500 models.

FAIRLANE TORINO SIX-CYLINDER SERIES

Model Number	Body/Style Number	Body Type & Seating	Factory Price	Shipping Weight	Production Total
T	54C	4-dr Sed-6P	2688	2965	Note 1
T	65C	2-dr HT Cpe-6P	2710	3001	Note 1
T	71E	4-dr Squire-6P	3032	3336	Note 1

NOTE 1: See Torino V-8 Series listing. Production was counted by series and body style only, with no breakout per engine type.

FAIRLANE TORINO V-8 SERIES I.D. NUMBERS: Fairlane Torino V-8 models used the same serial number sequence as the Fairlane and Fairlane 500 models.

FAIRLANE TORINO V-8 SERIES

Model Number	Body/Style Number	Body Type & Seating	Factory Price	Shipping Weight	Production Total
NA	54C	4-dr Sed-6P	2776	3159	17,962
NA	65C	2-dr HT Cpe-6P	2798	3195	35,964
NA	71E	4-dr Squire-6P	3119	3514	14,773

PRODUCTION NOTE: Total series output was 68,699 units. Ford does not indicate the number of each model produced with sixes and V-8s. Therefore, all production figures given above are total production of each body style with both engines.

1968 Ford, Falcon Futura four-door station wagon, V-8

1968 FALCON — OVERVIEW — The 1968 Falcons again used the same body shell as the previous two years, with only minor trim changes. The most noticeable change in the entire car is that the taillights were square, instead of the round type used on the car since its introduction in 1960. The grille was a stamped aluminum piece, with a rectangular mesh pattern, divided by the Falcon crest in the center. The simulated exhaust port, used on the front fender of the 1967 Falcons, was not continued into the year 1968.

FALCON SERIES — (ALL ENGINES) — The Falcons were the base trim level of the compact Falcon line for 1968 and included chrome windshield, rear window and rain gutter moldings; armrests on the front doors only; and a horn button, instead of the chrome horn ring found on the Futura models. The Falcon name, in script, appeared on the rear fenders, just ahead of the taillights and in block letters, across the vertical section of the trunk lid.

FALCON SERIES I.D. NUMBERS — (ALL ENGINES) — Falcons used the same serial number sequence as the full-size Fords and the Fairlane lines.

FALCON SERIES

Model Number	Body/Style Number	Body Type & Seating	Factory Price	Shipping Weight	Production Total
NA	54A	4-dr Sed-6P	2301	2714	29,166
NA	62A	2-dr Sed-6P	2252	2659	36,443
NA	71A	4-dr Sta Wag-6P	2617	3132	15,576

PRODUCTION NOTE: Total series output was 81,185 units. Ford does not indicate the number of each model produced with sixes and V-8s. Therefore, all production figures given above are total production of each body style with both engines.

FUTURA SERIES — (ALL ENGINES) — The Futura Series was the top trim level for 1968 and included all the standard Falcon features, plus a cigarette lighter; armrests and ashtrays on all doors; a chrome horn ring; nylon carpeting; special Futura moldings; trim, emblems and nameplates; and chrome side window frames. In addition, the sports coupe offered front bucket seats; special nameplates; a map light; ashtray; glovebox and trunk lights; 7.35 x 14 tires; a side chrome accent stripe; remote control outside driver's mirror; and Deluxe seat belts.

FUTURA SERIES I.D. NUMBERS: Futura models used the same serial number sequence as the full-size Fords, Fairlanes and Falcons.

FUTURA SERIES

Model Number	Body/Style Number	Body Type & Seating	Factory Price	Shipping Weight	Production Total
NA	54B	4-dr Sed-6P	2456	2719	18,733
NA	628	2-dr Sed-6P	2415	2685	10,633
NA	62C	2-dr Spts Cpe-5P	2541	2713	10,077
NA	71B	4-dr Squire-6P	2728	3123	10,761

PRODUCTION NOTES: Total series output was 50,204 units. Ford does not indicate the number of each model produced with sixes and V-8s. Therefore, all production figures given above are total production of each body style with both engines.

THUNDERBIRD SERIES — (ALL ENGINES) — The 1968 Thunderbird was a restyled version of the 1967 model, with very minor trim updating. The grille was very slightly revised from the 1967 offering and the taillights were mildly updated. New wheelcovers completed the face-lifting of the Thunderbird for 1968.

THUNDERBIRD SERIES I.D. NUMBER — (ALL ENGINES) — Thunderbird models began with the number '8,' assembly plant code 'Y' (Wixom), body type code, engine type code 'Z' or 'N' and, finally, the unit's production number, beginning at 100001 and going up.

THUNDERBIRD SERIES

Model Number	Body/Style Number	Body Type & Seating	Factory Price	Shipping Weight	Production Total
N/Z	65A	2-dr HT Cpe-6P	4716	4366	9,977
N/Z	65A	2-dr Landau-4P	4845	4372	33,029
N/Z	57B	4-dr Landau-4P	4924	4458	21,925

PRODUCTION NOTE: Total series output was 64,931 units. This figure includes 4,557 two-door hardtops; 13,924 two-door Landaus and 17,251 four-door Landaus equipped with bench seats.

ENGINES

FALCON/FAIRLANE SIX-CYLINDER: Overhead valves. Cast iron block. Displacement: 170 cid. Bore and stroke: 3.50 x 2.94 inches. Compression ratio: 8.7:1. Brake hp: 100 at 4000 rpm. Carburetion: Holley one-barrel. Seven main bearings. Serial number code "U."

FALCON/FAIRLANE/MUSTANG SIX-CYLINDER: Overhead valves. Cast iron block. Displacement: 200 cid. Bore and stroke: 3.68 x 3.13 inches. Compression ratio: 8.8:1. Brake hp: 115 at 3800 rpm. Carburetion: Holley one-barrel. Seven main bearings. Serial number code 'T' or export code "2."

FORD SIX-CYLINDER: Overhead valves. Cast iron block. Displacement: 240 cid. Bore and stroke: 4.00 x 3.18 inches. Compression ratio: 9.2:1. Brake hp: 150 at 4000 rpm. Carburetion: Holley one-barrel. Seven main bearings. Serial number code "V" or code "B" police; code "E" taxi; code '5' export.

CHALLENGER 289 V-8: Overhead valves. Cast iron block. Displacement: 289 cid. Bore and stroke: 4.00 x 2.87 inches. Compression ratio: 8.7:1. Brake hp: 195 at 4600 rpm. Carburetion: Holley two-barrel. Five main bearings. Serial number code "C."

302 V-8: Overhead valves. Cast iron block. Displacement: 302 cid. Bore and stroke: 4.00 x 3.00 inches. Compression ratio: 9.0:1. Brake hp: 210 at 4000 rpm. Carburetion: Motorcraft two-barrel. Five main bearings. Serial number code 'F' and export code "6."

302 FOUR-BARREL V-8: Overhead valve. Cast iron block. Displacement: 302 cid. Bore and stroke: 4.00 x 3.00 inches. Compression ratio: 10.0:1. Brake hp: 230 at 4800 rpm. Carburetion: Motorcraft four-barrel. Five main bearings. Serial number code "J."

THUNDERBIRD V-8: Overhead valves. Cast iron block. Displacement: 390 cid. Bore and stroke: 4.05 x 3.78 inches. Compression ratio: 9.5:1. Brake hp: 265 at 4400 rpm. Carburetion: Motorcraft four-barrel. Five main bearings. Serial number code "Z."

THUNDERBIRD V-8: Overhead valves. Cast iron block. Displacement: 390 cid. Bore and stroke: 4.05 x 3.78 inches. Compression ratio: 10.5:1. Brake hp: 280 at 4400 rpm. Carburetion: Motorcraft four-barrel. Five main bearings. Serial number code "X."

THUNDERBIRD FOUR-BARREL V-8: Overhead valves. Cast iron block. Displacement: 390 cid. Bore and stroke: 4.05 x 3.78 inches. Compression ratio: 10.5:1. Brake hp: 315 at 4600 rpm. Carburetion: Motorcraft four-barrel. Five main bearings. Serial number code "Z."

GT 390 V-8. Overhead valves. Cast iron block. Displacement: 390 cid. Bore and stroke: 4.05 x 3.78 inches. Compression ratio: 10.5:1. Brake hp: 325 at 4800 rpm. Carburetion: Holley four-barrel. Five main bearings. Serial number code "S."

THUNDERBIRD HIGH-PERFORMANCE V-8: Overhead valves. Cast iron block. Displacement: 427 cid. Bore and stroke: 4.23 x 3.78 inches. Compression ratio: 10.9:1. Brake hp: 390 at 4600 rpm. Carburetion: Motorcraft four-barrel. Five main bearings. Serial number code "W."

COBRA JET 428 V-8: Overhead valves. Cast iron block. Displacement: 428 cid. Bore and stroke: 4.13 x 3.98 inches. Compression ratio: 10.7:1. Brake hp: 335 at 5600 rpm. Carburetion: Holley four-barrel. Five main bearings. Serial number code 'Q' or police version code "P."

SUPER COBRA JET 428 V-8: Overhead valves. Cast iron block. Displacement: 428 cid. Bore and stroke: 4.13 x 3.98 inches. Compression ratio: 10.5:1. Brake hp: 360 at 5400 rpm. Carburetion: Holley four-barrel. Serial number code "R."

THUNDERBIRD 428 V-8: Overhead valves. Cast iron block. Displacement: 428 cid. Bore and stroke: 4.13 x 3.98 inches. Compression ratio: 10. 5:1. Brake hp: 340 at 5400 rpm. Carburetion: Motorcraft four-barrel. Serial number code "Q."

THUNDER-JET 429 V-8: Overhead valves. Cast iron block. Displacement: 429 cid. Bore and stroke: 4.36 x 3.59 inches. Compression ratio: 10.5:1. Brake hp: 360 at 4600 rpm. Carburetion: Motorcraft four-barrel. Serial number code "N."

FORD CHASSIS FEATURES: Wheelbase: 119 inches. Overall length: (station wagons) 213.9 inches; (other models) 213.3 inches. Tires: (hardtops) 8.15 x 15 four-ply tubeless blackwall; (station wagons) 8.45 x 15 four-ply tubeless blackwall; (other models) 7.75 x 15 four-ply tubeless blackwall.

FAIRLANE CHASSIS FEATURES: Wheelbase: (station wagons) 113 inches; (other models) 116 inches, overall length: (station wagons) 203.9 inches; (other models) 201 inches, tires: (station wagons) 7.75 x 14 tubeless blackwall; (GTs) F870 x 14; (other models) 7.35 x 14 tubeless blackwall.

FALCON CHASSIS FEATURES: Wheelbase: (station wagons) 113 inches; (other models) 110.9 inches. Overall length: (station wagons) 198.7 inches; (other models) 184.3 inches. Tires: (station wagons) 7.75 x 14 four-ply tubeless blackwall; (other models) 6.95 x 14 four-ply tubeless blackwall.

THUNDERBIRD CHASSIS FEATURES: Wheelbase: (four-door Landau) 117 inches: (other models) 115 inches. Overall length: (four-door Landau) 209.9 inches; (other models) 206.9 inches. Tires: (four-door Landau) 8.45 x 15 tubeless blackwall; (other models) 8.15 x 15 four-ply tubeless blackwall.

FORD OPTIONS: 210 hp: 302 cid V-8 engine ($110). 265 hp, 390 cid V-8 engine ($78 in XLs and LTDs; $184 in others). 315 hp 390 cid V-8 engine ($158 in XLs and LTDs; $265 in others). Cruise-O-Matic automatic transmission ($188 to $220, depending on engine choice). Power steering ($95). Power brakes ($42). Tinted windshield ($95). Air conditioning ($356). AM radio ($57). AM/FM stereo radio ($134). Vinyl roof ($74 on two-door hardtops; $83 on four-door models). White sidewall tires ($35).

STATION WAGON OPTIONS: All above, plus power tailgate window ($32). Luggage rack ($44). Deluxe adjustable luggage rack ($63).

FAIRLANE/TORINO OPTIONS: 210 hp, 302 cid V-8 engine ($107, standard on GT models). 390 cid V-8 engines ($184 for two-barrel version; $264 for the four-barrel version). Cruise-O-Matic automatic transmission ($188 to $220, depending on engine choice). Four-speed manual transmission ($184). AM radio ($57). Power steering ($84). Power tailgate window in station wagons ($32). Luggage rack on station wagons ($44). Two-tone paint ($22). White sidewall tires ($34). Wheelcovers ($41). Vinyl roofs on two-door hardtops ($74).

FALCON OPTIONS: 200 cid six-cylinder engine ($26). 289 cid V-8 engine ($132). 302 cid V-8 engine ($183). Cruise-O-Matic automatic transmission ($187). Four-speed manual transmission ($184). Power steering ($84). Power tailgate window on station wagons ($32). Tinted windshield ($21). Luggage rack on station wagons ($44). AM radio ($57). Eight-track stereo tape player ($128). Two-tone paint ($19). Vinyl roof on two-door sedans ($74). Wheelcovers ($21). White sidewall tires ($32).

THUNDERBIRD OPTIONS: 429 cid Thunder-Jet V-8 engine. Six-Way power driver's seat ($98). Power windows ($104). Cruise Control ($130). Air conditioning ($421). AM/8-track stereo radio ($128). AM/FM Multiplex stereo radio ($164). Two-tone paint ($25). White sidewall tires with red band ($52).

HISTORICAL FOOTNOTES: Ford products captured over 20 checkered flags in NASCAR stock car racing during 1968, with Ford driver David Pearson taking the overall championship. In USAC competition, Ford pilot A.J. Foyt was top driver of the year. Benny Parsons and Cale Yarborough also made Ford racing history this year, driving Fairlanes and Torinos in ARCA contests. A specially-trimmed Torino convertible paced the 52nd Indianapolis 500-Mile race. The new Fords were introduced to the public on Sept. 22, 1967. In Europe, Ford GT-40s competed in the international class races, attempting to repeat the success of 1967, when similar machines finished first, second and third in the French Grand Prix at LeMans. Early in 1968, Semon E. 'Bunkie' Knudsen became the chief executive officer of Ford Motor Co. Knudsen had held a similar position with Pontiac and Chevrolet during some of the most exciting years in automotive history.

1969 FORD

1969 FORDS — OVERVIEW — The year 1969 started out as a scramble for new Ford Motor Co. products. It was almost to the point where a scorecard was needed to keep track of all the models. A new series on scene was the Cobra, Ford's performance line in the Fairlane Series. Not to be left out, the Mustang stable added the hot Mach I and the luxurious Grande. The big news for 1969 came at midyear introduction time, when another horse, the Maverick, was introduced. The Maverick was designed to be direct competition for the Volkswagen and was intended to influence those who liked a small and economical car. With a base price of $1,995, it was the only Ford under $2,000. For the first time, economy was heavily promoted, with Ford announcing that the Maverick would average 22 mpg. By design, the Maverick was introduced April 17, 1969, exactly five years to the day, after the phenomenally successful Mustang.

FORD CUSTOM SERIES — (ALL ENGINES) — The 1969 full-size Fords were totally restyled and shared nothing with the previous year's offering. The lines of the new models were even rounder than in 1968. They looked more like big luxury cars, than Fords. Luxury, in fact, was very highly promoted. Velour interiors and vinyl tops were the order of the day in the LTD lineup. All full-size Fords shared the same body lines, with the LTD receiving it's own front end treatment, thus further segregating it from the 'ordinary' Galaxies. The Custom series was the base trim level Ford for 1969 and included chrome windshield and rear window moldings; a chrome horn ring; nylon carpeting; the Custom name, in script on the rear fender (just in front of the rear marker light); the Ford name, in block letters, across the rear escutcheon panel; and a single horizontal chrome strip along the center of the body.

CUSTOM SIX-CYLINDER SERIES I.D. NUMBERS: Custom six-cylinder models began with the number '9,' followed by the assembly plant code, engine designation 'V' and, finally, the unit's production number, according to the final assembly location. Each plant began at 100001 and went up.

CUSTOM SIX SERIES

Model Number	Body/Style Number	Body Type & Seating	Factory Price	Shipping Weight	Production Total
V	54E	4-dr Sed-6P	2674	3608	Note 1
V	62E	2-dr Sed-6P	2632	3585	Note 1
V	71D	4-dr Ranch Wag-6P	3074	4069	Note 1

NOTE 1: See Custom V-8 series listing. Production was counted by series and body style only, with no breakout per engine type.

CUSTOM V-8 SERIES

I.D. NUMBERS: Custom V-8 models began with the number '9,' followed by the assembly plant code, body type code, engine designation code and, finally, the unit's production number, according to the final assembly location. Each plant began at 100001 and went up.

CUSTOM V-8 SERIES

Model Number	Body/Style Number	Body Type & Seating	Factory Price	Shipping Weight	Production Total
NA	54E	4-dr Sed-6P	2779	3648	45,653
NA	62E	2-dr Sed-6P	2737	3625	15,439
NA	71D	4-dr Ranch Wag-6P	3179	4109	17,489

PRODUCTION NOTE: Total series output was 78,581 units. Ford does not indicate the number of each model produced with sixes and V-8s. Therefore, all production figures given above are total production of each body style with both engines.

CUSTOM 500 SERIES — (ALL ENGINES) — The Custom 500 was the upper trim level of the base-line Custom series and included all the Custom trim, plus special Custom 500 exterior trim and choices of four different upholsteries on the interior.

CUSTOM 500 SIX-CYLINDER SERIES I.D. NUMBERS: Custom 500 six-cylinder models used the same serial number sequence as the Custom models.

CUSTOM 500 SERIES

Model Number	Body/Style Number	Body Type & Seating	Factory Price	Shipping Weight	Production Total
V	54B	4-dr Sed-6P	2773	3620	Note 1
V	62B	2-dr Sed-6P	2731	3570	Note 1
V	71H	4-dr Ranch Wag-6P	3138	4082	Note 1
V	71J	4-dr Ranch Wag-10P	3251	4132	Note 1

NOTE 1: See Custom 500 V-8 series listings. Production was counted by series and body style only, with no breakout per engine type.

CUSTOM 500 V-8 SERIES I.D. NUMBERS: Custom 500 V-8 models used the same serial number sequence as the Custom models.

CUSTOM 500 V-8 SERIES

Model Number	Body/Style Number	Body Type & Seating	Factory Price	Shipping Weight	Production Total
NA	54B	4-dr Sed-6P	2878	3660	45,761
NA	62B	2-dr Sed-6P	2836	3610	7,585
NA	71H	4-dr Ranch Wag-6P	3243	4122	16,432
NA	71J	4-dr Ranch Wag-10P	3556	4172	11,563

PRODUCTION NOTE: Total series output was 81.341 units. Ford does not indicate the number of each model produced with sixes and V-8s. Therefore, all production figures given above are total production of each body style with both engines.

GALAXIE 500 SERIES — (ALL ENGINES) — The Galaxie 500 was the intermediate trim level for 1969 and included all the Custom series trim, plus stamped aluminum lower bodyside moldings and pleated interior trim.

GALAXIE 500 SIX-CYLINDER SERIES I.D. NUMBERS: Galaxie 500 six-cylinder models used the same serial number sequence as the Custom series.

GALAXIE 500 SIX SERIES

Model Number	Body/Style Number	Body Type & Seating	Factory Price	Shipping Weight	Production Total
V	54A	4-dr Sed-6P	2897	3670	Note 1
V	64B	2-dr FsBk Cpe-6P	2913	3680	Note 1
V	65C	2-dr FT Cpe-6P	2965	3635	Note 1
V	57B	4-dr HT Sed-6P	2966	3705	Note 1
V	76A	2-dr Conv-6P	3142	3840	Note 1
V	718	4-dr Cty Sed-6P	3257	4067	Note 1
V	71C	4-dr Cty Sed-10P	3373	3092	Note 1

NOTE 1: See Galaxie 500 V-8 series listing. Production was counted by series and body style only, with no breakout per engine type.

GALAXIE 500 V-8 SERIES.

I.D. NUMBERS: Galaxie 500 V-8 models used the same serial number sequence as the Custom series.

GALAXIE 500 V-8 SERIES

Model Number	Body/Style Number	Body Type & Seating	Factory Price	Shipping Weight	Production Total
NA	54A	4-dr Sed-6P	3002	3710	104,606
NA	63B	2-dr FsBk Cpe-6P	3018	3720	63,921
NA	65C	2-dr FT Cpe-6P	3070	3675	71,920
NA	57B	4-dr HT Sed-6P	3071	3745	64,031
NA	76A	2-dr Conv-6P	3247	3880	6,910
NA	71B	4-dr Cty Sed-6P	3362	4107	36,287
NA	17C	4-dr Cty Sed-10P	3487	4132	11,563

PRODUCTION NOTE: Total series output was 359,238 units. Ford does not indicate the number of each model produced with sixes and V-8s. Therefore, all production figures given above are total production of each body style with both engines.

GALAXIE 500XL SERIES — (ALL ENGINES) — The Galaxie 500XL was the sport trim version of the Galaxie 500. It came in 'Sportsroof' (two-door fastback coupe) and convertible styles. Standard equipment included bucket seats; wheelcovers; die-cast grille; retractable headlights; pleated, all-vinyl interior trim; and five vertical hash marks at the forward part of the front fenders, in addition to all the standard Galaxie 500 trim.

GALAXIE 500XL SIX-CYLINDER SERIES I.D. NUMBERS: The Galaxie 500XL six-cylinder models used the same serial number sequence as the Custom and Galaxie 500 series.

GALAXIE 500XL SIX SERIES

Model Number	Body/Style Number	Body Type & Seating	Factory Price	Shipping Weight	Production Total
V	63C	2-dr FsBk Cpe-5P	3052	3785	Note 1
V	76B	2-dr Conv-5P	3280	3935	Note 1

NOTE 1: See Galaxie 500XL V-8 series listing. Production was counted by series and body style only, with no breakout per engine data.

1969 Ford, XL two-door hardtop coupe, V-8

GALAXIE 500XL V-8 SERIES I.D. NUMBERS: Galaxie 500XLs used the same serial number sequence as the Custom and Galaxie 500 series.

GALAXIE 500XL V-8 SERIES

Model Number	Body/Style Number	Body Type & Seating	Factory Price	Shipping Weight	Production Total
NA	63C	2-dr FsBk Cpe-5P	3157	3825	54,557
NA	76B	2-dr Conv-5P	3385	3975	7,402

PRODUCTION NOTE: Total series output was 61,959 units. Ford does not indicate the number of each model produced with sixes and V-8s. Therefore, all production figures given above are total production of each body style with both engines.

LTD V-8 SERIES — (ALL ENGINES) — The LTD was the top trim level full-size Ford for 1969 and included all the Galaxie 500 trim, plus the 220 hp, 302 cid V-8 engine; SelectShift Cruise-O-Matic automatic transmission; electric clock; bright exterior moldings; and dual accent paint stripes. The LTD station wagon models (Country Squires) also had simulated woodgrain appliques on the bodysides. All LTDs also came with retractable headlights and die-cast grilles.

LTD V-8 SERIES I.D. NUMBERS: LTDs used the same serial number sequence as the Custom and Galaxie 500 series.

LTD V-8 SERIES

Model Number	Body/Style Number	Body Type & Seating	Factory Price	Shipping Weight	Production Total
NA	54C	4-dr Sed-6P	3192	3745	63,709
NA	57F	4-dr Sed-6P	3261	3840	113,168
NA	65A	2-dr FT Cpe-6P	3234	3745	111,565
NA	71E	4-dr Cty Sq-6P	3644	4202	46,445
NA	71A	4-dr Cty Sq-10P	3721	4227	82,790

PRODUCTION NOTE: Total series output was 417,677 units.

1969 FAIRLANE — (OVERVIEW) — Performance was the key word in the Fairlane lineup for 1969. Virtually all models, except four-door sedans, looked very fast. And most of them were. When equipped with the new Cobra Jet 428, the Fairlanes were awesome, as well as beautiful. They shared the same body as the 1968 models, with only very minor trim updating. The taillights were revised slightly and were squarer in shape than the 1968 type. The grille was revised slightly, with a more prominent center dividing bar than in 1968. At midyear introduction time, the incredible Talladega Torino was released in extremely limited quantities, to qualify the body shape for use in NASCAR racing. The front end was extended several inches and used a flat grille, mounted at the front of the opening, rather than several inches back, as on standard models. Also, the rear bumper from a standard Fairlane was used up front, because it was more aerodynamic than the original front bumper. All Talladegas were equipped with the Cobra Jet 428 engine and gave a choice of either SelectShift Cruise-O-Matic automatic transmission, or the bulletproof 'top-loader' four-speed manual gearbox.

FAIRLANE MODELS — (ALL ENGINES) — The Fairlane was the base trim level for 1969 and included chrome windshield and rear window moldings; chrome rain gutters and side window frames; a chrome horn ring; front and rear armrests; cigarette lighter; vinyl-coated rubber floor mats; and, the Fairlane name, in script, on the passenger side of the escutcheon panel. The Ford name was spelled out, in block letters, across the front of the hood and on the vertical section of the trunk lid.

FAIRLANE SIX-CYLINDER SERIES I.D. NUMBERS: Fairlane six-cylinder models began with the number '9,' followed by the assembly plant code, body type code, engine designation 'T' and, finally, the unit's production number, according to the final assembly location. Each plant began at 100001 and went up.

FAIRLANE SIX-CYLINDER SERIES

Model Number	Body/Style Number	Body Type & Seating	Factory Price	Shipping Weight	Production Total
T	54A	4-dr Sed-6P	2471	3010	Note 1
T	65A	2-dr HT Cpe-6P	2482	3025	Note 1
T	71B	4-dr Sta Wag-6P	2824	3387	Note 1

NOTE 1: See Fairlane V-8 series listing. Production was counted by series and body style only, with no breakout per engine data.

FAIRLANE V-8 SERIES I.D. NUMBERS: Fairlane V-8 models began with the number '9,' followed by the assembly plant code, body type code, engine designation code and, finally, the unit's production number, according to the final assembly location. Each plant began at 100001 and went up.

FAIRLANE V-8 SERIES

Model Number	Body/Style Number	Body Type & Seating	Factory Price	Shipping Weight	Production Total
NA	54A	4-dr Sed-6P	2561	3120	27,296
NA	65A	2-dr HT Cpe-6P	2572	3133	85,630
NA	71D	4-dr Sta Wag-6P	2914	3387	10,882

PRODUCTION NOTE: Total series output was 123,808 units. Ford does not indicate the number of each model produced with sixes and V-8s. Therefore, all production figures given above are total production of each body style with both engines.

FAIRLANE 500 SERIES — (ALL ENGINES) — The Fairlane 500 was the intermediate trim level for 1969 and included all Fairlane trim, plus special 500 trim and moldings; color-keyed carpeting (front and rear); and a choice of four nylon and vinyl upholsteries. Also included was an aluminum trim panel in the center of the rear escutcheon panel, between the taillights. The Fairlane 500 name, in script, appeared on the side of the rear fender, just in front of the taillights.

FAIRLANE 500 SIX-CYLINDER SERIES I.D. NUMBERS: Fairlane 500 six-cylinder model used the same serial number sequence as the Fairlane models.

FAIRLANE 500 SIX SERIES

Model Number	Body/Style Number	Body Type & Seating	Factory Price	Shipping Weight	Production Total
T	54B	4-dr Sed-6P	2551	3029	Note 1
T	65B	2-dr FT Cpe-6P	2609	3036	Note 1
T	63B	2-dr FsBk Cpe-6P	2584	3083	Note 1
T	76B	2-dr Conv-6P	2834	3220	Note 1
T	71B	4-dr Sta Wag-6P	2934	3415	Note 1

NOTE 1: See Fairlane 500 V-8 series listing. Production was counted by series and body style only, with no breakout per engine type.

FAIRLANE 500 V-8 SERIES I.D. NUMBERS: Fairlane 500 V-8 models used the same serial number sequence as the Fairlane models.

FAIRLANE 500 V-8 SERIES

Model Number	Body/Style Number	Body Type & Seating	Factory Price	Shipping Weight	Production Total
NA	54B	4-dr Sed-6P	2641	3135	40,888
NA	65B	2-dr FT Cpe-6P	2699	3143	28,179
NA	63B	2-dr FsBk Cpe-6P	2674	3190	29,849
NA	76B	2-dr Conv-6P	2924	3336	2,264
NA	71B	4-dr Sta Wag-6P	3024	3523	12,869

PRODUCTION NOTE: Total series output was 114,049 units. This figure includes 3.379 Formal Hardtop coupes (FT Cpe) produced with bucket seats; 7,345 Sportroofs (FsBk Cpe) produced with bucket seats and 219 convertibles produced with bucket seats. Ford does not indicate the number of each model produced with sixes and V-8s. Therefore, all production figures are total production of each body style.

1969 Ford, Torino GT two-door convertible, V-8

FAIRLANE TORINO SERIES — (ALL ENGINES) — The Fairlane Torino was the top trim level for 1969 and included all the Fairlane 500 trim, plus a polished aluminum rocker panel molding; special emblems and trim (inside and out) and a Torino crest on the 'C' pillars on the two-door hardtop and four-door sedan versions.

FAIRLANE TORINO SIX-CYLINDER SERIES I.D. NUMBERS: Fairlane Torino six-cylinder models used the same serial number sequence as the Fairlane and Fairlane 500 models.

FAIRLANE TORINOS

Model Number	Body Type Number	Body Type & Seating	Factory Price	Shipping Weight	Production Total
T	54C	4-dr Sed-6P	2716	3075	Note 1
T	65C	2-dr FT Cpe-6P	2737	3090	Note 1
T	71E	4-dr Squire-6P	3090	3450	Note 1

NOTE 1: See Fairlane Torino V-8 series listing. Production was counted by series and body style only, with no breakout per engine type.

FAIRLANE TORINO V-8 SERIES I.D. NUMBERS: Fairlane Torino V-8 models used the same serial number sequence as the Fairlane and Fairlane 500 models.

FAIRLANE TORINO V-8 SERIES

Model Number	Body/Style Number	Body Type & Seating	Factory Price	Shipping Weight	Production Total
NA	54C	4-dr Sed-6P	2806	3180	11,971
NA	65C	2-dr FT Cpe-6P	2827	3195	20,789
NA	71E	4-dr Squire-6P	3180	3556	14,472

PRODUCTION NOTE: Total series output was 47,232 units. Ford does not indicate the number of each model produced with sixes and V-8s. Therefore, all production figures given above are total production of each body style with both engines.

FAIRLANE TORINO GT SERIES — (ALL ENGINES) — The Fairlane Torino GT was the sporty version of the Fairlane 500 series and included all the Fairlane 500 features, plus the 220 hp, 302 cid V-8 engine; bucket seats and console; special name plaques and exterior trim; styled steel wheels; lower bodyside striping on two-door hardtop and two-door convertible versions; and a bodyside 'C' stripe on the two-door Sportsroof (FsBk Cpe) version. A high-performance version of this model, known as the Torino Cobra, was also offered. It included the 335 hp, 428 cid V-8 engine and four-speed manual transmission as standard equipment, as well as F70 x 14 wide oval tires.

FAIRLANE TORINO GT I.D. NUMBERS — (ALL ENGINES) — Fairlane Torino GTs used the same serial number sequence as the Fairlane and Fairlane 500 models.

FAIRLANE TORINO GT SERIES

Model Number	Body/Style Number	Body Type & Seating	Factory Price	Shipping Weight	Production Total
NA	65D	2-dr FT Cpe-5P	2848	3173	17,951
NA	63D	2-dr FsBk Cpe-5P	2823	3220	61,319
NA	76D	2-dr Conv-5P	3073	3356	2,552

FAIRLANE TORINO GT COBRA SUB-SERIES

Model Number	Body/Style Number	Body Type & Seating	Factory Price	Shipping Weight	Production Total
NA	65A	2-dr HT Cpe-5P	3208	3490	NA
NA	63B	2-dr FsBk Cpe-5P	3183	3537	NA

PRODUCTION NOTE: Total series output was 81,822 units, including the Cobra models (for which separate production figures are unavailable). Ford does not indicate the number of each model produced with sixes and V-8s. Therefore, all production figures are total production of each body style with both engines.

1969 Ford, Falcon two-door sedan, V-8

1969 FALCON — (OVERVIEW) — Falcons continued to use the same body style as in the past three years, with no major changes in either sheetmetal or trim. An optional V-8, new safety steering wheel and redesigned side marker lamps were the most noticeable revisions from the past. A full-width anodized aluminum grille helped impart a 'big car' appearance.

FALCON SERIES — (ALL ENGINES) — The Falcons were the base trim level for 1969 and included chrome windshield; rear window and rain gutter moldings; armrests on the front doors only and a horn button, instead of the chrome ring found on the Futura models. The Falcon name, in script, appeared on the rear fendersides and on the vertical section of the trunk lid (on the passenger side).

FALCON SERIES I.D. NUMBERS — (ALL ENGINES) — Falcons used the same serial number sequence as the full-size Fords and the Fairlane lines.

FALCON SERIES

Model Number	Body/Style Number	Body Type & Seating	Factory Price	Shipping Weight	Production Total
NA	54A	4-dr Sed-6P	2316/2431	2735	22,719
NA	62A	2-dr Sed-6P	2226/2381	2700	29,263
NA	71A	4-dr Sta Wag-6P	2643/2733	3110	11,568

PRODUCTION NOTE: Total series output was 63,550 units. Ford does not indicate the number of each model produced with sixes and V-8s. Therefore, all production figures are total production of each body style.

NOTE 2: The prices above the slash are for six/below slash for V-8.

FUTURA SERIES — (ALL ENGINES) — The Futura series was the top trim level for 1969 and included all the standard Falcon features, plus a cigarette lighter; armrests and ashtrays on all doors; a chrome horn ring; nylon carpeting; special Futura moldings, trim, emblems and nameplates; and chrome side window frames. In addition, the sports coupe offered front bucket seats; special nameplates; a map light; ashtray, glovebox and trunk lights; 7.35 x 14 fires; a side chrome accent stripe; polished aluminum rocker panel moldings and wheelwell trim; a remote-control outside driver's mirror; and Deluxe seat belts.

FUTURA SERIES I.D. NUMBERS — (ALL ENGINES) — Futura models used the same serial number sequence as the full-size Fords, Fairlanes and Falcon models.

FUTURA SERIES

Model Number	Body/Style Number	Body Type & Seating	Factory Price	Shipping Weight	Production Total
NA	54B	4-dr Sed-6P	2481/2571	2748	11,850
NA	62B	2-dr Sed-6P	2444/2534	2715	6,482
NA	62C	2-dr Spt Cpe-5P	2581/2671	2738	5,931
NA	71B	4-dr Sta Wag-6P	2754/2844	3120	7,203

PRODUCTION NOTE: Total series output was 31,466 units. Ford does not indicate the number of each model produced with sixes and V-8s. Therefore, all production figures are total production of each body style.

NOTE 2: The prices above slash are for six/below slash for V-8.

MAVERICK SERIES — (ALL ENGINES) — The Maverick was the midyear introduction model for 1969. It used a Falcon chassis and 170 cid six-cylinder engine to power the only body style available — a two-door sedan.

MAVERICK SERIES I.D. NUMBERS — (ALL ENGINES) — The Mavericks used the same serial number sequence as the full-size Fords, Fairlanes and Falcons.

MAVERICK SERIES

Model Number	Body/Style Number	Body Type & Seating	Factory Price	Shipping Weight	Production Total
T	91	2-dr Sed-6P	1995	2411	127,833

PRODUCTION NOTE: Total series output was 127,833 units.

1969 Ford, Thunderbird two-door Landau, V-8

THUNDERBIRD SERIES — (ALL ENGINES) — The Thunderbird continued to use the same body as the previous two years with minor trim changes and new frontal and taillight arrangements. The grille featured a horizontal division bar with the Thunderbird emblem in the center and three vertical moldings. The taillights of the 1969 Thunderbirds were large, rectangular units, with a single back-up light mounted in the center of the escutcheon panel. A power-operated sun roof was once again offered in the Thunderbird Sun Roof Landau.

THUNDERBIRD SERIES I.D. NUMBERS — (ALL ENGINES) — Thunderbird models began with the number '9,' assembly plant code 'Y' (Wixom), body type code, engine type code 'N' or 'Z' and, finally, the unit's production number beginning at 100001 and going up.

THUNDERBIRD SERIES

Model Number	Body/Style Number	Body Type & Seat,	Factory Price	Shipping Weight	Production Total
N/Z	65C	2-dr HT-4P	4807	4348	5,913
N/Z	65D	2-dr Landau-4P	4947	4360	27,664
N/Z	57C	4-dr Landau-4P	5026	4460	15,650

PRODUCTION NOTE: Total series output was 49,227 units. This figure includes 2,361 hardtops equipped with bucket seats; 12,425 Landau hardtops equipped with bucket seats and 1,981 Landau four-doors equipped with bucket seats.

ENGINES

FALCON SIX-CYLINDER: Overhead valves. Cast iron block. Displacement: 170 cid. Bore and stroke: 3.50 x 2.94 inches. Compression ratio: 8.7:1. Brake hp: 100 at 4000 rpm. Carburetion: Holley one-barrel. Seven main bearings. Serial number code "U."

FALCON/FAIRLANE/MUSTANG SIX-CYLINDER: Overhead valves. Cast iron block. Displacement: 200 cid. Bore and stroke: 3.68 x 3.13 inches. Compression ratio: 8.8:1. Brake hp: 115 at 3800 rpm. Carburetion: Motorcraft one-barrel. Seven main bearings. Serial number code "T" or (low-compression) "2."

FORD/MUSTANG SIX-CYLINDER: Overhead valve. Cast iron block. Displacement: 240 cid. Bore and stroke: 4.00 x 3.18 inches. Compression ratio: 9.2:1. Brake hp: 150 at 4000 rpm. Carburetion: Motorcraft one-barrel. Seven main bearings. Serial number code "V" or "B" (police); "E" (taxi) or "5" (low-compression.)

FORD SIX-CYLINDER: Overhead valves. Cast iron block. Displacement: 250 cid. Bore and stroke: 3.68 x 3.91 inches. Compression ratio: 9.0:1. Brake hp: 155 at 4000 rpm. Carburetion: Motorcraft one-barrel. Seven main bearings. Serial number code "L" or "3" (low-compression.

302 V-8: Overhead valves. Cast iron block. Displacement: 302 cid. Bore and stroke: 4.00 x 3.00 inches. Compression ratio: 9.5:1. Brake hp: 220 at 4600 rpm. Carburetion: Motorcraft two-barrel. Five main bearings. Serial number code "F" or "D" (police/taxi).

BOSS 302 V-8: Overhead valves. Cast iron block. Displacement: 302 cid. Bore and stroke: 4.00 x 3.00 inches. Compression ratio: 10. 5:1. Brake hp: 290 at 5600 rpm. Carburetion: Holley four-barrel. Five main bearings. Serial number code "G."

351 V-8: Overhead valve. Cast iron block. Displacement: 351 cid. Bore and stroke: 4.00 x 3.50 inches. Compression ratio: 9.5:1. Brake hp: 250 at 4600 rpm. Carburetion: Motorcraft two-barrel. Five main bearings. Serial number code "H."

351 FOUR-BARREL V-8: Overhead valves. Cast iron block. Displacement: 351 cid. Bore and stroke: 4.00 x 3.50 inches. Compression ratio: 10.7:1. Brake hp: 290 at 4800 rpm. Carburetion: Motorcraft four-barrel. Five main bearings. Serial number code "M."

INTERCEPTOR V-8: Overhead valves. Cast iron block. Displacement: 390 cid. Bore and stroke: 4.05 x 3.78 inches. Compression ratio: 9.5:1. Brake hp: 265 at 4400 rpm. Carburetion: Motorcraft two-barrel. Five main bearings. Serial number code "Y."

390 GT V-8: Overhead valves. Cast iron block. Displacement: 390 cid. Bore and stroke: 4.05 x 3.78 inches. Compression ratio: 10.5:1. Brake hp: 320 at 4600 rpm. Carburetion: Holley four-barrel. Five main bearings. Serial number code "S."

COBRA JET 428 V-8: Overhead valves. Cast iron block. Displacement: 428 cid. Bore and stroke: 4.13 x 3.98 inches. Compression ratio: 10.6:1. Brake hp: 335 at 5200 rpm. Carburetion: Holley four-barrel. Five main bearings. Serial number code "Q."

SUPER COBRA JET 428 V-8: Overhead valves. Cast iron block. Displacement: 428 cid. Bore and stroke: 4.13 x 3.98 inches. Compression ratio: 10.5:1. Brake hp: 360 at 5400 rpm. Carburetion: Holley four-barrel. Five main bearings. Serial number code "P."

THUNDER JET 429 V-8: Overhead valves. Cast iron block. Displacement: 429 cid. Bore and stroke: 4.36 x 3.59 inches. Compression ratio: 10.5:1. Brake hp: 320 at 4500 rpm. Carburetion: Motorcraft two-barrel. Five main bearings. Serial number code "K."

THUNDER JET 429 FOUR-BARREL V-8: Overhead valves. Cast iron block. Displacement: 429 cid. Bore and stroke: 4.36 x 3.59 inches. Compression ratio: 10.5:1. Brake hp: 360 at 4600 rpm. Carburetion: Motorcraft four-barrel. Five main bearings. Serial number code "N."

BOSS 429 V-8: Overhead valves. Cast iron block. Displacement: 429 cid. Bore and stroke: 4.36 x 3.59 inches. Compression ratio: 11.3:1. Brake hp: 375 at 5600 rpm. Carburetion: Holley four-barrel. Five main bearings. Serial number code "Z."

FORD CHASSIS FEATURES: Wheelbase: 121 inches. Overall length: (station wagons, 216.9 inches; (other models) 213.9 inches. Tires: (station wagons) 9.00 x 15 four-ply tubeless blackwall; (other models) 8.25 x 15 four-ply tubeless blackwall.

FAIRLANE CHASSIS FEATURES: Wheelbase: (station wagons) 113 inches; (other models) 116 inches. Overall length: (station wagons) 203.9 inches; (other models) 201 inches. Tires: (convertibles) 7.50 x 14 four-ply blackwall; (Cobras) F70 x 14; (other models) 7.35 x 14 four-ply tubeless blackwall.

FALCON CHASSIS FEATURES: Wheelbase: (station wagons) 113 inches; (other models) 110.9 inches. Overall length: (station wagon) 198.7 inches; (other models) 184.3 inches. Tires: (station wagons) 7.75 x 14 four-ply tubeless blackwall; (sports coupe) 7.35 x 14 four-ply tubeless blackwall; (other models) 6.95 x 14 four-ply tubeless blackwall.

MAVERICK CHASSIS FEATURES: Wheelbase: 103 inches. Overall length: 179.4 inches. Tires: 6.00 x 13 four-ply tubeless blackwall.

THUNDERBIRD SERIES CHASSIS FEATURES: Wheelbase: (four-door Landau) 117 inches; (other models) 115 inches. Overall length: (four-door Landau) 209.9 inches; (other models) 206.9 inches. Tires: (four-door Landau) 8.45 x 15 four-ply tubeless; (other models) 8.15 x 15 four-ply tubeless whitewall.

FORD OPTIONS: 265 hp, 390 cid V-8 engine ($58). 320 hp, 429 cid V-8 engine ($163). 360 hp, 429 cid V-8 engine ($237). Cruise-O-Matic automatic transmission ($222). Power steering ($100). Power brakes ($65 — front discs). Tinted windshield ($45). Air conditioning ($389). AM radio ($61). AM/FM stereo radio ($181). Vinyl roof ($100). White sidewall tires ($33).

FAIRLANE/FAIRLANE TORINO OPTIONS: 220 hp, 302 cid V-8 engine (no charge). 351 cid V-8 engine ($84). Cruise-O-Matic automatic transmission ($222). Four-speed manual transmission ($194 — standard on Cobras). AM radio ($61). Power steering ($100). Power tailgate window on station wagons ($35). Luggage rack on station wagons ($47). Two-tone paint ($27). White sidewall tires ($34). Vinyl roofs on two-door hardtops and four-door sedans ($90).

FALCON OPTIONS: 200 cid six-cylinder engine ($26). 302 cid V-8 engine ($79). Cruise-O-Matic automatic transmission ($175). Power steering ($89). Power tailgate window on station wagons ($35). Tinted windshield ($32). AM radio ($61). Wheelcovers ($21).

MAVERICK OPTIONS: Cruise-O-Matic automatic transmission ($175). AM radio ($61). White sidewall tires ($34).

THUNDERBIRD OPTIONS: 429 cid Thunder Jet V-8 engine ($237). Six-Way power seats ($99). Power windows ($109). Cruise-Control ($97). Air conditioning ($427). Climate Control air conditioning ($499). AM/FM stereo radio ($150). AM/8-track stereo ($128). Exterior Protection Group on two-doors ($25); on four-doors ($29).

HISTORICAL FOOTNOTES: The 1969 Ford lines were publicly introduced on Sept. 27, 1968. Calendar year production for America's number two automaker hit the 1,743,442 unit level this year. A total of 1,880,384 Fords were registered as new cars during calendar 1969. Semon E. Knudsen was, again, president of the company and continued to actively pursue a strong high-performance image. Stock car driver Richard Petty was enticed to drive for Ford in 1969, after a successful stint with Plymouth. He captured the checkered flag in the Riverside 500 Grand National Race. David Pearson, also driving Fords, won the NASCAR championship with 26 Grand National victories. The race cars were special Talladega streamlined Torinos that sold for $3,680. A total of 754 were built during January and February of 1969. It was the next to last season for the compact Falcon, which could not be modified to meet federal safety regulations at reasonable cost. The Falcon nameplate was used on a budget priced Torino added as a late-year model in 1970, then dropped entirely. Ford called its fastback cars "Sportsroof" models and used the name "Squire" on its fanciest station wagons.

1970 FORD

1970 FORDS — OVERVIEW — For model year 1970, Ford continued to expand its lineup with more and more models within each series. The full-size Fords were only slightly restyled for 1970, with a revamped rear end treatment. The taillights of the new model were positioned lower in the body and the grille was updated.

FORD CUSTOM SERIES — (ALL ENGINES) — The Custom series was the base trim level for 1970 and included chrome windshield and rear window moldings; nylon carpeting; the Custom name, in script, on the rear fenders and the Ford name, in block letters, across the front of the hood and in the rear escutcheon panel. The Custom 500 models offered the same trim, with the addition of a horizontal chrome strip along the mid-section of the body and a brushed aluminum trim strip at the front of the hood.

CUSTOM SIX-CYLINDER SERIES I.D. NUMBERS: Custom six-cylinder models began with the number 'O,' followed by the assembly plant code, engine designation 'V' and, finally, the unit's production number, according to the final assembly location. Each plant began at 100001 and went up.

CUSTOM SIX SERIES

Model Number	Body/Style Number	Body Type & Seating	Factory Price	Shipping Weight	Production Total
V	54E	4-dr Sed-6P	2771	3527	Note 1
V	54B	4-dr Sed-6P	2872	3567	Note 1

NOTE 1: See Custom V-8 series listing. Production was counted by series and body style only. with no breakout per engine type.

CUSTOM V-8 SERIES I.D. NUMBERS: Custom V-8 models began with the number 'O.' followed by the assembly plant code, body type code, engine designation code and, finally, the unit's production number according to the final assembly location. Each plant began at 100001 and went up.

CUSTOM V-8 SERIES

Model Number	Body/Style Number	Body Type & Seating	Factory Price	Shipping Weight	Production Total
NA	54E	4-dr Sed-6P	2850	3563	42,849
NA	71D	4-dr Ranch Wag-6P	3305	4079	15,086
NA	54B	4-dr Sed-6P	2951	3603	41,261
NA	71H	4-dr Ranch Wag-6P	3368	4049	15,304
NA	71J	4-dr Ranch Wag-10P	3481	4137	9,943

PRODUCTION NOTE: Total series output was 124,443 units. Ford does not indicate the number of each model produced with sixes and V-8s. Therefore, all production figures given above are total production of each body style with both engines.

GALAXIE 500 SERIES — (ALL ENGINES) — The Galaxie 500 was the intermediate trim level for 1969 and included all the Custom trim; plus a pleated vinyl interior; chrome side window and rain gutter moldings; and polished aluminum wheel opening moldings.

GALAXIE 500 SIX-CYLINDER SERIES I. D. NUMBERS: Galaxie 500 six-cylinder models used the same serial number sequence as the Custom series.

GALAXIE 500 SIX SERIES

Model Number	Body/Style Number	Body Type & Seating	Factory Price	Shipping Weight	Production Total
V	54A	4-dr Sed-6P	3026	3540	Note 1
V	578	4-dr HT Sed-6P	3096	3611	Note 1
V	65C	2-dr FT Cpe-6P	3094	3550	Note 1
V	63B	2-dr FsBk Cpe-6P	3043	3549	Note 1

NOTE 1: See Galaxie 500 V-8 series listing. Production was counted by series and body style only, with no breakout per engine type.

GALAXIE 500 V-8 SERIES I.D. NUMBERS: Galaxie 500 V-8 models used the same serial number sequence as the Custom series.

GALAXIE 500 V-8 SERIES

Model Number	Body/Style Number	Body Type & Seating	Factory Price	Shipping Weight	Production Total
NA	54A	4-dr Sed-6P	3137	3661	101,784
NA	57B	4-dr HT Sed-6P	3208	3732	53,817
NA	65C	2-dr FT Cpe-6P	3205	3671	57,059
NA	63B	2-dr FsBk Cpe-6P	3154	3670	50,825
NA	71B	4-dr Cty Sed-6P	3488	4089	32,209
NA	71C	4-dr Cty Sed-10P	3600	4112	22,645

PRODUCTION NOTE: Total series output was 318, 339 units. Ford does not indicate the number of each model produced with sixes and V-8s. Therefore, all production figures given above are total production of each body style with both engines.

FORD XL SERIES — (ALL ENGINES) — The Ford XL was the sport trim version of the full-size two-door convertible and two-door fastback models and included the features of the Galaxie 500s, plus the 302 cid V-8 engine; bucket seats; special wheelcovers; LTD style die-cast grille; retractable headlights; pleated, all-vinyl interior trim; and the XL designation, in block letters, in the center of the front of the hood.

FORD XL V-8 SERIES I.D. NUMBERS: Ford XLs used the same serial number sequence as the Custom and Galaxie 500 series.

FORD XL V-8 SERIES

Model Number	Body/Style Number	Body Type & Seating	Factory Price	Shipping Weight	Production Total
NA	63C	2-dr FsBk Cpe-5P	3293	3750	27,251
NA	76B	2-dr Conv-5P	3501	3983	6,348

PRODUCTION NOTE: Total series output was 33,599 units.

1970 Ford, LTD Brougham, two-door hardtop sports coupe, V-8

FORD LTD V-8 SERIES — (ALL ENGINES) — The LTD was the top trim level full-size Ford for 1970 and included all the Galaxie 500 trim, plus the 250 hp, 351 cid V-8 engine; Cruise-O-Matic automatic transmission; electric clock; bright exterior moldings; and dual accent paint stripes. The LTD station wagon models (Country Squires) also included simulated woodgrain appliques on the bodysides. All LTDs also included retractable headlights and a die-cast grille. The absolute top trim level for 1970 was the LTD Brougham two- and four-door hardtops and four-door sedan. These were LTDs with more lavish interiors than the regular LTD offered. Exterior trim remained the same as the standard LTD.

FORD LTD V-8 SERIES I.D. NUMBERS: LTDs used the same serial number sequence as the Custom and Galaxie 500 series.

FORD LTD V-8 SERIES

Model Number	Body/Style Number	Body Type & Seating	Factory Price	Shipping Weight	Production Total
NA	54C	4-dr Sed-6P	3307	3701	78,306
NA	57F	4-dr HT Sed-6P	3385	3771	90,390
NA	65A	2-dr HT Cpe-6P	3356	3727	96,324
NA	71E	4-dr Cty Sq-6P	3832	4139	39,837
NA	71A	4-dr Cty Sq-10P	3909	4185	69,077

LTD BROUGHAM SUB-SERIES

Model Number	Body/Style Number	Body Type & Seating	Factory Price	Shipping Weight	Production Total
NA	54	4-dr Sed-6P	3502	3829	NA
NA	57	4-dr HT Sed-6P	3579	4029	NA
NA	65	2-dr HT Cpe-6P	3537	3855	NA

PRODUCTION NOTE: Total series output was 373,934 units. Production is not broken down between LTD models and LTD Brougham models. Therefore, production figures represent total LTD model production.

FAIRLANE/TORINO — OVERVIEW — The Fairlane/Torino series was completely restyled, with a very sleek body shell and rounded fender contours. The top-line Torino series featured hidden headlights as part of its luxury package. The powerful Cobra models offered a functional hood scoop and rear window louvers as part of the Cobra package. The midyear 1969 introduction of the Maverick caused Falcon sales to plummet and, for 1970, the Falcon was nothing more than the lowest-price Fairlane model. It was available only as a two-door sedan, although all the high-performance engine options were offered in it.

FAIRLANE SERIES — (ALL ENGINES) — The Fairlane was the base trim level of the intermediate Fairlane/Torino series and included chrome windshield, rear window and rain gutter moldings; front and rear door armrests; cigarette lighter; nylon carpeting; the Fairlane 500 name, in script, on the rear fenders above the side marker lights; two chrome hash marks on the front fenders, behind the front wheel opening; and the Ford name, in block letters, on the driver's side of the hood and across the escutcheon panel.

FAIRLANE 500 SIX-CYLINDER SERIES I.D. NUMBERS: Fairlane 500 six-cylinder models began with the number 'O,' followed by the assembly plant code, body type code, engine designation 'L' and, finally, the unit's production number. according to the final assembly location. Each plant began at 100001 and went up.

19701/2 Ford Falcon, two-door sedan, V-8

FAIRLANE 500 SIX-CYLINDER SERIES

Model Number	Body/Style Number	Body Type & Seating	Factory Price	Shipping Weight	Production Total
FALCON SUB-SERIES					
L	54A	4-dr Sed-6P	2500	3116	Note 1
L	62A	2-dr Sed-6P	2460	3100	Note 1
L	71D	4-dr Sta Wag-6P	2767	3155	Note 1
FAIRLANE 500 SUB-SERIES					
L	54B	4-dr Sed-6P	2627	3116	Note 1
L	65B	2-dr HT Cpe-6P	2660	3128	Note 1
L	71B	4-dr Sta Wag-6P	2957	3508	Note 1

NOTE 1: See Fairlane 500 V-8 series listing. Production was counted by series and body style only, with no breakout per engine type.

FAIRLANE 500 V-8 SERIES I.D. NUMBERS: Fairlane 500 V-8 models began with the number 'O,' followed by the assembly plant code, body type code. engine designation code and, finally, the unit's production number, according to the final assembly location. Each plant began at 100001 and went up.

FAIRLANE 500 V-8 SERIES

Model Number	Body/Style Number	Body Type & Seating	Factory Price	Shipping Weight	Production Total
NA	54A	4-dr Sed-6P	2528	3216	30,443
NA	62A	2-dr Sed-6P	2479	3200	26,071
NA	71D	4-dr Sta Wag-6P	2856	3255	10,539
NA	54B	4-dr Sed-6P	2716	3216	25,780
NA	65B	2-dr HT Cpe-6P	2750	3228	70,636
NA	71B	4-dr Sta Wag-6P	3047	3608	13,613

PRODUCTION NOTE: Total series output was 177,091 units. Ford does not indicate the number of each model produced with sixes and V-8s. Therefore, all production figures given above are total production of each body style with both engines.

TORINO SERIES — (ALL ENGINES) — The Torino was the intermediate trim level for the intermediate size Fairlane/Torino series and included all the Fairlane 500 trim, plus a single horizontal chrome strip along the bodyside. The Torino name appeared in script, on the driver's side of the hood and in block letters on the side of the front fenders, behind the front wheel opening.

TORINO SIX-CYLINDER SERIES I.D. NUMBERS: Torino six-cylinder models used the same serial number sequence as the Fairlane 500 models.

TORINO SIX-CYLINDER SERIES

Model Number	Body/Style Number	Body Type & Seating	Factory Price	Shipping Weight	Production Total
L	54C	4-dr Sed-6P	2689	3158	Note 1
L	57C	4-dr HT Sed-6P	2795	3189	Note 1
L	65C	2-dr HT Cpe-6P	2722	3173	Note 1
L	63C	2-dr FsBk Cpe-6P	2810	3211	Note 1
L	71C	4-dr Sta Wag-6P	3074	3553	Note 1

NOTE 1: See Torino V-8 series listing. Production was counted by series and body style only, with no breakout per engine type.

TORINO V-8 SERIES I.D. NUMBERS: Torino V-8 models used the same serial number sequence as the Fairlane 500 models.

TORINO V-8 SERIES

Model Number	Body/Style Number	Body Type & Seating	Factory Price	Shipping Weight	Production Total
NA	54C	4-dr Sed-6P	2778	3258	30,117
NA	57C	4-dr HT Sed-6P	2885	3289	14,312
NA	65C	2-dr HT Cpe-6P	2812	3273	49,826
NA	63C	2-dr FsBk Cpe-6P	2899	3311	12,490
NA	71C	4-dr Sta Wag-6P	3164	3653	10,613

PRODUCTION NOTE: Total series output was 117,358 units. Ford does not indicate the number of each model produced with sixes and V-8s. Therefore, all production figures given above are total production of each body style with both engines.

TORINO BROUGHAM SERIES — (ALL ENGINES) — The Torino Brougham was the top trim level of the Torino series for 1970 and included all the Torino trim, plus polished aluminum wheel well and rocker panel moldings; retractable headlights; wheelcovers; and the 220 hp, 302 cid V-8 engine. The station wagon version included all of the above features, plus simulated woodgrain appliques and power front disc brakes.

TORINO BROUGHAM SERIES I.D. NUMBERS — (ALL ENGINES) — Torino Broughams used the same serial number sequence as the Fairlane 500 and Torino models.

TORINO BROUGHAM V-8 SERIES

Model Number	Body/Style Number	Body Type & Seating	Factory Price	Shipping Weight	Production Total
NA	57E	4-dr HT Sed-6P	3078	3309	14,543
NA	57E	2-dr HT Cpe-6P	3006	3293	16,911
NA	71E	4-dr Sq Wag-6P	3379	3673	13,166

PRODUCTION NOTE: Total series output was 44,620 units.

TORINO GT AND COBRA SERIES — (ALL ENGINES) — The Torino GT was the sport version of the Torino series and included all the Torino trim, plus outside color-keyed dual racing interior mirrors; hood scoop; trim rings with hubcaps; courtesy lights; carpeting; padded seats; GT emblems; 250 hp 351 cid V-8 engine and E70 x 15 fiberglass-belted white sidewall tires (F70 x 15 tires on convertible versions). The Torino Cobra was the high-performance version of the Torino series and included all the Torino trim, plus the 360 hp, 429 cid V-8 engine; four-speed manual transmission; competition suspension; seven inch wide wheels with hubcaps; black center hood; hood locking pins; bright exterior moldings; courtesy lights; Cobra emblems; and F70 x 15 fiberglass-belted black sidewall tires with raised white letters.

TORINO GT AND TORINO COBRA SERIES I.D. NUMBERS — (ALL ENGINES) — Torino GT and Cobra models used the same serial number sequence as Fairlane 500 and Torino models.

TORINO GT AND COBRA V-8 SERIES

Model Number	Body/Style Number	Body Type & Seating	Factory Price	Shipping Weight	Production Total
TORINO GT					
NA	63F	2-dr FsBk Cpe-6P	3105	3366	56,819
NA	76F	2-dr Conv-6P	3212	3490	3,939
TORINO GT COBRA					
NA	63H	2-dr FsBk Cpe-6P	3270	3774	7,675

PRODUCTION NOTE: Total series output was 68,433 units.

1970 Ford, Maverick Deluxe two-door sedan, 6-cyl

MAVERICK SERIES — (ALL ENGINES) — The Maverick, a midyear introduction model for 1969, was back for 1970. It again used a Falcon chassis and 170 cid six-cylinder engine and came only as a two-door sedan. Customer demand was so great for the 1969 version that Ford officials decided to leave a good thing alone and continued to offer the same car for 1970.

MAVERICK SERIES I.D. NUMBERS — (ALL ENGINES) — The Mavericks used the same serial number sequence as the full-size Fords, Fairlanes and Falcons.

MAVERICK SERIES

Model Number	Body/Style Number	Body Type & Seating	Factory Price	Shipping Weight	Production Total
T	91	2-dr Sed-6P	1995	2411	145,081

PRODUCTION NOTE: Total series output was 451,081 units.

THUNDERBIRD SERIES — (ALL ENGINES) — The 1970 Thunderbird featured a new grille, with a protruding center section, which was found to be very delicate and caused insurance companies to charge very high premiums to Thunderbird owners. The entire car was lower than in previous years and featured an inverted 'U' taillight arrangement. The length and lowness of the new Thunderbird was accented by a single horizontal feature line along the mid-section of the body. Color-keyed wheelcovers added to the rich look of the new Thunderbirds.

1970 Ford, Thunderbird two-door hardtop sports coupe, V-8

THUNDERBIRD SERIES I.D. NUMBERS — (ALL ENGINES) — Thunderbird models began with the number 'O,' assembly plant code 'Y' (Wixom), body type code, engine type code 'N' and, finally, the unit's production number, beginning at 100001 and going up.

THUNDERBIRD SERIES

Model Number	Body/Style Number	Body Type & Seating	Factory Price	Shipping Weight	Production Total
N	65C	2-dr HT-4P	4961	4354	5,116
N	65D	2-dr Landau-4P	5104	4630	36,847
N	57C	4-dr Landau-4P	5182	4464	8,401

PRODUCTION NOTE: Total series output was 50,364 units. This figure includes 1,925 two-door hardtops equipped with bucket seats; 16,953 two-door Landaus equipped with bucket seats and 5,005 four-door Landaus equipped with bucket seats.

ENGINES

MAVERICK SIX-CYLINDER: Overhead valves. Cast iron block. Displacement: 170 cid. Bore and stroke: 3.50 x 2.94 inches. Compression ratio: 9.0:1. Brake hp: 105 at 4400 rpm. Carburetion: Holley one-barrel. Seven main bearings. Serial number code "U."

MAVERICK SIX-CYLINDER: Overhead valves. Cast iron block. Displacement: 200 cid. Bore and stroke: 3.68 x 3.13 inches. Compression ratio: 8.0:1. Brake hp: 120 at 4400 rpm. Carburetion: Motorcraft one-barrel. Seven main bearings. Serial number code "T."

FORD/MUSTANG SIX-CYLINDER: Overhead valves. Cast iron block. Displacement: 240 cid. Bore and stroke: 4.00 x 3.18 inches. Compression ratio: 9.2:1. Brake hp: 150 at 4000 rpm. Carburetion: Motorcraft one-barrel. Seven main bearings. Serial number code "V."

FORD SIX-CYLINDER: Overhead valves. Cast iron block. Displacement: 250 cid. Bore and stroke: 3.68 x 3.91 inches. Compression ratio: 9.0:1. Brake hp: 155 at 4400 rpm. Carburetion: Motorcraft one-barrel. Seven main bearings. Serial number code "L."

302 V-8: Overhead valves. Cast iron block. Displacement: 302 cid. Bore and stroke: 4.00 x 3.00 inches. Compression ratio: 9.5:1. Brake hp: 220 at 4600 rpm. Carburetion: Motorcraft two-barrel. Five main bearings. Serial number code "F."

BOSS 302 V-8: Overhead valves. Cast iron block. Displacement: 302 cid. Compression ratio: 10.6:1. Brake hp: 290 at 5800 rpm. Carburetion: Holley four-barrel. Five main bearings. Serial code number "G."

351 V-8: Overhead valves. Cast iron block. Displacement: 351 cid. Bore and stroke: 4.00 x 3.50 inches. Compression ratio: 9.5:1. Brake hp: 250 at 4600 rpm. Carburetion: Motorcraft two-barrel. Five main bearings. Serial number code "H."

351 FOUR-BARREL V-8: Overhead valves. Cast iron block. Displacement: 351 cid. Bore and stroke: 4.00 x 3.50 inches. Compression ratio: 11.0:1. Brake hp: 300 at 5400 rpm. Carburetion: Motorcraft four-barrel. Five main bearings. Serial number code "M."

390 V-8: Overhead valves. Cast iron block. Displacement: 390 cid. Bore and stroke: 4.05 x 3.78 inches. Compression ratio: 9.5:1. Brake hp: 270 4400 rpm. Carburetion: Motorcraft two-barrel. Five main bearings. Serial number code "H."

COBRA JET 428 V-8: Overhead valve. Cast iron block. Displacement: 428 cid. Bore and stroke: 4.13 x 3.98 inches. Compression ratio: 10.6:1. Brake hp: 335 at 5200 rpm. Carburetion: Holley four-barrel. Five main bearings. Serial number code "Q."

SUPER COBRA JET 428 V-8: Overhead valves. Cast iron block. Displacement: 428 cid. Bore and stroke: 4.13 x 3.98 inches. Compression ratio: 10.5:1. Brake hp: 360 at 5400 rpm. Carburetion: Holley four-barrel. Five main bearings. Serial number code "J."

THUNDER JET 429 V-8: Overhead valves. Cast iron block. Displacement: 429 cid. Bore and stroke: 4.36 x 3.59 inches. Compression ratio: 10.5:1. Brake hp: 320 at 4400 rpm. Carburetion: Motorcraft two-barrel. Five main bearings. Serial number code "K."

THUNDER JET 429 FOUR-BARREL V-8: Overhead valves. Cast iron block. Displacement: 429 cid. Bore and stroke: 4.36 x 3.59 inches. Compression ratio: 10.5:1. Brake hp: 360 at 4600 rpm. Carburetion: Motorcraft four-barrel. Five main bearings. Serial number code "N."

POLICE INTERCEPTOR 429 V-8: Overhead valves. Cast iron block. Displacement: 429 cid. Bore and stroke: 4.36 x 3.59 inches. Compression ratio: 11.3:1. Brake hp: 370 at 5400 rpm. Carburetion: Holley four-barrel. Five main bearings. Serial number code "P."

BOSS 429 V-8: Overhead valves. Cast iron block. Displacement: 429 cid. Bore and stroke: 4.36 x 3.59 inches. Compression ratio: 11.3:1. Brake hp: 375 at 5600 rpm. Carburetion: Holley four-barrel Five main bearings. Serial number code "Z."

NOTE: Ram Air Boss 429 V-8: Same specifications as Boss 429.

FORD CHASSIS FEATURES: Wheelbase: 121 inches. Overall length: (station wagons) 216.9 inches; (other models) 213.9 inches. Tires: (Custom six-cylinder) F78 x 15 four-ply blackwall tubeless; (Custom and Custom 500 V-8) G78 x 15 four-ply tubeless blackwall; (Galaxie 500 and LTD) H78 x 15 four-ply tubeless blackwall.

FAIRLANE 500/TORINO CHASSIS FEATURES: Wheelbase: (station wagon) 114 inches; (other models) 117 inches. Overall length: (station wagon) 209 inches; (other models) 206.2 inches. Tires: (convertibles) F70 x 14 four-ply tubeless blackwall; (station wagons) G78 x 14; (GTs) E70 x 14; (other models) E78 x 14.

THUNDERBIRD CHASSIS FEATURES: Wheelbase: (two-doors) 114.7 inches; (other models) 117.1 inches. Overall length: 215 inches. Tires 215 x 15 radial blackwalls.

FORD OPTIONS: Power disc brakes ($65). Power steering ($105). Air conditioning ($389). Cruise-O-Matic automatic transmission ($201-$222). Tinted windshield ($45). AM radio ($61). AM/FM radio ($240). Vinyl roof ($105). White sidewall tires ($34). Custom series 265 hp, 390 cid V-8 engine ($131). Galaxie 500/XL/LTD 265 hp, 390 cid V-8 engine ($86). Custom series 320 hp, 429 cid V-8 engine ($213). Galaxie 500/XL/LTD 320 hp, 429 cid V-8 inch ($168). LTD Luxury trim package ($104).

FAIRLANE/TORINO OPTIONS: Power steering ($100). Air conditioning ($389). Cruise-O-Matic automatic transmission ($201-$222). Four-speed manual transmission ($194). AM radio ($61). Station wagon power tailgate window ($35). Station wagon rooftop luggage rack ($46). White sidewall tires ($34). Vinyl roof on two-door and four-door hardtops and sedan ($95). Fairlane/Torino 351 cid V-8 engine ($45).

PINTO OPTIONS: 100 hp 122 cid four-cylinder overhead cam engine ($50). Cruise-O-Matic automatic transmission ($175). AM radio ($61). Chrome window moldings ($60). White sidewall tires ($33).

THUNDERBIRD OPTIONS: Air conditioning ($427). Six-Way power seats ($198). Power side windows ($110). Cruise-Control ($97). Air conditioning with Climate Control ($499). AM/FM stereo radio ($150). AM radio with 8-track tape player ($150). Brougham interior package ($162). Limited-edition Fiera Brougham option package ($304).

1970 Ford, Falcon two-door sedan, V-8

HISTORICAL FOOTNOTES: The full-sized Fords were introduced in September 1969 and the Falcon/Torino appeared in dealer showrooms at midyear. Model year production peaked at 1,326,533 units. Calendar year production of 1,647,918 cars was recorded. Due to the new, reverse-curve Torino rear window design (and increased competition from the aerodynamic Dodge Daytona and Plymouth Superbird), Ford elected to race 1969 models this year. Only six stock car flags were taken by FoMoCo drivers. The DeTomaso Pantera, an Italian-built specialty sports car powered by a 310 hp 351 cid Ford 'Cleveland' V-8, made its debut in 1970. During the early months of 1970, the Falcon compact was still marketed in three styles, two- and four-door sedans and station wagons, but was replaced by the larger Fairlane based '70-1/2 Falcon during the summer.

1971 FORD

1971 FORDS — OVERVIEW — The complete restyling of two model lines and the introduction of the sub-compact Pinto line characterized 1972, a year which also saw the end of two Ford trademarks. The Fairlane was dropped, along with the 'FE' series big-block V-8 engine. The Fairlane name ceased to exist with the end of the 1970 model year and the big-block engine, in 390 and 428 cid sizes, was gradually phased-out during the production run. It was replaced by a new 400 cid 'Cleveland' V-8 and the 429 cid V-8.

FORD CUSTOM SERIES — (ALL ENGINES) — The full-size Fords received a total restyling. The grille was a full-width horizontal unit, with a larger, vertical center section which protruded forward. The hood peaked the center section of the grille and became wider toward the windshield. The Custom series was the base trim level full-size Ford for 1971 and included chrome windshield and rear window moldings; nylon carpeting and the Custom name, in block letters, on the rear fenders and rear escutcheon panel. The Custom 500 models included all the Custom trim, plus polished aluminum wheelwell moldings; argent and chrome appliques on the instrument panel; rear deck moldings; and Custom 500 ornamentation. The Custom and Custom 500 models were available with either the 140 hp 240 cid six-cylinder engine or the 210 hp 302 cid V-8 engine as standard equipment.

CUSTOM SERIES I.D. NUMBERS: Custom models began with the number '1,' followed by the assembly plant code, engine designation code and, finally, the unit's production number, according to the final assembly location. Each plant began at 100001 and went up.

CUSTOM SERIES

Model Number	Body/Style Number	Body Type & Seating	Factory Price	Shipping Weight	Production Total
BASE CUSTOM					
NA	54B	4-dr Sed-6P	3288/3363	3683/3724	41,062
NA	71B	4-dr Ranch Wag-6P	3890	4190	16,696

Model Number	Body/Style Number	Body Type & Seating	Factory Price	Shipping Weight	Production Total
CUSTOM 500					
NA	54D	4-dr Sed-6P	3426/3501	3688/3729	33,765
NA	71D	4-dr Ranch Wag-6P	3982	4215	25,957

PRODUCTION NOTE: Total series output was 117,480 units. The price and weight to the left of the slash indicate six-cylinder equipped models and the price and weight to the right of the slash indicate V-8 powered models.

GALAXIE 500 SERIES — (ALL ENGINES) — The Galaxie 500 was the intermediate trim level full-size Ford for 1971 and included all the Custom trim, plus woodgrain appliques on the interior doors and instrument panel; bodyside moldings, with black-painted inserts; partial polished aluminum wheelwell moldings; chrome window frames; deck and rear quarter extension moldings; Galaxie 500 ornamentation; 240 hp, 351 cid V-8 engine; and F78 x 15 belted black sidewall tires (H78 x 15 tires on Country Sedans).

GALAXIE 500 SERIES I.D. NUMBERS: Galaxie 500 models used the same serial number sequence as the Custom series.

GALAXIE 500 SERIES

Model Number	Body/Style Number	Body Type & Seating	Factory Price	Shipping Weight	Production Total
NA	54F	4-dr Sed-6P	3246/3367	3668/3826	98,130
NA	57F	4-dr HT Sed-6P	3665/3786	3723/3881	46,595
NA	65F	2-dr HT Cpe-6P	3628/3749	3668/3826	117,139
NA	71F	4-dr Cty Sed-6P	4074	4241	60,487
NA	71D	4-dr Cty Sed- 10P	4188	4291	NA

PRODUCTION NOTE: Total series output was 322,351 units. This figure does not include the 10-passenger four-door Country Sedan, for which separate production figures breakouts are not available. The price and weight to the left of the slash indicate six-cylinder equipped models and the price and weight to the right of the slash indicate V-8 powered models.

FORD LTD SERIES — (ALL ENGINES) — A more formal roofline was used in the LTD series and the interiors were completely restyled, with the emphasis on luxury or a luxury appearance in the lower-priced lines. The taillights were rectangular and were located at either end of the rear escutcheon panel, with the LTDs featuring an additional red, plastic reflector in the center. This gave the illusion of a single, full-width taillight. The LTD was the top trim level full-size Ford for 1971 and included all the Galaxie 500 trim, plus power front disc brakes; electric clock; luxury seat trim (except convertibles); left-hand outside rearview mirror; nylon carpeting; power top on convertibles; and G78 x 15 belted tires (in place of F78 x 15) on convertibles. The LTD Country Squire station wagons also included wheelcovers; power tailgate window; simulated woodgrain appliques on the bodyside panels; pleated vinyl trim; and H78 x 15 belted black sidewall tires. The LTD Brougham series included all the LTD trim, plus wheelcovers; unique Brougham seat trim; Deluxe steering wheel; front door courtesy light; cut-pile carpeting; front seat center armrest; and polished seat side shields; rear door courtesy light switches; special LTD 'C' pillar ornamentation; and highback bucket seats on the two-door hardtop.

LTD SERIES I.D. NUMBERS: LTDs used the same serial number sequence as the Custom and Galaxie 500 series.

LTD SERIES

Model Number	Body/Style Number	Body Type Number & Seating	Factory Price	Shipping Weight	Production Total
BASE LTD					
NA	53H	4-dr Sed-6P	3931	3913	92,260
NA	57H	4-dr HT Sed-6P	3969	3908	48,166
NA	65H	2-dr FT Cpe-6P	3923	3853	103,896
NA	76H	2-dr Conv-6P	4094	4091	5,750
NA	71H	4-dr Cty Sq-6P	4308	4308	130,644
NA	71H	4-dr Cty Sq-10P	4496	4358	NA
LTD BROUGHAM					
NA	53K	4-dr Sed-6P	4094	3949	26,186
NA	57K	4-dr HT Sed-6P	4140	3944	27,820
NA	65K	2-dr HT Cpe-6P	4097	3883	43,303

PRODUCTION NOTE: Total series output was 478,025 units. This figure includes the four-door, 10-passenger Country Squire, for which separate production figure breakouts are not available.

1971 Ford, Torino Cobra two-door hardtop sports coupe, V-8

TORINO SERIES — (ALL ENGINES) — Torinos for 1971 were merely 1970 bodies with updated trim and a very slightly revised grille. Standard equipment on the base Torino series included chrome windshield, rear window and rain gutter moldings; front and rear armrest on the doors; and the Torino name, in block letters, on the rear fenders. The Torino 500 Series had all the base Torino trim, plus color-keyed carpeting; cloth and vinyl interior trim; deck lid dock cover; Argent-painted eggcrate grille; and polished aluminum wheelwell and rocker panel moldings.

TORINO AND TORINO 500 SERIES I.D. NUMBERS: Torino 'and Torino 500s began with the number '1,' followed by the assembly plant code, body type code, engine designation code and, finally, the unit's production number, according to the final assembly location. Each plant began at 100001 and went up.

TORINO AND TORINO 500 SERIES

Model Number	Body/Style Number	Body Type & Seating	Factory Price	Shipping Weight	Production Total
BASE TORINO					
NA	54A	4-dr Sed-6P	2672/2767	3141/3220	29,501
NA	62A	2-dr HT Cpe-6P	2706/2801	3151/3230	37,518
NA	71D	4-dr Sta Wag-6P	3023/2950	3498/3577	21,570
TORINO 500					
NA	54C	4-dr Sed-6P	2855/2950	3146/3225	35,650
NA	57C	4-dr HT Sed-6P	2959/3054	3210/3289	12,724
NA	65C	2-dr HT Cpe-6P	2887/2982	3156/3235	89,966
NA	63C	2-dr FsBk Cpe-6P	2943/3038	3212/3291	11,150
NA	71C	4-dr Sta Wag-6P	3170/3265	3560/3639	23,270

PRODUCTION NOTE: Total series output was 261,349 units. The price and weight to the left of the slash indicate six-cylinder equipped models and the price and weight to the right of the slash indicate V-8 powered models.

TORINO BROUGHAM/TORINO GT/TORINO COBRA SERIES — (ALL ENGINES) — The Torino Brougham was the top trim level Torino for 1971 and included all the Torino 500 equipment, plus wheelcovers; chrome exterior moldings; soundproofing package; Brougham ornamentation; cloth interior trims (in choice of four colors); and 210 hp, 302 cid V-8 engine. The Squire wagon also included power front disc brakes; simulated woodgrain paneling on the bodysides; and G78 x 14 belted black sidewall tires. The Torino GT was the sporty version of the Brougham series and included all the basic Brougham trim, plus color-keyed outside racing mirrors (remote control on left-hand mirror); GT identification on the grille and rocker panels; simulated hood scoop; hubcaps with trim rings; chrome trim on the foot pedals; full-width taillight; and E70 x 14 white sidewall Wide-Oval tires. The convertible also had a power top. The Torino Cobra was the high-performance version of the Brougham series and included all the Brougham trim, plus 285 hp, 351 cid 'Cleveland' V-8 engine; four-speed manual transmission with Hurst shifter; special Cobra identification; heavy-duty suspension; seven inch wide, Argent-painted wheels with chrome hubcaps; black grille and lower escutcheon panel; black-finished hood with non-reflective paint; polished aluminum wheelwell moldings; F70 x 14 white sidewall Wide-Oval tires; 55 ampere heavy-duty battery; dual exhausts; and pleated vinyl seat trim.

TORINO BROUGHAM/GT/COBRA SERIES I.D. NUMBERS: — (ALL ENGINES) — Torino Brougham/GT/Cobra models used the same serial number sequence as the Torino and Torino 500 series.

TORINO BROUGHAM/GT/COBRA SERIES

Model Number	Body/Style Number	Body Type & Seating	Factory Price	Shipping Weight	Production Total
NA	57E	4-dr Brgm HT Sed	3248	3345	4,408
NA	65E	2-dr Brgm HT Cpe	3175	3390	8,593
NA	71E	4-dr Sq Wag-6P	3560	3663	15,805
NA	63F	2-dr GT Spt Cpe-6P	3150	3346	31,641
NA	76F	2-dr GT Conv-6P	3408	3486	1,613
NA	63H	2-dr Cobra HT Cpe	3295	3594	3,054

PRODUCTION NOTE: Total series output was 65,114 units. Styles 57E, 65E and 63H are 6-passenger models.

1971 Ford, Maverick 'Grabber' two-door sedan, V-8

MAVERICK SERIES — (ALL ENGINES) — The 1971 Maverick was unchanged from the previous two years, except for the addition of a four-door sedan and a 'Grabber' version of the two-door sedan. Also the 302 cid V-8 engine was available for the first time. The 302 proved to be a brisk performer in the small body and the special edition of the two-door sedan, called the 'Grabber,' was introduced to further enhance the performance image.

MAVERICK SERIES I.D. NUMBERS — (ALL ENGINES) — Maverick used the same serial number sequence as the full-size Fords and Torinos.

MAVERICK SERIES

Model Number	Body/Style Number	Body Type & Seating	Factory Price	Shipping Weight	Production Total
NA	54A	4-dr Sed-6P	2235/2404	2610/2803	73,208
NA	62A	2-dr Sed-6P	2175/2344	2478/2671	159,726
NA	62D	2-dr Grabber-6P	2354/2523	2570/2763	38,963

PRODUCTION NOTE: Total series output was 271,897 units. The price and weight to the left of the slash indicate six-cylinder equipped models and the price and weight to the right of the slash indicate V-8 powered models.

1971 PINTO — (OVERVIEW) — The new Pinto was introduced to serve the ever-growing small car market and to complete with Chevrolet's Vega and American Motor's Gremlin. Pintos were available with either a British-built 1600 cc overhead valve four-cylinder engine, or a second, more powerful (and much more popular) German-built 2000 cc motor, which was also a four. Both engines used a four-speed manual transmission, but only the larger engine was available with the three-speed Cruise-O-Matic transmission. While good fuel economy was the main objective of the new Pinto, those equipped with the larger engine and four-speed manual transmission provided quite brisk performance by any standards.

1971 Ford, Pinto two-door sedan, 4-cyl

PINTO SERIES — (ALL ENGINES) — The Pinto was the new sub-compact offering, built to compete with imports and domestic sub-compacts. It came only as a two-door sedan at first. Standard equipment included ventless door windows; highback, slim line bucket seats; all-vinyl upholstery; two-pod instrument cluster; glovebox; interior dome light; floor-mounted transmission controls; rack and pinion steering; hot water heater; DirectAire Ventilation system; and 6.00 x 13 rayon blackwall tires. In mid-season a three-door Runabout was added to the Pinto line. Its standard equipment was the same as above, plus fold-down rear seat with load floor color-keyed carpeting and passenger compartment color-keyed carpeting.

PINTO SERIES I.D. NUMBERS — (ALL ENGINES) — Pintos used the same serial number sequence as the full-size Fords, Torinos, Mavericks and Mustangs.

PINTO SERIES

Model Number	Body/Style Number	Body Type & Seating	Factory Price	Shipping Weight	Production Total
NA	62B	2-dr Sed-4P	1919	1949	288.606
NA	64B	2-dr Rbt-4P	2062	1994	63.796

PRODUCTION NOTE: Total series output was 352,402 units.

1971 Ford, Thunderbird two-door Landau, V-8

THUNDERBIRD SERIES — (ALL ENGINES) — The Thunderbird was essentially a 1970 model with only slight trim revisions. The grille had slightly wider bright metal blades at every third rung, giving a horizontally segmented look. There were also nine vertical division bars. New front side marker lamps with a one-piece lens were used. In addition, the front bumper wraparound edge was more massive.

THUNDERBIRD SERIES I.D. NUMBERS — (ALL ENGINES) — Thunderbirds began with the number '1,' assembly plant code 'Y' (Wixom), body type code, engine code 'N' and finally, the unit's production number, beginning at 100001 and going up.

THUNDERBIRD SERIES

Model Number	Body/Style Number	Body Type & Seating	Factory Price	Shipping Weight	Production Total
N	65A	2-dr HT Cpe-4P	5295	4399	9,146
N	65B	2-dr Landau-4P	5438	4370	20,356
N	57C	4-dr Landau-4P	5516	4509	6,553

PRODUCTION NOTE: Total series output was 36,055 units. This figure includes 2,992 two-door hardtops equipped with bucket seats; 8,133 two-door Landaus equipped with bucket seat and 4,238 four-door Landaus equipped with the split bench seat.

ENGINES:

PINTO FOUR: Overhead valves. Cast iron block. Displacement: 98 cid. Bore and stroke: 3.19 x 3.06 inches. Compression ratio: 8.4:1. Brake hp: 75 at 5000 rpm. Carburetor: one-barrel. Five main bearings.

PINTO FOUR: Overhead cam. Cast iron block. Displacement: 122 cid. Bore and stroke: 3.58 x 3.03 inches. Compression ratio: 9.0:1. Brake hp: 100 at 5600 rpm. Carburetion: Ford/Weber two-barrel. Five main bearings.

MAVERICK SIX-CYLINDER: Overhead valves. Cast iron block. Displacement: 170 cid. Bore and stroke: 3.50 x 2.94 inches. Compression ratio: 8.7:1. Brake hp: 100 at 4200 rpm. Carburetion: Motorcraft one-barrel. Seven main bearings. Serial number code "U."

MAVERICK SIX-CYLINDER: Overhead valves. Cast iron block. Displacement: 200 cid. Bore and stroke: 3.68 x 3.13 inches. Compression ratio: 8.7:1. Brake hp: 115 at 4000 rpm. Carburetion: Motorcraft one-barrel. Seven main bearings. Serial number code "T."

FORD/MAVERICK/MUSTANG SIX-CYLINDER: Overhead valves. Cast iron block. Displacement: 250 cid. Bore and stroke: 3.68 x 3.91 inches. Compression ratio: 9.0:1. Brake hp: 145 at 4000 rpm. Carburetion: Motorcraft one-barrel. Seven main bearings. Serial number code "L."

FORD SIX-CYLINDER: Overhead valves. Cast iron block. Displacement: 240 cid. Bore and stroke: 4.00 x 3.18 inches. Compression ratio: 8.9:1. Brake hp: 140 at 4000 rpm. Carburetion: Motorcraft one-barrel. Seven main bearings. Serial number code "V."

302 V-8: Overhead valves. Cast iron block. Displacement: 302 cid. Bore and stroke: 4.00 x 3.00 inches. Compression ratio: 9.0:1. Brake hp: 210 at 4600 rpm. Carburetion: Motorcraft two-barrel. Five main bearings. Serial number code "F."

351 V-8: Overhead valves. Cast iron block. Displacement: 351 cid. Bore and stroke: 4.00 x 3.50 inches. Compression ratio: 9.0:1. Brake hp: 240 at 4600 rpm. Carburetion: Motorcraft two-barrel. Five main bearings. Serial number code "H."

351 'CLEVELAND' TWO-BARREL V-8: Overhead valves. Cast iron block. Displacement: 351 cid. Bore and stroke: 4.00 x 3.50 inches. Compression ratio: 9.0:1. Brake hp: 240 at 4600 rpm. Carburetion: Motorcraft two-barrel. Five main bearings. Serial number code "H."

351 'CLEVELAND' FOUR-BARREL V-8: Overhead valves. Cast iron block. Displacement: 351 cid. Bore and stroke: 4.00 x 3.50 inches. Compression ratio: 10.7:1. Brake hp: 285 at 5400 rpm. Carburetion: Holley four-barrel. Five main bearings. Serial number code "M."

BOSS 351 V-8: Overhead valves. Cast iron block. Displacement: 351 cid. Bore and stroke: 4.00 x 3.50 inches. Compression ratio: 11.1:1. Brake hp: 330 at 5400 rpm. Carburetion: Holley four-barrel. Five main bearings. Serial number code "Q."

390 V-8: Overhead valves. Cast iron block. Displacement: 390 cid. Bore and stroke: 4.05 x 3.78 inches. Compression ratio: 8.6:1. Brake hp: 225 at 4400 rpm. Carburetion: Motorcraft two-barrel. Five main bearings. Serial number code "Y."

400 'CLEVELAND' V-8: Overhead valves. Cast iron block. Displacement: 400 cid. Bore and stroke: 4.00 x 4.00 inches. Compression ratio: 9.0:1. Brake hp: 260 at 4400 rpm. Carburetion: Motorcraft two-barrel. Five main bearings. Serial number code "S."

THUNDER JET 429 FOUR-BARREL V-8: Overhead valves. Cast iron block. Displacement: 429 cid. Bore and stroke: 4.36 x 3.59 inches. Compression ratio: 10.5:1. Brake hp: 360 at 4600 rpm. Carburetion: Motorcraft four-barrel. Five main bearings. Serial number code "N."

COBRA JET 429 V-8: Overhead valves. Cast iron block. Displacement: 429 cid. Bore and stroke: 4.36 x 3.59 inches. Compression ratio: 11.3:1. Brake hp: 370 at 5400 rpm. Carburetion: Holley four-barrel. Five main bearings. Serial number code "C."

SUPER COBRA JET 429 V-8: Overhead valves. Cast iron block. Displacement: 429 cid. Bore and stroke: 4.36 x 3.59 inches. Compression ratio: 11.3:1. Brake hp: 375 at 5600 rpm. Carburetion: Holley four-barrel (with Ram-Air induction). Five main bearings. Serial number code "J."

FORD CHASSIS FEATURES: Wheelbase: 121 inches. Overall length: 216.2 inches (219.2 inches on station wagons). Tires: F78 x 15 belted black sidewall (G78 x 15 on Galaxie 500s and LTDs and H78 x 15 on station wagons).

TORINO CHASSIS FEATURES: Wheelbase: 117 inches (114 on station wagons). Overall length: 206.2 inches (209 on station wagons). Tires: E78 x 14 belted blackwall (unless noted).

Standard Catalog of American Cars

MAVERICK CHASSIS FEATURES: Wheelbase: 103 inches. Overall length: 179.4 inches. Tires: 6.00 x 13 (6.50 x 13 on V-8 models).

PINTO CHASSIS FEATURES: Wheelbase: 115 inches (115 inches on four-door Landaus). Overall length: 215 inches. Tires: H78 x 15 belted black sidewall.

THUNDERBIRD CHASSIS FEATURES: Wheelbase: 115 inches (115 inches on four-door Landaus). Overall length: 215 inches. Tires: H78 x 15 belted black sidewall.

FORD OPTIONS: 260 hp 400 cid V-8 engine. 255 hp 390 cid V-8 engine ($98). 320 hp 429 cid V-8 engine ($168). 360 hp 429 cid V-8 engine ($268). Cruise-O-Matic automatic transmission ($217 to $238 depending on engine choice). Power steering ($115). Power front disc brakes ($52). Tinted windshield ($54). Air conditioning ($420). Cruise control ($84). AM radio ($66). AM /FM radio ($240). Vinyl roof on passenger cars ($113); on station wagons ($142). White sidewall tires ($34).

TORINO OPTIONS: 240 hp 351 cid V-8 engine ($45); 285 hp 351 cid V-8 engine ($93). 370 hp Cobra Jet 429 cid V-8 engine, in Cobra ($279); in all other Torinos ($372). Cruise-O-Matic automatic transmission, base Torino ($217); Cobra ($238). Four-speed manual transmission ($250). AM radio ($66). Power steering ($115). Power tailgate window on station wagons ($35). Luggage rack on station wagon ($52). Vinyl roof ($95). White sidewall tires ($34).

MAVERICK OPTIONS: 115 hp 200 cid six-cylinder engine ($39). 145 hp 250 cid six-cylinder engine ($79). 210 hp 302 cid V-8 engine. Cruise-O-Matic automatic transmission ($183). AM radio ($61). Power Steering ($95). White sidewall tires ($34).

PINTO OPTIONS: 100 hp 122 cid four-cylinder overhead cam engine ($50). Cruise-O-Matic automatic transmission ($175). AM radio ($61). Chrome window moldings ($60). White sidewall tires ($33).

THUNDERBIRD OPTIONS: Six-way power seats ($207). Power windows ($133). Cruise-Control ($97). Air conditioning ($448); with Climate control ($519). AM/FM stereo radio ($150); or AM/8-track stereo ($150). Electric rear window defogger ($48).

HISTORICAL FOOTNOTES: The full-sized Fords were introduced Sept. 18, 1970 and the other lines appeared in dealer showrooms the same day. Model year production peaked at 1,910,924 units. Calendar year production of 2,176,425 cars was recorded. (Note: The model year figure includes only Fords, Torinos, Mavericks, Pintos and Thunderbirds, while the calendar year figure covers all passenger and station wagon models). The Pinto Runabout was a two-door hatchback coupe. The more expensive full-sized Ford four-door sedans were advertised as 'pillared hardtops' this year. Fords captured only three NASCAR races in 1971, as the performance era wound to its close. Lee Iacocca became the president of Ford Motor Co. this season.

1972 FORD

1972 FORDS — OVERVIEW — For 1972, only two of the model lines received major restyling: the Torino and Thunderbird. All others either remained the same or received only very minor trim changes. It was a significant year in the respect that all engines were required to run on regular gasoline requiring a maximum compression ratio of around 9.0:1. Also, engines were no longer rated at brake horsepower. Beginning in 1972, all engines were rated in SAE Net horsepower or the theoretical power after deducting for the drain caused by the accessories and transmission. This fact notwithstanding, the 351 'Cleveland' V-8 still generated nearly 300 nhp, making it one of the most powerful engines being produced that year. Pollution requirements and rising insurance rates, plus the lower compression ratios, meant considerably restricted performance. As a result, 1971 is almost universally considered to be the end of the Ford muscle car era.

FORD CUSTOM AND CUSTOM 500 SERIES — (ALL ENGINES) — For 1972, the full-size Fords received only minor trim updating in the form of a slightly restyled grille set within the same grille opening. There was also a more protective front bumper. The rest of the body styling remained unchanged. The Custom was the base trim level for 1971 and included chrome windshield and rear window moldings; nylon carpeting; ignition key warning buzzer; 351 cid V-8 engine and Cruise-O-Matic automatic transmission (six-cylinder versions were available for fleet and taxi use, but will not be covered here due to limited collector interest). Power steering and F78 x 15 belted black sidewall tires were also standard. The Custom 500 versions included all the Custom trim, plus lower back panel and wheel lip moldings, and cloth and vinyl seating surfaces. Station wagons also included H78 x 15 belted black sidewall tires and power tailgate window.

CUSTOM SERIES I.D. NUMBERS: Custom models began with the number '2,' followed by the assembly plant code, engine designation code and, finally, the unit's production number, according to the final assembly location. Each plant began at 100001 and went up.

CUSTOM SERIES

Model Number	Body/Style Number	Body Type & Seating	Factory Price	Shipping Weight	Production Total
BASE CUSTOM					
NA	54B	4-dr Sed-6P	3288	3759	33,014
NA	71B	4-dr Ranch Wag-6P	3806	4317	13,064
CUSTOM 500					
NA	54D	4-dr Sed-6P	3418	3764	24,870
NA	71D	4-dr Ranch Wag-6P	3895	4327	16,834

PRODUCTION NOTE: Total series output was 87,782 units. Station wagon production was not broken down between six- and 10-passenger wagons.

GALAXIE 500 SERIES — (ALL ENGINES) — The Galaxie 500 was the intermediate trim level full-size Ford for 1972 and included all the Custom 500 trim, plus wheel lip and deck lid moldings, rocker panel moldings and woodgrain appliques on the instrument panel.

GALAXIE 500 SERIES I.D. NUMBERS: Galaxie 500 models used the same serial number sequence as the Custom Series.

GALAXIE 500 SERIES

Model Number	Body/Style Number	Body Type & Seating	Factory Price	Shipping Weight	Production Total
NA	54F	4-dr Sed-6P	3685	3826	104,167
NA	57F	4-dr HT Sed-6P	3720	3881	28,939
NA	65F	2-dr HT Cpe-6P	3752	3826	80,855
NA	71F	4-dr Cty Sed-6P	4028	4308	55,238

PRODUCTION NOTE: Total series output was 269,199 units. Station wagon production was not broken down between six and 10-passenger wagons.

1972 Ford, LTD Country Squire four-door station wagon, V-8

FORD LTD SERIES — (ALL ENGINES) — The LTD was the top trim level full-size Ford for 1972 and included all the Galaxie 500 trim, plus power front disc brakes; electric clock; luxury seat trim (except convertibles); rear bumper guards; woodgrain accents on interior door panels; front door courtesy lights; chrome trim on foot pedals; chrome armrest bases; F78 x 15 belted black sidewall tires on two-door hardtops; and G78 x 15 tires on all others-except wagons. Country Squire wagons also included full wheelcovers and reflective rear woodgrain paneling, in addition to the woodgrain paneling on the bodysides. LTD Brougham included all the standard LTD features, plus full wheelcovers; rocker panel moldings; unique Brougham seat and door trim; highback, flight-bench seats with center armrest; cut-pile carpeting; rear door courtesy light switches; front and rear dual armrests; and G78 x 15 belted black sidewall tires.

LTD SERIES I.D. NUMBERS: LTDs used the same serial number sequence as the Custom and Galaxie 500 Series.

LTD

Model Number	Body/Style Number	Body Type & Seating	Factory Price	Shipping Weight	Production Total
BASE LTD					
NA	53H	4-dr Sed-6P	3906	3913	104,167
NA	57H	4-dr HT Sed-6P	3941	3908	33,742
NA	65H	2-dr HT Cpe-6P	3898	3853	101,048
NA	76H	2-dr Conv-6P	4073	4091	4,234
NA	71H	4-dr Cty Sq-6P	4318	4308	121,419

Model Number	Body/Style Number	Body Type & Seating	Factory Price	Shipping Weight	Production Total
LTD BROUGHAM					
NA	53K	4-dr Sed-6P	4047	3949	36,909
NA	57K	4-dr HT Sed-6P	4090	3944	23,364
NA	65K	2-dr HT Cpe-6P	4050	3883	50,409

PRODUCTION NOTE: Total series output was 475,292 units. Station wagon production was not broken down between six and 10-passenger wagons.

1972 Ford, Gran Torino Sport two-door hardtop sport coupe, V-8

1972 TORINO — OVERVIEW — The 1972 Torino was one of two models completely restyled. The 'Coke bottle' shape was even more pronounced for 1972, than in previous years. There were rounded front fender profiles, and a rear fenderline which swept up toward the roof 'C' pillar, then tapered toward the rear of the car. Behind the car was a massive rear bumper, which housed rectangular taillights at each end. The grille was slightly reminiscent of the Cobra, being a large oval between the quad headlights. Automotive writer Tom McCahill observed that he thought the 1972 Torinos looked like, "land-locked Tunas sucking air." The top profile of the four-door sedans was rounder than in previous years, and the two-door fastback 'Sportsroof' featured an extremely low roofline.

TORINO SERIES — (ALL ENGINES) — Two basic lines of intermediate-sized Ford Torinos remained. Both the base Torino models and the top-line Gran Torinos were restyled from end-to-end. The Torino models featured chrome windshield, rear window and rain gutter moldings; highback bench seats; all-vinyl seat and door trim; floor mats; hubcaps with trim rings; 250 cid six-cylinder engine; and three-speed manual transmission. The Torino station wagon also included power front disc brakes and three-way tailgate. The Gran Torino was the top trim level for 1972 and included all the Torino features, plus manual front disc brakes and cloth and vinyl trim on seats and interior door panels; carpeting; lower bodyside, wheelwell and deck lid moldings; dual-note horn; trunk mat; Deluxe steering wheel; and chrome trim on the foot pedals. The Gran Torino Squire wagon also included the 140 hp, 302 cid V-8 engine; Deluxe pleated vinyl interior trim; wheelcovers; and woodgrain appliques on the bodysides, tailgate and instrument panel. The Gran Torino Sport was the sports version of the Gran Torino line and included all the Gran Torino features, plus the 140 hp, 302 cid V-8 engine; pleated, all-vinyl trim; hood scoops; color-keyed dual racing mirrors; and a unique grille.

TORINO AND GRAN TORINO SERIES I.D. NUMBERS: Torino and Gran Torino models began with the number '2,' followed by the assembly plant code, body type code, engine designation code and, finally, the unit's production number, according to the final assembly location. Each plant began at 100001 and went up.

TORINO AND GRAN TORINO SERIES

Model Number	Body/Style Number	Body Type & Seating	Factory Price	Shipping Weight	Production Total
BASE TORINO					
NA	538	4-dr HT Sed-6P	2641/2731	3469/3548	33,486
NA	65B	2-dr HT Cpe-6P	2673/2762	3369/3448	33,530
NA	71B	4-dr Sta Wag-6P	2955/3045	3879/3958	22,204
NA	53D	4-dr Sed-6P	2856/2947	3476/3555	102,300
GRAN TORINO					
NA	65D	2-dr HT-6P	2878/2967	3395/3474	132,284
NA	71D	4-dr Sta Wag-6P	3096/3186	3881/3960	45,212
NA	63R	2-dr FsBk Cpe-6P	3094	3496	60,794
NA	65R	2-dr Spt HT Cpe-6P	3094	3474	31,239
NA	71K	4-dr Sq Wag-6P	3486	4042	35,595

PRODUCTION NOTE: Total series output was 496,645 units. The price and weight to the left of the slash are for six-cylinder equipped models and the price and weight to the right of the slash are for V-8 powered models.

1972 Ford, Maverick four-door sedan, V-8

MAVERICK SERIES — (ALL ENGINES) — The Maverick Series was unchanged from the 1971 models.

MAVERICK SERIES I.D. NUMBERS: Mavericks used the same serial number sequence as the full-size Fords and Torino models.

MAVERICK SERIES

Model Number	Body/Style Number	Body Type & Seating	Factory Price	Shipping Weight	Production Total
NA	54A	4-dr Sed-6P	2245/2406	2833/2826	73,686
NA	62A	2-dr Sed-6P	2190/2350	2538/2731	145,931
NA	62D	2-dr Grabber-6P	2359/2519	2493/2786	35,347

PRODUCTION NOTE: Total series output was 254,964 units. The price and weight to the left of the slash are for six-cylinder equipped models and the price and weight to the right of the slash are for V-8 powered models.

1972 Ford, Pinto Runabout three-door hatch back coupe, 4-cyl

PINTO SERIES — (ALL ENGINES) — The Pintos were unchanged from the 1971 models, with the exception of a larger rear window on Runabout models and the addition of a two-door station wagon.

PINTO SERIES I.D. NUMBERS — (ALL ENGINES) — Pintos used the same serial number sequence as the full-size Fords, Torinos, Mavericks and Mustangs.

PINTO SERIES

Model Number	Body/Style Number	Body Type & Seating	Factory Price	Shipping Weight	Production Total
NA	62B	2-dr Sed-4P	1960	1968	181,002
NA	64B	2-dr Runabout-4P	2078	2012	197,920
NA	73B	2-dr Sta Wag-4P	2265	2293	101,483

PRODUCTION NOTE: Total series output was 480,405 units.

THUNDERBIRD SERIES — (ALL ENGINES) — Thunderbirds were completely restyled for 1972, a year that witnessed the introduction of the largest Thunderbirds ever. They were based on the Lincoln Continental Mark IV chassis and used the Mark IV body, with only minor changes, inside and outside. While the Thunderbird had lost most of its sportiness, it had gained all the luxury features of the Continental. The grille was a centrally located opening featuring horizontal grille bars between the quad headlights. The top had a very low profile, with a large 'C' pillar. At the rear, a single taillight lens was used once again, giving a massive appearance.

THUNDERBIRD SERIES I.D. NUMBERS — (ALL ENGINES) — Thunderbirds began with the number '2,' assembly plant code 'J' (Los Angeles) or 'Y' (Wixom), body type code, engine code 'A' or 'N' and, finally, the unit's production number, beginning at 100001 and going up.

THUNDERBIRD SERIES

Model Number	Body/Style Number	Body Type & Seating	Factory Price	Shipping Weight	Production Total
A/N	65K	2-dr HT-6P	5293	4420	57,814

1972 Ford, Thunderbird two-door hardtop, V-8

1972 ENGINES

PINTO FOUR-CYLINDER: Overhead valves. Cast iron block. Displacement: 98 cid. Bore and stroke: 3.19 x 3.06 inches. Compression ratio: 8.0:1. Net hp: 54 at 4600 rpm. Carburetion: Motorcraft one-barrel. Five main bearings.

PINTO FOUR-CYLINDER: Overhead cam. Cast iron block. Displacement: 122 cid. Bore and stroke: 3.58 x 3.03 inches. Compression ratio: 8.2:1. Net hp: 86 at 5400 rpm. Carburetion: Ford/Weber two-barrel. Five main bearings. Serial number code "X."

MAVERICK SIX-CYLINDER: Overhead valves. Cast iron block. Displacement: 170 cid. Bore and stroke: 3.50 x 2.94 inches. Compression ratio: 8.3:1. Net hp: 82 at 4400 rpm. Carburetion: Motorcraft one-barrel. Seven main bearings. Serial number code "U."

FORD SIX-CYLINDER: Overhead valves. Cast iron block. Displacement: 240 cid. Bore and stroke: 4.00 x 3.18 inches. Compression ratio: 8.5:1. Net hp: 103 at 3800 rpm. Carburetion: Motorcraft one-barrel. Seven main bearings. Serial number code "V."

MAVERICK/MUSTANG/TORINO SIX-CYLINDER: Overhead valves. Displacement: 250 cid. Bore and stroke: 3.68 x 3.91 inches. Compression ratio: 8.0:1. Net hp: 98 at 3400 rpm. Carburetion: Motorcraft one-barrel. Seven main bearings. Serial number code "L."

302 V-8: Overhead valves. Cast iron block. Displacement: 302 cid. Bore and stroke: 4.00 x 3.00 inches. Compression ratio: 8.5:1. Net hp: 140 at 4000 rpm. Carburetion: Motorcraft two-barrel. Five main bearings. Serial number code "F."

351 'WINDSOR' V-8: Overhead valves. Cast iron block. Displacement: 351 cid. Bore and stroke: 4.00 x 3.50 inches. Compression ratio: 8.3:1. Net hp: 153 at 3800 rpm. Carburetion: Motorcraft two-barrel. Five main bearings. Serial number code "H."

351 'CLEVELAND' V-8: Overhead valves. Cast iron block. Displacement: 351 cid. Bore and stroke: 4.00 x 3.50 inches. Compression ratio: 8.6:1. Net hp: 163 at 3800 rpm. Carburetion: Motorcraft two-barrel. Five main bearings. Serial number code "H."

351 'CLEVELAND' FOUR-BARREL V-8: Overhead valves. Cast iron block. Displacement: 351 cid. Bore and stroke: 4.00 x 3.50 inches. Compression ratio: 8.6:1. Net hp: 248 at 5400 rpm. Carburetion: Holley four-barrel. Five main bearings. Serial number code "M."

351 HO 'CLEVELAND' V-8: Overhead valves. Displacement: 351 cid. Bore and stroke: 4.00 x 3.50 inches. Compression ratio: 8.6:1. Net hp: 266 at 5400 rpm. Carburetion: Holley four-barrel. Five main bearings. Serial number code "Q."

400 'CLEVELAND' V-8: Overhead valves. Cast iron block. Displacement: 400 cid. Bore and stroke: 4.00 x 4.00 inches. Compression ratio: 8.5:1. Net hp: 172 at 4000 rpm. Carburetion: Motorcraft two-barrel. Five main bearings. Serial number code "S."

THUNDER JET 429 V-8: Overhead valves. Cast iron block. Displacement: 429 cid. Bore and stroke: 4.36 x 3.59 inches. Compression ratio: 8.5:1. Net hp: 205 at 4400 rpm. Carburetion: Motorcraft four-barrel. Five main bearings. Serial number code "K."

THUNDERBIRD 429 V-8: Overhead valves. Cast iron block. Displacement: 429 cid. Bore and stroke: 4.36 x 3.59 inches. Compression ratio: 8.5:1. Net hp: 212 at 4400 rpm. Carburetion: Motorcraft four-barrel. Five main bearings. Serial number code "N."

THUNDERBIRD 460 V-8: Overhead valves. Cast iron block. Displacement: 460 cid. Bore and stroke: 4.36 x 3.85 inches. Compression ratio: 8.5:1. Net hp: 224 at 4400 rpm. Carburetion: Motorcraft four-barrel. Five main bearings. Serial number code "A."

FORD CHASSIS FEATURES: Wheelbase: 121 inches. Overall length: 216.2 inches (219.2 inches on station wagons). Tires: F78 x 15 belted black sidewall (G78 x 15 on Galaxie 500 and LTDs and H78 x 15 on station wagons).

TORINO/GRAN TORINO CHASSIS FEATURES: Wheelbase: (four-door models) 118 inches; (other models) 114 inches. Overall length: (two-door models) 203.7 inches: (four-door models) 207.3 inches; (station wagons) 211.6 inches. Tires: (Torino two-door models) F78 x 14, (Gran Torino and Torino four-door models) F78 x 14, (station wagons) H78 x 14: (Gran Torino Sport hardtop) E70 x 14: (Gran Torino Sport Sportroof) F70 x 14. All tires were belted black sidewall.

MAVERICK CHASSIS FEATURES: Wheelbase: 103 inches. Overall length: 179.4 inches. Tires: (V-8s) C78 x 14 tubeless blackwall; (other models) 6.45 x 14 tubeless blackwall.

PINTO CHASSIS FEATURES: Wheelbase: 94 inches. Overall length: 163 inches. Tires: 6.00 x 13 rayon black sidewall (A78 x 13; A70 x 13 and 175Rl3 tires were optional).

THUNDERBIRD CHASSIS FEATURES: Wheelbase: 120.4 inches. Overall length: 214 inches. Tires: 215Rl5 belted Michelin radial blackwalls.

FORD OPTIONS: 172 hp, 400 cid, V-8 engine ($95). 205 hp, 429 cid V-8 engine ($222). Power front disc brakes, standard on LTDs ($50). Tinted windshield ($53). Air conditioning ($409); with climate control ($486). Cruise-Control ($99). AM radio ($64). AM/FM stereo radio ($234). Vinyl roof ($110); on station wagons ($148). White sidewall tires ($34).

Standard Catalog of American Cars

TORINO/GRAN TORINO OPTIONS: 163 hp, 351 cid 'Cleveland' V-8 engine ($44). 248 hp, 351 cid 'Cleveland' V-8 engine, two-door models only ($127). 205 hp, 429 cid V-8 engine ($99). Cruise-O-Matic automatic transmission ($21 to $211 depending on engine choice). Four-speed manual transmission ($200). AM radio ($64). AM/FM stereo radio ($208). Power steering ($112). Power tailgate window on station wagons ($34). Luggage rack on station wagons ($77). Vinyl roof ($93). White sidewall tires ($34).

MAVERICK OPTIONS: 200 cid six-cylinder engine ($38). 250 cid six-cylinder engine ($77). 302 cid V-8 engine. Cruise-O-Matic automatic transmission ($177). AM radio ($59). Power steering ($92). White sidewall tires ($34).

PINTO OPTIONS: 86 hp, 122 cid four-cylinder overhead cam engine ($49). Cruise-O-Matic automatic transmission ($170). AM radio ($59). Chrome window moldings. Luxury Decor Group ($137). Wheelcovers ($23). White sidewall tires ($42).

THUNDERBIRD OPTIONS: Six-Way power seats ($201). Power windows ($130). Cruise-Control ($103). Tilt steering wheel ($51). Climate Control air conditioning ($505). AM/FM stereo radio ($146). Electric rear window defogger ($36). Power sunroof ($505). Vinyl roof ($137). Turnpike convenience group ($132).

HISTORICAL FOOTNOTES: The 1972 Ford line was introduced Sept. 24, 1971. New options appearing this season included electric sliding sun roofs; electric deck lid release; tailgate power lock and bodyside moldings with vinyl inserts. Sun roofs were installed on 0.6 percent of all 1972 FoMoCo products, including Lincolns and Mercuries. As far as the Ford lines — Ford/Torino/Maverick/Pinto/Club Wagon/Thunderbird/Mustang — were concerned, model year output peaked at 1,855,201 vehicles this year. The calendar year production total was counted as 1,868,016 units. Henry Ford II was Ford Motor Company board chairman and Lee Iacocca was the firm's president. Ford Div. (also called Ford Marketing Corp.) was headed by J.B. Naughton, who held the title of vice-president and divisional general manager. The year 1972 was sales record-breaker and marked the first time in history that Ford dealers sold more than three million cars and trucks.

1973 FORD

1973 FORDS OVERVIEW — For 1973 the full-size Fords were the only models to receive significant restyling. The rest of the Ford lines received only very minor trim updating. More federally mandated safety requirements were initiated. They were reflected in the form of massive (and incredibly ugly) 'park bench' safety bumpers. These bumpers were supposed to be able to tolerate direct impact at five mph without damage. Pollution standards were tightened. The existing engines were further de-tuned or more emissions control equipment was added, making for some of the poorest performing and least fuel efficient motors ever built. The Arab embargo of oil products imported from the Middle East, also brought fuel economy into the spotlight and manufacturers began striving for improved mileage at the expense of performance and efficiency.

FULL-SIZE FORD SERIES — (ALL ENGINES) — Full-size Fords were restyled for 1973. The emphasis was placed on a more rounded profile, similar to the Torino series of the previous year. The 'Mercedes style' grille was the current craze and big Fords had their own version, complete with a spring-loaded hood ornament on the high trim-level models. At the rear, two rectangular taillights were used on all models and were very similar to those used on the lower-priced lines of the 1972 full-size Fords. The Custom 500 was the base trim level Ford for 1973 and included chrome windshield and rear window moldings; nylon carpeting; ignition key warning buzzer; 351 cid V-8 engine; Cruise-O-Matic automatic transmission; power steering; and G78 x 15 belted black sidewall tires. The Galaxie 500 was the intermediate trim level and included all the Custom 500 features, plus lower back panel wheel lip moldings; cloth and vinyl seating surfaces; rocker panel moldings; and woodgrain appliques on the instrument panel. The LTD was the top trim level and included all the Galaxie 500 features, plus deep-cushioned low-back bench seats; Deluxe two-spoke steering wheel; electric clock; chrome trim on the foot pedals; polished aluminum trim around the rear edge of the hood; bodyside moldings with vinyl inserts; and HR78 x 15 steel-belted radial tires. The LTD Brougham had all the LTD features, plus highback Flight-Bench seats with center armrests; ashtray and front door courtesy lights; full wheelcovers; cut-pile carpeting; carpeted lower door panels; polished rocker panel moldings and extensions; automatic seatback release (on two-door models); vinyl roof; and color-keyed seat belts. The Ranch Wagon contained all the features of the Galaxie 500 models, plus J78 x 15 tires. The Country Sedan contained all the features found in the Ranch Wagon, plus dual-note horn; woodgrain appliques on the instrument panel and front and rear door panels; special sound package; bodyside moldings; and a chrome-plated grille. The Country Squires contained all the features found in the LTDs, plus J78 x 15 tires and 400 cid V-8 engine.

FORD SERIES I.D. NUMBERS — (ALL ENGINES) — Fords began with the number '3,' followed by the assembly plant code, engine designation code and, finally, the unit's production number, according to the final assembly location. Each plant began at 100001 and went up.

FORD SERIES

Model Number	Body/Style Number	Body Type & Seating	Factory Price	Shipping Weight	Production Total
CUSTOM 500					
NA	53D	4-dr Sed-6P	3606	4078	42,549
NA	71D	4-dr Ranch Wag-6P	4050	4550	22,432
GALAXIE 500					
NA	53F	4-dr Sed-6P	3771	4110	85,654
NA	57F	4-dr HT Sed-6P	3833	4120	25,802
NA	65F	2-dr HT Cpe-6P	3778	4059	70,808
NA	71F	4-dr Cty Sed-6P	4164	4581	51,290
LTD					
NA	53H	4-dr Sed-6P	3958	4150	122,851
NA	57H	4-dr HT Sed-6P	4001	4160	28,608
NA	65H	2-dr HT Cpe-6P	3950	4100	120,864
NA	71H	4-dr Cty Sq-6P	4401	4642	142,933
LTD BROUGHAM					
NA	53K	4-dr Sed-6P	4113	4179	49,553
NA	57K	4-dr HT Sed-6P	4103	4189	22,268
NA	65K	2-dr HT Cpe-6P	4107	4128	68,901

PRODUCTION NOTE: Total series output was 941,054 units.

NOTE 2: The LTD four-door sedan was called a "pillared hardtop."

1973 TORINO — (OVERVIEW) — 1973 Torinos were unchanged from the 1972 models, with the exception of a revised grille. The opening was more rectangular than the 1972 version and blended well with the large front bumper. The remainder of the car was identical to the 1972 model. Improvements included larger standard rear brakes, an interior hood release and optional spare tire lock.

TORINO AND GRAN TORINO SERIES — (ALL ENGINES) — The 1973 Torino and Gran Torino models were very slightly modified from 1972 specifications. The Torino models were the base trim level and featured chrome windshield, rear window and rain gutter moldings; highback bench seats; all-vinyl seat and door trim; floor mats; hubcaps; 250 cid six-cylinder engine; and three-speed manual transmission. The Torino station wagon also included power front disc brakes and three-way tailgate. The Gran Torino was the top trim level for 1973 and included all the Torino trim, plus manual front disc brakes; cloth and vinyl trim on seats and interior door panels; carpeting; lower bodyside, wheelwell and deck lid moldings; dual-note horn; trunk mat; Deluxe two-spoke steering wheel; and chrome trim on the foot pedals. The Gran Torino Squire wagon also included the 138 hp 302 cid V-8 engine; Deluxe pleated vinyl interior trim; wheelcovers; and woodgrain appliques on the bodysides, tailgate and instrument panel. The Gran Torino Sport was the sports version of the Gran Torino line and included all the Gran Torino features, plus the 138 hp 302 cid V-8 engine; pleated, all-vinyl trim; hood scoops; color-keyed dual racing mirrors; and a unique grille.

TORINO AND GRAN TORINO SERIES I.D. NUMBERS — (ALL ENGINES) — The Torino and Gran Torino models began with the number '3,' followed by the assembly plant code, body type code, engine designation code and, finally, the unit's production number, according to the final assembly location. Each plant began at 100001 and went up.

TORINO SERIES

Model Number	Body/Style Number	Body Type & Seating	Factory Price	Shipping Weight	Production Total
NA	53B	4-dr Sed-6P	2701/2796	3597/3683	37,524
NA	65B	2-dr HT Cpe-6P	2732/2826	3528/3615	28,005
NA	71B	4-dr Sta Wag-6P	3198	4073	23,982

Model Number	Body/Style Number	Body Type & Seating	Factory Price	Shipping Weight	Production Total
GRAN TORINO SERIES					
NA	53D	4-dr Sed-6P	2890/2984	3632/3719	98,404
NA	65D	2-dr HT Cpe-6P	2921/3015	3570/3656	138,962
NA	71D	4-dr Sta Wag-6P	3344	4096	60,738
NA	71K	4-dr Squire-6P	3559	4124	40,023
NA	63R	2-dr Spt FsBk Cpe	3154	3670	51,853
NA	65R	2-dr Spt HT Cpe	3154	3652	17,090
GRAN TORINO BROUGHAM					
NA	53K	4-dr Sed-6P	3051/3140	3632/3719	NA
NA	65K	2-dr HT Cpe-6P	3071/3160	3590/3656	NA

PRODUCTION NOTE: Total series output was 496,581 units. Separate breakouts were not available for Gran Torino Broughams. Styles 53B, 53D and 53K were called four-door pillared sedans. Styles 63R and 65R were 6-passenger (6P) models.

NOTE 2: Prices and weights above slash are for sixes/below slash for V-8s.

MAVERICK SERIES — (ALL ENGINES) — The Maverick series was basically unchanged from the 1972 models. There was, however, a slightly new appearance up front because of the flatter, reinforced bumper.

MAVERICK SERIES I.D. NUMBERS: Mavericks used the same serial number sequence as full-sized Fords and Torino models.

1973 Ford, Maverick 'Grabber' two-door sedan, V-8

MAVERICK SERIES

Model Number	Body/Style Number	Body Type & Seating	Factory Price	Shipping Weight	Production Total
NA	54A	4-dr Sed-6P	2297/2419	2737/2900	110,382
NA	62A	2-dr Sed-6P	2240/2362	2642/2800	148,943
NA	62	2-dr Grabber-6P	2419/2541	2697/2855	32,350

PRODUCTION NOTE: Total series output was 291,675 units. The prices and weights to the left of the slash indicate six-cylinder equipped models and the prices and weights to the right of the slash indicate V-8 powered models.

PINTO SERIES — (ALL ENGINES) — The Pinto exterior remained basically the same as in the 1972 model year with the exception of front and rear bumpers. Front bumper guards were made standard equipment this year (but deleted in later years). Pinto styles included the two-door (sometimes called three-door) Runabout, which had a large rear hatch with gas-operated springs; plus the two-door sedan and station wagon. Because of the bumper design changes, the Pinto was actually about one and a half inches longer this year, although the bumper-to-bumper body length was not changed.

PINTO SERIES I.D. NUMBERS — (ALL ENGINES) — Pintos used the same serial number sequence as the full-size Fords, Torinos, Mavericks and Mustangs.

PINTO SERIES

Model Number	Body/Style Number	Body Type & Seating	Factory Price	Shipping Weight	Production Total
NA	62B	2-dr Sed-4P	1997	2124	116,146
NA	64B	2-dr Runabout-4P	2120	2162	150,603
NA	73B	2-dr Sta Wag-4P	2319	2397	217,763

1973 Ford Pinto Squire two-door station wagon, 4-cyl

PRODUCTION NOTE: Total series output was 484,512 units.

1973 Ford, Thunderbird two-door hardtop, V-8

THUNDERBIRD SERIES — (ALL ENGINES) — The 1973 Thunderbird continued to use the same body as introduced in 1972, with a few minor changes. An opera window was added to help eliminate the blind spot created by the massive 'C' pillar. Other product improvements included suspension system refinements; increased front and rear headroom; and steel-belted radial tires with white sidewalls as standard equipment. An inside hood release and spare tire lock were also new. The 1973 Thunderbird had an eggcrate grille in place of the bar type used the previous year. The two headlamps on either side of the grille were mounted in individual, square-shaped bezels. An unslotted bumper with vertical grille guards and new fender-notched parking lamp treatment were seen. The remainder of the car was unchanged.

THUNDERBIRD SERIES I.D. NUMBERS — (ALL ENGINES) — Thunderbirds began with the number '3,' assembly plant code 'J' (Los Angeles) or 'Y' (Wixom), body type code, engine designation code 'A' or 'N' and, finally, the unit's production number, beginning at 100001 and going up.

THUNDERBIRD SERIES

Model Number	Body/Style Number	Body Type & Seating	Factory Price	Shipping Weight	Production Total
A/N	65K	2-dr HT Cpe-6P	5577	4572	87,269

1973 ENGINES

PINTO FOUR-CYLINDER: Overhead cam. Cast iron block. Displacement: 122 cid. Bore and stroke: 3.58 x 3.03 inches. Compression ratio: 8.2:1. Net hp: 86 at 5400 rpm. Carburetion: Ford/Weber two-barrel. Five main bearings. Serial number code "X."

MAVERICK SIX-CYLINDER: Overhead valves. Cast iron block. Displacement: 200 cid. Bore and stroke: 3.68 x 3.13 inches. Compression ratio: 8.3:1. Net hp: 84 at 3800 rpm. Carburetion: Motorcraft single-barrel. Seven main bearings. Serial number code "U."

MAVERICK/MUSTANG/TORINO SIX-CYLINDER: Overhead valves. Cast iron block. Displacement: 250 cid. Bore and stroke: 3.68 x 3.91 inches. Compression ratio: 8.0:1. Net hp: 88 at 3200 rpm. Carburetion: Motorcraft single-barrel. Seven main bearings. Serial number code "L."

302 V-8: Overhead valves. Cast iron block. Displacement: 302 cid. Bore and stroke: 4.00 x 3.00 inches. Compression ratio: 8.0:1. Net hp: 135 at 4200 rpm. Carburetion: Motorcraft two-barrel. Five main bearings. Serial number code "F."

351 'WINDSOR' V-8: Overhead valves. Cast iron block. Displacement: 351 cid. Bore and stroke: 4.00 x 3.50 inches. Compression ratio: 8.0:1. Net hp: 156 at 3800 rpm. Carburetion: Motorcraft two-barrel. Five main bearings. Serial number code "H."

351 'CLEVELAND' V-8: Overhead valves. Cast iron block. Displacement: 351 cid. Bore and stroke: 4.00 x 3.50 inches. Compression ratio: 8.0:1. Net hp: 154 at 4000 rpm. Carburetion: Motorcraft two-barrel. Five main bearings. Serial number code "H."

351 'COBRA JET CLEVELAND' V-8: Overhead valves. Cast iron block. Displacement: 351 cid. Bore and stroke: 4.00 x 3.50 inches. Compression ratio: 8.0:1. Net hp: 266 at 5400 rpm. Carburetion: Holley four-barrel. Five main bearings. Serial number code "Q."

400 'CLEVELAND' V-8: Overhead valves. Cast iron block. Displacement: 400 cid. Bore and stroke: 4.00 x 4.00 inches. Compression ratio: 8.0:1. Net hp: 163 at 3800 rpm. Carburetion: Motorcraft two-barrel. Five main bearings. Serial number code "S."

THUNDER JET 429 V-8: Overhead valves. Cast iron block. Displacement: 429 cid. Bore and stroke: 4.36 x 3.59 inches. Compression ratio: 8.0:1. Net hp: 197 at 4400 rpm. Carburetion: Motorcraft four-barrel. Five main bearings. Serial number code "K."

THUNDERBIRD 429 V-8: Overhead valves. Cast iron block. Displacement: 429 cid. Bore and stroke: 4.36 x 3.59 inches. Compression ratio: 8.0:1. Net hp: 201 at 4400 rpm. Carburetion: Motorcraft four-barrel. Five main bearings. Serial number code "N."

THUNDERBIRD 460 V-8: Overhead valves. Cast iron block. Displacement: 460 cid. Bore and stroke: 4.36 x 3.85 inches. Compression ratio: 8.0:1. Net hp: 219 at 4400 rpm. Carburetion: Motorcraft four-barrel. Five main bearings. Serial number code "A."

ENGINE NOTE: Beginning with the 250 cid six-cylinder engine, Ford rated each engine with two or three different horsepower ratings, depending on the model each engine was installed in. Ratings shown in the engine section represent the lowest rating for each engine (except the '460,' which shows the highest rating). As body size and weight increased between models, horsepower ratings increased correspondingly. (i.e.: 302 cid V-8 rated at 135 hp in Maverick and 138 hp in Gran Torino). Most engine ratings varied between one and five horsepower, with the 460 cid V-8 varying 17 hp.

FORD CHASSIS FEATURES: Wheelbase: 121 inches. Overall length: 216.2 inches (219.2 inches on station wagons). Tires: F78 x 15 belted black sidewall (G78 x 15 on Galaxie 500 and LTDs and H78 x 15 on station wagons).

TORINO/GRAN TORINO CHASSIS FEATURES: Wheelbase: (four-door models) 118 inches; (other models) 114 inches. Overall length: (two-door models) 203.7 inches; (four-door models) 207.3 inches; (station wagons) 211.6 inches. Tires: (Torino two-door models) E78 x 14, (Gran Torino and Torino four-door models) F78 x 14, (station wagons) H78 x 14: (Gran Torino Sport hardtop) E70 x 14: (Gran Torino Sport fastback) F70 x 14. All tires were belted black sidewall.

MAVERICK CHASSIS FEATURES: Wheelbase: 103 inches. Overall length: 179.4 inches. Tires: (V-8s) C78 x 14 tubeless blackwall; (other models) 6.45 x 14 tubeless blackwall.

PINTO CHASSIS FEATURES: Wheelbase: 94 inches. Overall length: 163 inches. Tires: 6.00 x 13 rayon black sidewall (A78 x 13; A70 x 13 and 175RI3 tires were optional).

THUNDERBIRD CHASSIS FEATURES: Wheelbase: 120.4 inches. Overall length: 214 inches. Tires: 215RI5 belted Michelin radial blackwalls.

FORD OPTIONS: 172 hp, 400 cid V-8 engine ($95). 205 hp, 429 cid V-8 engine ($222). Power front disc brakes, standard on LTDs ($50). Tinted windshield ($53). Air conditioning ($409); with climate control ($486). Cruise-Control ($99). AM radio ($64). AM/FM stereo radio ($234). Vinyl roof ($110); on station wagons ($148). White sidewall tires ($34).

FORD OPTIONS: 171 hp, 400 cid V-8 engine ($95). 198 hp, 429 cid V-8 engine. 202 hp. 460 cid V-8 engine ($222). Tinted windshield ($53). Air conditioning ($409); with Climate Control ($486). Cruise Control ($99). AM radio ($64). AM/FM stereo radio ($234). Vinyl roof ($110); on station wagons ($148). White sidewall tires ($33).

TORINO/GRAN TORINO OPTIONS: 159 hp, 351 cid 'Cleveland' V-8 engine ($44). 168 hp, 400 cid 'Cleveland' V-8 engine. 197 hp, 429 cid V-8 engine ($99). Cruise-O-Matic automatic transmission ($211). Four-speed manual transmission ($200). AM radio ($64). AM/FM stereo radio ($208). Power steering ($112). Power tailgate window on station wagons ($34). Luggage racks on station wagons ($77). Vinyl roof ($93). White sidewall tires ($34).

MAVERICK OPTIONS: 200 cid six-cylinder engine ($77). 135 hp, 302 cid V-8 engine. Cruise-O-Matic automatic transmission ($177). AM radio ($59). Power steering ($92). White sidewall tires ($33).

PINTO OPTIONS: 86 hp, 122 cid four-cylinder overhead cam engine ($49). Cruise-O-Matic automatic transmission ($170). AM radio ($59). Luxury decor group ($137). Wheelcovers ($23). White sidewall tires ($42).

THUNDERBIRD OPTIONS: Six-Way power seats ($201). Power windows ($130). Cruise Control ($103). Tilt steering wheel ($51). Climate Control air conditioning ($505). AM/FM stereo radio ($146). Electric rear window defogger ($36). Power sunroof ($505). Vinyl roof ($137). Turnpike convenience group ($132).

HISTORICAL FOOTNOTES: The 1973 Ford line, except for Club Wagons, was publicly introduced on Sept. 22, 1972. Highlights of the year included the new impact-absorbing bumpers and an increased emphasis on making cars theft and vandal-proof. For example, a new fixed-length type radio antenna was adopted; inside hood release mechanisms became a regular feature in some models; and a spare tire lock was a new, extra-cost option. The Ford LTD was honored, by MOTOR TREND magazine, as the "Full-sized Sedan of the Year", while ROAD TEST magazine went further, calling it the "Car of the Year". Calendar year sales of 1,716,975 units were recorded. This included Club Wagons and some 1975 Fords (including Granada and Elite) made late in the calendar year. Model year production (1974 models only) hit 1,843,340 units, with 26,917 Falcon Club Wagons included. That gave the company a 22.69 percent share of America's total market. Important FoMoCo executives included board chairman, Henry Ford II; corporate president, Lee Iacocca and Ford Marketing Corp. vice president and divisional general manager B.E. Bidwell.

1974 FORD

1974 FORDS — (OVERVIEW) — With the exception of a totally restyled Mustang, 1974 Fords were basically 1973 models with refinements and slight trim updating. Emphasis continued to be placed on a luxury look and the addition of safety equipment. More federally mandated safety requirements were initiated, primarily in the form of massive rear 'safety' bumpers designed to withstand direct impact, at five mph without damage. When combined with the front safety bumpers adopted in 1973, the weight of a typical car was up nearly 350 pounds! Pollution standards were also further tightened, which, combined with weight increases, made 1974 models generally more sluggish than any available in the recent past. Pintos and Mavericks saw little technical innovation and all other lines were now limited to just V-8s under the hood. Torinos could be had with '302,' '351,' '400' and '460'engines. The bigger cars came with a base 351 cid V-8 or one of three options. They were a higher output '351,' the '400' or the '460.' The latter engine was the only one offered in Thunderbirds, as the powerful '429' was gone for all time.

1974 Ford, LTD four-door pillared hardtop (sedan), V-8

FULL-SIZED FORDS — (ALL ENGINES) — The full-sized Fords were slightly retrimmed versions of 1973 models. The main difference between cars of the two years appeared at the front. Extension caps were no longer used on the front fender corners, so that the vertical parking lamp lens was taller than the previous type and had a ribbed appearance. The overall shape of the grille was the same, but inserts with a finer mesh pattern were used. Also, the central section — below the protruding area of the hood — was surrounded by a rectangular housing that segmented it from the rest of the grille. This gave more of a 'Mercedes-Benz' look to the front of the car, or what some refer to as neo-classical styling. To heighten this image, a stand-up hood ornament was added to models with high-level trims. The profile of the 1974 Ford was much the same as previously seen, except that an upper, full-length horizontal feature line paralleled the upper body edge. It swept from the top of the parking lamps, to the rear of the car. In addition, the lower feature line now continued ahead of the forward wheel opening. Newly designed wheelcovers were seen and the rear end treatment was also enriched. The Custom 500 was the base trim level offering and included chrome windshield and rear window moldings; nylon carpeting; ignition key warning buzzer; power steering; automatic transmission; G78 x 15 belted black sidewall tires; and the 351 cid motor. The Galaxie 500 was the intermediate trim level and included all Custom 500 features, plus lower back panel and wheel lip moldings; cloth and vinyl seats; rocker panel moldings; and woodgrain appliques on the instrument panel. The LTD was the top trim level and included all the Galaxie 500 features, plus deep-cushioned, low-back bench seats; electric clock; Deluxe two-spoke steering wheel; chrome trim on the foot pedals; polished aluminum trim for the rear hood edge; and HR78 x 15 steel-belted radial tires. The LTD Brougham had all LTD features, plus highback Flight-Bench seats with center armrest; ashtray and front door courtesy lights; full wheelcovers; cut-pile carpeting; carpeted lower door panels; polished rocker panel moldings (with extensions); automatic seatback release (in two-door styles); vinyl roof; and color-keyed seat belts. The Ranch Wagon contained all the features of the Galaxie 500, plus J78 x 15 tires. The Country Sedan added a dual-note horn; woodgrain instrument panel applique; woodgrain front and rear door panel trim; special sound insulation package; bodyside moldings; and a special chrome-plated grille. The Country Squire contained all features found in LTDs, plus J78 x 15 tires and a base 400 cid V-8.

FORD SERIES I.D. NUMBERS: Fords began with the number '4,' followed by the assembly plant code, engine designation code and, finally, the unit's production number, according to final assembly location. Each plant began at 100001 and went up.

FULL-SIZED FORD SERIES

Model Number	Body/Style Number	Body Type & Seating	Factory Price	Shipping Weight	Production Total
CUSTOM 500/RANCH WAGON					
NA	53D	4-dr Sed-6P	3911	4180	28,941
NA	71D	4-dr Sta Wag-6P	4417	4654	12,104
GALAXIE 500/COUNTRY SEDAN					
NA	53F	4-dr Sed-6P	4093	4196	49,661
NA	57F	4-dr HT Sed-6P	4166	4212	11,526
NA	65F	2-dr HT Cpe-6P	4140	4157	34,214
NA	71F	4-dr Cty Sed-6P	4513	4690	22,400
LTD/COUNTRY SQUIRE					
NA	53H	4-dr Sed-6P	4299	4262	72,251
NA	57H	4-dr HT Sed-6P	4367	4277	12,375
NA	65H	2-dr HT Cpe-6P	4318	4215	73,296
NA	71H	4-dr Cty Sq-6P	4827	4742	64,047
LTD BROUGHAM					
NA	53K	4-dr Sed-6P	4576	4292	30,203
NA	57K	4-dr HT Sed-6P	4646	4310	11,371
NA	65K	2-dr HT Cpe-6P	4598	4247	39,084

PRODUCTION NOTES: Total series output was 519,916 units. Styles 53F, 53H and 53K were called four-door pillared hardtops.

1974 TORINO/GRAN TORINO — OVERVIEW — New grilles, front bumpers and some optional revisions in roof pillar treatments characterized the Torino models of 1974. The grille used a finer mesh and was now segmented by seven vertical division bars, with the parking lamps hidden behind the insert instead of being mounted on it. The bumper had a slightly more prominent center protrusion with the rubber-faced guards moved a bit closer together. Opera window treatments could be ordered, at extra cost, to 'fancy-up' the rear pillar of coupes. Side trim was revised to eliminate the wide, horizontally ribbed decorative panels used on high-trim models the previous season. Introduced at midyear was the Gran Torino Elite Series featuring full-length side trim with vinyl inserts; a chrome center molding across the grille; single headlamps (in square bezels); and parking lamps notched into the corners of front fenders. Stand-up hood ornaments were seen on many 1974 Torino models. The Torino Series was the base trim level and featured windshield, rear window and rain gutter moldings; highback bench seats; all-vinyl upholstery and trim; floor mats; hubcaps; three-speed manual transmission; HR78 x 14 tires (G78 x 14 on hardtops); and a base '302' V-8. The Torino station wagon also included power front disc brakes; H78 x 14 tires; and a three-way tailgate. The Gran Torino was the top trim level and included all above items, plus manual front disc brakes; cloth and vinyl seat trims; carpeting; lower bodyside, wheel well and deck lid moldings; dual-note horn; trunk mat; Deluxe two-spoke steering wheel; and chrome foot pedal trim. The Gran Torino Squire wagon also had Deluxe pleated vinyl interior trim; wheelcovers; woodgrain bodyside appliques; woodgrain tailgate trim; and woodgrain dashboard inserts. The Gran Torino Sport was the sporty version of the Gran Torino line. Its standard extras included pleated, all-vinyl trim; hood scoops; color-keyed dual outside racing mirrors and a unique grille.

TORINO/GRAN TORINO SERIES I.D. NUMBERS: The Torino and Gran Torino models began with the number '4,' followed by the assembly plant code, body type code, engine designation code and, finally, the unit's production number, according to the final assembly location. Each plant began at 100001 and went up.

TORINO/GRAN TORINO SERIES

Model Number	Body/Style Number	Body Type & Seating	Factory Price	Shipping Weight	Production Total
TORINO					
NA	53B	4-dr Sed-6P	3176	3793	31,161
NA	65B	2-dr HT Cpe-6P	3310	3509	22,738
NA	71B	4-dr Sta Wag-6P	3755	4175	15,393
GRAN TORINO					
NA	53D	4-dr Sed-6P	3391	3847	72,728
NA	65D	2-dr HT Cpe-6P	3485	3647	76,290
NA	71D	4-dr Sta Wag-6P	3954	4209	29,866
GRAN TORINO SPORT/SQUIRE					
NA	71K	4-dr Squire-6P	4237	4250	22,837
NA	65R	2-dr HT Spt Cpe	3761	3771	23,142
GRAN TORINO BROUGHAM					
NA	53K	4-dr Sed-6P	3903	3887	11,464
NA	65K	2-dr HT Cpe-6P	3912	3794	26,402
GRAN TORINO ELITE					
NA	65M	2-dr HT Cpe-6P	4374	4092	96,604

PRODUCTION NOTES: Total series output was 428,086 units. Styles 53D and 53K were called four-door pillared hardtops. Style 65R was a 6-passenger model. All 1974 Torinos were V-8 powered.

1974 Ford, Maverick 4-dr sedan, 6-cyl

MAVERICK SERIES — (ALL ENGINES) — The Maverick had a very slight frontal restyling for 1974 as energy-absorbing bumpers were adopted this year. A horizontal slot appeared in the center of the face bar, where the license plate indentation had formerly been positioned. Deluxe models featured side moldings with vinyl inserts; wheel cutout trim moldings and, on cars with vinyl roofs, a Maverick nameplate on the rear roof pillar. On all models, a similar nameplate was carried at the left-hand side of the grille.

MAVERICK SERIES I.D. NUMBERS: Mavericks used the same serial number system as other Ford products.

MAVERICK SERIES

Model Number	Body/Style Number	Body Type & Seating	Factory Price	Shipping Weight	Production Total
NA	54A	4-dr Sed-6P	2824/2982	2851/3014	137,728
NA	62A	2-dr Sed-6P	2742/2949	2739/2902	139,818
NA	62D	2-dr Grabber-6P	2923/3081	2787/2950	23,502

PRODUCTION NOTE: Total series output was 301,048 units. The prices and weights to the left of the slash are for six/to the right of the slash for V-8.

1974 Ford, Pinto Runabout three-door hatch back coupe, 4-cyl.

PINTO SERIES — (ALL ENGINES) — This was the year that energy-absorbing bumpers were added to the Pinto, too. This brought an obvious change to the front of the car, as the air slot opening in the gravel pan could no longer be seen. Also eliminated was the center-mounted license plate holder. It didn't look right with the massive new bumper, but then, hardly anything else did either. The bumper was plain on the base trim models, but came with rubber-faced vertical guards and a black vinyl impact strip on models with the Deluxe Decor package. Pinto wagons could be had with optional trim packages that included simulated woodgrain exterior paneling and rooftop luggage racks.

PINTO SERIES I.D. NUMBERS: Pintos used the same serial number system as full-sized Fords, Torinos and Mavericks.

PINTO SERIES

Model Number	Body/Style Number	Body Type & Seating	Factory Price	Shipping Weight	Production Total
NA	62B	2-dr Sed-4P	2527	2372	132,061
NA	64B	2-dr Hatch-4P	2631	2402	174,754
NA	73B	2-dr Sta Wag-4P	2771	2576	237,394

PRODUCTION NOTES: Total series output was 544,209 units. The two-door hatchback coupe was called the Pinto Runabout.

1974 Ford, Thunderbird two-door hardtop, V-8 (PH)

THUNDERBIRD SERIES — (ALL ENGINES) — The Thunderbird was left pretty much alone for 1974, except that the 460 cid V-8 was new under the hood. The side script plate was in its same location — above the side molding at the trailing edge of the front fender — but was slightly larger in size.

THUNDERBIRD SERIES I.D. NUMBERS: Thunderbirds began with the number '4.' followed by the assembly plant code 'J' (Los Angeles) or 'Y' (Wixom), body type code, engine designation code 'A' and, finally, the unit's production number, beginning at 100001 and going up.

THUNDERBIRD SERIES

Model Number	Body/Style Number	Body Type & Seating	Factory Price	Shipping Weight	Production Total
A	65K	2-dr HT Cpe-6P	7221	4825	58,443

1974 ENGINES

PINTO FOUR-CYLINDER: Overhead cam. Cast iron block. Displacement: 122 cid. Bore and stroke: 3.58 x 3.03 inches. Compression ratio: 8.2:1. Net hp: 86 at 5400 rpm. Carburetion: Ford/Weber two-barrel. Five main bearings. Serial number code "X."

PINTO/MUSTANG FOUR-CYLINDER: Overhead cam. Cast iron block. Displacement: 139 cid. Bore and stroke: 3.78 x 3.13 inches. Compression ratio: *8.6:1. Net hp: 80. Carburetion: Motorcraft two-barrel. Five main bearings. Serial number code "Y."

MAVERICK SIX-CYLINDER: Overhead valves. Cast iron block. Displacement: 200 cid. Bore and stroke: 3.68 x 3.13 inches. Compression ratio: 8.3:1. Net hp: 84 at 3800 rpm. Carburetion: Motorcraft one-barrel. Seven main bearings. Serial number code "T."

MAVERICK SIX-CYLINDER: Overhead valves. Cast iron block. Displacement: 250 cid. Bore and stroke: 3.68 x 3.91 inches. Compression ratio: 8.0:1. Net hp: 91 at 3200 rpm. Carburetion: Motorcraft one-barrel. Seven main bearings. Serial number code "L."

302 V-8 OVERHEAD VALVES: Cast iron block. Displacement: 302 cid. Bore and stroke: 4.00 x 3.00 inches. Compression ratio: 8.0:1. Net hp: 140 at 3800 rpm. Carburetion: Motorcraft two-barrel. Five main bearings. Serial number code "F."

351 'WINDSOR' V-8. OVERHEAD VALVE: Cast iron block. Displacement: 351 cid. Bore and stroke: 4.00 x 3.50 inches. Compression ratio: 8.2:1. Net hp: 163 at 4200 rpm. Carburetion: Motorcraft two-barrel. Five main bearings. Serial number code "H."

351 'CLEVELAND' V-8: Overhead valves. Cast iron block. Displacement: 351 cid. Bore and stroke: 4.00 x 3.50 inches. Compression ratio: 8.0:1. Net hp: 162 at 4000 rpm. Carburetion: Motorcraft two-barrel. Five main bearings. Serial number code "H."

351 'CLEVELAND' FOUR-BARREL V-8: Overhead valves. Cast iron block. Displacement: 351 cid. Bore and stroke: 4.00 x 3.50 inches. Compression ratio: 7.9:1. Net hp: 255 at 5600 rpm. Carburetion: Motorcraft four-barrel. Five main bearings. Serial number code "Q."

400 V-8: Overhead valves. Cast iron block. Displacement: 400 cid. Bore and stroke: 4.00 x 4.00 inches. Compression ratio: 8.0:1. Net hp: 170 at 3400 rpm. Carburetion: Motorcraft two-barrel. Five main bearings. Serial number code "S."

THUNDERBIRD 460 V-8: Overhead valves. Cast iron block. Displacement: 460 cid. Bore and stroke: 4.36 x 3.85 inches. Compression ratio: 8.0:1. Net hp: 215 at 4000 rpm. (220 hp in Thunderbirds). Carburetion: Carter four-barrel. Five main bearings. Serial number code "A."

FORD CHASSIS FEATURES: Wheelbase: 121 inches. Overall length: (passenger cars) 223 inches; (station wagons) 226 inches. Width: 80 inches. Tires: Refer to text.

TORINO CHASSIS FEATURES: Wheelbase: (two-door) 114 inches; (four-door) 118 inches. Overall length: (two-door passenger car) 212 inches; (four-door passenger car) 216 inches; (station wagons) 222 inches. Width: (passenger cars) 80 inches; (station wagon) 79 inches. Tires: Refer to text.

MAVERICK CHASSIS FEATURES: Wheelbase: (two-door) 103 inches; (four-door) 109.9 inches. Overall length: (two-door) 187 inches; (four-door) 194 inches. Width: 71 inches. Tires: (two-door) 6.45 x 14; (four-door) C78 x 14; (Grabber) D70-14.

PINTO CHASSIS FEATURES: Wheelbase: 94.2 inches. Overall length: (passenger car) 169 inches; (station wagon) 179 inches. Width: 70 inches. Tires: (passenger car) 6.00 x 13; (station wagon) A78 x 13.

THUNDERBIRD CHASSIS FEATURES: Wheelbase: 120.4 inches. Overall length: 225 inches. Width: 80 inches. Tires: LR78 x 15.

FORD OPTIONS: 170 hp 400 cid V-8, in Country Squires (standard); in other models ($94). 215 hp 460 cid V-8 ($304). Tinted glass ($55). Air conditioning, standard type ($426); Climate Control type ($506). Cruise Control ($103). AM radio ($67). AM/FM radio ($243). Vinyl roof, on passenger cars ($115); on station wagons ($148); on LTD Brougham (standard). White

sidewall tires ($33). AM/FM stereo with tape player ($378). Power seats ($106). Power windows ($134). Sunroof ($516). Country Squire Brougham option ($202). Country Squire Luxury package option ($545). Brougham Luxury Package option ($380).

TORINO OPTIONS: 162 hp 351 cid 'Cleveland' V-8 ($46). 170 hp 400 cid V-8 ($140). 215 hp 460 cid V-8 ($245). 225 hp 351 cid 'Cleveland' four-barrel V-8 ($132). Cruise-O-Matic transmission; with small V-8 ($219); with '460' V-8 ($241). AM radio ($67). AM/FM stereo radio ($217). Power steering ($117). Power disc brakes, on station wagons (standard); on passenger cars ($71). Power tailgate window ($35). Station wagon luggage rack ($80). Vinyl roof ($96). White sidewall tires ($33). Station wagon third passenger seat ($67). Sun roof ($490). AM/FM stereo radio with tape player ($378).

MAVERICK OPTIONS: 250 cid six ($42). 140 hp 302 cid V-8 ($122). Cruise-O-Matic transmission ($212). AM radio ($61). White sidewall tires ($33). Vinyl top ($83). Air conditioning ($383). Luxury Decor Group, except Grabber ($332).

PINTO OPTIONS: 90 hp 140 cid Four ($52). Cruise-O-Matic transmission ($212). AM radio ($61). AM/FM stereo radio ($222). Luxury Decor Group ($137). Full wheelcovers ($23). Forged aluminum wheels ($154). White sidewall tires ($44). Vinyl top ($83). Air conditioning ($383). Station wagon Squire package ($241).

THUNDERBIRD OPTIONS: Six-Way power seats ($105). Cruise Control ($107). Climate Control air conditioning ($74). Electric rear window defogger ($85). Power Moonroof ($798). Sunroof ($525). AM/FM radio with stereo tape ($311). Turnpike Convenience Group, includes Cruise Control, trip odometer and manual reclining passenger seat ($138). Burgundy Luxury Group package ($411).

OPTIONAL EQUIPMENT NOTES: Cruise-O-Matic automatic transmission and power front disc brakes were standard equipment on Torino station wagons. Automatic transmission, power steering and power front disc brakes were standard equipment on LTD, Custom 500, Galaxie and Thunderbird. Air conditioning, power windows and AM radio were also standard equipment in Thunderbirds.

HISTORICAL FOOTNOTES: Ford's 1974 model year resulted in 1,843,340 assemblies, including Falcon Club Wagons. Calendar year output was 1,716,975 units, again including the Falcon Club Wagon. (The Falcon Club Wagon was a light truck that Ford included, statistically, with passenger car production). The chief executives of the company were unchanged from 1973. Model year declines of some 130,000 units were caused by lagging buyer interest in 'big' Fords and Thunderbirds. Meanwhile, assemblies of the Mustang II tripled. Ford Motor Co.'s headquarters were listed as Southfield Rd. (at Rotunda Drive), P.O. Box 1509, Dearborn, MI 48121.

1975 FORD

1975 FORDS — OVERVIEW — With the exception of the slightly restyled full-size Fords, the 1975 models were, once again, basically the same as the year before. The big Fords were attractively face-lifted with the addition of a larger, Mercedes-style grille and new taillights. The most significant change occurred with the two-door hardtop model. The true pillarless hardtop was replaced by a coupe with fixed quarter windows and large 'opera' windows. The 1975 Torinos were unchanged from the previous year. The Gran Torino name was dropped and this car was now called the Elite. Once again, the Maverick and Pinto were unchanged, except for some very minor grille updating in each line. The big news for 1975 was the addition of the new Granada Series. The Granada was a new intermediate size car. Offered in four-door sedan and two-door sedan. As Ford was very proud to point out, the four-door had more than a passing resemblance to the Mercedes-Benz. Granadas could be fitted with options that created anything from a taxi to a mini-limousine. They came powered by engines ranging from the very sedate 250 cid six-cylinder to the 351 'Windsor' V-8. The latter motor produced not-so-sedate performance and these Granadas were, in fact, among the fastest of the 1975 Fords. The Thunderbird was exactly the same car as produced in 1974, with one small exception. The Thunderbird steering wheel had slightly different spokes (as did the steering wheels on all new Fords, except the Pinto). Pollution standards were stiffened once again and, in 1975, all cars were required to burn unleaded gasoline. The majority of the new models came with catalytic converters on the exhaust systems, to help reduce emissions and contaminates.

1975 Ford, LTD Landau two-door hardtop coupe, V-8

FULL-SIZE FORD SERIES — (ALL ENGINES) — The Custom 500 was the base trim level Ford for 1975. It included chrome windshield and rear window moldings; nylon carpeting; ignition key warning buzzer; 351 cid V-8 engine; Cruise-O-Matic automatic transmission; power steering; and G78 x 15 belted black sidewall tires. The LTD was the intermediate trim level. It included all the Custom 500 features, plus wheel lip moldings; cloth and vinyl seating surfaces; rocker panel moldings; and woodgrain appliques on the instrument panel. The LTD Brougham was the top trim level and included all the LTD features, plus deep-cushioned low-back bench seats; electric clock; Deluxe two-spoke steering wheel; chrome trim on the foot pedals; polished aluminum trim around the rear edge of the hood; bodyside moldings with vinyl inserts and HR78 x 15 steel-belted radial tires. The LTD Landau had all the Brougham features, plus highback Flight Bench seats (with center armrests); ashtray and front door courtesy lights; full wheelcovers; cut-pile carpeting; carpeted lower door panels; polished rocker panel moldings with extensions; automatic seatback release (on two-door models):

vinyl roof and color-keyed seat belts. The Ranch Wagon contained all the features of the LTD models, plus JR78 x 15 steel-belted radial tires. The Country Sedan contained all the features found in the Ranch Wagon, plus dual-note horn; woodgrain appliques on the instrument panel and front and rear door panels; special sound package; bodyside moldings and a chrome plated grille. The Country Squires contained all the features found in the LTD Country Sedans, plus JR78 x 15 steel-belted radial tires and the 400 cid V-8 engine.

FORD SERIES I.D. NUMBERS — (ALL ENGINES) — Fords began with the number '5,' followed by the assembled plant code, engine designation code and, finally, the unit's production number, according to the final assembly location. Each plant began at 100001 and went up.

FORD SERIES

Model Number	Body/Style Number	Body Type & Seating	Factory Price	Shipping Weight	Production Total
CUSTOM 500					
NA	53D	4-dr Sed-6P	4380	4377	31,043
NA	71D	4-dr Ranch Wag-6P	4970	4787	6,930
LTD					
NA	53H	4-dr Sed-6P	4615	4408	82,382
NA	60H	2-dr O/W Cpe-6P	4656	4359	47,432
NA	71H	4-dr Cty Sed-6P	5061	4803	22,935
LTD BROUGHAM					
NA	53K	4-dr Sed-6P	5016	4419	32,327
NA	60K	2-dr O/W Cpe-6P	5050	4391	24,005
NA	71K	4-dr Cty Sq-6P	5340	4845	41,550
LTD LANDAU					
NA	53L	4-dr Sed-6P	5370	4446	32,506
NA	60L	2-dr O/W Cpe-6P	5401	4419	26,919

PRODUCTION NOTES: Total series output was 390,714 units. Station wagon production was not broken down between six and 10-passenger wagons. The new body type designation O/W Cpe indicates the two-door coupe with opera windows.

TORINO/GRAN TORINO/ELITE SERIES — (ALL ENGINES) — The Torino line was the same as the previous year. The Torino models were the base trim level and featured chrome windshield, rear widow and rain gutter moldings; highback bench seats; all vinyl seat and door trim; floor mats; hubcaps; 302 cid V-8 engine and three-speed manual transmission. The Torino station wagon also included power front disc brakes and three-way tailgate. The Gran Torino was the intermediate trim level for 1975 and included all the Torino features, plus manual front disc brakes; cloth and vinyl trim on seats and interior door panels; carpeting; lower bodyside, wheelwell and deck lid moldings; dual-note horn; trunk mat; Deluxe two-spoke steering wheel and chrome trim on the foot pedals. The Gran Torino Squire wagon also included the 148 hp 351 cid V-8 engine; Cruise-O-Matic automatic transmission. Deluxe pleated vinyl interior trim, wheelcovers and woodgrain appliques on the bodysides, tailgate and instrument panel. The Gran Torino Brougham was the highest trim level and included all the Gran Torino features, plus power front disc brakes; power steering; cloth seating surfaces; bodyside moldings and padded vinyl top. The Elite continued to offer the same features as in 1974.

1975 Ford, Gran Torino Brougham 4-dr pillared hardtop, V-8

TORINO/GRAN TORINO/ELITE SERIES I.D. NUMBERS — (ALL ENGINES) — The Torino, Gran Torino and Elite models began with the number '5,' assembly plant code, body type code, engine designation code and, finally, the unit's production number, according to the final assembly location. Each plant began at 100001 and went up.

TORINO/GRAN TORINO/ELITE SERIES

Model Number	Body/Style Number	Body Type & Seating	Factory Price	Shipping Weight	Production Total
TORINO					
NA	53B	4-dr Sed-6P	3957	4059	22,928
NA	65B	2-dr O/W Cpe-6P	3954	3987	13,394
NA	71B	4-dr Sta Wag-6P	4336	4412	13,291
GRAN TORINO					
NA	53D	4-dr Sed-6P	4258	4090	53,161
NA	65D	2-dr O/W Cpe-6P	4234	3998	35,324
NA	71D	4-dr Sta Wag-6P	4593	4456	23,951
TORINO BROUGHAM					
NA	53K	4-dr Sed-6P	4791	4163	5,929
NA	65K	2-dr O/W Cpe-6P	4759	4087	4,849
TORINO SPORT					
NA	65R	2-dr Spt HT-6P	4744	4044	5,126
ELITE					
NA	65M	2-dr HT Cpe-6P	4721	4160	123,372

PRODUCTION NOTE: Total series output was 318,482 units.

1975 Ford, Maverick two-door sedan, 6-cyl

MAVERICK SERIES — (ALL ENGINES) — Originally scheduled to be replaced by the new Granada, the Maverick's existence was extended after the energy scare of 1974. The sedans and the sporty Grabber coupe featured refinements to interior and exterior trim; thicker, cut-pile carpeting; a Deluxe steering wheel as standard equipment and a 200 cid base V-6. Ford block lettering was added along the hood lip and the slot in the center of the front bumper was slightly decreased in width. New options included power disc brakes and a deck lid mounted luggage rack. A catalytic converter was required with the base engine, while the optional 350 cid Six or 302 cid V-8 came without this unpopular piece of equipment. Radial tires were also added to the regular equipment list. Buyers were given a choice of blue, black or tan interior combinations (as in the past) or new, light green trim.

MAVERICK SERIES I.D. NUMBERS — (ALL ENGINES) — Mavericks used the same serial number sequence as the full-size Fords and Torino models.

MAVERICK SERIES

Model Number	Body/Style Number	Body Type & Seating	Factory Price	Shipping Weight	Production Total
NA	54A	4-dr Sed-6P	3025/3147	2820/2971	90,695
NA	62A	2-dr Sed-6P	3061/3183	2943/3094	63,404
NA	62D	2-dr Grabber-6P	3224/3346	2827/2979	8,473

PRODUCTION NOTE: Total series output was 162,572 units. The price and weight to the left of the slash apply to six-cylinder equipped models and the price and weight to the right of the slash apply to V-8 powered models.

PINTO SERIES — (ALL ENGINES) — Changes to the Pinto were also of the minor type this year. There was little reason to go any further, since good fuel economy was helping sell the car. The optional 2.8 liter V-6 was available only with Cruise-O-Matic attachments and only in the station wagon, but wasn't very popular. Only 16 percent of all buyers added optional six-cylinder motors. Some other new accessories included power steering; power front disc brakes and a fuel-economy warning light. Standard motivation came from a U.S.-built 2.3 liter L4 equipped with either four-speed manual or three-speed automatic transmission.

1975 Ford, Pinto Runabout 3-dr hatch back coupe, 4-cyl

PINTO SERIES

Model Number	Body/Style Number	Body Type & Seating	Factory Price	Shipping Weight	Production Total
NA	62B	2-dr Sed-4P	2769	2495	64,081
NA	64B	3-dr Hatch-4P	2967/3220	2528/2710	68,919
NA	73B	2-dr Sta Wag-4P	3094/3347	2692/2874	90,763

PRODUCTION NOTE: Total series output was 223,763 units. The price and weight to the left of the slash apply to four-cylinder equipped models and the price and weight to the right of the slash apply to V-6 powered models.

GRANADA SERIES — (ALL ENGINES) — Ford referred to the Granada as a 'precision-sized' compact car. It was built off the Maverick four-door platform and came as a two-door coupe and four-door sedan. Its styling had a luxury flavor and was heavily influenced by European design themes. Even as a base model, it was quite elegant amongst cars in its class. The super-rich Ghia-optioned Granada went a step further where luxury was concerned. The 200 cid inline six was base Granada powerplant when attached to the three-speed manual gearbox. Ghias came standard with a 250 cid inline six; digital clock; Deluxe sound package and wide range of fancy seating surfaces. The base model could be ordered with the bigger six. Two-barrel V-8s, of 302 or 351 cid, were provided in both levels. Dealer sales of Granadas in the United States peaked at 241,297 cars, cutting substantially into the popularity of Mustang II.

GRANADA SERIES I.D. NUMBERS — (ALL ENGINES) — Granadas used the same serial number sequence as full-size Fords, Torinos, Mavericks and Pintos.

1975 Ford, Granada 4-dr sedan, V-8

GRANADA SERIES

Model Number	Body/Style Number	Body Type & Seating	Factory Price	Shipping Weight	Production Total
BASE					
NA	54H	4-dr Sed-6P	3756/3784	3293/3355	118,168
NA	66H	2-dr Sed-6P	3698/3826	3230/3306	100,810
GHIA					
NA	54K	4-dr Sed-6P	4240/4326	3361/3423	43,652
NA	66K	2-dr Sed-6P	4182/4268	3311/3373	40,028

PRODUCTION NOTE: Total series output was 302,649 units. The price and weight to the left of the slash apply to six-cylinder equipped models and the price and weight to the right of the slash apply to V-8 powered models.

1975 Ford, Thunderbird two-door hardtop, V-8

THUNDERBIRD SERIES — (ALL ENGINES) — The Thunderbird had certainly come a long ways since its 'two-seater' days. It was now FoMoCo's top-of-the-line personal/luxury car. A highly promoted new feature was the Sure-Trac rear brake anti-skid device. There were other chassis refinements, like four-wheel power disc brakes and the Hydro-Boost hydraulic brake boosting system. Standard features included automatic transmission; power steering; power brakes; power windows; air conditioning and AM/FM radio. Optional, for collector types, were Silver or Copper Luxury Groups with a special heavy-grained half-vinyl roof; velour or leather seats; Deluxe trunk lining and specific wheelcovers.

THUNDERBIRD SERIES I.D. NUMBERS — (ALL ENGINES) — Thunderbirds began with the number '5,' assembly plant code 'J' (Los Angeles) or 'Y' (Wixom), body type code, engine designation code 'A' and, finally, the unit's production number. beginning at 100001 and going up.

THUNDERBIRD SERIES

Model Number	Body/Style Number	Body Type & Seating	Factory Price	Shipping Weight	Production Total
A	65K	2-dr HT Cpe-6P	7701	4893	42,685

1975 ENGINES

PINTO FOUR-CYLINDER: Overhead cam. Cast iron block. Displacement: 144 cid. Bore and stroke: 3.78 x 3.13 inches. Compression ratio: 8.6:1. Net hp: 83. Carburetion: Motorcraft two-barrel. Five main bearings. Serial number code "Y."

PINTO/MUSTANG V-6: Overhead valves. Cast iron block. Displacement: 159 cid. Bore and stroke: 3.50 x 2.70 inches. Compression ratio: 8.0:1. Net hp: 97. Carburetion: Holley two-barrel. Four main bearings. Serial number code "Z."

MAVERICK SIX-CYLINDER: Overhead valves. Cast iron block. Displacement: 200 cid. Bore and stroke: 3.68 x 3.13 inches. Compression ratio: 8.3:1. Net hp: 75 at 3200 rpm. Carburetion: Motorcraft one-barrel. Seven main bearings. Serial number code "T."

MAVERICK/GRANADA SIX-CYLINDER: Overhead valves. Cast iron block. Displacement: 250 cid. Bore and stroke: 3.68 x 3.91 inches. Compression ratio: 8.0:1. Net hp: 72 at 2900 rpm. Carburetion: Motorcraft one-barrel. Seven main bearings. Serial number code "L."

302 V-8. OVERHEAD VALVES: Cast iron block. Displacement: 302 cid. Bore and stroke: 4.00 x 3.00 inches. Compression ratio: 8.0:1. Net hp: 129 at 3800 rpm. Carburetion: Motorcraft two-barrel. Five main bearings. Serial number code "F."

351 'WINDSOR' V-8: Overhead valves. Cast iron block. Displacement: 35N cid. Bore and stroke: 4.00 x 3.50 inches. Compression ratio: 8.2:1. Net hp: 143 at 3600 rpm. Carburetion: Motorcraft two-barrel. Five main bearings. Serial number code "H."

351 'MODIFIED' V-8: Overhead valves. Cast iron block. Displacement: 351 cid. Bore and stroke: 4.00 x 3.50 inches. Compression ratio: 8.0:1. Net hp: 148 at 3800 rpm. Carburetion: Motorcraft two-barrel. Five main bearings. Serial number code "H."

400 V-8: Overhead valves. Cast iron block. Displacement: 400 cid. Bore and stroke: 4.00 x 4.00 inches. Compression ratio: 8.0:1. Net hp: 158 at 3800 rpm. Carburetion: Motorcraft two-barrel. Five main bearings. Serial number code "S."

THUNDERBIRD 460 V-8: Overhead valves. Cast iron block. Displacement: 460 cid. Bore and stroke: 4.36 x 3.85 inches. Compression ratio: 8.0:1. Net hp: 218 at 4000 rpm. Carburetion: Motorcraft four-barrel. Five main bearings. Serial number code "A."

FORD CHASSIS FEATURES: Wheelbase; 121 inches. Overall length: (passenger cars) 224 inches; (station wagon) 226 inches. Width: 80 inches. Tires: HR78 x 15.

TORINO CHASSIS FEATURES: Wheelbase: (two-door) 114 inches. (four-door) 118 inches. Overall length: (two-door) 214 inches; (four-door) 218 inches. (station wagon) 223 inches. Width: 80 inches. Tire: HR78 x 14.

MAVERICK CHASSIS FEATURES: Wheelbase: (two-door) 103 inches, (four-door) 109.9 inches. Overall length: (two-door) 187 inches; (four-door) 194 inches. Width: 71 inches. Tires: (Grabber) DR70 x 14; (other two-doors) BR78 x 14; (four-doors) CR78 x 14.

PINTO CHASSIS FEATURES: Wheelbase: (passenger cars) 94.4 inches, (station wagon) 94.7 inches. Overall length: (passenger cars) 169 inches; (station wagons) 179 inches. Width: 70 inches. Tires: (all models) BR78 x 13B.

GRANADA CHASSIS FEATURES: Wheelbase: 109.9 inches. Overall length: (base models) 198 inches; (Ghia) 200 inches. Width: 74 inches. Tires: (Ghia four-door) ER7814; (other models) DR78-14.

THUNDERBIRD CHASSIS FEATURES: Wheelbase: 120.4 inches. Overall length: 226 inches. Width: 80 inches. Tires: LR78 x 15.

FORD: 158 hp 400 cid V-8 engine ($94, standard on Country Squires). 218 hp 460 cid V-8 engine ($304). Tinted glass ($55). Air conditioning ($426. Climate Control ($506). Cruise Control ($103). AM radio ($67). AM/FM stereo radio ($243). Vinyl roof ($115); on station wagons ($148). on LTD Landau (standard). White sidewall tires ($33).

TORINO/GRAN TORINO/ELITE OPTIONS: 158 hp 400 cid V-8 engine ($54). 218 hp 460 cid V-8 engine ($245). AM radio ($67). AM/FM stereo radio ($217). Power steering ($117). Power front disc brakes ($71); on station wagons (standard). Power tailgate window on station wagons ($35). Luggage rack on station wagons ($80). Vinyl top ($96). Air conditioning ($426). White sidewall tires ($33).

MAVERICK OPTIONS: 129 hp 302 cid V-8 engine. Cruise-O-Matic automatic transmission ($212). AM radio ($61). Power steering ($106). Luxury Decor Package ($392). White sidewall tires ($33).

PINTO OPTIONS: 159 cid V-6 engine ($229). Cruise-O-Matic automatic transmission ($212). AM radio ($61). AM/FM stereo radio ($222). Luxury Decor Group ($137). Forged aluminum wheels ($154). White sidewall tires ($33).

GRANADA OPTIONS: 129 hp 302 cid V-8 engine. 143 hp 351 'Windsor' V-8 engine. Cruise-O-Matic automatic transmission ($222). Power steering ($106). Power brakes ($45). AM radio ($61). AM/FM stereo radio ($222). Vinyl roof ($83). Air conditioning ($426). White sidewall tires ($33).

THUNDERBIRD OPTIONS: Six-Way power seats ($105). Cruise-Control ($107); with Turnpike Convenience Group (standard). Climate-Control air conditioning ($74). Electric rear window defroster ($85). Power moonroof ($798). Turnpike Convenience Group includes: Cruise-Control, trip odometer and manual passenger seat recliner ($138).

HISTORICAL FOOTNOTES: The 1975 Ford line was introduced Sept. 27, 1974. Model year sales, by United States dealers, included 282,130 Pintos; 207,944 Mustang IIs; 142,964 Mavericks; 241,297 Granadas; 158,798 Torinos; 102,402 Elite; 297,655 LTDs and 37,216 Thunderbirds. The production of 1975 models, in U.S. factories hit 1,302,205 cars. Calendar year production of Fords, in this country, peaked at 1,302,844 units. These figures do not include Falcon Club Wagons of which 17,431 were made for both the model and calendar years. Top executives influencing Ford Div. policy were Henry Ford II, Lee Iacocca and B.E. Bidwell. It was the final season for the long-lasting Custom 500 nameplate.

STANDARD CATALOG OF
MUSTANG
1964-1/2-1975

1965 Ford Mustang, 2+2 two-door fastback coupe, V-8 (Ford Motor Co.)

What a coup! To produce an extremely popular car, with virtually no competition. That is exactly what Ford did when they began marketing the Mustang in April, 1964. After the record-breaking success of the compact Falcon, Ford saw the need for a small sporty car in the lower price range — a working man's Thunderbird, perhaps.

By R. Perry Zavitz
Data compiled by John R. Smith

So, with relatively little effort, a new car was concocted using the Falcon's chassis and many of its components. This Mustang was introduced in mid-1964. The best time to introduce a new car is in the spring. Interest in new cars peaks then. Unlike the fall, there is not a profusion of new models.

The 1964-1/2 Mustang, officially considered an early 1965 model, came in a spunky-looking little hardtop coupe and convertible. Its wheelbase was 108 inches, overall length 181.6 inches and weight was just under 2,500 pounds. Base price was $2,368 for the hardtop.

The closest competition already on the market was the Corvair Monza Spyder at $2599. The Mustang's standard powerplant was a 170 cid 101 hp Six. Admittedly, that was anemic compared to the Spyder's 150 hp. But for just a few bucks extra, a 195 hp 289 cid V-8 was optional in the Mustang. That was where Ford had the drop on Chevrolet. Virtually any Ford-built engine (except the FE series blocks that had shock clearance problems) could be slipped under the early Mustang hood. The Corvair had no such possibilities, because of its flat-Six motor and rear mounting.

The Mustang was an instant hit. So great was its popularity, that the Dearborn factory (shared by Falcon) was not sufficient to meet the demand for new Mustangs. In July, additional production was begun at Ford's San Jose, Calif. plant. Soon after that, the Falcon assembly line at Metuchen, N.J., was changed over to Mustang production as well. History books are filled with instances where cars were extremely popular on introduction, but lack of finances and/or production capacity cooled public interest. When the problems were eventually overcome, the buyers were gone. The Mustang is the most outstanding exception to that sad fate.

By the end of 1964, Mustang had scored 263,434 sales. Despite its late start, the Mustang was outsold in the calendar year only by Impala, Galaxie 500, Bel Air and Chevelle. It even surpassed the Falcon, from which it was derived.

When the other Ford lines were altered for 1965, practically no changes were made to the Mustang. The standard six became the larger 200 cid 120 hp motor. Almost 27 percent of 1964 Mustangs had the six, which grew to over 35 percent popularity in the 1965 models. The rest, of course, were V-8s. The standard V-8 was the 200 hp edition of the "289" engine.

Options included 225 hp and 271 hp versions of the same engine.

A fastback body called the 2+2 was added to the hardtop and convertible choice. The 2+2 was not a hardtop in the sense of having pillarless styling, because it had no rear side windows. In the area where such windows are normally expected there was a set of louvers, used as the outlet for the flow-through ventilation.

Mustangs could be loaded with all the popular power accessories. Automatic or four-speed stick shift transmissions were on the option list, as well as power brakes, power steering and air-conditioning.

On April 17, 1965, the Mustang celebrated its first birthday. It took the cake by setting a new world record of over 418,000 sales in its first year on the market for a new model. It exceeded the previous record set by the Falcon, by about 1,000 units. It is good to remember that both these achievements came from the same company which, just a few years earlier, misjudged the market with the Edsel.

During calendar 1965, Mustang racked up a total of 518,252 registrations. It was second only to the Chevrolet Impala and almost equalled all models of Dodge combined.

For 1966, again, little change was made. A revised instrument panel, less like the Falcon's, was used. The grille, still the same shape, used horizontal bars. The bright accents were about the same, except for a strip on Mustangs with the $152 GT option. That accessory package (it was not a model) included clear lens fog lights mounted in the outer ends of the grille. The GT also featured racing stripes along the body sills. Only the 225 hp or 271 hp engines were available with the GT. Faster steering, stiffer suspension and front disc brakes were mechanical features standard on the GTs. Despite a general industry trend towards more V-8s, Ford heavily promoted sales of six-cylinder Mustangs for 1966. Thus, only 58 percent of the 'pony cars' were V-8 -powered. That was the lowest percentage in marque history.

Production of the 1966 Mustang reached an all-time peak of 607,568. By model year's end, there had been a total of 1,288,5567 Mustangs made.

For 1967, competition in the so-called pony car market was noticeably stiffer. The Mustang had caught other companies unprepared. Only the Plymouth Barracuda (introduced almost simultaneously with the Mustang) could be considered, more or less, in the same class as Mustang. The Dodge Charger, though of the same sports-personal character, was bigger and heavier and could not be classed as a 'pony car.'

Mercury introduced its version, the Cougar, for 1967. Chevrolet made no attempt to respond to the Mustang with the Corvair Monza Spyder, choosing instead to develop an entirely new car for 1967. This was the Camaro. The Firebird was Pontiac's version of the Camaro, brought out in mid-1967.

An all-new Mustang body was used on the 1967 models. It was said that the original dies were worn-out after making nearly 1.3 million copies, but competition, no doubt, was a major factor in the redesign. Styling, however, stayed almost the same. That was a wise move, because a big change in appearance could have hurt the Mustang's obvious appeal when there were other ponies to pick. The same three body types remained. Also the same engine availabilities were offered, plus a big 320 hp version of the 390 'cube' Thunderbird V-8. The GT option was obtainable with any V-8 Mustang, which meant some 70 percent of all 1967 editions. Nearly 16 percent of the Mustangs that year had factory air-conditioning.

Production of the 1967 models dropped over 22 percent, to 472,121 units, due to a smaller total Ford production that year

and increased competition. However, Mustang accounted for 6.2 percent of all 1967 cars built in the United States. Mustang production amounted to slightly more than twice American Motors' total production that year. In the pony car market, Mustang corralled 42.5 percent.

Only subtle appearance changes were made to the 1968 Mustang. The GT option included a choice of stripes. Either the rocker panel type or a reflecting "C" stripe was offered. The latter widened along the front fender ridge, crossed the door to the rear quarter panel, then swept around the depression ahead of the rear wheel and tapered along the bottom of the door.

Some new engine options were offered in 1968. The six and standard V-8 remained, but were down to 115 and 195 hp respectively. Optional V-8s included a "302" rated at 230 hp and a "390" developing 280 or 325 hp. The legendary 427 cid/390 hp V-8 was offered for just a short while, then replaced with a 428 cid 335 hp job. Seven power plant possibilities in '68s!

Production fell again in the 1968, dropping off to 317,404 units. Mustangs accounted for only 3.8 percent of the industry total. The Mustang had slipped from second place in production for 1965, to seventh rank for 1967. However, it still remained leader of the pony pack.

The body on 1969 Mustangs was altogether different than the 1968 type and reflected a major restyling of the five-year-old line. It kept the overall Mustang image. Dual headlights were used, with the outer pair in the fenders. The high-beam inner set were located in the grille ends.

Two new models were added. The Grande was a dressed-up edition of the hardtop. Vinyl roof and a plush interior were two of its standard features. It was priced $231 above the normal hardtop, comparably equipped. The Mach I was a variation of the fastback, now called a Sportsroof coupe. Beginning with the 1969 models, the Mustang fastbacks were true hardtops. The rear quarter louvers were gone and more glass area, by way of a small window, abutted the door window.

The Mach I was identifiable by special paint stripes along the sides and across the integral rear spoiler. Only the five optional V-8s were obtainable in the Mach I. They were the 250 and 290 hp versions of the 351 cid job; the 390 cid/320 hp V-8 and the 335 hp 428 Cobra-Jet Ram Air engine with cold air induction. The 428CJ option was quite evident, even in a parked Mustang. Its air intake protruded through a large hole in the so-called the "shaker" hood.

At the tame end of the engine options, it should be noted that Ford's 250 cid 155 hp six-cylinder motor was available for the first time in the Mustang. The standard six, optional six and standard 302 cid/220 hp V-8 could not be had in the Mach I.

V-8 power was installed in 81.5 percent of the 1969 Mustangs. Automatic transmission installations were running just over 71 percent, but the four-speed stick shift options (a choice of a wide- or close-ratio) were found in nearly 11 percent — a record high for Mustang. Power disc brakes were featured on 28 percent and power steering on nearly 66 percent of the 1969 Mustangs, with both options showing increased acceptance. Nevertheless, total production was down. The most potent powerplant for the Mustang was the 429 V-8, rated at 375 hp. Imagine 375 horses to pull a 3,000 pound car! Mustang was extending itself from the fancy little runabout to an all-out performance bomb. Oh yes, the sedate sixes were still available, but the Mustang also stressed "GO!" The hot Boss 302 listed for $3720, which was only $999 more than the base two-door hatchback hardtop.

A 1971 Mustang restyling featured a more European look. The cars were now longer, wider and heavier and seemed more like a mid-sized car than a pony car. The body was

slightly lower because of a flatter roof shape. Six models were available again, but the Boss 302 was renamed Boss 351 because it now had a 351 cid/330 hp engine.

Further emphasis on performance was evident by the omission of the "200" six. The standard engine became the 250 cid 145 hp six. Standard V-8 was the "302" at 210 hp. Options were 240 hp, 285 hp and 330 hp versions of the "351" V-8 and the 429/429 CJ/429 SCJ V-8s, the latter pair both rated at 370 hp.

For 1973 the convertible, which had been in the Mustang line since the start, was to become noteworthy as the final convertible to bear the Ford name. There were 16,302 Mustang ragtops built that model year. Total 1973 Mustang production was up nearly eight percent, to 134,867.

During the 10 Mustang model years (not lumping 1964 with 1965) nearly three million cars were built in an interesting variety, from adequate coupes to road-scorching racers. For collectors interested in Ford or specialty type cars, Mustangs are still around awaiting a good home. They can be had with virtually any degree of motor potency, in hardtops, convertibles or fastbacks, with just about any contemporary power accessory. (At the last, over 56 percent of them had factory air-conditioning, nearly 78 percent had power disc brakes and almost 93 percent had power steering.)

Luxury at an affordable price helped make the Mustang so phenomenally popular with the new car buyer. That will probably also hold true for the collector, now, and for some time to come.

1964 Ford Mustang, 2+2 two-door fastback coupe, V-8

1965 Ford Mustang, GT two-door convertible, V-8

1965 Ford Mustang, 2+2 two-door fastback coupe, V-8

1966 Ford Mustang, GT two-door convertible, V-8

1965 Ford Mustang, two-door convertible, 6-cyl

Standard Catalog of American Cars

1967 Ford Mustang, two-door convertible, V-8

1967 Ford Mustang, two-door hardtop coupe, V-8

1969 Ford Mustang, Sportsroof two-door fastback coupe, V-8

1969 Ford Mustang, Mach 1 two-door fastback coupe, V-8

1970 Ford Mustang, two-door convertible, V-8

1971 Ford Mustang, Mach 1 two-door fastback coupe, V-8

1972 Ford Mustang, Sprint two-door hardtop coupe, V-8

1972 Ford Mustang, Mach 1 two-door fastback coupe, V-8

1973 Ford Mustang, Mach 1 two-door fastback coupe, V-8

Standard Catalog of American Cars

1964-½ MUSTANG

1964-1/2 Ford Mustang, two-door convertible, V-8

1964-1/2 MUSTANG-(ALL ENGINES) — The biggest news for 1964 was not the restyled Galaxie, Fairlane, Falcon or Thunderbird, but, rather, the later introduction of a small, sporty car which caught the rest of the automotive industry totally off guard and caught the hearts of the American car buying public; the Ford Mustang. The Mustang was the midyear model that set records which have yet to be broken. It combined sporty looks, economy and brisk performance in a package which had a base price of $2368. Mustangs could be equipped to be anything from absolute economy cars, to luxury sports cars. The Mustang, with its lengthened and extended hood, shortened rear deck, sculptured body panels and sporty bucket seats provided a family-size sedan for grocery-getting mothers; an appearance for those people who yearned for another two-seat Thunderbird and plenty of power and handling options for the performance Ford enthusiast. So successful was the Mustang that a whole assortment of similar cars, by competitive manufacturers, came to be known as 'Pony Cars' or, in other words, cars in the original Mustang image. Mustangs came powered by everything from the very tame 101 hp, 170 cid six-cylinder engine, to a wild, solid-lifter high-performance 289 cid V-8, sporting 271 hp (and available only with the four-speed manual transmission). The basic standard equipment package found on all 1964-1/2 Mustangs included three-speed manual transmission with floor lever controls; front bucket seats; padded instrument panel; full wheelcovers; cloth and vinyl (hardtop) or all-vinyl upholstery; color-keyed carpeting; Sports steering wheel; cigarette lighter; door courtesy lights; glovebox light; and heater and defroster. The original base powerplants were the 170 cid six or the 260 cid V-8. In the fall of 1964, the 200 cid six or the 289 cid V-8 became the standard powerplants in the six and eight-cylinder Mustang lines, respectively.

VEHICLE I.D. NUMBERS: Vehicle Identification Numbers and other important encoded information will be found on the Ford Motor Co. data plate, located on the rear edge of the left front door. The data plate contains an upper row of codes that reveal body and trim information, plus (at center level) a Vehicle Warranty Number, that reveals other important data. In the upper row, the first three symbols are a body code with '65A' designating hardtop coupe and '76A' designating convertible. The fourth symbol is the paint code, as follows: 'A' = Raven Black; 'B' = Pagoda Green; 'D' = Dynasty Green; 'F' = Guardsman Blue; 'J' = Rangoon Red; 'K' = Silversmoke Gray; 'M' = Wimbeldon White; 'P' = Prairie Bronze; 'S' = Cascade Green; 'V' = Sunlight Yellow; 'X' = Vintage Burgundy; 'Y' = Skylight Blue; 'Z' = Chantilly Beige and '3' = Poppy Red. The next pair of symbols are the trim code. Many different interior trims, too numerous to catalog here, were available. The next group of symbols consisted of two numbers and a letter, which represent the assembly date code. The numbers give the day (i.e. '01' = first day) and the letter designates month of year, following normal progression (i.e. 'A' = January; 'B' = February, etc.), except that the letter 'I' is skipped. The next group of symbols is the DSO (district sales office) code, which is relatively unimportant to collectors. This is followed by a number or letter designating the axle ratio code. A number indicates conventional axle and a letter indicates EquaLock. The codes are as follows: '1' or 'A' = 3.00:1; '3' or 'C' = 3.20:1; '4' or 'D' 3.25:1; '5' or 'E' = 3.50:1; '6' or 'F' = 2.80:1; '7' or 'G' = 3.80:1; '8' or 'H' = 3.89:1 and '9' or 'I' = 4.11:1. The final code on the top row of symbols is a transmission code, as follows: 'I' = three-speed manual-, '5' = four-speed manual and '6' = C-4 Dual-Range automatic. The first symbol in the Vehicle Warranty Number is a '5' designating 1965 model year (all 1964-1/2 Mustangs were considered 1965 models). The second symbol is a letter designating the assembly point, as follows: Atlanta (A); Dallas (D); Mahwah (E); Dearborn (F); Chicago (G); Lorain (H); Los Angeles (J); Kansas City (K); Michigan Truck (L); Norfolk (N); Twin Cities (P); San Jose (R); Pilot Plant (S); Metuchen (T); Louisville (U); Wayne (W); Wixom (Y) and St. Louis (Z). The next two symbols are the body serial number and agree with the numbers listed in the second column of the specifications charts below (i.e. '07' = two-door hardtop). The fifth symbol is an engine code, which is listed with the engine specifications below. The next group of symbols is the consecutive unit number, beginning with 100001 and up at each factory.

MUSTANG SERIES

Model Number	Body/Style Number	Body Type & Seating	Factory Price	Shipping Weight	Production Total
NA	07	2-dr HT Cpe-4P	2368	2449	97,705
NA	08	2-dr Conv-4P	2614	2615	28,833

NOTE 1: Total series output was 121,538 units. In rounded-off figures, 32,700 were sixes and 88,900 were V-8s.

ENGINES

INLINE SIX: Overhead valves. Cast iron block. Displacement: 170 cid. Bore and stroke: 3.50 x 2.94 inches. Compression ratio: 8.7:1. Brake hp: 101 at 4400 rpm. Seven main bearings. Hydraulic valve lifters. Carburetion: Ford (Autolite) one-barrel Model C30F-9510-G. Serial number code 'U.'

V-8: Overhead valves. Cast iron block. Displacement: 260 cid. Bore and stroke: 3.80 x 2.87 inches. Compression ratio: 8.8:1. Brake hp: 164 at 4400 rpm. Five main bearings. Hydraulic valve lifters. Carburetor: Ford (Autolite) two-barrel Model C40F-9510E. Serial number code 'F.'

CHALLENGER V-8: Overhead valves. Cast iron block. Displacement: 289 cid. Bore and stroke: 4.00 x 2.87 inches. Compression ratio: 9.0:1. Brake hp: 210 at 4400 rpm. Five main bearings. Hydraulic valve lifters. Carburetor: Ford (Autolite) Model C4AF-9510B. Serial number code 'C.'

CHALLENGER FOUR-BARREL V-8: Overhead valves. Cast iron block. Displacement: 289 cid. Bore and stroke: 4.00 x 2.87 inches. Compression ratio: 9.8:1. Brake hp: 220 at 4800 rpm. Five main bearings. Hydraulic valve lifters. Carburetor: Ford (Autolite) four-barrel Model C5ZF-9510-C. Serial number code 'D.'

CHALLENGER HIGH-PERFORMANCE V-8: Overhead valves. Cast iron block. Displacement 289 cid. Bore and stroke: 4.00 x 2.87 inches. Compression ratio: 10.5:1 Brake hp: 271 at 6000 rpm. Five main bearings. Solid valve lifters. Carburetor: Ford (Autolite) four-barrel Model C40F-9510-AL. Serial number code 'K.'

CHASSIS FEATURES: Wheelbase: 108 inches. Overall length: 181.6 inches. Tires: (with V-8) 7.00 x 13 four-ply tubeless; (with high-performance '289' V-8) 7.00 x 14 four-ply tubeless blackwall; (other models) 6.50 x 13 four-ply tubeless blackwall.

OPTIONS: Accent Group ($27.70). Ford air conditioner ($283.20). Heavy-duty battery ($7.60). Front disc brakes ($58). Full-length center console ($51.50). Console with air conditioning ($32.20). Equa-Lock limited slip differential ($42.50). California type closed emissions system ($5.30). Challenger V-8 ($108). Challenger four-barrel V-8 engine ($162). Challenger high-performance four-barrel V-8 ($442.60). Early year only, 260 cid V-8 ($75). Emergency flashers ($19.60). Tinted glass with banded windshield ($30.90). Banded, tinted windshield only ($21.55). Back-up lights ($10.70). Rocker panel moldings ($16.10). Power brakes ($43.20). Power steering ($86.30). Power convertible top ($54.10). Push-button radio with antenna ($58.50). Rally-Pac instrumentation with clock and tachometer ($70.80). Deluxe retractable front seat safety belts ($7.55). Special Handling Package ($31.30). Padded sun visors ($5.70). Cruise-O-Matic transmission, with six ($179.80); with 200 and 225 hp V-8s ($189.60). Four-speed manual transmission, with six ($115.90); with V-8 ($75.80). Hardtop vinyl roof ($75.80). Visibility Group including remote-control mirror; day/nite mirror; two-speed electric wipers and windshield washers ($36). Wheelcovers with simulated knock-off hubs ($18.20). Wire wheelcovers, size 14 inch, ($45.80). Style steel wheels, size 14 inch ($122.30). NOTE: The MagicAire heater ($32.20 credit) and front seat belts ($11 credit) were 'delete options'. Size 6.50 x 13 whitewalls with six ($33.90). Size 6.95 x 14 tires, blackwall with six ($7.40); whitewall with six ($41.30); whitewall with V-8s, except high-performance type ($33.90); black nylon, except with high-performance V-8 ($15.80); Red Band nylon with V-8s, except high-performance V-8 ($49.60); Black nylon or white sidewall nylon with high-performance V-8 (No Charge).

HISTORICAL FOOTNOTES: Mustang was introduced April 17, 1964. Model year production peaked at 121,538 units. Lee Iacocca headed an eight-man committee that conceived the idea for the new car. Stylists Joe Oros, Gail Halderman and David Ash designed the car. So cleanly styled was the new Mustang that it was awarded the Tiffany Award for Excellence in American Design, the first and only automobile ever to be so honored by Tiffany & Company. Not only did the design purists like the new Mustang, so did the public. More than 100,000 were sold in the first four months of production, followed by 500,000 more in the next 12 months. More than 1,000,000 found buyers in less than 24 months. This set an automotive industry sales record which has yet to be equalled or eclipsed. A 1964-1/2 Mustang convertible was also selected as the Indy 500 pace car. Out of all the Mustangs built in the 1964 model run, some 49.2 percent featured an automatic transmission; 19.3 percent four-speed manual transmission; 73.1 percent V-8 engines; 26.9 percent six-cylinder engines; 77.8 percent radio; 99:1 percent heater; 30.9 percent power steering; 7.7 percent power brakes; 88.2 percent whitewalls; 48.3 percent windshield washers, 22.4 percent tinted windshields only; 8.0 percent all tinted glass; 44.6 percent back-up lights and 6.4 percent air conditioning

1965 MUSTANG

1965 Ford Mustang, two-door hardtop sports coupe, V-8

1965 MUSTANG — (ALL ENGINES) — One brand-new model and a number of very minor revisions were seen in the 1965 Mustang lineup. A 2+2 fastback body joined the hardtop and convertible, creating an expanded 'stable' of three Pony Cars. Perhaps the most significant change for 1965 was the use of an alternator in the place of the previously used generator. Engine choices remained the same as in late 1964, with one exception. The old workhorse I-block, 170 cid engine, was replaced by the 200 cid job as base six-cylinder powerplant. A number of small changes and some new options were seen on the 1965 models. While interior door handles on the earliest Mustangs were secured by 'C' clips, Allen screw attachments were a running production change adopted for later cars. Also, the spacing between the letters in the lower bodyside nameplates was modified, giving them a five inch measurement or about 1/4 inch longer than before. The push-down door lock buttons were chrome plated, in contrast to the 1964-1/2 type, which were colored to match the interior. Front

disc brakes were one new option. So was the GT Package, which included racing stripes as a standard, but deleteable, feature. The standard equipment list for 1965 was much the same as before, including heater and defroster; dual sun visors; Sports-type front bumpers; full wheelcovers; vinyl upholstery; seat belts; padded instrument panel; automatic courtesy lights; cigarette lighter; front and rear carpets; foam-padded front bucket seats; self-adjusting brakes; Sports steering wheel; five 6.50 x 13 four-ply tubeless black sidewall tires; and the 120 hp 200 cid six. The '289' V-8 and 6.95 x 14 size tires were standard in the Mustang V-8 Series.

VEHICLE I.D. NUMBERS: The numbering system and code locations were the same as on previous models. Several additions and deletions in exterior colors were seen. New codes and colors included: Code 'C' = Honey Gold; Code 'I' = Champagne Beige; Code 'O' = Tropical Turquoise and Code 'R' = Ivy Green. Colors deleted were Guardsman Blue (Code 'H'); Cascade Green (Code 'S') and Chantilly Beige (Code 'Z'). The 1965 date codes were changed in regards to the letter used to designate a specific month. Code 'N' designated January. Code 'O' was not used and the remaining months ran in normal alphabetical progression from Code 'P' (for February) through Code 'Z' (for December). The body serial number code for the new two-door fastback was '09'. The 1965 engine serial number codes are indicated in the engine data charts below. All other codes were the same used on 1964-1/2 models, except for interior trim codes which are not included in this catalog).

MUSTANG SERIES

Model Number	Body/Style Number	Body Type & Seating	Factory Price	Shipping Weight	Production Total
NA	65A (07)	2-dr HT Cpe-4P	2372	2465	409,260
NA	63A (09)	2-dr FsBk Cpe-4P	2589	2515	77,079
NA	76A (08)	2-dr Conv-4P	2614	2650	73,112

NOTE 1: Total model year output was 559,451 units. This figure includes 5,776 Luxury fastbacks; 22,232 Luxury hardtops: 14,905 bench seat equipped hardtops; 5,338 Luxury convertibles and 2,111 convertibles equipped with bench seats.
NOTE 2: In figures rounded-off to the nearest 100 units, the total included 198,900 sixes and 360,600 V-8s.

ENGINES

INLINE SIX: Overhead valves. Cast iron block. Displacement: 200 cid. Bore and stroke: 3.68 x 3.13 inches. Compression ratio: 9.2:1. Brake hp: 120 at 4400 rpm. Seven main bearings. Hydraulic valve lifters. Carburetor: Ford (Autolite) two-barrel Model C50F-9510-E. Serial number code 'T.'

CHALLENGER V-8: Overhead valves. Cast iron block. Displacement: 289 cid. Bore and stroke: 4.00 x 2.87 inches. Compression ratio: 9.3:1. Brake hp: 200 at 4400 rpm. Five main bearings. Hydraulic valve lifters. Carburetor: Ford (Autolite) two-barrel Model C5ZF-9510-A. Serial number code 'C.'

CHALLENGER FOUR-BARREL V-8: Overhead valves. Cast iron block. Displacement: 289 cid. Bore and stroke: 4.00 x 2.87 inches. Compression ratio: 10.0:1. Brake hp: 225 at 4800 rpm. Five main bearings. Hydraulic valve lifters. Carburetion: Ford (Autolite) four-barrel Model C5ZF-9510-C. Serial number code 'A.'

CHALLENGER HIGH-PERFORMANCE V-8: Overhead valves. Cast iron block. Displacement: 289 cid. Bore and stroke: 4.00 x 2.87 inches. Compression ratio: 10.5:1: Brake hp: 271 at 6000 rpm. Five main bearings. Solid valve lifters. Carburetor: Ford (Autolite) four-barrel Model C40F-9510-AL. Serial number code 'K.'

CHASSIS FEATURES: Wheelbase: 108 inches. Overall length: 181.6 inches. Tires: (V-8s) 7.00 x 13 four-ply tubeless blackwalls; (high-performance 289 V-8) 7.00 x 14 four-ply tubeless blackwall; (other models) 6.50 x 13 four-ply tubeless blackwall.

OPTIONS: Accent Group, on hardtop and convertible ($27.70); on fastback coupe ($14.20). Ford air conditioner ($283.20). Heavy-duty battery ($7.60). Front disc brakes with V-8 and manual brakes only ($58). Full-length center console ($51.50). Console for use with air conditioner ($32.20). Equa-Lock limited-slip differential ($42.50). California type closed emissions system ($5.30). Challenger 200 hp V-8 ($108). Challenger four-barrel 225 hp V-8 ($162). Challenger 271 hp high-performance V-8 including Special Handling Package and 6.95 x 14 nylon tires ($442.60). Emergency flashers ($19.60). Tinted glass with banded windshield ($30.90). Tinted-banded windshield glass ($21.55). Back-up lights ($10.70). Rocker panel moldings, except fastback coupe ($16.10). Power brakes ($43.20). Power steering ($86.30). Power convertible top ($54.10). Push-button radio with antenna ($58.50). Rally-Pac instrumentation with clock and tachometer ($70.80). Deluxe retractable front seat safety belts ($7.55). Special Handling package, with 200 or 225 hp V-8s ($31.30). Padded sun visors ($5.70). Cruise-O-Matic transmission, with six ($179.80); with 200 and 225 hp V-8s ($189.60). Four-speed manual transmission, with six ($115.90); with V-9 ($188). Vinyl roof, on two-door hardtop only ($75.80). Visibility Group, includes remote-control outside rearview mirror; day/nite inside rearview mirror; two-speed electric wipers and windshield washers ($36). Wheelcovers with knock-off hubs ($18.20). Fourteen inch wire wheelcovers ($45.80). Fourteen inch styled steel wheels ($122.30).

NOTE: Delete options and tire options same as 1964-1/2 models.

HISTORICAL FOOTNOTES: The 1965 Mustang was officially introduced on Oct. 1, 1964. Model year production peaked at 559,451 cars. Of these, 53.6 percent were equipped with automatic transmission; 14.5 percent with four-speed manual transmissions; 64.4 percent with V-8 engines; 35.6 percent with sixes; 78.9 percent with radio; 98.9 percent with heaters; 24.9 percent with power steering; 4.3 percent with power brakes; 97 percent with bucket seats; 100.00 percent with front seat safety belts; 83.6 percent with white sidewall tires; 47.3 percent with windshield washers; 24.8 percent with tinted windshields; 9 percent with all-tinted glass; 38.6 percent with back-up lights; 9.1 percent with air conditioning; 3.9 percent with dual exhausts and two percent with limited-slip differential. A total of 1.3 percent of all 1965 Mustangs, or 6,996 cars, were sold with the 271 hp V-8 (Code 'K') and all of these units had four-speed manual transmission. An interesting historical point is that Mustangs made in Germany were called Ford T-5 models, since the right to the Mustang name in that country belonged to another manufacturer.

1966 MUSTANG

1966 MUSTANG — (ALL ENGINES) — The 1966 Mustang continued to sell like 'hot cakes,' in spite of only very minor restyling in the trim department. The grille featured a floating Mustang emblem in the center, with no horizontal or vertical dividing bars. Brand new trim, on the rear fender, featured three chrome strips leading into the simulated scoop. This was the first year of federally mandated safety standards and all 1966 Fords included front and rear seat belts; padded instrument panel; emergency flashers; electric wipers; and windshield washers as standard equipment. In addition, the list of regular Mustang features was comprised of the following: front bucket seats; pleated vinyl upholstery and interior trim; Sports type steering wheel; five dial instrument cluster; full carpeting; heater and defroster; left-hand door outside rearview mirror; back-up lamps; door courtesy lights, rocker panel moldings; full wheelcovers; three-speed manual transmission with floor lever control; and 200 cid 120 hp six-cylinder engine. The fastback coupe also came with special Silent-Flo ventilation and the base V-8 engine was the 200 hp version of the '289.'

1966 Ford Mustang, two-door convertible, V-8

VEHICLE I.D. NUMBERS — (ALL ENGINES) — The numbering system and code location was the same as on previous models, although the size and color of the data plate itself was changed. The plate was narrower and the warranty number (formerly on the lower row) was now at the top left-hand corner of the plate. The data on the upper row of codes (body code, color code, trim code, etc.) was moved to a narrow, unfinished band that crossed the data plate, horizontally, nearly at its center. Another change was that previously data plates finished in black had indicated cars painted in conventional enamel, while gray finish had indicated cars done in acrylic enamel. This color-coding system was reversed for 1966. Reading along the top row of codes, the first symbol became a '6' to indicate 1966 model year. The next symbol was a letter designating the assembly plant (with the same codes as previously used). The next two symbols were the Body Serial Code ('07' = hardtop coupe; '09' = fastback coupe; '08' = convertible). The fifth symbol was a letter designating the type of engine, as indicated in the engine data listings below. The next six symbols in the upper row of codes were the consecutive unit number. The first three symbols in the lower row of codes represented the Body Style Number, as indicated in the second column of the charts below. The fourth symbol was a letter indicating the exterior color, as follows: Code 'A' Raven Black, Code 'F' Light Blue, Code 'H' Light Beige, Code 'K' Dark Blue Metallic, Code 'M' Wimbledon White, Code 'P' Medium Palomino Metallic; Code 'R' Dark Green Metallic; Code 'T' Candy Apple Red; Code 'U' Medium Turquoise Metallic; Code 'V' Emberglo Metalic; Code 'X' Maroon Metallic; Code 'Y' Light Blue Metallic; Code 'Z' Medium Sage Metallic;, Code '4' Medium Silver Metallic; Code '5' Signal Flare Red; and Code '8' Springtime Yellow. The fifth and sixth symbols were the interior trim code (not cataloged here). The next three symbols were the assembly date code, following the system used in 1964 (i.e. 21A = 21st day of January). The 10th and 11th symbols were numbers designating the District Sales Office code. The next symbol was a number designating the type of axle and the last (13th) symbol on the lower row was the transmission code. Axle codes and transmission codes are the same as those listed in the 1964 Mustang I.D. Number section.

MUSTANG SERIES

Model Number	Body/Style Number	Body Type & Seating	Factory Price	Shipping Weight	Production Total
NA	65A (07)	2-dr HT Cpe-4P	2416	2488	499,751
NA	63A (09)	2-dr FsBk Cpe-4P	2607	2519	35,698
NA	76A (08)	2-dr Conv-4P	2653	2650	72,119

NOTE 1: Total series output was 607,568 units. This figure included 7,889 Luxury fastbacks; 55,938 Luxury hardtops; 21,397 hardtops equipped with bench seats; 12,520 Luxury convertibles. and 3,190 convertibles equipped with bench seats.
NOTE 2: In figures rounded-off to the nearest 100 units, the total included 253,200 sixes and 354,400 V-8s.

ENGINES

INLINE SIX: Overhead valves. Cast iron block. Displacement: 200 cid. Bore and stroke: 3.68 x 3.1 25 inches. Compression ratio: 9.2:1. Brake hp: 120 at 4400 rpm. Seven main bearings. Hydraulic valve lifters. Carburetor: Ford (Autolite) one-barrel Model C60F-951 0-AD. Serial number code 'T.'

V-8: Overhead valves. Cast iron block. Displacement: 289 cid. Bore and stroke: 4.00 x 2.875 inches. Compression: 9.3:1. Brake hp: 200 at 4400 rpm. Five main bearings. Hydraulic valve lifters. Carburetor: Ford (Autolite) two-barrel Model C6DF-9510-A. Serial number code 'C.'

V-8: Overhead valves. Cast iron block. Displacement: 289 cid. Bore and stroke: 4.00 x 2.875 inches. Compression: 10.1:1. Brake hp; 225 at 4800 rpm. Five main bearings. Hydraulic valve lifters. Carburetor: Ford (Autolite) four-barrel Model C6ZF-9510-A. Serial number code 'A.'

V-8: Overhead valves. Cast iron block. Displacement: 289 cid. Bore and stroke: 4.00 x 2.875 inches. Compression ratio: 10.5:1. Brake hp: 271 at 6000 rpm. Five main bearings. Solid valve lifters. Carburetor: Ford (Autolite) four-barrel Model C60F-9510-C. Serial number code 'K.'

CHASSIS FEATURES: Wheelbase: 108 inches. Overall length; 181.6 inches. Tires: 6.95 x 14 four-ply tubeless blackwall; (high-performance V-8) 7.00 x 14 four-ply tubeless blackwall.

OPTIONS: Challenger 289 cid V-8 ($105.63). Challenger four-barrel 289 cid 225 hp 289 cid V-8 ($158.48). High-performance 289 cid 271 hp 289 cid V-8, in standard Mustang ($433.55); in Mustang GT ($381.97). NOTE: The total cost of the high-performance engine was $327.92 on regular Mustangs and $276.34 on Mustang GTs, plus the cost of the base V-8 attachment over the six (which was $105.63). Cruise-O-Matic automatic transmission, with six ($175.80); with standard V-8s ($185.39); with high-performance V-8 ($216.27). Four-speed manual floor-shift transmission, with six ($113.45); with all V-8s ($184.02). Power brakes ($42.29). Power steering ($84.47). Power convertible top ($52.95). Heavy-duty 55 ampere battery ($7.44). Manual disc brakes, with V-8 only ($56.77). GT Equipment group, with high-performance V-8 only, includes: dual exhausts; fog lamps; special ornamentation; disc brakes; GT racing stripes (rocker panel moldings deleted); and Handling Package components ($152.20). Limited-slip differential ($41.60). Rally-Pack instrumentation, includes clock and tachometer ($69.30). Special Handling Package, with 200 and 225 hp V-8 engines, includes increased rate front and rear springs, larger front and rear shocks; 22:1 overall steering ratio and large diameter stabilizer bar ($30.64). Fourteen inch styled steel wheels, on V-8 models only ($93.84). Two-speed electric windshield wipers ($12.95). Tinted-banded windshield only ($21.09). All glass tinted with banded windshield ($30.25). Deluxe, retractable front seat safety belts and warning lamp ($14.53). Visibility Group, includes remote-control outside rearview mirror; day/nite inside mirror and two-speed electric wipers ($29.81). Ford air conditioner ($310.90). Stereo tape player, AM radio mandatory ($128.49). Full-width front seat with

armrest, for Styles 65A and 76A only, ($24.42). Rear deck luggage rack, except fastback ($32.44). Radio and antenna ($57.51). Accent striping, less rear quarter ornamentation ($13.90). Full-length center console ($50.41). Console for use with air conditioning ($31.52). Deluxe steering wheel with simulated wood-grain rim ($31.52). Interior Decor Group, includes special interior trim; Deluxe wood-grain steering wheel; rear window door courtesy lights and pistol grip door handles ($94.13). Vinyl top, on hardtop ($74.36). Simulated wire wheelcovers ($58.24). Wheelcovers with simulated knock-off hubs ($19.48). Closed crankcase emissions system, except with high-performance V-8 ($5.19). Exhaust emissions control system, except with high-performance V-8 ($45.45). Tire options, exchange prices listed indicate cost above base equipment: 6.95 x 14 four-ply rated whitewall ($33.31); nylon blackwall ($15.67); nylon whitewall ($48.89); nylon with dual red band design, on cars with high-performance V-8 (no charge); all other ($48.97). No charge for substitution of nylon blackwalls or whitewalls on cars with high-performance V-8. MagicAire heater could be deleted for $45.45 credit. Air conditioning, three-speed manual transmission, power steering and U.S. Royal tires not available with high-performance V-8. Power brakes and accent striping not available with GT Equipment Group. Full-width front seat not available in cars with Interior Decor Group, or Model 63A or cars with console options.

HISTORICAL FOOTNOTES: The 1966 Mustangs were introduced Oct. 1, 1965, the same day as all other Fords. Model year production hit 607,568 Mustangs with the little 'Pony' pulling down a significant 7.1 percent share of all American car sales. Of all Mustangs built during the 1966 model run, only 7.1 percent had four-speed transmissions; 62.8 percent automatic transmission; 58.3 percent V-8 engines; 79.3 percent radio; 98.8 percent heater; 28.9 percent power steering; 3.3 percent power brakes; 9.5 percent vinyl tops; 29.1 percent tinted windshields; 7.3 percent all tinted glass; 6.7 percent disc brakes; 5 percent dual exhausts; 2.6 percent limited-slip differential; 17.9 percent a non-glare inside rearview mirror. 85.3 percent whitewalls and 9.5 percent air conditioning. Henry Ford II was Ford Motor Co. Board Chairman and Arjay Miller was the President. The Ford Div., which was actually responsible for Mustang sales, was headed by M.S. McLaughlin who had the titles of Vice-President and General Manager. For 1966, Mustang was the third best-selling individual nameplate in the American industry, an outstanding achievement for a car only three model years old.

1967 MUSTANG

1967 Ford Mustang GTA, two-door fastback 2+2 sports coupe, V-8

MUSTANG SERIES — (ALL ENGINES) — For the first time since its mid-1964 introduction the Mustang was significantly changed. The styling was similar to the original in its theme, but everything was larger. The grille featured a larger opening. The feature lines on the side led to a larger simulated scoop. The taillights took the form of three vertical lenses on each side of a concave indentation panel, with a centrally located gas cap. Standard equipment included all Ford Motor Co. safety features, plus front bucket seats; full carpeting; floor-mounted shift; vinyl interior trim; heater; wheelcovers; and cigarette lighter. The fastback came with wheelcovers; special emblems; and rocker panel moldings. There were five engine choices ranging from a 120 hp 200 cid six to a 320 hp 390 cid V-8. New options available included SelectShift Cruise-O-Matic.

VEHICLE I.D. NUMBERS — VIN stamped on top upper flange of left front fender apron. First symbol 7=1967. Second symbol indicates assembly plant: F=Dearborn, Mich.; R=San Jose, Calif.; T=Metuchen, N.J. Third and fourth symbols equated to Body Style Number: 63A=bucket seat fastback; 65A=bucket seat hardtop; 76A=bucket seat convertible; 63B=bucket seat luxury fastback; 65B=bucket seat luxury hardtop; 76B=bucket seat luxury convertible; 65C=bench seat hardtop; and 76C=bench seat convertible. Fifth symbol indicates engine: T=200 cid 120 hp six; 2=200 cid 200 hp V-8; 3=289 V-8 export; C=289 cid/200 hp V-8; A=289 cid/225 hp V-8; K=289 cid/271 hp; S=390 cid/320 hp V-8. The next six symbols are the sequential production number beginning at 100001 for each series at each factory. Body Number Plate located on left front door lock face indicates serial number, Body Style Number, color, trim, District Code, DSO Number, axle and transmission.

MUSTANG SERIES

Model Number	Body/Style Number	Body Type & Seating	Factory Price	Shipping Weight	Production Total
NA	07	2-dr HT Cpe-4P	2461	2578	356,271
NA	09	2-dr FsBk Cpe-4P	2592	2605	71,042
NA	08	2-dr Conv-4P	2698	2738	44,808

NOTE 1: Total series output was 472,121 units, including both sixes and V-8s.
NOTE 2: Series output includes 22,228 Luxury hardtops; 8,190 hardtops with bench seats; 17,391 Luxury fastbacks; 4,848 Luxury convertibles and 1,209 convertibles equipped with bench seats.
NOTE 3: In figures rounded-off to the nearest 100, the model year output of 1967 Mustangs included 141,500 sixes and 330,600 V-8s.

ENGINES

MUSTANG SIX-CYLINDER: Overhead valves. Cast iron block. Displacement: 200 cid. Bore and stroke: 3.68 x 3.13 inches. Compression ratio: 9.2:1. Brake hp: 120 at 4400 rpm. Carburetion: Holley one-barrel. Seven main bearings. Serial number code 'T.'

CHALLENGER 289 V-8: Overhead valves. Cast iron block. Displacement: 289 cid. Bore and stroke: 4.00 x 2.87 inches. Compression ratio: 9.3:1. Brake hp: 200 at 4400 rpm. Carburetion: Holley two-barrel. Five main bearings. Serial number code 'C.'

CHALLENGER 289 V-8: Overhead valves. Cast iron block. Displacement: 289 cid. Bore and stroke: 4.00 x 3.87 inches. Compression ratio: 9.8:1. Brake hp: 225 at 4800 rpm. Carburetion: Holley four-barrel. Five main bearings. Serial number code 'A.'

HIGH-PERFORMANCE 289 V-8: Overhead valves. Cast iron block. Displacement: 289 cid. Bore and stroke: 4.00 x 2.87 inches. Compression ratio: 10.5:1 Brake hp: 271 at 6000 rpm. Carburetion: Holley four-barrel. Five main bearings. Serial number code 'K.'

FOUR-BARREL V-8: Overhead valves. Cast iron block. Displacement: 390 cid. Bore and stroke: 4.05 x 3.78 inches. Compression ratio: 10.5:1. Brake hp: 320 at 4600 rpm. Carburetion: Holley four-barrel. Five main bearings. Serial number code 'Z.'

CHASSIS FEATURES: Wheelbase: 108 inches. Overall length: 183.6 inches. Tires: 6.95 x 14 four-ply tubeless blackwall.

OPTIONS: 200 hp V-8 ($106). 225 hp V-8 ($158). 271 hp V-8, included with GT Equipment Group, ($434). 320 hp V-8 ($264). Cruise-O-Matic three-speed automatic transmission, with six-cylinder ($188); with 200 and 225 hp V-8s ($198); with 271 and 320 hp V-8s ($232). Four-speed manual transmission; with six-cylinder or 225 hp V-8 ($184); with other V-8s ($233). Heavy-duty three-speed manual, required with 390 V-8 ($79). Power front disc brakes ($65). Power steering ($84). Power top, convertible ($53). GT Equipment Group, V-8s only ($205). Limited-slip differential ($42). Competition Handling Package, with GT Group only) ($62). Styled-steel wheels, 2+2 ($94); other models ($115). Tinted windows and windshield ($30). Convenience control panel ($40). Fingertip speed control, V-8 and Cruise-O-Matic required, ($71). Remote-control left door mirror, standard 2+2 ($10). Safety-glass rear window, convertible ($32). Select-Aire conditioning ($356). Push-button AM radio ($58). Push-button AM/FM radio ($134). Stereo-Sonic tape system, AM radio required ($128). "Sport Deck" option with folding rear seat and access door for 2+2 ($65). Full-width front seat, not available with 2+2 ($24). Tilt-Away steering wheel ($60). Deck lid luggage rack, not available on 2+2 ($32). Comfort-weave vinyl trim, not available on convertible ($25). Center console, radio ($50). Deluxe steering wheel ($32). Exterior Decor Group ($39). Lower back panel grille ($19). Interior Decor Group for convertible ($95), for other models ($108). Two-tone paint, lower back grille ($13). Accent stripe ($14). Vinyl roof, hardtop ($74). Wheelcovers, standard on 2+2 ($21). Wire wheelcovers, 2+2 ($58); other models ($80). Typical whitewall tire option ($33). Rocker panel moldings, standard on 2+2 ($16). Magic-Aire heater delete option ($32 credit).

HISTORICAL FOOTNOTES: The 1967 Mustang was introduced Sept. 30, 1966. Model year output peaked at 472,121 units. Dealer sales totaled 377,827 units, a 31.2 percent decline due to increased competition in the sports/personal car market, plus a strike in the final business quarter. Henry Ford II was chairman of Ford Motor Co. Mustang's creator, Lee Iacocca, was an executive vice-president in charge of North American Operations and was definitely on his way up to the corporate ladder, thanks to the success his 'Pony Car' had seen. Meanwhile, at Ford Corp., J.B. Naughton moved up to the slot of vice-president and general sales manager. About seven percent of all 1967 Mustangs had four-speed manual transmissions; 98 percent had bucket seats; nearly 15 percent vinyl tops and some 16 percent air conditioning. A rare feature was dual exhausts, found only on about 25,000 cars.

1968 MUSTANG

1968 Ford Mustang, two-door convertible, V-8

MUSTANG SERIES — (ALL ENGINES) — The 1968 Mustang continued to use the same body shell introduced the previous year, with minor trim changes. The Mustang emblem appeared to float in the center of the grille, with no horizontal or vertical bars attached to the emblem. Also, the side scoop had much cleaner chrome trim than the previous year, with no horizontal stripes connected to it.

VEHICLE I.D. NUMBERS — VIN stamped on aluminum tab on instrument panel, viewable through windshield. First symbol 8=1968. Second symbol indicates assembly plant: F=Dearborn, Mich.; R=San Jose, Calif.; T=Metuchen, N.J. Third and fourth symbols equated to Body Style Number: 63A=bucket seat fastback; 65A=bucket seat hardtop; 76A=bucket seat convertible; 63B=bucket or bench seat luxury fastback; 65B=bucket seat luxury hardtop; 76B=bucket or bench seat luxury convertible; 65C=bench seat hardtop; 76D= bench seat luxury hardtop; and 63D=bench seat luxury fastback. Fifth symbol indicates engine: T=200 cid/115 hp six; 2=200 cid six export; C=289 cid/195 hp V-8; J=302/230 hp V-8; X=390 cid/280 hp V-8; S=390 cid/325 hp; W=427 cid/390 hp V-8; G=302 cid/306 hp V-8; R=428 cid/335 hp Cobra-Jet V-8. The next six symbols are the sequential production number beginning at 100001 for each series at each factory. Body Number Plate located on left front door lock face indicates serial number, Body Style Number, color, trim, District Code, DSO Number, axle and transmission.

MUSTANG SERIES

Model Number	Body/Style Number	Body Type & Seating	Factory Price	Shipping Weight	Production Total
NA	65A	2-dr HT Cpe-4P	2602	2635	249,447
NA	63A	2-dr FsBk Cpe-4P	2712	2659	42,325
NA	76A	2-dr Conv-4P	2814	2745	25,376

NOTE 1: Total series output was 317,148 units. This figure included 9,009 Deluxe hardtops; 6,113 hardtops equipped with bench seats; 7,661 Deluxe fastbacks; 256 fastbacks equipped with bench seats; 853 Deluxe hardtops equipped with bench seats and 3,339 Deluxe convertibles.

ENGINES

MUSTANG SIX-CYLINDER: Overhead valves. Cast iron block. Displacement: 200 cid. Bore and stroke: 3.68 x 3.13 inches. Compression ratio: 8.8:1. Brake hp: 115 at 3800 rpm. Carburetion: Autolite model C80F-9510-E one-barrel. Seven main bearings. Serial number code 'T.'

CHALLENGER 289 V-8: Overhead valves. Cast iron block. Displacement: 289 cid. Bore and stroke: 4.00 x 2.87 inches. Compression ratio: 8.7:1. Brake hp: 195 at 4600 rpm. Carburetion: Autolite model C8AF-9510-AF two-barrel. Five main bearings. Serial number code 'C.'

302 FOUR-BARREL V-8: Overhead valve. Cast iron block. Displacement: 302 cid. Bore and stroke: 4.00 x 3.00 inches. Compression ratio: 10.0:1. Brake hp: 230 at 4800 rpm. Carburetion: Motorcraft four-barrel. Five main bearings. Serial number code 'J.'

302 HIGH-PERFORMANCE V-8: Overhead valve. Cast iron block. Displacement: 302 cid. Bore and stroke: 4.00 x 3.00 inches. Compression ratio: 10.0:1. Brake hp: 306 at 4800 rpm. Carburetion: Motorcraft four-barrel. Five main bearings. Serial number code' G'(?).

390 V-8: Overhead valves. Cast iron block. Displacement: 390 cid. Bore and stroke: 4.05 x 3.78 inches. Compression ratio: 10.5:1. Brake hp: 280 at 4800 rpm. Carburetion: Holley four-barrel. Five main bearings. Serial number code 'X.'

GT 390 V-8: Overhead valves. Cast iron block. Displacement: 390 cid. Bore and stroke: 4.05 x 3.78 inches. Compression ratio: 10.5:1. Brake hp: 325 at 4800 rpm. Carburetion: Holley four-barrel. Five main bearings. Serial number code 'S.'

HIGH-PERFORMANCE V-8: Overhead valves. Cast iron block. Displacement: 427 cid. Bore and stroke: 4.23 x 3.78 inches. Compression ratio: 10.9:1. Brake hp: 390 at 4600 rpm. Carburetion: Motorcraft four-barrel. Five main bearings. Serial number code 'W.'

COBRA JET 428 V-8: Overhead valves. Cast iron block. Displacement: 428 cid. Bore and stroke: 4.13 x 3.98 inches. Compression ratio: 10.7:1. Brake hp: 335 at 5600 rpm. Carburetion: Holley four-barrel. Five main bearings. Serial number code 'R.'

CHASSIS FEATURES: Wheelbase: 108 inches. Overall length: 183.6 inches. Tires: 6.95 x 14 four-ply tubeless blackwall (E70 x 14 four-ply tubeless blackwall, with Wide-Oval sport tire option).

OPTIONS: 289 cid two-barrel 195 hp V-8 ($106). 302-cid four-barrel 230 hp ($172). 390-cid four-barrel 325 hp V-8 ($158). 427-cid four-barrel 390 hp V-8 ($775). 428 cid four-barrel 335 hp Cobra-Jet V-8 ($245). Select-Shift Cruise-O-Matic three-speed automatic with six-cylinder ($19), with 289 V-8 ($201), with 390 V-8 ($233). Four-speed manual, not available with six-cylinder; with 289 V-8 ($184); with 390 V-8 ($233). Power front disc brakes, V-8s only, required with 390 V-8 or GT Equipment Group ($54). Power steering ($84). Power top, convertible ($53). GT Equipment Group, 230 or 325 hp V-8s with power brakes, not available with Sports Trim Group of optional wheelcovers, ($147). Tachometer, V-8s only ($54). Limited-slip differential, V-8s only ($79). Glass backlight, convertible ($39). Tinted glass ($30). Convenience Group, console required with Select-Aire ($32) Fingertip speed control, V-8 and Select-Shift required ($74). Remote-control left door mirror ($10). Select-Aire conditioner ($360). Push-button AM radio ($360). AM/FM stereo radio ($61). Stereo-Sonic Tape System, AM radio required, ($181). Sport deck rear seat, 2+2 only ($65). Full-width front seat, hardtop and 2+2 only, not available with console, ($32). Tilt-Away steering wheel ($66). Center console, radio required ($54). Interior Decor Group in convertibles and models with full-width front seat ($110), in others without full-width front seat ($124). Two-tone hood paint ($19). Accent paint stripe ($14). Vinyl roof, hardtop ($74). Wheelcovers, not available with GT or V-8 Sports Trim Group ($34). Whitewall tires ($33).

HISTORICAL FOOTNOTES: The 1968 Mustangs were introduced in September 1967. Model year production peaked at 317,148 units. The 427-powered Mustang was capable of moving from 0-60 mph in around six seconds. The price for this motor was $775 above that of the base Mustang V-8. The 427 was rare, but 428 V-8s were installed in 2,854 Mustangs built this model year. Side marker lights and other new federally mandated safety features were required on all Mustangs built this year. Ford went through a 60 day strike from late September to late November, 1967. This had a negative effect on sales and production. A very collectible model-option produced this year was the highly sought after "California Special" a variant of the coupe with special features like Shelby-type taillights. There was also the "High-Country Special," a similar regional edition model, produced for the Colorado Sales Zone.

1969 MUSTANG

MUSTANG SERIES — (ALL ENGINES) — The Mustang was different for 1969. It was enlarged considerably and significantly restyled for the new year. For the first time, Mustangs had quad headlights, the outboard units being mounted in deeply recessed openings at the outer edges of the fenders. The inboard units were mounted inside the grille opening. The side scoop was now located high on the rear fenders of fastback models. It was in the same location as before on the hardtops and convertibles, but now faced rearward. High-performance was the theme for Ford in 1969 and the hot new Mustangs were in the spotlight. The sizzling Mach I came with a 351 cid V-8 as standard equipment. The 390 cid V-8 and 428 CJ V-8 engines were optional. Trans-Am road racing was very popular at this time. To compete with the Chevrolet Camaro race cars, Ford introduced the famous and powerful Boss 302 Mustang. The top engine option for 1969 Mustangs became the incredibly awesome and huge Boss 429. Even though these monsters came with a factory horsepower rating of 375, actual output was much higher. They were definitely not machines for the weak-spirited individual. Only now, after being out of production for more than 24 years, is the true potential of these engineering masterpieces being fully realized.

VEHICLE I.D. NUMBERS — VIN stamped on aluminum tab on instrument panel, viewable through windshield. First symbol 9=1969. Second symbol indicates assembly plant: F=Dearborn, Mich.; R=San Jose, Calif.; T=Metuchen, N.J. Third and fourth symbols equated to Body Style Number: 63A=bucket or high-back bucket seat fastback; 65A=bucket seat or high-back bucket seat hardtop; 76A=bucket or high-back bucket seat convertible; 63B=bucket or high-back bucket seat luxury fastback; 65B=bucket seat or high-back bucket seat luxury hardtop; 76B=bucket or high-back bucket seat luxury convertible; 63C=high-back bucket seat Mach I; 65C=bench seat luxury hardtop; 65D= bench seat luxury hardtop; and 65E=bucket seat Grande hardtop. Fifth symbol indicates engine: T=200 cid/119 hp six; 2=200 cid six export; F=302 cid/220 hp V-8; 6=302 cid export V-8; H=351 cid/250 hp V-8; M=351 cid/290 hp V-8; S=390 cid/320 hp V-8; Q=428 CJ/335 hp V-8/R=428 SCJ/335 hp Ram-Air V-8; G=Boss 302 cid/290 hp V-8; and Z=429 cid/370 hp V-8. The next six symbols are the sequential production number beginning at 100001 for each series at each factory. Body Number Plate located on left front door lock face indicates serial number, Body Style Number, color, trim, District Code, DSO Number, axle and transmission.

1969 Ford Mustang, Grande two-door hardtop sports coupe, V-8

MUSTANG SERIES

Model Number	Body/Style Number	Body Type & Seating	Factory Price	Shipping Weight	Production Total
NA	65A	2-dr HT Cpe-4P	2618/2723	2690	127,954
NA	63A	2-dr FsBk Cpe-4P	2618/2723	2713	61,980
NA	76A	2-dr Conv-4	2832/2937	2800	14,746
NA	65E	2-dr Grande HT-4P	2849/2954	2981	22,182
NA	63C	2-dr Mach I FsBk-4P	/3122	3175	72,458

NOTE 1: Total series output was 299,824 units.
NOTE 2: Series output included 5,210 Deluxe hardtops; 4,131 hardtops equipped with bench seats; 5,958 Deluxe fastbacks; 504 Deluxe hardtops equipped with bench seats and 3,439 Deluxe convertibles.

ENGINES

MUSTANG SIX-CYLINDER: Overhead valves. Cast iron block. Displacement: 200 cid. Bore and stroke: 3.68 x 3.13 inches. Compression ratio: 8.8:1. Brake hp: 115 at 3800 rpm. Carburetion: Motorcraft one-barrel. Seven main bearings. Serial number code 'T.'

302 V-8: Overhead valves. Cast iron block. Displacement: 320 cid. Bore and stroke: 4.00 x 3.00 inches. Compression ratio: 9.5:1. Brake hp: 220 at 4600 rpm. Carburetion: Motorcraft two-barrel. Five main bearings. Serial number code 'F.'

302 V-8: Overhead valves. Cast iron block. Displacement: 320 cid. Bore and stroke: 4.00 x 3.00 inches. Compression ratio: 10.5:1. Brake hp: 290 at 5000 rpm. Carburetion: Motorcraft four-barrel. Five main bearings. Serial number code 'G' (export).

351 V-8: Overhead valve. Cast iron block. Displacement: 351 cid. Bore and stroke: 4.00 x 3.50 inches. Compression ratio: 9.5:1. Brake hp: 250 at 4600 rpm. Carburetion: Motorcraft two-barrel. Five main bearings. Serial number code 'H.'

351 FOUR-BARREL V-8: Overhead valves. Cast iron block. Displacement: 351 cid. Bore and stroke: 4.00 x 3.50 inches. Compression ratio: 10.7:1. Brake hp: 290 at 4800 rpm. Carburetion: Motorcraft four-barrel. Five main bearings. Serial number code 'M.'

390 GT V-8: Overhead valves. Cast iron block. Displacement: 390 cid. Bore and stroke: 4.05 x 3.78 inches. Compression ratio: 10.5:1. Brake hp: 320 at 4600 rpm. Carburetion: Holley four-barrel. Five main bearings. Serial number code 'S.'

COBRA JET 428 V-8: Overhead valves. Cast iron block. Displacement: 428 cid. Bore and stroke: 4.13 x 3.98 inches. Compression ratio: 10.6:1. Brake hp: 335 at 5200 rpm. Carburetion: Holley four-barrel. Five main bearings. Serial number code 'Q.'

SUPER COBRA JET 428 V-8: Overhead valves. Cast iron block. Displacement: 428 cid. Bore and stroke: 4.13 x 3.98 inches. Compression ratio: 10.5:1. Brake hp: 360 at 5400 rpm. Carburetion: Holley four-barrel. Ram-Air induction. Five main bearings. Serial number code 'R.'

BOSS 429 V-8: Overhead valves. Cast iron block. Displacement: 429 cid. Bore and stroke: 4.36 x 3.59 inches. Compression ratio: 11.3:1. Brake hp: 370 at 5600 rpm. Carburetion: Holley four-barrel Five main bearings. Serial number code 'Z.'

CHASSIS FEATURES: Wheelbase: 108 inches. Overall length: 187.4 inches. Tires: C78 x 14 four-ply tubeless blackwall (E78 x 14 four-ply on small V-8 equipped models and F70 x 14 four-ply on large V-8 equipped models).

OPTIONS: 302-cid two-barrel 220 hp V-8, not available in Mach I, ($105). 351-cid two-barrel 250 hp V-8, standard in Mach I ($163 in other models). 351-cid four-barrel 290 hp V-8, in Mach I ($26); in other models ($189). 390-cid four-barrel 320 hp V-8, in Mach I ($100); in other models ($158). 428-cid four-barrel 335 hp V-8, in Mach I ($224); in other models ($288). 428-cid four-barrel Cobra Jet V-8 including Ram Air, in Mach I ($357), in other models ($421). Select-Shift Cruise-O-Matic transmission; six-cylinder engines ($191); 302 and 351 V-8s ($201); 390 and 428 V-8s ($222). Four-speed manual; 302 and 351 V-8s ($205); 390 and 428 V-8s ($254). Power disc brakes, not available with 200-cid inline six, ($65). Power steering ($95). Power top. convertible ($53). GT Equipment Group, not available on Grande or with six-cylinder or 302-cid V-8, ($147). Tachometer, V-8s only ($54). Handling suspension, not available on Grande or with six-cylinder and 428 V-8 engines, ($31). Competition suspension, standard Mach I and GT; 428 V-8 required, ($31). Glass backlight, convertible ($39). Limited-slip differential, 250 inline six and 302 V-8 ($42). Traction-Lok differential, not available sixes and 302 V-8s ($64). Intermittent windshield wipers ($17). High-back front bucket seats, not available in Grande, ($85). Color-keyed dual racing mirrors, standard in Mach I and Grande, ($19). Power ventilation, not available with Select-Aire ($40). Electric clock, standard Mach I and Grande ($16). Tinted windows and windshield ($32). Speed control, V-8 and automatic transmission required ($74). Remote-control left door mirror ($13). Select-Aire conditioner, not available 200 inline six or 428 V-8 with four-speed ($380). Push-button AM radio ($61). AM/FM stereo radio ($181). Stereo-Sonic tape system, AM radio required ($134). Rear seat speaker, hardtop and Grande ($13). Rear seat deck, Sportsroof and Mach I ($97). Full-width front seat, hardtop, not available with console. ($32). Tilt-Away steering wheel ($66). Rim-Blow Deluxe steering wheel ($36). Console ($54). Interior Decor Group, not available on Mach I and Grande ($101), with dual racing mirrors ($88). Deluxe interior Decor Group. Sportsroof and convertible ($133), with dual racing mirrors ($120). Deluxe seat belts with reminder light ($16). Vinyl roof, hardtop ($84). Wheelcovers, not available on Mach I, Mustang GT or

Grande, but included with exterior Decor Group. ($21). Wire wheelcovers, not available Mach I and Mustang GT; standard on Grande, with Exterior Decor Group ($58), without Exterior Decor Group ($80). Exterior Decor Group, not available on Mach I and Grande, ($32). Chrome styled steel wheels, standard on Mach I; not available on Grande or with 200 inline six ($117); with GT Equipment Group ($78); with Exterior Decor Group ($95). Adjustable head restraints, not available on Mach I, ($17).

HISTORICAL FOOTNOTES: The 1969 Mustangs were introduced in September 1968. Model year production peaked at 299,824 units. Bunkie Knudsen was the chief executive officer of the company this year. The new fastback styling was called the "Sportsroof" treatment. The fantastic Boss 302 Mustang was styled and detailed by Larry Shinoda. Its standard equipment included the special competition engine; staggered shock absorbers: heavy-duty springs; CJ four-speed gearbox; power front disc brakes; heavy-duty rear drums: special ignition system (with high rpm cut-out feature); and F60 x 15 Goodyear Polyglas tires. A total of 1,934 Boss 302 Mustangs were built, almost twice as many as needed to qualify the model for SCCA Trans-Am racing.

1970 MUSTANG

1970 Ford Mustang, 'Boss 302' two-door Sportsroof coupe, V-8

MUSTANG SERIES — (ALL ENGINES) — For 1970, Mustangs were slightly revised versions of the 1969 models. The biggest change was the return to single headlights. They were located inside the new, larger grille opening. Simulated air intakes were seen where the outboard lights were on the 1969 models. The rear was also slightly restyled. There were flat taillight moldings and a flat escutcheon panel, taking the place of the concave panel and lights used in 1969. The year 1970 saw the introduction of the famous 351 'Cleveland' V-8 engine, in two-barrel and four-barrel configurations. Standard equipment in Mustangs included vinyl high-back bucket seats; carpeting; floor-mounted shift lever; instrument gauges; E78 x 15 tires; and either the '200' six or the '302' V-8. The Grande came with all above, plus Deluxe two-spoke steering wheel; color-keyed racing mirrors; wheelcovers; electric clock; bright exterior moldings; dual outside paint stripes; and luxury trim bucket seats. Convertibles had power-operated tops. The Mach I featured vinyl buckets; hood scoop; competition suspension; color-keyed racing mirrors; console-mounted shift controls; Deluxe steering wheel with rim-blow feature; rocker panel moldings; rear deck lid tape stripe; deep-dish sport wheelcovers; carpeting; E70-15 fiberglass-belted whitewall tires; and the 250 hp 351 cid two-barrel V-8. The Mustang Boss 302 had, in addition to the above, quick-ratio steering, functional front spoiler and Space Saver spare tire.

VEHICLE I.D. NUMBERS — VIN stamped on top of dash on driver side, viewable through windshield. First symbol 0=1970. Second symbol indicates assembly plant: F=Dearborn, Mich.; R=San Jose, Calif.; T=Metuchen, N.J. Third and fourth symbols equated to Body Style Number: 63A=bucket seat Sportsroof; 65A=bucket seat hardtop; 76A=bucket convertible; 63C=Mach I Sportsroof; 65E=bucket seat Grande hardtop. Fifth symbol indicates engine (See engine list below). The next six symbols are the sequential production number beginning at 100001 for each series at each factory. Vehicle Certification Label attached to driver's door has VIN, body code, color code, trim code, transmission code, rear axle code and special equipment codes.

MUSTANG SERIES

Model Number	Body/Style Number	Body Type & Seating	Factory Price	Shipping Weight	Production Total
NA	65B	2-dr HT Cpe-4P	2721/2822	2721/2923	82,569
NA	63B	2-dr FsBk-4P	2771/2872	2745/2947	45,934
NA	76B	2-dr Conv-4P	3025/3126	2831/3033	7,673
NA	65E	2-dr Grande-4P	2926/3028	2806/3008	13,581
NA	63C	2-dr Mach I-4P	3271	3240	40,970
NA	63	2-dr Boss 302	3720	3227	6,318

NOTE 1: Total series output was 190,727.
NOTE 2: Data above slash for six/below slash for V-8.

ENGINES

MUSTANG SIX-CYLINDER: Overhead valves. Cast iron block. Displacement: 200 cid. Bore and stroke: 3.68 x 3.13 inches. Compression ratio: 8.8:1. Brake hp: 115 at 3800 rpm. Carburetion: Motorcraft one-barrel. Seven main bearings. Serial number code 'T.'

FORD SIX-CYLINDER: Overhead valves. Cast iron block. Displacement: 250 cid. Bore and stroke: 3.68 x 3.91 inches. Compression ratio: 9.0:1. Brake hp: 155 at 4400 rpm. Carburetion: Motorcraft one-barrel. Seven main bearings. Serial number code 'L.'

302 V-8: Overhead valves. Cast iron block. Displacement: 302 cid. Bore and stroke: 4.00 x 3.00 inches. Compression ratio: 9.5:1. Brake hp: 220 at 4600 rpm. Carburetion: Motorcraft two-barrel. Five main bearings. Serial number code 'F.'

BOSS 302 V-8: Overhead valves. Cast iron block. Displacement: 302 cid. Compression ratio: 10.6:1. Brake hp: 290 at 5800 rpm. Carburetion: Holley four-barrel. Five main bearings.

351 V-8: Overhead valves. Cast iron block. Displacement: 351 cid. Bore and stroke: 4.00 x 3.50 inches. Compression ratio: 9.5:1. Brake hp: 250 at 4600 rpm. Carburetion: Motorcraft two-barrel. Five main bearings. Serial number code 'H.'

351 FOUR-BARREL V-8: Overhead valves. Cast iron block. Displacement: 351 cid. Bore and stroke: 4.00 x 3.50 inches. Compression ratio: 11.0:1. Brake hp: 300 at 5400 rpm. Carburetion: Motorcraft four-barrel. Five main bearings.

COBRA JET 428 V-8: Overhead valve. Cast iron block. Displacement: 428 cid. Bore and stroke: 4.13 x 3.98 inches. Compression ratio: 10.6:1. Brake hp: 335 at 5200 rpm. Carburetion: Holley four-barrel. Five main bearings. Serial number code 'Q.'

SUPER COBRA JET 428 V-8: Overhead valves. Cast iron block. Displacement: 428 cid. Bore and stroke: 4.13 x 3.98 inches. Compression ratio: 10.5:1. Brake hp: 360 at 5400 rpm. Carburetion: Holley four-barrel. Five main bearings. Serial number code 'R.'

BOSS 429 V-8: Overhead valves. Cast iron block. Displacement: 429 cid. Bore and stroke: 4.36 x 3.59 inches. Compression ratio: 11.3:1. Brake hp: 375 at 5600 rpm. Carburetion: Holley four-barrel Five main bearings. Serial number code 'Z.'

CHASSIS FEATURES: Wheelbase: 108 inches. Overall length: 187.4 inches. Tires: C78 x 14 four-ply tubeless blackwall (E78 x 14 four-ply on cars equipped with small V-8s and F70 x 14 four-ply on those with large V-8s). Boss 302 and Boss 429s used F70 x 15 tires.

OPTIONS: 250 hp 351 cid V-8, in Mach I (standard), in other Mustangs ($45). 300 hp 351 cid V-8 in Mach I ($48), in other Mustangs ($93). 335 hp 428 cid Cobra-Jet V-8 engine with Ram-Air induction, in Mach I ($376), in other Mustangs ($421). Cruise-O-Matic automatic transmission ($222). Four-speed manual transmission ($205). Power steering ($95). Power front disc brakes ($65). Limited-slip differential ($43). Styled steel wheels ($58). Magnum 500 chrome wheels ($129). AM radio ($61). AM/FM stereo radio ($214). AM/8-track stereo ($134). Center console ($54). Tilt steering wheel ($45). Exterior Decor group ($78). Vinyl roof ($84), on Grande ($26). Wheelcovers ($26). Rocker panel moldings ($16).

HISTORICAL FOOTNOTES: The 1970 Mustangs were introduced in September 1969. Model year production peaked at 190,727 units. Bunkie Knudsen was the chief executive officer of the company this year, but was in his last year at the helm. Ford Motor Co. chairman Henry Ford II fired Knudsen in 1971. Knudsen, of course, was famous for creating Pontiac's 'performance image' in the early 1960s. Part of his problem at FoMoCo was that auto sales were becoming less relative to high-performance marketing techniques in the early 1970s. For example, Ford ceased its official racing activities late in the 1970 calendar year. Others, however, suggested that Knudsen was the victim of Ford's traditional family controlled management system. He had tried to overstep the limits of his power and, for doing this, was dismissed on short notice. Before getting out of racing, Ford took the 1970 Trans-Am title with the Mustang.

1971 MUSTANG

1971 Ford Mustang, 'Boss 351' two-door Sportsroof coupe, V-8

MUSTANG SERIES — (ALL ENGINES) — The 1971 Mustangs were completely restyled. They were over two inches longer and had a new hood and concealed windshield wipers. The styling left little doubt that the cars were Mustangs, but they were lower, wider and heavier than any previous models. A full-width grille, incorporating the headlights within its opening, was used The Mustang corral was again seen in the center. The roof had a thinner appearance. New door handles fit flush to the body. New on the options list were the Special Instrumentation Group package; electric rear window defogger; and a Body Protection Group package that included side moldings and front bumper guards. The fastback-styled 'Sportsroof' was now available dressed in a vinyl top. Sadly, two of the most exotic engines were gone. The Boss 302 and Boss 429 power plants bit the dust. Although rumors persist that five cars were assembled with the 'Boss 429,' they are unconfirmed. There was a new Boss 351 Mustang that provided a more refined package, with a better weight distribution layout than the front-heavy Boss 429. Standard equipment on base Mustangs included color-keyed nylon carpeting; floor-shift; high-back bucket seats; steel guardrail door construction; DirectAire ventilation system; concealed windshield wipers with cowl air inlets; mini console with ashtray: armrests; courtesy lights; cigar lighter; heater and defroster; all-vinyl interior; glove box; E78-14 belted black sidewall tires; power convertible top; and either the 250 cid six or 302 cid V-8. The Mustang Grande coupe had the same basic features, plus bright pedal pads; Deluxe high-back bucket seats in cloth trim; Deluxe instrument panel; Deluxe two-spoke steering wheel; electric clock; molded trim panels with integral pull handles and armrests; right rear quarter panel trim with ashtray; dual paint accent stripes; dual color-keyed racing mirrors (left remote-control); rocker panel moldings; vinyl roof; wheelcovers; and wheel lip moldings. The Mustang Mach I had all of the basic equipment, plus color-keyed spoiler; hood moldings; fender moldings; and racing mirrors; a unique grille with Sportlamps; competition suspension; trim rings and hubcaps; high-back bucket seats; honeycomb texture back panel applique; pop-open gas cap; deck lid paint stripe; black or Argent Silver finish on lower bodysides (with bright molding at upper edge); E70 x 14 whitewalls; and the two-barrel 302 cid V-8. A NASA styled hood scoop treatment was a no-cost option. The Mustang Boss 351 had even more extras. In addition to the basic equipment, this model featured a functional NASA hood scoop; black or Argent Silver painted hood; hood lock pins; Ram-Air engine call-outs; color-keyed racing

mirrors (left remote-controlled); unique grille with Sportslamps; hubcaps with trim rings; bodyside tape stripes in black or Argent Silver; color-keyed hood and front fender moldings; Boss 351 call-out nomenclature; dual exhausts; power disc brakes; Space Saver spare tire; competition suspension with staggered rear shocks; 3.91:1 rear axle gear ratio with TractionLok differential; electronic rpm limiter; functional front spoiler (finished in black and shipped 'knocked-down'); 80 ampere battery; Instrumentation Group; F60-15 RWL tires; 330 hp High-Output 351 cid V-8 with four-barrel carburetion; special cooling package; and wide-ratio four-speed manual gearbox with Hurst shifter.

VEHICLE I.D. NUMBERS — VIN stamped on top of dash on driver side, viewable through windshield. First symbol 1=1971. Second symbol indicates assembly plant: F=Dearborn, Mich.; T=Metuchen, N.J. Third and fourth symbols equated to Body Style Number: 65D=standard two-door hardtop; 63D=standard two-door Sportsroof; 76D=standard convertible; 65F=Grande hardtop; 63R=Mach I Sportsroof. Fifth symbol indicates engine (See engine list below). The next six symbols are the sequential production number beginning at 100001 for each series at each factory. Vehicle Certification Label attached to driver's door has VIN, body code, color code, trim code, transmission code, rear axle code and special equipment codes.

MUSTANG SERIES

Model Number	Body/Style Number	Body Type & Seating	Factory Price	Shipping Weight	Production Total
NA	65D	2-dr HT Cpe-4P	2911/3006	2937/3026	65,696
NA	63D	2-dr FsBk-4P	2973/3068	2907/2993	23,956
NA	76D	2-dr Conv-4P	3227/3322	3059/3145	6,121
NA	65F	2-dr Grande-4P	3117/3212	2963/3049	17,406
NA	63	2-dr Boss 351-4P	4124	3281	NA
NA	63R	2-dr Mach I	3268	3220	36,449

NOTE 1: Total series output was 149,678 units.
NOTE 2: Data above slash for six/below slash for V-8.

ENGINES

SIX-CYLINDER: Overhead valves. Cast iron block. Displacement: 250 cid. Bore and stroke: 3.68 x 3.91 inches. Compression ratio: 9.0:1. Brake hp: 145 at 4000 rpm. Carburetion: Motorcraft one-barrel. Seven main bearings. Serial number code 'L.'

302 V-8: Overhead valves. Cast iron block. Displacement: 302 cid. Bore and stroker 4.00 x 3.00 inches. Compression ratio: 9.0:1. Brake hp: 210 at 4600 rpm. Carburetion: Motorcraft two-barrel. Five main bearings. Serial number code 'F.'

351 V-8: Overhead valves. Cast iron block. Displacement: 351 cid. Bore and stroker 4.00 x 3.50 inches. Compression ratio: 9.0:1. Brake hp: 240 at 4600 rpm. Carburetion: Motorcraft two-barrel. Five main bearings. Serial number code 'H.'

351 'CLEVELAND' FOUR-BARREL V-8: Overhead valves. Cast iron block. Displacement: 351 cid. Bore and stroke: 4.00 x 3.50 inches. Compression ratio: 10.7:1. Brake hp: 285 at 5400 rpm. Carburetion: Holley four-barrel. Five main bearings. Serial number code 'M.'

BOSS 351 V-8: Overhead valves. Cast iron block. Displacement: 351 cid. Bore and stroke: 4.00 x 3.50 inches. Compression ratio: 11.1:1. Brake hp: 330 at 5400 rpm. Carburetion: Holley four-barrel. Five main bearings. Serial number code 'Q.'

COBRA JET 429 V-8: Overhead valves. Cast iron block. Displacement: 429 cid. Bore and stroke: 4.36 x 3.59 inches. Compression ratio: 11.3:1. Brake hp: 370 at 5400 rpm. Carburetion: Holley four-barrel. Five main bearings. Serial number code 'C'.

COBRA JET 429 V-8: Overhead valves. Cast iron block. Displacement: 429 cid. Bore and stroke: 4.36 x 3.59 inches. Compression ratio: 11.3:1. Brake hp: 370 at 5400 rpm. Carburetion: Holley four-barrel. Five main bearings.

SUPER COBRA JET 429 V-8: Overhead valves. Cast iron block. Displacement: 429 cid Bore and stroke: 4.36 x 3.59 inches. Compression ratio: 11.5:1. Brake hp 375 at 5600 rpm. Carburetion: Holley four-barrel (with Ram-Air induction). Five main bearings. Serial number code 'J'.

CHASSIS FEATURES: Wheelbase: 109 inches. Overall length: 187.5 inches. Tires: E78 X 14 belted blackwall.

OPTIONS: 240 hp 351 cid V-8 engine ($45). 285 hp 351 cid 'Cleveland' V-8 engine ($93). 370 hp Cobra Jet 429 cid V-8 engine ($372). Cruise-O-Matic automatic transmission ($217-$238). Four-speed manual transmission ($216). Power steering ($115). Power front disc brakes ($70). Limited-Slip differential ($48). Magnum 500 chrome wheels ($129). AM radio ($66). AM/FM stereo radio ($214). AM/8-track stereo ($129). Center console ($60). Electric rear window defogger ($48). NASA style hood scoops (no charge). Drag-Pac rear axle 3.91:1 ratio ($155); 4.11:1 ratio ($207). Vinyl roof ($26). White sidewall tires ($34).

HISTORICAL FOOTNOTES: The 1971 Mustang were introduced Sept. 19, 1970. Model year production peaked at 149,678 units. Calendar year sales of 127,062 cars were recorded. J.B. Naughton was the chief executive officer of the Ford Div. this year. This branch of the corporation was also known as Ford Marketing Corp. Of all Mustangs built in the model year 1971, some 5.3 percent had four-speed manual transmissions; 5.6 percent had stereo eight-track tape players; 1.9 percent; had power windows and 29 percent had vinyl roofs.

1972 MUSTANG

MUSTANG SERIES — (ALL ENGINES) — The Mustang was a very versatile package. The original of 1964-1/2 was promoted as a sports/personal car. Later, the Mustang became a luxury auto and, then, a high-performance machine. Actually, the basic car itself was changed very little in overall concept. Yet, for 1972, it was suddenly being called Ford's "Sports Compact." It came in five two-door styles, two hardtops, two Sportsroofs (fastbacks) and a convertible. Styling was generally unaltered, the only appearance refinements being a color-keyed front bumper and redesigned deck latch panel nameplate. The color-keyed bumper was standard on Mach Is, while other models continued to use chrome front bumpers as standard equipment. A lot of customers ordered the monochromatic bumpers at slight extra-cost. Instead of spelling Mustang in block letters on the rear, a chrome signature script was used. The powerful 429 cid V-8 was no longer offered. The Cleveland 351 cid four-barrel job was the hairiest power plant around. Standard equipment in all body styles included concealed wipers: rocker panel and wheel lip moldings; lower back panel applique with bright moldings; color-keyed dual racing mirrors; recessed exterior door handles; wheelcovers; DirectAire ventilation; heater and defroster; high-back bucket seats; and bonded door trim panels with pull-type handles and armrests. At this point, the specific equipment in different styles varied. The hardtop and Sportsroof featured carpeting; mini-consoles; courtesy lights; Deluxe two-spoke steering wheel with wood-toned inserts; three-speed floor shift; E78 x 14 black belted tires; and a base 250 cid six. In addition to all of this, the Sportsroof also featured fixed rear quarter windows (except with power lifts) and a tinted backlight. The Mustang convertible also had a five-ply power-operated top; color-keyed top boot; tinted windshield and glass backlight; bright, upper back panel moldings; knitted vinyl seat trim; molded door handles; and black instrument panel appliques. The Mustang Grande featured — in addition to the above — a vinyl top with Grande script nameplates; unique bodyside tape stripes; unique wheelcovers: floor mat in trunk; Lambeth cloth and vinyl interior trim; bright pedal moldings; Deluxe camera grain instrument panel with wood-toned appliques; panel mounted electric clock; and rear ashtrays. The Mach I Sportsroof featured the following standard extras: competition suspension; NASA type hood scoops (listed as a no-cost option on all Mach Is, but essentially standard for the model); front spoiler-type bumper; color-keyed hood and rear fender moldings; black grille with integral Sportslamps; black panel applique; black or Argent Silver painted lower body, front and rear valance panels; rear tape stripes with Mach I decals; wheel trim rings and hubcaps; E70 x 14 bias-belted whitewall tires; and '302' two-barrel V-8.

1972 Ford, Mustang two-door hardtop sports coupe, V-8

VEHICLE I.D. NUMBERS — VIN stamped on top of dash on driver side, viewable through windshield. First symbol 2=1972. Second symbol indicates assembly plant: F=Dearborn, Mich. Third and fourth symbols equated to Body Style Number: 65D=standard two-door hardtop; 63D=standard two-door Sportsroof; 76D=standard convertible; 65F=Grande hardtop; 63R=Mach I Sportsroof. Fifth symbol indicates engine (See engine list below). The next six symbols are the sequential production number beginning at 100001 for each series at each factory. Vehicle Certification Label attached to driver's door has VIN, body code, color code, trim code, transmission code, rear axle code and special equipment codes.

MUSTANG SERIES

Model Number	Body/Style Number	Body Type & Seating	Factory Price	Shipping Weight	Production Total
NA	65D	2-dr HT Cpe-4P	2729/2816	2941/3025	57,350
NA	63D	2-dr FsBk -4P	2786/2873	2909/2995	15,622
NA	76D	2-dr Conv-4P	3015/3101	3061/3147	6,401
NA	65F	2-dr Grande-4P	2915/3002	2965/3051	18,045
NA	63R	2-dr Mach I-4P	3053	3046	27,675

NOTE 1: Total series output was 125,405 units.
NOTE 2: Data above slash for six/below slash for V-8.

ENGINES

MAVERICK/MUSTANG/TORINO SIX-CYLINDER: Overhead valves. Displacement: 250 cid. Bore and stroke: 3.68 x 3.91 inches. Compression ratio: 8.0:1. Net hp: 98 at 3400 rpm. Carburetion: Motorcraft one-barrel. Seven main bearings. Serial number code 'L.'

302 V-8: Overhead valves. Cast iron block. Displacement: 302 cid. Bore and stroke: 4.00 x 3.00 inches. Compression ratio: 8.5:1. Net hp: 140 at 4000 rpm. Carburetion: Motorcraft two-barrel. Five main bearings. Serial number code 'F.'

351 'CLEVELAND' V-8: Overhead valves. Cast iron block. Displacement: 351 cid. Bore and stroke: 4.00 x 3.50 inches. Compression ratio: 8.6:1. Net hp: 163 at 3800 rpm. Carburetion: Motorcraft two-barrel. Five main bearings. Serial number code 'H.'

351 'CLEVELAND' FOUR-BARREL V-8: Overhead valves. Cast iron block. Displacement: 351 cid. Bore and stroke: 4.00 x 3.50 inches. Compression ratio: 8.6:1. Net hp: 248 at 5400 rpm. Carburetion: Holley tour-barrel. Five main bearings. Serial number code 'M.'

351 HO 'CLEVELAND' V-8: Overhead valves. Cast iron block. Displacement: 351 cid. Bore and stroke: 4.00 x 3.50 inches. Compression ratio: 8.6:1. Net hp: 266 at 5400 rpm. Carburetion: Holley four-barrel. Five main bearings. Serial number code 'Q.'

CHASSIS FEATURES: Wheelbase: 109 inches. Overall length: 190 inches. Width: 75 inches. Tires: E78 x 14. (Note: Additional tire sizes are denoted in text when used as standard equipment on specific models).

OPTIONS: 177 hp 351 cid Cleveland V-8 ($41). 266 hp 351 cid Cleveland V-8 engine ($115). 275 hp 351 cid High-Output V-8 with four-barrel carburetion ($841-$870). Cruise-O-Matic transmission ($204). Four-speed manual transmission ($193). Power steering 9$103). Power front disc brakes ($62). Limited-slip differential ($43). Magnum 500 chrome wheels ($108-$139). Center console ($53-$97). Vinyl roof ($79). White sidewall tires ($34).

HISTORICAL FOOTNOTES: The 1972 Mustangs were introduced Sept. 24, 1971. Calendar year sales, by United States dealers, stopped at 120,589 units, a decline from the previous season. Ford had already stopped building Mustangs in San Jose, Calif. in 1971. Now, the Metuchen, N.J. factory was converted to Pinto production, leaving the sole Mustang assembly line in Dearborn. This would not last long, though. Sales took a sudden leap from 127,062 to 238,077 units and Mustang II production was soon resumed at San Jose, Calif. Model year production stopped at 111,015 cars. Of these, 2.7 percent had four-speed manual transmission, 3.9 percent had Tilt-Telescope steering: 6.2 percent wore optional styled wheels and 32.3 percent had vinyl tops. There were no changes in top Ford management, although B.E. Bidwell would soon be elected vice president and general manager of Ford Marketing Corp.

1973 MUSTANG

1973 Ford, Mustang two-door convertible, V-8

MUSTANG SERIES — (ALL ENGINES) — The 1973 Mustangs were virtually the same as the 1972 models. The Mustang convertible was the only car of that body style still offered by Ford, as well as one of the few remaining ragtops in the entire industry. All Mustangs featured a high-impact molded urethane front bumper that was color-keyed to the body. One design change for the new season was a revised cross-hatch design in the grille. New Mustang exterior colors and interior trims were provided. New options included forged aluminum wheels and steel-belted radial-ply tires. Headlights, still of single-unit design, were housed inside square panels that flanked the grille on each side. New features of the grille itself included a 'floating' pony badge at the center and an eggcrate style insert with vertical parking lights in the outboard segments. A new front valance panel was of unslotted design. Standard equipment included the 250 cid six or 302 cid V-8; three-speed manual transmission; floor-mounted shift control; E78 x 14 black sidewall tires; rocker panel and wheel lip moldings; lower back panel applique with bright molding; chrome, rectangular left-hand door mirror; all-vinyl upholstery and door trim; mini front console; color-keyed loop-pile carpets; Deluxe two-spoke steering wheel (with woodtone insert); cigarette lighter; seat belt reminder system; and door courtesy lamps. The Sportsroof style also included a tinted back window and fixed rear quarter windows. The convertible added under-dash courtesy lights; power-operated vinyl top; glass backlight; knit-vinyl seat trim; and power front disc brakes. Standard extras on the Mustang Grande, in addition to base equipment, was comprised of dual, color-keyed racing mirrors; vinyl roof; bodyside tape striping; special wheelcovers; trunk mat; Lambeth cloth and vinyl seat trim; molded door panels with integral armrests; bright pedal pads; Deluxe instrument panel; and electric clock. Also available was the Mustang Mach I, which came with all of the following: competition suspension package; choice of two hood designs (one with NASA-type scoops); size E70-14 whitewall tires of bias-belted wide-oval construction; color-keyed dual racing mirrors; black grille and back panel appliques; back panel tape stripe; wheel trim rings and hubcaps; tinted back window; all-vinyl upholstery and trim (with high-back bucket seats); and the 136 SAE nhp version of the two-barrel 302 cid V-8.

VEHICLE I.D. NUMBERS — VIN stamped on top of dash on driver side, viewable through windshield. First symbol 3=1973. Second symbol indicates assembly plant: F=Dearborn, Mich.; R=San Jose, Calif. Third and fourth symbols equated to Body Style Number: 65D=standard two-door hardtop; 63D=standard two-door Sportsroof; 76D=standard convertible; 65F=Grande hardtop; 63R=Mach I Sportsroof. Fifth symbol indicates engine (See engine list below). The next six symbols are the sequential production number beginning at 100001 for each series at each factory. Vehicle Certification Label attached to driver's door has VIN, body code, color code, trim code, transmission code, rear axle code and special equipment codes.

MUSTANG SERIES

Model Number	Body/Style Number	Body Type & Seating	Factory Price	Shipping Weight	Production Total
NA	65D	2-dr HT Cpe-4P	2760/2847	2984/3076	51,430
NA	63D	2-dr FsBk-4p	2820/2907	2991/3083	10,820
NA	76D	2-dr Conv-4P	3102/3189	3106/3198	11,853
NA	65F	2-dr Grande-4P	2946/3033	2982/3074	25,274
NA	63R	2-dr Mach I-4P	3088	3090	35,440

NOTE 1: Total series output was 134,867 units.
NOTE 2: Data above slash for six/below slash for V-8.
NOTE 3: This year the Mach I could be had with a 250 cid six.

ENGINES

MUSTANG SIX-CYLINDER: Overhead valves. Cast iron block. Displacement: 250 cid. Bore and stroke: 3.68 x 3.91 inches. Compression ratio: 8.0:1. Net hp: 88 at 3200 rpm. Carburetion: Motorcraft single-barrel. Seven main bearings. Serial number code 'L.'

302 V-8: Overhead valves. Cast iron block. Displacement: 302 cid. Bore and stroke: 4.00 x 3.00 inches. Compression ratio: 8.0:1. Net hp: 135 at 4200 rpm. Carburetion: Motorcraft two-barrel. Five main bearings. Serial number code 'F.'

351 'WINDSOR' V-8: Overhead valves. Cast iron block. Displacement: 351 cid. Bore and stroke: 4.00 x 3.50 inches. Compression ratio: 8.0:1. Net hp: 156 at 3800 rpm. Carburetion: Motorcraft two-barrel. Five main bearings. Serial number code 'H.'

351 'CLEVELAND' V-8: Overhead valves. Cast iron block. Displacement: 351 cid. Bore and stroke: 4.00 x 3.50 inches. Compression ratio: 8.0:1. Net hp 154 at 4000 rpm. Carburetion: Motorcraft two-barrel. Five main bearings. Serial number code 'H.'

CHASSIS FEATURES: Wheelbase: 109 inches. Overall length: 194 inches. Width: 75 inches. Tires: E78 x 14. (Note: Additional tire sizes are denoted in text. when used as standard equipment on specific models).

OPTIONS: 302 cid two-barrel V-8, standard in Mach I, in other models ($87). 351 cid two-barrel V-8 ($128). 351 cid four-barrel V-8, including 55 amp alternator; heavy-duty 55 amp battery; special intake manifold; special valve springs and dampers; large-capacity 4300-D carburetor; 2.5 inch diameter dual exhaust outlets; modified camshaft and four-bolt main bearing caps. Requires Cruise-O-Matic 3.25 axle ratio or four-speed manual transmission. 3.50 axle combination, power front disc brakes and competition suspension ($194). California emission testing ($14). Select-Shift Cruise-O-Matic transmission ($204). Four-speed manual with Hurst shifter, not available with six-cylinder ($193). Power front disc brakes, standard convertible; required with 351 V-8s, ($62). Power windows ($113). Power steering, required with Tilt-Away steering wheel, ($103). Select-Aire conditioning, including extra cooling package; not available on six-cylinder with three-speed manual transmission ($368). Console, in Grande ($53), in other models ($68). Convenience Group, including trunk light; glove compartment light; map light; underhood light; 'lights on' warning buzzer; automatic seatback releases; under-dash courtesy lights (standard on convertible); parking brake warning light; and glove compartment lock ($46). Electric rear window defroster, not available with convertible or six-cylinder ($57). Tinted glass, convertible ($14), others ($36). Instrumentation Group, including tachometer, trip odometer and oil pressure, ammeter and temperature gauges; included with Mach I Sports Interior, not available on six-cylinders; in Grande without console ($55); in other models ($71). Color-keyed dual racing mirrors, standard Grande, Mach I ($23). AM radio ($59). AM/FM stereo radio ($191). Sport deck rear seat Sportsroof, Mach I only ($86). Deluxe three-spoke Rim-Blow steering wheel ($35). Tilt-Away steering wheel, power steering required ($41). Deluxe leather-wrapped two-spoke steering wheel ($23). Stereo-Sonic Tape System, AM radio required ($120). Intermittent windshield wipers ($23). Optional axle ratios ($12). Traction-Lok differential ($43). Heavy-duty 70 amp per hour battery, standard hardtop and convertible with 351 two-barrel in combination with Instrument Group or Select-Aire ($14). Extra-cooling package, standard with Select-Aire, not available on six-cylinder ($13). Dual Ram Induction, 351 two-barrel V-8, including functional NACA-type hood with black or argent two-tone paint, hood lock pins, 'Ram-Air' engine decals, ($58). Rear deck spoiler with Sportsroof or Mach I only ($29). Competition suspension, including extra heavy-duty front and rear springs, extra heavy-duty front and rear shock absorbers, standard with Mach I and not available with six-cylinder ($28). Deluxe seat and shoulder belts package, standard without shoulder belts in convertible ($15). Deluxe Bumper Group including rear rubber bumper inserts and full-width horizontal strip ($25). Rear bumper guards ($14). Decor Group, including black or argent lower bodyside paint with bright upper edge moldings; unique grille with sport lamps; trim rings with hubcaps; [deletes rocker panel and wheel lip moldings with Decor Group] ($51). Door edge guards, included with Protection Group, ($6). Color-keyed front floor mats ($13). Metallic Glow paint ($35). Two-tone hood paint, for Mach I ($18), for other models ($34). Protection Group, including vinyl-insert bodyside moldings; spare tire lock; door edge guards [deletes bodyside tape stripe] on Grande ($23); on other models ($36), but not available on Mach I or Mustangs with Decor Group. Vinyl roof on hardtops, including C-pillar tri-color ornament [standard on Grande] ($80). Three-quarter vinyl roof for Sportsroofs only ($52). Mach I Sports Interior, for Mach I and V-8 Sportsroof only, including knitted vinyl trim; high-back bucket sets with accent stripes; Instrumentation Group; door trim panels with integral pull handles and armrests; color-accented, deep-embossed carpet runners; Deluxe black instrument panel applique with wood-tone center section; bright pedal pads and rear seat ashtray ($115). Black or argent bodyside stripes, with Decor Group only ($23). Trim rings with hubcaps [standard on Mach I and Mustangs with Decor Group], for Grande ($8), for other models ($31). Sports wheelcovers on Grande ($56), on Mach I or Mustangs with Decor Group ($48), on other models ($79). Forged aluminum wheels on Grande ($119), on Mach I or Mustangs with Decor Group ($111), on other models ($142).

HISTORICAL FOOTNOTES: Most 1973 Mustangs, 90.4 percent were equipped with the automatic, 6.7 percent had the three-speed manual, 2.9 percent had the four-speed manual, 92.9 percent had power steering, 77.9 percent had power brakes; 5.6 percent had a tilting steering wheel, 62.8 percent had tinted glass, 3.2 percent had power windows and 56.2 percent were sold with an air conditioner.

1974 MUSTANG

1974 Ford, Mustang II two-door hatch back coupe, 4-cyl

MUSTANG II SERIES — (ALL ENGINES) — Ford Motor Co. introduced its all-new Mustang II in 1974. It was billed as the 'right car at the right time.' The new pony measured seven inches shorter than the original 1965 Mustang and was a full 13 inches shorter than the 1973. Sales of the new entry were sluggish at first, since the company loaded most cars in the early mix with a lot of optional equipment. It didn't take long, however, for the marketing men to see that the car had greatest appeal as an economy job. The Mustang II was a combination of design motifs derived from both sides of the Atlantic. The Italian coach building firm of Ghia, recently acquired by Ford Motor Co., did some of the primary design work. Other ingredients came straight from the Ford/Mercury/Lincoln styling studios. Four models were available, the notch back coupe, three-door fastback, Ghia notch back coupe and fastback Mach I. Standard equipment included a 2.3 liter four; four-speed manual transmission with floor shift; solid state ignition; front disc brakes; tachometer; steel-belted whitewalls; low-back front bucket seats; vinyl upholstery and door trim; color-keyed carpeting; wood-tone instrument panel applique; European type armrests; and full wheelcovers. The 2+2 model added a fold-down rear seat and styled steel wheels. The Ghia notch back coupe also had, in addition to the base equipment, color-keyed Deluxe seat belts; dual color-keyed remote-control door mirrors; Super Sound Package; shag carpeting; wood-tone door panel accents; digital clock; super-soft vinyl or Westminster cloth interior trim; color-keyed vinyl roof; and spoke-style wheel-

covers. The Mach I had all 2+2 equipment, plus 2.8-liter V-6 engine; dual color-keyed remote-control door mirrors; Wide-Oval steel-belted BSW radial tires; black lower bodyside paint; deck lid striping; and styled steel wheels with trim rings.

VEHICLE I.D. NUMBERS — (ALL ENGINES) — VIN on top of dash, driver's side, viewable through windshield and prefixed and suffixed with "F" for Ford. First symbol of actual VIN is 4=1974. Second symbol identifies assembly plant: F=Dearborn, Mich; R=San Jose, Calif. Third/fourth symbols indicate body: 02=notch back; 03=hatchback; 04=Ghia notch back; 05=Mach I notch back. Fifth symbol is the engine code. (See Engine section below). Last six digits are sequential production number starting at 100001 at each plant. Vehicle Certification Label attached to driver's door has VIN, body code, color code, trim code, transmission code, rear axle code and special equipment codes.

MUSTANG II SERIES

NA	60F	2-dr HT Cpe-4P	3081	2620	177,671
NA	69F	3-dr FsBk-4P	3275	2699	74,799
NA	60H	2-dr Ghia-4P	3427	2866	89,477
NA	69R	2-dr Mach I-4P	3621	2778	44,046

NOTE 1: Total series output was 385,993 units.

ENGINES

MUSTANG FOUR-CYLINDER: Overhead cam. Cast iron block. Displacement: 140 cid. Bore and stroke: 3.78 x 3.13 inches. Compression ratio: 8.6:1. SAE Net hp: 85. Carburetion: Motorcraft two-barrel. Five main bearings. Serial number code 'Y.'

MUSTANG V-6: Overhead valves. Cast iron block. Displacement: 169 cid. Bore and stroke: 3.66 x 2.70 inches. Compression ratio: 8.0:1. SAE Net hp 105. Carburetion: two-barrel. Serial number code 'Z.'

CHASSIS FEATURES: Wheelbase: 96.2 inches. Overall length: 175 inches. Tires: B78 x 13 belted blackwall (BR78 x 13 on Ghia model).

OPTIONS: 2.8-liter (171 cid) 105 hp V-6, standard in Mach I; in other Mustang IIs ($229). Select-Shift Cruise-O-Matic ($212). Convenience Group includes: dual color-keyed remote-control door mirrors; right visor vanity mirror; inside day/night mirror; parking brake boot and rear ashtray, on Mustangs with Luxury Interior Group ($41); on Mach I or Mustangs with Rallye Package ($21); on other Mustangs ($57). Light Group includes: underhood, glovebox, map, ashtray and instrument panel courtesy lights, plus trunk or cargo area courtesy light and warning lamps for parking brake, 'door ajar' and 'headlamps-on' ($44). Luxury Interior Group includes: super-soft vinyl upholstery; Deluxe door panels with large armrests and woodtone accents; Deluxe rear quarter trim; 25 ounce cut-pile carpeting; sound package; parking brake boot; door courtesy lamps; rear ashtray; standard in Ghia, in other Mustangs ($100). Maintenance Group includes: shop manual; spare bulbs; fire extinguisher; flares; warning flag; fuses; tire gauge; bungee cord; lube kit; trouble light; pliers; screwdriver and crescent wrench ($44). Rallye Package, 2.8 V-8 required [not available on Ghia], includes Traction-Lok differential; steel-belted RWL tires; extra-cooling package; competition suspension; dual color-keyed remote-control door mirrors; styled steel wheels; sport exhaust system; digital clock and leather-wrapped steering wheel; on Mach I ($150), on 2+2 ($284), on others ($328). Select-Aire conditioning ($383). Anti-theft alarm system ($75). Traction-Lok differential ($45). Heavy-duty battery ($14). Color-keyed Deluxe seat belts, standard in Ghia, in others ($17). Front and rear bumper guards ($37). Digital clock, standard in Ghia, in others ($36). Console ($43). Electric rear window defroster ($59). California emission equipment ($19). Full tinted glass ($37). Dual color-keyed door mirrors, standard in Ghia and Mach I, in others ($36). Rocker panel moldings ($14). Vinyl-insert bodyside moldings ($50). Glamour paint ($36). Pinstripes ($14). Power brakes ($45). Power steering ($106). Radios, AM ($61); AM/FM monaural. ($124); AM/FM stereo ($222); AM/FM stereo with tape player ($346). Competition suspension, including heavy-duty springs; adjustable shocks; rear anti-roll bar and 195/70 B/WL tires ($37). Flip-out quarter windows, for 2+2 and Mach I fastbacks only ($29). Vinyl roof, hardtop only; standard on Ghia; on other models ($83). Fold-down rear seat ($61). Super Sound Package, standard in Ghia; in others ($22). Leather-wrapped steering wheel ($30). Sun roof ($149). Luggage compartment trim ($28). Picardy velour cloth trim, Ghia ($62). Wheel trim rings, standard on Ghia; on others ($32).

HISTORICAL FOOTNOTES: The new Mustang II was initially released as a luxury sub-compact in mid-1973 and, by the end of model year 1974, had recorded an impressive record of 338,136 assemblies, which compared to only 193,129 sales of the 'big' Mustangs the previous model year.

1975 MUSTANG

MUSTANG II — (FOUR/SIX) — SERIES 0 — Throughout its five years of availability, the Mustang II would see very little change. A 'moonroof' option and extra-cost V-8 engine were the major revisions for 1975. The design of the steering wheel was modified. A two-spoke type was used again, but the spokes bent downwards at each end instead of running nearly straight across as in the 1974 models. Ghia models had a new roofline with thicker, 'blind' rear quarters. This made the opera windows somewhat smaller. Another Ghia addition was a stand-up hood ornament. New hubcaps were featured with most decor-levels and, on cars with catalytic converters, unleaded fuel decals were affixed to the gas filler cap. In midyear, several changes took effect. The first was a slightly plainer Ghia coupe with restyled hubcaps and no hood ornament. The second was the Mustang II MPG, an economy leader that gave 26-28 highway miles per gallon. Standard equipment on the basic notchback hardtop included solid state ignition; front disc brakes; tachometer; steel-belted BR78 x 13 black sidewall tires; low-back front bucket seats; vinyl upholstery and trim; wood-grained dash appliques: armrests: full wheelcovers; four-speed manual transmission with floor shift; and the 2.3 liter four. The standard 2+2 fastback added a fold-down rear seat and styled steel wheels. The Ghia coupe had all base equipment, plus Deluxe color-keyed seat belts; dual color-keyed, remote controlled OSRV door mirrors; radial whitewalls; Super Sound package; shag carpeting; wood-grained door accent panels; digital clock; choice of Westminster cloth or super-soft vinyl trim; color-keyed vinyl roof; and spokestyle wheelcovers. The Mach I fastback model had all equipment used on the 2+2, plus color-keyed remote-control OSRV door mirrors; steel-belted BR70 x 13 wide oval tires; black lower bodyside paint; specific rear deck lid striping; styled steel wheels with trim rings; and the 2.8 liter V-6 engine.

VEHICLE I.D. NUMBERS: Vehicle Identification Numbers were located on the top left hand surface of the instrument panel and had eleven symbols. The first symbol '5' designated 1975 model year. The second symbol designated the assembly plant. The third symbol 'O' designated Mustang. The fourth symbol designated the Body Style Number, as follows: '2' = two-door notch back coupe; '3' = three-door fastback coupe; '4' = two-door Ghia notch back coupe and '5' = two-door fastback Mach I coupe. The fifth symbol designated the engine. The last six symbols were the sequential unit number beginning at 100001 and up. The third and fourth Symbols in the VIN (first and second columns of the chart below) were the same as the Ford Model Number.

1975 Ford, Mustang II Ghia two-door coupe, 4-cyl

MUSTANG II SERIES

Model Number	Body/Style Number	Body Type & Seating	Factory Price	Shipping Weight	Production Total
MUSTANG II LINE					
0	2	2-dr Cpe-4P	3529/3801	2660/2775	85,155
0	3	3-dr FsBk Cpe-4P	3818/4090	2697/2812	30,038
0	4	2-dr Ghia Cpe-4P	3938/4210	2704/2819	52,320
MUSTANG II MACH 1 LINE					
0	5	3-dr FsBk Cpe-4P	4188	2879	21,062

NOTE 1: Data above slash for four-cylinder/below slash for V-6s.

MUSTANG II ENGINES

BASE 2.3 LITRE FOUR: Inline Four. Overhead valves and camshaft. Cast iron block. Displacement: 140 cid. Bore and stroke: 3.78 x 3.12 inches. SAE Net hp: 83. Hydraulic valve lifters. Carburetor: Motorcraft two-barrel Model 5200.

BASE 2.8 LITRE V-6: V-6. Overhead valves and camshaft. Cast iron block. Displacement: 170.8 inches. Bore and stroke: 3.66 x 2.70 inches. SAE Net hp: 97. Carburetor: Motorcraft two-barrel Model 5200.

OPTIONAL 5.0 LITRE V-8: V-8. Overhead valves. Cast iron block. Displacement: 302 cid. Bore and stroke: 4.002 x 3.00 inches. SAE Net hp: 122. Carburetor: Motorcraft two-barrel Model 2150.

CHASSIS FEATURES: Wheelbase: (all models) 96.2 inches. Overall length: (all models) 175 inches. Front tread: (all models) 55.6 inches. Rear tread: (all models) 55.8 inches. Tires: Refer to text.

OPTIONS: Exterior Accent Group ($151). Select-Aire conditioning ($401). Anti-Theft alarm system ($71). Deluxe color-keyed seat belts, in Ghia (standard); in other models ($51). Front and rear bumper guards ($31). Digital quartz electric clock ($37). Console ($63). Electric rear window defroster ($59). California emissions equipment ($41). Fuel monitor warning light ($14). Deck lid Luggage rack ($43). Dual color-keyed OSRV door mirrors, standard Ghia/Mach I, on others ($36). Rocker panel moldings ($14). Color-keyed vinyl insert type bodyside moldings ($51). Power steering ($111). Glass moonroof ($422). Radio, AM ($63); AM/FM ($124); AM/FM stereo ($213); same with 8-track ($333). Glamour paint ($43). Vinyl roof for hardtop coupe, standard with Ghia, on others ($83). Fold-down rear seat, standard in fastbacks, on others ($61). Leather-wrapped steering wheel ($30). Pin striping ($18). Sun roof ($195). Competition suspension, includes heavy-duty springs; adjustable shock absorbers; rear anti-roll bar; and 195-70 blackwall or White Line tires, on Ghia or others with Exterior Accent Group ($43), on Mach I ($25), on others ($55). Velour cloth interior trim ($63). Flip-out rear quarter windows, on fastbacks ($31). Four-speed manual transmission with floor shift (standard). Select-Shift Cruise-O-Matic ($227). Mach I 2.8 litre, 171 cid V-6 engine, in Mach I (no charge), in other models ($253). 5.0 litre, 302 cid V-8 engine, in Mach I ($172), in other models ($199). Traction-Lok differential ($46). Heavy-duty battery ($14). Extended range fuel tank ($18).

OPTION PACKAGES: Convenience-Group, includes dual, color-keyed, remote-controlled OSRV door mirrors; right-hand visor/vanity mirror; inside day/nite mirror; parking brake boot; and rear ashtray, with Luxury Interior Group ($48), on Mach I or models with Rallye Package or Exterior Accent Group ($29), on other models ($65). Light Group, includes underhood; glove box; ashtray; dashboard courtesy lights; plus map, door ajar and headlamps-on warning lights ($33). Security Lock Group, includes locking gas cap; inside hood release lock and spare tire lock ($14). Luxury Interior Group, includes Super-Soft vinyl seats; door trim with large armrests; Deluxe rear quarter trim; door courtesy lights; color-keyed seat belts; shag carpets; parking brake boot; rear ashtray and Super-Sound package ($100). Ghia Sliver Luxury Group, (for Ghia coupe only), includes Silver metallic paint; silver Normande-grain half-vinyl roof; stand-up hood ornament; Cranberry striping; Silver bodyside moldings; all-Cranberry interior in Media velour cloth; color-keyed sun visors and headliner; plus center console ($151). Maintenance Group, includes shop manual; bulbs; fire extinguisher; flares; warning flag; fuses; tire gauge; bungee cloth; lube kit; trouble light; pliers; screwdriver; and crescent wrench ($45). Rallye Package, includes Traction-Lok differential; 195/70 RWL tires; extra-cooling package; bright exhaust tips; competition suspension package; dual, color-keyed, remote-control OSRV door mirrors; leather-wrapped steering wheel; and styled steel wheels with trim rings, on Mach I ($168), on 2+2 ($218), on other models ($262). Protection Group, includes door edge guards; front floor mats; and license plate frames; on Mach I ($19), on others ($27).

HISTORICAL FOOTNOTES: The 1975 Mustang II lineup was introduced in Sept., 1974, with the plainer Ghia coupe and Mustang II MPG bowing at midyear. Model year production of 188,575 cars was recorded. Lee Iacocca was chief executive officer of the company this year. The new Mustang II V-8 was capable of a top speed above 105 mph and could cover the standing start quarter-mile in 17.9 seconds with a terminal speed of 77 mph.

STANDARD CATALOG OF
FRAZER
1947-1951

1948 Frazer, Manhattan four-door sedan, 6-cyl

The Frazer is considered the senior line of Kaiser-Frazer. This is because of the price differential, running $100 to $300 more than the equivalent Kaiser model. Frazer shared the same basic bodies with Kaiser from 1947 through 1950. It was designed by 'Dutch' Darrin, with some modifications by other stylists.

By G. Marshall Naul

The initial Frazer, for 1947, had a subdued grille. There was a Frazer crest, above block letters, indicating the make across the hood nose. The fenderlines ran from front through the rear wheels without a break in the line. The theme of horizontal lines was extended to the interior. There the instrument panel was arranged with instruments and controls in a straight line. In addition, there was a horizontal metal strip, over the glove compartment, with the name Frazer. The rear view was quite simple, with small taillights low on the rear fenders and an indentation in the trunk lid for the license plate. Although all Frazers used split windshield glass, the initial rear window was one-piece. The latter was rather shallow in height, giving less than ideal rear views. The bumpers for the 1947 Frazer were horizontally ribbed, where those of the Kaiser were not.

Early 1947 models were built late in May, 1946. The Frazer line consisted of a standard sedan and a more expensive ver-

sion called Manhattan, the latter costing nearly $400 more. The exact production figures for the 1949-50 Frazers are not known, but have been estimated from registration figures.

Very few changes were made for the 1948 model year. Of a very minor nature, were slightly higher compression, stiffer engine blocks, improvements to eliminate vapor lock and reduce vibration, wider tires (Goodyear Super-Cushion) and 28 new one- and two-tone color combinations. For 1948, Frazer accounted for only about 1.5 percent of the U.S. cars built.

Frazer's 1949-1950 models were facelifted. An unusual four-door convertible was added to the lineup. Among technical changes was use of a previously optional dual downdraft carburetor as standard equipment. It helped increase horsepower on all Frazers from 100 to 112.

For 1951, the last year of production, Frazer added two models instead of cutting back its offerings. One new product was based on a utility sedan called the Vagabond, the name and design being adopted from the 1949 Kaiser. This body type combined the features of a sedan with the flexibility of a station wagon. It was the first hatchback automobile. Other cars of the era used similar themes, but Kaiser and Frazer used a unique design of dual rear hatches. In this system, one panel folded-down to form a tailgate, while the upper hatch opened upward to give nearly complete floor to ceiling interior access. The rear seat in the Vagabond folded flat, for-

ward and backward, to give a level floor similar to a station wagon.

The second new model was a hardtop sedan, in the Manhattan line. This was similar to the Kaiser Virginian of the year before. Although padded tops were supposedly available, few were seen. Some were produced, though. These new body types, and indeed the entire 1951 Fraser production run, were built using leftover unsold 1949 and 1950 Kaiser and Frazer bodies.

Continued for 1951 was the convertible sedan. It was not a popular model, as it cost over $700 more than competitive convertibles. Only 131 were built. Today, marque collectors value the survivors highly.

The demise of the Frazer was in part due to Joseph Frazer's leaving the company position he had held. Moreover, the sales of the Frazer were disappointingly small and the senior line was not considered to be profitable by Kaiser Motors.

1947 Frazer, four-door sedan, 6-cyl

1951 Frazer, Manhattan four-door hardtop sedan, 6-cyl.

1947 Frazer, Manhattan four-door sedan, 6-cyl

1951 Frazer, Vagabond four-door hatchback sedan, 6-cyl

1949 Frazer, four-door sedan, 6-cyl

1951 Frazer, four-door sedan, 6-cyl

Standard Catalog of American Cars

1947 FRAZER

FRAZER STANDARD — (6-CYL) — SERIES F47 — The Frazer, along with its twin the Kaiser, was the first American car to exhibit true postwar styling. It hit the market in June, 1946. Appearance features included sheet metal designed by the famous automotive craftsman Howard 'Dutch' Darrin. This was the first envelope type body, with fenderlines that ran from the front through the rear wheels without a break in contour. The theme of horizontal lines was extended to the interior where the instrument panel was arranged with instruments and controls in a straight line as well as a horizontal metal strip above the glove compartment with the name Frazer. The rear view was quite simple and featured small taillights low on the rear fenders and an indentation in the trunk lid to house the license plate. The one-piece radiator grille had five, full-length horizontal blades housed in a bright metal surround with solid parking lamp extensions at its outboard ends. Rectangular parking lights were set into these extensions, which nearly wrapped around the body corners. The entire grille curved smoothly in and out along its longitudinal axis. Frazer block lettering was seen above the grille, along with the corporate shield on the nose of the car. The bumpers had a unique, three-tier look and widely spaced vertical guards mounted almost in line with the headlamps.

FRAZER I.D. NUMBERS: The serial number was stamped on the left front door post. Frazer serial numbers consisted of a model prefix and a six digit figure which is 001,001 for the first car of the year. In 1947, the model prefix F47 denoted a standard sedan; the prefix F47C a Manhattan sedan. Serial numbers for 1947 were F47-001,001 to 037,120. Frazer engine numbers were stamped on a pad on the left front corner of the engine block and on a plate on the left side of the block. Motor numbers for 1947 were GP or F-10001 and up; 50120 to 82999 and 210001 to 306999. The prefix 'GP' denoted Graham-Paige, a company which Frazer evolved from, while the prefix 'F' denoted Frazer vehicles built after the Graham-Paige tie-in was officially dropped. Effective with the car having serial number F47-9940 and motor number F-50120 the prefix 'GP' was changed to 'F' for the balance of production. Frazers also carried a Body/Style Number code on a large plate attached to the firewall. The code was as follows: 'F476' — standard 1947 four-door sedan; 'F47C5' — Manhattan 1947 four-door sedan; '4855' — standard 1948 four-door sedan; '4855' — Manhattan 1948 four-door sedan. (Commencing 1949, these designations were revised and standardized on all K-F models, with '1' designating the four-door sedan and '2' the convertible; thus, for example, the 1949 standard Frazer carried body code '4951' while the Manhattan convertible carried body code '4962'.

FRAZER STANDARD SERIES F-47

Model Number	Body/Style Number	Body Type & Seating	Factory Price	Shipping Weight	Production Total
F47	47-5	4-dr Sed-5P	2053	3365	36,120

NOTE 1: Above are 1947 prices.
NOTE 2: Some sources list prices $2,152 and $2,295; weight of 3,340 pounds.

1947 Frazer, Manhattan four-door sedan, 6-cyl, Joseph Frazer on the left.

FRAZER MANHATTAN — (6-CYL) — SERIES F-47 — The Frazer Manhattan was based on the standard four-door sedan, enriched with upgraded interior appointments designed by company stylist Carleton B. Spencer. It was introduced on March 23, 1947 as a running addition to the line. The Deluxe trimmings included broadcloth upholstery; carpeting; rear seat armrest; fancier steering wheel and four front bumper guards. Five exterior colors were provided: Teal blue, Gunmetal: Doeskin tan; Linden green; Turf green. They came in six harmonizing interior/exterior color combinations, or two-tone finishes. Wide chrome moldings were seen on the rocker panel; trunk lid and window frames. Full chrome wheel discs; trim rings; concealed floor lamps; front seat assist handles; chrome instrument panel moldings and non-glare rearview mirrors were featured as well.

FRAZER MANHATTAN SERIES F47C

Model Number	Body/Style Number	Body Type & Seating	Factory Price	Shipping Weight	Production Total
F47C	47C5	4-dr Sed-5P	2550	3375	32,655

NOTE 1: Sources list a higher price of $2,712 for later Frazer Manhattans.

ENGINE: Inline. L-head six. Cast iron block. Displacement: 226.2 cid. Bore and stroke: 3-5/16 x 4-3/8 inches. Compression ratio: 6.9:1. Brake hp: 100 at 3600 rpm. Four main bearings. Solid valve lifters. Carburetor: Carter Type W-1 or WA-1 one-barrel Models 574S; 622S or 622SA.

CHASSIS FEATURES: Wheelbase: (All models) 123.5 inches. Overall length: (All models) 203 inches. Front tread: (All models) 58 inches. Rear tread: (All models) 60 inches. Tires: (All models) 6.50 x 15.

OPTIONS: Group AG1 includes front and rear bumper guards; heavy-duty (oil bath) air cleaner; storage tank for vacuum wipers; spare tire, tube and wheel and license plate holder guards, ($66). Stainless steel wheel trim rings. Exhaust pipe extension. Full wheel discs. Outside rearview mirror. Heater. Radio. External sun shade. Spotlights. Fog lamps. Plastic white sidewall discs. Three-speed manual transmission was standard. Overdrive transmission ($80). Automatic choke, standard, not an option. Oil-bath air cleaner. Vacuum booster fuel pump. Available rear axle gear ratios.

HISTORICAL FOOTNOTES: The 1947 Frazers were introduced June 29, 1946 and the Manhattan appeared in dealer showrooms March 23, 1947. Model year production peaked for both Kaisers and Frazers at 139,249 units. Calendar year production of 144,507 cars was recorded (these totals include Kaisers). Henry J. Kaiser was the chairman of the board of the company this year. Joseph W. Frazer was the president and general manager. Kaiser and Frazer automobiles were built off the same platform, with different decorative trims and upholstery appointments. The Kaiser-Frazer Corp. was incorporated Aug. 9, 1945 in the state of Nevada. Production was planned partly to occur in a West Coast factory owned by Kaiser, but most was done in a refurbished factory at Willow Run, Mich., not far from Detroit. Production of a front-wheel-drive Kaiser, with similar styling, was anticipated at first. At least one prototype was built before this plan was scuttled. The first body drop took place May 29, 1946 and the first cars were shipped on June 22 of the same year. However, deliveries were slow until the fall of 1946. The Fashion Academy, of New York City, awarded the 1947 Frazer Manhattan its Gold Medal for design achievement.

1948 FRAZER

FRAZER STANDARD — (6-CYL) — SERIES F48 — There were no major changes in 1948 Frazers, although the company promoted 35 mechanical and styling improvements. They included such things as a higher compression ratio; relocated fuel pump; relocated exhaust system; dual action fuel pump; new vibration dampener; standard Goodyear super-cushion tires; heavier springs and shock absorbers; aluminum master cylinder; counter sprung hood supports; lighter steel brake backing plates; and 15 other refinements. Appearance alterations included new colors; redesigned hubcaps; one-piece nameplate; front carpeting for Manhattans; leather upholstery options for Manhattans; and five other minor styling revisions. Some of these were actually running changes first seen on late 1947 cars. Four bumper guards were employed at the front of both 1947 and 1948 models.

FRAZER I.D. NUMBERS: The serial number was stamped on the left front door post. Frazer serial numbers consisted of a model prefix and a six digit figure which is 001,001 for the first car of the year. In 1947, the model prefix F485 denoted a standard sedan; the prefix F486 a Manhattan sedan. Serial numbers for 1948 were F485-1001 to 032480 on standard sedans; F4861001 to 021591 for Manhattans. Frazer engine numbers were stamped on a pad on the left front corner of the engine block and on a plate on the left side of the block. Motor numbers for 1948 continued from 1947. Frazers also carried a Body/Style Number code on a large plate attached to the firewall with these codes corresponding to the data in second column of charts below.

FRAZER STANDARD SERIES F48

Model Number	Body/Style Number	Body Type & Seating	Factory Price	Shipping Weight	Production Total
F48	F485	4-dr Sed 5P	2483	3340	29,480

1948 Frazer, Manhattan four-door sedan, 6-cyl

FRAZER MANHATTAN — (6-CYL) — SERIES F48 — For 1948 the Frazer Manhattan received front compartment carpeting; leather upholstery options; a Manhattan scriptplate located on the front fenders, just forward of the door; and a chrome molding strip running between the front and rear wheel openings. A 112 hp six-cylinder engine with two-barrel carburetion, as in 1947, was available in the Manhattan only.

FRAZER MANHATTAN SERIES F48

Model Number	Body/Style Number	Body Type & Seating	Factory Price	Shipping Weight	Production Total
F48	F486	4-dr Sed-6P	2746	3375	18,591

FRAZER STANDARD SERIES ENGINE: Inline. L-head Six. Cast iron block. Displacement: 226.2 cid. Bore and stroke: 3-5/16 x 4-3/8 inches. Compression ratio: 7.3:1. Brake hp: 100 at 3600 rpm. Four main bearings. Solid valve lifters. Carburetor: Carter Type WA-1 one-barrel Model 622SB.

CHASSIS FEATURES: Wheelbase: (all models) 123.5 inches. Overall length: (all models) 203 inches. Front tread: (all models) 58 inches; Rear tread: (all models) 60 inches; Tires: (all models) 7.10 x 15.

OPTIONS: Group AG1, includes same items as 1947 group, plus stainless steel wheel trim rings; tailpipe extension and rear seat cigar lighter ($105). Full wheel discs. Outside rearview mirror. Heater. Radio and antenna. Twin fog lamps. Twin spotlights. Retractable radio antenna. External sun shade. White sidewall tires. Leather upholstery. Two-tone exterior finish. Three-speed manual transmission was standard. Overdrive transmission ($80). Manhattan six-cylinder 226.2 cid 112 hp two-barrel engine. Heavy-duty air cleaner. Available rear axle gear ratios: (standard) 4.09:1; (optional) 3.73:1; (overdrive) 4.27:1.

The 1948 Frazers were introduced in December, 1947. The total Kaiser-Frazer production was 139,249 units. Calendar year production of 181,316 cars was recorded. Henry J. Kaiser was the chairman of the board of the company this year. Joseph W. Frazer was president and general manager. The 200,000th Kaiser-Frazer automobile was a 1948 Frazer Manhattan.

1949 FRAZER

FRAZER STANDARD — (6-CYL) — SERIES F49 — Several relatively minor changes were made in the Frazer for 1949, principally in the manner of trimming. The hood escutcheon or crest was lowered to a position just below the new grille and the name Frazer, in block letters, was on the grille. A wider chrome strip was fitted under the doors and new taillights were surrounded by a chromed casting. The grille was made into a massive eggcrate type with both horizontal and vertical bars. The previously optional 112 hp engine was standard equipment in both standard and Manhattan lines. For 1949, only about half as many Frazers were built and sold as there were in the previous year. By 1949, most other auto manufactures also had new postwar body designs and Kaiser and Frazer sales fell sharply in the face of this new competition.

FRAZER I.D. NUMBERS: The serial number was stamped on the left front door post. Frazer serial numbers consisted of a model prefix and a six digit figure which is 001,001 for the first car of the year. Body style prefixes changed to F4951 for standard Frazer sedan; F4961 for Frazer Manhattan sedan and F4962 for a new Frazer Manhattan four-door convertible. Serial Numbers were F495-1001 to 030480 for standard Frazers and F496-1001 to 019591 for Manhattan models. Frazer engine numbers were stamped on a pad on the left front corner of the engine block and on a plate on the left side of the block. Motor numbers F-M1001 and up were used for both series. Frazers also carried a Body/Style Number code on a large plate attached to the firewall with these codes corresponding to the data in second column of charts below.

FRAZER STANDARD SERIES F49

Model Number	Body/Style Number	Body Type & Seating	Factory Price	Shipping Weight	Production Total
F49	F4951	4-dr Sed-6P	2395	3386	14,700*

NOTE 1: Production totals are estimates; see 1950 notes.

1949 Frazer, Manhattan four-door sedan, 6-cyl

FRAZER MANHATTAN — (6-CYL) — SERIES F49 — The Frazer Manhattan lineup now included a four-door sedan and a four-door convertible sedan. Both had distinctive, twin molding lower bodyside strips fashioned of bright metal. The bottom strip was narrower than the upper band, which decorated the bottoms of the doors (plus all body panels on the same level) between the front and rear wheel openings. There was also a strip of chrome at upper beltline level, which ran from just below the windshield post to the curved portion of the rear fenders. Fender skirts, complete with dual trim moldings, were standard on the new convertible sedan. Despite its attractive and unique body styling, the four-door convertible remained a rarity with just 62 examples being built.

FRAZER MANHATTAN SERIES F49

Model Number	Body/Style Number	Body Type & Seating	Factory Price	Shipping Weight	Production Total
F49	F4961	4-dr Sed-6P	2595	3391	9,950*
F49	F4962	4-dr Conv-6P	3295	3726	70*

NOTE 1: Production totals are estimates; see 1950 notes.

ENGINE: Inline. L-head six. Cast iron block. Displacement: 226-2 cid. Bore and stroke: 3-5/16 x 4-3/8 inches. Compression ratio: 7.3:1. Brake hp: 112 at 3600 rpm. Four main bearings. Solid valve lifters. Carburetor. Carter Type WCD two-barrel Models 685S; 685SA or 723S.

CHASSIS FEATURES: Wheelbase (All models) 123.5 inches. Overall length: (All models) 207.5 inches. Front tread: (All models) 58 inches. Rear tread: (All models) 60 inches. Tires: (All models) 7.10 x 15.

CONVENIENCE OPTIONS: Group AG3 including electric clock; chrome wheel discs; spare tire, tube and rim; tailpipe extension; two front bumper guards; front cigarette lighter; oil filter and vacuum booster fuel pump ($80). Radio. Antenna. Heater and defroster. Twin spot lights. Twin fog lamps. External sun visor. Fender skirts. Full wheel discs. Wheel trim rings. License plate frames. External sun visor. Leather upholstery trim. Bumper windguards. Two-tone finish. White side wall tires. Hood ornament. Three-speed manual transmission was standard. Overdrive transmission ($96). Heavy-duty air cleaner. Available rear axle gear ratios: (Standard) 3.73:1; 3.91:1 and 4.09:1; (optional with overdrive) 4.27:1 or 4.55:1.

HISTORICAL FOOTNOTES: The 1949 Frazers were introduced in September 1948 and the Manhattan convertible appeared in dealer showrooms in January 1949. Model year production peaked at 24,923 units. Calendar year production of 60,405 cars was recorded;

including Kaisers. Henry J. Kaiser was the chairman of the board of the company this year. Joseph W. Frazer was vice-chairman of the board. Edgar Kaiser became the new president of Kaiser-Frazer Corp. A hood ornament was optional on Kaisers for the first time this year.

1950 FRAZER

FRAZER STANDARD — (6-CYL) — SERIES F50 — For 1950, Frazer claimed that its designers had "created a superb new Frazer that is the last word in luxury." In truth, there was nothing new at all, since the 1950 models were identical to 1949s in virtually all respects. Standard models could be identified by a few trim distinctions. Many were leftover 1949 models. They had narrow chrome strips below the doors. All models had "Frazer" across the front radiator grille. Company literature highlighted welded steel body construction; Tru-line steering with triple control; Super-Cushion low pressure tires; and interior fabrics, produced by famous mills and looms, which were color styled to blend with exterior finishes. Other important features included centrifuse brake drums; floating shoe brakes; three-point engine mountings; ball type mid ship bearings; double-channel box framing; hypoid rear axles; clear vision steering wheel; rubber cored spring brackets; spring leaf liners; V-mounted shock absorbers; directional signals; automatic choke; external engine oil filter; oil bath air cleaner; ball bearing water pump; sway eliminator bar; wraparound bumpers; coil front springs; 27 cubic-foot luggage compartment; push-button door latches; and large ash receivers.

FRAZER I.D. NUMBERS: The serial number was stamped on the left front door post. Frazer serial numbers consisted of a model prefix and a six digit figure which is 001,001 for the first car of the year. Body style prefixes changed to F5051 for standard Frazer sedan; F5061 for Frazer Manhattan sedan and F5062 for the Frazer Manhattan four-door convertible. Serial Numbers were F505-1001 to 20000 for standard Frazers and F-506-1001 to 11000 for Manhattan models. Frazer engine numbers were stamped on a pad on the left front corner of the engine block and on a plate on the left side of the block. Motor numbers were continued from 1949 in both Series. Frazers also carried a Body/Style Number code on a large plate attached to the firewall with these codes corresponding to the data in second column of charts below.

FRAZER STANDARD SERIES F50

Model Number	Body/Style Number	Body Type & Seating	Factory Price	Shipping Weight	Production Total
F50	F5051	4-dr Sed-6P	2395	3386	Note 1

NOTE 1: See 1949 production totals. Because 1950 Frazers were re-serial-numbered, it is not possible to break out model year totals.
NOTE 2: Total 1949-50 Frazer production was 24,923, estimated at 14,700 standards and 10,020 Manhattans.
NOTE 3: About 84 percent of the total were 1949 models and 15 percent were re-serial-numbered as 1950 models.

FRAZER MANHATTAN SERIES — (6-CYL) — SERIES F50 — The Frazer Manhattan series continued with two four-door models, the sedan and convertible. They could be identified by the wide 'double-level' chrome strip below the doors and the Manhattan script plate attached to the trailing edge of the upper front fender sides. Fender skirts, with 'double-level' moldings on their lower edge, were standard on the convertible sedan. Full chrome wheel discs; wheel trim rings; concealed floor lamps; front seats assist handles; chrome instrument panel moldings and non-glare rearview mirrors continued as standard equipment features.

FRAZER MANHATTAN SERIES F50

Model Number	Body/Style Number	Body Type & Seating	Factory Price	Shipping Weight	Production Total
F50	F5061	4-dr Sed-6P	2595	3391	Note 1
F50	F5062	4-dr Conv-6P	3295	3726	Note 1

NOTE 1: See Frazer Standard Note 2 above.

ENGINE: Inline. L-head six. Cast iron block. Displacement: 226-2 cid. Bore and stroke: 3-5/16 x 4-3/8 inches. Compression ratio: 7.3:1. Brake hp: 112 at 3600 rpm. Four main bearings. Solid valve lifters. Carburetor. Carter Type WCD two-barrel Models 685S; 685SA or 723S.

CHASSIS FEATURES: Wheelbase: (all models) 123.5 inches. Overall length: (all models) 207.5 inches. Front tread: (all models) 58 inches. Rear tread: (all models) 60 inches. Tires (all models) 7.10 x 15.

OPTIONS: Group AG-3 including electric clock; chrome wheel discs; spare tire, tube and rim; tail pipe extension; two bumper guards front and three bumper guards rear; heavy-duty air cleaner; front cigarette lighter; replaceable element oil filter; rear cigarette lighter; and vacuum booster fuel pump ($105). Air conditioned comfort heater. Radio. Antenna. Spotlight. Twin spotlights. Fog lights. Twin fog lights. Fender skirts on sedans. Full wheel discs. Wheel trim rings. White sidewall tires. License plate frames. External sun visor. Traffic viewer. Leather upholstery trims. Two-tone finish. Hood ornament. Outside rearview mirror. Three-speed manual transmission was standard. Overdrive transmission ($96). Vacuum booster fuel pump available with Group AG1 accessory package or individually. Heavy-duty air cleaner optional on Frazer Standard Series. Available rear axle gear ratios (standard) 3.73:l; 3.91:1 and 4.09:1 (optional with overdrive) 4.27:1 or 4.55:1.

HISTORICAL FOOTNOTES: The 1950 Frazers were introduced in November 1949. The production of 1950 models was included with 1949 production totals. Industry statistics suggest that 16 percent of the cars had 1950 Frazer serial numbers. Cars of the two years were actually the same, all having been leftover 1949s that were re-serial-numbered. It is not possible to break out model year totals. Total 1949-'50 Frazer production was 24,923, estimated at 14,700 standards and 10,020 Manhattans, of which about 84 percent were 1949 models and 16 percent were re-serial-numbered as 1950 models. On Nov. 7, 1949 all new and unused Frazers remaining in dealer stocks were re-coded as 1950 models. Many convertibles were sold as 1950 models, although total output of this style was only 68-72 units for both years combined. Kaiser-Frazer was America's 12th ranked automaker in 1950.

1951 FRAZER

FRAZER STANDARD — (6-CYL) — SERIES F51 — The Frazer was much facelifted for 1951, its last year of production. The new body design was based on styling proposals proposed by Howard Darrin, executed by Herb Weissinger. The car featured crisp, highly defined body lines with rakish windstream curves and unbroken fender contours. Elements included large sized taillights set into high-crowned rear fenders; sculptured crease lines on front and rear fendersides and around the rear wheel opening, plus a heavily chromed wind tunnel grille. The standard Frazer series comprised two body styles, the four-door sedan and the five-door Vagabond utility sedan. The latter body type combined the features of a conventional sedan with the flexibility of a station wagon. Other makes of the era used similar designs, but Frazer used a unique design of dual rear hatches. In this, one panel folded down to form a tailgate while the upper hatch opened upward to give nearly complete floor to ceiling access to the interior. The rear seat folded flat forward to give a station wagon like flat cargo floor. The word Frazer appeared on the rear door of standard sedans, and Frazer Vagabond on the utility model.

FRAZER I.D. NUMBERS: The serial number was stamped on the left front door post. Frazer serial numbers consisted of a model prefix and a six digit figure which is 001,001 for the first car of the year. Body style prefixes were changed as follows: F5151 = standard Frazer sedan; F5155 = standard Frazer Vagabond sedan; F5161 = Frazer Manhattan four-door hardtop sedan and F5162 = Frazer Manhattan four-door convertible. Serial numbers for standard Frazers were F515-1001 to 10931. Frazer engine numbers were stamped on a pad on the left front corner of the engine block and on a plate on the left side of the block. The motor numbers used on Manhattans were the same range used on the standard Frazers. Serial number prefixes for minor factories were 'A' for Long Beach; 'B' for Jackson and 'C' for Portland. Frazers also carried a Body/Style Number code on a large plate attached to the firewall with these codes corresponding to the data in second column of charts below.

STANDARD FRAZER SERIES F51

Model Number	Body/Style Number	Body Type & Seating	Factory Price	Shipping Weight	Production Total
F51	F5151	4-dr Sed-6P	2359	3456	Note 1
F51	F5155	4-dr Utly Sed-6P	2399	3556	Note 1

NOTE 1: Actual F515 total: 9,931.
NOTE 2: Estimated breakdown: 6,900 sedans, 3,000 Vagabonds.

FRAZER MANHATTAN — (6-CYL) — SERIES F51 — The 1951 Frazer Manhattan line consisted of a four-door hardtop sedan and four-door convertible sedan. The new hardtop sedan was similar to the Kaiser Virginian of 1950. Both the Manhattan and the Virginian attempted to combine convertible lines with the convenience of a steel roof. They were not true pillarless hardtops in that fixed side window frames and small glass panels (located above the center of the body) were used for added structural support. Both of these reinforcements prevented unobstructed view out the sides of the car. The Virginian (Kaiser) had featured padded nylon top coverings to provide an even more convertible-like appearance. This feature, however, was seen on only a handful of the new Frazers Manhattan sedans and all may have been prototypes. According to marque experts, all but one known model have unpadded roofs. Manhattan identification features include the model name, in script, on the rear door and the distinct body styles. Deluxe equipment was supplied as standard. It included a carpeted luggage compartment; automatic trunk light; door armrests; chrome trimmed steering wheel; and bright metal interior moldings and trim. A Manhattan sedan was announced at 1951 model introduction, but apparently not produced.

FRAZER MANHATTAN SERIES F51

Model Number	Body/Style Number	Body Type & Seating	Factory Price	Shipping Weight	Production Total
F51	F5161	4-dr HT Sed-6P	3075	3771	152
F51	F5162	4-dr Conv-6P	3075	3941	131

ENGINE: Inline L-head Six. Cast iron block. Displacement: 226.2 cid. Bore and stroke: 3-5/16 x 4-3/8 inches. Compression ratio: 7.3:1. Brake hp: 115 at 3650 rpm. Four main bearings. Solid valve lifters. Carburetor: Carter Type WCD two-barrel Model 723S or Carter Type WGD two-barrel Models 781S or 813S.

CHASSIS FEATURES: Wheelbase: (all models) 123.5 inches. Overall length: (Standard Vagabond) 207-11/16 inches; (other models) 211-3/8 inches. Front tread: (all models) 58 inches. Rear tread: (all models) 60 inches. Tires: (all models) 7.10 x 15.

CONVENIENCE OPTIONS: Chrome wheelcovers. Deluxe bumper guards. Directional signals. Rear cigarette lighter. Tailpipe extension. Tilt-type non-glare rearview mirror. Windshield washers. Chrome 'donut' wheel discs. Bumper guard ends. Electric clock. Chrome horn ring. Dual horns. Dual rear ashtrays. Tenite plastic steering wheel. Front vent wings. Four bumper guards. Air conditioned comfort heater. Radio. Radio antenna. Spotlights. Fog lights. wheel trim rings. External sun visors. Traffic light viewer. White sidewall tires. Two-tone paint. Leather upholstery trims. Special paint colors. Outside rearview mirror. Padded top on Manhattan sedan. Three-speed manual transmission was standard equipment on F515 models. Automatic transmission was standard equipment on Manhattan F516 models. Overdrive transmission was available on F515 standard models only ($96). Automatic transmission was optional on F515 standard models only ($159). heavy-duty air cleaner. Available rear axle gear ratios: (standard) 3.91:1; 4.55:1; (overdrive) 3.54: 1; (Hydra-Matic) 4.09:1 or 4.27:1.

1951 Frazer, Manhattan four-door hardtop sedan, 6-cyl

HISTORICAL FOOTNOTES: The 1951 standard Frazer line went on sale during March 1950. The Frazer Manhattan models were introduced in August 1950. Model year sales totaled 10,214 units. Calendar year sales of all Kaiser-Frazer products was 99,343 cars. The company was America's 14th ranked manufacturer this season. Production of Frazers was discontinued at the close of the 1951 model run when the stock of leftover bodies was used up. An attractive 'charging knight' hood ornament was used on 1951 Frazers.

HUDSON
1946-1957

Founded by Roy D. Chapin and financed by J.L. Hudson, the Hudson Motor Car Co. pioneered modestly-priced closed cars since its creation in 1909. The company made a small profit during the World War II building airplanes and landing craft engines and re-entered the automobile market, in 1946, with face-lifted prewar models.

Data compiled by Jack Miller and Charles Liskow of Hudson-Essex-Terraplane Club Introduction by Linda Clark

---

Hudson retained both its L-head six and eight engines with the Super Six accounting for two-thirds of Hudson's 1946 production. The wheelbase remained unchanged at 121 inches, but optional transmissions included Drive Master, Vacumotive Drive and overdrive. Except for minor exterior and interior changes, models were unchanged for 1947 and Hudson registered profits both years.

For 1948, Hudson introduced one of the great postwar designs with its unit-body Hudson, which was to continue through 1954. Being low and sleek, it had a low center of gravity and handled exceptionally well. Its dropped floorpan earned it the nickname Step Down. It was offered in four models — Commodore Six and Eight and Super Six and Eight — and sat on a 124 inch wheelbase. This same year, Hudson

introduced a new engine, the 262 cid Super Six, which developed 121 hp at 4000 rpm. In 1951 this same engine evolved into the '308' Hornet powerplant which, from 1951 through 1954, was the king of stock car racing.

Although the Step-Down proved to be one of America's most roadable cars from 1948-1954, Hudson lacked sufficient funds to add new models to the series, and combined with a lack of innovation, principally the lack of a V-8 engine in subsequent years, found sales dropping through the early 1950s.

Hudson introduced a Pacemaker model in 1950 which used a de-stroked version of the flathead Super Six and sold over 60,000 units. Mention should be made of Pacemakers' five inch shorter wheelbase and tighter turning radius. The Commodore Six and Eight were continued and all models offered optional Drive Master, Supermatic Drive and over-drive transmissions. Hydra-Matic was an option from 1951 on.

Carrying the same pricetag as the Commodore Eight, the legendary Hudson Hornet was introduced in 1951. Available in four body styles, the Hornet's six-cylinder powerplant produced 145 hp at 3800 rpm in stock form. In the hands of skilled tuners, though, it was capable of considerably more and the most noted of these, Marshall Teague, achieved 112 mph from a NASCAR-certified stock Hornet. In 1953 Hudson also offered factory severe-usage options which were designed for racing applications. Racing items were listed as "Export" options! These included 'Twin H-Power' for improved

breathing and a '7-X' racing engine which combined Twin H-power with other high-performance options to produce about 210 hp.

Tim Flock was the 1952 NASCAR champion in a Hornet. In 1953, Marshall Teague's Hornet won 12 of 13 AAA stock car events and drivers Herb Thomas, Dick Rathmann, Frank Mundy and Al Keller drove Hornets to 65 NASCAR victories through 1954. Although Hudson added and subtracted series throughout this period, its inability to add new body styles hurt sales. When the Hornet and the Hollywood hardtop were added in 1951, Hudson dropped the standard Pacemaker and Super Eight. In 1952, the Wasp replaced the Super Six and all the Commodores were dropped the next year. A new Hornet Special of 1954 failed to increase sales.

Hudson's ill-fated compact Jet appeared in 1953 and the luxurious Jet Liner of 1954 sold poorly. However, it inspired a two-passenger Grand Turismo, built on the Jet chassis and called the Italia. It was designed by Hudson's Frank Spring and built by Carrozzeria Touring of Milan, Italy. Powered by a 114 hp Jet engine, the Italia had an aluminum body with a wraparound windshield, doors cut into the roof, fender scoops for brake cooling, flow-through ventilation and a leather interior. In addition to the prototype, 25 production Italias were made, plus a four-door 'X-161' which was built on the Hornet's 124 inch wheelbase chassis.

By late 1953, Hudson sales were slumping and the company merged with Nash and moved production to Kenosha, Wis., after closing its Detroit plant on Oct. 30, 1954. The all new 1955 Hudson was really a restyled Nash using Hudson's 1954 dashboard instruments. Hudson front suspension components and Dual-Safe brakes were retained. Wasps were powered by the former '202' Jet engine and the big six was retained for the Hornet. The Hornet V-8 used a Packard 208 hp engine and a line of Ramblers and Metropolitans was offered.

In 1956, American Motors introduced its own 190 hp V-8 for the Hornet Special and a line of Hudson Ramblers, but modest styling and engineering advances contributed to decreasing sales. The 1957 Hornets were two inches lower and used 14 inch wheels and the new 327 cid AMC V-8 with a four-barrel carb and dual exhaust. Cars so-equipped were excellent performers. Like other Hudsons, they also carried price reductions, but it was still to be Hudson's last year. AMC decided to drop Hudson and Nash to concentrate on Rambler.

1946 Hudson, Commodore two-door coupe, six-cyl (JO)

1946 Hudson, Commodore four-door sedan, 8-cyl

1952 Hudson, Hornet four-door sedan, 6-cyl (JO)

1953 Hudson, Hornet four-door sedan, 8-cyl

1954 Hudson, Hornet two-door sedan, 8-cyl

1954 Hudson, Jet two-door sedan, 6-cyl

1955 Hudsons at Beacon Motor Sales (JO)

1955 Hudson, Hornet Custom Hollywood two-door hardtop, 6-cyl

1956 Hudson, Hornet Special, four-door sedan, 6-cyl (JO)

1955 Hudson, Hornet Custom four-door, 6-cyl (JO)

1955 Hudson, Hornet Custom four-door sedan, 6-cyl (JO)

1957 Hudson, Hornet Custom Country Club two-door hardtop, V-8

Standard Catalog of American Cars

1946 HUDSON

HUDSON SUPER — SERIES 51 SIX — SERIES 53 EIGHT — Hudson's big 1946 change was a new grille in the old postwar body. It now had a massive upper bar housing a Hudson badge. There were wide indentations at the center of each of the horizontal blades. The nose was smooth and no longer had a molding between the mascot and the grille, though a strip of chrome did run from the windshield base to the mascot. Nameplates alongside the rear of the hood revealed the model identity. The standard list was long, including dual brake system; dual carburetion; Auto Poise control; chrome alloy motor block; oil-cushioned clutch; center point steering; rear lateral stabilizer; teleflash signals; push-button starting; safety locking hood; hand-rubbed lacquer finish; Duo-Flo oiling; high-compression motor; large trunk; and Long Life spark plugs. The basic equipment assortment for all models comprised left-hand front door armrests; twin air horns; dashboard and rear ashtrays; woodgrained instrument panel; spring covers; front and rear stabilizers; twin wipers; stoplights; locking glove box; windshield and rear window reveal moldings; new oval headlamp rims with sealed beam bulbs; front door locks; pile carpet; and, for sedans, envelope type front seatback pockets. Supers were trimmed in blue and gray boucle waffle weave cloth.

1946 Hudson, Super Six two-door Convertible Brougham, 6-cyl

VEHICLE I.D. NUMBERS: Serial numbers were on the right door post. Engine numbers were the same and were found on a boss near the top left side of the cylinder block and also between the first two manifold flanges. The first symbol was a '3' in 1946. The second symbol corresponded to the second number in the series/model code. The following group of symbols designated production sequence. Super Sixes were numbered 31101 to 3195099; Commodore Sixes 32101 to 3295062; Super Eights 33101 to 3395085 and Commodore Eights 34101 to 3495100. Body Style Numbers not used through 1955. First columns in charts below show six-cylinder model numbers; second columns show eight-cylinder model numbers.

HUDSON SUPER SIX (SERIES 51)/SUPER EIGHT (SERIES 52)

Model Number	Model Number	Body Type & Seating	Factory Price	Shipping Weight	Production Total
51	53	4-dr Sed-6P	1555/1668	3085/3235	Note 1
51	NA	2-dr Brghm-6P	1511	3030	Note 1
51	53	2-dr Clb Cpe-6P	1553/1664	3015/3185	Note 1
51	NA	2-dr Cpe-3P	1481	2950	Note 1
51	NA	2-dr Conv Brghm-6P	1879	3195	Note 1

NOTE 1: Series production was 61,787 Super Six/3,961 Super Eight with no breakouts.
NOTE 2: Approximately 1,037 Super Six Convertible Broughams built.
NOTE 3: Sedan and Club Coupe came only as Super Eight.
NOTE 4: Data above slash for six/below slash for eight.

HUDSON COMMODORE — SERIES 52 SIX — SERIES 54 EIGHT — All basic features and Super Series equipment were standard on Commodores, plus blue gray plain cloth upholstery; air foam seat cushions; carpet insert front floor covering; crank type ventipanes; door step courtesy lights; black filled etched aluminum scuff plates; luggage compartment rubber floor mats; and vertical rear window bars. In addition, Deluxe level appointments included interior hardware; taillamps; passenger assist straps and door handles. Gold finish was used on Commodore instrument dial letters and dash panel finish plates. Chrome-nickel plating brightened the steering column, shift lever, brake hand grip and glove locker box. An 18-inch custom steering wheel with horn ring was used and so were right-hand sun visors and electric clocks. A quick look at the Commodore exterior would reveal front and rear bumper bar extensions; front fender lamps with chrome extension moldings; oversize tires with large hubcaps (wheelcovers); wide body moldings with wheel color stripes; and an extra chrome strip above the belt moldings. Sedans had rear seat center armrests, leather robe hangers and rear dome lamps.

HUDSON COMMODORE SIX (SERIES 52)/COMMODORE EIGHT (SERIES 54)

Model Number	Model Number	Body Type & Seating	Factory Price	Shipping Weight	Production Total
52	54	4-dr Sed-6P	1699/1774	3150/3305	Note 1
52	54	2-dr Clb Cpe-5/6P	1693/1760	3065/3235	Note 1
NA	54	2-dr Conv Brghm-P	2050	3410	Note 1

NOTE 1: Series production was 17,685 Commodore Sixes and 8,193 Commodore Eights with no breakouts.
NOTE 2: Approximately 140 Commodore Eight Convertibles Brougham were built.
NOTE 3: Convertible Brougham (convertible) came only as Commodore Eight.
NOTE 4: Data above slash for six/below slash for eight.

ENGINES

(SIX-CYLINDER) Inline. L-head six-cylinder. Chrome alloy block. Displacement: 212 cid. Bore and stroke: 3 x 5 inches. Compression ratio: 6.5:1. Brake hp: 103 at 4000 rpm. Three main bearings. Solid valve lifters. Carburetor: Carter two-barrel WDO type Model 501S.

(EIGHT-CYLINDER) Inline. L-head eight-cylinder. Chrome alloy block. Displacement: 254 cid. Bore and stroke: 3 x 4-1/2 inches. Compression ratio: 6.5:1. Brake hp: 128 at 4200 rpm. Five main bearings. Solid valve lifters. Carburetor: Carter two-barrel WDO type Model 502S.

1946 Hudson, Commodore Eight four-door sedan, 8-cyl

CHASSIS FEATURES: Wheelbase (all): 121 inches. Overall length: (all) 207-3/8 inches. Front tread (all): 56-5/16 inches. Rear tread (all) 59-1/2 inches. Tires: (Supers) 6.00 x 16; (Commodores) 6.50 x 15.

OPTIONS: Commodore front and rear seat cushions ($17); front only ($9). Commodore front and rear bumper bar extensions ($20). Commodore electric clock ($14). Commodore fender lamps ($16). Commodore horn ring with standard steering wheel ($6). Large hubcaps ($9). Custom 18 inch steering wheel with horn ring ($19). Right side visor ($3). Oversize 6.50 x 15 tires with four large hubcaps ($28). Right front door armrest ($4). Direction indicator for Supers ($26). Red or cream wheel color (no cost). Police car and taxi equipment ($11). Radio ($77). Heavy scale front and rear springs for sixes (no cost). Heavy scale rear springs (no cost). Weather Master heater ($50). Chrome wheel trim rings ($13). Three-quarter leather trim ($32-$53 depending on body style). Three-quarter leather grain trim ($25-$41 depending on body style). Vacumotive Drive ($40). Drive-Master, including Vacumotive Drive ($98). Oil bath air cleaner ($3). Power Dome with eight-cylinder engine ($10). Overdrive transmission ($88). Combination fuel and vacuum pump ($7). Rear axle with 4-1/9:1 gear ratio (no cost). Rear axle with 4-5/9:1 gear ratio (no cost). Factory delivered prices included leather-grain trims. Police/Taxi package included: larger clutch; heavy rear springs; 11 inch brakes; and heavy construction seats. Convertible Broughams included full-length trim; air foam seats, oversized tires; and extra sun visors. Blue-gray Shadow Weave Cloth (Supers) or blue-gray Bedford Cloth (Commodores) was used in combination with special three-quarter trim options. Note: First 10 equipment items listed above standard on Commodore, optional on Super.

HISTORICAL FOOTNOTES: Production of 1946 Hudsons began on Aug. 30, 1945. Dealer introductions were held Oct. 1, 1945. The company displayed a 1909 Hudson at the Automotive Golden Jubilee in Detroit, Mich. this year. Model year sales hit 95,000 units. Calendar year deliveries peaked at 93,870 cars. Hudson held ninth place on the industry's sales charts. The trunk emblem used in 1946 was made of plastic. Nine standard colors, two extra cost hues and four two-tone combinations were provided for 1946 Hudson. Royal red finish was $23 extra and Nepal ivory was $60 extra. Two-tone selections were all priced at $18 extra. Eight tire size and construction options were offered at exchange prices between $15 and $72, but whitewalls were not available. A unique Cab Pick-up, with passenger car type sheet metal, was marketed in 1946 and 1947.

1947 HUDSON

HUDSON SUPER — SERIES 171 SIX — SERIES 173 EIGHT — Minor styling changes and equipment revisions were seen on 1947 Hudsons. Plastic trunk emblems were replaced with bright metal types and the corporate logo badge, centered in the upper grille bar, was ever so sightly modified to a larger size. Standard features of Supers included diagonal check Boucle upholstery; single adjustable hinged sun visor; 30-hour wind-up clock; woodgrained window finish moldings; black rubber front floor covering; carryall luggage compartment with vertically housed spare tire; felt trunk mats; cord robe hangers in sedans; new hoodside ornaments; 17 inch steering wheel; latch type front ventipanes; twin standard taillamps; sliding pane rear quarter glass in sedans; and stationary rear quarter glass in Club Coupes.

VEHICLE I.D. NUMBERS: Serial numbers were on the right door post. Engine numbers were the same and were found on a boss near the top left side of the cylinder block and also between the first two manifold flanges. The numbering system was basically the same as in 1946, with numbers running in single consecutive order, regardless of series. The first three symbols were comprised of the new series/model codes, followed by a group of numbers beginning at 101. Super Sixes were numbered 171101 to 17195100. Commodore Sixes 172101 to 17295099; Super Eights 173101 to 17394992; and Commodore Eights 174101 to 17495088. Body Style Numbers not used through 1955. First columns in charts below show six-cylinder model numbers; second columns show eight-cylinder model numbers.

HUDSON SUPER SIX (SERIES 171)/SUPER EIGHT (SERIES 173)

Model Number	Model Number	Body Type & Seating	Factory Price	Shipping Weight	Production Total
171	173	4-dr Sed-6P	1749/1862	3110/3260	Note 1
171	NA	2-dr Brghm-6P	1704	3055	Note 1
171	173	2-dr Clb Cpe-6P	1744/1855	3040/3210	Note 1
171	NA	2-dr Cpe-3P	1628	2975	Note 1
171	NA	2-dr Conv Brghm-6P	2021	3220	Note 1

NOTE 1: Series production was 49,276 Super Sixes and 5,076 Super Eights with no breakouts.
NOTE 2: Approximately 1,462 Super Six Convertible Broughams were built.
NOTE 3: Sedan and Club Coupe were Super Eights only
NOTE 4: Data above slash for six/below slash for eight.

1947 Hudson Super Six two-door sedan

HUDSON COMMODORE — SERIES 172 SIX — SERIES 174 EIGHT — Standard equipment for Commodores included herringbone weave upholstery; electric clock; air foam seat cushions; rear seat center armrest in sedans; cigarette lighter; chrome window finish moldings; instrument dial dimmer (also used 1946); carpet insert rubber front floor mats; rubber trunk mat; leather robe hangers in sedans; side window reveal moldings; rear window bars; auxiliary belt moldings; new hood top ornament with plastic crest; hoodside ornaments; bumper bar wing extensions for front and rear; 18 inch Deluxe steering wheel with horn ring; crank type ventipanes; carryover window glass construction; Deluxe type twin taillamps; and front fender lamps. Commodores also used the new, chrome trunk medallion and heavier molding around the grille top medallion. They again came standard with 6.50 x 15 tires and large hubcaps, which were optional equipment on Supers.

COMMODORE SIX (SERIES 172)/COMMODORE EIGHT (SERIES 174)

Model Number	Model Number	Body Type & Seating	Factory Price	Shipping Weight	Production Total
172	174	4-dr Sed-6P	1896/1972	3175/3330	Note 1
172	174	2-dr Clb Cpe-6P	1887/1955	3090/3260	Note 1
NA	174	2-dr Conv Brghm-6P	2196	3435	Note 1

NOTE 1: Series production was 25,138 Commodore Sixes and 12,593 Commodore Eights with no breakouts were provided.
NOTE 2: Approximately 361 Commodore Eight Convertible Broughams were built.
NOTE 3: Convertible Brougham came only as an eight.
NOTE 4: Data above slash for six/below slash for eight.

ENGINES

(SIX-CYLINDER) Inline. L-head six-cylinder. Chrome alloy block. Displacement: 212 cid. Bore and stroke: 3 x 5 inches. Compression ratio: 6.5:1. Brake hp: 103 at 4000 rpm. Three main bearings. Solid valve lifters. Carburetor: Carter two-barrel WDO type Model 501S.

(EIGHT-CYLINDER) Inline. L-head eight-cylinder. Chrome alloy block. Displacement: 254 cid. Bore and stroke: 3 x 4-1/2 inches. Compression ratio: 6.5:1. Brake hp: 128 at 4200 rpm. Five main bearings. Solid valve lifters. Carburetor: Carter two-barrel WDO type Model 502S.

CHASSIS FEATURES: Wheelbase (all): 121 inches. Overall length (all): 207-3/8 inches. Front tread (all): 56-5/16 inches. Rear tread (all): 59-1/2 inches. Tires: (Supers) 6.00 x 16; (Commodores) 6.50 x 15.

OPTIONS: Air foam seat cushions, front and rear ($17); front only ($9). Front and rear bumper bar extensions ($20). Electric clock ($14). Fendertop lamps ($16). Horn ring with standard 17 inch steering wheel ($6). Large hubcaps ($9). Custom 18 inch steering wheel with horn ring ($19). Right side inside sun visor ($3). Oversize 6.50 x 15 tires with four large hubcaps ($28). Right fender door armrest ($4). Directional indicators for Super ($26). Red or cream wheel colors (no cost). Police and taxi equipment including large clutch; heavy rear springs; 11 inch brakes and heavy construction seats ($11). Radio ($77). Heavy scale front and rear springs for sixes (no cost). Heavy scale rear springs (no cost). Weather Master heater ($50). Chrome wheel trim rings ($13). Three-quarter leather trim ($32-53 extra per body style). Three-quarter leather grain trim ($25-41 per body style). [Note: Above trim options include special blue-gray Shadow Weave Cloth on Supers or special blue-gray Bedford Cloth on Commodores.] Full-leather upholstery with Air Foam seat cushions and an extra sun visor was standard in convertibles. Factory Town delivered prices included three-quarter leather grain trim. Royal red finish ($23). Nepal Ivory finish ($60). Two-tone finish ($18). Eight tire options were available at exchange prices from $14.60 to $72.80. Available sizes included 6.00 x 16 and 7.00 x 15 and all could be had in four or six-ply construction on specific body styles and models. Many tire options included four large hubcaps. Whitewall tires reappeared late in the year. Vacumotive Drive ($40). Drive-Master, including Vacumotive Drive ($98). Oil bath air cleaner ($3). Eight-cylinder Power Dome ($10). Overdrive manual transmission ($88). Combination fuel and vacuum pump ($7). Rear axle with 4-1/9:1 gear ratio (no cost). Rear axle with 4-5/9:1 gear ratio (no cost). Note: First 10 equipment items listed above standard on Commodore, optional on Super.

HISTORICAL FOOTNOTES: Sales of the 1947 Hudson line began in December 1946. Model year totals peaked at approximately 95,000 units. Calendar year sales were 100,393 cars. Hudson was rated the 13th largest producer in the United States. The company built its 3,000,000 car this season, which was proudly displayed and photographed besides a 1909 Hudson which was part of the factory's antique car collection. This latest Hudson milestone was a fancy Commodore Eight convertible photographed wearing white sidewall tires. Six prototype wooden bodied station wagons were built for special use on the factory grounds.

1948 HUDSON

HUDSON SUPER — SERIES 481 SIX — SERIES 483 EIGHT — In November, 1947, Hudson introduced a completely new line of slab-sided cars with the famous 'Step Down' design. They were sleek, low and aerodynamic with unit-body construction and many advanced body engineering features. Standard equipment for Super series models included striped Bedford Cord upholstery; gray salt and pepper carpet-like rubber front floor mats; rear carpeting; cord robe hangers in sedans; dark mahogany woodgrained dash on 1948 Super models; window garnish moldings; 30-hour wind-up clocks; 17 inch steering wheel; adjustable sun visors; armrests at ends of all seats; latch type ventipanes; wing type rear quarter windows in sedans; side window reveal moldings; full opening rear quarter windows in Club Coupes; front parking lamps; twin standard taillamps; carryall trunk with horizontal mount spare tire; luggage compartment floor mat; and hubcaps on Supers.

1948 Hudson Commodore four-door sedan, 8-cyl

VEHICLE I.D. NUMBERS: Serial numbers were on the right front door post. Engine numbers were the same and were found on the upper front right-hand side of six-cylinder blocks or between the first and second exhaust manifold flanges on eight-cylinder blocks. The first three symbols corresponded to the series/model code, followed by a group of numbers beginning at 101. Super Sixes were numbered 481101 to 481117300; Commodore Sixes 482101 to 482117301; Super Eights 483101 to 483111786 and Commodore Eights 484101 to 484117256. Body Style Numbers not used through 1955. First columns in charts below show six-cylinder model numbers; second columns show eight-cylinder model numbers.

HUDSON SUPER SIX (SERIES 481)/SUPER EIGHTS (SERIES 483)

Model Number	Model Number	Body Type & Seating	Factory Price	Shipping Weight	Production Total
481	483	4-dr Sed-6P	2222/2343	3500/3535	Note 1
481	NA	2-dr Brghm-6P	2172	3470	Note 1
481	483	2-dr Clb Cpe-6P	2219/2340	3480/3495	Note 1
481	NA	2-dr Clb Cpe-3P	2069	3460	Note 1
481	NA	2-dr Conv Brghm-6P	2836	3750	Note 1

NOTE 1: Series production was 49,388 Super Sixes and 5,338 Super Eights with no breakouts.
NOTE 2: Approximately 86 Super Six Convertible Broughams were built.
NOTE 3: Only the sedan and Club Coupe came as Super Eights.
NOTE 4: Data above slash for six/below slash for eight.

HUDSON COMMODORE — SERIES 482 SIX — SERIES 484 EIGHT — Standard specifications for the new 'Step Down' Commodores included Broadcloth upholstery (tan with green stripes or gray with blue stripes); air foam seat cushions; taupe colored carpet-like rubber front floor mats; rear compartment carpeting; cloth covered sedan robe hangers; 16 inch rear seat center armrest in Club Coupe; cigarette lighter; dark walnut and blonde grained instrument panel (two-tone); instrument panel dial dimmer; walnut grain window garnish moldings; twin adjustable swiveling sun visors; Plastic rimmed 18 inch Deluxe steering wheel with horn ring; electric clock; side window reveal moldings; crank type front door ventilating wings; wing type rear quarter window ventilation in sedans; full-opening rear quarter windows in Club Coupe; rubber trunk mat and Deluxe twin taillamps; and front parking lamps.

HUDSON COMMODORE SIX (SERIES 482)/COMMODORE EIGHT (SERIES 484)

Model Number	Model Number	Body Type & Seating	Factory Price	Shipping Weight	Production Total
482	484	4-dr Sed-6P	2399/2514	3540/3600	Note 1
482	484	2-dr Clb Cpe-6P	2374/2490	3550/3570	Note 1
482	484	2-dr Brghm Cnv-6P	3057/3138	3780/3800	Note 1

NOTE 1: Series production was 27,159 Commodore Sixes and 35,315 Commodore Eights with no breakouts.
NOTE 2: Approximately 49 Commodore Six convertibles and 65 Commodore Eight convertibles were built.
NOTE 3: Data above slash for six/below slash for eight.

ENGINES

(SIX-CYLINDER) Inline. L-head six-cylinder. Chrome alloy block. Displacement: 262 cid. Bore and stroke: 3-9/16 x 4-3/8 inches. Compression ratio: 6.5:1. Brake hp: 121 at 4000 rpm. Four main bearings. Solid valve lifters. Carburetor: Carter two-barrel WDO type Model 647S.

(EIGHT-CYLINDER) Inline. L-head eight-cylinder. Chrome alloy block. Displacement: 254 cid. Bore and stroke: 3 x 4-1/2 inches. Compression ratio: 6.5:1. Brake hp: 128 at 4200 rpm. Five main bearings. Solid valve lifters. Carburetor: Carter two-barrel WDO type Model 647S.

CHASSIS FEATURES: Wheelbase (all) 124 inches. Overall length: (all) 207-1/2 inches. Front tread (all) 58-1/2 inches. Rear tread (all); 55-1/2 inches. Tires: (all) 7.10 x 15.

OPTIONS: Red or cream wheelcovers (no cost). Front fender ornaments on Supers ($6). Front bumper guard on Supers ($13). Convertible Brougham top rear window glass ($21). Rear window reveal moldings on Supers ($4). Weather Control heater ($64). Radio ($84). Foam rubber front seatback ($16). Directional indicators ($20). Commodore steering wheel on Supers ($20). Foam rubber seat cushions on Supers ($28). Wheel trim rings ($13). Hydraulic window regulators on Super Six convertibles ($63) Large hubcaps ($10). Foam rubber front seat cushions on Supers ($14). Electric clock on Supers ($17). Leather trim options for closed cars were available at prices between $83 and $145, with the cost depending on body style. Leather trims came in Russet, gray or dark red colors. Convertible Broughams came standard with 7.60 x 15 tires, antique grain Maroon leather trim and hydraulic window regulators (except Super Six). Brown cloth and maroon leather or gray cloth and maroon leather trims were no cost convertible options. Convertible tops came in black, gray or maroon. Specific upholstery trim and top colors were recommended with certain exterior body colors, although variations were possible. Note: Equipment choices specifically listed above as Super Series options were standard on Commodores. Tire options included white sidewalls, oversized 7.60 x 15 tires, and extra-ply construction. Six-cylinder aluminum cylinder head ($11). Eight-cylinder aluminum cylinder head ($13). Vacumotive Drive ($44). Drive-Master, including Vacumotive Drive ($112). Oil bath air cleaner, six ($6); Eight ($8). Overdrive manual transmission ($101). Vacuum booster pump ($9). Standard rear axle gear ratio was 4.1:1 on all models. Optional 4-5/9:1 or 4.3:1 gear ratios were available at no extra cost. With Overdrive transmission, the 4-5/9:1 rear axle was standard and 4.1:1 or 4.3:1 axles were no cost options. The 4.1:1 gear ratio rear axle was used in conjunction with DriveMaster.

HISTORICAL FOOTNOTES: The new styling introduced on 1948 models was created by a group of Hudson designers under the direction of Frank Spring. The 1948 line was offered for sale in December 1947. Model year sales hit the 117,200 unit level, while calendar year sales peaked at 142,454 cars. Hudson was ranked as America's 11th largest maker this season. The Vacumotive system automatically controlled the operation of the clutch. The Drive-Master system automatically controlled both clutching and gear shifting operations. Hudson dealers in New York City began one of the first television automobile advertising campaigns in 1947. Some body styles were not available at the beginning of the season. Four-door sedans, Brougham sedans and Club Coupes appeared first in late 1947. The Convertible Brougham did not show up until August 1948.

1949 HUDSON

HUDSON SUPER — SERIES 491 SIX — SERIES 493 EIGHT — There were very minor annual revisions in the 1949 Hudson Models and all were found inside the cars. The Super Series standard equipment list included all previous features, plus non-glare dashboard top finish and leather grained trim on the following items: valance panels under windows; kick pads on all doors; rear quarter panels of Broughams and Club Coupes; recessed panel shelves; and top of armrests. Cloth covered robe hangers were now used in all models, except the three-passenger coupe. A new, ribbed type front rubber floor mat with simulated carpet pattern was seen.

1949 Hudson, Super Six two-door Convertible Brougham, 6-cyl

VEHICLE I.D. NUMBERS: Serial numbers were on the right front door post. Engine numbers were the same and they were found on the upper front right-hand side of six-cylinder blocks or between the first and second exhaust manifold flanges on eight-cylinder blocks. The first three symbols changed to correspond to new model numbers. Super Sixes were numbered 491-101 to 491159201; Commodore Custom Sixes 492-101 to 492159081; Super Eights 493-101 to 49315919 and Commodore Custom Eights 494-101 to 494159159. Body Style Numbers not used through 1955. First columns in charts below show six-cylinder model numbers; second columns show eight-cylinder model numbers.

HUDSON SUPER SIX (SERIES 491)/SUPER EIGHT (SERIES 493)

Model Number	Model Number	Body Type & Seating	Factory Price	Shipping Weight	Production Total
491	493	4-dr Sed-6P	2207/2296	3555/3565	Note 1
491	493	2-dr Brghm-6P	2156/2245	3515/3545	Note 1
491	493	2-dr Clb Cpe-6P	2203/2292	3480/3550	Note 1
491	NA	2-dr Cpe-3P	2053	3485	Note 1
491	493	2-dr Conv Brghm-6P	2799	3750	Note 1

NOTE 1: Production was 91,333 Super Sixes and 6,365 Super Eights with no breakouts.
NOTE 2: Approximately 1,868 Super Six Convertible Broughams were built.
NOTE 3: Sedan, Brougham Sedan and Club Coupe only came as Super Eights.
NOTE 4: Data above slash for six/below slash for eight.

HUDSON COMMODORE CUSTOM — SERIES 492 SIX — SERIES 494 EIGHT — Upper series models were now called Commodore Customs and looked identical to 1948 Commodores on the outside. The standard equipment list was essentially the same, with the following minor changes: a new brown front floor mat was made of rubber and had a ribbed, simulated carpet pattern. Non-glare finish was used on top of the instrument panel. Envelope type pockets were now used on the front seatbacks of convertibles, instead of only on sedans. Leather graining was seen on the door kick pads and rear quarter panels of Broughams and Club Coupes. Two large parcel compartments, with locks, were now incorporated at each side of the Commodore Custom dashboard, the left-hand locker being new. As usual, Commodore Customs had such distinguishing features as bumper guards; metal hand rails on back of front seat; rear window reveal moldings; and 18 inch Deluxe steering wheel with full circle horn ring. Much of this could be ordered, as optional equipment, on Supers.

COMMODORE SIX (SERIES 492)/COMMODORE CUSTOM EIGHT (SERIES 494)

Model Number	Model Number	Body Type & Seating	Factory Price	Shipping Weight	Production Total
492	494	4-dr Sed-6P	2383/2472	3625/3650	Note 1
492	494	2-dr Clb-Cpe-6P	2359/2448	3585/3600	Note 1
492	494	2-dr Conv Brghm-6P	2952/3041	3780/3800	Note 1

NOTE 1: Series production was 32,715 Commodore Custom Sixes and 28,687 Commodore Custom Eights with no breakouts.
NOTE 2: Approximately 656 Commodore Custom Six convertibles and 596 Commodore Custom Eight convertibles were built.
NOTE 3: Data above slash for six/below slash for eight.

ENGINES

(SIX-CYLINDER) Inline. L-head six-cylinder. Chrome alloy block. Displacement: 262 cid. Bore and stroke: 3-9/16 x 4-3/8 inches. Compression ratio: 6.5:1. Brake hp: 121 at 4000 rpm. Four main bearings. Solid valve lifters. Carburetor: Carter two-barrel WDO type Model 647S.

(EIGHT-CYLINDER) Inline. L-head eight-cylinder. Chrome alloy block. Displacement: 254 cid. Bore and stroke: 3 x 4-1/2 inches. Compression ratio: 6.5:1. Brake hp: 128 at 4200 rpm. Five main bearings. Solid valve lifters. Carburetor: Carter two-barrel WDO type Model 647S.

CHASSIS FEATURES: Wheelbase (all) 124 inches. Overall length: (all) 207-1/2 inches. Front tread (all) 58-1/2 inches. Rear tread (all); 55-1/2 inches. Tires: (all) 7.10 x 15.

OPTIONS: Red or cream wheelcovers (no cost). Front fender ornaments on Supers ($6). Front bumper guard on Supers ($13). Convertible Brougham top rear window glass ($21). Rear window reveal moldings on Supers ($4). Weather Control heater ($64). Radio ($84). Foam rubber front seatback ($16). Directional indicators ($20). Commodore steering wheel on Supers ($20). Foam rubber seat cushions on Supers ($28). Wheel trim rings ($13). Hydraulic window regulators on Super Six convertibles ($63) Large hubcaps ($10). Foam rubber front seat cushions on Supers ($14). Electric clock on Supers ($17). Leather trim options for closed cars were available at prices between $83 and $145, with the cost depending on body style. Leather trims came in Russet, gray or dark red colors. Convertible Broughams came standard with 7.60 x 15 tires, antique grain Maroon leather trim and hydraulic window regulators (except Super Six). Brown cloth and maroon leather or gray cloth and maroon leather trims were no cost convertible options. Convertible tops came in black, gray or maroon. Specific upholstery trim and top colors were recommended with certain exterior body colors, although variations were possible. Note: Equipment choices specifically listed above as Super Series options were standard on Commodores. Tire options included white sidewalls, oversized 7.60 x 15 tires, and extra-ply construction. Six-cylinder aluminum cylinder head ($11). Eight-cylinder aluminum cylinder head ($13). Vacumotive Drive ($44). Drive-Master, including Vacumotive Drive ($112). Oil bath air cleaner, six ($6); Eight ($8). Overdrive manual transmission ($101). Vacuum booster pump ($9). Standard rear axle gear ratio was 4.1:1 on all models. Optional 4-5/9:1 or 4.3:1 gear ratios were available at no extra cost. With Overdrive transmission, the 4-5/9:1 rear axle was standard and 4.1:1 or 4.3:1 axles were no cost options. The 4.1:1 gear ratio rear axle was used in conjunction with DriveMaster.

HISTORICAL FOOTNOTES: The 1949 Hudson line was introduced to the public in November 1948. Hudson retained its 11th rank in industry with model year sales of 159,100 cars and calendar year sales of 142,462 units. The firm celebrated its 40th anniversary this season.

1950 HUDSON

1950 Hudson, Pacemaker four-door sedan, 6-cyl

HUDSON PACEMAKER — SERIES 500 — SERIES 50A DELUXE — A shorter Hudson was Hudson's new 'baby' in 1950. This Pacemaker was not much smaller than conventional styles, but seemed to be back then. It had the season's new look, which included a grille with four horizontal blades widening as they neared the bumper and twin struts forming a triangle with a company medallion at the top. Though only the grille was drastically changed, all the cars seemed lower. Basic equipment on all models included Durafab plastic interior trims; 18 inch steering wheel; twin, adjustable visors; full opening rear quarter windows for Club Coupes; new, two-piece curved Full-View windshield; front dome lamp; lockable parcel compartment; large trunk with mat and horizontal spare and; a rearview mirror. Several Pacemaker features,

including lighted grille/hood medallions; standard twin taillamps; latch type front ventipanes; and a new streamlined hood ornament, were shared with Supers. Distinctive Pacemaker equipment included striped, Bedford Cord upholstery; front and rear rubber floor mats; Blue Spruce two-spoke steering wheel; fabric finish dash; seatback pockets in sedans only; ashtrays in front seatback and dash; trumpet horn; and parking lamps under the lower grille bar. Deluxe Pacemakers had a bit of extra trim and slightly richer appointments.

VEHICLE I.D. NUMBERS: Serial numbers were on the right front door post. Engine numbers were the same and they were found on the upper front right-hand side of six-cylinder blocks or between the first and second exhaust manifold flanges on eight-cylinder blocks. Serial numbers followed the same system. The first three symbols correspond with new model numbers. Pacemaker 500s were numbered 500-101 to 500121481; Pacemaker Deluxes 50A-101 to 50A121505; Super Sixes 501-101 to 501121508; Commodore Sixes 502-101 to 502121504; Super Eights 503-101 to 503121491 and Commodore Eights 504-101 to 504121500. Body Style Numbers not used through 1955. First columns in charts below show Pacemaker 500 or six-cylinder model numbers; second columns show Pacemaker Deluxe or eight-cylinder model numbers.

HUDSON PACEMAKER 500 (SERIES 500)/PACEMAKER DELUXE (SERIES 50A)

Model Number	Model Number	Body Type & Seating	Factory Price	Shipping Weight	Production Total
500	50A	4-dr Sed-6P	1933/1959	3510/3520	Note 1
500	50A	2-dr Brghm-6P	1912/1928	3475/3485	Note 1
500	50A	2-dr Clb Cpe-6P	1933/1959	3460/3470	Note 1
500	50A	2-dr Cpe-3P	1807	3445	Note 1
500	50A	2-dr Conv Brghm-6P	2428/2444	3655/3665	Note 1

NOTE 1: Series production was 39,455 Pacemaker 500s and 22,297 Pacemaker Deluxes with no breakouts available.
NOTE 2: Approximately 1,865 Pacemaker 500 convertibles were built.
NOTE 3: Approximately 660 Pacemaker Deluxe convertibles were built.
NOTE 4: The three-passenger coupe came only as a Pacemaker 500.
NOTE 5: Data slash for Pacemaker 500/below slash for Pacemaker Deluxe.

HUDSON SUPER — SERIES 501 SIX — SERIES 503 EIGHT — Supers were basically a 1949 carryover with the newly designed 1950 grille appearance. A small 'spear tip' ornament at the front of the body contour line, just above the wheel opening, served as a Super identifier. A broad sill panel molding was used as the only major bodyside trim. No fendertop ornaments were seen and the new, streamlined hood ornament matched that on Pacemakers. The Super equipment list comprised all basic features and items shared with Pacemakers, plus striped Bedford cloth upholstery; two-tone woodgrained dash; wind-up clock; Cord robe hangers; light tan steering wheel; and door pillar assist straps. In addition, the following items were shared with Custom Commodores: ribbed carpet-like front mats; rear carpets; armrests at seat ends; sedan rear ventipanes; bright metal windows and windshield reveal moldings; larger sedan and Brougham rear window; parking lamps in lower grille bar; license lamps in center rear bumper guards; fender skirts; twin air horns, ashtrays in seat ends; and dashboard and envelope style seatback pockets in all models.

HUDSON SUPER SIX (SERIES 501)/SUPER EIGHT (SERIES 503)

Model Number	Model Number	Body Type & Seating	Factory Price	Shipping Weight	Production Total
501	503	4-dr Sed-6P	2105/2189	3590/3605	Note 1
501	503	2-dr Brghm-6P	2068/2152	3565/3575	Note 1
501	503	2-dr Clb Cpe-6P	2102/2186	3555/3560	Note 1
501	NA	2-dr Conv Brghm-6P	2629	3750	Note 1

NOTE 1: Series production included 17,246 Super Sixes and 1,074 Super Eights. No body style breakouts were provided.
NOTE 2: Approximately 464 Super Six Convertible Broughams were built.
NOTE 3: Prices and shipping weights above slashes are for sixes, below slash for eights.

HUDSON CUSTOM COMMODORE — SERIES 502 SIX — SERIES 504 EIGHT — Commodores had upper level trim and enriched interiors. Four bumpers guards were seen, as were front fendertop ornaments. Side trim consisted of the broad sill panel and a strip of molding that followed the body contour line several inches below it. At the front of this molding were model nameplates, while the rear portion widened and curved into the sill panel behind the enclosed rear wheelhousing. The Custom Commodore equipment list included all basic features and the additional items shared with Supers, plus nylon Bedford Cord upholstery (in tan with brown stripes or blue-gray with blue stripes); foam rubber seat cushions; Durafab covered robe hangers; bright metal seatback hand grips; 16 inch rear seat center armrest; pop-out cigarette lighter; dash dimmer switch; leather grain dash and window garnish molding finish; three-spoke steering wheel; electric clock; crank type ventipanes; two rear dome lights (in sedans and Club Coupes); and inner and outer bumper guards, front and rear. Basic items on Custom Commodores were slightly upgraded. For example, the rearview mirror was an extra large Deluxe type.

CUSTOM COMMODORE 6 (SERIES 502)/CUSTOM COMMODORE 8 (SERIES 504)

Model Number	Model Number	Body Type & Seating	Factory Price	Shipping Weight	Production Total
502	504	4-dr Sed-6P	2282/2366	3655/3675	Note 1
502	504	2-dr Clb Cpe-6P	2257/2341	3640/3575	Note 1
502	504	2-dr Conv Brghm-6P	2809/2893	3840/3865	Note 1

NOTE 1: Series production included 24,605 Custom Commodore Sixes and 16,731 Custom Commodore Eights with no body style breakouts provided.
NOTE 2: Approximately 700 Custom Commodore Six convertibles and 426 Custom Commodore Eight convertibles were built.
NOTE 3: Factory prices and shipping weights above slashes are for sixes, below slash for eights.

ENGINES

(PACEMAKER SIX) Inline. Six-cylinder. Flathead. Chrome alloy block. Displacement: 232 cid. Bore and stroke: 3-9/16 x 3-7/8 inches. Compression ratio: 6.7:1. Brake hp: 112 at 4000 rpm. Four main bearings. Solid valve lifters. Carburetor: Carter one-barrel WA-1 type Model 749S.

(SUPER/COMMODORE SIX) Inline. Six-cylinder. Flathead. Chrome alloy block. Displacement: 262 cid. Bore and stroke: 3-9/16 x 4-3/8 inches. Compression ratio: 6.7:1. Brake hp: 123 at 4000 rpm. Four main bearings. Solid valve lifters. Carburetor: Type WGD Model 776S with L-shaped air horns.

(SUPER/COMMODORE EIGHT) Inline. eight-cylinder. Flathead. Chrome alloy block. Displacement: 254 cid. Bore and stroke: 3 x 3-1/2 inches. Compression ratio: 6.7:1. Brake hp: 128 at 4200 rpm. Five main bearings. Solid valve lifters. Carburetor: Carter Type WGD Model 773S with L-shaped air horns.

1950 Hudson, Commodore Eight four-door sedan, 8-cyl

CHASSIS FEATURES: Wheelbase: (Pacemaker) 119 inches; (other models) 124 inches. Overall length: (Pacemaker) 201-1/2 inches; (other models) 208-3/32 inches. Front tread: (all) 58-1/2 inches. Rear tread: (all) 55-1/2 inches. Tires: (convertibles) 7.60 x 15; (all others) 7.10 x 15.

OPTIONS: Foam rubber Pacemaker seat cushions. Rear wheelcovers (fender skirts) for Pacemaker. Mechanical or electric clock in Pacemaker. Pacemaker front bumper outer guards. White sidewall tires. Super front bumper outer guards. Foam rubber cushions in Supers. Super side ornamentation. Hydraulic window lifts for Super convertible. Radio. Heater. Overdrive manual transmission ($95). Drive Master semi-automatic transmission ($105). Supermatic ($199). Aluminum cylinder head with 7.2:1 compression ratio. Rear axle ratios including 4.10:1 (standard); 4.55:1 (standard Supermatic) or 3.82:1 gears at no extra cost. Oil bath air cleaner. Vacuum booster pump.

HISTORICAL FOOTNOTES: The new Hudsons were introduced on Nov. 18, 1949. The firm slid to 13th rank in the American industry, with model year sales of 121,408 cars; calendar year output of 143,586 units. Prices were slightly reduced from the previous year and Hudson reported a $12 million profit on sales of $267 million. Canadian production, suspended during war, was resumed at the Hudson factory in Tilbury, Ontario, April, 1950. The Convertible Brougham, in both Commodore and Hornet series, came with hydraulic windows and leather trim. The same upholstery was featured on Super Series convertibles, but hydraulic window lifts were optional. Convertible top colors were tan, black or maroon. A 'Fold Away' rear window was optional with all convertibles.

1951 HUDSON

1951 Hudson, Pacemaker four-door sedan, 6-cyl

PACEMAKER CUSTOM — SIX — SERIES 4A — The Hudson grille was changed again this year. It now had three horizontal blades. The top two were bowed to meet the bottom bar. A twin-strut triangle was seen near the center. Rectangular parking lights were housed outboard of the main grille bars on either side. The lamp housings were slightly rounded where they wrapped around the Pacemaker body corners, but looked squarer on other models. The sides of Pacemakers were trimmed only by 'spear tip' ornaments (without spears) and broad lower sill panels that stretched, from behind the front wheel opening, to the extreme rear of the car. Standard on Pacemakers were Hudson basics like Twin-Contour wipers; gas gage; Teleflash 'idiot lights;' water temperature gage; windshield/defroster vents; Cushion-Action door latches; theft-proof locks; push-button door handles; windshield and side window reveals; dash ashtray; rearview mirror; twin sun visors; full opening crank-out rear quarter windows in Club Coupes and Broughams; front dome light; lockable parcel compartment; twin air horns; and illuminated grille medallion. Pacemakers had the rear ashtray in the front seatback and door pillar assist straps in Brougham sedans. Upholstery was gray special-weave cord with red and brown stripes and Dura-fab plastic trim.

VEHICLE I.D. NUMBERS: Serial numbers were on the right front door post. Engine numbers were the same and they were found on the upper front right-hand side of six-cylinder blocks or between the first and second exhaust manifold flanges on eight-cylinder blocks. Serial numbers followed the same system. The first two symbols correspond with new model designations and were a number and letter. Pacemaker Customs were numbered 4A-1001 to 132072; Super Customs 5A-1001 to 132246; Commodore Customs (Six) 6A-1001 to 132586; Hornets 7A-1001 to 132915 and Commodore Customs (Eight) 8A-1001 to 132028. Body Style Numbers not used through 1955. First columns in charts below show Pacemaker 500 or six-cylinder model numbers; second columns show Pacemaker Deluxe or eight-cylinder model numbers.

PACEMAKER CUSTOM SIX (SERIES 4A)

Model Number	Model Number	Body Type & Seating	Factory Price	Shipping Weight	Production Total
4A	NA	4-dr Sed-6P	2145	3460	Note 1
4A	NA	2-dr Brghm-6P	2102	3430	Note 1
4A	NA	2-dr Clb Cpe-6P	2145	3410	Note 1
4A	NA	2-dr Cpe-3P	1964	3380	Note 1
4A	NA	2-dr Conv Brghm-6P	2642	3600	Note 1

NOTE 1: Series production included 34,495 Pacemaker Customs. No body style breakouts were provided.
NOTE 2: Approximately 425 Pacemaker convertibles were built.

SUPER CUSTOM — SIX — SERIES 5A — For 1951, Supers were given the new frontal treatment and basically the type of side trim used on 1950 Commodores, but without standard outer grille guards. Small hubcaps were seen. The regular assortment of equipment was identical to that listed for Pacemakers, with only a few exceptions. Variations included rear ashtrays housed in recess panels on the doors and inner rear quarter panels (instead of front seatback) and wing-type ventipanes for sedan rear quarter windows. Upholstery was in tan Bedford cloth with brown and maroon stripes. A new Hollywood model, with two-door pillarless hardtop styling, was introduced in September of 1951 as a late-year addition to the line. A new, rounded corner traphazoid shaped front center grille guard was seen on all 'big' Hudsons, including the Supers.

SUPER CUSTOM SIX (SERIES 5A)

Model Number	Model Number	Body Type & Seating	Factory Price	Shipping Weight	Production Total
5A	NA	4-dr Sed-6P	2287	3565	Note 1
5A	NA	2-dr Brghm-6P	2238	3535	Note 1
5A	NA	2-dr Clb Cpe-6P	2287	3525	Note 1
5A	NA	2-dr Holly HT-6P	2605	3590	Note 1
5A	NA	2-dr Conv Brghm-6P	2827	3720	Note 1

NOTE 1: Series production included 22,532 Super Custom Sixes. No body style breakouts were provided.
NOTE 2: Approximately 1,100 Hollywood two-door hardtops and 282 convertibles were built in this series.

COMMODORE CUSTOM — SERIES 6A SIX — SERIES 8A EIGHT — No longer the flagship of the Hudson fleet, the Commodore Six was priced under a new Hudson Hornet line, while Commodore Eights were marketed at equal-to-Hornet prices. Distinguishing Commodores from lower series were larger front fender nameplates; outer grille guards front and rear; metal hand grips on front seatbacks; rear window reveal moldings and three dimensional weave upholstery with stripes and Antique Crush Dura-fab trim. These features were also used in and on Hornets. The balance of equipment was the same found on Super Customs, plus a 16 inch rear center armrest to provide a two-person seating arrangement. The Commodore convertible came in nine standard or four extra cost colors with dark red or blue genuine top grain leather upholstery and harmonizing leather grain trim. It again had hydraulic window lifts and a hydraulic roof with tan, black or maroon top material. A large, plastic rear window was optional.

CUSTOM COMMODORE SIX (SERIES 6A)/EIGHT (SERIES 8A)

Model Number	Model Number	Body Type & Seating	Factory Price	Shipping Weight	Production Total
6A	8A	4-dr Sed-6P	2480/2568	3600/3620	Note 1
6A	8A	2-dr Clb Cpe-6P	2455/2543	3585/3600	Note 1
6A	8A	2-dr Holly HT-6P	2780/2869	3640/3650	Note 1
6A	8A	2-dr Conv Brghm-6P	3011/3099	3785/3800	Note 1

NOTE 1: Series production included 16,979 Custom Commodore Sixes and 14,243 Custom Commodore Eights. No body style breakouts were provided.
NOTE 2: In the Custom Commodore Six series, approximately 819 Hollywoods and 211 convertibles were built.
NOTE 3: In the Custom Commodore Eight series, approximately 669 Hollywoods and 181 convertibles were built.
NOTE 4: Factory prices and shipping weights above slashes are for sixes, below slash for eights.

HUDSON HORNET — SIX — SERIES 7A — The first of the famed Hudson Hornets was really a Commodore with a special high-performance six and a few distinctive identification and appointment details. Special features included a gold and chrome plated 'Skyliner Styling' hood mascot; pillar assist straps in coupes and sedans; Deluxe robe hanger, hand grips and tailored pockets on back of the lounge-wide front seat; Hornet H-145 type medallions in each front door valance panel; indirectly lighted precision instruments set into a polished chrome dash housing on a leather grained panel with non-glare Dura-fab top; and gleaming, rocketship-shaped "Badges of Power" in front of the bodyside rub moldings and on the trunk. These badges showed a rocket piercing two vertically angled bars, with Hornet lettering turning them into a letter 'H'. Upholstery was of the Commodore type and came in tan-brown with gold stripes or blue-gray with blue stripes. Antique Crush type leather grained Dura-fab trim combinations were used. The high-compression, aluminum 'Power-Dome' cylinder head was standard on the Hornet engine, but the regular iron alloy head was a no-cost option.

HUDSON HORNET H-145 SIX (SERIES 7A)

Model Number	Model Number	Body Type & Seating	Factory Price	Shipping Weight	Production Total
7A	NA	4-dr Sed-6P	2568	3600	Note 1
7A	NA	2-dr Clb Cpe-6P	2543	3580	Note 1
7A	NA	2-dr Holly HT-6P	2869	3630	Note 1
7A	NA	2-dr Conv Brghm-6P	3099	3780	Note 1

NOTE 1: Series production included 43,666 Hudson Hornets. No body style breakouts were provided.
NOTE 2: Approximately 2,101 Hollywood two-door hardtops and 551 convertibles were built in this series.

(PACEMAKER SIX) Inline. Six-cylinder. Flathead. Chrome alloy block. Displacement: 232 cid. Bore and stroke: 3-9/16 x 3-7/8 inches. Compression ratio: 6.7:1. Brake hp: 112 at 4000 rpm. Four main bearings. Solid valve lifters. Carburetor: Carter one-barrel WA-1 type Model 749S.

(SUPER/COMMODORE SIX) Inline. Six-cylinder. Flathead. Chrome alloy block. Displacement: 262 cid. Bore and stroke: 3-9/16 x 4-3/8 inches. Compression ratio: 6.7:1. Brake hp: 123 at 4000 rpm. Four main bearings. Solid valve lifters. Carburetor: Type WGD Model 776S with L-shaped air horns.

(COMMODORE EIGHT) Inline. eight-cylinder. Flathead. Chrome alloy block. Displacement: 254 cid. Bore and stroke: 3 x 3-1/2 inches. Compression ratio: 6.7:1. Brake hp: 128 at 4200 rpm. Five main bearings. Solid valve lifters. Carburetor: Carter Type WGD Model 773S with L-shaped air horns.

1951 Hudson, Hornet four-door sedan, 6-cyl.

(HORNET SIX) Inline. L-head six. Chrome alloy block. Displacement: 308 cid. Bore and stroke: 3-13/16 x 4-1/2 inches. Compression ratio: 7.2:1. Brake hp: 145 at 3800 rpm. Four main bearings. Solid valve lifters. Carburetor: Carter two-barrel type WGD model 776S.

CHASSIS FEATURES: Wheelbase: (4A) 119-7/8 inches; (5A, 6A, 7A and 8A) 123-7/8 inches. Overall length: (4A) 201-1/2 inches; (5A, 6A, 7A and 8A) 208-1/2 inches. Front tread: (all) 58-1/2 inches. Rear tread: (all) 55-1/2 inches. Overall width: (4A and 5A) 77-1/16 inches; (6A, 7A and 8A) 77-21/32 inches. Tires: (5A, 6A 7A and 8A convertibles) 7.60 x 15; (4A convertible and all other models) 7.10 x 15.

OPTIONS: Foam rubber Pacemaker seat cushions. Rear wheelcovers (fender skirts) for Pacemaker. Mechanical or electric clock in Pacemaker. Pacemaker front bumper outer guards. White sidewall tires. Super front bumper outer guards. Foam rubber cushions in Supers. Super side ornamentation. Hydraulic window lifts for Super convertible. Radio. Heater. Overdrive manual transmission ($100). Drive Master semi-automatic transmission for Pacemaker/Super only ($99). Supermatic, all except Hornet ($158). Hydra-Matic for Commodore or Hornet ($158). Available rear axles included units with 4.55:1, 4.10:1 and 3.58:1 gear ratios. The Power-Dome cylinder head was optional on lower series at extra cost. The standard cylinder head was optional on Hornets at no extra cost.

HISTORICAL FOOTNOTES: The new Hudson line was introduced in September 1950 and continued in extended production through January, 1952. Hollywood hardtops were a late edition to the 1951 line. Model year deliveries hit 131,915 units. Calendar year sales dropped to 92,859 cars. Hudson was ranked 15th in the American industry. A loss of $1,125,210 was reported on sales volume of $186,050,832. Labor unrest and delays in getting government authorization to raise prices, during the Korean conflict, was responsible for the poor business year. The Hudson factory help support stock car racing efforts with the new Hornets by providing special 'export' and 'severe usage' parts suitable for high-performance applications. Hudsons were able to win 12 of the 41 NASCAR Grand National contests held in 1951. Top Hudson Hornet drivers included Marshall Teague, Herb Thomas, Tim Flock and Dick Rathmann. A special dual carburetion package helped Herb Thomas take a checkered flag in the second Southern 500 Race, at Darlington, S.C., with an 86.21 mph average speed. MOTOR TREND and MECHANIX ILLUSTRATED determined the top speed of the stock 1951 Hudson Hornet at 97 mph. Herb Thomas captured Top Driver honors on the NASCAR circuit this season.

1952 HUDSON

PACEMAKER/WASP — SIX — SERIES 4B/5B — The Pacemaker was slightly downgraded for 1952 and had a plainer look. The twin-strut grille arrangement was deleted and fender skirts were optional. The 'spear tips' had a staggered look and a boomerang shaped fin became the hood mascot. The rear end was spartan, having small oval taillamp lenses and only outer bumper guards. Standard specifications included fancy gray special-weave cord upholstery with red and brown stripes; ribbed rubber floor mats; dark brown painted dash; two-spoke light tan steering wheel; friction type front ventipanes; two assist straps in sedan, one in Club Coupe; pop-out cigarette lighter; dash and seatback ashtrays; windshield and window reveal moldings; twin air horns; armrests at front seat end (plus rear seat end on sedan and Club Coupe); seatback pockets; woven trunk mat; and 232 cid engine. Prices were up about $165 over 1951. The new Wasp Six was built off the Pacemaker platform. Wasps were an inch longer, since they came with center rear bumper guards which protruded out that much further. In terms of price, the Wasp replaced the Super. In terms of character, it was to the Pacemaker what the Hornet was to the Commodore Eight: a slightly fancier and more powerful version of the same car. (This is borne out by name changes of 1953, when the Pacemaker was renamed Wasp and the term Super Wasp was applied if the bigger motor was used.) Standard 1952 Wasp specifications included tan special-weave cord upholstery with red and brown stripes; rear compartment carpeting; dark brown leather grain dash; door courtesy lamps; wind-up clock; three-spoke steering wheel with half-circle horn ring; armrests at seat ends, except convertible and Brougham rear seat; robe hanger and hand grips on front seatback; friction front ventipanes; windshield and window reveal moldings; rear center guard with license lamp; woven fabric trunk mat; fender skirts; pop-out lighter; dash ashtray (and front seatback type in sedans); distinctive Hudson triangle grille ornament; front fendertop ornaments; seatback pockets; side body rub rail moldings; and twin-strut front grille guard.

VEHICLE I.D. NUMBERS: Serial numbers were on the right front door post. Engine numbers were the same and they were found on the upper front right-hand side of six-cylinder blocks or between the first and second exhaust manifold flanges on eight-cylinder blocks. Serial numbers followed the same system. The first two symbols correspond with new model designations, the second symbol of the prefix changing to a letter 'B'. Pacemakers were numbered 132916 to 202512; Wasps 132916 to 202715; Commodore Sixes 132916 to 198220; Hornets 132916 to 202916 and Commodore Eights 132916 to 200201. Body Style Numbers not used through 1955. First columns in charts below show Pacemaker or six-cylinder model numbers; second columns show Wasp or eight-cylinder model numbers.

1952 Hudson, Wasp two-door Hollywood hardtop, 6-cyl

PACEMAKER SIX (SERIES 4B)/WASP SIX (SERIES 5B)

Model Number	Model Number	Body Type & Seating	Factory Price	Shipping Weight	Production Total
4B	5B	4-dr Sed-6P	2311/2466	3390/3485	Note 1
4B	5B	2-dr Brghm-6P	2264/2413	3355/3470	Note 1
4B	5B	2-dr Clb Cpe-6P	2311/2466	3335/3435	Note 1
4B	NA	2-dr Cpe-3P	2116	3305	Note 1
NA	5B	2-dr Holly HT-6P	2812	3525	Note 1
NA	5B	2-dr Conv Brghm-6P	3048	3635	Note 1

NOTE 1: Series 4B production included 7,486 Pacemakers; no breakouts.
NOTE 2: Series 5B production included 21,876 Wasps; no breakouts.
NOTE 3: Approximately 1,320 Hollywood two-door hardtops and 220 convertibles in Wasp series.
NOTE 4: Data above slash for 4B/below slash for 5B.
NOTE 5: The three-passenger coupe came only as a Pacemaker; the Hollywood and Convertible Brougham came only as a Wasp.

COMMODORE — SIX — SERIES 6B — The 1952 Commodore line featured new Hudson-Aire identification and appointment items. They included double rub rail moldings that ran along the body contour line, from the front fenders to the rear fenders, with a downward sweep towards the back bumper; twin-strut grille and arrangement; front and rear center bumper guards; front fender nameplates; rocker sill beauty panels; large Deluxe hubcaps and taillights styled to form a continuous horizontal trim line. Standard equipment on sixes was markedly different than on eights. It included six-tone Bedford cord upholstery with tan and brown stripes; leather grain Dura-Fab trim; rear compartment carpets; dark brown leather grain dash; wind-up clock; three-spoke, half-ring steering wheel; armrests at ends of all seats (except convertible and Brougham); center rear seat armrest in sedan, Club Coupe and Hollywood; pop-out lighter; ashtrays at seat ends; dash ashtray; friction front ventipanes; leather grain window garnish moldings; reveal moldings; woven fabric trunk mat; fender skirts; Hudson triangle hood ornament; seatback pockets; front dome lamp (two side lamps in Hollywood); rear quarter dome lamps in sedan, Club Coupe and Hollywood; robe hanger and hand grips on seatback and front fendertop ornaments.

COMMODORE — EIGHT — SERIES 8B — The Commodore Eight had the following differences from the Commodore Six: nylon three-dimensional weave upholstery in tan-Brown with gold stripes or blue-Gray with blue stripes; foam rubber seat cushions; front and rear carpets; cord type, Dura-Fab covered robe hangers in all models; instrument lighting dimmer switch; Deluxe steering wheel; electric clock; crank type front ventipanes; printed jute trunk mat and Inline. eight-cylinder motor. The front fender 'spear tips' on sixes were decorated with a number '6'; on eights with a number '8'. Front parking lenses for all Commodores were of the wraparound style seen on Wasps, but not on Pacemakers.

COMMODORE SIX (SERIES 6B)/COMMODORE EIGHT (SERIES 8B)

Model Number	Model Number	Body Type & Seating	Factory Price	Shipping Weight	Production Total
6B	8B	4-dr Sed-6P	2674/2769	3595/3630	Note 1
6B	8B	2-dr Clb Cpe-6P	2647/2742	3550/3580	Note 1
6B	8B	2-dr Holly HT-6P	3000/3095	3625/3660	Note 1
6B	8B	2-dr Conv Brghm-6P	3247/3342	3750/3770	Note 1

NOTE 1: Series 6B production included 1,592 Commodore Sixes; no breakouts.
NOTE 2: Series 8B production included 3,125 Commodore Eights; no breakouts.
NOTE 3: Approximately 100 Hollywood two-door hardtops and 20 convertibles were built in the Commodore Six series.
NOTE 4: Approximately 190 Hollywood two-door hardtops and 30 convertibles were built in the Commodore Eight series.
NOTE 5: Factory prices and shipping weights above slashes are for sixes, below slash for eights.

HUDSON HORNET — SIX — SERIES 7B — The Hornet for 1952 was based on the Commodore Eight. Special features seen on the Hornet included dark blue or brown leather grain window garnish moldings; Hornet 'Flying-H' identification on the side of front fenders and rear deck; gold and chrome hood mascot; Hornet medallions on front door valance panels; and the high-compression H-145 six-cylinder engine. All other specifications matched those of the Commodore Eight. On a model for model basis, the two series were again priced identically, with the 8A models weighing 30 pounds more than Hornets.

HUDSON HORNET SIX (SERIES 7B)

Model Number	Model Number	Body Type & Seating	Factory Price	Shipping Weight	Production Total
7B	NA	4-dr Sed-6P	2749	3600	Note 1
7B	NA	2-dr Clb Cpe-6P	2722	3550	Note 1
7B	NA	2-dr Holly HT-6P	3071	3630	Note 1
7B	NA	2-dr Conv Brghm-6P	3318	3750	Note 1

NOTE 1: Series production included 35,921 Hornets; no breakouts.
NOTE 2: Approximately 2,160 Hollywood two-door hardtops and 360 convertibles were built in the Hornet Series.

ENGINES

(PACEMAKER SIX) L-head six. Chrome alloy block. Displacement: 232 cid. Bore and stroke: 39/16 x 3-7/8 inches. Compression ratio: 6.7:1. Brake hp: 112 at 4000 rpm. Four main bearings. Solid valve lifters. Carburetor: Carter one-barrel type WA-1 model 749S.

(WASP/COMMODORE SIX) Inline. L-head six. Chrome alloy block. Displacement: 262 cid. Bore and stroke: 3-9/16 x 4-3/8 inches. Compression ratio: 6.7:1. Brake hp: 127 at 4000 rpm. Four main bearings. Solid valve lifters. Carburetor: Carter one-barrel type WA-1 model 776S.

(COMMODORE EIGHT) Inline. eight-cylinder. Flathead. Chrome alloy block. Displacement: 254 cid. Bore and stroke: 3 x 3-1/2 inches. Compression ratio: 6.7:1. Brake hp: 128 at 4200 rpm. Five main bearings. Solid valve lifters. Carburetor: Carter Type WGD Model 773S with L-shaped air horns.

1952 Hudson, Hornet four-door sedan, 6-cyl

(HORNET SIX) Inline. L-head six. Chrome alloy block. Displacement: 308 cid. Bore and stroke: 3-13/16 x 4-1/2 inches. Compression ratio: 7.2:1. Brake hp: 145 at 3800 rpm. Four main bearings. Solid valve lifters. Carburetor: Carter two-barrel type WGD model 776S.

CHASSIS FEATURES: Wheelbase: (4B and 5B) 119 inches; (all other models) 124 inches. Overall length: (4B) 201-1/2 inches; (5B) 202-1/2 inches; (all other models) 208-1/2 inches. Front tread: (all) 58-1/2 inches. Rear tread: (all) 55-1/2 inches. Tires: Low-pressure, high-volume Super-Cushion 7.10 x 15 tires were standard on all models except Hornet and Commodore convertibles, which were equipped with size 7.60 x 15 tires. Size 7.60 x 15 was optional on all other models at extra cost. White sidewall tires were optional at extra cost, with availability limited by Korean War production restrictions.

OPTIONS: Fender skirts for Pacemaker. Center bumper guards for Pacemaker. Large hubcaps for Pacemaker and Wasp. Front fender ornaments for Pacemaker. Radio. Radio antenna, roof mount type. Heater. wind-up clock in Pacemaker. Electric clock in Wasp or Commodore Six. External windshield sun visor. Side window sun shields. Wheel trim rings. Oversize tires. Hydraulic window lifts in Wasp convertible (standard in other convertibles). Plastic rear window for convertible. Other standard factory and dealer installed accessories. Pacemaker models were available in five solid colors with six special hues optional at extra cost. All other Hudsons were available in 11 solid colors plus black, 19 two-tones. Convertibles came only in solid colors. Hudson Motor Car Co. released a special 'High-Output' options catalog this year. It included the high compression Pacemaker Six with optional aluminum 7.2:1 compression cylinder head; the super high-output H-127 Wasp/Commodore Six with the same optional head and the high-output Super-Eight engine with this 'Power Dome' cylinder head. Also, the 'Miracle H-Power' Hornet engine was available with both 7.2:1 aluminum head and 6.7:1 iron alloy head, plus a 7.2:1 iron alloy head. A dual-carburetor induction system with dual intake manifolds was released for the Hornet engine as the 'Twin-H' power package. Overdrive transmission was available was available for $111 extra. Hydra-Matic Drive could be ordered for $175.71 extra. Numerous types of extra-special performance components were offered by the factory to professional stock car racers this year. Iron alloy 'Power Dome' cylinder heads were also available for Super Six and Super Eight motors.

HISTORICAL FOOTNOTES: The 1952 Hudson line was introduced January, 1952. Hudson Hornet stock cars won 27 NASCAR races out of a total 34 Grand Nationals held this year. Hudson drivers in NASCAR included Herb Thomas and Tim Flock. Marshall Teague began driving Hudsons in AAA competition, after taking the 1952 NASCAR Daytona stock car race in a Hornet. The car was torn down after the race and proved to be 100 percent stock. In AAA racing, Teague took 14 checkered flags for Hudson, while other drivers captured a total of five. For the year, the Hornets had captured 40 wins in 48 major stock car races. It was quite a feat! With model year sales of 70,000 cars and calendar year deliveries of 79,117 units, the company's sales rank moved up one notch to 14th position. In May, 1952, Hudson announced that it was starting to tool-up for production of a new compact-sized line of 1953 models. This car became the Hudson Jet.

1953 HUDSON

1953 Hudson, Super Jet four-door sedan, 6-cyl

SERIES 1C JET — SERIES 2C SUPER JET — SIX — A down-sized Hudson flew on the scene in 1953. It was called the Jet. Marked by slab sided styling with conventional notch back lines, the Jet looked different from other Hudsons. A fake air scoop decorated the front of the hood. The grille had a flat oval appearance with a chrome molding highlighting the upper opening. Super Jet scripts appeared on the fenders of the more highly trimmed line, which also had an air scoop ornament. Fender skirts were optional on both lines. Standard 'custom car' equipment on the base model included Teleflash 'idiot lights;' water temperature and gasoline gages; Twin-Contour vacuum wipers; defroster vents; rotary door latches; theft-proof locks; push-button door handles; lock buttons; dash ashtray; wing type front ventipanes; twin stop and taillamps; front parking lamps; manual dome light; lockable parcel compartment; twin horns and visors; and lighted ignition switch keyway. Upholstery was done in gray weave worsted striped red and brown. Super Jet extras included oversize tires; wing type rear ventipanes; automatic dome lamps; and a host of features attached to the front seatback, such as pockets, coat hooks, cigarette lighter, robe hanger and ash receiver. Super Jets also had two-tone blue or green woven wool upholstery with Dura-fab leather grain trim.

VEHICLE I.D. NUMBERS: Serial numbers were on the right front door post. Engine numbers were the same and they were found on the upper front right-hand side of six-cylinder blocks or between the first and second exhaust manifold flanges on eight-cylinder blocks. Serial numbers followed the same system. The first two symbols were a prefix corresponding with model designations, with the second symbol changing to a 'C' in 1953. Jets were numbered 202917 to 268963; Super Jets 202917 to 269059; Wasps 202917 to 267518; Super Wasps 202917 to 267451 and Hornets 202917 to 267453. Body Style Numbers not used through 1955. First columns in charts below show lower series; second columns show higher series; Hornet offered only in one series coded in column one.

JET SIX (SERIES 1C)/SUPER JET SIX (SERIES 2C)

Model Number	Model Number	Body Type & Seating	Factory Price	Shipping Weight	Production Total
1C	2C	4-dr Sed-6P	1858/1954	2650/2700	Note 1
NA	2C	2-dr Cpe Sed-6P	1933	2695	Note 1

NOTE 1: Series production included 21,143 Jets and Super Jets combined. No body style breakouts.
NOTE 2: The two-door Coupe Sedan came only as a Super Jet.
NOTE 3: Factory prices and shipping weights above slash are for Jets, below slash for Super Jets.

WASP SERIES 4C — SUPER WASP SERIES 5C — SIX — The Wasp now became a mid-size Hudson offering with traditional Step Down styling on the 119 inch wheelbase. Appearance changes included deletion of the twin-strut grille guard and the addition of an air scoop hood. Upholstery was in tan weave cord with red and brown stripes and Dura-fab trim. Power came from the former Pacemaker Six. A standard steering wheel, plain-top fenders and small hubcaps were identification features. Super Wasp models were comparable to the 1952 Wasp. They were upholstered in new nylon combinations with special check weave and Dura-fab trim. Two-tone green was standard with six solid exterior colors and twelve two-tone combinations. Two-tone blue was standard with four different solids and nine two-tones. However, both upholstery choices were optional with opposite colors at no extra cost. Leather upholstery was also a no-cost option on the Super Wasp convertible. Standard equipment on Super Wasps also included a special 127 hp six-cylinder engine; large hubcaps; front fendertop ornaments; combination fuel and vacuum pump; foam rubber front seat cushions; and Deluxe steering wheel.

WASP SIX (SERIES 4C)/SUPER WASP SIX (SERIES 5C)

Model Number	Model Number	Body Type & Seating	Factory Price	Shipping Weight	Production Total
4C	5C	4-dr Sed-6P	2311/2466	3380/3480	Note 1
4C	5C	2-dr Sed-6P	2264/2413	3350/3460	Note 1
4C	5C	2-dr Clb Cpe-6P	2311/2466	3340/3455	Note 1
NA	5C	2-dr Holly HT-6P	2812	3525	Note 1
NA	5C	2-dr Conv Brghm-6P	3048	3655	Note 1

NOTE 1: Series production included 17,792 Wasps and Super Wasps combined. No body style breakouts were provided.
NOTE 2: Approximately 590 two-door Hollywood hardtops and 50 Convertible Broughams were built in the Super Wasp Series.
NOTE 3: The Hollywood and the Convertible Brougham came only as Super Wasps.
NOTE 4: Factory prices and shipping weights above slashes are for Wasps, below slash for Super Wasps.

HUDSON HORNET — SIX — SERIES 7C — the 1953 Hudson Hornet was very similar to the previous model bearing the same name, except that the strut bar look was eliminated from the grille and the air scoop hood look was used in its place. Hornets had most equipment used on Wasps, plus front rectangular bumper guards; front outer bumper guards; electric clock; large hubcaps; front and rear foam seat cushions; and hydraulic window regulators for convertibles. The rocketship-shaped Hornet front fender and trunk ornaments were seen again. Special decorator check weave nylon upholstery was featured (same colors as Wasp interior) and a slim three-spoke steering wheel, with specially positioned horn button, was seen. Below the hood was the H-145 six-cylinder engine, with 'Power Dome' aluminum cylinder head standard.

HUDSON HORNET SIX (SERIES 7C)

Model Number	Model Number	Body Type & Seating	Factory Price	Shipping Weight	Production Total
7C	NA	4-dr Sed-6P	2769	3570	Note 1
7C	NA	2-dr Clb Cpe-6P	2742	3530	Note 1
7C	NA	2-dr Holly HT-6P	3095	3610	Note 1
7C	NA	2-dr Conv Brghm-6P	3342	3760	Note 1

NOTE 1: Series production included 27,208 Hornets. No body style breakouts were provided.
NOTE 2: Approximately 910 Hornet Hollywood two-door hardtops were built.

1953 Hudson, Super Wasp four-door sedan, 6-cyl

ENGINES

(JET/SUPER JET SIX) Inline. L-head six. Chrome alloy block. Displacement: 202 cid. Bore and stroke: 3 x 4-3/4 inches. Compression ratio: 7.5:1. Brake hp: 104 at 4000 rpm. Four main bearings. Solid valve lifters. Carburetor: Carter one-barrel type WA-1 Models 2009S or 2009SA.

(WASP SIX) L-head six. Chrome alloy block. Displacement: 232 cid. Bore and stroke: 39/16 x 3-7/8 inches. Compression ratio: 6.7:1. Brake hp: 112 at 4000 rpm. Four main bearings. Solid valve lifters. Carburetor: Carter one-barrel type WA-1 model 749S.

(SUPER WASP SIX) Inline. L-head six. Chrome alloy block. Displacement: 262 cid. Bore and stroke: 3-9/16 x 4-3/8 inches. Compression ratio: 6.7:1. Brake hp: 127 at 4000 rpm. Four main bearings. Solid valve lifters. Carburetor: Carter one-barrel type WA-1 model 776S.

(HORNET SIX) Inline. L-head six. Chrome alloy block. Displacement: 308 cid. Bore and stroke: 3-13/16 x 4-1/2 inches. Compression ratio: 7.2:1. Brake hp: 145 at 3800 rpm. Four main bearings. Solid valve lifters. Carburetor: Carter two-barrel type WGD model 776S.

1953 Hudson, Wasp four-door sedan, 6-cyl

CHASSIS FEATURES: Wheelbase: (Jets) 105 inches; (Wasps) 119 inches; (Hornet) 124 inches. Overall length: (Jets) 180-11/16 inches; (Wasps) 201-1/2 inches; (Super Wasps) 202-1/2 inches; (Hornet) 208-1/2 inches. Front tread: (Jets) 54 inches; (all others) 58-1/2 inches. Rear tread: (Jets) 52 inches; (all others) 55-1/2 inches. Tires: (Jets) 5.90 x 15 (Super Jets) 6.40 x 15; (Hornet convertible) 7.60 x 15; (all others) 7.10 x 15.

OPTIONS: Two-door sedan rear seat armrests ($4). Front rectangular bumper guard ($24). Front outer bumper guards ($15). Electric clock, Jets ($22); Wasps ($19). Exhaust deflector ($2). Direction indicator, Jets ($21); Wasps ($24); Hornet ($24). Large hubcaps ($11). Cigar lighter ($4). Back-up lights, Super Jet ($18); Wasps and Hornet ($24). Glareproof mirror ($5). Outside rearview mirror, Jets ($5); others ($6). Front fendertop ornaments ($7). Large plastic rear window for convertible ($10). Eight-tube push-button radio ($100). Six-tube manual radio ($82). Front foam seat cushions, Jets ($13); Wasp ($14). Rear foam seat cushions (same price per model). Heavy-duty shock absorbers ($14). Solex glass with sunshade windshield ($42). Deluxe steering wheel ($20). Wheel trim rings ($15). Orion convertible top ($134). Window and wing vent shades, except convertible and Hollywood hardtop ($18). Outside sun visor with traffic light viewer ($33). Remote control Weather Control heater, Jets ($73); others ($74). Rear fender skirts [Hudson called them "wheelcovers."] ($15). Custom wheel discs Jets and Wasp ($20); Super Wasp and Hornet ($18). Windshield washer ($11). Hydraulic window regulators for Super Wasp convertible ($67). Hand-buffed genuine leather trim ($132-146 per body style). Note: leather trim not available on base Jet or blue combinations not available on base Wasps. Dura-fab trim ($53). Special solid paint colors on Jets ($27); other models ($28). Two-tone paint combinations on Super Jet only ($27); on Super Wasp or, Hornet only ($31). Note: Special and two-tone colors were not available on base Jet or base Wasp. Tire options for Jets and Super Jets included whitewalls, six-ply and Super Jet size on Jet at exchange prices from $6 to $50. Tire options on the Hornet convertible included whitewalls at $41 and six-ply blackwalls at $54 (exchange prices). Tire options on other Hornets, Wasps and Super Wasps included 7.60 x 15 size, whitewalls and special order six-ply choices at exchange prices from $22 to $72. Oil bath air cleaner ($8). Two oil bath air cleaners with 'Twin-H' power package ($16). Aluminum cylinder head, Wasps ($14); Jets ($12). Special 127 hp Super Wasp Six for Wasp ($37). Hydra-Matic Drive ($176). Oil filter ($14). Overdrive for Jets ($102); for other models ($111). Combination fuel and vacuum pump for base Wasp ($12); for Jet/Super Jet ($11). 'Twin-H' Power for all models, twin oil bath air cleaners mandatory on Wasp 4C ($85.60). Available rear axles included units with 4.09:1, 4.10:1 4.55:1, 4.27:1, 3.54:1, 3.31:1 and 3.07:1 gear ratios. Specific applications of axle ratios varied with models and transmissions, but options available were no extra cost. Cost of the high-performance 7-X engine from Hudson Dealer Parts Departments was $385.

HISTORICAL FOOTNOTES: The 1953 Hudson line was introduced in November, 1952. Model year sales were 66,143 units. Calendar year production peaked at 67,089 cars. Hudson was the 15th ranked producer. A special 7-X engine package was released for "severe usage," such as stock car racing. An official power rating was not published, but 200 hp was estimated for cars with this option. Hudsons captured 22 (out of 37) major NASCAR races, with driver Herb Thomas winning championship honors for the season. In AAA competition 13 (out of 16) races went to Hudson. The Hornets took checkered flags in 35 of 53 contests. Rumors of an impending merger between Hudson and another independent manufacturer began circulating in Detroit.

1954 HUDSON

JET SIX — SERIES 1D — The 1954 Jet grille had four ribs on each side of the main blade and a center embossment. Standard equipment was the same as the previous year. Tan worsted weave upholstery with brown and red stripes was featured, in combination with brown Plasti-hide trim. The base model lacked robe cords; courtesy lamps; front seatback pockets; wing type rear ventipanes; coat hooks; and a rear ashtray. Even a cigar lighter was extra. Two-tone paint was not available and the sole upholstery option was gray Plasti-hide with leather trim. On April 12, 1954, a new Family Club Sedan was added to the line as a stripped economy model. Priced $216 under the base sedan, this two-door had a non-scoop hood, plainer grille, black rubber windshield surround and even more spartan appointments.

VEHICLE I.D. NUMBERS: Serial numbers were on the right front door post. Engine numbers were the same and they were found on the upper front right-hand side of six-cylinder blocks or between the first and second exhaust manifold flanges on eight-cylinder blocks. The system of numbering Hudsons was changed. Each serial number had seven symbols. The first designated model, the others were the consecutive unit number. The starting number for all series was 269060 and they ran in mixed production. Engine numbers were the same. The serial number was on the right door post and, in Jet models, on the top right frame rail flange near the dash panel. Engine numbers were at the right front corner of the block near the top. Charts below list the lower series Model Number in first column and upper series Model Number in second column when two series are offered.

JETS SIX (SERIES 1D)

Model Number	Model Number	Body Type & Seating	Factory Price	Shipping Weight	Production Total
1D	NA	4-dr Sed-6P	1858	2675	Note 1
1D	NA	2-dr Fam Clb Sed	1621	2635	Note 1
1D	NA	2-dr Utl Sed-6P	1837	2715	Note 1

NOTE 1: Mixed production with Super Jet/Jetliner series below.

1954 Hudson, Jetliner two-door sedan, 6-cyl

SERIES 2D SUPER JET — SERIES 3D JETLINER — SIX — Block letters spelled out Super Jet on the front fenders of this one-step-up model. Features included hood air scoop ornamentation; horizontal front fender and door moldings; robe cords; wing type rear door ventipanes; front seatback pockets; rear ashtray; courtesy door lights; coat hooks; and cigar lighter. Two-tone green or blue decorator selected worsted upholstery fabrics in a handsome check pattern, with solid Plasti-hide trim, were used. The Jetliner was a new, top-level offering characterized by Jetliner fender block lettering; rear wheelcovers (skirts); Custom wheel discs; rear fender horizontal rub moldings; body sill highlights; bright rear gravel shields; and chrome rear taillight trim. Most Super Jet appointments were included, plus front and rear foam seat cushions and smartly pleated antique white Plastic-hide upholstery with headliner and bolsters of the same material in blue, green or red. Worsted cloth Super Jet combinations were optional at no extra cost.

SUPER JET SIX (SERIES 2D)/JETLINER SIX (SERIES 3D)

Model Number	Model Number	Body Type & Seating	Factory Price	Shipping Weight	Production Total
2D	3D	4-dr Sed-6P	1954/2057	2725/2760	Note 1
2D	3D	2-dr Clb Sed-6P	1933/2046	2710/2740	Note 1

NOTE 1: Series production included 14,224 Jets, Super Jets and Jetliners combined. No body style breakouts available.
NOTE 2: Data above slash for Super Jet/below slash for Jetliner.

WASP SERIES 4D — SUPER WASP SERIES 5D — SIX — New styling, resembling that of the Jets, was applied to regular Hudsons this year. The grille had a heavy, bowed molding tracing the upper radiator opening. There was a full-width, flat horizontal loop surrounding the wedge shaped parking lights at each end. The main bar (top of the loop) was ribbed towards the middle and held a triangular Hudson medallion in a finned housing at its center. Behind this bar was an angled plate with four additional, wide-spaced ribs. Block letters spelled out Hudson below the scoop on the nose of the hood. Wasp or Super Wasp signature scripts were placed on the front fender tips above a full-length horizontal rub molding. Two-door hardtops had Hollywood scripts at the upper rear edge of front fenders. A panoramic one-piece windshield and protruding tip taillamps were new. Bright metal gravel shields with windsplit vents decorated the rear fendersides. Standard equipment on Wasps included fender skirts; cigar lighter; robe cord; front seatback pockets; rear ashtray; and special pattern cloth upholstery with blue or green Plasti-hide trim. Super Wasps had the same features, plus the following additions or changes: large hubcaps; front foam seat cushions; Custom steering wheel; passenger assist handles; crank type front ventipanes on Hollywoods and convertibles; courtesy door lights; combination fuel and vacuum pump; and two-tone blue or green check pattern tweed cloth upholstery with worsted bolster material and Plasti-hide trim. In Super Wasp convertibles blue, maroon or green leather cushions with Plasti-hide side trim was standard. The Super Wasp Hollywood hardtop had brown, blue or green nylon cord seats with snowflake design cloth upholstery and harmonizing Plasti-hide bolsters.

WASP SIX (SERIES 4D)/SUPER WASP SIX (SERIES 5D)

Model Number	Model Number	Body Type & Seating	Factory Price	Shipping Weight	Production Total
4D	5D	4-dr Sed-6P	2256/2466	3440/3525	Note 1
4D	5D	2-dr Clb Sed-6P	2209/2413	3375/3490	Note 1
4D	5D	2-dr Clb Cpe-6P	2256/2466	3360/3475	Note 1
NA	5D	2-dr Holly HT-6P	2704	3570	Note 1
NA	5D	2-dr Conv Brghm-6P	3004	3680	Note 1

NOTE 1: Series production included 11,603 Wasps and Super Wasps combined. No body style breakouts available.
NOTE 2: Industry trade magazines indicate that, on a calendar year basis, Hudson built 2,654 Hollywoods and 222 convertibles (note change from earlier editions of SCAC) with no series breakouts.
NOTE 3: Data above slash for Wasp/below slash for Super Wasps.

HORNET SPECIAL SERIES 6D — HORNET SERIES 7D — SIX — Hornets seemed a little more like Super Wasps this year, although the longer 124 inch wheelbase was still used. The appearance change to the Jet-like look brought an end to the front fender rocketship ornaments. Hudson signature scripts were seen on the fenders, but only the trunk lid had a special badge. As on Super Wasps, two-door hardtops also had Hollywood scripts at the high trailing edge of front fenders, above the full-length horizontal body rub moldings. Hornets had most Super Wasp equipment, plus the following additions or changes: crank type front ventipanes on all models; cast aluminum 'high-compression' head; electric clock; foam rubber rear seat cushions; Custom wheel discs; hydraulic window lifts (in convertibles); and special trims. Sedans and Club Coupes were upholstered in 15 percent nylon worsted Bedford cloth with broadcloth bolsters and Plastihide trim in different shades of the same colors; brown, blue or green. The Hornet Hollywood had similarly toned, snowflake design nylon cord seats with Plasti-hide bolsters. The convertible was done in blue, maroon or green genuine leather (with Plasti-hide side trim). Convertible tops were available in maroon, black or tan. Specific combinations of top colors with car finishes were recommended, but not considered mandatory. Also, the Hollywood hardtop could be had with tri-colored seat and headlining combinations of antique white Plasti-hide and red, blue and green bolsters, at no extra cost. The last models introduced by Hudson, in Detroit, were the Hornet Specials. They appeared March 19, 1954 at prices $115 to $140 lower than comparable Hornets. They had Hornet Special front fender scripts; Hornet engine and subdued level of exterior brightwork, but Super Wasp interior trim.

1954 Hudson, Hornet four-door sedan, 6-cyl

HORNET SPECIAL SIX (SERIES 6D)/HORNET SIX (SERIES 7D)

Model Number	Model Number	Body Type & Seating	Factory Price	Shipping Weight	Production Total
6D	7D	4-dr Sed-6P	2619/2769	3560/3620	Note 1
6D	NA	2-dr Clb Sed-6P	2571	3515	Note 1
6D	7D	2-dr Clb Cpe-6P	2619/2742	3505/3570	Note 1
NA	7D	2-dr Holly HT-6P	2988	3655	Note 1
NA	7D	2-dr Conv Brghm-6P	3288	3800	Note 1

NOTE 1: Series production included 24,833 Hornet Specials and Hornets combined. No body style breakouts.
NOTE 2: The Club Sedan came as a Hornet Special only; the Hollywood hardtop and Convertible Brougham came as Hornets only.
NOTE 3: Data above slash for Hornet Special/below slash for Hornet.

HUDSON ITALIA — CUSTOM SERIES — SIX — Twenty-six Hudson Italia coupes were built in 1954 on the Jet platform. The Italia body was styled and crafted by Carrozzeria Touring, of Milan, Italy, based on original sketches by Hudson's own Frank Spring. The sporty GT had aluminum coachwork; functional front fender scoops with brake cooling ducts; wraparound windshield; flow through ventilation; contoured leather bucket seats with three different densities of foam for proper support; deep-pile Italian floor carpeting; Borrani wire spoke wheels; white sidewall tires; radio; heater; back-up lights; and turn signals stacked in Jet-tube pipes tunneled into rear fenders. The Italia was announced, as a production model, on Jan. 14, 1954, the same day Hudson's merger with Nash Motors was approved. The 26 cars were actually designed and custom built as four-passenger Grand Touring 'image' cars to steal attention from Chevy Corvettes, Ford T-Birds and Ghia Chrysler show cars. Twenty-five were actually sold as production models, while a coupe prototype and four-door X-161 pilot model were also created. Twenty-one of these cars are known to still exist.

HUDSON ITALIA SIX (CUSTOM SERIES)

Model Number	Model Number	Body Type & Seating	Factory Price	Shipping Weight	Production Total
NA	NA	2-dr GT Spt Cpe-4P	4800	2710	27

HUDSON METROPOLITAN — (SERIES E) — FOUR — On May 1, 1954 Hudson Motor Car Co. became a division of American Motors Corp. Hudson dealers then undertook the sale of four-cylinder Metropolitans, previously marketed as a Nash offering in the United States. Hudson dealers were supplied with replacement grille center inserts having an 'H' instead of an 'M.' These were to be installed in Metropolitans sold as Hudson. The cars were otherwise identical to Nash Metropolitans, which are mentioned elsewhere in this catalog. Even serial and engine numbers were the same. Hudson Metropolitan were marketed through 1956. Since these were early "captive imports," rather than a true domestic automobile, specifications are not listed in this catalog. They can be found in Krause Publication's STANDARD CATALOG of IMPORTED CARS.

ENGINES

(JET/SUPER JET SIX) Inline. L-head six. Chrome alloy block. Displacement: 202 cid. Bore and stroke: 3 x 4-3/4 inches. Compression ratio: 7.5:1. Brake hp: 104 at 4000 rpm. Four main bearings. Solid valve lifters. Carburetor: Carter one-barrel type WA-1 Models 2009S or 2009SA.

(WASP SIX) Inline. L-head six. Chrome alloy block. Displacement: 232 cid. Bore and stroke: 3-9/16 x 3.7/8 inches. Compression ratio: 7.0:1. Brake hp: 126 at 4400 rpm. Four main bearings. Solid valve lifters. Carburetor: Carter one-barrel type WA-1 model 749S.

(SUPER WASP SIX) Inline. L-head six. Chrome alloy block. Displacement: 262 cid. Bore and stroke: 3-9/16 x 4-3/8. Compression ratio: 7.0:1. hp: 140 at 4000 rpm. Four main bearings. Solid valves lifters. Carburetor: Carter two-barrel type WGD Model 2115S.

(HORNET 'BIG' SIX) Inline. L-head six. Chrome alloy block. Displacement: 308 cid. Bore and stroke: 3-15/16 x 4-1/2 inches. Compression ratio: 7.5:1. Brake hp: 160 at 3800 rpm. Four main bearings. Solid valve lifters. Carburetor: Carter two-barrel type WGD Model 2115S.

(ITALIA SIX) Inline. L-head six. Chrome alloy block. Displacement: 201.5 cid (202). Bore and stroke: 3.00 x 4.75 inches. Compression ratio: 7.5:1. Brake hp: 114 at 4000 rpm. Four main bearings. Solid valve lifters. Induction system: Twin-H Power package with dual manifolding and carburetion (Carter carburetors).

1954 Hudson, Hornet Special two-door sedan, 6-cyl

CHASSIS FEATURES: Wheelbase: (Jets) 105 inches; (Wasps) 119 inches; (Hornets) 124 inches; (Italia) 105 inches. Overall length: (Jets) 180-11/16 inches; (Wasp) 201/1-2 inches; (Super Wasp) 202-15/32 inches; (Hornets) 268-7.8 inches. Front tread: (Jets/Italia) 54 inches; (other models) 58.5 inches. Rear tread: (Jets/Italia) 52 inches; (other models) 55.5 inches. Tires: (Jet) 5.90 x 15; (Super Jet/Jetliner) 6.40 x 15; (Hornet convertible) 7.60 x 15; (other models, except Italia) 7.10 x 15.

OPTIONS: Wasp two-door sedan rear armrest ($4). Power brakes, except Jets ($43). Electric clock, in Jets ($22); in Wasps ($19). Exhaust deflector ($2). Direction indicators, in Jets ($16); in others ($20). Large hubcaps, Wasp only ($11). Jet cigar lighter ($4). Super Jet/Jetliner back-up lights ($18); same on Wasps and Hornets ($24). Glare-proof mirror ($5). Outside rearview mirror (OSRV), in Jets ($5); all others ($6). Plastic convertible rear window ($10). Eight-tube push-button radio ($100). Six-tube manual radio, Jets only ($82). Front foam seats, in Jet/Super Jet ($13); in Wasp ($14). Rear foam seats, Jet/Super Jet ($13); in Wasp/Super Wasp ($14). Extra-heavy-duty shock absorbers, in Jets ($5); other models ($14). Solex glass with sunshade windshield ($33). Heavy scale springs, front and rear or rear only, separate no-cost option in Jets and other models. Power steering, Wasps and Hornets only ($177). Custom steering wheel, in Jet/Wasp ($20); in Super Jet/Jetliner ($19). Wheel trim rings, Jets and Wasps ($15). Orion, convertible top ($134). Window and wing vent shades, except convertible and Hollywood hardtop ($18). Outside visor with traffic light viewer in Wasps and Hornets ($33). Weather Control heater with remote control, in Jets ($73); in others ($74). Rear wheelcovers (skirts), in Jet/Super Jet only ($15). Custom wheel discs, on Jet/Super Jet and base Wasp ($20); on Super Hornet ($18). Wheels painted upper body color, (no cost with two-tone paint). Windshield washer ($11). Hydraulic window regulators in Super Wasp convertible ($67). Safety Group including back-up lights; directionals; glare proof and OSRV mirrors and windshield washer in Super Wasp and Hornet ($66). Safety Group with all above items plus combination fuel/vacuum pump in Wasp ($78); in Super Jet/Jetliner ($66). Safety Group with all above, less back-up lights in Jet ($49). Chrome plated wire wheels, except Jets. Velchrome painted wire wheels, (Special order in all models). The following equipment was available on models indicated, when sold as taxis or Police cars: Extra-wide 2-1/4 inch brake (standard in 5D, 7D; special order in 4D). Heavy-duty clutch (standard in 5D, 7D; special order in 1-2-3-4D). Heavy-duty battery (special order in 1-2-3D). Police/taxi special seat construction (special order in 1-2-3D). Color and Trim Options: Roman bronze or Pasture green special paint (no charge, except Jet/Wasp base models). Algerian blue, Coronation cream, St. Clair gray, or Lipstick red solid colors (extra cost). Model 1D Gray Plasti-hide trim (extra cost). Model 2D blue or green Plasti-hide trim (extra cost). Model 3D worsted upholstery (no cost). Model 4D Pioneer grain leather trim (extra cost). Model 5D maroon Pioneer grain or green Antique grain leather trim (extra cost). Model 5D Hollywood Plasti-hide trim (no cost). Model 7D sedan and Club Coupe, blue, maroon or green Antique grain leather trim (extra cost). Model 7D Hollywood blue or maroon leather trim (extra cost). Tire options included white sidewalls, oversize or extra-ply construction types at a variety of exchange prices based on series, model and body style. A continental tire extension kit was offered as a dealer installed accessory. Oil bath air cleaner ($8). Twin oil bath air cleaners for 'Twin-H' package mandatory on base Wasp equipped with 'Twin H'($16). Aluminum cylinder head optional on all, except Italia/Hornet, on Jets ($12); on others ($14). Super Wasp Six for base Wasp ($48). Hydra-Matic Drive ($178). Oil filter, no charge on Super Jet/Jetliner with Hydra-Matic; (other models $14). Overdrive transmission, on Jets ($102); on all others ($111). Combination fuel/vacuum pump, on Jets ($11); on all others ($12). 'Twin-H' power with dual carburetion and manifolding, 170 hp, dual air cleaners mandatory on base Wasp ($86).

HISTORICAL FOOTNOTES: Oct. 2, 1953 was the dealer introduction date for 1954 Hudson and Jet Utility Sedans. The Jetliner Series was introduced 10 days later. Model year production totaled 51,314 cars. Calendar year production peaked at 32,287 cars, including 4,239 Ramblers. On Jan. 14, 1954, Hudson directors approved a merger with Nash-Kelvinator. On March 24, 1954, Hudson stockholders approved the merger. On April 12, 1954 the Jet Family Club Sedan was added to the line. On May 1, 1954. Hudson officially became part of American Motors Corp. Twenty-six days later, Hudson employees were notified that production was being switched to the Nash automobile factory in Kenosha, Wis. On Oct. 30, 1954, the 1954 Hudson model run ended in Detroit. Eleven days later the first Hornet/Rambler departed the Kenosha plant. On Dec. 28, 1954, the first 1955 Hudson Hornet V-8 was built at Kenosha. An era in Hudson's history had ended.

1955 HUDSON

HUDSON RAMBLER — SERIES 5500 — SIX — The year 1955 found 11 Nash Ramblers, thinly disguised with grille badge inserts and hubcaps with a letter 'H' in the center, at Hudson dealerships. Two 'Fleet Specials' were stripped, three-passenger economy jobs with painted lamp rims, rubber windshield surrounds and spartan appointments. Next in price came a Deluxe series with plated headlamp rims, Deluxe front fender scripts, plain air scoop, no hood ornament and slightly up-market interior trim. A hood ornament and air scoop trim band were seen on the Super series, priced in the next higher bracket. At the top of the heap was a Custom series, with Custom front fender scripts, standard continental spare tire, enriched interior and all other Super features. These Hudson Ramblers were identical to the latest editions of the comparable Nash Rambler in features, trim and price.

VEHICLE I.D. NUMBERS: [HUDSON/RAMBLER] Serial numbers were located on a plate attached to the center cowl panel, below the hood. Cars built in Kenosha were numbered D205001 to D-276099. Cars built at El Segundo, California were numbered DC-15001 to DC-23325. Engine numbers were on the upper left corner of the block (with air-conditioning at the left front side of the block) and ran H-45001 to H-131414. Nash and Hudson Ramblers were built in mixed production. Body type identification was possible, with (Body Style) model numbers stamped on a plate located at the right side of dash, below hood. These numbers correspond to the Model Numbers in column two of charts below. [WASP/HORNET SUPER/HORNET CUSTOM] Wasps (built in Kenosha,Wis.) were numbered W1001 to W-8026. Kenosha-built Hornet Sixes were numbered X-1001 to X-7523; V-8s Y-1001 to Y-7170. El Segundo-built Hornet Sixes were numbered XC-1001 to XF-1048; V-8s YC-1001 to YC-1048. Engine number locations were on a machined surface on the left-hand side of block (at side of second cylinder) for Series 40 (Wasp Six) and Series 60 (Hornet Six) and were on a machined surface on right-hand side of block (at side of cylinder number eight below exhaust manifold) for Series 80 (Hornet V-8). Engine numbers were M-1001 to M-8026 (Wasp Six); F-1001 to F-7523 (Hornet Six) and P-1001 to P-7170 (Hornet V-8). Body type identification was now possible with (Body Style) model numbers stamped on a plate at the center of cowl panel, below hood. These numbers correspond to model numbers in column two of charts below.

1955 Hudson, Rambler Custom four-door sedan, 6-cyl

HUDSON RAMBLER SIX (SERIES 2500/5500)

Series Number	Body Model Number	Body Type & Seating	Factory Price	Shipping Weight	Production Total
FLEET SPECIAL SERIES					
n.a.	5504	2-dr Utl Wag-3P	1570	2500	21
n.a.	5512	2-dr Del Bus Sed	1457	2400	34
DELUXE SERIES					
n.a.	5515	4-dr Sed-6P	1695	2567	Note 1
n.a.	5516	2-dr Clb Sed-5P	1585	2432	0
n.a.	5514	2-dr Sub-5P	1771	2528	0
SUPER SERIES					
n.a.	5516-1	2-dr Clb Sed-5P	1683	2450	2,970
n.a.	5514-1	2-dr Sub-5P	1869	2532	1,335
n.a.	5515-1	4-dr Sed-6P	1798	2570	Note 1
n.a.	5518-1	4-dr Cty Clb-6P	1975	2675	0
CUSTOM SERIES					
n.a.	5515-2	4-dr Sed-6P	1989	2606	Note 1
n.a.	5518-2	4-dr Cr Ctry-6P	2098	2685	12,023
n.a.	5517-2	4-dr Cty Clb-5P	1995	2518	601

NOTE 1: Production of 7,210 Hudson Rambler four-door sedans was recorded with only the partial model breakouts shown here available.

WASP SUPER AND CUSTOM — SERIES 40 — SIX — The post-AMC merger Hudsons were introduced at the Chicago Auto Show, Feb. 23, 1955. Styling and engineering, though based on the Nash unit body and platform, were planned to give Hudsons a distinct character. For example, the former Jet engine was under the hood and the Hudson dual braking system was retained. Gone, however, was the traditional Hudson 'crab tread' stance. The Wasp front tread was 3/16 inches less than its rear tread. As far as the sheet metal went, the only panel interchangeable between Nashes and Hudsons was the rear deck lid. Overall styling was pleasant. A massive eggcrate grille filled the area below and between the single headlamps, with an inverted steer horn shaped bar bordering the top. This upper border bar had a Hudson badge set into a housing at its center. Hudson block letters decorated the hood, which no longer had a simulated air scoop. It have a full-width cowl vent near the windshield base. Horizontal moldings stretched across the front fenders and doors. A higher molding swept rearwards from the wraparound windshield post towards the upper back fender region. A stand-up hood ornament and Wasp front fender nameplates were seen on Super models, which also had Super scripts on the sides of the cowl. Customs had a flatter hood ornament and Custom cowl side script and included a continental spare tire as standard. Wrapover rear roof pillars were seen on all models.

WASP SIX AND CUSTOM SIX (SERIES 40)

Series Number	Body Model Number	Body Type & Seating	Factory Price	Shipping Weight	Production Total
STANDARD SERIES					
n.a.	35545-1	4-dr Sed-6P	2290	3254	Note 1
CUSTOM SERIES 40-2					
n.a.	35545-2	4-dr Sed-6P	2460	3347	5,551
n.a.	35547-2	2-dr Holly HT-6P	2570	3362	1,640

NOTE 1: Production of Super Wasp four-door sedans is included in Custom Wasp four-door sedan total.

HORNET SUPER AND CUSTOM — SERIES 60 SIX — SERIES 80 V-8 — The Hornet for 1955 had the same styling as the new Wasps on a longer wheelbase platform. Hornet nameplates were seen on the front fenders. Hardtops had Hollywood cowlside scripts as well. Very high quality interiors and standard continental spare tire carriers were regular equipment distinguishing Custom level cars. The Custom interior included 16 inch table-like rear seat armrests; transparent sun visors; roof package net; and padded dashboard. Hornet engine choices included the standard (160 hp) or 'Twin-H' (170 hp) versions of the big 308 cid six or a new V-8 built and supplied by Packard. Packard's new Twin Ultramatic transmission was both standard and mandatory in Hudsons equipped with V-8.

HORNET SUPER AND CUSTOM SIX (SERIES 60)/V-8 (SERIES 80)

Series Number	Body Model Number	Body Type & Seating	Factory Price	Shipping Weight	Production Total
SUPER SIX SERIES 60-1					
NA	35565-1	4-dr Sed-6P	2565	3495	Note 1

CUSTOM SIX SERIES 60-2

NA	35565-2	4-dr Sed-6P	2760	3562	5,357
NA	35557-2	2-dr Holly HT-6P	2880	3587	1,554

NOTE 1: Production of Hornet Super Six four-door sedans is included in Hornet Custom Six four-door sedan total.

SUPER V-8 SERIES 80-1

NA	35585-1	4-dr Sed-6P	2825	3806	Note 1

CUSTOM V-8 SERIES 80-2

NA	35585-2	4-dr Sed-6P	3015	3846	4,449
NA	35587-2	2-dr Holly HT-6P	3145	3876	1,770

NOTE 1: Production of Hornet Super V-8 four-door sedans is included in Hornet Custom V-8 four-door sedan total.

1955 Hudson, Wasp four-door sedan, 6-cyl

ENGINES

(RAMBLER 'FLYING SCOT' SIX) Inline. L-head six. Cast iron block. Displacement: 195.6 cid. Bore and stroke: 3-1/8 x 4-1/4 inches. Compression ratio: 7.3:1. Brake hp: 90 at 3800 rpm. Four main bearings. Solid valve lifters. Carburetor: Carter one-barrel type YF Model 2014S.

(WASP SIX) Inline. L-head Six. Cast iron block. Displacement: 202 cid. Bore and stroke: 3 x 4-3/4 inches. Compression ratio: 7.5:1. Brake hp: 120 at 4000 rpm. Four main bearings. Solid valve lifters. Carburetor: Carter one-barrel type WA-1 Model 20138.

(HORNET 'BIG' SIX) Inline. L-head six. Chrome alloy block. Aluminum cylinder head. Displacement: 308 cid. Bore and stroke: 3-13/16 x 4-1/2 inches. Compression ratio: 7.5:1. Brake hp: 160 at 3800 rpm. Four main bearings. Solid valve lifters. Carburetor: Carter one-barrel type WA-1 Model 2113S.

(PACKARD EIGHT) V-8. Overhead valves. Cast iron block. Displacement: 320 cid. Bore and stroke: 3-13/16 x 3-1/2 inches. Compression ratio: 7.8:1. Five main bearings. Brake hp: 208 at 4200 rpm. Five main bearings. Non-adjustable hydraulic valve lifters. Carburetor: Carter two-barrel type WGD Model 2231 SA.

1955 Hudson, Custom Hornet four-door sedan, 6-cyl

1955 Hudson Hornet Hollywood two-door hardtop

CHASSIS FEATURES: Wheelbase: (Rambler four-door) 108 inches; (Rambler two-door) 100 inches; (Wasps) 114-1/4 inches; (Hornets) 121-1/4 inches. Overall length: (Rambler four-door) 186-1/4 inches or 193-3/8 inches with continental spare, (Rambler two-door) 178-1/4 inches or 185-3/8 inches with continental spare; (Wasps) 202-1/4 inches or 212-1/4 inches with continental spare; (Hornets) 209-1/4 inches or 2191/4 inches with continental spare.

Front tread: (Rambler) 54-5/8 inches; (all Hudson) 59-1/2 inches. Rear tread: (Rambler) 53 inches; (Wasp) 59-11/16 inches; (Hornet) 60-1/2 inches. Tires: (Rambler) 6.40 x 15; (Wasp) 6.70 x 15; and (Hornet) 7.10 x 15.

OPTIONS: Rambler radio ($76). Rambler heater ($74). Rambler air conditioning ($345). Hudson air conditioning with heater ($395). Hudson twin speaker radio ($98). Hudson Weather Eye heater and defroster ($77). Power steering ($140). Power brakes ($39). Power windows ($128). Continental spare tire, except Customs. Reclining seats. Twin-Travel bed. Air mattress. Detachable window screens. Full wheel discs. Wasp 'Twin-H' six with two (2) Carter one-barrel type WA-1 Model 2013S carburetors, 8.0:1 compression aluminum cylinder head and 130 hp at 4000 rpm. Hornet 'Twin-H' six with two (2) Carter one-barrel type WA-1 carburetors, 7.5:1 compression and 170 hp at 4000 rpm. Hornet Special V-8 with one Carter two-barrel type WGD Model 2352S carburetor, 8.25:1 compression and 215 hp at 4600 rpm. Hydra-Matic transmission ($179). Packard Twin Ultramatic transmission (mandatory on V-8 Hornets and included in factory price of these models). Overdrive manual transmission ($104). Available rear axle gear ratios: (Rambler) 3.77:1 and 4.4:1 (Hudson) 3.15:1, 3.54:1, 3.58:1, 4.1:1 and 4.4:1.

HISTORICAL FOOTNOTES: Model year production included 25,214 Ramblers, 7,191 Wasps, 6,911 Hornets, and 6,219 V-8s for a total of 45,535 Hudsons. Sales promotions such as a 'Dealer Volume Investment Fund' and 'Sun Valley Sweepstakes' (for salesmen) helped Hudson move upwards by seven percent in the sales volume ranking charts. A national contest offering new Hudsons and trips to Disneyland as prizes was open to public participation. Although Hudson's headquarter address was still 14250 Plymouth Road, Detroit 32, Mich., all production of 1955 models was quartered at the AMC factory, Kenosha, Wis.

1956 HUDSON

1956 Hudson, Rambler Custom four-door sedan, 6-cyl

HUDSON RAMBLER — (6-CYL) — SERIES 5600 — The Hudson Jet was discontinued, but Hudson dealers still had small cars to sell under the AMC 'family plan.' These were totally badge-engineered cars including the imported Metropolitan. "American" cars from American Motors included Hudson Ramblers built at Kenosha, Wis. They were, in fact, identical to 1956 Nash Ramblers, except for having hubcaps with an 'H' in the center and 'H' logo circular grille inserts.

VEHICLE I.D. NUMBERS: The numbering system was the same as for previous models. Letter prefixes indicated model and place of origin. [HUDSON RAMBLER] Serial numbers were D-276101 for Kenosha built cars; DKD-5601 for unassembled export and DT-5401 for Canadian models. [WASP] Serial numbers for Kenosha built Wasps were W-8101 to W-10619. [HORNET] Serial numbers for Kenosha built Hornet Sixes were X-7601 to X-10665. Serial numbers for Kenosha built Hornet V-8s were Y-7201 to Y-10191. [HORNET SPECIAL] Serial numbers for Kenosha built Hornet Special V-8s were Z-1001 to Z-2757. Hudson Rambler engine numbers started at B-1001 and up. Wasp and Hornet engine numbers were as follows: (Wasp Six) M-8701 and up (with M-10001 to M-10100 previously assigned to 1955 models); (Hornet Six) F-8601 and up (Hornet V-8s) P-21001 to P-28804 and (Hornet Special V-8s) G-1001 to G-7288.

HUDSON RAMBLER SERIES

Model Number	Body/Style Number	Body Type & Seating	Factory Price	Shipping Weight	Production Total
DELUXE LINE					
n.a.	5615	4-dr Sed-6P	1826	2891	Note 1
SUPER LINE					
n.a.	5615-1	4-dr Sed-6P	1936	2906	Note 1
n.a.	5618-1	4-dr Sta Wag-6P	2230	2992	Note 1
n.a.	5613-2	4-dr HT Wag-6P	2491	3095	Note 1
CUSTOM LINE					
n.a.	5615-2	4-dr Sed-6P	2056	2929	Note 1
n.a.	5619-2	4-dr HT Sed-6P	2221	2990	Note 1
n.a.	5618-2	4-dr HT Wag-6P	2326	3110	Note 1

NOTE 1: Production of 1956 Hudson Ramblers was 20,496 with no breakouts.

HUDSON WASP — (SIX) — SERIES 40 — A completely new, V-shaped grille with a Hudson medallion set into another V-shaped dip in the center was a new styling trademark for 1956. Other changes included new hood ornaments and new rectangular front parking lamps set into wedge-shaped chrome moldings that accented the V-shape of the grille. There were air-scoop fendertop ornaments and new bodyside rub rail moldings, which also had a V-shaped dip on the rear doors or fenders. In addition, the taillights were redesigned. The Wasp models could be identified by their Wasp nameplates inside the V-shaped dip in the rub rail molding. They could also be spotted by the chrome-enclosed panel on the rear fender sides that was finished in lower body color. Popular features included Deep Coil ride; Triple-Safe hydraulic brakes (with a reserve mechanical system); positive action handbrake; Double-Safe single unit construction; tubeless tires; Select-O-Lift starter; drawer-type glove compartment;

wraparound windshield and rear window; and double-acting airplane type shock absorbers. The only model available in the 1956 Wasp lineup was the Super trim level four-door sedan. Twin-H power was optionally available.

HUDSON WASP SIX

Model Number	Body Style Number	Body Type & Seating	Factory Price	Shipping Weight	Production Total
SUPER LINE					
n.a.	35645-1	4-dr Sed-6P	2416	3264	2,519

HUDSON HORNET — (SIX/V-8) — SERIES 50/80 — The 1956 Hornet had the same general styling changes as the new Wasp, but came with richer interior appointments and more standard equipment. All Hornet models had identification nameplates in the V-shaped dip in the side rub rail moldings. Custom trim level Hornets had a continental style spare tire and a chrome enclosed, gold-finished panel just to the rear of the V-shaped dip in the side molding. However, Super Hornets did not use either of these features, having the chrome-enclosed rear fender panel painted lower body color. In 1956 Hornet V-8s the Packard-built engine was used. Ultramatic transmission was again a mandatory option with this particular powerplant. Hornet Sixes came with the famous 308 cid Hudson 'Championship' six and could be had with three-speed manual, overdrive, or Hydra-Matic transmission. Series 80 Hornet V-8s were on the longer 121-1/4 inch wheelbase. Super and Custom trim versions were offered as sixes and Customs only could be fitted with the V-8.

HUDSON HORNET SERIES

Model Number	Body/Style Number	Body Type & Seating	Factory Price	Shipping Weight	Production Total
SUPER LINE SIX					
60	35665-1	4-dr Sed-6P	2777	3545	Note 1
CUSTOM LINE SIX					
60	35665-2	4-dr Sed-6P	3019	3636	3,022
60	35667-2	2-dr Holly HT-6P	3136	3646	358
CUSTOM LINE V-8					
80	35685-2	4-dr Sed-6P	3286	3862	1,962
80	35687-2	2-dr Holly HT-6P	3429	3872	1,053

NOTE 1: Production of the Super Six included in total for Custom Six sedan.

HUDSON HORNET SPECIAL — (V-8) — SERIES 50 — On March 5, 1956 the Hornet Special returned. It was a different type of car than the Hornet Special of 1954. The early Hornet Specials represented a cheaper version of the standard wheelbase Hornet. The 1956 Hornet Special had a cheaper price, but was actually something of a high-performance car. It came with a new AMC built 250 cid overhead valve V-8 in the 114-1/4 inch wheelbase Wasp chassis. Exterior trim and interior appointments were comparable to Super Hornets. Three-speed manual transmission was standard and both overdrive or Hydra-Matic Drive were available at extra cost.

HUDSON HORNET SPECIAL V-8 SERIES 50

Model Number	Body/Style Number	Body Type & Seating	Factory Price	Shipping Weight	Production Total
SUPER LINE					
50	35655-1	4-dr Sed-6P	2626	3467	1,528
50	35657-1	2-dr Holly HT-6P	2741	3486	229

1956 Hudson, Wasp four-door sedan, 6-cyl

1956 Hudson, Custom Hornet four-door sedan, 6-cyl

ENGINES

(HUDSON-RAMBLER SIX) Inline. L-head six. Cast iron block. Displacement: 195.6 cid. Bore and stroke: 3-1/8 x 4-1/4 inches. Compression ratio: 7.47:1. Brake hp: 120 at 4200 rpm. Four main bearings. Solid valve lifters. Carburetor: Carter type YF one-barrel Model 2014S.

(BASE WASP SIX) Inline. L-head six. Cast iron block. Displacement: 202 cid. Bore and stroke: 3 x 4.75 inches. Compression ratio: 7.5:1. Brake hp: 120 at 4000 rpm. Four main bearings. Solid valve lifters. Carburetor: Carter Type WA1 one-barrel Model 2009S.

(WASP TWIN-H SIX) Inline. L-head six. Cast iron block. Displacement: 202 cid. Bore and stroke: 3 x 4.75 inches. Compression ratio: 8.0:1. Brake hp: 130 at 4000 rpm. Four main bearings. Solid valve lifters. Carburetor: Two (2) Carter Type WA1 one-barrels Model 2013S.

(BASE HORNET SIX) Inline. L-head six. Cast iron block. Displacement: 308 cid. Bore and stroke: 3-13/16 x 4-1/2 inches. Compression ratio: 7.5:1. Brake hp: 165 at 3800 rpm. Four main bearings. Hydraulic valve lifters. Carburetor: Carter Type WGD two-barrel Model 2252S.

(HORNET TWIN-H SIX) Inline. L-head six. Cast iron block. Displacement: 308 cid. Bore and stroke: 3-13/16 x 4-1/2 inches. Compression ratio: 7.5:1. Brake hp: 175 at 4000 rpm. Four main bearings. Hydraulic valve lifters. Carburetor: Two (2) Carter Type WA1 one-barrel Model 2113S.

(PACKARD EIGHT) V-8. Overhead valves. Cast iron block. Displacement: 352 cid. Bore and stroke: 4 x 3-1/2 inches. Compression ratio: 9.55:1. Brake hp: 220 at 4600 rpm. Five main bearings. Hydraulic valve lifters. Carburetor: Carter Type WGD two-barrel Model 2231SA.

(HORNET SPECIAL EIGHT) V-8. Overhead valves. Cast iron block. Displacement: 250 cid. Bore and stroke: 3-1/2 x 3-1/4 inches. Compression ratio: 8.0:1. Brake hp: 190 at 4900 rpm. Five main bearings. Hydraulic valve lifters. Carburetor: Carter Type WGD two-barrel Model 2352S.

CHASSIS FEATURES: Wheelbase: (Rambler) 108 inches. (Wasp/Hornet Special) 114.25 inches; (Hornet) 121.25 inches. Overall length: (Rambler) 191.14 inches; (Rambler with Continental tire) 198.89 inches; (Wasp/Hornet Special) 202.25 inches; (Hornet Special with Continental tire) 212.25 inches; (Hornet) 209.25 inches; (Hornet with Continental tire) 219.25 inches; (Rambler wagons) 198.89 inches. Front tread: (Rambler) 57.75 inches; (wasp/Hornet Special) 59.5 inches. (Hornet) 59.5 inches. Rear tread: (Rambler) 58 inches; (Wasp/Hornet Special) 59-11/16 inches; (Hornet) 60.5 inches. Tires: (Rambler) 6.40 x 15; (Wasp/Hornet Special) 6.70 x 15; (Hornet Six) 7.10 x 15; (Hornet V-8) 7.60 x 15.

OPTIONS: Power steering, in Rambler ($80). Air conditioning, in Rambler ($345). Radio, in Rambler ($76). Heater, in Rambler ($74). All-Season air conditioning with heater, in Hudson ($395). Twin speaker radio, in Hudson ($98). Hudson Weather-Eye heater and defroster ($77). Power steering, in Hudson ($140). Power brakes, in Hudson ($39). Power windows, in Hudson ($128). Reclining seats and twin beds. Continental rear mount tire. Directional signals. White sidewall tires. Other standard options and accessories. Note: Power steering, power brakes and power windows were available on Hornets and Wasps only, continental rear-mounted tires and reclining seats with twin beds were standard on all Custom models except station wagons, which were not available with the continental tire. Three-speed manual transmission was standard. Ultramatic automatic transmission was a mandatory option in Hornets with the 352 cid V-8. Overdrive transmission ($107). Automatic transmission ($188). Twin-H carburetion. Heavy-duty air cleaner. Available rear axle gear ratios: 3.07:1; 3.31:1; 3.58:1; 3.54:1; 3.15:1; 4.0:1; 4.09:1; 4.40:1; 4.60:1.

HISTORICAL FOOTNOTES: Introduction date for the 1956 Hudson Wasp, Hornet Six and Hornet V-8 was Nov. 30, 1955. The 1956 Hudson Ramblers were then introduced on Dec. 15, 1955. It wasn't until March 5, 1956 that the Hornet Special V-8 appeared and thereafter began showing up in dealer showrooms. Calendar year output amounted to 10,671 units. Model year production hit its peak at 22,588 assemblies, excluding Hudson Ramblers. Seat belts were an option in 1956 and the 12-volt electrical system was introduced. Some 1956 Hudson factory literature included the weights of various options as follows: Hydra-Matic (105-125 pounds); overdrive (30-50 pounds); radio (13-18 pounds); Weather-Eye (18-22 pounds); air conditioning (120 pounds); power steering (42-50 pounds); power brakes (18 pounds); power windows (12 to 18 pounds) and continental tire carrier (65 pounds).

1957 HUDSON

HUDSON HORNET — (V-8) — SERIES 80 — Hudson trimmed its model lineup by an amazing figure of 11 cars in 1957, while its roofline was trimmed two inches. The Hudson Rambler, Wasp and Hornet Special Series were dropped. Other new features included 14 inch wheels; a new Hydra-Matic with parking gear; standard 327 cid V-8 with dual exhausts; ball joint front suspension; interiors restyled along more modern lines (with new materials and colors) and standard padded dashboard in all lines. Styling changes included a new 'V' medallion in the center of the grille; dual-fin front fender ornaments; rear tailfin fenders with vertical lamps and a new side trim treatment with front fender and door accent panels. On Supers, the accent panel was painted. There were Hornet and Hollywood nameplates on the hardtops, as well as rear fender 'H' medallions. The Super Sedan had Hornet front door nameplates and no 'H' medallions. Hornet Customs could be identified by textured aluminum insert panels used on the front fenders, between the trim moldings. Nameplate and medallion placements were the same as on comparable Super styles.

1957 Hudson, Hornet four-door sedan, V-8

VEHICLE I.D. NUMBERS: The numbering system was the same as for previous models. Number plates were on a plate under the hood at the top center of dash on Hornets. Body Style Numbers took the form 357( )( ) with the first symbol indicating Hudson; the second

and third symbols indicating model year; the fourth symbol indicating the car-line or series and the fifth symbol indicating body type. Serial number Y-10501 to Y-14376 were used. Engine numbers were below the right rear exhaust port on V-8s. Engine numbers were N-1001 and up.

HUDSON HORNET

Model Number	Body/Style Number	Body Type & Seating	Factory Price	Shipping Weight	Production Total
SUPER V-8 LINE					
NA	35785-1	4-dr Sed-6P	2821	3631	1,103
NA	35787-1	2-dr HT Cpe-6P	2911	3655	266
CUSTOM V-8 LINE					
NA	35785-2	4-dr Sed-6P	3011	3678	1,256
NA	35785-2	2-dr HT Cpe-6P	3101	3693	483

NOTE 1: Total 5700 Series production, including exports, was 4,108 units.

NOTE 2: An additional 72 model 35660 Hudson Sixes were shipped overseas in 'knocked-down' form.

ENGINE: V-8. Overhead valves. Cast iron block. Displacement: 327 cid. Bore and stroke: 4 x 3.25 inches. Compression ratio: 9.0:1. Brake hp: 255 at 4700 rpm. Five main bearings. Hydraulic valve lifter. Carburetor: four-barrel.

CHASSIS FEATURES: Wheelbase: (Hornet) 121.25 inches. Overall length: (Hornet) 209.25 inches. Front tread: (Hornet) 59-1/16 inches. Rear tread: (Hornet) 60-1/2 inches. Tires (Hornet) 8.00 x 14.

POWERTRAIN OPTIONS: Three-speed manual transmission was standard. Overdrive transmission ($110). Automatic transmission ($232). Available rear axle gear ratios 3.15:1; 4.10:1.

OPTIONS: Power brakes on Super ($40); on Custom (standard). Power steering ($100). Air conditioning ($415); Power windows ($109.50).

HISTORICAL FOOTNOTES: The last Hudsons were introduced on Oct. 25, 1957.

KAISER

1947-1955

Shipbuilder Henry J. Kaiser decided to make the automotive industry his port of call after the close of World War II. Teaming with Graham-Paige executive Joseph Frazer — in an association often shaken by personality conflicts — Kaiser moved quickly to beat the major makers into production of an all-new postwar car. The result was a novel-looking, straight-sided design with definite appeal to buyers of the day.

Data Compiled by G. Marshall Naul
Introduction by John A. Gunnell

Competing in a crowd of basically prewar cars that looked like the 'mothball fleet,' Kaiser leaped to an encouraging start. Over 70,000 sales were achieved by the 1947 models and the future, indeed, looked bright. It wasn't very long, however, before the more established brands threw off their prewar image and started to catch up. Being rather high-priced, the Kaisers (and companion Frazer models) simply could not compete. Sales began to decline in 1949 and financial problems ensued. But for a massive loan from the postwar Reconstruction Finance Corporation, the firm may not have survived past this point.

After the loan was granted, Kaiser did survive for a time, although Frazer passed from the scene in 1951. To revitalize the remaining products, master craftsman Howard 'Dutch' Darrin was employed to restyle the line. Heavy emphasis was

also placed on upgraded interior appointments, with major responsibility in this area falling to designer Carlton Spencer, who accomplished an outstanding job. To finish the task of re-making the cars, a powerful six from Continental Engines Co. — a Kaiser Industries subsidiary firm — was improved with new manifolding to produce more get-up-and-go. The 115 hp produced by this 'Supersonic Six' made the 1951 Kaiser something less than a high-performance machine, but nevertheless it was a very fine engine.

Another area in which Kaiser did some fine, if unappreciated work, was in the creation of unique body styles. One was a hatchback sedan called the Vagabond in Deluxe trim, and Traveler in standard form. The company also marketed a four-door convertible and a four-door Virginian hardtop sedan. The latter looked like a ragtop, but was actually a full-pillared automobile. None of these beautiful models sold very well, nor did a Taxicab Special of 1949-1950.

Innovation with Kaiser did not stop with the above, since a number of unique products were also developed in the 1952-1954 period. One was the compact-sized Henry, J (also marketed through Sears, Roebuck and Company as the Allstate). This model is covered separately in the rear section of this catalog devoted to low-production postwar cars and Alternative automobiles.

A second innovation was the Kaiser-Darrin sports car. This spectacular-looking, fiberglass-bodied two-seater was developed and sold as a Kaiser product, as covered in this section.

Later, it was later revived, by Howard Darrin himself, between 1955 and 1958 (see the "Minor Makes" section).

By 1952, Kaiser sales fell to the 32,000 unit level, which brought some interesting results. For example, in some years the company fell far short of selling the number of cars it had produced. In such cases, the leftovers were sometimes redecorated, given new serial numbers and re-introduced as the next line of cars. When all were sold, a new series would be introduced, without regard to the normal duration of the current model year. The 1952 Virginian (no longer a four-door hardtop) was such a car.

When the true 1952 Kaisers were introduced, in March of that calendar year, several new model names appeared. The Manhattan was the top-level series, while bottom-of-the-line cars were called Deluxe models. Added in 1953 was a fully-equipped luxury model called the Dragon. It was named after the texture of its seating surface material, which was thought to be like the skin of the mythological beast. An option was a padded roof covered in special 'Bambu' vinyl.

If all of this sounds like a desperate attempt to reach out for new buyers, you've got a clear picture of the way things were in the company's last few years of domestic automobile production. On the other hand, you can imagine how modern collectors enjoy owning a car that was virtually the next thing to custom-built. Sales at this point were down to some 22,000 units per year and Kaiser was going broke.

Kaiser, of course, wasn't the only independent manufacturer having problems at this time and the trend was for the smaller companies to merge together, in order to survive against the 'Big Three.' In 1954, the same year that Nash and Hudson combined to form American Motors, Kaiser Motors bought Willys-Overland of Toledo, Ohio. The result became known as Kaiser-Willys, which thereafter operated as a subsidiary of Kaiser Industries. The Kaiser factory, in Willow Run, Mich., was sold to General Motors. Eventually, all production was transferred to Toledo.

For the 1954 model year, there were, again, two series of cars. The first consisted of 1953 leftovers that carried Body number plates from Michigan and Serial number plates from Ohio. However, all units of the later series were products constructed at the Willys plant. A new feature was a supercharged, 'Super-Power' six, which developed 140 bhp in Manhattan models. When sales for the calendar year peaked at only 17,000 units, Henry Kaiser could see the handwriting on the wall.

In 1955, Kaiser-Willys announced its intentions to pull out of the passenger car building business, at least in the United States. In the future, the company would concentrate solely on the domestic commercial vehicle market, where its Jeep product line was enjoying much stronger sales. Just over 1,000 Kaiser automobiles were turned out in 1955, with the majority shipped to South America to fill an Argentina order. In the following months, the body dies and manufacturing equipment were also sent to Argentina, where the Kaiser would be marketed, as the Carabella, for another seven years.

While the Kaiser lasted for only 10 years in this country, marque enthusiasts are quick to point out the contributions made by these outstanding cars. In terms of styling, 1951 was the first year of the new second-generation Kaiser style. The 1952 models built upon the lead and can justly lay claim to helping to develop a new school of automotive design emphasizing sleek, low looks. Kaiser was also among the first to provide a full instrument panel crash pad as standard equipment. Kaiser is also given credit for being among the first to incorporate pop-out windshields. The company was one of the few automakers to offer seat belts at the time. In addition, Kaiser pioneered use of dual purpose taillamps designed to serve as side safety markers, as well as stop and directional lights. Emphasis on the use of sound-deadening interior insulation, lavish upholstery trim options and supercharging as standard equipment are three other Kaiser milestones later accepted as industry standard.

1947 Kaiser, four-door sedan, 6-cyl

1948 Kaiser Special, four-door sedan, 6-cyl

1954 Kaiser-Darrin two-door roadster, 6-cyl

1954 Kaiser, Manhattan four-door sedan, 6-cyl

Standard Catalog of American Cars

1947 KAISER

1947 Kaiser, Special four-door sedan, 6-cyl

KAISER SPECIAL — (6-CYL) — K100 SERIES — The Kaiser was first conceived as a front-wheel-drive sedan, designated the K-85, of which two working prototypes were built. Engineering difficulties and costs kept the K-85 from reaching production. The 1947 production models were introduced in August, 1946. They were based on the same body used for 1947 Frazers, which had been designed by Howard 'Dutch' Darrin. Both of these cars had the first true postwar sheet metal with envelope bodies and fenderlines that ran front to rear in an unbroken contour. Features included welded all-steel construction; between the wheel seating; exceptionally wide wheel rims; low center of gravity; low, luxurious seats; large luggage compartment; curved wraparound bumpers; dual horns; twin sun visors; dash mounted starter switch; two combination stop and taillights; automatic dome lights; and large, hydraulic self-centering brakes. The Kaiser radiator grille was a strange mixture of vertical and horizontal blades with rectangular parking lamps placed outside the grillework, under the headlamps. A large hood badge bearing the letter 'K' above a buffalo shield was an obvious identification feature.

KAISER I.D. NUMBERS: Serial number stamped on a tag on left front door post. Serial numbers consisted of a Model number prefix and a six digit figure which is 001001 for the first car of the year. For 1947, prefix K-100=Special sedan; Prefix K-101=Custom sedan. Serial numbers for 1947 were K100-1001 to 66062 for Specials and K101-2000001 to 2005412 for Customs. Engine numbers were stamped on a pad on the left front upper corner of the engine block and on a plate on the left side of the block. Engine numbers for 1947 were K-100001 and up for both series. Kaisers also carried a numerical Body (Style) Number, which was identical to the Body numbers used on Frazers.

KAISER SPECIAL SERIES K100

Model Number	Body/Style Number	Body Type & Seating	Factory Price	Shipping Weight	Production Total
K100	1005	4-dr Sed-6P	1868	3305	65,062

NOTE 1: Prices and weights above are those in effect during April, 1947.
NOTE 2: Prices changed to $1,967 and $2,104 later.
NOTE 3: Late-year factory weight was 3,295 pounds.

KAISER CUSTOM — (6-CYL) — SERIES K101 — The Custom was a more Deluxe version of the basic Kaiser sedan. This model was introduced on Sept. 25, 1947. Features included a special dashboard; window control knobs; custom styled back seats; robe holder; new ashtrays and package shelf; more interior trim; bright metal windshield frames; upholstered trunk compartment; passenger assist handles; chrome highlighted foot rests; courtesy lamps; bright finished hand brake lever; and lengthwise seamed headliner. Rocker panel moldings and Custom front fender scripts were seen, as well as chrome wheel trim rings. Four front bumper guards were standard equipment. The Custom interiors were carefully keyed to harmonize with special exterior shades such as Onyx; Linden Green; Clay Pipe Gray; Coral Sand; Horizon Blue and Hickory Brown Metallic.

KAISER CUSTOM SERIES K101

Model Number	Body/Style Number	Body Type & Seating	Factory Price	Shipping Weight	Production Total
K101	1015	4-dr Sed-6P	2301	3295	5,412

NOTE 1: The price for the 1947 Kaiser Custom sedan later increased to $2,456.

ENGINE: Inline. L-head six. Cast iron block. Displacement: 226.2 cid. Bore and stroke: 3-15/16 x 4-3/8 inches. Compression ratio: initially 6.86:1, changed to 7.3:1 near end of model year. Brake hp: 100 at 3600 rpm. Four main bearings. Solid valve lifters. Carburetor: Carter Type W-1 or WA-1 one-barrel Models 574S; 622S or 622SA.

CHASSIS FEATURES: Wheelbase: 123.5 inches. Overall length: 203 inches. Front tread: 58 inches. Rear tread: 60 inches. Tires: 6.50 x 15.

CONVENIENCE OPTIONS: Defroster and heater ($48). Radio. Radio antenna. Stainless steel wheel trim rings. Tailpipe extension. Full wheel discs. Outside rearview mirror. External sun visor. Spot lights. Fog lamps. Plastic white side wall discs. Front bumper guards. Rear bumper guards. White sidewall tires (when available). Clip-on vanity mirror. Locking gas cap. Three-speed manual transmission was standard. Automatic choke. Oil-bath air cleaner. Vacuum booster fuel pump. Kaiser-Frazer Club Archives lists five available rear axle gear ratios.

HISTORICAL FOOTNOTES: The 1947 Kaiser Specials were introduced in August, 1946 and the Kaiser Custom appeared in dealer showrooms after Sept. 25, 1947. Model year production peaked at 70,474 units. Calendar year sales of 144,490 cars including Frazers were recorded. Henry J. Kaiser was the chairman of the board for the company this year. Joseph W. Frazer was president and general manager. Frazer was also the chief executive officer of Graham-Paige Motors. On Feb. 1, 1947 the automotive assets of Graham-Paige were sold to the new

Kaiser-Frazer company. Hood ornaments were not used on 1947 Kaiser-Frazer automobiles, although aftermarket mascots were available which were custom designed for both cars. Kaiser-Frazer of Canada, Ltd. was formed in 1947.

1948 KAISER

1948 Kaiser, Special four-door sedan, 6-cyl

KAISER — (6-CYL) — SERIES K481 — There were minor changes in the Kaiser for 1948 and most were alterations adopted at some point in the 1947 model run. They included new bumper guards with a more angular, staggered look; a darker color field behind the large 'K' in the hood name badge; the elimination of two thin moldings at the outboard ends of the radiator grille opening; and removal of Special nameplates from the grille and rear deck (which appeared only on very early 1947 cars anyway). Effective with car number 36,446 the use of beige colored instrument faces, instead of green ones, was begun. Higher compression ratios were listed as a 1948 improvement, but use of this 7.3:1 ratio head began late in 1947 and was carried over for 1948 models. Apparently, only the earliest 1947s had a 6.86:1 ratio head design and this was actually a running production change. The horsepower rating was not affected. About 25 other technical changes, most of minor significance, were promoted by the company for the new year for both Kaisers and Frazers. The use of larger 7.10 x 15 tires was one of them.

KAISER I.D. NUMBERS: Serial number stamped on a tag on left front door post. Serial numbers consisted of a Model number prefix and a six digit figure which is 001001 for the first car of the year. The 1948 Body Style number prefix changed to K481 for the lowest-priced line and K482 for Customs. The first symbol 'K' indicated Kaiser. The second and third symbols '48' indicated 1948 model. The fourth symbol was used for series designation. Serial numbers K481-1001 to 093587 were used on standard Kaiser models. Serial numbers K482-1001 to 002263 were used on Kaiser Customs. Motor numbers continued from 1947 or fell into a new range of numbers beginning at K100 and up.

KAISER SIX SERIES K481

Model Number	Body/Style Number	Body Type & Seating	Factory Price	Shipping Weight	Production Total
K481	K4811	4-dr Sed-6P	2244	3295	90,588

KAISER CUSTOM — (6-CYL) — SERIES K482 — The Custom continued as a more Deluxe version of the Kaiser Special with control knobs; clock; richer upholstery; custom styled back seats; robe holder; ashtrays; package shelf; bright metal windshield and window reveals; upholstered trunk compartment; passenger assist handles; chrome trimmed foot rests; courtesy lamps; bright metal hand brake lever; and headliner with seams running lengthwise. The exterior of Custom models was distinguished by identification scripts placed high on the trailing edge of the front fendersides (cowl side region) and bright rocker panel moldings. Front compartment carpeting was a new, running change.

KAISER CUSTOM SERIES K482

Model Number	Body/Style Number	Body Type & Seating	Factory Price	Shipping Weight	Production Total
K482	K4821	4-dr Sed-6P	2466	3295	1,263

ENGINES

(BASE SIX) Inline: L-head six. Cast iron block. Displacement: 226.2 cid. Bore and stroke: 3-15/16 x 4-3/8 inches. Compression ratio: 7.3:1. Brake hp: 100 at 3600 rpm. Four main bearings. Solid valve lifters. Carburetor: Carter Type W-1 or WA-1 one-barrel Models 574S; 622S or 622SA.

(DUAL MANIFOLD SIX) Inline. L-head six. Cast iron block. Displacement: 226.2 cid. Bore and stroke: 3-15/16 x 4-3/8 inches. Compression ratio: 7.3:1. Brake hp: 112 at 3600 rpm. Four main bearings. Solid valve lifters. Carburetor: Carter Type WCD or WAI Dual manifold motor introduced at midyear.

CHASSIS FEATURES: Wheelbase: 123-1/2 inches. Overall length: 203 inches. Front tread: 58 inches. Rear tread: 60 inches. Tires: 7.10 x 15.

OPTIONS: Defroster and heater ($48). Radio. Radio antenna. Stainless steel wheel trim rings. Tailpipe extension. Round shaped outside rearview mirror. External sun visor. Clip-on vanity mirror. Locking gas cap. Spotlights. Fog lamps. Authentic white sidewall tires. Bumper guards. Accessory Group AG-1 including bumper guards front and rear; heavy-duty air cleaner; vacuum storage tank for wipers; spare tire and tube on wheel; license holder and guards; wheel trim rings; tailpipe extension; rear seat cigar lighter ($105). Three-speed manual transmission was standard. Automatic choke. Oil-bath air cleaner. Vacuum booster fuel pump. Several available rear axle ratios.

HISTORICAL FOOTNOTES: Sales of 1948 Kaisers began in December, 1947. Model year production peaked at 91,851 cars. Henry J. Kaiser was Chairman of the Board again this year. Joseph W. Frazer was President, Edgar F. Kaiser General Manager. A proud addition to the Harrah's Automobile Collection (now National Automobile Museum), in Reno, Nevada, for many years was a one-off 1948 Kaiser made for Edward Hunt's wife. (Hunt was the director

of the company's Detroit Engine Div.). Hunt's wife was physically handicapped, so this car featured a styling and seating configuration not available in regular production cars. The rear doors were welded closed and had the seams filled in, thereby making it a two-door sedan. A U-shaped, Davenport style seat was found in the rear compartment. Called the Pinconning Special (after Hunt's hometown in Michigan), the two-door had a dark green roof and fenders, but was colored light green on the hood, rear deck and body above the belt. It is usually referred to as the "conference" car, although Pinconning Special scripts adorn both front fenders. Business disputes, revolving around corporate finances, erupted this season between Henry J. Kaiser and Cyrus Eaton of Otis & Co., a stock market firm. The overall effect was less than beneficial to Kaiser-Frazer's financial stability at the time.

1949 KAISER

1949 Kaiser, Special four-door sedan, 6-cyl

KAISER SPECIAL — (6-CYL) — SERIES K49 — With a styling program estimated to have cost $10 million, Kaiser-Frazer extensively revamped its 1949 models to make them look longer, lower and more modern. Actually, the height of the body was unchanged, but a full-width horizontal grille and fenders with 3-1/2 extra inches of overhang made for a lower appearance. The grille featured three wide, horizontal moldings that ran end-to-end and slightly around the front body corners. Rectangular parking lamps were set into the outboard ends of the center bar. On the nose of the car, right above the grille, was a rather large, wing-shaped chrome molding incorporating the company's large K-and-buffalo logo. The 'K' rose above the piece of plated pot metal, while the buffalo - against a black color field - was in the lower mid-section of the badge. Cloisonne finish was no longer used on the badge, as it was now strictly painted metal. Another obvious revision, among 42 styling changes claimed by designers, was larger taillights with more massive chrome housings. Rocker panel moldings were now used on all models. They were placed an inch or two above the edge of the lower body sill, between the front and rear wheelhousings. No hood ornaments were used and the low-priced Special had no exterior side nameplates. Interior treatments included a two-spoke steering wheel with a full horn-blowing ring that had a circular indentation at the top. There was a chrome plated bottom support bar between the wheel's outer rim and the bright metal horn ring. In the center was a light-colored insert decorated with a large K-and-buffalo badge. The dash top was of painted metal; instrument panel trim was stainless steel; the emergency brake handle was chrome plated and rubber floor mats were used. The circular housing on the glovebox door was filled with a plain insert, unless a clock (standard in Deluxes) was ordered as optional equipment. A new model was the unique Traveler utility sedan. Priced less than $100 above the conventional sedan, the Traveler's standard equipment included heavy-duty springs; heavy-duty shock absorbers; a special license plate holder; fold-down rear seatback; plastic seat covers; and hatchback style rear construction. The car was turned into a combination workhorse and carryall by welding the left rear door shut; moving the spare tire to a vertical mounting behind the driver's seat and horizontally splitting the rear deck sheet metal. Thus, the upper deck and window became a liftgate, while the lower deck was converted into a drop-down tailgate. It took a lot of braces, supports and structural re-engineering (plus repositioning of the bumper guards) to make things work just right, but the result was a combination passenger car and station wagon with a large cargo bed. For 1949-1950, Kaiser also built heavy-duty taxicabs in the low-trim line. They had a beefed-up suspension and more durable upholstery fabrics to suit the task at hand.

KAISER I.D. NUMBERS: Serial number stamped on a tag on left front door post. Serial number consisted of a model number prefix and a six digit figure which is 001001 for the first car of the year. Serial numbers K-491-1001 to 052740 were used on Special models. Serial numbers K-492-1001 to 045050 were used on Deluxe models. The first symbol 'K' designated Kaiser. The second and third symbols '49' designated 1949 model year. The fourth symbol designated the trim level series, as follows: the lower number '1' indicated Special (low-trim) models and the higher number '2' indicated Deluxe (high-trim) models. A fifth symbol, shown in Body/Style Number column of charts below, was added to code different body styles. Motor numbers for both series continued from 1948, with the range KM 1001 and up now specified for Deluxes.

KAISER SPECIAL SERIES K491

Model Number	Body/Style Number	Body Type & Seating	Factory Price	Shipping Weight	Production Total
K491	K4911	4-dr Sed-6P	1995	3311	Note 2
K491	K4915	4-dr Utl Sed-6P	2088	3456	Note 2
K491	K4916	4-dr Taxi-6/8P	2216	3345	Note 2

NOTE 1: "Production Total" may actually be a sales total, as serial number range ran through 53,996 instead of 52,740. Some cars were built and not sold.

NOTE 2: Kaiser's 1949-1950 production counted as a single total; see 1950.

NOTE 3: References list Traveler four-door, though left rear door was fixed.

KAISER DELUXE — (6-CYL) — SERIES K492 — The Deluxe Series was characterized by richer interior and exterior appointments, the offering of a distinctive four-door hardtop called the Virginian and the late introduction of a four-door convertible. Sedans had paint color name listed as chrome script on side of the cowl. Standard equipment on Deluxe sedans included all Special sedan features, plus wheel trim rings; front compartment carpets; Deluxe two-spoke steering wheel with semi-circular horn-blowing ring; glovebox clock; padded dashboard; wood-grained front dash panel inserts; color-keyed interior parts (the brake controls, sun visors, headlining, rear ashtrays, pedal pads and gearshift knob were all in harmonizing color tones); richer upholstery fabrics; and 112 hp six-cylinder engine. The Vagabond was the Deluxe trim version of the utility sedan. It had special front fender model scripts, standard fender skirts and wider rocker panel moldings. Genuine leather upholstery was optional in this style. The Virginian four-door hardtop sedan also had Deluxe dashboard trim; front carpets; wide rocker moldings; fender skirts with rocker panel extension moldings; suitable front fender identification scripts; chrome plated lower window/belt reveal moldings; plated roof trim moldings; nylon top in black or tan with colored-keyed inner liner; three-section rear window; and special, color-keyed interior trims. Released later in the run, as an option priced around $200, was the Custom Virginian package, including Custom script plates; Stockholm and Volta cloth upholstery; Imperial Crush floor coverings; extra brightwork; and carpeted lower door panels. Very few Custom Virginians were made and most of them served as company show cars. In January, 1949, Kaiser added a four-door convertible (a true convertible sedan) to the Deluxe model lineup. It was styled and trimmed like the Virginian, except that it lacked front fender scripts and usually came with black, top grain leather seating surfaces. Some sources classify all the convertibles as 1950 models, since November, 1949 was considered the starting point for sales of '1950' Kaisers. However, the earliest Kaiser convertibles were coded as body style K4922, which makes them true 1949 models (1950 convertibles were recoded K5022).

KAISER DELUXE SERIES K492

Model Number	Body/Style Number	Body Type & Seating	Factory Price	Shipping Weight	Production Total
DELUXE SERIES					
K492	K4921	4-dr Sed-6P	2195	3341	Note 1
K492	K4922	4-dr Conv-6P	3195	3725	Note 1
VIRGINIAN SERIES					
K492	K4923	4-dr HT Sed-6P	2995	3541	Note 1
VAGABOND SERIES					
K492	K4925	4-dr Utl Sed-6P	2288	3501	Note 1

NOTE 1: Kaiser's 1949-1950 production counted as a single total; see 1950.

ENGINES

(BASE SIX) Inline: L-head six. Cast iron block. Displacement: 226.2 cid. Bore and stroke: 3-15/16 x 4-3/8 inches. Compression ratio: 7.3:1. Brake hp: 100 at 3600 rpm. Four main bearings. Solid valve lifters. Carburetor: Carter Model 622SB single downdraft carburetor on Specials.

(DUAL MANIFOLD SIX) Inline: L-head six. Cast iron block. Displacement: 226.2 cid. Bore and stroke: 3-15/16 x 4-3/8 inches. Compression ratio: 7.3:1. Brake hp: 112 at 3600 rpm. Four main bearings. Solid valve lifters. Carburetor: Carter Type WCD or WAI with dual manifold. (Offered on Special taxicabs).

CHASSIS FEATURES: Wheelbase: 123-1/2 inches. Overall length: 203 inches. Front tread: 58 inches. Rear tread: 60 inches. Tires: 7.10 x 15.

OPTIONS: Defroster and heater ($48). Radio. Radio antenna. Stainless steel wheel trim rings. Tailpipe extension. Round shaped outside rearview mirror. External sun visor. Clip-on vanity mirror. Locking gas cap. Spotlights. Fog lamps. Authentic white sidewall tires. Bumper guards. Accessory Group AG-1 including bumper guards front and rear; heavy-duty air cleaner; vacuum storage tank for wipers; spare tire and tube on wheel; license holder and guards; wheel trim rings; tailpipe extension; rear seat cigar lighter ($105). Three-speed manual transmission was standard. Automatic choke. Oil-bath air cleaner. Vacuum booster fuel pump. Several available rear axle ratios. Two-tone paint. Rear fender skirts. Option Accessory Groups: [Group AG1] includes oil-bath air cleaner and directional signal lights ($17.85). [Group AG2] includes oil-bath air cleaner; directional signals; rear cigar lighter; chrome wheel-covers; and Deluxe bumper guards ($60). [Group AG3] includes electric clock; chrome wheel discs; spare tire and tube on wheel; tailpipe extension; two front and three rear bumper guards; heavy-duty air cleaner; front cigar lighter; replaceable oil filter element; rear cigar lighter; and dual-action fuel pump ($105). [Group AG8] includes heavy-duty grille and air cleaner; spare tire and tube on wheel; three rear bumper guards; front cigar lighter; replaceable oil filter element; and dual-action fuel pump in Vagabond ($40); in taxicab (standard). On Virginians and Vagabonds, rear fender skirts appear to have been what is called a 'standard option.' In other words, they are extra-cost items, but were probably installed on all cars unless specifically deleted.

HISTORICAL FOOTNOTES: The 1949 Kaiser sedan was publicly announced on Sept. 19, 1948. A handful of Kaiser convertibles have 1949 model coding. Kaiser-Frazer was America's 12th ranked automobile manufacturer this year. The new models were styled by a design team working under chief stylist Bob Cadwalloder. Color and trim combinations, which were most imaginative, were created by Carlton Spencer. An interesting point is that paint call-out nameplates were seen on the front fenders of Kaiser Deluxe models. They carried the name of the main body color, for example, 'Executive Green' or 'Caribbean Coral.'

1950 KAISER

KAISER SPECIAL — (6-CYL) — SERIES K501 — Kaiser originally planned to market a face-lifted line of cars for the 1950 model year, but was unable to accomplish the changes on schedule, due to lack of money for development work. By October, 1949 it was clear the revisions could not be ready in time. Therefore, the company decided to recode leftover 1949s as 1950 models and to save the new ideas for the following season. On Nov. 3, 1949, company dealers were sent a letter advising that, within four days, a factory representative would arrive with new serial number plates for installation on 1949 models remaining in stock. The sales agents were specifically told not to represent the cars as being different from the previous product. Technically speaking, the 1950 Kaiser model year lasted only from the time that the serial number plates were switched (beginning Nov. 7, 1949), until March 15, 1950, when the all-new 1951 Kaiser line was introduced. Inspection of calendar year registration and production figures indicates that approximately 16 percent of the cars originally built to 1949 specifications were sold during this four month period. It has also been determined, by automotive historians, that most of these were fancier and higher-priced models, such as Virginians and four-door convertibles. Important features promoted in all of these cars included All-Direction roominess; sway eliminator bar; coil front springs; Super-Cushion tires; double channel frame construction; ball type midship bearings; two-piece propeller shaft; floating shoe brakes; Centrifuse brake drums; three-point engine mounting; vibration

dampener; direct-acting shock absorbers; spring leaf liners; rubber cored spring shackles; hypoid rear axle; Clear-Vision steering wheel; external oil filter; ball bearing water pump; and automatic choke. The Kaiser Special could be identified by continued use of narrow chrome rocker panel strips below the doors and lack of front fender insignia.

KAISER I.D. NUMBERS: Serial number stamped on a tag on left front door post. Serial numbers consisted of a Model number prefix and a six digit figure which is 001001 for the first car of the year. The cars were recoded with a Serial number plate having the prefix K501 for Specials and K502 for Deluxes. The first symbol 'K' indicated Kaiser. The second and third symbols '50' indicated 1950 model. The fourth symbol indicated car-line. A fifth symbol indicating body type is listed in Body/Style Number column of charts below. Sequential unit numbers for 1950 did not change from those used in 1949, although the ending number was arbitrarily raised to 600000 for Specials and 500000 for Deluxes. Based on the 1949 sequences previously listed, car number K501-1052741 was the first 1950 Special; car number K502-045051 the first 1950 Deluxe. Since the 1950 ending numbers are arbitrary, there is no way to pinpoint the exact model year output.

KAISER SPECIAL SERIES K501

Model Number	Body/Style Number	Body Type & Seating	Factory Price	Shipping Weight	Production Total
K501	K5011	4-dr Sed-6P	1995	3311	32,429
K501	K5015	4-dr Trav Utl Sed-6P	2088	3456	19,605
K501	K5016	4-dr Taxi-6/8P	NA	NA	2,641

NOTE 1: Kaiser's 1949-1950 production counted as a single total.
NOTE 2: Approximately 16 percent of total sold as 1950 models.

KAISER DELUXE — (6-CYL) — SERIES K502 — The Kaiser Deluxe models were also unchanged in specifications and received updated Serial numbers sometime after Nov. 7, 1949. After the numbers were changed, they were sold as 1950 automobiles. In addition to the features listed for Specials, the Kaiser Deluxe utilized the 112 hp powerplant having a dual intake manifold and dual-throat carburetor as standard equipment. Deluxe sedans and Utility sedans were identified by wider chrome rocker panels below the doors. There were Virginian or Vagabond front fender nameplates or scripts bearing main body colors, such as "Linden Green," on convertibles and sedans. The four-door convertible and Virginian had the same special equipment features as in 1949. Marque experts suggest that, due to their higher prices, most of these cars were sold as 1950 models.

KAISER DELUXE SERIES K502

Model Number	Body/Style Number	Body Type & Seating	Factory Price	Shipping Weight	Production Total
DELUXE SERIES					
K502	K5021	4-dr Sed-6P	2195	3341	37,756
K502	K5022	4-dr Conv-6P	3195	3726	42
VIRGINIAN SERIES					
K502	K5023	4-dr Vir HT Sed-6P	2995	3541	986
VAGABOND SERIES					
K502	K5025	4-dr Trav Utl Sed-6P	2288	3501	4,507

NOTE 1: Kaiser's 1949-1950 production counted as a single total.
NOTE 2: Approximately 16 percent of total sold as 1950 models.

ENGINES

(BASE SIX) Inline: L-head six. Cast iron block. Displacement: 226.2 cid. Bore and stroke: 3-15/16 x 4-3/8 inches. Compression ratio: 7.3:1. Brake hp: 100 at 3600 rpm. Four main bearings. Solid valve lifters. Carburetor: Carter Model 622SB single downdraft carburetor on Specials.

(DUAL MANIFOLD SIX) Inline: L-head six. Cast iron block. Displacement: 226.2 cid. Bore and stroke: 3-15/16 x 4-3/8 inches. Compression ratio: 7.3:1. Brake hp: 112 at 3600 rpm. Four main bearings. Solid valve lifters. Carburetor: Carter Type WCD or WAI with dual manifold. (Offered on Special taxicabs).

CHASSIS FEATURES: Wheelbase: 123-1/2 inches. Overall length: 203 inches. Front tread: 58 inches. Rear tread: 60 inches. Tires: 7.10 x 15.

OPTIONS: Defroster and heater ($48). Radio. Radio antenna. Stainless steel wheel trim rings. Tailpipe extension. Round shaped outside rearview mirror. External sun visor. Clip-on vanity mirror. Locking gas cap. Spotlights. Fog lamps. Authentic white sidewall tires. Bumper guards. Accessory Group AG-1 including bumper guards front and rear; heavy-duty air cleaner; vacuum storage tank for wipers; spare tire and tube on wheel; license holder and guards; wheel trim rings; tailpipe extension; rear seat cigar lighter ($105). Three-speed manual transmission was standard. Automatic choke. Oil-bath air cleaner. Vacuum booster fuel pump. Several available rear axle ratios. Two-tone paint. Rear fender skirts. Option Accessory Groups: [Group AG1] includes oil-bath air cleaner and directional signal lights ($17.85). [Group AG2] includes oil-bath air cleaner; directional signals; rear cigar lighter; chrome wheel-covers; and Deluxe bumper guards ($60). [Group AG3] includes electric clock; chrome wheel discs; spare tire and tube on wheel; tailpipe extension; two front and three rear bumper guards; heavy-duty air cleaner; front cigar lighter; replaceable oil filter element; rear cigar lighter; and dual-action fuel pump ($105). [Group AG8] includes heavy-duty grille and air cleaner; spare tire and tube on wheel; three rear bumper guards; front cigar lighter; replaceable oil filter element; and dual-action fuel pump in Vagabond ($40); in taxicab (standard). On Virginians and Vagabonds, rear fender skirts appear to have been what is called a 'standard option.' In other words, they are extra-cost items, but were probably installed on all cars unless specifically deleted.

HISTORICAL FOOTNOTES: The exact model year production of 1949-1950 Kaisers was 95,175 units. Some reference sources indicate the beginning of the 1950 model year as Jan. 9, 1950. However, the leftover 1949 cars were re-coded in November 1949. Possibly, the company waited until all cars were converted, before officially announcing the start of the new model year. Henry J. Kaiser was chairman of the board. Joseph W. Frazer was vice chairman of the board.

1951 KAISER

KAISER SPECIAL — (6-CYL) — SERIES K511 — The 1951 Kaiser was completely redesigned in a style which would remain essentially unchanged through the end of marque production in 1955. The new design was again the product of Howard 'Dutch' Darrin's skills. The general lines were less boxy than in the past, with greatly increased glass areas. There was a break in the fenderlines, at the rear doors, which eliminated the old pontoon shape. Gone also, was the bull-nosed frontal appearance, which was replaced with a more pleasing shape having a prominent center crease. The grille was formed by two horizontal bars, the main top member running the full width of the body and wrapping around the corners. The lower bar stretched only to the extremities of the radiator opening. A K-and-buffalo badge sat in front of the hood and a dart-like mascot enhanced its overall appearance. A unique 'Darrin Dip' was incorporated at the front of the roof. In this treatment, the upper windshield header had a gently curved contour on each side, with the curves dipping together, in a 'V' at the middle. The resulting 'sea gull's wing' shape would remain a Kaiser trademark until the end. The overall appearance was called "Anatomic Design," as it was claimed that the car fit the anatomy of the human body. It certainly allowed greater passenger comfort, with substantial increases in headroom and legroom. Features included the largest windshield in the auto industry; safety locks on rear doors; scientifically achieved weight distribution; Direct-View instrumentation cluster; Tuck-Away spare tire well; rubber body mountings; steel covered rear springs; wraparound bumpers; insulated body; large diameter drive shaft; Hotchkiss drive; air-cooled clutch; and a 115 hp high-compression six with mushroom tappets, vibration dampener, full-length water jacketing, fully-balanced crankshaft and external oil filter. Early 1951 Kaiser Specials were identifiable by the lack of chrome bodyside trim, although a narrow chrome side strip was added later in the run. It was of three-quarter length, being mounted low on the body and running from behind the front wheelhousing to above the rear bumper wraparound.

KAISER I.D. NUMBERS: Serial number stamped on a tag on left front door post. Serial numbers consisted of a Model number prefix and a six digit figure which is 001001 for the first car of the year. Serial numbers K511-001001 to 067256 were used on Specials built at the Willow Run, Mich. factory. Serial numbers K512-001001 to 079757 were used on Deluxes built at the Willow Run, Mich. factory. Cars built at three other assembly points carried a specific alphabetical serial number prefix, as follows: A=Long Beach, Calif.; B=Jackson, Mich. and C=Portland, Ore. Motor numbers 100000 and up or 2000000 and up were used on Kaisers and were continued into 1952. Body style codes show up as the fifth symbol in second column of charts below.

KAISER SPECIAL SERIES K511

Model Number	Body/Style Number	Body Type & Seating	Factory Price	Shipping Weight	Production Total
K511	K5111	4-dr Sed-6P	2212	3126	39,078
K511	K5110	2-dr Trav Utl Sed-6P	2265	3210	915
K511	K5113	2-dr Bus Cpe-3P	1992	3061	746
K511	K5114	2-dr Sed-6P	2160	3106	8,166
K511	K5115	4-dr Trav Utl Sed-6P	2317	3270	1,829

NOTE 1: Body style production totals based on estimates by historians.

1951 Kaiser, Deluxe two-door coupe, 6-cyl

KAISER DELUXE — (6-CYL) — SERIES K512 — The Kaiser Deluxe models had the same new styling as Specials with additional trim features. They also had richer appointments and more standard equipment. They could be easily identified by a wide strip of chrome around the bottom of the body; foam rubber seat cushions; Deluxe dashboard treatments; and rear seat ashtrays. Also included were bumper end wing guards, stainless steel belt moldings; bright window reveals; cotton headliner with wool facing; front compartment carpeting; padded vinyl dashboard; and Tenite plastic Deluxe steering wheel with horn-blowing ring. Deluxe interior combinations included Stockholm, Beaumont or Normandie cloths, genuine leather options and pleated, patterned vinyl in Travelers. A two-door Club Coupe with six-passenger seating replaced the three-passenger business coupe in the Deluxe line. Otherwise, the high-trim body styles were a match for those in the Special Series. Both 1951 lines were introduced in February, 1950. This was due to Kaiser's carryover of 1949 models into model year 1950. The company now had the resources to make changes originally planned earlier. Thus, the company's 1951 model year lasted from the spring of 1950 thru winter of 1951. In November, 1950, the famous Kaiser Dragon trim option was initially marketed. Named for their heavy seat surfacing material - which was jokingly compared to the skin of a dragon - Kaisers sold with this option seem to have all come with certain other features, including Hydra-Matic transmission; white sidewall tires; and interior/exterior enrichments. The first series Dragons were sold through Feb. 6, 1951. They came with a choice of nine different exterior color combinations, each of which complemented a specific 'Dragon vinyl' trim combination, with seven selections catalogued. On these earliest Dragons the roof was painted, sometimes in a contrasting shade. Second series Dragons had padded tops. So did a third series offered after April 27, 1951. The second series models had three exterior color choices and were named after them. For example, Golden Dragons came with Arena yellow exteriors and black dinosaur vinyl trim; Silver Dragons came in Mariner gray with Scarlet dinosaur vinyl trim; and Emerald Dragons were painted Cape Verde green (metallic) with matching dinosaur vinyl fabrics. Third series cars came only as Tropical green 'Jade Dragons' with straw-colored interiors. Some Dragon features, such as a removal armrest in second series editions and padded 'Sport Topping' roof treatments, later became separate options for other Kaisers. Also, the armrest was not standard in third series Dragons to lower the price a bit. The GM made Hydra-Matic four-speed automatic transmission was also available as an individual option for the first time in 1951.

KAISER DELUXE SERIES K512

Model Number	Body/Style Number	Body Type & Seating	Factory Price	Shipping Weight	Production Total
K512	K5121	4-dr Sed-6P	2328	3171	56,723
K512	K5120	2-dr Trav Utl Sed-6P	2380	3285	367
K512	K5124	2-dr Sed-6P	2275	3151	8,888
K512	K5125	4-dr Trav Utl Sed-6P	2380	3285	984
K512	K5127	2-dr Clb Cpe-6P	2296	3111	4,606

NOTE 1: Body style production totals based on estimates by historians.

ENGINE: Inline L-head six. Cast iron block. Displacement: 226.2 cid. Bore and stroke: 3-15/16 x 4-3/8 inches. Compression ratio: 7.3:1. Brake hp: 115 at 3650 rpm. Four main bearings. Solid valve lifters. Carburetor: Carter Type WGD two-barrel Model 781S.

CHASSIS FEATURES: Wheelbase: 118.5 inches. Overall length: (Special) 208.5 inches; (Deluxe) 210-3/8 inches. Front tread: 58 inches. Rear tread: 58.75 inches. Tires: 6.70 x 15.

OPTIONS: Defroster and heater ($48). Radio. Radio antenna. Stainless steel wheel trim rings. Tailpipe extension. Round shaped outside rearview mirror. External sun visor. Clip-on vanity mirror. Locking gas cap. Spotlights. Fog lamps. Authentic white sidewall tires. Bumper guards. Automatic choke. Oil-bath air cleaner. Vacuum booster fuel pump. Several available rear axle ratios. Two-tone paint. Rear fender skirts. Conditioned air system. Radio. Spotlight. Accessory Groups: [Group AG1] included directionals and oil bath air cleaner ($17.85). [Group AG2] included oil bath cleaner; directional signals; rear cigar lighter; chrome wheelcovers; and Deluxe bumper guards ($60). [Group AG3] included front cigar lighter; replaceable oil filter element; rear cigarette lighter; dual-action fuel pump; wheel discs; electric clock; spare and tube on wheel; tailpipe extension; two front/three rear bumper guards; and oil-bath air cleaner ($105). [Group AG21] included front cigar lighter; front vent wings; full wheelcovers; chrome horn ring; dual horns; folding rear seat; Stockholm or Dragon vinyl upholstery; door trim moldings; armrest; right interior sun visor; four bumper guards; and dual rear ashtrays ($180.95). [Group AG9] included oil bath air cleaner; directionals; rear cigar lighter; tilt-type rearview mirror; Deluxe front and rear bumper guards; chrome wheelcovers; tailpipe extension; electric clock; Tenite plastic Deluxe steering wheel; and electric windshield wipers ($113.59). Three-speed manual column-mounted transmission was standard equipment. Overdrive transmission ($98). Hydra-Matic four-speed automatic transmission ($162). Replaceable element oil filter.

HISTORICAL FOOTNOTES: The 1951 Kaiser line was publicly introduced on Feb. 16, 1950. The Allstate, built by Kaiser, but marketed by Sears, Roebuck And Company, was introduced Dec. 20, 1951 as a new model. The Allstate is covered in the "Alternative Cars" section of THE STANDARD CATALOG of AMERICAN CARS 1946-1975. The 1951 Henry J, being essentially the same car as the Allstate, was introduced in October 1950. Kaiser-Frazer started assembly plant operations in Israel, Canada and Japan during the 1951 model year; a facility in Rotterdam, Netherlands began operations in 1949. Kaiser-Frazer's management stayed basically the same this year. The exact model year production of 1951 Kaisers was 145,031 units. Calendar year registrations peaked at 52,286 cars, but, of course, many 1951 models were registered in calendar 1950. Hydra-Matic transmission was a popular new Kaiser option. In calendar 1950, a total of 16,343 Kaisers built to 1951 specifications were equipped with this feature. In calendar 1951, a total of 13,868 Kaisers and Frazers had Hydra-Matic transmissions installed, while 15,898 Kaisers came with manual overdrive transmissions. On Nov. 1, 1951 the Office of Price Stabilization (a Korean War era government agency) allowed Kaiser-Frazer to increase the price of its full-sized models $42-$52.

1952 KAISER

KAISER VIRGINIAN SPECIAL — (6-CYL) — SERIES K521 — There were two different series of 1952 Kaisers. The first series, called Virginians, was simply a carryover of 1951 offerings with new serial number codes. There were no essential changes in these cars, which hit the market on Dec. 15, 1951. Even the prices were the same as for comparable 1951 models, with slight adjustments in shipping weights being the main statistical change. The front grille was of the 1951 type. A Virginian script appeared on the front fenders. Continental tire kits were factory optional.

KAISER I.D. NUMBERS: Serial number stamped on a tag on left front door post. Serial numbers consisted of a Model number prefix and a six digit figure. This year only the starting serial number (proceeded by a factory code) was 1,001,001, instead of 001001. The third symbol was changed to a '2' to indicate 1952 model year. Serial numbers K521-1001001 and up were used on Virginian Specials built at Willow Run. Serial numbers K522-1001001 and up were used on Virginian Deluxes built at Willow Run. Serial number prefixes used at the Long Beach, Jackson and Portland assembly plants were the same as for 1951. Virginian Motor numbers continued from 1951.

KAISER VIRGINIAN SPECIAL SERIES K521

Model Number	Body/Style Number	Body Type & Seating	Factory Price	Shipping Weight	Production Total
K521	K5211	4-dr Sed-6P	2212	3150	Note 1
K521	K5215	4-dr Trav Utl Sed-6P	2317	3260	Note 1
K521	K5214	2-dr Sed-6P	2160	3110	Note 1
K521	K5210	2-dr Trav Utl Sed-6P	2265	3210	Note 1
K521	K5213	2-dr Bus Cpe-3P	1992	3060	Note 1

NOTE 1: Total production of Special and Deluxe Virginians was 5,579.
NOTE 2: No model or body style breakouts available.

KAISER VIRGINIAN DELUXE — (6-CYL) — SERIES K522 — The Virginian Deluxe was also a carryover of the 1951 Kaiser Deluxe. A Virginian front fender script was added. There were slightly revised shipping weights and new data plate coding. Virginians in both lines lasted only until March 14, 1952, at which point the true 1952 Kaisers were introduced. Today, Virginians are valued about the same as Deluxe 1951 Kaisers, although some collectors will pay a slight premium for a Virginian Club Coupe.

KAISER VIRGINIAN DELUXE SERIES

Model Number	Body/Style Number	Body Type & Seating	Factory Price	Shipping Weight	Production Total
K522	K5221	4-dr Sed-6P	2328	3180	Note 1
K522	K5225	4-dr Trav Utl Sed-6P	2433	3310	Note 1
K522	K5224	2-dr Sed-6P	2275	3145	Note 1
K522	K5220	2-dr Trav Utl Sed-6P	2380	3290	Note 1
K522	K5227	2-dr Clb Cpe-6P	2296	3125	Note 1

NOTE 1: Total production of Special and Deluxe Virginians was 5,579.
NOTE 2: No model or body style breakouts available.

ENGINE: Inline L-head six. Cast iron block. Displacement: 226.2 cid. Bore and stroke: 3-15/16 x 4-3/8 inches. Compression ratio: 7.3:1. Brake hp: 115 at 3650 rpm. Four main bearings. Solid valve lifters. Carburetor: Carter Type WGD two-barrel Model 781S.

CHASSIS FEATURES: Wheelbase: 118.5 inches. Overall length: (Special) 208.5 inches; (Deluxe) 210-3/8 inches. Front tread: 58 inches. Rear tread: 58.75 inches. Tires: 6.70 x 15.

OPTIONS: Defroster and heater ($48). Radio. Radio antenna. Stainless steel wheel trim rings. Tailpipe extension. Round shaped outside rearview mirror. External sun visor. Clip-on vanity mirror. Locking gas cap. Spotlights. Fog lamps. Authentic white sidewall tires. Bumper guards. Automatic choke. Oil-bath air cleaner. Vacuum booster fuel pump. Several available rear axle ratios. Two-tone paint. Rear fender skirts. Conditioned air system. Radio. Spotlight. Continental tire kit. Accessory Groups: [Group AG1] included directionals and oil bath air cleaner ($17.85). [Group AG2] included oil bath cleaner; directional signals; rear cigar lighter; chrome wheelcovers; and Deluxe bumper guards ($60). [Group AG3] included front cigar lighter; replaceable oil filter element; rear cigarette lighter; dual-action fuel pump; wheel discs; electric clock; spare and tube on wheel; tailpipe extension; two front/three rear bumper guards; and oil-bath air cleaner ($105). [Group AG21] included front cigar lighter; front vent wings; full wheelcovers; chrome horn ring; dual horns; folding rear seat; Stockholm or Dragon vinyl upholstery; door trim moldings; armrest; right interior sun visor; four bumper guards; and dual rear ashtrays ($180.95). [Group AG9] included oil bath air cleaner; directionals; rear cigar lighter; tilt-type rearview mirror; Deluxe front and rear bumper guards; chrome wheelcovers; tailpipe extension; electric clock; Tenite plastic Deluxe steering wheel; and electric windshield wipers ($113.59). Three-speed manual column-mounted transmission was standard equipment. Overdrive transmission ($98). Hydra-Matic four-speed automatic transmission ($162). Replaceable element oil filter.

HISTORICAL FOOTNOTES: The Virginian was simply the 1951 Kaiser with a new name. This change was made at the time when most other manufacturers were introducing their new models. Kaiser made the change to stay competitive, without spending a lot of money.

1952 Kaiser Virginian club coupe

KAISER DELUXE — (6-CYL) — SERIES K521 — The year 1952 was certainly a strange one for Kaiser. First the company brought out the Virginian models, which were really 1951 Kaisers with different fender badges and 1952 data plate codes. Then, on March 14, 1952, the company brought out an entirely new range of offerings, which were the real 1952 models, but used the same series codes as Virginians. These cars had new styling elements and higher prices. The grille had one, large full-width bar that ran horizontally across the front of the car. Below it was a more massive 'bridge' type grille guard which housed the license plate. Larger taillamps were seen at the rear, along with a more massive bumper having large, chrome pods at each end. The trunk lid was redone and seemed to be better integrated into the overall package. The Deluxe Series was now the base-trim level and could be identified by the words Kaiser Deluxe on the sides of the front fenders. A curved, one-piece windshield was new, as was the lance-like hood ornament. A key-operated starter switch replaced the old button type. Standard features included airplane type shock absorbers; mechanical hand brake; X-member frame construction; freeze-proof door locks; five-inch wide safety wheel rims; center point steering; and the 115 hp six with chrome piston rings, automatic warm-up feature, full-pressure lubrication system and dual-throat carburetion.

KAISER I.D. NUMBERS: Serial number stamped on a tag on left front door post. Serial numbers consisted of a model number prefix (shown in second column of charts below) and a six digit figure. The numbers at each factory were as follows: (Willow Run) K521-1200000 to 1218587; (Jackson) K521-B1001001 to 1218587; (Portland) K521C1001001 to 1218587. Motor numbers 1165001 to 20530001 (Kaiser six with manual transmission); 2114001 (Kaiser six with Hydra-Matic); 165001 (Continental six with manual transmission) and 1218001 (Continental six with Hydra-Matic) were used. Manhattans used serial numbers K522-1200000 to 1207965, with the same factory prefixes and engine numbers.

KAISER DELUXE SERIES

Model Number	Body Style Number	Body Type & Seating	Factory Price	Shipping Weight	Production Total
K521	K5211	4-dr Sed-6P	2537	3195	4,801
K521	K5215	4-dr Trav Utl Sed-6P	2643	3260	NA
K521	K5214	2-dr Sed-6P	2484	3145	1,487
K521	K5210	2-dr Trav Utl Sed-6P	2590	3210	NA
K521	K5213	2-dr Bus Cpe-3P	2296	3060	NA

NOTE 1: Body style production totals based on estimates by historians.

1952 Kaiser, Manhattan four-door sedan, 6-cyl

KAISER MANHATTAN SERIES — (6-CYL) — SERIES K522 — The Manhattan now represented the top trim level in the Kaiser model range. Manhattans could be identified by the words Kaiser Manhattan on the sides of front fenders and by the wide chrome trim around the bottom of the body. They had the same new styling features as 1952 Kaiser Deluxes. There was also a wide, dart-shaped beltline molding with embossed treatment; Deluxe instrument panel with padded crash pad; chrome horn-blowing ring and Deluxe steering wheel. Full

carpeting and lavish upholstery trims were standard equipment. Many options were available, too. Technically, the Manhattan could be had in any of the normally available styles, but experts seem to feel that no Manhattan Travelers were built outside of a few prototypes.

KAISER MANHATTAN SERIES

Model Number	Body/Style Number	Body Type & Seating	Factory Price	Shipping Weight	Production Total
K522	K5221	4-dr Sed-6P	2654	3220	15,839
K522	K5225	4-dr Trav Utl Sed-6P	2759	3310	NA
K522	K5224	2-dr Sed-6P	2601	3185	1,315
K522	K5220	2-dr Trav Utl Sed-6P	2707	3290	NA
K522	K5227	2-dr Clb Cpe-6P	2622	3185	263

NOTE 1: Body style production totals based on estimates by historians.

ENGINE: Inline. L-head six. Cast iron block. Displacement: 226.2 cid. Bore and stroke: 3-5/16 x 4-3/8 inches. Compression ratio: 7.3:1. Brake hp: 115 at 3650 rpm. Five main bearings. Solid valve lifters. Carburetor: Carter Type WGD two-barrel Model 999S.

CHASSIS FEATURES: Wheelbase: 118.5 inches. Overall length: (Special) 208.5 inches; (Deluxe) 210-3/8 inches. Front tread: 58 inches. Rear tread: 58.75 inches. Tires: 6.70 x 15.

OPTIONS: Conditioned air system. Chrome 'donut' style wheel discs. Tailpipe extension. Two-tone paint ($14). E-Z-Eye tinted glass ($15). White sidewall tires ($20). Defroster and heater ($48). Radio. Radio antenna. Stainless steel wheel trim rings. Tailpipe extension. Round shaped outside rearview mirror. External sun visor. Clip-on vanity mirror. Locking gas cap. Spotlights. Fog lamps. Authentic white sidewall tires. Bumper guards. Automatic choke. Oil-bath air cleaner. Vacuum booster fuel pump. Several available rear axle ratios. Two-tone paint. Rear fender skirts. Conditioned air system. Radio. Spotlight. Continental tire kit. Accessory Groups: [Group AG1] included directionals and oil bath air cleaner ($17.85). [Group AG2] included oil bath cleaner; directional signals; rear cigar lighter; chrome wheelcovers; and Deluxe bumper guards ($60). [Group AG3] included front cigar lighter; replaceable oil filter element; rear cigarette lighter; dual-action fuel pump; wheel discs; electric clock; spare and tube on wheel; tailpipe extension; two front/three rear bumper guards; and oil-bath air cleaner ($105). [Group AG21] included front cigar lighter; front vent wings; full wheelcovers; chrome horn ring; dual horns; folding rear seat; Stockholm or Dragon vinyl upholstery; door trim moldings; armrest; right interior sun visor; four bumper guards; and dual rear ashtrays ($180.95). [Group AG9] included oil bath air cleaner; directionals; rear cigar lighter; tilt-type rearview mirror; Deluxe front and rear bumper guards; chrome wheelcovers; tailpipe extension; electric clock; Tenite plastic Deluxe steering wheel; and electric windshield wipers ($113.59). Three-speed manual column-mounted transmission was standard equipment. Overdrive transmission ($98). Dual-Range Hydra-Matic four-speed automatic transmission ($179). Replaceable element oil filter.

HISTORICAL FOOTNOTES: The 1952 Kaiser Deluxe and Manhattan lines were introduced on March 14, 1952. The 1952 Allstate was introduced on Dec. 20, 1951 and the 1952 Henry J was introduced Dec. 20, 1951. Both of these Kaiser-related marques are covered in the section of this catalog devoted to low production postwar cars. Model year production (beginning February, 1952) peaked at 32,131 units. Kaiser was involved in production of war materials including aircraft engines and C-119 Air Force cargo planes. On June 23, 1952, the company established a new electronics division. On Sept. 26, 1952 Kaiser Corp. announced its intention to market a plastic-bodied sports car designed by Howard 'Dutch' Darrin. The 700,000th Kaiser-Frazer automobile was built on Oct. 6, 1952. Henry J. Kaiser continued as Chairman of the Board, with Joe Frazer serving as Vice-Chairman and Edgar F. Kaiser as President. Chief Engineer was G.C. Harbert and Chief Stylist was Herbert Weissinger. During calendar 1952, Kaiser fitted 12,320 cars (excluding Henry Js) with overdrive transmissions, while 26,362 additional units featured Hydra-Matic Drive.

1953 KAISER

KAISER DELUXE — (6-CYL) — SERIES K531 — Kaiser's passenger car business was on the decline in 1953 and economy measures were effected by reducing the number of body styles available. Still, some refreshing design changes were seen in this model year. They represented mainly detail refinements that could be accomplished at minimum cost. A chrome strip was added to the tops of rear fenders to create miniature tailfins. Concealed hinges on the rear deck made for a more modern appearance. Wider chrome caps were added to the headlights, patterned after the aftermarket chrome 'eye brows' which were in vogue at this time. A new, bird-in-flight type hood mascot was adopted. The Deluxe Series was the base trim level and could be identified by Kaiser Deluxe front fender scripts; the lack of bumper end caps; the use of small hubcaps; unskirted rear fenders; untrimmed window sills; and side trim consisting of a narrow chrome spear running from behind the frontwheel housing to the rear of the car on the lower body. Features being promoted included oversized, self-centering brakes; Safety-First lighting; wraparound bumpers and bin-type glove compartments.

KAISER I.D. NUMBERS: Serial number stamped on a tag on left front door post. Serial numbers consisted of a model number prefix (shown in second column of charts below) and a six digit figure. Serial numbers for Kaiser Deluxe began at K31001001 and up. Serial numbers for Kaiser Manhattans began at K532-001001 and up. The K538 Series Carolina models and K530 Series Kaiser Dragon 'hardtops' were added to the line. Their serial numbers followed the same basic pattern, with the series code as the prefix and same sequential number range. Motor numbers for all series were 2059001 and up (Kaiser six with stick shift); 2130001 and up (Kaiser six with Hydra-Matic); 1173001 and up (Continental six with manual transmission) and 1219001 and up (Continental six with Hydra-Matic). The body style symbol for the new Dragon hardtop was the digit '1,' usually prefixed with the K530 Series code.

KAISER DELUXE SERIES K531

Model Number	Body/Style Number	Body Type & Seating	Factory Price	Shipping Weight	Production Total
K531	K5311	4-dr Sed-6P	2513	3200	5,069
K531	K5314	2-dr Sed-6P	2459	3150	1,227
K531	K5315	4-dr Trav Utl Sed-6P	2619	3315	946

NOTE 1: Body style production totals based on estimates by historians.

KAISER MANHATTAN — (6-CYL) — SERIES K532 — Manhattans featured the same styling refinements as Kaiser Deluxe models and, officially, came in the same three body styles. However, it's likely that no Manhattan Travelers were ever built. Identifying features of the higher trim level cars included dart-shaped window sill moldings; a wide chrome side spear running from front to rear fender; bumper wing caps; fender skirts with wide chrome moldings; full wheel discs; and a series nameplates high on the trailing edge of the front fendersides.

KAISER MANHATTAN SERIES K532

Model Number	Body Style Number	Body Type & Seating	Factory Price	Shipping Weight	Production Total
K532	K5321	4-dr Sed-6P	2650	3265	18,603
K532	K5324	2-dr Clb Sed-6P	2597	3235	2,342
K532	K5325	4-dr Trav Utl Sed-6P	2755	3375	0

NOTE 1: Body style production totals based on estimates by historians.

1953 Kaiser, Dragon four-door sedan, 6-cyl

KAISER DRAGON — (6-CYL) — SERIES K530 — The new Kaiser Dragon was introduced, as an addition to the line, on Oct. 31, 1952. . . Halloween day. This model was certainly a treat, but was also quite "trick" as well. In fact, some buyers could have been tricked into thinking that it was a Packard or Cadillac. Standard equipment included all features normally listed as part of Kaiser's Group 100 options package, which carried a retail value of $1,273.98. The extras included all of the following: Hydra-Matic transmission; E-Z-Eye tinted glass; radio with antenna and rear speaker; white sidewall tires; Deluxe wheelcovers; windshield washer; heater; defroster; air conditioning; shaded backlight; gold-plated hood and fender nameplates; door lock shields; personalized owner's glovebox nameplate; and padded 'bambu' vinyl top. This latter material was also used for most of the interior appointments. As with the previous Dragons, three different series were released for the 1953 run, each having specific interior and exterior paint, fabric and trim combinations. An interesting point is that some Kaiser Deluxe models have been found with Dragon features. Also, the Dragons were not true pillarless hardtops, but sedans with the padded top applied in a manner resembling the style of hardtops (a border showing body color was left around the window openings). They were, however, beautiful and luxurious cars and are true collector's items today.

KAISER DRAGON SERIES K530

Model Number	Body/Style Number	Body Type & Seating	Factory Price	Shipping Weight	Production Total
K530	K5301	4-dr Sed-6P	3924	3320	1,277

KAISER CAROLINA — (6-CYL) — SERIES K538 — The Kaiser Carolina sedan and club sedan were a running addition to the line on March 20, 1953. They were, conceptually, the opposite of the Dragon or, in other words, a stripped economy offering with less chrome, plainer upholstery and fewer standard equipment features. There were no sweep spears on the side of the Carolina bodies; no pads atop the dashboards, no chrome horn rings and inexpensive vinyl upholstery. Also, there were virtually no extra sales gained by marketing these low-budget cars. The Kaiser body simply didn't come off well when the chrome accents were removed.

KAISER CAROLINA SERIES K538

Model Number	Body/Style Number	Body Type & Seating	Factory Price	Shipping Weight	Production Total
K538	K5381	4-dr Sed-6P	2373	3185	1,136
K538	K5384	2-dr Clb Sed-6P	2313	3135	308

NOTE 1: Body style production totals based on estimates by historians.

ENGINE: Inline. L-head six. Cast iron block. Displacement: 226.2 cid. Bore and stroke: 3-5/16 x 4-3/8 inches. Compression ratio: 7.3:1. Brake hp: 118 at 3650 rpm. Four main bearings. Solid valve lifters. Carburetor: Carter two-barrel.

CHASSIS FEATURES: Wheelbase: (all models) 118-1/2 inches. Overall length: (all models) 211-1/8 inches. Front tread: 58 inches. Rear tread: 58-3/4 inches. Tires: (Dragon) 7.10 x 15; (others) 6.70 x 15.

OPTIONS: Radio. Heater and defroster. Conditioned Air system. Power steering ($131). Spot lights. Fog lights. Wire wheels ($290). Two-tone paint. Wheel trim rings. Full wheel discs. Tailpipe extension. Front bumper guards. Rear bumper guards. Accessory Groups: [Group AG31] includes chrome horn ring; narrow rub rail moldings; directional signals; and oil-bath air cleaner, on Deluxe sedan and Traveler (standard); on Carolinas and Deluxe Club Sedan ($38). [Group AG32] includes tilt-type rearview mirror; rear cigar lighter; directionals; oil bath air cleaner; bumper bridge caps; full wheel discs; exhaust deflector; Deluxe steering wheel; electric wipers; and electric clock, on Manhattan (standard); on others, except Dragon ($114). [Group AG39] includes: dual-action pump; front cigar lighter; right-hand visor; dual rear ashtrays; front vent wings; front and rear bumper guards; dual horns; full wheelcovers; chrome horn rings and stationary rear seat and deck lid ($83). [Group 100] includes all items in Group AG32, plus E-Z-Eye tinted glass and banded windshield; 7.10 x 15 white sidewall tires; dual-range Hydra-Matic transmission; Laguna and Bambu upholstery; radio (eight-tube Deluxe) and antenna; rear seat speaker; Calpoint custom carpeting on floor and in trunk; heater and defroster; special sun visors; windshield washer; gold-finished glovebox door medallion; Bambu vinyl or Poplin 'Sport Topping'; special body finish in selected color; bright metal scalp and dart-shaped belt moldings; gold hood ornament and nose medallion; gold trunk handle with nameplate; gold trunk lock cover; gold front fender nameplates; chromed lower dash panel; chrome garnish moldings; upholstered trunk and glovebox walls; Bambu vinyl windlacing; and package shelf and interior quarter panels, on Dragon (standard); on other styles ($1184). Dual-Range Hydra-Matic transmission was standard in Dragons. Three-speed manual transmission with column controls was standard in all other models. Hydra-Matic, as option ($179). Overdrive ($107).

HISTORICAL FOOTNOTES: Model year production was counted from September, 1952 and hit only 31,272 units (excluding Henry J). A prototype Darrin sports car was exhibited by Kaiser on Feb. 22, 1953. On April 28, 1953 Kaiser Motors formally purchased Willys-Overland. Kaiser-Frazer Corp. got a name change to Kaiser Motors Corp. The acquisition of Willys created Willys Motors, Inc. and Kaiser Motors became part of Willys. Kaiser-Willys Sales Corp. marketed Kaiser vehicles. The first power steering unit was installed in a Kaiser on May

15, 1953. On Oct. 20, 1953 Kaiser reported a net operating loss of $10,796,754 in the first half of the year. Henry J. Kaiser was Chairman of the Board. Edgar F. Kaiser was company President. Joe Frazer's name no longer appeared on the list of Kaiser executives. Company headquarters were moved from Willow Run, Mich. to Toledo, Ohio.

1954 KAISER

KAISER SPECIAL — (6-CYL) — SERIES K545 — General styling changes for 1954 Kaisers are said to have been inspired by Buick's famous XP-300 show car. They included a new "jet airscoop" grille. It had a bowed oval shape and multiple vertical louvers. There was a matching "air intake" chrome vent at the front of a simulated hood scoop. Massive, hooded headlamp units now enclosed the front parking lamps. The taillamp clusters were redesigned to be visible from the side as well as rear. The new front bumper had vertical crease at its center and twin, vertical guards replaced the single unit 'bridge' type arrangement. A confusing situation was the offering of two distinctly different type Kaiser Specials for 1954. It seems that several thousand 1953 models were leftover at the beginning of the year. It was decided to turn them into 1954 Specials. About 3,500 cars were converted this way by adding new grilles, taillights, trim and data plates. These cars had one piece, non-wraparound rear windows, wide, three-quarter length lower body moldings, 1953 style interior and chassis features and Kaiser-Frazer (Willow Run) firewall code plates. A Kaiser script was on the left edge of the hood, with Kaiser Special signatures on the front fenders. When all of the leftovers were sold, a second series of Specials appeared. These later cars had much thinner, three-quarter length lower bodyside moldings and somewhat less chrome on the roof gutters and around the windows. They also featured the trimmer new crash panel dashboard and three-piece wraparound rear window, as introduced earlier on 1954 Manhattans. In addition, the firewall trim plates identified these units as products of Kaiser-Willys Corp., of Toledo, Ohio. They used cheaper interior appointments than the first series Specials, too. For example, rubber floor mats, all-cloth headliners and uninspired vinyl patterned fabrics were seen. Regular equipment on all 1954 Kaiser Specials included wheelcovers; bumper guards; chrome exhaust deflector; Deluxe steering wheel; electric wipers and clock; oil-bath air cleaner; directional signals; rear cigarette lighter (except two-door Special sedan) and tilt-type rearview mirror. This was actually a case of clearing options off the shelf, rather than offering more fully-equipped cars. Prices were increased accordingly.

KAISER I.D. NUMBERS: Serial number stamped on a tag on left front door post. Serial numbers consisted of a model number prefix (shown in second column of charts below) and a six digit figure. The third symbol in the serial number was changed to a '4' to indicate 1954 model year. All production was quartered at Toledo, Ohio. Serial numbers for Kaiser Specials were K545-001001 to 023114 and serial numbers for Kaiser Manhattans were K542-001001 to 005440. Engine numbers continued from 1953. Kaiser Darrin sports cars had serial numbers 161-001001 and up and engine numbers 3495001 and up.

KAISER SPECIAL

Model Number	Body/Style Number	Body Type & Seating	Factory Price	Shipping Weight	Production Total
FIRST SERIES (1953 TYPE)					
K545	K5451	4-dr Sed-6P	2192	3315	Note 1
K545	K5454	2-dr Clb Sed-6P	2141	3275	Note 1
SECOND SERIES (1954 TYPE)					
K545	K5451	4-dr Sed-6P	2192	3305	749
K545	K5454	2-dr Clb Sed-6P	2141	3265	180

NOTE 1: Body style production totals based on estimates by historians.
NOTE 2: An estimated 3,500 1953 Kaisers were sold as 1954 Kaiser Specials.

1954 Kaiser, Manhattan four-door sedan, 6-cyl

SUPERCHARGED KAISER MANHATTAN — (6-CYL) — SERIES K542 — The 1954 Kaiser Manhattan had the same general styling changes outlined for Kaiser Specials, plus the three-section wraparound rear window (also used on second series 1954 Kaiser Specials). This window treatment featured curved glass, chrome division bars and curved outer glass panels that swept around the rear quarter region of the roof. The Manhattan interior was also redone with an aircraft inspired treatment. It had a vertically pleated, full-width padded dashboard, inverted 'U' shaped speedometer and lever type controls at the driver's left. Standard equipment (actually required options) used on Manhattans included bumper guards and wings; chrome wheelcovers; tailpipe extension; oil-bath air cleaner; directional signals; rear cigar lighter; tilt-type rearview mirror; windshield washer and 'donut' style chrome wheel trim rings. Kaiser lettering appeared, in script, on the left-hand tip of the hood and Kaiser Manhattan chrome signatures decorated the upper front fendersides. The really big news, however, was under the hood. On Manhattans, a McCulloch centrifugal supercharger was

standard. It turned the old 'Super Sonic Six' into the 140 hp 'Super Power Six' which had the same 226.2 cid motor.

SUPERCHARGED KAISER MANHATTAN SERIES K542

Model Number	Body/Style Number	Body Type & Seating	Factory Price	Shipping Weight	Production Total
K542	K5421	4-dr Sed-6P	2454	3375	4,107
K542	K5424	2-dr Clb Cpe-6P	2404	3335	218

NOTE 1: Body style production totals based on estimates by historians.

1954 Kaiser, Darrin two-door roadster convertible, 6-cyl

KAISER DARRIN — (6-CYL) — SERIES 161 — Largely the brainchild of Howard Darrin (after whom it was named) the new Darrin sports car had first been announced on Sept. 26, 1952 with initial prototypes shown on Feb. 22, 1953. It appeared in limited numbers, mainly for testing and exhibition, during November, 1953. That was about two months after production had actually commenced in Kaiser's Jackson, Mich. warehouse. The Willys merger and move to Toledo slowed the pace, but on Jan. 6, 1954 the car was finally released for public sale. Some sources indicate that actual deliveries began the same day. The fiberglass-bodied vehicle incorporated a number of radical ideas, including doors that slid forward, into the front fenders. 'Dutch' Darrin had first conceived of such an arrangement as early as 1922. Other features of the Kaiser Darrin included a three-position convertible top and a 161 cid/90 hp Willys F-head six with one-barrel carburetion. Early experimental versions used a special L-head six. Later units, sold by Howard Darrin after Kaiser dropped the sports car (in mid-1954), could be had with McCulloch superchargers and 304 hp Cadillac V-8s.

KAISER DARRIN SERIES 161

Model Number	Body/Style Number	Body Type & Seating	Factory Price	Shipping Weight	Production Total
161	161	2-dr Spt Conv-2P	3655	2175	435

NOTE 1: Production total given is for production-type Kaiser-Darrin.
NOTE 2: Between 12-62 pre-production experimental cars were built.
NOTE 3: Howard Darrin later sold some 50 leftover cars.

ENGINES

(SPECIAL SIX) Inline: L-head six. Cast iron block. Displacement: 226.2 cid. Bore and stroke: 3-5/16 x 4-3/8 inches. Compression ratio: 7.3:1. Brake hp: 118 at 3650 rpm. Four main bearings. Solid valve lifters. Carburetor: Carter Type WGD two-barrel Model 999S.

(SUPERCHARGED MANHATTAN SIX) Inline: L-head six. Cast iron block. Displacement: 226.2 cid. Bore and stroke: 3-5/16 x 4-3/8 inches. Compression ratio: 7.3:1. Brake hp: 140 at 3900 rpm. Four main bearings. Solid valve lifters. Carburetor: Carter Type WCD two-barrel Model 2146S.

(PRODUCTION TYPE KAISER DARRIN SIX) Inline: F-head six. Cast iron block. Displacement: 161 cid. Bore and stroke: 3-1/8 x 3-1/2 inches. Compression ratio: 7.6:1. Brake hp: 90 at 4200 rpm. Four main bearings. Solid valve lifters. Carburetor: Carter Type YF one-barrel.

(EXPERIMENTAL L-HEAD SIX) Inline: L-head six. Cast iron block. Aluminum Edmund's cylinder head. Displacement: 161 cid. Bore and stroke: 3.12 x 3.50 inches. Compression ratio: 8.0:1. Brake hp: 100 at 4200 rpm. Four main bearings. Solid valve lifters. Carburetor: Three (3) Holley one-barrel with dual headers and exhaust. Special camshaft.

(EXPERIMENTAL SUPERCHARGED L-HEAD SIX) Inline: L-head six. Cast iron block. Displacement: 161 cid. Bore and stroke: 3.12 x 3.50 inches. Compression ratio: (not available). Brake hp: (not available). Four main bearings. Solid valve lifters. Induction: Carter. Type YF one-barrel carburetor and McCulloch centrifugal supercharger.

CHASSIS FEATURES: Wheelbase: (Special and Manhattan) 118.5 inches; (Darrin) 100 inches. Overall length: (Special and Manhattan) 211-1.8 inches; (Darrin) 183 inches. Front tread: (Special and Manhattan) 56 inches; (Darrin) 54 inches. Rear tread: (Special and Manhattan) 58.5 inches; (Darrin) 54 inches. Tires: (Special and Manhattan) 6.70 x 15; (Darrin) 5.90 x 15.

OPTIONS: Power brakes. Power steering ($131). Air conditioning. Eight-tube radio ($89). Heater ($68). White sidewall tires ($22). E-Z-Eye tinted glass ($16). Two-tone paint, Manhattans ($15). Leather upholstery, Manhattans ($250). Pin-crush vinyl trim, Manhattans ($125). Wire wheels ($290). Three-speed manual transmission was standard. Overdrive transmission ($107). Automatic transmission ($178). Available rear axle gear ratios: 3.91:1; 3.31:1; 4.55:1; 4.10:1.

HISTORICAL FOOTNOTES: The 1954 Kaiser Darrin sports car was introduced Jan. 6, 1954. The 1954 Kaiser Manhattan was introduced on Feb. 3, 1954 along with the first series type Kaiser Special. The second series Kaiser Special was introduced on March 23, 1954. Production of cars built to 1954 specifications was halted on June 30, 1954. On July 19, some 400 workers were put on furlough and the car building assembly lines were utilized for manufacturing Willys commercial vehicles and Jeeps. Model year production of Kaisers was counted at only 5,818 units, of which 435 were Kaiser Darrin sports cars. On Oct. 5, 1954 Board Chairman Henry J. Kaiser and Willys Motor's President Edgar F. Kaiser signed a contract to produce cars, trucks and Jeeps in Argentina.

1955 KAISER

KAISER MANHATTAN — (6-CYL) — SERIES K516 — The 1955 Kaiser Manhattan was the only model marketed for 1955. The Manhattan retained the basic styling of 1954, but the height of the center fin decorating the simulated hood scoop was increased. Also, two smaller side fins were added. This gave a total of five decorative fins surrounding the scoop. Model year output was exactly 1,231 cars, of which 1,021 were built to fill an order from Argentina. Apparently, the remaining 210 cars were sold in the United States, along with another 270 leftover units retitled as 1955 models. All 1955 Manhattans were supercharged. The company ceased passenger car operations after shipping the final cars off to Argentina. The name Kaiser and the design did not, however, completely disappear. The tooling was sold to IKA, in Argentina, where the Kaiser was built from 1958 through 1962.

KAISER I.D. NUMBERS: The numbering system and code locations were the same as for previous models with the third and fourth symbols changed to '16'to indicate 1955 Series. Serial numbers were 51357-10001 and up for sedans and 51467-1001 and up for club sedans.

KAISER MANHATTAN SERIES K516

Model Number	Body/Style Number	Body Type & Seating	Factory Price	Shipping Weight	Production Total
RETITLED 1954 SERIES					
516	51367	4-dr Sed-6P	2670	3375	226
516	51467	2-dr Clb Sed-6P	2617	3335	44
1955 SERIES (DOMESTIC)					
516	41367	4-dr Sed-6P	2670	3375	Note 1
516	51467	2-dr Clb Sed-6P	2617	3335	Note 1
1955 SERIES (ARGENTINA)					
516	51367	4-dr Sed-6P	2670	3375	Note 2
516	51467	2-dr Clb Sed-6P	2617	3335	Note 2

NOTE 1: Available statistics indicate 210 units made in 1955 for U.S. sale.
NOTE 2: Available statistics indicate 1,021 cars built for sale in Argentina

ENGINES

(SPECIAL SIX) Inline L-head six. Cast iron block. Displacement: 226.2 cid. Bore and stroke: 3-5/16 x 4-3/8 inches. Compression ratio: 7.3:1. Brake hp: 118 at 3650 rpm. Four main bearings. Solid valve lifters. Carburetor: Carter Type WGD two-barrel Model 999S.

(SUPERCHARGED MANHATTAN SIX) Inline: L-head six. Cast iron block. Displacement: 226.2 cid. Bore and stroke: 3-5/16 x 4-3/8 inches. Compression ratio: 7.3:1. Brake hp: 140 at 3900 rpm. Four main bearings. Solid valve lifters. Carburetor: Carter Type WCD two-barrel Model 2146S.

1955 Kaiser, Manhattan four-door sedan, 6-cyl

CHASSIS FEATURES: Wheelbase: (Special and Manhattan) 118.5 inches; (Darrin) 100 inches. Overall length: (Special and Manhattan) 211-1.8 inches; (Darrin) 183 inches. Front tread: (Special and Manhattan) 56 inches; (Darrin) 54 inches. Rear tread: (Special and Manhattan) 58.5 inches; (Darrin) 54 inches. Tires: (Special and Manhattan) 6.70 x 15; (Darrin) 5.90 x 15.

OPTIONS: Power brakes. Power steering ($131). Air conditioning. Eight-tube radio ($89). Heater ($68). White sidewall tires ($22). E-Z-Eye tinted glass ($16). Two-tone paint, Manhattans ($15). Leather upholstery, Manhattans ($250). Pin-crush vinyl trim, Manhattans ($125). Wire wheels ($290). Three-speed manual transmission was standard. Overdrive transmission ($107). Automatic transmission ($178). Available rear axle gear ratios: 3.91:1; 3.31:1; 4.55:1; 4.10:1.

HISTORICAL FOOTNOTES: The 1955 Kaiser line was introduced Jan. 6, 1955. The last Kaisers built in the United States were shipped to Argentina in June, 1955. Kaiser Motors was renamed Kaiser Industries, Inc. and was the platform for the actual creation of publicly held Kaiser business operations. Willys Motors, Inc. continued commercial vehicle operations as a subsidiary of Kaiser Industries Corp. Leftover Kaiser Darrin sports cars were marketed by some Kaiser dealers during the 1955 model year.

STANDARD CATALOG OF
LINCOLN
1946-1975

Like most American cars, the 1946-1948 Lincolns were warmed-over prewar models. When you had a gorgeous automobile like the Continental, that wasn't bad. It was one of those rare cars that became an instant Classic. Although highly regarded for its styling, sales were not good. But it did help Lincoln's image.

By Charles Webb

When the first postwar Lincolns debuted in early 1948 (1949 models), the company had nothing to compare with the Continental. The top-of-the-line Cosmopolitan looked too much like the standard Lincoln series, which in turn resembled Mercury, with which it shared bodies.

In 1952, Lincoln dramatically changed its appearance. It bore no resemblance to the previous year's model, but shared the corporate look all Ford Motor Co. cars had that year. Although Lincolns had participated in previous Pan American Road races, this was the first year the make dominated the event, winning the first four spots (using 1953 models).

The "hot car" image nurtured by the racing victories was fully exploited by the company. As an ad for 1955 models said, "The first function of a fine car is outstanding performance." Fortunately for Lincoln, the Pan American Road Race was discontinued in 1954. Its days as a Road Race winner were about to end. Chrysler came out with its potent 300 Letter Car in 1955.

The Continental returned in 1956. The beautiful Mark II captured the spirit of the original Continental, yet was thoroughly modern in design. Despite early waiting lists, it suffered the same fate as its predecessor: low demand.

The 1956 Continental was also very attractive. If anyone had doubts about Continental's status as a prestige car, they were vanquished this year. Regrettably, styling was jazzed up a bit for 1957. And the following year, Continental was completely changed.

The 1958 to 1960 models were the biggest American cars of the postwar era. In certain parts of the country, owners were obligated by law to place red reflectors on the rear of their new Continentals and amber clearance lights on the front. These huge Continentals came on the automotive scene at a time when Detroit was being widely criticized for building cars that were too big. Continental sales declined in 1958 and continued to drop until the restyled 1961s were introduced.

As in 1956, the 1961 Continental showed the world just how beautiful a production American automobile could be. It made most of its contemporaries look like they had been designed by Soupy Sales. Stylistically, it was the most influential car of the decade. Continental kept the same basic styling until 1969.

One benefit of styling consistency was that it established a "Continental look." Cadillac had long been aware of the value of continuity in styling, something early postwar Continentals didn't have. With an easily identifiable look all its own, Ford Motor Co. was able to make its less expensive cars classier by giving them Continental styling traits.

In the spring of 1968, the 1969 Continental Mark III was introduced. It looked like a Mark II that had gone "Hollywood." The Mark III proved to be very popular and a sales success. Its design would influence Continental styling throughout the 1970s.

1946 Lincoln, four-door sedan, V-12 (AA)

1947 Lincoln, two-door convertible, V-12

LINCOLN SERIES — SERIES 66H — The new 1946 Lincolns were warmed over 1942s. They had a more massive bumper, different nameplate on the sides of the hood and a heavier grille with horizontal and vertical bars. The push-button Continental style door openers introduced on the 1942 models were kept.

LINCOLN I.D. NUMBERS: Serial numbers were the same as engine numbers. They ranged from H136,6255 to 138,051; H138,052 to 152,839. The first letter (H) indicates the series (66H).

LINCOLN

Model Number	Body/Style Number	Body Type & Seating	Factory Price	Shipping Weight	Production Total
66H	73	4-dr Sed-6P	2337	3980	Note 1
66H	76	2-dr Conv-6P	2883	4210	Note 1
66H	77	2-dr Clb Cpe-6P	2318	3380	Note 1

NOTE 1: Total production of all body types was 16,645 units.

LINCOLN SERIES — SERIES 76H — Styling changes for 1947 were minor. The push-button door handles were replaced by conventional ones. The word 'Lincoln' was written in chrome on both sides of the hood. The raised hexagon center wheelcovers of the previous year were replaced by plainer ones.

LINCOLN I.D. NUMBERS: Serial numbers were the same as engine numbers. They ranged from 7H 152,840 to 174,289.

LINCOLN

Model Number	Body/Style Number	Body Type & Seating	Factory Price	Shipping Weight	Production Total
76H	73	4-dr Sed-6P	2554	4015	Note 1
76H	76	2-dr Conv-6P	3142	4245	Note 1
76H	77	2-dr Clb Cpe-6P	2533	3915	Note 1

NOTE 1: Total production of all body types was 19,891 units.

1946 Lincoln-Continental, two-door cabriolet, V-12

1947 Lincoln-Continental, two-door coupe, V-12 (TVB)

CONTINENTAL SERIES — SERIES 66H — The Continental was a luxurious, beautiful, handcrafted automobile built for boulevard cruising. The 1946 model received a larger, criss-cross pattern grille and a heavier bumper. Lincoln Continental was written in chrome on the side of the hood.

CONTINENTAL

Model Number	Body/Style Number	Body Type & Seating	Factory Price	Shipping Weight	Production Total
66H	52	2-dr Conv-5P	4474	4090	201
66H	57	2-dr Club Cpe-5P	4392	4100	265

BASE ENGINE: V-12: L-head. Cast iron block. Displacement: 305 cid. Bore and stroke: 2.93 x 375 inches. Compression ratio: 7.20:1. Brake hp: 130 at 3600 rpm. Four main bearings. Carburetor: Chandler-Grove two-barrel.

CHASSIS FEATURES: Wheelbase: 125 inches. Overall length: 216 inches. Front tread: 59 inches. Rear tread: 60.6 inches. Tires: 7.00 x 15.

OPTIONS: Custom interior ($149 in Lincoln sedan and coupe). Radio. Whitewall tires. Heater. A three-speed manual transmission was standard. Overdrive was optional.

HISTORICAL FOOTNOTES: The 1946 Continental was pace car at the 1946 Indianapolis 500. This beautiful car was introduced to the press on Sept. 13, 1945. Only 569 cars were made by the end of the calendar year, although a total of 13,496 were built in calendar 1946. Model year production of 16,645 helped Lincoln place 16th in the domestic sales race.

CONTINENTAL SERIES — SERIES 76H — The best way to tell a 1947 Continental from a 1946 (or 1948) is to ask the owner. The only exterior changes were in the wheelcovers and, in mid-model year, the hood ornament. Mechanical improvements were made to the generator and starter drive.

CONTINENTAL

Model Number	Body/Style Number	Body Type & Seating	Factory Price	Shipping Weight	Production Total
76H	52	2-dr Conv-5P	4746	4135	738
76H	57	2-dr Clb Cpe-6P	4662	4125	831

BASE ENGINE: V-12: L-head. Cast iron block. Displacement: 305 cid. Bore and stroke: 2.93 x 3.75 inches. Compression ratio: 7.20:1. Brake hp: 130 at 3600 rpm. Four main bearings. Carburetor: Chandler-Grove two-barrel.

CHASSIS FEATURES: Wheelbase: 125 inches. Overall length: 216 inches. Front tread: 59 inches. Rear tread: 60.6 inches. Tires: 7.00 x 15.

OPTIONS: Custom interior, in Lincoln sedan and coupe ($168). Whitewall tires. Radio. Heater. A three-speed manual transmission was standard and overdrive was optional.

HISTORICAL FOOTNOTES: The year 1947 was the best yet for Lincoln-Continental sales. Production hit 1,569 vehicles, but calendar year production of Lincolns and Continentals was 29,275. Lincoln came in 18th in domestic sales.

LINCOLN SERIES — SERIES 9EL — The first all-new postwar Lincolns were introduced on April 22, 1948. They had a more streamlined appearance than the 1948s. However, the new, two-piece windshield seemed a bit out of sync with the 'modern' styling. At a distance, it was hard to tell a Lincoln from a Mercury. Recessed headlights and a shinier front end set it apart.

LINCOLN I.D. NUMBERS: Serial numbers were the same as engine numbers. They started at 9ELI and went up to 9EL73,559. Cosmopolitan numbers ranged from 9EH1 to 73,563.

1948 Lincoln, four-door sedan, V-12

LINCOLN SERIES — SERIES 876H — Lincoln Div. was working frantically to bring out the new postwar model. So the 1948s were basically just leftover 1947s.

LINCOLN I.D. NUMBERS: Serial numbers were the same as engine numbers. They ranged from 8H174,290 to 182,129.

LINCOLN

Model Number	Body/Style Number	Body Type & Seating	Factory Price	Shipping Weight	Production Total
876H	73	4-dr Sed-6P	2554	4015	Note 1
876H	76	2-dr Conv-6P	3142	4245	Note 1
876H	77	2-dr Clb Cpe-6P	2533	3915	Note 1

NOTE 1: Total production of all body types was 6,470.

1949 Lincoln, four-door sedan, V-8 (AA)

LINCOLN

Model Number	Body/Style Number	Body Type & Seating	Factory Price	Shipping Weight	Production Total
9EL	72	2-dr Clb Cpe-6P	2527	3959	Note 1
9EL	74	4-dr Spt Sed-6P	2575	4009	Note 1
9EL	76	2-dr Conv-6P	3116	4224	Note 1

NOTE 1: Total 9EL Series production was 38,384 units.

1948 Continental, two-door cabriolet, V-12

CONTINENTAL SERIES — SERIES 876H — The Continental was virtually unchanged for 1948.

CONTINENTAL

Model Number	Body/Style Number	Body Type & Seating	Factory Price	Shipping Weight	Production Total
876H	56	2-dr Conv-6P	4746	4135	452
876H	57	2-dr Clb Cpe-6P	4662	4125	847

BASE ENGINE: V-12: L-head. Cast iron block. Displacement: 305 cid. Bore and stroke: 2.93 x 3.75 inches. Compression ratio: 7.20:1. Brake hp: 130 at 3600 rpm. Four main bearings. Carburetor: Chandler-Grove two-barrel.

CHASSIS FEATURES: Wheelbase: 125 inches. Overall length: 216 inches. Front tread: 59 inches. Rear tread: 60.6 inches. Tires: 7.00 x 15.

OPTIONS: Custom interior ($168 in Lincoln sedan and coupe). Whitewall tires. Radio. Heater. A three-speed manual transmission was standard. Overdrive optional.

HISTORICAL FOOTNOTES: In 1951, the Museum of Modern Art selected the Continental as one of eight automotive 'works of art.' Eight years later, TIME magazine ranked it in their top 10 choice of the 100 best-designed commercial products. The 1948 model year began on Nov. 1, 1947 and lasted only six months. Calendar year sales were 43,938 units. Model year production was 1,299 Continentals. This made Lincoln the 17th largest U.S. automaker.

1949 Lincoln, Cosmopolitan four-door Sport Sedan, V-8 (AA)

COSMOPOLITAN SERIES — SERIES 9EH — The Continental was gone. The new top-of-the-line Lincoln was the Cosmopolitan. While it resembled the standard series, most of the sheetmetal was different. A one-piece windshield and what appeared to be a huge horizontal gob of chrome on each front fender, were a couple of its main distinguishing features. Power windows and power seats were standard.

COSMOPOLITAN

Model Number	Body/Style Number	Body Type & Seating	Factory Price	Shipping Weight	Production Total
9EH	72	2-dr Clb Cpe-6P	3186	4194	7,685
9EH	73	4-dr Twn Sed-6P	3238	3274	7,302
9EH	74	4-dr Spt Sed-6P	3238	4259	18,906
9EH	76	2-dr Conv-6P	3948	4419	1,230

NOTE 1: The Town Sedan was the only 1949 Lincoln with fastback styling.

BASE ENGINE: V-8: L-head. Cast iron block. Displacement: 336.7 cid. Bore and stroke: 3.5 x 4.37 inches. Compression ratio: 7.00:1. Brake hp: 152 at 3600 rpm. Carburetor: Holley two-barrel.

CHASSIS FEATURES: Wheelbase: (Series 9EL) 121 inches; (Cosmopolitan) 125 inches. Overall length: (Series 9EL) 213 inches; (Cosmopolitan) 220.5 inches. Front tread: 58.5 inches. Rear tread: 60 inches. Tires: 8.20 x 15.

OPTIONS: Hand-brake signal. Radio. Vacuum antenna. Power windows. Heater. A three-speed manual transmission was standard. 'Touch-O-Matic' overdrive was optional. Late in the model year, Hydra-Matic automatic transmission became optional.

HISTORICAL FOOTNOTES: Lincolns won two of the nine National Association for Stock Car Auto Racing (NASCAR) Grand National races held in 1949. The 1949 Lincoln's recessed headlights were originally planned to be hidden. The 1949 Lincolns were introduced April 22, 1948. Model year production was 73,507 cars. Calendar year assemblies totaled 33,132 units. Lincoln came in 17th in sales for the second year running.

1950 Lincoln two-door coupe, V-8 (AA)

LINCOLN SERIES — SERIES 0EL — A new horizontal bar grille with vertical elements enhanced the appearance of the standard Lincoln. Its name was in the same location on the front fender as last year, but it was larger. In mid-model year, the Lido Coupe was added to the line. It featured a vinyl top and custom interior.

LINCOLN I.D. NUMBERS: 0EL Series serial numbers ranged from 50LP5,001L to 20,082L and 50LA5,001L to 72,521. Lincoln Cosmopolitan serial numbers ranged from 50LP5,001L to 15,701H. See I.D. numbers for assembly plant code. Assembly plant codes: LA = Los Angeles; LP = Lincoln Plant; SL = St. Louis.

LINCOLN

Model Number	Body/Style Number	Body Type & Seating	Factory Price	Shipping Weight	Production Total
0EL	L-72	2-dr Clb Cpe-6P	2529	4090	Note 1
0EL	L-72C	2-dr Lido Cpe-6P	2721	4145	Note 1
0EL	L-74	4-dr Spt Sed-6P	2576	4115	11,714

NOTE 1: Total production of body styles L-72 and L-72C was 5,748.

COSMOPOLITAN SERIES — SERIES 0EH — The Cosmopolitan received a new grille and dash for 1950. Its name was now written in chrome on the lower front fenders. The Cosmopolitan Capri had a padded leather roof and custom interior. It also had an additional horizontal gobs of chrome on the rear quarter panels parallel to the ones on the front fenders. The Capri was introduced to make up for Continental's lack of a two-door hardtop.

1950 Lincoln, Cosmopolitan four-door sedan, V-8

COSMOPOLITAN

Model Number	Body/Style Number	Body Type & Seating	Factory Price	Shipping Weight	Production Total
0EH	H-72	2-dr Clb Cpe-6P	3187	4375	1,315
0EH	H-72C	2-dr Capri Cpe-6P	3406	4385	509
0EH	H-74	4-dr Spt Sed-6P	3240	4410	8,332
0EH	H-76	2-dr Conv-6P	3950	4640	536

BASE ENGINE: V-8: L-head. Cast iron block. Displacement: 336.7 cid. Bore and stroke: 3.5 x 4.37 inches. Compression ratio: 7.00:1. Brake hp: 152 at 3600 rpm. Carburetor: Holley 885-FFC two-barrel.

CHASSIS FEATURES: Wheelbase: (Series 0EL) 121 inches; (Cosmopolitan) 125 inches. Overall length: (Series 0EL) 213.8 inches; (Cosmopolitan) 212.2 inches. Front tread: 58.5 inches. Rear tread: 60 inches. Tires: (Series 0EL) 8.00 x 15; (Cosmopolitan) 8.20 x 15.

OPTIONS: Heater. Power windows (standard in Cosmopolitan). Power antenna. Whitewall tires. Radio. A three-speed manual transmission was standard. Overdrive and Hydra-Matic automatic transmission were extra-cost options.

HISTORICAL FOOTNOTES: Lincolns won two of the 19 NASCAR Grand National races held in 1950.

1951 Lincoln, four-door sedan, V-8 (TVB)

LINCOLN SERIES — SERIES 1EL — The front of the 1951 Lincoln looked like a 1950 model that had gotten into a fight...and lost. The grille bar only extended from the center section between the bumper guards. A forward slanting, vertical piece was added to the front fender side chrome. The word Lincoln was written behind it. The glamorous Lido coupe came with a canvas or vinyl roof, fender skirts, rocker panel molding and custom interior.

LINCOLN I.D. NUMBERS: Series 1EL serial numbers began with either 41LP5,001L or 51 LA5,001L. Cosmopolitan serial numbers ranged from 51LP5,001H to 20,813H.

LINCOLN

Model Number	Body/Style Number	Body Type & Seating	Factory Price	Shipping Weight	Production Total
1EL	L-72B	2-dr Clb Cpe-6P	2505	4065	Note 1
1EL	L72C	2-dr Lido Cpe-6P	2702	4100	Note 1
1EL	L-74	4-dr Spt Sed-6P	2553	4130	12,279

NOTE 1: Total production for body styles L-72B and L-72C was 4,482 units.

1951 Lincoln, Cosmopolitan four-door sedan, V-8

COSMOPOLITAN SERIES — SERIES 1EH — Except for the chrome rocker panels, the new Cosmopolitan looked pretty much like the standard Lincoln. The distinctive gobs of chrome on the front fenders of the previous two years were mercifully removed. Also, the Cosmopolitan name was placed on the upper front fenders. Next to the convertible, the snazziest model was the Capri coupe. It featured a canvas or vinyl roof, Deluxe upholstery and (like all Cosmopolitans) fender skirts.

COSMOPOLITAN

Model Number	Body/Style Number	Body Type & Seating	Factory Price	Shipping Weight	Production Total
1EH	H-72B	2-dr Clb Cpe-6P	3129	4340	1,476
1EH	H-72C	2-dr Capri Cpe-6P	3350	4360	1,251
1EH	H-74	4-dr Spt Sed-6P	3182	4415	12,229
1EH	H-76	2-dr Conv-6P	3891	4615	857

BASE ENGINE: V-8: L-head. Cast iron block. Displacement: 336.7 cid. Bore and stroke: 3.5 x 4.38 inches. Compression ratio: 7.00:1. Brake hp: 154 at 3600 rpm. Carburetor: Holley 885-FFC two-barrel.

CHASSIS FEATURES: Wheelbase: (Series 1EL) 121 inches; (Cosmopolitan) 125 inches. Overall length: (Series 1EL) 214.8 inches; (Cosmopolitan) 222.5 inches. Front tread: 58.5 inches. Rear tread: 60 inches. Tires (Series 1EL) 8.00 x 15; (Cosmopolitan) 8.20 x 15.

OPTIONS: Heater. Power windows. Whitewall tires. Radio. A three-speed manual transmission was standard. Overdrive and Hydra-Matic automatic transmission were optional.

HISTORICAL FOOTNOTES: This season set an all-time output record for Lincoln at 390,439 cars . . . more than the company had ever sold since being acquired by Ford Motor Co. in 1922. In November, 1951, the 124 inch wheelbase series was discontinued. This season's dealer introductions were staged for Nov. 15, 1950. Production of models built to 1951 specifications was quartered at Detroit and Los Angeles assembly plants, although a new factory

in Wayne, Mich. was nearly completed this season and went into operations for production of 1952 Lincolns. Benson Ford was the general manager of the Lincoln-Mercury Division this year.

1952 LINCOLN

1952 Lincoln, Cosmopolitan four-door sedan, V-8 (AA)

COSMOPOLITAN SERIES — SERIES 2H — Lincoln was completely restyled for 1952. It had a lean, racy look. The bumper and grille were integrated. Instead of being recessed, the headlights seemed to stick out slightly from the fenders. Side trim consisted of a nearly full-length spear which divided a wide, slanted rear fender molding. The large vertical taillights were vaguely similar to last year's. A wraparound windshield and rear window added a 'modern' touch to the car's styling. New ball-joint suspension improved its handling and ride.

I.D. NUMBERS: Cosmopolitan serial numbers ranged from 52LP5,001 to 52WA29,217H. Capri serial numbers ranged from 52LA5,001H to 52LA7,761H; 52SL5,001H to 52SL5,072H; plus those found in the Cosmopolitan I.D. numbers section. Assembly plant code: LA = Los Angeles; LP = Lincoln plant; SL = St. Louis; WA = Wayne, Mich.

COSMOPOLITAN

Model Number	Body/Style Number	Body Type & Seating	Factory Price	Shipping Weight	Production Total
2H	60C	2-dr HT Spt Cpe-6P	3293	4155	4,545
2H	73A	4-dr Sed-6P	3198	4125	Note 1

NOTE 1: Total production for Cosmopolitan and Capri four-door sedans was 15,854.

1952 Lincoln, Capri two-door hardtop sport coupe, V-8 (AA)

CAPRI SERIES — SERIES 2H — The Capri was now Lincoln's top-of-the-line model. The sedan featured fabric and leather upholstery. Like the Cosmopolitan that it resembled, its gas tank filler was hidden behind the rear license plate.

CAPRI

Model Number	Body/Style Number	Body Type & Seating	Factory Price	Shipping Weight	Production Total
2H	60A	2-dr HT Cpe-6P	3518	4235	5,681
2H	73B	4-dr Sed-6P	3331	4140	Note 1
2H	76A	2-dr Conv-6P	3665	4350	1,191

NOTE 1: See Cosmopolitan note.

BASE ENGINE: V-8: Overhead valves. Cast iron block. Displacement: 317.4 cid. Bore and stroke: 3.8 x 3.5 inches. Compression ratio: 7.50:1. Brake hp: 160 at 3900 rpm. Carburetor: Holley two-barrel.

CHASSIS FEATURES: Wheelbase: 123 inches. Overall length: 214 inches. Front tread: 58.5 inches. Rear tread: 58.5 inches. Tires: 8.00 x 15.

OPTIONS: Heater. Power front seat and power windows (both standard in convertible). Whitewall tires. Radio. Spotlight. Grille guard. Hydra-Matic automatic transmission was standard. A 'maximum duty kit' was available for owners who wanted to race their Lincolns.

HISTORICAL FOOTNOTES: Lincolns came in first, second, third and fourth at the 1952 Pan American Road Race in Mexico. However, 1953 models were used.

1953 LINCOLN

COSMOPOLITAN SERIES — SERIES 8H — With the exception of an emblem inside a chrome 'V' on the upper section of the grille and the word Lincoln printed across the face of the hood, styling was basically the same as last year.

I.D. NUMBERS: Serial numbers in 1953 ranged from 53WA5,001H to 39,566H; 53LA5,001H to 10,995H and 53SL5,001H. Assembly plant code: LA = Los Angeles; LP = Lincoln plant; SL = St. Louis; WA = Wayne, Mich.

COSMOPOLITAN

Model Number	Body/Style Number	Body Type & Seating	Factory Price	Shipping Weight	Production Total
8H	60C	2-dr HT Spt Cpe-6P	3322	4155	6,562
8H	73A	4-dr Sed-6P	3226	4135	7,560

1953 Lincoln, Capri two-door convertible, V-8

CAPRI SERIES — SERIES 8H — The most expensive series continued to be the Capri. Except for the chrome rocker panels, it was difficult to tell them from Cosmopolitans.

CAPRI

Model Number	Body/Style Number	Body Type & Seating	Factory Price	Shipping Weight	Production Total
8H	60A	2-dr HT Cpe-6P	3549	4165	12,916
8H	73B	4-dr Sed-6P	3453	4150	11,352
8H	76A	2-dr Conv-6P	3699	4310	2,372

BASE ENGINE: V-8: Overhead valves. Cast iron block. Displacement: 317.5 cid. Bore and stroke: 3.8 x 3.5 inches. Compression ratio: 8.00:1. Brake hp: 205 at 4200 rpm. Five main bearings. Carburetor: Holley 2140 four-barrel.

CHASSIS FEATURES: Wheelbase: 123 inches. Overall length: 214.1 inches. Front tread: 58.5 inches. Rear tread: 58.5 inches. Tires: 8.00 x 15; (Convertible) 8.20 x 15.

OPTIONS: Power brakes. Four-way power seat. Power steering. Electric windows. Tinted windows. Whitewall tires. Radio. Hydra-Matic automatic transmission was standard.

HISTORICAL FOOTNOTES: For the second year in a row, Lincolns captured the top four spots at the Pan American Road Race. A fire at General Motors' Livonia, Mich. transmission plant stopped production of the Hydra-Matic equipped Lincolns for 55 days. This reportedly caused Lincoln to lose 7,000 sales. Eighty-seven percent of 1953 Lincolns had power brakes and sixty-nine percent had power steering.

1954 LINCOLN

COSMOPOLITAN SERIES — Lincolns grew an inch in length and width this year. The Lincoln name was now written on the front fenders. The wide, slanted rear fender chrome piece was replaced by a rear fender stone shield. The straight, side molding was higher and longer than that used on the 1953s. The company emblem and 'V' were on the face of the hood and the top bumper/grille bar was straight.

I.D. NUMBERS: Serial numbers ranged from 54WA5,001H to 36,840H and 54LA5.001 H to 9,891H. Assembly plant code: LA = Los Angeles; LP = Lincoln plant; SL = St. Louis; WA = Wayne, Mich.

COSMOPOLITAN

Model Number	Body/Style Number	Body Type & Seating	Factory Price	Shipping Weight	Production Total
NA	60C	2-dr HT Spt Cpe-6P	3625	4155	2,994
NA	73A	4-dr Sed-6P	3522	4135	4,447

1954 Lincoln, Capri two-door convertible, V-8 (AA)

CAPRI SERIES — Except for the chrome rocker panels and roof trim, it was hard to tell a Capri from a Cosmopolitan without looking at the nameplate.

CAPRI

Model Number	Body/Style Number	Body Type & Seating	Factory Price	Shipping Weight	Production Total
NA	60A	2-dr HT Cpe-6P	3869	4250	14,003
NA	738	4-dr Sed-6P	3711	4245	13,598
NA	76A	2-dr Conv-6P	4031	4310	1,951

BASE ENGINE: V-8: Overhead valves. Cast iron block. Displacement: 317.5 cid. Bore and stroke: 3.8 x 3.5 inches. Compression ratio: 8.0:1. Brake hp: 205 at 4200 rpm. Five main bearings. Carburetor: Holley 2140 four-barrel.

CHASSIS FEATURES: Wheelbase: 123 inches. Overall length: 215 inches. Tires: 8.00 x 15; (Convertible) 8.20 x 15.

CONVENIENCE OPTIONS: Power brakes. Power steering. Four-Way power seat. Tinted glass. Whitewall tires. Radio. Heater. Hydra-Matic automatic transmission was standard.

HISTORICAL FOOTNOTES: Lincolns took first and second place at the 1954 Pan American Road Race.

1955 LINCOLN

CUSTOM SERIES — The 1955 Lincoln was a refined version of the 1954 model. Removal of the lower vertical bars on the grille gave it a cleaner look. The headlight treatment seemed very Ford-like. The Lincoln name was (as in 1953) printed on the front of the hood. Although the full-length side chrome spear remained, the rear fender stone shield was changed. The taillight design and hood ornament were also new. Custom two-door hardtops came with chrome rocker panels.

CUSTOM I.D. NUMBERS: Serial numbers ranged from 55WA5,001H to 28,595H and 55LA5,001H to 8,519H. Assembly plant code: LA = Los Angeles; LP = Lincoln plant; SL = St. Louis; WA = Wayne, Mich.

CUSTOM

Model Number	Body/Style Number	Body Type & Seating	Factory Price	Shipping Weight	Production Total
NA	60C	2-dr HT Spt Cpe-6P	3666	4185	1,362
NA	73A	4-dr Sed-6P	3563	4235	2,187

CAPRI SERIES — Its nameplate. chrome rocker panels and a different rear roof pillar trim, distinguished the exterior of the Capri from the lower-priced Custom. The convertible had leather upholstery.

CAPRI

Model Number	Body/Style Number	Body Type & Seating	Factory Price	Shipping Weight	Production Total
NA	60A	2-dr HT Cpe-6P	3910	4305	11,462
NA	73B	4-dr Sed-6P	3752	4245	10,724
NA	76A	2-dr Conv-6P	4072	4415	1,487

BASE CUSTOM ENGINE: V-8: Overhead valves. Cast iron block. Displacement: 341 cid. Bore and stroke: 3.93 x 3.5 inches. Compression ratio: 8.50:1. Brake hp: 225 at 4400 rpm. Carburetor: Holley four-barrel.

CHASSIS FEATURES: Wheelbase: 123 inches. Overall length: 215.6 inches. Tires-. 8.00 x 15; (Convertible and cars with air conditioning) 8.20 x 15.

1955 Lincoln, Capri two-door hardtop sport coupe, V-8

CONVENIENCE OPTIONS: Air conditioning. Power steering. Power brakes. Power windows. Tinted glass. Heater. Radio. Power seats. Whitewall tires. Turbo-Drive automatic transmission was standard.

HISTORICAL FOOTNOTES: Ninety-three percent of 1955 Lincolns had power steering; ninety-four percent power brakes; ninety-one percent power seats; eighty-two percent power windows; ninety-eight percent radios; ninety-nine percent heaters and eighty-nine percent tinted glass. This was the first year Lincoln used its own automatic transmission. It had been equipping cars with GM's Hydra-Matic. Also, on April 18, 1955, Lincoln became a separate division of the Ford Motor Co. Since October, 1945 it had been part of the Lincoln-Mercury Div.

1956 LINCOLN

CAPRI SERIES — Lincoln was attractively restyled for 1956. It was based on the XL-500 and XM-800 dream cars. It had hooded headlights and a bumper-integrated, center horizontal bar grille with thinner horizontal bars above and below it. Taillight treatment was similar to last year. Bumper ports beneath the taillights served as exhaust exits. A full-length, tire-level side molding was incorporated onto the standard fender skirts. All 1956 Lincolns came equipped with power steering, automatic transmission and dual exhaust.

I.D. NUMBERS: Serial numbers ranged from 56WA-5,001L to 480,056 and 56LA5,001 L to 122,88L. Assembly plant code: LA = Los Angeles; LP = Lincoln plant; SL = St. Louis; WA = Wayne, Mich.

CAPRI

Model Number	Body/Style Number	Body Type & Seating	Factory Price	Shipping Weight	Production Total
NA	60E	2-dr HT Spt Cpe-6P	4119	4305	4,355
NA	73A	4-dr Sed-6P	4212	4315	4,436

1956 Lincoln, Premiere two-door hardtop coupe, V-8

PREMIERE SERIES — It is easy to see why the Premiere hardtop was able to win an award from the Industrial Designers Institute for excellence in automotive design. Outside of rear fender medallions and fancier wheelcovers, it was difficult to tell the Premiere from the less costly Capri. Like all Ford Motor Co. products in 1956, the Premiere had a lot of safety features. Improved door latches, deep-dish steering wheel, heavily padded seatbacks and door panels. Power windows and four-way power front seat were standard.

PREMIERE

Model Number	Body/Style Number	Body Type & Seating	Factory Price	Shipping Weight	Production Total
NA	60B	2-dr HT Cpe-6P	4601	4357	19,619
NA	738	4-dr Sed-6P	4601	4347	19,465
NA	76B	2-dr Conv-6P	4747	4452	2,447

1956 Lincoln-Continental, Mark II two-door hardtop coupe, V-8

MARK II SERIES — The Lincoln-Continental returned this year with the introduction of the Mark II. It made its debut on Oct. 6, 1955 at the Paris Auto Show. A long hood, short deck, restrained use of chrome and near perfect proportions helped the Mark II show the world just how beautiful a production American automobile could be. Like its predecessors, it was an instant classic. Yet it was not an imitation of the original. The Mark II was unmistakenly modern in design. Being priced in the then lofty $10,000 range seemed to only accentuate how special this car was.

MARK II

Model Number	Body/Style Number	Body Type & Seating	Factory Price	Shipping Weight	Production Total
NA	60A	2-dr Spt Cpe-6P	9966	4825	2,550

BASE ENGINE: V-8: Overhead valves. Cast iron block. Displacement: 368 cid. Bore and stroke: 4 x 3.65 inches. Compression ratio: 9.0:1. Brake hp: 285 at 4600 rpm. Carburetor: Lincoln four-barrel.

MARK II ENGINE: V-8: Overhead valves. Cast iron block. Displacement: 368 cid. Bore and stroke: 4 x 3.65 inches. Compression ratio: 10.00:1. Brake hp: 300 at 4800 rpm. Carburetor: Carter four-barrel.

CHASSIS FEATURES: [Lincoln] Wheelbase: 126 inches. Overall length: 223 inches. Overall width: 79.9 inches. Tires: 8.00 x 15; (Convertible and cars with air conditioning) 8.20 x 15. [Mark II] Wheelbase: 126 inches. Overall length: 218.5 inches. Overall width: 77.5 inches. Tires: 8.00 x 15; (Cars with air conditioning) 8.20 x 15.

CONVENIENCE OPTIONS: [Lincoln] Air conditioning. Power brakes. Push-button lubrication. Power windows. Power Four-Way front seat. Automatic headlight dimmer. Heater. Radio. Whitewall tires. Turbo-Drive automatic transmission was standard. [Mark II] The only option was air-conditioning. Power steering; power brakes; power seat; radio; whitewall tires and a heater were all standard equipment.

HISTORICAL FOOTNOTES: Ninety-eight percent of 1956 Lincolns were equipped with power brakes; 85 percent power seats; 86 percent power windows; 94 percent radios; 99 percent heaters and 98 percent whitewall tires. In 1956, Lincoln switched from 6-volt to a 12-volt electrical system.

1957 LINCOLN

1957 Lincoln, Capri two-door hardtop sport coupe, V-8

CAPRI SERIES — Lincolns received a facelift this year that was stylistically equivalent to putting a beehive hairdo on the Mona Lisa. The main change included the addition of two more headlights (actually they functioned as auxiliary lights), wider parking and signal lights, full-length center bodyside chrome and exaggerated tailfin enclosed taillights.

I.D. NUMBERS: Serial numbers ranged from 57W45,001L to 46,232L. Assembly plant code: LA = Los Angeles; LP = Lincoln plant; SL = St. Louis; WA = Wayne, Mich.

CAPRI

Model Number	Body/Style Number	Body Type & Seating	Factory Price	Shipping Weight	Production Total
NA	57A	4-dr Lan HT Sed	5294	4538	1,451
NA	58A	4-dr Sed-6P	2794	4349	1,476
NA	60A	2-dr HT Cpe-6P	4649	4373	2,973

1957 Lincoln, Premiere 4-dr Landau hardtop sedan, V-8 (AA)

PREMIERE SERIES — Except for the nameplate and star medallion on the front fenders, exterior differences between the Premiere and Capri were nil. Advertising promoted the 300 hp V-8 as a 'safety feature.' Power seats, power steering, electric windows and power brakes were standard.

PREMIERE

Model Number	Body/Style Number	Body Type & Seating	Factory Price	Shipping Weight	Production Total
NA	57B	4-dr Lan HT Sed	5294	4538	11,223
NA	58B	4-dr Sed-6P	5294	4527	5,139
NA	60B	2-dr HT Cpe-6P	5149	4451	15,185
NA	76B	2-dr Conv-6P	5381	4676	3,676

1957 Lincoln-Continental, Mark II two-door hardtop, V-8 (AA)

MARK II SERIES — This was the second and last year for the beautiful Mark II. Outside of a slightly lighter model, it was identical to last year's model. Two convertibles were specially built. Power steering; power brakes; carpeting; radio; heater; power seats; power windows and whitewall tires were standard.

MARK II

Model Number	Body/Style Number	Body Type & Seating	Factory Price	Shipping Weight	Production Total
NA	60A	2-dr HT Spt Cpe-6P	9695	4797	444
NA	76A	2-dr Conv-4P	10,000	NA	2

BASE ENGINE: V-8: Overhead valves. Cast iron block. Displacement: 368 cid. Bore and stroke: 4 x 3.65 inches. Compression ratio: 10.00:1. Brake hp: 300 at 4800 rpm. Carburetor: Carter four-barrel.

MARK II ENGINE: V-8: Overhead valves. Cast iron block. Displacement: 368 cid. Bore and stroke: 4 x 3.65 inches. Compression ratio: 10.00:1. Brake hp: 300 at 4800 rpm. Carburetor: Carter four-barrel.

CHASSIS FEATURES: [Lincoln] Wheelbase: 126 inches. Overall length: 224.6 inches. Front tread: 58.5 inches. Rear tread: 60 inches. Tires: 8.00 x 15; (Convertible and with air conditioning) 8.20 x 15. [Mark II] Wheelbase: 126 inches. Overall length: 218.5 inches. Overall width: 77.5 inches. Tires: 8.00 x 15; (With air conditioning) 8.20 x 15.

CONVENIENCE OPTIONS: [Lincoln] Air conditioning. Tinted glass. Whitewall tires. Front license plate frame. Padded instrument panel. Seat belts. Spotlight. Power vent windows. Three-tone leather trim. Six-Way power seat. Auxiliary driving lights. Electric door locks. Automatic headlight dimmer. Town and Country radio. Power radio antenna. push-button lubrication. Dual control heater. Padded sun visors. Directed Power differential. [Mark II] Air conditioning.

HISTORICAL FOOTNOTES: Only 22 percent of 1957 Lincolns came equipped with air conditioning.

1958 LINCOLN

CAPRI SERIES — The Capri was totally restyled for 1958. It had a unique roof design, slanting headlight pods, stylized front and rear bumpers and wraparound front and rear windows. The grille was mainly horizontal, with several vertical accent bars that seemed to make the car look wider than it already was. The side chrome spears were lower and not as

long as those used on last year's model. Automatic transmission; power steering; power brakes; windshield washers; padded instrument panel; and a V-8 engine were standard on all 1958 Lincolns.

LINCOLN I.D. NUMBERS: Serial numbers ranged from H8Y-400,001 to 429,624. The first letter (H) stood for the 430 cid V-8 with four-barrel carburetor. The first letter (J) stood for the same engine with three (3) two-barrel carburetors. The second digit (8) referred to the year (1958). The 'Y' referred to the Wixom, Mich. assembly plant. The fourth digit indicated the series and body styles as follows: 'A' = 1958-1959 Capri two-door hardtop; 1959 four-door sedan; 1959 four-door hardtop sedan. 'B' = 1958 Capri four-door hardtop; 1959 Premier four-door sedan; 1959 Premier four-door hardtop; 1959 Premiere two-door hardtop; 1959 Continentals. 'D' = 1959 Premier four-door hardtop. 'E' or 'F' = 1958 Continental two-door hardtop. 'K' = Capri four-door sedan. 'L' = 1958 Premier four-door sedan. 'M' = 1958 Continental four-door sedan. The fifth digit ('4') refers to the Lincoln Division. The last five digits are the production numbers.

CAPRI SERIES

Model Number	Body/Style Number	Body Type & Seating	Factory Price	Shipping Weight	Production Total
NA	53A	4-dr Sed-6P	4951	4799	1,184
NA	57A	4-dr Lan HT Sed	4951	4810	3,084
NA	63A	2-dr HT Cpe-6P	4803	4735	2,591

1958 Lincoln, Premier four-door Landau hardtop sedan, V-8

PREMIERE SERIES — A chrome rocker panel, a star at the forward tip of the side chrome spear and its distinct nameplate were the easiest ways to tell the Premier series from the lower priced Capri. Buyers could get either leather and fabric or all-fabric upholstery.

PREMIERE SERIES

Model Number	Body/Style Number	Body Type & Seating	Factory Price	Shipping Weight	Production Total
NA	53B	4-dr Sed-6P	5505	4802	1,660
NA	578	4-dr HT Sed-6P	5505	4798	5,572
NA	63B	2-dr HT Cpe-6P	5259	4734	3,043

1958 Lincoln-Continental, Mark III two-door convertible, V-8

CONTINENTAL MARK III — The Mark II of 1956-1957 had as much in common with the new Mark III as a thoroughbred Kentucky Derby winner has with TV's "Mr. Ed," the talking horse. A criss-cross pattern aluminum grille, full-length lower-body molding and a grid pattern rear panel were exclusive to the Mark III. The coupe and four-door had an unusual rear window that could be lowered. The coupe's roof style was shared with the convertible. The Mark III had the same standard equipment as Premieres and Capris.

CONTINENTAL SERIES

Model Number	Body/Style Number	Body Type & Seating	Factory Price	Shipping Weight	Production Total
NA	54A	4-dr Sed-6P	6012	4888	1,283
NA	65A	2-dr HT Cpe-6P	5765	4802	2,328
NA	68A	2-dr Conv-6P	6223	4927	3,048
NA	75A	4-dr HT Sed-6P	6012	4884	4,891

BASE ENGINE: V-8: Overhead valves. Cast iron block. Displacement: 430 cid. Bore and stroke: 4.29 x 3.7 inches. Compression ratio: 10.50:1. Brake hp: 375 at 4800 rpm. Carburetor: Holley 4150 four-barrel.

CHASSIS FEATURES: Wheelbase: 131 inches. Overall length: 229 inches. Tires: 9.00 x 14; [Optional on Mark III] 9.50 x 14.

OPTIONS: Special paint ($39.10). Air-conditioner and heater ($610.70). Power windows ($120.40). Power vent windows ($66). Power Six-Way seat over manual ($106.50). Six-Way power seat over Four-Way ($45.20). Whitewall tires, five, rayon ($55.50); five nylon whitewall tires ($85.40). Tinted glass ($48.40). Automatic headlight dimmer ($49.50). Translucent sun visors ($26.90). Power lubricator ($43). Leather interior, except standard in convertible, ($100). Seat belts ($23.70). Air suspension. Directed power differential. A 430 cid V-8 with three (3) two-barrel carburetors and 400 hp at 4600 rpm. was available at extra cost.

HISTORICAL FOOTNOTES: One of the least popular options in 1958 was air suspension. Only two percent of Lincolns came with it. Lincoln switched to unitized body construction this year. The chassis was eliminated. The suspension, driveline and engine units were fastened to the body structure.

1959 LINCOLN

CAPRI SERIES — The 1959 Capri was a couple inches shorter than last year's model, but at 227 inches, nobody confused it with a Rambler American. The canted headlights were integrated into the restyled grille. Side chrome was a bit gaudier. Brushed-aluminum trim covered the lower quarter panel and was connected to a chrome spear above the rear tires that continued almost to the front fender. The rear panel pattern was redesigned.

LINCOLN I.D. NUMBERS: Serial numbers ranged from H9Y-400,001 up. The first letter (H) stood for the 430 cid V-8 with four-barrel carburetor. The first letter (J) stood for the same engine with three (3) two-barrel carburetors. The second digit (9) referred to the year (1959). The 'Y' referred to the Wixom, Mich. assembly plant. The fourth digit indicated the series and body styles as follows: 'A' = 1958-1959 Capri two-door hardtop; 1959 four-door sedan; 1959 four-door hardtop sedan. 'B' = 1958 Capri four-door hardtop; 1959 Premier four-door sedan; 1959 Premier four-door hardtop; 1959 Premiere two-door hardtop; 1959 Continentals. 'D' = 1959 Premier four-door hardtop. 'E' or 'F' = 1958 Continental two-door hardtop. 'K' = 1958 Capri four-door sedan. 'L' = 1958 Premier four-door sedan. 'M' = 1958 Continental four-door sedan. The fifth digit ('4') refers to the Lincoln Division. The last five digits are the production numbers.

CAPRI SERIES

Model Number	Body/Style Number	Body Type & Seating	Factory Price	Shipping Weight	Production Total
NA	53A	4-dr Sed-6P	5090	5030	1,312
NA	57A	4-dr HT Sed-6P	5090	5000	4,417
NA	63A	2-dr HT Cpe-6P	4902	4925	2,200

1959 Lincoln, Premiere two-door hardtop coupe, V-8

PREMIERE SERIES — Once again, the best way to identify a Premiere was to look for its nameplate. On the outside, it looked the same as the lowest-priced Lincoln series. All 1959 Lincolns were equipped with automatic transmission; power brakes; power steering; dual exhausts; electric clock; windshield washer and remote-control outside mirror. In addition, Premieres came with power windows, rear license plate frame and Four-Way power front seat.

PREMIERE SERIES

Model Number	Body/Style Number	Body Type & Seating	Factory Price	Shipping Weight	Production Total
NA	53B	4-dr Sed-6P	5594	5030	1,282
NA	57B	4-dr HT Sed-6P	5594	5015	4,606
NA	63B	2-dr HT Cpe-6P	5347	4920	1,963

CONTINENTAL MARK IV — The Mark IV featured a criss-cross pattern grille, full-length lower body molding (but no side spear), four taillights and reverse slant rear window that could be lowered. Even the back window of the convertible was made of glass and was retractable. Mark IVs were equipped with Six-Way power seats; tinted glass; 'Travel-Tuner' radio with dual speakers; power vent windows and were available in three metallic paints exclusive to the series.

1959 Lincoln-Continental, Mark IV four-door Landau hardtop sedan, V-8

CONTINENTAL SERIES

Model Number	Body/Style Number	Body Type & Seating	Factory Price	Shipping Weight	Production Total
NA	23A	Exec Limo-6P	10,230	5450	49
NA	23B	4-dr Fml Sed-6P	9,208	5450	78
NA	54A	4-dr Sed-6P	6,845	5155	955
NA	65A	2-dr HT Cpe-6P	6,598	5050	1,703
NA	68A	2-dr Conv-6P	7,056	5175	2,195
NA	75A	4-dr HT Sed-6P	6,845	5155	6,146

BASE ENGINE: V-8. Overhead valves. Cast iron block. Displacement: 430 cid. Bore and stroke: 4.29 x 3.7 inches. Compression ratio: 10.00:1. Brake hp: 350 at 4400 rpm. Carburetor: Carter AFB-2853S four-barrel.

CHASSIS FEATURES: Wheelbase: 131 inches. Overall length: 227.1 inches. Tires: 9.50 x 14.

OPTIONS: Travel Tuner radio ($144.20). FM tuner radio ($114). Leather upholstery ($85). Remote control trunk release ($40). Power lubricator ($40). Electronic headlight dimmer ($51). Power vents ($65). Six-Way power seats ($98). Tinted glass ($48). Power windows ($94.70). Air conditioner with heater ($385). Power differential ($52).

HISTORICAL FOOTNOTES: Almost all 1959 Lincolns (99.6 percent) had a radio and 40.8 percent came with an air-conditioner.

1960 LINCOLN

LINCOLN SERIES — The biggest changes for 1960 were, a full-length mid-body chrome spear; larger tailfins wrapped in chrome; new instrument panel; altered horizontal theme grille; more conventional style front bumper and Ford-like square roofline. The back-up and taillights were rectangular. All 1960 Lincolns came with power brakes; power steering, heater and defroster; undercoating; whitewall tires; clock: radio; windshield washer; padded dash: center rear armrest and dual exhaust.

LINCOLN I.D. NUMBERS: Lincoln serial numbers contained eleven digits. The first indicated model year. as follows: '0' = 1960; '1' = 1961 etc. The second indicated the assembly plant as follows: 'Y' = Wixom, Mich.; 'S' = Allen Park, Mich. The third and fourth digits referred to the series and body style model numbers. The fifth indicated the type of engine as follows: 'A' = 460 cid V-8 with four-barrel carb; 'G' = 462 cid V-8 with four-barrel carb; 'S' = 400 cid V-8 with two-barrel carb. The last six digits were the sequential vehicle production numbers.

LINCOLN SERIES

Model Number	Body/Style Number	Body Type & Seating	Factory Price	Shipping Weight	Production Total
NA	53A	4-dr Sed-6P	5441	5016	1,093
NA	57A	4-dr HT Sed-6P	5441	5012	4,397
NA	63A	2-dr HT Cpe-6P	5253	4929	1,670

PREMIERE SERIES — The Premiere looked virtually the same as the standard Lincoln, except for a small front fender medallion. All Premieres came with power windows, rear compartment reading lights and four-way power seats.

PREMIERE SERIES

Model Number	Body/Style Number	Body Type & Seating	Factory Price	Shipping Weight	Production Total
NA	53B	4-dr Sed-6P	5945	5072	1,010
NA	578	4-dr HT Sed-6P	5945	5068	4,200
NA	638	2-dr HT Cpe-6P	5696	4987	1,364

CONTINENTAL MARK V — A criss-cross "dot-in-a-square" pattern grille; circular tail and back-up lights; lower front fender chrome bars and a reverse slanted, retractable rear window, set the top-of-the-line Mark V apart from the other series. Standard features included a Six-Way power seat, tinted glass and power vent windows.

CONTINENTAL SERIES

Model Number	Body/Style Number	Body Type & Seating	Factory Price	Shipping Weight	Production Total
NA	23A	4-dr Exec Limo-6P	10,230	5495	34
NA	23B	4-dr Town Car-6P	9207	5286	136
NA	54A	4-dr Sed-6P	6854	5157	807
NA	65A	2-dr HT Cpe-6P	6598	5070	1,461
NA	68A	2-dr Conv-6P	7056	5176	2,044
NA	75A	4-dr HT Sed-6P	6845	5153	6,604

1960 Lincoln-Continental, Mark V two-door convertible, V-8

BASE ENGINE: V-8: Overhead valves. Cast iron block. Displacement: 430 cid. Bore and stroke: 4.29 x 3.7 inches. Compression ratio: 10.00:1. Brake hp: 315 at 4100 rpm. Carburetor: Carter ABD-2965S two-barrel.

CHASSIS FEATURES: Wheelbase: 131 inches Overall length: 227.2 inches. Overall width: 80,3 inches. Tires: 9.50 x 14.

1960 Lincoln-Continental, Mark V Executive four-door limousine, V-8

OPTIONS: Air-conditioner with heater ($475.20). Electronic headlight dimmer ($56). Electric door locks, on two-doors ($39 45); on four-doors ($63.65). Power lubricator ($46.90). FM radio attachment ($129). Four-Way power seat ($87). Six-Way power seat ($118.95). Six-Way power seat over a Four-Way power seat ($49.50). Power vent windows ($75,60). Remote control trunk lid ($45.60). Chrome curb guard ($26 90). Directed power differential ($57.50).

HISTORICAL FOOTNOTES: Almost half of all 1960 Lincolns (49 percent) came equipped with an air-conditioner. Lincolns had a new Hotchkiss rear suspension.

1961 LINCOLN

1961 Lincoln-Continental, four-door sedan, V-8

CONTINENTAL SERIES — Once again. Lincoln proved it could produce a strikingly beautiful car. The 1961 Continental became one of the most influential automobile designs of the 1960s. The four headlights were embedded in a criss-cross pattern grille (with emphasis on the horizontal bars). The front and rear wraparound bumpers blended well into the overall design. Side trim was limited to full-length upper body molding and a chrome rocker panel. The rear doors opened to the center. All 1961 Continentals had automatic transmission; a radio with rear speaker; heater; power brakes; power steering; power windows; walnut applique or padded instrument panel; carpeting and power door locks.

I.D. NUMBERS: VIN stamped on right inner fender apron under hood. First symbol 1=1961. Second symbol indicates assembly plant: Y=Wixom, Mich. Third and fourth symbols indicate model and series: 82=Continental sedan; 86=Continental convertible. Fifth symbol indicates engine: H=430 cid/300 hp V-8 and K=low-compression Export version of 430 cid V-8. Last six symbols are sequential production number. Body plate riveted to front body pillar between door hinges gives body, color, trim, date, engine, transmission and axle codes.

CONTINENTAL SERIES

Model Number	Body/Style Number	Body Type & Seating	Factory Price	Shipping Weight	Production Total
82	54A	4-dr Sed-6P	6067	4927	22,303
86	74A	4-dr Conv-6P	6713	5215	2,857

BASE ENGINE: V-8. Overhead valves. Cast iron block. Displacement: 430 cid. Bore and stroke: 4.29 x 3.7 inches. Compression ratio: 10.00:1. Brake hp: 300 at 4100 rpm. Carburetor: Carter ABD two-barrel.

CHASSIS FEATURES: Wheelbase: 123 inches. Overall length: 212.4 inches. Tires: (Sedan) 9.00 x 14; (Convertible) 9.50 x 14.

OPTIONS: Air-conditioner with heater ($504.60). Six-Way power seat ($118.95). Speed control ($96.80). Special interior trim ($100). Tinted glass ($53.65). Directed power differential ($57.50).

HISTORICAL FOOTNOTES: Sixty-five percent of 1961 Continentals were equipped with an air-conditioner. Every new Continental underwent a 12-mile road test before it left the factory. The Industrial Design Institute awarded the designers of the 1961 Lincoln-Continental a bronze medal. Few other automobiles have ever been so honored.

1962 LINCOLN

1962 Lincoln-Continental, four-door convertible, V-8

CONTINENTAL SERIES — Removal of the front bumper guards, the use of a new type of individual headlight trim, a narrower center grille bar and a semi-honeycomb style grille treatment (repeated on the rear panel) were the main changes for 1962. The new Continentals were also slightly lower, longer and narrower than the 1961 models. Broadcloth upholstery was standard in the sedan, all-vinyl in the convertible. Like last year's model, the convertible top retracted into the trunk. All Continentals had power brakes; automatic transmission; power steering; power windows; a radio with a rear speaker; carpeting; electric clock; power door locks; walnut applique or padded instrument panel; dual exhaust and folding center armrests.

I.D. NUMBERS: VIN stamped on right inner fender apron under hood. First symbol 2=1962. Second symbol indicates assembly plant: Y=Wixom, Mich. Third and fourth symbols indicate model and series: 82=Continental sedan; 84=Continental four-door hardtop; 86=Continental convertible. Fifth symbol indicates engine: H=430 cid/300 hp V-8 and K=low-compression Export version of 430 cid V-8. Last six symbols are sequential production number. Body plate riveted to front body pillar between door hinges gives body, color, trim, date, engine, transmission and axle codes.

CONTINENTAL SERIES

Model Number	Body/Style Number	Body Type & Seating	Factory Price	Shipping Weight	Production Total
82	53A	4-dr Sed-6P	6074	4929	27,849
86	74A	4-dr Conv-6P	6720	5213	3,212

NOTE 1: Four Lincoln-Continental four-door hardtops (body code 57C) may have been built.

BASE ENGINE: V-8. Overhead valves. Cast iron block. Displacement: 430 cid. Bore and stroke: 4.29 x 3.7 inches. Compression ratio: 10.00:1. Brake hp: 300 at 4100 rpm. Carburetor: Carter ABD two-barrel.

CHASSIS FEATURES: Wheelbase: 123 inches. Overall length: 213 inches. Tires: (Sedan) 9.00 x 14; (Convertible) 9.50 x 14.

OPTIONS: Air-conditioner and heater ($505.60). Automatic headlight dimmer ($45.60). Special interior trim ($100). Power vent windows ($75.60). Electric radio antenna ($32.60). Automatic trunk release ($53.40). Six-Way power seat ($118.95). Speed control ($96.80). Tinted glass ($53.65). Directed power differential ($57.50).

HISTORICAL FOOTNOTES: Almost three out of four 1962 Continentals were sold with air-conditioning, 96 percent came with power seats.

1963 LINCOLN

1963 Lincoln-Continental, four-door sedan, V-8

CONTINENTAL SERIES — A different rear panel design and new grille treatment were the main changes for 1963. The Continental was also about a third of an inch longer. The dash was changed slightly to give more knee room. All new Continentals came equipped with:

automatic transmission; power brakes; power windows; heater; Six-Way power seat; power radio antenna; radio with rear speaker; dual exhausts; carpeting; electric clock; power steering; walnut applique or padded instrument panel; power vent windows, chrome curb guards; visor vanity mirror; remote control outside rearview mirror; and power door locks.

I.D. NUMBERS: VIN stamped on right inner fender apron under hood. First symbol 3=1963. Second symbol indicates assembly plant: Y=Wixom, Mich. Third and fourth symbols indicate model and series: 82=Continental sedan; 86=Continental convertible. Fifth symbol indicates engine: N=430 cid/320 hp V-8 and 7=low-compression Export version of 430 cid V-8. Last six symbols are sequential production number. Body plate riveted to front body pillar between door hinges gives body, color, trim, date, engine, transmission and axle codes.

CONTINENTAL

Model Number	Body/Style Number	Body Type & Seating	Factory Price	Shipping Weight	Production Total
82	54A	4-dr Sed-6P	6270	4950	28,095
86	74A	4-dr Conv-6P	6916	5360	3,138

BASE ENGINE: V-8. Overhead valves. Cast iron block. Displacement: 430 cid. Bore and stroke: 4.29 x 3.7 inches. Compression ratio: 10.00:1. Brake hp: 320 at 4600 rpm. Carburetor: Carter AFB four-barrel.

CHASSIS FEATURES: Wheelbase: 123 inches. Overall length: 213.3 inches. Tires: (Sedan) 9.00 x 14: (Convertible) 9.50 x 14.

OPTIONS: Air-conditioner and heater ($504.60). Tinted glass ($53.65). Power trunk lock ($53.40). Speed control ($96.80). Front seat belts ($16.80). Automatic headlight dimmer ($45.60). AM/FM push-button radio ($84.70). Special leather trim, except standard in convertible ($100). Directed power differential ($57.50).

HISTORICAL FOOTNOTES: Seventy-three percent of all 1963 Continentals had air conditioners, 94.4 percent tinted glass and 20.6 percent a locking differential.

1964 LINCOLN

1964 Lincoln-Continental, four-door convertible, V-8

CONTINENTAL SERIES — The Continental grew a bit in 1964. Still, styling changes continued to be mild. Among them were, a new dash; full-length lower body molding; flat side glass; horizontal theme rear end trim and the replacement of the thick center grille bar, formerly connecting the headlights, by five vertical bars. All Continentals were equipped with automatic transmission; radio; power seats; power windows; power brakes and power steering.

I.D. NUMBERS: VIN stamped on right inner fender apron under hood. First symbol 4=1964. Second symbol indicates assembly plant: Y=Wixom, Mich. Third and fourth symbols indicate model and series: 82=Continental sedan; 86=Continental convertible. Fifth symbol indicates engine: N=430 cid/320 hp V-8 and 7=low-compression Export version of 430 cid V-8. Last six symbols are sequential production number. Body plate riveted to front body pillar between door hinges gives body, color, trim, date, engine, transmission and axle codes.

CONTINENTAL

Model Number	Body/Style Number	Body Type & Seating	Factory Price	Shipping Weight	Production Total
82	53A	4-dr Sed-6P	6292	5055	32,969
86	74A	4-dr Conv-6P	6938	5393	3,328

BASE ENGINE: V-8: Overhead valves. Cast iron block. Displacement: 430 cid. Bore and stroke: 4.29 x 3.7 inches. Compression ratio: 1 0.00:1. Brake hp: 320 at 4600 rpm. Carburetor: Carter C3VE-9510B four-barrel.

CHASSIS FEATURES: Wheelbase: 126 inches. Overall length: 216.3 inches. Width: 78.6 inches. Tires: 9.15 x 15.

OPTIONS: Air-conditioner and heater ($504.60). Speed control ($96.80). Tinted glass ($53.65). AM/FM push-button radio ($84.70). Power trunk lock ($53.40). Automatic headlight dimmer ($45.60). Movable steering wheel. Directed Power differential.

HISTORICAL FOOTNOTES: One of the least popular Lincoln options in 1964 was the movable steering wheel. Only seven percent of the cars came with this feature.

1965 LINCOLN

1965 Lincoln-Continental, four-door sedan, V-8

CONTINENTAL SERIES — The Continental received a relatively major facelift in 1965. Although basic styling remained the same, it had a flat horizontal grille theme and wraparound signal lights. The hood was also new. Among the many standard features were; automatic transmission; power steering; dual exhausts; visor vanity mirror; trip odometer; transistorized radio with rear speaker; undercoating; walnut applique or padded instrument panel; heater and defroster; Six-Way power seat; power radio antenna; remote control outside rearview mirror; power brakes; carpeting; windshield washer and power door locks.

I.D. NUMBERS: VIN stamped on right inner fender apron under hood. First symbol 5=1965. Second symbol indicates assembly plant: Y=Wixom, Mich. Third and fourth symbols indicate model and series: 82=Continental sedan; 86=Continental convertible. Fifth symbol indicates engine: N=430 cid/320 hp V-8 and 7=low-compression Export version of 430 cid V-8. Last six symbols are sequential production number. Body plate riveted to front body pillar between door hinges gives body, color, trim, date, engine, transmission and axle codes.

CONTINENTAL

Model Number	Body/Style Number	Body Type & Seating	Factory Price	Shipping Weight	Production Total
82	53A	4-dr Sed-6P	6292	5075	36,824
86	74A	4-dr Conv-6P	6798	5475	3,356

BASE ENGINE: V-8: Overhead valves. Cast iron block. Displacement: 430 cid. Bore and stroke: 4.29 x 3.7 inches. Compression ratio: 10.00:1. Brake hp: 320 at 4600 rpm. Carburetor: Carter C3VE-9510B four-barrel.

CHASSIS FEATURES: Wheelbase: 126 inches. Overall length: 216.3 inches. Width: 78.6 inches. Tires: 9.15 x 15.

OPTIONS: Air conditioner and heater ($504.50). Vinyl roof ($104.30). Individually adjustable front seats ($281.40). Power trunk lock ($53.40). Automatic headlight dimmer ($45.60). Emergency flasher ($12.80). AM/FM push-button radio ($84.70). Speed control ($96.80). Movable steering wheel ($60.00). Special leather trim, except standard in convertible ($100). Tinted glass ($53.65). Door edge guards ($6.90). Closed crankcase emission reduction system ($5.30). Directed power differential ($57.50).

HISTORICAL FOOTNOTES: Only about one in four 1965 Continentals had a movable steering wheel, but 90.6 percent were sold with air-conditioning.

1966 LINCOLN

CONTINENTAL SERIES — The Continental grew another four inches in 1966. The turn signals returned to the bumper, which now extended to the front tire openings. An emblem was on the front fender above the bumper. For the first time in five years, the taillights did not wraparound the rear fenders. Other changes included a return to curved side glass and a new instrument panel. Among the many standard features were; automatic transmission; power seats; power steering; front disc brakes; power windows; carpeting and windshield washer.

1966 Lincoln-Continental, four-door convertible, V-8

I.D. NUMBERS: VIN stamped on right inner fender apron under hood. First symbol 6=1966. Second symbol indicates assembly plant: Y=Wixom, Mich. Third and fourth symbols indicate model and series: 82=Continental sedan; 86=Continental convertible; 89=Continental two-door hardtop. Fifth symbol indicates engine: G=462 cid/340 hp V-8. Last six symbols are sequential production number. Body plate riveted to front body pillar between door hinges gives body, color, trim, date, engine, transmission and axle codes.

CONTINENTAL

Model Number	Body/Style Number	Body Type & Seating	Factory Price	Shipping Weight	Production Total
82	53A	4-dr Sed-6P	5750	5085	35,809
86	74A	4-dr Conv-6P	6383	5480	3,180
NA	65A	2-dr HT Cpe-6P	5485	4985	15,766

BASE ENGINE: V-8. Overhead valves. Cast iron block. Displacement: 462 cid. Bore and stroke: 4.38 x 3.830 inches. Compression ratio: 10.25:1. Brake hp: 340 at 4600 rpm. Carburetor: Carter C6VF-9510B four-barrel.

CHASSIS FEATURES: Wheelbase: 126 inches. Overall length: 220.9 inches. Width: 79.7 inches. Tires: 9.15 x 15.

OPTIONS: Air-conditioner and heater ($504.60). Vinyl roof ($104.30). Individually adjustable front seats ($281.40). Power trunk lock ($53.40). Automatic headlight dimmer ($45.60). AF/FM push-button radio ($84.70). Speed control ($96.80). Movable steering wheel ($60). Tinted glass ($53.65). Directed power differential. 3.00:1 rear axle were optional.

HISTORICAL FOOTNOTES: Slightly more than one in three Continentals had a movable steering wheel, 93.5 percent came with air-conditioning, 14.3 percent with a locking differential and 97.7 percent with tinted glass.

1967 LINCOLN

1967 Lincoln-Continental, four-door sedan, V-8

CONTINENTAL SERIES — Styling changes for 1967 were minor. Once again the center section of the grille was slightly protruding. The grille pattern featured horizontal bars accentuated by vertical ones. All new Continentals were equipped with; automatic transmissions; power steering; power brakes; power windows; visor vanity mirror; trip odometer; front and rear seat belts; Two-Way power seat; dual exhaust; carpeting; electric clock; remote control outside mirror; windshield washer and heater and defroster. The convertible also had leather trim, remote control trunk release and rear glass window.

I.D. NUMBERS: VIN stamped on right inner fender apron under hood. First symbol 7=1967. Second symbol indicates assembly plant: Y=Wixom, Mich. Third and fourth symbols indicate model and series: 82=Continental sedan; 86=Continental convertible; 89=Continental two-door hardtop. Fifth symbol indicates engine: G=462 cid/340 hp V-8; 7=Export version. Last six symbols are sequential production number. Body plate riveted to front body pillar between door hinges gives body, color, trim, date, engine, transmission and axle codes.

CONTINENTAL

Model Number	Body/Style Number	Body Type & Seating	Factory Price	Shipping Weight	Production Total
82	53A	4-dr Sed-6P	5795	5049	32,331
86	74A	4-dr Conv-6P	6449	5505	2,276
89	65A	2-dr HT Cpe-6P	5553	4940	11,060

BASE ENGINE: V-8. Overhead valves. Cast iron block. Displacement: 462 cid. Bore and stroke: 4.38 x 3.830 inches. Compression ratio: 10.25:1. Brake hp: 340 at 4600 rpm. Carburetor: Carter 4362 four-barrel.

CHASSIS FEATURES: Wheelbase: 126 inches. Overall length: 220.9 inches. Width: 79.7 inches. Tires: 9.15 x 15.

POWERTRAIN OPTIONS: SelectShift Turbo-Drive automatic transmission was standard. Directed power differential and a high torque axle were optional at extra cost.

1967 Lincoln-Continental, four-door Lehman-Peterson limousine, V-8

OPTIONS: Manual air-conditioner ($471.05). Air-conditioner with automatic temperature control ($523.55). Leather with vinyl trim, standard in convertible, ($124.30). Automatic headlight dimmer ($50.05). Emission control exhaust ($50). Speed actuated power door locks, in convertible and sedan ($68.50); in coupe, ($44.85). Six-Way power seat ($83.23). Six-Way power seat with passenger side recliner and power adjustable headrest ($181.68). Two-Way contour power seat, individually adjustable, with passenger side recliner ($290.58). Individually adjustable power contour seat, Six-Way for driver, Two-Way reclining for passenger ($373.86). Power vent windows ($71.64). AM radio with power antenna ($161.27). AM/FM signal seeking radio with power antenna ($244.54). AM radio and stereosonic tape system with power antenna ($244.54). Shoulder belts ($32). Embassy roof for coupe. ($131.60); for sedan ($136.85). Tilting steering wheel ($58.74). Remote control trunk release with warning light ($33.19). Tinted glass ($52.53). Speed control ($94.77).

HISTORICAL FOOTNOTES: Most 1967 Continentals, 96.5 percent, were sold with an air-conditioning.

1968 LINCOLN

1968 Lincoln-Continental, two-door hardtop sport coupe, V-8

CONTINENTAL SERIES — A new hood accentuated the protruding center section of the 1968 Lincoln-Continental grille. Wraparound signal lights, similar to those on the 1965 models, and wraparound taillights returned. Otherwise, styling was little changed from the previous year. All 1968 Continentals were equipped with automatic transmission; power steering; seat belts; remote-control outside rearview mirror; windshield washer; power windows; dual exhaust; electric clock; padded instrument panel; four-way emergency flashers; power disc brakes and Two-Way power seat.

I.D. NUMBERS: VIN on tag on dashoard visible through windshield. First symbol 8=1968. Second symbol indicates assembly plant: Y=Wixom, Mich. Third and fourth symbols indicate model and series: 82=Continental sedan; 80=Continental two-door hardtop; 89=Mark III Coupe. Fifth symbol indicates engine: A=460 cid/365 hp V-8; 1=Export version of 460 cid V-8; G=462 cid/340 hp V-8; 7=462 cid Export V-8. Last six symbols are sequential production number. Body plate riveted to front body pillar between door hinges gives body, color, trim, date, engine, transmission and axle codes.

CONTINENTAL

Model Number	Body/Style Number	Body Type & Seating	Factory Price	Shipping Weight	Production Total
80	65A	2-dr HT Cpe-6P	5736	4883	9,415
82	53A	4-dr Sed-6P	5970	4978	29,719

CONTINENTAL MARK III SERIES — The big news at Lincoln was the introduction of the Mark III. It arrived in April of 1968, as a 1969 model. It was a personal luxury car in the long-hood, short-deck tradition. The rear deck spare tire hump was also reminiscent of the first 'Mark.' Among the many standard features were all items available on the Continental, plus individually adjustable front seats; front and rear center folding armrests; Flow-Thru ventilation system and rear lamp monitoring system.

CONTINENTAL MARK III

Model Number	Body/Style Number	Body Type & Seating	Factory Price	Shipping Weight	Production Total
89	65A	2-dr HT Cpe-5P	6585	4739	Note 1

NOTE 1: Mark III is considered a 1969 production vehicle; see 1969 for first year production total.

BASE ENGINE: V-8. Overhead valves. Cast iron block. Displacement: 462 cid. Bore and stroke: 4.38 x 3.830 inches. Compression ratio: 10.25:1. Brake hp: 340 at 4600 rpm. Carburetor: Carter C8VF-9510E four-barrel.

MARK III ENGINE: V-8: Overhead valves. Cast iron block. Displacement: 460 cid. Bore and stroke: 4.36 x 3.85 inches. Compression ratio: 10.50:1. Brake hp: 365 at 4600 rpm. Carburetor: four-barrel.

CHASSIS FEATURES: Wheelbase: 126 inches. Overall length: 221 inches. Tires: 9.15 x 15.

OPTIONS: Manual control air-conditioner ($503.90). Air-conditioner with automatic temperature control ($523.55). Remote control right-hand outside mirror ($13.15). Automatic headlight dimmer ($50.05). Front seat shoulder belts ($32). Rear seat shoulder belts ($32). Tinted glass ($52.53). Rear window defogger ($42.50). Spare tire cover ($10.95). Manually adjustable head rests ($52.50). Power door locks in coupe ($47.45); in sedan ($68.50). Combination AM radio with stereosonic tape system, including two front and rear speakers and power antenna ($244.54). AM/FM signal-seeking radio with power antenna ($244.54). Vinyl covered roof ($136.85). Automatic ride leveler suspension ($97.15). Individually adjustable contour seats with Six-Way power for driver, Two-Way power reclining passenger side ($334.46). Six-Way power bench seat ($83.28). Six-Way power seat with reclining passenger side ($142.28). Tilting steering wheel ($66.95). Speed control ($94.77). Power vent windows ($71.64). Stereo-sonic tape system ($130.10). Leather with vinyl trim ($137.26). Five four-ply dual chamber whitewall tires ($196.80). Directed power differential. High torque (3.00:1) axle.

HISTORICAL FOOTNOTES: Most 1968 Lincolns, 75.6 percent, had a vinyl top, 98.7 percent had air conditioning and 99.3 percent came with tinted glass. The one-millionth Lincoln, a four-door sedan, was built this year. The new Continental MK III was introduced in April, 1968.

1969 LINCOLN

CONTINENTAL SERIES — The most noticeable changes made to the 1969 Lincoln were a revised grille pattern and the appearance of the Continental name printed above the grille. This was the last year the basic 1961 Continental body shell (and unit body construction) was used. Among the standard features were, automatic transmission; power steering; power brakes; self-adjusting front disc brakes; dual exhaust; vanity mirror; power windows and Two-Way power seat.

I.D. NUMBERS: VIN on tag on dashoard visible through windshield. First symbol 9=1969. Second symbol indicates assembly plant: Y=Wixom, Mich. Third and fourth symbols indicate model and series: 82=Continental sedan; 80=Continental two-door hardtop; 89=Mark III coupe. Fifth symbol indicates engine: A=460 cid/365 hp V-8. Last six symbols are sequential production number. Body plate riveted to front body pillar between door hinges gives body, color, trim, date, engine, transmission and axle codes.

CONTINENTAL

Model Number	Body/Style Number	Body Type & Seating	Factory Price	Shipping Weight	Production Total
80	65A	2-dr HT Cpe-6P	5813	4916	9,032
82	53A	4-dr Sed-6P	9046	5011	29,351

BASE ENGINE: V-8: Overhead valves. Cast iron block. Displacement: 460 cid. Bore and stroke: 4.36 x 3.85 inches. Compression ratio: 10.50:1. Brake hp: 365 at 4600 rpm. Carburetor: Autolite C8VF-9510J four-barrel.

1969 Lincoln-Continental, Mark III two-door hardtop, V-8

CONTINENTAL MARK III SERIES — Production of the new Continental Mark III coupe continued from April 1968 without interruption, with all cars in the series considered 1969 models. The new car was a far cry from its namesake, the Mark III of 1958. Rather, it was a personal luxury car in the long-hood, short-deck tradition of the Mark I. The rear deck spare tire hump was also reminiscent of the first 'Mark.' However, basic styling was in tune with that of standard Lincolns. Among the many standard features offered on the Mark III were the same items available on the Continental, plus individually adjustable front seats; front and rear center folding armrests; Flow-Thru ventilation system and rear lamp monitoring system.

CONTINENTAL MARK III

Model Number	Body/Style Number	Body Type & Seating	Factory Price	Shipping Weight	Production Total
89	65A	2-dr HT Cpe-5P	6741	4475	30,858

BASE ENGINE: V-8: Overhead valves. Cast iron block. Displacement: 460 cid. Bore and stroke: 4.36 x 3.85 inches. Compression ratio: 10.50:1. Brake hp: 365 at 4600 rpm. Carburetor: Autolite C8VF-9510J four-barrel.

CHASSIS FEATURES: Wheelbase: (Continental) 126 inches; (Mark III) 117.2 inches. Overall length: (Continental) 224 inches; (Mark III) 216 inches. Tires: (Continental) 9.15 x 15; (Mark III) 8.55 x 15.

OPTIONS: Manual air-conditioner ($503.70). Automatic temperature control air-conditioner ($523.30). Automatic headlight dimmer ($51.20). Rear window defogger with environment control in Continental ($42). Rear window defogger in Mark III ($26.30). Rear window defroster in Mark III ($85.30). Remote-control deck lid release ($40.70). Leather with vinyl interior ($137.80). Power door locks in two-doors ($47.30); in four-doors ($68.20). Six-Way power seat in Continental ($89.20). Six-Way power seat in Mark III ($179.70). Six-Way power seat with reclining passenger side seat, in Continental ($149.60); in Mark III ($238.70). Power vent windows in Continental (72.20). AM radio with power antenna ($161.40). AM/FM signal-seeking radio with power antenna in Continental ($244). AM radio/sterosonic tape system with power antenna, in Continental ($245.30); in Mark III ($258.40). AM/FM radio with power antenna, in Continental ($288.60); in Mark III ($326.60). Vinyl roof ($152.20). Individually

adjustable seats, in Continental ($334.50). Speed control ($94.50). Sure-Track brake system in Mark III ($195.80). Tilting steering wheel ($72.20). Tinted glass ($56.40). Town Car interior in Continental ($249.20). Four-ply fiberglass belted 9.15 x 15 whitewall tires ($196.80). Directed power differential. High torque axle.

HISTORICAL FOOTNOTES: All but 0.3 percent of Mark IIIs had an air-conditioner. Just over one in three came with a movable steering wheel. The vast majority of 1969 Continentals, 83.8 percent were sold with a vinyl roof.

1970 LINCOLN

1970 Lincoln-Continental, four-door sedan, V-8

CONTINENTAL SERIES — The Continental was restyled for 1970. A resemblance to past models was clearly evident. Hidden headlights, a protruding grille (with horizontal grille pieces) and wraparound front fenders gave it a sort of refined 'Batmobile' look. The Continental also had a new bumper-integrated taillight rear end treatment. The doors were wider on both the hardtop and sedan. The sedan's rear door now opened in the conventional way. Standard equipment included, automatic transmission; fender skirts; custom pinstripe; padded windshield pillar; map and reading lights; cut-pile carpeting; electric clock; vanity mirror; simulated woodgrain dash panel applique; power windows; power steering; power front disc brakes; front and rear ashtrays and cigarette lighters; Two-Way power bench seat and flashing side marker lights.

I.D. NUMBERS: VIN on tag on dashoard visible through windshield. First symbol 9=1969. Second symbol indicates assembly plant: Y=Wixom, Mich. Third and fourth symbols indicate model and series: 82=Continental sedan; 80=Continental two-door hardtop; 89=Mark III coupe. Fifth symbol indicates engine: A=460 cid/365 hp V-8. Last six symbols are sequential production number. Body plate riveted to front body pillar between door hinges gives body, color, trim, date, engine, transmission and axle codes.

CONTINENTAL

Model Number	Body/Style Number	Body Type & Seating	Factory Price	Shipping Weight	Production Total
81	65A	2-dr HT Cpe-6P	5976	4669	3,073
82	53A	4-dr Sed-6P	6211	4719	28,622

1970 Lincoln-Continental, Mark III two-door hardtop, V-8

CONTINENTAL MARK III SERIES — The biggest changes in the 1970 Mark III were hidden windshield wipers and new wheelcovers. The signal and taillights were also altered. The parking lights now remained on when the headlights were being used. In addition to the items standard on the Continental, the Mark III also came equipped with: Sure-Track brake system; Cartier electric chronometer; walnut dash panel and steering wheel applique; head console with warning lights; spare tire cover; rear lamp monitor system and vinyl roof.

CONTINENTAL MARK III

Model Number	Body/Style Number	Body Type & Seating	Factory Price	Shipping Weight	Production Total
89	65A	2-dr HT Cpe-6P	7281	4675	21,432

BASE ENGINE: V-8: Overhead valves. Cast iron block. Displacement: 460 cid. Bore and stroke: 4.36 x 3.85 inches. Compression ratio: 10.00:1. Brake hp: 365 at 4600 rpm. Carburetor: four-barrel.

CHASSIS FEATURES: Wheelbase: (Continental) 127 inches; (Mark III) 117.2 inches. Overall length: (Continental) 224 inches; (Mark III) 216 inches. Tires: (Continental) 9.15 x 15, (Mark III) 225 x 15.

OPTIONS: Manual air-conditioner ($503.70). Automatic temperature control air-conditioner ($523.20). Automatic headlight dimmer ($51.20). Cross-Country ride package in Continental ($17.10). Automatic ride control ($97.10). Sun roof in Mark III ($459.10). Leather with vinyl interior, in Mark III ($164); in Continental ($157-40). 'Moondust' paint ($131.20). Remote-control deck lid release in Mark III ($40.70). Power door locks in Mark III ($47.30). Six-Way power seat. in Continental ($89.20); in Mark III ($179.70). Six-Way power seat with reclining passenger side seat, in Continental ($149.60); in Mark III ($242.70). Twin Comfort Six-way/Two-way power seats in Continental ($220.40). Twin Comfort Six-way/Two-way power seats with reclining passenger seat ($280.70). AM radio with power antenna ($161.40). AM/FM radio with power antenna ($301.70). AM radio with Stereosonic tape system and power antenna ($296.50). TractionLok differential. High ratio rear axle.

HISTORICAL FOOTNOTES: All but four percent of 1970 Continentals came with an air-conditioner and tinted glass. Most Marks IIIs, 83.9 percent, had a tilting steering wheel. Many chassis parts on Lincoln's new body mounted on a frame construction, were interchangeable with full-size Mercurys and Fords. The 1970 Mark III was the first American car to come with steel-belted radial tires as standard equipment.

1971 LINCOLN

1971 Lincoln-Continental, four-door sedan, V-8

CONTINENTAL SERIES — Styling was little changed from 1970. Unlike last year, the grille's horizontal bars were not extended to the headlight covers. This toned down the front end a bit. Standard equipment included; automatic temperature control air-conditioning; automatic transmission; power front disc brakes; power steering; Two-Way power seat; fender skirts; cut-pile carpeting; carpeted luggage compartment; folding center armrests in front and rear; remote-control outside mirror; vanity mirror; tinted glass; electric clock: trip odometer and power ventilation system.

I.D. NUMBERS: VIN on tag on dashoard visible through windshield. First symbol 1=1971 Second symbol indicates assembly plant: Y=Wixom, Mich. Third and fourth symbols indicate model and series: 82=Continental sedan; 81=Continental two-door hardtop; 89=Mark III coupe. Fifth symbol indicates engine: A=460 cid/365 hp V-8. Last six symbols are sequential production number. Body plate riveted to front body pillar between door hinges gives body, color, trim, date, engine, transmission and axle codes.

CONTINENTAL

Model Number	Body/Style Number	Body Type & Seating	Factory Price	Shipping Weight	Production Total
81	65A	2-dr HT Cpe-6P	7172	5032	8,205
82	53A	4-dr Sed-6P	7419	5072	27,346

1971 Lincoln-Continental, Mark III two-door hardtop, V-8

CONTINENTAL MARK III SERIES — The Mark III was virtually unchanged for 1971. It had the same standard features as the Continental plus, high-back front seats with individual armrests; Cartier chronometer; monitor system for brakes; spare tire cover and vinyl roof (five vinyl top covers were available).

CONTINENTAL MARK III

Model Number	Body/Style Number	Body Type & Seating	Factory Price	Shipping Weight	Production Total
89	65A	2-dr HT Cpe-5P	8421	5003	27,091

BASE ENGINE: V-8. Overhead valves, Cast iron block. Displacement: 460 cid. Bore and stroke: 4.36 x 3.85 inches. Compression ratio: 10.50:1. Brake hp: 365 at 4600 rpm. Carburetor: four-barrel.

CHASSIS FEATURES: Wheelbase: (Continental) 127 inches. (Mark III) 117.2 inches. Overall length: (Continental) 225 inches; (Mark III) 216.1 inches. Tread width: (Continental) 64.3 inches; (Mark III) 62.3 inches. Tires: 225-15 steel belted Michelin.

OPTIONS: Sure Track brake system, standard in Mark III; in Continental ($196.80). Front bumper guards, in Continental ($19.70). Rear window defogger ($31.50). Automatic headlight dimmer ($51.20). Automatic load adjuster, in Continental ($97.10). Power deck lid release, in Mark III ($46). Power door locks, in Mark III ($49.90). Lock release group, in Continental ($106.30). Moondust metallic paint ($131.20). Six-Way power seat, in Continental ($91.90); in Mark III, ($183.70). Six-Way power bench seat with recliner, in Continental ($152.50). Six-Way power seat with reclining passenger seat, in Mark III ($242.70). Six-Way/Two-Way twin comfort power seat, in Continental ($223). Rear window defroster ($85.30). Six-Way/Two-Way Twin Comfort power seat, in Mark III ($246.60). Six-Way /Two-Way power twin comfort seat with passenger recliner, in Continental ($283.30). Cross-Country ride package ($17.10). Speed control ($94.50). AM signal-seeking radio ($161.40). AM/FM stereo radio ($306.90). AM radio with stereo tape system ($301.70). Vinyl roof, in Continental ($156.10). Leather seat trim, in Continental ($173.20); in Mark III ($183.70). Tilting steering wheel ($72.20). Luxury wheelcovers, in Continental ($59.10). Intermittent windshield wipers, in Continental ($26.30). Traction-Lok differential. Higher ratio rear axle.

HISTORICAL FOOTNOTES: Only 12.3 percent of 1971 Continentals had a locking differential. Most Mark IIIs, 88 percent, came with a tilting steering wheel. Nineteen seventy-one was the golden anniversary of Lincoln.

1972 LINCOLN

CONTINENTAL SERIES: Full-length upper body moldings and a new criss-cross pattern grille, were the most noticeable styling changes for 1972. A hood ornament with the Lincoln emblem was also added. Standard equipment included, fender skirts; automatic temperature control air-conditioning; power front disc brakes; cut-pile carpeting; electric clock; carpeted luggage compartment; left-hand remote-control outside rearview mirror; front and rear armrests; tinted glass; visor vanity mirror; AM radio with power antenna; Two-Way power seat; power ventilation; power windows and seat belts.

I.D. NUMBERS: VIN on tag on dashboard visible through windshield. First symbol 2=1972. Second symbol indicates assembly plant: Y=Wixom, Mich. Third and fourth symbols indicate model and series: 82=Continental sedan; 81=Continental two-door hardtop; 89=Mark III coupe. Fifth symbol indicates engine: A=460 cid V-8. Last six symbols are sequential production number. Body plate riveted to front body pillar between door hinges gives body, color, trim, date, engine, transmission and axle codes.

1972 Lincoln-Continental, four-door sedan, V-8

CONTINENTAL

Model Number	Body/Style Number	Body Type & Seating	Factory Price	Shipping Weight	Production Total
81	65A	2-dr HT Cpe-6P	7068	4906	10,408
82	53A	4-dr Sed-6P	7302	4958	35,561

CONTINENTAL MARK IV SERIES — The new Mark IV was four inches longer, about half an inch lower and a fraction of an inch wider than last year's Mark III. The radiator style grille was longer and used fewer vertical bars. It also bore a Mark IV emblem with a hood ornament on top. A new roof design featured an oblong opera window. Four rectangular bumper integrated taillights replaced the vertical wraparound ones. The distinctive spare-tire hump on the trunk remained. The Mark IV had more leg and shoulder room for rear seat passengers. In addition to the standard features offered on the Continental, the Mark IV was equipped with, Sure Track power brake system; spare tire cover; luxury wheelcovers; Cartier electric clock; Six-Way power Twin Comfort lounge seat; vinyl roof and automatic seatback release.

1972 Lincoln-Continental, Mark IV two-door hardtop, V-8

CONTINENTAL MARK IV

Model Number	Body/Style Number	Body Type & Seating	Factory Price	Shipping Weight	Production Total
89	65A	2-dr HT Cpe-6P	8640	4792	48,591

CONTINENTAL ENGINE: V-8: Overhead valves. Cast iron block. Displacement: 460 cid. Bore and stroke: 4.36 x 3.85 inches. Compression ratio: 8.5:1. SAE nhp: 212 at 4400 rpm. Carburetor: four-barrel.

CONTINENTAL MARK IV ENGINE: V-8: Overhead valves. Cast iron block. Displacement: 460 cid. Bore and stroke: 4.36 x 3.85 inches. Compression ratio: 8.5:1. SAE nhp: 224 at 4400 rpm. Carburetor: four-barrel.

CHASSIS FEATURES: Wheelbase: (Continental) 127 inches; (Mark IV) 120.4 inches. Overall length: (Continental) 225 inches; (Mark IV) 220.1 inches. Tires: 225-15 Michelin radial.

CONVENIENCE OPTIONS: Sure Track brake system, on Continental ($191.83). Opera window, in Mark IV ($81.84). Front bumper guards ($19.19). Rear window defroster ($83.13). Automatic headlight dimmer ($49.88). Cornering lamps, in Mark IV ($35.81). Moondust metallic paint ($127.88). Power lock/release group, in Continental ($103.59). Lock convenience group, in Mark IV ($93.36). AM radio with stereo tape player ($136.84). Seats with leather trim, in Continental ($168.80); in Mark IV ($179.04). Leather trimmed seats with passenger recliner ($61.39 extra in Mark IV). Six-Way power bench seat with passenger recliner ($148.35 Continental). Six-Way power bench seat, in Continental ($89.52). Six-Way/Two-Way power Twin Comfort seats, in Continental ($217.40). Six-Way/Two-way power Twin Comfort seats with passenger recliner, in Continental ($276.23). Tilting steering wheel ($70.35). Town Car package for Continental four-door sedan ($446.67). Town Car package with leather trim for Continental four-door sedan ($635.47). Speed control ($92.08). Vinyl roof, on Continental ($152.19). Luxury wheelcovers, on Continental ($57.56). TractionLok differential. High-ratio rear axle.

HISTORICAL FOOTNOTES: Most 1972 Continentals, 77.3 percent came with a tilting steering wheel.

1973 LINCOLN

1973 Lincoln-Continental, four-door sedan, V-8

CONTINENTAL SERIES — The Continental name was printed above the grille of the 1973 model. It hadn't been seen in this location for three years. An improved bumper with bumper guards was another change. Otherwise, the new Continental looked virtually the same as last year's. Among the standard features were: automatic transmission; power steering; white sidewall tires; Deluxe wheelcovers; dual custom stripes; power windows; Two-Way power seat; AM radio with power antenna; cut-pile carpeting; seat belt warning buzzer; electric clock; folding center armrests in front and rear; carpeted luggage compartment; tinted glass; remote control left-hand outside mirror; visor mounted vanity mirror; spare tire lock and cornering lights.

I.D. NUMBERS: VIN on tag on dashoard visible through windshield. First symbol 3=1973. Second symbol indicates assembly plant: Y=Wixom, Mich. Third and fourth symbols indicate model and series: 82=Continental sedan; 81=Continental two-door hardtop; 89=Mark III coupe. Fifth symbol indicates engine: A=460 cid V-8. Last six symbols are sequential production number. Body plate riveted to front body pillar between door hinges gives body, color, trim, date, engine, transmission and axle codes.

Model Number	Body/Style Number	Body Type & Seating	Factory Price	Shipping Weight	Production Total
81	65A	2-dr HT Cpe-6P	7230	5016	13,348
82	53A	4-dr Sed-6P	7474	5049	45,288

CONTINENTAL MARK IV SERIES — The main changes to the new Mark IV were restyled, wraparound signal lights and an improved front bumper that covered up the lower part of the grille (this area had been exposed in 1972). The Mark IV featured the same standard items as the Continental, plus vinyl roof; opera windows; Twin Lounge seats with Six-Way power; cloth and vinyl upholstery; deep cut-pile carpeting; reading lights; carpeted spare tire cover; Cartier electric clock; inside hood latch release; Sure-Track brake system and customer monograms.

CONTINENTAL MARK IV

Model Number	Body/Style Number	Body Type & Seating	Factory Price	Shipping Weight	Production Total
89	65A	2-dr HT Cpe-5P	8984	4908	69,437

1973 Lincoln-Continental, Mark IV two-door hardtop, V-8

ENGINE: V-8. Overhead valves. Cast iron block. Displacement: 460 cid. Bore and stroke: 4.36 x 3.85 inches. Compression ratio: 8.0:1. SAE nhp: 208 at 4400 rpm. Carburetor: four-barrel.

CHASSIS FEATURES: Wheelbase: (Continental) 127 inches; (Mark IV) 120.4 inches. Overall length: (Continental) 229.5 inches; (Mark IV) 224 inches. Tires: 230R15 steel-belted radial.

OPTIONS: Town Car package including power vent windows, rear door quarter armrest inserts. 'C' pillar lights and vinyl covered 'B' pillar, on four-door models; also, on both two and four-door models, including vinyl roof; seatback robe cords; seatback carpet inserts; personalized owner's initials; distinctive Town Car insignia; flocked headlining and sun visors and glovebox vanity mirror, for two-door Continentals ($567); for four-door Continentals ($635). Sun roof ($611.28). Rear window defroster ($83.13). Remote control right-hand mirror $26.67. Tilting steering wheel ($70.35). Automatic headlight dimmer ($49.88). Mark IV Silver Luxury group, including silver grained vinyl roof, red interior and silver 'Moondust' metallic paint ($400). AM/FM stereo radio ($141.96). AM radio with stereo tape system ($136.84). Continental seats with leather trim ($168.80). Speed control ($92.08). Seats with leather trim and passenger recliner ($240.43). Six-Way/Two-Way Twin Comfort power seats, in Continental ($217.40). Six-Way/Two-Way Twin Comfort power seats with recliner, in Continental ($276.23). Six-Way power bench seat in Continental ($89.52). Six-Way power bench seat with recliner, in Continental ($148.35). Bodyside vinyl insert molding ($33.25). Interval windshield wipers ($25.57). TractionLok differential. High-ratio rear axle.

HISTORICAL FOOTNOTES: Ninety-three percent of 1973 Mark IVs came with a tilting steering wheel.

1974 LINCOLN

CONTINENTAL SERIES — The Continental received a minor, but attractive facelift this year. New wraparound signal lights, clean headlight doors and a vertical bar style grille seemed to have been influenced by the Mark IV. Standard features included power windows; power ventilation system; Six-Way power seat; automatic temperature control; AM radio with power antenna; Cartier electric clock; visor-mounted vanity mirror; tinted glass; automatic parking brake release; Deluxe wheelcovers; spare tire lock; remote control outside rearview mirror; power steering; fender skirts; power front disc brakes; cornering lights and carpeted luggage compartment.

I.D. NUMBERS: VIN on tag on dashoard visible through windshield. First symbol 4=1974. Second symbol indicates assembly plant: Y=Wixom, Mich. Third and fourth symbols indicate model and series: 82=Continental sedan, 81=Continental two-door hardtop; 89=Mark III coupe. Fifth symbol indicatos engine: A=460 cid V-8. Last six symbols are sequential production number. Body plate riveted to front body pillar between door hinges gives body, color, trim, date, engine, transmission and axle codes.

1974 Lincoln-Continental, four-door Town Car sedan, V-8

CONTINENTAL

Model Number	Body/Style Number	Body Type & Seating	Factory Price	Shipping Weight	Production Total
81	65A	2-dr HT Cpe-6P	8053	5366	7,318
82	53A	4-dr Sed-6P	8238	5361	29,351

1974 Lincoln-Continental, Mark IV two-door hardtop, V-8

CONTINENTAL MARK IV SERIES — The Mark IV's styling was virtually unchanged for 1974. However, new sound insulation and thicker carpeting helped give it a quieter ride. In addition to most of the standard features offered on Continentals, the Mark IV came equipped with Sure Track power brake system; carpeted spare tire cover; digital clock; rear bumper guard; luxury steering wheel; front and rear rub strips; vinyl roof; Six-Way Twin Comfort power seat and engine compartment light.

CONTINENTAL MARK IV

Model Number	Body/Style Number	Body Type & Seating	Factory Price	Shipping Weight	Production Total
89	65A	2-dr HT Spt Cpe-6P	10,194	5362	57,316

CONTINENTAL ENGINE: V-8: Overhead valves. Cast iron block. Displacement: 460 cid. Bore and stroke: 4.36 x 3.85 inches. Compression ratio: 8.0:1. SAE net hp: 215 at 4000 rpm. Carburetor: four-barrel.

MARK IV ENGINE: V-8: Overhead valves. Cast iron block. Displacement: 460 cid. Bore and stroke: 4.36 x 3.85 inches. Compression ratio: 8.0:1. SAE net hp 220 at 4000 rpm. Carburetor: four-barrel.

CHASSIS FEATURES: Wheelbase: (Continental) 127.2 inches; (Mark IV) 120.4 inches. Overall length: (Continental) 232.6 inches; (Mark IV) 228.4 inches. Tires: (Continental) 234RI five steel belted radial; (Mark IV) 230 x 15 steel belted radial.

OPTIONS: Anti-theft alarm system ($77). Sure-Track brake system, on Continental ($191.82). Quick Defrost defroster, in Mark IV ($306.70). Rear window defroster ($83.13). Dual exhaust, on Mark IV ($52). Right-hand remote control outside rearview mirror ($26.67). Illuminated visor vanity mirror ($86.70). Body side moldings with vinyl insert ($33.25). Moondust metallic paint ($127.88). Diamond Fire metallic paint ($167). AM/FM multiplex radio ($141.96). AM/FM Multiplex radio with stereo tape system, in Continental ($26.33), in Mark IV ($127.37). Speed control ($92.08). Bench seat with passenger recliner ($58.83). Six-Way Twin Comfort power seat, in Continental ($217.15). Six-Way Twin Comfort power seat with passenger recliner, in Continental ($278.48). Tilting steering wheel ($70.35). Sun roof ($611.28). Power sun roof with steel panel, in Mark IV ($611.28). Space Saver spare tire, for Mark IV ($77.40). Leather interior trim, in Mark IV ($179.04); in Continental ($168.80). Mark IV velour interior trim ($179.70). Vinyl roof, on Continental ($152.19). Luxury wheelcovers, on Continental ($76). Power vent windows, in Continental four-door ($68). Interval windshield wipers ($25.57). Mark IV Silver Luxury package including silver grained vinyl roof, silver metallic paint, red leather or velour interior, or silver leather interior ($400). As above, with power glass sun roof ($777.40). Gold Luxury package including gold grained vinyl roof, gold diamond fire metallic paint, tan leather interior with brown suede accents and tan components ($438 Mark IV). As above, with power glass sun roof ($770.40). Town Car package including vinyl roof; Six-Way power bench seat in vinyl with leather seating surfaces; full-width head restraints; front seatback robe cords; carpeted front seatbacks; glovebox vanity mirror; distinctive insignia; flocked headlining and sun visors; and personalized initials, in two-door Continentals ($567.47); in four-door Continentals ($635.47). TractionLok differential and high ratio rear axle were optional.

1975 LINCOLN

1975 Lincoln-Continental, Mark IV two-door coupe, V-8

1975 Lincoln-Continental two-door Town coupe, V-8

CONTINENTAL SERIES — Several changes were made to the Continental for 1975. Among these were, a new roof design; new taillights; rotary valve steering gear; new brakes; Continental name written in chrome on the rear fenders; full-length lower body molding; a vertical bar grille containing several heavier accent bars and the extension of the grille below the upper front bumper. Some of the many standard Continental features included, power steering; power front discs brakes; solid-state ignition; automatic temperature control air-conditioning; tinted glass; power windows; AM/FM Multiplex stereo radio with power antenna; Cartier digital clock; vinyl roof; power door locks; power trunk lid release; tilting steering wheel; trip odometer; door edge guards; Deluxe wheelcovers; Six-Way cloth and vinyl power seat; cut-pile carpeting; door-closing assist straps; folding center armrests; visor mounted vanity mirror; left-hand remote-control outside rearview mirror; spare tire cover and lock; personalized initials and license plate frames.

I.D. NUMBERS: VIN on tag on dashoard visible through windshield. First symbol 5=1975. Second symbol indicates assembly plant: Y=Wixom, Mich. Third and fourth symbols indicate model and series: 82=Continental sedan; 81=Continental two-door hardtop; 89=Mark III coupe. Fifth symbol indicates engine: A=460 cid V-8. Last six symbols are sequential production number. Body plate riveted to front body pillar between door hinges gives body, color, trim, date, engine, transmission and axle codes.

CONTINENTAL

Model Number	Body/Style Number	Body Type & Seating	Factory Price	Shipping Weight	Production Total
81	65A	2-dr HT Spt Cpe-6P	9214	5219	21,185
82	53A	4-dr Sed-6P	9656	5229	33,513

CONTINENTAL MARK IV SERIES — The 1975 Mark IV was a virtual clone of last year's model. However, there was a new Landau vinyl roof option. It featured a 'frenched' rear window and bright chrome band vaguely reminiscent of the 1955-1956 Ford Crown Victorias. Standard features included most of those offered on the Continental plus, four-wheel disc brakes; wiper-mounted windshield washers; speed control; Six-Way power Twin Comfort lounge seats with cloth upholstery and engine compartment light.

CONTINENTAL MARK IV

Model Number	Body/Style Number	Body Type & Seating	Factory Price	Shipping Weight	Production Total
89	65A	2-dr HT Spt Cpe-6P	11,082	5145	47,145

CONTINENTAL ENGINE: V-8: Overhead valves. Cast iron block. Displacement: 460 cid. Bore and stroke: 4.36 x 3.85 inches. Compression ratio: 8.00:1. SAE net hp: 215 at 4000 rpm. Carburetor: four-barrel.

CONTINENTAL MARK IV ENGINE: V-8: Overhead valves. Cast iron block. Displacement: 460 cid. Bore and stroke: 4.36 x 3.85 inches. Compression ratio: 8.00:1. SAE net hp: 220 at 4000 rpm. Carburetor: four-barrel.

CHASSIS FEATURES: Wheelbase: (Continental) 127.2 inches; (Mark IV) 120.4 inches. Overall length: (Continental) 232.9 inches; (Mark IV) 228.1 inches. Tires: (Continental/Mark IV) 230-15 steel belted radial.

CONVENIENCE OPTIONS: Town Car/Town Coupe package included power vent windows; coach lamps; exterior nameplate; Six-Way power seat with leather seating surfaces; special seat trim and door panels; deep cut-pile carpeting; glovebox vanity mirror; luggage compartment carpeting and interior nameplate with gold accent, in Continental two-door ($567.47); in Continental four-door ($635.47). Mark IV Silver Luxury group ($400). Lipstick and White Mark IV luxury group ($400). Mark IV forged aluminum wheels ($287). AM/FM stereo radio with tape player ($139). Leather interior trim, in Continental ($168.80); in Mark IV ($179.04). Rear window defroster (83.13). Speed-control, on Continental ($92.08). Six-Way Twin Comfort seat with passenger recliner, in Mark IV ($61.39). Add $97.40 for above with power lumbar back support. Moondust metallic paint ($141.96). Diamond fire metallic paint ($167). Right-hand remote control outside rearview mirror ($26.67). Power sun roof ($611.28). Mark IV power sun roof with glass panel ($777.40). Space Saver spare tire ($77.40). Anti-theft alarm system ($77). TractionLok differential and high ratio rear axle were optional.

MERCURY
1946-1975

The Lincoln-Mercury Div. was formed in 1945, but it wasn't until 1949 models appeared, in early 1948, that Mercury was able to shed (temporarily) its image as a glorified Ford.

The 1949 to 1951 Mercurys became very popular with customizers and hot rodders. Actor James Dean, driving one in the classic 1950s youth movie "Rebel Without A Cause," helped assure the cars' cult status.

By Charles Webb

The fancy Ford look returned in 1952. Mercury was supposed to have received a new overhead valve V-8 that year, but it wasn't ready in time. So the flathead V-8 was kept two more years. The flathead had a reputation as a hot engine. However, this was mainly because it was so easy to soup-up.

In addition to an overhead valve V-8, the 1954 Mercury offered one of the most unique cars available that year. Its Sun Valley, like Ford's Skyliner, had a plexiglass section over the front half of the roof. Although not exactly the most practical idea, it did show how innovative Ford Motor Co. was.

Considering that they were based on Fords, the 1955 and 1956 Mercurys featured distinctive styling. In 1957, the make received its own body, which it shared with no one. That may have been just as well. The man largely responsible for the 1957 Mercury design said, years later, "You could see how we could get the reputation as real hacks and chrome merchants: because looking at those cars, it would be hard to deny."

Ford once again shared a body with Mercury in 1960, when they introduced the successful compact Comet.

Full-size Fords and Mercurys shared bodies in 1961, 1962 and 1963, when the intermediate Fairlane and Meteors also shared bodies.

The "Breezeway" roof, with its retractable rear window (first used on the 1957 Turnpike Cruiser), was reintroduced in 1963. Mercury was the only make to have this unique and useful style roof. Fastback Marauder hardtops were offered because their roofline was more aerodynamic and improved the make's chance of winning stock car races.

"It's now in the Lincoln Continental tradition," proclaimed ads for the 1965 Mercury. That same year, Ford group vice president Lee A. Iacocca was put in charge of a program to improve Lincoln-Mercury sales. He pushed to further identify the make with Lincoln. The results of his efforts are very evident in the 1969 and up models.

While full-size Mercurys became plusher, the compact Comet series expanded and certain models (Caliente and Cyclone) began to earn well-deserved reputations as hot street machines. Mid-size Mercurys of the late 1960s and early 1970s were especially potent when equipped with one of several high-powered engines available.

Mercury entered the 'pony car' market in 1967. Its Cougar was offered with some powerful performance packages the first several years, but by 1971, became primarily a sporty personal car.

Small Mercurys reappeared in the early 1970s. Comet returned and was joined by Bobcat. The mid-size Monarch came on the scene in 1975.

1947 Mercury, two-door sedan-coupe, V-8

1962 Mercury, Monterey Custom two-door convertible, V-8

1950 Mercury, two-door convertible, V-8

1969 Mercury, Montego MX two-door convertible, V-8

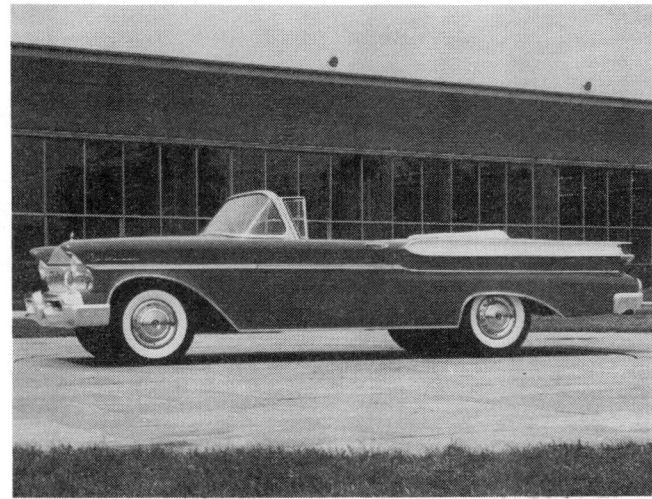

1957 Mercury, Monterey two-door convertible, V-8

1970 Mercury, Marquis two-door convertible, V-8

Standard Catalog of American Cars

1946 MERCURY

1946 Mercury, two-door sedan, V-8

MERCURY SERIES — SERIES 69M — A new grille was the most noticeable difference between the 1942 and 1946 Mercurys. It had thin, vertical bars surrounded by a trim piece painted the same color as the car. The Liquamatic Drive automatic transmission option was also eliminated. The most distinctive new Mercury was the Sportsman convertible. It featured wood body panels.

MERCURY I.D. NUMBERS: Serial numbers were the same as engine numbers. They ranged from 99A50280 to 1,412,707.

MERCURY

Model Number	Body/Style Number	Body Type & Seating	Factory Price	Shipping Weight	Production Total
69M	71	2-dr Sptmn Conv	2209	3407	205
69M	70	2-dr Sed-6P	1448	3240	13,108
69M	72	2-dr Sed Cpe-6P	1495	3190	24,163
69M	73	4-dr Twn Sed-6P	1509	3270	40,280
69M	76	2-dr Conv-6P	1711	3340	6,044
69M	79	4-dr Sta Wag-8P	1729	3540	2,797

MERCURY ENGINE: V-8: L-head. Cast iron block. Displacement: 239.4 cid. Bore and stroke: 3.19 x 3.75 inches. Compression ratio: 6.75:1. Brake hp: 100 at 3800 rpm. Three main bearings. Carburetor: Holley 94 two-barrel.

CHASSIS FEATURES: Wheelbase: 118 inches. Overall length: 201.8 inches. Front tread: 58 inches. Rear tread: 60 inches. Tires: 6.50 x 15.

POWERTRAIN OPTIONS: A three-speed manual transmission was standard.

CONVENIENCE OPTIONS: Radio with foot control. Heater. Fog lamps.

HISTORICAL FOOTNOTES: Mercury's model year production for 1946 was 86.603 cars. Sales for the calendar year were counted as 70,955 vehicles. This made the company America's 12th largest automaker. Production difficulties and parts shortages delayed Mercury introductions until Feb. 8, 1946.

1947 MERCURY

1947 Mercury, four-door sedan, V-8 (AA)

MERCURY SERIES — SERIES 79M — Styling changes were slight this year. The Mercury name was placed on the side of the hood. Different hubcaps were used. The border around

the grille was chrome plated. There was also new trunk trim. More chrome was used on the interior and the dash dial faces were redesigned. The convertible and station wagon came with leather upholstery. The other body styles used fabric.

MERCURY I.D. NUMBERS: Serial numbers were the same as engine numbers. They ranged from 799A1,412,708 to 2,002,282.

MERCURY

Model Number	Body/Style Number	Body Type & Seating	Factory Price	Shipping Weight	Production Total
79M	70	2-dr Sed-5P	1592	3268	34
79M	72	2-dr Sed Cpe-6P	1645	3218	29,284
79M	73	4-dr Twn Sed-6P	1660	3298	42,281
79M	76	2-dr Conv-6P	2002	3368	10,221
79M	79	4-dr Sta Wag-8P	2207	3571	3,558

MERCURY ENGINE: V-8. L-head. Cast iron block. Displacement: 239.4 cid. Bore and stroke: 3.19 x 3.75 inches. Compression ratio: 6.75:1. Brake hp: 100 at 3800 rpm. Three main bearings. Carburetor: Holley 94 two-barrel.

CHASSIS FEATURES: Wheelbase: 118 inches. Overall length: 201-8 inches. Front tread: 58 inches. Rear tread: 60 inches. Tires: 6.50 x 15.

POWERTRAIN OPTIONS: A three-speed manual transmission was standard.

CONVENIENCE OPTIONS: Radio with foot control. Fog lamps. Heater. Whitewall tires.

HISTORICAL FOOTNOTES: The 1947 model year began Jan. 1, 1947. By the time it ended, Mercury produced 86,383 vehicles. Calendar year sales were 124,612 cars. This gave the company ninth rank in the American industry. Technical innovations included a moisture-sealed distributor and oil-resistant electrical wiring.

1948 MERCURY

1948 Mercury four-door station wagon, V-8

MERCURY SERIES — SERIES 89M — If you liked the 1947 Mercurys, you liked the 1948s. For all practical purposes, they were identical. The major changes consisted of different dial faces and no steering column lock.

MERCURY I.D. NUMBERS: Serial numbers were the same as engine numbers. They ranged from 899A1, 990,957 to 2,374,315.

MERCURY

Model Number	Body/Style Number	Body Type & Seating	Factory Price	Shipping Weight	Production Total
89M	72	2-dr Sed Cpe-6P	1645	3218	16,476
89M	73	4-dr Twn Sed-6P	1660	3298	24,283
89M	76	2-dr Conv-6P	2002	3368	7,586
89M	79	4-dr Sta Wag-8P	2207	3571	1,889

MERCURY ENGINE: V-8. L-head. Cast iron block. Displacement: 239.4 cid. Bore and stroke: 3.19 x 3.75 inches. Compression ratio: 6.75:1. Brake hp: 100 at 3800 rpm. Three main bearings. Carburetor: Mercury two-barrel.

CHASSIS FEATURES: Wheelbase: 118 inches. Overall length: 201.8 inches. Front tread: 58 inches. Rear tread: 60 inches. Tires: 6.50 x 15.

POWERTRAIN OPTIONS: A three-speed manual transmission was standard.

CONVENIENCE OPTIONS: Radio with foot control. Fog lamps. Heater. Whitewall tires.

HISTORICAL FOOTNOTES: The new 1948 models bowed in the showrooms on Nov. 1, 1947. During the model year, 50,268 cars were built. This made Mercury 10th in U.S. car sales.

1949 MERCURY

MERCURY SERIES — SERIES 9CM — The first all-new postwar Mercurys were introduced on April 29, 1948. In a break with tradition they did not look like fancy Fords, but rather, shared Lincoln styling (and basic body shells). The grille resembled a shiny coil divided in the center

by a large vertical piece of chrome. A nearly full-length, mid-body chrome spear stretched across the sides. The 1949 Mercury also had wraparound front and rear bumpers. The wood bodied station wagon was replaced by one that used only wood trim. As before, the sedan rear doors opened to the center.

MERCURY I.D. NUMBERS: Serial numbers were the same as engine numbers. They ranged from 9CM101 to 302,439.

MERCURY

Model Number	Body/Style Number	Body Type & Seating	Factory Price	Shipping Weight	Production Total
9cm	72	2-dr Cpe-6P	1979	3321	120,616
9cm	74	4-dr Spt Cpe-6P	2031	3386	155,882
9cm	76	2-dr Conv-6P	2410	3591	16,765
9cm	79	2-dr Sta Wag-8P	2716	3626	8,044

1949 Mercury, four-door sedan, V-8 (AA)

MERCURY ENGINE: V-8: L-head. Cast iron block. Displacement: 255.4 cid. Bore and stroke: 3.19 x 4 inches. Compression ratio: 6.80:1. Brake hp: 110 at 3600 rpm. Three main bearings. Carburetor: Holley 885FFC two-barrel.

CHASSIS FEATURES: Wheelbase: 118 inches. Overall length: 206.8 inches. Front tread: 58.5 inches. Rear tread: 60 inches. Tires: 7.10 x 5.

POWERTRAIN OPTIONS: A three-speed manual transmission was standard. Touch-O-Matic overdrive was optional.

CONVENIENCE OPTIONS: Radio. Heater. Rear fender shields. Foam rubber seat cushions. Whitewall tires.

HISTORICAL FOOTNOTES: The first all-new postwar models were introduced by Mercury on April 29, 1948. Mercury placed ninth in industry sales with 203,339 calendar year deliveries. Model year production for 1949 was 301,319 cars.

1950 MERCURY

MERCURY SERIES — SERIES 0CM — For 1950, the letters of the word Mercury were imbedded in chrome on the front of the hood. The signal lights were chrome encased, in a fashion similar to that used on the 1948 Cadillac. The design of the trunk chrome was altered, as was the tip on the side spear. The biggest change was made to the dash. It was completely restyled. Improvements were made to the carburetor, parking brake and steering. To compete with GM and Chrysler two-door hardtops, Mercury introduced the Monterey coupe. It featured a padded canvas or vinyl top and custom leather interior.

1950 Mercury, Monterey two-door coupe, V-8 (AA)

MERCURY I.D. NUMBERS: Serial numbers were the same as engine numbers. For 1950 they were: 50DA1,001M to 79,027M; 50LA1,001M to 44,958M; 50ME1,001M to 97,749M and 50SL1,001M to 110,459M. The plant codes were DA = Dearborn; LA = Los Angeles; ME = Metuchen; SL = St. Louis and W = Wayne.

1950 Mercury, two-door station wagon, V-8 (TVB)

MERCURY

Model Number	Body/Style Number	Body Type & Seating	Factory Price	Shipping Weight	Production Total
0CM	M-72A	2-dr Cpe-3P	1875	3345	Note 1
0CM	M-72B	2-dr Clb Cpe-6P	1980	3430	Note 1
0CM	M-72C	2-dr Mont Cpe	2146	3626	Note 1
0CM	M-74	4-dr Spt Sed-6P	2032	3470	132,082
0CM	M-74	2-dr Conv-6P	3412	3710	8,341
0CM	M-79	2-dr Sta Wag-8P	2561	3755	1,746

NOTE 1: A total of 151,489 Mercury coupes were made in 1950.

MERCURY ENGINE: V-8: L-head. Cast iron block. Displacement: 255.4 cid. Bore and stroke: 3.19 x 4 inches. Compression ratio: 6.80:1. Brake hp: 110 at 3600 rpm. Three main bearings. Carburetor: Holley 885FFC two-barrel.

CHASSIS FEATURES: Wheelbase: 118 inches. Overall length: (Passenger cars) 206.8 inches; (Station wagon) 213.5 inches. Front tread: 58.5 inches. Rear tread: 60 inches. Tires: 7.10 x 15.

POWERTRAIN OPTIONS: A three-speed manual transmission was standard. Touch-0-Matic overdrive was optional.

CONVENIENCE OPTIONS: Radio. Power windows (standard in convertible). Power seat. Oil bath air cleaner. Heater. Two-tone paint. Whitewall tires.

HISTORICAL FOOTNOTES: The one-millionth Mercury built was a 1950 four-door sedan. Mercurys won two NASCAR Grand National races this year. Mercury was the official pace car at the 1950 Indianapolis 500.

1951 MERCURY

1951 Mercury, four-door sedan, V-8 (TVB)

MERCURY SERIES — SERIES 1CM — A new grille that was integrated with the signal lights appeared in 1951. Vertical taillights replaced the horizontal type found on the 1949 and 1950 Mercurys. New, lower, rear quarter panel trim made the wraparound bumper appear to extend even further than before. Chrome gravel shields and rocker panels, a vinyl or canvas roof and custom interior were standard on the Monterey coupe.

MERCURY I.D. NUMBERS: Serial numbers for 1951 were: 51DA51DA10,001M to 67,910M; 51LA10,001M to 46,772M; 51ME10,0001M to 103,515M and 51SL10,001M to 127,830M. The plant codes were DA = Dearborn; LA = Los Angeles; ME = Metuchen; SL = St. Louis and W = Wayne.

MERCURY

Model Number	Body/Style Number	Body Type & Seating	Factory Price	Shipping Weight	Production Total
1CM	M-72B	2-dr Spt Cpe-6P	1947	3485	Note 1
1CM	M-72C	2-dr Mont Cpe	2116	3485	Note 1
1CM	M-72C	2-dr Mont Cpe	2127	3485	Note 1
1CM	M-74	4-dr Spt Sed-6P	2000	3550	157,648
1CM	M-76	2-dr Conv-6P	2380	3760	6,759
1CM	M-79	2-dr Sta Wag-8P	2530	3800	3,812

NOTE 1: A total of 142,168 Mercury coupes were made in 1951.

NOTE 2: The higher priced Monterey included a vinyl top covering.

MERCURY ENGINE: V-8: L-head. Cast iron block. Displacement: 255.4 cid. Bore and stroke: 3.19 x 4 inches. Compression ratio: 6.80:1. Brake hp: 112 at 3600 rpm. Three main bearings. Carburetor: Holley 885FFC two-barrel.

CHASSIS FEATURES: Wheelbase: 118 inches. Overall length: 206.8 inches: (Station Wagons) 213.5 inches. Front tread: 58.5 inches. Rear tread: 60 inches. Tires: 7.10 x 15.

POWERTRAIN OPTIONS: A three-speed manual transmission was standard. Overdrive and Merc-O-Matic automatic transmission were optional.

CONVENIENCE OPTIONS: Radio. Fender skirts. Heater. Whitewall tires.

HISTORICAL FOOTNOTES: Approximately one in every three 1951 Mercurys were sold with an automatic transmission. In 1951, Mercurys came in first at two NASCAR Grand National races.

1952 MERCURY

1952 Mercury, Custom two-door hardtop coupe, V-8 (AA)

CUSTOM SERIES — SERIES 2M — Like all Ford Motor Co. cars, Mercury was completely restyled for 1952. It had frenched headlights; a one-piece curved windshield; wraparound rear window; fake hood scoop; massive integrated bumper/grille; and vertical tail/back-up lights encased in chrome in manner that made them look like extensions of the rear bumper. The fender level hood line helped give the Custom an aggressive look.

CUSTOM I.D. NUMBERS: Serial numbers for 1952 were: 52SL10,001M to 86,300M; 52LP10,001M to 52WA19,422M; 52LA10,001M to 38,763M and 52ME10,001 to 65,500M. The plant codes were DA = Dearborn; LA = Los Angeles; ME = Metuchen; SL = St. Louis and W = Wayne.

CUSTOM

Model Number	Body/Style Number	Body Type & Seating	Factory Price	Shipping Weight	Production Total
2M	60E	2-dr Spt Cpe-6P	2100	3435	30,599
2M	70B	2-dr Sed-6P	1987	3335	25,812
2M	73B	4-dr Sed-6P	2040	3390	Note 1
2M	79B	4-dr Sta Wag-6P	2525	3795	Note 1
2M	79D	4-dr Sta Wag-8P	2570	3795	Note 1

NOTE 1: The total production of all 1952 Custom and Monterey four-door sedans was 83,475. The total production of all station wagons was 2,487.

CUSTOM ENGINE: V-8: L-head. Cast iron block. Displacement: 255.4 cid. Bore and stroke: 3.19 x 4 inches. Compression ratio: 7.20:1. Brake hp: 125 at 3700 rpm. Three main bearings. Carburetor: Holley 885FFC two-barrel.

1952 Mercury, Monterey two-door convertible, V-8 (AA)

MONTEREY SERIES — SERIES 2M — Except for the chrome rocker panels and fancier wheelcovers, exterior styling resembled the lower-priced Custom series. Standard Monterey features included a two-tone paint job and leather and vinyl interior. Suspended pedals were new to both series. The rear doors of Mercury sedans now opened in the conventional manner.

MONTEREY I.D. NUMBERS: Serial numbers for 1952 were: 52SL10,001M to 86,300M; 52LP10,001M to 52WA19,422M; 52LA10,001M to 38,763M and 52ME10,001 to 65,500M.

MONTEREY

Model Number	Body/Style Number	Body Type & Seating	Factory Price	Shipping Weight	Production Total
2M	608	2-dr HT Cpe-6P	2225	3520	24,453
2M	73C	4-dr Sed-6P	2115	3375	Note 1
2M	76B	2-dr Conv-6P	2370	3635	5,261

MONTEREY ENGINE: V-8: L-head. Cast iron block. Displacement: 255.4 cid. Bore and stroke: 3.19 x 4 inches. Compression ratio: 7.20:1. Brake hp: 125 at 3700 rpm. Three main bearings. Carburetor: Holley 885FFC two-barrel.

CHASSIS FEATURES: Wheelbase: 118 inches. Overall length: 202.2 inches. Front tread: 58 inches. Rear tread: 56 inches. Tires: 7.10 x 15; (Convertible and station wagons) 7.60 x 15.

POWERTRAIN OPTIONS: A three-speed manual transmission was standard. Overdrive and Merc-O-Matic automatic transmission were optional.

CONVENIENCE OPTIONS: Radio. 'Merc-O-Matic' heater. Bumper grille guard. Fender skirts (standard on Monterey). Whitewall tires.

HISTORICAL FOOTNOTES: Almost half of all 1952 Mercurys came with automatic transmission and about 33 percent of the manual shift cars were equipped with a three-speed manual with overdrive. This was the first year for a Mercury two-door hardtop.

1953 MERCURY

CUSTOM SERIES — SERIES 3M — A major styling change for 1953 was made to the grille. It was still integrated with the bumper, but the bumper guards were now bullet-shaped. The trunk featured a new medallion. Side chrome trim consisted of a full-length, mid-body spear and rear fender molding. The doors could stay in position either halfway or fully opened.

CUSTOM I.D. NUMBERS: Serial numbers for 1953 were: 53LA10,601M to 50,946M; 53WA10,001M to 45,383; 53ME10,001M and up and 53SL10,001M to 14,285M. The plant codes were DA = Dearborn; LA = Los Angeles; ME = Metuchen; SL = St. Louis and W = Wayne.

CUSTOM

Model Number	Body/Style Number	Body Type & Seating	Factory Price	Shipping Weight	Production Total
3M	60E	2-dr Spt Cpe-6P	2117	3465	39,547
3M	70B	2-dr Sed-6P	2004	3405	50,183
3M	73B	4-dr Sed-6P	2057	3450	59,794

CUSTOM ENGINE: V-8: L-head. Cast iron block. Displacement: 255.4 cid. Bore and stroke: 3.19 x 4 inches. Compression ratio: 7.20:1. Brake hp: 125 at 3800 rpm. Three main bearings. Carburetor: Holley 1901 FFC two-barrel.

1953 Mercury, Monterey two-door convertible, V-8 (AA)

MONTEREY SERIES — SERIES 3M — Two-tone paint, fender skirts and chrome rocker panels were standard on Mercurys top-of-the-line series. The Monterey name was placed on the upper front fenders (except on those built early in the model year). The rear side windows of the station wagon featured sliding glass.

MONTEREY I.D. NUMBERS: Serial numbers for 1953 were: 53LA10,601M to 50,946M; 53WA10,001M to 45,383; 53ME10,001M and up and 53SL10,001M to 14,285M. The plant codes were DA = Dearborn; LA = Los Angeles; ME = Metuchen; SL = St. Louis and W = Wayne.

MONTEREY

Model Number	Body/Style Number	Body Type & Seating	Factory Price	Shipping Weight	Production Total
3M	60B	2-dr HT Cpe-6P	2244	3465	76,119
3M	73C	4-dr Sed-6P	2133	3425	64,038
3M	76B	2-dr Conv-6P	2390	3585	8,463
3M	79B	4-dr Sta Wag-6P	2591	3765	7,719

MONTEREY ENGINE: V-8: L-head. Cast iron block. Displacement: 255.4 cid. Bore and stroke: 3.19 x 4 inches. Compression ratio: 7.20:1. Brake hp: 125 at 3800 rpm. Three main bearings. Carburetor: Holley 1901 FFC two-barrel.

CHASSIS FEATURES: Wheelbase: 118 inches. Overall length: 202-2 inches. Front tread: 58 inches. Rear tread: 56 inches. Tires: 7.10 x 15; (Convertible and station wagon) 7.60 x 15.

POWERTRAIN OPTIONS: A three-speed manual transmission was standard. Overdrive and Merc-O-Matic automatic transmission were optional.

CONVENIENCE OPTIONS: Wheelcovers. Power steering. Power seat. Electric windows. Whitewall tires. Bumper grille guard. Radio. Power brakes.

HISTORICAL FOOTNOTES: An enlarged tailpipe and new, straight-through muffler greatly reduced back pressure. Power brakes were first offered in April of 1953. Fifteen percent of Mercurys were equipped with them. A month later, power steering was introduced. Only eight percent of 1953 Mercurys were sold with this option. The 40 millionth vehicle built by Ford Motor Co. was a 1953 Mercury convertible now in the Imperial Palace Auto Collection.

1954 MERCURY

CUSTOM SERIES — Wraparound vertical taillights were the most noticeable change made for 1954. The grille was modestly restyled but was still integrated with the front bumper. 'Mercury' was written in chrome on the rear fenders, above the mid-body spear. New ball joint front suspension improved handling and ride qualities.

CUSTOM I.D. NUMBERS: Serial numbers ranged from 54WA10,001M to 75,348M. The plant codes were DA = Dearborn; LA = Los Angeles; ME = Metuchen; SL = St. Louis and W = Wayne.

CUSTOM

Model Number	Body/Style Number	Body Type & Seating	Factory Price	Shipping Weight	Production Total
NA	60E	2-dr HT Cpe-6P	2315	3485	15,234
NA	70B	2-dr Sed-6P	2194	3435	37,146
NA	73B	4-dr Sed-6P	2251	3480	32,687

CUSTOM ENGINE: V-8: Overhead valves. Cast iron block. Displacement: 256 cid. Bore and stroke: 3.62 x 3.10 inches. Compression ratio: 7.50:1. Brake hp: 162 at 4400 rpm. Carburetor: Holley 2140 four-barrel.

1954 Mercury, Monterey Sun Valley two-door hardtop, V-8 (AA)

MONTEREY SERIES — The Monterey featured its name written in chrome above the side trim on the rear fender. It had a medallion near, the tip of the side chrome spear on the front fenders. Chrome rocker panels and fender skirt were standard. The most unique Monterey was the Sun Valley. The front half of its roof contained a green tinted, plexiglass section. As in previous years, the station wagon had simulated wood trim.

MONTEREY I.D. NUMBERS: Serial numbers ranged from 54WA10,001M to 75,348M. The plant codes were DA = Dearborn; LA = Los Angeles; ME = Metuchen; SL = St. Louis and W = Wayne.

MONTEREY

Model Number	Body/Style Number	Body Type & Seating	Factory Price	Shipping Weight	Production Total
NA	60B	2-dr HT Cpe-6P	2452	3520	79,533
NA	60F	2-dr SV HT-6P	2582	3535	9,761
NA	73C	4-dr Sed-6P	2333	3515	65,995
NA	768	2-dr Conv-6P	2610	3620	7,293
NA	79B	4-dr Sta Wag-8P	2776	3735	11,656

MONTEREY ENGINE: V-8: Overhead valves. Cast iron block. Displacement: 256 cid. Bore and stroke: 3.62 x 3.10 inches. Compression ratio: 7.50:1. Brake hp: 162 at 4400 rpm. Carburetor: Holley 2140 four-barrel.

CHASSIS FEATURES: Wheelbase: 118 inches. Overall length: 206.2 inches. Tires 7.10 x 15; (Convertible and station wagon) 7.60 x 15.

POWERTRAIN OPTIONS: A three-speed manual was standard. Overdrive and Merc-O-Matic Drive automatic transmission were optional.

CONVENIENCE OPTIONS: Power steering. Power brakes. Four-Way power seat. Radio. Heater. Fender skirts (Custom). Chrome rocker panels (Custom). Whitewall tires Solex glass.

1955 MERCURY

CUSTOM SERIES — Mercurys were restyled this year. They were longer, lower and wider. Yet they bore a definite resemblance to the 1954 models. The bumper-integrated grille had

three heavy vertical bars between the upper and lower bumper. The tall vertical taillights had a 'chubby cheeks' look. The Custom had slightly different side chrome than the other series. Its rear fender molding was plainer. The Custom station wagon did not have fake wood trim. All 1955 Mercurys featured a wraparound windshield and hooded headlights.

1955 Mercury, Custom two-door sedan, V-8

CUSTOM I.D. NUMBERS: Custom serial numbers were: 55WA10,001M to 94,613M and 55LA10,001M to 48,892. The plant codes were DA = Dearborn; LA = Los Angeles; ME = Metuchen; SL = St. Louis and W = Wayne.

CUSTOM

Model Number	Body/Style Number	Body Type & Seating	Factory Price	Shipping Weight	Production Total
NA	60E	2-dr HT Cpe-6P	2341	3480	7,040
NA	708	2-dr Sed-6P	2218	3395	31,295
NA	738	4-dr Sed-6P	2277	3450	21,219
NA	79B	4-dr Sta Wag-6P	2686	3780	13,134

CUSTOM ENGINE: V-8: Overhead valves. Cast iron block. Displacement: 292 cid. Bore and stroke: 3.75 x 3.30 inches. Compression ratio: 7.60:1. Brake hp 188 at 4400 rpm. Carburetor: four-barrel.

1955 Mercury, Monterey four-door sedan, V-8

MONTEREY SERIES — The rear fender trim was lower on the Monterey than on the Custom. It also had chrome rocker panels and a bright band of molding under the windows. 'Monterey' was written in chrome on the front fenders of the sedan and hardtop. The name was placed on the rear doors of the station wagon. A round medallion was placed next to the nameplate.

MONTEREY I.D. NUMBERS: Custom serial numbers were: 55WA10,001M to 94,613M and 55LA10,001M to 48,892. The plant codes were DA = Dearborn; LA = Los Angeles; ME = Metuchen; SL = St. Louis and W = Wayne.

MONTEREY

Model Number	Body/Style Number	Body Type & Seating	Factory Price	Shipping Weight	Production Total
NA	60B	2-dr HT Cpe-6P	2465	3510	69,093
NA	73C	4-dr Sed-6P	2400	3500	70,392
NA	79C	4-dr Sta Wag-8P	2844	3770	11,968

MONTEREY ENGINE: V-8: Overhead valves. Cast iron block. Displacement: 292 cid. Bore and stroke: 3.75 x 3.30 inches. Compression ratio: 7.60:1. Brake hp 188 at 4400 rpm. Carburetor: four-barrel.

1955 Mercury, Montclair four-door sedan, V-8

MONTCLAIR SERIES — In addition to a round medallion and the model name on the front fenders, Montclairs also had a narrow band of chrome under the side windows, which outlined a small panel. They were slightly lower than other Mercurys. The Sun Valley had a tinted plexiglass section over the front half of its roof.

MONTCLAIR I.D. NUMBERS: Serial numbers were: 55ME10,001M to 87,345M and 55SL10,001M to 13,753M. The plant codes were DA = Dearborn; LA = Los Angeles; ME = Metuchen; SL = St. Louis and W = Wayne.

MONTCLAIR

Model Number	Body/Style Number	Body Type & Seating	Factory Price	Shipping Weight	Production Total
NA	58A	4-dr Sed-6P	2685	3600	20,624
NA	64A	2-dr HT Cpe-6P	2631	3490	71,588
NA	64B	2-dr SV HT	2712	3560	1,787
NA	76B	2-dr Conv-6P	2712	3685	10,668

MONTCLAIR ENGINE: V-8: Overhead valves. Cast iron block. Displacement: 292 cid. Bore and stroke: 3.75 x 3.30 inches. Compression ratio: 8.50:1. Brake hp: 198 at 4400 rpm. Carburetor: four-barrel.

CHASSIS FEATURES: Wheelbase: (Passenger cars) 119 inches: (Station wagons) 118 inches. Overall length: (Passenger cars) 206.3 inches; (Station wagons) 201.7 inches. Overall height: (Montclairs) 58.6 inches: (Station wagons) 62.45 inches (others) 61.2 inches. Tires: (Convertible) 7.10 x 15; (Station wagons) 7.60 x 15.

POWERTRAIN OPTIONS: A three-speed manual transmission was standard. Overdrive and Merc-O-Matic automatic were optional. A 198 hp V-8 was available at extra cost on cars with the automatic.

CONVENIENCE OPTIONS: Power brakes. Power steering. Whitewall tires. Four-Way power seat. Heater. Power windows. Radio. Custom two-tone paint. Custom fender skirts.

HISTORICAL FOOTNOTES: Mercury shared honors with Chevrolet as MOTOR TREND magazine's 'car of the year'. Part of the credit for this belonged to the Merc's improved, ball-and-socket joint front-end suspension. Since 1945, Mercury had been under combined management with Lincoln. Both became separate divisions in the spring of 1955.

1956 MERCURY

1956 Mercury, Medalist two-door sedan, V-8

MEDALIST SERIES — The new Medalist was Mercury's low-priced car. It was introduced in midyear. The Medalist featured a more frugal use of side chrome and lacked the front bumper guards found on the more expensive series. Like all 1956 Mercs, it had a big 'M' medallion on the front of the hood and the word 'Mercury' was spelled out in block letters on the center horizontal grille bar.

MEDALIST I.D. NUMBERS: Medalist serial numbers were: 56WA10,001M to 89,958M and 56LA10,001M to 51,292M. The plant codes were DA = Dearborn; LA = Los Angeles; ME = Metuchen; SL = St. Louis and W = Wayne.

MEDALIST

Model Number	Body/Style Number	Body Type & Seating	Factory Price	Shipping Weight	Production Total
NA	57D	4-dr HT Sed-6P	2458	3530	6,685
NA	64E	2-dr HT Cpe-6P	2389	3545	11,892
NA	70C	2-dr Sed-6P	2254	3430	20,582
NA	73D	4-dr Sed-6P	2313		

MEDALIST ENGINE: V-8: Overhead valves. Cast iron block. Displacement: 312 cid. Bore and stroke: 3.8 x 3.44 inches. Compression ratio: 8.00:1. Brake hp: 210 at 4600 rpm. Carburetor: four-barrel.

CUSTOM SERIES — Chrome window trim was the main styling difference between the Custom and the Medalist. (The Medalist two-door sedan also used slightly less side trim.)

CUSTOM I.D. NUMBERS: Medalist serial numbers were: 56WA10,001M to 89,958M and 56LA10,001M to 51,292M. The plant codes were DA = Dearborn; LA = Los Angeles; ME = Metuchen; SL = St. Louis and W = Wayne.

CUSTOM

Model Number	Body/Style Number	Body Type & Seating	Factory Price	Shipping Weight	Production Total
NA	57C	4-dr HT Sed-6P	2555	3550	12,187
NA	64C	2-dr HT Cpe-6P	2485	3560	20,857
NA	70B	2-dr Sed-6P	2351	3505	16,343
NA	73B	4-dr Sed-6P	2410	3520	15,860
NA	76A	2-dr Conv-6P	2712	3665	2,311
NA	79B	4-dr Sta Wag-6P	2819	3860	9,292
NA	79D	4-dr Sta Wag-6P	2722	3790	8,478

CUSTOM ENGINE: V-8: Overhead valves. Cast iron block. Displacement: 312 cid. Bore and stroke: 3.8 x 3.44 inches. Compression ratio: 8.00:1. Brake hp: 210 at 4600 rpm. Carburetor: four-barrel.

1956 Mercury, Monterey four-door sedan, V-68

MONTEREY SERIES — The 1956 Monterey looked a lot like last year's model. The hooded headlights. vertical 'chubby cheek' taillights, and bumper integrated grille were little changed. Montereys featured heavy chrome trim around the side windows and chrome rocker panels. The side body molding made a sort of lightning bolt pattern. 'Monterey' was written in chrome on the front fenders.

MONTEREY I.D. NUMBERS: Monterey serial numbers were: 56ME10,001M to 100,055M; 56SL10,001M to 125,006M. The plant codes were DA = Dearborn; LA = Los Angeles; ME = Metuchen; SL = St. Louis and W = Wayne.

MONTEREY

Model Number	Body/Style Number	Body Type & Seating	Factory Price	Shipping Weight	Production Total
NA	57B	4-dr HT Sed-6P	2700	3800	10,726
NA	58B	4-dr Spt Sed-6P	2652	3550	11,765
NA	64C	2-dr HT Cpe-6P	2630	3590	42,863
NA	73C	4-dr Sed-6P	2555	3570	26,735
NA	79C	4-dr Sta Wag-8P	2977	3885	13,280

MONTEREY ENGINE: V-8: Overhead valves. Cast iron block. Displacement: 312 cid. Bore and stroke: 3.8 x 3.44 inches. Compression ratio: 8.00:1. Brake hp: 210 at 4600 rpm. Carburetor: four-barrel.

1956 Mercury, Montclair two-door hardtop, V-8

MONTCLAIR SERIES — Top-of-the-line Montclairs had a narrow color panel surrounded by chrome trim below the side windows and chrome rocker panels. A round medallion was placed near the tip of the front fender side trim. 'Montclair' was written, in chrome, on the front fenders. The four-door Sport sedan was replaced, early in the model year, by a four-door hardtop 'Phaeton.'

MONTCLAIR I.D. NUMBERS: Serial numbers were: 56ME10,001M to 100,055M; 56SL10,001M to 125,006M. The plant codes were DA = Dearborn; LA = Los Angeles; ME = Metuchen; SL = St. Louis and W = Wayne.

MONTCLAIR

Model Number	Body/Style Number	Body Type & Seating	Factory Price	Shipping Weight	Production Total
NA	57A	4-dr HT Sed-6P	2835	3640	23,493
NA	58A	4-dr Spt Sed-6P	2786	3610	9,617
NA	64A	2-dr HT Cpe-6P	2765	3620	50,562
NA	768	2-dr Conv-6P	2900	3725	7,762

MONTCLAIR ENGINE: V-8: Overhead valves. Cast iron block. Displacement: 312 cid. Bore and stroke: 3.8 x 3.44 inches. Compression ratio: 8.00:1. Brake hp: 210 at 4600 rpm. Carburetor: four-barrel.

CHASSIS FEATURES: Wheelbase: (Passenger cars) 119 inches; (Station wagons) 118 inches. Overall length: 206.4 inches. Overall width: 76.4 inches. Tires: 7.10 x 15; (Convertible and Station wagons) 7.60 x 15 inches.

POWERTRAIN OPTIONS: A three-speed manual transmission was standard. Overdrive and Merc-O-Matic Drive automatic transmission were optional. Cars equipped with an automatic came with a 225 hp 312 cid V-8 with four-barrel carburetor. In midyear, a new camshaft raised the output in the standard and 225 hp V-8s by 10. Also, the M-260 package (two four-barrel carburetors, 260 hp) was offered in all series later in the year.

CONVENIENCE OPTIONS: Power lubrication. Power brakes. Power steering. Four-Way power seat. Air conditioning. Seat belts. Whitewall tires. Radio. Power windows. Padded dash.

HISTORICAL FOOTNOTES: Dual exhausts were standard on all Montclairs and Montereys. Almost 90 percent of all 1956 Mercurys were sold with automatic transmission, 78.4 percent had whitewall tires, 88 percent back-up lights and 96 percent heaters. Only 1.1 percent were equipped with an air conditioner. Mercury won five NASCAR Grand National races in 1956.

1957 MERCURY

MONTEREY SERIES — Mercurys were completely restyled for 1957. For the first time, the make had bodies that were the exclusive to it and not based on Fords or Lincolns. A concave vertical bar grille; front hinged hood; 'V' shaped taillights; upper rear fender and rear deck sculpturing and cowl vent intakes were several of the new features. A chrome 'M' was placed between the grille and bumper. Early models had two headlights; later ones had four.

MONTEREY I.D. NUMBERS: Monterey serial numbers were: 57WA10,001M to 90,490M and 57LA10,001M to 40,854M. The plant codes were DA = Dearborn; LA = Los Angeles; ME = Metuchen; SL = St. Louis and W = Wayne.

MONTEREY

Model Number	Body/Style Number	Body Type & Seating	Factory Price	Shipping Weight	Production Total
NA	57A	4-dr HT Sed-6P	2763	3915	22,475
NA	58A	4-dr Sed-6P	2645	3890	53,839
NA	63A	2-dr HT Cpe-6P	2693	3870	42,199
NA	64A	2-dr Sed-6P	2576	3875	33,982
NA	76A	2-dr Conv-6P	3005	4035	5,003

MONTEREY ENGINE: V-8: Overhead valves. Cast iron block. Displacement: 312 cid. Bore and stroke: 3.8 x 3.44 inches. Compression ratio: 9.70:1. Brake hp: 255 at 4600 rpm. Carburetor: Holley four-barrel.

1957 Mercury, Montclair two-door convertible, V-8

MONTCLAIR SERIES — Chrome headlight rims, nameplates on the upper front fenders and an emblem ornament on the rear shelf of sedans and hardtops were the main differences between Montclairs and Montereys. Convertibles in both series had a plexiglass wraparound rear window.

MONTCLAIR I.D. NUMBERS: Serial numbers were: 57WA10,001M to 90,490M and 57LA10,001M to 40,854M. The plant codes were DA = Dearborn; LA = Los Angeles; ME = Metuchen; SL = St. Louis and W = Wayne.

MONTCLAIR

Model Number	Body/Style Number	Body Type & Seating	Factory Price	Shipping Weight	Production Total
NA	57B	4-dr HT Sed-6P	3317	3925	21,156
NA	58B	4-dr Sed-6P	3188	3905	19,836
NA	63B	2-dr HT Cpe-6P	3236	3900	30,111
NA	76B	2-dr Conv-6P	3430	4010	4,248

MONTCLAIR ENGINE: V-8: Overhead valves. Cast iron block. Displacement: 312 cid. Bore and stroke: 3.8 x 3.44 inches. Compression ratio: 9.70:1. Brake hp: 255 at 4600 rpm. Carburetor: Holley four-barrel.

1957 Mercury, Turnpike Cruiser two-door hardtop, V-8

TURNPIKE CRUISER SERIES — The Turnpike Cruiser was one of the most gadget- laden cars ever built. It was said to have been based on the XM-Turnpike Cruiser, although the opposite is true. All power items were standard. Other special features included: an overhanging roof with retractable rear window; air ducts mounted on top of the windshield (with fake aerial sticking out of them); power seat with a memory dial; rubber instrument bezels; special starter button; clock/odometer; sliding door locks; and gold anodized insert in the upper rear fender concave section, which lead to the taillights.

TURNPIKE CRUISER I.D. NUMBERS: Serial numbers were: 57ME10,001M to 85,895M and 57SL10,001M to 98,451M. The plant codes were DA = Dearborn; LA = Los Angeles; ME = Metuchen; SL = St. Louis and W = Wayne.

TURNPIKE CRUISER

Model Number	Body/Style Number	Body Type & Seating	Factory Price	Shipping Weight	Production Total
NA	65A	2-dr HT Cpe-6P	3758	4005	7,291
NA	75A	4-dr HT Sed-6P	3849	4015	8,305
NA	76S	2-dr Conv-6P	4103	4100	1,265

TURNPIKE CRUISER ENGINE: V-8: Overhead valves. Cast iron block. Displacement: 368 cid. Bore and stroke: 4 x 3.65 inches. Compression ratio: 9.70:1. Brake hp: 290 at 4600 rpm. Five main bearings. Carburetor: Holley four-barrel.

1957 Mercury, Voyager four-door hardtop station wagon, V-8

STATION WAGON SERIES — Station wagons were a separate series this year. The top of-the-line model was the Colony Park. It featured four-door hardtop styling and fake wood trim. The mid-priced wagon was the Voyager. It had a rear vent window like the Colony Park, but did not have wood trim. The lowest priced wagon, the Commuter, looked about the same as the Voyager but lacked a rear vent window.

STATION WAGON I.D. NUMBERS: Serial numbers were: 57WA10,001M to 90,490M and 57LA10,001M to 40,854M. The plant codes were DA = Dearborn; LA = Los Angeles; ME = Metuchen; SL = St. Louis and W = Wayne.

STATION WAGON

Model Number	Body/Style Number	Body Type & Seating	Factory Price	Shipping Weight	Production Total
NA	56A	2-dr Comm-6P	2903	4115	4,885
NA	56B	2-dr Voy-6P	3403	4240	2,283
NA	77A	4-dr Comm-6P	2973	4195	11,990
NA	77B	4-dr Col Prk	3677	4240	7,386
NA	77C	4-dr Comm-8P	3070	4195	5,752
NA	77D	4-dr Voy-8P	3403	4240	3,716

STATION WAGON ENGINE: Commuter and Voyager same as Monterey. Colony Park same as Turnpike Cruiser.

CHASSIS FEATURES: Wheelbase: 122 inches. Overall length: 211.1 inches. Overall width: 79.1 inches. Tires: 8.00 x 14; (Convertibles and station wagons) 8.50 x 14.

POWERTRAIN OPTIONS: A three-speed manual transmission was standard in the station wagons and Monterey. Overdrive and Merc-0-Matic automatic transmission were optional. An automatic was standard in the Turnpike Cruiser and Montclair. A 290 hp 368 cid V-8 was optional for the Commuter, Voyager, Montclair and Monterey. The M-335 power package (two four-barrel carbs, 335 hp 368 cid V-8) was optional on Montereys.

CONVENIENCE OPTIONS: Continental kit. Seat-O-Matic. Power steering. Power brakes. Radio. Heater. Whitewall tires. Air conditioning.

HISTORICAL FOOTNOTES: About one-third (32.6 percent) of 1957 Mercurys came with four headlights. All but 3.9 percent had automatic transmission. Three of the least popular options were air conditioning (1.5 percent), power windows (7.3 percent) and overdrive (1.4 percent). In 1959, MOTOR TREND magazine claimed the 1957 Monterey hardtop was one of the most popular used mid-priced cars. Mercury was the Official Pace Car at the 1957 Indianapolis 500 race.

1958 MERCURY

MEDALIST SERIES — The 1958 Mercury grille was divided into two sections enclosed in the massive bumpers. A chrome 'M' was in the center of the grille. The sculptured rear fenders remained, but the 'V' shaped taillights were altered a bit. There was now a 'projectile' light attached to them. The hood and fenders were new for 1958. Side window trim on the Medalist was painted.

1958 Mercury, Medalist two-door sedan, V-8

MEDALIST I.D. NUMBERS: Serial numbers were: W500,001 to 547,046. The plant codes were DA = Dearborn; LA = Los Angeles; ME = Metuchen; SL = St. Louis and W = Wayne.

MEDALIST

Model Number	Body/Style Number	Body Type & Seating	Factory Price	Shipping Weight	Production Total
NA	58C	4-dr Sed-6P	2617	3875	10,982
NA	64B	2-dr Sed-6P	2547	3790	7,750

MEDALIST ENGINE: V-8: Overhead valves. Cast iron block. Displacement: 312 cid. Bore and stroke: 3.80 x 3.44 inches. Compression ratio: 9.70:1. Brake hp: 235 at 4600 rpm. Five main bearings. Carburetor: Holley four-barrel.

MONTEREY SERIES — A single full-length chrome strip, which started at the headlights, was used on Monterey wagons and two-door hardtops. An extra trim piece, running parallel to the first, extended from the front fender to slightly past the front doors on four-door styles. The rear bumper pods contained concave dividers. The Monterey name was on the front fenders.

MONTEREY I.D. NUMBERS: Serial numbers were: W500,001 to 547,046 and J500,001 and up. Plant code: W = Wayne; J = Los Angeles; T = Metuchen; Z = St. Louis.

MONTEREY

Model Number	Body/Style Number	Body Type & Seating	Factory Price	Shipping Weight	Production Total
NA	57A	4-dr HT Sed-6P	2840	4150	6,909
NA	58A	4-dr Sed-6P	2721	4160	28,892
NA	63A	2-dr HT Cpe-6P	2769	4075	13,693
NA	64A	2-dr Sed-6P	2652	4080	10,526
NA	76A	2-dr Conv-6P	3,081	4,225	2,292

MONTEREY ENGINE: V-8: Overhead valves. Cast iron block. Displacement: 383 cid. Bore and stroke: 3.25 x 3.29 inches. Compression ratio: 10.5:1. Brake hp: 312 at 4600 rpm. Five main bearings. Carburetor: Holley four-barrel.

MONTCLAIR SERIES — Distinguishing features of the Montclair were two full-length side chrome strips, with silver trim between them, and chrome headlight rims. The Turnpike Cruiser was now part of the Montclair series. It featured an overhanging rear roof, retractable rear window and twin air intakes on the roof above both sides of the windshield.

MONTCLAIR I.D. NUMBERS: Serial numbers were the same as for Montereys, plus T500,001 and up and, also, Z500,001 and up. The plant codes were DA = Dearborn; LA = Los Angeles; ME = Metuchen; SL = St. Louis and W = Wayne.

MONTCLAIR

Model Number	Body/Style Number	Body Type & Seating	Factory Price	Shipping Weight	Production Total
NA	57B	4-dr HT Sed-6P	3365	4165	3,609
NA	58B	4-dr Sed-6P	3236	4155	4,801
NA	63B	2-dr HT Cpe-6P	3284	4085	5,012
NA	65A	2-dr TP Crs-6P	3498	4150	2,864
NA	85A	4-dr TP Crs-6P	3597	4230	3,543
NA	76B	2-dr Conv-6P	3536	4295	844

MONTCLAIR ENGINE:

V-8: Overhead valves. Cast iron block. Displacement: 383 cid. Bore and stroke: 4.29 x 3.29 inches. Compression ratio: 10.5:1. Brake hp: 330 at 4600 rpm. Five main bearings. Carburetor: Holley four-barrel (standard in Montclair).

V-8: Overhead valves. Cast iron block. Displacement: 430 cid. Bore and stroke: (Turnpike Cruiser V-8) V-8: Overhead valves. Cast iron block. Displacement: 430 cid. Bore and stroke: 4.29 x 3.7 inches. Compression ratio: 10.50:1. Brake hp: 360 at 4600 rpm. Carburetor: Holley four-barrel.

1958 Mercury, Park Lane four-door hardtop sedan, V-8

PARK LANE SERIES — The new Park Lane was introduced to compete with Buick's Roadmaster. Front fender ornaments, rear roof panel nameplates, chrome headlight rims and rectangular pattern trim in the rear bumper pods were styling features of the Park Lane. Like the Montclair, the Park Lane convertible had a wraparound rear window.

PARK LANE I.D. NUMBERS: Serial numbers were: T500,001 and up and, also, Z500,001 and up. The plant codes were DA = Dearborn; LA = Los Angeles; ME = Metuchen; SL = St. Louis and W = Wayne.

PARK LANE

Model Number	Body/Style Number	Body Type & Seating	Factory Price	Shipping Weight	Production Total
NA	57C	4-dr HT Sed-6P	3944	4390	5,241
NA	63C	2-dr HT Cpe-6P	3867	4280	3,158
NA	76C	2-dr Conv-6P	4118	4405	853

PARK LANE ENGINE: V-8: Overhead valves. Cast iron block. Displacement: 430 cid. Bore and stroke: (Turnpike Cruiser V-8) V-8: Overhead valves. Cast iron block. Displacement: 430 cid. Bore and stroke: 4.29 x 3.7 inches. Compression ratio: 10.50:1. Brake hp: 360 at 4600 rpm. Carburetor: Holley four-barrel.

1958 Mercury, Colony Park four-door hardtop station wagon, V-8

STATION WAGON SERIES — The 1958 Mercury wagons were based on the Montclair. The Colony Park had simulated wood trim. Like the Voyager and Commuter, it featured a pillarless hardtop look.

STATION WAGON I.D. NUMBERS: See Park Lane I.D. numbers. The plant codes were DA = Dearborn; LA = Los Angeles; ME = Metuchen; SL = St. Louis and W = Wayne.

STATION WAGON

Model Number	Body/Style Number	Body Type & Seating	Factory Price	Shipping Weight	Production Total
NA	56A	2-dr Comm-6P	3035	4400	1,912
NA	56B	2-dr Voy-6P	3535	4435	568
NA	77A	4-dr Comm-6P	3105	4485	8,601
NA	77B	4-dr Col Prk-6P	3775	4605	4,474
NA	77C	4-dr Comm-9P	3201	4525	4,227
NA	77D	4-dr Voy-6P	3635	4540	2,520

STATION WAGON ENGINE: Commuter, same as Monterey. Voyager and Colony Park, same as Montclair.

POWERTRAIN OPTIONS: A three-speed manual was standard on station wagons, Medalists and Monterey. Overdrive and Merc-O-Matic automatic transmissions were optional. Merc-O-Matic was standard on the Montclair. Multi-Drive automatic was standard on the Park Lane. A 360 hp 430 cid V-8 was optional on the Montclair. A 400 hp 430 cid V-8 with three two-barrel carburetors was optional on all series. Dual exhausts were a $32.30 option.

CHASSIS FEATURES: Wheelbase: (Park Lane) 125 inches; (others) 122 inches. Overall length: (Station wagons) 214.2 inches; (Park Lane) 220.2 inches; (others) 213.2 inches. Tires: (Convertibles, Park Lane and station wagons) 8.50 x 14; (others) 8.00 x 14.

CONVENIENCE OPTIONS: Tinted glass ($34.40). Two-tone paint ($17.20). Power lubricator ($43). Power steering ($107.50). Power windows ($107.50). Power brakes ($37.70). Four-Way power seat ($69.90). Seat-O-Matic ($96.80). Radio with electric antenna ($149.50). Push-button radio ($100). Rear speaker ($16.20). Manual heater and defroster ($91.40). Heater and defroster with Climate Control ($109.49). Electric clock ($15.10). Air conditioner and heater ($458.75). Padded instrument panel ($21.50). Power retracting station wagon window ($32.30). Windshield washer ($14). Speed limit safety monitor ($12.90). Wheelcovers ($12.90). Nylon four-ply 8.00 x 14 whitewall tires ($67.40); Rayon four-ply 8.00 x 14 whitewall tires ($41). Foam rubber cushions ($21.90).

HISTORICAL FOOTNOTES: Only one percent of all 1958 Mercurys came with a manual transmission and overdrive.

1959 MERCURY

MONTEREY SERIES — Mercurys once again shared a strong family resemblance with Fords, at least from the front. The bumper-integrated grille of last year was replaced by a separate honeycomb grille and plain, wraparound bumper which contained the signal lights. The concave side body sculpturing now extended almost to the front fenders. The wraparound windshield was larger and curved upward. Glass area size of the back window was also increased. The backlights on four-door and two-door hardtop models curved upwards. Four-door and two-door sedans had a unique roof line and a large wraparound rear window. In addition to distinct front fender nameplates, Montereys had a horizontal ribbed rear panel and three chrome bands on the upper rear fenders, in front of the taillights.

SERIAL NUMBER: Code consisted of 10 symbols. The first represented the engine: P 312 cid two-barrel; N = 383 cid two-barrel; M = 383 cid four-barrel; L = 430 cid four-barrel; K = 430 cid six-barrel. The second symbol stands for the year (9 = 1959). The third symbol represents the assembly plant: J = California; W = Michigan; Z = Missouri and T = New Jersey. The fourth symbol indicates the series: A = Monterey; B = Montclair; C = Park Lane and D = station wagons. The fifth symbol (5) stands for the Mercury Division. The following group of digits is the sequential vehicle production number.

1959 Mercury, Monterey two-door hardtop, V-8 (AA)

MONTEREY

Model Number	Body/Style Number	Body Type & Seating	Factory Price	Shipping Weight	Production Total
NA	57A	4-dr HT Sed-6P	2918	4065	11,355
NA	58A	4-dr Sed-6P	2832	4140	43,570
NA	63A	2-dr HT Sed-6P	2854	4215	17,232
NA	64A	2-dr Sed-6P	2768	3975	12,694
NA	76A	2-dr Conv-6P	3150	4295	4,426

MONTEREY ENGINES: V-8: Overhead valves. Cast iron block. Displacement: 312 cid. Bore and stroke: 3.79 x 3.43 inches. Compression ratio: 8.75:1. Brake hp: 210 at 4400 rpm. Five main bearings. Carburetor: Holley 2300 two-barrel.

1959 Mercury, Montclair two-door hardtop, V-8 (AA)

MONTCLAIR SERIES — The Montclair had four chrome bands on the upper rear fender, full-length lower body moldings, bright metal 'cubed' grid pattern appliques on the rear panel and special nameplates under the chrome spears on the front fenders. A fabric and vinyl interior, padded dash, windshield washer, electric clock, parking brake warning light and foam rubber cushions were standard.

MONTCLAIR I.D. NUMBERS: Montclair serial numbers started with: (　)9(　)B500,00l. Code consisted of 10 symbols. The first represented the engine: P 312 cid two-barrel; N = 383 cid two-barrel; M = 383 cid four-barrel; L = 430 cid four-barrel; K = 430 cid six-barrel. The second symbol stands for the year (9 = 1959). The third symbol represents the assembly plant: J = California; W = Michigan; Z = Missouri and T = New Jersey. The fourth symbol indicates the series: A = Monterey; B = Montclair; C = Park Lane and D = station wagons. The fifth symbol (5) stands for the Mercury Division. The above group of digits is the sequential vehicle production number.

MONTCLAIR

Model Number	Body/Style Number	Body Type & Seating	Factory Price	Shipping Weight	Production Total
NA	57B	4-dr HT Sed-6P	3437	4275	6,713
NA	58B	4-dr Sed-6P	3308	4240	9,514
NA	63B	2-dr HT Cpe-6P	3357	4150	7,375

MONTCLAIR ENGINE: V-8: Overhead valves. Cast iron block. Displacement: 383 cid. Bore and stroke: 4.30 x 3.30 inches. Compression ratio: 10.0:1. Brake hp: 322 at 4600 rpm. Five main bearings. Carburetor: Mercury four-barrel.

1959 Mercury, Park Lane four-door hardtop (AA)

PARK LANE SERIES — Styling distinctions of the Park Lane included, chrome-plated projec-tiles on the rear fender coves, full-length lower body moldings, large aluminum gravel guards on the lower rear quarter panels, bright roof moldings and front fender (instead of hood) ornaments. Rear panel trim was the same as on the Montclair. Once again, the Park Lane convertible (like the Monterey) had a wraparound rear window. Park Lanes came equipped

with the same items as Montclairs, plus power steering, power self-adjusting brakes, dual exhaust, back-up lights, rear center armrest and rear cigarette lighter.

PARK LANE I.D. NUMBERS: Serial numbers started at (　)9(　)C500,001. Code consisted of 10 symbols. The first represented the engine: P 312 cid two-barrel; N = 383 cid two-barrel; M = 383 cid four-barrel; L = 430 cid four-barrel; K = 430 cid six-barrel. The second symbol stands for the year (9 = 1959). The third symbol represents the assembly plant: J = California; W = Michigan; Z = Missouri and T = New Jersey. The fourth symbol indicates the series: A = Monterey; B = Montclair; C = Park Lane and D = station wagons. The fifth symbol (5) stands for the Mercury Division.

PARK LANE

Model Number	Body/Style Number	Body Type & Seating	Factory Price	Shipping Weight	Production Total
NA	57C	4-dr HT Sed-6P	4031	4445	7,206
NA	63C	2-dr HT Cpe-6P	3955	4365	4,060
NA	76C	2-dr Conv-6P	4206	4575	1,257

PARK LANE ENGINE: V-8: Overhead valves. Cast iron block. Displacement: 430 cid. Bore and stroke: 4.3 x 3.7 inches. Compression ratio: 10.0:1. Brake hp: 345 at 4400 rpm. Five main bearings. Carburetor: AFB-2853S four-barrel.

COUNTRY CRUISER STATION WAGON SERIES — The Commuter wagons shared trim styling with Montereys. Voyager and Colony Park station wagon trim was like that used on Montclairs, except the Colony Park had simulated wood panels.

COUNTRY CRUISER STATION WAGONS I.D. NUMBERS: Serial numbers started at (　)9(　)D500,001. Code consisted of 10 symbols. The first represented the engine: P 312 cid two-barrel; N = 383 cid two-barrel; M = 383 cid four-barrel; K = 430 cid six-barrel. The second symbol stands for the year (9 = 1959). The third symbol represents the assembly plant: J = California; W = Michigan; Z = Missouri and T = New Jersey. The fourth symbol indicates the series: A = Monterey; B = Montclair; C = Park Lane and D = station wagons. The fifth symbol (5) stands for the Mercury Division.

COUNTRY CRUISER STATION WAGONS

Model Number	Body/Style Number	Body Type & Seating	Factory Price	Shipping Weight	Production Total
NA	56A	2-dr Comm-6P	3035	4400	1,051
NA	77A	4-dr Comm-6P	3105	4485	15,122
NA	77B	4-dr Col Prk-6P	3932	4650	5,959
NA	77D	4-dr Voy-6P	3793	4565	2,496

PRODUCTION NOTE: A two-door Voyager station wagon may have been built and sold in limited quantities.

STATION WAGON ENGINES: (Voyagers and Colony Park) V-8: Overhead valves. Cast iron block. Displacement: 383 cid. Bore and stroke: 4.30 x 3.30 inches. Compression ratio: 10.0:1. Brake hp: 322 at 4600 rpm. Five main bearings. Carburetor: Mercury four-barrel.

1959 Mercury Park Lane, two-door convertible, V-8

(COMMUTER) V-8: Overhead valves. Cast iron block. Displacement: 383 cid. Bore and stroke: 4.29 x 3.29 inches. Compression ratio: 10.00:1. Brake hp: 280 at 4400 rpm. Carburetor: four-barrel.

POWERTRAIN OPTIONS: A three-speed manual was standard on Montereys and Commuter station wagons. Merc-O-Matic automatic was standard in Montclair, Colony Park and Voyager. It was a $173.30 option in Montereys and Commuters. Multi-Drive Merc-O-Matic was standard in Park Lane and an extra cost option on other series. A 280 hp 383 cid V-8 was optional on the Monterey. A 322 hp 383 cid V-8 with four-barrel carburetor was optional in Montereys. A 345 hp 430 cid V-8 with four-barrel carburetor was optional in Montereys and Montclairs.

CHASSIS FEATURES: Wheelbase: (Park Lane) 128 inches; (others) 126 inches. Overall length: (Station wagons) 218.2 inches; (Park Lane) 222.8 inches; (others) 217.8 inches. Tires: (Monterey) 8.00 x 14; (others) 8.50 x 14.

CONVENIENCE OPTIONS: Push-button radio ($68.75). Signal-seeking radio ($90.25). Rear seat radio speaker ($9.30). Electric clock in Monterey and Commuter ($14.20). Windshield washer ($11.75). Tinted glass ($34.90). Tinted windshield ($19.79). Air conditioner with heater ($385). Heater and defroster ($71.15). Heater and defroster with Climate Control ($84.95). Power steering ($83.50). Power brakes ($34.55). Four-Way power seat ($60.40). Seat-O-Matic power seat ($82.20). Power windows ($84.50). Dual exhausts ($25.80). Commuter power tailgate window ($26.80). Safety speed monitor ($12). Padded dash in Monterey and Commuter ($17.10). Back-up lights ($8.90). Courtesy light group ($9.30 Monterey). Whitewall tires ($32.95). Two-tone paint ($14.25). Lower back panel reflector ($10.90). Third seat for station wagons ($90.70). Optional Monterey trim ($30.60). Clear plastic seat covers ($29.95). Undercoating ($15). Outside rearview mirror ($6.95). Seat belts ($12.25 each).

HISTORICAL FOOTNOTES: The majority of 1959 Mercurys, 69.7 percent, came with power steering, 47.2 percent had tinted glass and 52.5 percent had power brakes.

Standard Catalog of American Cars

1960 MERCURY

COMET SERIES — Mercury introduced its compact Comet in March of 1960. It was the first car of the make to be powered by a six-cylinder engine. The grille was similar to the one used on full-size Mercurys, but the rear fins and slanting taillights on sedans were distinctive to the Comet. The wagon used a different rear end style and larger, rounded horizontal taillights. It looked like a dressed-up Falcon. Full-length chrome trim was placed on the bodysides.

COMET I.D. NUMBERS: Serial numbers started at OHO( )S800.001. Serial number code: The first symbol designates the year. The second symbol designates the assembly plant as follows: R = California; K = Missouri; H = Ohio. The third and fourth symbols designate the body type as follows: four-door sedan = 12 or 02; two-door sedan = 11 or 01; four-door station wagon = 22 or 07; two-door station wagon = 21 or 06. The fifth symbol designates the engine as follows: S = 144 cid Six; U = 170 cid Six. See Monterey I.D. numbers for V-8s. The last six digits are the sequential vehicle production numbers.

COMET

Model Number	Body/Style Number	Body Type & Seating	Factory Price	Shipping Weight	Production Total
NA	54A	4-dr Sed-6P	2053	2433	47,416
NA	59A	2-dr Sta Wag-6P	2310	2548	5115
NA	62A	2-dr Sed-6P	1998	2399	45,374
NA	71A	4-dr Sta Wag-6P	2365	2581	18,426

COMET ENGINE: Six: Overhead valves. Cast iron block. Displacement: 144.3 cid. Bore and stroke: 3.5 x 2.5 inches. Compression ratio: 8.70:1. Brake hp: 90 at 4200 rpm. Four main bearings. Carburetor: Holley one-barrel.

CHASSIS FEATURES: Wheelbase: (Passenger cars) 114 inches; (Station Wagons) 109.5 inches. Overall length: (Passenger cars) 194.8 inches; (Station Wagons) 191.8 inches. Tires: (Passenger cars) 6.00 x 13; (Station Wagons) 6.50 x 13.

POWERTRAIN OPTIONS: A three-speed manual transmission was standard. Ford-O-Matic automatic was a $172 option.

CONVENIENCE OPTIONS: Deluxe trim package ($58). Heater and defroster ($74.30). Back-up lights ($10.70). Padded instrument panel and visors ($22.40). Two-tone paint ($19.40). Push-button radio ($58.80). Electric station wagon tailgate window ($29.90). Whitewall tires, on sedans, ($43.40); on station wagons, ($33). Tinted windshield ($10.30). Wheelcovers ($16). Windshield washers ($13.70). Two-speed electric windshield wipers ($9.65).

HISTORICAL FOOTNOTES: The Comet had originally been planned as the successor to the Edsel. Twenty-four percent of Comets came with tinted glass, four percent had power windows and 62 percent had automatic transmission.

1960 Mercury, Monterey two-door hardtop, V-8

MONTEREY SERIES — The basic body shell was unchanged from 1959, but, except for the windshield and roof treatment, it was hard to see any resemblance. Unlike the previous few models, the new Mercury looked as if the people who designed the front and rear were from the same planet. The four-door sedan featured a wraparound back window. Flared fins and massive vertical taillights, integrated into the bumper, highlighted the rear end treatment. Outside of full-length upper side body level moldings, the Monterey was relatively free of stylistic 'doo-dads.' Its rear deck panel had enamel finish.

MERCURY I.D. NUMBERS: Serial numbers started at O( ) ( ) ( ) ( ) 500,001. Serial number code: The first symbol designates the year. The second the assembly plant as follows: A = Atlanta; B = Oakville, Ontario; E = Mahwah; F = Dearborn; G = Chicago; H = Lorain; J = Los Angeles; K = Kansas City; N = Norfolk; P = Twin Cities; R = San Jose; S = Allen Park; T = Metuchen; U = Louisville; W = Wayne; X = St. Thomas, Ontario; Y = Wixom; Z = St. Louis. The third and fourth numbers designate the body style number. The fifth symbol designates the engine as follows: Four-cylinder = Y; Six-cylinder: S = 144 cid; T = 200 cid (one-barrel) U = (thru 1972) 170 cid (one-barrel); V = (60 to 65) 223 cid (one-barrel); (1966) 240 cid (one-barrel); Z = (1975) 170 cid (two-barrel). Eight-cylinder: A = (1960s) 289 cid (four-barrel), (1973-1975) 460 cid (four-barrel); B = (1960s) 406 cid (four-barrel); C = (1966 to 1967) 289 cid (two-barrel); D = (1960s) 406 cid (three (3) two-barrels); F = (1960s) 406 cid (three (3) two-barrels); (1970) 'Boss' 302 cid (four-barrel); H = (1970-1975) 351 cid (two-barrel); J = (1971-1972) Ram Air 429 cid (four-barrel); K = (1960s) 289 cid (four-barrel); (1970-1971) 429 cid (two-barrel); L = (1960s) 221 cid; (1970-1975) 250 cid (one-barrel); M = (1966) 410 cid (four-barrel); (1960s) 430 cid; (1970-1971) 351 cid (four-barrel); N — (1960s) 383 cid (two-barrel); (1970-1973) 429 cid (four-barrel); P = (1960s) 312 cid (two-barrel); (1970-1971) 429 cid (four-barrel); Q = (to 1966) 428 cid (four-barrel); (1970) 429 cid (four-barrel); (1972-1974) 351 cid (four-barrel); R = (1960s) 427 cid (dual four-barrel); (1970) Ram Air 429 cid (four-barrel); S = (1970-1975) 400 cid (two-barrel); W = (1960s) 292 cid (two-barrel); (1966) 427 cid (four-barrel); (1970) 351 cid (four-barrel); X = (1960s) 352 cid (two-barrel), (1966) 352 cid (four-barrel); Y = (1960-1970) 390 cid (two-barrel); Z = (1960s) 390 cid (four-barrel); (1970) Boss 429 cid (four-barrel). The last six digits are the sequential vehicle production numbers.

MONTEREY

Model Number	Body/Style Number	Body Type & Seating	Factory Price	Shipping Weight	Production Total
NA	57A	4-dr HT Sed-6P	2845	4061	9,536
NA	58A	4-dr Sed-6P	2730	4029	49,594
NA	63A	2-dr HT Cpe-6P	2781	3984	15,790
NA	64A	2-dr Sed-6P	2631	3952	21,557
NA	76A	2-dr Conv-6P	3077	4161	6,062

MONTEREY ENGINE: V-8. Overhead valves. Cast iron block. Displacement: 312 cid. Bore and stroke: 3.8 x 3.44 inches. Compression ratio: 8.90:1. Brake hp: 205 at 4000 rpm. Five main bearings. Carburetor: Holley 2300 two-barrel.

MONTCLAIR SERIES — Montclairs could be identified by their distinctive bright metal horizontal bar pattern rear deck panel and three vertical chrome bars on the back doors of four-door models and on the panel in front of the rear tires on two-doors. They also had full-length lower body moldings. A model nameplate appeared on the rear fenders. Standard features included: electric clock, wheelcovers, padded dash, courtesy light group and back-up lights.

MONTCLAIR

Model Number	Body/Style Number	Body Type & Seating	Factory Price	Shipping Weight	Production Total
NA	57B	4-dr HT Sed-6P	3394	4330	5,548
NA	58B	4-dr Sed-6P	3280	4298	8,510
NA	63B	2-dr HT Cpe-6P	3331	4253	5,756

MONTCLAIR ENGINE: V-8. Overhead valves. Cast iron block. Displacement: 430 cid. Bore and stroke: 4.3 x 3.7 inches. Compression ratio: 10.0:1. Brake hp: 310 at 4100 rpm. Five main bearings. Carburetor: Carter ABD-2965S two-barrel.

PARK LANE SERIES — The Park Lane had special 'cubed' pattern, bright metal trim between the trunk lid and rear bumper. Chrome also decorated the rocker and rear quarter panels. In addition, five vertical bars of chrome were placed in a row on the panel in front of the rear tires. Standard features included those found on the Montclair, plus power brakes, power steering, windshield washer and inside non-glare mirror.

PARK LANE

Model Number	Body/Style Number	Body Type & Seating	Factory Price	Shipping Weight	Production Total
NA	57F	4-dr HT Sed-6P	3858	4421	5,788
NA	63F	2-dr HT Cpe-6P	3794	4344	2,974
NA	76D	2-dr Conv-6P	4018	4525	1,525

PARK LANE ENGINE: V-8. Overhead valves. Cast iron block. Displacement: 430 cid. Bore and stroke: 4.3 x 3.7 inches. Compression ratio: 10.0:1. Brake hp: 310 at 4100 rpm. Five main bearings. Carburetor: Carter ABD-2965S two-barrel.

1960 Mercury Commuter four-door hardtop station wagon, V-8

COUNTRY CRUISER STATION WAGONS SERIES — The Commuter wagon was based on the Monterey series. The simulated wood-trimmed Colony Park came with the same standard equipment as Montclair, plus a power rear window. Both wagons had four-door hardtop styling.

COUNTRY CRUISER STATION WAGONS

Model Number	Body/Style Number	Body Type & Seating	Factory Price	Shipping Weight	Production Total
NA	77A	4-dr Comm-6P	3127	4303	14,949
NA	778	4-dr Col Prk-6P	3837	4568	7,411

COUNTRY CRUISER STATION WAGON ENGINES: Commuter engine: see 1960 Monterey Series engine data. Colony Park: See 1960 Montclair Series engine data.

CHASSIS FEATURES: Wheelbase: 126 inches. Overall length: 219.2 inches. Tires: (Montclair, Colony Park) 8.50 x 14; (Park Lane) 9.00 x 14; (Other models) 8.00 x 14.

POWERTRAIN OPTONS: A three-speed manual transmission was standard on Montereys and Commuter station wagons. Merc-O-Matic automatic was standard on Montclairs and Colony Park station wagons. Multi-Drive automatic transmission was standard on Park Lane. Merc-O-Matic transmission was optional on Monterey and Commuter. Multi-Drive was also available, but not with the standard engine. Multi-Drive was a $25.50 option on Montclair and Colony Park. A 280 hp 383 cid V-8 (four-barrel) and a 310 hp 430 cid V-8 were optional on Monterey and Commuter.

CONVENIENCE OPTIONS: Tinted glass ($43.10). Air conditioner with heater ($472.10). Electric clock ($17). Heater and defroster ($78.70). Padded instrument panel in Monterey, Commuter ($21.30). Two-tone paint ($17). Power brakes ($43.20). Power rear tailgate window in Commuter ($32). Four-Way power seats ($76.50). Power steering ($106.20). Power windows ($106.20). Rear fender shields ($11.60). Push-button radio ($86). Rear seat radio speaker ($10.70). Tinted windshield ($29. Third seat for station wagons ($113.30). Trim option in Monterey, Commuter ($27.20). Wheelcovers Monterey, Commuter ($19.20). Five Rayon whitewall tires ($43.10). Visual aid group ($57).

HISTORICAL FOOTNOTE: Power windows and power seats were relatively unpopular options. Less than eight percent of full-size Mercurys were so equipped in 1960.

1961 MERCURY

COMET SERIES — A new grille and the addition of three vertical chrome pieces to the front fenders were the main difference between the 1961 Comet and last year's model. Mercury considered Comet a 'family-sized' compact. Advertising bragged the make was roomier and longer than most of its competition.

COMET/S-22 I.D. NUMBERS: VIN on top surface of left-hand brace to firewall. First symbol 1 = 1961. Second symbol identifies assembly plant: H = Lorain, Ohio; R = San Jose, Calif. Third and fourth symbols are body code (first two numbers in Body/Style Number in charts below). Fifth symbol identifies engine: S = 144 cid six; D = 144 cid six (low-compression); U = 170 cid six; E = 170 cid six (low-compression). Last six symbols are sequential production number starting at 500001. Body plate on front body pillar gives VIN, body code, color, trim, date, engine, transmission and axle codes.

COMET SERIES

Model Number	Body/Style Number	Body Type & Seating	Factory Price	Shipping Weight	Production Total
NA	54A	4-dr Sed-6P	2053	2411	85,332
NA	59A	2-dr Sta Wag-6P	2310	2548	4199
NA	62A	2-dr Sed-6P	1998	2376	71,563
NA	71A	4-dr Sta Wag-6P	2353	2581	22,165

S-22 SERIES — The new S-22 coupe was basically a dressed-up Comet two-door sedan. It was introduced in midyear to cash in on the popularity of sporty compacts. Buyers could choose from 10 exterior colors. Standard features included front bucket seats with a vinyl-clad steel console between them, deep-loop yarn carpeting, front and rear armrests, Deluxe steering wheel and horn ring, rear fender medallion, extra insulation and factory-applied undercoating.

S-22 SERIES

Model Number	Body/Style Number	Body Type & Seating	Factory Price	Shipping Weight	Production Total
NA	62C	2-dr Sed-5P	2282	2432	14,004

1961 Mercury, Meteor '600' two-door sedan, V-8

METEOR 600 SERIES — Mercurys once again began to look like glamorous Fords. The concave, vertical bar grille housed four chrome rimmed headlights. The unusual roof lines of last year were replaced with square, crisp styling. Meteors had a mid-body chrome spear that ran from almost the tip of the rear fender to the front tires. The taillights were small and circular. They extended slightly. An ornament was on top of each front fender.

MERCURY I.D. NUMBERS: First symbol 1 = 1961. Second symbol identifies assembly plant: E = Mahwah, NJ; H = Lorain, Ohio; J = Los Angeles, Calif.; K = Kansas City, Kan.; R = San Jose, Calif.; W = Wayne, Mich.; Y = Wixom, Mich.; Z = St. Louis, Mo. Third and fourth symbols are body code (first two numbers in Body/Style Number in charts below). Fifth symbol identifies engine: (Monterey) V = 223 cid six; W = 292 cid V-8; T = 292 cid V-8 (export); X = 352 cid V-8; (Mercury) same as Meteor, plus Z = 390 cid V-8; R = 390 cid V-8 export. Last six symbols are sequential production number starting at 500001. Body plate on front body pillar gives VIN, body code, color, trim, date, engine, transmission and axle codes.

METEOR 600

Model Number	Body/Style Number	Body Type & Seating	Factory Price	Shipping Weight	Production Total
NA	58A	4-dr Sed-6P	2587	3714	Note
NA	64A	2-dr Sed-6P	2533	3647	18,117

NOTE: Four-door sedan production total not available.

METEOR 800 SERIES — Three horizontal chrome bars on the front fenders, rocker panel molding, chromed tailfin tips and more roof panel trim, helped distinguish the 800 Series from the lower priced 600. Back-up lights and an electric clock were a couple of standard extras.

1961 Mercury, Meteor '800' two-door hardtop sport coupe, V-8

METEOR 800

Model Number	Body/Style Number	Body Type & Seating	Factory Price	Shipping Weight	Production Total
NA	54A	4-dr Sed-6P	2765	3762	Note
NA	62A	2-dr Sed-6P	2711	3680	35,005
NA	65A	2-dr HT-6P	2772	3694	Note
NA	75A	4-dr HT-6P	2837	3780	Note

NOTE: Production totals not available.

1961 Mercury, Monterey two-door hardtop sport coupe, V-8

MONTEREY SERIES — Chrome rear fender stone guards and full-length bodyside moldings were the main exterior styling features of the Monterey. The interior was plusher than the other series and a padded dash was standard.

MONTEREY

Model Number	Body/Style Number	Body Type & Seating	Factory Price	Shipping Weight	Production Total
NA	54B	4-dr Sed-6P	2869	3777	22,881
NA	65B	2-dr HT-6P	2876	3709	10,942
NA	75B	4-dr HT-6P	2941	3795	9,252
NA	76A	2-dr Conv-6P	3126	3872	7,053

STATION WAGONS SERIES — The Commuter wagon looked like a Meteor. However, it only had two taillights, instead of six, and they were semi-rectangular rather than round. The Colony Park had imitation wood trim and a power tailgate window. It shared the same standard features as the Monterey.

STATION WAGONS

Model Number	Body/Style Number	Body Type & Seating	Factory Price	Shipping Weight	Production Total
NA	71A	4-dr Comm-6P 2922	4115	8,951	
NA	71B	4-dr Col Prk-6P	3118	4131	7,887

COMET/S22 BASE ENGINE: Six: Overhead valves. Cast iron block. Displacement: 144.3 cid. Bore and stroke: 3.5 x 2.5 inches. Compression ratio: 8.70:1. Brake hp: 85 at 4200 rpm. Four main bearings. Carburetor: Holley 1908 one-barrel.

METEOR BASE ENGINE: Six: Overhead valves. Cast iron block. Displacement: 223 cid. Bore and stroke: 3.62 x 3.6 inches. Compression ratio: 8.40:1. Brake hp: 135 at 4000 rpm. Four main bearings. Carburetor: one-barrel.

MONTEREY BASE ENGINE: V-8: Overhead valves. Cast iron block. Displacement: 292 cid. Bore and stroke: 3.75 x 3.3 inches. Compression ratio: 8.80:1. Brake hp: 175 at 4200 rpm. Five main bearings. Carburetor: Mercury two-barrel.

STATION WAGON ENGINE: Commuter: See 1961 Meteor 600 Series engine data. Colony Park: See 1961 Monterey Series engine data.

COMET/S-22 CHASSIS FEATURES: Wheelbase: (Station wagon) 109.5 inches; (others) 114 inches. Overall length: (wagons) 191.8; (others) 194.8. Tires: (wagons) 6.50 x 13; (others) 6.00 x 13.

METEOR/MERCURY CHASSIS FEATURES: Wheelbase: 120 inches. Overall length: (station wagons) 214.4 inches; (others) 214.6 inches. Tires: (Convertible and station wagons) 8.00 x 14; (others) 7.50 x 14.

COMET/S-22 OPTIONS: Fashion group interior and exterior trim ($86.90). Heater and defroster ($7.430). Back-up lights ($10.70). Padded instrument panel and visors ($22.40). Two-tone paint ($19.40). Push-button radio ($58.80). Electric tailgate window ($29.90). Whitewall tires, on passenger cars ($43.40); on station wagons ($33). Tinted windshield ($10.30). Wheelcovers ($16). Windshield washers ($13.70). Two-speed electric windshield wipers ($9.65). A three-speed manual was standard. Ford-O-Matic automatic was optional. A 101 hp 170 cid six with one-barrel carburetor was available at extra cost.

METEOR/MERCURY OPTIONS: Air conditioner with heater ($436). Electric clock ($14.60). Courtesy light group ($13.30). Back-up lights ($10.70). Heater and defroster ($75.10). Padded instrument panel ($21.30). Power brakes ($43.20). Power tailgate window ($32.30 Commuter). Four-Way power seat ($63.80). Two-tone paint ($22). Power steering ($81.70). Power windows ($102.10). Push-button radio ($65). Tinted glass ($43). Station wagon third seat ($70.20). Whitewall tires, on station wagons ($37); on other models ($48). Trim options, on Meteor 800 and Commuter ($27.20). Wheelcovers ($19.20). Windshield washer ($13.70). Two-speed windshield wipers ($11.60). A three-speed manual transmission was standard. Overdrive was optional on the Meteor and wagons. Merc-O-Matic and Multi-Drive automatics were optional. A 175 hp 292 cid V-8 (with two-barrel carburetor) was optional on the Meteor Series and Commuter. A 220 hp Marauder 352 cid V-8 (two-barrel); 300 hp Marauder 390 cid V-8 (four-barrel) and a 330 hp Marauder 390 cid V-8 (four-barrel) were optional. A power transfer rear axle was optional.

HISTORICAL FOOTNOTES: The vast majority of 1961 Mercurys had automatic transmission and power steering. About one in 10 came with air conditioning. Mercury once again shared its body shell with Ford. Most 1961 Comets, 64.7 percent, were equipped with automatic transmission.

1962 MERCURY

1962 Mercury, Meteor Custom four-door sedan, V-8

1962 Mercury, Comet Custom four-door sedan, 6-cyl

COMET SERIES — A new, fine-patterned, vertical bar grille, round taillights and the repositioning of the Comet nameplates, from rear to front fenders, were the main styling changes for 1962. The model name was now, officially, Mercury Comet. Increased sound insulation, a roomier trunk and easier to read instrument panel gauges were among the less obvious improvements.

MERCURY & COMET I.D. NUMBERS: VIN on left firewall brace of Comets and Meteors and right frame rail, ahead of cowl on Mercurys. First symbol 2 = 1962. Second symbol identifies assembly plant: E = Mahwah, NJ; F = Dearborn, Mich.; H = Lorain, Ohio; J = Los Angeles, Calif.; K = Kansas City, Kan.; R = San Jose, Calif.; S = Pilot; T = Metuchen, NJ; W = Wayne, Mich.; Y = Wixom, Mich.; Z = St. Louis, Mo. Third and fourth symbols are body code (first two numbers in Body/Style Number in charts below). Fifth symbol identifies engine: (Comet) S = 144 cid six; D = 144 cid six (low-compression); U = 170 cid six; E = 170 cid six (low-compression); (Monterey) U = 170 cid six; E = 170 cid six (low-compression); L = 221 cid V-8; C = 221 cid V-8 (export); F = 260 cid V-8; (Mercury) V = 223 cid six; W = 292 cid V-8; T = 292 cid V-8 (export); X = 352 cid V-8; Z = 390 cid V-8; R = 390 cid V-8 (export); P = 390 cid V-8 high-perf.; B = 406 cid V-8; G = 406 cid V-8 high-perf. Last six symbols are sequential production number starting at 500001. Body plate on front body pillar gives VIN, body code, color, trim, date, engine, transmission and axle codes).

COMET

Model Number	Body/Style Number	Body Type & Seating	Factory Price	Shipping Weight	Production Total
NA	54A	4-dr Sed-6P	2139	2457	70,227*
NA	69A	2-dr Sta Wag-6P	2483	2642	2,121*
NA	62A	2-dr Sed-6P	2084	2420	73,800*
NA	71A	4-dr Sta Wag-6P	2526	2679	16,7580*

(*) Production figures include Custom and S-22 series.

COMET CUSTOM SERIES — Outside of the fender nameplates and side window chrome trim, the exterior of the Custom resembled the standard Comet series. However, its interior featured Deluxe upholstery, white steering wheel, bright horn ring, rear seat armrest, carpeting, front door dome light switch and cigarette lighter.

COMET CUSTOM

Model Number	Body/Style Number	Body Type & Seating	Factory Price	Shipping Weight	Production Total
NA	54B	4-dr Sed-6P	2226	2468	Note *
NA	59B	2-dr Sta Wag-6P	2483	2642	Note *
NA	628	2-dr Sed-6P	2171	2431	Note *
NA	71B	4-dr Sta Wag-6P	2526	2679	Note *

NOTE: (*) See Comet production total.

COMET SPECIAL SERIES — The sporty S-22 two-door sedan had six taillights (rather than the four on other Comets), a medallion above the trim on the roof panel and red wheel rims. The all-vinyl interior featured front bucket seats with a storage console between them. Back-up lights, whitewall tires and loop-yarn carpeting were among the standard items found on the S-22. The Villager station wagon had simulated wood trim.

COMET SPECIAL

Model Number	Body/Style Number	Body Type & Seating	Factory Price	Shipping Weight	Production Total
NA	62C	2-dr S-22 Sed-5P	2368	2358	Note *
NA	71C	4-dr Vill Wag	2710	2612	2,318

(*) See Comet production total.

METEOR SERIES — The Meteor was now a midsize car. It shared the same basic body as Ford's Fairlane, but featured styling similar to the big Mercurys. Meteors had a wavy, fine-pattern vertical bar grille; bumper integrated signal lights; full-length side body moldings (that started above the headlights); a lower chrome spear, which began at the rear bumper and ran about half way across the car (with three thin chrome horizontal bars under it); and cylindrical taillights that stuck out from the tips of the tailfins. Buyers had their choice of 14 solid and 36 two-tone color combinations. The interiors were trimmed in crushed vinyl and cloth.

METEOR

Model Number	Body/Style Number	Body Type & Seating	Factory Price	Shipping Weight	Production Total
NA	54A	4-dr Sed-6P	2340	2877	9,183
NA	62A	2-dr Sed-6P	2278	2843	3,935

METEOR CUSTOM SERIES — Chrome side window trim, rocker panel moldings, lower rear-quarter panel gravel shields and more roof side panel brightwork visually distinguished Meteor Customs from standard Meteors. Interiors were available in cloth and vinyl or all-vinyl. Twisted loop carpeting was standard.

METEOR CUSTOM

Model Number	Body/Style Number	Body Type & Seating	Factory Price	Shipping Weight	Production Total
NA	54B	4-dr Sed-6P	2428	2885	23,484
NA	62A	2-dr Sed-6P	2366	2851	9,410

METEOR S-33 SERIES — The S-33 looked like a Meteor Custom two-door sedan. However, it had special wheelcovers, a vinyl interior and front bucket seats with a storage console between them.

METEOR S-33

Model Number	Body/Style Number	Body Type & Seating	Factory Price	Shipping Weight	Production Total
NA	62C	2-dr Sed-6P	2509	2851	5,900

1962 Mercury, Monterey four-door hardtop sedan, V-8

MONTEREY SERIES — The most noticeable styling change was seen in the taillights. They protruded from the tailfins. The new grille had a horizontal bar pattern, with an emblem, at its center, connecting the headlights. Side chrome was at two levels, joined in the middle by a slight chrome arch. The Monterey was one inch lower than last year's model.

MONTEREY

Model Number	Body/Style Number	Body Type & Seating	Factory Price	Shipping Weight	Production Total
NA	54A	4-dr Sed-6P	2726	3721	18,975
NA	62A	2-dr Sed-6P	2672	3644	5,117
NA	65A	2-dr HT-6P	2733	3661	5,328
NA	71A	4-dr Comm Wag	2920	4069	8,389
NA	75A	4-dr HT-6P	2798	3737	2,691

MONTEREY CUSTOM SERIES — Full-length lower body moldings and a large, rectangular chrome trim piece on the forward sides of the front fenders, were found on the Custom. The Colony Park station wagon had imitation wood trim, a power tailgate window, carpeting and either cloth and vinyl or all-vinyl interior.

MONTEREY CUSTOM

Model Number	Body/Style Number	Body Type & Seating	Factory Price	Shipping Weight	Production Total
NA	54A	4-dr Sed-6P	2965	3836	27,591
NA	65B	2-dr HT-6P	2972	3772	10,814
NA	71B	4-dr Col Park Wag	3219	4186	9,596
NA	75B	4-dr HT-6P	3037	3851	8,932
NA	76A	Conv-6P	3222	3938	5,489

MONTEREY CUSTOM S-55 SERIES — The S-55 was basically a trim and performance option. Front fender ornaments and special wheelcovers were the main exterior differences from a standard Custom. The S-55 had front bucket seats, console, red safety-light in the doors, carpeting and a more powerful standard V-8.

MONTEREY CUSTOM S-55

Model Number	Body/Style Number	Body Type & Seating	Factory Price	Shipping Weight	Production Total
NA	65C	2-dr HT-5P	3488	3772	2,772
NA	76B	2-dr Conv-5P	3738	3938	1,315

COMET BASE ENGINE: Six: Overhead valves. Cast iron block. Displacement: 144.3 cid. Bore and stroke: 3.5 x 2.5 inches. Compression ratio: 8.70:1. Brake hp: 85 at 4200 rpm. Four main bearings. Carburetor: Holley 1909 one-barrel.

METEOR BASE ENGINE: Six: Overhead valves. Cast iron block. Displacement: 170 cid. Bore and stroke: 3.5 x 2.94 inches. Compression ratio: 8.70:1. Brake hp: 101 at 4400 rpm. Four main bearings. Carburetor: Holley 1909 one-barrel.

MONTEREY BASE ENGINE: Six: Overhead valves. Cast iron block. Displacement: 223 cid. Bore and stroke: 3.62 x 3.6 inches. Compression ratio: 8.40:1. Brake hp: 138 at 4200 rpm. Four main bearings. Carburetor: Holley one-barrel.

MONTEREY CUSTOM ENGINE: V-8: Overhead valves. Cast iron block. Displacement: 292 cid. Bore and stroke: 3.75 x 3.3 inches. Compression ratio: 8.80:1. Brake hp: 170 at 4200 rpm. Five main bearings. Carburetor: Ford two-barrel.

MONTEREY CUSTOM S-55 ENGINE: V-8: Overhead valves. Cast iron block. Displacement: 390 cid. Bore and stroke: 4.05 x 3.78 inches. Compression ratio: 9.60:1. Brake hp: 300 at 4600 rpm. Carburetor: four-barrel.

COMET CHASSIS FEATURES: Wheelbase: (Station wagons) 109.5 inches; (others) 114 inches. Overall length: (Station wagons) 191.8 inches; (others) 194.8 inches. Tires: (Station wagons) 6.50 x 13; (others) 6.10 x 13.

METEOR CHASSIS FEATURES: Wheelbase: 116.5 inches. Overall length: 203.8 inches. Tires: 6.50 x 14; (7.00 x 14 optional).

MERCURY CHASSIS FEATURES: Wheelbase: 120 inches. Overall length: (Station wagons) 121.1 inches; (others) 215.5 inches. Tires: (Station wagons and convertible) 8.00 x 14; (others) 7.50 x 14.

COMET OPTIONS: Back-up lights ($10.70). Station wagon luggage rack ($39). Air conditioning ($270.90). Convenience group ($25.80). Padded instrument panel ($16.40). Padded visors ($4.50). Push-button radio ($58.80). Two-tone paint ($19.40). Electric tailgate window ($29.75). Tinted glass ($30.90). Tinted windshield ($12.95). Whitewall tires, on passenger cars ($29.90); on station wagons ($33). Wheelcovers ($16). Windshield washers ($13.70). Two-speed electric windshield wipers ($9.65). A three-speed manual transmission was standard. Merc-O-Matic automatic transmission was a $171.70 option. A 101 hp 170 cid six was optional at $45.10.

METEOR OPTIONS: Air conditioning ($231.70). Padded instrument panel ($19.95). Outside remote-control rearview mirror ($12). Padded visors ($5.20). Power steering ($81.70). Tinted glass ($40.30). Whitewall tires ($37). Wheelcovers ($18.60). Windshield washer ($13.70). Push-button radio ($58.50). Front seat belts ($16.80). Two-tone paint ($22). A three-speed manual transmission was standard. Overdrive and Merc-O-Matic automatic transmission were optional at extra cost. A 145 hp 221 cid V-8 (two-barrel) and a 164 hp 260.8 cid V-8 were offered.

MERCURY OPTIONS: Air conditioner with heater ($360.90). Electric clock ($14.60). Back-up lights ($10.70). Station wagon luggage rack ($39). Padded visors ($5.80). Two-tone paint ($22). Power brakes ($43.20). Power tailgate window, in Commuter ($32.30). Power windows ($102.10). Four-Way power seat ($63.80). Power steering ($81.70). Push-button radio ($58.50). Smog reduction system ($5.70). Tinted glass ($43). Tinted windshield ($21.55). Station wagon third seat ($70.20). Wheelcovers ($19.20). Windshield washer ($13.70). Two-speed windshield wipers ($7.75). Whitewall tires, on passenger cars, ($52.60); on station wagons ($37). A three-speed manual transmission was standard. Four-speed manual and Multi-Drive automatic transmissions were optional. A 170 hp 292 cid V-8 (two-barrel) was optional in Montereys. A 220 hp 352 cid V-8 (two-barrel); 300 hp 390 cid V-8 (four-barrel); 330 hp 390 cid V-8 (four-barrel); 385 hp 406 cid V-8 (four-barrel); 405 hp 406 cid V-8 (three [3] two-barrels) and power transfer rear axle were available at extra cost.

HISTORICAL FOOTNOTES: Less than five percent of all 1962 Montereys were equipped with a manual transmission. A mere 17 percent were sold with a six-cylinder engine. Mercurys and Checkers were the only medium-priced cars available with a six-cylinder engine in 1962. Most 1962 Comets, 64.7 percent were equipped with automatic transmission, 47.4 percent had a radio, 31.9 percent had tinted glass and .9 percent had air conditioning. The vast majority of 1962 Meteors came with a V-8 engine and automatic transmission.

1963 MERCURY

1963 Mercury, Comet S-22 two-door convertible, V-8

COMET SERIES — The new Comet looked a lot like last year's model. Chrome now outlined the side body sculpturing. The four circular taillights protruded from the rear deck panel. The grille featured a horizontal bar theme and the four headlights had chrome rims.

MERCURY & COMET I.D. NUMBERS: VIN on left inner fender of Comets and Meteors and right cowl tab on Mercurys. First symbol 3 = 1963. Second symbol identifies assembly plant: E = Mahwah, NJ; F = Dearborn, Mich.; H = Lorain, Ohio; J = Los Angeles, Calif.; K = Kansas City, Kan.; R = San Jose, Calif.; S = Pilot; T = Metuchen, NJ; W = Wayne, Mich.; Y = Wixom, Mich.; Z = St. Louis, Mo. Third and fourth symbols are body code (See Body/Style Number column in charts below). Fifth symbol identifies engine: (Comet) S = 144 cid six; 2 = 144 cid six (export); U = 170 cid six; 4 = 170 cid six (export); F = 260 cid V-8; 8 = 260 cid V-8 (export); (Meteor) U = 170 cid six; 4 = 170 cid six (export); T = 200 cid 'big six'; L = 221 cid six; 3 = 221 cid V-8 (export); F = 260 cid V-8; 8 = 260 cid V-8 (export); K = 289 cid V-8; (Mercury) Y = 390 cid V-8 2V; Z = 390 cid V-8 4V; 9 = 390 cid V-8 (export); P = 390 cid V-8 high-perf.; B = 406 cid/385 hp V-8; G = 406 cid/405 hp V-8 high-perf.; Q = 427 cid/410 hp V-8; R = 427 cid/425 hp V-8. Last six symbols are sequential production number starting at 500001. Body plate on front body pillar gives VIN, body code, color, trim, date, engine, transmission and axle codes.

COMET

Model Number	Body/Style Number	Body Type & Seating	Factory Price	Shipping Weight	Production Total
NA	02	4-dr Sed-6P	2139	2499	24,230
NA	21	2-dr Sta Wag-6P	2440	2644	623
NA	01	2-dr Sed-6P	2084	2462	24,351
NA	22	4-dr Sta Wag-6P	2483	2681	4,419

COMET CUSTOM SERIES — Chrome window trim and three horizontal bars on the rear quarter panel and on front fenders of wagons, except the Villager, were distinguishing features of the Custom series. The interior came with such items as bright horn ring; rear seat armrests and ashtrays; front door dome light switch; cigarette lighter and carpeting. The Villager wagon had simulated wood trim and a power tailgate window. Front bucket seats were optional.

COMET CUSTOM

Model Number	Body/Style Number	Body Type & Seating	Factory Price	Shipping Weight	Production Total
NA	12	4-dr Sed-6P	2226	2508	27,498
NA	23	2-dr Sta Wag-6P	2527	2659	272
NA	11	2-dr Sed-6P	2171	2471	11,897
NA	13	2-dr HT Cpe-6P	2300	2572	9,432
NA	24	4-dr Sta Wag-6P	2570	2696	5,151
NA	26	4-dr Villager Wag	2754	2736	1,529
NA	15	2-dr Conv-6P	2557	2784	7,354

COMET SPECIAL S-22 SERIES — Six taillights made it easy to identify the Special S-22 Series from the rear. Outside of the front fender ornaments, they looked about the same as Customs. The Custom interiors featured individually adjustable bucket seats with center console and deep, loop-pile carpeting.

COMET SPECIAL S-22

Model Number	Body/Style Number	Body Type & Seating	Factory Price	Shipping Weight	Production Total
NA	19	2-dr Sed-5P	2368	2512	6,303
NA	17	2-dr HT Cpe-6P	2400	2572	5,807
NA	18	2-dr Conv-5P	2710	2825	5,757

1963 Mercury, Meteor Custom two-door hardtop, V-8

METEOR SERIES — The protruding cone-shaped taillights of 1962 remained on this season's Meteor station wagons, but were replaced on other body types. They now looked like part of the tailfin, rather than an add-on. A slightly sloping full-length chrome spear graced the bodyside. The grille resembled the one used on the 1962 Comet. Once again, bright metal trim was used on the roof quarter panels.

METEOR

Model Number	Body/Style Number	Body Type & Seating	Factory Price	Shipping Weight	Production Total
NA	32	4-dr Sed-6P	2340	2959	9,183
NA	31	2-dr Sed-6P	2278	2920	3,935
NA	38	4-dr Sta Wag-6P	2631	3237	2,359

METEOR CUSTOM SERIES — Chrome side window trim, full-length lower body moldings and more chrome on the roof quarter panels were features that set the Custom series apart from the standard Meteors. They also had special interiors and carpeting. The Country Cruiser wagon had simulated wood paneling.

METEOR CUSTOM

Modal Number	Body/Style Number	Body Type & Seating	Factory Price	Shipping Weight	Production Total
NA	42	4-dr Sed-6P	2428	2965	14,498
NA	41	2-dr Sed-6P	2366	2926	2,704
NA	43	2-dr HT Cpe-6P	2448	2944	7,565
NA	49	4-dr Ctry Cr	2886	3253	1,485
NA	48	4-dr Sta Wag-6P	2719	3245	3,636

METEOR S-33 SERIES — Triple horizontal chrome bars on the front fenders, rear fender insignia and special medallions on the roof quarter panels were exclusive to the S-33. The interior featured front bucket seats with a center console between them.

METEOR S-33

Model Number	Body/Style Number	Body Type & Seating	Factory Price	Shipping Weight	Production Total
NA	47	2-dr HT Cpe-6P	2628	2964	4,865

1963 Mercury, Monterey four-door hardtop sedan, V-8

MONTEREY SERIES — Basic Monterey styling seemed more in tune with the 1961 models than the 1962s. Six taillights were (as in 1961) located in the rear deck panel. Side body moldings ran from the tailfins to the headlights. Chrome trim was on the roof quarter panels. A concave, vertical bar grille housed four chrome-rimmed headlights. Mercury's fondness for unusual designs surfaced again this year. The Breezeway roof featured a roll-down back window. In midyear, the Marauder two-door hardtop, with fastback styling, was introduced.

MONTEREY

Model Number	Body/Style Number	Body Type & Seating	Factory Price	Shipping Weight	Production Total
NA	52	4-dr Sed-6P	2887	3994	18,177
NA	51	2-dr Sed-6P	2834	3854	4,640
NA	57	2-dr Fsbk Cpe	3083	3875	Note 1
NA	53	2-dr HT Cpe-6P	2930	3869	2,879
NA	54	4-dr HT Sed-6P	2995	3959	1,692

NOTE 1: The Marauder Fastback Sport Coupe was introduced as a running addition to the 1963 Mercury line. Specific production totals for this style, model number 57, are not available.

MONTEREY CUSTOM SERIES — Tire level full-length moldings, three rectangular chrome pieces on the rear fender and front fender nameplates distinguished the Custom from the standard Monterey. All Customs came equipped with back-up lights, courtesy light group, electric clock and two-speed windshield wipers.

MONTEREY CUSTOM

Model Number	Body/Style Number	Body Type & Seating	Factory Price	Shipping Weight	Production Total
NA	62	4-dr Sed-6P	3075	3959	39,542
NA	66	2-dr Fsbk Cpe-6P	3083	3887	7,298
NA	63	2-dr HT Cpe-6P	3083	3881	10,693
NA	76	4-dr Sta Wag-6P	3295	4306	6,447

Model Number	Body/Style Number	Body Type & Seating	Factory Price	Shipping Weight	Production Total
NA	76	4-dr Sta Wag-9P	3365	4318	7,529
NA	64	4-dr HT Sed-6P	3148	3971	8,604
NA	65	2-dr Conv-6P	3333	4043	3,783

NOTE: Model number 66, the fastback coupe, was called the Marauder. Models numbered 76 were called Colony Park station wagons.

MONTEREY S-55 SERIES — The S-55 insignia in front of the rear fender chrome bars and special wheelcovers were the most noticeable exterior differences between the S-55 and the Custom. Inside, the S-55 featured vinyl upholstery, front bucket seats with the center console, front and rear armrests and padded dash. Buyers could have an automatic or a four-speed manual transmission at no extra cost.

MONTEREY S-55

Model Number	Body/Style Number	Body Type & Seating	Factory Price	Shipping Weight	Production Total
NA	68	2-dr Fsbk Cpe-6P	3650	3900	2,317
NA	67	2-dr HT Cpe-6P	3650	3894	3,863
NA	60	4-dr HT Sed-5P	3715	3984	1,203
NA	69	2-dr Conv-5P	3900	4049	1,379

NOTE: Model number 68, the fastback coupe, was called the Marauder.

COMET BASE ENGINE: Six: Overhead valves. Cast iron block. Displacement: 144.3 cid. Bore and stroke: 3.5 x 2.5 inches. Compression ratio: 8.70:1. Brake hp: 85 at 4200 rpm. Four main bearings. Carburetor: Ford C3GF-9510 one-barrel.

METEOR BASE ENGINE: Six: Overhead valves. Cast iron block. Displacement: 170 cid. Bore and stroke: 3.5 x 2.94 inches. Compression ratio: 8.70:1. Brake hp: 101 at 4400 rpm. Four main bearings. Carburetor: Ford C30F-9510-A one-barrel.

MONTEREY BASE ENGINE: V-8: Overhead valves. Cast iron block. Displacement: 390 cid. Bore and stroke: 4.05 x 3.78 inches. Compression ratio: 8.90:1. Brake hp: 250 at 4400 rpm. Five main bearings. Carburetor: Ford C3MF-9510 two-barrel.

COMET CHASSIS FEATURES: Wheelbase: (Station wagon) 109.5 inches; (other models) 114 inches. Overall length: (Station wagons) 191.8 inches; (other models) 194.8 inches. Tires: (Station wagon and convertible) 6.50 x 13; (other models) 6.00 x 13.

METEOR CHASSIS FEATURES: Wheelbase: (Passenger cars) 116.5 inches; (Station wagons) 115.5 inches. Overall length: (Passenger cars) 203.8 inches; (Station wagons) 202.3 inches. Tires: 6.50 x 14.

MERCURY CHASSIS FEATURES: Wheelbase: 120 inches. Overall length: (Passenger cars) 215 inches; (Station wagons) 212.1 inches. Tires: (Passenger cars) 7.50 x 14; (Station wagons) 8.00 x 14.

COMET OPTIONS: Back-up lights ($10.70). Luggage rack for station wagons ($39). Air conditioning ($270.90). Comet convenience group ($25.80). Padded instrument panel ($16.40). Padded visors ($4.50). Push-button radio ($58.80). Two-tone paint ($19.40). Electric tailgate

window for station wagons ($29.75). Tinted glass ($30.90). Tinted windshield ($12.95). Whitewall tires on passenger cars ($29.90): on station wagons ($33). Wheelcovers ($16). Windshield washers ($13.70). Two-speed electric windshield wipers ($9.65). A three-speed manual transmission was standard. Four-speed manual and Merc-O-Matic automatic transmissions were optional. A 101 hp 170 cid (one-barrel) and a 164 hp 260 cid V-8 (two-barrel) were optional.

METEOR OPTIONS: Two-speed windshield wipers ($7.75). Air conditioning ($231.70). Padded instrument panel ($19.95). Outside remote-control rearview mirror ($12). Padded visors ($5.20). Power steering ($81.70). Tinted glass ($40.30). Whitewall tires ($37). Wheelcovers ($18.60). Windshield washer ($13.70). Push-button radio ($58.50). Front seat belts ($16.80). Two-tone paint ($22). Third station wagon seat ($43.50). Station wagon power rear window ($32.30). A three-speed manual transmission was standard. Overdrive, four-speed manual and Merc-O-Matic automatic transmissions were optional. A 145 hp 221 cid V-8 (two-barrel) and a 164 hp 260.8 cid V-8 were available.

MERCURY OPTIONS: Air-conditioner with heater ($360.90). Electric clock ($14.60). Back-up lights ($10.70). Station wagon luggage rack ($45.40). Outside remote control rearview mirror ($12). Padded dash ($21.30). Padded visors ($5.80). Two-tone paint ($22). Power brakes ($43.20). Power driver's bucket seat in S-55 ($92.10). Power steering ($106.20). Power windows ($102.10). Push-button radio ($58.50). AM/FM radio ($129.30). Front seat belts ($16.80). Swing-away steering wheel ($50). Tinted glass ($43). Tinted windshield ($28). Whitewall tires ($52.60). Monterey sedan trim option ($34.80). Wheelcovers ($19.20). Windshield washer ($13.70). Courtesy light group ($14.80). Two-speed windshield wipers ($7.75). A three-speed manual transmission was standard on Monterey and Custom series. Multi-Drive automatic or four-speed manual transmissions were standard in the S-55. Automatic transmission was optional on all series. The four-speed manual transmission was available on all, but the Colony Park. A 300 hp cid V-8 (four-barrel); 330 hp 390 cid V-8 (four-barrel); 385 hp 406 cid (four-barrel) and a 405 hp 406 cid V-8 were optional. The last two choices were offered only on cars equipped with four-speed manual transmission. A 427 V-8 was also available in 410 hp and 425 hp formats, with manual transmissions only.

HISTORICAL FOOTNOTES: Just over 64 percent of 1963 Comets were equipped with an automatic transmission. Most Meteors, 79.6 percent, came with an automatic transmission, 91.4 percent had a V-8 engine, 47 percent had power steering, 68.6 percent had a radio, 46 percent had tinted glass and five percent had air conditioning. The majority of 1963 full-size Mercurys came with automatic transmission, power steering, power brakes, radio and tinted glass. About one in 10 had power windows. Twenty percent were sold with an air-conditioner. Mercury won one NASCAR Grand Nationals race in 1963. This was the first year for the 427 cid V-8 in big Mercurys.

1964 MERCURY

COMET 202 SERIES — The 1964 Comet had a Lincoln Continental style grille. The same theme was repeated on the rear deck panel. A wraparound trim piece was seen on the tips of the front fenders. Three thin, vertical trim slashes were on the sides of the front fenders. The signal lights remained embedded in the front bumper.

MERCURY & COMET I.D. NUMBERS: VIN on left inner fender of Comets and Meteors and right cowl tab on Mercurys. First symbol 4 = 1964. Second symbol identifies assembly plant: E = Mahwah, NJ; F = Dearborn, Mich.; H = Lorain, Ohio; J = Los Angeles, Calif.; K = Kansas City, Kan.; R = San Jose, Calif.; S = Pilot; T = Metuchen, NJ; W = Wayne, Mich.; Y = Wixom, Mich.; Z = St. Louis, Mo. Third and fourth symbols are body code (See Body/Style Number column in charts below). Fifth symbol identifies engine: (Comet) U = 170 cid six; 4 = 170 cid six (export); F = 260 cid V-8; 6 = 260 cid V-8 (export); D = 289 cid/210 hp cid V-8; K = 289 cid/271 hp V-8; R = 427 cid/425 hp V-8; (Mercury) Y = 390 cid/250 hp V-8 2V; H = 390 cid/266 hp V-8 2V; Z = 390 cid/300 hp V-8 4V; P = 390 cid/330 hp V-8 4V high-performance; 9 = 390 cid (export); Q = 427 cid/410 hp V-8; R = 427 cid/425 hp V-8. Last six symbols are sequential production number starting at 500001. Body plate on front body pillar gives VIN, body code, color, trim, date, engine, transmission and axle codes).

COMET 202

Model Number	Body/Style Number	Body Type & Seating	Factory Price	Shipping Weight	Production Total
NA	02	4-dr Sed-6P	2182	2580	29,147
NA	01	2-dr Sed-6P	2126	2539	33,824
NA	32	4-dr Sta Wag-6P	2463	2727	5,504

COMET 404 SERIES — Full-length bodyside moldings were the most obvious exterior difference between the Comet 404 and lower priced Comet 202. Interior trims were available in cloth and vinyl or all-vinyl. The Villager station wagon featured imitation wood trim.

COMET 404

Model Number	Body/Style Number	Body Type & Seating	Factory Price	Shipping Weight	Production Total
NA	12	4-dr Sed-6P	2269	2588	25,136
NA	11	2-dr Sed-6P	2213	2551	12,512
NA	34	4-dr Sta Wag-6P	2550	2741	6,918
NA	36	4-dr Sta Wag-6P	2734	2745	1,980

NOTE: Model number 36 was called the Villager station wagon.

1964 Mercury, Comet Caliente two-door hardtop sport coupe, V-8

1964 Mercury, Colony Park four-door station wagon, V-8

CALIENTE SERIES — "Every bit as hot as it looks!", was how sales literature described the Caliente. It had a wide, full-length molding, on its sides and a nameplate on the lower front fenders. A padded instrument panel with walnut grain trim and deep-loop carpeting were a couple of standard luxury features. Caliente hardtops and convertibles were available only in solid colors.

CALIENTE

Model Number	Body/Style Number	Body Type & Seating	Factory Price	Shipping Weight	Production Total
NA	22	4-dr Sed-6P	2350	2668	27,218
NA	23	2-dr HT Cpe-6P	2375	2688	31,204
NA	25	2-dr Conv-6P	2636	2861	9,039

CYCLONE SERIES — This two-door hardtop was the first macho Comet. Literature told of "under the hood, a whiplash of surging power" and of the "masculine feel of black vinyl in the instrument panel." As a safety feature the "bucket seats are contoured to hold you more securely in turns." (Apparently, Mercury felt a lot of people were falling out of their bucket seats when driving around corners.) Fender nameplates, full-length lower body moldings, vinyl roof coverings and 'chrome wheel look' wheelcovers distinguished the Cyclone. A three-spoke steering wheel, front bucket seats with center console and a tachometer were standard. The engine came with special chromed parts, including air cleaner, dip stick, oil filter, radiator cap and rocker arm covers.

CYCLONE

Model Number	Body/Style Number	Body Type & Seating	Factory Price	Shipping Weight	Production Total
NA	27	2-dr HT Cpe-5P	2655	2688	7,454

MONTEREY SERIES — Although obviously based on the 1963 models, the new full-size Mercurys now seemed closer in styling to Continentals than Fords. The rear end appeared to be influenced by the 1959 Continental Mark IV. Six rectangular tail/back-up lights were set in the rear deck panel. The slightly recessed grille featured bent vertical bars and four chrome rimmed headlights. The signal lights were in the bumper. The unusual Breezeway roof, with its retractable rear window, was offered once again. Full-length upper body moldings and tire level chrome spears decorated the sides.

MONTEREY

Model Number	Body/Style Number	Body Type & Seating	Factory Price	Shipping Weight	Production Total
NA	42	4-dr Sed-6P	2892	3985	20,234
NA	48	4-dr HT Fsbk-6P	2957	4017	4,143
NA	41	2-dr Sed-6P	2819	3895	3,932
NA	47	2-dr HT Fsbk-6P	2884	3916	8,760
NA	43	2-dr HT Sed-6P	2884	3910	2,926
NA	45	2-dr Conv-6P	3226	4027	2,592

NOTE: Models number 48 and 47, the pillarless fastback styles, were called Marauders.

MONTCLAIR SERIES — Montclairs had three horizontal chrome pieces on the front fenders. nameplates on the rear fenders and a wide band of chrome on the rear quarter panel. Buyers had their choice of cloth and vinyl or all-vinyl interiors.

MONTCLAIR

Model Number	Body/Style Number	Body Type & Seating	Factory Price	Shipping Weight	Production Total
NA	52	4-dr Sed-6P	3116	3996	15,520
NA	58	4-dr HT Fsbk-6P	3181	4017	8,655
NA	57	2-dr HT Fsbk-6P	3127	3927	6,459
NA	53	2-dr HT Cpe-6P	3127	3921	2,329

NOTE: Models number 57 and 58, the pillarless fastback styles, were called Marauders.

PARK LANE SERIES — The Park Lane returned as Mercury's top-of-the-line series. A wide band of tire level chrome trim, running across the bodysides, set it apart from other Mercurys. Its interior featured nylon face, biscuit-design upholstery and large, walnut-tone door panel inserts. The Park Lane convertible. like the Monterey version, came with a glass rear window.

PARK LANE

Model Number	Body/Style Number	Body Type & Seating	Factory Price	Shipping Weight	Production Total
NA	62	4-dr Sed-6P	3348	4035	6,230
NA	68	4-dr HT Fsbk-5P	3413	4056	3,658
NA	67	2-dr HT Fsbk-5P	3359	3966	2,721
NA	63	2-dr HT Cpe-6P	3359	3960	1,786
NA	64	4-dr HT Sed-6P	3413	4050	2,402
NA	65	2-dr Conv-6P	3549	4066	1,967

NOTE: Models number 67 and 68, the pillarless fastback styles, were called Maurauders.

STATION WAGONS SERIES — The Commuter station wagon was based on the Monterey. The Colony Park had mahogany-toned side paneling.

STATION WAGONS

Model Number	Body/Style Number	Body Type & Seating	Factory Price	Shipping Weight	Production Total
NA	72	4-dr Comm-6P	3236	4259	3,484
NA	76	4-dr Col Prk-6P	3434	4275	4,234
NA	72	4-dr Comm-9P	3306	4271	1,839
NA	76	4-dr Col Prk-9P	3504	4287	5,624

COMET BASE ENGINE: Six: Overhead valves. Cast iron block. Displacement: 170 cid. Bore and stroke: 3.5 x 2.93 inches. Compression ratio: 8.70:1. Brake hp: 101 at 4400 rpm. Four main bearings. Carburetor: Ford C3YF-9510E one-barrel.

CYCLONE BASE ENGINE: V-8: Overhead valves. Cast iron block. Displacement: 289 cid. Bore and stroke: 4 x 2.37 inches. Compression ratio: 9.00:1. Five main bearings. Brake hp: 210 at 4400 rpm. Carburetor: Ford C5MF-9510A two-barrel.

MERCURY BASE ENGINE: V-8: Overhead valves. Cast iron block. Displacement: 390 cid. Bore and stroke: 4.05 x 3.78 inches. Compression ratio: 9.40:1. Brake hp: 250 at 4400 rpm. Five main bearings. Carburetor: Ford C4MF-9510D two-barrel.

COMET CHASSIS FEATURES: (Passenger cars) 114 inches; (station wagons) 109.5 inches. Overall length: (passenger cars) 195.1 inches; (station wagons) 191.8 inches. Tires (passenger cars) 6.50 x 14; (station wagons) 7.00 x 14.

MERCURY CHASSIS FEATURES: Wheelbase: 120 inches. Overall length: (passenger cars) 215.5; (station wagons) 210.3 inches. Tires: 8.00 x 14.

COMET OPTIONS: Power steering ($86). Air conditioning ($232). Heavy-duty battery ($7.60). Tinted glass ($27.10). Tinted windshield ($18.10). Station wagon luggage rack ($64.35). Outside remote control rearview mirror ($12). Padded instrument panel ($18.40). Padded visors ($4.50). Two-tone paint ($19.40). Power brakes ($43.20). Push-button AM radio ($58.50). Tachometer ($43.10). Wheelcovers ($19.20). Windshield washer and wipers ($21.80). A three-speed manual transmission was standard. Four-speed manual, Merc-0-Matic and Multi-Drive automatic transmissions were optional. A 116 hp 200 cid six (one-barrel); 164 hp 260 cid V-8 (two-barrel); 210 hp 289 cid. V-8 (two-barrel) and a 271 hp 289 cid V-8 (four-barrel) were available. A limited number of Comets with 427 cid/425 hp engines were built as lightweight factory drag racing cars.

MERCURY CONVENIENCE OPTIONS: Air conditioner ($430). Heavy-duty battery ($42.50). Bucket seats ($160.90). Console and tachometer ($88.80). Courtesy light group ($23.20). Electric clock in Monterey ($16.10). Power steering ($106). Tinted glass ($43). Tinted windshield ($28). Station wagon luggage rack ($64.40). Padded dash ($21.30). Two-tone paint ($22). Power brakes ($43.20). Six-Way power seats ($96.50). Power windows ($106.20). Push-button AM radio ($61.10). AM/FM radio ($148.60). Speed control ($92.70). Tilting steering wheel ($43.10). Windshield washer ($13.70). Vinyl roof ($88.80). Wire Wheelcovers ($45.20). A three-speed manual transmission was standard. Four-speed manual and Multi-Drive automatic transmissions were optional. The four-speed was not available in station wagons. A power transfer rear axle was offered at extra cost. Optional engines included: 266 hp 390 cid V-8 (station wagons only); 300 hp 390 cid V-8 (four-barrel); 330 hp 390 cid V-8 (four-barrel); 410 hp 427 cid V-8 (four-barrel) and 425 hp 427 cid V-8 (dual four-barrels). The last two engines were not available in station wagons.

HISTORICAL FOOTNOTES: Most 1964 Comets, 68 percent, had automatic transmission, 24 percent had power steering and only four percent had power brakes. A team of Comet Calientes, powered by 271 hp 289 cid V-8s, traveled over 100,000 miles at average speeds in excess of 100 mph. Three of the least popular options on full-size Mercurys this year (and their installation rates) were four-speed manual transmission (.9 percent), locking differential (four percent) and tilting steering wheel (two percent). Maurauder was the name given full-size Mercury fastback two-door and four-door hardtops. Mercurys won five NASCAR Grand National races in 1964. The Comet Boss 427 Dragster, Mercury's counterpart to Ford's Fairlane Thunderbolt, was introduced.

1965 MERCURY

COMET 202 SERIES — The restyled Comet had vertical headlights which made it look more like a Ford than a Merc. The grille used a horizontal bar theme. Side chrome was limited to the roof quarter panel and three thin horizontal pieces on the front fenders. Wraparound rectangular taillights were used on all body types, except the station wagon, which used square ones. Front seat belts, a heater and defroster and front and rear armrests were standard equipment.

MERCURY & COMET I.D. NUMBERS: VIN on left inner fender of Comets and Meteors and right cowl tab on Mercurys. First symbol 5 = 1965. Second symbol identifies assembly plant: E = Mahwah, NJ; F = Dearborn, Mich.; H = Lorain, Ohio; J = Los Angeles, Calif.; K = Kansas City, Kan.; R = San Jose, Calif.; S = Pilot; T = Metuchen, NJ; W = Wayne, Mich.; Y = Wixom, Mich.; Z = St. Louis, Mo. Third and fourth symbols are body code (See Body/Style Number

column in charts below). Fifth symbol identifies engine: (Comet) U = 170 cid six; 4 = 170 cid six (export); F = 260 cid V-8; 6 = 260 cid V-8 (export); D = 289 cid/210 hp V-8; K = 289 cid/271 hp V-8; R = 427 cid/425 hp V-8; (Mercury) Y = 390 cid/250 hp V-8 2V; H = 390 hp/266 hp V-8 2V; Z = 390 hp/300 hp V-8 4V; P = 390 hp/330 hp V-8 4V high-performance; 9 = 390 cid (export); Q = 427 cid/410 hp V-8; R = 427 cid/425 hp V-8. Last six symbols are sequential production number starting at 500001. Body plate on front body pillar gives VIN, body code, color, trim, date, engine, transmission and axle codes).

COMET 202

Model Number	Body/Style Number	Body Type & Seating	Factory Price	Shipping Weight	Production Total
202	01	4-dr Sed-6P	2163	2335	23,501
202	02	2-dr Sed-6P	2108	2295	32,425
202	32	4-dr Sta Wag-6P	2438	2495	4,814

COMET 404 SERIES — Full-length bodyside chrome and side window moldings set the 404 apart from the 202 series. The Villager Station Wagon had imitation wood paneling and came with a power tailgate window.

COMET 404

Model Number	Body/Style Number	Body Type & Seating	Factory Price	Shipping Weight	Production Total
404	11	4-dr Sed-6P	2248	2340	18,628
404	12	2-dr Sed-6P	2193	2305	10,900
404	34	4-dr Sta Wag-6P	2523	2500	5,226
404	36	4-dr Sta Wag-6P	2703	2500	1,592

NOTE: Model number 36, a woodgrain panelled station wagon, was called the Villager.

CALIENTE SERIES — The most luxurious Comet remained the Caliente. It had a special horizontal chrome bar taillight treatment that blended into the rear deck panel. In addition, it featured a mid-tire level molding. Carpeting, a padded dash and door courtesy lights were among the standard items offered on the Caliente. The convertible had a power top.

CALIENTE

Model Number	Body/Style Number	Body Type & Seating	Factory Price	Shipping Weight	Production Total
NA	22	4-dr Sed-6P	2327	2370	20,337
NA	23	2-dr HT Cpe 6P	2352	2395	29,247
NA	25	2-dr Conv-6P	2607	2588	6,035

1965 Mercury, Comet Cyclone two-door hardtop sport coupe, V-8

CYCLONE SERIES — A vinyl roof, chrome wheels, curb moldings, distinctive grille, designs, two hood scoops, bucket seats with console and a tachometer were standard on the Cyclone two-door hardtop.

CYCLONE

Model Number	Body/Style Number	Body Type & Seating	Factory Price	Shipping Weight	Production Total
NA	27	2-dr HT Cpe-5P	2625	2994	12,347

MONTEREY SERIES — The 1965 Monterey had a horizontal bar grille with the mid-section protruding slightly. Thin vertical signal lights were located at the tips of the front fenders. Outside of the large front fender trim pieces and rocker panel moldings, the Monterey's sides were relatively clean of 'doo-dads'. The taillights were vertical and fully integrated into the bumper and rear fenders. Carpeting, front seat belts and a heater and defroster were among the standard features. The Breezeway sedan, with its retractable rear window, was offered once again.

MONTEREY

Model Number	Body/Style Number	Body Type & Seating	Factory Price	Shipping Weight	Production Total
NA	44	4-dr Sed-6P	2782	3853	23,363
NA	43	2-dr Sed-6P	2711	3788	5,775
NA	47	2-dr Fsbk-6P	2843	3823	16,857
NA	42	4-dr Brzway-6P	2845	3898	19,569
NA	48	4-dr HT Fsbk-6P	2918	3893	10,047
NA	45	2-dr Conv-6P	3165	3928	4762

NOTE: Models number 47 and 48, the pillarless hardtop styles. were called Marauders. Model number 42, the Breezeway. was a sedan with slanting and retractable rear window styling.

MONTCLAIR SERIES — The Montclair had a full-length, chrome middle body spear. Its nameplate was on the rear fenders. As in the Monterey Series, the Breezeway model had chrome trim on the roof quarter panels. In addition to the standard items found in Montereys, Montclair buyers received wheelcovers, electric clocks and interval selector windshield wipers.

MONTCLAIR

Model Number	Body/Style Number	Body Type & Seating	Factory Price	Shipping Weight	Production Total
NA	52	4-dr Brzway-6P	3074	3933	18,924
NA	58	4-dr HT Fsbk-6P	3145	3928	16,977
NA	57	2-dr HT Fsbk-6P	3072	3848	9,645

NOTE: Models number 57 and 58, the pillarless hardtop styles, were Marauders. Model number 52, the Breezeway was a sedan with slanting and retractable rear window styling.

1965 Mercury, Park Lane four-door hardtop sedan, V-8

PARK LANE SERIES — Rectangular rear fender nameplates, chrome gravel shields and a band of molding above the rocker panels, were three styling features of Park Lanes. They had more luxurious interiors than cars in the other series. Standard equipment included, padded dash, padded visors, courtesy lights, visor-mounted vanity mirrors and a trip odometer.

PARK LANE

Model Number	Body/Style Number	Body Type & Seating	Factory Price	Shipping Weight	Production Total
NA	62	4-dr Brzway-6P	3301	3988	8,335
NA	68	4-dr HT Fsbk-6P	3372	3983	14,211
NA	67	2-dr HT Fsbk-6P	3299	3908	6,853
NA	65	2-dr Conv-6P	3526	4013	3,008

NOTE: Models number 67 and 68, the pillarless hardtop styles, were called Mauraders. Model number 62, the Breezeway, was a sedan with slanting and retractable rear window styling.

STATION WAGONS SERIES — The third seat, in Mercury wagons equipped with such an option, faced the rear. The rear quarter panels contained wind vanes. The Colony Park had simulated wood paneling.

STATION WAGONS

Model Number	Body/Style Number	Body Type & Seating	Factory Price	Shipping Weight	Production Total
NA	72	4-dr Comm-6P	3169	4178	8,081
NA	76	4-dr Col Prk-6P	3364	4213	15,294

COMET BASE ENGINE: Six: Overhead valves. Cast iron block. Displacement: 200 cid. Bore and stroke: 3.68 x 3.12 inches. Compression ratio: 9.20:1. Brake hp: 120 at 4400 rpm. Seven main bearings. Carburetor: Ford C50F-9510E one-barrel.

CYCLONE BASE ENGINE: V-8: Overhead valves. Cast iron block. Displacement: 289 cid. Bore and stroke: 4 x 2.87 inches. Compression ratio: 9.30:1. Brake hp: 200 at 4400 rpm. Five main bearings. Carburetor: Ford C5MF-9510A two-barrel.

MONTEREY BASE ENGINE: V-8: Overhead valves. Cast iron block. Displacement: 390 cid. Bore and stroke: 4.05 x 3.78 inches. Compression ratio: 9.40:1. Brake hp: 250 at 4400 rpm. Five main bearings. Carburetor: Ford C5MF-9519-A two-barrel.

PARK LANE BASE ENGINE: V-8: Overhead valves. Cast iron block. Displacement: 390 cid. Bore and stroke: 4.05 x 3.78 inches. Compression ratio: 10.10:1. Brake hp: 300 at 4600 rpm. Five main bearings. Carburetor: Ford C5AF-9510E four-barrel.

COMET CHASSIS FEATURES: Wheelbase: (Passenger cars) 114 inches: (109.5) (Station Wagons). Overall length: (passenger cars) 195.3 inches; (station wagons) 191.8 inches. Tires: 6.95 x 14.

MERCURY CHASSIS FEATURES: (passenger cars) 123 inches; (station wagons) 119 inches. Overall length: (passenger cars) 218.4 inches; (station wagons) 214.5 inches. Tires: 8.15 x 15.

COMET OPTIONS: Air conditioner ($257.50). Heavy-duty battery ($7.60). Elapsed-time clock ($20). Courtesy light group ($14.80). Remote-control trunk lid release ($11). Emergency flasher ($12.80). Tinted glass ($27.80). Tinted windshield ($18.10). Back-up lights ($10.70). Station wagon luggage rack ($64.35). Remote-control outside rearview mirror ($12). Curb molding ($16.10). Padded dash ($18.40). Padded visors ($4.50). Two-tone paint ($19.40). Power brakes ($43.20). Power steering ($86.30). Station wagon power tailgate window ($29.75). Push-button AM radio ($58.50). AM/FM radio ($129.30). Rally Pac ($83); same in Cyclone ($40). Retractable front seat belts ($7.10). Front bucket seats with console in Caliente hardtop and convertible ($131.30). Front bucket seats in two-door sedan only ($70.80). Size 6.95 x 14 whitewall tires. Tachometer ($43.10). Vacuum gauge ($20). Wheelcovers ($19.20). Wire Wheelcovers ($64.40): same on Cyclone ($43.20). Windshield washer and wipers ($21.80). Vinyl roof on hardtop ($75.80). A three-speed manual transmission was standard. Four-speed manual and Multi-Drive automatic transmissions were optional. A 200 hp Cyclone 289 cid V-8 (two-barrel) and a 225 hp Super Cyclone 289 cid V-8 (four-barrel) were optional. A performance handling package could be had for $20.80. A power transfer axle cost $38. A power booster fan was $16.10.

MERCURY OPTIONS: Air conditioner ($430). Bucket seats in Monterey hardtop and convertible ($160.90). Reclining passenger side bucket seat in Park Lane ($45. 10). Console and tachometer in Monterey ($88.80). Courtesy light group ($23.20). Remote-control trunk lid release ($110). Decor group in Monterey sedans ($34.80); in Monterey hardtops and Commuter ($21.90); in Monterey convertible ($14.20). Power door locks in two-doors ($37.30); in four doors ($52.80). Speed-actuated rear door locks ($25.80). Electric clock ($16.10). Tinted windshield ($3.00). Tinted glass ($43). Luggage rack ($64.40). Padded dash ($21.30). Padded visors ($5.80). Two-tone paint ($22). Power antenna ($29.60). Power brakes ($43.20). Four-way power bucket seat, driver's side ($92.10). Six-Way power seats ($96.50). Power windows ($106.20). Power vent windows ($52.80). Push-button AM radio ($61.10). AM/FM Push-button radio with rear speaker ($148.60). Rear seat speaker ($19.30). Studio-sonic rear speaker ($53.50). Third seat in station wagons ($76.80). Retractable front seat belts ($7.10). Speed control ($92.70). Sports package in Park Lane two-door hardtop and convertible ($423). Tilting steering wheel ($43.10). Whitewall tires ($40.56). All-vinyl Deluxe trim in Monterey hardtops and four-door sedans ($70.80). Leather trim in Park Lanes with bench seats ($98.80). Visibility group in Monterey ($30.80). Trip odometer ($8.90). Wheelcovers with spinners on Monterey ($38.40); on Montclair and Park Lane ($19.20). Deluxe wheelcovers on Monterey ($19.20). Custom wheelcovers on Monterey ($54.10); on Montclair and Park Lane ($34.90). Wire wheelcovers on Monterey ($64.40); on Montclair and Park Lane ($45.20). Vinyl roof ($88.80). Windshield washer ($13.70). A three-speed manual transmission was standard. Overdrive, four-speed manual and Multi-Drive Merc-O-Matic automatic transmissions were optional. A 255 hp 390 cid V-8 (two-barrel) was standard on Montclairs and station wagons equipped with automatic. A 300 hp 390 cid V-8 (four-barrel); a 330 hp 390

cid V-8 (four-barrel) and a 425 hp 427 cid V-8 (dual four-barrel) were optional. The latter engine was offered only with cars that had a four-speed manual gearbox. It was not available in station wagons. A power transfer axle could be had for $42.50.

HISTORICAL FOOTNOTES: Most 1965 Comets, 65.5 percent, had automatic transmission, 51.3 percent had a six-cylinder engine and only 1.9 percent came with power windows. Just .3 percent of full-size Mercs came with a four-speed manual gearbox. Other rare options included a tilting steering wheel (6.4 percent) and locking differential (4.5 percent). Mercurys won one NASCAR Grand National race in 1965. The 427 cid single-overhead cam engine was specially available in Comet "Boss" lightweight drag cars/funny cars for 1965.

1966 MERCURY

1966 Mercury, Comet '202' two-door sedan, 6-cyl

COMET 202 SERIES — The Comet grew this year, from a compact to an intermediate. A stacked headlight arrangement was continued. The two-level grille consisted of crisscross pieces. Three bent vertical bars were on the front fenders. A heater and defroster were standard equipment.

MERCURY & COMET I.D. NUMBERS: VIN on left inner fender of Comets and Meteors and right cowl tab on Mercurys. First symbol 6 = 1966. Second symbol identifies assembly plant: A = Atlanta, Ga.; Oakville, (Canada); D = Dallas, Texas; E = Mahwah, NJ; F = Dearborn, Mich.; G = Chicago, Ill.; H = Lorain, Ohio; J = Los Angeles, Calif.; K = Kansas City, Kan.; N = Norfolk, Va.; P = Mpls. St.Paul, Minn.; R = San Jose, Calif.; S = Pilot; T = Metuchen, NJ; W = Wayne, Mich.; Y = Wixom, Mich.; Z = St. Louis, Mo. Third and fourth symbols are body code (See Body/Style Number column in charts below). Fifth symbol identifies engine: (Comet) T = 200 cid six; 2 = 200 cid six (export); C = 289 cid/200 hp V-8/ 3 = 289 cid V-8 (export); Y = 390 cid/ 265 hp V-8; H = 390 cid/275 hp V-8 (Mercury) Y = 390 cid/265 hp V-8 2V; H = 390 cid/275 hp V-8 2V; M = 410 cid/330 hp V-8; P = 428 cid/360 hp V-8 4V high-perf.; 8 = 428 cid (export); Q = 428 cid/345 hp V-8; R = 427 cid/345 hp V-8. Last six symbols are sequential production number starting at 500001. Body plate on front body pillar gives VIN, body code, color, trim, date, engine, transmission and axle codes).

COMET 202

Model Number	Body/Style Number	Body Type & Seating	Factory Price	Shipping Weight	Production Total
202	01	2-dr Sed-6P	2206	2779	35,964
202	02	4-dr Sed-6P	2263	2823	20,440

COMET CAPRI SERIES — Rocker panel moldings, front fender medallions and chrome side window trim were styling features of the Capri intermediate. Carpeting was standard.

COMET CAPRI

Model Number	Body/Style Number	Body Type & Seating	Factory Price	Shipping Weight	Production Total
NA	12	4-dr Sed-6P	2378	2844	15,635
NA	13	2-dr HT Cpe-6P	2400	2876	15,031

CALIENTE SERIES — Calientes had chrome trimmed wheelwell openings and moldings above the rocker panels. Their interiors were a bit plusher than those on other Comets.

CALIENTE

Model Number	Body/Style Number	Body Type & Seating	Factory Price	Shipping Weight	Production Total
NA	22	4-dr Sed-6P	2453	2846	17,933
NA	23	2-dr HT Cpe-6P	2475	2882	25,862
NA	25	2-dr Conv-6P	2735	3143	3,922

1966 Mercury, Comet Cyclone 'GT' two-door hardtop, V-8

CYCLONE SERIES — A special front fender nameplate, body strips above the rocker panels and a different, horizontal bar grille, made it easy to tell a Cyclone from other Comets. Bucket seats and chromed wheels were standard.

CYCLONE

Model Number	Body/Style Number	Body Type & Seating	Factory Price	Shipping Weight	Production Total
NA	27	2-dr HT Cpe-5P	2700	3074	6,889
NA	29	2-dr Conv-5P	2961	3321	1,305
NA	26	2-dr GT Conv-5P	3152	3595	2,158
NA	28	2-dr GT Cpe-5P	2891	3315	13,812

MONTEREY SERIES — The new 1966 Mercury grille consisted of horizontal bars and a thin vertical piece in the center. Small signal lights wrapped around the front fenders. Large, chrome ringed taillights, at the ends of the rear fenders, appeared to be bumper-integrated. The Mercury name was written on the hood and trunk lid. A Monterey nameplate appeared on the rear fenders. A large, criss-cross pattern trim piece was on the front fenders. Carpeting with fabric and vinyl upholstery were standard, except in the convertible, which had an all-vinyl interior.

Model Number	Body/Style Number	Body Type & Seating	Factory Price	Shipping Weight	Production Total
NA	42	4-dr Brzway-6P	2917	3966	14,174
NA	43	2-dr Sed-6P-	2783	3835	2,487
NA	44	4-dr Sed-6P	2854	3903	18,998
NA	45	2-dr Conv-6P	3237	4039	3,279
NA	47	2-dr HT Cpe-6P	2915	3885	19,103
NA	48	4-dr HT Sed-6P	2990	3928	7,647

NOTE: Model number 42, the four-door Breezeway, was a sedan with slanting and retractable rear window styling.

1966 Mercury, Montclair two-door hardtop, V-8

MONTCLAIR SERIES — Fender-to-fender upper body moldings and chrome rocker panels were two styling features of the Montclair. An electric clock, interval selector windshield wipers. Deluxe steering wheel and Wheelcovers were standard.

MONTCLAIR

Model Number	Body/Style Number	Body Type & Seating	Factory Price	Shipping Weight	Production Total
NA	54	4-dr Sed-6P	3087	3921	11,856
NA	57	2-dr HT Cpe-6P	3144	3887	11,290
NA	58	4-dr HT Sed-6P	3217	3971	15,767

PARK LANE SERIES — A wide, full-length molding (at tire level) on the bodysides and rear deck panel trim, were distinguishing features of the Park Lane.

PARK LANE

Model Number	Body/Style Number	Body Type & Seating	Factory Price	Shipping Weight	Production Total
NA	62	4-dr Brzway-6P	3389	4051	8,696
NA	65	2-dr Conv-6P	3608	4148	2,546
NA	67	2-dr HT Cpe-6P	3387	3971	8,354
NA	68	4-dr HT Sed-6P	3460	4070	19,204

NOTE: Model number 62, the four-door Breezeway, was a sedan with slanting and retractable rear window styling.

MERCURY S-55 SERIES — The sporty S-55 had full-length mid-body chrome trim, chrome rocker panels and a rear fender medallion. Bucket seats, a center console and dual exhausts, were a few of its standard features.

1966 Mercury, Parklane four-door Breezeway sedan, V-8

MERCURY S-55 SERIES

Model Number	Body/Style Number	Body Type & Seating	Factory Price	Shipping Weight	Production Total
NA	46	2-dr Conv-5P	3614	4148	669
NA	49	2-dr HT Cpe-5P	3292	4031	2916

COMET STATION WAGON SERIES — The Voyager was based on the Comet Capri series. The Villager was a bit more luxurious and featured simulated woodgrain body panels.

STATION WAGONS

Model Number	Body/Style Number	Body Type & Seating	Factory Price	Shipping Weight	Production Total
NA	06	4-dr Voy-6P	2553	3201	7,595
NA	16	4-dr Vill-6P	2,780	3,244	3,880

COMET BASE ENGINE: Six: Overhead valves. Cast iron block. Displacement: 200 cid. Bore and stroke: 3.68 x 3.13 inches. Compression ratio: 9.20:1. Brake hp: 120 at 4400 rpm. Seven main bearings. Carburetor: Ford C3PF-9510-A one-barrel.

CYCLONE BASE ENGINE: V-8: Overhead valves. Cast iron block. Displacement: 289 cid. Bore and stroke: 4 x 2.87 inches. Compression ratio: 9.30:1. Brake hp: 200 at 4400 rpm. Five main bearings. Carburetor: Ford C40F-9510-AM two-barrel.

MERCURY MONTEREY BASE ENGINE: V-8: Overhead valves. Cast iron block. Displacement: 390 cid. Bore and stroke: 4.05 x 3.78 inches. Compression ratio: 9.50:1. Brake hp: 265 at 4400 rpm. Five main bearings. Carburetor: Ford C6AF-9510-AM two-barrel.

MERCURY PARK LANE BASE ENGINE: V-8: Overhead valves. Cast iron block. Displacement: 410 cid. Bore and stroke: 4.05 x 3.98 inches. Compression ratio: 10.50:1. Brake hp: 330 at 4600 rpm. Carburetor: Ford C6MF-9510-E four-barrel.

S-55 BASE ENGINE: V-8: Overhead valves. Cast iron block. Displacement: 428 cid. Bore and stroke: 4.13 x 3.98 inches. Compression ratio: 10.50:1. Carburetor: Ford C6AF-9510-AD four-barrel.

STATION WAGON BASE ENGINE: Six: Overhead valves. Cast iron block. Displacement: 200 cid. Bore and stroke: 3.68 x 3.13 inches. Compression ratio: 9.20:1. Brake hp: 120 at 4400 rpm. Carburetor: Ford C3PF-9510-A one-barrel.

COMET & WAGON CHASSIS FEATURES: Wheelbase: (Passenger cars) 116 inches; (Station wagons) 113 inches. Overall length: (Passenger cars) 203 inches; (Station wagons) 199.9 inches. Tires: (Passenger cars) 6.95 x 14; (Station wagons) 7.75 x 14.

COMET & WAGON OPTIONS: Air conditioner ($257.50). Heavy-duty battery ($7.60). Elapsed-time clock ($20). Courtesy light group ($14.80). Remote-control trunk lid release ($11). Emergency flasher ($12.80). Tinted glass ($27.10). Tinted windshield ($18.10). Back-up lights ($10.70). Station wagon luggage rack ($64.35). Remote-control outside rearview mirror ($12). Curb molding ($16.10). Padded dash ($18.40). Padded visors ($4.50). Two-tone paint ($19.40). Power brakes ($43.20). Power steering ($86.30). Power tailgate window ($29.75). Push-button AM radio ($58.50). AM/FM radio ($129.30). Rally Pac, in Cyclone ($40); in other models ($83). Retractable front seat belts ($7.10). Caliente hardtop convertible front bucket seats with console ($131.30). Front bucket seats only in two-door sedan ($79.80). Size 6.95 x 14 whitewall tires. Tachometer ($43.10). Vacuum gauge ($20). Wheelcovers ($19.20). Wire Wheelcovers in Cyclone ($43.20); in other ($64.40). Windshield washer and wipers ($21.80). Vinyl roof on hardtops ($75.80). A three-speed manual transmission standard. Four-speed manual and Merc-O-Matic transmissions were optional. A 200 hp 289 cid V-8 (two-barrel); 265 hp 390 cid V-8 (two-barrel); 275 hp 390 cid V-8 (four-barrel) and a 335 hp 390 cid V-8 were offered. The last engine was standard with the GT option. It also included twin hood scoops; body strips; distinctive grille; special emblems; heavy-duty suspension; power booster fan, and dual exhaust. The Cyclone option was called GTA if ordered with an automatic transmission. A power transfer axle was also available.

1966 BIG STATION WAGON SERIES — Commuters were trimmed like Montclairs and shared the same standard features. The Colony Park had simulated wood panels and Deluxe wheelcovers. A power tailgate window was standard in the top-of-the-line station wagon.

STATION WAGONS

Model Number	Body/Style Number	Body Type & Seating	Factory Price	Shipping Weight	Production Total
NA	72	4-dr Comm-6P	3240	4280	6,847
NA	76	4-dr Col Prk-6P	3502	4332	18,894

1966 MERCURY OPTIONS: Air conditioner ($430). Bucket seats in Monterey hardtop and convertible. ($160.90) Reclining passenger side bucket seat in Park Lane ($45.10). Console and tachometer in Monterey ($88.80). Courtesy light group ($23.20). Remote-control trunk lid release ($11). Decor group in Monterey sedans ($34.80); in Monterey hardtop and Commuters ($21.90); in Monterey convertible ($14.20). Power door locks in two-doors ($37.30); in four-doors ($52.80). Speed actuated rear door locks ($25.80). Electric clock ($16.10). Tinted windshield ($3). Tinted glass ($43). Luggage rack ($64.40). Padded dash ($21.30. Padded visors ($5.80). Two-tone paint ($22). Power antenna ($29.60). Power brakes ($43.20). Four-Way power bucket seat driver's side ($92.10). Six-Way power seats ($96.50). Power windows ($106.20). Power vent windows ($52.80). Push-button AM radio ($61.10). AM/FM push-button radio with rear speaker ($148.60). Rear seat speaker ($19.30). Studiosonic rear speaker ($53.50). Third seat in station wagons ($75.80). Retractable front seat belts ($7.10). Sports package in Park Lane two-door hardtop and convertible ($423). Tilting steering wheel ($43.10). Whitewall tires ($40.56). All-vinyl Deluxe trim in Monterey hardtops and four-door sedans ($70.80). Leather trim in Park Lane bench seats ($98.80). Visibility group in Monterey ($30.80). Trip odometer ($8.90). Wheelcovers with spinners in Monterey ($38.40);

in Montclair and Park Lane ($19.20). Deluxe wheelcovers on Monterey ($19.20). Custom wheelcovers on Monterey ($54.10); on Montclair and Park Lane ($34.90). Wire wheelcovers on Monterey ($64.40); on Montclair and Park Lane ($45.20). Vinyl roof ($88.80). Windshield washer ($13.70). Cornering lights. A three-speed manual transmission standard in all but the S-55, which came with either a four-speed manual or Multi-Drive automatic transmission. These transmissions were both optional in the other series, except the four-speed was not available in station wagons. A 275 hp 390 cid V-8 (two-barrel); a 330 hp 410 cid V-8 (four-barrel) and a 345 hp 428 cid V-8 (four-barrel) were offered. A power transfer and a high performance axle were optional.

HISTORICAL FOOTNOTE: Most 1966 Comets, 72 percent had automatic transmissions. A V-8 engine was ordered in 63.7 percent of these cars. The millionth Comet built was a Caliente four-door sedan. The Cyclone GT was chosen as the official pace car at the 1966 Indianapolis 500 race.

1967 MERCURY

COMET 202 SERIES — Comet styling was close to that of the Ford Fairlane it was based on. The horizontal grille, with a vertical piece in the center, was framed by stacks of two headlights on each fender. The sides were clean, except for a '202' nameplate on the front fenders. The vertical taillights were on the ends of the rear fenders. About the only extras not optional on the '202' were a dome light and a cigarette lighter.

MERCURY I.D. NUMBERS: VIN on cowl extension tab below hood consists of 11 symbols. First symbol 7 = 1967. Second symbol indicates assembly plant: F = Dearborn, Mich. (Cougar); J = Los Angeles, Calif. (Comet); H = Lorain, Ohio (Comet); W = Wayne, Mich. (Mercury); and Z = St. Louis, Mo. (Mercury). Third and fourth symbols are Body Style Number in charts below. Fifth symbol identifies engine code. Last six symbols are sequential production number starting at 100001 at each plant. Body Number Plate on left front door lock face panel provides additional information on model year, assembly point, body type, engine, color, trim, axle and transmission.

COMET 202

Model Number	Body/Style Number	Body Type & Seating	Factory Price	Shipping Weight	Production Total
NA	01	2-dr Sed-6P	2284	2787	14,251
NA	02	4-dr Sed-6P	2336	2825	10,281

CAPRI SERIES — The Capri had nearly full-length, mid-bodyside moldings and nameplates on the rear quarter panel. Vinyl and fabric or all-vinyl upholstery, deep-loop carpeting and rear armrests were among standard features.

CAPRI

Model Number	Body/Style Number	Body Type & Seating	Factory Price	Shipping Weight	Production Total
NA	06	4-dr Sed-6P	2436	2860	9,292
NA	07	2-dr HT Cpe-6P	2459	2889	11,671

CALIENTE SERIES — Bright fender ornaments, rocker panel and wheel openings moldings and full-length upper-body pinstripes set the Caliente apart from other Comets. Its interior featured woodgrained dash and door panels, luxury armrests and paddle-type door handles.

CALIENTE SERIES

Model Number	Body/Style Number	Body Type & Seating	Factory Price	Shipping Weight	Production Total
NA	10	4-dr Sed-6P	2535	2871	9,153
NA	11	2-dr HT Cpe-6P	2558	2901	9,966
NA	12	3-dr Conv-6p	2818	3170	1,539

CYCLONE SERIES — The Cyclone looked about the same as the Caliente, less the fender ornaments. Its grille had fewer horizontal pieces. The rear deck panel was blacked-out and the word Cyclone was spelled out on it. Bucket seats and all-vinyl upholstery were standard.

CYCLONE SERIES

Model Number	Body/Style Number	Body Type & Seating	Factory Price	Shipping Weight	Production Total
NA	15	2-dr HT Cpe-5P	2737	3075	6,101
NA	16	2-dr Conv-5P	2997	2229	809

COMET STATION WAGON SERIES — The Voyager wagon had a distinctive elongated U-shaped chrome piece on its front fenders. The Villager featured woodgrained side and tailgate panels. It came with crinkle vinyl trim and a dual-action tailgate.

Model Number	Body/Style Number	Body Type & Seating	Factory Price	Shipping Weight	Production Total
NA	03	4-dr Voy Wag-6P	2604	3230	4930
NA	08	4-dr Vill Wag-6P	2841	3252	3140

1967 Mercury Cougar two-door hardtop sport coupe, V-8

COUGAR SERIES — The new Cougar was basically a dressed-up Mustang. It featured disappearing headlights, wraparound front and rear fenders and triple taillights (with sequential turn signals). The front and rear end styling were similar. Cougars came equipped with all-vinyl bucket seats, three-spoke 'sports-style' steering wheel, deep-loop carpeting, Deluxe seat belts and floor-mounted three-speed manual transmission.

COUGAR

Model Number	Body/Style Number	Body Type & Seating	Factory Price	Shipping Weight	Production Total
NA	91	2-dr HT Cpe-5P	2851	3005	123,672

COUGAR XR-7 SERIES — The XR-7 was introduced in mid-model year. Except for a medallion on the roof's quarter panel, it looked like the standard Cougar, but it came with a woodgrained dashboard insert and fancier interior.

COUGAR XR-7

Model Number	Body/Style Number	Body Type & Seating	Factory Price	Shipping Weight	Production Total
NA	93	2-dr HT Cpe-5P	3081	3015	27,221

MONTEREY SERIES — The center section of the horizontal bar grille protruded slightly and the signal lights were now located in the front bumpers. Wheelwell openings had chrome moldings. The only additional side trim on the Monterey was a front fender criss-cross pattern trim piece and the Monterey name on the rear fenders. A fabric and vinyl interior was standard, except in the convertible, which had all-vinyl upholstery. An S-55 sports package was optional on the Monterey convertible and two-door hardtop.

MONTEREY

Model Number	Body/Style Number	Body Type & Seating	Factory Price	Shipping Weight	Production Total
NA	44	4-dr Sed-6P	2904	3798	15,177
NA	44	4-dr Brzwy-6P	2904	3847	5910
NA	45	2-dr Conv-6P	3311	3943	2673
NA	47	2-dr HT Cpe-6P	2985	3820	16,910
NA	48	4-dr HT Sed-6P	3059	3858	8013

NOTE 1: The Breezeway sedan had a slanting and retractable rear window.

MONTCLAIR SERIES — The Montclair had full-length upper body moldings. A nameplate was located on the rear fenders. Standard features included Deluxe wheelcovers, electric clock, Deluxe steering wheel and Deluxe front and rear seat belts with reminder light. Regular equipment was listed as: carpeting; padded dash and visors; two-speed windshield wipers; windshield washers; emergency flasher; courtesy light group; and remote-control outside rearview mirror. These same features were also found in Monterey models for 1967.

MONTCLAIR

Model Number	Body/Style Number	Body Type & Seating	Factory Price	Shipping Weight	Production Total
NA	54	4-dr Sed-6P	3187	3863	5783
NA	54	4-dr Brzwy-6P	3187	3881	4151
NA	57	2-dr HT Cpe-6P	3244	3848	4118
NA	58	4-dr HT Sed-6P	3316	3943	5870

NOTE 1: The Breezeway sedan had a slanting and retractable rear window.

PARK LANE SERIES — Full-length tire level moldings, wheelwell chrome trim and front fender emblems were styling features of the Park Lane. Standard equipment included an automatic parking brake release, rear seat armrests, vanity mirror, spare tire cover and power front disc brakes.

PARK LANE

Model Number	Body/Style Number	Body Type & Seating	Factory Price	Shipping Weight	Production Total
NA	64	4-dr Brzwy-6P	3736	4011	4163
NA	65	2-dr Conv-6P	3984	4114	1191
NA	67	2-dr HT Cpe-6P	3752	3947	2196
NA	68	4-dr HT Sed-6P	3826	3992	5412

NOTE 1: The Breezeway sedan had a slanting and retractable rear window.

BROUGHAM SERIES — Broughams were basically similar to the Park Lane models, which they resembled, but were slight fancier. Extra body insulation, unique interior and exterior ornamentation and woodgrain steering wheel and trim were standard features.

BROUGHAM

Model Number	Body/Style Number	Body Type & Seating	Factory Price	Shipping Weight	Production Total
NA	61	4-dr Brzwy-6P	3896	3980	3325
NA	62	4-dr HT Sed-6P	3986	4000	4189

NOTE 1: The Breezeway sedan had a slanting and retractable rear window.

MARQUIS SERIES — Two noticeable features of the new Marquis two-door hardtop were a vinyl roof and five, full-length, lower body pinstripes. Power front disc brakes; woodgrain interior trim; Deluxe body insulation; electric clock; courtesy light group; spare tire cover; and plush, fabric and vinyl upholstery were among the many standard items in the Marquis. The front seats had individual fold-down armrests.

MARQUIS

Model Number	Body/Style Number	Body Type & Seating	Factory Price	Shipping Weight	Production Total
NA	69	2-dr HT Cpe-6P	3989	3995	6510

STATION WAGONS SERIES — The Commuter station wagon had full-length upper body moldings. The Colony Park had woodgrain panels outlined by chrome trim. Both wagons had a heater and defroster and dual-action tailgate. In addition, the Colony Park came with an electric clock; Deluxe wheelcovers; Deluxe steering wheel; power rear tailgate window; power front disc brakes; and all-vinyl or parchment Mosaic fabric interiors.

STATION WAGONS

Model Number	Body/Style Number	Body Type & Seating	Factory Price	Shipping Weight	Production Total
NA	72	4-dr Col Pk Wag	3289	4178	7898
NA	76	4-dr Col Pk Wag-6	3657	4258	18,680

1967 Mercury, Comet Cyclone 'GT' two-door hardtop coupe, V-8

MERCURY BASE ENGINES

(COMET/CAPRI 202/COMET WAGON) SIX: Overhead valves. Cast iron block. Displacement: 200 cid. Bore and stroke: 3.68 x 3.13 inches. Compression ratio: 9.20:1. Brake hp: 120 at 4400 rpm. Seven main bearings. Carburetor: Autolite C7DF-9510-Z one-barrel. (Engine Code T)

(CYCLONE/COUGAR/XR-7) V-8: Overhead valves. Cast iron block. Displacement: 289 cid. Bore and stroke: 4 x 2.87 inches. Compression ratio: 9.30:1. Brake hp: 200 at 4400 rpm. Five main bearings. Carburetor: Autolite C7DF-9510-Z two-barrel. (Code C)

(MONTEREY/MONTCLAIR/WAGON) V-8: Overhead valves. Cast iron block. Displacement: 390 cid. Bore and stroke: 4.05 x 3.78 inches. Compression ratio: 10.50:1. Brake hp: 270 at 4400 rpm. Five main bearings. Carburetor: Holley C70F-9510-A four-barrel. (Engine Code H)

(PARK LANE/BROUGHAM/MARQUIS) V-8: Overhead valves. Cast iron block. Displacement: 410 cid. Bore and stroke: 4.05 x 3.98 inches. Compression ratio: 10.50:1. Brakes hp: 330 at 4600 rpm. Carburetor: C7AF-9510-AE four-barrel.

1967 Mercury, Marquis two-door hardtop sports coupe, V-8 (Engine Code M)

CHASSIS FEATURES: Wheelbase: (passenger cars) 116 inches; (station wagons) 113 inches. Overall Length: (four-doors and convertibles) 203.5; (two-doors) 196 inches; (station wagons) 199.9 inches. Tires: (passenger cars) 7.35 x 14; (station wagons and Cyclone GT) 7.75 x 14.

COUGAR CHASSIS FEATURES: Wheelbase: 111 inches. Overall length: 190 inches. Tires: 7.35 x 14.

MERCURY CHASSIS FEATURES: Wheelbase: (passenger cars) 123 inches; (station wagons) 119 inches. Overall length: (passenger cars) 218.5 inches; (station wagons) 213.5 inches. Tires: (passenger cars) 8.15 x 15; (station wagons) 8.45 x 15.

COMET OPTIONS: Air conditioning ($355.95). Heavy-duty battery ($7.44). Bright window frames ($17.70). Electric clock ($15.76). Remote-control deck lid release ($12.65). Tinted glass ($28.50). Tinted windshield ($19.50). Luggage rack on station wagons ($66.99). Right-hand side view mirror ($6.95). Outside rearview mirror with remote-control ($9.60). Curb molding ($15.76). Oxford roof ($84.25). Two-tone paint ($27.06). Power brakes ($42.29). Power disc brakes ($84.25). Four-Way power bench seat ($62.45). Power steering ($95). Power windows ($100.10). AM radio with antenna ($60.05). AM/FM radio with antenna ($133.65). Rear seat speaker ($15.60). Deluxe seat belts, front and rear with warning light ($10.40). Station wagon third seat with two belts ($51.31). Shoulder belts ($27.06). Stereo-sonic tape system ($128.50). Dual-action station wagon tailgate ($45.40). Tachometer ($47.30). Vinyl interior for Comet 202 models ($27.47). Wire wheelcovers ($69.52). Styled steel wheels ($115.15). Interval selector windshield wipers ($11.59). Courtesy light group ($19.69). Wide oval, whitewall nylon tires ($82.94). A three-speed manual transmission was standard. Four-speed manual and Merc-0-Matic automatic transmissions were optional. A 200 hp 289 cid V-8 (two-barrel); 270 hp 390 cid V-8 (two-barrel) and a 320 hp 390 cid V-8 (four-barrel) were available. The last engine was standard in the Cyclone GT performance package, which also included dual exhausts; racing stripes; wide oval nylon whitewall tires; heavy-duty suspension; 3.25:1 axle ratio; power booster fan; twin hood scoops and power disc brakes. A performance handling package was offered on cars equipped with the 270 hp 390 cid V-8. It featured, higher rate front and rear springs, large diameter stabilizer bar and heavy-duty shocks. Buyers could also order a high-performance or power transfer axle.

COUGAR OPTIONS: Air conditioner ($355.95). Heavy-duty battery ($7.44). Rear bumper guards ($12.95). Electric clock ($15.76). Courtesy light group ($16.85). Door edge guards ($4.40). Tinted glass ($30.25). Tinted windshield ($21.09). Deck lid luggage carrier ($32.45). Oxford roof ($84.25). Two-tone paint ($27.06). Power brakes ($42.29). Power disc brakes ($84.25). Power steering ($95). AM radio ($60.05). AM/FM radio ($133.65). AM radio with Stereo-Sonic tape system ($188.50). Front bench seat with center armrest ($24.42). Shoulder belts ($27.06). Speed control ($71.30). Sports console ($57). Tilting steering wheel ($60.05). Comfort-weave vinyl interior ($33.05). Deluxe wheelcovers ($18.79). Wire wheelcovers ($69.51). Visual check panel ($39.50). Styled steel wheels ($115.15). A three-speed manual transmission was standard, except in the XR-7, which came with a four-speed manual gearbox. The four-speed was optional in the standard Cougar. Merc-0-Matic SelectShift

automatic transmission was optional in both series. A 225 hp 289 cid V-8 (four-barrel) and a 320 hp 390 cid V-8 (four-barrel) were available. The GT performance package included: 390 cid V-8; performance handling package; wide-oval whitewall tires; low back pressure exhausts; power disc brakes and medallions. A power transfer axle was available.

MERCURY OPTIONS: Air conditioner ($421.28). Heavy-duty battery ($7.44). Deck lid release with remote control for all passenger cars ($12.65). Door edge guards, in two-doors ($4.40); in four-doors ($6.66). Dual exhausts ($31.52). Electric clock ($15.76). Tinted glass ($42.09). Tinted windshield ($27.41). Automatic headlight dimmer ($41.60). Cornering lights ($33.28). Luggage rack ($62.99). Right-hand side view mirror ($6.95). Remote-control mirror ($9.60). Curb molding ($15.81). Oxford roof, on two-door hardtops ($88.99); on four-door hardtops and sedans ($99.47); on station wagons ($131.65). Two-tone paint ($27.06). Power antenna. ($28.97). Power brakes ($42.29). Power door locks. in two-doors ($44.23); in four-doors ($67.62). Power rear windows ($31.62). Six-Way power seats: bucket type ($84.25); bench type ($94.45). Power seat for S-55: bucket type ($168.40); lounge type ($84.25); driver and passenger ($168.40). Power steering ($103.95). Power vent windows ($51.68). Power windows ($103.95). AM push-button radio ($62.15). AM/FM push-button radio ($150.84). AM radio with stereo tape system ($190.65). Deluxe front and rear seat belts ($10.40). Monterey and Commuter shoulder belts ($27.06). Spare tire cover ($3.90). Speed control ($90.74). Tilting steering wheel ($42.19). Station wagon third seat ($95.36). Deluxe interior trim, in Commuter ($69.30); in Colony Park ($77.80). Leather with vinyl trim, in Park Lane and Marquis hardtops ($109.45). Mondero all-vinyl trim in Monterey ($69.30). Visual safety-check panel ($31.42). Deluxe wheelcovers on Monterey and Commuter ($18.79). Wheelcovers with spinners, in Monterey ($18.79); in Commuter ($37.59). Wire wheelcovers, on Monterey ($69.50); on others ($50.75). A three-speed manual transmission was standard in all, but the Park Lane and Brougham. These came with four-speed manual or Merc-O-Matic SelectShift transmission. Both of these gearboxes were optional in the other series. The four-speed was not available in station wagons. A 330 hp 410 cid V-8 (four-barrel); 345 hp 427 cid V-8 (four-barrel) and a 360 hp 428 cid V-8 (four-barrel) were optional. The 345 hp engine was standard in the S-55 performance package, which also included dual exhausts; engine dress-up kit; heavy-duty battery; power disc brakes; Deluxe wheelcovers with.spinners; deck lid applique; side paint stripe; door trim panels; bucket seats; sports console; Deluxe steering wheel; Deluxe sound package; and S-55 ornamentation. High-performance and power transfer axles were available.

HISTORICAL FOOTNOTES: Three of the most popular Comet options (and their attachment rates) were automatic transmission (82.4 percent), V-8 engine (67.4 percent) and power steering (49.6 percent). A total of 3,419 Cyclone hardtops and 378 convertibles were sold with the GT performance package. Only 7,412 Cougars came with the optional front bench seat. Just 5.3 percent were equipped with a four-speed manual transmission. The most popular options in full-size 1967 Mercurys included: automatic transmission (98.2 percent) power steering (97 percent) tinted glass (69.7 percent) and power brakes (65.6 percent).

1968 MERCURY

COMET SERIES — The new Comet was restyled for 1968. It looked like a full-size Mercury that had gone on a diet. The Comet had a horizontal grille, rocker panel molding, side marker lights and chrome-encased, vertical taillights. Among the standard features were an energy-absorbing steering column and steering wheel; front and rear seat belts; shoulder belts; padded dash; padded sun visors; dual brakes with warning light; and two-speed windshield wipers and washers.

MERCURY I.D. NUMBERS: VIN on tag on top right-hand side of instrument panel, visible through windshield. VIN consists of 11 symbols. First symbol 8 = 1968. Second symbol indicates assembly plant: F = Dearborn, Mich. (Cougar); J = San Jose, Calif. (Cougar); H = Lorain, Ohio (Montego/Comet); and Z = St. Louis, Mo. (Mercury). Third and fourth symbols are Body Style Number in charts below. Fifth symbol identifies engine code. Last six symbols are sequential production number starting at 100001 at each plant. Body Number Plate on left front door lock face panel provides additional information on model year, assembly point, body type, engine, color, trim, axle and transmission.

COMET

Model Number	Body/Style Number	Body Type & Seating	Factory Price	Shipping Weight	Production Total
NA	01	2-dr HT Cpe-6P	2477	3078	16,693

1968 Mercury, Montego MX two-door hardtop sports coupe, V-8

MONTEGO SERIES — The Montego looked about the same as the Comet. It had the same standard features as well, plus curb moldings, cigar lighter and glovebox lock.

MONTEGO

Model Number	Body/Style Number	Body Type & Seating	Factory Price	Shipping Weight	Production Total
NA	06	4-dr Sed-6P	2504	2982	18,492
NA	07	2-dr HT Cpe-6P	2552	3057	15,002

MONTEGO MX SERIES — Full-length upper and lower body trim, chrome wheelwell trim and a vinyl top were styling features of the Montego MX. It also had bright metal upper door frames, simulated wood inserts in the lower body molding, woodgrain door trim panels inserts and carpeting.

MONTEGO MX

Model Number	Body/Style Number	Body Type & Seating	Factory Price	Shipping Weight	Production Total
NA	08	4-dr Sta Wag-6P	2876	3379	9,328
NA	10	4-dr Sed-6P	2657	3007	15,264
NA	11	2-dr HT Cpe-6P	2675	3081	25,827
NA	12	2-dr Conv-6P	2935	3293	3,248

CYCLONE SERIES — Cyclones had a mid-tire level body tape stripe. Those with the GT option had an upper body level racing stripe; bucket seats; wide tread whitewalls; special wheelcovers; all-vinyl interior; and special handling package.

CYCLONE

Model Number	Body/Style Number	Body Type & Seating	Factory Price	Shipping Weight	Production Total
NA	15	2-dr Fsbk Cpe-6P	2768	3254	12,260
NA	17	2-dr HT Cpe-6P	2768	3208	1,368

1968 Mercury, Cougar XR-7 two-door hardtop coupe (GT-E), V-8

COUGAR SERIES — If you liked the 1967 Cougar, you probably liked the 1968. The biggest change was the addition of side marker lights. Standard equipment included: dual hydraulic brake system with warning light; front and rear seat belts; outside rearview mirror; padded dash; padded sun visors; two-speed windshield wipers and washers; four-way emergency flasher; and back-up lights.

COUGAR

Model Number	Body/Style Number	Body Type & Seating	Factory Price	Shipping Weight	Production Total
NA	91	2-dr HT Cpe-5P	2933	3094	81,014

XR-7 SERIES — Rocker panel moldings, special wheelcovers, deck lid medallions and XR-7 plaques on the rear roof pillars set the top-of-the-line Cougar apart from the basic series. Standard equipment included: an overhead console (with map and warning lights); deep loop carpeting; tachometer; trip odometer; gauges; leather-trimmed vinyl seats; and walnut tone instrument-panel.

XR-7

Model Number	Body/Style Number	Body Type & Seating	Factory Price	Shipping Weight	Production Total
NA	93	2-dr HT Cpe-5P	3232	3134	32,712

MONTEREY SERIES — The Monterey had a new, equal-size horizontal bar grille which protruded at the center. The vertical signal lights wrapped around the front fenders. Rear end treatment resembled last year's. As before, the back window on cars with the Breezeway option could be lowered. Standard features included; dual brakes with warning light; energy-absorbing steering column and steering wheel; seat belts; padded dash; padded sun visors; outside rearview mirror; side marker lights; heater/defroster; ashtray light; trunk light; four-way emergency flasher; glovebox light; and shoulder belts.

MONTEREY

Model Number	Body/Style Number	Body Type & Seating	Factory Price	Shipping Weight	Production Total
NA	44	4-dr Sed-6P	3052	3798	30,727
NA	45	2-dr Conv-6P	3436	4114	1,515
NA	47	2-dr HT Cpe-6P	3133	3820	15,145
NA	48	4-dr HT Sed-6P	3207	3858	8,927

MONTCLAIR SERIES — Deluxe wheelcovers and full-length, tire level moldings were two exterior differences between the Montclair and the lower-priced Monterey. An electric clock was among the many standard features.

MONTCLAIR

Model Number	Body/Style Number	Body Type & Seating	Factory Price	Shipping Weight	Production Total
NA	54	4-dr Sed-6P	3331	3863	7,255
NA	57	2-dr HT Cpe-6P	3387	3848	3,497
NA	58	4-dr HT Sed-6P	3459	3943	4,008

PARK LANE SERIES — The Park Lane had full-length, tire level moldings that looked like two thin parallel strips with a narrow band of chrome between them. The wheelwell lips were also chromed and there were three slanted trim pieces on the roof quarter panels. Like all full-size Mercurys for 1968, the Park Lane had a redesigned, clustered dash (i.e. dash instruments were placed in close proximity to the driver). The electrical system was improved as well. A seldom-ordered Park Lane option was 'yacht paneling,' a fancy name for exterior woodgrained appliques on passenger cars.

PARK LANE

Model Number	Body/Style Number	Body Type & Seating	Factory Price	Shipping Weight	Production Total
NA	64	4-dr Sed-6P	3552	4011	7,008
NA	65	2-dr Conv-6P	3822	4114	1,112
NA	67	2-dr HT Cpe-6P	3575	3947	2,584
NA	68	4-dr HT Sed-6P	3647	3992	10,390

MARQUIS SERIES — The Marquis was trimmed similar to the Montclair, except it came with a vinyl-covered roof. Its interior was also plusher.

MARQUIS

Model Number	Body/Style Number	Body Type & Seating	Factory Price	Shipping Weight	Production Total
NA	69	2-dr HT Cpe-6P	3685	3995	3,965

1968 Mercury, Colony Park four-door station wagon, V-8

STATION WAGON SERIES — Both station wagons had full-length, tire level moldings and chrome trimmed wheel openings. The Colony Park had plank style woodgrain applique on its sides. A dual-action tailgate was standard on both.

STATION WAGONS

Model Number	Body/Style Number	Body Type & Seating	Factory Price	Shipping Weight	Production Total
NA	72	4-dr Comm Wag-6P	3441	4178	8,688
NA	76	4-dr Col Prk Wag-6P	3760	4258	21,179

NOTE 1: A total of 5,191 Commuter and 15,505 Colony Park wagons came with either a rear facing or dual-center facing rear seats.

MERCURY BASE ENGINES

(COMET/MONTEGO/MONTEGO MX) SIX: Overhead valves. Cast iron block. Displacement: 200 cid. Bore and stroke: 3.68 x 3.13 inches. Compression ratio: 8.80:1. Brake hp: 115 at 3800 rpm. Seven main bearings. Carburetor: Autolite C80F-9510-E one-barrel. (Engine Code T)

(CYCLONE/COUGAR/COUGAR XR-7) V-8: Overhead valves. Cast iron block. Displacement: 302 cid. Bore and stroke: 4 x 3 inches. Compression ratio: 9.0:1. Brake hp: 210 at 4600 rpm. Carburetor: Autolite C8AF-9510-AF two-barrel. (Engine Code F; Released Jan. 1968)

(MONTEREY/MONTCLAIR/MERCURY WAGON) V-8: Overhead valves. Cast iron block. Displacement: 390 cid. Bore and stroke: 4.05 x 3.78 inches. Compression ratio: 9.50:1. Brake hp: 265 at 4400 rpm. Carburetor: Autolite C8AF-9510-M two-barrel. (Engine Code Y)

(PARK LANE/MARQUIS) V-8: Overhead valves. Cast iron block. Displacement: 390 cid. Bore and stroke: 4.05 x 3.78 inches. Compression ratio: 10.50:1. Brake hp: 315 at 4600 rpm. Carburetors: Autolite C8AF-9510-B four-barrel. (Engine Code Z)

1968 Mercury, Cyclone GT two-door hardtop sports coupe, V-8

COMET/MONTEGO CHASSIS FEATURES: Wheelbase: (Passenger cars) 116 inches; (Station wagons) 113 inches. Overall length: (Cyclone fastback) 206.1 inches; (others) 206 inches. Tires: 7.74 x 14.

COUGAR CHASSIS FEATURES: Wheelbase: 111 inches. Overall length: 190.3 inches. Tires: E70 x 14.

MERCURY CHASSIS FEATURES: Wheelbase: (Passenger cars) 123 inches; (Station wagons) 119 inches. Overall length: (Passenger cars) 220.1 inches; (Station wagons) 215.4 inches. Tires: 8.15 x 15.

COMET/MONTEGO OPTIONS: Brougham interior option includes: exterior 'C' pillar ornament, unique seat and door trim, Brougham script on instrument panel and Deluxe steering wheel for Montego MX four-door sedan and two-door hardtop ($77.80). Appearance protection group, includes: vinyl twin front and rear floor mats, door edge guards and license plate frames, for two-doors, ($25.28); for four-doors ($29.17). Appearance special equipment group, includes Deluxe wheelcovers; whitewall tires; courtesy light group; Comfort Stream ventilation ($64.85). Decor group includes: wheel lip moldings; right upper door frames for four-door only; unique lower back panel applique; Deluxe wheelcovers for hardtop only, for hardtop with special appearance equipment group ($42.11); for hardtop without ($60.95); for sedan ($54.45). Light group, includes: two instrument panel lights; glovebox light; ashtray light; luggage compartment light; cargo light on wagons; rear door jam switches for four-door models ($19.50). Heavy-duty battery ($7.44). Deluxe seat belts and seat belt reminder light includes: Deluxe front seat shoulder belts Deluxe buckle and color-keyed webbing with black webbing on convertible ($29.61). Front seat shoulder belts includes regular buckle and black webbing; rear seat shoulder belts with regular buckle and black webbing; power disc front brakes, electric clock sports console ($50). Rear window defogger ($21.25). Tinted glass ($35.05). Tinted windshield ($21.09). Pair of adjustable head rests ($42.75). Luggage carrier for station wagons only ($62.99). Remote control left-hand mirror ($9.60). Two-tone paint ($30.96). AM radio with antenna ($61.40). AM/FM radio stereo with antenna ($184.95). Reflective tape stripe ($16.85). Oxford roof on two-door hardtop ($94.55); on four-door sedan ($94.55). Bucket seats ($110.15). Third, rear-facing seat in station wagons only ($51.31). Four-Way power bench seat ($62.45). Four-Way power bucket seats ($62.45). Dual rear seat speakers ($26). Power steering ($95). Deluxe steering wheels ($13.90). Tachometer ($48). Dual-action tailgate for station wagons only ($45.40). Comfort weave vinyl bench seat ($24.47). Ventilation system ($15.60). Visual check group, includes: low fuel, parking brake and door ajar warning lights ($32.45). Deluxe wheelcovers ($21.29). Deluxe wheelcovers with spinners ($20.10). Wheelcovers ($41.40). Wire wheelcovers with GT group or HT group ($50.75); without ($72.05). Styled steel wheels with GT or HT group ($96.36); without ($117.65). Power rear windows for station wagons ($31.62). Power side windows ($100.10). Two-speed interval selector windshield wipers ($14.19). Heavy-duty three-speed, four-speed manual and Merc-0-Matic SelectShift automatic transmissions were optional. The heavy-duty three-speed transmission was only available with the 335 hp 390 cid V-8. The four-speed manual transmission was not available with the six or 427 cid V-8. A 210 hp 302 cid V-8 (two-barrel); 230 hp 302 cid V-8 (four-barrel); 265 hp 390 cid V-8 (two-barrel); 335 hp 390 cid V-8 (four-barrel); 335 hp 428 cid V-8 (four-barrel); and a 390 hp 427 cid V-8 (four-barrel) were optional. The latter two engines were offered only in hardtops. The 335 hp 390 cid V-8 was not available in station wagons. High-performance and power transfer axles were optional. A special handling package was offered on V-8 powered two-door hardtops and convertibles. It included: higher rate front and rear springs, a large diameter stabilizing bar and heavy-duty shocks.

COUGAR OPTIONS: Air conditioner ($360.90). Heavy-duty battery ($7.44). Deluxe seat belt with reminder light ($13.05). Deluxe front seat shoulder belts ($29.61). Deluxe rear seat shoulder belts ($29.61). Front seat shoulder belts ($27.06). Power disc brakes ($64.85). Electric clock ($15.76). Sports console ($57). Sports console for XR-7 only ($72.55). Rear window defogger ($21.25). Tinted glass ($30.25). Tinted windshield ($21.09). Door edge guards ($4.40). Rear bumper guards ($12.95). Adjustable front seat headrests ($42.75). Remote control left-hand mirror ($9.60). Visual check panel ($39.50). Two-tone paint ($31.10). AM radio with antenna ($60.90). AM/FM stereo ($21.25). Oxford roof ($41.60). Speed control ($71.30). Power steering ($95). Tilt-away steering wheel ($66.05). Stereo-sonic tape system ($195.15). Three-speed manual transmission ($79). Four-speed manual transmission ($184.02). Four-speed manual transmission with GT group ($105.02). Merc-O-Matic transmission with "302" engine ($206.65). Merc-O-Matic transmission with "390" engine ($226.10). Merc-O-Matic transmission with GT group ($147.10). Deluxe wheelcovers ($21.29). Deluxe wheelcovers with spinners on XR-7 ($18.79). Deluxe wheelcovers, except on XR-7 ($72.05). Styled steel wheels on XR-7 ($96.36). Styled steel wheels (117.65). Blackwall tubeless tires ($36.35). Whitewall tubeless tires ($36.35-$73.40). Red band tubeless tires ($38.95). Space-Saver spare tires ($6.55-$19.50). Heavy-duty three-speed, four-speed manual, and Select-Shift Merc-0-Matic automatic transmissions were optional. The heavy-duty three-speed gearbox was only available with the 325 hp engine. The four-speed manual was not available with the 280 or 390 hp V-8s. A 230 hp 302 cid V-8 (four-barrel); 280 hp 390 cid V-8 (two-barrel); 325 hp 390 cid V-8 (four-barrel); and a 335 hp 428 cid V-8 (four-barrel) were optional. The 325 hp engine was standard with the GT option. This package also included; stiffer front and rear springs, heavy-duty shocks, low back pressure dual exhausts, power booster fan and a large diameter stabilizer bar. The 428 cid V-8 was standard in the 7.0 Litre GT-E package. It featured: twin hood scoops; styled steel wheels; quadruple trumpet exhausts; modified grille and taillight design; silver grey trim on the lower body; extra stiff front and rear springs; heavy-duty shocks; and wide-thread radial-ply tires.

MERCURY OPTIONS: Appearance and protection group, includes: door edge guards, license plate frames, vinyl twin front and rear floor mats, in two-doors ($25.30); in four-doors ($29.15). Brougham option, includes: exterior Brougham script on 'C' pillar; Brougham script on glovebox; unique door trim panels; dual upper body paint stripes; twin comfort lounge seats; luxury level seat trim; in Park Lane four-door models with Oxford roof ($272.05); without Oxford roof ($172.58). Decor group, for Monterey and Commuter sedans, includes: color-keyed interior rear window moldings on vehicles without Breezeway; Deluxe steering wheel; and rear door courtesy switch ($21.49). Decor group for four-door hardtop and Commuter, includes: bright drip moldings, Deluxe steering wheel, rear-door courtesy switch ($21.49). Decor group for two-door hardtop and convertibles includes: Deluxe steering wheel ($13.90). Whisperaire air conditioner ($421.28). Power antenna ($28.97). Heavy-duty battery ($7.44). Deluxe seat belts and seat belt reminder light, includes Deluxe buckle on all six belts and color-keyed webbing ($13.05). Shoulder belts, includes regular buckle and black webbing, front seat ($27.06); back seat ($27.06). Deluxe shoulder belts, includes Deluxe buckle and color-keyed webbing, front seat ($29.61); back seat ($29.61). Power disc brakes ($71.30). Electric clock ($15.76). Spare tire cover ($5.25). Tinted glass ($42.75). Tinted windshield ($27.41). Adjustable front seat head rests ($42.75). Power door locks for two-doors ($45.40); for four-doors ($68.65). Luggage carrier for wagons only ($62.99). Manual right-hand side view mirror ($6.95). Remote control left-hand mirror ($9.60). Protective bodyside moldings ($45.40). Two-tone paint ($30.96). Visual-Check panel includes door-ajar warning light, seat belt reminder light, low-fuel reminder light and parking brake warning light ($32.45). AM radio with antenna ($63.40). AM/FM radio stereo with antenna (189.34). Remote control deck lid release ($14). Oxford roof for two-door ($99.47); for four-door ($99.47); for station wagons ($131.65). Rear-facing third seat in wagons ($128.11). Dual center-facing seat in wagons ($95.36). Six-Way power seat, bench ($94.80); driver's seat ($84.25); driver's and passenger's side ($168.40). Twin comfort lounge seats ($77.80). Dual rear seat speakers ($25.90). Speed control ($90.74). Power steering ($115.65). Tilt steering wheel ($42.75). Stereo-sonic tape system/AM radio combination ($197.25). Trim includes: door panels, seat trim and front seat courtesy lights in Colony Park with Deluxe interior ($84.25); in Monterey with Deluxe cloth-and-vinyl ($84.25). Breezeway ventilation for sedans ($58.35). Comfort Stream and heating system ventilation ($40.10). Deluxe wheelcovers ($21.29). Deluxe wheelcovers with medallion for Monterey and Commuter ($40.14); others ($18.79). Wire wheelcovers for Monterey and Commuter ($72.05); others ($50.75). Power rear window for Commuter and Colony Park ($31.62). Power side windows ($103.95). Power vent windows ($52.98). Two-speed interval selector windshield wipers ($14.19). A three-speed manual transmission was standard, except in the Park Lane and Marquis. Parklane/Marquis came with SelectShift Merc-0-Matic transmission. This automatic was optional in the other series. A 280 hp 390 cid V-8 (two-barrel); 315 hp 390 cid V-8 (four-barrel); 335 hp 390 cid V-8 (four-barrel); 340 hp 428 cid V-8 (four-barrel); and 360 hp 428 cid V-8 (four-barrel) were optional. High-performance and power transfer axles were available.

HISTORICAL FOOTNOTES: Mercury built a total of 6,105 Cyclone fastbacks and 334 two-door Cyclone hardtops with the Cyclone GT option. Mercurys won seven NASCAR Grand National races in 1968. Only 2.7 percent of all 1968 Cougars were equipped with a four-speed manual gearbox, 86.8 percent had an automatic transmission 87.3 percent power steering

and 38.6 percent power brakes. An XR-7 'G' was available on special order. It had hood pins, hood scoop, running lights and a vinyl top with sun roof. The vast majority of 1968 full-size Mercurys, 99.6 percent were equipped with automatic transmission, 99.2 percent had power steering, 42.5 percent had a tilting steering wheel, 59.5 percent had air conditioning and 32.8 percent had power windows.

1969 MERCURY

COMET SERIES — The new Comet had a framed horizontal bar grille. It protruded slightly in the center section, where a Comet emblem was housed. The side marker lights were now at bumper level. Teakwood-toned appliques were used on the instrument panel. The upholstery was cloth and vinyl.

MERCURY I.D. NUMBERS: VIN on metal tag affixed to left-hand top of dash and viewable through windshield. VIN consists of 11 symbols. First symbol 9 = 1969. Second symbol indicates assembly plant: F = Dearborn, Mich. (Cougar); H = Lorain, Ohio (Montego); R = San Jose, Calif. (Cougar); and Z = St. Louis, Mo. (Mercury). Third and fourth symbols are Body Style Number in charts below. Fifth symbol identifies engine code. Last six symbols are sequential production number starting at 100001 at each plant. Body Number Plate on left front door lock face panel provides additional information on model year, assembly point, body type, engine, color, trim, axle and transmission.

COMET

Model Number	Body/Style Number	Body Type & Seating	Factory Price	Shipping Weight	Production Total
NA	01	2-dr HT Cpe-6P	2515	3087	14,104

MONTEGO SERIES — Montegos had moldings above the rocker panels and trunk lid. There were fender-to-fender upper body twin pinstripes. Carpeting and cloth and vinyl, or all-vinyl upholstery were standard.

MONTEGO

Model Number	Body/Style Number	Body Type & Seating	Factory Price	Shipping Weight	Production Total
NA	06	4-dr Sed-6P	2538	3060	21,950
NA	07	2-dr HT Cpe-6P	2588	3074	17,785

MONTEGO MX SERIES — Full-length lower body moldings, chromed wheel lip openings, fender-to-fender upper-body chrome trim, trunk lid appliques and wood-tone appliques on the lower dash panel were features of the Montego MX. The convertible had all-vinyl interior and a power top with glass rear window.

MONTEGO MX

Model Number	Body/Style Number	Body Type & Seating	Factory Price	Shipping Weight	Production Total
NA	08	4-dr Sta Wag-6P	2962	3458	10,590
NA	10	4-dr Sed-6P	2701	3094	17,738
NA	11	2-dr HT Cpe-6P	2719	3106	22,909
NA	12	2-dr Conv-6P	2979	3356	1,725

NOTE 1: 3,621 Montego MX station wagons came with woodgrain side trim.

NOTE 2: Brougham option on 1,590 four-door sedans and 1,226 two-door hardtops.

NOTE 3: Only 363 of the convertibles were sold with bucket seats.

CYCLONE SERIES — The sporty Cyclone fastback had rocker panel and wheel lip opening moldings. It also featured twin racing stripes, which ran from the front bumper and across the sides to the end of the rear fenders. Standard items included: carpeting, all-vinyl upholstery, ventless windows, tinted rear window and wood-tone appliques on the instrument cluster and lower dash.

CYCLONE

Model Number	Body/Style Number	Body Type & Seating	Factory Price	Shipping Weight	Production Total
NA	15	2-dr Fsbk Cpe-6P	2754	3273	5,882

CYCLONE CJ SERIES — A blacked-out grille was framed in chrome and had a single chrome piece in the middle running from each end of the grille. There was also a Cyclone emblem in the center, highlighting the front of the Cyclone CJ. Additional features included wheelwell opening moldings; dual exhausts; a 3.50:1 rear axle; engine dress-up kit; hood tape stripe; and competition handling package.

CYCLONE CJ

Model Number	Body/Style Number	Body Type & Seating	Factory Price	Shipping Weight	Production Total
NA	16	2-dr Fsbk Cpe-6P	3207	3615	3,261

COUGAR SERIES — The Cougar's grille now had horizontal pieces that protruded slightly at the center. Retractable headlights were used again. Rocker panel strips, wheelwell opening moldings and two parallel full-length upper body pinstripes decorated the Cougar's sides. The back-up lights wrapped around the rear fenders and the taillights were trimmed with concave vertical chrome pieces. A vinyl interior with foam-padded bucket seats and carpeting was standard.

COUGAR

Model Number	Body/Style Number	Body Type & Seating	Factory Price	Shipping Weight	Production Total
NA	65	2-dr HT Cpe-5P	2999	3380	66,331
NA	76	2-dr Conv-5P	3365	3499	5,796

NOTE 1: 1,615 Cougar hardtops ordered with optional front bench seats.

COUGAR XR-7 SERIES — The XR-7 looked about the same as the basic Cougar from the outside. Its standard extras included: rim-blow steering wheel; courtesy light group; visual check panel; left-hand remote-control racing mirror; electric clock; Deluxe armrests; walnut-toned instrument panel with tachometer and trip odometer; leather with vinyl upholstery; vinyl door trim panels; and special wheelcovers.

COUGAR XR-7

Model Number	Body/Style Number	Body Type & Seating	Factory Price	Shipping Weight	Production Total
NA	65	2-dr HT Cpe-5P	3298	3420	23,918
NA	76	2-dr Conv-5P	3578	3539	4,024

MONTEREY SERIES — The Monterey had a new, horizontal bar grille with a vertical piece in the center. Signal lights wrapped around the front fenders. The concave, rectangular taillights were clustered in the rear deck panel, which was heavily trimmed with vertical chrome pieces. The wheelhouse openings, trunk lid and roof quarter panels had moldings. Standard features included: ventless side windows; nylon carpeting; wood-toned dash and door panels; heater and defroster and dome light. The convertible had an all-vinyl interior, while other body types had cloth and vinyl trims.

MONTEREY

Model Number	Body/Style Number	Body Type & Seating	Factory Price	Shipping Weight	Production Total
NA	44	4-dr Sed-6P	3141	3963	23,009
NA	45	2-dr Conv-6P	3523	4108	1,297
NA	47	2-dr HT Cpe-6P	3220	3927	9,865
NA	48	4-dr HT Sed-6P	3296	3998	6,066
NA	72	4-dr Sta Wag-6P	3519	4272	5,844

NOTE 1: A total of 3,839 Monterey wagons came with an optional third seat.

MONTEREY CUSTOM SERIES — Rocker panel moldings and Deluxe wheelcovers were two exterior differences between the Custom and the basic Monterey. The Custom also had a Deluxe steering wheel; leather door pulls; woodgrained vinyl appliques; front seat center armrest; bright seat side shields; and rear door courtesy light.

MONTEREY CUSTOM

Model Number	Body/Style Number	Body Type & Seating	Factory Price	Shipping Weight	Production Total
NA	54	4-dr Sed-6P	3360	3968	7,103
NA	56	2-dr HT Cpe-6P	2442	3959	2,898
NA	58	4-dr HT Sed-6P	3516	4000	2,827
NA	74	4-dr Sta Wag-6P	3740	4384	1,920

NOTE 1: A total of 967 Monterey Custom station wagons came with a third seat.

1969 Mercury, Marquis Brougham four-door hardtop sedan, V-8

MARQUIS SERIES — The attractive front-end styling of the Marquis was influenced by the Continental Mark III. The integrated bumper grille had a horizontal bar theme and a prominent center section. Hidden headlight covers blended into the grille. Dual lower body pinstripes ran above the full-length bright curb moldings. Except for two back-up lights, the rear deck panel was a solid row of concave, rectangular, chrome-accented taillights. The interior featured deep-pile nylon carpeting, buried-walnut vinyl paneling on the dash and doors, front door courtesy lights, electric clock and a steering wheel with wood-toned spokes and rim.

MARQUIS

Model Number	Body/Style Number	Body Type & Seating	Factory Price	Shipping Weight	Production Total
NA	63	4-dr Sed-6P	3840	4144	31,388
NA	66	2-dr HT Cpe-6P	3902	3927	18,302
NA	68	4-dr HT Sed-6P	3973	4184	29,389
NA	65	2-dr Conv-6P	4107	4380	2,319
NA	76	4-dr Col Prk Wag-6P	3878	4457	25,604

NOTE 1: 18,003 Colony Park station wagons came with the optional third seat.

MARAUDER SERIES — The Marauder had a Marquis front end, special tunneled rear window treatment and twin upper body pinstripe. There was a unique sculptured section, with five short, horizontal chrome pieces just behind the doors. The six tail and two back-up lights were embedded in the rear deck panel. Set between them was a blacked-out section with the Marauder name written in chrome. A cloth and vinyl interior was standard.

MARAUDER

Model Number	Body/Style Number	Body Type & Seating	Factory Price	Shipping Weight	Production Total
NA	60	2-dr HT Cpe-6P	3351	4009	9,031

MARAUDER X-100 SERIES — The Marauder X-100 features a two-tone paint job; fender skirts; leather with vinyl interior; rim-blow steering wheel; electric clock; glass-belted wide-tread tires; and styled aluminum wheels.

MARAUDER X-100

Model Number	Body/Style Number	Body Type & Seating	Factory Price	Shipping Weight	Production Total
NA	61	2-dr HT Cpe-6P	4074	4009	5,635

MERCURY BASE ENGINES

(COMET/MONTEGO/MONTEGO MX) SIX: Overhead valves. Cast iron block. Displacement: 250 cid. Bore and stroke: 3.68 x 3.91 inches. Compression ratio: 8.60:1. Brake hp: 155 at 4000 rpm. Carburetor: Autolite C90F-9510-BD one-barrel. (Engine Code L)

(CYCLONE) V-8: Overhead valves. Cast iron block. Displacement: 302 cid. Bore and stroke: 4 x 3 inches. Compression ratio: 9.50:1. Brake hp: 220 at 4400 rpm. Carburetor: Autolite C8AF-9510-B four-barrel. (Engine Code F)

(CYCLONE CJ) V-8: Overhead valves. Cast iron block. Displacement: 428 cid. Bore and stroke: 4.13 x 3.98 inches. Compression ratio: 10.60:1. Brake hp: 335 at 5200 rpm. Carburetor: Autolite C8AF-9510-B four-barrel. (Engine Code Q)

(CYCLONE SPOILER) V-8: Overhead valves. Cast iron block. Displacement: 351 cid. Bore and stroke: 4 x 3.5 inches. Compression ratio: 10.7:1. Brake hp: 290 at 5200 rpm. Carburetor: Autolite four-barrel. (Engine Code M)

(COUGAR/COUGAR XR-7) V-8: Overhead valves. Cast iron block. Displacement: 351 cid. Bore and stroke: 4 x 3.5 inches. Compression ratio: 9.5:1. Brake hp: 250 at 4800 rpm. Carburetor: Autolite two-barrel. (Engine Code H)

(MONTEREY/MONTEREY CUSTOM/MARAUDER) V-8: Overhead valves. Cast iron block. Displacement: 390 cid. Bore and stroke: 4.05 x 3.78 inches. Compression ratio: 9.50:1. Brake hp: 265 at 4400 rpm. Carburetor: Autolite C9AF-9510-B two-barrel. (Engine Code Y)

(MARQUIS/MARQUIS BROUGHAM) V-8: Overhead valves. Cast iron block. Displacement: 429 cid. Bore and stroke: 4.36 x 3.59 inches. Compression ratio: 10.50:1. Brake hp: 320 at 4400 rpm. Carburetor: Autolite C9AF-9510-J two-barrel. (Engine Code K)

(MARAUDER X-100) V-8: Overhead valves. Cast iron block. Displacement: 429 cid. Bore and stroke: 4.36 x 3.59 inches. Compression ratio: 10.50:1. Brake hp: 360 at 4600 rpm. Carburetor: four-barrel. (Engine Code N)

COMET/MONTEGO/CYCLONE CHASSIS FEATURES: Wheelbase (passenger cars) 116 inches; (station wagons) 113 inches. Overall length: (passenger cars) 206.2 inches; (Cyclone and Cyclone CJ) 203.2 inches; (station wagons) 193.8 inches. Tires: (Cyclone) 7.75 x 14; (others) 7.35 x 14.

COUGAR CHASSIS FEATURES: Wheelbase: 111 inches. Overall length: 193.8 inches. Tires: E78 x 14.

MERCURY CHASSIS FEATURES: (Station wagons and Marauder) 121 inches; (other models) 124 inches. Overall length: (Marquis) 224.3 inches; (Monterey and Custom) 221.8 inches; (Marauder and X-100) 219.1 inches; (Colony Park) 220.5 inches; (Monterey and Custom station wagons) 218 inches. Tires: (Marquis and station wagons) 8.55 x 15; (X100) H70 x 15; (other models) 8.25 x 15.

COMET/CYCLONE/MONTEGO OPTIONS: Heavy-duty battery ($7.80). Electric clock ($15.60). Courtesy light group includes: twin dash panel lights; glovebox, and ashtray and luggage compartment lights; cargo light on station wagon and rear door light switch on sedans ($19.50). Cross-country ride package ($13). Competition handling package ($31.10). Curb moldings ($15.60). Decor group, includes: bright wheel lip moldings; trunk lid applique and bright upper door frames in sedans; Deluxe wheelcovers on hardtops and Montego sedan ($54.50); on Montegos with special appearance group ($42.80); on Montego without special appearance group ($60.90). Tinted glass ($35). Front head restraints ($17). Hood lock pins for Cyclone and Cyclone CJ ($7.80). Luggage carrier on MX wagons ($46.70). Left-hand remote-control racing mirror on Cyclone and Cyclone CJ ($13). Left-hand remote-control mirror ($10.40). Right-hand manual racing ($6.50). MX Brougham, includes: Comfort Stream ventilation; remote-control mirror; rear roof pillar Brougham identification; luxury-level cloth/ vinyl interior; vinyl-covered door pull handles; Brougham dash panel nameplate and rim-blow steering wheel for Montego MX hardtop or sedan ($90.70). Two-tone paint ($31.10). Dual paint tape stripes for Cyclone and Cyclone CJ ($31.10). Power disc brakes ($64.80). Four-Way bench seat ($73.90). Power steering ($94.60). Tailgate and power window for MX station wagon ($35). Power windows, except on Comet and Montego, ($104.90). AM radio ($60.90). AM/FM stereo with twin speakers ($185.30). Dual rear-seat speakers, except in convertible and station wagon ($25.90). Deluxe seat belts for convertibles, includes a seat belt reminder light ($13). Deluxe front shoulder seat belts, except for convertibles, includes a seat belt reminder light ($15.60). Bucket seats without console for Montego MX, Cyclone hardtops and MX convertible ($110.10). Third seat MX wagon ($51.20). Sports console for Montego MX, Cyclone and Cyclone CJ ($155.70). Special appearance group includes: Deluxe wheelcovers; whitewall tires; courtesy light group and Comfort Stream ventilation, except Cyclone CJ ($64.80). Sports appearance group includes: bucket seats; remote-control left-hand racing mirror; turbine wheelcovers and rim-blow steering wheel for Cyclone CJ ($149). Rim-blow steering wheel ($35). Tachometer ($48). Comfortweave vinyl interior for Montego MX except station wagons and Cyclone ($24.70). Vinyl roof ($99.80). Deluxe wheelcovers with spinners, over hubs ($41.50); other ($20.80). Styled steel wheels, over hubs ($116.60); other ($95.90). Interval windshield wipers ($16.90). Yacht deck paneling for MX wagon ($149). A three-speed manual transmission was standard except in the Cyclone CJ, which came with a four-speed manual gearbox. Four-speed and SelectShift automatic transmissions were optional in the other series. A 220 hp 302 cid V-8 (two-barrel); 250 hp 351 cid V-8 (two-barrel); 290 hp 351 cid V-8 (four-barrel); 320 hp 390 cid V-8 (four-barrel); 335 hp 428 cid V-8 (four-barrel); 360 hp 429 cid V-8 (four-barrel); and a 390 hp 427 cid V-8 (four-barrel) were optional. High-performance and power transfer axles were available. A special handling package and traction-lok differential were optional.

COUGAR OPTIONS: Heavy-duty battery ($7.80). Front bumper guards ($l3). Rear window defogger for hardtop ($22.10). Decor group includes: Deluxe wheelcovers; curb molding; rim-blow steering wheel; custom grade seat; door and quarter trim; door mounted courtesy lights; rear seat armrests and windshield pillar and roof rail pads ($90.70). Door edge guards ($5.20). Dual exhausts ($31.10). Tinted glass ($29.80). GT appearance group for Cougar Cyclone, includes: comfortweave vinyl bucket seats; rim-blow steering wheel; remote-control left-hand racing mirror; turbine design wheelcovers; GT decal; GT dash nameplate and F70 x 14 fiberglass belted tires ($168.40). Front head restraints ($17). Hood lock pins ($7.80). Front and rear rubber floor mats ($13). Left-hand remote-control racing mirror ($13). Left-hand remote control mirror ($10.40). Two-tone paint ($31.10). Power steering ($99.80). Sun roof with vinyl roof ($459.80). Power windows ($104.90). AM radio ($60.90). AM/FM stereo with twin speakers ($185.30). AM radio and stereosonic tape system ($195.60). Rear seat speaker ($15.60). Deluxe seat belts in convertibles ($13). Deluxe front shoulder seat belts, all except convertibles ($15.60). Full-width front seat with center armrest in hardtop ($24.70). Speed control ($71.30). Sports console ($57. 10). Tilt away steering wheel ($68.70). Vinyl roof ($89.40). Visual Check panel includes: door-ajar, low-fuel warning lights ($25.90). Deluxe wheelcovers ($20.80). Deluxe wheelcovers, with spinners over hubs ($41.50); other ($20.80). Wire wheelcovers, over hubs ($72.60); other ($51.90). Styled steel wheels, over hubs ($95.90); other in hardtops ($16.90); Interval windshield wipers ($16.90). A three-speed manual transmission was standard. Heavy-duty three-speed, four-speed manual and Select-Shift automatic transmissions were optional. A 290 hp 351 cid V-8 (four-barrel); 290 hp 302 cid V-8 (four-barrel); 320 hp 390 cid V-8 (four-barrel); 335 hp 'CJ' 428 cid V-8 (four-barrel); and a 360 hp 429 cid V-8 (four-barrel) were available. The 302 cid V-8 was standard in the 'Eliminator' performance package. It featured a two-speed street rear axle; blacked-out grille; ram-air hood scoop: special side body stripe and front and rear spoilers. The 290 hp 351 cid V-8 was standard in the '351' performance package. This option included: competition handling package, dual stripes and a power dome hood. The ram-air induction option came with a 428 V-8, hood scoop and F70 x 14 tires. High-performance rear axles and heavy-duty traction-Lok differential were optional. Also note that two Cougars were produced with the Boss 429 cid engine.

MERCURY OPTIONS: Air conditioner ($421). Heavy-duty battery ($6.50). Carpeted load floor on wagons ($15.60). Rear window defogger ($22.10). Electric clock ($15.60); Fender skirts for Marauder ($36.30). Tinted glass ($42.80). Tinted windshield, feet only ($27.30). Front head restraints ($17). Luggage-rack carrier for wagons, with air deflector ($94.60); without air deflector ($73.90). Front and rear rubber floor mats ($13). Outside rearview mirror with remote-control ($10.40). Two-tone paint ($36.30). Two-tone paint Marauder ($45.40). Power antenna ($31.10). Front disc brakes ($71.30). Power locks, in two-doors ($45.40); in four-doors ($68.70). Rear power window on station wagons ($35). Six-Way bench seat ($99.80). Six-Way twin comfort lounge driver's side ($84.20); driver's and passenger's side ($168.40). Power steering ($115.30). Remote-control trunk release ($14.30). Power windows ($110.10). AM radio with antenna ($63.50). AM/FM radio, stereo with antenna ($190.40). AM radio stereosonic tape system ($198.20). Dual rear speakers ($25.90); automatic ride control ($79.10). Deluxe seat belts with reminder light on all convertibles ($13). Deluxe front and rear shoulder seat belts ($15.60). Bucket seat with console, Marauder ($162). Twin comfort lounge, Marquis ($77.80). Center seat facing rear, station wagons ($91.90). Reclining passenger seat, Marauder and Marquis ($41.50). Twin comfort lounge, Marquis ($162). Single-key locking system ($3.90). Speed control ($63.50). Rim-blow steering wheel, Monterey and Marauder ($35); others ($19.50). Tilt steering wheel ($45.40). All-vinyl Deluxe trim, Monterey ($28.50). Leather with vinyl trim, Marquis ($110.10). Visual safety-check panel, includes: low fuel, door ajar, headlamps-on warning lights, headlamps-on warning buzzer and seat belt reminder light ($32.40). Vinyl roof on passenger cars ($115.30); on station wagons ($142.50). Styled aluminum wheels, Monterey and Marauder ($116.60). Styled aluminum wheels Monterey, Marquis ($95.90). Deluxe wheelcovers ($20.80). Deluxe wheelcovers with medallion for Monterey and Marauder ($45.40); for Monterey and Marquis ($24.70). Wire wheels, Marauder ($72.60); others ($51.90). Marauder fender skirts ($20.80). Interval selector windshield wipers ($16.90). Appearance protection group, includes: door edge guards; license plate frames; twin vinyl front; and rear floor mats for two-doors, except Marauder ($25.90); for four-doors, except Marquis ($29.80). Brougham option for Marquis includes exterior 'C' pillar trim; twin comfort lounge seats; upper body peak molding; luxury-level seat trim; unique door trim panels; rear seat center armrest; and vinyl roof ($272). Decor group, includes: woodgrain rim steering wheel, curb molding and Deluxe wheelcovers on Monterey and Monterey station wagons ($57.10). Cooling package ($36). A three-speed manual transmission was standard, except in the Marquis and X-100, both of which came with SelectShift automatic. The automatic transmission was optional in the other models. A 280 hp 390 cid V-8 (two-barrel); 320 hp 390 cid V-8 (four-barrel); 335 hp 428 cid V-8 (four-barrel); and a 360 hp 429 cid V-8 (four-barrel) were offered. A competition handling package, which included heavy-duty shocks and larger stabilizer bar, was a $31.10 option on the Marauder and X-100. High-performance and power transfer axles were also offered.

1969 Mercury, Cougar (Eliminator) two-door hardtop coupe, V-8

HISTORICAL FOOTNOTES: Over five percent of all 1969 Montegos had bucket seats, 26.9 percent had vinyl covered roofs, 1.8 percent had four-speed manual transmission and about one percent came with power seats. Mercurys won four NASCAR Grand National races in 1969. The vast majority of 1969 Cougars, 92.4 percent had power steering, 89.4 percent had automatic transmission, 57 percent had tinted glass and 58.9 percent had power brakes. Most full-size 1969 Mercurys, 99.5 percent of Montereys, 99.7 percent of Customs and 99.5 percent of Marauders, were equipped with automatic transmission. Mercury also built the Cyclone Spoiler II, Mercury's equivalent to Ford's NASCAR racer the Torino Talladega.

1970 MERCURY

MONTEGO SERIES — The protruding hood Mercury had been using for the past few years was carried to extremes on the new Montego. Its grille looked like the front end of a coffin. It had horizontal bars on it and an emblem in the center. The signal lights were placed in the front fenders. Wheelwell and roof drip moldings were used. There were four hooded taillights, each evenly divided into four sections by chrome trim pieces. Standard equipment included: concealed wipers; front and rear side markers; cloth and vinyl or all-vinyl interior; wood-tone applique on dash; and front and rear armrests.

MONTEGO

Model Number	Body/Style Number	Body Type & Seating	Factory Price	Shipping Weight	Production Total
NA	01	2-dr HT-6P	2473	3161	21,298
NA	02	4-dr Sed-6P	2560	3246	13,988

MONTEGO MX SERIES — The Montego MX had mid-bodyside molding and chrome trim around the trunk lid on all models and the window frames of four-doors. The interior featured loop carpeting, pleated cloth and vinyl or all-vinyl upholstery; and a teakwood applique on the steering wheel.

MONTEGO MX

Model Number	Body/Style Number	Body Type & Seating	Factory Price	Shipping Weight	Production Total
NA	08	4-dr Sta Wag-6P	2996	3709	5,094
NA	06	4-dr Sed-6P	2662	3253	16,708
NA	07	2-dr HT Cpe-6P	2563	3186	31,670

MONTEGO MX BROUGHAM SERIES — Concealed headlights, chrome rocker panels, wheelwell moldings, dual upper body pinstripes, six-pod taillights; and silver or black appliques on the rear deck panel set the Brougham apart from the other Montegos. Standard equipment included a cloth and vinyl interior, nylon loop carpeting and a woodgrain vinyl insert in the steering wheel.

MONTEGO MX BROUGHAM

Model Number	Body/Style Number	Body Type & Seating	Factory Price	Shipping Weight	Production Total
NA	10	4-dr Sed-6P	2712	3153	3,315
NA	11	2-dr HT Cpe-6P	2730	3186	8,074
NA	12	4-dr HT Sed-6P	2844	3206	3,685
NA	18	4-dr Vill Wag-6P	3090	3624	2,682

1970 Mercury, Cyclone GT two-door hardtop sports coupe, V-8

CYCLONE SERIES — The protruding center section of the Cyclone grille was outlined by a chrome square. It was equally divided into four pieces, with a chrome circle in the center. Rectangular running lights were embedded in the grille. The lower back panel was either silver or black. Loop carpeting, all-vinyl interior and a competition handling package were standard.

CYCLONE

Model Number	Body/Style Number	Body Type & Seating	Factory Price	Shipping Weight	Production Total
NA	15	2-dr HT Cpe-6P	3037	3449	1,695

CYCLONE GT SERIES — Concealed headlights, non-functional performance scooped hood, full-length lower bodyside molding, left-hand remote-control and right-hand manual racing mirrors, high-back comfortweave vinyl bucket seats, special door panel trim and a three-spoke sports style steering wheel were standard GT features.

CYCLONE GT

Model Number	Body/Style Number	Body Type & Seating	Factory Price	Shipping Weight	Production Total
NA	16	2-dr HT Cpe-5P	3025	3434	10,170

CYCLONE SPOILER SERIES — The 'Spoiler' was aptly named. It had front and rear spoilers; exposed headlights; mid-bodyside stripes; traction belted tires; scooped hood; dual racing mirrors; competition handling package; and full instrumentation.

CYCLONE SPOILER

Model Number	Body/Style Number	Body Type & Seating	Factory Price	Shipping Weight	Production Total
NA	17	2-dr HT Cpe-5P	3530	3464	1,631

COUGAR SERIES — The clean Cougar grille of 1969 was replaced by a center hood extension and 'electric shaver' style insert reminiscent of the 1967 and 1968 models. Basic trim was upper body pinstripes, wheel opening and roof moldings and windshield rear window chrome. The interior featured high-back bucket seats, courtesy lights, carpeted door panels, vinyl headliner and rosewood toned dash panel. The convertible had comfortweave vinyl interior, door-mounted courtesy lights, three-spoke steering wheel and power top with folding rear glass window.

COUGAR

Model Number	Body/Style Number	Body Type & Seating	Factory Price	Shipping Weight	Production Total
NA	91	2-dr HT Cpe-6P	2917	3307	49,479
NA	92	2-dr Conv-5P	3264	3404	2,322

1970 Mercury, Cougar XR-7 two-door convertible, V-8

COUGAR XR-7 SERIES — The XR-7 had distinctive wheelcovers, rocker panel moldings, remote-control racing mirror and an emblem on the rear roof pillar. Interior features included vinyl high-back bucket seats with leather accents; map pockets on the seatbacks; tachometer;

trip odometer; rocker switch display; burled walnut vinyl applique on the instrument panel; rear seat armrests; map and courtesy light; visual check panel; loop yarn nylon carpeting; and an electric clock with elapsed-time indicator.

COUGAR XR-7

Model Number	Body/Style Number	Body Type & Seating	Factory Price	Shipping Weight	Production Total
NA	93	2-dr HT Cpe-6P	3201	3333	18,565
NA	94	2-dr Conv-5P	3465	3430	1,977

MONTEREY SERIES — The Monterey grille had thin, bi-level horizontal bars outlined in heavier chrome; a slender vertical emblem in the middle; four recessed chrome rimmed headlights; and large, wraparound signal lights. There were bright moldings on the wheelwell openings, rear roof pillar base and windows. The two large narrow, rectangular deck panel taillights were centrally divided by back-up lamps. The interior featured nylon carpeting; dark teakwood vinyl instrument panel appliques; color-keyed steering wheel; adjustable head restraints; steering column lock; pleated design cloth and vinyl upholstery (all-vinyl in the convertible); and heavy sound insulation.

MONTEREY

Model Number	Body/Style Number	Body Type & Seating	Factory Price	Shipping Weight	Production Total
NA	44	4-dr Sed-6P	3029	3940	29,432
NA	47	2-dr HT Cpe-6P	3107	3904	9,359
NA	48	4-dr HT Sed-6P	3179	3975	5,032
NA	45	2-dr Conv-6P	3429	4085	581
NA	72	4-dr Sta Wag-6P	3440	4249	5,164

MONTEREY CUSTOM SERIES — The Custom had full-length, mid-bodyside chrome spears with vinyl inserts, Deluxe wheelcovers and curb moldings. On the inside was the cloth and vinyl or all-vinyl upholstery, front seat armrest, teakwood toned inserts in the steering wheel, vinyl-covered door pull handles and rear courtesy light switches.

MONTEREY CUSTOM

Model Number	Body/Style Number	Body Type & Seating	Factory Price	Shipping Weight	Production Total
NA	54	4-dr Sed-6P	3288	3945	4,823
NA	56	2-dr HT Cpe-6P	3365	3936	1,194
NA	58	4-dr HT Sed-6P	3436	3987	1,357

1970 Mercury Marquis, four-door hardtop sedan, V-8

MARQUIS SERIES — The Marquis received a modest facelift for 1970. Vertical pieces were added to the bumper integrated grille and to the signal lights. Dual, pinstripes ran from fender to fender, at tire level, and also above the wheelwell openings, outlining them. There were bright and black curb moldings and chrome trim on the lower front fenders. A luxury rim-blow steering wheel, front door courtesy lights and wood-toned door panel inserts graced the Marquis interior.

MARQUIS

Model Number	Body/Style Number	Body Type & Seating	Factory Price	Shipping Weight	Production Total
NA	40	4-dr Sed-6P	3793	4121	14,384
NA	41	2-dr HT Cpe-6P	3952	4072	6,229
NA	42	4-dr HT Sed-6P	3910	4141	8,411
NA	65	2-dr Conv-6P	4047	4337	1,233
N	74	4-dr Sta Wag-6P	3930	4434	2,388
NA	76	4-dr Col Pk Wag-6P	4,123	4,480	19,204

NOTE 1: 1,429 Marquis wagons and 14,549 Colony Parks sold with third seat.

MARQUIS BROUGHAM SERIES — Instead of pinstripes, the Brougham used upper body moldings which ran from the face of the front fenders to the back of the rear. Also seen on these luxury models were chromed wheel openings and a vinyl roof. The interior featured individually adjustable, twin comfort lounge seats, with two folding armrests. The door trim panels were wood toned and the door pull handles were covered with vinyl.

MARQUIS BROUGHAM

Model Number	Body/Style Number	Body Type & Seating	Factory Price	Shipping Weight	Production Total
NA	63	4-dr Sed-6P	4092	4166	14,920
NA	66	2-dr HT Cpe-6P	4151	4119	7,113
NA	68	4-dr HT Sed-6P	4219	4182	11,623

MARAUDER SERIES — Except for its name spelled out in chrome on the face of the hood, the Marauder looked the same as the Marquis from the front. Side trim consisted of twin upper body pinstripes, window moldings and a sculptured section with five short horizontal chrome pieces behind the doors. A tunneled rear window remained a Marauder styling highpoint. The same distinctive taillight treatment used last year was on the 1970 model.

MARAUDER

Model Number	Body/Style Number	Body Type & Seating	Factory Price	Shipping Weight	Production Total
NA	60	2-dr HT Cpe-6P	3271	3986	3,397

Standard Catalog of American Cars

MARAUDER X-100 SERIES — Fender skirts, wheel opening moldings and special wheelcovers distinguished the X-100 from the standard Marauder. Interior differences included high-back, all-vinyl bucket seats with center console (or twin comfort lounge seats), luxury steering wheel and bright seat side shields.

MARAUDER X-100

Model Number	Body/Style Number	Body Type & Seating	Factory Price	Shipping Weight	Production Total
NA	61	2-dr HT Cpe-6P	3873	4128	2,646

(MONTEGO/MONTEGO MX/MONTEGO BROUGHAM) SIX: Overhead valves. Cast iron block. Displacement: 250 cid. Bore and stroke: 3.68 x 3.91 inches. Compression ratio: 9.00:1. Brake hp: 155 at 4000 rpm. Carburetor: one-barrel. (Engine Code L)

(CYCLONE/MARAUDER X-100) V-8: Overhead valves. Cast iron block. Displacement: 429 cid. Bore and stroke: 4.36 x 3.59 inches. Compression ratio: 10.50:1. Brake hp: 360 at 4600 rpm. Carburetor: four-barrel. (Engine Code N)

(CYCLONE GT/COUGAR/COUGAR XR-7) V-8: Overhead valves. Cast iron block. Displacement: 351 cid. Bore and stroke: 4 x 3.5 inches. Compression ratio: 9.50:1. Brake hp: 250 at 4600 rpm. Carburetor: two-barrel. (Engine Code H)

(CYCLONE SPOILER) V-8: Overhead valves. Cast iron block. Displacement: 429 cid. Bore and stroke: 4.36 x 3.59 inches. Compression ratio: 11.30:1. Brake hp: 370 at 5400 rpm. Carburetor: four-barrel. (Engine Code N)

(MONTEREY/MONTEREY CUSTOM) V-8: Overhead valve. Cast iron block. Displacement: 390 cid. Bore and stroke: 4.05 x 3.78 inches. Compression ratio: 9.50:1. Brake hp: 265 at 4400 rpm. Carburetor: two-barrel. (Engine Code Y)

(MARQUIS/MARQUIS BROUGHAM/MARAUDER) V-8: Overhead valves. Cast iron block. Displacement: 429 cid. Bore and stroke: 4.36 x 3.59 inches. Compression ratio: 10.50:1. Brake hp: 320 at 4400 rpm. Carburetor: two-barrel. (Engine Code K)

MONTEGO/CYCLONE CHASSIS FEATURES: Wheelbase: (Passenger cars) 117 inches; (Station wagons) 114 inches. Overall length: (Passenger cars) 209.9 inches; (Station wagons) 209 inches. Tires: (Cyclone series) G70-14; (other models) E78-14.

COUGAR CHASSIS FEATURES: Wheelbase: 111.1 inches. Overall length: 196.1 inches. tires: E78-14.

MERCURY CHASSIS FEATURES: Wheelbase: (Wagons, Marauder and X-100) 121 inches; (others) 124 inches. Overall length: (Marquis and Brougham) 224.3 inches; (Marquis wagons) 220.5 inches; (Monterey and Custom) 221.8 inches; (Monterey wagons) 218 inches; (Marauder and X-100) 219.1 inches. Tires: (Monterey and Custom) G78-15; (Marquis, Brougham, Marauder) H78-15; (Monterey wagons) H70-15 X-100.

MONTEGO/CYCLONE OPTIONS: Air-conditioner ($388.60). Heavy-duty 55 amp alternator ($20.80). Heavy-duty battery ($7.80). Extra cooling ($7.80). Cross-country ride ($9.10). Tinted glass ($36.30). Tinted glass Windshield, fleet only ($25.90). Heater and defroster ($22. 10). Low gear lockout ($6.50). Luggage carrier with adjustable roof rails for MX wagon without air deflector ($54.50); with air deflector ($73.90). left-hand remote-control racing mirror ($13). Front disc brakes ($64.80). Four-Way bench seat ($73.90). Power steering ($104.90). Power windows ($104.90). Protective vinyl bodyside molding ($25.90). AM radio ($60.90). AM/FM stereo radio ($212.50). Dual rear seat speaker ($27.30). Deluxe seat and front shoulder belts ($15.60). Deluxe seat belts with automatic seatback release on two-doors ($38.90). High-back bucket seats with comfort vinyl trim ($119.20). Rear facing third seat MX station wagon ($63.70). Rim-blow steering wheel ($35). Sun roof Montego two-door hardtops ($375.70). Upbeat spectrum stripe MX two-door with bench seats ($32.40). Comfort weave vinyl MX with bench seats ($32.40). Upbeat watch plaid MX with bench seats ($32.40). High level ventilation ($15.50). Vinyl roof ($99.80). Deluxe wheelcovers ($25.90). Luxury wheelcovers ($41.50). Styled steel wheels ($38.90). Interval windshield wipers ($25.90). Mud and snow tires ($7.80). F78-14 whitewall tires, with 250 or 302 engines ($31.10); with 351 engines ($49.30). G 78-14 whitewall tires, with 351 engine ($49.30); with 429 engines ($64.80); with 351 engines ($46.70). F70-14 traction tires, with 250, 302 engines ($77.80); with 351 engines ($59.60). G70-14 whitewall tires, with 250, 302 engines ($83); with 351 engines ($64.80). G70-14 traction tires, with 250, 302 engines ($95.90); with 351 engine ($77.80); with 429 engine ($59.60). Instrumentation group includes: tachometer, oil temperature and ammeter gauges ($77.80). Trailer-towing package includes: 351 two-barrel engine; power disc brakes; competitive handling package; extra-cooling package; heavy-duty alternator; heavy-duty battery, with air conditioner ($151.60); without air conditioner ($159.40). A three-speed manual transmission was standard, except in the Cyclone and Spoiler. Both came with a four-speed manual and Hurst shifter. Four-speed manual and SelectShift automatic transmissions were optional. A 220 hp 351 cid V-8 (two-barrel); 250 hp 351 cid V-8 (two-barrel); a 300 hp 351 cid V-8 (four-barrel); 360 hp Thunder Jet 429 cid V-8 (four-barrel); 370 hp Cobra Jet 429 cid V-8 (four-barrel); and a 375 hp Super Cobra Jet 429 cid V-8 (four-barrel) were offered. A limited production Boss 429 cid V-8 (four-barrel) was available on special order. Drag pack, drag-pack super and ram-air induction options were offered in the Cyclone, GT and Spoiler series. A higher ratio rear axle and Trac-Lok differential were available at extra cost.

COUGAR OPTIONS: Air-conditioner ($375.70). Electric clock ($15.60). Sports console ($57.10). Tinted glass ($32.40). Tinted windshield, fleet only ($22.10). Heater and defroster ($22.10). Left-hand remote-control racing mirror ($13). Two-tone paint ($31.10). Front disc brakes ($64.80). Power steering ($105.90). AM radio ($60.90). AM/FM stereo radio ($212.50). AM radio/stereo sonic tape ($195.60). Rear seat speaker ($15.60). Deluxe front seat and shoulder belts ($15.60). Rim-blow steering wheel ($35). Vinyl sun roof ($459.80). Tilt steering wheel ($45.40). Houndstooth cloth and vinyl trim $32.40). Vinyl roof includes roof and bright roof moldings ($89.40). Deluxe wheelcovers ($25.90). Ralley wheelcovers over hubs ($41.50); others ($15.60). Wire wheelcovers, over hubs ($74.90); others ($48). Styled steel wheels, over hubs ($116.60); others ($90.70). Interval windshield wipers ($25.90). Mud and snow tires ($7.80). Tires: E78-14 whitewall wide tread ($29.80); F70-14 whitewall belted ($63.50); F70-14 traction belted ($76.50); F70-14 traction belted ($13). Appearance protection group includes: front bumper guards, door edge guards, rear floor mats ($31.10). Courtesy light group includes: rear roof pillar, trunk, underhood and map lights, headlamps on warning buzzer with light ($19.50). Decor group includes: Deluxe wheelcovers; curb molding; three-spoke rim-blow steering wheel; custom grade door; and quarter trim; door courtesy lights; rear quarter armrests; Comfortweave vinyl high-back bucket seats ($90.70); on Eliminator ($70). Drag-pack option ($207.30). Eliminator option ($129.60). Ram-air induction option includes: ram-air induction system and functional hood scoop in body color; hood stripes (black or argent); color-keyed stripe with CJ 428 logo ($64.80). Visual-Check panel includes door-ajar, low-fuel warning lights ($25.90). A three-speed manual transmission was standard. Four-speed manual and SelectShift automatic transmissions were optional. A 300 horsepower 351 cid V-8 (four-barrel); a 290 hp Boss 302 cid V-8 (four-barrel); 335 hp Cobra Jet 428 cid V-8 (four-barrel); and a 375 hp Boss 429 cid V-8 (four-barrel) were available. The 300 hp engine was standard in the Eliminator performance package. The Boss 302 was only offered in the Eliminator. Drag-pack and ram-air induction options could also be ordered. A high performance rear axle and Traction-Lok differential were available at extra cost.

MERCURY OPTIONS: Air-conditioner ($421). Heavy-duty 55 amp alternator ($20.80). Heavy-duty 65 amp alternator ($86.80). Heavy-duty battery ($7.80). Carpeted load floor wagons ($19.50). Heavy-duty cooling ($36.30). Cross-country ride ($23.40). Electric rear window defroster ($53.20). Door edge guards in two-doors ($6.50); in four-doors ($10.40). Tinted glass ($36.30). Tinted windshield, fleet only ($27.30). Luggage carrier with adjustable roof rails in wagons ($73.90); with air deflector ($94.60). Front and rear floor mats ($13). Two-tone paint ($36.30). Two-tone paint Marauder ($45.40). Power antenna ($31.10). Front disc brakes ($71.30). Power door locks, two-doors ($45.40); four-doors ($68.70); wagons including power lock for tailgate ($77.80). Automatic seatback release ($25.90 two-doors). Six-Way bench seat ($99.80). Power steering ($115.30). Remote control trunk release ($14.30). Power windows ($110.10). Protective vinyl bodyside moldings in Monterey ($25.90). AM radio ($63.50). AM/FM stereo radio ($239.60). AM radio stereo-sonic tape ($198.20). Automatic ride control ($28.10). Deluxe front seat and shoulder belts ($15.60). Heavy-duty front-seating, fleet only ($33.70). Center-facing rear seats Mercury wagons includes tailgate step pad ($91.90). Single key locking system ($3.90). Speed control ($63.50). Rim-blow steering wheel ($19.50). Tilt steering wheel ($45.40). Deluxe vinyl interior Monterey Marauder ($28.50). Vinyl roof ($115.30); wagons ($142.50). Deluxe wheelcovers Monterey and Marauder ($25.90). Luxury wheelcovers ($46.70). Styled aluminum wheels, over hubs ($116.60); over Deluxe ($90.70); Monterey, Marauder X-100 over luxury ($44. 10); Marauder over Marauder appearance group ($90.70). Interval windshield wipers ($25.90). Mud and snow tires ($7.80). G7815 whitewall or blackwall belted Monterey, Custom, Marauder ($31.10). H78-15 whitewall belted on Mercurys ($33.70); on Marauder, Monterey, Custom H70-15 blackwall wide tread ($51.90); on Mercurys ($49.30); on Monterey, Monterey Custom, Marauder ($67.40). Appearance protection group includes: door edge guards; license plate frames; front and rear rubber floor mats, two-door ($25.90); four-door ($29.80). Competition handling group, Marauder ($31.10). Decor group, Monterey, includes: Deluxe steering wheel (with woodgrain spoke accents); curb molding: Deluxe wheelcovers ($57.10). Marauder appearance group includes: Marauder wheelcovers, fender skirts and wheel opening molding ($57.10). A three-speed manual transmission was standard in Marauder, Monterey. and Custom. SelectShift automatic was standard in Marquis, Brougham and X-100. The automatic was optional in the other series. A 320 hp 429 cid V-8 (two-barrel) and a 360 hp 429 cid V-8 (four-barrel) were optional. A higher ratio rear axle was available.

HISTORICAL FOOTNOTES: Most 1970 Montegros, 92.6 percent, were equipped with automatic transmission, 87 percent had a V-8 engine, 49.5 percent had air conditioning, 88.1 percent had power steering, 42.1 percent disc brakes and one percent had power seats. Mercurys won four NASCAR Grand National races in 1970. The majority of 1970 Cougars, 67.6 percent were equipped with power brakes, 95.6 percent had power steering, 63.9 percent tinted glass and 92.2 percent had automatic transmission. A total of 3,507 Monterey station wagons were equipped with the optional third rear-facing seat. Most 1970 Marquis Broughams, 99.6 percent, were equipped with air conditioning. Over 99 percent of all full-size Mercurys that had a three-speed manual listed as standard equipment were sold with an automatic.

1971 MERCURY

1971 Mercury, Comet two-door sedan, V-8

COMET SERIES — Comet returned as a compact this year. It looked basically like a Maverick with make-up. The horizontal bar grille protruded slightly (harmonizing with the 'power dome' hood). The center horizontal bar was chromed. Rectangular signal lights were placed alongside the grille. The two headlights were recessed into a chromed background. Side trim consisted of wheel opening moldings and twin pinstripes, which ran from the tip of the headlights to the door handles. Taillights were of the pod variety used on Montegos. Standard features included: front and rear armrests, carpeting, vinyl headliner, cigar lighter, two-spoke steering wheel and light grey and gold check cloth and vinyl upholstery. A do-it-yourself repair manual was offered to Comet buyers.

MERCURY I.D. NUMBERS: VIN on metal tag affixed to left-hand top of dash and viewable through windshield. VIN consists of 11 symbols. First symbol 1 = 1971. Second symbol indicates assembly plant: F = Dearborn, Mich. (Cougar); H = Lorain, Ohio (Montego); K = Kansas City, Kan. (Comet) and Z = St. Louis, Mo. (Mercury). Third and fourth symbols are Body Style Number in charts below. Fifth symbol identifies engine code. Last six symbols are sequential production number starting at 100001 at each plant. Vehicle Certification label on left front door lock face panel provides additional information on model year, assembly point, body type, engine, color, trim, axle and transmission.

COMET

Model Number	Body/Style Number	Body Type & Seating	Factory Price	Shipping Weight	Production Total
NA	30	2-dr Sed-4P	2217	2335	54,884
NA	31	4-dr Sed-4P	2276	2366	28,116

MONTEGO SERIES — The Montegos protruding grille was toned down a bit for 1971. It now had a criss-cross pattern. Side trim consisted of wheel opening and window moldings. Last year's pod style taillights remained. The instrument panel had woodgrain trim.

MONTEGO

Model Number	Body/Style Number	Body Type & Seating	Factory Price	Shipping Weight	Production Total
NA	01	2-dr HT Cpe-6P	2777	3124	9,623
NA	02	4-dr Sed-6P	2772	3125	5,718

MONTEGO MX SERIES — The MX had chrome rocker panels and its name written on the rear fenders. Fancier wheelcovers and a slightly plusher interior were the main differences between the MX and the basic Montego.

MONTEGO MX

Model Number	Body/Style Number	Body Type & Seating	Factory Price	Shipping Weight	Production Total
NA	06	4-dr Sed-6P	2891	3131	13,559
NA	07	2-dr HT Cpe-6P	2891	3130	13,719
NA	08	4-dr Sta Wag-6P	3215	3547	3,698

1971 Mercury, Montego MX Brougham four-door hardtop sedan, V-8

MONTEGO MX BROUGHAM SERIES — Upper body twin pinstripes and wheel opening and rocker panel moldings were styling features of the MX Brougham. It also had Deluxe wheelcovers. The upholstery was cloth and vinyl or all-vinyl. The door panels had woodgrain vinyl appliques. The Villager station wagon had wood-toned panels framed with chrome trim. A dual action tailgate was standard.

MONTEGO MX BROUGHAM

Model Number	Body/Style Number	Body Type & Seating	Factory Price	Shipping Weight	Production Total
NA	10	4-dr Sed-6P	3073	3154	1,565
NA	11	2-dr HT Cpe-6P	3085	3171	2,851
NA	12	4-dr HT Sed-6P	3157	3198	1,156
NA	18	4-dr Vill Wag-6P	3456	3483	2,121

MONTEGO CYCLONE — SERIES — The new Cyclone looked virtually the same as last year's model. It came with a performance hood (having an integral scoop); running lights; cross country ride package; deep loop carpeting; dual racing mirrors; concealed wipers; and flow-thru ventilation.

MONTEGO CYCLONE

Model Number	Body/Style Number	Body Type & Seating	Factory Price	Shipping Weight	Production Total
NA	15	2-dr HT Cpe-6P	3369	3587	444

MONTEGO CYCLONE GT SERIES — The GT had the same standard equipment as the basic Cyclone, plus high-back bucket seats; Deluxe wheelcovers; full instrumentation (tachometer, oil gauge, temperature gauge and ammeter); three-spoke steering wheel; and concealed headlights.

MONTEGO CYCLONE GT

Model Number	Body/Style Number	Body Type & Seating	Factory Price	Shipping Weight	Production Total
NA	16	2-dr HT Cpe-5P	3681	3493	2,287

MONTEGO CYCLONE SPOILER SERIES — Higher positioned side body stripes and a less potent standard engine were the most noticeable changes made to the Spoiler in 1971. It came with front and rear spoilers; hubcaps with bright trim rings and Traction-Lok differential with 3.25:1 gear ratio rear axle.

MONTEGO CYCLONE SPOILER

Model Number	Body/Style Number	Body Type & Seating	Factory Price	Shipping Weight	Production Total
NA	17	2-dr HT Cpe-5P	3801	3580	353

COUGAR SERIES — The Cougar's front end was restyled. The four headlights were exposed and recessed. The signal lights wrapped around the front fenders. The protruding center grille had vertical bars and was framed in chrome. An ornament was set in its center. Triple, mid-tire level pinstripes ran from fender to fender. There were moldings on the wheelwell openings. The rear bumper was integrated into the rear deck panel, which housed the large rectangular taillights. Standard features included: high-back bucket seats; cigar lighter; concealed wipers; consolette with illuminated ashtray; glovebox and panel courtesy lights; and flow-thru ventilation system.

COUGAR

Model Number	Body/Style Number	Body Type & Seating	Factory Price	Shipping Weight	Production Total
NA	91	2-dr HT Cpe-5P	3289	3285	34,008
NA	92	2-dr Conv-5P	3681	3415	1,723

1971 Mercury Cougar XR-7 two-door hardtop, V-8

COUGAR XR-7 SERIES — The XR-7 had chrome rocker panels, distinctive wheelcovers and ornamentation and a unique vinyl covered half-roof. It also provided highback bucket seats with leather seating surfaces, a fully instrumented dash panel (i.e. tach, trip odometer, toggle switches) and a remote-control left-hand racing mirror. The instrument board and steering wheel had woodgrain appliques. The convertible had a tinted windshield.

COUGAR XR-7

Model Number	Body/Style Number	Body Type & Seating	Factory Price	Shipping Weight	Production Total
NA	93	2-dr HT Cpe-5P	3629	3314	25,416
NA	94	2-dr Conv-5P	3877	3454	1,717

MONTEREY SERIES — The Monterey's wraparound grille was a wave of horizontal bars that came to a point at the center. The four chrome-rimmed headlights were recessed into the grille. Signal lights were located in the front bumper. There was no side trim other than the Monterey name, written in chrome, on the lower quarter panel. The large, rectangular bumper-integrated taillights wrapped around the rear fenders. Standard features included: cloth and vinyl upholstery; carpeting; courtesy and trunk compartment lights; power vent system; recessed outside door handles; dual ashtrays and temperature and braking system warning lights.

1971 Mercury, Monterey two-door hardtop coupe, V-8

MONTEREY

Model Number	Body/Style Number	Body Type & Seating	Factory Price	Shipping Weight	Production Total
NA	44	4-dr Sed-6P	3423	4028	22,744
NA	47	2-dr HT Cpe-6P	3465	3958	9,099
NA	48	4-dr HT Sed-6P	3533	4024	2,483
NA	72	4-dr Sta Wag-6P	4283	4384	4,160

MONTEREY CUSTOM SERIES — Rocker panel and lower side window moldings, plus a full-length, mid-bodyside chrome spear, set the Custom apart from the plain Monterey. It also had Deluxe wheelcovers and a plusher interior.

MONTEREY CUSTOM

Model Number	Body/Style Number	Body Type & Seating	Factory Price	Shipping Weight	Production Total
NA	54	4-dr Sed-6P	3958	4105	12,411
NA	56	2-dr HT Cpe-6P	4141	4028	4,508
NA	58	4-dr HT Sed-6P	4113	4104	1,397

MARQUIS SERIES — Changes in the Marquis for 1971 were evolutionary, yet noticeable. The word Mercury replaced 'Marquis' on the left headlight door. The protruding type horizontal bar grille was outlined, at the top, by a larger piece of chrome and was no longer centrally divided by the bumper. A full-length chrome stripe ran at slightly above mid tire-level. There was chrome trim on the front wheel openings and on the standard fender skirts. The taillight treatment was the same as that used on the Monterey, except for the trunk lid molding and distinct center rear deck panel trim.

MARQUIS

Model Number	Body/Style Number	Body Type & Seating	Factory Price	Shipping Weight	Production Total
NA	40	4-dr Sed-6P	4474	4311	16,030
NA	41	2-dr HT Cpe-6P	4557	4240	7,726
NA	42	4-dr HT Sed-6P	4624	4306	5,491
NA	74	4-dr Sta Wag-6P	4547	4411	2,158
NA	76	4-dr Col Prk Wag-6P	4806	4471	20,004

MARQUIS BROUGHAM SERIES — The Brougham had full-length, upper body moldings, a vinyl covered roof and color-keyed wheelcovers (i.e. the center hub of the covers was the same color as the car). Like the basic Marquis, it came with most power equipment standard.

MARQUIS BROUGHAM

Model Number	Body/Style Number	Body Type & Seating	Factory Price	Shipping Weight	Production Total
NA	63	4-dr Sed-6P	4880	4354	25,790
NA	66	2-dr HT Cpe-6P	4963	4271	14,570
NA	68	4-dr HT Sed-6P	5033	4341	13,781

(COMET) SIX: Cast iron block. Displacement: 170 cid. Bore and stroke: 3.68 x 3.91 inches. Compression ratio: 9.00:1. Brake hp: 100 at 4200 rpm. Carburetor: one-barrel. [Code U]

(MONTEGO/MX/MX BROUGHAM) SIX: Cast iron block. Displacement: 250 cid. Bore and stroke: 3.68 x 3.91 inches. Compression ratio: 9.00:1. Brake hp: 145 at 4000 rpm. Carburetor: one-barrel. [Code L]

(MONTEGO CYCLONE/SPOILER) V-8: Overhead valves. Cast iron block. Displacement: 351 cid. Bore and stroke: 4 x 3.5 inches. Compression ratio: 10.70:1. Brake hp: 285 at 5400. [Code H]

(MONTEGO CYCLONE GT/COUGAR/XR-7/MONTEREY) V-8: Overhead valves. Cast iron block. Displacement: 351 cid. Bore and stroke: 4 x 3.5 inches. Compression ratio: 9.00:1. Brake hp: 240 at 4600 rpm. Carburetor: two-barrel. [Code M]

(MONTEREY CUSTOM) V-8: Overhead valves. Cast iron block. Displacement: 400 cid. Bore and stroke: 4 x 4 inches. Compression ratio: 9.00:1. Brake hp: 260 at 4400 rpm. Carburetor: two-barrel. [Code S]

(MARQUIS/MARQUIS BROUGHAM) V-8: Overhead valves. Cast iron block. Displacement: 429 cid. Bore and stroke: 4.36 x 3.59. Compression ratio: 10.50:1. Brake hp: 320 at 4400 rpm. Carburetor: two-barrel. [Code K]

COMET CHASSIS FEATURES: Wheelbase: 103 inches. Overall length: 181.7 inches. Tires: 6.45 x 14.

MONTEGO/CYCLONE CHASSIS FEATURES: Wheelbase: (passenger cars) 117 inches; (station wagons) 114 inches. Overall length: (passenger cars) 209.9 inches; (station wagons) 211.8 inches. Tires: (Montego MX) F78-14; (station wagons and Cyclone GT) G78-14; (Cyclone and Spoiler) G70xl4; (other models) E78xl4.

COUGAR CHASSIS FEATURES: Wheelbase: 112.1 inches. Overall length: 196.9 inches. Tires: E78 x 14.

MERCURY CHASSIS FEATURES: Wheelbase (passenger cars) 124 inches; (station wagons) 121 inches. Overall length: (passenger cars) 224.7 inches; (station wagons) 220.5 inches. Tires: (Monterey) G78 x 15; (Marquis and wagons) H78 x 15.

COMET OPTIONS: GT package includes: black-out grille; dual body tape stripes; high-back bucket seats; wheel trim rings; hood scoop; dual racing mirrors; bright window frames; Deluxe door trim panels; and black instrument panel ($178.80). Heavy-duty battery ($12). Consolette with clock ($41.80). Rear window defogger ($28.60). Tinted glass ($37). Front and rear bumper guards ($23.90). Two-tone paint ($28.60). Power steering ($115.30). AM radio ($60.80). Vinyl roof ($77.50) Floor-mounted shifters, with automatic or three-speed manual transmissions ($13.10). Deluxe trim option ($39.40). Vinyl trim ($17.90). Deluxe wheelcovers ($23.90). Convenience group ($26.30). Exterior decor group ($52.50). Air conditioner ($370.60). A three-speed manual transmission was standard. SelectShift automatic was optional for $183. A 115 hp 200 cid six (one-barrel); 155 hp 200 cid six (one-barrel) and a 210 hp 302 V-8 (two-barrel) were available at extra cost. A handling and suspension package cost $12 extra.

MONTEGO/CYCLONE OPTIONS: Heavy-duty battery ($13). Electric clock ($18.20). Extra-duty cooling package ($7.80). Console ($60.90). Rear window defroster ($48). Tinted glass ($42.80). Luggage carrier on MX station wagon ($59.60); on MX station wagon with air deflector ($79.10). Remote-control left-hand mirror ($13). Bodyside molding ($33.70). Front disc brakes ($70). Four-Way power seat ($77.80). Power steering ($115.30). Power windows ($115.30). Power tailgate window ($35). AM radio ($66.10). AM/FM stereo radio ($218.90). Vinyl covered roof ($99.80). Deluxe seat and shoulder belts ($38.90). High-back bucket seats ($132.20). Houndstooth Cyclone interior ($32.40). Third seat for station wagons ($80). Two-tone Comfortweave seats in Montego MX ($32.40). Rim-blow steering wheel ($35). Tilting steering wheel ($45.40). Hubcaps with trim rings in Cyclones ($31.10). Deluxe wheelcovers ($25.90). Luxury wheelcovers ($18.20). Courtesy light group ($20.80). Instrumentation group ($84.20). Trailer towing package ($120.50). Air conditioner ($408). A three-speed manual transmission was standard in the Montego, MX and MX Brougham. A four-speed manual gearbox with Hurst shifter was standard in the Cyclone and Spoiler. The Cyclone GT came with SelectShift automatic. Four-speed and automatic transmissions were optional in the other series. The four-speed was not offered in station wagons. The cross-country ride package, which included heavy-duty springs, front stabilizer bar and shocks cost $16.90. Ram-air induction was available on Cyclones with the 429 cid Cobra Jet V-8 for $64.80. A higher ratio and Traction-Loc axle were optional. The following V-8 engines were available: 210 hp 302 cid (two-barrel); 240 hp 351 cid (two-barrel); 285 hp 351 cid (four-barrel); 370 hp Cobra Jet 429 cid (four-barrel); and 370 hp Super Cobra Jet 429 cid (four-barrel).

COUGAR OPTIONS: Air conditioner ($408). Heavy-duty battery ($13). Sports console with clock ($76.50). Rear window defroster ($48); on convertibles ($15.60). Tinted glass ($37.60); on convertibles ($15.60). Left-hand remote-control racing mirror ($15.60). Power front disc brakes ($70). Four-Way power driver's seat ($77.80). Power steering ($115.30). Power windows ($115.30). Vinyl roof with power sun roof ($483.10). AM radio ($66.10). AM/FM stereo radio ($218.90). AM radio with stereo tape system ($200.80). Vinyl roof ($89.40). Deluxe wheelcovers ($25.90). Wire wheelcovers ($84.20). Styled steel wheels ($58.30). Appearance protection group ($32.40). Convenience group on closed cars ($48); on convertibles ($32.40). Decor group ($90.70). A console-mounted three-speed manual transmission was standard. A four-speed manual gearbox with Hurst shifter and SelectShift automatic transmission were optional. The following V-8s were available: 285 hp 351 cid (four-barrel) and 370 hp Super Cobra Jet 429 cid (four-barrel). A GT package was offered for $129.60. It featured a high-ratio axle; competition suspension; dual racing mirrors; hood scoop (non-functional except with the 429 Cobra Jet V-8 and Ram-Air); performance cooling package; tachometer; rim-blow steering wheel; F78 x 14 whitewall tires; hubcaps with bright trim rings; GT fender identification badges; and black-finished instrument panel. A higher ratio axle cost $13 extra and a competition handling package was a $32.40 option.

MERCURY OPTIONS: Air conditioning ($441.70). Air conditioning with automatic temperature controls ($520.70). Heavy-duty cooling package ($36.30). Rear window defogger ($31.10). Rear window defroster ($63.50). Tinted glass ($51.90). Cornering lamps ($36.30). Automatic load adjuster ($79.10). Luggage carrier with air deflector ($94.60). Luggage carrier with air deflector on Colony Park ($20.80). Metallic paint ($38.90). Power antenna ($33.40). Power front disc brakes ($71.30). Power door locks in two-doors ($45.40); in four-doors ($68.70). Six-Way power seat ($104.90); driver's side power seat ($89.40); both seats power operated ($178.80). Remote-control trunk release ($14.30). Power steering on Monterey sedan and hardtops ($125.70). Power windows ($132.20). AM radio ($66.10). AM/FM stereo radio ($239.60). AM radio with stereo tape system ($200.80). Dual, rear-seat speakers ($33.70). Vinyl roof on Monterey ($119.20); on station wagons ($142.50). Vinyl 'Halo' roof on Marquis ($128.30). Deluxe seat and shoulder belts ($15.60). Center-facing third seat on station wagons ($128.60). Reclining passenger seat ($44.10). Twin comfort lounge seats ($77.80). Vinyl interior trim in Monterey ($28.50). Fender skirts in Monterey and Custom ($36.30). Speed control ($68.70). Tilting steering wheel ($45.40). Luxury wheelcovers on

---

Monterey ($59.60). Rear window washer on station wagons ($38.90). Convenience group on two-doors ($46.70); on four-doors ($23.40). Appearance protection group ($38.90); same on station wagons ($25.90). Decor group on Monterey ($80.40). Suspension ride package ($23.40). Trailer towing package ($90.70). SelectShift automatic transmission was standard in all, but the basic Monterey sedan and hardtop. They came with a three-speed manual transmission, but could be ordered with the automatic at extra cost. The following V-8 engines were available: 260 hp 400 cid (two-barrel); 320 hp 429 cid (two-barrel); 360 hp 429 cid (four-barrel); and a 370 hp 429 cid (four-barrel). Higher ratio and Traction-Lok axles were optional.

HISTORICAL FOOTNOTES: Most 1971 Comets, 81 percent, came with automatic transmission, 61.9 percent had a six, 48.3 percent had power steering, 33.2 percent had tinted glass and 24.6 percent had air conditioning. Most 1971 Montegos, 97.1 percent, were equipped with automatic transmission, 91.5 percent had a V-8 engine, 94.5 percent had power steering, 49.5 percent had power brakes, 8.5 percent had power windows; and 58.3 percent had an air conditioner. Mercurys won 11 NASCAR Grand National races in 1971. Most 1971 Cougars, 96.9 percent, were equipped with automatic transmission, 75 percent had an air conditioner, 98.5 percent had power steering, 77.9 percent had tinted glass, 79.7 percent had disc brakes, 4.6 percent had power seats and 8.9 percent had power windows. Most full-size 1971 Mercurys, 90 percent, were equipped with an air conditioner, 28.5 percent had a tilting steering wheel, 27.6 percent had power windows and 90.4 percent had tinted glass.

1972 MERCURY

1972 Mercury, Comet two-door sedan, V-8

COMET SERIES — Comet's biggest styling change for 1972 was its dual, full-length upper body pin stripes. Aside from that, it looked the same as last year's model. Standard features included; locking steering column; two-speed windshield wipers/washers; left-hand outside rearview mirror, padded dash, door-operated courtesy lights, carpeting and heater.

COMET

Model Number	Body/Style Number	Body Type & Seating	Factory Price	Shipping Weight	Production Total
NA	30	4-dr Sed-4P	2398	2674	29,092
NA	31	2-dr Sed-4P	2342	2579	53,267

MONTEGO SERIES — The protruding, chrome outlined grille of the new Montego featured a criss-cross pattern that was carried over to the headlight panels. Wheelwell opening moldings were about the only side trim used. The four large rectangular taillights were bumper integrated. Interiors were trimmed in either cloth and vinyl or all-vinyl.

1972 Mercury, Montego MX Brougham two-door hardtop coupe, V-8

MONTEGO

Model Number	Body/Style Number	Body Type & Seating	Factory Price	Shipping Weight	Production Total
NA	02	4-dr Sed-6P	2843	3454	8,658
NA	03	2-dr HT Cpe-6P	2848	3390	9,963

MONTEGO MX SERIES: Dual upper body pinstripes running from the front fenders to the rear side windows, and bright rocker panel moldings, were two features of the Montego MX. Deluxe sound insulation, carpeting and, on the wagon a three-way tailgate, were standard features for the MX line.

MONTEGO MX

Model Number	Body/Style Number	Body Type & Seating	Factory Price	Shipping Weight	Production Total
NA	04	4-dr Sed-6P	2951	3485	23,387
NA	07	2-dr HT Cpe-6P	2971	3407	25,802
NA	08	4-dr Sta Wag-6P	3264	3884	6,268

MONTEGO MX BROUGHAM SERIES — Rocker sill, lower rear quarter panel and upper body moldings were styling features of the Montego MX Brougham, which also came with Deluxe wheelcovers, 'flight-bench' folding armrest seats and a woodgrain applique on the steering wheel. The Villager wagon had woodgrained side body and tailgate paneling.

MONTEGO MX BROUGHAM

Model Number	Body/Style Number	Body Type & Seating	Factory Price	Shipping Weight	Production Total
NA	10	4-dr Sed-6P	3127	3512	17,540
NA	11	2-dr HT Cpe-6P	3137	3433	28,417
NA	18	4-dr Vill Wag-6P	3438	3907	9,237

MONTEGO GT SERIES — The GT had full-length, tire-level bodyside moldings; a performance hood; dual racing mirrors; louvres behind the doors; a tachometer; gauges; and a special black-finished instrument panel.

MONTEGO GT

Model Number	Body/Style Number	Body Type & Seating	Factory Price	Shipping Weight	Production Total
NA	16	2-dr HT Fsk BK-5P	3346	3517	5,820

MONTEREY SERIES — A waffle pattern grille was the biggest Monterey styling change for 1972. Standard features included: power steering; simulated Cherrywood instrument cluster; color-keyed two-spoke steering wheel; power front disc brakes; nylon loop carpeting; and cloth and vinyl upholstery.

MONTEREY

Model Number	Body/Style Number	Body Type & Seating	Factory Price	Shipping Weight	Production Total
NA	44	2-dr Sed-6P	3793	4136	19,012
NA	46	2-dr HT Cpe-6P	3832	4086	6,731
NA	48	4-dr HT Sed-6P	3896	4141	1,416
NA	74	4-dr Sta Wag-6P	4445	4539	4,644

MONTEREY CUSTOM SERIES — Full-length mid-bodyside moldings. Deluxe wheelcovers and chrome rocker panels helped distinguish Customs from basic Montereys. The Custom's cloth and vinyl interior was also more luxurious.

MONTEREY CUSTOM

Model Number	Body/Style Number	Body Type & Seating	Factory Price	Shipping Weight	Production Total
NA	54	4-dr Sed-6P	3956	4225	16,879
NA	56	2-dr HT Cpe-6P	4035	4175	5,910
NA	58	4-dr HT Sed-6P	4103	4230	1,583

MARQUIS SERIES — A new ice-cube-tray-pattern grille and similar treatment in the center section of the rear deck panel were the main styling changes for 1972. Standard equipment included: power front disc brakes; power steering; Deluxe sound insulation; power ventilation; 100 percent nylon loop carpeting; Deluxe wheelcovers; woodgrain instrument panel; electric clock; map light; luggage compartment light; twin ashtray; and courtesy lights.

MARQUIS

Model Number	Body/Style Number	Body Type & Seating	Factory Price	Shipping Weight	Production Total
NA	63	4-dr Sed-6P	4493	4386	14,122
NA	66	2-dr HT Cpe-6P	4572	4336	5,507
NA	68	4-dr HT Sed-6P	4637	4391	1,583
NA	74	4-dr Sta Wag-6P	4445	4539	2,085

1972 Mercury, Cougar XR-7 two-door hardtop sports coupe, V-8

MARQUIS BROUGHAM SERIES — The Brougham had fender-to-fender upper body moldings. In addition to standard Marquis features, it came with a vinyl robe cord; cut-pile nylon carpeting; front door courtesy lights; vanity mirror on the right hand sunvisor; power windows; vinyl roof; color-keyed; wheelcovers; interior pillar lights; and ashtrays and lighters in the rear seat armrests.

MARQUIS BROUGHAM

Model Number	Body/Style Number	Body Type & Seating	Factory Price	Shipping Weight	Production Total
NA	62	4-dr Sed-6P	4890	4436	38,242
NA	64	2-dr HT Cpe-6P	4969	4386	20,064
NA	67	4-dr HT Sed-6P	5034	4441	12,841
NA	76	4-dr Sta Wag-6P	4550	4579	20,192

NOTE 1: Model 76 uses same V-8 as Monterey station wagons.

COUGAR SERIES — The fine, criss-cross pattern on the wraparound front signal lights was replaced by a design of horizontal lines. Otherwise, the 1972 Cougar looked virtually the same as last year's model. Among the standard features were: high-back bucket seats; sequential turn signals; locking steering column; back-up lights; consolette with illuminated ashtray; concealed two-speed windshield wipers; dual racing mirrors; two-spoke steering wheel; Deluxe wheelcovers; instrument panel courtesy lights; glovebox light; and flow-thru ventilation.

COUGAR

Model Number	Body/Style Number	Body Type & Seating	Factory Price	Shipping Weight	Production Total
NA	91	2-dr HT Cpe-5P	3016	3282	23,731
NA	92	2-dr Conv-5P	3370	3412	1,240

COUGAR XR-7 SERIES — The XR-7 came with an emblem in the center of the grille; a half-vinyl roof; bucket seats with leather seating; tachometer; sissy bar; alternator gauge; oil pressure gauge; and nylon carpeting.

COUGAR XR-7

Model Number	Body/Style Number	Body Type & Seating	Factory Price	Shipping Weight	Production Total
NA	93	2-dr HT Cpe-5P	3323	3298	26,802
NA	94	2-dr Conv-5P	3547	3451	1,929

MERCURY BASE ENGINES

(COMET) SIX: Cast iron block. Displacement: 170 cid. Bore and stroke: 3.68 x 3.91 inches. Compression ratio: 9.00:1. SAE net hp: 82 at 4400 rpm. Carburetor: one-barrel. (Code U)

(MONTEGO/MX/MX BROUGHAM) SIX: Cast iron block. Displacement: 250 cid. Bore and stroke: 3.68 x 3.91. Compression ratio: 9.00:1. SAE net hp: 95 at 3500 rpm. Carburetor: one-barrel. [Code L]

(MONTEGO GT) V-8: Overhead valves. Cast iron block. Displacement: 302 cid. Bore and stroke: 4 x 3 inches. Compression ratio: 8.50:1. SAE net hp: 140 at 4000 rpm. Carburetor: two-barrel. [Code F]

(COUGAR/XR-7) V-8: Overhead valves. Cast iron block. Displacement: 351 cid. Bore and stroke: 4 x 3.5 inches. Compression ratio: 8.60:1. SAE net hp: 163 at 3800 rpm. Carburetor: two-barrel. [Code H]

(MONTEREY/MONTEREY CUSTOM PASSENGER CARS) V-8: Overhead valves. Cast iron block. Displacement: 351 cid. Bore and stroke: 4 x 3.5 inches. Compression ratio: 8.60:1. SAE net hp: 163 at 3800 rpm. Carburetor: two-barrel. [Code H]

(MONTEREY/MONTEREY CUSTOM WAGONS) STATION WAGON V-8: Overhead valves. Cast iron block. Displacement: 400 cid. Bore and stroke: 4 x 4 inches. Compression ratio: 8.40:1. SAE net hp: 172 at 4000 rpm. Carburetor: two-barrel. [Code S]

(MARQUIS/MARQUIS BROUGHAM) V-8: Overhead valves. Cast iron block. Displacement: 429 cid. Bore and stroke: 4.36 x 3.59 inches. Compression ratio: 8.50:1. SAE net hp: 208 at 4400 rpm. Carburetor: four-barrel. [Code N]

COMET CHASSIS FEATURES: Wheelbase: 110 inches. Overall length: (four-door) 187 inches; (two-door) 182 inches. Tires: 6.45 x 14.

MONTEGO CHASSIS FEATURES: Wheelbase: (four-door) 118 inches; (two-door) 114 inches. Overall length: (four-door) 213 inches; (two-door) 209 inches; (station wagon) 216 inches. Front tread: 62.8 inches. Rear tread: 62.9 inches. Tires: (MX and GT) F78 x 14; (station wagons) F78 x 14; (other models) E78 x 14.

COUGAR CHASSIS FEATURES: Wheelbase: 112.1 inches. Overall length: 196.1 inches. Front tread: 61.5 inches. Rear tread: 61 inches. Tires: E78 x 14.

MERCURY CHASSIS FEATURES: Wheelbase: (passenger cars) 124 inches; (station wagons) 121 inches. Overall length: (passenger cars) 225 inches; (station wagons) 221 inches. Front tread: 63.3 inches. Rear tread: 64.3 inches. Tires: H78 x 15.

COMET OPTIONS: GT package included: high-back bucket seats; Deluxe door trim panels; hood scoop; dual racing mirrors; hubcaps with bright trim rings; bright window frames; dual body tape stripes; black-out grille, headlamp doors and lower back panel paint treatment and black dash panel with bright moldings ($173.34). Air conditioner ($359.59). Front and rear bumper guards ($23.11). Consolette with clock ($40.45). Rear-window defogger ($27.73). Door edge guards on two-doors ($5.78); four-doors ($8.10). Tinted windows ($52.01). Bodyside moldings ($30.05). Two-tone paint ($27.73). Glamour paint ($34.66). Power steering ($92.45). AM radio ($58.94). AM/FM radio ($123.65). Vinyl-covered roof ($72.12). Bucket seats ($72.12). Vinyl trim on two-doors ($17.34). Deluxe trim ($38.14). Trim rings with hubcaps ($27.73). Deluxe wheelcovers ($23.11). Convenience group ($25.54). Exterior decor group ($50.84). A three-speed manual transmission was standard. SelectShift automatic was optional. A 91 hp 200 cid six (one-barrel); 98 hp 250 cid six (one-barrel); and a 138 hp 302 cid V-8 (two-barrel) were available at extra cost.

MONTEGO OPTIONS: Air conditioner ($397.91). Front bumper guards ($15.14). Electric clock ($17.67). Console ($59.32). Tinted windows ($41.66). Carpeted load floor in station wagons ($25.24). Dual racing mirrors ($12.62). Left-hand remote-control mirror ($12.62). Glamour paint ($37.86). Power front disc brakes ($68.14). Power door locks in two-doors ($44.17); in four-doors ($66.89); in station wagons ($75.72). Six-Way power bench seat ($102.22). Power steering ($112.33). Power windows ($112.33). Power tailgate window in station wagons ($34.08) AM radio ($58.94). AM/FM stereo radio ($213.29). Vinyl-covered roof ($97.18). High-back bucket seats ($128.72). Rear-facing third seat in station wagons ($75.81). Hubcaps with trim rings ($30.29). Deluxe wheelcovers ($25.24). Luxury wheelcovers ($17.67). Interval windshield wipers ($25.24). Appearance group on passenger cars ($31.55); on station wagons ($25.54). Convenience group on two-doors ($47.96); on four-doors ($25.24). Instrumentation group ($99.71). Cross-country ride package ($16.41). Visibility group ($25.24). A three-speed manual transmission was standard. A four-speed manual gearbox (with Hurst shifter) and SelectShift automatic transmission were optional. Buyers of the Cyclone option package (which included: functional dual hood scoop; Traction-Lok differential; wide oval tires; special striping; dual racing mirror; and three-spoke steering wheel) could choose either four-speed or automatic transmissions. A 140 hp 302 cid V-8 (two-barrel); a 161 hp 351 cid V-8 (two-barrel); a 248 hp CJ 351 cid V-8; a 168 hp 400 cid V-8 (two-barrel) and a 201 hp 429 cid V-8 (four-barrel) were optional. A higher ratio axle cost $12.62. Traction-Lok differential sold for $46.76. A competition handling package was $27.76 extra.

COUGAR OPTIONS: Air conditioning ($364.01). Front bumper guards ($13.87), Sports console with clock ($68.18). Rear window defroster ($42.76). Tinted windows in closed cars ($33.52); in convertibles ($13.87). Dual racing mirrors with left-hand remote-control ($23.11). Protective bodyside molding ($30.05). Glamour paint ($34.66). Power front disc brakes ($62.40). Four-Way power seat ($69.34). Power steering ($102.86). Power sun roof ($431.04). Power windows ($102.86). AM radio ($58.94). AM/FM stereo radio ($195.30). AM radio with stereo tape system ($179.12). Vinyl roof ($79.73). Tilting steering wheel ($40.45). Upbeat stripe cloth trim (no charge with decor group). Deluxe wheelcovers ($23.11). Wire wheelcovers ($75.12). Interval windshield wipers ($23.11). Appearance protection group ($28.89). Convenience group ($42.76). Exterior decor group ($80.89).

MERCURY OPTIONS: Air conditioner ($430.58); with automatic temperature controls ($507.55) Deluxe seat and shoulder belts ($50.49). Heavy-duty battery ($12.62). Front bumper guards ($8.84). Electric rear window defroster ($61.84). Tinted glass ($50.49). Cornering lamps ($35.34). Automatic load adjuster ($76.99). Luggage carrier with air deflector on station wagons ($92.13). Glamour paint ($37.86). Sure-Track brake system ($189.30).

Power door locks in two-doors ($44.17); in four-doors ($66.89). Six-Way power bench seat ($102.22). Six-Way left- and right-hand power seat ($174.16). Power sun roof ($495.97). Power windows ($128.72). Remote-control trunk release ($13.89). AM radio ($64.37). AM/FM stereo radio ($233.47). AM radio with stereo tape system ($195.62). Vinyl roof Monterey and Custom ($97.18); station wagons ($138.82); Marquis ($124.95). Center-facing third seat ($122.27). Twin comfort lounge seat ($75.72). Speed control ($66.89). Tilting steering wheel ($44.17). Vanity mirror ($3.79). Deluxe wheelcovers Monterey and wagons ($25.24). Luxury wheelcovers ($32.82). Interval windshield wipers ($25.24). Rear windshield washer on station wagons ($37.89). Appearance protection group ($37.36). Convenience group on two-doors; ($58.05); on four-doors ($35.34). Cross-country ride package ($22.71). Trailer-towing package ($88.34). A three-speed manual transmission was standard. Four-speed manual transmission (with a Hurst shifter) and a SelectShift automatic gearbox were offered. A 262 hp 351 cid V-8 (four-barrel) and a 266 hp CJ 351 cid V-8 were optional. The latter engine came with dual exhaust and competition suspension. The $115.96 GT options package included higher axle ratio; hood scoop; tachometer; performance cooling package; Deluxe steering wheel; trim rings; black instrument panel and dual racing mirrors. A competition handling package was available for $28.89. Higher ratio axles and Traction-Lok differentials were also available. SelectShift automatic transmission was standard. A 172 hp 400 cid V-8 (two-barrel); 208 hp 429 cid V-8 (four-barrel); and a 224 hp 460 cid V-8 were optional.

HISTORICAL FOOTNOTES: Most 1972 Comets, 88 percent, were sold with an automatic transmission, 38.3 percent had a V-8 engine, 38.5 percent had tinted glass, 64.8 percent had power steering, 89 percent had radios, 13.6 percent had bucket seats and 36.3 percent had a vinyl roof. Only 3.3 percent of 1972 Montegos came with bucket seats, 60.8 percent had a vinyl roof, 97.1 percent had a radio, 99.2 percent had automatic transmission, 97.2 percent had a V-8 engine, 97.8 percent had power steering and 14.8 percent had power windows. Most full-size 1972 Mercurys, 73.5 percent, came with a vinyl roof. The vast majority of 1972 Cougars, 98.5 percent were equipped with an automatic, 87.9 percent had power brakes, 98.1 percent had a radio, 78.9 percent had vinyl roofs, 21.9 percent had tilting steering wheels, 5.7 percent had power seats, and 99.1 percent had power steering.

1973 MERCURY

COMET SERIES — Comet received a new, criss-cross pattern grille and energy-absorbing bumpers. However, basic styling remained the same as it had since 1971. Standard features included: dual hydraulic brakes with warning light system; blend-air heater; wheel lip moldings; rocker panel moldings; carpeting; front and rear ashtrays and cloth and vinyl upholstery.

COMET

Model Number	Body/Style Number	Body Type & Seating	Factory Price	Shipping Weight	Production Total
NA	30	4-dr Sed-4P	2389	2904	28,984
NA	31	2-dr Sed-4P	2432	2813	55,707

1973 Mercury, Comet two-door sedan, 6-cyl

MONTEGO SERIES — Larger, energy-absorbing bumpers were the most noticeable change made to Montegos for 1973. The standard interior was vinyl and cloth.

MONTEGO

Model Number	Body/Style Number	Body Type & Seating	Factory Price	Shipping Weight	Production Total
NA	02	4-dr Sed-6P	2916	3719	7,459
NA	03	2-dr HT Cpe-6P	2926	3653	7,082

MONTEGO MX SERIES — Like last year, rocker panel moldings and dual, upper body pinstripes helped set the MX apart from the basic Montego. It also had Deluxe sound insulation and color-keyed deep loop carpeting.

MONTEGO MX

Model Number	Body/Style Number	Body Type & Seating	Factory Price	Shipping Weight	Production Total
NA	10	4-dr Sed-6P	3009	3772	25,300
NA	11	2-dr HT Cpe-6P	3041	3683	27,812
NA	08	4-dr Sta Wag-6P	3417	4124	7,012

MONTEGO MX BROUGHAM SERIES — Bright upper body moldings and Deluxe wheelcovers were two distinguishing exterior features of the Brougham, which came with 'flight bench' seats. These were bench seats with backs that resembled buckets and a folding armrest between them. The steering wheel had a woodgrain insert.

MONTEGO MX BROUGHAM

Model Number	Body/Style Number	Body Type & Seating	Factory Price	Shipping Weight	Production Total
NA	10	4-dr Sed-6P	3189	3813	24,329
NA	11	2-dr HT Cpe-6P	3209	3706	40,951
NA	18	4-dr Vill Wag-6P	3606	4167	12,396

1973 Mercury, Montego MX Brougham two-door hardtop coupe, V-8

MONTEGO GT SERIES — New energy-absorbing bumpers and the placing of the letter 'G' over 'T' on the front fender nameplate, were the styling changes made for 1973. Standard features included: Deluxe sound insulation; Deluxe wheelcovers; sports-type three-spoke steering wheel; deep loop carpeting; dual racing mirrors; and performance hood with non-functional dual scoops.

MONTEGO GT

Model Number	Body/Style Number	Body Type & Seating	Factory Price	Shipping Weight	Production Total
NA	16	2-dr HT FsBk-6P	3413	3662	4,464

COUGAR SERIES — Styling changes for 1973 consisted mainly of vertical chrome pieces in the headlight panels, a more refined radiator-look grille and vertical trim pieces on the taillights. Standard equipment included: sequential turn signals; high-back bucket seats; two-spoke color-keyed steering wheel; consolette with ashtray; and power front disc brakes.

COUGAR

Model Number	Body/Style Number	Body Type & Seating	Factory Price	Shipping Weight	Production Total
NA	91	2-dr HT-6P	3372	3396	21,069
NA	92	2-dr Conv-5P	3726	3524	1,284

1973 Mercury, Cougar XR-7 two-door hardtop sports coupe, V-8

COUGAR XR-7 SERIES — Chrome rocker panels and the XR-7 emblem on top of the grille were two ways to tell the top-of-the-line Cougar from the standard one. In addition to the features offered on the basic Cougar line, XR-7 buyers received special wheelcovers; toggle switches; remote-control mirror, vinyl roof; tachometer; trip odometer; alternator gauge; oil pressure gauge; and a map light. The high-back bucket seats had leather seating surfaces.

COUGAR XR-7

Model Number	Body/Style Number	Body Type & Seating	Factory Price	Shipping Weight	Production Total
NA	93	2-dr HT Cpe-5P	3679	3416	35,110
NA	94	2-dr Conv-5P	3903	3530	3,165

MONTEREY SERIES — The new Monterey was about two inches shorter than last year's model, but nobody mistook it for a Comet. Its ice-cube-tray grille was outlined in chrome. The horizontal bars on the recessed headlight panels carried over to the large wraparound signal lights. A full-length, mid-bodyside chrome spear, chrome wheelwell openings and chrome rocker panels graced the Monterey's sides. Six square, chrome trimmed taillights and two back-up lights were located on the rear deck panel. Between them was trim which matched the grille's pattern. All 1973 Montereys came equipped with power steering, nylon loop carpeting, front bumper guards, automatic parking brake release, energy-absorbing bumper and power front disc brakes. A cloth and vinyl interior was standard.

MONTEREY

Model Number	Body/Style Number	Body Type & Seating	Factory Price	Shipping Weight	Production Total
NA	44	4-dr Sed-6P	3961	4225	16,622
NA	46	2-dr HT Cpe-6P	4004	4167	6,452
NA	72	4-dr Sta Wag-6P	4379	4673	4,275

NOTE 1: One (1) Monterey four-door hardtop was made.

MONTEREY CUSTOM SERIES — The Custom was basically a standard Monterey with a plusher interior and a more powerful engine.

MONTEREY CUSTOM

Model Number	Body/Style Number	Body Type & Seating	Factory Price	Shipping Weight	Production Total
NA	54	4-dr Sed-6P	4124	4295	20,873
NA	56	2-dr HT Cpe-6P	4207	4239	6,962

NOTE 1: Two (2) Monterey Custom four-door hardtops were made.

MARQUIS SERIES — Changes in the Marquis for 1973 included energy-absorbing bumpers; finger grille squares; wraparound signal lights; a free standing hood ornament and full-length lower body and wheelwell opening moldings. Automatic parking brake release; fender skirts; electric clock; inside hood latch release; power front disc brakes; and power steering were among the many standard features.

MARQUIS

Model Number	Body/Style Number	Body Type & Seating	Factory Price	Shipping Weight	Production Total
NA	62	4-dr Sed-6P	5072	4547	15,250
NA	66	2-dr HT Cpe-6P	4727	4411	5,973
NA	68	4-dr HT Sed-6P	5206	4565	2,185
NA	74	4-dr Sta Wag-6P	4608	4695	2,464

MARQUIS BROUGHAM SERIES — The Brougham had fender-to-fender upper-bodyside moldings; power windows; halo vinyl roof; shag cut-pile carpeting; vanity mirror on right-hand sun visor; rear pillar and luggage compartment lights; and Deluxe wheelcovers with inserts. The Colony Park station wagon came with a three-way tailgate, power rear window and Cherry woodgrain yacht deck exterior paneling.

1973 Mercury, Marquis Brougham four-door sedan, V-8

MARQUIS BROUGHAM

Model Number	Body/Style Number	Body Type & Seating	Factory Price	Shipping Weight	Production Total
NA	62	4-dr Sed-6P	5072	4547	46,624
NA	64	2-dr HT Cpe-6P	5151	4475	22,770
NA	67	4-dr HT Sed-6P	5206	4565	10,613
NA	76	4-dr Col Prk Wag-6P	4713	4730	23,283

MERCURY BASE ENGINES

(COMET) SIX: Cast iron block. Displacement: 200 cid. Bore and stroke: 3.68 x 3.1 3 inches. Compression ratio: 8.30:1. SAE net hp: 94 at 3800 rpm. Carburetor: one-barrel.

(MONTEGO/MX CAR/MX BROUGHAM CAR) SIX: Overhead valves. Cast iron block. Displacement: 250 cid. Bore and stroke: 3.68 x 3.91 inches. Compression ratio: 8.00:1. SAE net hp: 92 at 3200 rpm. Carburetor: one-barrel.

(MONTEGO/MX/MX BROUGHAM WAGON) V-8: Overhead valves. Cast iron block. Displacement: 302 cid. Bore and stroke: 4 x 3 inches. Compression ratio: 8.00:1. SAE net hp: 137 at 4200 rpm. Carburetor: two-barrel.

(COUGAR/XR-7) V-8: Overhead valves. Cast iron block. Displacement: 351 cid. Bore and stroke: 4 x 3.5 inches. Compression ratio: 8.00:1. SAE net hp: 168 at 4000 rpm. Carburetor: two-barrel.

(MONTEREY CAR) V-8: Overhead valves. Cast iron block. Displacement: 351 cid. Bore and stroke: 4 x 3.5 inches. Compression ratio: 8.00:1. SAE net hp: 159 at 4000 rpm. Carburetor: two-barrel.

(MONTEREY/MARQUIS/MARQUIS BROUGHAM WAGON) V-8: Overhead valves. Cast iron block. Displacement: 400 cid. Bore and stroke: 4 x 4 inches. Compression ratio: 8.00:1. SAE net hp: 171 at 3600 rpm. Carburetor: two-barrel.

(MARQUIS/MARQUIS BROUGHAM) V-8: Overhead valves. Cast iron block. Displacement: 429 cid. Bore and stroke: 4.36 x 3.59 inches. Compression ratio: 8.00:1. SAE net hp: 198 at 4400 rpm. Carburetor: four-barrel.

COMET CHASSIS FEATURES: Wheelbase: (two-doors) 103 inches; (four-doors) 109.9 inches. Overall length: (two-doors) 185.4 inches; (four-doors) 192.3 inches. Tires: 6.45 x 14.

MONTEGO CHASSIS FEATURES: Wheelbase: (two-door) 114 inches; (four-doors and station wagons) 118 inches. Overall length: (two-doors) 211.3 inches; (four-door) 215.3 inches; (station wagons) 218.5 inches. Tires: (station wagons) F78 x 14 GT or G78 x 14; (other models) E78 x 14.

COUGAR CHASSIS FEATURES: Wheelbase: 112.1 inches. Overall length: 199.5 inches. Tires: E78 x 14.

MERCURY CHASSIS FEATURES: Wheelbase: (Passenger cars) 124 inches; (Station wagons) 121 inches. Overall length: (Passenger cars) 222.5 inches; (station wagons) 223.4 inches. Tires: (Passenger cars) HR78 x 15 steel belted radials; (station wagons) JR78 x 15 steel-belted radials.

COMET OPTIONS: GT package including high-back bucket seats: Deluxe door trim panels; hood scoop; dual racing mirrors; hubcaps with bright trim rings; bright window frames; dual body tape stripe; blacked-out grille, headlamp door. lower back panel and hood paint treatment and black dash panel with bright moldings ($173.34). Air conditioner ($359.59). Front and rear bumper guards ($23.11). Consolette with clock ($40.45). Rear window defogger ($27.73). Door edge guards on two-doors ($5.78); on four-doors ($8.10). Tinted windows ($52.01). Bodyside moldings ($30.05). Two-tone paint ($27.73). Glamour paint ($34.66). Power steering ($92.45). AM radio ($58.94). AM/FM radio ($123.65). Vinyl covered roof ($72.12). Bucket seats ($72.12). Vinyl trim on two-doors ($17.34). Deluxe trim ($38.14). Trim rings with hubcaps ($27.73). Deluxe wheelcovers ($23.11). Convenience group ($25.54). Exterior decor group ($50.84). Custom option including Deluxe sound package; grained vinyl roof; radial tires; driver's side remote-control mirror; reclining expanded vinyl bucket seats; mid-side body moldings and distinctive dash ($346). A three-speed manual transmission was standard. SelectShift automatic transmission was optional. An 88 hp 250 cid six (one-barrel) and a 138 hp 302 cid V-8 (two-barrel) were available at extra cost.

MONTEGO OPTIONS: Air conditioner ($397.91). Front bumper guards ($15.14). Electric clock ($17.67). Console ($59.32). Tinted windows ($41.66). Carpeted load floor in station wagon ($25.24). Dual racing mirrors ($12.62). Left-hand remote-control mirror ($12.62). Glamour paint ($37.86). Power front disc brakes ($68.14). Power door locks in two-doors ($44.17); in four-doors ($66.89); in station wagons ($75.72). Six-Way power bench seat ($102.22). Power steering ($112.33). Power window ($121.33). Power tailgate window in station wagons ($34.08). AM radio ($58.94). AM/FM stereo radio ($213.29). Vinyl covered roof ($97.18). High-back bucket seats ($128.72). Rear facing third seat in station wagons ($75.81). Hubcaps with trim rings ($30.92). Deluxe wheelcovers ($25.24). Luxury wheelcovers ($17.64). Interval windshield wipers ($25.24). Appearance group on station wagons ($25.54); On other models ($31.55). Convenience group on two-doors ($47.96); on four-doors ($25.24). Instrumentation group ($99.71). Cross country ride package ($16.41). Visibility group ($25.24). A three-speed manual transmission was standard. A four-speed manual gearbox (with Hurst shifter) and SelectShift automatic transmission were optional. A 137 hp 302 cid V-8 (two-barrel); 161 hp 351 cid V-8 (two-barrel); 248 hp CJ 351 cid V-8; 168 hp 400 cid V-8 (two-barrel); and a 201 hp 429 cid V-8 (four-barrel) were optional. A higher ratio axle, Traction-Lok differential; and a competition handling package were available.

COUGAR OPTIONS: Air conditioning ($364.01). Front bumper guards ($13.87). Sports console with clock ($68.18). Rear window defroster ($42.76). Tinted windows ($33.52). Tinted windows in convertibles ($13.87). Dual racing mirrors with left-hand remote-control ($23.11). Protective bodyside molding ($30.05). Glamour paint ($34.66). Power front disc brakes ($62.40). Four-Way power seat ($69.34). Power steering ($102.86). Power sun roof ($431.04). Power windows ($102.86). AM radio ($58.94). AM/FM stereo radio ($195.30). AM radio with stereo tape system ($179.12). Vinyl roof ($79.73). Tilting steering wheel ($40.45). Upbeat stripe cloth trim (no charge with decor group). Deluxe wheelcovers ($23.11). Wire wheelcovers ($75.12). Interval windshield wipers ($23.11). Appearance protection group ($28.89). Convenience group ($42.76). Exterior decor group ($80.89). SelectShift automatic transmission was standard. A four-speed manual gearbox was optional. A 264 hp CJ 351 cid V-8 was available at extra cost. A higher ratio axle and Traction-Lok differential were also available. Air conditioner ($430.58). Air conditioner with automatic temperature controls ($507.55). Deluxe seat and shoulder belts ($50.49). Heavy-duty battery ($12.62). Front bumper guards ($8.84). Electric rear window defroster ($61.84). Tinted glass ($50.49). Cornering lamps ($35.34). Automatic load adjuster ($75.99). Luggage carrier with air deflector ($92.13). Glamour paint ($37.86). Sure-Track brake system ($189.30). Power door locks on two-doors ($44.17); on four-doors ($68.99). Six-Way power bench seat ($102.22). Six-Way in left and right-hand power seat ($174.16). Power sun roof ($495.97). Power windows ($128.72). Remote control trunk release ($13.89). AM radio ($64.37). AM/FM stereo radio ($233.47). AM radio with stereo tape system (195.62). Vinyl roof ($124.95). Center-facing third seat ($122.27). Twin comfort lounge seat ($75.72). Speed control ($66.89). Tilting steering wheel ($44.17). Vanity mirror ($3.79). Luxury wheelcovers ($32.82). Interval windshield wipers ($25.24). Rear windshield washer on station wagon ($37.89). Appearance protection group ($37.36). Convenience group on two-doors ($58.05); on four-doors ($35.34). Cross-country ride package ($22.71). Trailer-towing package ($88.34). SelectShift automatic transmission was standard. A 171 hp 400 cid V-8; 198 hp 429 cid V-8 (four-barrel); and a 267 hp 460 cid V-8 (four-barrel) were optional.

HISTORICAL FOOTNOTES: Most full-size Mercurys, 75.7 percent, came with a vinyl roof. Most 1973 Comets, 91.82 percent, had radios, 35.2 percent had bucket seats, 37.4 percent had vinyl roofs, 90 percent had automatic transmissions, 45.9 percent had V-8s and 50.4 percent had tinted glass. Just 3.2 percent of 1973 Montegos came with bucket seats, 63.4 percent had vinyl roofs, 97 percent had a radio and 99.2 percent were powered by a V-8 engine. Most 1973 Cougars, 98 percent, had a radio, 94.7 percent had a vinyl roof, 28 percent had a tilting steering wheel, 99.3 percent had automatic transmission and 84.5 percent had air conditioning.

1974 MERCURY

COMET SERIES — New front and rear bumpers and slightly different upper and lower body moldings were the biggest Comet styling changes for 1974. Standard features included dual hydraulic brakes with warning light system: Blend-Air heater; windshield washers; locking steering column; cigar lighter; energy-absorbing steering wheel; and two-speed windshield wipers.

COMET

Model Number	Body/Style Number	Body Type & Seating	Factory Price	Shipping Weight	Production Total
NA	30	4-dr Sed-4P	2489	2904	60,944
NA	31	2-dr Sed-4P	2432	2813	64,751

1974 Mercury, Comet two-door sedan, 6-cyl

MONTEGO SERIES — The slightly protruding, chrome-outlined Montego grille had a criss-cross pattern. The four headlights were nestled in chrome panels. wheelwell openings and center mid body moldings were seen on the sides. Taillights were located on the rear deck panel and wrapped around the fenders. Standard features included front disc brakes; impact-resistant bumpers; locking steering column; concealed windshield wipers; inside hood release and color-keyed deep loop carpeting.

MONTEGO

Model Number	Body/Style Number	Body Type & Seating	Factory Price	Shipping Weight	Production Total
NA	02	4-dr Sed-6P	3360	4062	5,674
NA	03	2-dr HT-6P	3327	3977	7,645

MONTEGO MX SERIES — Rocker panel moldings and nameplates on the lower front fenders, were two identifying traits of the MX. In addition to a slightly plusher interior than the base Montego, the MX had Deluxe sound insulation.

MONTEGO MX

Model Number	Body/Style Number	Body Type & Seating	Factory Price	Shipping Weight	Production Total
NA	04	4-dr Sed-6P	3478	4092	19,446
NA	07	2-dr HT Cpe-6P	3443	3990	20,957
NA	08	4-dr Sta Wag-6P	4083	4426	4,085

1974 Mercury, Montego MX Brougham four-door Sed, V-8

MONTEGO MX BROUGHAM SERIES — Upper body and lower rear quarter panel moldings, plus a super sound-insulation package and woodgrain applique on the instrument panel were Brougham features. The Villager station wagon had simulated woodgrain bodyside and tailgate paneling, outlined with bright moldings, power tailgate window; flight-bench seat with center armrest and imitation Cherry wood instrument and dash panel appliques.

MONTEGO MX BROUGHAM

Model Number	Body/Style Number	Body Type & Seating	Factory Price	Shipping Weight	Production Total
NA	10	4-dr Sed-6P	3680	4143	13,467
NA	11	2-dr HT Cpe-6P	3646	4010	20,511
NA	18	4-dr Vill Wag-6P	4307	4463	6,234

1974 Mercury, Cougar XR-7 two-door hardtop sports coupe, V-8

COUGAR XR-7 SERIES — Front end styling was similar to last year's model, except the grille was wider and had the previous emblem replaced by a hood ornament. Side trim consisted of upper body chrome (running from the tip of the fenders to the rear fenders where it connected with a chrome band that went across the roof), full-length upper tire level moldings and a rear roof quarter panel opera window. The rear deck panel taillights wrapped around the fenders. Standard features included: soft, vinyl bucket seats or twin comfort lounge seats; steel-belted radial tires; power steering; performance instrumentation; luxury steering wheel; cut-pile carpeting and inside hood release.

COUGAR XR-7

Model Number	Body/Style Number	Body Type & Seating	Factory Price	Shipping Weight	Production Total
NA	93	2-dr HT Cpe-5P	4706	4255	91,670

MONTEREY SERIES — The Monterey had a squares-within-squares. chrome framed grille. This pattern was carried over to the headlight panels. Signal lights wrapped around the front fenders. Rear quarter pillar nameplate and trim, full-length mid-body spear and wheel opening and rocker panel molding were sedan on the sides. Among the standard features were: nylon carpeting; glovebox light; power steering; automatic parking brake release; solid state ignition and cloth and vinyl interior.

Model Number	Body/Style Number	Body Type & Seating	Factory Price	Shipping Weight	Production Total
NA	44	4-dr Sed-6P	4367	4559	6,185
NA	46	2-dr HT Cpe-6P	4410	4506	2,003
NA	72	4-dr Sta Wag-6P	4731	4916	1,669

MONTEREY CUSTOM SERIES — The Custom series script on the rear roof quarter panel. Deluxe wheelcovers, a Deluxe steering wheel and all-vinyl interior were standard features of the Custom.

MONTEREY CUSTOM

Model Number	Body/Style Number	Body Type & Seating	Factory Price	Shipping Weight	Production Total
NA	54	4-dr Sed-6P	4480	4561	13,113
NA	56	2-dr HT Cpe-6P	4523	4504	4,510

MARQUIS SERIES — The Marquis grille had rectangular vertical pieces with finder bars within them. The hidden headlight doors had horizontal bars which extended around the wraparound signal lights. Mercury was spelled out in chrome above the grille. Side trim consisted of full-length, lower body moldings. The six square taillights and two back-up lights were located in the rear deck panel. Standard features on Marquis included power front disc brakes; power steering; Deluxe sound insulation; loop-pile carpeting; courtesy lights; fender skirts and power ventilation. The interior was cloth and vinyl.

MARQUIS

Model Number	Body/Style Number	Body Type & Seating	Factory Price	Shipping Weight	Production Total
NA	63	4-dr Sed-6P	5080	4757	6,910
NA	66	2-dr HT Cpe-6P	5080	4698	2,633
NA	68	4-dr HT Sed-6P	4080	4753	784
NA	72	4-dr Sta Wag-6P	4960	4973	1,111

1974 Mercury, Marquis Brougham four-door sedan, V-8

MARQUIS BROUGHAM SERIES — Full-length upper body molding, halo vinyl roof, power windows; door pull straps, left-hand remote-control mirror; Deluxe wheelcovers with inserts; pillar lights and lights under the instrument panel, were Brougham features.

MARQUIS BROUGHAM

Model Number	Body/Style Number	Body Type & Seating	Factory Price	Shipping Weight	Production Total
NA	62	4-dr Sed-6P	5519	4833	24,477
NA	64	2-dr HT Cpe-6P	5519	4762	10,207
NA	67	4-dr HT Sed-6P	5519	4853	4,189
NA	76	4-dr Col Prk Wag-6P	5066	5066	10,802

(COMET) SIX: Overhead valves. Cast iron block. Displacement: 200 cid. Bore and stroke: 3.68 x 3.13 inches. Compression ratio: 8.30:1. SAE net hp: 84 at 3800 rpm. Carburetor: one-barrel.

(MONTEGO/MX/BROUGHAM) V-8: Overhead valves. Cast iron block. Displacement: 302 cid. Bore and stroke: 4 x 3 inches. Compression ratio: 8.00:1. SAE net hp: 140 at 3800 rpm. Carburetor: two-barrel.

(COUGAR XR-7) V-8: Overhead valves. Cast iron block. Displacement: 351 cid. Bore and stroke: 4 x 3.5 inches. Compression ratio: 8.00:1. SAE net hp: 168 at 4000 rpm. Carburetor: two-barrel.

(MONTEREY/MONTEREY CUSTOM) V-8: Overhead valves. Cast iron block. Displacement: 400 cid. Bore and stroke: 4 x 4 inches. Compression ratio: 8.00:1. SAE net hp: 170 at 3600 rpm. Carburetor: two-barrel.

(MARQUIS/MARQUIS BROUGHAM) V-8: Overhead valves. Cast iron block. Displacement: 460 cid. Bore and stroke: 4.36 x 3.85 inches. Compression ratio: 8.00:1. SAE net hp: 195 at 4400 rpm. Carburetor: four-barrel.

COMET CHASSIS FEATURES: Wheelbase: (two-door) 103 inches; (four-door) 109 inches. Overall length: (two-door) 187.7 inches; (four-door) 196.3 inches. Tires: 6.45 x 14.

MONTEGO CHASSIS FEATURES: Wheelbase: (two-doors) 114 inches; (four-doors and station wagons) 118 inches. Overall length: (two-doors) 215.5 inches; (four-doors) 219.5 inches; (station wagons) 223.1 inches. Tires: (station wagons) H78 x 14; (Villager Station wagon) HR78 x 14; (other models) G78 x 14.

COUGAR CHASSIS FEATURES: Wheelbase: 114 inches. Overall length: 214.2 inches. Tires: HR78 x 14.

MERCURY CHASSIS FEATURES: Wheelbase: (Passenger cars) 124 inches; (Station wagons) 121 inches. Overall length: (Passenger cars) 226.7 inches; (Station wagons) 225.6 inches. Tires: (Passenger cars) HR78 x 15; (Station wagons) JR78 x 15.

COMET OPTIONS: Air conditioner ($382.70). Heavy-duty battery ($13.60). Manual front disc brakes ($33.90). Rear window defogger ($30). Tinted glass ($37.50). Solid state ignition ($37.80). Left-hand remote-control dual racing mirrors ($25.10). Bodyside moldings ($32.50). Two-tone paint ($30). Glamour paint ($36.50). Power steering ($106.20). Push-button AM radio ($61.40). AM radio with special speakers ($115.50). AM/FM multiplex with dual front door and rear seat speakers ($221.60). AM/FM monoral ($129.10). Embassy roof ($83.20). Bucket seats ($126.40). Floor shifter ($13.80). All-vinyl trim ($13.80). Deluxe interior ($91.30). Deluxe wheelcovers ($25.10). Forged aluminum wheels with regular equipment ($153.80); with GT option ($123.80). Appearance protection group including floor mats with carpet inserts; door edge guards; license plate frames and spare tire lock on two-door ($36.50); on four-door ($39.10). Bumper protection group including front and rear rubber strips and rear bumper guards on cars without Custom group ($31.32); with Custom group ($23.50). Convenience group including glovebox, trunk, instrument panel courtesy and dual dome lights; day/night mirror; color-keyed seat/shoulder belts; Deluxe and left-hand remote-control racing mirrors, on cars with Deluxe trim or bucket seats ($31.30); with dual racing mirrors ($39.10); with dual racing mirrors and bucket seats or GT option ($23.50). Custom option including DR78 x 14 steel-belted whitewall radial tires; Deluxe wheelcovers with color-keyed inserts; left-hand remote-control mirror; dual body paint stripe; wheel lip and rocker panel moldings; tan interior; 25 oz. carpeting; higher level NVH package and Odense-grain vinyl roof, on

sedans ($408.30); on Villagers ($123.70). GT option including high-back bucket seats; Deluxe sound insulation; leather-wrapped steering wheel; cut-pile carpeting; color-keyed hood scoop; dual racing mirrors; black hubcaps with bright trim rings; black-out hood and black-finished front and lower back panels, on two-doors ($243.70). A three-speed manual transmission was standard. SelectShift automatic transmission was optional. A 91 hp 250 cid six (one barrel) and a 140 hp 302 cid V-8 were available at extra cost.

MONTEGO OPTIONS: Air conditioner ($397.91). Automatic temperature control air conditioner ($507.55). Anti-theft alarm system ($79). Traction-Lok differential axle ($46.70). Deluxe seat belts ($15.14). Load floor carpeting ($25.24). Electric clock ($17.67). Electric rear window defroster in Passenger cars ($46.70); in Station wagons ($61.84). Heavy-duty electrical system ($27.76). Tinted glass ($41.66). Solid-state ignition ($38.20). Luggage carrier with air deflector for station wagons ($76.99). Dual racing mirrors, left-hand mirror remote-control ($38.20). Illuminated visor vanity mirror ($35.60). Bodyside moldings ($32.82). Front disc brakes for station wagons ($68.14). Power door locks in two-doors ($44.17); in four-doors ($66.89). Six-Way bench seat ($102.22). Power steering ($112.33). Power windows in two-doors ($85.60); in four-doors ($112.33). AM/FM multiplex with stereo tape ($363.20). AM/FM multiplex with dual front door and rear seat speakers ($213.29). Dual rear speakers with AM radio ($30.29). Vinyl roof ($97.18). Embassy roof ($115.80). Rear facing center seat ($75.81). Automatic speed control ($98.70). Tilt steering wheel ($44.80). Standard wheelcovers ($25.24). Deluxe wheelcovers on Brougham, Villager ($7.90). Luxury wheelcovers ($42.91); same on Brougham, Villager ($17.67). Deluxe wheelcovers ($32.90). Styled steel wheels ($117.10); on Brougham, Villager ($92.10). Opera windows on two-doors with vinyl roof ($80.30). Interval-selector windshield wipers ($25.24). Appearance protection group including floor mats with carpet inserts; door edge guards; license plate frames and spare tire lock ($38.20). Brougham Custom trim option including Arden velour seating surfaces; door panel inserts; comfort lounge seats; luxury steering wheel; Cherry wood cluster cover; instrument panel applique with teakwood inlays; super-soft vinyl seat facings and door panels; trunk side lining boards; Deluxe color-keyed wheelcovers. Door-pull assist straps; 25 oz. carpet; visor vanity mirror and Lavant-grain or Odense-grain Embassy vinyl roof ($315.80). Bumper protection group including front and rear rubber strips and rear bumper guards, on passenger cars ($35.60); on Station wagons ($23.70). Convenience group including remote-control left and visor vanity mirrors; automatic seatback release with two-doors and spare tire extractor on Station wagon, two-doors ($51.40); four-doors ($29); station wagons ($31.60). Cross-country ride package ($16.41). Sports appearance group including fuel; ammeter; oil pressure and temperature gauges; trip odometer; clock; tachometer; sporty hood; dual racing mirrors; black hubcaps with bright trim rings; lower body tape stripe; G70 x 14 blackwall tires with raised white letters; lower panel black-out paint; leather-wrapped steering wheel; bright trim pedal pads and H70 x 14 blackwall tires with RL and 460 engine in two-doors ($310.29). Trailer-towing package class II ($32.82); class III ($117.18): station wagons ($80.01). Visibility light group ($29). A three-speed manual transmission was standard. SelectShift automatic transmission was optional. A 162 hp 351 cid V-8 (two-barrel); 246 hp CJ 351 cid V-8; 168 hp 400 cid V-8 (two-barrel) and a 244 hp 460 cid V-8 (four-barrel) were available. The last engine was not offered in station wagons. The 246 hp engine was not available in the MX Brougham series. A high-performance axle and Traction-Lok differential were optional.

COUGAR OPTIONS: Air conditioner ($397.54). Automatic temperature control with air conditioner ($475). Anti-theft alarm system ($79). Traction-Lok differential axle ($46.70). Deluxe seat belts ($15.14). Electric rear window defroster ($61.81). Heavy-duty electrical system ($27.70). Tinted glass ($36.61). Solid-state ignition ($38.20). Left-hand remote-control dual racing mirrors ($38.20). Illuminated visor vanity mirrors ($35.60). Bodyside moldings ($32.82). Power door locks ($44.80). Six-Way left-hand power seat ($90.80). Electric sun roof ($471.10). Power windows on two-doors ($85.60); on four-doors ($112.33). AM radio with special speakers ($97.40). AM/FM multiplex with stereo tape ($363.20). AM/FM multiplex with dual front door and rear seat speakers ($213.29). Dual rear speakers with AM radio ($30.30). Vinyl roof ($33.20). Tilt steering wheel ($44.17). Leather-wrapped steering wheel ($6.07). Leather upholstery trim with bucket or twin comfort seats ($167.10). Velour upholstery with twin comfort seats ($77.70). Sporty wheelcovers ($61.90). Styled steel wheels ($79). Appearance protection group including floor mats with carpet inserts; door edge guards; license plate frames and spare tire lock ($32.90). Bumper protection group including front and rear rubber strips and rear bumper guards ($35.60). Convenience group including visor vanity mirror; left-hand remote-control mirror and automatic seatback release. on two-doors, includes Deluxe CC seat belts ($50). Trailer towing package, class II ($32.90); class III ($177.10). Visibility light group ($29). SelectShift automatic was standard. A 264 hp CJ 351 cid V-8; 170 hp 400 cid V-8 (two-barrel) and a 220 hp 460 cid V-8 were optional. A high performance axle and Traction-Lok differential were available at extra cost.

MERCURY OPTIONS: Air conditioner ($430.58). Anti-theft alarm system. for station wagons without appearance protection group ($79); with appearance protection group ($73.70); Executive wagons without appearance protection group ($84.30); with appearance protection group ($78.95). Heavy-duty battery in Monterey and wagons ($12.62). Deluxe seat and shoulder belts ($15.14). Electric clock in Monterey ($17.67). Digital clock in Monterey ($39.50). Electric rear window defroster ($61.84). Rear fender skirts except Monterey wagons and Marquis passenger cars ($35.34). Floor mats in Monterey Custom ($23.70). Tinted glass ($50.49). Cornering lights ($35.24). Automatic load adjuster on wagons ($76.99). Luggage carrier with air deflector on wagons ($92.13). Visor vanity illuminated mirror on Monterey and Marquis ($35.60). Bodyside molding ($32.82); on Monterey, ($14.47). Rocker panel on Monterey Custom ($25). Sure-track power brakes ($189.30 with 460 engines). Six-Way bench seat ($102.22); same on Marquis ($87.08). Six-Way left and right power seat on Marquis ($174.15). Electric power sun roof on Executive wagons ($495.97). Electric windows ($140.79). Power tailgate window on MX wagons ($34.08). Power vent windows (four-doors $64.47). Remote-control trunk release on Executive wagons ($13.89). AM radio with special speakers ($97.40). AM/FM multiplex with stereo tape ($363.20). AM/FM multiplex with dual front-door and rear-seat speakers ($233.47). Dual rear speakers ($32.82). Vinyl roof on Executive wagons ($116.11); on other station wagons ($138.82). Halo roof on Marquis Executive wagon ($124.95). Dual-facing third seat on station wagons ($122.27). Twin comfort lounge seats ($75.72). Vinyl bench seat on Monterey ($27.76). Passenger-side reclining seat ($42.91). Automatic speed control ($66.89). Tilt steering wheel ($44.17). Storage compartment with locks on wagons ($32.90). Recreation table on wagons ($42.11). Trailer brake control ($38.20. Trailer hitch equalizer platform ($88.20). Deluxe cargo area trim, including lockable storage compartment and padded quarter trim on wagons ($65). Luggage compartment trim on Executive wagons including carpeting, spare tire cover and side lining board ($40.80). Luxury wheelcovers ($32.82). Interval selector wipers ($25.24). Rear tailgate window washer on wagons ($37.86). Appearance protection group including floor mats with carpet inserts; door edge guards; license plate frames; spare tire lock; rear mats with carpet inserts and hood lock, on station wagons ($46.10), on Executive wagons ($47.40) Bumper protection group including front and rear rubber strips and rear bumper guards, on station wagons ($23.68); on Executive wagons, ($35.53). Cross-country ride package ($22.7 1). Decor group including Deluxe steering wheel and wheelcovers, wheel lip and rocker panel moldings on Monterey ($63.16). Grand Marquis luxury trim including digital clock; carpeted trunk with side lining boards and flap; hood and deck lid stripes; perforated vinyl headlining with Corinthian grain vinyl covered visors; assist handles; unique head rest and seat trim; dash panel and cluster applique; door and quarter trim panels; dome map/reading lamp; luxury steering wheel; 25 oz. carpeting on Marquis without light group, ($325); Marquis with light group ($311.90); wagons without light group ($390.80); wagons with light group ($377.70). Lock convenience group including power door locks; trunk lid release; left-hand remote-control mirror; automatic seatback release on two-doors and power tailgate on station wagons, on two-doors with power windows ($82.89); four-doors with power windows ($80.26); wagons without power windows ($88.16); wagons with power windows ($75.54): two-doors without power windows ($96.05); four-doors without power windows ($93.42). Marquis-Colony Park luxury trim including instrument panel lights; door-pull straps; Brougham wheelcovers; Brougham split bench seat and door trim panels; 25 oz. carpeting; visor vanity mirror; Brougham level sound package; front door courtesy lights; rear door armrest cigar lighters and Brougham trim ($184.21). Trailer towing package class I ($35.84); class II ($32.82); class III ($88.34). Visibility light group on Monterey ($56.60); on Mercury ($47.40); on Marquis ($39.50). SelectShift automatic transmission was standard. A 195 hp 460 cid V-8 was optional. A high-performance axle and TractionLok differential were available at extra cost.

HISTORICAL FOOTNOTES: Most 1974 Comets, 82.2 percent, came with a radio, 36.2 percent had a vinyl roof and 24.1 percent had bucket seats. The vast majority of 1974 Montegos, 90.1 percent, had a radio and 65.7 percent came with a vinyl roof. Most Cougars, 90.9 percent were equipped with radio, 38.7 percent had bucket seats, 32.6 percent had a tilting steering wheel and 20.6 percent came with speed control. Seventy-eight percent of all full-size 1974 Mercurys came with a vinyl roof.

1975 MERCURY

1975 Mercury, Comet four-door sedan, 6-cyl

COMET SERIES — The styling department must have been in hibernation. The new Comet looked virtually the same as last year's model. Standard features included; locking steering column, Deluxe sound insulation package, deluxe steering wheel, color-keyed instrument panel with lighted dash, dual hydraulic-brake system with warning light and cut-pile carpeting. Buyers had their choice of four colors of cloth and vinyl interior.

MERCURY I.D. NUMBERS: VIN located on left-hand top of dash, viewable through windshield. VIN has 11 symbols. First symbol 5 = 1975. Second symbol indicates assembly plant: A = Atlanta, Ga. (Cougar); H = Lorain, Ohio (Montego); K = Kansas City, Mo. (Comet) and Z = St. Louis, Mo. (Mercury). Third and fourth symbols are Body Style Number in second column of charts below. Fifth symbol identifies engine: 1974 Engine Codes A,C,F,H,L,Q,S,T available, plus new Y = 139 cid (2.3L) four and Z = 169 cid (2.8L) four. Final six symbols are sequential production code. Certification Label on rear edge of driver's door indicates manufacturer, build dates (month and year), VIN, body code, color, trim, transmission and axle data.

COMET

Model Number	Body/Style Number	Body Type & Seating	Factory Price	Shipping Weight	Production Total
NA	30	4-dr Sed-4P	3270	3193	31,080
NA	31	2-dr Sed-4P	3236	3070	22,768

BOBCAT SERIES — The new Bobcat was based on Ford's Pinto. It had an attractive, chrome-framed grille with vertical bars and the word Mercury spelled out above it. Both headlights were recessed into bright moldings. The long, rectangular vertical taillights were placed on the rear deck panel.

BOBCAT

Model Number	Body/Style Number	Body Type & Seating	Factory Price	Shipping Weight	Production Total
NA	20	3-dr Hatch-4P	3189	NA	20,651
NA	21	2-dr Sta Wag-4P	3481	NA	13,583

NOTE: Model number 20, the three-door hatchback coupe, was called a Runabout. Model number 21, the two-door station wagon, was called the Villager.

MONARCH SERIES — Mercury called the new Monarch a "precision-size luxury car." It had a chrome-framed grille with vertical bars and Mercury spelled out above it. The two headlights were enclosed in square molding 'boxes' and the signal lights wrapped around the front fenders. Full-length trim (that continued around the rear of the car), wheel lip and window moldings and chrome rocker panels were sedan on the sides. The wraparound rectangular taillights were located on the rear deck panel. The word Mercury was printed in a chrome-framed section between the taillights. Standard equipment included, individually reclining bucket seats, front disc brakes, foot operated parking brake. solid-state ignition, locking glovebox and inside hood release.

MONARCH

Model Number	Body/Style Number	Body Type & Seating	Factory Price	Shipping Weight	Production Total
NA	34	4-dr Sed-5P	3822	3284	34,307
NA	35	2-dr Sed-5P	3764	3234	29,151

1975 Mercury, Monarch four-door Ghia sedan, V-8

MONARCH GHIA SERIES — Wide, full-length upper tire level moldings and upper body pinstripes made it easy to distinguished the Ghia from the basic Monarch. It came with a Deluxe sound insulation package; left-hand remote-control outside mirror; Odense-grain vinyl roof; unique wire spoke wheelcovers; carpeted luggage compartment; digital clock and luxury steering wheel.

MONARCH GHIA

Model Number	Body/Style Number	Body Type & Seating	Factory Price	Shipping Weight	Production Total
NA	37	4-dr sedan-5P	4349	3352	22,723
NA	38	2-dr Sed-5P	4291	3302	17,755

MONTEGO SERIES — Twin slots in the center of the lower front bumper were the main changes to Montego styling for 1975. Standard features included power brakes, power steering, solid state ignition, locking steering column, cut-pile carpeting. concealed windshield wipers and front bumper guards. Buyers could choose from a cloth and vinyl or all-vinyl interior in black, tan, or blue.

MONTEGO

Model Number	Body/Style Number	Body Type & Seating	Factory Price	Shipping Weight	Production Total
NA	02	4-dr Sed-6P	4128	4066	4,142
NA	03	2-dr HT Cpe-6P	4092	4003	4,051

1975 Mercury, Montego MX two-door hardtop, V-8

MONTEGO MX SERIES — Upper body pinstripes and rocker panel moldings were sedan on the MX. It also had extra sound insulation and a slightly fancier interior.

MONTEGO MX

Model Number	Body/Style Number	Body Type & Seating	Factory Price	Shipping Weight	Production Total
NA	04	4-dr Sed-6P	4328	4111	16,033
NA	07	2-dr HT Cpe-6P	4304	4030	13,666
NA	08	4-dr Sta Wag-6P	4674	4464	4,508

MONTEGO MX BROUGHAM SERIES — The Brougham had upper body moldings; door-pull straps; super sound-insulation package; vinyl roof; woodgrain applique on the steering wheel and wiper mounted windshield washer jets. The Villager wagon had woodgrain vinyl paneling on its sides and tailgate; power tailgate window; Deluxe steering wheel and flight bench seat with folding center armrest.

MONTEGO MX BROUGHAM

Model Number	Body/Style Number	Body Type & Seating	Factory Price	Shipping Weight	Production Total
NA	10	4-dr Sed-6P	4498	4130	8,235
NA	11	2-dr HT Cpe-6P	4453	4054	8,791
NA	18	4-dr Vill Wag-6P	4909	4522	5,754

1975 Mercury, Cougar XR-7 two-door hardtop sports coupe, V-8

COUGAR XR-7 SERIES — Two rectangular openings between the front bumper guards, on the lower bumper, was the extent of styling changes made to Cougars in 1975. They came with power steering; bucket seats with console (or Twin Comfort lounge seats); luxury steering wheel; deep cut-pile carpeting; passenger assist handle; inside hood release; locking steering column and power front disc brakes.

Model Number	Body/Style Number	Body Type & Seating	Factory Price	Shipping Weight	Production Total
NA	93	2-dr HT Cpe-5P	5218	4108	62,987

MARQUIS SERIES — The 1975 Marquis' chrome framed-grille consisted of six rectangular chrome pieces, each containing five vertical bars. A single vertical bar evenly divided the grille in two. The concealed headlight doors looked like music boxes. Both had an emblem in the center. The wraparound signal lights were circled by four thin chrome bands. Side trim consisted of full-length lower-body molding and upper body pinstripes. Mercury was spelled out on the center rear deck panel between the wraparound, rectangular taillights. Standard features included power steering; power front disc brakes; woodgrain applique on instrument panel; left-hand remote-control mirror; power ventilation system; Deluxe wheelcovers and cut-pile carpeting.

MARQUIS

Model Number	Body/Style Number	Body Type & Seating	Factory Price	Shipping Weight	Production Total
NA	63	4-dr Sed-6P	5115	4513	20,058
NA	66	2-dr HT Cpe-6P	5049	4470	6,807
NA	74	4-dr Sta Wag-6P	5411	4880	1,904

1975 Mercury, Marquis Brougham two-door hardtop coupe, V-8

MARQUIS BROUGHAM SERIES — The Brougham had full-length upper body moldings; vinyl roof; deep cut-pile carpeting; electric clock: power windows, fender skirts; Brougham wheelcovers and a visor mounted vanity mirror. The Colony Park station wagon featured simulated Rosewood paneling on the sides and tailgate; flight bench seat with center armrest, door-pull and seatback assist straps; Brougham wheelcovers; Deluxe seat and shoulder belts; visor mounted vanity mirror and three-way tailgate.

MARQUIS BROUGHAM

Model Number	Body/Style Number	Body Type & Seating	Factory Price	Shipping Weight	Production Total
NA	62	4-dr Sed-6P	6037	4799	19,667
NA	64	2-dr HT Cpe-6P	5972	4747	7,125
NA	76	4-dr Col Prk-6P	5598	4,953	11,652

1975 Mercury, Grand Marquis four-door Sed, V-8

GRAND MARQUIS SERIES — A wide, upper tire level band of molding across its sides set the Grand Marquis apart from the other series. It came with deep, shag cut-pile carpeting: dual map-reading lamps; left-hand remote-control mirror; vinyl roof; carpeted luggage compartment; hood and deck lid paint stripes and passenger assist straps.

GRAND MARQUIS I.D. NUMBERS: See 1960 Monterey I.D. numbers.

GRAND MARQUIS

Model Number	Body/Style Number	Body Type & Seating	Factory Price	Shipping Weight	Production Total
NA	60	4-dr Sed-6P	6469	4815	12,307
NA	61	2-dr HT Cpe-6P	6403	4762	4,945

(COMET/MONARCH) SIX: Overhead valves. Cast iron block. Displacement: 200 cid. Bore and stroke: 3.68 x 3,13 inches. Compression ratio: 8.30:1. SAE net hp: 75 at 3800 rpm. Carburetor: one-barrel.

(BOBCAT) FOUR: Overhead camshaft. Cast iron block. Displacement: 140 cid. Bore and stroke: 3.78 x 3.13 inches. Compression ratio: 8.40:1. SAE net hp: 83 at 4800 rpm. Carburetor: one-barrel

(MONARCH/MONARCH GHIA) SIX: Overhead valve. Cast iron block. Displacement: 250 cid. Bore and stroke: 3.68 x 3.91 inches. Compression ratio: 8.00:1. SAE net hp: 72 at 2900 rpm. Carburetor: one-barrel.

(MONTEGO/MX/MX BROUGHAM/COUGAR XR-7) V-8: Overhead valves. Cast iron block. Displacement: 351 cid. Bore and stroke: 4 x 3.5 inches. Compression ratio: 8.00:1. SAE net hp: 148 at 3800 rpm. Carburetor: two-barrel.

(MARQUIS CAR/MARQUIS BROUGHAM WAGON) V-8: Overhead valves. Cast iron block. Displacement: 460 cid. Bore and stroke: 4 x 4 inches. Compression ratio: 8.00:1. SAE net hp: 158 at 3800 rpm. Carburetor: two-barrel.

(MARQUIS BROUGHAM/GRAND MARQUIS CAR) V-8: Overhead valves. Cast iron block. Displacement: 460 cid. Bore and stroke: 4.36 x 3.85. Compression ratio: 8.00:1 SAE net hp: 218 at 4000 rpm. Carburetor: four-barrel.

COMET CHASSIS FEATURES: Wheelbase: (four-door) 109 inches; (two-door) 103 inches. Overall length: (four-door) 196.9 inches; (two-door) 190 inches. Tires: (four-door) CR78 x 14; (two-door) BR78 x 14.

BOBCAT CHASSIS FEATURES: Wheelbase: (Runabout) 94.5 inches; (Villager) 94.8 inches. Overall length: (Runabout) 169 inches; (Villager) 179 inches. Tires: B78 x 13.

MONTEGO CHASSIS FEATURES: Wheelbase (two-door) 114 inches, (four-door and station wagons) 118 inches. Overall length (two-door) 215.5 inches; (four-door) 219.5 inches; (station wagons) 224.4 inches. Tires: HR78 x 14.

MONARCH CHASSIS FEATURES: Wheelbase 109.9 inches. Length: 200 inches. Tires: DR78 x 14.

COUGAR CHASSIS FEATURES: Wheelbase: 114 inches. Overall length: 215.5 inches. Tires: HR78 x 14.

MERCURY CHASSIS FEATURES: Wheelbase: (passenger car) 124 inches; (station wagon) 121 inches. Overall length: (passenger car) 229 inches; (station wagon) 227 inches. Tires: (passenger cars) JR78 x 15; (Marquis) HR78 x 15.

COMET OPTIONS: Air conditioner ($382.70). Heavy-duty battery ($13.60). Manual front disc brakes ($33.90). Rear window defogger ($30). Tinted glass ($37.50). Solid-state ignition ($37.80). Left-hand remote-control dual racing mirrors ($25.10). Bodyside moldings ($32.50). Two-tone paint ($30). Glamour paint ($36.50). Power steering ($106.20). Push-button AM radio ($61.40). AM radio with special speakers ($115.50). AM/FM multiplex with dual front door and rear seat speakers ($221.60). AM/FM monaural ($129.10). Embassy roof ($83.20). Bucket seats ($126.40). Floor shifter ($13.80). All-vinyl trim ($13.80). Deluxe interior ($91.30). Deluxe wheelcovers ($25.10). Forged aluminum wheels ($153.80); same with GT option ($123.80). Appearance protection group including floor mats with carpet inserts; door edge guards; license plate frames and spare tire lock in two-doors ($36.50); in four-doors ($39.10). Bumper protection group including front and rear rubber strips and rear bumper guards, on models without Custom group ($31.32); on models with Custom group ($23.50). Convenience group including glovebox, trunk, instrument panel courtesy and dual dome lights; day/night mirror; color-keyed seat/shoulder belts; Deluxe and left-hand remote-control racing mirror, on cars with Deluxe trim or bucket seats ($31.30); cars with dual racing mirrors ($39.10); cars with dual racing mirrors and bucket seat or GT option ($23.50). Custom option including DR78xl4 steel-belted whitewall radial tires; Deluxe wheelcovers with color-keyed inserts; left-hand remote-control mirror; dual body paint stripe; wheel lip and rocker panel moldings; tan interior; 25 oz. carpeting; higher level NVH package and Odense-grain vinyl roof, on sedan ($408.30); on Villager ($123.70). GT option includes high-back bucket seats; Deluxe sound insulation; leather-wrapped steering wheel; cut-pile carpeting; color-keyed hood scoop; dual racing mirrors; black hubcaps with bright trim rings; black-out hood, front and lower back panel, on two-doors ($243.70). A three-speed manual transmission was standard. SelectShift automatic transmission was optional. A 91 hp 250 cid six and a 140 hp 302 cid V-8 (two-barrel) were available at extra cost.

BOBCAT OPTIONS: Air conditioning ($416). Vinyl top on Runabout ($83). Deluxe wheelcovers ($25.10). Luggage rack on Villager ($71). Sunroof ($210). AM radio ($61.40). AM/FM radio ($218). Aluminum wheels ($136). Power steering ($106). Sports accent group ($269). A three-speed manual transmission was standard. SelectShift automatic transmission was optional. A 97 hp 170 cid six was available.

MONARCH OPTIONS: Air conditioning ($416). Vinyl roof ($92). AM radio ($61.40). AM/FM stereo radio ($225). AM/FM stereo radio with tape system ($347). Power seats ($104). Power sun roof ($517). Power windows ($85.60). Power steering ($112.33). Power brakes ($68). Rear window defroster ($46.70). Upholstery with leather seating surfaces. Grand Ghia package. Illuminated visor vanity mirror. Decor package including vinyl seat trim with map pocket and assist rails. A three-speed manual transmission was standard. SelectShift automatic was optional. A 72 hp 250 cid six (one-barrel); 129 hp 302 cid V-8 (two-barrel) and a 154 hp 351 cid V-8 (two-barrel) were available.

MONTEGO OPTIONS: Air conditioner ($397.91). Automatic temperature control air conditioner ($507.55). Anti-theft alarm system ($79). Traction-Lok differential axle ($46.70). Deluxe seat belts ($15.14). Load floor carpet ($25.24). Electric clock ($17.67). Electric rear window defroster in passenger cars ($46.70); in station wagons ($61.84). Heavy-duty electrical system ($27.76). Tinted glass ($41.66). Solid state ignition ($38.20). Luggage carrier with air deflector ($76.99). Dual racing mirrors with remote control left-hand unit ($38.20). Illuminated visor vanity mirror ($35.60). Bodyside moldings ($32.82). Front disc brakes on wagons ($68.14). Power door locks in two-doors ($44.17), four-doors ($66.89). Six-Way bench seat ($124). Power steering ($112.33). Power windows in two-doors ($85.60); four-doors ($112.33). AM/FM multiplex with stereo tape ($383.20). AM/FM multiplex with dual front door and rear seat speakers ($238.29). Dual rear speakers with AM radio ($30.29). Vinyl roof ($97.18). Embassy roof ($115.80). Rear facing center seat ($86). Automatic speed control ($98.70). Tilt steering wheel ($44.80). Standard wheelcovers ($25.24). Deluxe wheelcovers for Brougham, Villager ($7.90). Luxury wheelcovers ($42.91); same on Brougham, Villager ($17.67). Deluxe wheelcovers ($32.90). Styled steel wheels ($117.10); same on Brougham, Villager ($92.10). Opera windows in two-doors with vinyl roof ($80.30). Interval-selector windshield wipers ($25.24). Appearance protection group including floor mats with carpet inserts; door edge guards; license frames and spare tire lock ($38.20). Brougham Custom trim option including Ardenvelour seating surfaces; door panel inserts; comfort lounge seats; luxury steering wheel; Cherrywood cluster cover; instrument panel applique with teakwood inlays; super-soft vinyl seat facings and door panels; trunk side lining boards; Deluxe color-keyed wheelcovers; door-pull assist straps; 25 oz. carpet; visor vanity mirror and Lavant-grain or Odense-grain Embassy vinyl roof ($384.80). Bumper protection group including front and rear rubber strips and rear bumper guards, on passenger cars ($35.60); on station wagons ($23.70). Convenience group including remote-control left-hand and visor vanity mirrors; automatic seatback release with two-doors and spare tire extractor with station wagons, on two-doors ($51.40); on four-doors ($29); on station wagons ($31.60). Cross-country ride package ($16.41). Sports appearance group including fuel; ammeter; oil pressure and temperature gauges; trip odometer; clock; tachometer; sports hood; dual racing mirrors; black hubcaps with bright trim rings; lower body tape stripe; G70xl4 blackwall tires with raised white letters (or H70 x 14 blackwall tires with raised letters and 460 engine); lower panel black-out paint; leatherwrapped steering wheel; bright trim pedal pads, for two-doors ($260). Trailer-towing package class II ($32.82); class III ($117.18); station wagons ($80.01). Visibility light group ($29). SelectShift automatic was standard. A 158 hp 400 cid V-8 (two-barrel) and a 216 hp 460 cid V-8 were optional. A high-performance axle and Traction-Lok differential were available at extra cost.

COUGAR OPTIONS: Air conditioner ($397.54). Automatic temperature control air conditioner ($475). Anti-theft alarm system ($79). Traction-Lok differential axle ($46.70). Deluxe seat belts ($15.14). Electric rear window defroster ($61.81). Heavy-duty electrical system ($27.70). Tinted glass ($36.61). Solid-state ignition ($38.20). Left-hand remote-control dual racing mirrors ($38.20). Illuminated visor vanity mirror ($35.60). Bodyside moldings ($32.82). Power door locks ($44.80). Six-Way left-hand power seat ($124). Electric sun roof ($525). Power windows, on two-door ($85.60); four-door ($112.33). AM radio with special speakers ($97.40). AM/FM multiplex with stereo tape ($393.20). AM/FM multiplex with dual front door and rear seat speakers ($213.29). Dual rear speakers with AM radio ($30.30). Vinyl roof ($33.20). Tilt steering wheel ($44.17). Leather-wrapped steering wheel ($6.07). Leather upholstery trim with bucket or twin comfort seats ($167.10). Velour upholstery with twin comfort seats ($77.70). Sporty wheelcovers ($61.90). Styled steel wheels ($79). Appearance protection group including floor mats with carpet inserts; door edge guards; license plate frames and spare tire lock ($32.90). Bumper protection group including front and rear rubber strips and rear bumper guards ($35.60). Convenience group including visor vanity mirror; left-hand remote-control mirror; automatic seatback release, on two-doors and Deluxe color-coordinated seat belts ($50). Trailer towing package class II ($32.90); class III ($117.10). Visibility light group ($29). SelectShift automatic was standard. A 158 hp 400 cid V-8 (two-barrel) and a 216 hp 460 cid V-8 (four-barrel) were optional. A high-performance axle and Traction-Lok differential could be ordered.

MERCURY OPTIONS: Air conditioner ($430.58). Anti-theft alarm system, for station wagons without appearance protection group ($84.30); with appearance protection group ($78.95). Heavy-duty battery, station wagons ($12.62). Deluxe seat and shoulder belts ($15.14). Digital clock ($39.50). Electric rear window defroster ($61.84). Tinted glass ($50.49). Cornering lights ($35.24). Automatic load adjuster, station wagons $76.99). Luggage carrier with air deflector ($96.00). Visor vanity illuminated mirror ($35.60). Bodyside molding ($32.82). Sure-Track power brakes with 460 cid V-8 ($189.30). Six-Way bench seat ($124). Six-Way left and right hand power seat ($174.16). Electric power sun roof ($495.97). Electric windows ($140.79). Remote control trunk release ($13.89). AM radio with special speakers ($97.40). AM/FM multiplex with stereo tape ($363.20). AM/FM multiplex with dual front door and rear seat speakers ($233.47). Dual rear speakers ($32.82). Vinyl roof ($637). Dual facing third seat, wagons ($112.27). Twin comfort lounge seats ($75.72). Passenger side reclining seat ($42.91). Automatic speed control ($66.89). Tilt steering wheel ($44.17). Storage compartment with locks, station wagons ($32.90). Recreation table, station wagons ($42.11). Trailer brake control ($38.20). Trailer hitch equalizer platform ($88.20). Deluxe cargo area trim, including lockable storage and padded quarter trim, station wagons ($65). Luggage compartment trim, for station wagons, including: carpeting; spare tire cover and side lining board ($40.80). Luxury wheelcovers ($32.82). Interval selector wipers ($25.24). Rear tailgate window washer, station wagons ($37.86). Appearance protection group, including floor mats with carpet inserts; door edge guards; license plate frames; spare tire lock; rear mats with carpet inserts and hood lock, on station wagons ($47.40). Bumper protection group including front and rear rubber bumper strips and rear bumper guards, on station wagons ($23.68); on executive wagons ($35.53). Cross country ride package ($22.71). Grand Marquis luxury trim including digital clock; carpeted trunk with side lining boards and flap, hood and deck lid stripes; perforated vinyl headlining with Corinthian-grain vinyl covered visors; assist handles; unique headrests and seat trim; dash panel and cluster applique; door and quarter trim panels; dome map/reading lamp; luxury steering wheel and 25 oz. carpeting, on Marquis without light group ($325); Marquis with light group ($311.90); station wagons without light group ($390.80); station wagons with light group ($377.70). Marquis/Colony Park luxury trim, including instrument panel lights, door-pull straps; Brougham wheelcovers; Brougham split bench seat and door trim panels; 25 oz. carpeting; visor vanity mirror; Brougham level sound package; front door courtesy lights; rear door armrest cigar lighters and Brougham trim ($184.21). Trailer-towing package class I ($36.84); class II ($32.82) and class III ($88.34). Visibility light group ($39.50). SelectShift automatic transmission was standard. A 218 hp 460 cid V-8 (four-barrel) was optional.

HISTORICAL FOOTNOTES: Most 1975 Comets, 82.5 percent, were equipped with a radio, 13.2 percent had bucket seats and 39.2 percent came with a vinyl-covered roof. Most 1975 Bobcats, 75 percent, came with radios and 10.5 percent had vinyl roofs. Only 6.3 percent of 1975 Monarchs came with a stereo tap system, 50.6 percent had a vinyl roof and 88.4 percent had a radio. Most 1975 Montegos, 89.1 percent, were equipped with a radio, 59.3 percent had vinyl roofs, 3.7 percent had a stereo tape system and 12.4 percent had a tilting steering wheel. Approximately one in three 1974 full-size Mercurys came with speed control.

STANDARD CATALOG OF
NASH
1946-1957

1955 Nash, four-door sedan, 6-cyl

Charles W. Nash and James Storrow purchased the Thomas B. Jeffery Co. of Kenosha, Wis. in 1916. Nash was a former vice-president of General Motors. Jeffery was best known for making the Rambler of the early 1900s.

Cars bearing the Nash name started to appear during 1917, although the first Nash-designed car was a 1918 model.

The firm's first post World War II models were similar to the Nash 600, created in 1941 as a car that could get up to 600 miles on one fill up of its 20 gallon gasoline tank. George W. Mason, a former Chrysler works manager, became president in 1936 when Nash and Mason's Kelvinator Corp. merged to form Nash-Kelvinator.

Data compiled by Larry Daum

The 1946 Nash 600 carried its prewar sheet metal on a 112-inch wheelbase chassis powered by an L-head six. It was marketed together with the fancier Ambassador, which used an overhead valve engine in a 121 inch wheelbase car. The Ambassador chassis was quite different from that of the 600. The smaller car had unitized construction, while the Ambassador retained the body-on-frame type. Also, the 600 had coil springs all around, while the Ambassador used semi-elliptic springs at the rear.

Nash, unlike other independent automakers, avoided a major restyling in the earlier post World War II years. The 600 became its bread-and-butter model. The Ambassador had richer appointments inside and out. These handsome looking cars were similar in style to contemporary Cadillacs, but Nash was headed in a new postwar direction and would continue building this type of vehicle only through 1948.

Strong sales were registered throughout the period, due primarily to America's dire need for cars from a period when manufacturing was artificially restricted. The ability to have some product on hand was helpful and probably played a role in having a unique honor bestowed upon Nash for the first and last time in 1947. The company was asked to supply the Official Pace Car for the Indianapolis 500-Mile Race. It was an Ambassador sedan.

Dramatically new for 1949, the Nash Airflyte series offered unit-construction in a fastback body that looked like a baby Packard. These cars carried over features popular with buyers, such as an overhead valve six in the Ambassador series, full coil spring suspension, large 15 inch tires and the efficiency of an overdrive transmission. Styling features included fully enclosed front and rear wheelhousings, one-piece windshields, fold-down travel bed seats and the 'Uniscope' dash instrument cluster that put all the gauges in one place.

In his plans for the changing marketplace of the '50s, George Mason saw that the early postwar seller's market would not last and he tried to merge all the independent auto-

makers together. He was unable to do so, but did accomplish the introduction of the first compact car in 1950. Mason's small car interest was shared by George Romney, who joined Nash-Kelvinator in 1948 as Mason's administrative assistant.

Nash re-introduced the Rambler nameplate in 1950, affixing it to the midyear compact model built off a new platform. It first came only as an equipment-loaded convertible-landau. This was basically like a two-door hardtop with a soft-top. When the roof was lowered on rails, the windows and frames remained in a fixed-upright position. The Rambler's engine was the original Nash 600 motor. It could go even further on a gallon of gas in the small Rambler.

A second model was soon added. This two-door station wagon was announced at the same price as the convertible. Mason's idea to make the compact marketable was to introduce fancier models first to gain respectability for the compact. This followed the old Nash advertising motto 'Built up to a standard, not down to a price' and it worked.

The year 1951 brought a two-door hardtop to the Rambler line. It was called the Country Club coupe. This was the first modern compact hardtop. It had loads of trim and a fashionable continental spare tire. The larger models were basically carried over in 1951, with a few detail changes.

Nash's Golden Anniversary was celebrated in 1952. There was new styling for the Ambassador and Statesman. A new notch back body created by Italy's Pininfarina was the fashion hit of the marque's 50th year. The fastback look was gone and eye appeal was greatly enhanced.

Shortly before George Mason's death in 1954, his dream of joining all the independent auto companies into one came partly true. Nash and Hudson merged, in May, 1954, to form American Motors. Then, it fell to George Romney to lead the fledgling enterprise in its formative and perhaps most significant years. Also in 1954, a two-door sedan version of the Rambler American was finally introduced, along with a four-door sedan.

It took George Romney several years to fully integrate Nash and Hudson operations and fully develop AMC. During the interim, some of the autocracy of the two firms was retained. Both Nashes and Hudsons continued to appear in separate showrooms. Each kept some styling distinctions, although the basic Nash body was used for both. Hudson dealers were also supplied with a "badge-engineered" Rambler. It had Hudson nameplates, hubcaps and grille medallions. Both companies also sold badge-engineered versions of the first American-designed sub-compact. However, this pint-sized Metropolitan was built by Austin, in England. Like the hybrid Nash-Healey, also British-made, it falls beyond the scope of this catalog of "American" automobiles.

The Rambler and Ambassador were both restyled for 1955. Full front wheel openings were the major change for the smaller car, along with new exterior trim design. The Ambassador and Statesman received a new slab-cornered front end treatment. It had larger, but not full, front wheel cutouts along with a wraparound windshield and larger oval grille that incorporated the headlights. The Packard Clipper V-8 was made available in the full-sized Nash Ambassador, along with Packard's Ultramatic transmission. Nash sixes continued to use GM's Hydra-Matic.

The big news for 1956 was a completely new type of Ramblers that debuted in the spring. They were based on the 1954 four-door models'108-inch wheelbase. Cars in this series featured many Rambler firsts, including a new overhead valve six, two-tone exterior sweep panel treatments and optional Hydra-Matic. The fancier and larger economy class cars accounted for 82,000 of the 104,00 units sold during the year.

The grand finale came for both Nash and Hudson in 1957. By this stage of the merger program, Hudson production in Detroit, Mich. had ceased completely and almost all AMC assemblies were done at the Nash facilities in Kenosha, Wis. The Ambassador was face-lifted for the last time, with new emphasis placed on sportiness, luxury and V-8 power. In fact, AMC had its own V-8 since the middle of 1956.

No amount of effort was quite enough to turn the tide. In fact, merely over 10,000 Nashes found buyers during the calendar year. The same basic product in Hudson trim sold just over 4,000.

When 1958 rolled around, both marques were relegated into the history books. The Nash and Hudson names were dropped at the last minute, just before the new models were introduced. Rambler became the name of the marque. The timing for the change was perfect. In 1958, rising auto prices and a general economic recession combined to boost buyer interest in small cars. The only such domestic product around at that time was the Rambler. For awhile, it would be a success.

1946 Nash 600, four-door sedan, 6-cyl

1949 Nash, four-door sedan, 6-cyl

Standard Catalog of American Cars

1947 Nash, four-door Suburban, 6-cyl

1948 Nash, four-door Suburban, 6-cyl

1949 Nash, Statesman Super four-door, 8-cyl (JL)

1950 Nash, Rambler two-door landau convertible, 6-cyl

1952 Nash, Ambassador two-door hardtop, 6-cyl

1954 Nash, Statesman Super, four-door sedan, 6-cyl

1954 Nash, Statesman Super four-door sedan, 6-cyl

1955 Nash, Ambassador Custom four-door sedan, V-8

Standard Catalog of American Cars

1946 NASH

1946 Nash '600' Coupe, 6-cyl

NASH 600 — SERIES 40 — (6-CYL) — Nash, like most manufacturers after World War II, brought out cars based on prewar models with minor modifications. A significant change in the 600 was the use of a conventional wishbone front suspension. It replaced the Lancia-inspired 1941-1942 "sliding-pillar" type. Other changes included a wider front grille, the movement of turn signals from atop the front fenders (in 1942) to a position inboard of the front headlights, and a new hood crest showing the Nash coat of arms. This emblem was less stylized and ornate than in 1942. Like the 1941 original, the new '600' had unitized construction. The model name reflected the fact that Nash claimed the car would go 600 miles on a full 20-gallon tank of gas. Technical features included sealed-in manifolding; full-pressure lubrication; full-length water jackets; steel-strut aluminum alloy pistons; extra-hard cylinder blocks; double-automatic spark control; air-cooled voltage generator; radial balanced crankshaft; three-point rubber-insulated engine mounting; crankshaft vibration dampener; and 20-gallon fuel tank. Standard equipment varied by model as follows: [Deluxe] spare wheel and tire; no-draft ventilation; hi-test safety glass; Deluxe bumpers; twin bumper guards front and rear; dual horns, sun visors and windshield wipers; front door armrests; dome light; cigar lighter; instrument panel ashtray; and center-rear compartment ashtray. [Four-door sedan] rear quarter compartment ashtray and robe cord. [Two- and four-door sedan) assist cords. [Custom] Wind-up type clock; metal rear fender gravel pads; door locks; glove compartment locks; Deluxe steering wheel; rear quarter vent windows; combination plastic and lacquered radio grille; rotary door locks; sealed beam headlights; stainless steel running board moldings; carpet insert in front floor mat and voltage control generator.

NASH I.D. NUMBERS: Vehicle Identification Plate located on the right-hand side of the cowl below the hood contains motor-serial number and number codes for model, paint and trim. Motor-serial number matches the serial number. Model number has four symbols. The first two symbols indicate model year, 46 = 1946. The third symbol indicates series: 4 = 600; 6 = Ambassador. The fourth symbol indicates body style. (All four numbers appear in Body/Style Number column of charts below). Motor numbers located on right-hand side of crankcase towards front and on front upper left-hand side of block. Motor-serial numbers for 1946 were: [600] K-77701 to K-135801; [Ambassador] R-393101 to R-429001.

NASH 600 SERIES 40

Model Number	Body/Style Number	Body Type & Seating	Factory Price	Shipping Weight	Production Total
40	4640	4-dr Trk Sed-6P	1342	2740	7,300
40	4643	2-dr Brgm Sed-6P	1293	2685	8,500
40	4648	4-dr FsBk Sed-6P	1298	2780	42,300

1946 Nash, Ambassador four-door sedan, 6-cyl (TVB)

NASH AMBASSADOR — SERIES 60 — (6-CYL) — The Ambassador shared the looks and detail changes seen on the 600, but had a nine inch longer wheelbase. Instead of unitized construction, it featured separate chassis/frame engineering. However, the sheet metal and body construction were the same as for 600s from the cowl back. The car's extra nine inches of sheet metal was originally planned for a Nash overhead valve straight eight. The inline eight engine was dropped from production after World War II. The Ambassador now used a slightly

updated overhead valve six with 112 hp. Technical features included sealed-in manifolding; full-pressure lubrication; full-length water jackets; steel-strut aluminum alloy pistons with four rings; extra-hard cylinder block; double automatic spark control; air-cooled voltage generator; radial-balanced crankshaft with vibration dampener; four-point rubber insulated engine mounting; oil filter; six quart crankcase; and 20-gallon fuel tank.

AMBASSADOR 60 SERIES

Model Number	Body/Style Number	Body Type & Seating	Factory Price	Shipping Weight	Production Total
60	4660	4-dr Trk Sed-6P	1511	3335	3,875
60	4663	2-dr Brgm Sed-6P	1453	3260	4,825
60	4664	4-dr Sub-6P	1929	3470	275
60	4668	4-dr FsBk Sed-6P	1469	3360	26,925

ENGINES

(NASH 600 SIX) Inline. L-head six: Cast iron block. Displacement: 172.6 cid. Bore and stroke: 3-1/8 x 3-3/4 inches. Compression ratio: 6.8:1. Brake hp: 82 at 3800 rpm. Four main bearings. Solid valve lifters. Carburetion: Carter one-barrel WA1-611S.

(AMBASSADOR SIX) Inline six: Overhead valves. Cast iron block. Displacement: 234.8 inches. Bore and stroke: 3-3/8 x 4-3/8 inches. Compression ratio: 6.8:1. Brake hp: 112 at 3400 rpm. Seven main bearings. Solid valve lifters. Carburetion: Carter one-barrel Model YF.

CHASSIS FEATURES: Wheelbase: (600) 112 inches; (Ambassador) 121 inches. Overall length: (600) 199-9/16 inches; (Ambassador) 208-9/16 inches. Front tread: (600) 56-13/16 inches; (Ambassador) 57-1/2 inches. Rear tread: (600) 59-3/4 inches; (Ambassador) 60-1/2 inches. Tires: (600) 6.00 x 16; (Ambassador) 6.50 x 15.

OPTIONS: Foam rubber cushions. Conditioned air system. Vacuum booster pumper. Radio and antenna. Directional signals. Oil bath air cleaner. Oil filter. There were no available engine options. The standard gearbox was a three-speed manual type with overdrive offered as an option on the Ambassador only.

HISTORICAL FOOTNOTES: From 1946-1948 Nash produced a wood-bodied four-door sedan in the style of the Chrysler Town & Country. A total of 1,000 of these wood covered 'Suburbans' were built in this three-year period. The fastback sedan was called the Slip Stream. Nash built 98,769 cars in calendar 1946 for eighth place in auto industry sales rankings.

1947 NASH

1947 Nash, '600' four-door sedan, 6-cyl

NASH 600 — SERIES 40 — (6-CYL) — The Nash 600 for 1947 received few changes from 1946. The front grilles were widened again and new raised center hubcaps were used.

NASH I.D. NUMBERS: Vehicle Identification Plate located on the right-hand side of the cowl below the hood contains motor-serial number and number codes for model, paint and trim. Motor-serial number matches the serial number. Model number has four symbols. The first two symbols indicate model year, 47 = 1947. The third symbol indicates series: 4 = 600; 6 = Ambassador. The fourth symbol indicates body style. (All four numbers appear in Body/Style Number column of charts below). Motor numbers located on right-hand side of crankcase towards front and on front upper left-hand side of block. Motor-serial numbers for 1946 were: [600] K-136001 to K-153244; [Ambassador] R-429201 to R-440922.

NASH 600 SERIES 40

Model Number	Body/Style Number	Body Type & Seating	Factory Price	Shipping Weight	Production Total
40	4740	4-dr Trk Sed-6P	1464	2786	21,500
40	4743	2-dr Brgm-6P	1415	2731	12,100
40	4748	4-dr FsBk Sed-6P	1420	2826	27,700

NASH AMBASSADOR — SERIES 60 — (6-CYL) — The only changes for the 1947 Ambassador was the addition of the same front grille as used on Nash 600s, plus the same raised center hubcaps. The four-door Nash Suburban was distinguished by wooden side panels. The fastback sedan was called the Slip Stream.

AMBASSADOR 60 SERIES

Model Number	Body/Style Number	Body Type & Seating	Factory Price	Shipping Weight	Production Total
60	4760	4-dr Trk Sed-6P	1809	3387	15,927
60	4763	2-dr Brgm-6P	1751	3312	8,673
60	4764	4-dr Sub-6P	2227	3522	595
60	4768	4-dr FsBk Sed-6P	1767	3412	14,505

ENGINES

(NASH 600 SIX) Inline. L-head six: Cast iron block. Displacement: 172.6 cid. Bore and stroke: 3-1/8 x 3-3/4 inches. Compression ratio: 6.8:1. Brake hp: 82 at 3800 rpm. Solid valve lifters. Carburetion: Carter one-barrel WA1-611S.

(AMBASSADOR SIX) Inline six: Overhead valves. Cast iron block. Displacement: 234.8 inches. Bore and stroke: 3-3/8 x 4-3/8 inches. Compression ratio: 6.8:1. Brake hp: 112 at 3400 rpm. Seven main bearings. Solid valve lifters. Carburetion: Carter one-barrel Model YF.

CHASSIS FEATURES: Wheelbases: (600) 112 inches; (Ambassador) 121 inches. Overall length: (600) 199-9/16 inches; (Ambassador) 208-9/16 inches. Front tread: (600) 56-13/16 inches; (Ambassador) 57-1/2 inches. Rear tread: (600) 59-3/4 inches; (Ambassador) 60-1/2 inches. Tires: (600) 6.00 x 16; (Ambassador) 6.50 x 15.

1947 Nash, Ambassador, four-door sedan, 6-cyl (IMS)

OPTIONS: Foam rubber cushions. Cruising gear (Ambassador only). Conditioned air system. Vacuum booster pump. Radio and antenna. Directional signals. Oil bath air cleaner. Oil filter (600 only). There were no available optional engines. The standard gearbox was a three-speed manual type with Warner Gear overdrive available at extra cost.

HISTORICAL FOOTNOTES: Production for calendar year 1947 increased to 113,315 cars and Nash came in 10th in sales. A one-of-a-kind 12-passenger Nash limousine was built to carry executives and VIPs around the plant. It had four doors on each side. A Nash Ambassador was Official Pace Car for the Indianapolis 500-Mile Race. The five percent of total U.S. auto sales earned by Nash this season was a strong showing for an independent manufacturer. New assembly sites in El Segundo, Calif. and Toronto, Ontario, Canada were acquired by Nash-Kelvinator Corp. this year. George W. Mason was chairman of the board and president of the company. Production of the 1947 line commenced in December, 1946.

1948 NASH

1948 Nash, '600' four-door sedan, 6-cyl

NASH 600 SERIES 40 — (6-CYL) — Changes to the 1948 Nash consisted of the removal of a chrome molding just below the beltline, giving the cars a clean sided look. Hoodside moldings did not run as far forward and the hood badge design was changed. In addition, the model line was expanded to meet an anticipated upsurge in buyer demand. Included, for the first time since before World War II, was a three-passenger business coupe and upgraded Custom versions of the two-door Brougham and the four-door Slip Stream and Trunk sedan.

NASH I.D. NUMBERS: Vehicle Identification Plate located on the right-hand side of the cowl below the hood contains motor-serial number and number codes for model, paint and trim. Motor-serial number matches the serial number. Model number has four symbols. The first two symbols indicate model year, 48 = 1948. The third symbol indicates series: 4 = 600 Super/Deluxe; 5 = 600 Custom; 6 = Ambassador Super; 7 = Ambassador Custom. The fourth symbol indicates body style. (All four numbers appear in Body/Style Number column of charts below). Motor numbers located on right-hand side of crankcase towards front and on front upper left-hand side of block. [600 SERIES] Serial numbers ran from K196901 to K259792. Motor numbers ran from KE55001 to KE120132 and no longer matched serial numbers. [AMBASSADOR SERIES] Serial numbers ran from R468501 to R514594. Motor-serial numbers ran from RE40001 to RE82095.

NASH 600 SERIES 40

Model Number	Body/Style Number	Body Type & Seating	Factory Price	Shipping Weight	Production Total
SUPER LINE/DELUXE COUPE					
40	4840	4-dr Trk Sed-6P	1587	2786	25,103
40	4843	2-dr Brgm-6P	1538	2731	11,530
40	4848	4-dr FsBk Sed-6P	1534	2826	25,044
40	4842	2-dr Bus Cpe-3P	1478	2635	925
CUSTOM LINE					
40	4850	4-dr Trk Sed-6P	1776	2786	346
40	4853	2-dr Brgm-6P	1727	2731	170
40	4858	4-dr FsBk Sed-6P	1732	2826	332

1948 Nash, Ambassador two-door convertible, 6-cyl.

NASH AMBASSADOR — SERIES 60 — (6-CYL) — The 1948 Ambassador also had the chrome molding just below the beltline removed for a cleaner side appearance. In addition, the model line was also expanded to meet an anticipated surge in sales caused by the return to full postwar production after the settling of labor disputes and the relaxation of materials restrictions. Added were Custom versions of the two-door Brougham and the four-door Slip Stream (fastback) and Trunk sedan. Also, for the first time since 1941 a convertible was added to the line, but only 1,000 were made. This was to be the last full-size Nash convertible ever made, although a 1950 Nash Rambler compact size convertible would be produced. Not until 1965 would Nash Motor's successor, AMC, build a full-sized convertible again.

AMBASSADOR 60 SERIES

Model Number	Body/Style Number	Body Type & Seating	Factory Price	Shipping Weight	Production Total
SUPER LINE					
60	4860	4-dr Trk Sed-6P	1916	3387	14,248
60	4863	2-dr Brgm-6P	1858	3312	7,221
60	4864	4-dr Sub-6P	2239	3522	130
60	4868	4-dr FsBk Sed-6P	1874	3412	14,777
CUSTOMLINE					
60	4870	4-dr Trk Sed-6P	2105	3387	4,102
60	4873	2-dr Brgm Sed-6P	2047	3312	929
60	4878	4-dr FsBk Sed-6P	2063	3412	4,143
60	4871	2-dr Conv-6P	2355	3465	1,000

ENGINES

(NASH 600 SIX) Inline. L-head six: Cast iron block. Displacement: 172.6 cid. Bore and stroke: 3-1/8 x 3-3/4 inches. Compression ratio: 6.8:1. Brake hp: 82 at 3800 rpm. Four main bearings. Solid valve lifters. Carburetion: Carter one-barrel WA1-6625.

(AMBASSADOR SIX) Inline six: Overhead valves. Cast iron block. Displacement: 234.8 inches. Bore and stroke: 3-3/8 x 4-3/8 inches. Compression ratio: 6.8:1. Brake hp: 112 at 3400 rpm. Seven main bearings. Solid valve lifters. Carburetion: Carter one-barrel model YF.

CHASSIS FEATURES: Wheelbase: (600) 112 inches; (Ambassador) 121 inches. Overall length: (600) 200 inches; (Ambassador) 209-3/16 inches. Front tread: (all) 57-1/2 inches. Rear tread (600) 59-11/16 inches; (Ambassador) 60-1/2 inches. Tires: (600) 6.40 x 15 Super Cushion; (Ambassador) 6.50 x 15; 7.10 x 15 Super Cushion optional.

OPTIONS: Foam rubber cushions. Cruising gear (Ambassador only). Conditioned air system. Vacuum booster pump. Radio and antenna. Directional signals. Oil bath air cleaner. Oil filter (600 only). There were no available optional engines. The standard gearbox was a three-speed manual type with Warner Gear overdrive available at extra cost.

HISTORICAL FOOTNOTES: Charles Nash died on June 6, 1948 at the age of 84. The 1948 Ambassadors were the last Nashes to use separate frames. Production began at the El Segundo, Calif. factory this year. The starting month for production of Nash products built to 1948 specifications was November, 1947. This would be the last year that Nash used the term "Brougham" to describe its club coupe. (Starting with the 1949 Nash Airflyte, the Brougham model became a two-door sedan featuring two individual "lounge-chair" style seats, angled towards the center of the car, with a permanent center armrest between them.) Calendar year production peaked at 118,621 units or 3.04 percent of total domestic sales for the entire industry. George W. Mason retained the top corporate posts and George Romney served as Nash-Kelvinator vice president. The fastback sedan was again called a Slip Stream.

1949 NASH

NASH 600 — SERIES 40 — (6-CYL) — Nash introduced its first totally redesigned postwar car line in 1949. The Nash Airflyte series, as it was called, featured single-unit construction, one-piece curved windshield, 'Uniscope' gauge cluster (a pod atop the steering column containing all instruments) and fully reclining front seatbacks. In 1949, Nash was the first U.S. manufacturer of mass produced autos to totally commit to unitized, single-unit construction and one of the first in the world to do so. These 'bathtub' Nashes (as they were known) were styled with an eye toward aerodynamics. At 60 mph in wind tunnel tests, the Airflyte had only 113 pounds of drag. (In comparison a similar looking 1949 Packard had around 171 pounds of drag.)

NASH I.D. NUMBERS: Vehicle Identification Plate located on the right-hand side of the cowl below the hood contains motor-serial number and number codes for model, paint and trim. Motor-serial number matches the serial number. Model number has four symbols. The first two symbols indicate model year, 49 = 1949. The third symbol indicates series: 2 = 600 Special; 4 = 600 Super; 5 = 600 Custom; 6 = Ambassador Super; 7 = Ambassador Custom; 9 = Ambassador Super Special. The fourth symbol indicates body style. (All four numbers appear in Body/Style Number column of charts below). Motor numbers located on right-hand side of crankcase towards front and on front upper left-hand side of block. [600 SERIES] The starting serial number for the Nash 600 of 1949 was K-260501 for cars assembled in Kenosha, Wis. Unassembled export serial numbers began 4KD-1401. Starting serial numbers for El

Segundo, Calif. was KC-1001. Starting engine serial number for all 1949 Nash 600s was S-1001. [AMBASSADOR SERIES] The starting serial number for the Ambassador six of 1949 was: R-515501 for Kenosha, Wis.; 6KD-1501 for unassembled export and RC-1001 for El Segundo. Starting engine serial numbers for all 1949 Ambassadors was A-1001.

1949 Nash 600 four-door sedan, 6-cyl

NASH 600 SERIES 40

Model Number	Body/Style Number	Body Type & Seating	Factory Price	Shipping Weight	Production Total
SUPER SPECIAL LINE					
40	4923	2-dr Brgm-5P	1846	2960	2,564
40	4928	4-dr Sed-6P	1849	2960	23,606
40	4929	2-dr Sed-6P	1824	2935	9,605
SUPER LINE					
40	4943	2-dr Brgm-5P	1808	2960	2,954
40	4948	4-dr Sed-6P	1811	2950	31,194
40	4949	2-dr Sed-6P	1786	2935	17,006
CUSTOM LINE					
40	4953	2-dr Brgm-5P	1997	2970	17
40	4958	4-dr Sed-6P	2000	2985	199

1949 Nash, Ambassador Custom four-door sedan, 6-cyl (TVB)

NASH AMBASSADOR — SERIES 60 — (6-CYL) — The Nash Ambassador for 1949 shared all the styling changes of the 1949 Nash 600. The difference was largely that the Ambassador had a nine inch longer wheelbase due to its longer front end. Coil spring suspension and torque tube drive were featured on both the Ambassador and the Nash 600. The same three series or trim levels were available in the Ambassador: Super, Super Special and Custom.

NASH AMBASSADOR SERIES 60

Model Number	Body/Style Number	Body Type & Seating	Factory Price	Shipping Weight	Production Total
SUPER LINE					
60	4963	2-dr Brgm-5P	2191	3390	1,541
60	4968	4-dr Sed-6P	2195	3385	17,960
60	4969	2-dr Sed-6P	2170	3365	4,602
CUSTOM LINE					
60	4973	2-dr Brgm-5P	2359	3415	1,837
60	4978	4-dr Sed-6P	2363	3415	6,539
60	4979	2-dr Sed-6P	2338	3400	691

Model Number	Body/Style Number	Body Type & Seating	Factory Price	Shipping Weight	Production Total
SUPER SPECIAL LINE					
60	4993	2-dr Brgm-5P	2239	3390	807
60	4998	4-dr Sed-6P	2243	3385	6,777
60	4999	2-dr Sed-6P	2218	3365	2,072

ENGINES

(NASH 600 SIX) Inline. L-head six: Cast iron block. Displacement: 172.6 cid. Bore and stroke: 3-1/8 x 3-3/4 inches. Compression ratio: 6.8:1. Brake hp: 82 at 3800 rpm. Four main bearings. Solid valve lifters. Carburetion: Carter one-barrel WA1-6945.

(AMBASSADOR SIX) Inline six: Overhead valves. Cast iron block. Displacement: 234.8 inches. Bore and stroke: 3-3/8 x 4-3/8 inches. Compression ratio: 6.8:1. Brake hp: 112 at 3400 rpm. Seven main bearings. Solid valve lifters. Carburetion: Carter one-barrel WA1-683S.

CHASSIS FEATURES: Wheelbase: (600) 112 inches; (Ambassador) 121 inches. Overall length: (600) 201 inches; (Ambassador) 210 inches. Front tread: (all) 5411/16 inches. Rear tread: (600) 59-11/16 inches; (Ambassador) 60-1/2 inches. Tires: (600) 6.40 x 15; (Ambassador) 7.10 x 15.

OPTIONS: Bed, single ($19); double ($39). Exhaust pipe extensions ($2). Fog lights, pair ($13). Spotlight, door mounted ($20). Back-O-Matic Lights, pair ($9). Fuel purifier ($2). License plate frames ($2). Electric snap up gas cap ($5). Magnalite trouble light ($4). Non-glare mirror ($4). Rearview mirror, right and left ($3). Visor vanity mirror ($l). Deluxe fiber seat covers (interwoven pattern, blue color) in two-door sedan and four-door sedan ($25); in Broughams ($31). Deluxe fiber Sportster type seat covers in all two-door and four-door sedans ($28); in Broughams ($35). Rayon twill seat covers with maroon, blue or brown color, in all sedans ($48); in Broughams ($51). Trim rings ($12). Wheel discs ($17). Tissue Dispensers ($3). Hood ornaments ($9). Windshield washer ($7). Rear window wiper ($14). Front grille guard ($25). Rear grille guard ($20). Fender guard, pair, ($10). Nash Karvisor ($26). Directional signals ($16). Radio ($82). Manual antenna ($7). Vacuum antenna ($14). Warner Gear overdrive.

HISTORICAL FOOTNOTES: The 1949 Nash line began production in October, 1948. A total of 130,000 units was produced for the model year. Calendar year production was counted at 142,592 cars or 2.78 percent of the total domestic auto business. Nine Ambassadors were built by the engineering department (under the direction of M.F. Moore, vice-president of Nash Research) with automatic transmissions. Three-passenger models and the wood-veneered Suburban sedan were dropped this year. Nash was America's 10th ranked maker of the season.

1950 NASH

1950 Nash, Statesman, four-door sedan, 6-cyl

NASH STATESMAN — SERIES 40 — (6-CYL) — The Nash 600 was renamed Statesman for 1950 and its L-head six-cylinder engine had a one-quarter inch larger stroke. This increased displacement from 172.6 cid to 184 cid and increased horsepower from 82 to 85. One significant styling change made this year was a much larger rear window, which was very helpful to the driver considering that the fastback design made seeing the traffic behind very difficult. The bumper guards grew slightly thicker and the cars had a Statesman script on their front fenders. Seat belts were available with the Statesman and the Ambassador in their first use on a U.S. built car. Both the Statesman and the Ambassador came in two basic trim levels, Super and Custom for 1950. The Statesman also had a low-priced 'line leader' Deluxe Business Coupe. Custom models had rear seat armrests; carpets; courtesy lights; a Custom steering wheel; and full wheel discs. Some 1950 models were built in the new Canadian factory. Production figures for Canada are unavailable.

NASH I.D. NUMBERS: Vehicle Identification Plate located on the right-hand side of the cowl below the hood contains motor-serial number and number codes for model, paint and trim. Motor-serial number matches the serial number. Model number has four symbols. The first two symbols indicate model year, 50 = 1950. The third symbol indicates series: 2 = Rambler; 3 = Statesman; 4 = Super Statesman; 5 = Custom Statesman; 6 = Ambassador Super; 7 = Ambassador Custom. The fourth symbol indicates body style. (All four numbers appear in Body/Style Number column of charts below). Motor numbers located on right-hand side of crankcase towards front and on front upper left-hand side of block. [STATESMAN]: Serial numbering for Statesman sixes built in Kenosha were at K-340001 to K-436892; in El Segundo, KC-9501 to KC-23007; in Canada, KT-1001 and up; and for unassembled export units 4KD-2301 and up. Engine numbers for 1950 Statesman sixes began at S-92001 to S-205947. [AMBASSADOR]: Serial numbering for Ambassador sixes built in Kenosha were R-556001 to R-599704; in El Segundo, RC-3501 to RC-8488; and for unassembled export units RD-2101 and up. (No Ambassadors assembled in Canada). Engine numbers for 1950 Ambassadors were A-46001 to A-96151. [RAMBLER] The serial numbers were D-1001 to D-12263. Engine numbers were F-1001 to F-12574.

NASH STATESMAN SERIES 40

Model Number	Body/Style Number	Body Type & Seating	Factory Price	Shipping Weight	Production Total
NASH STATESMAN SERIES 40					
40	5032	2-dr Bus Cpe-3P	1633	2830	1,198
SUPER LINE					
40	5043	2-dr Brgm-5P	1735	2940	1,489
40	5048	4-dr Sed-6P	1738	2965	60,090
40	5049	2-dr Sed-6P	1713	2930	34,196
CUSTOM LINE					
40	5053	2-dr Brgm-5P	1894	2965	132
40	5058	2-dr Sed-6P	1897	2990	11,500
40	5059	2-dr Sed-6P	1872	2950	2,693

NASH AMBASSADOR — SERIES 60 — (6-CYL) — The 1950 Nash Ambassador had a longer hood than the 1949 model, as well as the enlarged back window. Otherwise, there were not many significant changes. An Ambassador script appeared on the fenders for identifi-

cation. The year's major innovation was the introduction of a GM built Hydra-Matic transmission, available only on the 1950 Nash Ambassador. A new cylinder head design was also introduced for the 234.8 cid overhead valve Ambassador engine and raised the output to 115 hp. Custom models differed from the Supers by featuring a rear seat with a folding center armrest; front floor carpeting; courtesy lights; a Custom steering wheel; and large wheel discs.

1950 Nash, Ambassador Custom four-door sedan, 6-cyl

NASH AMBASSADOR SERIES 60

Model Number	Body/Style Number	Body Type & Seating	Factory Price	Shipping Weight	Production Total
SUPER LINE					
60	5063	2-dr Brgm-5P	2060	3335	716
60	5068	4-dr Sed-6P	2064	3350	27,523
60	5069	2-dr Sed-6P	2039	3325	7,237
CUSTOM LINE					
60	5073	2-dr Brgm-5P	2219	3385	108
60	5078	4-dr Sed-6P	2223	3390	12,427
60	5079	2-dr Sed-6P	2198	3365	1,045

1950 Nash — Rambler two-door convertible, 6-cyl

NASH RAMBLER — SERIES 10 — (6-CYL) — Nash introduced the compact Nash Rambler Convertible Landau in March, 1950. The first cars built by Nash's predecessor, the Thomas B. Jeffery Co. of Kenosha, Wis., also used this name. The compact car had a 100 inch wheelbase and used the 82 hp six-cylinder engine from the Nash 600. The first model introduced was the two-door Convertible Landau. A two-door station wagon was introduced two months later on June 23. Both models came loaded with options such as radio and antenna; Custom steering wheel; turn signals; wheel discs; electric clock; courtesy lights; Custom upholstery; and foam seat cushions. On the convertible only, a sliding top (in black or tan fabric) could be raised over 'bridge beam' side rails above the doors. The Rambler used Hotchkiss drive, unlike the torque tube drive of the conventional Nash.

NASH RAMBLER SERIES 10

Model Number	Body/Style Number	Body Type & Seating	Factory Price	Shipping Weight	Production Total
10	5021	2-dr Cus Conv-5P	1808	2430	9,330
10	5024	2-dr Cus Sta Wag-5P	1808	2515	1,712
10	5026	2-dr Cus Trk Sed	—	—	6
10	5114	2-dr Sup Sta Wag	—	—	1
10	5124	2-dr Cus Sta Wag	—	—	1
10	5121	2-dr Cus Conv-5P	1808	2430	378

NOTE 1: 378 convertibles built in Calif. July/Aug. 1950 possibly prototypes.

ENGINES

(STATESMAN SIX) Inline. L-head six. Cast iron block. Displacement: 184.0 cid. Bore and stroke: 3-1/8 x 3-3/4 inches. Compression ratio: 7.0:1. Brake hp: 85 at 3800 rpm. Four main bearings. Solid valve lifters. Carburetor: Carter one-barrel Model WAI-694S.

(AMBASSADOR SIX) Inline. Overhead valve six. Displacement: 234.8 cid. Bore and stroke: 3-3/8 x 4-3/8 inches. Compression ratio: 7.3:1. Brake hp: 115 at 3400 rpm. Seven main bearings. Solid valve lifters. Carburetor: Carter one-barrel type WA-1 Model 746S.

(RAMBLER SIX) Inline. L-head six. Cast iron block. Displacement: 172.6 cid. Bore and stroke: 3-1/8 x 3-3/4 inches. Compression ratio: 7.25:1. Brake hp: 82 at 3800 rpm. Four main bearings. Solid valve lifters. Carburetor: Carter one barrel type YF model 757S.

CHASSIS FEATURES: Wheelbase: (Statesman) 112 inches; (Ambassador) 121 inches; (Rambler) 100 inches. Overall length: (Statesman) 201 inches; (Ambassador) 210 inches;

(Rambler) 176 inches. Front tread: (Statesman and Ambassador) 54-11/16 inches; (Rambler) 53-1/4 inches. Rear tread: (Statesman) 59-11/16 inches; (Ambassador) 60-1/2 inches; (Rambler) 53 inches. Tires: (Statesman) 6.40 x 15; (Ambassador) 7.10 x 15; (Rambler) 5.90 x 15.

OPTIONS: Electric clock (standard on Custom models). Mechanical clock. Overdrive. Two-tone colors. Directional signals (standard on Custom models). Emergency brake alarm. Fender signal. Floor mat pads. Foam rubber seat cushion (standard on custom). Fuel purifier. Locking gas cap. Electric locking gas cap. Fender guards. Grille guards. Trunk guards. Hood ornament. Hydra-Matic transmission (Ambassador). License frames. Back-O-Matic lights. Fog lights, (pair). Spotlight, (front door). Spotlight (with rearview mirror). Trouble light. Mattress. Zipper case for bed. Rearview mirror. Deluxe rearview outside mirror. Visor vanity mirror. Oil filter (Statesman and Ambassador). Heavy-duty oil bath air cleaner (Statesman and Ambassador). Opto-shade inside sun shield. Custom radio with manual antenna. Custom radio with vacuum antenna. Deluxe radio with vacuum antenna. Rear speaker for Deluxe radio. Rear door safety locks. Front divided seatback for four-door sedan w/bed (standard on Custom models). Reclining front seat. Fiber Regal seat covers. Fiber Majestic seat covers. Top-Flyte Custom rayon seat covers in maroon, blue and green. Custom steering wheel (standard equipment in Custom models). White sidewall tires, size 6.40 x 14 four-ply. White sidewall tires, size 6.40 x 15 six-ply. White sidewall tires, size 7.10 x 15 four-ply. White sidewall tires, size 7.10 x 15 six-ply. Tissue dispenser packet. Tool pouch. Set of five stainless steel chrome trim rings. Leather upholstery. Outside window visors for two-door; four-door. Visor shade. Weather-Eye conditioned air system. Five chrome stainless steel wheel discs (standard on Custom models). Window screen for two-door; four-door. Windshield washer. Rear window wiper.

HISTORICAL FOOTNOTES: Production of 1950 Nash products began in September 1949. A total of 145,782 Statesman and Ambassador models, along with 26,000 Ramblers, were produced for the model year. Sales were counted at 191,865 cars, putting Nash 10th in the auto sales race. This broke the all-time record for Nash production. The official model introduction date for the new Rambler convertible was April 14, 1950. Together, the two Rambler body styles helped Nash achieve the assembly of 7.1 percent of all convertibles and 3.6 percent of all station wagons built in the U.S. in calendar 1950. The compact line was an immediate success. Nash calendar year production leaped to 189,543 cars or 2.84 percent of total auto industry sales. The three-passenger Nash was reintroduced this year, as a back seat-less business car intended strictly for commercial use. Several Nash models competed successfully in stock car races during 1950. Their greater fuel economy meant that less pit stops were required. Many Nash owners reported 25-30 mpg in normal operation, according to the company's advertisements.

1951 NASH

NASH STATESMAN — SERIES 40 — (6-CYL) — The 1951 Nash Statesman featured a new "electric shaver" type grille and side marker lights along with new rear fenders and fender lights. Statesman scripts were on the front fender for identification. Super models had basic features. Customs also had foam seat cushions; front floor carpets; courtesy lights; a rear seat center armrest; Custom steering wheel; and full wheel discs. Hydra-Matic automatic transmission made its debut on the Statesman in 1951.

NASH I.D. NUMBERS: Vehicle Identification Plate located on the right-hand side of the cowl below the hood contains motor-serial number and number codes for model, paint and trim. Motor-serial number matches the serial number. Model number has four symbols. The first two symbols indicate model year. 51 = 1951. The third symbol indicates series: 0 = Rambler Utility; 1 = Rambler Super 2 = Rambler Custom; 3 = Statesman; 4 = Super/Deluxe Statesman; 5 = Custom Statesman; 6 = Ambassador Super; 7 = Ambassador Custom. The fourth symbol indicates body style. (All four numbers appear in Body/Style Number column of charts below). Motor numbers located on right-hand side of crankcase towards front and on front upper left-hand side of block. [NASH STATESMAN SERIES 40 I.D. NUMBERS]: Serial numbers for 1951 Nash Statesman models built at Kenosha, Wis. were K-438001 to K518763; 4KD-3201 and up for unassembled export; KC-23501 and up for El Segundo, Calif. and KT-22501 and up for cars made in the Toronto, Ontario, Canada assembly plant. Engine numbers for the Statesman six were S-207001 to S-306795 for all assembly points. [NASH AMBASSADOR SERIES 60 I.D. NUMBERS]: Serial numbers for the 1951 Nash Ambassador models built at Kenosha, Wis. were R-600501 to R-655753; 6KD-2071 and up for unassembled exports and RC-8701 and up for El Segundo, Calif. Ambassadors were not manufactured at the Canadian plant. Engine numbers for all Ambassador six engines were A-97001 to A-160453. [NASH RAMBLER SERIES I.D. NUMBERS]: The serial numbers for 1951 Ramblers built in Kenosha, Wis. were D-12501 to D-78917; DKD-1201 for unassembled export and DC1501 for El Segundo, Calif. Engine numbers for 1951 Ramblers were F-1001 to F-83778. The Rambler Deliveryman utility wagon line had serial numbers D66495 and up/motor numbers F-69802 and up.

1951 Nash, Statesman four-door sedan, 6-cyl.

NASH STATESMAN SERIES 40

Model Number	Body/Style Number	Body Type & Seating	Factory Price	Shipping Weight	Production Total
SUPER/DELUXE LINES					
40	5132	2-dr Del Bus Cpe-3P	1710	2835	52
40	5143	2-dr Brgm-5P	1812	2935	152
40	5148	4-dr Sed-6P	1815	2970	52,325
40	5149	2-dr Sed-6P	1790	2930	22,261
CUSTOM LINE					
40	5153	2-dr Brgm-5P	1971	2950	38
40	5158	4-dr Sed-6P	1974	2990	14,846
40	5159	2-dr Sed-6P	1949	2940	2,141

1951 Nash, Ambassador Custom four-door sedan, 6-cyl

NASH AMBASSADOR SERIES 60 — (6-CYL) — The 1951 Nash Ambassador received the same revised front grille and side marker lights and new rear fenders as the 1951 Statesman. The major difference from the Statesman was the Ambassador's nine inch longer front end. Supers had basic features. Customs had a rear seat with a folding center armrest; courtesy lamps; front carpeting; Custom steering wheel; and large wheel discs.

NASH AMBASSADOR SERIES 60

Model Number	Body/Style Number	Body Type & Seating	Factory Price	Shipping Weight	Production Total
SUPER LINE					
60	5163	2-dr Brgm-5P	2158	3370	40
60	5168	4-dr Sed-6P	2162	3410	34,935
60	5169	2-dr Sed-6P	2137	3370	4,382
CUSTOM LINE					
60	5173	2-dr Brgm-5P	2317	3395	37
60	5178	4-dr Sed-6P	2321	3445	21,071
60	5179	2-dr Sed-6P	2296	3380	1,118

1951 Nash, Rambler Country Club two-door hardtop coupe, 6-cyl

NASH RAMBLER — SERIES 10 — (6-CYL) — The major change for 1951 was the introduction of a new Rambler model called the Country Club hardtop. This was the first two-door compact hardtop to be introduced in the U.S. This body style had been popularized by the introduction of two-door hardtops in several GM car-lines in 1949.

NASH RAMBLER SERIES 10

Model Number	Body/Style Number	Body Type & Seating	Factory Price	Shipping Weight	Production Total
10	5104	2-dr Utl Wag-3P	1673	2415	1,569
10	5114	2-dr Sta Wag-5P	1723	2515	5,568
10	5117	2-dr HT Cpe-5P	—	—	1
10	5121	2-dr Conv-5P	1837	2430	14,881
10	5124	2-dr Cus Sta wag-5P	1837	2515	28,617
10	5126	2-dr Clb Sed-5P	—	—	50
10	5127	2-dr Cty Clb-5P	1968	2420	19,317

ENGINES

(STATESMAN SIX) Inline. L-head six. Cast iron block. Displacement: 184.0 cid. Bore and stroke: 3-1/8 x 3-3/4 inches. Compression ratio: 7.0:1. Brake hp: 85 at 3800 rpm. Four main bearings. Solid valve lifters. Carburetor: Carter one-barrel Model YF-824S.

(AMBASSADOR SIX) Inline. Overhead valve six. Displacement: 234.8 cid. Bore and stroke: 3-3/8 x 4-3/8 inches. Compression ratio: 7.3:1. Brake hp: 115 at 3400 rpm. Seven main bearings. Solid valve lifters. Carburetor: Carter one-barrel type WA-1 Model 746S.

(RAMBLER SIX) Inline. L-head six. Cast iron block. Displacement: 172.6 cid. Bore and stroke: 3-1/8 x 3-3/4 inches. Compression ratio: 7.25:1. Brake hp: 82 at 3800 rpm. Four main bearings. Solid valve lifters. Carburetor: Carter one barrel type YF model 757S.

CHASSIS FEATURES: Wheelbase: (Statesman) 112 inches; (Ambassador) 121 inches; (Rambler) 100 inches. Overall length: (Statesman) 201 inches; (Ambassador) 211 inches; (Rambler) 176 inches. Front tread: (Statesman and Ambassador) 54-11/16 inches; (Rambler) 53-1/4 inches. Rear tread: (Statesman) 59-11/16 inches; (Ambassador) 60-1/2 inches; (Rambler) 53 inches. Tires: (Statesman) 6.40 x 15; (Ambassador) 7.10 x 15; (Rambler) 5.90 x 15.

OPTIONS: Radio. Vacuum control antenna. Spotlight with mirror. Door-top outside mirror. Door mount outside mirror. Back-up lights. Fog lights. Non-glare rearview mirror. Visor vanity mirror. Curb-L-Arm. Custom seat covers. License plate frame. Exhaust extension. Protect-O-Mat for floor. Automatic windshield washer. Rear window wiper. Opto-shade for windshield. Vent shades. Outside windshield visor. Magnalite trouble light. Gas cap lock. Tissue dispenser. Bed mattress. Plastic screens.

HISTORICAL FOOTNOTES: In 1951, Nash introduced Rambler hardtop, suburban and Deliveryman (utility wagon) models; suspended operations in Canada and received a defense contract to built Pratt & Whitney aero engines. Korean War allocations prevented introduction of the Rambler four-door sedan this season. Annual model introductions were held on Sept. 22, 1950. The Nash Rambler Country Club hardtop was introduced, as an addition to the line, on June 28, 1951. In November, 1951, the company received permission from the Economic Stability Agency to increase prices. The subsequent jump was $64 in Rambler; $48-55 in Statesman and $61-66 in Ambassador retail prices. Model year production counted 125,203 standard-sized models and 80,000 compact Ramblers, with the production run beginning in September, 1950. Calendar year production hit 161,209 units or 3.02 percent of total American industry output. Over 82,731 Nash products were assembled with optional overdrive transmission, while another 64,775 cars had automatic drives. (GM Hydra-Matic). The new Deliveryman was a wagon type vehicle, with only one seat, intended strictly for commercial package carrying work. In most reference sources it was listed as a truck and described as a utility wagon, which is how it appears in the specifications charts above. During 1951, Nash made 6.9 percent of all convertibles, 3.9 percent of all hardtops and 15.2 percent of all station wagons produced in the U.S. During the calendar year, 25,962 automatic transmission attachments were sold, while 82,731 cars had the optional Warner Gear overdrive.

1952 NASH

NASH STATESMAN — SERIES 40 — (6-CYL) — The year 1952 marked the 50th anniversary of Nash Motor Co. and it's predecessor Thomas B. Jeffery Co. Nash used the occasion to introduce a totally redesigned line of big cars called Nash Golden Airflytes. These were partly styled by Italian designer Pinin Farina and had more conventional lines than the 1949-1951 models. The Statesman and the Ambassador again shared sheet metal from the cowl back. The 1952 Statesman had its wheelbase increased to 114-1/4 inches and the engine was stroked 1/4 inch to 195.6 cid. This increase in displacement boosted the Statesman engine's output to 88 hp at 3800 rpm.

NASH I.D. NUMBERS: Vehicle Identification Plate located on the right-hand side of the cowl below the hood contains motor-serial number and number codes for model, paint and trim. Motor-serial number matches the serial number. Model number has four symbols. The first two symbols indicate model year, 52 = 1952. The third symbol indicates series: 0 = Rambler Utility; 1 = Rambler Super 2 = Rambler Custom; 4 = Super Statesman; 5 = Custom Statesman; 6 = Ambassador Super; 7 = Ambassador Custom. The fourth symbol indicates body style. (All four numbers appear in Body/Style Number column of charts below). Motor numbers located on right-hand side of crankcase towards front and on front upper left-hand side of block. [NASH STATESMAN SERIES 40 I.D. NUMBERS]: Serial numbers for 1952 Statesman models built at Kenosha were K-519001 to K-562291; for unassembled export KD-4301 and up; for El Segundo KC-37001 to KC-42976; and for Toronto, Canada, KT-6101 and up. Engine numbers for the Statesman sixes were S-308001 to S-361836 for all assembly points. [NASH AMBASSADOR SERIES 60 I.D. NUMBERS]: Serial numbers for 1952 Ambassador models built at Kenosha were R-656001 to R-691337; for unassembled export 6KD3501 and up; for El Segundo RC-14501 to RC-18798. There was no Canadian production for this series. Engine numbers for the Ambassador sixes were A-165001 to A-205789 for all assembly points. [NASH RAMBLER SERIES 10 I.D. NUMBERS]: Serial numbers for 1952 Rambler models built at Kenosha were D-79501 to D-127045; for unassembled export DKD-2301 and up; and for El Segundo DC-4101 to DC-8914. Engine numbers for all 1952 Nash Ramblers were F-85001 to F-139394. [NASH-HEALEY I.D. NUMBERS]: Serial numbers N-2001 to N-2109 were used on cars built at Warwick, England as 1951 models. Motor Numbers were NHA-1001 and up. The beginning number for cars built at Warwick as 1952 models was N-2086. However, the beginning 1952 number was then followed by N-2103, N-2104, N-2106 and N-2200 with numbers following in sequence after N-2200. Motor Numbers for 1952 were NHA-1088 and up, but did not necessarily follow each other in sequence. The model number for the Nash-Healey was 25162 (1951) and 25262 (1952). The first two symbols indicate the series. The third symbol indicates model year. The fourth and fifth symbols are the equivalent of a body style number.

NASH STATESMAN SERIES 40

Model Number	Body/Style Number	Body Type & Seating	Factory Price	Shipping Weight	Production Total
SUPER LINE					
40	5245	4-dr Sed-6P	2178	3045	27,304
40	5246	2-dr Sed-6P	2144	3025	6,795
CUSTOM LINE					
40	5255	4-dr Sed-6P	2332	3070	13,660
40	5256	2-dr Sed-6P	2310	3050	1,872
40	5257	2-dr Cty Clb HT-6P	2433	3095	869

1952 Nash, Ambassador Custom two-door sedan, 6-cyl

AMBASSADOR — SERIES 60 (6-CYL) — The 1952 Nash Ambassador shared the same styling and design changes as the 1952 Nash Statesman, the major difference being the seven inch longer front end. The 1952 Nash Ambassador came in two series: Super and Custom. Supers had basic features. Customs added foam seat cushions; two-tone upholstery; an electric clock; directional signals; chrome wheel discs; and front and rear courtesy lights. For 1952, the Ambassador engine was bored 1/8 inch, yielding 252.6 cid.

NASH AMBASSADOR SERIES 60

Model Number	Body/Style Number	Body Type & Seating	Factory Price	Shipping Weight	Production Total
SUPER LINE					
60	5265	4-dr Sed-6P	2557	3430	16,838
60	5266	2-dr Sed-6P	2521	3410	1,871
CUSTOM LINE					
60	5275	4-dr Sed-6P	2716	3480	19,585
60	5276	2-dr Sed-6P	2695	3450	1,178
60	5277	2-dr HT Cpe-6P	2829	3550	1,228

1952 Nash, Rambler Greenbriar two-door station wagon, 6-cyl (TVB)

NASH RAMBLER — SERIES 10 — (6-CYL) — The 1952 Nash Rambler line received no major changes from 1951. Custom models came with the Nash "Weather-Eye" conditioned air system and a radio as standard equipment. The Greenbrier station wagon was an upgraded model with two-tone paint and richer trim.

NASH RAMBLER SERIES 10

Model Number	Body/Style Number	Body Type & Seating	Factory Price	Shipping Weight	Production Total
10	2204	2-dr Utl Wag-5P	1842	2415	1,248
10	5214	2-dr Sta Wag-5P	2003	2515	2,970
10	5221	2-dr Conv-5P	2119	2430	3,108
10	5224	2-dr Sta Wag-5P	2119	2515	19,889
10	5227	2-dr Cty Clb-5P	2094	2420	25,785

NOTE 1: Station wagon production included 4,425 Greenbriers.

NASH-HEALEY — SERIES 25 — SIX — The Nash-Healey sports car had a special two-passenger open body made of aluminum, an adjustable steering wheel and leather upholstery. The first Nash-Healey, model 25162, used the 234.8 cid Nash six and is sometimes called a "1951" model. The second version, model number 25262, switched to the 252.6 cid "LeMans" engine with dual carburetion. The English-build sports car's styling traits included a grille of outward curved vertical chrome bars entirely circled by a heavy chrome molding. There were model designations on the front fenders and in back of the wheel opening. The full hood had a unique hatch cover (air scoop) at the center with a vertical grille at the opening. These cars were built at Warwick, England and sold by Nash dealers. Styling by Pinin Farina was seen on 1952 models and late in the year, the more powerful LeMans engine was released. According to WARD'S AUTOMOTIVE YEARBOOK 1953 the official introduction date of the Nash-Healey, in the U.S., was Feb. 16, 1951. Since the Nash-Healey was of foreign manufacture, it will not be covered fully in this catalog, beyond the data given below.

NASH-HEALEY SERIES N-25

Model Number	Body/Style Number	Body Type & Seating	Factory Price	Shipping Weight	Production Total
N-25	25162	2-dr Spts Conv-2P	4063	2690	104
N-25	25262	2-dr Spts Conv-2P	5909	2750	150

NOTE 1: Style 25162 usually considered a 1951 model; 25262 the 1952 model.

ENGINES

(STATESMAN SIX): Inline. L-head six. Cast iron block. Displacement: 195.6 cid. Bore and stroke: 3-1.8 x 4-1/4 inches. Compression ratio: 7.10:1. Brake hp: 88 at 3800 rpm. Four main bearings. Solid valve lifters. Carburetor: Carter one-barrel Type YF model 824S.

(AMBASSADOR SIX) Inline six. Overhead valves. Displacement: 252.6 cid. Bore and stroke: 3.50 x 4.375 inches. Compression ratio: 7.3:1. Brake hp: 120 at 3700 rpm. Seven main bearings. Solid valve lifters. Carburetor: Carter one-barrel Type WA (side-inlet).

(RAMBLER SIX) Inline. L-head six. Cast iron block. Displacement: 172.6 cid. Bore and stroke: 3-1/8 x 3-3/4 inches. Compression ratio: 7.25:1. Brake hp: 82 at 3800 rpm. Four main bearings. Solid valve lifters. Carburetor: Carter one-barrel type YF model 757S.

(NASH-HEALEY SIX) Inline six. Overhead valves. Displacement: 234.8 cid. Bore and stroke: 3.375 x 4.375. Compression ratio: 8.0:1. Brake hp: 125 at 4000 rpm.

(LE MANS SIX) Inline. LeMans six. Overhead valves. Displacement: 252.6 cid. Bore and stroke: 3.50 x 4.375. Compression ratio: 8.0: 1. Brake hp: 140 at 4000 rpm.

CHASSIS FEATURES: Wheelbase: (Statesman) 114-1/4 inches; (Ambassador) 121-1/4 inches; (Rambler) 100 inches. Overall length: (Statesman) 202-1/4 inches; (Ambassador) 209-1/4 inches; (Rambler) 176 inches. Front tread: (Statesman) 55-1/2 inches; (Ambassador) 55-5/8 inches; (Rambler) 55-3/8 inches. Rear tread: (Statesman) 59-11/16 inches; (Ambassador) 60-1/2 inches; (Rambler) 53 inches. Tires: (Statesman) 6.70 x 15; (Ambassador) 7.10 x 15; (Rambler Super) 5.90 x 15; (Rambler Custom) 6.40 x 15.

OPTIONS: Radio. Vacuum control antenna. Spotlight with mirror. Door-top outside mirror. Door mount outside mirror. Back-up lights. Fog lights. Non-glare rearview mirror. Visor vanity mirror. Curb-L-Arm. Custom seat covers. License plate frame. Exhaust extension. Protect-O-Mat for floor. Automatic windshield washer. Rear window wiper. Opto-shade for windshield. Vent shades. Outside windshield visor. Magnalite trouble light. Gas cap lock. Tissue dispenser. Bed mattress. Plastic screens. Rambler grille guard. Windshield washer. Rambler trunk guard. Trunk light. Rooftop carrier. Overdrive indicator. Visor pouch. Continental tire mount. Statesman 7.35:1 high-compression cylinder head. Ambassador 8.25:1 high-compression cylinder head. Rambler 7.6:1 high-compression cylinder head.

HISTORICAL FOOTNOTES: The 1952 Nash Ambassador and Statesman models were introduced March 14, 1952. The updated Rambler appeared on April 1, 1952. The Nash-Healey (sometimes considered a 1951 model) made its American debut as a 1952 Nash offering. Production hit a peak of 152,141 units or 3.51 percent of American auto sales. Model year production included 99,086 Statesman/Ambassador models and 55,055 Ramblers. Over 20 percent of all Nash products, or 28,950 cars, had Hydra-Matic Drive this year. The optional Warner Gear overdrive was installed in 74,535 units. The Nash-Healey took first place in its class in the French Grand Prix, at LeMans, plus a third place overall. These racing models used the LeMans "Dual-Jetfire" Ambassador engine, later released as a production car powerplant.

1953 NASH

1953 Nash, Custom Statesman two-door sedan, 6-cyl

NASH STATESMAN — SERIES 40 — (6-CYL) — The 1952 Golden anniversary styling for the Statesman went almost unchanged for 1953. The only outward change was the addition of vertical chrome stripes in the fresh air intake just below the front windshield. Supers had basic features. Customs added foam seat cushions; two-tone upholstery; an electric clock; directional signals; chrome wheel discs; and front and rear courtesy lights.

NASH I.D. NUMBERS: Vehicle Identification Plate located on the right-hand side of the cowl below the hood contains motor-serial number and number codes for model, paint and trim. Motor-serial number matches the serial number. Model number has four symbols. The first two symbols indicate model year, 53 = 1953. The third symbol indicates series: 0 = Rambler Utility; 1 = Rambler Super 2 = Rambler Custom; 3 = Statesman; 4 = Super Statesman; 5 = Custom Statesman; 6 = Ambassador Super; 7 = Ambassador Custom. The fourth symbol indicates body style. (All four numbers appear in Body/Style Number column of charts below). Motor numbers located on right-hand side of crankcase towards front and on front upper left-hand side of block. [NASH STATESMAN SERIES 40 I.D. NUMBERS]: Serial numbers for the Statesman six were K-563501 to K-615291 for Kenosha, Wis.; 4KD-4801 and up for unassembled export; KC-43001 to KC-47173 for El Segundo, Calif. and KT-6901 and up for Toronto, Canada. Engine serial numbers were S-365001 to S-425053. [NASH AMBASSADOR SERIES 60 I.D. NUMBERS]: Serial numbers for the Ambassador six were R-692101 to R-721686 for Kenosha, Wis.; 6KD-3901 and up for unassembled export and RC-19001 to RC-21984 for El Segundo, Calif. Engine serial numbers were A-210001 to A-243959. (LeMans Dual-Jetfire engine numbers prefixed by LMA. [NASH RAMBLER SERIES 10 I.D. NUMBERS]: Serial numbers for 1953 were D-127501 to D-155727 for Kenosha, Wis. built cars; DKD-2701 and up for unassembled export and DC-9001 to DC-12299 for El Segundo, Calif. Engine serial numbers were F-140001 to F-166688 for cars without Hydra-Matic and H-1001 for cars with Hydra-Matic.

Model Number	Body Style Number	Body Type & Seating	Factory Price	Shipping Weight	Production Total
SUPER LINE					
40	5345	4-dr Sed-6P	2178	3045	28,445
40	5346	2-dr Sed-6P	2144	3025	7,999
CUSTOM LINE					
40	5355	4-dr Sed-6P	2332	3070	11,476
40	5356	2-dr Sed-6P	2309	3050	1,305
40	5357	2-dr HT Cpe-6P	2433	3095	7,025

NOTE 1: Beginning 1953, Nash often publicized FAP (factory as-delivered prices) rather than ADP (advertised delivered prices) retail costs. FAP did not include federal tax and some preparation and handling charges, while ADP did. Earlier editions of this catalog reflected FAPs for 1953 and up models. This edition shows the ADPs based on March issues of industry trade journals through 1956.

1953 Nash, Ambassador Country Club two-door hardtop coupe, 6-cyl

AMBASSADOR — SERIES 60 — (6-CYL) — The 1952 Golden anniversary styling from 1952 for the 1953 Ambassador went almost unchanged for 1953. The only outward change was the addition of vertical chrome strips in the fresh air intake just below the front windshield. The 1953 Nash Ambassador again came in two series: Super and Custom. Supers had basic features. Customs added foam seat cushions; two-tone upholstery; an electric clock; directional signals; chrome wheel discs; and front and rear courtesy lights. In addition, a new dual-carburetor 'Le Mans Dual Jetfire' engine (similar to the motor used in the Nash-Healeys raced at LeMans and named after them) was made optional on 1953 Ambassadors. This engine produced 140 hp at 4000 rpm.

NASH AMBASSADOR SERIES 60

Model Number	Body/Style Number	Body Type & Seating	Factory Price	Shipping Weight	Production Total
SUPER LINE					
60	5365	4-dr Sed-6P	2557	3430	12,489
60	5366	2-dr Sed-6P	2521	3410	1,273
CUSTOM LINE					
60	5375	4-dr Sed-6P	2716	3480	12,222
60	5376	2-dr Sed-6P	2695	3450	428
60	5377	2-dr HT Cpe-6P	2829	3550	6,438

1953 Nash, Rambler Custom two-door hardtop, 6-cyl

NASH RAMBLER — SERIES 10 — (6-CYL) — The 1953 Nash Rambler was completely restyled for 1953 and distinguished by a lowered hood, single bar front grille and enclosed front and rear fenders. The new styling was credited to Pinin Farina and had many of the styling features of the 1952 and 1953 Golden Anniversary Ambassador and Statesman. Custom models came with the Nash "Weather-Eye" conditioned air system and a radio as standard equipment. Custom convertible and Country Club hardtop included continental spare tire. Dual-Range Hydra-Matic became an option available for the first time on the 1953 Nash Rambler with Hydra-Matic equipped cars receiving an engine with five more brake horsepower than manual transmission cars.

NASH RAMBLER SERIES 10

Model Number	Body/Style Number	Body Type & Seating	Factory Price	Shipping Weight	Production Total
10	2304	2-dr Deliveryman	—	—	9
10	5314	2-dr Sta Wag-5P	2003	2555	1,114
10	5321	2-dr Conv-5P	2150	2590	3,284
10	5324	2-dr Sta Wag-5P	2119	2570	10,598
10	5327	2-dr CtyClb-5P	2125	2550	15,255

NOTE 1: Includes three model 5306 — two-door sedan Deluxe.

NOTE 2: Includes 3536 Greenbriar station wagon and 7035 DiNoc station wagons.

ENGINES

(STATESMAN SIX): Inline. L-head six. Cast iron block. Displacement: 195.6 cid. Bore and stroke: 3-1/8 x 4-1/4 inches. Compression ratio: 7.45:1. Brake hp: 100 at 3800 rpm. Four main bearings. Solid valve lifters. Carburetor: Carter two-barrel WCD-2034S.

(AMBASSADOR SIX) Inline six. Overhead valves. Displacement: 252.6 cid. Bore and stroke: 3.50 x 4.375 inches. Compression ratio: 7.3:1. Brake hp: 120 at 3700 rpm. Seven main bearings. Solid valve lifters. Carburetor: Carter one-barrel Type YH-895-S or YH-895-SA).

(AMBASSADOR "LE MANS" SIX) Inline. LeMans six. Overhead valves. Displacement: 252.6 cid. Bore and stroke: 3.50 x 4.375. Compression ratio: 8.0:1. Brake hp: 140 at 4000 rpm. Carburetors: (Front) Carter YH 973S; (Rear) Carter YH 974S.

(RAMBLER SIX) Inline. L-head six. Cast iron block. Displacement: 184.1 cid. Bore and stroke: 3-1/8 x 4 inches. Compression ratio: 7.25:1. Brake hp: 85 at 3800 rpm. Four main bearings. Solid valve lifters. Carburetor: Carter one- barrel type YF model 2014S.

(RAMBLER HYDRA-MATIC SIX) Inline. Six-cylinder. L-head. Cast iron block. Displacement: 195.6 inches. Compression ratio: 7.3:1. Four main bearings. Solid lifters. Brake hp: 90 at 3800 rpm. Carburetion: Carter one-barrel Model YF.

CHASSIS FEATURES: Wheelbase: (Statesman) 114-1/4 inches; (Ambassador) 121-1/4 inches; (Rambler) 100 inches. Overall length: (Statesman) 202-1/4 inches; (Ambassador) 209-1/4 inches; (Rambler Super) 176 inches; (Rambler Custom with continental tire extension) 185-3/8 inches. Front tread: (Statesman) 55-1/2 inches; (Ambassador) 55-5/8 inches; (Rambler) 55-3/8 inches. Rear tread: (Statesman) 59-11/16 inches; (Ambassador) 60-1/2 inches; (Rambler) 53 inches. Tires: (Statesman) 6.70 x 15; (Ambassador) 7.10 x 15; (Rambler Super) 5.90 x 15; (Rambler Custom) 6.40 x 15.

OPTIONS: Weather-Eye conditioned air system. Reclining seat and twin bed. Hydra-Matic automatic transmission. Automatic overdrive. Radio with twin speakers. White sidewall tires. Two-tone paint. Solex glass. Power steering (Ambassador only). Oil bath air cleaner. Rambler higher-compression engine with Hydra-Matic transmission.

HISTORICAL FOOTNOTES: Calendar year production amounted to 93,504 Nash models and 41,825 Ramblers. In calendar year 1953, Nash built 3,501 convertibles; 13,533 station wagons; and 34,356 hardtops.

1954 NASH

NASH STATESMAN — SERIES 40 — (6-CYL) — The 1954 Nash Statesman carried over the 1952-1953 Golden Anniversary styling with a minor facelift of the body. Changes included a new front concave grille and new chrome head light bezels. Continental rear tire carriers were added as standard on all Custom models. New interiors and instrument panels on both the Statesman and Ambassador appeared for 1954 also.

NASH I.D. NUMBERS: Vehicle Identification Plate located on the right-hand side of the cowl below the hood contains motor-serial number and number codes for model, paint and trim. Motor-serial number matches the serial number. Model number has four symbols. The first two symbols indicate model year, 54 = 1954. The third symbol indicates series: 0 = Rambler Deluxe; 1 = Rambler Super; 2 = Rambler Custom; 4 = Statesman Super; 5 = Statesman Custom; 6 = Ambassador Super; 7 = Ambassador Custom. The fourth symbol indicates body style. (All four numbers appear in Body/Style Number column of charts below). Motor numbers located on right-hand side of crankcase towards front. [NASH STATESMAN SERIES 40 I.D. NUMBERS]: Starting serial numbers for the Nash Statesman were K-615501 for Kenosha, Wis.; 4KD-5101 for unassembled export, KC-47201 for El Segundo, Calif. and KT-9101 for Toronto, Canada. Starting engine serial numbers were J-1001 for 1954. [NASH AMBASSADOR SERIES 60 I.D. NUMBERS]: Starting serial numbers for the Nash Ambassador were R-722501 for Kenosha, Wis.; 6KD-4201 for unassembled export and RC-22001 for El Segundo, Calif. Starting engine serial numbers were A246001 for 1954. [NASH RAMBLER SERIES 10 I.D. NUMBERS]: Starting serial numbers for the 1954 Nash Rambler were D-171501 for Kenosha, Wis.; DKD-3001 for unassembled export, and DC-12301 for El Segundo, Calif. Starting engine serial numbers for the 1954 Nash Rambler were F-170001.

NASH STATESMAN SERIES 40

Model Number	Body/Style Number	Body Type & Seating	Factory Price	Shipping Weight	Production Total
SUPER LINE					
40	5445	4-dr Sed-6P	2178	3045	11,401
40	5446	2-dr Sed-6P	2130	3025	1,855
CUSTOM LINE					
40	5455	4-dr Sed-6P	2362	3095	4,219
40	5456	2-dr Sed-6P	2340	3050	24
40	5457	2-dr HT Cpe-6P	2468	3120	2,726

1954 Nash, Ambassador Custom four-door sedan, 6-cyl

NASH AMBASSADOR — SERIES 60 — (6-CYL) — The 1954 Nash Ambassador, with a seven inch longer wheelbase than the 1954 Nash Statesman, shared the same changes as the Statesman for 1954. They included a new front concave grille and new chrome headlight bezels, new instrument panel and new interior. Continental rear tire carriers were standard on all Custom models.

NASH AMBASSADOR SERIES 60

Model Number	Body/Style Number	Body Type & Seating	Factory Price	Shipping Weight	Production Total
SUPER LINE					
60	5465	4-dr Sed-6P	2412	3430	7,433
60	5466	2-dr Sed-6P	2360	3025	283
CUSTOM LINE					
60	5475	4-dr Sed-6P	2595	3095	10,131
60	5477	2-dr HT Cpe-6P	2730	3120	3,581

1954 Nash, Rambler Country Club two-door hardtop coupe, 6-cyl

NASH RAMBLER — SERIES 10 — (6-CYL) — The 1954 Nash Rambler received no major appearance changes for 1954. However several new models were added to the lineup. New for 1954 were a four-door sedan and a four-door station wagon on a new longer 108 inch wheelbase, also added were a Deluxe and Super two-door sedan on the 100 inch wheelbase as low-line price leaders. To cut costs, radios and heaters were changed from standard equipment to options.

NASH RAMBLER SERIES 10

Model Number	Body/Style Number	Body Type & Seating	Factory Price	Shipping Weight	Production Total
10	2404	2-dr Utl Wag-5P	1444	2425	56
10	5406	2-dr Del Sed-5P	1550	2425	7,273
10	5414	2-dr Sub-5P	1945	2520	504
10	5415	4-dr Sup Sed-5P	1995	2570	4,313
10	5416	2-dr Sup Sed-5P	1865	2425	300
10	5417	2-dr CtyClb-5P	1945	2465	1,071
10	5421	2-dr Conv-5P	2125	2555	221
10	5424	2-dr Sta Wag-5P	2095	2535	2,202
10	5425	4-dr Cus Sed-5P	2175	2630	7,640
10	5427	2-dr Cus HT Cpe-5P	2095	2515	3,612
10	5428	4-dr Cus Sta Wag-5P	2200	2715	9,039

ENGINES

(STATESMAN SIX): Inline. L-head six. Cast iron block. Displacement: 195.6 cid. Bore and stroke: 3-1/8 x 4-1/4 inches. Compression ratio: 8.5:1. Brake hp: 110 at 4000 rpm. Four main bearings. Solid valve lifters. Carburetor: Carter two-barrel WCD-2098S; or Carter YF-2137-S; or Carter YF-2137-SA.

(AMBASSADOR SIX) Inline six. Overhead valves. Displacement: 252.6 cid. Bore and stroke: 3.50 x 4.375 inches. Compression ratio: 7.6:1. Brake hp: 130 at 3700 rpm. Seven main bearings. Solid valve lifters. Carburetor: Carter one-barrel Type YH-895-S or YH-895-SA).

(LEMANS "DUAL-JETFIRE" SIX) Inline. LeMans six. Overhead valves. Displacement: 252.6 cid. Bore and stroke: 3.50 x 4.375. Compression ratio: 8.0:1. Brake hp: 140 at 4000 rpm. Carburetors: (Front) Carter YH 973S; (Rear) Carter YH 974S.

(RAMBLER SIX) Inline. L-head six. Cast iron block. Displacement: 184.1 cid. Bore and stroke: 3-1/8 x 4 inches. Compression ratio: 7.25:1. Brake hp: 85 at 3800 rpm. Four main bearings. Solid valve lifters. Carburetor: Carter one-barrel type YF model 2014S.

(RAMBLER HYDRA-MATIC SIX) Inline. Six-cylinder. L-head. Cast iron block. Displacement: 195.6 inches. Compression ratio: 7.3:1. Four main bearings. Solid lifters. Brake hp: 90 at 3800 rpm. Carburetion: Carter one-barrel Model YF.

CHASSIS FEATURES: Wheelbase: (Statesman) 114.3 inches; (Ambassador) 121.3 inches; (Rambler 10) 100 inches; (Rambler four-door) 108 inches. Overall length: (Statesman) 202.3 inches; (Statesman with continental kit) 212.3 inches; (Ambassador) 209.3 inches; (Ambassador with continental kit) 219.3 inches; (Rambler 10 Super) 178.3 inches; (Rambler 10 Custom with continental tire extension) 185.4 inches; (Rambler four-door) 186.3 inches; (Rambler four-door with continental kit) 193.4 inches. Front tread: (Statesman) 55.5 inches; (Ambassador) 59.7 inches; (Rambler) 53.4 inches. Rear tread: (Statesman) 55.6 inches; (Ambassador) 60.5 inches; (Rambler) 53 inches. Tires: (Statesman) 6.70 x 15; (Ambassador) 7.10 x 15; (Rambler Super) 5.90 x 15; (Rambler Custom) 6.40 x 15.

OPTIONS: Rambler (general prices). Oil bath air cleaner (price $7.50). Airliner reclining seats only ($111.45); and twin beds ($18.00). Air mattresses for twin bed ($15.00). Electric clock ($17.00). Two-tone color ($16.00). Directional signals ($16.00). Le Mans Dual-Jetfire engine for Ambassador (price n.a.). Foam cushions front or rear ($10.00); both front and rear ($20.00). Solex glass ($19.00). Hydra-Matic transmission ($179.00). Overdrive ($104.00). Power brakes (price n.a.). Power steering (price n.a.). Radio and antenna standard Rambler. Custom steering wheel ($14.00); with overdrive power pass ($18.95). Heavy springs and shocks ($8.00). White sidewall tires, size 6.40 x 15 ($25.00). White sidewall tires, size 5.90 x 15 ($22.00). Upholstery options ($80.00). Electric window lifts (Ambassador only price n.a.). Wheel discs, four ($21.00). Weather-Eye (standard Rambler) optional Statesman and Ambassador.

HISTORICAL FOOTNOTE: On April 22, 1954 Nash and Hudson merged to form American Motors Corp. The official date for the beginning of AMC was May 1. George Mason hoped to bring Studebaker and Packard into the new corporation as well, but he passed away before this could be accomplished. Nash, in 1954, was the first to introduce low price air-conditioning systems to mass market autos. The system Nash invented for use then is the basis for all modern auto air-conditioning systems. Previously, air-conditioning was very expensive and available only on very expensive autos in limited quantities and filled half the trunk area. Nash's system was much more compact and easily serviced and integrated into the underhood area of the car. Calendar year production included 37,779 Ramblers and 29,371

Nash. The total of 67,150 cars made Nash America's 13th largest automaker. Model year production was 62,911 units made to 1954 specifications. The LeMans "Dual-Jetfire" six was advertised as an engine "that has won many Grand Prix d'Endurance awards." In calendar year 1954, Nash was credited with building 6,065 hardtops, 11,800 station wagons; and four convertibles.

1955 NASH

NASH STATESMAN — SERIES 40 — (6-CYL) — The 1955 Nash Statesman had a completely revised version of 1952's Golden Anniversary styling. A "Scena-Ramic" wraparound windshield appeared. Another new feature was a long character molding from front to rear fenders. The headlights were enclosed in a redesigned oval grille. The new concave grille had multiple chrome dividers. Custom models had the continental spare tire mount.

NASH I.D. NUMBERS: Vehicle Identification Plate located on the right-hand side of the cowl below the hood contains motor-serial number and number codes for model, paint and trim. Motor-serial number matches the serial number. Model number has four symbols. The first two symbols indicate model year, 55 = 1955. The third symbol indicates series: 0 = Rambler Deluxe; 1 = Rambler Super; 2 = Rambler Custom; 4 = Statesman Super; 5 = Statesman Custom; 6 = Ambassador Super; 7 = Ambassador Custom. The fourth symbol indicates body style. (All four numbers appear in Body/Style column of charts below). Motor numbers located on right-hand side of crankcase towards front. [NASH STATESMAN SERIES 40 I.D. NUMBERS]: Serial numbers for the Statesman six were K-635001 to K-649123 for Kenosha, Wis.; 4KD-5401 and up for unassembled export; KC-48101 and up for El Segundo, Calif. and KT-10501 and up for Toronto, Canada. Engine serial numbers were S-440001 to S-453100 for single-carburetor jobs and J-30001 to J-33070 for dual-carburetor jobs. [NASH AMBASSADOR SERIES 60 I.D. NUMBERS]: Serial numbers for the Ambassador six were R-742901 to R-757866 for Kenosha, Wis.; 6KD-4401 and up for unassembled export and RC-23001 and up for El Segundo, Calif., with no Canadian production of this series. Starting engine serial numbers were A-270001 to A-278691 for single carburetor Super Six and LMA-270001 to LMA-277002 for dual-carburetor jobs. [NASH AMBASSADOR SERIES 80 I.D. NUMBERS]: Serial numbers for the Ambassador V-8s were V-1001 to V-11444 for Kenosha, Wis.; 8KD-1001 and up for unassembled export and VC-1001 and up for El Segundo, Calif. Starting engine serial number for all Ambassador Eights was P-1001 to P-11444. [NASH RAMBLER SERIES 10 I.D. NUMBERS]: Serial numbers for Ramblers were D-205001 to D-276099 for Kenosha, Wis.; DKD-3701 and up for unassembled export and DC-15001 to (Nash) DC-23325/(Hudson) DC-23325 for El Segundo, Calif. Engine serial number for all Ramblers was H45001 to H-131414.

NASH STATESMAN SERIES 40

Model Number	Body/Style Number	Body Type & Seating	Factory Price	Shipping Weight	Production Total
SUPER LINE					
40	5545-1	4-dr Sup Sed-6P	2215	3134	12,877
CUSTOM LINE					
40	5547-2	2-dr HT Cpe-6P	2495	3220	1,395
40	5545-2	4-dr Cus Sed-6P	2385	3204	Note 1

NOTE 1: Custom four-door production included with Super four-door total.

1955 Nash, Ambassador Country Club two-door hardtop, V-8

AMBASSADOR — SERIES 60 — (6-CYL) — The 1955 Nash Ambassador six received the same type of appearance changes as the 1955 Nash Statesman including: new wraparound windshield, new long character moldings from front to rear fenders; and headlights enclosed in a redesigned oval-concave grille.

NASH AMBASSADOR SERIES 60

Model Number	Body/Style Number	Body Type & Seating	Factory Price	Shipping Weight	Production Total
SUPER					
60	5565-1	4-dr Sup Sed-6P	2480	3538	13,809
CUSTOM LINE					
60	5567-2	2-dr HT Cpe-6P	2795	3593	1,395
60	5565-2	4-dr Cus Sed-6P	2675	3576	Note 1

NOTE 1: Custom four-door production included with Super four-door total.

NASH AMBASSADOR SERIES 80 — (8-CYL) — The year 1955 marked the introduction of an overhead valve V-8 engine in the Ambassador line. The new power plant was a 320 cid engine purchased from Packard. It was only available with Twin Ultramatic transmission. The 1955 Nash Ambassador V-8 was distinguished by V-8 emblems on its rear fenders and Ambassador (Custom or Super) V-8 emblems on front fenders. Styling was otherwise the same as on the Ambassador six.

NASH AMBASSADOR SERIES 80

Model Number	Body/Style Number	Body Type & Seating	Factory Price	Shipping Weight	Production Total
SUPER					
80	5585-1	4-dr Sup Sed-6P	2775	3795	8,805
CUSTOM LINE					
80	5587-2	2-dr HT Cpe-6P	3095	3839	1,775
80	5585-2	4-dr Cus Sed-6P	2965	3827	Note 1

NOTE 1: Custom four-door production included with Super four-door total.

1955 Nash, Rambler Country Club two-door hardtop, 6-cyl (TVB)

NASH RAMBLER — SERIES 10 — (6-CYL) — The 1955 Nash Rambler received a minor facelift over 1954. New features included the addition of a new cellular grille and full wheel cutouts in the front fenders. Both Nash and Hudson marketed versions of the Rambler in 1955.

NASH RAMBLER SERIES 10

Model Number	Body/Style Number	Body Type & Seating	Factory Price	Shipping Weight	Production Total
FLEET (100" WHEELBASE)					
10	2504	2-dr Utl Wag-5P	—	2500	14
DELUXE (100" W.B. TWO-DOOR/108" W.B. FOUR-DOOR)					
10	5512	2-dr Del Bus Sed-3P	1328	2400	43
10	5516	2-dr Del Clb Sed-5P	1585	2432	Note 1
10	5515	4-dr Del Sed-6P	1695	2567	Note 1
SUPER (100" W.B. TWO-DOOR/108" W.B. FOUR-DOOR)					
10	5516-1	2-dr Sup Clb Sed-5P	1683	2450	8979
10	5514-1	2-dr Sup Sub-5P	1869	2532	2379
10	5515-1	4-dr Sup Sed-6P	1798	2570	15,998
10	5518-1	4-dr Sup Cr Cty-6P	1807	2675	Note 1
CUSTOM (100" W.B. TWO-DOOR/108" W.B. FOUR-DOOR)					
10	5517-2	2-dr Cus Cty Clb HT-5P	1995	2518	2,993
10	5515-2	4-dr Cus Sed-6P	1989	2606	Note 1
10	5518	4-dr Cus Sta Wag-5	2098	2685	25,617

NOTE 1: Production included with same Style Number in other trim lines.

ENGINES

(STATESMAN SIX): Inline. L-head six. Cast iron block. Displacement: 195.6 cid. Bore and stroke: 3-1/8 x 4-1/4 inches. Compression ratio: 7.45:1. Brake hp: 100 at 3800 rpm. Four main bearings. Solid valve lifters. Carburetor: Carter one-barrel YF-22585.

(STATESMAN SIX DUAL CARB): Inline. Overhead six. Cast iron block. Displacement: 195.6 cid. Bore and stroke: 3-1/8 x 4-1/4 inches. Compression ratio: 8.0:1. Brake hp: 110 at 4000 rpm. Four main bearings. Solid valve lifters. Carburetor: Carter one-barrel (front) YH-973S; (rear) YH-974S.

(AMBASSADOR SIX) Inline six. Overhead valves. Displacement: 252.6 cid. Bore and stroke: 3.50 x 4.375 inches. Compression ratio: 7.6:1. Brake hp: 130 at 3700 rpm. Seven main bearings. Solid valve lifters. Carburetor: Carter one-barrel Type YH-895-S).

(LEMANS "DUAL-JETFIRE" SIX): Inline. LeMans six. Overhead valves. Displacement: 252.6 cid. Bore and stroke: 3.50 x 4.375. Compression ratio: 7.6:1. Brake hp: 140 at 4000 rpm. Carburetors: (Front) Carter YH 973S; (Rear) Carter YH 974S.

(RAMBLER SIX) Inline. Six-cylinder. L-head. Cast iron block. Displacement: 195.6 inches. Compression ratio: 7.3:1. Four main bearings. Solid lifters. Brake hp: 90 at 3800 rpm. Carburetion: Carter one-barrel Model YF.

(AMBASSADOR V-8) V-8. Overhead valves. Cast iron block. Displacement: 320 inches. Bore and stroke: 313/16 x 3-1/2 inches. Compression ratio: 7.8:1. Brake hp: 208 at 4200 rpm. Non-adjustable hydraulic valve lifters. Five main bearings. Carburetor: Carter two-barrel Model WGD.

CHASSIS FEATURES: Wheelbase: (Statesman) 114.3 inches; (Ambassador) 121.3 inches; (Rambler 10) 100 inches; (Rambler four-door) 108 inches. Overall length: (Statesman) 202.3 inches; (Statesman with continental kit) 212.3 inches; (Ambassador) 209.3 inches; (Ambassador with continental kit) 219.3 inches; (Rambler 10 Super) 178.3 inches; (Rambler 10 Custom with continental tire extension) 185.4 inches; (Rambler four-door) 186.3 inches; (Rambler four-door with continental kit) 193.4 inches. Front tread: (Statesman) 55.5 inches; (Ambassador) 59.7 inches; (Rambler) 53.4 inches. Rear tread: (Statesman) 55.6 inches; (Ambassador) 60.5 inches; (Rambler) 53 inches. Tires: (Statesman) 6.70 x 15; (Ambassador) 7.10 x 15; (Rambler) 5.90 x 15; (Rambler Custom) 6.40 x 15.

OPTIONS: [Rambler]: Rambler oil bath air cleaner ($8). Reclining seats ($11); with twin bed ($18). Air mattress for twin bed ($15). All season air conditioning ($345). Electric clock ($17). Two-tone color ($16). Directional signals ($16). Foam seat cushions front or rear ($10). Foam seat cushions front and rear ($20). Solex glass ($19). Hood ornament ($11). Hydra-Matic transmission ($179). Overdrive ($104). Radio and antenna ($76). Heavy-duty springs ($8). White sidewall tires, size 6.40 x 15 ($27). Black sidewall tires, size 6.40 x 15 ($37). White sidewall tires, size 6.40 x 15, six-ply tubeless construction($70). Upholstery ($55). Vacuum booster pump ($3). Weather-Eye heater ($74). [Nash]: Radio. Electric antenna. Visor vanity mirror. Non-glare rearview mirror. Outside mirror. Spotlight and mirror. Wire wheelcovers. Back-up lights. Windshield washer. Fog lights. Rear window wiper. Trunk light. Electric clock. Air mat. Hand spotlight. Plastic screens. Luggage carrier. Door top shades. Curb-L-arms. Sola-cell cooling system. Dyna-Flyte dual plate distributor. Oil filter. Fuel filter. Gas filler guard. Hood ornament. Door edge guards. Exhaust extension. License plate frame.

HISTORICAL FOOTNOTES: Nash had a slow start in 1955, but, once started, moved along at a warm pace. The company wound up the year with model year sales of 109,102 units. Calendar year output was 83,852 Ramblers and 51,315 Nashes for 10th place in the industry. Dealer contests and sales promotions were instrumental in stimulating deliveries. A total of 81,237 Nash/Hudson units were built, highest run for the line in history. An added feather in Rambler's cap was its consistent holding of number one spot in used car value, as reflected in NADA reports. Nash's more powerful, 'Speedline' styled 1956 models were unveiled Nov. 17, 1955. Dealer introductions took place Nov. 23, 1954. Two new engines were introduced: the top-powered 220 hp Ambassador Jetfire V-8 with Twin Ultramatic and a Statesman six overhead valve powerplant. Model year production began October, 1954 and included 40,133 Statesman/Ambassadors and 56,023 Ramblers. Calendar year production included 7,442 two-door hardtops and 28,163 station wagons.

1956 NASH

NASH STATESMAN — SERIES 40 — (6-CYL) — The 1956 Nash Statesman received a major facelift. The front and rear fenders were restyled. There were larger, more visible front running lights and, also, new taillights. A revised hood ornament and one-piece rear windows were seen. Chrome side stripping revisions included a shallow 'Z' shape on the side of the car and outline moldings on the hood and rear fender sides. The only Statesman model available for 1956 was the four-door Super sedan. Its engine was redesigned to an overhead valve configuration.

NASH I.D. NUMBERS: Vehicle Identification Plate located on the right-hand side of the cowl below the hood contains motor-serial number and number codes for model, paint and trim. Motor-serial number matches the serial number. Model number has four symbols. The first two symbols indicate model year, 56 = 1956. The third symbol indicates series: 0 = Rambler Deluxe; 1 = Rambler Super; 2 = Rambler Custom; 4 = Statesman Super; 5 = Statesman Custom; 6 = Ambassador Super; 7 = Ambassador Custom. The fourth symbol indicates body style. (All four numbers appear in Body/Style Number column of charts below.) Motor numbers located on right-hand side of crankcase towards front. [NASH STATESMAN SERIES 40 I.D. NUMBERS]: Starting serial numbers for the Statesman six were K-649201 for Kenosha, Wis.; 4KD-5701 for unassembled export and KT-11101 for Toronto, Canada. Starting engine serial number was DB-1001. [NASH AMBASSADOR SERIES 60 I.D. NUMBERS]: Starting serial numbers for the Ambassador six were R-757901 for Kenosha, Wis., and 6KD-4601 for unassembled export. Starting engine serial numbers were A-279001 for single-carburetor jobs and LMA-277001 for the dual-carburetor jobs. [NASH AMBASSADOR SERIES 80 I.D. NUMBERS]: Starting serial numbers for Ambassador Eights were V-11501 for Kenosha, Wis. and 8KD-1101 for unassembled export. Starting engine serial numbers were P-21001 for Ambassador Eights. [NASH AMBASSADOR SPECIAL SERIES 50 I.D. NUMBERS]: Starting serial numbers were U-1001 for Kenosha, Wis.; UKD-1001 for unassembled export and UT-1001 for cars built in Toronto, Canada. Starting engine serial number was G-1001 for all series 50 Ambassador V-8s. [NASH RAMBLER SERIES 10 I.D. NUMBERS]: Starting serial numbers for 1956 Ramblers were D-276101 for Kenosha, Wis.; DKD-5601 for unassembled export and KT-5401 for Toronto, Canada. Starting engine serial number for all Ramblers was B1001.

NASH STATESMAN SERIES 40

Model Number	Body/Style Number	Body Type & Seating	Factory Price	Shipping Weight	Production Total
40	5645-1	4-dr Sup Sed-6P	2385	3199	7,438

NASH AMBASSADOR — SERIES 60 — (6-CYL) — The 1956 Nash Ambassador six available in only one body style, the four-door Super sedan. It shared all the styling changes of 1956 Statesman models on the seven inch longer wheelbase of the Ambassador platform. An Ambassador Super script appeared on front fenders.

NASH AMBASSADOR SERIES 60

Model Number	Body/Style Number	Body Type & Seating	Factory Price	Shipping Weight	Production Total
60	5665-1	4-dr Sup Sed-6P	2689	3555	5,999

1956 Nash, Ambassador Custom four-door sedan, V-8

NASH AMBASSADOR — SERIES 80 — (8-CYL) — The 1956 Nash Ambassador eight shared the same styling changes as the Ambassador six. The Super V-8 sedan was equipped and trimmed similar to the Super Six sedan. Customs had the name "Ambassador Custom" on the front fenders and "Ambassador Country Club" on the hardtops. On later production models, vertical chrome moldings are added to the front fenders of Customs. The V-8 was, again, a Packard built engine, and a larger 352 cid displacement block was used. This motor was only available with Packard's Ultramatic transmission attached.

NASH AMBASSADOR SERIES 80

Model Number	Body/Style Number	Body Type & Seating	Factory Price	Shipping Weight	Production Total
80	5685-1	4-dr Sup Sed-6P	2956	3748	3,885
80	5685-2	4-dr Cus Sed-6P	3195	3846	Note 1
80	5687-2	2-dr Cus HT Cpe-6P	3338	3854	796

NOTE 1: Production of Super and Custom four-door is counted as a single total.

NASH AMBASSADOR SPECIAL — SERIES 50 — (8-CYL) — The Nash Ambassador Special V-8 was introduced as a midyear 1956 model. It came out in April with a V-8 engine of AMC's own design and manufacture. The Ambassador Special was available in three models, a Super four-door sedan, a Custom four-door sedan and a two-door hardtop coupe. Supers had single side rub-rail moldings and chrome moldings across the front of the hood and fenders. Power brakes, an "Airliner" reclining seat and continental tire mounting were standard on Custom models. They also had double chrome side rub-rail moldings enclosing a separate color area and a chrome band across the front of the hood and fenders, down to the bumper wings. On later production models, vertical chrome moldings are added to the front fenders of Customs.

NASH AMBASSADOR SERIES 50

Model Number	Body/Style Number	Body Type & Seating	Factory Price	Shipping Weight	Production Total
50	5655-1	4-dr Sup Sed-6P	2355	3397	4,145
50	5655-2	4-dr Cus Sed-6P	2462	3418	Note 1
50	5657-2	2-dr Cus Sed-6P	2541	3567	706

NOTE 1: Production of Super/Custom four-doors is counted as a single total.

1956 Nash, Rambler Custom Cross Country four-door wagon, 6-cyl

NASH RAMBLER — SERIES 10 — (6-CYL) — The 1956 Nash Rambler received a major redesign of the long-wheelbase four-door sedan and station wagon. The short-wheelbase cars were dropped. (They would re-appear, with a few minor changes, as the 1958 American.) The 1956 models were totally re-designed on the outside, with a new oval-shaped grille housing the headlights located inside the grille. Running lights (front parking lights that stayed on even when the headlights were turned on) were set high in each front fender. They complemented the new rear fenders and revisions to the rear deck. Chrome trim and color treatments with three-tone color combinations were available and a wraparound rear window appeared. Also introduced was the first four-door hardtop station wagon. Nash production was discontinued at the El Segundo, Calif. plant.

NASH RAMBLER SERIES 10

Model Number	Body/Style Number	Body Type & Seating	Factory Price	Shipping Weight	Production Total
DELUXE (108" WHEELBASE)					
10	5615	4-dr Del Sed-6P	1829	2891	21,966
SUPER (108" WHEELBASE)					
10	5615-1	4-dr Sup Sed-6P	1939	2906	Note 1
10	5618-1	4-dr Sup Sta Wag-6P	2233	2992	21,554
CUSTOM (108" WHEELBASE)					
10	5613-2	4-dr Cty Clb Wag-6P	2491	3095	402
10	5615-2	4-dr Cus Sed-6P	2056	2990	Note 1
10	5618-2	4-dr Cus Crs Cty Wag-6P	2326	3110	Note 1
10	5619-2	4-dr Cus HT Sed-6P	2224	2990	2,155

NOTE 1: If two models have same first four symbols in Body Style Numbers the production of cars with different levels of trim is not separately broken out.

BASE ENGINES

(STATESMAN SIX) Six-cylinder. Overhead valves. Cast iron block. Displacement: 195.6 cid. Bore and stroke: 3-1/8 x 4-1/4 inches. Compression ratio: 7.47:1. Brake hp: 130 at 4500 rpm. Four main bearings. Solid valve lifters. Carburetor: Carter two barrel WCD 2350S or Stromberg BVX-25 Model 380288. A 12-volt electrical system was used for the first time.

(AMBASSADOR SIX) Inline six. Overhead valves. Displacement: 252.6 cid. Bore and stroke: 3.50 x 4.375 inches. Compression ratio: 7.6:1. Brake hp: 135 at 3700 rpm. Seven main bearings. Solid valve lifters. Carburetor: Carter one-barrel Type YH 2368S.

(LEMANS "DUAL-JETFIRE" SIX) Inline. LeMans six. Overhead valves. Displacement: 252.6 cid. Bore and stroke: 3.50 x 4.375. Compression ratio: 7.6:1. Brake hp: 145 at 4000 rpm. Carburetors: (Front/Rear) Carter YH 2369S.

(AMBASSADOR/PACKARD V-8) V-8. Overhead valves. Displacement: 352 cid. Bore and stroke: 4 x 3-1/2 inches. Compression ratio: 9.55:1. Brake hp: 220 at 4600 rpm. Five main bearings. Hydraulic lifters. Carburetion: Carter two-barrel WGD 2231S.

(AMBASSADOR/AMC V-8) V-8. Overhead valve. Cast iron block. Displacement: 250 cid. Bore and stroke: 3-1/2 x 3-1/4 inches. Compression ratio: 8.0:1. Brake hp: 190 at 4900 rpm. Five main bearings. Non-adjustable hydraulic lifters. Carburetion: Carter two-barrel WGD.

(RAMBLER SIX) Six-cylinder. Overhead valve. Cast Iron block. Displacement: 195.6 cid. Bore and stroke: 3-1/8 x 4-1/4 inches. Compression ratio: 7.47:1. Brake hp: 120 at 4200 rpm. Four main bearings. Solid valve lifters. Carburetion: Carter one-barrel Model AS-2349S.

CHASSIS FEATURES: Wheelbase: (Rambler) 108 inches; (Statesman) 114.3 inches; (Ambassador 50/60) 121.3 inches. Overall length: (Rambler) 191.1 inches; (Rambler Custom with continental kit) 198.9 inches; (Statesman) 202.3 inches; (Ambassador 50/60) 209.3 inches. Front tread: (Rambler) 57.8 inches; (Statesman/Ambassador 50 and 60) 56.6 inches. Rear tread: (Rambler) 58 inches; (Statesman) 59.7 inches; (Ambassador 50/60) 60.5 inches. Tires: (Rambler) Four-ply tubeless, size 6.40 x 15; (Statesman) 6.70 x 15; (Ambassador 50) 7.60 x 15; (Ambassador 60) 7.10 x 15.

OPTIONS: (All models) Radio. Hood ornament. Outside mirror. Non glare rearview mirror. Spotlight mirror. Back-up lights. Windshield washer. Air screens. Center pillar overlay (four-door sedan). Locking gas cap. Filler neck guard. Cross country cargo straps. Power brakes.

Exhaust extension. Curb indicators. Trunk light. Door top shades. Door edge guards. Rear window wiper (Statesman and Ambassador). Oil filter. Sola-cell. Seat belts. Rear door safety locks.

HISTORICAL FOOTNOTES: Dealer introductions of 1956 models took place on Nov. 22, 1955. Cars were sold by both Hudson and Nash dealers and the Series 10 models were known as American Motors Ramblers. The Hudson and Nash products were comparable, except for hood medallions and their "N" or "H" wheelcover insignias. The company's automotive division sustained a sizable loss while its appliance division enjoyed its most profitable year since 1950. During the year the corporation completed the sale of idle plants and equipment (El Segundo, Calif. and the Hudson-Gratiot plant in Detroit) for a net amount of $5.3 million. Year 1956 saw production by American Motors of 104,190 cars (79,166 Ramblers, 17,842 Nashes, 7,182 Hudsons). American Motors Corp. produced its 2,000,000th single-unit construction car March 27, 1956. Genuine leather trims were available in the following 1956 models: Ambassador Six and Ambassador V-8 sedans; Ambassador Country Club hardtop; Rambler sedan; Rambler Country Club station wagon; Rambler four-door hardtop and Rambler Country Club station wagon.

1957 NASH

1957 Nash, Ambassador four-door sedan, V-8

NASH AMBASSADOR SERIES 80 — (V-8) — The Nash Ambassador for 1957 was available only with a 327 cubic inch AMC V-8 engine in two-door hardtops and four-door sedan. Super and Custom trim levels were provided. The Nash Ambassador six and Statesman six were discontinued. The new Ambassador received a major face-lift incorporating the first four-beam headlight system used on any U.S. car. Also seen was completely new front end styling, including a new cellular grille, front parking lights on top of the front fenders and new lightning streak side trim. The Ambassador Super had its name on the front fenders in script, small hubcaps and single lightning streak side trim with no upper beltline molding. Ambassador Customs had scripts with that name on the fenders, dual molding lightning streak trim and full wheelcovers. This was the last year for Nash production.

NASH I.D. NUMBERS: Vehicle Identification Plate located on the right-hand side of the cowl below the hood contains motor-serial number and number codes for model, paint and trim. Motor-serial number matches the serial number. Model number has four symbols. The first two symbols indicate model year, 57 = 1957. The third symbol indicates series: 1 = Rambler; 8 = Ambassador Super; 7 = Ambassador Custom. The fourth symbol indicates body style. (All four numbers appear in Body/Style Number column of charts below). Suffixes are added behind the four numbers on some models, as follows: 1 = Super; 2 = Custom. No suffix means Deluxe. Motor numbers located on right-hand side of crankcase towards front. [NASH AMBASSADOR SERIES 80 I.D. NUMBERS]: Starting serial number for the Nash Ambassador was V-16501, with all Nash Ambassadors built in Kenosha, Wis. Starting engine serial number is N1001. [RAMBLER SIX SERIES 10 I.D. NUMBERS]: Starting serial number for the 1957 Rambler six was D-341001. Starting engine serial numbers were B-73001 for the standard engine and CB-2001 for the optional six-cylinder engine. [RAMBLER V-8 SERIES 20 I.D. NUMBERS]: Starting serial numbers for the 1957 Rambler V-8 was A-1001. Starting engine serial number was G7501. [RAMBLER REBEL SERIES 30 I.D. NUMBERS]: Starting serial numbers for the Rambler Rebel was F-1001. Starting engine serial number was CN1001.

NASH AMBASSADOR SERIES 80

Model Number	Body/Style Number	Body Type & Seating	Factory Price	Shipping Weight	Production Total
80	5785-1	4-dr Sup Sed-6P	2821	3639	3,098
80	5785-2	4-dr Cus Sed-6P	3011	3701	5,627
80	5787-1	2-dr Sup HT-6P	2910	3655	608
80	5787-2	2-dr Cus HT-6P	3101	3722	997

NOTE 1: Prices given for 1957 models are ADP figures from OFFICIAL AUTOMOBILE GUIDE (87th edition) effective Jan. 1, 1957.

RAMBLER SIX SERIES 10 — (6-CYL) — The Rambler six for 1957 continued the 108 inch wheelbase with a few minor changes. Included were new vertical, front running lights, with horizontal bright metal dividers positioned below the headlights; a new wing-shaped ornament on top of the rectangular grille section and the elimination of side color accent trim running over the roof. Three series were again available. Deluxe models had the lowest level of trim and equipment and were essentially built for fleet customers. Super series models carried a single, full-length side molding with the word Super, in script, on the rear fenders. Deluxe models came with no series name or side moldings. The Custom series models came with Rambler Custom scripts on the front fenders and dual side moldings, with a round medallion at the forward end.

RAMBLER SIX SERIES 10

Model Number	Body/Style Number	Body Type & Seating	Factory Price	Shipping Weight	Production Total
DELUXE LINE					
10	5715	4-dr DeL Sed-6P	1961	1962	9,402
10	5718	4-dr DeL Sta Wag	2291	3034	75

1957 Nash, Super Cross Country four-door station wagon, 6-cyl

Model	Body/Style	Body Type	Factory	Shipping	Production
SUPER LINE					
10	5715-1	4-dr Sup Sed-6P	2123	2914	16,320
10	5718-1	4-dr Sup Sta Wag	2410	3042	14,083
10	5719-1	4-dr Sup HT-6P	2208	2936	612
CUSTOM LINE					
10	5715-2	4-dr Cus Sed-6P	2213	2938	10,520
10	5718-2	4-dr Cus Sta Wag	2500	3076	17,745

NOTE 1: The Deluxe station wagon, Style 5718, was for fleet use only.

1957 Nash, Custom four-door hardtop sedan, V-8

RAMBLER V-8 SERIES 20 — (V-8) — The Rambler, for 1957, was also available with a V-8 engine of 250 cid. The same four-door station wagon and sedan styles were offered with this brand new Rambler power plant. Super and Custom trim levels were provided. Super series models carried a single, full-length side molding with the word Super, in script, on the rear fenders. Deluxe models came with no series name or side moldings. The Custom series models came with Rambler Custom scripts on the front fenders and dual side moldings, with a round medallion at the forward end.

RAMBLER V-8 SERIES 20

SUPER LINE

Model Number	Body/Style Number	Body Type & Seating	Factory Price	Shipping Weight	Production Total
20	5725-1	4-dr Sup Sed-6P	2253	3223	3,555
20	5728-1	4-dr Sup Sta Wag	2540	3359	2,461
CUSTOM LINE					
20	5723-2	4-dr Cus HT Sta Wag	2715	3409	182
20	5725-2	4-dr Cus Sed-6P	2343	3259	3,199
20	5728-2	4-dr Cus Sta Wag-6P	2630	3392	4,560
20	5729-2	4-dr Cus HT Sed-6P	2428	3269	485

RAMBLER REBEL — 30 SERIES — (V-8) — The 1957 Rambler Rebel used the Ambassador 327 cid engine in a Rambler V-8 body. This limited-production car was available exclusively in light silver-gray metallic finish. It had black nylon and silver gray vinyl upholstery. However, many of the cars were later repainted by dealers, due to excessive fading of the silver gray

paint. The 1957 Rebel featured a side molding of bronze/gold anodized aluminum, which ran the full length of the car. The four-door hardtop body style was the only one available. The Rebel was the first attempt by American Motors to build a high performance car. In fact, this was the first time a large engine had been placed in a true intermediate-sized chassis (an idea Pontiac would find great success with in the GTO) by any automaker. In an April, 1957, MOTOR TREND test it was found that the only car capable of a faster 0-to-60 time than the Rebel was the fuel-injected Corvette. Fuel-injection had actually been planned for the 1957 Rebel with 288 hp possible. However, problems with the electric control unit prevented its production. Thus, a mildly re-worked 327 cid Ambassador engine was used.

RAMBLER REBEL SERIES 30

Model Number	Body/Style Number	Body Type & Seating	Factory Price	Shipping Weight	Production Total
30	5739-2	4-dr Cus HT Sed-6P	2786	3353	1,500

1957 Nash, Rebel four-door hardtop, V-8

BASE ENGINES

[AMBASSADOR EIGHT] V-8: Overhead valves. Displacement: 327 cid. Bore and stroke: 4 x 3-1/4 inches. Compression ratio: 9.0:1. Brake hp: 255 at 4700 rpm. Five main bearings. Hydraulic valve lifters. Carburetor: Carter four-barrel model WCFB-2593SA. Dual exhaust. 12-volt electrical system.

(RAMBLER SIX) Six-cylinder. Overhead valve. Cast Iron block. Displacement: 195.6 cid. Bore and stroke: 3-1/8 x 4-1/4 inches. Compression ratio: 8.25:1. Brake hp: 125 at 4200 rpm. Four main bearings. Solid valve lifters. Carburetion: Carter one-barrel model AS-2580S.

(RAMBLER EIGHT) V-8. Overhead valve. Cast iron block. Displacement: 250.1 cid. Bore and stroke: 3-1/2 x 3-1/4 inches. Compression ratio: 8.0:1. Brake hp: 190 at 4900 rpm. Five main bearings. Non-adjustable hydraulic lifters. Carburetion: Carter two-barrel model WGD-2352-SA.

[RAMBLER REBEL EIGHT] V-8. Overhead valves. Cast iron block. Displacement: 326.7 cid. Bore and stroke: 4 x 3-1/4 inches. Compression ratio: 9.0:1. Brake hp: 255 at 4700 rpm. Five bearings. Solid valve lifters. Carburetion: Carter four-barrel model WCBF-2593-SA.

CHASSIS FEATURES: [NASH AMBASSADOR] Wheelbase: 121.3 inches. Overall length: 209.3 inches (219.3 inches with continental tire mount). Front tread: 59.1 inches. Rear tread: 60.5 inches. Tires: 8.00 x 14. [RAMBLER]: Wheelbase: 108 inches. Overall length: (Station wagon) 193.61 inches; (four-door sedan) 191.14 Inches; (four-door sedan with continental kit 198.89 inches). Front tread: 57-3/4 inches. Rear tread: 58 inches. Tires: (six) 6.40 x 15; (V-8) 6.70 x 15.

OPTIONS: [AMBASSADOR] Power steering. Power brakes (standard on Custom). Powerlift windows. Weather-Eye heating and ventilating system. All-season air conditioning. Airliner reclining seats (standard on Custom). Electric clock (standard on Customs). Oil filter. Oil bath air cleaner. Hydra-Matic. Automatic overdrive. Continental tire mount. Twin speaker radio. Whitewall tubeless tires. Solex glass. Back-O-Matic lights. Windshield washer. Special leather seat trim (for Custom only). Two-tone paint. Three-tone paint (Custom only). Heavy-duty springs and shocks. Factory applied undercoating. Padded sun visors (standard on Custom). Dealer-installed seat belts. [RAMBLER] Six-cylinder engine with two-barrel carburetor and Power Pack (135 hp). Weather-Eye heating and ventilating system. All-Season air conditioning. Radio. Airliner reclining seats. Rear foam cushions (standard on all except Deluxe). Padded instrument panel and padded sun visors. Directional signals. Electric clock. Cigarette lighter (standard on all except Deluxe). Continental tire mount (not available on station wagon). Chrome wheelcovers. Power steering. Power brakes. Automatic or overdrive transmission. Oil filter. Oil bath air cleaner on six-cylinder. Solex glass. Hood ornament. Special leather seat trim (for Customs only). Back-O-Matic lights. Windshield washer. Size 6.70 x 15 tires. Heavy-duty springs and shocks. Seat belts. Travel rack leather straps. Child guard door locks.

HISTORICAL FOOTNOTES: Dealer introductions for the 1957 models were held Oct. 25, 1956. Calendar year production of 3,561 Nash automobiles gave the marque a .06 percent market share. The Rambler nameplate did somewhat better with calendar year production of 109,178 cars for a 1.78 percent slice of the pie.

OLDSMOBILE

1946-1975

1947 Oldsmobile 98, two-door convertible, 8-cyl.

Oldsmobile has the longest historical trail of the existing domestic car builders. Over the years the Lansing, Mich. based General Motors division has offered a genuine variety of motorcars and even a few trucks. Oldsmobiles powered by a selection of single-, twin-, six- and eight-cylinder engines with inline and V-block construction and fueled by either gasoline or diesel, have rolled the roads since 1897.

By Dennis F. Casteele

Success came to the company early and just after the turn of the century Oldsmobile was the most popular car on the road. Several editions of the nimble little Curved Dash model were marketed. Like other GM namesakes David Buick and Louis Chevrolet, Ransom Eli Olds left the firm carrying his name in the early going. Unlike Messrs. Buick and Chevrolet, Olds made a successful re-entry into the automotive field. By 1905 his new firm REO was working its way up the automotive ladder.

Joining the fledgling General Motors group in 1908, Oldsmobile slipped into the lower production, higher-quality automotive realm through the early 1920s. After a series of six-cylinder cars built to more modest price standards from the early 1920s through 1928, Olds introduced a companion car in 1929. The new line was called Viking and came upon the scene in the worst of times with a overcrowded market-

place and economic Depression. By 1930 the Viking was just a somewhat bitter memory. In 1933 things looked so bleak for GM that serious consideration was given to combining or eliminating Buick, Oldsmobile and Pontiac. Things gradually got better for Oldsmobile, however, and GM retained all of its automotive arms. Through the shortened 1942 model year Olds offered first two and then three automotive series, powered by a six- or eight-cylinder inline motor. For most of this time Oldsmobile was content to hold a sales slot near the bottom rung of the industry's top 10, offering solid, if unspectacular, transportation.

The lone indication of things to come began with introduction of the Hydra-Matic transmission in 1940. For years the auto industry had flirted with the fully automatic transmission. Certainly Oldsmobile's Hydra-Matic was not the first automatic, but up until that point it probably was the best. Several years before Oldsmobile had shared with Buick the so-called Safety Automatic Transmission. It was really a semi-automatic unit and had very limited marketing success. The Hydra-Matic, backed by the research of giant GM, caught on quickly in the Oldsmobile showrooms and soon Cadillac was offering Hydra-Matic as well.

Like most of the established car building firms, Oldsmobile hit the postwar streets with warmed-over 1942 models as 1946s. The same was true in 1947 and for the junior series of 1948. It was a different story (and a strong indication of things on the immediate Oldsmobile horizon) with the 1948 Ninety-

Eight models. Here an all-new appearance package called Futuramic was introduced. In 1949, Futuramic styling got the underhood boost it deserved, the new high-compression overhead valve Rocket V-8 engine. Coupled with the time-proven Hydra-Matic, the real postwar Oldsmobiles were dynamite. A big-engined/small-bodied Rocket 88 series was king of the roads and champ of the budding NASCAR stock car racing circuit in the early 1950s.

Gradually, Oldsmobile was upstaged in the performance arena by the Chrysler Hemi and the high-winding small-block Chevrolet V-8. Oldsmobile did continue to offer a variety of pleasing, well-styled, and popular cars through 1956. In 1957 Oldsmobile made another move into the high-performance arena. Divisional engineers elected to fight the competition's more exotic and more expensive fuel-injection and super-charging systems with a tri-carb based J-2 option available on most 1957 and 1958 models.

Oldsmobile, like most of the domestic car builders, moved into an automotive space age of sorts with the 1958 models. In 1961, two big developments came from the Oldsmobile camp. The personal luxury Starfire bowed as a convertible (a companion hardtop was added in 1962) and the folks from Lansing also joined the GM compact car parade with their F-85/Cutlass Series. Eventually the Cutlass nameplate would grow into the best-selling single model of the 1970s.

By the early 1960s Oldsmobile was on the move upwards on many sales and engineering fronts. An innovative chief engineer named John Beltz would move into the general manager's chair in this era. A lot of great automotive con-cepts were advanced by this auto enthusiast/executive. The Cutlass had once seen a brief fling with high-performance in its turbocharged Jetfire models in 1962 and 1963. Now more was on the way.

In 1964, Oldsmobile made a bold move back into the high-performance field with its 4-4-2 package. First as an F-85/Cutlass option, later as a full-fledged series, this Oldsmobile intermediate package was a real hit with the performance crowd. For those seeking a bit more zing, the potent W-cars were offered in the late 1960s. Finally, buyers who wanted to taste more luxury with their high-performance Cutlass were tempted by the limited-production Hurst/Olds.

One of the uniquely different cars of the postwar era emerged from Oldsmobile, in 1966, with the introduction of the front-wheel-drive Toronado. This quickly became the Oldsmobile banner-carrier on the personal/luxury front while the Starfire was dropped. The Toronado garnered a basket full of 'buff book' and engineering awards, but never captured the market share Oldsmobile officials hoped for.

By the 1970s, the Cutlass had grown into a powerful market force beyond the high-performance arena covered by the W-cars, Hurst/Olds and 4-4-2. This position got even stronger with the introduction of the Colonnade styled Cutlass Supreme coupe in 1973. Coupled with solid sales performances from the traditional Eighty-Eight and Ninety-Eight models and a boost from the addition of the smaller Omega and new Starfire, Oldsmobile rode into third place in the industry sales race.

1947 Oldsmobile, Special Sixty four-door station wagon, 6-cyl

1950 Oldsmobile, 88 Series Holiday two-door hardtop, V-8

1950 Oldsmobile, 88 Series two-door convertible, V-8

1956 Oldsmobile, 98 Series Holiday two-door hardtop, V-8

Standard Catalog of American Cars

1961 Oldsmobile, Super 88 Holiday four-door hardtop, V-8

1962 Oldsmobile, 98 Holiday four-door hardtop, V-8

1964 Oldsmobile, Starfire two-door hardtop, V-8

1968 Hurst-Oldsmobile, two-door hardtop coupe, V-8

1970 Oldsmobile, Cutlass 'S' Rallyee 350 two-door hardtop, V-8

1970 Oldsmobile, 4-4-2 W-30 Force-Air two-door hardtop, V-8

1970 Oldsmobile, 4-4-2 two-door hardtop coupe, V-8

1971 Oldsmobile, 4-4-2 W-30 Force-Air two-door convertible, V-8

1946 OLDSMOBILE

1946 Oldsmobile, 60 Series four-door station wagon, 6-cyl (DC)

SPECIAL — SIXTY SERIES — The Special or Sixty series was Oldsmobile's lowest- priced group of cars in 1946. Specials came only with six-cylinder power, although in other years an eight-cylinder was offered. In this series interiors were done in tan mixture pattern cloth. Standard tire size was 6.00 x 16 inches. Leather interiors were offered on convertibles. Technical features included electro hardened aluminum pistons, full-pressure lubrication and automatic choke with fast idle mode.

OLDSMOBILE I.D. NUMBERS: Serial number (VIN) on left front door hinge pillar. Motor number on front of block above water pump and on plate on end of floorboard inside the right front door. VIN starts with a prefix having two or three symbols. First two symbols indicate series: 66=Series 66 six-cylinder; 76=Series 76 six-cylinder; 78=Series 78 eight-cylinder and 98=Series 98 eight-cylinder. Third symbol (if used) indicates assembly plant: no symbol= Lansing, Mich.; K=Kansas City; L=Linden, N.J.; C=California (Los Angeles). Beginning and ending numbers by plant and series (check prefix) were [Lansing] 66-112001 to 66-131546; 76-92001 to 76-133098; 78-33001 to 78-48769; and 98-32001 to 98-42567. [Kansas City] 66K-1001 to 66K-2431; 76K-1001 to 76K-2997; 78K-1001 to 78K-2096; and 98K-1001 to 98K-1660. [Linden] 66L-14001 to 66L-18098; 76L-13001 to 76L-18939; 78L-5001 to 78L-7588; and 98L-7001 to 98L-8956. [Los Angeles] 66C-12001 to 66C-14468; 76C-9001 to 76C-12618; 78C-5001 to 78C-6500; and 98C-5001 to 98C-6181. Engines carried mixed production serial numbers with no specific relationship to a particular assembly plant. Beginning and ending engine numbers were: (six-cylinder) 6-1001 to 6-82337; (eight-cylinder) 8-1001 to 8-36397.

SPECIAL SIXTY SERIES

Model Number	Body/Style Number	Body Type & Seating	Factory Price	Shipping Weight	Production Total
60	3527	2-dr Clb Cpe-5P	1108	3325	4,537
60	3507	4-dr Clb Sed-5P	1134	3330	11,721
60	3519	4-dr Sed-6P	1169	3355	12,747
60	3567	2-dr Conv-5P	1327	3605	1,409
60	3581	4-dr Sta Wag-6P	1795	3785	140

1946 Oldsmobile, 78 Series two-door sedanette, 8-cyl (DC)

DYNAMIC — SEVENTY SERIES — Again this year the middle Oldsmobile series, the Seventy, was restricted to just two models of fastback design. Standard equipment for the Seventy series included front and rear bumper guards, vacuum booster pump, dual sun visors, cigarette lighter and plastic radiator ornament. Deluxe equipment for this series included wider door trim, foam rubber seat cushion, special steering wheel, Deluxe instrument cluster, electric clock, chrome wheel trim rings and rear seat armrest. Six-cylinder cars in this series were known as 76s, eight-cylinders as 78s. Cars in this series came standard with 6.50 x 16 inch tires. Technical features included: Electro-hardened aluminum pistons, I-beam connecting rod design and automatic choke with fast idle feature.

DYNAMIC SEVENTY SERIES

Model Number	Body/Style Number	Body Type & Seating	Factory Price	Shipping Weight	Production Total
SIX-CYLINDER					
76	3607	2-dr Clb Sed-5P	1184	3460	32,862
76	3609	4-dr Sed-5P	1234	3655	20,604
EIGHT-CYLINDER					
78	3607	2-dr Clb Sed-5P	1264	3650	10,911
78	3609	4-dr Sed-5P	1313	3799	10,042

NOTE 1: D Style Number suffix = Deluxe; Deluxe items available on standards.

1946 Oldsmobile, 98 Series four-door sedan, 8-cyl (DC)

CUSTOM CRUISER — NINETY SERIES — The Custom Cruiser or Ninety series Oldsmobile was the top of the line. Just three models were offered and all eight-cylinder powered. Most equipment found standard on the 60 and 70 series cars was also standard on the 90 models. Other series standard equipment included: wraparound bumpers, Deluxe instrument cluster and clock, rear seat armrest and foam rubber seat cushions. Tire size was 7.00 x 15 inches. Available upholstery spanned either leather, broadcloth or Bedford cord.

CUSTOM CRUISER NINETY SERIES

Model Number	Body/Style Number	Body Type & Seating	Factory Price	Shipping Weight	Production Total
46-90	3969	4-dr Sed-5P	1490	3795	11,031
46-90	3907	2-dr Clb Sed-5P	1442	3715	2,459
46-90	3967	2-dr Conv-3P	1840	4075	874

ENGINES

(OLDSMOBILE 60/70 SERIES SIX) Inline. Six-cylinder. L-head. Cast iron block. Displacement: 238 cid. Bore and stroke: 3-1/2 x 4-1/8 inches. Compression ratio: 6.5:1. Brake hp: 100 at 3400 rpm. Five main bearings. Solid valve lifters. Carburetor: Carter one-barrel Model WA1-504S.

(OLDSMOBILE 70/90 SERIES EIGHT) Inline. Eight-cylinder. L-head. Cast Iron block. Displacement: 257 cid. Bore and stroke: 3-1/4 x 3-7/8 inches. Compression ratio: 6.5:1. Brake hp: 110 at 4600 rpm. Six main bearings. Solid valve lifters. Carburetor: Carter two-barrel Model WD0-503S.

CHASSIS FEATURES: Wheelbase: (Special) 119 inches; (Dynamic) 125 inches; (Custom) 125 inches. Overall length: (Special) 204 inches; (Dynamic) 214 inches; (Custom) 216 inches. Front tread: (All) 58 inches. Rear tread: (All) 61-1/2 inches.

OPTIONS: Condition-air heater and ventilating system. Dual-flow heater with defroster. Deluxe radio. Standard radio. Deluxe plastic steering wheel. Electric clock. Directional signals. Safety spotlight. Auxiliary driving and fog lights. Back-up light. Trunk light. Rear fender skirts. Gas tank cover lock. A three-speed manual transmission with column shifter was standard equipment on all 1946 Oldsmobiles. A fully automatic Hydra-Matic transmission — introduced by Oldsmobile on its 1940 models — was available as on option on any model.

HISTORICAL FOOTNOTES: Car production began on Oct. 15, 1945, but a United Auto Workers strike on Nov. 21, 1945 brought the production lines to a halt. They did not start again until April 1, 1946. This held Oldsmobile's model year production to 119,388 units and kept calendar year production to 114,674 cars. Olds was the seventh largest U.S. automaker for the year. Olds woodie station wagon bodies were made by both Ionia and Hercules in 1946. The rare wagons came in a limited range of colors: black, Ambassador red, Pawnee beige and Forest green. Fender skirts were a rare option offered exclusively on the big Ninety Series Oldsmobiles.

1947 OLDSMOBILE

SPECIAL — SIXTY SERIES — More models were offered in the low-priced Special series than in the other two series offered by Oldsmobile in 1947. This model year saw the return of the eight-cylinder engine to the Special series and there were 66 and 68 versions of each body style offered. Standard equipment included: safety glass, spare wheel and tire, dual horns, vacuum booster pump and cigarette lighter. The standard interior fabric was tan mixture cloth and standard tire size was 6.00 x 16 inches.

OLDSMOBILE I.D. NUMBERS: Serial number (VIN) on left front door hinge pillar. Motor number on front of block above water pump and on plate on end of floorboard inside the right front door. VIN starts with a prefix having two or three symbols. First two symbols indicate series: 66=Series 66 six-cylinder; 76=Series 76 six-cylinder; 68=68 eight-cylinder; 78=Series 78 eight-cylinder and 98=Series 98 eight-cylinder. Third symbol (if used) indicates assembly plant: no symbol=Lansing, Mich.; A=Atlanta, Ga.; K=Kansas City; L=Linden, N.J.; C=California (Los Angeles); W=Wilmington, Del. Beginning and ending numbers by plant and series (check prefix) were [Lansing] 66-132001 to 66-163261; 76-134001 to 76-162749; 68=13001 to 68-24077; 78-50001 to 78-70213; and 98-43001 to 98-64483. [Atlanta] 66A-1001 to 66A-1045; 76A-1001 to 76A-1035; 68A-1001 to 68A-1020; 78A-1001 to 78A-1025; and 98A-1001 to 98A-1001. [Kansas City] 66K-1001 to 66K-8124; 76K-4001 to 76K-8509; 68K-1001 to 68K-2538; 78K-3001 to 78K-6132; and 98K-2001 to 98K-5269. [Linden] 66L-19001 to 66L-29555; 76L-2801 to 76L-29949; 68L-4001 to 68L-7037; 78L-8001 to 78L-14896; and 98L-10001 to 98L-18787. [Los Angeles] 66C-15001 to 66C-19520; 76C-13001 to 76C-17239; 68C4001 to 68C-5401; 78C-7001 to 78C-10011; and 98C-7001 to 98C-10515. Engines carried mixed production serial numbers with no specific relationship to a particular assembly plant. Beginning and ending engine numbers were: (six-cylinder) 6-83001 to 6-186314; (eight-cylinder) 8-37001 to 8-125584.

1947 Oldsmobile, 66 Series four-door sedan, 6-cyl (DC)

SPECIAL SIXTY SERIES

Model Number	Body/Style Number	Body Type & Seating	Factory Price	Shipping Weight	Production Total
66/68	47-3567	2-dr Conv-4P	1627	3520	6,528
66/68	47-3527	2-dr Clb Cpe-4P	1308	3315	14,297
66/68	47-3507	4-dr Clb Sed-5P	1334	3330	28,488
66/68	47-3519	4-d Sed-5P	1369	3375	22,660
66/68	47-3581	4-dr Sta Wag-6P	2175	3715	1,460

NOTE 1: Prices and weights are for 66 model.
NOTE 2: Production figures are for 66 and 68 models.

1947 Oldsmobile, 78 Series four-door sedan, 8-cyl (DC)

DYNAMIC — SEVENTY SERIES — The middle series for Oldsmobile consisted of just a pair of fastback body styles. Power came from either inline six- or eight-cylinder engines, hence the designations 76 or 78. There were Deluxe and standard versions of both body styles. Standard equipment included the same items that were standard on the lower series Special cars. Deluxe equipment included: a special instrument cluster, Deluxe clock and steering wheel, foam rubber seat cushions and rear center armrests. The Deluxe package cost around $100, depending on what model it was fitted and represented a substantial savings over purchasing the same accessories individually. Interior fabric choices were modern-weave cloth and custom broadcloth. Tire size was 7.00 x 15 inches.

DYNAMIC SEVENTY SERIES

Model Number	Body/Style Number	Body Type & Seating	Factory Price	Shipping Weight	Production Total
76/68	47-3607	2-dr Clb Sed-5P	1392	3460	44,849
76/78	47-3609	4-dr Sed-5P	1459	3525	38,825

NOTE 1: Deluxe models had the suffix D on the style number.
NOTE 2: Prices and weights shown are for 76 six-cylinder models.

1947 Oldsmobile, 98 Series convertible, 8-cyl (DC)

CUSTOM CRUISER — NINETY-EIGHT SERIES — Three body styles were again used in the top-of-the-line Oldsmobile series. This was the last year that the Ninety-Eight used a styling package which could be directly traced to the 1941 models. All Ninety-Eights were powered by the straight-eight motor. Standard Ninety-Eight equipment included the same items as the Special Series, plus a solenoid starter system. Upholstery was done in either custom broadcloth or leather. Standard tire size was 7.00 x 15 inches.

CUSTOM CRUISER NINETY-EIGHT SERIES

Model Number	Body/Style Number	Body Type & Seating	Factory Price	Shipping Weight	Production Total
98	47-3907	2-dr Clb Sed-5P	1642	3690	8,475
98	47-3967	2-dr Conv-5P	2040	4023	3,940
98	47-3969	4-dr Sed-5P	1690	3775	24,733

ENGINES

(68/78 SERIES SIX) Inline. Six-cylinder. Cast iron block. L-head side valve design. Displacement: 238 cid. Bore and stroke: 3-1/2 x 4-1/8 inches. Compression ratio: 6.5:1. Developed hp: 100. Electro-hardened aluminum pistons. Full pressure lubrication. Carter WA1-504S downdraft carburetor fitted with automatic choke and fast idle system.

(68/78/88 SERIES EIGHT) Eight-cylinder: L-head straight eight design. Cast iron block. Displacement: 257 cid. Compression ratio: 6.5:1. Bore and stroke: 3-1/4 x 3-7 /8 inches. Electro-hardened aluminum pistons. I-beam construction connecting rods. Carter WCD-665S two-barrel downdraft carburetion. Automatic choke with fast idle system.,

CHASSIS FEATURES: (Special Series) Wheelbase: 119 inches; overall length: 204 inches; front tread: 58 inches; rear tread: 62 inches. (Dynamic Series) Wheelbase: 125 inches; overall length: 213 inches; front tread: 58 inches; rear tread: 62 inches. (Custom Cruiser Series) Wheelbase: 127 inches; overall length: 216 inches; front tread: 58 inches; rear tread: 62 inches.

OPTIONS: Condition-Air heater ($52.90). Dual-flow heater/defroster ($31.80). Chrome wheel trim rings ($10.60). Plastic white sidewall discs ($12.10). Luggage compartment light ($1.75). Chrome exhaust extension ($1.75). Left-hand outside mirror ($3.40). Visor vanity mirror ($2.50). Underhood light ($2. 10). License plate frame ($2.10). Electric clock ($17.40). Gas tank fender door lock ($1.90). Fender skirts ($17.35). Deluxe steering wheel ($17.14). Directional signals ($14.75). Fog and driving lamps ($15.55). Cadet outside visor ($30.25). Back-up light ($7.75). Rear-window wiper ($15.20). Standard 5-tube radio ($72.75) and Deluxe 6-tube radio ($82.75). All 1947 Oldsmobiles came standard with a column-shifted, three-speed manual transmission. The Hydra-Matic transmission could be ordered on any 1947 Olds for $135 extra. Special and Dynamic models came either as six-cylinder 66 or 76 models, or as eight-cylinder 68 or 78 models. Ninety-Eights (98s) were available only with an eight.

HISTORICAL FOOTNOTES: Model year production was 194,388 units and calendar year output amounted to 191,454 cars for a seventh rank in industry. On June 7, 1947 GM engineering genius Charles "Boss" Kettering put an overhead valve V-8 engine in a 1947 Oldsmobile sedan and demonstrated the car at the summer meeting of the Society of Automotive Engineers. It had a 12.5:1 compression ratio and required 94 octane gas. All 1947 Oldsmobile wood-bodied station wagons had Ionia bodies.

1948 OLDSMOBILE

1948 Oldsmobile 98 convertible

DYNAMIC — SIXTY SERIES — This year Oldsmobile dropped the Special series designation and tagged both the former Special and 70 series cars as Dynamics. The 60 series Dynamics were, physically, the smallest Oldsmobiles offered in 1948 and this series offered the greatest variety of body styles. Either six- or eight-cylinder power could be fitted and the car became a 66 or 68 depending upon engine selection. Standard 60 series equipment included: dual horns, dual sun visors and a cigarette lighter. The Deluxe equipment package included the standard items, plus foam rubber seat cushions, Deluxe steering wheel, Deluxe instrument cluster, clock and chrome wheel trim rings. Standard tires were 6.00 x 16 and upholstery was Bedford cord or broadcloth.

OLDSMOBILE I.D. NUMBERS: Serial number (VIN) on left front door hinge pillar. Motor number on front of block above water pump and on plate on end of floorboard inside the right front door. VIN starts with a prefix having two or three symbols. First two symbols indicate series: 66=Series 66 six-cylinder; 76=Series 76 six-cylinder; 68=68 eight-cylinder; 78=Series 78 eight-cylinder and 98=Series 98 eight-cylinder. Third symbol (if used) indicates assembly plant: no symbol=Lansing, Mich.; A=Atlanta, Ga.; B= (Boston) Framingham, Mass.; K=Kansas City; L=Linden, N.J.; C=California (Southgate/Los Angeles); W=Wilmington, Del. Beginning and ending numbers by plant and series (check prefix) were [Lansing] 66-165001 to 66-185604; 76-164001 to 76-177725; 68=25001 to 68-33599; 78-72001 to 78-82294; and 98-65001 to 98-96882. [Atlanta] 66A-2001 to 66A-3864; 76A-2001 to 76A-3414; 68A-2001 to 68A-2817; 78A-2001 to 78A-2983; and 98A-1001 to 98A-3485. [Framingham, Mass.] 66B-9001 to 66B-2868; 76B1001 to 76B-2443; 68B-1001 to 68B-1824; 78B-no 78s made at Framingham; 98B-1001 to 98B-4559. [Kansas City] 66K-9001 to 66K-13202; 76K-9001 to 76K-12182; 68K-3001 to 68K-4851; 78K-7001 to 78K-9315; and 98K-6001 to 98K-12126. [Linden] 66L-31001 to 66L-34067; 76L-31601 to 76L-33442; 68L-8001 to 68L-9359; 78L-16001 to 78L-17830; and 98L-20001 to 98L-27179. [Los Angeles] 66C-21001 to 66C-24356; 76C-18001 to 76C-20549; 68C-6001 to 68C-7509; 78C-11001 to 78C-12951; and 98C-11001 to 98C-18076. Engines carried mixed production serial numbers with no specific relationship to a particular assembly plant. Beginning and ending engine numbers were: (six-cylinder) 6-188021 to 6-256090; (eight-cylinder) 8-127001 to 8-164285.

DYNAMIC SIXTY SERIES

Model Number	Body/Style Number	Body Type & Seating	Factory Price	Shipping Weight	Production Total
66/68	48-3527	2-dr Clb Cpe-5P	1609	3240	9,326
66/68	48-3507	4-dr Clb Sed-5P	1776	3285	23,732
66/68	48-3519	4-dr Sed-5P	1677	3320	18,142
66/68	48-3567X	2-dr Conv-5P	1725	3550	3,892
66/68	48-3562	4-dr Sta Wag-6P	2614	3620	2,707

NOTE 1: Deluxes have suffix "D."
NOTE 2: Prices and weights for 66 models.

1948 Oldsmobile, 70 Series four-door sedan, 8-cyl (DC)

DYNAMIC — SEVENTY SERIES — Again this year, the middle Olds series was restricted to just two cars of fastback design. Standard equipment for the 70s included front and rear bumper guards, vacuum booster pump, dual sun visors, cigarette lighter and plastic radiator ornament. Deluxe equipment included wider door trim, foam rubber seat cushions, special steering wheel, Deluxe instrument cluster, electric clock, chrome wheel trim rings and rear seat armrest. Upholstery was broadcloth or Bedford cord. Standard tire size was 7.60 x 15 inches.

Model Number	Body/Style Number	Body Type & Seating	Factory Price	Shipping Weight	Production Total
76/78	48-3609	4-dr Sed-5P	1801	3525	24,646
76/78	48-3607	2-dr Clb Sed-5P	1726	3460	25,172

NOTE 1: Deluxe cars had the suffix "D" along with the body style number.

1948 Oldsmobile, 98 Series two-door sedanette, 8-cyl. (DC)

FUTURAMIC — NINETY-EIGHT SERIES — For the first time in quite a while, Oldsmobile offered two totally different types of styling during a single model year. The top-of-the-line series drew heavily on the new Futuramic styling concept that would be used across the board in 1949 by Oldsmobile. Standard equipment on the Ninety-Eights included a solenoid starter, fender skirts, E-Z-I rearview mirror and foam rubber seat cushions. The Ninety-Eights also included standard items from the Sixty and Seventy Dynamic models. Deluxe equipment on the Ninety-Eight consisted of front and rear floor mats, Deluxe steering wheel, wheel trim rings, rear seat armrests and hydraulic window, seat, and top controls on convertibles. Upholstery was in either broadcloth or leather. The standard tire size was 6.50 x 16.

Model Number	Body/Style Number	Body Type & Seating	Factory Price	Shipping Weight	Production Total
98	48-3807	4-dr Clb Sed-5P	2708	3465	14,260
98	48-3869	4-dr Sed-5P	2151	3705	38,061
98	48-3867X	2-dr Conv-5P	2624	4035	12,914

NOTE 1: Deluxe model had "D" suffix on style number.

ENGINES

(66/76 SERIES SIX) Inline. Six-cylinder. L-head. Cast iron block. Displacement: 238 cid. Bore and stroke: 3-1/2 x 4-1/8 inches. Compression ratio: 6.5:1. Developed hp: 100 at 3400 rpm. High carbon crankshaft. Four main bearings. Aluminum alloy pistons. Carter WA1-651S one-barrel downdraft carburetor with automatic choke.

(68/78 SERIES EIGHT) Inline. Eight cylinder. L-head. Cast iron block. Displacement: 257 cid. Compression ratio: 6.5:1. Bore and stroke: 3-1/4 x 3-7/8 inches. Brake hp: 110 at 3600 rpm. Aluminum pistons and I-beam connecting rods. Carter WDO-650S two-barrel downdraft carburetor with automatic choke.

(98 SERIES EIGHT) Inline. Eight-cylinder. L-head. Cast iron block. Bore and stroke: 3-1/4 x 3-7/8 inch. Displacement: 257 cid. Compression ratio: 7 to 1. Brake hp: 115 hp at 3600 rpm. Carter WDO-650 SA dual downdraft carburetion with built-in automatic choke.

CHASSIS FEATURES: Wheelbase: (Sixty) 119 inches; (Seventy and Ninety-Eight) 125 inches. Overall length: (Sixty) 204 inches; (Seventy and Ninety-Eight) 213 inches. Front tread: (Sixty and Seventy) 58 inches; (Ninety-Eight) 57 inches. Rear tread: (Sixty and Seventy) 62 inches; (Ninety-Eight) 59 inches.

OPTIONS: Solenoid starter ($7). Fender skirts ($17). Dual flow heater and defroster ($32). Condition-air heater and defroster ($58). Windshield washer ($9). Standard 5-tube radio ($84). Super Deluxe radio 6-tube ($94). Chrome wheel trim rings ($10). Glovebox and map lights ($2). Fog and driving lamps ($15). Safety spot light ($20). Tilting glare proof mirror ($5). Visor vanity mirror ($2). Back-up light ($9). Turn signals ($16). Cadet sunvisor ($30). Rear window wiper ($14). All models came standard with a column-shifted manual transmission. Each 1948 Oldsmobile could be ordered with the optional Hydra-Matic Drive ($175). Engine options included the heavy-duty air cleaner ($4) and oil filter ($7).

HISTORICAL FOOTNOTES: Production was 173,661 cars for the model year and 194,755 for the calendar year. This put Oldsmobile seventh in the U.S. auto sales race for the third year in a row. The 1948 station wagons had new combination wood and metal Fisher Body Co. bodies. The 98s featured all-new styling and engineering. They were introduced around February 1948, while the carryover "prewar" style models bowed on Jan. 15, 1948. It was the last year for the Oldsmobile 66, 68 and 78 car-lines.

1949 OLDSMOBILE

1949 Oldsmobile, 76 Series four-door station wagon, 6-cyl (DC)

SEVENTY-SIX SERIES — Oldsmobile would retain a six-cylinder engine through 1950, but 1948 was the last year for three different-sized series. The Seventy-Six was now the bottom-line Oldsmobile. The Seventy-Six and Eighty-Eight were nearly identical, except for their power plants. Standard Seventy-Six equipment included: safety glass, bumper guards, dual horns, dual sun visors, cigarette lighter and solenoid starter. Deluxe equipment featured foam rubber seat cushions, front and rear floor mats, special external chrome moldings, clock, Deluxe steering wheel, wheel trim rings and turn signals. Upholstery choices were Bedford cord, broadcloth and leather. Standard tire size was 7.10 x 15 inches.

OLDSMOBILE I.D. NUMBERS: Serial number located on left front door pillar on right side of cowl. Motor number on block above water pump; and on plate on floor inside right door; and on left corner of block above generator; and on front of left cylinder head at negative battery terminal. Olds 76 numbers took the form 496( )1001 to 496( )ending number. Olds 88 numbers took the form 498( )1001 to 498( )ending number. Olds 98 numbers took the form 499( )1001 to 499( )ending number. First two symbols indicate model year: 49=1949. Third symbol indicates series: 6=76; 8=88; 9=98. Fourth symbol in ( ) indicated assembly plant as follows: A=Atlanta; B=Boston (Framingham); K=Kansas City; M=Michigan (Lansing); L=Linden (New Jersey); C=California (Los Angeles/Southgate); and W=Wilmington, Del. Remaining symbols were the unit's sequential production number. Starting number at each assembly plant was 1001. Ending numbers, by series, at each coded plant were: [76] M48479; A6595; B7168; K11687; L8703; C9069; and W8794. [88] M46245; A7203; B8544; K13460; L10496; C10512; and W13460. [98] M46908; A6327; B7508; K11676; L9576; C9508; and W8750. Motor numbers (unrelated to assembly plants) were: [Six-cylinder] 6A1001 to 6A96888; [V-8] 8A1001 to 8A193864. Motors with an "H" prefix on Hydra-Matic cars.

SEVENTY-SIX SERIES

Model Number	Body/Style Number	Body Type & Seating	Factory Price	Shipping Weight	Production Total
76	49-3527	2-dr Clb Cpe-5P	1630	3260	12,683
76	49-3507	2-dr Clb Sed-5P	1790	3290	32,019
76	49-3569	4-dr Sed-5P	1725	3335	37,505
76	49-3508	4-dr Twn Sed-5P	1715	3625	6,466
76	49-3567X	2-dr Conv-5P	2025	3845	5,338
76	49-3561	4-dr Sta Wag-6P	2735	3945	1,545

NOTE 1: Deluxe equipped models had a suffix "D" after style number.

EIGHTY-EIGHT SERIES — Introduced a bit later than the other two series, the Eighty-Eight was the logical combination of the all-new Rocket V-8 motor, from the Ninety-Eight series, into the new, lightweight Futuramic Seventy-Six chassis. Standard equipment and Deluxe equipment packages were nearly identical to those listed in the Seventy-Six series section. Upholstery selection could be made from leather, leather and cloth combinations, Bedford cord or broadcloth. Standard tire were 7.60 x 15 inches. Thirteen standard colors were offered with eight factory sanctioned two-tone combinations.

EIGHTY-EIGHT SERIES

Model Number	Body/Style Number	Body Type & Seating	Factory Price	Shipping Weight	Production Total
88	49-3527	2-dr Clb Cpe-5P	2025	3550	11,561
88	49-3507	2-dr Clb Sed-5P	2050	3585	28,707
88	49-3569	4-dr Sed-5P	2120	3610	46,386
88	49-3508	4-dr Twn Sed-5P	2110	3625	5,833
88	49-3567DX	2-dr Conv-5P	2420	3845	5,434
88	49-3561	4-dr Sta Wag-6P	3120	3945	1,355

NOTE 1: Suffix "D" was on all Deluxe equipped cars.

Standard Catalog of American Cars

1949 Oldsmobile, 88 Series two-door club sedan, V-8 (DC)

FUTURAMIC NINETY-EIGHT SERIES — This was the second year for Futuramic styling in the top-of-the-line Oldsmobile series and the first year for Rocket V-8 power. Standard equipment included all items basic to the lower two series, plus foam rubber seat cushions, windshield washer and turn signals. The Deluxe 98 package had a rear center seat armrest, front and rear floor mats, special chrome body moldings, electric clock, Deluxe steering wheel, stainless steel wheel trim rings and hydraulic window, seat and top controls on convertibles. Upholstery choices were Bedford cord, broadcloth, leather and leather/cloth combinations. Standard tire size was 7.60 x 15 inches. Oldsmobile used this year's 98 series to introduce its popular two-door Holiday hardtop model.

NINETY-EIGHT SERIES

Model Number	Body/Style Number	Body Type & Seating	Factory Price	Shipping Weight	Production Total
98	49-3807	2-dr Clb Sed-5P	2380	3835	20,049
98	49-3869	4-dr Sed-5P	2360	3890	57,821
98	49-3867X	2-dr Conv-5P	2810	4200	12,602
98	49-3837X	2-dr 2-dr Hol HT-5P	2973	3945	3,006

NOTE 1: Cars with "D" suffix are Deluxes.
NOTE 2: Cars with "DX" suffix have hydraulic powered accessories.

1949 Oldsmobile, 98 Series two-door convertible, V-8 (DC)

ENGINES

(SERIES 76 SIX) Inline. Six-cylinder. Cast iron block. Bore and stroke: 3-17/32 x 4-3/8 inches. Displacement: 231 cid. Compression ratio: 6.5:1. Brake hp: 105 at 3400 rpm. Solid lifters. Carter WA1-709 S single-barrel downdraft carburetor with built-in choke.

(SERIES 88/98 EIGHT) Vee-block. Overhead valves. Cast iron block. Bore and stroke: 3-3/4 x 3-7/16 inches. Brake hp: 135 at 3600 rpm. Compression ratio: 7.25:1. A Carter WGD-714S dual downdraft carburetor was fitted with an automatic choke.

CHASSIS FEATURES: Wheelbase: (Seventy-Six and Eighty-Eight) 119-1/2 inches; (Ninety-Eight): 125 inches. Overall length: (Seventy-Six and Eighty-Eight) 202 inches; (Ninety-Eight) 213 inches. Front tread: 57 inches. Rear tread: 59 inches.

OPTIONS: Standard radio ($88). Super Deluxe radio ($96). Condition-Air heater /defroster ($67). Traffic light viewer ($5). Cadet visor ($30). Hood ornament ($5). Stainless steel wheel rings ($10). Auxiliary driving and fog lights ($19). Spotlight ($26). Turn signals ($21). Glovebox light ($2). Underhood light ($2). Trunk light ($2). Outside rearview mirror ($3). Vanity visor mirror ($2). Exhaust extension ($2). License plate frame ($9). Windshield washer ($9) Back-up lights ($15). A column-shifted three-speed manual transmission was standard equipment on all Seventy-Six models. Eighty-Eight and Ninety-Eights came standard with the Hydra-Matic transmission, which was an $185 option on the Seventy-Six. A heavy-duty air cleaner cost $4.40, while an oil filter cost $9.

HISTORICAL FOOTNOTES: Model year output was 288,310 cars...a new Oldsmobile record! The company retained seventh slot in the U.S. industry with 282,885 cars made in the calendar year. New-car introductions took place in Sept. 1948 and the Holiday Hardtop was added at midyear. The 1949 Olds 88 sedan could go 0-60 mph in 12.2 seconds and run the quarter-mile in 19.9 seconds, which was hot stuff for the time. Red Byron won the 1949 stock car race on the sand at Daytona Beach, Fla., with a Rocket 88 coupe and Oldsmobile took five of eight NASCAR Grand Nationals held in 1949. Byron was named the national champion. An Olds 88 also served as the Official Pace Car for the year's Indy 500-Mile Race. Among its special features was a see-through plexiglas hood to show off the Rocket 88 V-8. This item was made available as a factory option, too.

1950 OLDSMOBILE

SEVENTY-SIX SERIES — This was the final year for both the Seventy-Six series and also the six cylinder "Big Six" engine. Olds would not offer another six-cylinder motor until the mid-1960s and that would be an engine built by another GM division. The Seventy-Six models were again nearly identical to the Eighty-Eight offerings. Standard equipment on the base

models included: bumper guards, dual horns, parking lamps, dome light, rubber front floor mats, aluminum sill plates. Deluxe equipment included: foam rubber seat cushions, robe rails, stainless steel gravel shields and extra chrome moldings. Upholstery choices were striped cloth, broadcloth, nylon surrey weave and leather. Standard tire size was 7.10 x 15 inches. For 1950 a Holiday coupe was added to the Seventy-Six and Eighty-Eight series and this marked the last year for an Oldsmobile station wagon until 1957.

1950 Oldsmobile, 76 Series two-door sedan, 6-cyl (DC)

OLDSMOBILE I.D. NUMBERS: Serial number located on left front door pillar; on right side of cowl. Motor number on block above water pump; on plate on floor inside right door; on left corner of block above generator; and on front of left cylinder head at negative battery terminal. Olds 76 numbers took the form 506( )1001 to 506( )ending number. Olds 88 numbers took the form 508( )1001 to 508( )ending number. Olds 98 numbers took the form 509( )1001 to 509( )ending number. First two symbols indicate model year: 50=1950. Third symbol indicates series: 6=76; 8=88; 9=98. Fourth symbol in ( ) indicated assembly plant as follows: A=Atlanta; B=Boston (Framingham); K=Kansas City; M=Michigan (Lansing); L=Linden (New Jersey); C=California (Los Angeles/Southgate); and W=Wilmington, Del. Remaining symbols were the unit's sequential production number. Starting number at each assembly plant was 1001. Ending numbers, by series, at each coded plant were: [76] M17502; A3149; B2879; K4931; L3501; C3715; and W3657. [88] M114848; A20617; B20092; K40988; L26001; C25800; and W26826.[98] M51635; A7949; B7412; K14934; L10157; C10157; and W10280. Motor numbers (unrelated to assembly plants) were: [Six-cylinder] 6A97001 to 6A130440; [V-8] 8A194001 to 8A568689. Motors with an "H" prefix on Hydra-Matic cars.

SEVENTY-SIX SERIES

Model Number	Body/Style Number	Body Type & Seating	Factory Price	Shipping Weight	Production Total
76	503507	2-dr Clb Sed-5P	1640	3260	5,105
76	50-3511	2-dr Sed-5P	1655	3290	6,354
76	50-3527	2-dr Clb Cpe-5P	1615	3295	3,364
76	50-3537	2-dr Hol HT-5P	1885	3335	538
76	50-3567X	2-dr Conv-5P	2010	3585	973
76	50-3569	4-dr Sed-5P	1710	3340	16,555
76	50-3562	4-dr Sta Wag-6P	2360	3610	368

NOTE 1: Style numbers for Deluxe cars carried the suffix "D".

1950 Oldsmobile, 88 Series two-door club sedan, V-8 (DC)

EIGHTY-EIGHT SERIES — In its second year the Eighty-Eight continued to be a strong seller. It was also one of the hottest performers available off the showroom floor. Body and chassis were quite similar to the Seventy-Six series. Standard and Deluxe equipment packages were identical to those listed for the Seventy-Six. Upholstery choices included broadcloth, striped cloth, nylon and a variety of colored leathers. Standard tire size was 7.60 x 15 inches.

EIGHTY-EIGHT SERIES

Model Number	Body/Style Number	Body Type & Seating	Factory Price	Shipping Weight	Production Total
88	50-3707	2-dr Clb Sed-5P	1790	3460	31,093
88	50-3711	2-dr Sed-5P	1805	3490	50,561
88	50-3727	2-dr Clb Cpe-5P	1725	3485	21,456
88	50-3737	2-dr Hol HT-5P	2035	3535	12,682
88	50-3762	4-dr Sta Wag-6P	2585	3810	2,382
88	50-3767	2-dr Conv-5P	2160	3746	9,127
88	50-3769	4-dr Sed-5P	1860	3540	141,111

NOTE 1: Style numbers for Deluxe models carried the suffix "D".

1950 Oldsmobile, 98 Series two-door convertible, V-8 (DC)

NINETY-EIGHT SERIES — In 1950 Oldsmobile did the same thing as in 1948 with its top of the line series. The 1950 Ninety-Eights differed significantly from other series cars and more closely resembled 1951 models. Standard equipment included all items from the Eighty-Eight series, plus foam rubber seat cushions, chrome interior trim hardware, lined luggage compartment and counter-balanced trunk lid. Deluxe Ninety-Eight equipment included rear seat center armrest, Deluxe electric clock, Deluxe steering wheel and horn button, special door trim and stainless steel wheel trim rings. Upholstery choices spanned nylon fabric, striped broadcloth or leather. Standard tire size was 7.60 x 15 inches.

NINETY-EIGHT SERIES

Model Number	Body/Style Number	Body Type & Seating	Factory Price	Shipping Weight	Production Total
98	50-3807	2-dr Clb Sed-5P	2095	3685	11,989
98	50-3869	4-dr Sed-5P	2165	3765	80,265
98	50-3808	4-dr Twn Sed-5P	2135	3750	1,778
98	50-3837	2-dr Hol HT-5P	2245	3775	8,263
98	50-3867X	2-dr Conv-5P	2615	4150	3,925

NOTE 1: Deluxe cars carried the suffix "D" in style number.

ENGINES

(SERIES 76 SIX) Inline. Six-cylinder. Cast iron block. L-head. Bore and stroke: 3.531 x 4.375 inches. Displacement: 231.5 cid. Brake hp: 105 at 3400 rpm. Compression ratio: 6.5:1. Solid lifters. Carter single-barrel downdraft carburetor model WA1-764A with automatic choke.

(SERIES 88/98 ROCKET 88 V-8) Vee-block. Overhead valve. Cast iron block. Hydraulic valve lifters. Bore and stroke: 3-3/4 x 3-7/16 inches. Displacement: 303.7 cid. Brake hp: 135 at 3600 rpm. Compression ratio: 7.25:1. Five main bearings. Carter model WGD-714S dual-downdraft carburetor.

CHASSIS FEATURES: Wheelbase: (Seventy-Six and Eighty-Eight) 119-1/2 inches; (Ninety-Eight) 122 inches. Overall length: (Seventy-Six and Eighty-Eight) 202 inches, all except station wagon, 205 inches; (Ninety-Eight) 209 inches. Front tread: (Seventy-Six and Eighty-Eight) 57 inches; (Ninety-Eight) 59 inches. Rear tread: (Seventy-Six and Eighty-Eight) 59 inches; (Ninety-Eight) 61-1/2 inches.

OPTIONS: Standard Condition-Air heater and defroster ($45). Deluxe condition air heater and defroster ($60). Standard radio ($85). Deluxe radio ($110). Futuramic electric clock ($15). Deluxe steering wheel and horn ring ($20). Stainless steel wheel trim rings ($10). Deluxe wheelcovers ($17). Turn signals ($23). Safety spotlight ($23). Auxiliary driving and fog lights ($16). Back-up lights ($15). Traffic light view ($5). Center bumper guard ($5). Under hood light ($2). glovebox light ($2). License plate frames ($2). Outside rearview mirror ($3). Visor vanity mirror ($3). Exhaust deflector ($2). Windshield washer ($7) and Cadet sun visor ($27). Standard transmission on all 1950s was a column-shifted manual three-speed. Hydra-Matic was available on any 1950 Olds. Heavy-duty oil bath air cleaners were available or both the "Big Six" and the Rocket V-8. A full flow oil filter was a V-8 option.

HISTORICAL FOOTNOTES: Model year output: 407,889. Calendar year output: 396,757. Rank in U.S. industry: sixth. The 1950 Oldsmobiles were introduced in Dec., 1949. During the calendar year, the company would produce 6.6 percent (13,571) of all American convertibles; 8 percent (21,482) of the hardtops; and 1.7 percent (2,650) of the domestic station wagons. With the weak showing in wagon-making, Olds would drop this model for the next six years. There were 19 big NASCAR stock car races during 1950. Oldsmobiles took 10 of them, with driver Bill Rexford winning the championship. Hershell McGriff and Ray Elliott won the 1950 Mexican Road Race in their number 52 Olds coupe, a 1951 model. Car owner Roy Sundstrom, of Portland, Ore., was awarded 150,000 pesos for the victory. That sounds impressive, but equated to $17,341.04 in U.S. currency. McGriff, a 32-year-old lumber truck driver, won the race by a one minute and 19 second margin. His Rocket 88 was one of 13 Oldsmobiles that competed. At the Olds factory in Lansing, Mich., S.E. Skinner sat behind the general manager's desk. His designers turned out the "Palm Beach" dream car. Based on the Holiday hardtop, it featured alligator hide and basketweave wicker trim.

1951 OLDSMOBILE

STANDARD/DELUXE 88 SERIES — This series was also known as the 88-A and offered vehicles similar to the 1950 Eighty-Eight series. Near the end of the model year, 88-A production was dropped altogether and the car disappeared from later editions of the 1951 catalog. Gone for 1951 was the long running inline six-cylinder engine. Just a pair of body styles were offered. Standard features included: bumper guards, cigarette lighter, dome light, rubber floor mats, stainless steel moldings and lined luggage compartment. Deluxe cars had extras including foam seat cushions, rear ash receiver and stainless steel gravel shields. Upholstery choices were nylon or nylon cord. Standard tire size was 7.60 x 15 inches. Just two body styles were available.

OLDSMOBILE I.D. NUMBERS: Serial number located on left front door pillar on right side of cowl. Motor number on block above water pump; and on plate on floor inside right door; and on left corner of block above generator; and on front of left cylinder head at negative battery terminal. Olds 88 numbers took the form 517( )1001 to 517( )ending number. Olds Super

88 numbers took the form 518( )1001 to 508( )ending number. Olds 98 numbers took the form 519( )1001 to 519( )ending number. First two symbols indicate model year: 51=1951. Third symbol indicates series: 7=88; 8=Super 88; 9=98. Fourth symbol in ( ) indicated assembly plant as follows: A=Atlanta; B=Boston (Framingham); K=Kansas City; M=Michigan (Lansing); L=Linden (New Jersey); C=California (Los Angeles/Southgate); and W=Wilmington, Del. Remaining symbols were the unit's sequential production number. Starting number at each assembly plant was 1001. Ending numbers, by series, at each coded plant were: [88] M19934; A2960; B2835; K4989; L3571; C3555; and W3592. [Super 88] M66062; A12364; B11103; K20775; L14291; C15413; and W15340. [98] M42674; A8556; B7590; K15277; L11584; C11027; and W10857. Motor numbers (unrelated to assembly plants) were: [V-8] 8C1001 to 8C287312. Motors with at "B" prefix on synchromesh cars.

EIGHTY-EIGHT SERIES

Model Number	Body/Style Number	Body Type & Seating	Factory Price	Shipping Weight	Production Total
88A	51-3711	2-dr Sed-5P	1815	3585	11,792
88A	51-3769	4-dr Sed-5P	1871	3610	22,848

SUPER EIGHTY-EIGHT — This middle series was styled completely different than the Eighty-Eight series. Only a Rocket V-8 was available for engine power. With its five body styles the Super 88 offered the Olds buyer more selection than the other Olds series. A Deluxe package of equipment was offered on this series. It included items from both the standard and Deluxe Eighty-Eight packages, plus low pressure tires, special interior chrome door trim, exposed chromed roof bows and dual rear quarter courtesy lights. Upholstery choices were colored leathers, nylon cloth or nylon cord. Standard tire size was 7.60 x 15 inches.

1951 Oldsmobile, Super 88 two-door Deluxe Holiday coupe, V-8 (DC)

SUPER EIGHTY-EIGHT SERIES

Model Number	Body/Style Number	Body Type & Seating	Factory Price	Shipping Weight	Production Total
S-88	51-3627D	2-dr Clb Cpe-5P	1928	3628	7,328
S-88	51-3611D	2-dr Sed-5P	1969	3642	34,963
S-88	51-3637D	2-dr Hol HT-5P	2231	3659	14,180
S-88	51-3667DX	2-dr Conv-5P	2333	3896	3,854
S-88	51-3669D	4-dr Sed-5P	2025	3675	90,131

NOTE 1: DX suffix indicates hydraulically-operated seat and windows.

1951 Oldsmobile, 98 Series two-door Holiday hardtop coupe, V-8 (DC)

NINETY-EIGHT SERIES — Topping the Oldsmobile lineup again for 1951 was the Ninety-Eight. Three body styles were available. The four-door sedan and convertible came only with Deluxe equipment, while the Holiday coupe could be had in either Deluxe or Standard trim. Ninety-Eight standard equipment included all items from the lower series, plus illuminated ashtray, foam rubber seat cushions and extra chrome moldings. Deluxe equipment included a special rear door ornament, rear center seat armrests, Deluxe electric clock, Deluxe steering wheel and horn ring and special chrome trim. Upholstery choices were nylon cord, nylon cloth and leather.

NINETY-EIGHT SERIES

Model Number	Body/Style Number	Body Type & Seating	Factory Price	Shipping Weight	Production Total
98	51-3837	2-dr Hol HT-5P	2267	3762	17,929
98	51-3869D	4-dr Sed-5P	2277	3787	78,122
98	51-3867DX	2-dr Conv-5P	2644	4107	4,468

NOTE 1: Deluxe models had D suffix; suffix "X" indicated hydraulic controls.

ENGINE: V-8. Cast-iron block. Overhead valves. Hydraulic lifters. Five main bearings. Bore and stroke: 3-3/4 x 3-7/16 inches. Displacement: 303 cid. Brake hp: 135 at 3600 rpm. Torque: 263 foot pounds at 1800 rpm. Compression ratio: 7.5:1. Carburetor: Rochester BB two-barrel.

CHASSIS FEATURES: Wheelbase (Eighty-Eight) 119-1/2 inches; (Super Eighty-Eight) 120 inches; (Ninety-Eight) 122 inches. Overall length; (Eighty-Eight) 202 inches; (Super Eighty-Eight) 204 inches; (Ninety-Eight) 208 inches. Front tread: (Eighty-Eight and Super Eighty-Eight) 57 inches; (Ninety-Eight) 59 inches. Rear tread: (Eighty-Eight and Super Eighty-Eight) 59 inches; (Ninety-Eight) 61-1/2 inches.

OPTIONS: Radio antenna ($7). Deluxe radio ($88). Super Deluxe signal seeking radio ($113). Electric clock ($15). Deluxe wheelcovers ($17). Exhaust extension ($2). Deluxe condition air heater/defroster ($42). Back-up lights ($18). Fog and driving lights ($19). Under hood light ($2). Spotlight with rearview mirror ($25). Outside rearview mirror ($4). Visor mirror ($2). Turn signals ($21). Rear radio speaker ($18). Chrome ventshades ($14). Cadet outside sun visor ($32). Traffic light viewer ($5). Battery vitalizer ($5). Windshield washer ($10). All 1951 Oldsmobiles were fitted with the same Rocket V-8 engine. Standard equipment transmission in all series was the synchromesh three-speed column shifted manual unit. A Hydra-Matic was a $150 option on any model, any series. An optional $6 oil filter was available on any Rocket V-8. Rear end ratios were 3.42; 3.64 and 3.9 to 1.

HISTORICAL FOOTNOTES: The 1951 Oldsmobiles appeared in showrooms in Jan., 1951. Model year production was 285,615 units, while the calendar year production total included only 19 additional cars. The total of 285,634 for the January-to-December count brought Oldsmobile in seventh again. Olds built 10,500 more hardtops in 1951 than 1952. On a calendar year basis, the hardtops' popularity was 32,109 sales. However, this was a lower 6.7 percent of the hardtops' industry-wide share of market. The 1.3 percent drop for Olds was due to many other automakers bringing out their own hardtops. In the calendar year, Olds also built 5.9 percent (8,322) of all U.S. convertibles, but no wagons. Hydra-Matic transmission was installed in 278,717 cars made in calendar 1951. In racing, the marque captured 20 of 41 stock car racing checkered flags, but lost the annual crown to Hudson. The dropping of the Holiday hardtop, club coupe and two-door fastback in the 1951 Rocket 88 series had a negative effect on winning races. The remaining models were heavier and less aerodynamic. A famous Olds driver was Curtis "Pops" Turner. On the corporate front, Jack Wolfrom became the 13th general manager of Oldsmobile Div.

1952 OLDSMOBILE

DELUXE EIGHTY-EIGHT — In 1952, Oldsmobile maintained its three series structure. On the bottom end of things was a two-model series known as the Deluxe Eighty-Eight. Wheelbase, chassis features and most body features, minus a bit of extra trim, were shared with the Super Eighty-Eight group. A slightly lower-powered version of the Rocket V-8 was fitted. Standard equipment included: bumper guards, gray rubber floor mats front and rear, electric clock, dual horns, aluminum door sill plates and rubber gravel shields. Upholstery was done in a gray basket weave corded cloth. Standard tire size was 7.60 x 15 inches.

1952 Oldsmobile 88 two-door sedan

OLDSMOBILE I.D. NUMBERS: Serial number located on left front door pillar on right side of cowl. Motor number on block above water pump; and on plate on floor inside right door; and on left corner of block above generator; and on front of left cylinder head at negative battery terminal. Olds 88/Super 88 numbers took the form 528( )1001 to 528( )ending number. Olds 98 numbers took the form 529( )1001 to 529( )ending number. First two symbols indicate model year: 52=1952. Third symbol indicates series: 8=88 or Super 88; 9=98. Fourth symbol in ( ) indicated assembly plant as follows: A=Atlanta; B=Boston (Framingham); K=Kansas City; M=Michigan (Lansing); L=Linden (New Jersey); C=California (Los Angeles/Southgate); and W=Wilmington, Del. Remaining symbols were the unit's sequential production number. Starting number at each assembly plant was 1001. Ending numbers, by series, at each coded plant were: [88/Super 88] M62915; A11269; B8235; K20968; L12276; C13379; and W13681. [98] M36565; A6008; B4730; K10793; L8605; C8403; and W7733. Motor numbers (unrelated to assembly plants) were: [V-8] 8R1001 to 8R214478.

DELUXE EIGHTY-EIGHT

Model Number	Body/Style Number	Body Type & Seating	Factory Price	Shipping Weight	Production Total
D-88	52-3611	2-dr Sed-5P	2050	3565	6,402
D-88	52-3669	4-dr Sed-5P	2110	3608	12,215

1952 Oldsmobile, Super 88 Series four-door sedan, V-8 (DC)

SUPER EIGHTY-EIGHT — Similar to the Deluxe Eighty-Eight group, the five model Super Eighty-Eight lineup was the most popular Olds series. Standard equipment included items from the Deluxe Eighty-Eight series, plus foam rubber seat cushions, stainless steel gravel shields and turn signals. Upholstery choices were broadcloth, nylon sharkskin, nylon Bedford cord or leather. Standard tire size was 7.60 x 15 inches.

SUPER EIGHTY-EIGHT SERIES

Model Number	Body/Style Number	Body Type & Seating	Factory Price	Shipping Weight	Production Total
S-88	52-3627D	2-dr Clb Cpe-5P	2126	3597	2,050
S-88	52-3611D	2-dr Sed-5P	2172	3603	24,963
S-88	52-3637D	2-dr Hol HT-5P	2430	3640	15,777
S-88	52-3667TDX	2-dr Conv-5P	2595	3867	5,162
S-88	52-3669D	4-dr Sed-5P	2234	3649	70,606

1952 Oldsmobile, 98 Series two-door convertible, V-8 (DC)

NINETY-EIGHT SERIES — The top of the line Oldsmobiles remained as the long-standing Ninety-Eight models. The series shared the new, higher output, 160 hp Rocket V-8 with the Super Eighty-Eight series cars. Standard-equipment on the three body styles included all items from the Super Eighty-Eight group, plus carpeting front and rear, electric clock, stainless steel wheel trim rings, windshield washer and Deluxe steering wheel and horn ring. Upholstery selection was broadcloth or six colors of leather. Standard tire size was 8.00 x 15.

NINETY-EIGHT SERIES

Model Number	Body/Style Number	Body Type & Seating	Factory Price	Shipping Weight	Production Total
98	52-3037D	2-dr Hol HT-5P	2750	3874	14,150
98	52-3067DX	2-dr Conv-5P	2940	4111	3,544
98	52-3069D	4-dr Sed-5P	2532	3764	58,550

BASE ENGINES

(DELUXE 88) V-8. Cast iron. Overhead valves. Hydraulic valve lifters. Bore and stroke: 3-3/4 x 3-7/16 inches. Displacement: 303 cid. Brake hp: 145 at 3600 rpm. Torque: 280 foot pounds. Compression ratio: 7.5:1. Five main bearings. Carburetor: Rochester model BB two-barrel or Carter.

(SUPER 88/98) V-8. Cast iron block. Overhead valves. Hydraulic valve lifters. Bore and stroke: 3-3/4 x 3-7/16 inches. Displacement: 303 cid. Brake hp 160 at 3600 rpm. Torque 283 foot pounds. Compression ratio: 7.5:1. Five main bearings. Carburetor either Rochester 4GC or Carter WGD four-barrel.

CHASSIS FEATURES: Wheelbase: (Deluxe and Super Eighty-Eight) 120 inches; (Ninety-Eight) 124 inches. Overall length: (Deluxe and Super Eighty-Eight) 204 inches; (Ninety-Eight) 213 inches. Front tread: 58 inches. Rear tread: 59 inches.

OPTIONS: Deluxe Condition-Air heater/defroster ($79). Deluxe 6-tube radio ($100). Deluxe radio with rear speaker ($121). Super Deluxe 8-tube radio with signal seeking ($129). Windshield washer ($10). Back-up lights ($21). Deluxe steering wheel and horn ring ($14). Cadet visor ($32). Turn signals ($24). Electric clock ($8). Self-winding steering wheel mounted car watch ($35). Compass ($8). Stainless steel wheel trim rings ($14). Hydraulic steering ($185). Accessory group Z exhaust extension, visor vanity mirror, trunk, under hood and glovebox and hand brake. All cars were Rocket V-8 powered with Super Eighty-Eight and Ninety-Eight models having slightly higher output engines. An optional oil filter was available for $10; A heavy-duty air cleaner cost $11. All cars came standard with a three-speed manual transmission that was column-shifted. The optional Hydra-Matic could be ordered on any model, any series for $165.

HISTORICAL FOOTNOTES: Model year production: 213,419. Calendar year production: 228,452. Rank in industry: fourth (a new high for Oldsmobile). Power steering was a new option. During 1952, Oldsmobile continued to be the top-selling Hydra-Matic-equipped car in America. A grand total of 1,737,351 Oldsmobiles had been made with this popular drive system since the division developed it in 1940. (All in all, 3,837,443 American cars — including 223,581 Olds built in calendar 1952 — had been equipped with Hydra-Matic by the end of

1952.) During the calendar year run, Olds also made 9,509 convertibles and 33,119 hardtops, both slightly increased. The Southern 500 stock car race at Darlington, S.C., on Labor Day 1952, was the biggest of three NASCAR events Oldsmobiles would win in 1952.

1953 OLDSMOBILE

1953 Oldsmobile, 88 Series two-door sedan, V-8 (DC)

DELUXE EIGHTY-EIGHT — Oldsmobile continued to offer a relatively modest bottom series with just two body styles populating the Deluxe Eighty-Eight series. Again a lower horsepower version of the Rocket V-8 was exclusive to this series. Standard equipment included: bumper guards, electric clock, lined luggage compartment, dual horns, cigarette lighter, chrome moldings and twin interior sun visors. A total of 17 colors were available with 15 factory approved two-tone combinations on the order form. Upholstery was done in a two-tone pattern cloth. Standard tire size was 7.60 x 15 inches.

OLDSMOBILE I.D. NUMBERS: Serial number located on left front door pillar on right side of cowl. Motor number on block above water pump; and on plate on floor inside right door; and on left corner of block above generator; and on front of left cylinder head at negative battery terminal. Olds 88 numbers took the form 537( )1001 to 537( )ending number. Olds Super 88 numbers took the form 538( )1001 to 538( )ending number. Olds 98 numbers took the form 539( )1001 to 539( )ending number. First two symbols indicate model year: 53=1953. Third symbol indicates series: 7=88; 8=Super 88; 9=98. Fourth symbol in ( ) indicated assembly plant as follows: A=Atlanta; B=Boston (Framingham); K=Kansas City; M=Michigan (Lansing); L=Linden (New Jersey); C=California (Los Angeles/Southgate); and W=Wilmington, Del. Remaining symbols were the unit's sequential production number. Starting number at each assembly plant was 1001. Ending numbers, by series, at each coded plant were: [88] M19106; A3184; B3254; K4613; L3317; C3028; and W3298. [Super 88] M107336; A13333; B11410; K24976; L15787; C17946; and W16346. [98] M49567; A7826; B6610; K13956; L10234; C9887; and W9034. Motor numbers (unrelated to assembly plants) were: [V-8] R215001 to R549482.

DELUXE EIGHTY-EIGHT SERIES

Model Number	Body/Style Number	Body Type & Seating	Factory Price	Shipping Weight	Production Total
S-88	53-3611	2-dr Sed-5P	2065	3514	12,400
S-88	53-3669	4-dr Sed-5P	2126	3622	20,400

1953 Oldsmobile, Super 88 Series two-door Holiday coupe, V-8 (DC)

SUPER EIGHTY-EIGHT — Again Oldsmobile's middle series offered the most variety of body styles and also sold the most cars. Body and chassis wise, the Super Eighty-Eight was very similar to the Deluxe Eighty-Eight. The Super Eighty-Eight shared a higher horsepower version of the Rocket V-8 with the Ninety-Eight. This series carried the same standard equipment as the Deluxe Eighty-Eight, plus rear seat robe rails, special rear stainless steel trim and chrome window ventipanes. Upholstery selection included nylon cloth or leather.

SUPER EIGHTY-EIGHT SERIES

Model Number	Body/Style Number	Body Type & Seating	Factory Price	Shipping Weight	Production Total
S-88	53-3611D	2-dr Sed-5P	2253	3634	36,824
S-88	53-3637D	2-dr Hol HT-5P	2448	3670	34,500
S-88	53-3667DX	2-dr Conv-5P	2615	4080	8,310
S-88	53-3669	4-dr Sed-5P	2252	3681	119,317

1953 Oldsmobile, Fiesta two-door convertible, V-8 (DC)

NINETY-EIGHT SERIES — The normally plush Ninety-Eight series got an even richer limited production model late in the year. It was the very rare Fiesta. This model predicted 1954 styling features like curved windshields and also had virtually every Olds option offered, except factory air conditioning. The regular Ninety-Eight models had all items from the lower series cars as standard equipment plus the padded dash, windshield washers and Deluxe steering wheel and horn ring. Upholstery selections were broadcloth, gabardine or leather. Standard tire size was 8.00 x 15.

NINETY-EIGHT SERIES

Model Number	Body/Style Number	Body Type & Seating	Factory Price	Shipping Weight	Production Total
98	53-3037DX	2-dr Hol HT-5P	2771	3906	27,920
98	53-3067DX	2-dr Conv-5P	2963	4123	7,521
98	53-3069D	4-dr Sed-5P	2552	3798	64,431
98	53-3067SDX	2-dr Fiesta Conv-5P	5715	4459	458

BASE ENGINES

(DELUXE 88) V-8. Cast iron block. Overhead valves. Hydraulic valve lifters. Bore and stroke: 3-3/4 x 3-7/16 inches. Displacement: 303 cid. Compression ratio: 8.0:1. Brake hp: 150 at 3600 rpm. Torque: 280 foot pounds at 1800 rpm. Carburetor: Carter WGD two-barrel.

(SUPER 88/98) V-8. Cast iron block. Overhead valves. Hydraulic valve lifters. Bore and stroke: 3-3/4 x 3-7/16 inches. Displacement: 303 cid. Compression ratio: 8.0.1. Brake hp: 165 at 3600 rpm. Torque: 284 foot pounds at 1800 rpm. Carburetor: either Rochester 4GC or Carter WCFB four-barrels.

(FIESTA) V-8. Cast iron block. Overhead valves. Hydraulic valve lifters. Bore and stroke: 3-3/4 x 3-7/16 inches. Displacement: 303 cid. Compression ratio: 8.3:1 Brake hp: 170 at 4000 rpm. Carburetor: Rochester 4GC four-barrel.

CHASSIS FEATURES: Wheelbase: (Deluxe and Super Eighty-Eights) 120 inches; (Ninety-Eight and Fiesta) 124 inches. Overall length: (Deluxe and Super Eighty-Eights) 204 inches; (Ninety-Eight and Fiesta) 215 inches. Tread: (front and rear all series) 59 inches.

OPTIONS: Deluxe Condition-Air heater/defroster ($79). Deluxe radio, 6-tube push-button ($100). Rear seat speaker ($20). Super Deluxe radio, 8-tube, signal seeking ($129). Back-up lights ($14). Hand brake signal ($6). Windshield washer ($10). Deluxe steering wheel and horn ring ($14). Cadet visor ($33). Safety padded instrument panel ($15). Electric clock ($18). Autronic eye ($50). Tinted glass ($30). Hydraulic window and seat controls ($131). Oldsmobile/Frigidaire air conditioning ($550). Stainless steel wheel trim rings ($12). Power steering ($165). Power brakes ($33). This year all Oldsmobiles were equipped, for the first time, with 12-volt electrical systems. All models, except the Fiesta, came standard with a three-speed manual, column-shifted transmission. Hydra-Matic, which was standard on the Fiesta, cost $132 on any other model in any series. An optional oil filter cost $10 and a heavy-duty air cleaner was a good buy at $6. During this model year a fire destroyed the General Motors Hydra-Matic plant and a number of Oldsmobiles were built with the Buick Dyna-Flow transmission.

HISTORICAL FOOTNOTES: Jan. 9, 1953 was the day that 1953 Oldsmobiles were introduced. By the end of the year, 334,462 cars built to 1953 model specs were made. A calendar year run of 319,414 units put Olds in seventh place. The Fiesta limited-production convertible was brought out. There were big increases in the calendar year production of convertibles (16,000 built) and hardtops (62,500 built). The fiberglass-bodied Starfire was seen at the year's auto shows. In stock car racing, the release of heavy-duty factory parts helped make '53 Oldsmobiles more competitive in NASCAR racing. Checkered flags were captured in nine events, including Buck Baker's win at the Southern 500. Bob Pronger set a new mark of 113.38 mph in the Flying-Mile at Daytona driving an Olds 88 two-door sedan. Later, he rolled the car on the beach race course during the 160-mile Daytona stock car race, which Bill Blair took with another Olds.

1954 OLDSMOBILE

EIGHTY-EIGHT SERIES — A rather complete styling change was made across the board for Oldsmobile in 1954. The lowest Olds series was known again as the Eighty-Eight. Gone was the rather misleading Deluxe Eighty-Eight terminology. The bottom series was powered by slightly de-tuned version of the Rocket V-8. A third model was added to this series — the popular two-door Holiday coupe. Standard Eighty-Equipment included: bumper guards, rubber simulated carpets front and rear, electric clock, lined luggage compartment, dual horns, cigarette lighter, aluminum door sill plates and turn signals. Eighteen standard paint colors were offered in 1954 with 18 factory sanctioned two-tone combinations in place. Upholstery in this series was in either gray, green or blue pattern cloth. Standard tire size was 7.60 x 15 inches.

OLDSMOBILE I.D. NUMBERS: Serial number located on left front door pillar on right side of cowl. Motor number on block above water pump; and on plate on floor inside right door; and on left corner of block above generator; and on front of left cylinder head at negative battery terminal. Olds 88 numbers took the form 547( )1001 to 547( )ending number. Olds Super 88 numbers took the form 548( )1001 to 548( )ending number. Oldsmobile 98 numbers

took the form 549( )1001 to 549( )ending number. First two symbols indicate model year: 54=1954. Third symbol indicates series: 7=88; 8=Super 88; 9=98. Fourth symbol in ( ) indicated assembly plant as follows: A=Atlanta; B=Boston (Framingham); K=Kansas City; M=Michigan (Lansing); L=Linden (New Jersey); C=California (Los Angeles/Southgate); T=Texas (Arlington); and W=Wilmington, Del. Remaining symbols were the unit's sequential production number. Starting number at each assembly plant was 1001. Ending numbers, by series, at each coded plant were: [88] M31457; A6390; T3992; B5394; K10213; L9056; C7066; and W7293. [Super 88] M8842; A15328; T7612; B12411; K24104; L23190; C16267; and W17294. [98] M44758; A7278; T4101; B6362; K10921; L11436; C8426; and W7779. Motor numbers (unrelated to assembly plants) were: [V-8] V1001 to V355083.

1954 Oldsmobile, 88 Series two-door sedan, V-8 (DC)

EIGHTY-EIGHT SERIES

Model Number	Body/Style Number	Body Type & Seating	Factory Price	Shipping Weight	Production Total
88	54-3611	2-dr Sed-5P	2066	3684	18,013
88	54-3637	2-dr Hol HT-5P	2230	3703	25,820
88	54-3669	4-dr Sed-5P	2126	3707	29,028

1954 Oldsmobile, Super 88 Series two-door convertible, V-8 (DC)

SUPER EIGHTY-EIGHT SERIES — Oldsmobile featured a new look in 1954 and the Super Eighty-Eight continued to be the division's bread-and-butter series. One of the most noticeable 1954 features was the so-called panoramic windshield previewed on the limited-production 1953 Fiesta. Standard equipment on this series included all items from the Eighty-Eight series, plus chrome rocker panel moldings, deck lid ornament and foam rubber seat cushions. Upholstery selections spanned a nylon and orlon cloth combination or a variety of colored leathers. Standard tire size was 7.60 x 15 inches.

SUPER EIGHTY-EIGHT SERIES

Model Number	Body/Style Number	Body Type & Seating	Factory Price	Shipping Weight	Production Total
S-88	54-3611D	2-dr Sed-5P	2189	3713	27,882
S-88	54-3637D	2-dr Hol HT-5P	2448	3758	42,155
S-88	54-3667DTX	2-dr Conv-5P	2615	3985	6,452
S-88	54-3669D	4-dr Sed-5P	2251	3755	111,326

NINETY-EIGHT SERIES — A three model Ninety-Eight series was atop the Olds lineup for this year. Some new two-toning concepts seemed to fit the top line Olds series well. This year Olds dubbed its Ninety-Eight series convertibles 'Starfires' after the previous year's dream car. A slightly higher horsepower Rocket V-8 was shared with Super Eighty-Eight models. Standard Ninety-Eight equipment included items from the bottom two series, plus padded instrument panel, brake signal light, courtesy light package, stainless steel wheel discs, windshield washer and Deluxe steering wheel and horn ring. Upholstery choices were nylon and leather in a variety of colors. Standard tire size was 8.00 x 15 inches.

NINETY-EIGHT SERIES

Model Number	Body/Style Number	Buy Type & Seating	Factory Price	Shipping Weight	Production Total
98	54-3037	2-dr Hol HT-5P	2570	3840	38,553
98	54-3067DX	2-dr Conv-5P	2963	4159	6,800
98	54-3069D	4-dr Sed-5P	2552	3863	47,972

ENGINES

(88 SERIES) V-8. Cast iron block. Overhead valves. Hydraulic lifters. Bore and stroke: 3-7/8 x 3-7/16 inches. Displacement: 324 cid. Hp: 170 at 4000 rpm. Compression ratio: 8.5:1. Torque 300 foot pounds at 1400 rpm. Carburetor Carter dual downdraft WGD.

(SUPER 88 SERIES) V-8. Cast iron block. Overhead valves. Hydraulic lifters. Bore and stroke: 3-7/8 x 3-7/16 inches. Displacement: 324 cid. Hp: 185; Torque 300 foot pounds. Compression ratio: 8.25:1. Carburetor: Carter WCFB or Rochester 4GC, both four-barrels.

CHASSIS FEATURES: Wheelbase: (Eighty-Eight and Super Eighty-Eight) 122 inches; (Ninety-Eight) 126 inches. Overall length: (Eighty-Eight and Super Eighty-Eight) 205.26 inches; (Ninety-Eight) 214.26 inches. Front tread: 59 inches. Rear tread: 58 inches.

1954 Oldsmobile, 98 Series two-door Holiday hardtop coupe, V-8 (DC)

OPTIONS: Deluxe heater/defroster ($79). Power steering ($125). Deluxe radio ($100). Electric antenna ($20). Rear seat speaker ($14). Super Deluxe radio ($129). Back-up lights ($14). Courtesy light package ($4). Windshield washer ($10). Tinted glass ($30). Cadet sunvisor ($33). Padded dash ($17). Power brakes ($37). Air conditioning ($550). Oversize tires ($18). Whitewall tires ($30). Autronic eye ($45). Hydraulic window lifts/4-way power seats ($165). Electric 4-way seat ($65). Stainless steel wheel trim rings ($8). Deluxe wheel discs ($30). Mimetic wire wheel discs ($60). Accessory group Z — exhaust extension, visor vanity mirror and luggage compartment under hood and glove box lights ($10). Oil filter ($10). Air cleaner ($5). Hydra-Matic Drive ($165).

HISTORICAL FOOTNOTES: The new Oldsmobiles were introduced Jan. 20, 1954. Added to the line later were Deluxe 88 and Classic 98 Deluxe Holiday hardtops and the Classic 98 Holiday convertible or Starfire convertible. Model year production was 354,001 units. Olds took fourth place in industry output with calendar year production of 433,810 units. The '54s were the fastest Olds ever with up to 170 hp coming from the 324 cid block. They could do 0-60 mph in 12.4 seconds and cover the quarter-mile in 18. Calendar year body type production included 11,575 convertibles and 144,000 hardtops, with sales of the latter more than doubling from the prior 12 months. The Cutlass F-88 dream car was on the show circuit for Oldsmobile in 1954. In racing, the Oldsmobiles took 11 NASCAR victories, but then heavy-duty factory parts kits were banned.

1955 OLDSMOBILE

1955 Oldsmobile, 88 Series two-door sedan, V-8 (DC)

EIGHTY-EIGHT — Again the bottom Olds series was the Eighty-Eight with its three body styles. Exclusive to this series was a slightly de-tuned version of the Rocket V-8 engine, although the higher horsepower Rocket was an option. Standard Eighty-Eight equipment included: directional signals, bumper guards, stainless steel moldings, dual horns, cigarette lighter, front and rear floor mats and inside rearview mirror. Oldsmobile continued to offer a number of a stylish two-tone combinations highlighted by an attractive molding package. Upholstery choices were gray, green or blue pattern cloth or moroceen and pattern cloth. Standard tire size was 7.60 x 15 inches.

OLDSMOBILE I.D. NUMBERS: Serial number located on left front door pillar on right side of cowl. Motor number on block above water pump; and on plate on floor inside right door; and on left corner of block above generator; and on front of left cylinder head at negative battery terminal. Olds 88 numbers took the form 557( )1001 to 557( )ending number. Olds Super 88 numbers took the form 558( )1001 to 558( )ending number. Oldsmobile 98 numbers took the form 559( )1001 to 559( )ending number. First two symbols indicate model year: 55=1955. Third symbol indicates series: 7=88; 8=Super 88; 9=98. Fourth symbol in ( ) indicated assembly plant as follows: A=Atlanta; B=Boston (Framingham); K=Kansas City; M=Michigan (Lansing); L=Linden (New Jersey); C=California (Los Angeles/Southgate); T=Texas (Arlington); and W=Wilmington, Del. Remaining symbols were the unit's sequential production number. Starting number at each assembly plant was 1001. Ending numbers, by series, at each coded plant were: [88] M83115; A25284; T13728; B14033; K26765; L30220; C26134; and W18188. [Super 88] M95087; A24050; T14606; B35211; K26765; L30220; C26134; and W18874. [98] M48385; A12463; T7937; B7338; K12237; L16111; C12655; and W9117. Motor numbers (unrelated to assembly plants) were: [V-8] V400001 to V983275.

EIGHTY-EIGHT SERIES

Model Number	Body/Style Number	Body Type & Seating	Factory Price	Shipping Weight	Production Total
88	55-3611	2-dr Sed-5P	2297	3690	37,507
88	55-3637	2-dr Hol HT-5P	2474	3705	85,767
88	55-3669	4-dr Sed-5P	2362	3710	57,777
88	55-3639	4-dr Hol HT-5P	2546	3695	41,310

1955 Oldsmobile, Super 88 Series four-door Holiday sedan, V-8 (DC)

SUPER EIGHTY-EIGHT — This year the higher output Ninety-Eight series engine was slipped into the Eighty-Eight body to make the Super Eighty-Eight series. An Olds buyer had more choice in this series than any other, since there were four available body styles. Standard equipment included all items from the Eighty-Eight series, plus foam rubber seat cushions, stainless steel rocker panel moldings, front seatback robe cord, spun glass underhood insulation and rear window ventipanes. Upholstery choices were pattern cloth, leather and pattern cloth combinations and two colored leather combinations.

Model Number	Body/Style Number	Body Type & Seating	Factory Price	Shipping Weight	Production Total
S-88	55-3611D	2-dr Sed-5P	2436	3755	11,950
S-88	55-3637D	2-dr Hol HT-5P	2714	3765	62,534
S-88	55-3667DTX	2-dr Conv-5P	2894	3795	9,007
S-88	55-3669D	4-dr Sed-5P	2503	3760	111,316
S-88	55-36395D	4-dr Hol HT-5P	2788	3780	47,385

1955 Oldsmobile, 98 Series two-door Starfire convertible, V-8 (DC)

NINETY-EIGHT SERIES — This year's Ninety-Eight was again a physically larger machine than the Eighty-Eight. These top line Oldsmobiles were well appointed. Standard equipment included items from the Eighty-Eight and Super Eighty-Eight series, plus electric clock, stainless steel wheel discs, custom cushion lounge seats front and rear, hand brake signal light, courtesy light package, safety padded dash, Deluxe steering wheel and horn ring and windshield washer. Upholstery choices were covert and pattern cloth, leather and pattern cloth, leather and nylon and leather and dimple leather. Standard tire size was 7.60 x 15 inches.

NINETY-EIGHT SERIES

Model Number	Body/Style Number	Body Type & Seating	Factory Price	Shipping Weight	Production Total
98	55-3037	2-dr Hol HT-5P	3069	3805	38,363
98	55-3067DX	2-dr Starfire Conv-5P	3276	3890	9,149
98	55-3069D	4-dr Sed-5P	2833	3865	39,847
98	55-3039SDX	4-dr Hol HT-5P	3140	3875	31,267

NOTE 1: Deluxe Holiday hardtop coupe carried the suffix "DX" in style number.

ENGINES

(88 SERIES) V-8. Cast iron block. Overhead valves. Hydraulic valve lifters. 3-7/8 x 3-7/16 inches. Displacement: 324 cid. Hydraulic valve lifters. Hp: 185 at 4000 rpm. Torque: 320 pound feet at 2000 rpm. Compression ratio: 8.5:1. Carburetor: Rochester 2GC dual downdraft.

(SUPER 88/98 SERIES) V-8. Cast iron block. Overhead valves. Hydraulic valve lifters. Bore and stroke: 3-7/8 x 37/16 inches. Displacement: 324 cid. Hydraulic valve lifters. Compression ratio: 8.5:1. Hp: 202 at 4000 rpm. Torque: 332 foot pounds at 2400 rpm. Carburetor: Rochester 4GC Quadra-Jet.

CHASSIS FEATURES: Wheelbase: (Eighty-Eight and Super Eighty-Eight) 122 inches; (Ninety-Eight) 126 inches. Overall length: (Eighty-Eight and Super Eighty-Eight) 203 inches. (Ninety-Eight) 123.5 inches. Front tread: 59 inches. Rear tread: 58 inches.

OPTIONS: Condition-air heater/defroster ($74). Safety power steering ($120). Deluxe radio ($94). Electric radio antenna ($21). Rear seat radio speaker ($12). Super Deluxe radio ($21). Back-up lights ($13). Hand brake signal light ($5). Windshield washer ($11). Deluxe steering wheel and horn ring ($15). Safety padded instrument panel ($32). Spotlight ($23).-Air Condi-tioning ($550). Pedal-Ease power brakes ($58). Electric clock ($11). Autronic Eye ($45). Electric 2-way seat ($50). Electric 4-way seat ($65). Electric windows ($80). Hydra-Matic ($165). Heavy-duty air cleaner ($10). Oil filter ($6).

HISTORIC FOOTNOTES: Nov. 5, 1954 was the date of factory introductions of 1955 Oldsmobiles. Exactly two weeks later, the dealer introductions were held in auto showrooms across America. Public announcements of the 1955 Holiday Sedan were made Jan. 6, 1955, two days after Buick announced its own Riviera four-door hardtop. Sales of this totally new body style, by Oldsmobile dealers, began in March 1955. This helped make it the best-ever model year for the company with production of 583,179 units. The calendar year output was 643,549 cars, good for fifth slot in the industry's production sweepstakes. On a calendar year basis, the new four-door Holiday sedan outsold the Riviera sedan 174,207 to 173,527. However, the Oldsmobile lead in four-door hardtop sales lasted only the one year. Olds also increased calendar year production of convertibles to 20,218 units and Holiday Coupes to 195,866. In the performance field, the extraction of 32 more horsepower from the 324 cid V-8 helped the 1955 Super 88 sedan trim its 0-60 time to 10.6 seconds and its quarter-mile time to 17.6 seconds. Drivers Dick Rathman and Jim Pascal raced Oldsmobiles for the Wood Racing Team. This year's factory show car was the Delta, with cast aluminum wheels and anodized aluminum bodyside trim predictive of the late 1950s and a tachometer and console like a 1960s muscle car.

1956 OLDSMOBILE

1956 Oldsmobile, 88 Series two-door sedan, V-8 (DC)

EIGHTY-EIGHT — Oldsmobile stayed with its three series format in 1956. The Eighty-Eight was again the bottom line offering. The series was expanded this year and comprised of four body styles including a new four-door Holiday hardtop. Standard equipment items were: armrests, bumper guards, lined luggage compartment, rotary door latches, dual horns, cigarette lighter, directional signals, rubber floor mats, aluminum door sill plates and sun visors. Twenty-one factory colors were available with 26 sanctioned two-tone layouts. Upholstery choices on this series included pattern cloth in a variety of colors and trim materials. Standard tire size was 7.10 x 15 inches.

OLDSMOBILE I.D. NUMBERS: Serial number located on left front door pillar on right side of cowl. Motor number on block above water pump; and on plate on floor inside right door; and on left corner of block above generator; and on front of left cylinder head at negative battery terminal. Olds 88 numbers took the form 567( )1001 to 567( )ending number. Olds Super 88 numbers took the form 568( )1001 to 568( )ending number. Olds 98 numbers took the form 569( )1001 to 569( )ending number. First two symbols indicate model year: 56=1956. Third symbol indicates series: 7=88; 8=Super 88; 9=98. Fourth symbol in ( ) indicated assembly plant as follows: A=Atlanta; B=Boston (Framingham); K=Kansas City; M=Michigan (Lansing); L=Linden (New Jersey); C=California (Los Angeles/Southgate); T=Texas (Arlington); and W=Wilmington, Del. Remaining symbols were the unit's sequential production number. Starting number at each assembly plant was 1001. Ending numbers, by series, at each coded plant were: [88] M81004; A23776; T12624; B13634; K23009; L27865; C21622; and W20657. [Super 88] M68628; A18370; T11317; B9624; K19777; L23452; C19208; and W15808. [98] M37834; A9354; T6069; B5403; K8944; L13210; C9179; and W8063. Motor numbers (unrelated to assembly plants) were: [V-8] A001001 to A385513.

EIGHTY-EIGHT SERIES

Model Number	Body/Style Number	Body Type & Seating	Factory Price	Shipping Weight	Production Total
88	56-3611	2-dr Sed-5P	2166	3705	31,949
88	56-3637	2-dr Hol HT-5P	2330	3715	74,739
88	56-3669	4-dr Sed-5P	2226	3761	57,092
88	56-3639	4-dr Hol HT-5p	2397	3776	52,239

SUPER EIGHTY-EIGHT — With its five body styles the Super Eighty-Eight continued to give the Olds buyer the most selection and was responsible for the most sales. Standard equipment included all items from the Eighty-Eight series, plus front and rear carpeting, foam rubber seat cushions, courtesy lights, front fender medallions and deck lid '88' numerals. Upholstery choices included pattern cloth and leather in a variety of colors and combinations. Standard tire size for the series was 7.60 x 15 inches.

SUPER EIGHTY-EIGHT

Model Number	Body/Style Number	Body Type & Seating	Factory Price	Shipping Weight	Production Total
S-88	56-3611D	2-dr Sed-5P	2301	3835	5465
S-88	56-3637SD	2-dr Hol HT-5P	2520	3838	43,054
S-88	56-3669D	4-dr Sed-5P	2363	3897	59,728
S-88	56-3639SD	4-dr Hol HT-5P	2586	3905	61,192
S-88	56-3667DTX	2-dr Conv-5P	2726	3947	9,561

1956 Oldsmobile, Super 88 Series two-door Holiday coupe, V-8 (DC)

NINETY-EIGHT — Again in 1956, the top of the line Oldsmobile series rolled on an exclusive wheelbase four inches longer than the two Eighty-Eight series cars. Power came from a 240 hp Rocket V-8 shared with Super Eighty-Eight models. Standard equipment included all items found on the lower series cars plus back-up lamp moldings, electric clock, Jetaway Hydra-Matic Drive, padded dash, courtesy lights, power steering, windshield washers and Deluxe steering wheel. Upholstery choices were pattern cloth and leather in a variety of colors and combinations. Standard tire size was 8.00 x 15 inches either U.S. Royal, Goodrich or Firestone.

NINETY-EIGHT SERIES

Model Number	Body/Style Number	Body Type & Seating	Factory Price	Shipping Weight	Production Total
98	56-3037SDX	2-dr Hol HT-5P	3138	3978	19,433
98	56-3069D	4-dr Sed-5P	2969	4047	20,105
98	56-3039SDX	4-dr Hol HT-5P	3204	4061	42,320
98	56-3067DX	2-dr Starfire Conv-5P	3380	4107	8,581

1956 Oldsmobile, 98 Series Starfire two-door convertible, V-8 (DC)

ENGINES

(88 SERIES) Cast-iron overhead valve V-8 engine. Bore and stroke: 3-7/8 x 3-7/16 inches. Displacement: 324 cid. Hydraulic valve lifters. Compression ratio: 9.25:1. Hp: 230 at 4400 rpm. Torque: 340 foot pounds at 2400 rpm. Carburetor: Rochester 2GC dual downdraft. Super Eighty-Eight engine optional in this series.

(SUPER 88/98 SERIES) Cast-iron overhead valve V-8 engine. Bore and stroke: 3-7/8 x 3-7/16 inches. Displacement: 324 cid. Hydraulic valve lifters. Compression ratio: 9.25:1. Hp: 240 at 4400 rpm. Torque: 350 foot pounds at 2800 rpm. Carburetor: Rochester 4GC Quadra-Jet.

CHASSIS FEATURES: Wheelbase: (Eighty-Eight and Super Eighty-Eight) 122 inches; (Ninety-Eight) 126 inches. Overall length: (Eighty-Eight and Super Eighty-Eight) 203.29 inches; (Ninety-Eight) 212.29 inches. Front tread: 59 inches. Rear tread: 58 inches.

OPTIONS: Deluxe heater and defroster ($77). Power steering ($100). Deluxe 6-tube push-button radio ($96). Electric antenna ($21). Rear speaker ($14). Super Deluxe 8-tube signal seeking radio ($121). Back-up lights ($13). Parking brake signal light ($5) Front courtesy lights ($4). Windshield washer ($10). Deluxe steering wheel and horn ring ($13). Deluxe horn ($10). Tinted glass ($30). Cadet visor ($33). Padded dash ($18). Power brakes ($37). Electric clock ($18). Air conditioning ($400). Whitewall tires ($33). Dual exhaust ($38). Exhaust extension ($2). Autronic eye ($46). Electric 6-way seat ($86). Electric windows ($90) Deluxe wheel discs ($28). Heavy-duty air cleaner ($10). Oil filter ($6). Super Hydra-Matic Drive ($175). Jetaway Hydra-Matic ($190 on 98s only). Heavy-duty manual transmission with clutch cover and special propeller shaft (Lansing-built cars only, $15).

HISTORICAL FOOTNOTES: Factory introductions of 1956 Oldsmobiles were done Oct. 25, 1955. The dealer-level intros took place on Nov. 3. Model year assemblies came to 485,459 units, equaling 7.7 percent of all U.S. output. Calendar year totals were 432,903 vehicles including 17,795 convertibles; 121,304 two-door hardtops; 128,640 four-door hardtops; and 689 (1957) early-production station wagons. Leather trim was available in the Olds 98 Starfire convertible; the 98 Deluxe Holiday Sedan; the 98 Deluxe Holiday Coupe; the Super 88 convertible; and the Super 88 Holiday Sedan and Holiday Coupe. Even with 38 extra horses, the 1956 Olds Super 88 four-door hardtop was slower than the 1955 four-door sedan. It needed an extra .20 seconds for both 0-60 and the quarter-mile, due to the extra 107 pounds it was carrying. Olds took only one big NASCAR race in 1956, although Lee Petty was able to establish a new Flying-Mile record of 144 mph with an Oldsmobile at Daytona Beach, Fla.

1957 OLDSMOBILE

GOLDEN ROCKET EIGHTY-EIGHT — To honor GM's upcoming 50th anniversary, Olds picked 1957 to tag its bottom line series the Golden Rockets. A mild restyle greeted Olds fans this year with a novel rear window treatment. Olds buyers could order a station wagon for the first time since 1950. Standard equipment included: armrests, bumper guards, directional signals, rubber floor mats and sun visors. Upholstery choices included a variety of colors and fabrics. Standard tire size was 8.50 x 14 inches.

1957 Oldsmobile, 88 Series two-door sedan, V-8 (DC)

OLDSMOBILE I.D. NUMBERS: Serial number located on left front door pillar on right side of cowl; on cowl under hood; on flange on left frame, just ahead of cowl; on metal plate on top of left front end of frame; on engine number plate. Motor number on block above water pump; and on plate on floor inside right door; on left corner of block above generator; and on front of left cylinder head at negative battery terminal. Olds 88 numbers took the form 577( )1001 to 577( )ending number. Olds Super 88 numbers took the form 578( )1001 to 578( )ending number. Olds 98 numbers took the form 579( )1001 to 579( )ending number. First two symbols indicate model year: 57=1957. Third symbol indicates series: 7=88; 8=Super 88; 9=98. Fourth symbol in ( ) indicated assembly plant as follows: A=Atlanta; B=Boston (Framingham); K=Kansas City; M=Michigan (Lansing); L=Linden (New Jersey); C=California (Los Angeles/Southgate); T=Texas (Arlington); and W=Wilmington, Del. Remaining symbols were the unit's sequential production number. Starting number at each assembly plant was 1001. Ending numbers, by series, at each coded plant were: [88] M70862; A18289; T10149; B9961; K19003; L19547; C16888; and W15960. [Super 88] M52348; A13297; T9490; B6879; K14818; L16542; C14280; and W11689. [98] M33963; A8105; T5873; B4877; K8378; L10933; C7994; and W7260. Motor numbers (unrelated to assembly plants) were: [V-8] A001001 and up.

GOLDEN ROCKET EIGHTY-EIGHT

Model Number	Body/Style Number	Body Type & Seating	Factory Price	Shipping Weight	Production Total
88	57-3611	2-dr Sed-6P	2478	4110	18,477
88	57-3637	2-dr Hol HT-6P	2591	4119	49,187
88	57-3639	4-dr Hol HT-6P	2663	4188	33,830
88	57-3669	4-dr Sed-6P	2538	4137	53,923
88	57-3667TX	2-dr Conv Cpe-6P	2895	4392	6,423
88	57-3662F	4-dr Sta Wag-6P	2914	4433	5,052
88	57-3665F	4-dr HT Sta Wag-6P	3017	4472	5,767

NOTE 1: All 1957 Oldsmobile station wagons are called Fiestas.

1957 Oldsmobile, Super 88 four-door hardtop Fiesta station wagon, V-8

SUPER EIGHTY-EIGHT — The middle Oldsmobile series, the Super Eighty-Eight, continued to find popularity with buyers. Wheelbase and body shells were shared with the Golden Rocket Eighty-Eights. Offered were six body styles and the newly returned Fiesta station wagon could be found in this series. Standard equipment included all items from the Golden Rocket Eighty-Eight group plus, front fender chrome script, exposed chrome roof bows and side interior courtesy lights. A variety of colored cloth and leather upholstery combinations could be offered. Standard tire size was 8.50 x 14 inches.

SUPER EIGHTY-EIGHT

Model Number	Body/Style Number	Body Type & Seating	Factory Price	Shipping Weight	Production Total
S-88	57-3637SD	2-dr Hol HT-6P	2884	4171	31,155
S-88	57-3611D	2-dr Sed-6P	2687	4164	2,983
S-88	57-3639SD	4-dr Hol HT-6P	2950	4251	39,162
S-88	57-3669D	4-dr Sed-6P	2745	4186	42,696
S-88	57-3667DTX	2-dr Conv Cpe-6P	3132	4445	7,128
S-88	57-3665SDF	4-dr Sta Wag-6P	3220	4537	8,981

1957 Oldsmobile, 98 Series Starfire four-door sedan, V-8 (DC).

STARFIRE NINETY-EIGHT — Again the top of the line Oldsmobile series was the Ninety-Eight group, this year's series officially being titled the Starfire Ninety-Eights. Offered in just four models, the top series cars were longer and heavier than either type of Eighty-Eight. Standard equipment included all items standard on the Super Eight-Eight plus, electric windows, special emblems, power steering, power brakes and Jetaway Hydra-Matic. Upholstery choices included a variety of cloth, morocceen and leather. Standard tire size was 9.00 x 14 inches.

STARFIRE NINETY-EIGHT

Model Number	Body/Style Number	Body Type & Seating	Factory Price	Shipping Weight	Production Total
98	57-3037SDX	2-dr Hol HT-6P	3578	4458	17,791
98	57-3067DX	2-dr Conv-6P	3838	4747	8,278
98	57-3069D	4-dr Sed-6P	3396	4450	21,525
98	57-3939SDX	4-dr Hol HT-6P	3649	4525	32,099

BASE ENGINES

(88/SUPER 88/98 SERIES) Cast iron overhead valve V-8 engine. Bore and stroke: 4 x 3-11/16 inches. Displacement: 371 cid. Hydraulic valve lifters. Compression ratio: 9.5:1. Torque: 400 pound feet at 2800 rpm. Brake hp: 277 at 4400 rpm. Carburetor: Quadra-Jet four-barrel.

CHASSIS FEATURES — Wheelbase: (Golden Rocket Eighty-Eight and Super Eighty-Eight) 122 inches; (Starfire Ninety-Eight) 126 inches. Overall length: (Golden Rocket Eighty-Eight and Super Eighty-Eight) 208.2 inches; (Ninety-Eight) 216.7 inches. Front tread: 59 inches. Rear tread: 58 inches.

OPTIONS: Hydra-Matic transmission ($215). Heater/defroster ($85). Power steering ($100). Deluxe radio ($96). Electric antenna ($22). Rear speakers ($16). Super Deluxe signal seeking radio ($121). Back-up lights ($15). Windshield washer ($11). Padded dash ($20). Power brakes ($37). Electric clock ($19). Air conditioning ($430). Autronic eye ($46). Deluxe wheelcovers ($30). Remote-control mirror ($9). Seat belts ($23). Cadet visor ($33). J-2 induction system (300 hp) with three two-barrel carburetors ($83). Special J-2 induction system (312 hp) not recommended for street use and offered to drag racers and stock car racers for off-road use ($395). Note: The Jetaway Hydra-matic was standard on Ninety-Eights and optional on all other models.

HISTORICAL FOOTNOTES: The 1957 Oldsmobiles were introduced Nov. 9, 1956. Model year production peaked at 384,390 units. Calendar year sales of 390,091 cars were recorded, including 21,840 ragtops, 98,300 hardtop coupes, 104,930 hardtop sedans and 19,500 wagons. This made Oldsmobile the fifth best-selling American automobile maker with a 6.2 percent share of market. J.F. Wolfram was the chief executive officer of the company this year. The Oldsmobile Mona Lisa show car was seen on the auto show circuit during 1957. Richard Petty drove Oldsmobiles in NASCAR stock car races, joining the Olds team with his father Lee Petty. Their aim was to win races behind the wheels of Oldsmobiles with the hot J-2 engine option. However, NASCAR ultimately banned multi carburetor engines and Olds wound up with only five Grand National wins, before pulling out of factory-backed racing efforts.

1958 OLDSMOBILE

DYNAMIC EIGHTY-EIGHT — A major styling change was made in 1958 and the three series format was again retained. Since the Seventy-Six designation was dropped in 1951, the bottom line series had been called the Eight-Eight. In 1958, the bottom line series designation became the Dynamic Eighty-Eight. Seven models were found here. Seventeen standard colors were available with five extra cost, high metallic colors offered. Upholstery choices in the series spanned a variety of colored morocceen and cloth combinations. Standard series equipment included: four beam headlights, oil filter, turn signals, printed circuit instrument cluster and aluminum anodized grille. Standard tire size was 8.50 x 14 inches.

OLDSMOBILE I.D. NUMBERS: Serial number located on left front door pillar on right side of cowl; on cowl under hood; on flange on left frame, just ahead of cowl; on metal plate on top of left front end of frame; on engine number plate. Motor number on block above water pump; and on plate on floor inside right door; on left corner of block above generator; and on front of left cylinder head at negative battery terminal. Oldsmobile 88 numbers took the form 587( )1001 to 587( )ending number. Olds Super 88 numbers took the form 588( )1001 to 588( )ending number. The Oldsmobile 98 numbers took the form 589( )1001 to 589( )ending number. First two symbols indicate model year: 58=1958. Third symbol

indicates series: 7=88; 8=Super 88; 9=98. Fourth symbol in ( ) indicated assembly plant as follows: A=Atlanta; B=Boston (Framingham); K=Kansas City; M=Michigan (Lansing); L=Linden (New Jersey); C=California (Los Angeles/Southgate); T=Texas (Arlington); and W=Wilmington, Del. Remaining symbols were the unit's sequential production number. Starting number at each assembly plant was 1001. Ending numbers, by series, at each coded plant not available. Motor numbers were B00-1001 and up were for engineering purposes only and no longer useful for identification.

1958 Oldsmobile, two-door Holiday 88 hardtop coupe, V-8 (DC)

DYNAMIC EIGHTY-EIGHT SERIES

Model Number	Body/Style Number	Body Type & Seating	Factory Price	Shipping Weight	Production Total
88	58-3611	2-dr Sed-5P	2772	4102	11,833
88	58-3637	2-dr Hol HT-5P	2893	4112	35,036
88	58-3669	4-dr Sed-5P	2837	4161	60,429
88	48-3639	4-dr Hol HT-5P	2971	4185	28,241
88	58-3667TX	2-dr Conv-6P	3221	4198	4,456
88	58-3693	4-dr Sta Wag-6P	3284	4441	3,249
88	58-3695	4-dr HT Sta Wag-6P	3395	4417	3,323

NOTE 1: All 1958 Oldsmobile station wagons are Fiestas.
NOTE 2: The Holiday Fiesta was the hardtop-style wagon.

1958 Oldsmobile, four-door hardtop Super 88 Fiesta station wagon, V-8 (AA)

SUPER EIGHTY-EIGHT — The middle Oldsmobile series again was the Super Eighty-Eight, sharing its wheelbase with the Dynamic Eighty-Eight and its engine with the Ninety-Eight. The model lineup spanned five body styles. Upholstery choices included various combinations of leather, cloth and morocceen. Standard equipment included all Dynamic Eighty-Eight equipment plus: padded dash, foam rubber padded seat cushions, courtesy lights, parking brake signal light, special side moldings and chrome rocker panel moldings. Standard tire size was 8.50 x 14 inches.

SUPER EIGHT-EIGHT SERIES

Model Number	Body/Style Number	Body Type & Seating	Factory Price	Shipping Weight	Production Total
S-88	58-3637D	2-dr Hol HT-5P	3262	4153	18,653
S-88	58-3667DTX	2-dr Conv-5P	3529	4217	3,799
S-88	58-3669D	4-dr Sed-5P	3112	4185	33,844
S-88	58-3639SD	4-dr Hol HT-5P	3339	4223	27,521
S-88	58-3695	4-dr Sta Wag-6P	3623	4471	5,175

NINETY-EIGHT — Again Oldsmobile's top of the line cars were found in the long-running Ninety-Eight series. This group rode on its own exclusive wheelbase of 126-1/2 inches, while sharing the more powerful Rocket V-8 engine with the Super Eighty-Eight models. Just four body styles were available. Standard series equipment included all items offered as standard on the two Eighty-Eight series, plus Hydra-Matic transmission, power steering and brakes, dual exhausts, electric clock, color accented wheel discs and chrome wheel frames. Interiors could be ordered in a variety of colored leathers, cloth and morocceen. Standard tires were 8.50 x 14 inches.

NINETY-EIGHT SERIES

Model Number	Body/Style Number	Body Type & Seating	Factory Price	Shipping Weight	Production Total
98	58-3037SDX	2-dr Hol HT-5P	4020	4454	11,012
98	58-3069D	4-dr Sed-5P	3824	4474	16,595
98	58-3039SDX	4-dr Hol HT-5P	4096	4559	27,063
98	48-3067DX	2-dr Conv-5P	4300	4504	5,605

1958 Oldsmobile, two-door Ninety-Eight convertible, V-8 (DC)

BASE ENGINES

(DYNAMIC 88 SERIES) Cast iron overhead valve V-8 engine. Bore and stroke: 4 x 3-11/16 inches. Displacement: 371 cid. Hydraulic valve lifters. Compression ratio: 10:1. Torque: 390 pound feet at 2400 rpm. Brake hp: 265 at 4400 rpm. Carburetor: "Economy" two-barrel. Super Eighty-Eight or J-2 engine optional in series.

(SUPER 88/98 SERIES) Cast iron overhead valve V-8 engine. Bore and stroke: 4 x 3-11/16 inches. Displacement: 371 cid. Hydraulic valve lifters. Compression ratio: 10:1. Brake hp: 305 at 4600 rpm. Torque: 410 pound feet at 2800 rpm. Carburetor: Quadra-Jet four-barrel.

CHASSIS FEATURES: Wheelbase: (Dynamic Eighty-Eight and Super Eighty-Eight) 122.5 inches; (Ninety-Eight) 126.5 inches. Overall length: (Dynamic Eighty-Eight and Super Eighty-Eight) 208.2 inches; (Ninety-Eight) 216.7 inches. Front tread: 59 inches. Rear tread: 58 inches.

OPTIONS: Jetaway Hydra-Matic drive. Heater/defroster. Power steering. Power brakes. Deluxe radio. Electric antenna. Rear radio speaker. Super Deluxe signal seeking radio. Trans-Portable radio. Windshield washer. Back-up lights. E-Z-Eye tinted glass. Cadet sun visor. Electric clock. Air conditioning. Autronic eye. Power seat. Power windows. New-Matic air suspension. All 1958 Oldsmobiles were powered by a Rocket V-8 engine. The 265 hp version was standard on Dynamic Eighty-Eights; the 305 hp motor optional on any Dynamic Eighty-Eight standard on all other models. A triple carbureted J-2 engine option could be ordered on any other 1958 Olds. It boosted power to 312 hp. Other engine options were a heavy-duty air cleaner and a heavy-duty crankcase ventilation system. A three-speed manual transmission was standard on cars in the Eighty-Eight and Super Eighty-Eight series. The Jetaway Hydra-Matic was standard on all Ninety-Eights, optional on all other models.

HISTORICAL FOOTNOTES: Factory announcements took place Oct. 30, 1957 and the 1958 models were introduced Nov 8, 1957. Model year production peaked at 296,374 units for a seven percent market share. Calendar year sales of 310,795 cars were recorded, for a fourth place in the sales race. J.F. Wolfram was the chief executive officer of the company again this year. Oldsmobile was solidly established as the sales leader in the medium-price class of the U.S. auto market. Its calendar year output included 13,705 convertibles; 63,259 two-door hardtops, 95,577 four-door hardtops and 13,265 station wagons. The 305 hp J-2 equipped Oldsmobile Super 88 Holiday Sedan was capable of 0-to-60 in 8.7 seconds and 17.3 second quarter-miles. The four millionth Hydra-Matic was built on April 8, 1958. Some Oldsmobile options and accessories with low installation rates included: air suspension (6.1 percent); limited slip differential (2.3 percent); air conditioning (12.5 percent); power windows (17.7 percent) and power seat (19.5 percent).

1959 OLDSMOBILE

1959 Oldsmobile, two-door Dynamic 88 convertible, V-8 (DC)

DYNAMIC EIGHTY-EIGHT — For the second consecutive year a new styling package greeted Oldsmobile buyers. On the bottom of the lineup was the Dynamic Eight-Eight series offering six body styles, the most of any Olds series. For the first time in a while, Olds offered a smaller displacement engine on the Dynamic Eighty-Eight models. Standard series equipment included: oil filter, turn signals, air scoop brakes, panoramic windshield and Safety spectrum speedometer. Upholstery was available in a variety of cloth and morocceen combinations. Standard tire size was 8.50 x 14 inches.

OLDSMOBILE I.D. NUMBERS: Serial number located on left front door pillar on right side of cowl; on cowl under hood; on flange on left frame, just ahead of cowl; on metal plate on top of left front end of frame; on engine number plate. Motor number on block above water pump;

and on plate on floor inside right door; on left corner of block above generator; and on front of left cylinder head at negative battery terminal. Oldsmobile 88 numbers took the form 597( )1001 to 597( )ending number. Olds Super 88 numbers took the form 598( )1001 to 598( )ending number. The Oldsmobile 98 numbers took the form 599( )1001 to 599( )ending number. First two symbols indicate model year: 59=1959. Third symbol indicates series: 7=88; 8=Super 88; 9=98. Fourth symbol in ( ) indicated assembly plant as follows: A=Atlanta; B=Boston (Framingham); K=Kansas City; M=Michigan (Lansing); L=Linden (New Jersey); C=California (Los Angeles/Southgate); T=Texas (Arlington); and W=Wilmington, Del. Remaining symbols were the unit's sequential production number. Starting number at each assembly plant was 1001 took the above format. Ending numbers, by series, at each coded plant not available. Motor numbers were C00-1001 for the 371 cid V-8 and D00-1001 for the 394 cid V-8. Motor numbers were for engineering purposes only and no longer useful for identification.

DYNAMIC EIGHTY-EIGHT

Model Number	Body/Style Number	Body Type & Seating	Factory Price	Curb Weight	Production Total
88	59-3211	2-dr Sed Cpe-5P	2837	4214	16,123
88	59-3237	2-dr Hol HT-5P	2958	4235	38,488
88	59-3267	2-dr Conv-5P	3286	4279	8,491
88	59-3219	4-dr Sed-5P	2902	4281	70,995
88	59-3239	4-dr Hol HT-5P	3036	4231	48,707
88	59-3235	4-dr Sta Wag-6P	3365	4619	11,298

NOTE 1: All 1959 Oldsmobile station wagons are called Fiestas.
NOTE 2: All 1959 Oldsmobile hardtops are called Holidays.

SUPER EIGHTY-EIGHT — The middle series of Oldsmobile was again the Super Eighty-Eight group which offered five body styles for 1959. Standard equipment included all items from the Dynamic Eighty-Eight series, plus: rocker panel moldings, special emblems, parking brake signal light, sponge vinyl headliner and deep twist carpeting. Upholstery was in a variety of colored leather, morocceen or cloth. Standard tire size was 9.00 x 14 inches.

1959 Oldsmobile, four-door Super 88 Holiday sedan, V-8 (DC)

SUPER EIGHTY-EIGHT

Model Number	Body/Style Number	Body Type & Seating	Factory Price	Shipping Weight	Production Total
S-88	59-3537	2-dr Hol HT-5P	3328	4260	20,259
S-88	59-3519	4-dr Sed-5P	3178	4280	37,024
S-88	59-3539	4-dr Hol HT-5P	3405	4274	38,467
S-88	59-3567	2-dr Conv-5P	3595	4340	4,895
S-88	59-3535	4-dr Sta Wag-6P	3669	4470	7,015

1959 Oldsmobile, two-door Ninety-Eight convertible, V-8

NINETY-EIGHT — Olds stayed with its successful top series format by offering a limited number of body styles (four) on an exclusive (126.3 inch) wheelbase. A Ninety-Eight buyer continued to buy a well-equipped vehicle, even with just the basic equipment. All items standard on the Super Eighty-Eight were found on the Ninety-Eight, as well as: special emblems and moldings; electric clock; wheel trim moldings; power steering; power brakes; and Jetaway Hydra-Matic Drive. Interiors were selected from either leather, morocceen or cloth in different colors. Standard tire size was 9.00 x 14 inches.

NINETY-EIGHT

Model Number	Body/Style Number	Body Type & Seating	Factory Price	Shipping Weight	Production Total
98	59-3837	2-dr Hol HT-5P	4086	4505	13,699
98	59-3867	2-dr Conv-5P	4366	4545	7,514
98	59-3819	4-dr Sed-5P	3890	4530	23,106
98	59-3839	4-dr Hol HT-5P	4163	4538	36,813

BASE ENGINES

(DYNAMIC 88 SERIES) Cast iron overhead valve V-8 engine. Bore and stroke: 4 x 3-11/16 inches. Displacement: 371 cid. Hydraulic lifters. Compression ratio: 9.75:1. Torque: 390 pound feet. Brake hp: 270 at 4600 rpm. Carburetor: Rochester 2GC "Econ-o-way" two-barrel.

(SUPER 88/98 SERIES) Cast iron overhead valve V-8. Bore and stroke: 4-1/8 x 3-11/16 inches. Displacement: 394 cid. Hydraulic valve lifters. Compression ratio: 9.75:1. Torque: 435 pound feet. Brake hp: 315 at 4600 rpm. Carburetor: Rochester 4GC Quadra-Jet.

CHASSIS FEATURES: Wheelbase: (Dynamic Eighty-Eight and Super Eighty-Eight) 123 inches; (Ninety-Eight) 126.3 inches. Overall length: (Dynamic Eighty-Eight and Super Eighty-Eight) 218.4 inches; (Ninety-Eight) 223 inches. Front tread: 61 inches. Rear tread: 61 inches.

OPTIONS: Power steering ($107). Power brakes ($43). Power windows ($107). Six-Way power seat ($102). Heater/defroster ($101). Deluxe radio ($129). Air conditioning ($430). Deluxe horns. Tinted glass. Electric clock. Autronic eye. Deluxe wheel discs. All 1959 Oldsmobiles were powered by Rocket V-8 engines. The Dynamic Eighty-Eight models were powered by a 371 cid version, the other two series with a slightly larger bore 394 cid motor. The Quadra-Jet carburetor was standard on 394 cid motors, optional on 371 cid engines. Dual exhausts and heavy-duty air cleaner were optional on cars not fitted with that equipment standard. The Jetaway Hydra-Matic was standard on all Ninety-Eight models, optional on all other series. Another drive train option was an anti-spin differential.

HISTORICAL FOOTNOTES: The 1959 Oldsmobiles were introduced Oct. 3, 1958. Model year production peaked at 382,865 units or a 6.9 percent share of market. Calendar year production of 366,305 cars were recorded. J.F. Wolfram was the chief executive officer of the company again this year. The sleek, flat-roofed Holiday four-door hardtop styles were the company's second most popular offering. A total of 116,064 four-door Oldsmobiles were built. Two-door hardtops (Holidays) accounted for 65,926 production units or 18 percent of total output. Six percent of all 1959 Oldsmobiles were convertibles. Rare options and their installation rates included air suspension (0.5 percent); limited slip differential (5.2 percent), dual exhausts (5.3 percent) and air conditioning (1 5.2 percent). Running without open factory support, Lee Petty drove a 1959 Oldsmobile two-door hardtop to a photo finish in the first Daytona 500-Mile stock car race.

1960 OLDSMOBILE

DYNAMIC EIGHTY-EIGHT — This marked the final year Oldsmobile would stay with its traditional three series format: a pair of Eighty-Eights and a Ninety-Eight. The Dynamic Eighty-Eight, with its seven models, was again the bottom-of-the-line Olds. Standard equipment for the series included: safety-vee steering wheel; turn signals; air scoop brakes; electric windshield wipers; Safety-spectrum speedometer and carpets with rubber inserts. Upholstery choices included cloth, morocceen or leather in an assortment of colors. Standard tire size was 8.50 x 14 inches.

1960 Oldsmobile, four-door Dynamic 88 sedan, V-8

OLDSMOBILE I.D. NUMBERS: Serial number located on left front door pillar on right side of cowl; on cowl under hood; on flange on left frame, just ahead of cowl; on metal plate on top of left front end of frame; on engine number plate. Motor number on block above water pump; and on plate on floor inside right door; on left corner of block above generator; and on front of left cylinder head at negative battery terminal. Oldsmobile 88 numbers took the form 607( )1001 to 607( )ending number. Olds Super 88 numbers took the form 608( )1001 to 608( )ending number. The Oldsmobile 98 numbers took the form 609( )1001 to 609( )ending number. First two symbols indicate model year: 60=1960. Third symbol indicates series: 7=88; 8=Super 88; 9=98. Fourth symbol in ( ) indicated assembly plant as follows: A=Atlanta; B=Boston (Framingham); K=Kansas City; M=Michigan (Lansing); L=Linden (New Jersey); C=California (Los Angeles/Southgate); T=Texas (Arlington); and W=Wilmington, Del. Remaining symbols were the unit's sequential production number. Starting number at each assembly plant was 1001 took the above format. Ending numbers, by series, at each coded plant not available. Motor numbers were C00-1001 or H00-1001 for the 371 cid V-8 and D00-1001 for the 394 cid V-8. Motor numbers were for engineering purposes only and no longer useful for identification.

DYNAMIC EIGHTY-EIGHT

Model Number	Body/Style Number	Body Type & Seating	Factory Price	Shipping Weight	Production Total
88	60-3211	2-dr Sed-5P	2835	4052	13,545
88	60-3237	2-dr Hol HT-5P	2956	4061	29,368
88	60-3219	4-dr Sed-5P	2900	4109	76,377
88	60-3239	4-dr Hol HT-5P	3034	4067	43,761
88	60-3267	2-dr Conv-5P	3284	4184	12,271
88	60-3235	4-dr Sta Wag-5P	3363	4278	8,834
88	60-3245	4-dr Sta Wag-7P	3471	4299	5,708

1960 Oldsmobile, two-door Super 88 Sceni-Coupe, V-8 (AA)

SUPER EIGHTY-EIGHT — The middle of the line Olds series again shared the wheelbase of the Dynamic Eighty-Eight with the more powerful engine from the Ninety-Eight series. Standard equipment included all items from the Dynamic Eighty-Eighty plus: padded dash, courtesy lamps, wheel trim rings, Star-lite headliner, two-speed windshield wipers and chrome roof side moldings. Interiors were done in either cloth, leather and morocceen. Standard tire size was 8.50 x 14 inches.

SUPER EIGHTY-EIGHT

Model Number	Body/Style Number	Body Type & Seating	Factory Price	Shipping Weight	Production Total
S-88	60-3537	2-dr Hol HT-5P	3325	4080	16,464
S-88	60-3519	4-dr Sed-5P	3176	4128	35,094
S-88	60-3539	4-dr Hol HT-5P	3402	4086	33,285
S-88	60-3567	2-dr Conv-5P	3592	4203	5,830
S-88	60-3535	4-dr Sta Wag-5P	3665	4298	3,765
S-88	60-3545	4-dr Sta Wag-7P	3773	4306	3,475

1960 Oldsmobile, two-door Ninety-Eight convertible, (IMS)

NINETY-EIGHT — Once again the top of the line Oldsmobile series was the Ninety-Eight, a physically larger and better-fitted car than either of the Eighty-Eights. Standard equipment included all items from the Super Eighty-Eight series, plus: Jetaway Hydra-Matic transmission; power steering; power brakes, windshield washers, electric clock and deep twist carpeting. Upholstery selections came from either fabric, leather or morocceen in a variety of colors. Tire size for the Ninety-Eight was 9.00 x 14 inches.

NINETY-EIGHT

Model Number	Body/Style Number	Body Type & Seating	Factory Price	Shipping Weight	Production Total
98	60-3837	2-dr Hol HT-5P	4083	4312	7,635
98	60-3819	4-dr Sed-5P	3887	4353	17,188
98	60-3839	4-dr Hol HT-5P	4159	4364	27,257
98	60-3867	2-dr Conv-5P	4362	4412	7,284

BASE ENGINES

(DYNAMIC 88 SERIES) Cast iron overhead valve V-8 engine. Bore and stroke: 4 x 3-11/16 inches. Displacement: 371 cid. Hydraulic valve lifters. Compression ratio: 8.75:1. Torque 375 pound feet at 2400 rpm. Brake hp: 240 at 4600 rpm. Carburetor: Two-barrel Econ-o-way Rochester Model 2GC.

(SUPER 88/98) Cast iron overhead valve V-8 engine. Bore and stroke: 4-1/8 x 3-11/16 inches. Displacement: 394 cid. Hydraulic valve lifters. Compression ratio: 9.75:1. Torque: 435 pound feet at 2800 rpm. Brake hp: 315 at 4600 rpm. Carburetor: Multi-jet Rochester 4GC four-barrel.

CHASSIS FEATURES: Wheelbase: (Dynamic Eighty-Eight and Super Eighty-Eight) 123 inches; (Ninety-Eight) 126.3 inches. Overall length: (Dynamic Eighty-Eight and Super Eighty-Eight) 217.6 inches; (Ninety-Eight) 220.9 inches. Front tread: 61 inches. Rear tread: 61 inches.

OPTIONS: Heater/defroster ($97). Power steering ($107). Deluxe radio ($88). Electric antenna ($23). Deluxe radio ($124). Back-up lamps ($9). Parking brake signal lamp ($4). Windshield washer ($11). Deluxe tri-tone horns ($11). Padded dash ($15). Power brakes ($43). Electric clock ($19). Outside rearview mirror ($4). Power windows ($106). Power seat ($68). Fiesta luggage carrier ($98). Dual exhausts ($26). Heavy-duty air cleaner/breather system ($5). Jetaway Hydra-Matic Drive, optional 88s only ($231). Anti-Spin differential ($47).

HISTORICAL FOOTNOTES: The 1960 Oldsmobiles were introduced Oct. 1, 1959. Model year production peaked at 347,141 units. Calendar year sales of 363,300 cars were recorded. J.F. Wolfram was the chief executive officer of the company again this year. The calendar year sales figure given above includes 19,800 assemblies of the F-85, built late in the 1960

calendar year. Installation rates on rare options included: Dual exhausts (3.1 percent); limited slip differential (5.3 percent); air conditioning (18.8 percent); power seats (19 percent) and power windows (18 percent).

1961 OLDSMOBILE

1961 Oldsmobile, four-door F-85 sedan, V-8 (DC)

F-85 — For the first time Oldsmobile broke with their three series format in 1961. On the bottom of the Oldsmobile lineup was the all new F-85 compact series. Smaller than any other postwar Oldsmobile, the F-85 was powered by a unique aluminum 215 cid V-8. It joined small-car offerings from Buick and Pontiac, but was the only one to use a V-8 as regular equipment. Standard equipment on the series included foam-cushioned front seat; front armrests; dual sun visors; turn signals; stabilizer bar and self-energizing brakes. Cloth or vinyl trimmed interiors were offered. Standard tire size was 6.59 x 11 inches. The F-85 was built in the Lansing and Southgate assembly plants.

OLDSMOBILE I.D. NUMBERS: Serial number located on left front door pillar on right side of cowl; on cowl under hood; on flange on left frame, just ahead of cowl; on metal plate on top of left front end of frame; on engine number plate. Motor number on block above water pump; and on plate on floor inside right door; on left corner of block above generator; and on front of left cylinder head at negative battery terminal. Olds F-85 numbers took the form 610( )01001 and up. Oldsmobile 88 numbers took the form 612( )01001 and up. Olds Super 88 numbers took the form 615( )01001 and up. Olds Starfire numbers took the form 616( )01001 and up (611( )01001 for Deluxe F-85). Oldsmobile 98 numbers took the form 618( )01001 and up. First two symbols indicate model year: 61=1961. Starting this year, the third symbol indicating series is the same as the second digit of the Body/Style Numbers in the second column of the charts below (i.e., 0=F-85; 2=88, etc.). Fourth symbol in ( ) indicated assembly plant as follows: A=Atlanta; K=Kansas City; M=Michigan (Lansing); L=Linden (New Jersey); C=California (Los Angeles/Southgate); T=Texas (Arlington); and W=Wilmington, Del. Remaining symbols were the unit's sequential production number. Starting number at each assembly plant was 1001 took the above format. Ending numbers, by series, at each coded plant not available. Motor numbers started with a prefix indicating displacement: S001001 for 215 cid V-8; F001001 for 394 cid /250 hp V-8; G001001 for 394 cid/325 hp V-8 and D001001 for 394 cid/330 hp Starfire V-8. Engine numbers were for engineering purposes only and not designed to aid in vehicle identification.Hydra-Matic Drive was standard equipment on the Ninety-Eights and a $231 option on the Eighty-Eights. Option S-1 was $47 anti-spin differential.

F-85 SERIES

Model Number	Body/Style Number	Body Type & Seating	Factory Price	Shipping Weight	Production Total
85	61-3027	2-dr Cpe-5P	2502	2712	2,336
85	61-3019	4-dr Sed-5P	2384	2666	19,192
85	61-3035	4-dr Sta Wag-5P	2654	2742	6,677
85	61-3045	4-dr Sta Wag-7P	2694	2816	10,087

DELUXE

Model Number	Body/Style Number	Body Type & Seating	Factory Price	Shipping Weight	Production Total
85	61-3119	4-dr Sed-5P	2519	2798	26,311
85	61-3135	4-dr Sta Wag-5P	2789	2815	526
85	61-3117	2-dr Cut Spt Cpe-4P	2753	2712	9935
85	61-3145	4-dr Sta Wag-7P	3091	2837	757

1961 Oldsmobile, two-door Dynamic 88 hardtop sport coupe, V-8

DYNAMIC EIGHTY-EIGHT — With the addition of the compact F-85 car line the Dynamic Eighty-Eight series was moved up a notch. This remained Oldsmobile's most diverse series with seven models offered. Standard series equipment included: padded dash, Safety spectrum speedometer, floating propeller shaft and air scoop brakes. Interiors were done in either vinyl or cloth. Standard tire size was 8.00 x 14 inches.

DYNAMIC EIGHTY-EIGHT SERIES

Model Number	Body/Style Number	Body Type & Seating	Factory Price	Shipping Weight	Production Total
D88	61-3211	2-dr Sed-5P	2835	4152	4,920
D88	61-3237	2-dr Hol HT-5P	2956	3969	19,878
D88	61-3269	4-dr Sed-5P	2900	4024	42,584
D88	51-3239	4-dr Hol HT-5P	3034	4037	51,562
D88	61-3267	2-dr Conv-5P	3284	4244	9,049
D88	61-3235	4-dr Sta Wag-5P	3663	4317	5,374
D88	61-3245	4-dr Sta Wag-7P	3471	4334	4,013

1961 Oldsmobile, four-door Super 88 station wagon, V-8 (DC)

SUPER EIGHTY-EIGHT — For full-size buyers the Super Eighty-Eight models continued to be popular with the smaller body design shared with the Dynamic Eighty-Eights and the more powerful engine from the Classic Ninety-Eight series. Series standard equipment included all items from the Dynamic Eighty-Eight group plus: two-speed windshield wipers, Safety-Vee steering wheel, parking brake signal lamp, courtesy lamps and oil filter. Upholstery could be selected from a variety of colored vinyls and fabrics. Standard tire size was 8.00 x 14 inches.

SUPER EIGHTY-EIGHT

Model Number	Body/Style Number	Body Type & Seating	Factory Price	Shipping Weight	Production Total
S88	61-3537	2-dr Hol HT-5P	3325	4003	7,009
S88	61-3569	4-dr Sed-5P	3176	4063	15,328
S88	61-3539	4-dr Hol HT-5P	3402	4092	23,272
S88	61-3567	2-dr Conv-5P	3592	4275	2,624
S88	61-3535	4-dr Sta Wag-5P	3665	4357	2,761
S88	61-3545	4-dr Sta Wag-7P	3773	4378	2,170

1961 Oldsmobile, two-door Starfire convertible, V-8

STARFIRE — Oldsmobile bolstered its top line coverage of the market with an offering in the personal luxury category — the Starfire. This model was late coming to the Olds lineup. It was not available until Jan. 1, 1961. It came as a convertible, sharing its wheelbase with the Eighty-Eights, and was powered by a slightly more powerful motor than other 1961 Rocket powered Oldsmobiles. Standard equipment included all items from the Super Eighty-Eight group plus: brushed aluminum side panels, console, tachometer, power seats and a special dual exhaust system. Upholstery was done in leather. Standard tire size was 8.50 x 14 inches. Starfires were built only in Lansing.

STARFIRE

Model Number	Body/Style Number	Body Type & Seating	Factory Price	Shipping Weight	Production Total
ST	61-3667	2-dr Starfire Conv-5P	4647	4305	7,800

CLASSIC NINETY-EIGHT — The Olds top-of-the-line series was the old Ninety-Eight group, this year with the misnomer Classic as a prefix. Buyers found five body styles to chose from and the all new Starfires must have cut a bit into Ninety-Eight sales. Standard equipment included all items from the Super Eighty-Eight group plus: windshield washer, electric clock, Hydra-Matic transmission, power steering and power brakes. Upholstery came in a variety of colored vinyl, cloth and leather. Standard tire size was 8.50 x 14 inches.

CLASSIC NINETY-EIGHT SERIES

Model Number	Body/Style Number	Body Type & Seating	Factory Price	Shipping Weight	Production Total
98	61-3837	2-dr Hol HT-5P	4072	4156	4,445
98	61-3819	4-dr Twn Sed-5P	3887	4208	9,087
98	61-3839	4-dr Spt Sed-5P	4083	4187	12,343
98	61-3829	4-dr Hol HT-5P	4021	4179	13,331
98	61-3867	2-dr Conv-5P	4363	4224	3,804

BASE ENGINES

(F-85 SERIES) Aluminum block. Overhead valve. Liquid cooled V-8 engine. Bore and stroke: 3.5 x 2.8 inches. Displacement: 215 cid. Hydraulic valve lifters. Compression ratio: 8.75 to 1. Torque: 210 pound feet at 3200 rpm. Brake hp: 155 at 3200 rpm. Carburetor: two-barrel, Rochester 2GC.

(DYNAMIC 88 SERIES) Cast iron. Overhead valve. V-8. Bore and stroke: 4-1/8 x 3-11/16 inches. Displacement: 394 cid. Hydraulic valve lifters. Compression ratio: 8.75:1. Torque: 405 pound feet at 2400 rpm. Brake hp: 250 at 4400 rpm. Carburetor: Econ-o-way Rochester Model 2GC.

(SUPER 88/98) Cast iron, overhead valve, V-8 engine. Bore and stroke: 4-1/8 x 3-11/16 inches. Displacement: 394 cid. Hydraulic valve lifters. Compression ratio: 10 to 1. Brake hp: 325 at 4600 rpm. Torque: 435 pound feet at 2800 rpm. Carburetor: Rochester four-barrel 4GC.

(STARFIRE SERIES) Overhead valves. Cast iron V-8 engine. Bore and stroke: 4-1/8 x 3-11/16 inches. Displacement: 394 cid. Hydraulic valve lifters. Compression ratio: 10.25:1. Brake hp: 330 at 4600 rpm. Torque: 440 pound feet at 2800 rpm. Carburetor: four-barrel Rochester 4GC.

CHASSIS FEATURES: Wheelbase: (F-85) 112 inches; (Dynamic Eighty-Eight, Super Eighty-Eight and Starfire) 123 inches; (Classic Ninety-Eight) 126 inches. Overall length: (F-85) 188.2 inches; (Dynamic Eighty-Eight, Super Eighty-Eight and Starfire) 212 inches; (Classic Ninety-Eight) 218 inches. Front tread: (F-85) 56 inches; (all others) 61 inches. Rear tread: (F-85) 56 inches; (all others) 61 inches.

OPTIONS: [F-85] Heater/defroster ($74). Power steering ($86). Deluxe radio ($65). Back-up lights ($7). Windshield washer ($11). Padded dash ($12). Electric clock ($16). Air conditioning ($378). Outside mirror ($4). All F-85s were powered by the aluminum block "Rockette" V-8 engine. A power pack option consisted of high-compression heads, four-barrel carburetor and dual exhausts. It boosted horsepower by 30 to 185. Other engine options were heavy-duty air cleaner, full-flow oil filter and positive crankcase ventilation system. All F-85s came standard with a three-speed manual transmission with Hydra-Matic a popular $189 option. [OLDSMOBILE] Heater/defroster ($97). Rear window defroster ($21). Power steering ($107). Deluxe radio ($88). Electric antenna ($23). Super Deluxe signal seeking radio ($124). Back-up lights ($9). Courtesy lamps ($5). Windshield washer ($12). Padded dash ($12). Power brakes ($43). Electric clock ($19). Air conditioning ($430). Power windows ($106). Fiesta luggage carrier ($98). All full-sized Oldsmobiles were powered by one of the three versions of the 394 cid Rocket V-8. The 250 hp version was standard equipment on Dynamic Eighty-Eights. The 325 hp motor was standard on Classic Ninety-Eights and Super Eighty-Eights, optional on Dynamic Eighty-Eights. A 330 hp V-8 was exclusive to the Starfire series. Other engine options included dual exhausts, heavy-duty oil filter and positive crankcase ventilation system. Hydra-Matic was standard on all Classic Ninety-Eights, optional on all other models for $231. Option S-1 was the $47 anti-spin differential.

HISTORICAL FOOTNOTES: The full-sized Oldsmobiles were introduced Oct. 6, 1960 and the F-85 appeared in dealer showrooms the same day. Model year production peaked at 242,323 Oldsmobiles and 76,446 F-85s. Calendar year sales of 321,838 cars were recorded. J.F. Wolfram was the chief executive officer of the company this year.

1962 OLDSMOBILE

F-85 — Oldsmobile expanded its small-sized series in 1962 with the F-85 moving into its second year. In a bold marketing stroke, a Cutlass convertible and coupe were added, along with several Deluxe versions. In an effort to get back into the high-performance mainstream a special turbocharged Jetfire coupe was available. Standard Series equipment included: heater; defroster; coil springs; foam cushion seats and three-speed synchromesh transmission. Upholstery was available in several types of cloth and vinyl. Standard tire size was 6.50 x 13 inches.

1962 Oldsmobile, two-door Cutlass F-85 convertible, V-8

OLDSMOBILE I.D. NUMBERS: Serial number located on left front door pillar on right side of cowl; on cowl under hood; on flange on left frame, just ahead of cowl; on metal plate on top of left front end of frame; on engine number plate. Motor number on block above water pump; and on plate on floor inside right door; on left corner of block above generator; and on front of left cylinder head at negative battery terminal. Olds F-85 numbers took the form 620( )01001 and up. Olds F-85 Deluxe numbers took the form 621( )010001 and up. Oldsmobile 88 numbers took the form 622( )01001 and up. Olds Super 88 numbers took the form 625( )01001 and up. Olds Starfire numbers took the form 626( )01001 and up. Oldsmobile 98 numbers took the form 628( )01001 and up. First two symbols indicate model year: 62=1962. Third symbol indicating series is the same as the second digit of the Body/Style

Numbers in the second column of the charts below (i.e., 0=F-85; 1=F-85 Deluxe, etc.). Fourth symbol in ( ) indicated assembly plant as follows: A=Atlanta; K=Kansas City; M=Michigan (Lansing); L=Linden (New Jersey); C=California (Los Angeles/Southgate); T=Texas (Arlington); and W=Wilmington, Del. Remaining symbols were the unit's sequential production number. Starting number at each assembly plant was 1001. Ending numbers, by series, at each coded plant not available. Motor numbers started with a prefix indicating displacement: S=215 cid/155 hp V-8; SG=215 cid/185 hp V-8; ST=215 cid/215 hp Jetfire V-8; F=394 cid/280 hp V-8; FL=394 cid/260 hp V-8; G=394 cid/330 hp V-8; GS=394 cid/345 hp V-8. (Notes: Engines with G as second letter of code are high-compression. Engines with E or H as second letter behind the above symbols are low-compression versions for export. Engine numbers for each type started at 1001001 and up and were for engineering purposes only.)

F-85 SERIES

STANDARD

Model Number	Body/Style Number	Body Type & Seating	Factory Price	Shipping Weight	Production Total
F-85	3027	2-dr Clb Cpe-5P	2403	2691	7,909
F-85	3019	4-dr Sed-5P	2457	2719	8,074
F-85	3067	2-dr Conv-5P	2760	2780	3,660
F-85	3035	4-dr Sta Wag-6P	2754	2805	3,204
F-85	3045	4-dr Sta Wag-9p	2835	2820	1,887

DELUXE

Model Number	Body/Style Number	Body Type & Seating	Factory Price	Shipping Weight	Production Total
F-85	3117	2-dr Cpe-5P	2694	2698	32,461
F-85	3119	4-dr Sed-5P	2592	2725	18,736
F-85	3167	2-dr Conv-5P	2971	2785	9,898
F-85	3135	4-dr Sta Wag-5P	2889	2815	4,974

JETFIRE TURBOCHARGED

Model Number	Body/Style Number	Body Type & Seating	Factory Price	Shipping Weight	Production Total
F-85	3147	2-dr Spt Cpe-5P	3045	2744	3,765

DYNAMIC EIGHTY-EIGHT — Restyling came to the Eighty-Eights this year with the Dynamic series offering the largest model selection found in the full-size Oldsmobiles. Standard equipment on the series included: padded dash; guard beam frame; live rubber body cushions; coil springs; and foam rubber seats. Interiors were done in a variety of colored fabric and cloth. Standard tire size was 8.00 x 14 inches.

DYNAMIC EIGHTY-EIGHT

Model Number	Body/Style Number	Body Type & Seating	Factory Price	Shipping Weight	Production Total
D-88	3247	2-dr Hol HT Cpe-6P	3054	4165	39,676
D-88	3269	4-dr Sed-6P	2997	4179	68,467
D-88	3239	4-dr Hol HT Sed-6P	3131	4173	53,438
D-88	3235	4-dr Sta Wag-6P	3460	4305	8,527
D-88	3245	4-dr Sta Wag-9P	3568	4325	6,417
D-88	3267	2-dr Conv-6P	3381	4255	12,212

NOTE 1: Oldsmobile station wagons are called Fiestas.

1962 Oldsmobile, four-door Super 88 sedan, V-8 (DC)

SUPER EIGHTY-EIGHT — The fancier of the two Eighty-Eight series was the Super Eighty-Eight. It shared its 123 inch wheelbase with the Dynamic Eighty-Eight and Starfire models and used the same power plant as the Ninety-Eight series cars. Standard equipment included all items from the Dynamic Eighty-Eight series, plus: two-speed windshield wipers; parking brake signal lamps; courtesy lamp package; and special moldings. Upholstery selection was from a variety of colored fabrics, vinyls and leathers. Standard tire size was 8.00 x 14 inches.

SUPER EIGHTY-EIGHT

Model Number	Body/Style Number	Body Type & Seating	Factory Price	Shipping Weight	Production Total
S88	3547	2-dr Hol HT-6P	3422	4182	9,010
S88	3569	4-dr Sed-6P	3273	4199	24,125
S88	3539	4-dr Hol HT-6P	3499	4197	21,175
S88	3535	4-dr Sta Wag-6P	3763	4312	3,837

1962 Oldsmobile, two-door Starfire hardtop sport coupe, V-8

STARFIRE — After a midyear introduction in 1961, a second Starfire model, the two-door hardtop coupe, joined the convertible. This was Oldsmobile's attempt to grab a greater share of the personal/luxury car market. The Starfire was a well-equipped model. In standard trim it included all items standard on the Super Eighty-Eight, plus sports console; tachometer; Hydra-Matic drive with console shifter; power brakes; power steering; brushed aluminum side trim; and dual exhausts with fiberglass packed mufflers. Leather upholstery was fitted. Standard tire size was 8.00 x 14 inches.

STARFIRE

Model Number	Body/Style Number	Body Type & Seating	Factory Price	Shipping Weight	Production Total
SF	62-3647	2-dr Hol HT-5P	4131	4335	34,839
SF	62-3667	2-dr Conv-5P	4744	4488	7,149

NINETY-EIGHT — The largest Oldsmobiles for 1962 were the Ninety-Eights. A five model lineup was available. It had three four-doors and open and closed two-door. Cars in this series were well-appointed with all equipment from the Super Eighty-Eight series, plus Hydra-Matic transmission; power brakes; power steering; power windows; and power seat. Interiors could be ordered in leather, vinyl or cloth in a variety of colors. Standard tire size was 8.50 x 14 inches.

NINETY-EIGHT

Model Number	Body/Style Number	Body Type & Seating	Factory Price	Shipping Weight	Production Total
98	62-3847	2-dr Hol HT-5P	4180	4375	7,546
98	62-3819	4-dr Twn Sed-5P	3984	4392	12,167
98	62-3839	4-dr Spts Sed-5P	4256	4384	33,095
98	62-3829	4-dr Sed-5P	4118	4399	7,653
98	62-3867	2-dr Conv-5P	4459	4488	3,693

BASE ENGINES

(F-85 SERIES) Aluminum block, overhead valve, liquid-cooled V-8 engine. Bore and stroke: 3.5 x 2.8 inches. Displacement: 215 cid. Hydraulic valve lifters. Compression ratio: (F85) 8.75:1; (Cutlass and Jetfire) 10.25:1. Torque (F-85) 210 pounds-feet at 4800 rpm.; (Cutlass) 230 pounds-feet at 4800 rpm.; (Jetfire) 300 pounds-feet at 3200 rpm. Brake hp: (F-85) 155 at 4800 rpm.; (Cutlass) 185 at 4800 rpm.; (Jetfire) 215 at 4800 rpm. Carburetor: (F-85) Rochester 2GC; (Cutlass) Rochester 4GC; (Jetfire) Turbocharged and fluid-injected.

(DYNAMIC 88 SERIES) Cast iron, overhead valve, V-8 engine. Bore and stroke: 4-1/8 x 3-11/16 inches. Displacement: 394 cid. Hydraulic valve lifters. Compression ratio: 10.25:1. Torque: 430 pound feet at 2400 rpm. Brake hp: 280 at 4400 rpm. Carburetor: Econ-o-way Rochester 2GC.

(SUPER 88/98 SERIES) Cast iron, overhead valve, V-8 engine. Bore and stroke: 4-1/8 x 3-11/16 inches. Displacement: 394 cid. Hydraulic valve lifters. Compression ratio: 10.25:1. Brake hp: 330 at 4600 rpm. Torque: 440 pound feet at 2800 rpm. Carburetor: Rochester 4GC four-barrel.

(STARFIRE SERIES) Cast iron block, overhead valve, V-8 engine. Bore and stroke: 4-1/8 x 3-11/16 inches. Displacement: 394 cid. Hydraulic valve lifters. Compression ratio: 10.50:1. Torque: 440 pound feet at 3200 rpm. Brake hp: 345 at 4600 rpm. Carburetor: Rochester 4GC four-barrel.

CHASSIS FEATURES: Wheelbase: (F-85) 112 inches; (Dynamic Eighty-Eight, Super Eighty-Eight and Starfire) 123 inches; (Ninety-Eight) 126 inches. Overall length: (F-85) 188.2 inches; (Dynamic Eighty-Eight, Super Eighty-Eight and Starfire) 213.9 inches; (Ninety-Eight) 220 inches. Front tread: (F-85) 56 inches; (All others) 61 inches. Rear tread: (F-85) 56 inches; (All others) 61 inches.

OPTIONS: [F-85]: Power steering ($89). Deluxe radio ($65). Back-up lights ($7). Windshield washer ($12). Padded dash ($13). Electric clock ($15). Air conditioning ($385). Outside mirror ($5). All F-85s were powered by the aluminum block "Rockette" V-8 engine. This engine produced 155 hp in standard form and 185 hp in the higher powered option version. A 215 hp turbocharged, liquid injected V-8 was exclusive to the Jetfire. Standard transmission was a manual three-speed with Hydra-Matic optional on all models.[OLDSMOBILE] Rear window defroster ($22). Power steering ($109). Deluxe radio ($91). Electric antenna ($23). Super Deluxe signal seeking radio ($126). Back-up lights ($10). Courtesy lamps ($5). Windshield washer ($13). Power brakes ($44). Electric clock ($20). Air conditioning ($435). Power windows ($108). All full-sized Oldsmobiles were powered by one of four versions of the 394 cid Rocket V-8. The base Dynamic Eighty-Eight motor was a 280 hp V-8 with a 260 hp, lower compression ratio V-8 as a no cost option. Standard powerplant on the Super Eighty-Eight and Ninety-Eight was the 330 hp V-8 and this motor was optional on the Dynamic Eighty-Eight. A 345 hp V-8 was standard on the Starfire Series cars and optional on the Super Eighty-Eight and Ninety-Eight models.

HISTORICAL FOOTNOTES: The full-sized Oldsmobiles were introduced Sept. 22, 1961 and the F-85 models appeared in dealer showrooms at the same time. Model year production peaked at 447,594 units. Calendar year sales of 458,359 cars were recorded. J.F. Wolfram was the chief executive officer of the company this year. The turbocharged F-85 Jetfire was announced in April, 1962. Oldsmobile claimed this to be the first car in the U.S. industry to offer one horsepower per cubic inch. Interestingly, Chrysler had made the same claim for its 1956 300-B and Chevrolet for its fuel-injected 1957 V-8. The Jetfire, however, was the first car to classify as both a regular production model and a one-to-one ratio car. For the 1962 model year, only 4.7 percent of all full-sized Oldsmobiles had power tailgate windows; 11.9 percent

had bucket seats; 13.1 percent had dual exhausts and 7.8 percent had limited-slip rear axles. For F-85s, 2.1 percent had power windows; 2.6 percent had power brakes; 2.4 percent four-speed manual gear boxes and 48.8 percent bucket seats.

1963 OLDSMOBILE

F-85 — After standing pat for two years with its styling, a slight restyle was in order for the compact F-85 Series this year. Three standard models; two Deluxes; two Cutlass models and the turbocharged Jetfire coupe comprised this automotive group. Standard F-85 items included: aluminized muffler; self-adjusting brakes; tubeless tires; front stabilizer bar; fiberglass hood insulation; and cigarette lighter. Deluxe equipment included standard items, plus carpets; front and rear foam seat cushions; special chrome moldings; rocker panel moldings; and Deluxe steering wheel. F-85s were made in the Lansing, Kansas City and Southgate assembly plants.

1963 Oldsmobile, Jetfire two-door hardtop sport coupe, V-8

OLDSMOBILE I.D. NUMBERS: VIN located on left front door pillar. Engine unit number on left cylinder head. Serial number takes the form of four symbols, plus sequential production number. First two symbols identify year: 63=1963. Third symbol indicates series and matches second digit in Body/Style Number column of charts below. Fourth symbol indicates assembly plant: T=Texas (Arlington); A=Atlanta, Ga.; B=Boston (Framingham), Mass.; K=Kansas City, Kan.; M=Michigan (Lansing); L=Linden, N.J.; C=California (Southgate); W=Wilmington, Del. Remaining symbols are the sequential production number starting at 001001 at each factory. Ending VINs not available. Engine numbers consist of a alphabetical prefix and a production sequence number starting at 200001 for F-85 and 001001 for all other models. Prefixes for 1963 engines were: [215 cid V-8] S=155 hp, SE=export, SG=195 hp or 185 hp; SH=export; ST=215 hp turbocharged. [394 cid Dynamic 88 V-8] H=280 hp; HE=export; HL=260 hp; J=330 hp; JE=export; JS=345 hp. Ending engine numbers not available.

Model Number	Body/Style Number	Body Type & Seating	Factory Price	Shipping Weight	Production Total
STANDARD LINE					
F-85	3019	4-dr Sed-6P	2512	2747	8,937
F-85	3027	2-dr Clb Cpe-6P	2403	2684	11,276
F-85	3035	4-dr Sta Wag-6P	2889	2814	3,348
DELUXE LINE					
F-85	3119	4-dr Sed-6P	2592	2767	29,269
F-85	3117	2-dr Cut Cpe-5P	2694	2704	41,343
F-85	3167	2-dr Cut Conv-5P	2971	2784	12,149
F-85	3135	4-dr Sta Wag-6P	2889	2846	6,647
JETFIRE LINE					
F-85	3147	2-dr HT Cpe-5P	3048	2884	5,842

1963 Oldsmobile, two-door Dynamic 88 convertible, V-8 (DC)

DYNAMIC EIGHTY-EIGHT — A mildly restyled series awaited buyers of the full-sized Oldsmobiles. Again on the lowest rung of the ladder was the Dynamic Eight-Eight series. A total of six different models were available. Standard series equipment included: die cast grille; deep pile carpeting; 21-gallon fuel tank; full-flow oil filter; foam seat cushions; and foot-operated parking brake. Upholstery was offered in a variety of vinyls, leather and cloth combinations. Standard tire size was 8.00 x 14 inches. Dynamic 88s were built in Lansing, Atlanta, Kansas City, Linden, Southgate, Wilmington and Arlington.

DYNAMIC EIGHTY-EIGHT

Model Number	Body/Style Number	Body Type & Seating	Factory Price	Shipping Weight	Production Total
D88	3247	2-dr Hol HT-6P	3052	4165	39,071
D88	3269	4-dr Sed-6P	2995	4184	68,611
D88	3239	4-dr Hol HT-6P	3130	4172	62,351
D88	3267	2-dr Conv-5P	3379	4240	12,551
D88	3235	4-dr Sta Wag-6P	3459	4280	9,615
D88	3245	4-dr Sta Wag-9P	3566	4292	7,116

SUPER EIGHTY-EIGHT — For this model just four body styles were available. Again, the smaller 123 inch wheelbase was shared with the Dynamic Eighty-Eight. However, the larger Sky Rocket engine from the Ninety-Eight series, was underhood. Standard equipment included all items from the Dynamic Eighty-Eight series, plus: two-speed windshield wipers; special molding package; Deluxe steering wheel; map light; heavy-duty air cleaner and courtesy lights. Interiors could be done in either cloth, vinyl or leather in a variety of colors. Standard tire size was 8.00 x 14 inches. Super Eighty-Eights were made at the Lansing, Kansas City, Atlanta, Linden, Southgate, Wilmington and Arlington assembly plants.

SUPER EIGHTY-EIGHT

Model Number	Body/Style Number	Body Type & Seating	Factory Price	Shipping Weight	Production Total
S88	3547	2-dr Hol HT-6P	3408	4184	8,930
S88	3569	4-dr Sed-6P	3246	4196	24,575
S88	3539	4-dr Hol HT-6P	3473	4202	25,387
S88	3535	4-dr Sta Wag-6P	3748	4314	3,878

STARFIRE — The Starfire was in its third year as a two-model series tucked between the Eighty-Eight and Ninety-Eight. Starfires were well-appointed automobiles. All items from the Super Eighty-Eight series were standard plus: windshield washer; Hydra-Matic Drive; dual exhausts: power steering; special wheelcovers; courtesy lights; electric clock and power brakes. Interiors were done in leather or vinyl in several colors. Standard tire size was 8.00 x 14 inch.

STARFIRE

Model Number	Body/Style Number	Body Type & Seating	Factory Price	Shipping Weight	Production Total
SF	3657	2-dr Hol HT-5P	4129	4349	21,489
SF	3667	2-dr Conv-5P	4742	4492	4,401

1963 Oldsmobile, four-door Ninety-Eight hardtop sedan, V-8

NINETY-EIGHT — Again the top of line Oldsmobiles came from the Ninety-Eight series which rode on an exclusive 126 inch wheelbase. In a rather unusual move the Ninety-Eight Custom Sports Coupe was the only car in the series offered with the Starfire engine. The Ninety-Eights continued to be a well-appointed car. Standard equipment included all items from the Super Eighty-Eight series, plus Hydra-Matic Drive, power brakes, power steering, special rocker panel moldings, self-regulating electric clock, dual rear seat cigarette lighters and special headliner. Interiors could be done in either cloth, leather or vinyl. Standard tire size was 8.50 x 14 inches. Ninety-Eights were made at Lansing, Kansas City, Linden, South Gate, and Wilmington.

NINETY-EIGHT

Model Number	Body/Style Number	Body Type & Seating	Factory Price	Shipping Weight	Production Total
98	3847	2-dr Hol HT-6P	4178	4390	4,984
98	3819	4-dr Twn Sed-6P	3982	4395	11,053
98	3829	4-dr Lux Sed-6P	4332	4411	19,252
98	3839	4-dr Hol HT-6P	4254	4396	23,330
98	3867	2-dr Conv-5P	4457	4465	4,267
98	3947	2-dr Cus Spt Cpe-5P	4381	4384	7,422

BASE ENGINES

(F-85 SERIES) Aluminum block. Overhead valve. Liquid-cooled V-8 engine. Bore and stroke: 3.5 x 2.8 inches. Displacement: 215 cid. Hydraulic valve lifters. Compression ratio (F85) 8.75 to 1; (Cutlass) 10.25 to 1; (Jetfire) 10.75 to 1. Torque (F-85) 210 pound feet; (Cutlass) 230 pound feet; (Jetfire) 300 pound feet. Brake hp: (F-85) 155; (Cutlass) 185; (Jetfire) 215. Carburetor: (F-85) two-barrel model 2GC; (Cutlass) four-barrel model 4GC; (Jetfire) Turbocharged, fluid-injected Model RC.

(88 SERIES) Cast iron block. Overhead valve. V-8. Bore and stroke: 4-1/8 x 3-11/16 inches. Displacement: 394 cid. Hydraulic valve lifters. Compression ratio: 10.25 to 1. Torque: 430 pound feet. Brake hp: 280. Carburetor: two-barrel Rochester 2 GC.

(SUPER 88/98 SERIES) Cast iron. Overhead valve. V-8. Bore and stroke: 4-1/8 x 3-11/16 inches. Displacement: 394 cid. Hydraulic valve lifters. Compression ratio: 10.25 to 1. Torque: 440 pound feet. Brake hp: 330. Carburetor Rochester four-barrel Model 4GC.

(98 CUSTOM/STARFIRE SERIES) Cast iron. Overhead valve. V-8. Bore and stroke: 4-1/8 x 3-11/16 inches. Displacement: 394 cid. Hydraulic valve lifters. Compression ratio: 10.50 to 1. Torque: 440 pound feet. Brake hp: 345. Carburetor Rochester four-barrel Model 4GC.

CHASSIS FEATURES: Wheelbase: (F-85) 112 inches, (Dynamic Eighty-Eight, Super Eighty-Eight and Starfire) 123 inches; (Ninety-Eight) 126 inches. Overall Length: (F-85) 192.2 inches; (Dynamic Eighty-Eight, Super Eighty-Eight and Starfire) 214.4 inches, (Ninety-Eight) 221.5 inches. Front tread: (F-85) 56 inches; (all others) 62.2 inches. Rear tread: (F-85) 56 inches; (all others) 61 inches.

OPTIONS: [F-85]: Tinted glass ($31). Electric windows. ($102). Seat belts. Power trunk release. Vinyl top. Air conditioning ($378). Remote control outside mirror. Power brakes. Power steering ($86). Back-up lights ($11). Electric clock ($19). Luggage carrier for station wagons ($65). All F-85's were powered by an aluminum block Rockette engine. This engine produced 155 hp in standard form, 185 hp in the optional Cutlass version. This was the last year for the 215 hp turbocharged, liquid-injected V-8 Jetfire coupe. All F-85s came standard with a three-speed manual transmission optional with either a four-speed manual unit or Hydra-Matic. [OLDSMOBILE] Tinted glass ($43). Electric windows ($106). Seat belts. Electric seats ($97). Vinyl roof. Windshield washer ($5). Air conditioning ($430). Remote control outside mirror. Power steering ($108). Tilt steering wheel. Back-up lights ($11). AM/FM radio ($124). Deluxe radio ($89). Super Deluxe signal seeking radio ($124). Electric antenna ($26). Bi-phonic radio speakers. All full-sized Oldsmobiles were powered by one of three versions of the 394 cubic V-8. Exclusive to the Dynamic Eighty-Eight series was the 280 hp Rocket V-8. Shared in the Super Eight-Eight and Ninety-Eight series was the 330 hp Sky Rocket engine. Exclusive to the Ninety-Eight Custom Sports Coupe and two Starfire models was the 345 hp Starfire motor. Other drivetrain options for full-sized cars included: G-80 anti-spin differential, G-90 mountain axle package; G-96 expressway axle package and VOI special engine cooling package. The Ninety-Eights and Starfires came with Hydra-Matic as standard equipment. All others were fitted with three-speed manual transmissions as standard equipment.

HISTORICAL FOOTNOTES: The full-sized Oldsmobiles were introduced Oct. 4, 1962 and the F-85 line appeared in dealer showrooms the same day. Model year production peaked at 476,753 units. Calendar year sales of 504,555 cars were recorded. J.F. Wolfram was the chief executive officer of the company again this year. Optional tilt-type steering wheels; crankcase ventilation systems; self-adjusting brakes and Delcotron generators for all models were highly promoted this year. Because of a new 'sway control' feature, Oldsmobiles this year had a three-foot smaller turn circle. For the model year, 99.5 percent of all full-sized Oldsmobiles had automatic transmissions, 91.7 percent had radios and 98.5 percent had power steering, but only 8.5 percent had posi-traction and 9.2 percent had bucket seats. In the F-85 Series, 88.5 percent had automatic transmission (4.3 percent had manual four-speed). 1.8 percent had power windows; 50.2 percent had bucket seats and 19 percent had seat belts. ·

1964 OLDSMOBILE

1964 Oldsmobile, Cutlass 4-4-2 two-door hardtop. V-8 (DC)

F-85 — The F-85/Cutlass Series grew up quite a bit in the 1964 model year. The wheelbase was increased three inches. Gone was the aluminum block 215 cid V-8 and in its place a variety of V-6 or cast iron V-8 Rocket motors appeared. This was also the first season for the midyear 4-4-2 option package. This $136 option package carried the RPO code B09. The name (in 1964) translated as 4=four-barrel; 4=four-speed; and 2=dual exhausts. Other 4-4-2 goodies included a heavy-duty suspension; dual-snorkel air cleaner; over-sized redline tires; and special 4-4-2 identification badges. F-85s could be ordered in either standard or Deluxe trim. Standard equipment included: heater/defroster; self-adjusting brakes; oil filter; front stabilizer; and dual sun visors. Deluxe and Cutlass equipment included items from the standard list plus: Deluxe steering wheel, padded dash and carpets. Interiors were done in either vinyl or cloth. Standard tire size was 6.50 14 inches. F-85s were built in Lansing, Atlanta, Kansas City, Linden, Southgate and Arlington.

OLDSMOBILE I.D. NUMBERS: VIN located on left front door pillar. Motor number (V-8) stamped on machined pad on left cylinder head above center exhaust port; (V-6) on front of right cylinder head. Serial number takes the form of four symbols, plus sequential production number. First symbol identifies engine type: 6=six; 8=V-8. Second symbol indicates series and matches second digit in Body/Style Number column of charts below. Third symbol identifies model year: 4=1964. Fourth symbol indicates assembly plant: T=Texas (Arlington); A=Atlanta, Ga.; B=Boston (Framingham), Mass.; K=Kansas City, Kan.; M=Michigan (Lansing); L=Linden, N.J.; C=California (Southgate); W=Wilmington, Del. Remaining symbols are the sequential production number starting at 001001 at each factory. Ending VINs not available. Engine numbers consist of a alphabetical prefix and a production sequence number. Prefixes for 1964 engines were: [225 cid V-6] KH=155 hp; KJ=export. [330 cid V-8] T=230 hp; TE=export; TG=290 hp; TH=export; V or TV=442 high-performance 310 hp; TK=245 hp. [394 cid V-8] H=280 hp; HE=export; HL=260 hp; J=330 hp; JE=export; JS=345 hp. Ending engine numbers not available.

F-85 SERIES

F-85

Model Number	Body/Style Number	Body Type & Seating	Factory Price	Shipping Weight	Production Total
F-85 STANDARD					
F-85	64-3027	2-dr Clb Cpe-6P	2332	2875	16,298
F-85	64-3035	4-dr Sta Wag-6P	2688	3254	4,047
F-84	64-3069	4-dr Sed-6P	2386	2980	12,106

F-85 DELUXE

Model Number	Body/Style Number	Body Type & Seating	Factory Price	Shipping Weight	Production Total
F-85	64-3127	2-dr Spts Cpe-6P	2404	3025	6,594
F-85	64-3135	4-dr Sta Wag-6P	2876	3290	10,793
F-85	64-3169	4-dr Sed-6P	2663	3140	42,237

F-85 CUTLASS

Model Number	Body/Style Number	Body Type & Seating	Factory Price	Shipping Weight	Production Total
F-85	64-3227	2-dr Cpe-5P	2663	3140	15,440
F-85	64-3237	2-dr Hol HT-5P	2773	3155	36,153
F-85	64-3267	2-dr Conv-5P	2973	3307	12,822

VISTA CRUISER — Most Oldsmobile enthusiasts tend to think of the Vista Cruiser as an F-85 model, but it was a physically larger vehicle riding on a larger wheelbase. This was the first year for the stylish station wagon and it was a late introduction. The Vista Cruiser had an elevated roof over the cargo area. The roof windows in the elevated section resembled the 1954 GM/Greyhound scenic-cruiser. Standard equipment included coil springs; three-speed manual transmission; self-adjusting air scoop brakes; and aluminized exhaust system. Either cloth or vinyl upholstery was offered. Standard tire size was 7.50 x 14 inches. Vista Cruisers were built in Lansing, Atlanta, Kansas City, Linden, Southgate and Arlington.

VISTA CRUISER

Model Number	Body/Style Number	Body Type & Seating	Factory Price	Shipping Weight	Production Total
VC	64-3055	4-dr Sta Wag-6P	2938	3553	1,305
VC	64-3065	4-dr Sta Wag-9P	3072	3658	2,089

VISTA CRUISER CUSTOM

Model Number	Body/Style Number	Body Type & Seating	Factory Price	Shipping Weight	Production Total
VC	64-3255	4-dr Sta Wag-6P	3055	3582	3,320
VC	64-3265	4-dr Sta Wag-9P	3122	3687	7,286

1964 Oldsmobile, four-door Jetstar 88 hardtop, V-8 (DC)

JETSTAR EIGHTY-EIGHT — In a confusing bit of marketing, a pair of Jetstar nameplates were added to the Oldsmobile lineup in 1964. The new bottom line Eight-Eight series group was now the Jetstar Eighty-Eight. Four body styles were included in the series. Standard equipment for the series included: foam padded front seat; carpeting; padded dash; wheel opening and rocker panel moldings; and automatic dome light. Upholstery was done in either vinyl or leather. These cars were made in the same assembly plant that built Vista Cruisers. Standard tire size was 7.50 x 14 inches.

JETSTAR EIGHTY-EIGHT

Model Number	Body/Style Number	Body Type & Seating	Factory Price	Shipping Weight	Production Total
J88	64-3347	2-dr Hol HT-6P	2981	3720	14,663
J88	64-3367	2-dr Conv-6P	3308	3817	3,903
J88	64-3369	4-dr Sed-6P	2924	3739	24,614
J88	64-3339	4-dr Hol HT-6P	3058	3758	19,325

DYNAMIC EIGHTY-EIGHT — Due to adding the Jetstar Eighty-Eight, the Dynamic Eighty-Eight moved up a rung on the Oldsmobile ladder. Six models were found in this series. Standard equipment on these models included: foam rubber padded front seat; chrome side moldings; carpeting; padded dash; automatic dome light; courtesy and map lights; and electric rear window on Fiesta. Upholstery was in a variety of colored cloth, vinyl and leather. Standard tire size was 8.00 x 14 inches. Dynamic 88s were built at the Lansing, Atlanta, Kansas City, Linden, Southgate and Arlington plants.

DYNAMIC EIGHTY-EIGHT

Model Number	Body/Style Number	Body Type & Seating	Factory Price	Shipping Weight	Production Total
D88	64-3447	2-dr Hol HT-6P	3051	3912	32,369
D88	64-3469	4-dr Sed-6P	2924	3952	57,590
D88	64-3467	2-dr Conv-6P	3378	4005	10,042
D88	64-3439	4-dr Hol HT-6P	3129	3980	50,327
D88	64-3435	4-dr Sta Wag-6P	3458	4155	10,747
D88	64-3445	4-dr Sta Wag-9P	3565	4180	6,599

SUPER EIGHTY-EIGHT — A reduced model line was offered in several new Oldsmobile series this year and the long running Super Eighty-Eight series was affected. Standard equipment on the remaining 'Supers' included all items from the Dynamic Eighty-Eight group plus: special chrome molding package, chrome window frames, parking brake signal lamp and rear fold-down armrest. Upholstery selection was from cloth, leather or vinyl. Standard tire size was 8.00 x 14 inches. Super 88s were made in the same plants as Dynamic 88s.

SUPER EIGHTY-EIGHT

Model Number	Body/Style Number	Body Type & Seating	Factory Price	Shipping Weight	Production Total
S88	64-3539	4-dr Hol HT-5P	3472	4054	17,778
S88	64-3569	4-dr Sed-5P	3250	4021	19,736

JETSTAR I — Added as a companion car to the Starfire Series was a second Jetstar for 1964, the Jetstar I. This car was in a single-model series. Standard equipment on this line included: bucket seats; center console; foam padded front seats; padded dash; carpets; special molding package; and windshield washer. Upholstery was in vinyl, cloth or leather. Standard tire size was 8.00 x 14 inches. Jetstar Is were built with Dynamic 88s.

JETSTAR I

Model Number	Body/Style Number	Body Type & Seating	Factory Price	Shipping Weight	Production Total
J1	64-3457	2-dr Spts Cpe-5P	3592	4028	16,084

1964 Oldsmobile, two-door Starfire convertible, V-8 (DC)

STARFIRE — The two-model Starfire series was continued for 1964. This series continued to be powered by the most powerful V-8 engine Olds offered and Starfire features afforded the best luxury Oldsmobile could provide. Standard equipment for this series included: Hydra-Matic transmission; power windows; seat; steering and brakes; whitewall tires; windshield washer; Deluxe steering wheel and wheel disc; bucket seats; console; and tachometer. Interiors were done in cloth, vinyl or leather. Standard tire size was 8.00 x 14 inches.

STARFIRE

Model Number	Body/Style Number	Body Type & Seating	Factory Price	Shipping Weight	Production Total
SF	64-3667	2-dr Conv-5P	4742	4275	2,410
SF	64-3657	2-dr Cpe-5P	4128	4153	13,753

NINETY-EIGHT — Again, the top of the line Ninety-Eights were accepted by the Oldsmobile buying public. This year six models were offered in two-door, four-door and convertible configurations. Standard equipment on the series included: Hydra-Matic transmission; power steering and brakes; power windows and seats; windshield washer; special wheel discs; clock; courtesy and map lights; and padded dash. Upholstery was offered in a variety of colored cloth, vinyl and leather. Standard tire size was 8.50 x 14 inches. All Ninety-Eights were now built in Lansing, Mich.

NINETY-EIGHT

Model Number	Body/Style Number	Body Type & Seating	Factory Price	Shipping Weight	Production Total
98	64-3847	2-dr Hol HT-6P	4177	4175	6,139
98	64-3947	2-dr Spt Cpe-6P	4391	4254	4,594
98	64-3867	2-dr Conv-6P	4457	4315	4,004
98	64-3829	4-dr Lux Sed-6P	4331	4238	17,346
98	64-3819	4-dr Twn Sed-6P	3982	4189	11,380
98	64-3839	4-dr Spts Sed-6P	4254	4231	24,791

BASE ENGINES

(F-85/VISTA CRUISER SIX) Inline Six. Overhead valves. Cast iron block. Displacement: 225 cid. Bore and stroke: 3.75 x 3.4 inches. Compression ratio: 9.0:1. Brake hp: 155 at 4400 rpm. Carburetor: Rochester one-barrel Model BC.

(F-85/VISTA CRUISER V-8) V-8. Overhead valves. Displacement: 330 cid. Bore and stroke: 3.93 x 3.38 inches. Compression ratio: 9.0:1. Brake hp: 210 at 4400 rpm. Hydraulic valve lifters. Carburetor: Rochester two-barrel Model 2GC.

(JETSTAR SERIES) V-8. Overhead valves. Cast iron block. Displacement: 330 cid. Bore and stroke: 3.93 x 3.38 inches. Compression ratio: 10.25:1. Brake hp: 245 at 4600 rpm. Carburetor: two-barrel Rochester Model 2GC.

(DYNAMIC 88 SERIES) V-8. Cast iron block. Displacement: 394 cid. Bore and stroke: 4-1/8 x 3-11/16 inches. Compression ratio: 10.25:1. Brake hp: 280 at 4400 rpm. Carburetor: Rochester two-barrel Model 2GC.

(SUPER 88/98 SERIES) V-8. Displacement: 394 cid. Bore and stroke: 4-1/8 x 3-11/16 inches. Compression ratio: 10.25:1. Brake hp: 330 at 4600 rpm. Carburetor: Rochester four-barrel Model 4GC.

(JETSTAR I/STARFIRE/98 CUSTOM SERIES) V-8. Cast iron block. Displacement: 394 cid. Bore and stroke: 4-1/8 x 3-11/16 inches. Compression ratio: 10.50:1. Brake hp: 345 at 4800 rpm. Carburetor: Rochester four-barrel Model 4GC.

CHASSIS FEATURES: Wheelbase: (F-85) 115 inches; (Vista Cruiser) 120 inches; (Jetstar 88, Jetstar I, Dynamic 88, Super 88 and Starfire) 123 inches; (Ninety-Eight) 126 inches. Overall length: (F-85) 203 inches; (Vista Cruiser) 208 inches; (Jetstar 88, Jetstar I, Dynamic 88, Super 88 and Starfire) 215.3 inches; (Ninety-Eight) 222.3 inches. Front tread: (F-85 and Vista Cruiser) 58 inches; (All others) 62.2 inches. Rear tread: (F-85 and Vista Cruiser) 58 inches; (All others) 61 inches.

OPTIONS: Power brakes ($43). Power steering ($107). Air conditioning ($430). Power seats ($71). Clock ($16). Convenience lamps ($8). Outside mirror ($4). Two-tone paint ($17). AM/FM radio ($150). Deluxe push-button radio ($88). Super Deluxe signal seeking radio ($124). Power antenna ($26). Rear speaker ($16). Cruise Control ($91). Tilt steering ($43). Trunk release ($10). Rear window defroster ($21). Tinted glass ($43). Automatic transmission ($231). Three-speed manual floor shift transmission ($43). Four-speed manual floor shift transmission ($188). F-85 V-8: 330 cid/290 hp Cutlass engine ($34). Jetstar 88 V-8: 330 cid/290 hp Jetfire engine ($37). Dynamic 88 V-8: 394 cid/330 hp Rocket engine ($37). All 88 and 98 models V-8: 394 cid/345 hp Starfire engine ($64). Positive traction rear axle ($47). Midyear: 4-4-2 package as F-85 option with RPO B09 code ($136).

HISTORICAL FOOTNOTES: Oldsmobile selected Sept. 24, 1963 as the date of introduction for its 1964 models. Model year sales included some 177,600 'senior-compact' F-85s and 368,500 full-sized Oldsmobiles. New car sales of 546,112 units in 1964 were 6.3 percent ahead of year 1963 with its 486,410. F-85, in its fifth season, maintained its uninterrupted climb with sales of 173,816 units, 38.5 percent above 1963's 125,514. Divisional general manager, H.N. Metzel, was smiling for most of the year.

1965 OLDSMOBILE

1965 Oldsmobile, two-door Cutlass convertible w/4-4-2 opt., V-8 (DC)

1965 Oldsmobile, two-door Jetstar I hardtop sports coupe, V-8

F-85 — The F-85 series was mildly restyled this model year and it continued to grow in popularity within the Oldsmobile model mix. In mid-1964 the 4-4-2 package was introduced on the F-85 group, and in 1965 that optional handling and performance package more widely known by the buying public. The engine in the 442 was a 400 cid 345 hp V-8. The "442" translated as 4=400 cid; 4=four-barrel carburetor and 2=dual exhaust this year. Basically three types of F-85s were offered this year: standard, Deluxe and increasingly popular Cutlass. Standard F-85 equipment consisted of: heater/defroster; self-adjusting brakes; aluminized muffler; front seat belts; electric windshield wipers; dual sun visors; and oil filter. Standard on the Deluxe and Cutlass models were all items listed on F-85 plus: Deluxe steering wheel; padded dash; and carpeting. Interiors could be ordered in either vinyl or cloth. Standard tire size was 7.35 x 14 inches. F-85s were built in the Lansing, Baltimore, Kansas City and Fremont assembly plants.

OLDSMOBILE I.D. NUMBERS: VIN located on left front door pillar. Motor number on right cylinder head of V-6 and V-8. Serial number takes the form of seven symbols, plus sequential production number. First symbol identifies GM division: 3=Oldsmobile. Second to fifth symbols indicate series and match the last four digits in Body/Style Number column of charts below. Sixth symbol identifies model year: 5=1965. Seventh symbol indicates assembly plant: C=Southgate, Calif.; D=Atlanta, Ga.; E=Linden, N.J.; G=Framingham, Mass.; M=Lansing, Mich.; Z=Fremont, Calif.; X=Kansas City, Kan.; R=Arlington, Texas. Remaining symbols are the sequential production number starting at 100001 at each factory. Ending VINs not available. Engine numbers consist of a alphabetical prefix and a production sequence number. Prefixes for 1965 engines were: [225 cid V-6] LH=155 hp; LJ=export. [330 cid V-8] T=250 hp; TE=export, TG=315 hp; TH=export. [330 cid JETSTAR 88] U=260 hp; UL=250 hp; UE=export two-barrel; UH=export four-barrel; UG=315 hp. [400 cid high-performance 4-4-2 V-8] V=345 hp four-barrel. [425 cid V-8] M=310 hp; ME=export two-barrel; ML=300 hp; N=360 hp; NE=export four-barrel; NS=370 hp. Ending engine numbers not available.

F-85

Model Number	Body/Style Number	Body Type & Seating	Factory Price	Shipping Weight	Production Total
STANDARD WITH V-6					
F-85	65-3327	2-dr Clb Cpe-6P	2344	2655	5,289
F-85	65-3335	4-dr Sta Wag-6P	2689	3236	714
F-85	65-3369	4-dr Sed-6P	2505	2991	3,089
STANDARD WITH V-8					
F-85	65-3427	2-dr Spts Cpe-6P	2415	2789	7,720
F-85	65-3435	4-dr Sta Wag-6P	2797	3258	2,496
F-85	65-3469	4-dr Sed-6P	2465	3167	5,661
DELUXE WITH V-6					
F-85	65-3527	2-dr Spts Cpe-6P	2538	2984	6,141
F-85	65-3535	4-dr Sta Wag-6P	2797	3274	659
F-85	65-3569	4-dr Sed-6P	2505	3024	4,989
DELUXE WITH V-8					
F-85	65-3635	4-dr Sta Wag-6P	2868	3456	10,365
F-85	65-3669	4-dr Sed-6P	2576	3209	47,767
CUTLASS					
F-85	65-3827	2-dr Spts Cpe-6P	2643	2784	26,441
F-85	65-3837	2-dr Hol HT-6P	2784	2799	46,138
F-85	65-3867	2-dr Conv-6P	2983	2901	12,628

VISTA CRUISER — Now in its second year, the Oldsmobile Vista Cruiser was among the most attractive station wagons available for 1965. Sheetmetal came from the Cutlass/F-85 dies, but the wheelbase and overall length were longer than wagons from those series. Standard equipment included: tinted Vista roof; underfloor luggage compartment; electric windshield wipers and self-adjusting brakes. Custom equipment included: Deluxe steering wheel; padded dash; chrome window frames and foam padded seat cushions. Interiors were done in either vinyl or cloth. Tire size was 7.75 x 14 inches. Vista Cruisers were built in the same plants as F-85s.

VISTA CRUISER

Model Number	Body/Style Number	Body Type & Seating	Factory Price	Shipping Weight	Production Total
VC	65-3455	4-dr Sta Wag-6P	2937	3685	2,110
VC	65-3855	4-dr Cus Sta Wag-6P	3146	3747	9,335
VC	65-3465	4-dr Sta Wag-9P	3072	3762	3,335
VC	65-3865	4-dr Cus Sta Wag-9P	3270	3814	17,205

JETSTAR EIGHTY-EIGHT — The Jetstar group continued to be the bottom line of the Eighty-Eight offerings in 1965. A restyling was made on the full-sized Oldsmobile this year. Standard equipment on the Jetstar Eighty-Eight series included: foam padded front seats; padded dash; rocker panel moldings; automatic dome light; electric windshield wipers; carpeting and parking brake signal light. Interiors were done in either vinyl or cloth. Standard tire size was 7.75 x 14 inches. The following letters were codes for Jetstar 88 assembly plants: M, R, T, D, X, E and C.

JETSTAR EIGHTY-EIGHT

Model Number	Body/Style Number	Body Type & Seating	Factory Price	Shipping Weight	Production Total
J88	65-5237	2-dr Hol HT-6P	2995	3701	13,911
J88	65-5267	2-dr Conv-6P	3337	3853	2,879
J88	65-5267	4-dr Sed-6P	2938	3734	22,725
J88	65-5239	4-dr Hol HT-6P	3072	3755	15,922

JETSTAR I — Continued as a single model series in 1965 was the Jetstar I. It featured the smaller body with the big Starfire V-8 engine and wound-up being a budget version of the or expensive Starfire offering. Standard equipment included: bucket seats; center control console; carpeting; parking brake signal lamp; courtesy lamps; padded dash; windshield washer; Deluxe steering wheel; special wheelcovers and clock. Interiors were done in vinyl. Standard tire size was 8.25 x 14 inches. The following letters were codes for Jetstar I assembly plants: M, R, T, D, X, E and C.

JETSTAR I

Model Number	Body/Style Number	Body Type & Seating	Factory Price	Shipping Weight	Production Total
J-1	65-5457	2-dr Spts Cpe-5P	3602	3936	6,552

DYNAMIC EIGHTY-EIGHT — The Dynamic Eighty-Eight group continued to be a popular full-size Oldsmobile offering. This year the sub-series Delta models were added to the standard Dynamic offerings. In total, seven models were built. Standard Dynamic equipment included: padded dash; foam front seat cushion; carpeting; parking brake signal lamp and electric windshield wipers. Additional equipment with the Delta package included: special moldings; chrome door frames; Deluxe interior trim; folding center armrest and courtesy lamps. Upholstery was done in either cloth, vinyl or leather. Standard tire size was 8.25 x 14 inches. For city assembly plant code letters see 1965 Jetstar 88.

DYNAMIC EIGHTY-EIGHT

Model Number	Body/Style Number	Body Type & Seating	Factory Price	Shipping Weight	Production Total
D88	65-5637	2-dr Hol HT-6P	3065	3847	24,746
D88	65-5669	4-dr Cel Sed-6P	3088	3914	47,030
D88	65-5639	4-dr Hol HT-6P	3143	3942	38,889
D88	65-5667	2-dr Conv-6P	3408	4036	8,832
DELTA					
D88	65-5837	2-dr Hol HT-6P	3253	3907	23,194
D88	65-5869	4-dr Cel Sed-6P	3158	3948	29,915
D88	65-5839	4-dr Hol HT-6P	3253	3959	37,358

STARFIRE — This would be the final year for the Starfire to carry the Oldsmobile personal luxury banner by itself. Next year the Toronado would join the team. Meanwhile, this series continued to offer just two well-equipped models. Standard equipment on both the coupe and convertible included: T-stick controlled Turbo Hydramatic transmission; power steering and brakes; courtesy lamps; bucket seats; center control console; tachometer; padded dash; parking brake signal lamp; Deluxe steering wheel; special wheelcovers; windshield washers and electric wipers and power windows and seat. Upholstery was done in vinyl, leather or cloth. Standard tire size 8.25 x 14 inches.

STARFIRE

Model Number	Body/Style Number	Body Type & Seating	Factory Price	Shipping Weight	Production Total
SF	65-6657	2-dr Cpe-5P	4148	4132	13,024
SF	65-6667	2-dr Conv-5P	4778	4347	2,236

NINETY-EIGHT — Five models rolled on the exclusive Ninety-Eight wheelbase in 1965. The top of the line Oldsmobiles continued to be well-appointed in just standard equipment form. As with most full-sized models, the new, larger 425 cid V-8 made for more powerful driving in the pre-gasoline crunch days. Standard equipment on the series included: Turbo Hydra-Matic transmission; power steering and brakes; power windows; clock; padded dash; foam padded seats; parking brake signal lamp; Deluxe steering wheel; special wheelcovers; windshield washer and two-speed electric wipers; courtesy and glovebox lamps and front seat belts. Upholstery was done in either leather, vinyl or cloth. Standard tire size was 8.55 x 14 inches. Ninety-Eights were built only in Lansing, Mich.

NINETY-EIGHT

Model Number	Body/Style Number	Body Type & Seating	Factory Price	Shipping Weight	Production Total
98	65-8437	2-dr Spts Cpe-6P	4197	4164	12,166
98	65-8467	2-dr Conv-6P	4493	4335	4,903
98	65-8469	4-dr Twn Sed-6P	4001	4201	13,266
98	65-8439	4-dr Hol HT-6P	4273	4232	28,480
98	65-8669	4-dr Lux Sed-6P	4351	4249	33,591

BASE ENGINES

(F-85 & VISTA CRUISER SERIES/SIX) V-6. Overhead valves. Cast iron block. Displacement: 225 cid. Bore and stroke: 3.75 x 3.40 inches. Compression ratio: 9.0:1. Brake hp: 155 at 4400 rpm. Four main bearings. Hydraulic valve lifters. Carburetor: Rochester Type BC one-barrel.

(F-85 & VISTA CRUISER SERIES/V-8) V-8. Overhead valves. Cast iron block. Displacement: 330 cid. Bore and stroke: 3.939 x 3.39 inches. Compression ratio: 9.0:1. Brake hp: 250 at 4800 rpm. Five main bearings. Hydraulic valve lifters. Carburetor: Rochester Type 2GC two-barrel.

(JETSTAR SERIES) V-8. Overhead valves. Cast iron block. Displacement: 330 cid. Bore and stroke: 3.939 x 3.385 inches. Compression ratio: 10.25:1. Brake hp: 260 at 4800 rpm. Five main bearings. Hydraulic valve lifters. Carburetor: Rochester Type 4GC four-barrel.

(JETSTAR I/STARFIRE SERIES) V-8. Overhead valves. Cast iron block. Displacement: 425 cid. Bore and stroke: 4.125 x 3.975 inches. Compression ratio: 10.25:1. Brake hp: 370 at 4800 rpm. Five main bearings. Hydraulic valve lifters. Carburetor: Rochester Type 4GC four-barrel.

(DYNAMIC 88 SERIES) V-8. Overhead valves. Cast iron block. Displacement: 425 cid. Bore and stroke: 4.125 x 3.975 inches. Compression ratio: 9.0:1. Brake hp: 300 at 4400 rpm. Five main bearings. Hydraulic valve lifters. Carburetor: Rochester Type 2GC two-barrel.

(98 SERIES) V-8. Overhead valves. Cast iron block. Displacement: 425 cid. Bore and stroke: 4.125 x 3.975 inches. Compression ratio: 10.25:1. Brake hp: 360 at 4800 rpm. Five main bearings. Hydraulic valve lifters. Carburetor: Rochester Type 4GC four-barrel.

CHASSIS FEATURES: Wheelbase: (F-85) 115 inches; (Vista Cruiser) 120 inches; (Jetstar 88, Jetstar I, Dynamic 88 and Starfire) 123 inches; (Ninety-Eight) 126 inches. Overall length: (F-85) 204.3 inches; (Vista Cruiser) 207.7 inches; (Jetstar 88, Jetstar I, Dynamic 88 and Starfire) 216.9 inches; (Ninety-Eight) 222.9 inches. Front tread: (F-85 and Vista Cruiser) 58 inches; (all others) 62 inches. Rear tread: (F-85 and Vista Cruiser) 58 inches; (all others) 64 inches.

OPTIONS: Power brakes ($45). Power steering ($109). Air conditioning ($441). Power seats ($71). Clock ($16). Courtesy lamps ($9). Outside mirror ($5). AM/FM radio ($165). Push-button radio ($88). Power antenna ($27). Rear speaker ($21). Cruise control ($91). Tilt steering ($44). Rear window defogger ($22). High-performance 4-4-2 Handling and Performance Package ($156). Three-speed manual transmission was standard on all except Ninety-Eight and Starfire. Automatic transmission ($245). Three-speed manual floor shift transmission ($45). Four-speed manual floor shift transmission ($205). V-8 330 cid 260 hp Jetfire engine ($30). V-8 330 cid 315 hp Jetfire engine ($55). V-8 425 cid/360 hp Super engine ($60). V-8 425 cid 370 hp Starfire engine ($78). Positive traction rear axle ($51).

HISTORICAL FOOTNOTES: The full-sized Oldsmobiles were introduced Sept. 24, 1964 and the F-85 models appeared in dealer showrooms the same day. Model year production peaked at 592,804 units. Calendar year production of 650,801 cars was recorded. H.N. Metzel was the chief executive officer of the company this year. Record sales were achieved by Oldsmobile Div. this season.

1966 OLDSMOBILE

1966 Oldsmobile, two-door Cutlass F-85 convertible, V-8

F-85 — The F-85 continued to grow in popularity. Traditional full-sized car buyers began looking to the Oldsmobile intermediate series. This year there were several sub-groups under the F-85 heading: Standard, Deluxe, Cutlass and 4-4-2. New to the series this year was the first inline six since 1950. F-85 standard equipment consisted of front and rear seat belts; padded dash; windshield washer; two-speed wipers; back-up lights; outside rearview mirror; and vinyl floor covering. Deluxe equipment consisted of all items from the standard list, plus foam padded seat cushions; carpeting; chrome roof moldings; and Deluxe steering wheel. Cutlass models included all items from the Deluxe list, plus bucket or Custom seats; Deluxe armrests; and courtesy lamp package. Upholstery was done in either vinyl or cloth. Standard tire size was 7.35 x 14. F-85s built in Lansing, Michigan were coded with an M, while those built in Fremont, California were coded with a Z.

OLDSMOBILE I.D. NUMBERS: VIN located on left front door pillar. Motor number on inline six on right side of block behind distributor. Motor number for V-8 on machined pad on front of right cylinder head. Serial number takes the form of seven symbols, plus sequential production number. First symbol identifies GM division: 3=Oldsmobile. Second to fifth symbols indicate series and match the four digits in Body/Style Number column of charts below. Sixth symbol identifies model year: 6=1966. Seventh symbol indicates assembly plant: C=Southgate, Calif.; D=Atlanta, Ga.; E=Linden, N.J.; G=Framingham, Mass.; M=Lansing, Mich.; Z=Fremont, Calif.; X=Kansas City, Kan.; R=Arlington, Texas. Remaining symbols are the sequential production number starting at 100001 at each factory. Ending VINs not available. Engine numbers consist of a alphabetical prefix and a production sequence number. Prefixes for 1966 engines were: [250 cid I6] VA/VB/VC=155 hp; VJ=export; VE/VF/VG=155 hp (automatic). [330 cid F-85/Cutlass V-8] W=250 hp; WE=export two-barrel; WL=310 hp; WG=320 hp; WH=export four-barrel. [Jetstar 88 330 cid V-8] X=260 hp; XE=export two-barrel; XG=320 hp; XH=export four-barrel; XL=250 hp. [400 cid high-performance 4-4-2 V-8] V=350 hp four-barrel

and 360 hp Tri-Carb. [425 cid Dynamic 88/Delta 88/Ninety-Eight V-8] M=310 hp; ME=export two-barrel; ML=300 hp; N=365 hp; NS=375 hp. [425 cid 98 only] NE=four-barrel export. [425 cid Toronado only V-8] NT=385 hp. Ending engine numbers not available.

F-85 SERIES

Model Number	Body/Style Number	Body Type & Seating	Factory Price	Shipping Weight	Production Total
STANDARD 6-CYLINDER					
F-85	66-3335	4-dr Sta Wag-6P	2605	3350	2,160
F-85	66-3307	2-dr Clb Cpe-6P	2322	2855	12,694
F-85	66-3369	4-dr Sed-6P	2384	3023	6,616
STANDARD 8-CYLINDER					
F-85	66-3407	2-dr Clb Cpe-6P	2418	3150	6,353
F-85	66-3435	4-dr Sta Wag-6P	2764	3437	1,652
F-85	66-3469	4-dr Sed-6P	2471	3185	3,754
DELUXE 6-CYLINDER					
F-85	66-3517	2-dr Hol HT-6P	2495	2955	19,942
F-85	66-3569	4-dr Sed-6P	2479	3058	31,020
F-85	66-3539	4-dr Hol HT-6P	2610	3043	7,013
F-85	66-3535	4-dr Sta Wag-6P	2773	3386	8,492
DELUXE 8-CYLINDER					
F-85	66-3617	2-dr Hol HT-6P	2583	3188	16,968
F-85	66-3669	4-dr Sed-6P	2567	3207	27,452
F-85	66-3639	4-dr Hol HT-6P	2699	3273	6,911
F-85	66-3635	4-dr Sta Wag-6P	2793	3458	8,058
CUTLASS					
F-85	66-3807	2-dr Spts Cpe-5P	2614	3185	17,455
F-85	66-3817	2-dr Hol HT-6P	2750	3197	44,633
F-85	66-3867	2-dr Conv-5P	2944	3197	12,154
F-85	66-3839	4-dr Sup HT-6P	2895	3255	30,871

VISTA CRUISER — The demand for family station wagons continued this year and families wanting a little more space could find it in the stylish Vista Cruiser line. Standard equipment here included: foam padded seats; padded dash; windshield washer; two-speed wipers; heavy-duty clutch; back-up lamps; and left outside rearview mirror. Custom equipment included all above, plus carpets; special chrome moldings; Deluxe steering wheel; and Deluxe armrests. Upholstery was done in either cloth or vinyl. Standard size tires were 8.25 x 14. Vista Cruisers were built in F-85 plants.

VISTA CRUISER SERIES

Model Number	Body/Style Number	Body Type & Seating	Factory Price	Shipping Weight	Production Total
STANDARD					
VC	66-3455	4-dr Sta Wag-6P	2914	3753	1,660
VC	66-3465	4-dr Sta Wag-9P	3065	3787	1,869
CUSTOM					
VC	66-3855	4-dr Sta Wag-6P	3114	3769	8,910
VC	66-3865	4-dr Sta Wag-9P	3278	3804	14,167

JETSTAR EIGHTY-EIGHT — In its final year as an Oldsmobile series was the bottomline, full-sized offering named Jetstar Eighty-Eight. Just three styles were offered in 1966. Standard equipment was front and rear seat belts; special chrome moldings; padded instrument panel; windshield washer; two-speed wipers; carpeting; back-up lamps; Deluxe armrests; left outside rearview mirror and parking brake lamp. Upholstery was done in either cloth or vinyl. Standard tire size was 7.75 x 14. Plant codes for Jetstar 88s were M, D, X, E and C.

JETSTAR EIGHTY-EIGHT SERIES

Model Number	Body/Style Number	Body Type & Seating	Factory Price	Shipping Weight	Production Total
J88	66-5237	2-dr Hol HT-6P	2962	3752	8,575
J88	66-5269	4-dr Cel Sed-6P	2907	3776	13,734
J88	66-5239	4-dr Hol HT-6P	3038	3752	7,938

DYNAMIC EIGHTY-EIGHT — For 1966 the Delta Eighty-Eight group was pulled out as a sub-series within this group and stood on its own. For the year, just four Dynamic Eighty-Eight models were available to buyers in the over-populated Eighty-Eight group. Standard equipment on the series included: Deluxe wheel discs; front and rear seat belts; carpeting; padded dash; windshield washer and two-speed wipers; foam seat cushions; chrome window moldings; back-up lamps; courtesy lamps and parking brake signal lamp. Interiors were done in vinyl, leather or cloth. Standard tire size was 8.25 x 14 inches. Assembly plant codes were the same listed for Jetstar Eighty-Eights.

DYNAMIC EIGHTY-EIGHT

Model Number	Body/Style Number	Body Type & Seating	Factory Price	Shipping Weight	Production Total
D88	66-5637	2-dr Hol HT-6P	3048	4913	20,857
D88	66-5667	2-dr Conv-6P	3381	4017	5,540
D88	66-5669	4-dr Cel Sed-6P	2992	3930	38,742
D88	66-5639	4-dr Hol HT-6P	3123	3945	30,784

DELTA EIGHTY-EIGHT — For the first time this model year, the Delta Eighty-Eight stood alone as a separate series. Four models were available in this top Eighty-Eight lineup. Standard equipment was: special wheel discs; front and rear seat belts; carpeting; padded dash; windshield washer and two-speed wipers; Deluxe steering wheel; foam seat cushions; back-up lamps; courtesy and map lights; special armrests; and parking brake signal lamp. Upholstery could be done in vinyl, leather or cloth. Standard tire size was 8.25 x 14 inches. These cars were built in the same plants as Dynamic 88s.

DELTA EIGHTY-EIGHT

Model Number	Body/Style Number	Body Type & Seating	Factory Price	Shipping Weight	Production Total
D88	66-5837	2-dr Hol HT-6P	3230	3917	20,587
D88	66-5857	2-dr Conv-6P	3564	4055	4,303
D88	66-5839	4-dr Hol HT-6P	3306	3984	33,326
D88	66-5869	4-dr Cel Sed-6P	3138	3963	30,140

1966 Oldsmobile, two-door Starfire hardtop sports coupe, V-8

STARFIRE — The Starfire saw its personal luxury market cramped increasingly by the Ninety-Eight two-door models and the introduction of all new Toronado this model year. This would be the final year for the Starfire, which was introduced in 1961. Only a coupe was offered. As usual the standard equipment list was quite complete for this model. It included: sports console; bucket seats; foam seat cushions; front and rear seat belts; carpeting; windshield washers and two-speed wipers; special wheel discs; electric clock; chrome molding package; courtesy lamps; outside rearview mirror; and back-up lamps. Interiors could be ordered in vinyl, leather or cloth. Standard tire size was 8.25 x 14 inches.

STARFIRE

Model Number	Body/Style Number	Body Type & Seating	Factory Price	Shipping Weight	Production Total
SF	66-5457	2-dr HT-5P	3540	4013	13,019

NINETY-EIGHT — Some luxury market buyers purchased either Starfires or the new Toronados, but the Ninety-Eight remained the full-sized top-of-the-market series for Oldsmobile in 1966. Five models, including a trio of four-doors, were available this year. As usual the Ninety-Eight was a well-appointed car. Standard equipment included: Turbo Hydra-Matic transmission; power steering and brakes; power windows and seat; special wheelcovers; front and rear seat belts; carpeting; windshield washer and two-speed wipers; foam seat cushions; electric clock and special armrests on selected models. Upholstery was offered in cloth, vinyl and leather. Standard tire size was 8.55 x 14 inches. Built in same plants as Dynamic 88s and Delta 88s.

NINETY-EIGHT

Model Number	Body/Style Number	Body Type & Seating	Factory Price	Shipping Weight	Production Total
98	66-8437	2-dr Hol HT-6P	4129	4140	11,488
98	66-8467	2-dr Conv-6P	4413	4245	4,568
98	66-8439	4-dr Hol HT-6P	4204	4184	23,048
98	66-8469	4-dr Twn Sed-6P	4001	4197	10,892
98	66-8669	4-dr Lux Sed-6P	4279	4197	38,123

1966 Oldsmobile, two-door Toronado fastback coupe, V-8

TORONADO — Ranking with such block-buster Oldsmobile introductions as the Hydra-Matic transmission in 1940 and the Rocket V-8 in 1949, Oldsmobile introduced its front-wheel-drive Toronado in 1966. The first practical, domestic, full-sized front-wheel-drive car since the Cords of the 1930s, the Toronado offered a number of engineering innovations. Like the Ninety-Eights of the previous few years, the early "Toros" were built exclusively in Lansing, Mich. Standard equipment was extensive and included: Turbo-Hydramatic transmission; power steering and power brakes; Strato-bench front seat; foam seat cushions; special chrome molding package; carpeting; electric clock; back-up lamps; Deluxe armrests; instrument panel and courtesy lamps; outside rearview mirror; and parking brake signal lamp. Interiors could be ordered in vinyl, leather or cloth. Standard tire size was 8.85 x 15 inches.

TORONADO SERIES

Model Number	Body/Style Number	Body Type & Seating	Factory Price	Shipping Weight	Production Total
STANDARD					
T	66-9487	2-dr Cpe-5P	4585	4366	6,333
DELUXE					
T	66-9687	2-dr Cpe-5P	4779	4410	34,630

BASE ENGINES

(F-85 SERIES) Inline Six. Overhead valves. Cast iron block. Displacement: 250 cid. Bore and stroke: 3.875 x 3.53 inches. Compression ratio: 8.5:1. Brake hp: 155 at 4200 rpm. Seven main bearings. Hydraulic valve lifters. Carburetor: Rochester Type BV one-barrel.

(F-85 SERIES) V-8. Overhead valves. Cast iron block. Displacement: 330 cid. Bore and stroke: 3.985 x 3.385 inches. Compression ratio: 10.25:1. Brake hp: 310. Five main bearings. Hydraulic valve lifters. Carburetor: Rochester Type 2GC two-barrel.

(VISTA CRUISER/JETSTAR SERIES) V-8. Cast iron block. Overhead valves. Displacement: 330 cid. Bore and stroke: 3.985 x 3.385 inches. Compression ratio: 10.25:1. Brake hp: 250. Five main bearings. Hydraulic valve lifters. Carburetor: Rochester Type 2GC two-barrel.

(DYNAMIC 88/DELTA 88 SERIES) V-8. Overhead valves. Cast iron block. Displacement: 425 cid. Bore and stroke: 4.125 x 3.975 inches. Compression ratio: 10.25:1. Brake hp: 310. Five main bearings. Hydraulic valve lifters. Carburetor: Rochester 2GC two-barrel.

(STARFIRE SERIES) V-8. Overhead valves. Cast iron block. Displacement: 425 cid. Bore and stroke: 4.125 x 3.975 inches. Compression ratio: 10.5:1. Brake hp: 375. Five main bearings. Hydraulic valve lifters. Carburetor: Rochester 4GC four-barrel.

(NINETY-EIGHT SERIES) V-8. Overhead valves. Cast iron block. Displacement: 425 cid. Bore and stroke: 4.125 x 3.975 inches. Compression ratio: 10.25:1. Brake hp: 365. Five main bearings. Hydraulic valve lifters. Carburetor: Rochester 4GC four-barrel.

(TORONADO SERIES) V-8. Overhead valve. Cast iron block. Displacement: 425 cid. Bore and stroke: 4.125 x 3.975 inches. Compression ratio: 10.5:1. Brake hp: 385. Five main bearings. Hydraulic valve lifters. Carburetor: Rochester 4GC four-barrel.

CHASSIS FEATURES: Wheelbase: (F-85) 115 inches; (Vista Cruiser) 120 inches; (Toronado) 119 inches; (Jetstar 88/Dynamic 88) 123 inches; (Delta 88/Starfire) 123 inches; (Ninety-Eight) 126 inches. Overall length: (F-85) 204.2 inches; (Vista Cruiser) 209.1 inches; (Toronado) 211 inches; (Jetstar 88/Dynamic 88) 217 inches; (Delta 88/Starfire) 217 inches; (Ninety-Eight) 223 inches. Front tread: (F-85/Vista Cruiser) 58 inches; (Jetstar 88) 61.8 inches; (Toronado) 63.5 inches; (all others) 62.5 inches. Rear tread: (F-85/Vista Cruiser) 59 inches; (all others) 63 inches. Tires: See text.

OPTIONS: Power brakes ($41). Power steering ($94). Air conditioning ($343). Tinted windows ($30). Power seat ($69). Power trunk ($12). Floor mats ($7). Vinyl roof ($74). Sports console ($68). Cruise control ($41). Tilt steering column ($41). Wire wheel discs ($61). Tachometer ($52). Electric clock ($15). Radio ($64). Power antenna ($29). Rear radio speaker ($15). AM/FM radio ($147). Power door locks ($68). Rear defroster ($21). The 4-4-2 package consisted of a special 400 cid/350 hp V-8, heavy-duty chassis items and special internal and external trim. It was offered on F-85 and Cutlass two-door models ($152). Three-speed manual transmission was standard on all models, except Olds 98 and Toronado. Automatic transmission ($23). Three-speed manual floor shift transmission ($84). Hurst shifter, F-85. Four-speed manual floor shift transmission ($184). Close-ratio four-speed manual transmission with floor shift ($184). V-8: 330 cid/310 hp Cutlass engine ($33). V-8: 425 cid/365 hp Super Rocket engine ($36). V-8: 425 cid/375 hp Starfire engine ($100). Positive traction rear axle ($46). Heavy-duty clutch ($5). Available rear axle gear ratios: 2.73: 1; 3.93:1; 3.08:1; 3.23:1; 3.42:1; 3.90:1.

HISTORICAL FOOTNOTES: Model year sales peaked at 586,381 cars. Calendar year sales were counted at 594,069 units. MOTOR TREND magazine picked Toronado as its 'Car of the Year.' Oldsmobile Div. got a brand new administration building this year. A total of 21,997 cars were sold with the optional 4-4-2 equipment package.

1967 OLDSMOBILE

F-85 — The F-85 continued to be the base series for the F-85 group, but Olds intermediate buyers were ordering more luxury with their cars and Cutlass models became more popular. This year just three basic F-85's were offered with either the L-head six-cylinder or a Rocket V-8 for power. Standard equipment for this series included: vinyl floor covering; seat belts; electric windshield wipers; heater/defroster; and back-up lights. Standard tire size was 7.75 x 14 inches. Interiors could be ordered in either cloth or vinyl. F-85s were made at Lansing, Bloomfield, N.J. and Fremont, Calif. this year.

OLDSMOBILE I.D. NUMBERS: VIN located on left front door pillar. Motor number on right side of six-cylinder block; front of right cylinder head on V-8. Serial number takes the form of seven symbols, plus sequential production number. First symbol identifies GM division: 3=Oldsmobile. Second to fifth symbols indicate series and match the four digits in Body/Style Number column of charts below. Sixth symbol identifies model year: 7=1967. Seventh symbol indicates assembly plant: C=Southgate, Calif.; D=Atlanta, Ga.; E=Linden, N.J.; G=Framingham, Mass.; M=Lansing, Mich.; Z=Fremont, Calif.; X=Kansas City, Kan.; R=Arlington, Texas. Remaining symbols are the sequential production number starting at 100001 at each factory. Ending VINs not available. Engine numbers consist of a alphabetical prefix and a production sequence number. Prefixes for 1967 engines were: [250 cid inline six-cylinder] FVA/FVB/FVC/FVD/FVE/FVF/FVG/FVH=155 hp; FVJ=export [330 cid F-85/Cutlass V-8] W=260 hp; WE=250 hp. [330 cid Delmont 88 V-8] XE=250 hp; X=260 hp; XG=320 hp. [350 cid F-85/Cutlass/Cutlass Supreme V-8] WG/WH=320 hp. [400 cid high-performance 4-4-2 V-8] VG=350 hp four-barrel and 360 hp Force-Air. [400 cid Turnpike Cruiser V-8] V=300 hp; [425 cid Dynamic 88/Delta 88/Delta 88 Custom/Ninety-Eight V-8] PL=300 hp; P=310 hp; R=365 hp; RS=375 hp; PE= export two-barrel; RE=export four-barrel. [425 cid Toronado only V-8] RT=385 hp. Ending engine numbers not available.

F-85 SERIES

Model Number	Body/Style Number	Body Type & Seating	Factory Price	Shipping Weight	Production Total
6-CYLINDER					
F-85	67-3307	2-dr Clb Cpe-6P	2410	2965	5,349
F-85	67-3369	4-dr Sed-6P	2457	3015	2,458
F-85	67-3335	4-dr Sta Wag-6P	2749	3200	2,749
8-CYLINDER					
F-85	67-3407	2-dr Clb Cpe-6P	2480	3184	6,700
F-85	67-3369	4-dr Sed-6P	2527	3211	5,126
F-85	67-3335	4-dr Sta Wag-6P	2818	3463	1,625

F-85 SERIES ENGINES

VISTA CRUISER — Two and three-seat versions of the Vista Cruisers were offered in 1967. This was again the biggest Oldsmobile station wagon offered. Sheetmetal was nearly identical to the Cutlass/F-85 models, but the Vista Cruiser rolled on a five inch longer wheelbase. Standard equipment on this series included: heavy-duty clutch; heavy-duty vinyl floor covering and foam padded seats. Custom equipment included: Deluxe armrests; carpeting; special interior light package; special moldings and Deluxe steering wheel. Upholstery was offered in either cloth or vinyl. Standard tire size was 8.25 x 14 inches. Vista Cruisers were assembled in F-85 factories.

VISTA CRUISER

Model Number	Body/Style Number	Body Type & Seating	Factory Price	Shipping Weight	Production Total
VC	67-3465	4-dr Sta Wag-8P	3135	3820	2,748

CUSTOM

Model Number	Body/Style Number	Body Type & Seating	Factory Price	Shipping Weight	Production Total
VC	67-3855	4-dr Sta Wag-6P	3228	3789	9,513
VC	67-3865	4-dr Sta Wag-8P	3339	3897	15,293

CUTLASS — The fancier version of the F-85, the Cutlass had now attained series status of its own and began a climb that would take it to the most popular nameplate for a U.S. built car. Either six-cylinder or V-8 power could be had in any of five Cutlass models. Upholstery was in either cloth or vinyl. Standard equipment on the Cutlass models included: carpeting; courtesy lamps; chrome molding package; foam seat cushions and Deluxe steering wheel. Standard tire size was 7.75 x 15 inches. Cutlasses were also assembled in F-85 factories.

CUTLASS SERIES

Model Number	Body/Style Number	Body Type & Seating	Factory Price	Shipping Weight	Production Total
6-CYLINDER					
Cut	67-3517	2-dr Hol HT-6P	2574	2965	2,564
Cut	67-3567	2-dr Conv-6P	2770	3145	567
Cut	67-3569	4-dr Twn Sed-6P	2552	3054	2,219
Cut	67-3539	4-dr Hol HT-6P	2683	3074	644
Cut	67-3535	4-dr Sta Wag-6P	2848	3200	365
8-CYLINDER					
Cut	67-3617	2-dr Hol HT-6P	2644	3216	29,799
Cut	67-3667	2-dr Conv-6P	2839	3304	3,777
Cut	67-3669	4-dr Twn Sed-6P	2622	3229	29,062
Cut	67-3639	4-dr Hol HT-6P	2753	3298	7,344
Cut	67-3635	4-dr Sta Wag-6P	2917	3478	8,130

CUTLASS SUPREME — Another new series for Olds this year came with the Cutlass Supreme, introduced as just a single model the previous year. The Supreme was the only series in which the popular 4-4-2 and the high-mileage Turnpike Cruising option could be ordered. The 4-4-2 performance packages were sold with 24,829 cars. The new 400 cid "Force-Air" engine optionally available for 4-4-2s had a ram-induction system. Its output was advertised at the same rating as the 1966 Tri-Carb engine. Five models were offered in this top-of-the-line F-85 range. Standard equipment consisted of: Deluxe armrests; carpeting; courtesy lamp package; special molding group; foam seats; and Deluxe steering wheel. Upholstery was done either in vinyl or cloth. Standard tire size was 7.75 x 14 inches. Cutlass Supremes were assembled in F-85 factories.

CUTLASS SUPREME SERIES

Model Number	Body/Style Number	Body Type & Seating	Factory Price	Shipping Weight	Production Total
CS	67-3807	2-dr Spt Cpe-6P	2694	3140	18,256
CS	67-3867	2-dr Conv-6P	3067	3385	10,897
CS	67-3869	4-dr Twn Sed-6P	2726	3262	8,346
CS	67-3839	4-dr Hol HT-6P	2900	3284	22,571
CS	67-3817	2-dr Hol HT-6P	2831	3152	57,858

DELMONT EIGHTY-EIGHT — A new nameplate was placed on the bottom-line Eight Eights in 1967: Delmont 88. Two sub-series were offered here: the 330 and the 425. The numerals referred to the engine displacement, either 330 cid or 425 cid, depending upon which motor was fitted. Three models could be ordered either way, but the convertible came only as a 425. Standard equipment included: Deluxe armrests; carpeting; lamp package; special wheelcovers; and chrome body moldings. Interiors were done in either vinyl, leather or cloth. Standard tire size was 8.55 x 14 inches. Full-size Oldsmobiles were made in the Lansing, Linden, Kansas City and Southgate assembly plants this year.

DELMONT EIGHTY-EIGHT SERIES

Model Number	Body/Style Number	Body Type & Seating	Factory Price	Shipping Weight	Production Total
330 MODELS					
88	67-5287	2-dr Hol HT-6P	3063	3876	10,786
88	67-5239	4-dr Hol HT-6P	3139	3894	10,600
88	67-5269	4-dr Twn Sed-6P	3008	3850	15,076
425 MODELS					
88	67-5687	2-dr Hol HT-6P	3126	3781	16,669
88	67-5639	4-dr Hol HT-6P	3202	3987	21,909
88	67-5669	4-dr Twn Sed-5P	3071	3955	21,511
88	67-5667	2-dr Conv-6P	3462	4058	3,525

DELTA EIGHTY-EIGHT — With the continued proliferation of Eighty-Eight models, the Delta series got into the act. It how had two sub-series: the standard Delta Eighty-Eight and the Delta Eighty-Eight Custom. Four models were offered as standard Deltas, while just two were available as Customs. Standard trim consisted of: Deluxe armrests; carpeting; lamp package; molding package; foam seat cushions; special wheelcovers; and Deluxe steering wheel. Interiors could be done in vinyl cloth or leather. Standard tire size was 8.55 x 14 inches.

DELTA EIGHTY-EIGHT SERIES

Model Number	Body/Style Number	Body Type & Seating	Factory Price	Shipping Weight	Production Total
STANDARD					
D88	67-5887	2-dr Hol HT-6P	3310	3915	2,447
D88	67-5867	2-dr Conv-6P	3646	4178	14,471
D88	67-5869	4-dr Twn Sed-6P	3218	3993	21,909
D88	67-5839	4-dr Hol HT-6P	3386	3951	22,270
CUSTOM					
D88	67-5487	2-dr Hol HT-6P	3522	3975	12,192
D88	67-5439	4-dr Hol HT-6P	3582	4027	14,306

1967 Oldsmobile, two-door Ninety-Eight convertible, V-8

NINETY-EIGHT — Gone for good was the sporty elegance of the Starfire. The Ninety-Eight and Toronado series were where the Olds buyers had to look for their luxury cars now. This year, as back in the 1930s, an Olds buyer could select from a variety of Ninety-Eights. There were five models to pick from. Standard Ninety-Eight trim included: armrests; power brakes; dual cigarette lighters; electric clock; carpeting; lamp package; molding package; seat belts; power seats; power steering; Turbo Hydramatic; and power windows. Upholstery was done in either cloth, vinyl or leather. Standard tire size was 8.85 x 14 inches. Ninety-Eight models were built in Lansing.

NINETY-EIGHT SERIES

Model Number	Body/Style Number	Body Type & Seating	Factory Price	Shipping Weight	Production Total
98	67-8457	2-dr Hol HT-6P	4214	4184	10,476
98	67-8467	2-dr Conv-6P	4498	4405	3,769
98	67-8469	4-dr Twn Sed-6P	4009	4222	8,900
98	67-8439	4-dr Hol HT-6P	4276	4285	17,533
98	67-8669	4-dr Lux Sed-6P	4351	4247	35,511

1967 Oldsmobile, two-door Toronado fastback coupe, V-8

TORONADO — In its second year the Toronado made a unique offering in the domestic luxury auto market. Changes were few from the introductory model of 1966, but there were some subtle improvements. Standard trim included: power brakes; rear cigarette lighters; electric clock; carpeting; interior lamp package; chrome molding package; foam seat cushions; Deluxe steering wheel; and Turbo-Hydramatic transmission. The Deluxe package included all standard items plus: center front seat armrests; Strato bench seat; and special wheel trim rings. Upholstery could be ordered in vinyl, cloth or leather. Standard tire size was 8.85 x 15 inches. Toronado engines had the letter code RT. All Toronado models were built in Lansing, Mich. and carried the letter M in the Vehicle Identification Number.

TORONADO SERIES

Model Number	Body/Style Number	Body Type & Seating	Factory Price	Shipping Weight	Production Total
T	67-9487	2-dr Cpe-5P	4674	4330	1,770
T	67-9687	2-dr Del Cpe-5P	4869	4357	20,020

BASE ENGINES

(F-85) Inline Six. Overhead valves. Cast iron block. Displacement: 250 cid. Bore and stroke: 3.875 x 3.53 inches. Compression ratio: 8.5:1. Brake hp: 155 at 4200 rpm. Seven main bearings. Hydraulic valve lifters. Carburetor: Rochester Type BV one-barrel.

(F-85/CUTLASS) Inline Six. Overhead valves. Cast iron block. Displacement: 250 cid. Bore and stroke: 3.875 x 3.53 inches. Compression ratio: 8.5:1. Brake hp: 155 at 4200 rpm. Seven main bearings. Hydraulic valve lifters. Carburetor: Rochester Type BV one-barrel.

(F-85/CUTLASS/VISTA CRUISER SERIES) V-8. Overhead valves. Cast iron block. Displacement: 330 cid. Bore and stroke: 3.985 x 3.385 inches. Compression ratio: 9.0:1. Brake hp: 250. Five main bearings. Hydraulic valve lifters. Carburetor: Rochester Type 2GC two-barrel.

(CUTLASS SUPREME SERIES) V-8. Overhead valves. Cast iron block. Displacement: 330 cid. Bore and stroke: 3.9385 x 3.385 inches. Compression ratio: 10.25 to 1. Brake hp: 320 at 4800 rpm. Five main bearings. Hydraulic valve lifters. Carburetor: Rochester 4GC four-barrel.

(DELMONT "330" EIGHTY-EIGHT SERIES) V-8. Overhead valves. Displacement: 330 cid. Bore and stroke: 3.9385 x 3.385 inches. Compression ratio: 9 to 1. Brake hp: 250 at 4800 rpm. Five main bearings. Hydraulic valve lifters. Carburetor: Rochester 2GC two-barrel.

(DELMONT "425" EIGHTY-EIGHT/TURNPIKE CRUISER SERIES) V-8. Overhead valves. Displacement: 425 cid. Bore and stroke: 4.125 x 3.975 inches. Compression ratio: 9 to 1. Brake hp: 300 at 4800 rpm. Five main bearings. Carburetor: Rochester 2GC two-barrel.

(NINETY-EIGHT SERIES) V-8. Overhead valves. Cast iron block. Displacement: 425 cid. Bore and stroke: 4.125 x 3.975 inches. Compression ratio: 10.25 to 1. Brake hp: 365 at 4800 rpm. Five main bearings. Hydraulic valve lifters. Carburetor: Rochester 4GC four-barrel.

(TORONADO/TORONADO DELUXE SERIES) V-8. Overhead valves. Cast iron block. Displacement: 425 cid. Bore and stroke: 4.125 x 3.975 inches. Compression ratio: 10.5 to 1. Brake hp: 385 at 4800 rpm. Five main bearings. Hydraulic valve lifters. Carburetor: Rochester 4GC four-barrel.

CHASSIS FEATURES: Wheelbase: (F-85 /Cutlass/Cutlass Supreme) 115 inches; (Vista Cruiser) 120 inches; (Toronado) 119 inches; (Delmont/Delta 88) 123 inches; (Ninety-Eight) 126 inches. Overall length: (F-85/Cutlass/Cutlass Supreme) 204.2 inches; (Vista Cruiser) 209.5 inches; (Toronado) 211 inches; (Delmont/Delta 88) 217 inches; (Ninety-Eight) 223 inches. Front tread: (F-85/Cutlass/Cutlass Supreme/Vista Cruiser) 58 inches; (Toronado) 63.5 inches; (all others) 62.5 inches. Rear tread: (F85/Cutlass/Cutlass Supreme/Vista Cruiser) 59 inches; (all others) 63 inches. Tires: See text for tire sizes.

OPTIONS: Power brakes ($104). Power steering ($94). Air conditioning ($343). Tinted windshield ($21). Seat shoulder belts ($23). Floor mats ($7). Vinyl roof ($84). Remote-control outside mirror ($8). Sports console ($54). Cruise Control ($44). Tilt steering wheel ($24). Rocket rallye packet instruments ($84). Electric clock ($35). AM/FM radio ($133). Rear speaker ($16). Push-button AM radio ($64). Stereo tape player ($124). AM/FM stereo ($238). Tach/clock ($84). Cornering lights ($38). Wire wheel discs ($68). Power windows ($104). Power seats ($94). Power door locks ($44). Rear window defogger ($21). GT paint stripe ($10). The 4-4-2 package was available only on Cutlass Supreme series. It consisted of a special 400 cid/350 hp engine and special redline tires, special handling package and 4-4-2 emblems. Three-speed manual transmission was standard on all but Toronado and Olds 98. Automatic transmission ($236). Three-speed manual floor shift transmission ($84). Four-speed manual floor shift transmission ($184). Wide-ratio four-speed manual transmission with floor shift ($184). V-8: 330 cid/310 hp Jetfire engine ($33). V-8: 330 cid/320 hp Jetfire engine ($33). V-8: 425 cid/365 hp Super Rocket engine ($36). V-8: 425 cid/375 hp Starfire engine ($100). High- Energy ignition ($100). Air induction package ($33). Positive traction rear axle ($42). Axle ratios: 2.41; 2.73; 2.78; 2.93; 3.08; 3.21; 3.23; 3.42; 3.55; 3.90; 3.91.

HISTORICAL FOOTNOTES: Model year sales were 548,390 cars. On a calendar year basis, 558,762 transactions involving new Oldsmobiles were registered. The division became America's sixth ranked automobile manufacturer that year, according to the sales charts. The 4-4-2 performance packages were sold with 24,829 cars. The 400 cid "Force-Air" engine optionally available for 4-4-2s had a ram-induction system. Its output was advertised at the same rating as the 1966 Tri-Carb engine.

1968 OLDSMOBILE

F-85 — The growth in the F-85 series was coming in the fancier intermediate lines like the Cutlass, Cutlass Supreme and 4-4-2. This year, however, a two-model F-85 series remained. Power came from either a Chevy inline six-cylinder or an Olds Rocket V-8. Standard equipment was sparse on this series and consisted of: dual master brake cylinder; four-way flashers; padded dash; back-up lights; chrome hubcaps; and seat belts. Interiors were available in either cloth or vinyl. Standard tire size was 7.75 x 14 inches. Production of the F-85 and other Oldsmobile intermediates was quartered at the Lansing, Fremont, Linden, Framingham and Oshawa (Canada) assembly plants.

OLDSMOBILE I.D. NUMBERS: VIN located on top left of dashboard viewable through windshield. Motor number on right of block (I-6) or right cylinder head (V-8). Serial number takes the form of seven symbols, plus sequential production number. First symbol identifies GM division: 3=Oldsmobile. Second to fifth symbols indicate series and match the four digits in Body/Style Number column of charts below. Sixth symbol identifies model year: 8=1968. Seventh symbol indicates assembly plant: C=Southgate, Calif.; D=Doraville (Atlanta), Ga.; E=Linden, N.J.; G=Framingham, Mass.; M=Lansing, Mich.; Z=Fremont, Calif.; X=Fairfax (Kansas City), Kan.; R=Arlington, Texas; 1=Oshawa, Canada. Remaining symbols are the sequential production number starting at 100001 at each factory. Ending VINs not available. Engine numbers consist of a alphabetical prefix and a production sequence number. Prefixes for 1968 engines were: [250 cid/155 hp inline six-cylinder] VA/VB/VF/VE; [350 cid F-85/Cutlass/Cutlass Supreme V-8] QI/QJ=250 hp manual; QA/QB=250 hp automatic; QV/QX=310 hp manual; QN/QP=310 hp automatic; T=250 hp; TB/TD=250 hp automatic; TN=310 hp. [400 cid V-8] QL=290 hp; QR/QS/QT=325 hp; QW/QU=350 hp; QT=360 hp "W-30" optional. [455 cid V-8] UC/UC=310 hp; UN/UO=365 hp; UA/UB=320 hp; US/UT=375 hp; UW=400 hp (Toronado only) and UX=390 hp (Toronado only). Ending engine numbers not available.

F-85 SERIES

Model Number	Body/Style Number	Body Type & Seating	Factory Price	Shipping Weight	Production Total
SIX-CYLINDER					
F-85	3177	2-dr Clb Cpe-6P	2512	3065	4,052
F-85	3169	4-dr Sed-6P	2560	3115	1,847
V-8					
F-85	3277	2-dr Clb Cpe-6P	2617	3277	5,426
F-85	3269	4-dr Twn Sed-6P	2665	3206	3,984

CUTLASS — Just as Olds had a proliferation of full-sized models several years before, the same tactic was now being used on Cutlass models. It's interesting to note that four-doors in the Olds intermediate series now rode on longer wheelbase than two-door models. Olds took its mid-size four-doors for 1968 and tagged them Cutlass models, while the two-doors were Cutlass 'S' models. A completely new styling package was used on 1968 Olds intermediates. Standard Cutlass equipment included: dual master cylinder; four-way flashers; energy-absorbing steering column; padded dash; back-up lights; full fiberglass hood insulation; and Deluxe steering wheel. Interiors were done in either vinyl or cloth. Standard tire size was 7.75 x 14 inches.

Model Number	Body/Style Number	Body Type & Seating	Factory Price	Shipping Weight	Production Total
SIX CYLINDER					
C	3539	4-dr Hol HT-6P	2804	3174	265
C	3569	4-dr Twn Sed-6P	2674	3154	1,305
C	3535	4-dr Sta Wag-6P	2969	3345	354
V-8					
C	3639	4-dr Hol HT-6P	2909	3351	7,839
C	3669	4-dr Twn Sed-6P	2779	3328	25,994
C	3635	4-dr Sta Wag-6P	3074	3562	9,291

1968 Oldsmobile, Cutlass 'S' two-door hardtop sports coupe, V-8

CUTLASS S — The new nameplates of Cutlass 'S' applied to the shorter wheelbased Cutlass coupes this year. A total of three Cutlass 'S' models were offered. They carried the same standard equipment as Cutlass models. Also, the same tire sizes and upholstery was provided.

CUTLASS 'S' SERIES

Model Number	Body/Style Number	Body Type & Seating	Factory Price	Shipping Weight	Production Total
SIX-CYLINDER					
C	3577	2-dr Spts Cpe-6P	2632	3216	1,181
C	3587	2-dr Hol HT-6P	2696	3099	1,492
C	3567	2-dr Conv-6P	2949	3245	410
V-8					
C	3677	2-dr Spts Cpe-6P	2737	3412	14,586
C	3687	2-dr Hol HT-6P	2801	3294	59,577
C	3667	2-dr Conv-6P	3055	3415	13,667

CUTLASS SUPREME — The ultimate in intermediate-sized Oldsmobile luxury for 1968 was the three model Cutlass Supreme series. No six-cylinders were offered in this line and a slightly more powerful version of the new 350 Rocket V-8 was standard equipment. Other regular features were: dual master cylinder; four-way flasher; back-up lights; side marker lights; seat belts; new high-performance starter; fiberglass hood insulation; and Deluxe steering wheel. Upholstery was done either in vinyl or cloth. Standard tire size was 7.75 x 14 inches.

CUTLASS SUPREME SERIES

Model Number	Body Style Number	Body Type & Seating	Factory Price	Shipping Weight	Production Total
CS	4287	2-dr Cpe-6P	2982	3335	33,518
CS	4269	4-dr Twn Sed-6P	2884	3334	5,524
CS	4239	4-dr Hol HT-6P	3057	3240	15,067

4-4-2 — Since 1964 the 4-4-2 had been a high-performance option, which continued to grow in popularity. In 1968, the 4-4-2 was accorded series status. Standard equipment included all Cutlass items plus: heavy-duty springs; stabilizer bar; special shock absorbers and wheels; special emblems; hood louvers; paint stripe; special tires and a high output engine. Upholstery could be ordered in vinyl or cloth. Standard tire size was F70-14. The Hurst/Olds option was first available in 1968. It consisted of special black and silver paint; special handling package; various luxury options; and a special 455 cid V-8. A total of 515 were made, all based on 4-4-2 models.

4-4-2 SERIES

Model Number	Body/Style Number	Body Type & Seating	Factory Price	Shipping Weight	Production Total
442	4477	2-dr Spts Cpe-5P	3087	3450	4,282
442	4487	2-dr Hol HT-5P	3150	3470	24,183
442	4467	2-dr Conv-5P	3341	3540	5,142

VISTA CRUISER — The largest station wagon offered by Oldsmobile, again this year, was the Vista Cruiser. It came in both a two-seat and three-seat version. Standard equipment on this series included: dual master cylinder; four-way flasher; padded dash; back-up lights; seat belts; cross-flow radiator; folding second seat; fiberglass hood insulation; underfloor compartment; and Deluxe steering wheel. Upholstery could be ordered in either cloth or vinyl. Standard tire size was 8.25 x 14 inches.

VISTA CRUISER SERIES

Model Number	Body/Style Number	Body Type & Seating	Factory Price	Shipping Weight	Production Total
VC	4855	4-dr Sta Wag-6P	3367	3842	13,375
VC	4865	4-dr Sta Wag-8P	3508	3957	22,768

DELMONT EIGHTY-EIGHT — Bottom of the line for full-sized Oldsmobiles, again this year, was the Delmont Eighty-Eight. Four models were offered. Like all big cars, they were mildly restyled this year. Standard Delmont Eighty-Eight equipment was: dual master cylinder; four-way flashers; back-up lights; fiberglass hood insulation; cross-flow radiator; map lights; molding package; and central dome light. Standard upholstery was done in either vinyl, cloth or leather. Tire size was 8.55 x 14 inches. Factory codes M, X, E, C and D were on the big Oldsmobiles.

DELMONT EIGHTY-EIGHT SERIES

Model Number	Body/Style Number	Body Type & Seating	Factory Price	Shipping Weight	Production Total
88	5487	2-dr Hol HT-6P	3202	3874	18,391
88	5469	4-dr Twn Sed-6P	3146	3922	24,365
88	5439	4-dr Hol HT-6P	3278	3977	21,056
88	5467	2-dr Conv-6P	3515	3964	2,812

DELTA EIGHTY-EIGHT — The heart of the Eighty-Eight sales picture could be found in the Delta Eighty-Eight series. Three models were offered in standard trim, with two additional Custom models provided. Standard equipment included: dual master cylinder; four-way flasher; energy-absorbing steering column; padded dash; extra sound deadening; back-up lights; larger battery; fiberglass hood insulation; and chrome wheel discs. The Custom models carried all standard features plus: electric clock; courtesy lamp package; molding package; special speedometer; and Deluxe steering wheel. Upholstery could be ordered in vinyl, cloth or leather. Standard tire size was 8.55 x 14 inches.

DELTA EIGHTY-EIGHT SERIES

Model Number	Body/Style Number	Body Type & Seating	Factory Price	Shipping Weight	Production Total
STANDARD					
D88	6487	2-dr Hol HT-6P	3449	3990	18,501
D88	6469	4-dr Twn Sed-6P	3357	3998	33,689
D88	6439	4-dr Hol HT-6P	3525	4080	30,048
CUSTOM					
D88	6687	2-dr Hol HT-6P	3661	4055	9,540
D88	6639	4-dr Hol HT-6P	3721	4155	10,727

1968 Oldsmobile, four-door Holiday 98 hardtop sedan, V-8

NINETY-EIGHT — Once again, Oldsmobile rolled out a series of well-appointed Ninety-Eights. Five models were offered for 1968. All Ninety-Eights were well-equipped, too. Standard equipment included: dual master cylinder, four-way flasher; energy-absorbing steering column; back-up lights; side marker lights; seat belts; cross-flow radiator; rear armrest ashtrays; power brakes; electric clock; special moldings; shoulder belts, Deluxe steering wheel; power steering; carpeted trunk; and Turbo-Hydramatic transmission. Upholstery was done in either vinyl, cloth or leather. Standard tire size was 8.85 x 14 inches. Ninety-Eight production was quartered exclusively in Lansing, Mich.

NINETY-EIGHT SERIES

Model Number	Body/Style Number	Body Type & Seating	Factory Price	Shipping Weight	Production Total
98	8457	2-dr Hol HT-6P	4360	4247	15,319
98	8467	2-dr Conv-6P	4618	4295	3,942
98	8439	4-dr Hol HT-6P	4422	4347	21,147
98	8469	4-dr Twn Sed-6P	4155	4258	10,584
98	8669	4-dr Lux Sed-6P	4497	4318	40,755

TORONADO — In its third year as the top-of-the-line Oldsmobile, the Toronado received a mild restyling effort. There was even an optional, high-performance version. This special extra-cost package included cold air induction. Standard Toronado equipment included: Turbo-Hydramatic transmission; electric clock; carpets; concealed headlamps; special headliner; fiberglass hood insulation; courtesy lamp package; chrome molding package; foam padded seat cushions; rolling dial speedometer; power steering; Deluxe steering wheel; power brakes; trunk floor carpeting; torsion bar front suspension; and door-opening assist springs. Upholstery was done in vinyl, leather or cloth. Standard tire size was 8.85 x 15 inches. All Toronados were built in Lansing, Mich. and contained the letter code M in the Vehicle Identification Number.

1968 Oldsmobile, two-door Toronado hardtop sports coupe, V-8

TORONADO SERIES

Model Number	Body/Style Number	Body Type & Seating	Factory Price	Shipping Weight	Production Total
T	9487	2-dr Cpe-5P	4750	4280	3,957
CUSTOM					
T	9687	2-dr Cpe-5P	—	4328	22,497

BASE ENGINES

(F-85) Inline Six. Overhead valves. Cast iron block. Displacement: 250 cid. Bore and stroke: 3.875 x 3.53 inches. Compression ratio: 8.5:1. Brake hp: 155 at 4200 rpm. Seven main bearings. Hydraulic valve lifters. Carburetor: Rochester Type BV one-barrel model 7026028.

(F-85/CUTLASS) Inline Six. Overhead valves. Cast iron block. Displacement: 250 cid. Bore and stroke: 3.875 x 3.53 inches. Compression ratio: 8.5:1. Brake hp: 155 at 4200 rpm. Seven main bearings. Hydraulic valve lifters. Carburetor: Rochester Type BV one-barrel model 7026028.

(F-85/CUTLASS) V-8. Overhead valves. Cast iron block. Displacement: 350 cid. Bore and stroke: 4.057 x 3.385 inches. Compression ratio: 9.0:1. Brake hp: 250 at 4400 rpm. Five main bearings. Hydraulic valve lifters. Carburetor: Rochester 4GC four-barrel model 7028250.

(CUTLASS SUPREME/VISTA CRUISER SERIES) V-8. Overhead valves. Cast iron block. Displacement: 350 cid. Bore and stroke: 4.057 x 3.385 inches. Compression ratio: 10.25:1. Brake hp: 310 at 4800 rpm. Five main bearings. Hydraulic valve lifters. Carburetor: Rochester 4GC, four-barrel model 7028250.

(4-4-2 SERIES) V-8. Overhead valves. Cast iron block. Displacement: 400 cid. Bore and stroke: 3.870 x 4.25 inches. Compression ratio: 10.5:1. Brake hp: 350 at 4800 rpm. Five main bearings. Hydraulic valve lifters. Carburetor: Rochester 4GC, four-barrel model 7028251.

(DELMONT EIGHTY-EIGHT SERIES) V-8. Overhead valves. Cast iron block. Displacement: 350 cid. Bore and stroke: 4.057 x 3.385 inches. Compression ratio: 9.0:1. Brake hp: 250 at 4400 rpm. Five main bearings. Hydraulic valve lifters. Carburetor: Rochester 2GC two-barrel model 7029250.

(DELTA EIGHTY-EIGHT SERIES) V-8. Overhead valves. Cast iron block. Displacement: 455 cid. Bore and stroke: 4.126 x 4.250 inches. Compression ratio: 9.0:1. Brake hp: 310 at 4200 rpm. Five main bearings. Hydraulic valve lifters. Carburetor: Rochester 2GC, two-barrel model 709250.

(NINETY-EIGHT SERIES) V-8. Overhead valves. Cast iron block. Displacement: 455 cid. Bore and stroke: .126 x 4.250 inches. Compression ratio: 10.25:1. Brake hp: 365 at 4600 rpm. Five main bearings. Hydraulic valve lifters. Carburetor: Rochester 4GC four-barrel model 7029250.

(TORONADO SERIES) V-8. Overhead valves. Cast iron block. Displacement: 455 cid. Bore and stroke: 4.126 x 4.250 inches. Compression ratio: 10.25:1. 375 hp at 4600 rpm. Five main bearings. Hydraulic valve lifters. Carburetor: Rochester 4MV four-barrel.

CHASSIS FEATURES: Wheelbase: (Cutlass 'S'/4-4-2/Cutlass Supreme, two-doors) 112 inches; (F-58/Cutlass/Cutlass Supreme, four-doors) 116 inches; (Delmont/Delta 88) 123 inches; (Vista Cruiser) 121 inches; (Toronado) 119 inches; (Ninety-Eight) 126 inches. Overall length: (Cutlass 'S'/4-4-2/Cutlass Supreme, two-doors) 201.6 inches; (F-85/Cutlass/Cutlass Supreme, four-doors) 205.6 inches; (Delmont/ Delta 88) 217.8 inches; (Vista Cruiser) 217.5 inches; (Toronado) 211.4 inches; (Ninety-Eight) 223.7 inches. Front tread: (F-85/Cutlass/Cutlass 'S'/4-4-2/Cutlass Supreme/Vista Cruiser) 59 inches; (all others) 62.5 inches. Rear tread: (F-85/Cutlass/Cutlass 'S'/44-2/Cutlass Supreme/Vista Cruiser) 59 inches; (all others) 63 inches. Tires: See text for tire sizes.

OPTIONS: Power brakes ($53). Power steering ($98). Air conditioning ($411). Power antenna ($35). Electric clock ($79). Cruise Control ($79). Air deflector, station wagons ($17). Rear defogger ($17). Wire wheel hubcaps ($89). Tissue dispenser ($5). Lamp package ($8). Guidematic headlamp control ($46). Rooftop luggage carrier, wagons ($52). Rooftop ski carrier ($36). Floor mats ($7). Remote-control mirror ($12). Door edge moldings ($8). Push-button AM radio ($78). AM/FM radio ($134). AM/FM stereo radio ($219). Stereo tape player ($116). Rear radio speaker ($13). Power trunk lid release ($12). Three-speed manual transmission was standard except Toronado and Olds 98. Automatic transmission was standard except Olds 98 and Toronado. Automatic transmission ($158). Three-speed manual floor shift transmission ($43). Four-speed manual floor shift transmission ($189). V-8 350 cid/310 hp Rocket engine ($38). V-8: 400 cid/290 hp Turnpike Cruiser engine ($98). V-8: 400 cid/325 hp Rocket engine ($89). V-8: 455 cid/365 hp Rocket engine ($57). V-8: 455 cid/400 hp Rocket engine ($190).

HISTORICAL FOOTNOTES: It was 562,459 sales for the model run in 1968, good for retention of sixth industry rank. CARS magazine picked 4-4-2 as its 'Performance Car of the Year.' Yet, even Toronado was 'hot' in competition, taking one-two-three in the Pikes Peak Hill Climb. There was also some strong performance advertising associated with Lansing this year. 'Dr. Oldsmobile' played a starring role in the lead-footed media blitz. The 290 hp Olds 4-4-2 had a top speed of 116 mph. The 360 hp Olds 4-4-2 could hit about 123 mph at top end. The 390 hp Olds 4-4-2 need 6.5 seconds to reach 60 mph and did the quarter-mile in 12.97 seconds. Hurst-Olds were assembled on an "off-line" basis by Hurst Performance Products, Co.

1969 OLDSMOBILE

F-85 — For 1969 the Cutlass series was reduced to just a single coupe model. Most of the sales activity for the Olds intermediates had moved to the high-performance market and more luxury-equipped cars came up into the Cutlass line. Standard F-85 equipment included: four-way flashers; front armrests; cigarette lighter; vinyl floor covering; seat belts and shoulder harnesses; outside rearview mirror and chrome hubcaps. Interiors were in vinyl. Standard tire size was 7.75 x 14 inches. The 1969 Olds intermediates had M, Z and E assembly plant codes.

OLDSMOBILE I.D. NUMBERS: VIN located on top left of dashboard viewable through windshield. Motor number (6) right side of block; (V-8) front of right cylinder head. Serial number takes the form of seven symbols, plus sequential production number. First symbol identifies GM division: 3=Oldsmobile. Second to fifth symbols indicate series and match the four digits in Body/Style Number column of charts below. Sixth symbol identifies model year: 9=1969. Seventh symbol indicates assembly plant: C=Southgate, Calif.; D=Doraville (Atlanta), Ga.; E=Linden, N.J.; G=Framingham, Mass.; M=Lansing, Mich.; Z=Fremont, Calif.; X=Fairfax (Kansas City), Kan.; R=Arlington, Texas; 1=Oshawa, Canada. Remaining symbols are the sequential production number starting at 100001 at each factory. Ending VINs not available. Engine numbers consist of a alphabetical prefix and a production sequence number. Prefixes for 1969 engines were: [250 cid inline six] VD/VJ=export; VA/VB/VF/VE;=155 hp [350 cid V-8] QI=250 hp manual; QA/QB/QJ=250 hp automatic; QV/QN/QP=310 hp manual; QX="W-31" with 325 hp; TL/TB/TO/TC=250 hp. [400 cid V-8] QW=350 hp; QR/QS=325 hp; QU/QT="W-30" with 360 hp. [455 cid V-8] UC/UD/UJ=310 hp; UN/UO=365 hp; UL=390 hp; US/UT/UV=Toronado 375 hp; UW=Toronado 400 hp; UX=380 hp in Hurst-Olds. Ending engine numbers not available.

F-85

Model Number	Body/Style Number	Body Type & Seating	Factory Price	Shipping Weight	Production Total
SIX-CYLINDER					
F-85	3177	2-dr Spts Cpe-5P	2561	3221	2,899
V-8					
F-85	3277	2-dr Spts Cpe-5P	2672	3421	5,541

CUTLASS — The next step up the Oldsmobile ladder in 1969 was the Cutlass series. For all Olds intermediates this year, a shorter wheelbase was used on two-door models than four-doors. The two-door offerings in the Cutlass class were also tagged Cutlass S. This year high-performance became even more fashionable for Olds intermediate buyers and this trend now extended beyond the 4-4-2 buyer. A very potent "W-31" package was available in Cutlass and Cutlass Supreme models. It was based on a "Force-Air" inducted 350 cid V-8 with special equipment. Standard Cutlass features included all items from the F-85 list plus: hood louvers; insulated fiberglass hood blanket; nylon blend carpeting; special molding package; and Deluxe steering wheel. Standard tire size was 7.75 x 14 inches. Upholstery choices were vinyl or cloth.

CUTLASS

Model Number	Body Style Number	Body Type & Seating	Factory Price	Shipping Weight	Production Total
SIX-CYLINDER					
C	3577	2-dr Spts Cpe-5P	2681	3327	483
C	3587	2-dr Hol HT-5P	2742	3277	566
C	3567	2-dr Conv-5P	2998	3336	236
C	3569	4-dr Twn Sed-5P	2772	3300	137
C	3539	4-dr Hol HT-5P	2853	3353	236
C	3535	4-dr Sta Wag-5P	3055	3701	180
V-8					
C	3677	2-dr Spts Cpe-5P	2792	3437	10,682
C	3687	2-dr Hol HT-5P	2855	3465	66,495
C	3667	2-dr Conv-5P	3109	3534	13,498
C	3669	4-dr Twn Sed-5P	2883	3489	24,251
C	3639	4-dr Hol HT-5P	2964	3548	7046
C	3635	4-dr Sta Wag-5P	3157	3900	8,559

CUTLASS SUPREME — The ultimate luxury in Oldsmobile's intermediate line seemed to be embodied in the Cutlass Supreme lineup for 1969. This three-model series remained one of Oldsmobile's best sellers. Standard Supreme equipment included all items from the Cutlass standard equipment list plus: loop-pile carpeting; oval outside rearview mirror; molding package; inside day/night mirror; front stabilizer bar; and dual-latched hood. Upholstery came in either vinyl or cloth. Standard tire size was 7.75 x 14 inches.

CUTLASS SUPREME

Model Number	Body/Style Number	Body Type & Seating	Factory Price	Shipping Weight	Production Total
CS	4287	2-dr Hol HT-5P	3036	3496	24,193
CS	4269	4-dr Twn Sed-5P	2938	3509	4,522
CS	4239	4-dr Hol HT-5P	3111	3586	8,714

1969 Oldsmobile, two-door Cutlass 4-4-2 hardtop, V-8

4-4-2 — Available in its second year as a series was the high-performance 4-4-2. Three basic models were available this year. If a 4-4-2 buyer wanted a little more performance a special "W-30" package could be ordered. It was based on a special "Force-Air" inducted 360 hp version of the 400 cid V-8. A well-tuned, factory blue-printed 4-4-2 with the 400 cid V-8 was among the fastest stock showroom domestic cars available to the general public in 1969. Stock 4-4-2 equipment included all items from the Cutlass list plus: special grille; special stripes and emblems; bucket seats; heavy-duty drive shaft; special handling package; heavy-duty wheels; and straight-through exhaust system. Interiors were done in either vinyl or cloth. Tire size was F-70 x 14 inches.

4-4-2

Model Number	Body/Style Number	Body Type & Seating	Factory Price	Shipping Weight	Production Total
442	4477	2-dr Spts Cpe-5P	3141	3665	2,475
442	4487	2-dr Hol HT-5P	3204	3675	19,587
442	4467	2-dr Conv-5P	3395	3743	4,295
442/HO	4487H	2-dr Hurst/Olds-5P	4500-4900	3705	906

VISTA CRUISER — Oldsmobile continued to offer station wagons on two different wheelbases and the Vista Cruiser was the longer of the two groups. Despite the fact the Vista Cruiser was a physically larger car, it shared a great deal of the Cutlass sheet metal. Standard series equipment included: Deluxe armrests; cigar lighter; dome light; molding package; foam seat cushions; dual front head restraints; Vista roof treatment; and recessed windshield wipers. Standard tire size was 8.25 x 14 inches. Upholstery was either vinyl or cloth.

VISTA CRUISER

Model Number	Body/Style Number	Body Type & Seating	Factory Price	Shipping Weight	Production Total
VC	4855	4-dr Sta Wag-5P	3457	4101	11.879
VC	4865	4-dr Sta Wag-7P	3600	4237	21,508

1969 Oldsmobile four-door Delta 88 Holiday hardtop sedan, V-8

DELTA EIGHTY-EIGHT — Three different series of Eighty-Eight models were available this year and the plain Delta 88 was the bottom of the line. A total of four body styles were available in this full-size series. Standard Delta equipment included: armrests front and rear; cigar lighter; carpeting; woodgrain instrument panel trim; lamp package; chrome molding package; front head restraints; and Flo-Thru body ventilation. Upholstery could be done in either vinyl or cloth. Standard tire size was 8.55 x 15 inches. Assembly plant codes: M, X, E, C and D will be discovered on full-size 1969 Oldsmobiles, with production of some models specific to a single factory.

DELTA EIGHTY-EIGHT

Model Number	Body/Style Number	Body Type & Seating	Factory Price	Shipping Weight	Production Total
D88	5437	2-dr Hol HT-5P	3277	4070	41,947
D88	5469	4-dr Twn Sed-5P	3222	4098	49,995
D88	5439	4-dr Hol HT-5P	3353	4148	42,690
D88	5467	2-dr Conv-5P	3590	4129	5,294

DELTA EIGHTY-EIGHT CUSTOM — The next step up the ladder on the full-sized Oldsmobile lineup was the Delta Eighty-Eight Custom. Just three models were offered in this series and the convertible was not available as a Custom. Later in the model year, the larger 455 cid motor became standard equipment on this series. Standard equipment also included all items from the Delta Eighty-Eight series, plus: foam seats; seat molding package; lamp switches at all doors; and a special interior lamp package. Standard tire size was 8.55 x 15 inches. Interiors were done either in cloth or vinyl.

DELTA EIGHTY-EIGHT CUSTOM

Model Number	Body/Style Number	Body Type & Seating	Factory Price	Shipping Weight	Production Total
DC88	6437	2-dr Hol HT-5P	3525	4169	22,083
DC88	6469	4-dr Twn Sed-5P	3432	4189	31,012
DC88	6439	4-dr Hol HT-5P	3600	4254	36,502

DELTA EIGHTY-EIGHT ROYALE — A single car series this year was the Delta Eighty-Eight Royale. It's interesting to note that Oldsmobile picked up this nameplate from REO, which itself was named for Ransom E. Olds. REO used the Royale name on a classic 1930s model it built. Standard 1969 Oldsmobile Delta Eighty-Eight Royale equipment included all items from the Delta Eighty-Eight Custom series, plus: body paint stripes; vinyl roof covering; Custom Sport front seat; front center armrest; and electric clock. Standard tire size was 8.55 x 15 inches. Upholstery was either vinyl or leather.

DELTA EIGHTY-EIGHT ROYALE

Model Number	Body/Style Number	Body Type & Seating	Factory Price	Shipping Weight	Production Total
DR88	6647	2-dr Hol HT-5P	3836	4197	22,564

NINETY-EIGHT — As far as conventional front engine/rear drive cars went, the Ninety-Eight remained the top of the line for Oldsmobile buyers. It was the physically largest product offered by Oldsmobile and rode on a 127 inch wheelbase. A Ninety-Eight buyer had six body styles to select from. The Ninety-Eight was a well-appointed car and standard equipment included: power brakes; electric clock; full carpeting; courtesy lamps; paint stripes; power seat adjuster; seat belts; and shoulder harnesses; power steering; Deluxe steering wheel; power windows; and Turbo-Hydramatic transmission. Standard tire size was 8.85 x 15 inches. Upholstery could be ordered in vinyl, cloth or leather. All Ninety-Eights were built in Lansing, Mich. and contained the letter code M.

NINETY-EIGHT

Model Number	Body/Style Number	Body Type & Seating	Factory Price	Shipping Weight	Production Total
98	8457	2-dr Hol HT-5P	4462	4359	27,041
98	8469	4-dr Twn Sed-5P	4256	4372	11,169
98	8639	4-dr Lux Sed-5P	4693	4447	25,973
98	8439	4-dr Hol HT-5P	4524	4456	17,294
98	8467	2-dr Conv-5P	4729	4457	4,288
98	8669	4-dr Lux Sed-5P	4599	4515	30,643

1969 Oldsmobile, two-door Toronado hardtop sports coupe, V-8

TORONADO — The Olds Toronado continued to be a unique automobile, sharing honors with the Cadillac Eldorado as the only full-sized front-wheel-drive automobiles offered in the domestic market. Just two body styles were made. The standard equipment list was long: power brakes; electric clock; full carpeting; courtesy lamps; power steering; Flo-Thru ventilation; and Turbo-Hydramatic transmission. Standard tire size was 8.85 x 15 inches. Upholstery was done in vinyl, leather or cloth.

TORONADO

Model Number	Body/Style Number	Body Type & Seating	Factory Price	Shipping Weight	Production Total
T	9487	2-dr Cpe-5P	4836	4478	3,421
CUSTOM					
T	9687	2-dr Cpe-5P	—	4505	25,073

BASE ENGINES

(F-85/CUTLASS SERIES) Inline six-cylinder. Overhead valves. Cast iron block. Displacement: 250 cid. Bore and stroke: 3-7/8 x 3.53 inches. Compression ratio: 8.5:1. Brake hp: 155 at 4200 rpm. Seven main bearings. Hydraulic valve lifters. Carburetor: Rochester MV, one-barrel.

(F-85/CUTLASS SERIES) V-8. Overhead valves. Cast iron block. Displacement: 350 cid. Bore and stroke: 4.057 x 3.385 inches. Compression ratio: 9:1. Brake hp: 250 at 4400 rpm. Five main bearings. Hydraulic valve lifters. Carburetor: 2GC, two-barrel.

(CUTLASS SUPREME/VISTA CRUISER SERIES) V-8. Overhead valves. Cast iron block. Displacement: 350 cid. Bore and stroke: 4.057 x 3.385 inches. Compression ratio: 10.25:1. Brake hp: 310 at 4800 rpm. Five main bearings. Hydraulic valve lifters. Carburetor: Rochester 4GC, four-barrel.

(4-4-2 SERIES) V-8. Overhead valves. Cast iron block. Displacement: 350 cid. Bore and stroke: 3.87 x 4.25 inches. Compression ratio: 10.5:1. Brake hp: 325 (automatic transmission); 350 (manual transmission) at 4800 rpm. (W31). Five main bearings. Hydraulic valve lifters. Carburetor: Rochester 4GC, four-barrel.

(DELTA EIGHTY-EIGHT SERIES) V-8. Overhead valves. Cast iron block. Displacement: 350 cid. Bore and stroke: 4.057 x 3.385 inches. Compression ratio: 9:1. Brake hp: 250 at 4400 rpm. Five main bearings. Hydraulic valve lifters. Carburetor: Rochester 4GC, four-barrel.

(DELTA EIGHTY-EIGHT CUSTOM/ROYALE SERIES) V-8. Overhead valves. Cast iron block. Displacement: 455 cid. Bore and stroke: 4.125 x 4.250 inches. Compression ratio: 9 to 1. 310 hp at 4400 rpm. Five main bearings. Hydraulic valve lifters. Rochester 2GC two-barrel.

(NINETY-EIGHT SERIES) V-8. Overhead valves. Cast iron block. Displacement: 455 cid. Bore and stroke: 4.125 x 4.250 inches. Compression ratio: 10.25:1. Brake hp: 365 at 4600 rpm. Five main bearings. Hydraulic valve lifters. Carburetion: Rochester 4GC, four-barrel.

(TORONADO SERIES) V-8. Overhead valves. Cast iron block. Displacement: 455 cid Bore and stroke: 4.125 x 4.250 inches. Compression ratio: 10.25:1. Brake hp: 375 at 4600 rpm. Five main bearings. Hydraulic valve lifters. Carburetor: Rochester: 4GC four-barrel.

CHASSIS FEATURES: Wheelbase: (Cutlass/Cutlass Supreme sedans) 116 inches; (4-42/Cutlass S/F-85 two-doors) 112 inches; (Vista Cruiser) 121 inches; (Delta/Delta Custom/Royale 88s) 124 inches; (Ninety-Eight) 127 inches; (Toronado) 119 inches. Overall length: (Cutlass/Supreme sedans) 205.9 inches; (4-4-2, Cutlass S, F-8 two-doors) 201.9 inches; (Vista Cruiser) 217.6 inches; (Delta/Delta Custom/Royale 88s) 218.6 inches; (Ninety-Eight) 224.4 inches; (Toronado) 214.8 inches. Front tread: (F85/Cutlass S/Supreme/4-4-2/Vista Cruiser) 59 inches. (Toronados) 63.5 inches; (all others) 62.5 inches. Rear tread: (F-85/Cutlass S/Supreme/4-4-2/Vista Cruiser) 59 inches; (all others) 63 inches.

OPTIONS: Power brakes ($41). Power steering ($100). Air conditioning ($375). Tinted glass ($38). Power trunk release ($17). Power door locks ($44). Floor mats ($7). Rear defogger ($44). Sports console ($61). Super-Stock wheels ($73). Tilt steering wheel ($46). Rallye instruments ($84). Stereo tape player ($133). AM/FM radio ($238). Power antenna ($31). Rear speakers ($16). Vinyl roof ($121). Power seats ($100). Cornering lamps ($38). Special order paint ($83). W-31 package including special Force-Air 350 cid engine option for Cutlass ($310). W-30 special 400 cid Force-Air engine package for 4-4-2 ($264). Three-speed manual transmission was standard on all except 98 and Toronado. Automatic transmission ($227). Three-speed manual floor shift transmission ($84). Wide-ratio four-speed manual transmission with floor shift ($184). Close-ratio four-speed manual transmission with floor shift ($184). V-8: 350 cid/310 hp Rocket engine ($47). V-8: 400 cid/325 hp Rocket engine ($47). V-8: 455 cid/365 hp Rocket engine ($110). V-8: 455 cid/390 hp High-Performance Rocket engine ($141). V-8: 455 cid/400 hp Toronado engine ($47). Force-Air induction package ($42). Positive traction rear axle ($43). Cruise control ($57).

HISTORICAL FOOTNOTES: The 1969 Oldsmobiles, F-85s and Toronados were introduced Sept. 12, 1968. Oldsmobile moved ahead of Plymouth to take fifth place in industry sales with 655,241 units moved in 1969. The 12-millionth Oldsmobile was built in November, 1969. In the F-85 car-lines 82 percent of the cars had standard V-8s; 15.5 percent had optional V-8s; 4.9 percent had four-speed transmission; nine percent had AM/FM; 26.3 percent had bucket seats; and 39.3 percent had vinyl tops. In the full-size Oldsmobile series, 77.3 percent of the cars had standard V-8s and the rest had optional V-8s. Only 1.9 percent of the big Olds models had bucket seats; 8.1 percent had Posi-Traction; and 6.6 percent had Cruise Control. Option installation rates for Toronados included 7.2 percent bucket seats; 88.9 percent with power windows; 53.2 percent with front disc brakes; 22 percent with power door locks; and 19.2 percent with Cruise Control. During the year, John Beltz replaced Harold Metzel as general manager of Oldsmobile. Metzel had held the job five years.

1970 OLDSMOBILE

F-85 — The bottom-of-the-line Oldsmobile offering this year continued as a single model F-85. Only the sports coupe was marketed in 1970. Standard equipment on this most basic Oldsmobile included: padded head restraints; seat and shoulder belts; anti-theft steering column; locking glovebox; and heavy-duty three-speed manual transmission. Standard tire size was F78 x 14 inches. Upholstery was done in either cloth or vinyl. Option W-45 was the Rallye 350 Package, which was fitted on 3,547 Cutlass 'S' coupes and F-85 coupes. The package included Sebring yellow paint, special decals and a special 350 motor. Assembly plant codes found on mid-size Oldsmobiles this year were M, Z, E, and G.

OLDSMOBILE I.D. NUMBERS: VIN located on top left of dashboard viewable through windshield. Motor production code number indicating approximate production date and a motor serial number matching the VIN located on engine. Serial number takes the form of seven symbols, plus sequential production number. First symbol identifies GM division: 3=Oldsmobile. Second to fifth symbols indicate series and match the four digits in Body/Style Number column of charts below. Sixth symbol identifies model year: 0=1970. Seventh symbol indicates assembly plant: C=Southgate, Calif.; D=Doraville (Atlanta), Ga.; E=Linden, N.J.; G=Framingham, Mass.; M=Lansing, Mich.; Z=Fremont, Calif.; X=Fairfax (Kansas City), Kan. Remaining symbols are the sequential production number starting at 100001 at each factory. Ending VINs not available. Engine numbers consist of a alphabetical prefix and a production sequence number. Prefixes for 1970 engines were: [250 cid inline six] VB/VF=155 hp; [350 cid V-8] QI/QA/QJ/TC/TD/TL=250 hp; QN/QP/QV=310 hp; QD/QX=325 hp. [455 cid V-8] UC/UD/UJ=310 hp; TX/TY=320 hp; TP/TQ/TU/TV/TW/UN/UO=365 hp; TS/TT=370 hp; US/UT=375 hp; UL=390 hp; UV/UW=400 hp. Ending engine numbers not available.

F-85

Model Number	Body/Style Number	Body Type & Seating	Factory Price	Shipping Weight	Production Total
SIX-CYLINDER					
F-85	3177	2-dr Spts Cpe-5P	2676	3294	2,836
V-8					
F-85	3277	2-dr Spts Cpe-5P	2787	3505	8,274

1970 Oldsmobile, two-door Cutlass Supreme hardtop coupe, V-8

CUTLASS — The first move up the Oldsmobile intermediate ladder was the Cutlass series. Again, the two-door Cutlass models rolled on a shorter wheelbase and carried the Cutlass S nameplate. Only closed cars were found in this series for 1970, including a pair of two-doors, a pair of four-doors and a four-door station wagon. Standard equipment included all items from the F-85 list plus: special chrome moulding package; Deluxe steering wheel; interior light package; and special hood design. Standard tire size was G78 x 14 inches. Interiors were done in vinyl or cloth. Option W-45 was the Rallye 350 Package, which was fitted on 3,547 Cutlass 'S' coupes and F-85 coupes. The package included Sebring yellow paint, special decals and a special 350 motor.

CUTLASS

Model Number	Body/Style Number	Body Type & Seating	Factory Price	Shipping Weight	Production Total
SIX-CYLINDER					
C	3535	4-dr Sta Wag-5P	3234	3749	85
C	3587	2-dr Hol HT-5P	2859	3342	729
C	3577	2-dr Spts Cpe-5P	2796	3305	484
C	3539	4-dr Hol HT-5P	2968	3430	238
C	3569	4-dr Twn Sed-5P	2837	3361	1,171
V-8					
C	3635	4-dr Sta Wag-5P	3334	3956	7,680
C	3687	2-dr Hol HT-5P	2970	3556	88,578
C	3677	2-dr Spt Cpe-5P	2907	3520	10,677
C	3639	4-dr Hol HT-5P	3,079	3641	9,427
C	3669	4-dr Twn Sed-5P	2948	3572	35,239

CUTLASS SUPREME — Three models were available under the Cutlass Supreme nameplate, including a convertible. Also available, exclusively in this series, was the new 'SX' package. It included some special engine items, coupled with distinct internal and external markings. Standard equipment on this series included all items from the Cutlass group plus: Flo-Thru ventilation; special dash; V-8 engine; Deluxe steering wheel; and Custom Sport seat. Standard tire size was G-78 x 14 inches. Interiors could be done in cloth or vinyl.

CUTLASS SUPREME

Model Number	Body/Style Number	Body Type & Seating	Factory Price	Shipping Weight	Production Total
CUTLASSSUPREME					
CS	4257	2-dr Hol HT-5P	3151	3574	11,354
CS	4267	2-dr Conv-5P	3335	3614	4,867
CS	4239	4-dr Hol HT-5P	3226	3662	10,762

4-4-2 — Continuing as a series this year was the 4-4-2 group. High-performance continued to sell well for Oldsmobile in 1970 and this series was the division's performance leader. Three models, all two-doors, were available as 4-4-2s. Standard equipment included all items from the Cutlass list plus: foam padded seats; special handling package; external and internal emblems; Deluxe steering wheel; special engine; low-restriction exhaust system and special paint stripes. Standard tires were G-70 x 14 RWL. Upholstery was done in either vinyl or cloth.

4-4-2

Model Number	Body/Style Number	Body Type & Seating	Factory Price	Shipping Weight	Production Total
442	4487	2-dr Hol HT-5P	3376	3817	14,709
442	4477	2-dr Spts Cpe-5P	3312	3801	1,688
442	4467	2-dr Conv-5P	3567	3844	2,933

VISTA CRUISER — Found in both a two-seat and three-seat version for this model year was the Oldsmobile Vista Cruiser station wagon. The Vista Cruiser continued to be a physically larger car than the Cutlass Cruiser and found good sales in the station wagon market. Standard equipment for this series included: special underfloor storage compartment; seat belts and shoulder harness; energy-absorbing steering column; side marker lights; anti-theft ignition system; divided front seat; V-8 engine; tinted roof-top vista window; and Deluxe Steering wheel. Standard tire size was H78 x 14 inches. Upholstery could be ordered in vinyl or cloth.

VISTA CRUISER

Model Number	Body/Style Number	Body Type & Seating	Factory Price	Shipping Weight	Production Total
VC	4855	4-dr Sta Wag-5P	3636	4183	10,758
VC	4865	4-dr Sta Wag-7P	3778	4284	23,336

1970 Oldsmobile two-door Delta 88 Royale hardtop sports coupe, V-8

DELTA EIGHTY-EIGHT — The Delta 88 line remained the basic full-line series for Oldsmobile. Four basic body styles were offered: coupe, convertible and two four-doors. One of the latter was a pillared Town Sedan and the other a pillarless Holiday Sedan. Standard equipment included: seat belts and shoulder harnesses; energy-absorbing steering column; anti-theft ignition; side marker lights; four-way flashers; dual hood latches; Deluxe steering wheel; and full wheel discs. Standard tire size was H78 x 15 inches. Upholstery was done in vinyl or cloth. The full-size Olds assembly plant codes were: M, X, E, C and D.

DELTA EIGHTY-EIGHT

Model Number	Body/Style Number	Body Type & Seating	Factory Price	Shipping Weight	Production Total
88	5437	2-dr Hol HT-5P	3590	4034	33,017
88	5439	4-dr Hol HT-5P	3666	4120	37,695
88	5467	2-dr Conv-5P	3903	4119	3095
88	5469	4-dr Twn Sed-5P	3534	4078	47,067

DELTA EIGHTY-EIGHT CUSTOM — The next rung up the full-sized Oldsmobile model ladder was the Delta Eighty-Eight Custom. Three models were found here, but the convertible was not offered as a Custom. Standard equipment included all items from the Delta Eighty-Eight list plus: Custom Sport seat; special moldings; interior light package; and special wheel discs. Standard tire size was H78 x 15 inches. Interiors were done in vinyl or leather.

DELTA EIGHTY-EIGHT CUSTOM

Model Number	Body/Style Number	Body Type & Seating	Factory Price	Shipping Weight	Production Total
D88C	6437	2-dr Hol HT-5P	3848	4133	16,149
D88C	6469	4-dr Twn Sed-5P	3755	4174	24,727
D88C	6439	4-dr Hol HT-5P	3924	4221	28,432

DELTA EIGHTY-EIGHT ROYALE — Oldsmobile again topped-off Eighty-Eight group with a single model Delta Eighty-Eight Royale series. Standard equipment here included all items from the Custom series, plus: vinyl roof covering; electric clock; double padded seats; special front fender trim; and paint stripes. Standard tire size was H78 x 15 inches. Interiors could be ordered in vinyl or cloth.

DELTA EIGHTY-EIGHTY ROYALE

Model Number	Body/Style Number	Body Type & Seating	Factory Price	Shipping Weight	Production Total
D88R	6647	2-dr Hol HT-5P	4,159	4,136	13,249

NINETY-EIGHT — Once again, the Ninety-Eight models were the physically largest Oldsmobiles to hit the road. They still shared the luxury side of Oldsmobile's business with the Toronado. Standard equipment on this series was rather complete. It included: Turbo-Hydramatic 400 transmission; power steering; power brakes with front discs; power windows; power seats; Deluxe steering wheel; electric clock; and full wheel discs. Standard tire size was J78 x 15 inches. Interiors were done in leather, vinyl or cloth. All Ninety-Eights were built in Lansing, Mich. and the letter code M was contained in the Vehicle Identification Number.

NINETY-EIGHT

Model Number	Body/Style Number	Body Type & Seating	Factory Price	Shipping Weight	Production Total
98	8457	2-dr Hol HT-5P	465	4391	21,111
98	8467	2-dr Conv-5P	4914	4423	3,161
98	8669	4-dr Lux Sed-5P	4793	4490	29,005
98	8639	4-dr Lux HT-5P	4888	4535	19,377
98	8439	4-dr Hol HT-5P	4582	4463	14,098
98	8469	4-dr Twn Sed-5P	4451	4397	9,092

1970 Oldsmobile, two-door Toronado hardtop sports coupe, V-8

TORONADO — Once again the top-of-the-line Oldsmobile was the front-wheel-driven Toronado. The 'Toro' carried the Oldsmobile banner into the personal luxury field with a car that was well-equipped even in standard form. Regular equipment included: Turbo-Hydra-

matic transmission; power steering; power brakes; foam-padded front seat; special V-8 engine; Deluxe steering wheel; and electric clock. Standard tire size was J78 x 15 inches. Interiors could be done in vinyl, cloth or leather.

TORONADO

Model Number	Body/Style Number	Body Type & Seating	Factory Price	Shipping Weight	Production Total
T	9487	2-dr Cpe-5P	5023	4459	2,351

CUSTOM

Model Number	Body/Style Number	Body Type & Seating	Factory Price	Shipping Weight	Production Total
T	9687	2-dr Cpe-5P	5216	4498	23,082

BASE ENGINES

(F-85/CUTLASS SERIES) Inline six-cylinder. Overhead valves. Cast-iron block. Displacement: 250 cid. Bore and stroke: 3.875 x 3.530 inches. Compression ratio: 8.5:1. Brake hp: 155 at 4200 rpm. Seven main bearings. Hydraulic valve lifters. Carburetor: Rochester Model MV one-barrel.

(F-85/CUTLASS SERIES) V-8. Overhead valves. Displacement: 350 cid. Bore and stroke: 4.057 x 3.385 inches. Compression ratio: 9:1. Brake hp: 250 at 4400 rpm. Five main bearings. Hydraulic valve lifters. Carburetor: Rochester two-barrel Model 2GC.

(CUTLASS SUPREME SERIES) V-8. Overhead valve. Cast iron block. Displacement: 350 cid. Bore and stroke: 4.057 x 3.385 inches. Compression ratio: 10.25:1. Brake hp: 310 at 4600 rpm. Five main bearings. Hydraulic valve lifters. Carburetor: Rochester Model 4GC four-barrel.

(4-4-2 SERIES) V-8. Overhead valves. Cast iron block. Displacement: 455 cid. Bore and stroke: 4.125 x 4.250 inches. Compression ratio: 10.50:1. Brake hp: 365 at 5000 rpm. Five main bearings. Hydraulic valve lifters. Carburetor: Rochester Model 4GC four-barrel.

(VISTA CRUISER SERIES) V-8. Overhead valves. Cast iron block. Displacement: 350 cid. Bore and stroke: 4.057 x 3.385 inches. Compression ratio: 9:1. Brake hp: 250 at 4400 rpm. Five main bearings. Hydraulic valve lifters. Carburetor: Rochester Model 2GC two-barrel.

(DELTA 88/CUSTOM/ROYALE SERIES) V-8. Overhead valves. Cast iron block. Displacement: 4.125 x 4.250 inches. Compression ratio: 9:1. Brake hp: 310 at 4200 rpm. Five main bearings. Hydraulic valve lifters. Carburetion: Rochester Model 2GC two-barrel.

(NINETY-EIGHT SERIES) V-8. Overhead valves. Displacement: 455 cid. Bore and stroke: 4.125 x 4.250 inches. Compression ratio: 10.25:1. Brake hp: 365 at 4600 rpm. Five main bearings. Hydraulic valve lifters. Rochester Model 4GC four-barrel carburetor.

(TORANADO SERIES) V-8. Overhead valves. Cast iron block. Displacement: 455 cid. Bore and stroke: 4.125 x 4.250 inches. Compression ratio: 10.25:1. 375 hp at 4600 rpm. Five main bearings. Hydraulic valve lifters. Carburetor: Rochester Model 4GC four-barrel.

CHASSIS FEATURES: Wheelbase: (Cutlass/F-85 4-4-2 two-door) 112 inches; (Cutlass/Cutlass Supreme four-door) 116 inches; (Vista Cruiser) 121 inches; (Delta 88) 124 inches; (Ninety-Eight) 127 inches; (Toronado) 119 inches. Overall length: (F-85/Cutlass/4-4-2 two-door) 203.2 inches; (Cutlass/Cutlass Supreme four-door) 207.2 inches; (Vista Cruiser) 218.2 inches; (Delta 88) 219.1 inches; (Ninety-Eight) 225.2 inches; (Toronado) 214.3 inches. Front tread: (all F-85/ Cutlass/Supreme/ Vista Cruiser) 59 inches; (Toronado) 63.5 inches; (all others) 62.5 inches. Rear tread: (all F-85/Cutlass/Supreme/Vista Cruiser) 59 inches; (all others) 63 inches.

OPTIONS: Power brakes ($55). Power steering ($109). Air conditioning ($431). Aluminum axle carrier ($157). AM radio ($69). AM/FM stereo ($238). Rear speaker ($16). Deck lid spoiler ($73). Rear air deflector/station wagons ($20). Superlift rear shocks ($42). Roof luggage rack ($64). Power windows ($110). Tilt steering wheel ($46). Electric clock ($16). Cruise control ($62). Three-speed manual transmission was standard on all except 98 and Toronado. Option W-45 was the Rallye 350 Package. Three-speed manual floor shift transmission ($51). Four-speed manual floor shift transmission ($137). V-8: 350 cid/310 hp Rocket engine ($81). V-8: 350 cid/325 hp W-31 engine ($585). V-8: 455 cid/320 hp Rocket engine ($87). V-8: 455 cid/365 hp Rocket engine ($115). V-8: 455 cid/370 hp W-30 engine ($597). V-8: 455 cid/400 hp Toronado engine ($212). Air-induction package with W-30 or W-31. Positive traction rear axle ($42).

HISTORICAL FOOTNOTES: In 1970, Oldsmobile sales were 633,981 units, putting the division fifth in the rankings. In the intermediate (F-85) lines 96 percent of all cars had automatic transmission; three percent had four-speed manual transmission; 75 percent had V-8s; 89 percent had AM radios; six percent had AM/FM; four percent had stereos; 26 percent had bucket seats; 48 percent had a vinyl roof; 10 percent had a limited-slip axle and 18 percent had styled wheels. In the full-size Oldsmobile lines, all cars had automatic transmission; 85 percent had V-8s; 12 percent had power door locks; 41 percent had power windows; only one percent had bucket seats; 71 percent had vinyl tops; 86 percent had air conditioning and 23 percent had option full wheel discs. Only seven percent of Toronados had bucket seats; 73 percent had a movable steering column; and 28 percent had Cruise Control.

1971 OLDSMOBILE

F-85 — The F-85 series hung on for another year as a one-model series. This year the only available body style was a four-door sedan. Standard series equipment included: front door armrests, cigarette lighter, dome lamp, dual head restraints, seat belts and shoulder harnesses, and chrome hubcaps. Standard tire size F78 x 14 inches. Interiors were done in either vinyl or cloth. Assembly plant codes for 1971 F-85s were R, G, Z and M.

OLDSMOBILE I.D. NUMBERS: VIN located on top left of dashboard viewable through windshield. Motor production code number indicating approximate production date and a motor serial number matching the VIN located on engine. Serial number takes the form of seven symbols, plus sequential production number. First symbol identifies GM division: 3=Oldsmobile. Second to fifth symbols indicate series and match the four digits in Body/Style Number column of charts below. Sixth symbol identifies model year: 1=1971. Seventh symbol indicates assembly plant: E=Linden, N.J.; G=Framingham, Mass.; M=Lansing, Mich.; Z=Fremont, Calif.; X=Fairfax (Kansas City) Kan.; R=Arlington, Texas. Remaining symbols are the sequential production number starting at 100001 at each factory. Ending VINs not available. Engine numbers consist of a alphabetical prefix and a production sequence number. Prefixes for 1970 engines were: [250 cid inline six] ZB/ZG/VB/VF=145 hp; [350 cid V-8] QI/QA/QJ/TC/TD/TE=240 hp; QN/QP/QB/QD=260 hp. [455 cid V-8] UC/UD/UE/TY/TX=280 hp; TA/TN/TP/TQ/TU/TV/TW/UN/UO=320 hp; TT/TL/TS/TB=340 hp; US/UT=350 hp. Ending engine numbers not available.

Model Number	Body/Style Number	Body Type & Seating	Factory Price	Shipping Weight	Production Total
F-85	3169	4-dr Twn Sed-5P	2884	3358	769
V-8					
F-85	3269	4-dr Twn Sed-5P	3005	3569	3,650

CUTLASS — A mild restyling job was given the Oldsmobile intermediates this year. The Cutlass group consisted of three body styles with either six or V-8 power plants. Standard equipment included all items from the F-85 list plus: Deluxe armrests, carpeting, molding packages, Flo-Thru ventilation and recessed windshield wipers. Standard tire size was F78 x 14 inches. Upholstery was done in either cloth or vinyl.

CUTLASS

Model Number	Body/Style Number	Body Type & Seating	Factory Price	Shipping Weight	Production Total
SIX-CYLINDER					
C	3536	4-dr Sta Wag-5P	3453	3680	47
C	3569	4-dr Twn Sed-5P	2998	3358	618
C	3187	2-dr Hol HT-5P	2900	3339	1,345
V-8					
C	3636	4-dr Sta Wag-5P	3574	4054	6,742
C	3669	4-dr Twn Sed-5P	3119	3598	31,904
C	3287	2-dr Hol HT-5P	3021	3552	32,278

1971 Oldsmobile, two-door Cutlass 'S' hardtop sports coupe, V-8

CUTLASS 'S' — This year the Cutlass 'S' nameplate took on a bit different meaning. A pair of coupe models were offered powered by either a six or eight-cylinder motor. Standard equipment included: front and rear armrests, cigarette lighter, carpeting, dome light, chrome molding package, radio antenna in windshield, seat belts and shoulder harnesses and Deluxe steering wheel.

CUTLASS 'S'

Model Number	Body/Style Number	Body Type & Seating	Factory Price	Shipping Weight.	Production Total
SIX-CYLINDER					
CS	3587	2-dr Hol HT-5P	3020	3346	297
CS	3577	2-dr Spts Cpe-5P	2957	3334	113
V-8					
CS	3687	2-dr Hol HT-5P	3141	3561	63,145
CS	3677	2-dr Spts Cpe-5P	3078	3550	4339

CUTLASS SUPREME — The most luxury filled Oldsmobile intermediates were the Cutlass Supreme models. A total of three body styles were available including a convertible, in its next to the last year as a Cutlass offering. Standard equipment included: armrests, cigarette lighter, V-8 engine, carpeting, woodgrain dash, interior light package, moldings, seat belts and shoulder harnesses, Deluxe steering wheel and chrome hubcaps. Standard tire size was F78 x 14 inches. Upholstery was done in either vinyl or cloth.

CUTLASS SUPREME

Model Number	Body/Style Number	Body Type & Seating	Factory Price	Shipping Weight	Production Total
CSU	4267	Conv-5P	3506	3631	10,255
CSU	4239	4-dr Hol HT-5P	3397	3690	10,458
CSU	4257	2-dr Hol HT-5P	3332	3562	60,599

4-4-2 — High performance motoring at Oldsmobile and most other manufacturers began a downhill run in 1971. This was the final year the 4-4-2 would hold model status at Oldsmobile. Standard series equipment included: special 455 cid motor, dual exhausts, carpeting, special springs, stabilizer bars, special engine mounts, strato bucket seats, heavy-duty wheels, special emblems and Deluxe steering wheel. Standard tire was G70 x 14 inches. Upholstery was done in either vinyl or cloth.

4-4-2

Model Number	Body/Style Number	Body Type & Seating	Factory Price	Shipping Weight	Production Total
442	4487	2-dr Hol HT-5P	3551	3835	6,285
442	4467	2-dr Conv-5P	3742	3792	1,304

VISTA CRUISER — For the first time in quite a while the Vista Cruiser was not the largest Olds wagon offered. The honor went this year to the Custom Cruiser. The Vista Cruiser now filled the middle slot in the Olds wagon lineup and it was available as either a two- or three-seat model. Standard equipment included: woodgrain trim, cigarette lighter, V-8 motor, carpeting, moldings, windshield radio antenna, seat belts and shoulder harnesses, vista roof and chrome hubcaps. Upholstery was done in either vinyl or cloth. Standard tire size was H78 x 14 inches.

VISTA CRUISER

Model Number	Body/Style Number	Body Type & Seating	Factory Price	Shipping Weight	Production Total
VC	4856	4-dr Sta Wag-5P	3865	4293	9,317
VC	4866	4-dr Sta Wag-7P	4007	4414	20,566

DELTA EIGHTY-EIGHT — The basic full-sized series again this year for Oldsmobile was the Delta Eighty-Eight. Three models were available in this series. This new body was the final body until 1977's down-sized models. Standard equipment included: front and rear armrests, power front disc brakes, carpeting, inside hood release, dome light, lamp package, windshield antenna, seat belts and shoulder harnesses and Flo-Thru ventilation. Standard tire size was H78 x 15 inches. Upholstery was done in either vinyl or cloth. Assembly plant codes found on 1971 full-size Oldsmobiles were X, M and E, with production of high trim level models limited to specific factories.

DELTA EIGHTY-EIGHT

Model Number	Body/Style Number	Body Type & Seating	Factory Price	Shipping Weight	Production Total
88	5457	2-dr Hol HT-5P	3826	4165	27,031
88	5439	4-dr Hol HT-5P	3888	4221	31,420
88	5469	4-dr Twn Sed-5P	3770	4198	38,298

DELTA EIGHTY-EIGHT CUSTOM — The second step up the full-sized Oldsmobile ladder was the Delta Eighty-Eight Custom series. Just three models were available in the series. Standard equipment included: front and rear armrests, power front disc brakes, cigarette lighter, carpeting, inside hood release, lamp package, seat belt and shoulder harnesses, power steering and chrome hubcaps. Standard tire size was H78 x 15 inches. Upholstery could be ordered in vinyl or cloth.

DELTA EIGHTY-EIGHT CUSTOM

Model Number	Body/Style Number	Body Type & Seating	Factory Price	Shipping Weight	Production Total
88C	6439	4-dr Hol HT-5P	4134	4335	24,251
88C	6457	2-dr Hol HT-5P	4059	4277	14,067
88C	6469	4-dr Twn Sed-5P	3966	4308	22,209

DELTA EIGHTY-EIGHT ROYALE — The top-of-the line offering in the 88 group was the Delta Eighty-Eight Royale. Just two body styles were available as the convertible joined a hardtop coupe in this series. Standard series equipment included: power front disc brakes, electric clock, carpeting, interior hood release, courtesy lamps, moldings, body paint stripes, vinyl top (on coupes), power steering, Deluxe steering wheel, Flo-Thru ventilation and special wheel discs. Standard tire size was H78 x 15 inches. Upholstery was done in vinyl, leather or cloth.

DELTA EIGHTY-EIGHT ROYALE

Model Number	Body/Style Number	Body Type & Seating	Factory Price	Shipping Weight	Production Total
88R	6647	2-dr Hol HT-5P	4317	4254	8,397
88R	6667	2-dr Conv-5P	4325	4233	2,883

1971 Oldsmobile, four-door Custom Cruiser station wagon, V-8

CUSTOM CRUISER — The new addition to Oldsmobile's full-size lineup this year was this full-sized wagon. It used sheet metal from the Eighty-Eight models, but shared the Ninety-Eight series wheelbase. Both two-seat and three-seat versions were offered. Standard equipment included: power front disc brakes, carpeting, V-8 engine, moldings, windshield radio antenna, power steering, Deluxe steering wheels and heavy-duty wheels. Standard tire size was L78 x 15 inches. Upholstery was done in vinyl or leather.

CUSTOM CRUISER

Model Number	Body/Style Number	Body Type & Seating	Factory Price	Shipping Weight	Production Total
CC	6835	4-dr Sta Wag-5P	4539	4888	4049
CC	6845	4-dr Sta Wag-7P	4680	5008	9,932

NINETY-EIGHT — Once again the largest and most luxury filled-Oldsmobile was in the Ninety-Eight series. This year offerings were cut to just four models. All cars in this series were well-appointed. Standard equipment included: armrests front and rear, power brakes with front discs, electric clock, V-8 engine, carpeting, inside hood latch, lamp package, power seat, power steering and Turbo-Hydramatic transmission. Standard tire size was J78 x 15 inches. Interiors were done in vinyl, cloth or leather. The 1971 Ninety-Eights were built at both Linden and Lansing.

NINETY-EIGHT

Model Number	Body/Style Number	Body Type & Seating	Factory Price	Shipping Weight	Production Total
98	8437	2-dr Hol HT-5P	4828	4482	8,335
98	8637	2-dr Lux Cpe-5P	5103	4582	14,876
98	8439	4-dr Hol HT-5P	4890	4548	15,025
98	8639	4-dr Lux Sed-5P	5197	4598	45,055

TORONADO — The front-drive Toronado continued to be the mainstay for Oldsmobile in the competitive personal/luxury market. Just two coupe models were available and the Toronado continued to be exclusively manufactured at Olds main plant complex in Lansing, Mich. Standard equipment included: power brakes, cigarette lighter, electric clock, dual exhausts, remote control outside mirror, custom seats, power steering, Deluxe steering wheel and Turbo-Hydramatic transmission. Standard tire size was J78 x 15 inches. Upholstery could be done in cloth, vinyl or leather. Tornados were built at Lansing, Mich. only.

TORONADO

Model Number	Body/Style Number	Body Type & Seating	Factory Price	Shipping Weight	Production Total
T	9657	2-dr Cpe-5P	5449	4532	20,184

BROUGHAM TRIM

T	9857	2-dr Cpe-5P	—	4551	8,796

BASE ENGINES

(F-85/CUTLASS/CUTLASS 'S' SERIES) Inline six-cylinder. Overhead valves. Cast iron block. Displacement: 250 cid. Bore and stroke: 3.875 x 3.530 inches. Compression ratio: 8.5:1. Brake hp: 145 at 4200 rpm. Seven main bearings. Carburetion: Rochester MV, one-barrel.

(F-85/CUTLASS/CUTLASS 'S' SERIES) V-8. Overhead valves. Cast iron block. Displacement: 350 cid. Bore and stroke: 4.057 x 3.385 inches. Compression ratio: 8.5:1. Brake hp: 240 at 4400 rpm. Five main bearings. Hydraulic valve lifters. Carburetor: Rochester 2GC, two-barrel.

(CUTLASS SUPREME SERIES) V-8. Overhead valves. Cast iron block. Displacement: 350 cid. Bore and stroke: 4.057 x 3.385 inches. Compression ratio: 8.5:1. Brake hp: 260 at 4600 rpm. Five main bearings. Hydraulic valve lifters. Carburetor: Rochester 4MC, four-barrel.

(4-4-2 SERIES) V-8. Overhead valves. Cast iron block. Displacement: 455 cid. Bore and stroke: 4.125 x 4.250 inches. Compression ratio: 8.5:1. Brake hp: 340 at 4600 rpm. Five main bearings. Hydraulic valve lifters. Carburetor: Rochester 4MC, four-barrel.

(VISTA CRUISER/DELTA 88 SERIES) V-8. Overhead valves., Cast iron block. Displacement: 350 cid. Bore and stroke: 4.057 x 3.385 inches. Compression ratio: 8.5:1. Brake hp: 240 at 4200 rpm. Five main bearings. Hydraulic valve lifters. Carburetor: Rochester 2GC, two-barrel.

(DELTA 88 CUSTOM/ROYALE/CUSTOM CRUISER SERIES) V-8. Overhead valves. Cast iron block. Displacement: 455 cid. Bore and stroke: 4.125 x 4.250 inches. Compression ratio: 8.5:1. Brake hp: 280 at 4400 rpm. Carburetor: Rochester 2GC, two-barrel.

(NINETY-EIGHT SERIES) V-8. Overhead valves. Cast iron block. Displacement: 445 cid. Bore and stroke: 4.125 x 4.250 inches. Compression ratio: 8.5:1. Brake hp: 320 at 4400 rpm. Five main bearings. Hydraulic valve lifters. Carburetor: Rochester 4MC four-barrel.

(TORONADO SERIES) V-8. Overhead valves. Cast iron block. Displacement: 455 cid. Bore and stroke: 4.125 x 4.250 inches. Compression ratio: 8.5:1. Brake hp: 350 at 4400 rpm. Five main bearings. Hydraulic valve lifters. Carburetor: Rochester 4MC four-barrel.

CHASSIS FEATURES: Wheelbase: (intermediate two-doors) 112 inches; (intermediate four-doors) 116 inches; (all 88s) 124 inches; (98 and Custom Cruiser) 127 inches; (Vista Cruiser) 121 inches; (Toronado) 122.3 inches. Overall length: (Intermediate two-doors) 203.6 inches; (intermediate four-doors) 207.6 inches; (all 88s) 220.2 inches; (98s) 226.1 inches; (Toronados) 219.9 inches; (Vista Cruiser) 218.3 inches; (Custom Cruisers) 225.3 inches. Front tread: (all intermediates and Vista Cruisers) 59.7 inches; (all 88s and 98s) 64.1 inches; (Toronado) 63.1 inches. Rear tread: (all intermediates and Vista Cruiser) 59 inches; (all 88s and 98s) 64 inches; (Toronados) 63.3 inches.

OPTIONS: Power brakes ($69). Power steering ($115). Air conditioning ($407). Power windows ($115). Tinted windows ($43). Power trunk latch ($14). Floor mats ($7). Power door locks ($47). Windshield washer ($17). Remote control mirror ($12). Sports mirrors ($22). Vinyl roof ($102). Rear window defogger ($63). Sports console ($36). Two-tone finish ($36). Tilt steering wheel ($45). Super stock wheels ($75). Rallye pack instruments ($84). Stereo tape player ($133). AM/FM stereo radio ($239). AM radio ($74). Rear speaker ($16). Rear deck spoiler ($73). Power seat ($105). Headlamp off delay system ($12). Bumper guards ($34). Three-speed manual transmission was standard on all but 98s and Toronados. Automatic transmission ($242). Three-speed manual floor shift transmission ($84). Four-speed manual floor shift transmission ($195). Wide-ratio four-speed manual transmission with floor shift ($195). V-8: 350 cid/260 hp Rocket engine ($47). V-8: 455 cid/320 hp Rocket engine ($47). V-8: 455 cid/ 335 hp Rocket engine ($138). V-8: 455 cid/350 hp W-30 engine ($369). Positive traction rear axle ($44).

HISTORICAL FOOTNOTES: On Sept. 10, 1970, the 1971 Oldsmobiles bowed to the public. A production total of 558,889 units put Olds in sixth place. On the big Oldsmobiles, 72.9 percent had vinyl roofs; 81.3 percent had air conditioning and 8.7 percent had a special automatic air conditioning system; 1.6 percent had styled wheels; and 2.1 percent had dual exhausts. On F-85s, 0.8 percent had a four-speed manual transmission; 4.7 percent had dual exhausts; 2.3 percent had power door locks; 18.6 percent had power windows; and 19.2 percent had bucket seats. As for Toronados, 93.5 percent had a vinyl top; 36. 8 percent had Cruise Control; 74.6 percent had a movable steering column; and 65.6 percent had tape decks.

1972 OLDSMOBILE

F-85 — Once again the F-85 was retained as the bottom-of-the-line, single model in the Oldsmobile intermediate car lineup. The only F-85 offered his model year was a four-door Town Sedan. Gone was the Chevrolet built inline six-cylinder power plant. Now an F-85 could be fitted with either a 350 cid or 455 cid Rocket V-8 motor. Standard series equipment included: plastic fender inner liners; fiberglass hood insulation; side reflector markers; four-way flashers; left outside mirror; cigarette lighter; head restraints; and aluminized exhaust system. Standard tire size was F78 x 14 inches. Interiors were done in vinyl or cloth. Olds plant codes found on 1972 intermediates included M, Z, G and R.

OLDSMOBILE I.D. NUMBERS: VIN located on top left of dashboard viewable through windshield. Motor production code number indicating approximate production date and a motor serial number matching the VIN located on engine. Serial number takes the form of seven symbols, plus sequential production number. First symbol identifies GM division: 3=Oldsmobile. Second symbol changed to a letter indicating series: D=F-85; F=Cutlass hardtop; G=Cutlass 'S'; J=Cutlass Supreme; K=Vista Cruiser; L=Delta 88; N=Delta 88 Royale; R=Custom Cruiser; U=98; V=Luxury; Y=Toronado; X=Toronado chassis. Third and fourth symbols indicate body style and match second two digits of Body/Style Number in charts below. Fifth symbol indicates type of engine: [350 cid V-8] H, J, K, M; [455 cid V-8] S,T,U,V,W,X. Sixth symbol identifies model year: 2=1972. Seventh symbol indicates assembly plant: E=Linden, N.J.; G=Framingham, Mass.; M=Lansing, Mich.; Z=Fremont, Calif.; X=Fairfax (Kansas City), Kan.; R=Arlington, Texas. Remaining symbols are the sequential production number starting at 100001 at each factory. Ending VINs not available. Engine numbers consist of an alphabetical prefix and a production sequence number. Prefixes for 1972 engines were: [350 cid V-8] QA=160 hp; QB/QC/QN=175 hp; QD/QE/QJ/QK/QP=180 hp. QM=200 hp; [455 cid V-8] WX=250 hp; UD/UE/UA/UB=270 hp; US/UT=225 hp; UL/UN/UO=300 hp. Ending engine numbers not available.

F-85

Model Number	Body/Style Number	Body Type & Seating	Factory Price	Shipping Weight	Production Total
F-85	D69	4-dr Twn Sed-5P	2958	3536	3,792

CUTLASS — The Cutlass, once Oldsmobile's fanciest intermediate, had now drifted down to the bottom of the lineup. Just two body styles, a sedan and coupe, were found in the Cutlass group this year. All items from the F-85 were standard on the Cutlass plus: front and rear armrests; rear armrest ashtrays; full carpeting; fiberglass hood insulation; special molding package; and Deluxe steering wheel. Standard tire size was F78 x 14 inches. Upholstery could be done in either vinyl or cloth.

CUTLASS

Model Number	Body/Style Number	Body Type & Seating	Factory Price	Shipping Weight	Production Total
C	F87	2-dr Cpe-5P	2973	3509	37,790
C	G69	4-dr Twn Sed-5P	3066	3549	38,893

1972 Oldsmobile, two-door Cutlass 4-4-2 hardtop sports coupe, V-8

CUTLASS 'S' — A pair of two-door styles were the models that made up the Cutlass 'S' series in 1972. The 4-4-2 was lifted from a full series status this year and returned to optional status. A lot of cars in this series were 4-4-2 optioned, but by now the package had been reduced to a handling and appearance item. Standard equipment series included all items from the Cutlass group plus; simulated chrome hood louvers; Deluxe bench seats and special foam seat cushions. Standard tire size was F78 x 14 inches. Upholstery was done in cloth or vinyl.

CUTLASS 'S'

Model Number	Body/Style Number	Body Type & Seating	Factory Price	Shipping Weight	Production Total
CS	G87	2-dr Hol HT-5P	3087	3509	78,461
CS	G77	2-dr Spts Cpe-5P	3027	3503	4,141

CUTLASS SUPREME — Atop the Olds intermediate group was the Cutlass Supreme series. This series offered a bit of everything, with a coupe, four-door sedan and a convertible. This would be the final year a true Cutlass convertible would be offered. Standard equipment included all items from the Cutlass list plus: a larger output 350 cid engine; a special die-cast grille; woodgrain dash treatment; and Strato bucket seats. Standard tire size was F78 x 14 inches. Upholstery could be done in vinyl or cloth.

CUTLASS SUPREME

Model Number	Body/Style Number	Body Type & Seating	Factory Price	Shipping Weight	Production Total
CSU	J57	2-dr Hol HT-5P	3258	3520	105,087
CSU	J67	2-dr Conv-5P	3433	3614	11,571
CSU	J39	4-dr Hol HT-5P	3329	3582	14,955

CUTLASS CRUISER — Oldsmobile again offered three station wagons this year and the smallest of the trio was the Cutlass Cruiser. Standard equipment was identical to that of the Cutlass. Upholstery was done in either vinyl or cloth. Standard tire size was H78 x 14 inches.

CUTLASS CRUISER

Model Number	Body/Style Number	Body Type & Seating	Factory Price	Shipping Weight	Production Total
CC	G36	4-dr Sta Wag-5P	3498	4049	7,979

VISTA CRUISER — This year the mid-size Oldsmobile station wagon was the Vista Cruiser, which was in its ninth year. Cutlass sheet metal was used, but the Vista Cruiser was a physically larger car than other Oldsmobile intermediates. Standard equipment on the series was front and rear armrests; woodgrain decals; carpeting; V-8 engine; moldings; foam seat cushions; Deluxe steering wheel; drop or swing tailgate; heavy-duty wheels; and vista roof treatment. Standard tire size was H78 x 14 inches. Interiors were done in either cloth or vinyl.

VISTA CRUISER

Model Number	Body/Style Number	Body Type & Seating	Factory Price	Shipping Weight	Production Total
VC	K56	4-dr Sta Wag-5P	3774	4285	10,573
VC	K66	4-dr Sta Wag-7P	3908	4373	21,340

1972 Oldsmobile, two-door Delta 88 Royale hardtop coupe, V-8

DELTA EIGHTY-EIGHT — Just two Eighty-Eight series were offered in 1972, as the Custom was no longer an Eighty-Eight nameplate. Three body styles were available in the Delta Eighty-Eight group, a pair of sedans and a coupe. Standard series equipment included cigarette lighter; carpeting; 350 cid V-8; lamp package; moldings; windshield radio antenna; power steering; Deluxe steering wheel; Turbo-Hydramatic transmission; power brakes (with front discs); and chrome wheelcovers. Upholstery was done in vinyl or cloth. Standard tire size was H78 x 15 inches. Full-size Oldsmobiles carried assembly plant codes M, E or X, with production of some trim levels quartered in particular plants.

DELTA EIGHTY-EIGHT

Model Number	Body/Style Number	Body Type & Seating	Factory Price	Shipping Weight	Production Total
D88	L57	2-dr Cpe-5P	4001	4296	32,036
D88	L39	4-dr Hol HT-5P	4060	4375	35,538
D88	L69	4-dr Twn Sed-5P	3948	4324	46,092

DELTA EIGHTY-EIGHT ROYALE — This was the fancier of the two Eighty-Eight series and the only area where a full-size convertible was offered. A total of four body styles populated this series. Standard equipment included all items from the Delta Eighty-Eight series, plus Deluxe carpeting; special grille; interior light package; and side moldings. Upholstery was done in vinyl, leather or cloth. Standard tire size was H78 x 15 inches.

DELTA EIGHTY-EIGHT ROYALE

Model Number	Body/Style Number	Body Type & Seating	Factory Price	Shipping Weight	Production Total
D88R	N57	2-dr Cpe-5P	4179	4316	34,345
D88R	N39	4-dr Hol HT-5P	4238	4404	42,606
D88R	N69	4-dr Twn Sed-5P	4101	4369	34,150
D88R	N67	2-dr Conv-5P	4387	4442	3,900

CUSTOM CRUISER — King of the Oldsmobile station wagon fleet, again this year, was the mighty Custom Cruiser. Sandwiched between an Eighty-Eight and a Ninety-Eight, the Custom Cruiser was available as either a two- or three-seater. Standard equipment included woodgrain trim; power brakes with front discs; 455 cid motor; interior hood latch; interior lamp package; molding package; windshield radio antenna; foam seat cushions; power steering; and Turbo-Hydramatic transmission.

CUSTOM CRUISER

Model Number	Body/Style Number	Body Type & Seating	Factory Price	Shipping Weight	Production Total
CC	R35	4-dr Sta Wag-5P	4700	5109	6,907
CC	R45	4-dr Sta Wag-7P	4834	5204	18,087

NINETY-EIGHT — A pair of coupes and a pair of sedans were the body styles offered in the Ninety-Eight series for 1972. This series of cars was Oldsmobile's best-appointed. The long standard equipment list included: Deluxe armrests; dual ashtrays; power brakes with front discs; electric clock; carpeting; interior hood release; remote control outside mirror; molding package; interior light package; windshield radio antenna; power seat; power steering; spare tire cover; and Turbo-Hydramatic transmission.

NINETY-EIGHT

Model Number	Body/Style Number	Body Type & Seating	Factory Price	Shipping Weight	Production Total
98	U37	2-dr Hol HT-5P	4748	4537	9,624
98	V37	2-dr Lux Cpe-5P	5009	4459	24,452
98	U39	4-dr HT-5P	4807	4608	17,572
98	V39	4-dr Lux HT-5P	5098	4658	69,920

NOTE 1: A mid-year version of style 8639 was called the Regency and was produced to specially honor Oldsmobile's 75th year in the vehicle building business.

1972 Oldsmobile, two-door Toronado hardtop sports coupe, V-8

TORONADO — The division's entry in the personal luxury area continued to be the front-drive Toronado. Just two models were offered, the Custom coupe. Standard equipment was quite complete and included Deluxe armrests; dual ashtrays; power brakes with front discs; cigarette lighter; electric clock; special 455 cid engine; dual exhausts; interior hood latch; molding package; remote mirror; windshield radio antenna; power steering; and Turbo-Hydramatic transmission. Interiors were done in vinyl leather or cloth. Standard tire size was J78 x 15 inch. All Toronados were made in Lansing.

TORONADO

Model Number	Body/Style Number	Body Type & Seating	Factory Price	Shipping Weight	Production Total
T	Y57	2-dr Cpe-5P	5341	4540	31,076

BROUGHAM

T	9857	2-dr Cpe-5P	5494	4570	17,824

BASE ENGINES

(F-85/CUTLASS/CUTLASS 'S'/CUTLASS CRUISER/DELTA 88 & DELTA 88 ROYALE SERIES) V-8. Overhead valves. Cast iron block. Displacement: 350 cid. Bore and stoke: 4.057 x 3.385 inches. Compression ratio: 8.5:1. Brake hp: 160 at 4000 rpm. Five main bearings. Hydraulic valve lifters. Carburetor: Rochester 2GC two-barrel.

(CUTLASS SUPREME SERIES) V-8. Overhead valves. Cast iron block. Displacement: 350 cid. Bore and stroke: 4.057 x 3.385 inches. Compression ratio: 8.5:1. Brake hp: 180 at 4000 rpm. Five main bearings. Hydraulic valve lifters. Carburetor: Rochester 4MC four-barrel.

(CUSTOM CRUISER/NINETY-EIGHT SERIES) V-8. Overhead valves. Cast iron block. Displacement: 455 cid. Bore and stroke: 4.125 x 4.250 inches. Compression ratio: 8.5:1. Brake hp: 225 at 4000 rpm. Five main bearings. Hydraulic valve lifters. Carburetor: Rochester 4MC four-barrel.

(TORONADO SERIES) V-8. Overhead valves. Cast iron block. Displacement: 455 cid. Bore and stroke: 4.125 x 4.250 inches. Compression ratio: 8.5:1. Brake hp: 250 at 4000 rpm. Five main bearings. Hydraulic valve lifters. Carburetor: Rochester 4MC four-barrel.

CHASSIS FEATURES: Wheelbase: (F-85/Cutlass/Cutlass Supreme four-doors) 116 inches; (Cutlass 'S'/Supreme/two-doors) 112 inches; (Vista Cruiser) 121 inches; (Toronado) 122 inches; (All 88 models) 124 inches; (Custom Cruiser/98) 127 inches. Overall length: F-85/Cutlass/Supreme four-doors) 207.6 inches; (Cutlass 'S'/Supreme two-doors) 203.6 inches; (Vista Cruiser) 218.3 inches; (Toronado) 220.6 inches; (all 88 models) 221 inches; (98) 227.8 inches; (Custom Cruiser) 227 inches. Front tread: (all intermediates) 59.3 inches; (all 88/98 models) 63.6 inches; (Toronado) 63.7 inches. Rear tread: (all intermediates) 59 inches; (Toronado) 63.6 inches; (all others) 64 inches.

OPTIONS: Power brakes ($69). Power steering ($115). Air conditioning ($407). Tinted window ($43). Power seats ($78). Window defogger ($63). Cruise control ($64). Tilt steering wheel ($45). Super stock wheels ($73). Wire wheel discs ($115). AM radio ($73). AM /FM radio ($139). Stereo tape player ($133). Electric clock ($19). Rallye pack instruments ($84). Power trunk lid ($14). Headlamp-off delay ($12). Cornering lamps ($36). Bumper guards ($16). Outside thermometer ($12). Three-speed manual transmission was standard in all intermediates. Automatic transmission ($221). Four-speed manual floor shift transmission ($195). V-8: 350 cid/180 hp L34 engine ($47). V-8: 455 cid/270 hp L-75 engine ($188). V-8: 455 cid/300 hp W-30 engine ($648). Force-Air induction package with W-30.

HISTORICAL FOOTNOTES: A Hurst/Olds package was offered in 1972 on Cutlass coupes and convertibles. A total of 629 were made.

1973 OLDSMOBILE

1973 Oldsmobile, two-door Omega hatchback coupe V-8

OMEGA — A new Oldsmobile series was added this model year with the Omega nameplate. It was the smallest and least expensive Oldsmobile. Oldsmobile adopted the Chevy Nova body, which had remained essentially unchanged since its 1968 introduction. Standard equipment on the new series included: armrests, cigarette lighter, carpeting, dome light, moldings, space saver spare tire and Deluxe steering wheel. Upholstery was done in either cloth or vinyl. Standard tire size was E78 x 14 inches. The letter codes L and W identify the factories where Omegas were made this year.

OLDSMOBILE I.D. NUMBERS: VIN located on top left of dashboard viewable through windshield. Motor production code number indicating approximate production date and a motor serial number matching the VIN located on engine. Serial number takes the form of seven symbols, plus sequential production number. First symbol identifies GM division: 3=Oldsmobile. Second symbol is a letter indicating series: F=Cutlass hardtop; G=Cutlass 'S'; J=Cutlass Supreme; K=Vista Cruiser; B=Omega; L=Delta 88; N=Delta 88 Royale; Q=Custom Cruiser; R=Custom Cruiser with woodgrain; T=98; V=98 Luxury; X=98 Regency; Y=Toronado Custom. Third and fourth symbols indicate body style and match second two digits of Body/Style Number in charts below. Fifth symbol indicates type of engine: [250 cid six]=D; [350 cid V-8]=H,K,M; [455 cid V-8]=T,U,V,W. Sixth symbol identifies year. Seventh symbol indicates assembly plant: L=Van Nuys; E=Linden, N.J.; G=Framingham, Mass.; M=Lansing, Mich.; X=Fairfax (Kansas City), Kan.; R=Arlington, Texas; W=Willow Run. Remaining symbols are the sequential production number starting at 100001 at each factory. Ending VINs not available. Engine numbers consist of a alphabetic prefix and a production sequence number. Prefixes for 1973 engines were: [250 cid six] CCC/CCD/CCA/CCB=100 nhp; [350 cid V-8] QN/QO/QP/QQ/QS/QT=160 nhp; QA/QB/QJ/QK/QU/QV/QC/QD/QE/QL=180 nhp. [455 cid V-8] UA/UB/UD/US/UT/UU/UV=225 nhp; T=250 hp; W=270 nhp. Ending engine numbers not available.

OMEGA

Model Number	Body/Style Number	Body Type & Seating	Factory Price	Shipping Weight	Production Total
0	B-27	2-dr Cpe-5P	2612	3094	26,126
0	B-17	2-dr Hatch-5P	2761	3283	21,433
0	B-69	4-dr Sed-5P	2640	3117	12,804

CUTLASS — The all new 1973 body was introduced one year later due to a GM strike. All two-door models had fixed rear side windows that could not be rolled down. Bottom of the line in the intermediate group was the Cutlass series, which contained just two models, a coupe and sedan. Standard equipment on the series included armrests, front disc brakes, cigarette lighter, dome light, interior hood latch, moldings, windshield radio antenna, Deluxe steering wheel and chrome hubcaps. Upholstery could be ordered in either cloth or vinyl. Standard tire size was F78 x 14 inches. Intermediate-size Oldsmobiles carried assembly plant codes: M, G and R.

CUTLASS

Model Number	Body/Style Number	Body Type & Seating	Factory Price	Shipping Weight	Production Total
C	F-37	2-dr Cpe-5P	3048	3905	22,002
C	G-29	4-dr Sed-5P	3136	3917	35,578

CUTLASS 'S' — Offered in just a single body style for 1973 was the newly styled Cutlass 'S.' The 4-4-2 option was available again in 1973, but it amounted to only a handling and appearance option. Standard equipment on this series included: armrests, ashtrays, cigarette lighter, carpeting, dome light, special hood treatment, moldings, windshield radio antenna, seat belts and shoulder harness, Deluxe steering wheel and chrome hubcaps. Standard tire size was F78 x 14 inches. Upholstery was done in either vinyl or leather.

CUTLASS 'S'

Model Number	Body/Style Number	Body Type & Seating	Factory Price	Shipping Weight	Production Total
CS	G-37	2-dr HT-5P	3158	3840	77,558

1973 Oldsmobile, two-door Cutlass 'S' Colonnade coupe, V-8

CUTLASS SUPREME — Atop the Olds intermediate group was the all-new Cutlass Supreme. This was a hands-down favorite with the intermediate buying public. A main styling feature was a special window treatment. Standard equipment on this series included: armrests, ashtrays, front disc brakes, carpeting, interior hood latch, dome light, molding package, windshield radio antenna, seat belts and shoulder harness, Deluxe steering wheel and chrome hubcaps. Upholstery was done in either vinyl or cloth. Standard tire size was F78 x 14 inches.

CUTLASS SUPREME

Model Number	Body/Style Number	Body Type & Seating	Factory Price	Shipping Weight	Production Total
CSU	J-57	2-dr Cpe-5P	3323	3920	219,857
CSU	J-29	4-dr Sed-5P	3394	3824	26,099

VISTA CRUISER — A bit of realignment was in order for the Vista Cruiser series. For years the Vista Cruiser was longer than the Cutlass series offering, but for 1973 the 116 inch wheelbase was shared by the intermediate four-doors. The Vista Cruiser's elevated rear roof was now discontinued. In place of it was a glass sun roof. Gone this year were the Cutlass Cruiser station wagons. Standard series equipment included: ashtrays, woodgrain trim, power brakes with front discs, cigarette lighter, carpeting, interior hood release, moldings, radio antenna in windshield, Deluxe steering wheel and special roof ventilator. Standard tire size was H78 x 14 inches. Upholstery was done in either vinyl or leather.

VISTA CRUISER

Model Number	Body/Style Number	Body Type & Seating	Factory Price	Shipping Weight	Production Total
VC	J-35	2S Sta Wag-5P	3788	4357	10,894
VC	J-45	3S Sta Wag-7P	3901	4392	13,531

DELTA EIGHTY-EIGHT — Again this year a pair of Eighty-Eight models were available with the bottom offering the three model Delta Eighty-Eight series. Standard equipment on the series included: power brakes with front discs, cigarette lighter, carpeting, dome light, molding package, windshield radio antenna, power steering, Deluxe steering wheel and Turbo-Hydramatic transmission. Standard tire size was H78 x 15 inches. Upholstery was done in either vinyl or cloth. Plant codes M, E and X were seen in the big cars' serial numbers.

DELTA EIGHTY-EIGHT

Model Number	Body/Style Number	Body Type & Seating	Factory Price	Shipping Weight	Production Total
D88	L-57	2-dr Cpe-5P	4047	4313	27,096
D88	L-39	4-dr Hol HT-5P	4108	4420	27,986
D88	L-69	4-dr Twn Sed-5P	3991	4379	42,476

DELTA EIGHTY-EIGHT ROYALE — A bit fancier than the Delta Eighty-Eight was the Delta Eighty-Eight Royale series. This series offered the only convertible for 1973. Also available were a pair of sedans and a coupe. Standard equipment on this series included: power brakes with front discs, cigarette lighter, carpeting, interior hood release, dome light, light package, molding package, windshield radio antenna, power steering, Deluxe steering wheel, Turbo-Hydramatic transmission and Flo-Thru ventilation. Standard tire size was H78 x 15 inches. Upholstery was done in either leather, vinyl or cloth.

DELTA EIGHTY-EIGHT ROYALE

Model Number	Body/Style Number	Body Type & Seating	Factory Price	Shipping Weight	Production Total
D88R	N-57	2-dr Cpe-5P	4221	4341	43,315
D88R	N-39	4-dr HT Sed-5P	4293	4448	49,145
D88R	N-69	4-dr Twn Sed-5P	4156	4379	42,672
D88R	N-67	2-dr Conv-5P	4442	4430	7,088

CUSTOM CRUISER — The largest Oldsmobile station wagon in 1973 continued to come from the Custom Cruiser group. Both two and three-seat models were available this year. Standard series equipment included: armrests, power brakes with front discs, cigarette lighter, carpeting, inside hood release, dome light, molding package, windshield radio antenna, foam seat cushions, power steering, Deluxe steering wheel, Turbo-Hydramatic transmission and wheel opening covers. Standard tire size was L78 x 15 inches. Upholstery was done in either vinyl or cloth.

CUSTOM CRUISER

Model Number	Body/Style Number	Body Type & Seating	Factory Price	Shipping Weight	Production Total
CC	Q-35	2S Sta Wag-5P	4630	5002	5,275
CC	Q-45	3S Sta Wag-7P	4769	5070	7,341

WITH WOODGRAIN TRIM

Model Number	Body/Style Number	Body Type & Seating	Factory Price	Shipping Weight	Production Total
CC	R-35	2S Sta Wag-5P	4785	5005	7,142
CC	R-45	3S Sta Wag-7P	4924	5072	19,163

1973 Oldsmobile, two-door Luxury 98 hardtop coupe, V-8

NINETY-EIGHT — A five model Ninety-Eight series greet buyers looking at the upper end of the Oldsmobile lineup for 1973. In 1972, Olds made a midyear addition to this series with the Regency model. This popular offering saw its first full year of production in 1973. Standard equipment included: Deluxe armrests, dual ashtrays, power brakes with front discs, interior hood latch, lamp package, molding package, windshield radio antenna, power seats, power steering, Deluxe steering wheel, spare tire cover and Turbo-Hydramatic transmission. Standard tire size was J78 x 15 inches. Upholstery was done in vinyl, cloth or leather.

NINETY-EIGHT

Model Number	Body/Style Number	Body Type & Seating	Factory Price	Shipping Weight	Production Total
98	T-37	2-dr Cpe-5P	4798	4545	7,850
98	V-37	2-dr Lux Cpe-5P	5070	4601	26,925
98	T-39	4-dr Sed-5P	4859	4611	13,989
98	V-39	4-dr Lux Sed-5P	5163	4686	55,695
98	X-39	4-dr Regy Sed-5P	5417	4659	34,009

1973 Oldsmobile, two-door Toronado sports coupe, V-8

TORONADO — Oldsmobile continued in the personal luxury field in 1973 with the Toronado. The Toronado was a well appointed car even in standard trim, which included: armrests, ashtrays, power brakes with front discs, bumper guards, cigarette lighter, electric clock, door-pull handles, dual exhausts, interior hood release, molding package, windshield radio antenna, power steering, Deluxe steering wheel and Turbo-Hydramatic transmission. Standard tire size was J78 x 15 inches. Upholstery was done in either vinyl, leather or cloth. As usual, the M plant code was found in all Toronado serial numbers.

TORONADO

Model Number	Body/Style Number	Body Type & Seating	Factory Price	Shipping Weight	Production Total
T	Y-57	2-dr Cpe-5P	5440	4654	28,193

BROUGHAM

Model Number	Body/Style Number	Body Type & Seating	Factory Price	Shipping Weight	Production Total
T	Z-57	2-dr Cpe-5P	5594	4676	27,728

BASE ENGINES

(OMEGA SERIES)

Inline six-cylinder. Overhead valves. Cast-iron block. Displacement: 250 cid. Bore and stroke: 3.88 x 3.53 inches. Compression ratio: 8.25:1. Brake hp: 100 at 3600 rpm. Seven main bearings. Hydraulic valve lifters. Carburetor: Rochester, MV one-barrel.

(CUTLASS/CUTLASS 'S'/CUTLASS SUPREME/VISTA CRUISER SERIES) V-8. Overhead
valves. Cast iron block. Displacement: 350 cid. Bore and stroke: 4.057 x 3.385 inches. Compression ratio: 8.5:1. Brake hp 180 at 3800 rpm. Five main bearings. Hydraulic valve lifters. Carburetor 4MC four-barrel.

(DELTA 88/DELTA 88 ROYALE SERIES) V-8. Overhead valves. Cast iron block.
Displacement: 350 cid. Bore and stroke: 4.057 x 3.385 inches. Compression ratio: 8.5:1. Brake hp: 160 at 3800 rpm. Five main bearings. Hydraulic valve lifters. Carburetor: Rochester 2GC, two-barrel.

(CUSTOM CRUISER/NINETY-EIGHT SERIES) V-8. Overhead valves. Cast iron block.
Displacement: 455 cid. Bore and stroke: 4.125 x 4.250 inches. Compression ratio: 8.5:1. Brake hp: 275 at 3600 rpm. Five main bearings. Hydraulic valve lifters. Carburetion: Rochester 4MC, four-barrel.

(TORONADO SERIES) V-8. Overhead valves. Cast iron block. Displacement: 455 cid. Bore
and stroke: 4.125 x 4.250 inches. Compression ratio: 8.5:1. Brake hp: 250 at 4000 rpm. Five main bearings. Hydraulic valve lifters. Carburetor: Rochester 4MC, four-barrel.

CHASSIS FEATURES: Wheelbase: (Omega) 111 inches; (Intermediate two-doors) 112 inches; (intermediate four-doors/Vista Cruiser) 116 inches; (Eighty-Eights) 124 inches; (Ninety-Eights/Custom Cruiser) 127 inches; (Toronados) 122 inches. Overall length: (Omega) 197.5 inches; (Intermediate two-doors) 207 inches; (intermediate four-doors/Vista Cruiser) 211 inches; (Eighty-Eights) 225 inches; (Ninety-Eights/Custom Cruiser) 230.2 inches; (Toronados) 226.8 inches. Front tread: (Omega) 59.1 inches; (all Cutlass) 61.4 inches;, (Eighty-Eights/Ninety-Eights) 63.7 inches; (Toronados) 63.5 inches. Rear tread: (Omega) 58.8 inches; (all Cutlass) 60.7 inches; (Eighty-Eights/Ninety-Eights) 64 inches; (Toronados) 63.6 inches.

OPTIONS: Power brakes ($46). Power steering ($113). Air conditioning ($397). Tinted windows ($30). Trunk release ($14). Power windows ($75). Power door locks ($69). Floor mats ($7). Vinyl roof ($99). Rear window defogger ($62). Sport mirrors ($22). Cruise-Control ($62). Super stock wheels ($72). Instrument gauges ($31). Electric clock ($18). AM radio ($73). AM/FM radio ($135). Rear speaker ($18). AM/FM stereo radio ($233). Paint stripe ($21). Power seat ($103). Litter container ($5). Wire wheel disc ($82). Power antenna ($32). Three-speed manual transmission was standard on all Cutlass and Omega. Automatic transmission was standard on all others. 4-4-2 appearance and handling option ($121). Automatic transmission ($215). Four-speed manual floor shift transmission ($190). V-8: 350 cid/180 hp L-34 engine ($164). V-8: 455 cid/250 hp L-75 engine ($137). V-8: 455 cid/275 hp L-74 engine ($169). Positive traction rear axle ($43).

HISTORICAL FOOTNOTES: Option W-45 was a Hurst/Olds package. It was available on selected Cutlass 'S' coupes and 1,097 were made.

1974 OLDSMOBILE

1974 Oldsmobile, two-door Omega hatchback coupe, V-8

OMEGA — In its second year was the Oldsmobile Omega series, which continued as the smallest and least expensive group of cars offered by Oldsmobile. Again in 1974, a trio of models was offered. Standard equipment included: armrests; ashtrays; cigarette lighter; carpeting; dome light; molding package; space saver spare tire; and chrome hubcaps. Standard tire size was E-78 x 14 inches. Upholstery was done in either vinyl or cloth. The L and W plant codes show up in 1974 Omega serial numbers.

OLDSMOBILE I.D. NUMBERS: VIN located on top left of dashboard viewable through windshield. Motor production code number indicating approximate production date and a motor serial number matching the VIN located on engine. Serial number takes the form of seven symbols, plus sequential production number. First symbol identifies GM division: 3=Oldsmobile. Second symbol is a letter indicating series: B=Omega; F=Cutlass hardtop; G=Cutlass 'S'; H=Cutlass wagon; J=Cutlass Supreme; K=Vista Cruiser; L=Delta 88; N=Delta 88 Royale; Q=Custom Cruiser; R=Custom Cruiser with woodgrain; T=98; V=98 Luxury; X=98 Regency; Y=Toronado Custom; Toronado Brougham. Third and fourth symbols indicate body style and match second two digits of Body/Style Number in charts below. Fifth symbol indicates type of engine: [250 cid six]=D; [350 cid V-8]=K,M; [455 cid V-8]=T,U,W. Sixth symbol identifies model year: 4=1974. Seventh symbol indicates assembly plant: D=Doraville (Atlanta), Ga.; L=Van Nuys; E=Linden, N.J.; G=Framingham, Mass.; M=Lansing, Mich.; X=Fairfax (Kansas City), Kan.; R=Arlington, Texas; W=Willow Run. Remaining symbols are the sequential production number starting at 100001 at each factory. Ending VINs not available. Engine numbers consist of a alphabetical prefix and a production sequence

number. Prefixes for 1974 engines were: [250 cid six] DCC/DCD/DCA/DCB=100 nhp; [350 cid V-8] KB/KC/KL/KO/KU/KW/MB/MC/ML/MO=180 hp. [455 cid V-8] UC/UD/UL/UN/UP/UO/UR/UV/UX=225 nhp; T=250 hp; W=270 nhp. Ending engine numbers not available.

OMEGA

Model Number	Body/Style Number	Body Type & Seating	Factory Price	Shipping Weight	Production Total
O	B27	2-dr Cpe-5P	2762	3334	27,075
O	B17	2-dr Hatch-5P	2911	3438	12,449
O	B69	4-dr Twn Sed-5P	2790	3382	10,756

CUTLASS — The basic Oldsmobile intermediate this year again was the Cutlass. Just a mild restyling was added to last year's complete styling overhaul. Standard series equipment included: armrests; ashtrays; front disc brakes; V-8 engine; carpeting; dome light; molding package; windshield radio antenna; power steering; Deluxe steering wheel; and Turbo-Hydramatic transmission. Standard tire size was G78 x 14 inches. Upholstery was done in vinyl or cloth. Plant codes found on mid-size Olds were M, G and R.

CUTLASS

Model Number	Body/Style Number	Body Type & Seating	Factory Price	Shipping Weight	Production Total
C	F-37	2-dr Cpe-5P	3453	3984	16,063
C	G-29	4-dr Sed-5P	3528	4040	25,718

CUTLASS 'S' — Remaining as a single body style series was the Cutlass 'S'. Standard equipment in this series included: armrests; ashtrays; cigarette lighter; carpeting; interior hood release; dome light; molding package; radio antenna in windshield; Deluxe steering wheel; front disc brakes; power steering; and Turbo-Hydramatic transmission. Standard tire size was F78 x 14 inches. Upholstery was done in either cloth or vinyl.

CUTLASS 'S'

Model Number	Body/Style Number	Body Type & Seating	Factory Price	Shipping Weight	Production Total
CS	G37	2-dr Cpe-5P	3550	3993	50,860

1974 Oldsmobile, two-door Cutlass Supreme Colonnade coupe, V-8

CUTLASS SUPREME — This immensely popular Oldsmobile series continued to attract buyers in 1974. A total of two body styles were offered this year. An interesting new offering was the Salon package, which attempted to bring a bit of European touring sedan influence to the Oldsmobile lineup. Standard equipment in this series included: front disc brakes; cigarette lighter; carpeting; interior hood release; dome light; molding package; windshield radio antenna; power steering; Deluxe steering wheel; and Turbo-Hydramatic transmission. Standard tire size was F78 x 14 inch. Upholstery choices were vinyl or cloth.

CUTLASS SUPREME

Model Number	Body/Style Number	Body Type & Seating	Factory Price	Shipping Weight	Production Total
CSU	J29	4-dr Sed-5P	3816	4085	12,525
CSU	J57	2-dr Cpe-5P	3745	3998	172,360

CUTLASS SUPREME/VISTA CRUISER — Oldsmobile brought back the Cutlass nameplate in the station wagon series this year. The official tag was the Cutlass Supreme Cruiser and it was coupled with the long running Vista Cruiser to form one series. The basic differences between the two nameplates were the Vista Cruiser had woodgrain exterior decals and a special roof treatment. The Cutlass Supreme Cruiser had neither. Standard series equipment included: power brakes with front discs; cigarette lighter; carpeting; bumper impact strips; interior hood release; lamp package; molding package; windshield radio antenna; power steering; Deluxe steering wheel; and Turbo-Hydramatic transmission. Standard tire size was H78 x 14 inches. Upholstery was done in vinyl or cloth.

CUTLASS SUPREME/VISTA CRUISER

Model Number	Body/Style Number	Body Type & Seating	Factory Price	Shipping Weight	Production Total
CSUC	H35	4-dr Sta Wag-6P	3970	4485	3,437
CSUC	H45	4-dr Sta Wag-8P	4083	4521	3,101
VC	J35	4-dr Sta Wag-6P	4180	4496	4,191
VC	J45	4-dr Sta Wag-8P	4293	4532	7,013

DELTA EIGHTY-EIGHT — Again the basic full-sized model for this year was the long running Delta Eighty-Eight. Three body styles, a pair of sedans and a coupe, populated this series. A major restyling effort was carried out this time in this group. Standard equipment included: armrests; ashtrays; power brakes with front discs; cigarette lighter; interior hood release; dome light; molding package; windshield radio antenna; and Turbo-Hydramatic transmission. Standard tire size was H78 x 15 inches. Interiors were done in either cloth or vinyl. Plant codes found on big Olds were M, E, X and D.

1974 Oldsmobile, two-door Delta 88 Royale hardtop coupe, V-8

DELTA EIGHTY-EIGHT

Model Number	Body/Style Number	Body Type & Seating	Factory Price	Shipping Weight	Production Total
D88	L57	2-dr Cpe-5P	4120	4515	11,615
D88	L39	4-dr HT Sed-5P	4181	4568	11,941
D88	L-69	4-dr Twn Sed-5P	4064	4536	17,939

DELTA EIGHTY-EIGHT ROYALE — The fancier Eighty-Eight model again in 1974 was the Royale. A pair of sedans and a coupe joined the only convertible left in the Olds lineup. Standard equipment included: armrests; ashtrays; cigarette lighter; carpeting; power brakes with front discs; molding package; lamp package; windshield radio antenna; power steering; Deluxe steering wheel; and Turbo-Hydramatic transmission. Standard tire size was H78 x 15 inches. Upholstery was done in leather, vinyl or cloth.

DELTA EIGHTY-EIGHT ROYALE

Model Number	Body/Style Number	Body Type & Seating	Factory Price	Shipping Weight	Production Total
D88R	N57	2-dr HT Cpe-5P	4275	4537	27,515
D88R	N69	4-dr Twn Sed-5P	4204	4554	22,504
D88R	N39	4-dr HT Sed-5P	4341	4602	26,363
D88R	N67	2-dr Conv-5P	4490	4594	3,716

CUSTOM CRUISER — The big wagon continued in the Oldsmobile series for 1974 under the nameplate Custom Cruiser. This Olds heavy hauler was available in either two- or three-seat versions. Standard equipment included: armrests; ashtrays; bodyside moldings; cigarette lighter; power brakes with front discs; carpeting; interior hood latch; lamp package; windshield radio antenna; power steering; Deluxe steering wheel; heavy-duty wheels and Turbo-Hydramatic transmission. Standard tires were L78 x 15 inches. Upholstery was done in either vinyl or cloth.

CUSTOM CRUISER

Model Number	Body/Style Number	Body Type & Seating	Factory Price	Shipping Weight	Production Total
CC	Q-35	4-dr Sta Wag-6P	4665	5110	1,481
CC	Q-45	4-dr Sta Wag-8P	4804	5161	2,528

WITH WOODGRAIN PANELING

Model Number	Body/Style Number	Body Type & Seating	Factory Price	Shipping Weight	Production Total
CC	R-35	4-dr Sta Wag-6P	4820	5122	2,960
CC	R-45	4-dr Sta Wag-8P	4959	5186	8,947

NINETY-EIGHT — Oldsmobile's longest running series, the Ninety-Eight dated back to the 1940s and it was still a popular offering. A total of five models were offered this year with the new addition being a Regency coupe. Even in standard trim the Ninety-Eight was a well appointed car. Standard equipment included: power brakes with front discs; cigarette lighter; electric clock; interior hood release; lamp package; molding package; remote control outside mirror; windshield radio antenna; power steering; Deluxe steering wheel; spare tire cover; power windows; power seat; and Turbo-Hydramatic transmission. Standard tire size was J78 x 15 inches. Upholstery was done in cloth, vinyl or leather.

NINETY-EIGHT

Model Number	Body/Style Number	Body Type & Seating	Factory Price	Shipping Weight	Production Total
98	V-37	2-dr Cpe-5P	5141	4778	9,236
98	X-37	2-dr Regy Cpe-5P	5403	4789	10,719
98	T-39	4-dr Sed-5P	4930	4870	4,395
98	V-39	4-dr Lux Sed-5P	5234	4892	21,896
98	X-39	4-dr Regy Sed-5P	5496	4802	24,310

TORONADO — Once again the front-wheel-drive Toronado was atop the Olds model lineup. Just two models — the Custom coupe and Brougham — were offered. Standard equipment on this series included: armrests; ashtrays; power brakes with front discs; electric digital clock; door-pull handles; dual exhausts; carpeting; headlamp warning system; windshield radio antenna; power steering; Deluxe steering wheel; moldings; and Turbo-Hydramatic transmission. All Toronados had the M factory code.

1974 Oldsmobile, two-door Toronado sports coupe, V-8

TORONADO

Model Number	Body/Style Number	Body Type & Seating	Factory Price	Shipping Weight	Production Total
T	Y-57	2-dr Cpe-5P	5559	4726	8,094

BROUGHAM

Model Number	Body/Style Number	Body Type & Seating	Factory Price	Shipping Weight	Production Total
T	Z-57	2-dr Cpe-5P	5713	4770	19,488

BASE ENGINES

(OMEGA SERIES) Inline six. Overhead valves. Cast iron block. Displacement: 250 cid. Bore and stroke: 3 7/8 x 3.53 inches. Compression ratio: 8.0:1. SAE Net Brake hp: 100 at 3600 rpm. Seven main bearings. Hydraulic valve lifters. Carburetor: Rochester MV one-barrel.

(CUTLASS/CUTLASS 'S'/CUTLASS SUPREME/VISTA CRUISER/DELTA 88/DELTA 88 ROYALE SERIES) V-8. Overhead valves. Cast iron block. Displacement: 350 cid. Bore and stroke: 4.057 x 3.385 inches. Compression ratio: 8.5:1. Brake hp 180 at 3800 rpm. Five main bearings. Hydraulic valve lifters. Carburetor: Rochester 4MC four-barrel.

(CUSTOM CRUISER/NINETY-EIGHT SERIES) V-8. Overhead valves. Cast iron block. Displacement: 455 cid. Bore and stroke: 4.125 x 4.250 inches. Compression ratio: 8.5 to 1. 210 nhp at 4000 rpm. Five main bearings. Hydraulic valve lifters. Carburetor: Rochester 4MC four-barrel.

(TORONADO SERIES) V-8. Overhead valves. Cast iron block. Displacement: 455 cid. Bore and stroke: 4.125 x 4.250 inches. Compression ratio: 8.5 to 1. 230 nhp at 4000 rpm. Five main bearings. Hydraulic valve lifters. Carburetors: Rochester 4MC four-barrel.

CHASSIS FEATURES: Wheelbase (Omega) 111 inches; (Intermediate two-doors) 112 inches; (Intermediate four-doors) 116 inches; (all 88s) 124 inches; (Toronados) 122 inches; (98 Custom Cruiser) 127 inches. Overall length: (Omega) 199.5 inches; (intermediate two-doors) 211.5 inches; (intermediate four-doors) 214.6 inches; (all 88s) 226.91 inches; (Toronado) 228 inches; (98) 232.4 inches; (Custom Cruiser) 231.2 inches. Front tread: (Omega) 59.1 inches; (all intermediates) 61.4 inches; (88/98) 63.7 inches; (Toronado) 63.5 inches. Rear tread: (Omega) 58.8 inches; (all intermediates) 60.7 inches; (98/88) 64 inches; (Toronado) 63.6 inches.

OPTIONS: Power brakes ($48). Power steering ($114). Air conditioning ($411). Super stock wheels ($72). Sports console ($59). Sport steering wheel ($31). Sport mirrors ($22). Salon option ($361). Vinyl roof ($123). Cruise control ($67). Tilt steering wheel ($44). Electric digital clock ($38). Power trunk release ($14). Station wagon luggage rack ($63). Power antenna ($32). AM/FM stereo radio with tape player ($342). Engine block heater ($10). True track braking system ($192). AM radio ($74). AM/FM radio ($135). Three-speed manual transmission was standard on Omega. Automatic transmission was standard on all others. Automatic transmission ($237). Four-speed manual floor shift transmission ($197). V-8: 350 cid/180 hp L-34 engine ($111). V-8: 455 cid/230 hp L-75 engine ($98).

HISTORICAL FOOTNOTES: In 1974 a Hurst/Olds was offered and it served as a pace car for the 1974 Indianapolis 500.

1975 OLDSMOBILE

STARFIRE — For a number of years Oldsmobile worked on beefing up the top end of their model lineup, but in more recent years it concentrated on the bottom end. First came the Omega. In 1975 the Starfire, based on the Chevy Monza, was added. Rolling on a wheelbase of 97 inches, the Starfire was the physically smallest Oldsmobile to appear in many years. Standard equipment on the series included: armrests; power brakes with front discs; power steering; cigarette lighter; bumper rub strips; V-6 engine; carpeting; electronic ignition; stowaway spare tire; custom sport steering wheel; and four-speed transmission. Standard tire size was BR78 x 13 inches. Upholstery was done in vinyl or cloth. All Starfires were made in the GM plant at St. Therese in Quebec, Canada.

1975 Oldsmobile, two-door Starfire hatchback coupe, V-6

OLDSMOBILE I.D. NUMBERS: VIN located on top left of dashboard viewable through windshield. Motor production code number indicating approximate production date and a motor serial number matching the VIN located on engine. Serial number takes the form of seven symbols, plus sequential production number. First symbol identifies GM division: 3=Oldsmobile. Second symbol is a letter indicating series: D=Starfire; B=Omega; C=Omega Salon; F=Cutlass hardtop; G=Cutlass 'S'; H=Cutlass Supreme Cruiser; J=Cutlass Supreme/Vista Cruiser; K=Cutlass Salon; L=Delta 88; N=Delta 88 Royale; Q=Custom Cruiser; R=Custom Cruiser with woodgrain; V=98 Luxury; X=98 Regency; Y=Toronado Custom; Z=Toronado Brougham. Third and fourth symbols indicate body style and match second two digits of Body/Style Number in charts below. Fifth symbol indicates type of engine: [231 cid V-6]=C; [250 cid six]=D; [260 cid V-8]=F; [350 cid V-8]=H,J,K,M. [400 cid V-8]=R,S. [455 cid V-8]=T,W. Sixth symbol identifies model year: 5=1975. Seventh symbol indicates assembly plant: D=Doraville (Atlanta), Ga.; 2=St. Therese; L=Van Nuys; E=Linden, N.J.; G=Framingham, Mass.; M=Lansing, Mich.; X=Fairfax (Kansas City), Kan.; R=Arlington, Texas; W=Willow Run. Remaining symbols are the sequential production number starting at 100001 at each factory. Ending VINs not available. Engine numbers consist of a alphabetical prefix and a production sequence number. Prefixes for 1975 engines were: [250 cid six] CJU/

CJT/CJL=105 nhp. [231 cid V-6] FP/FR/FS=110 nhp; [350 cid V-8] RS/RT=145 nhp; [260 cid V-8] QA/QB/QC/QD/QE/QJ/QK/QN/QP/QQ/TA/TE/TD/TN/TP/TQ=110 nhp; [350 cid V-8] PA/PB/Q2/Q3/Q4/Q5/QL/QO/QX/RN/RW/RX/TL/TO/TX=165 nhp; M=170 nhp dual-exhaust. [400 cid V-8] YH/YJ=170/175 nhp; YM/YT=190 nhp. [455 cid V-8] UB/UC/UD/UE/UP/VB/VC/VD/VE/VP/YM/YT=190 nhp; W=215 nhp dual exhausts.

STARFIRE

Model Number	Body/Style Number	Body Type & Seating	Factory Price	Shipping Weight	Production Total
SF	DO-7	2-dr Cpe-4P	4156	2937	28,131
SF	TO-7	2-dr Cpe-4P	3872	3601	2,950

1975 Oldsmobile, two-door Omega coupe, V-8

OMEGA — For the first time in 1975 there were two Omega series. The standard Omega series had three body styles: a pair of coupes and a four-door sedan. Standard equipment included: armrests; front disc brakes; electronic ignition; carpeting; dome light; molding package; three-speed manual transmission; and inline six cylinder engine. Standard tire size was FR78 x 14 inches. Interiors could be ordered in cloth or vinyl. Plant codes W and L were used for Omegas.

OMEGA

Model Number	Body/Style Number	Body Type & Seating	Factory Price	Shipping Weight	Production Total
O	B-17	2-dr Hatch-5P	3558	3426	6,287
O	B-27	2-dr Cpe-5P	3435	3518	14,306
O	B-69	4-dr Sed-5P	3463	3471	13,971

OMEGA SALON — The addition of the Salon package worked well in the Cutlass series, so Oldsmobile marketing decided to do the same thing in 1975 for the Omega. All three Omega body styles were available as Salons. Standard equipment included everything from the Omega list plus: a console; remote control outside mirror; reclining bucket seats; and Turbo-Hydramatic transmission. Standard tires were size FR78 x 14 inch radials. Upholstery was done in vinyl or cloth.

OMEGA SALON

Model Number	Body/Style Number	Body Type & Seating	Factory Price	Shipping Weight	Production Total
OS	C-17	2-dr Hatch-5P	4310	3601	1,636
OS	C-27	2-dr Cpe-5P	4194	3512	2,176
OS	C-69	4-dr Sed-5P	4205	3651	1,758

CUTLASS — The bottom line for the Oldsmobile intermediate series remained the two model Cutlass series. A coupe and sedan were available. Standard equipment included: front disc brakes; six-cylinder engine; carpeting; inside hood release; dome light; molding package; lamp package; power steering; Deluxe steering wheel; and three-speed manual transmission. Standard tire size was FR78 x 14 inches. Upholstery was done in vinyl or cloth. Plant codes M, R, D and Z were seen on Cutlasses, plus K for the new factory in Leeds, Mo.

CUTLASS

Model Number	Body/Style Number	Body Type & Seating	Factory Price	Shipping Weight	Production Total
C	F-37	2-dr Cpe-5P	3755	3773	12,797
C	G-29	4-dr Sed-5P	3830	3845	30,144

1975 Oldsmobile, two-door Cutlass 'S' Colonnade coupe, V-8

CUTLASS 'S' — Remaining as a single model series in 1975 was the Cutlass 'S'. Just a coupe was available. Standard equipment included: armrests; ashtrays; cigarette lighter; carpeting; inside hood release; bumper impact strips; lamp package; molding package; dome light; power steering; front disc brakes; Deluxe steering wheel; three-speed manual transmission; and inline six-cylinder engine. Standard tire size was FR78 x 14 inches. Upholstery was done in either vinyl or cloth.

CUTLASS 'S'

Model Number	Body/Style Number	Body Type & Seating	Factory Price	Shipping Weight	Production Total
CS	G-37	2-dr Cpe-5P	3852	3779	42,921

CUTLASS SUPREME — Again near the top of the intermediate lineup was the Cutlass Supreme nameplate. Just a pair of models were found here: a coupe and sedan. Standard equipment here included: front disc brakes; cigarette lighter; six-cylinder inline engine; carpeting; inside hood release; bumper impact strips; lamp package; molding package; power steering; Deluxe steering wheel; and three-speed manual transmission. Standard tire size was FR78 x 14 inches. Upholstery was done in vinyl or cloth.

CUTLASS SUPREME

Model Number	Body/Style Number	Body Type & Seating	Factory Price	Shipping Weight	Production Total
CSU	J-57	2-dr Cpe-5P	4047	3793	150,874
CSU	J-29	4-dr Sed-5P	4104	3891	15,517

CUTLASS SALON — Well received in previous years, the Cutlass Salon continued to be popular with Oldsmobile intermediate buyers. This was the only Cutlass model in 1975 to come standard with V-8 power, utilizing the 260 cid motor. Standard equipment on this series included: front disc brakes; electronic ignition system; carpeting; spring-loaded hood ornament; inside hood release; lamp package; molding package; power steering; Deluxe steering wheel and Turbo-Hydramatic transmission.

CUTLASS SALON

Model Number	Body/Style Number	Body Type & Seating	Factory Price	Shipping Weight	Production Total
CSA	K-57	2-dr Cpe-5P	4654	4033	39,050
CSA	K-29	4-dr Sed-5P	4726	4133	5,810

CUTLASS SUPREME/VISTA CRUISER — Again Oldsmobile offered a pair of intermediate station wagons in 1975. Both were available in either two- or three-seat models. The Vista Cruiser had the woodgrain decal package and a special roof vent and the Cutlass Supreme Cruiser had neither item as standard equipment. Standard equipment for both included: power front disc brakes; 350 cid power plant; cigarette lighter; carpeting; inside hood release; lamp package; molding package; spare tire extractor; power steering; Deluxe steering wheel; heavy-duty wheels; and Turbo-Hydramatic transmission. Standard tire size was HR78 x 115 inches. Upholstery was done in either vinyl or cloth.

CUTLASS SUPREME/VISTA CRUISER

Model Number	Body/Style Number	Body Type & Seating	Factory Price	Shipping Weight	Production Total
CSC	H-35	4-dr Sta Wag-5P	4678	4492	4,490
CSU	H-45	4-dr Sta Wag-7P	4791	4594	3,739
VC	J-35	4-dr Sta Wag-5P	4888	4517	4,963
VC	J-45	4-dr Sta Wag-7P	5001	4619	9,226

DELTA EIGHTY-EIGHT — In the full-size department for 1975, Oldsmobile offered two series. The Delta Eighty-Eight had three models, a pair of sedans and a coupe. Standard equipment included: power brakes with front discs; cigarette lighter; 350 cid engine; High-Energy ignition system; inside hood release; dome lamp; lamp package; molding package; power steering; and Turbo-Hydramatic transmission. Standard tire size was HR78 x 15 inches. Upholstery was done in vinyl or cloth. Factory codes M, E and X were found on this year's big Olds.

DELTA EIGHTY-EIGHT

Model Number	Body/Style Number	Body Type & Seating	Factory Price	Shipping Weight	Production Total
D88	L-57	2-dr Cpe-5P	4843	4483	8,522
D88	L-39	4-dr HT Sed-5P	4904	4544	9,283
D88	L-69	4-dr Twn Sed-5P	4787	4496	16,112

DELTA EIGHTY-EIGHT ROYALE — The only series that retained a convertible for the Oldsmobile lineup in 1975 was the Delta Eighty-Eight Royale. It joined the coupe and a pair of four-door sedans. Standard equipment on this group included: power brakes with front discs; cigarette lighter; electronic ignition system; 350 cid engine; carpeting; inside hood release; bumper impact strips; dome light; lamp package; molding package; power steering; Deluxe steering wheel and Turbo-Hydramatic transmission. Standard tire size was HR78 x 15 inches. Upholstery was vinyl, leather or cloth.

DELTA EIGHTY-EIGHT ROYALE

Model Number	Body/Style Number	Body Type & Seating	Factory Price	Shipping Weight	Production Total
D88R	N-57	2-dr Cpe-5P	4998	4525	23,465
D88R	N-69	4-dr Twn Sed-5P	4927	4578	21,038
D88R	N-39	4-dr HT Sed-5P	5064	4546	32,481
D88R	N-67	2-dr Conv-5P	5213	4595	7,181

CUSTOM CRUISER — Oldsmobile continued in the big wagon business with two- and three-seat versions of its huge Custom Cruiser in 1975. The Custom Cruiser was available both with and without the woodgrain side trim. Standard equipment on this series included: power brakes; bumper guards; cigarette lighter; electronic ignition; 455 cid engine; carpeting; lamp package; molding package; spare tire extractor; Deluxe steering wheel; power steering; and Turbo-Hydramatic transmission. Standard tire size was LR78 x 15 inches. Upholstery was done in either vinyl or cloth.

CUSTOM CRUISER

Model Number	Body/Style Number	Body Type & Seating	Factory Price	Shipping Weight	Production Total
CC	Q-35	4-dr Sta Wag-5P	5426	5059	1,458
CC	Q-45	4-dr Sta Wag-7P	5565	5119	2,315

WOODGRAIN SIDE TRIM

Model Number	Body/Style Number	Body Type & Seating	Factory Price	Shipping Weight	Production Total
CC	R-35	4-dr Sta Wag-5P	5581	5072	2,837
CC	R-45	4-dr Sta Wag-7P	5720	5129	9,458

1975 Oldsmobile, four-door Regency 98 hardtop sedan, V-8

NINETY-EIGHT — A reduction in the number of Ninety-Eight models was in order for 1975. A total of four models were available, coupes and sedan in Luxury and Regency trim. The Ninety-Eight remained a well-appointed car, even in standard trim. Standard equipment included: power brakes with front discs; cigarette lighter; electric clock; electronic ignition; hood release; bumper impact strips; lamp package; 455 cid engine; molding package; remote-controlled outside mirror; power seat; power windows; power steering; Deluxe steering wheel; chrome wheel discs; and Turbo-Hydramatic transmission. Standard size tires were JR78 x 15 inches. Upholstery was done in vinyl, leather or cloth.

NINETY-EIGHT

Model Number	Body/Style Number	Body Type & Seating	Factory Price	Shipping Weight	Production Total
98	V-37	2-dr Lux Cpe-5P	5963	4731	8,798
98	X-37	2-dr RegyCpe-5P	6225	4761	16,697
98	V-39	4-dr Lux Sed-5P	6104	4883	18,091
98	X-39	4-dr Regy Sed-5P	6366	4895	35,264

TORONADO — For model year 1975 the front-drive Toronado series was expanded to include a second model. Both were coupes, the Custom and the Brougham. The Toronado remained Oldsmobile's mainstay in the personal/luxury market and one of the few full-size front-wheel-drive cars built domestically. The standard equipment list was impressive on this series. It included: Deluxe armrests; power brakes with front discs; cigarette lighter; electric digital clock; High-Energy ignition; carpeting; inside hood release; molding package; light package; power windows; power seat; power steering; Deluxe steering wheel; and Turbo-Hydramatic transmission. Standard tire size was JR78 x 15 inches. Upholstery was done in vinyl, cloth or leather. Once again, all Toronados were assembled in Michigan and had the M code for the Lansing factory in their serial number.

TORONADO

Model Number	Body/Style Number	Body Type & Seating	Factory Price	Shipping Weight	Production Total
T	Y-57	2-dr Cus Cpe-5P	6536	4787	4,419
T	Z-57	2-dr Brgm Cpe-5P	6766	4793	18,882

BASE ENGINES

(STARFIRE SERIES) V-6. Overhead valve. Cast-iron block. Displacement: 231 cid. Bore and stroke: 3.8 x 3.4 inches. Compression ratio: 8 to 1. Brake hp: 125 at 3500 rpm. Five main bearings. Hydraulic valve lifters. Carburetor: Rochester 2GC two-barrel.

(OMEGA/OMEGA SALON/CUTLASS/CUTLASS 'S'/ SERIES) Inline. Six cylinder. Overhead valves. Cast iron block. Displacement: 250 cid. Bore and stroke: 3 7/8 x 3.53 inches. Compression ratio: 8 to 1. Brake hp: 100 at 3400 rpm. Seven main bearings. Hydraulic valve lifters. Carburetor: Rochester MV one-barrel.

(CUTLASS SALON SERIES) V-8. Overhead valves. Cast iron block. Displacement: 260 cid. Bore and stroke: 3.5 x 3.385 inches. Compression ratio: 8 to 1. Brake hp: 150 at 3800 rpm. Five main bearings. Hydraulic valve lifters. Carburetor: Rochester Model 2GC two-barrel.

(CUTLASS SUPREME/VISTA CRUISER/DELTA 88/DELTA 88 ROYALE SERIES) V-8. Overhead valves. Cast iron block. Displacement: 350 cid. Bore and stroke: 4.057 x 3.385 inches. Compression ratio: 8.5 to 1. Brake hp: 180 at 4000 rpm. Five main bearings. Hydraulic valve lifters. Carburetor: M4MC four-barrel.

(CUSTOM CRUISER/NINETY-EIGHT SERIES) V-8. Overhead valves. Cast iron block. Displacement: 455 cid. Bore and stroke: 4.125 x 4.250 inches. Compression ratio: 8.5 to 1. Brake hp: 210 at 4000 rpm. Five main bearings. Hydraulic valve lifters. Carburetor: M-4MC four-barrel.

(TORONADO SERIES) V-8. Overhead valves. Cast-iron block. Displacement: 455 cid. Bore and stroke: 4.125 x 4.250 inches. Compression ratio: 8.5 to 1. Brake hp: 230 at 4000 rpm. Five main bearings. Hydraulic valve lifters. Carburetor: M-4MC four-barrel.

CHASSIS FEATURES: Wheelbase: (Starfire) 97 inches; (Omega) 111 inches; (Intermediate two-door) 112 inches; (Intermediate four-door) 116 inches; (88) 124 inches; (98/Custom Cruiser) 127 inches; (Toronado) 122 inches. Overall length: (Starfire) 179.3 inches; (Omega) 196.6 inches; (intermediate two-door) 211.7 inches; (Intermediate four-door) 215.7 inches; (88) 226.9 inches; (98) 232.4 inches; (Toronado) 227.6 inches; (Custom Cruiser) 231.2 inches. Front tread: (Starfire) 54.7 inches; (Omega) 61.3 inches; (all Intermediates) 61.1 inches; (Toronado) 63.6 inches; (all others) 63.7 inches. Rear tread: (Starfire) 53.6 inches; (Omega) 59 inches; (all Intermediates) 60.7 inches; (Toronado) 63.5 inches; (all others) 63.7 inches.

OPTIONS: Power brakes ($55). Power steering ($129). Air conditioning ($487). Power trunk release ($16). Door locks ($56). Floor mats ($7). Vinyl roof ($107). Sports mirrors ($25). Two-tone finish ($38). Super stock wheel ($79). Gauges ($33). AM radio ($73). AM/ FM stereo radio ($329). Rear speaker ($19). Fuel economy meter ($24). 4-4-2 package ($128). Power seat ($116). Power windows ($149). Electric clock ($19). Locking gas cap ($6). Opera roof ($142). Pulse wipers ($26). Four-speed manual transmission was standard on Starfire. Three-speed manual transmission was standard on Omega and Cutlass. Automatic transmission was standard on others. Automatic transmission ($237). V-8: 350 cid/180 hp L-77 engine ($180). V-8: 455 cid/210 hp L-74 engine ($298). V-8: 260 cid/150 hp LV-8 engine ($78). Positive traction rear axle ($49).

HISTORICAL FOOTNOTES: The 1975 Oldsmobiles were introduced Sept. 27, 1974. The division achieved third ranking in industry sales with 628,720 deliveries for the calendar year. The 'last' Oldsmobile convertible was a red Delta 88 Royale rag-top built on July 11, 1975. Of potential interest to collectors this season was a Hurst/Olds package, priced at $1,095 over the base cost of the J-57 Cutlass Supreme hardtop coupe. Of the total 7,181 Delta 88 Royale convertibles built this year, 245 cars were equipped with a 400 cid V-8. Also produced were 212 Cutlass style F-37 coupes and 6,015 Cutlass 'S' style G-37 coupes with the 4-4-2 package installed. Oldsmobile also reported building 32 Toronados that were specially packaged for mobile homes and 150 Oldsmobile Ninety-Eight chassis with a 150 inch wheelbase for the professional car building firm Cotner-Bevington. R.J. Cook was the general manager of Oldsmobile this year.

PACKARD

1946-1958

1955 Packard Caribbean, two-door convertible, V-8 (AA)

The postwar history of Packard Motor Car Co. is a sad tale to relate. One of America's oldest car makers, Packard continued to create outstanding automobiles from 1946 to 1958. The cars failed to find popularity with a new breed of buyers who wanted a radically different type of product after the fighting in Europe and Asia subsided.

by G. Marshall Naul

For years, Packard's business philosophy was built on the foundation of thought that high-priced car buyers did not care for radical change on an annual, model year basis. The directors of the company felt that such customers preferred a quality product that could retain its style value one season after the next. This was no longer the case in the industry, after 1949, when style consciousness came to play an ever more important role in the marketing of cars on a high-volume basis.

Also contributing to the eventual demise of the Packard nameplate was the company's independent status. Without full-range market coverage and the resources of a giant corporation to back it up, Packard was unable to adjust very quickly to the new postwar trends. This meant that even after the problems had been identified, there was no feasible way to solve them. Packard simply could not afford to create all-new styling one year and sufficiently change it the next.

Of course, for the modern enthusiast, yesterday's problems have turned into a blessing of sorts. This is because many of those tradition-bound, quality-constructed Packards of the late 1940s and early 1950s now represent valuable collector's items. Endowed with the magic of the Packard name, such automobiles are durable, beautiful and rare.

The first postwar Packards saw daylight on a chilly, grey October morning in 1945 and were, indeed, cars built to the same high standards held by this manufacturer since 1899. All of America wanted a new car at this time, so the fact that they looked much like the 1942 models had little effect on sales. It was due to other factors, such as a labor unrest and difficulty getting raw materials, that only 30,793 Twenty-First Series (1946) Packards were sold. Even at that, Packard was able to keep pace with other competitors within its own price class.

For 1947, the Packard saw little change, but began losing precious ground in terms of keeping abreast of new trends. The problem was not of major proportion yet, since the only all-new cars to be had were those from smaller companies like Studebaker and Kaiser-Frazer. In fact, the company's long-time rival, Cadillac, was merely one notch up in the charts. (Only about three percent of the 1946-1950 Packards were in the Cadillac price range, however, and the company actually saw Buick as the big competitor in that period.)

The year 1948 brought a different ball game. That was when Cadillac introduced P-38 type tailfins and sleekly-styled

sheet metal on a few of its lines. Packard countered with a new look as well. It was one that seemed to have mass appeal. Praised and honored by a number of internationally respected design organizations, the Twenty-Second Series models earned 146,441 deliveries for calendar 1948 and 1949.

Suddenly it was late 1949 and three things began to happen. First, production by all manufacturers got back into full-swing, satisfying just about all demand for new cars. Second, the large makers came forth with completely new and much modernized styling. The General Motors' hardtops were the fashion hit of the season. The third factor was one where Packard's weakness began to show. Though labeled as new, Twenty-Third Series "Golden Anniversary" models, the late 1949 and 1950 offerings looked basically the same as before. One important innovation was Ultramatic transmission, a type considered the best of its day by the public and auto experts alike.

In contrast to the models from other firms, buyers began viewing Packard as an old-fashioned 'fogie' in a brave, new world. Helping little to combat the image, was a lack of a modern overhead valve V-8 engine, although Packard made the largest straight eight available at the time. It was standard on the 23rd Series Custom Eights of 1949 and an option on all '49 Packards by year's end.

Avoiding or neglecting the need for a V-8 motor, Packard made a valiant attempt to get back on the right track in 1951. There was an almost completely new car, except for the huge straight eight. It featured all-new sheet metal and trim, new frames and updated interior styling. The addition of the handsome Mayfair hardtop was a move in the right direction, along with increased acceptance of Ultramatic. The result was a 115 percent increase in business over 1950. This should have been a sign of the proper pattern to follow year after year.

Unfortunately, the indicators were ignored. Despite some wonderfully creative reworkings that resulted in flashier and fancier models in 1953 and 1954, the new Packards remained virtually unchanged in basic terms.

Sales and production figures, in themselves, did not paint an exceptionally bleak picture until 1954. Packard was the 16th largest producer in 1951, selling some 76,000 cars. The

following season, it was 16th again, with 63,000 deliveries. It even achieved 14th rank and found 81,000 customers for 1953. Yet, the overall market was consistently expanding. Packard's business was not keeping pace with that of the major firms. There was no real growth. When a general downturn hit after the Korean War, 1954 assemblies peaked at 27,593 cars. It was yet another bad sign.

Forced into a corner, Packard went to new body shells and V-8 power for 1955. There were three-tone color combinations, hooded headlights, torsion bars, wraparound windshields, a hint of tailfins and, even, a medium-priced Clipper line.

As in the past, the high degree of change brought immediate benefits. Sales climbed to 70,000 cars. The new Packards drew rave reviews. But, the revisions came with bills for new tooling, technology and factory expansion. These were costs that Packard could no longer bear alone, so the company's president, James Nance, went looking for a financial partner in 1954. This culminated in the purchase of Studebaker, a move which seemed logical on the surface, but actually brought more problems.

Like the other independent manufacturers at this time, Studebaker was over-extended in trying to compete with the 'Big Three' automakers and actually pulled a somewhat healthy parent to its grave. When sales dropped to 13,000 cars in the depressed market of 1956, Nance bailed out. Curtiss-Wright Corp. gained management control of Studebaker-Packard, primarily as a tax write-off, and quickly decided to consolidate its holdings at Studebaker's South Bend, Ind. facilities. Many profitable aspects of the auto company (defense contracts, etc.) were acquired by Curtiss-Wright. What remained of Studebaker-Packard was eventually released under its own management.

For the next two years, the Packard became a badge-engineered car to fulfill dealer contracts and was built off a Studebaker platform. Though technically a fine automobile, and certainly rare and unique, this new type of Packard was unable to attract repeat customers due to its lack of identity and some controversial styling. After 1958, the name Packard disappeared from the automotive scene. Many say the passing was unavoidable. "How could a car with enduring quality and grace survive in an age in which the basis of success is planned obsolescence?," they asked.

1948 Packard, four-door Station Sedan, 8-cyl

1949 Packard, Custom Eight two-door convertible, 8-cyl

1946 Packard, Clipper Super Custom four-door sedan, 8-cyl (AA)

CLIPPER SIX — (6-CYL) — SERIES 2100 — Although given a new designation as Twenty-First Series models, the 1946 Packards were an extension of the 1942 Clipper line with practically no changes. The Clipper design had been started in 1941, but with pent-up demand for new cars built-up over four war years, there was no time nor any need for all new-models. A single body stamping was used for Packards, even though length of the wheelbase varied by series. Changes in length were taken up ahead of the firewall with longer front end sheet metal. Clippers were easy to spot. Unlike other models, the horizontal grille extension bars running below the headlights did not wrap around the front body corners. In addition, the six did not carry model identification scripts below the vent windows on the front doors. Available body types included a two-door Club Sedan with a fastback roofline and a conventional four-door sedan with a notch back (or 'humped' back) look. Also provided, with six-cylinder power only, were a taxicab sedan and a taxicab sedan with a driver's partition.

CLIPPER SIX SERIES

Series Number	Body/Style Number	Body Type & Seating	Factory Price	Shipping Weight	Production Total
2100	1685	2-dr Clb Sed-6P	1680	3450	Note 1
2100	1682	4-dr Tr Sed-6P	1730	3495	Note 1
2100	1686	4-dr Taxi-6P	1945	3670	Note 1
2100	1684	4-dr Part. Taxi-6P	2069	3730	Note 1

NOTE 1: 15,892 Clipper Sixes built.
NOTE 2: No body style breakouts available.

PACKARD I.D. NUMBERS: Packard motor numbers were the most important of three types of manufacturer's codes. They were stamped on a white-painted boss on the upper left-hand side of the cylinder block. A vehicle number was also stamped on a plate attached to the left top side of the cowl and was the same as a Body/Style Number, since it identified the model or style. These numbers correspond to the Body/Style Number in the second column of our charts, with the first two symbols changing from 16 to 21 to indicate Twenty-First Series. A Body Number was provided and was also stamped on the plate attached to the left top side of the cowl, below the hood. The Body Number does not provide model identification, but seems to represent a production sequence record used mainly for factory purposes. The Body/Style Number appeared as the first four digits of the Packard serial number, followed by the motor number. Motor numbers for the Clipper Six were F-1501 to F-14999. Motor numbers for Clipper and Clipper Deluxe Eights were F-300001 to F-319999. Motor numbers for Super Clipper and Custom Clipper Eights ranged from F-500001 to 505999 with both built in mixed production and sharing the same range of numbers.

CLIPPER STANDARD/DELUXE EIGHT — (8-CYL) — SERIES 2101/2111 — The basic Clipper Eight was marketed only in four-door trunk sedan (notch back) form. It carried a door script to identify the series designation and was listed as the only car in the 2101 Series. A Deluxe 2111 Series included both this model and the fastback Club Sedan. Identification for the fancier cars was achieved by placing special bi-level scripts on the door, below the front vent window. Deluxes also featured wraparound type grille extension bars, fancier wheel trim treatments, more window moldings and richer interior trim. Taxicabs were not normally provided on the eight-cylinder chassis.

CLIPPER EIGHT SERIES

Series Number	Body/Style Number	Body Type & Seating	Factory Price	Shipping Weight	Production Total
STANDARD					
2101	1692	4-dr Tr Sed-6P	1802	3575	1,500
DELUXE					
2111	1615	2-dr Clb Sed-6P	1817	3625	Note 1
2111	1612	4-dr Tr Sed-6P	1869	3670	Note 1

NOTE 1: 5,714 Clipper Deluxe Eights built.
NOTE 2: No body style breakouts available.

SUPER CLIPPER EIGHT — (8-CYL) — SERIES 2103 — The Super Clipper Eight was on a seven inch longer wheelbase than lower-priced Packards. It featured wraparound grille extension bars, upgraded wheel trim treatments, a 'humpier' looking rear deck and a single-level door signature script reading 'Super Clipper.' In terms of body styles, both a four-door and a two-door were offered in a single level of trim. The Club Sedan was a fastback.

SUPER CLIPPER EIGHT SERIES

Series Number	Body/Style Number	Body Type & Seating	Factory Price	Shipping Weight	Production Total
2103	1675	2-dr Clb Sed-6P	2241	3950	Note 1
2103	1672	4-dr Tr Sed-6P	2290	3995	Note 1

NOTE 1: 4,924 Super Clipper Eights built.
NOTE 2: No body style breakouts available.

CUSTOM SUPER CLIPPER EIGHT — (8-CYL) — SERIES 2106/2126 — In a case of subtle prestige, Packard's top-flight cars appeared without front door scripts to identify their upper crust status. They did, however, have wraparound grille extension bars to help avoid confusion with low priced Clipper Sixes on the behalf of buyers unable to detect differences in size. Of course, a look at the rich interior appointments served to further distinguish the high-dollar machines. As might be expected, they were built off two of Packard's longest platforms, either the 127 inch wheelbase chassis, shared with Super Clippers, or the 148 inch wheelbase extended chassis used for seven-passenger sedans and limousines. The biggest Packard motor, with its smooth nine bearing crankshaft and silent hydraulic lifters, was nestled under the hoods of these cars. Like all Packards, they had a 6-volt, positive ground electrical system.

CUSTOM SUPER CLIPPER EIGHT SERIES

Series Number	Body/Style Number	Body Type & Seating	Factory Price	Shipping Weight	Production Total
STANDARD WHEELBASE LINE					
2106	1625	2-dr Clb Sed-6P	2913	4000	Note 1
2106	1622	4-dr Tr Sed-6P	3047	4060	Note 1
EXTENDED WHEELBASE LINE					
2126	1651	4-dr Sed-7P	4332	4870	Note 2
2126	1650	4-dr Limo-7P	4496	4900	Note 2

NOTE 1: 1,472 standard wheelbase Custom Super Clippers built.
NOTE 2: 1,291 long wheelbase Custom Super Clippers built.
NOTE 3: No body style breakouts available.

ENGINES

(CLIPPER SIX) Inline. L-head six. Displacement: 245.3 cid. Bore and stroke: 3-1/2 x 4-1/4 inches. Compression ratio: 6.7:1. Brake hp: 105 at 3600 rpm. Four main bearings. Solid valve lifters. Carburetor: Carter Type WA1 one-barrel Model 530S.

(CLIPPER STANDARD/DELUXE EIGHT) Inline. L-head eight. Displacement: 282.04 cid. Bore and stroke: 3-1/4 x 4-1/4 inches. Compression ratio: 6.85:1. Brake hp: 125 at 3600 rpm. Five main bearings. Solid valve lifters. Carburetor: Carter Type WDO two-barrel Model 512S.

(SUPER/CUSTOM SUPER CLIPPER EIGHT) Inline. L-head eight. Displacement: 356 cid. Bore and stroke: 3-1/2 x 4-5/8 inches. Compression ratio: 6.85:1. Brake hp: 165 at 3600 rpm. Nine main bearings. Hydraulic valve lifters. Carburetor: Carter Type WDO two-barrel Model 531S.

CHASSIS FEATURES: Wheelbase: (Series 2100, 2101 and 2111) 120 inches; (Series 1203 and 2106) 127 inches; (Series 2126) 148 inches. Overall length: (Series 2100, 2101 and 2111) 208.4 inches. (Series 2103 and 2106) 215.5 inches. Front tread: (all) 59-1/4 inches. Rear tread: (Series 2100) 60-9/16 inches; (Series 2101 and 2111) 60-13/16 inches; (Series 2103, 2106 and 2126) 60-11/16 inches. Tires: (Series 2103, 2106) 7.00 x 15; (Series 2126) 7.50 x 16; (other series) 6.50 x 15. Packard advertising for 1946 highlighted such chassis features as roll control bar; fifth shock absorber; car wider than high and low center of gravity.

OPTIONS: Heater. Radio. Fender skirts. Wheel trim rings. Roof-mount radio antenna. Two-tone paint. Electromatic clutch. Overdrive.

HISTORICAL FOOTNOTES: Postwar Packards were reintroduced to the market in October, 1945. A limited number of standard body styles were available at first. The full line of standard Packards was seen in production by about April, 1946. Super Eights started rolling from the assembly line a month later, followed by manufacture of a complete line by June of the same year. A total of 30,793 cars found buyers. Calendar year deliveries peaked at 42,102 units, making Packard America's 14th largest producer. Instruments were said to be grouped in a newly redesigned panel offering "at-a-glance" readability. Highly promoted were such beneficial devices as automatic chokes, rotary door catches, safety glass, counter-balanced trunk lids and "chatterproof" glove compartments. The Classic Car Club of America accepts 1946-1947 Custom Super Clippers as authentic Classic Cars, upon individual application by owners. The Milestone Car Society and Veteran Motor Car Club of America have designated the Custom Super Clipper as a Milestone Car.

1947 PACKARD
(21st SERIES)

1947 Packard Custom Super Clipper four-door sedan

CLIPPER SIX — (6-CYL) — SERIES 2100 — There were virtually no changes in Packard models for 1947, save for serial numbers, price and weight increases. Taxi sedans, with or without driver's partitions, continued to be offered as six-cylinder only models.

PACKARD I.D. NUMBERS: Packard motor numbers were the most important of three types of manufacturer's codes. They were stamped on a white-painted boss on the upper left-hand side of the cylinder block. A vehicle number was also stamped on a plate attached to the left top side of the cowl and was the same as a Body/Style Number, since it identified the model

or style. These numbers correspond to the Body/Style Number in the second column of our charts, with the first two symbols changing from 16 to 21 to indicate Twenty-First Series. A Body Number was provided and was also stamped on the plate attached to the left top side of the cowl, below the hood. The Body Number does not provide model identification, but seems to represent a production sequence record used mainly for factory purposes. The Body/Style Number appeared as the first four digits of the Packard serial number, followed by the motor number. Motor numbers for the Clipper Six were F-15001 to F-50999. Motor numbers for Clipper and Clipper Deluxe Eights were F-320001 to F-399999. Motor numbers for Super Clipper and Custom Clipper Eights ranged from F-506001 to 521999 with both built in mixed production and sharing the same range of numbers.

CLIPPER SIX SERIES

Series Number	Body/Style Number	Body Type & Seating	Factory Price	Shipping Weight	Production Total
2100	2182	4-dr Sed-6P	1745	3495	Note 1
2100	2185	2-dr Clb Sed-6P	1695	3480	Note 1
2100	2186	4-dr Taxi-6P	2024	3705	Note 1
2100	2184	4-dr Part Taxi-6P	2148	3765	Note 1

NOTE 1: 14,949 Clipper Sixes built.
NOTE 2: No body style breakouts available.
NOTE 3: Prices of $1,912 (Club Sedan); $1,937 (four-door sedan) at midyear.

CLIPPER EIGHT — (8-CYL) — SERIES 21 11 — A standard Clipper Eight, Series 2101 model, is listed by some 1947 references, but no prices, weights or other data are provided for this car. This suggests that the model was either dropped, or that no examples were sold. For all practical purposes, only the two Clipper Deluxe Eights remained. Both were unchanged from their 1946 specifications.

CLIPPER DELUXE EIGHT SERIES

Series Number	Body/Style Number	Body Type & Seating	Factory Price	Shipping Weight	Production Total
2111	2115	2-dr Clb Sed-6P	1895	3625	Note 1
2111	2112	4-dr Sed-6P	1947	3670	Note 1

NOTE 1: 23,855 Deluxe Clipper Eights were built.
NOTE 2: No breakout per body style is available.
NOTE 3: Prices of $2,124 (Club Sedan); $2,149 (four-door sedan) at midyear.

SUPER CLIPPER EIGHT — (8-CYL) — SERIES 2103 — As with the other 1947 models, there was virtually no change in the new Super Clipper Eight models. Cars in this series continued to sell with the biggest Packard engine and the middle-sized platform. Once again, they took their identification from scripts placed on the upper part of the front door, below the ventipanes.

SUPER CLIPPER EIGHT SERIES

Series Number	Body/Style Number	Body Type & Seating	Factory Price	Shipping Weight	Production Total
2103	2175	2-dr Clb Sed-6P	2342	3950	Note 1
2103	2172	4-dr Sed-6P	2391	3995	Note 1

NOTE 1: 4,802 Super Clipper Eights built.
NOTE 2: No breakout per body style available.
NOTE 3: Prices of $2,747 (Club Sedan); $2,772 (four-door sedan) at midyear.

CUSTOM SUPER CLIPPER EIGHT — (8-CYL) — SERIES 2106/2126 — Customs continued to come with distinctive interior trims and no external identifiers, such as door scripts. Special carpeting was featured again, along with upholstery in rich broadcloth and leather combinations. Imitation wood paneling was used on the interior of Custom models to add an even finer flavor. The model lineup was the same as provided the previous season.

CUSTOM SUPER CLIPPER EIGHT SERIES STANDARD WHEELBASE LINE

Series Number	Body/Style Number	Body Type & Seating	Factory Price	Shipping Weight	Production Total
2106	2125	2-dr Clb Sed-6P	3140	4000	Note 1
2106	2122	4-dr Sed-6P	3274	4060	Note 1
EXTENDED WHEELBASE LINE					
2126	2151	4-dr Sed-7P	4357	4870	Note 2
2126	2150	4-dr Limo-7P	4521	4900	Note 2

NOTE 1: 5,690 standard wheelbase Custom Super Clippers built.
NOTE 2: 1,790 extended wheelbase Custom Super Clippers built.
NOTE 3: No breakouts per body style available.
NOTE 4: Prices of $3,384 (Club Sedan); $3,449 (six-passenger sedan); $4,504 (seven-passenger sedan); and $4,668 (limousine) at midyear.

ENGINES

(CLIPPER SIX) Inline. L-head six. Displacement: 245.3 cid. Bore and stroke: 3-1/2 x 4-1/4 inches. Compression ratio: 6.7:1. Brake hp: 105 at 3600 rpm. Four main bearings. Solid valve lifters. Carburetor: Carter Type WA1 one-barrel Model 530S.

(CLIPPER STANDARD/DELUXE EIGHT) Inline. L-head eight. Displacement: 282.04 cid. Bore and stroke: 3-1/4 x 4-1/4 inches. Compression ratio: 6.85:1. Brake hp: 125 at 3600 rpm. Five main bearings. Solid valve lifters. Carburetor: Carter Type WDO two-barrel Model 512S.

(SUPER/CUSTOM SUPER CLIPPER EIGHT) Inline. L-head eight. Displacement: 356 cid. Bore and stroke: 3-1/2 x 4-5/8 inches. Compression ratio: 6.85:1. Brake hp: 165 at 3600 rpm. Nine main bearings. Hydraulic valve lifters. Carburetor: Carter Type WDO two-barrel Model 531S.

CHASSIS FEATURES: Wheelbase: (Series 2100, 2101 and 2111) 120 inches; (Series 1203 and 2106) 127 inches; (Series 2126) 148 inches. Overall length: (Series 2100, 2101 and 2111) 208.4 inches. (Series 2103 and 2106) 215.5 inches. Front tread: (all) 59-1/4 inches. Rear tread: (Series 2100) 60-9/16 inches; (Series 2101 and 2111) 60-13/16 inches; (Series 2103, 2106 and 2126) 60-11/16 inches. Tires: (Series 2103, 2106) 7.00 x 15; (Series 2126) 7.50 x 16; (other series) 6.50 x 15. Packard advertising for 1946 highlighted such chassis features as roll control bar; fifth shock absorber; car wider than high and low center of gravity.

OPTIONS: White sidewall tires ($21). Heater. Radio. Fender skirts. Wheel trim rings. Roof-mount radio antenna. Two-tone paint. Electromatic clutch. Overdrive.

HISTORICAL FOOTNOTES: Packard slipped into the 16th spot on auto industry sales charts this season. Sales rankings were based on calendar year deliveries of 55,477 vehicles, as opposed to a strong model year production total of 81,879 cars. The unusually large spread between the two is related to the changeover to the all-new Twenty-Second Series (1948-1949) models that were manufactured late in the 1947 calendar year. The Classic Car Club of America accepts the 1946-1947 Custom Super Clipper as a full Classic, upon individual application by owners. The Milestone Car Society and the VMCCA have designated the Custom Super Clipper a Milestone Car. The millionth Packard was built during 1947. It was a Twenty-Second Series Super Eight convertible.

1948-49 PACKARD
(22nd SERIES)

1948 Packard two-door sedan, 8-cyl

STANDARD EIGHT/DELUXE EIGHT — (8-CYL) — SERIES 2202/2222 — The Twenty-Second Series Packards were merchandised as 1948 and 1949 models, since Packard did not adhere to a model year changeover system. Effective Nov. 1, 1948, for purposes of registration, 1948 Series 2200 Packards became 1949 Series 2200-9 models. When they were first introduced, these were all-new postwar cars. General appearance changes included a longer hood; an "ox-yoke" shaped upper grille: full-width, wraparound lower grille; a pair of simplified, vertical front bumper guards; and smoother, rounded body lines. Their styling is often referred to as the "inverted bathtub" or "pregnant elephant" look. Standard Eights were the base offering (except for six-cylinder taxi and export-only models). They came in two conventional passenger car versions; Club Sedan or touring sedan. They had the plainest and cheapest looking Packard hood ornament; single rocker panel strips; upper belt moldings running from below the front ventipanes to the rear; and no lower belt moldings at mid-body level. Deluxe Eights were the same basic cars with extra exterior trim and shared some richer interior appointments with Super Eights. Most had more elaborate, horizontally 'veed' hood ornaments (with disc-shaped protrusions at the forward tip). These were called 'Winged Goddess' mascots. (Four styles of ornaments were available.) Fancier wheel trim treatments were another common aid in spotting Deluxe Eights. An almost all-steel, wagon-like, Station Sedan was provided as a Standard Eight model only. It had genuine northern birch wood body paneling that was structural only in the tailgate region.

PACKARD I.D. NUMBERS: Packard motor numbers were the most important of three types of manufacturer's codes. They were stamped on a white-painted boss on the upper left-hand side of the cylinder block. A vehicle number was also stamped on a plate attached to the left top side of the cowl and was the same as a Body/Style Number, since it identified the model or style. These numbers correspond to the Body/Style Number in the second column of our charts, with the first two symbols changing from 21 to 22 to indicate Twenty-Second series. A Body Number was provided and was also stamped on the plate attached to the left top side of the cowl, below the hood. The Body Number does not provide model identification, but seems to represent a production sequence record used mainly for factory purposes. The Body/Style Number appeared as the first four digits of the Packard serial number, followed by the motor number. Motor numbers for six-cylinder taxis and exported sixes were G-1501 to G-10,000. Motor numbers for the Standard/Deluxe Eights were G-200001 to G-303000 for 1948 (Series 2200) models and continuing through G-350,000 for 1949 (Series 2200-9) models. Motor numbers for Super Eights were G-400001 to G-432000 for 1948 (Series 2200) models and continuing through G-475000 for 1949 (Series 2200-9) models. Motor numbers for Custom Eights were G-600001 to G-612000 for 1948 (Series 2200) models and continuing through G-650000 for 1949 (Series 2200-9) models.

PACKARD EIGHT SERIES

Series Number	Body/Style Number	Body Type & Seating	Factory Price	Shipping Weight	Production Total
STANDARD LINE					
2201	2292	4-dr Sed-6P	2150	3815	Notes 1/2
2201	2295	2-dr Clb Sed-6P	2125	3755	Notes 1/2
2201	2293	4-dr Sta Sed-6P	3350	4080	Notes 1/2
DELUXE LINE					
2211	2262	4-dr Sed-6P	2375	3850	Notes 3/4
2211	2265	2-dr Clb Sed-6P	2350	3770	Notes 3/4

NOTE 1: 12,803 Series 2200 (1948) Standard Eights built.
NOTE 2: 12,532 Series 2200-9 (1949) Standard Eights built.
NOTE 3: 47,790 Series 2200 (1948) Deluxe Eights built.
NOTE 4: 27,438 Series 2200-9 (1949) Deluxe Eights built.
NOTE 5: No breakouts per body type available.

SUPER EIGHT — (8-CYL) — SERIES 2202/2222/2232 — Packard's middle line emphasized technical benefits, as indicated by 1948 promotional messages such as "A new performance thrill awaits the buyers of the spirited Super Eight... the motor car that makes distance disappear." These cars came with enriched interior appointments and streamlined 'Goddess of Speed' hood ornaments. Exterior trim was not very much different than that of the Standard Eights, except on the Super Deluxe sedan, which was trimmed in the manner of the Deluxe Eight and also had slightly fancier taillamp doors with short chrome divider bars. Three sub-series were coded. The first included Club and touring sedans on a 120 inch wheelbase chassis. The second featured four closed body styles on an extended 141 inch wheelbase. An all-new Victoria Convertible was the third entry. It was Packard's first open car since 1942. The Super convertible had single rocker panel strips and fender skirts were standard. It was built off the standard wheelbase chassis, but drew much buyer interest.

SUPER EIGHT SERIES

Series Number	Body/Style Number	Body Type & Seating	Factory Price	Shipping Weight	Production Total!
STANDARD WHEELBASE (CLOSED)					
2202	2272	4-dr Sed-6P	2690	3855	Notes 1/2
2202	2275	2-dr Clb Sed-6P	2665	3790	Notes 1/2
LONG WHEELBASE (CLOSED)					
2222	2277	4-dr Sed-7P	3300	4460	Notes 3/4
2222	2271	4-dr Del Sed-7P	3650	4590	Notes 3/4
2222	2276	4-dr Limo-7P	3450	4525	Notes 3/4
2222	2270	4-dr Del Limo-7P	3800	4610	Notes 3/4
VICTORIA CONVERTIBLE COUPE					
2232	2279	2-dr Conv-6P	3250	4025	Notes 6/7

NOTE 1: 12,929 Series 2200 (1948) standard wheelbase Super Eights built.
NOTE 2: 5,871 Series 2200-9 (1949) standard wheelbase Super Eights built.
NOTE 3: 1,740 Series 2200 (1948) extended wheelbase Super Eights built.
NOTE 4: 865 Series 2200-9 (1949) extended wheelbase Super Eights built.
NOTE 5: No breakout per body type available on closed cars.
NOTE 6: 4,750 Series 2200 (1948) Super Eight Victoria Convertibles built.
NOTE 7: 4,250 Series 2200-9 (1949) Super Eight Convertible Victorias built.

1948 Packard, Custom Eight Victoria convertible 8-cyl. AA

CUSTOM EIGHT — (8-CYL) — SERIES 2206/2226/2233 — Packard's luxury line had the highest horsepower, but not the highest power-to-weight ratio. The luxury-per-pound factor was excellent though. Eggcrate style grille insert designs were exclusive to these cars and a beauty panel of similar patterning stretched across the lower rear body to encase the taillamps with its bright metal gridwork. Rear wheel shrouds (fender skirts) were standard equipment and double rocker panel trim strips underscored the body sides. A graceful, vertical cormorant or pelican mascot was seen raising its wings over the nose of the car. Interiors were done in rich cloth and leather combinations and all-leather on the Victoria Convertible. The standard Custom wheelbase was 127 inches. Seven passenger styles had a 148 inch stance.

CUSTOM EIGHT SERIES

Series Number	Body/Style Number	Body Type & Seating	Factory Price	Shipping Weight	Production Total
STANDARD WHEELBASE (CLOSED)					
2206	2252	4-dr Sed-6P	3750	4175	Note 1
2206	2255	2-dr Clb Sed-6P	3700	4110	Note 1
LONG WHEELBASE (CLOSED)					
2226	2251	4-dr Sed-7P	4704	4860	Note 3/4
2226	2250	4-dr Limo-7P	4868	4880	Note 3/4
VICTORIA CONVERTIBLE COUPE					
2233	2259	2-dr Conv-6P	4295	4380	Note 6/7

NOTE 1: 5,935 Series 2200 (1948) standard wheelbase Custom Eights built.
NOTE 2: 2,989 Series 2200-9 (1949) standard wheelbase Custom Eights built.
NOTE 3: 231 Series 2200 (1948) long-wheelbase Custom Eights built.
NOTE 4: 49 Series 2200-9 (1949) long-wheelbase Custom Eights built.
NOTE 5: No breakouts per body type available on closed cars.
NOTE 6: 1,103 Series 2200 (1948) Custom Eight Victoria Convertibles built.
NOTE 7: 215 Series 2200-9 (1949) Custom Eight Victoria Convertibles built.

ENGINES

(STANDARD/DELUXE EIGHT) Inline. L-head eight. Cast iron block. Displacement: 288 cid. Bore and stroke: 3-1/2 x 3-3/4 inches. Compression ratio: 7.0:1. Brake hp: 130 at 3600 rpm. Five main bearings. Solid valve lifters. Carburetor: Carter Type WDO two-barrel Model 644SA.

(SUPER EIGHT) Inline. L-head eight. Cast iron block. Displacement: 327 cid. Bore and stroke: 3-1/2 x 4-1/4 inches. Compression ratio: 7.0:1. Brake hp: 145 at 3600 rpm. Solid valve lifters. Five main bearings. Carburetor: Carter Type WDO two-barrel Model 643SA.

(CUSTOM EIGHT) Inline. L-head eight. Cast iron block. Displacement: 356 cid. Bore and stroke: 3-1/2 x 4-5/8 inches. Compression ratio: 7.0:1. Brake hp: 160 at 3600 rpm. Nine main bearings. Hydraulic valve lifters. Carburetor: Carter Type WDO two-barrel Model 531S or 531SA.

CHASSIS FEATURES: Wheelbase: (Standard/Deluxe/Super Eight 2202/2232) 120 inches; (Super Eight 2222) 141 inches; (Custom Eight 2206 and 2233) 127 inches; (Custom Eight 2226) 148 inches. Overall length: (Standard/Deluxe/Super Eight 2202/2232) 204-5/8 inches; (Super Eight 2222) 225-5/8 inches; (Custom Eight 2206 and 2233) 212-5/8 inches; (Custom Eight 2226) 233-5/8 inches. Front tread: (Standard/Deluxe) 59-11/32; (Super) 59-19/32; (Custom) 60-3/32 inches. Rear tread: (Standard /Deluxe) 60-15/32; (Super) 60-23/32: (Custom) 60-47/64 inches. Tires: (Standard/Deluxe) 6.50 x 16; (Super) 7.60 x 15, except seven-passenger styles had 7.00 x 15 size; (Custom) 7.00 x 15, except convertible had 7.00 x 16 size.

OPTIONS: Comfort-Aire ventilation system. Radio. Cowl mount radio antenna. Rear fender shrouds (standard on Custom and both convertibles). Rear master bumper guards and protection rail. Front master bumper guard assembly. Exhaust pipe chrome extensions. License plate frames. Front fog lamps. Outside rear view mirror (left-hand or/and right-hand). Wheel trim rings. White sidewall tires. Overdrive ($87). Electromatic clutch with overdrive ($123). Oil bath air cleaner ($7) (standard on Super and Custom). Available rear axle ratios included: 3.54:1, 3.90:1, 4.09:1, 4.1:1 and 4.36:1.

HISTORICAL FOOTNOTES: The first 22nd Series Packards to appear in August, 1947, were the new convertibles. Packard did not adhere to a model year coding system until 1951. The company's official posture was that its traditional series production system wasn't relative to model year changeovers. The so-called "1948" models were actually built from August, 1947, through May, 1949. In November, 1948, dealers were instructed to remove data plates on all unsold 22nd Series Packards and return them to the factory. They were replaced by similar plates with the suffix '9' added to the Body/Style Number. Retails were then increased on some models. Packard 2201/2211 models went up an average $125 on 1949 price sheets; 2202 models went up $137; 2222 went up $200; and convertibles and Custom Eight model prices remained unchanged. The 2200-9 coded cars were considered 1949 Packards for registration purposes. OLD CARS does not recommend seeking 1948-1949 Packard parts or information on the basis on model year only. The total production of 22nd Series models hit 146,441 cars. Calendar year sales of 98,898 Packards was good for the 14th rank in industry. The new Packard body styling was awarded a 'Fashion Car of the Year' gold medal by the New York Fashion Academy. At automobile salons and concours d'elegance exhibits throughout the world, the new Custom Victoria Convertible Coupe was honored for its beauty and elegance. A dashboard with black-lighted 'Flite-Glo' instrumentation was a gimmicky new feature. Tool kits were still provided with each new Packard sold. On April 19, 1948, Alvan Macauley retired. He had served as Packard president from 1916 to 1938 and chairman from 1938 to 1948. George T. Christopher moved from the position of company president to replace him. A total of 1,317 (1948) and 24 (recoded 1949) taxicabs were built. A total 1,927 (1948) and 683 (recoded 1949) Export units were built. All of these were six-cylinder powered. Packard Custom Eights built through 1950 are certified Milestone Cars. Dick Bachman, PO Box 875, Post Falls, ID 83854 has done extensive personal research on serial numbers, motor numbers, model charts and production totals for 22nd and 23rd Series Packards and is interested in contacting owners of such cars to obtain information that may help refine his charts on these models.

1949 PACKARD
(23rd SERIES)

STANDARD EIGHT/DELUXE EIGHT — (8-CYL) — SERIES 2301 -Twenty-Third Series "Golden Anniversary" models went on sale in May, 1949. They looked much like the previous cars, but had some noticeable differences. The front bumpers had chromed centers instead of the painted type used in 1948. A thin spear of chrome ran down the middle of the bodysides, stopping just forward of the taillamps on base Packard Eights. Above this molding, on the front fenders, Packard block lettering appeared and was underlined in chrome. The taillight lenses were set in protruding oval-shaped bright metal housings, except on Station Sedans. The size of the rear window (backlight) was enlarged 33 percent. Inside, oval clutch/brake pedals were used. A Packard nameplate was placed between the speedometer and clock opening. A new illuminated switch turned the engine on. The Deluxe Eight had chromed 13 inch diameter hubcaps. The Standard Eight had 10 inch diameter hubcaps. A "Goddess of Speed" hood mascot was standard with both levels of trim. Automatic transmission was introduced in November, 1949, for all models. The 120 inch wheelbase continued.

PACKARD I.D. NUMBERS: Packard motor numbers were the most important of three types of manufacturer's codes. They were stamped on a white-painted boss on the upper left-hand side of the cylinder block. A vehicle number was also stamped on a plate attached to the left top side of the cowl and was the same as a Body/Style Number, since it identified the model or style. These numbers correspond to the Body/Style Number in the second column of our charts, with the first two symbols changing from 22 to 23 to indicate Twenty-Third series. A Body Number was provided and was also stamped on the plate attached to the left top side of the cowl, below the hood. The Body Number does not provide model identification, but seems to represent a production sequence record used mainly for factory purposes. The Body/Style Number appeared as the first four digits of the Packard serial number, followed by the motor number. Motor numbers for the Standard/Deluxe Eights were H-200001 to H-291000 for 1949 (Series 2300) models and continued through H-295000 for 1950 (Series 2300-5) models. Motor numbers for Super Eights were H-400001 to H-416000 for 1949 (Series 2300) models and continued through H-425,000 for 1950 (Series 2300-5) models. Motor numbers for Custom Eights were H-600001 to H-602000 for 1949 (Series 2300) models and continued through H-610000 for 1950 (Series 2300-5) models.

PACKARD EIGHT SERIES

Series Number	Body/Style Number	Body Type & Seating	Factory Price	Shipping Weight	Production Total
STANDARD LINE					
2301	2392	4-dr Sed-6P	2249	3815	Note 1
2301	2395	2-dr Clb Sed-6P	2224	3740	Note 1
2301	2393	4-dr Sta Sed-6P	3449	4075	Note 1
DELUXE LINE					
2301	2362	4-dr Sed-6P	2383	3840	Note 1
2301	2365	2-dr Clb Sed-6P	2358	3770	Note 1

NOTE 1: 49,280 Series 2300 (1949) Standard/Deluxe Eights built.
NOTE 2: No breakouts per body style are available.

SUPER/SUPER DELUXE EIGHT — (8-CYL) — SERIES 2302/2322/2332 — The Super Eight was trimmed somewhat like lower series cars. It shared the same horizontal grille, "Goddess of Speed" hood ornament and a chrome molding below the windows that stopped at the rear fender center. However, it had a slightly longer bodyside molding which overlapped the taillamp housings. The Super Deluxe was a new model. It was really something special, approximating a short "Custom Eight." For example, it had front and rear eggcrate grilles; cast chromium extensions from the upper belt molding to windshield wipers; bullet type bumper guards; pelican hood ornament; and an ivory-colored Tenite steering wheel with plated inlaid handgrips. Seats were upholstered in rich, pinstriped wool cloth with bolster-type back rests and door panels. The instrument board, upper seatback panels and window frames had woodgrained finish. Standard equipment included fender shrouds; wheel trim rings; day/night rear view mirror; Select-O-Matic spring cushions; and added acoustical insulation. The Convertible Victoria was appointed in similar fashion, but limousines had the standard Super type bar grille.

1949 Packard, Deluxe Eight four-door sedan, 8-cyl

SUPER SERIES

Series Number	Body/Style Number	Body Type & Seating	Factory Price	Shipping Weight	Production Total
STANDARD LINE					
2302	2382	4-dr Sed-6P	2633	3870	Note 1
2302	2385	2-dr Clb Sed-6P	2608	3800	Note 1
DELUXE LINE					
2302	2372	4-dr Sed-6P	2919	3925	Note 1
2302	2375	2-dr Clb Sed-6P	2894	3855	Note 1
LONG WHEELBASE (CLOSED)					
2322	2371	4-dr Sed-7P	3950	4600	Note 3
2322	2370	4-dr Limo-7P	4100	4620	Note 3
VICTORIA CONVERTIBLE COUPE					
2332	2379	2-dr Conv-6P	3350	4260	671

NOTE 1: 8,565 Series 2300 (1949) Super Eights built.
NOTE 2: No breakouts per body style for Series 2302 models.
NOTE 3: Four Series 2322 (1949) seven-passenger sedans and limos were built.
NOTE 4: No breakouts per body style for Series 2322 models.

1949 Packard, Custom Eight four-door sedan, 8-cyl (AA)

CUSTOM EIGHT — (8-CYL) — SERIES 2306/2333 — On Custom Eights the chrome molding below the windows extended completely down the rear fenders and around the trunk lid. This was about the only external distinction over Super Deluxe Eights, plus the use of cloisonne hubcap medallions as a standard feature. Color-keyed Bedford cloth and leather upholstery combinations were exclusive trims found inside Custom Eights. Ultramatic transmission became standard equipment on Custom Eights before November, 1949. It was then made optional on other Packards.

CUSTOM EIGHT SERIES

Series Number	Body/Style Number	Body Type & Seating	Factory Price	Shipping Weight	Production Total
2306	2352	4-dr Sed-6P	3750	4310	810
2333	2359	2-dr Conv-6P	4295	4530	60

ENGINES

(STANDARD/DELUXE EIGHT) Inline. L-head eight. Cast iron block. Displacement: 288 cid. Bore and stroke: 3-1/2 x 3-3/4 inches. Compression ratio: 7.0:1. Brake hp: 130 at 3600 rpm. Five main bearings. Solid valve lifters. Carburetor: Carter Type WDO two-barrel Model 644SA.

(SUPER EIGHT) Inline. L-head eight. Cast iron block. Displacement: 327 cid. Bore and stroke: 3-1/2 x 4-1/4 inches. Compression ratio: 7.0:1. Brake hp: 145 at 3600 rpm. Solid valve lifters. Five main bearings. Carburetor: Carter Type WDO two-barrel Model 643SA.

(CUSTOM EIGHT) Inline. L-head eight. Cast iron block. Displacement: 356 cid. Bore and stroke: 3-1/2 x 4-5/8 inches. Compression ratio: 7.0:1. Brake hp: 160 at 3600 rpm. Nine main bearings. Hydraulic valve lifters. Carburetor: Carter Type WDO two-barrel Model 531S or 531SA.

HISTORICAL FOOTNOTES: Both model year and calendar year sales totals were 59,390 vehicles. This includes only the 23rd Series models sold as late 1949 cars. Packard celebrated its 50th year as an automaker this season, a most notable achievement. As part of the ceremonies surrounding this accomplishment, a total of 2,000 cars were finished in Custom gold paint, a non-standard color. These cars were driven from the Packard Proving Grounds, in Utica, Mich. by dealers and salesmen. The dealers and salesmen took them to locations throughout North America as part of a driveaway honoring the company's longevity. In October, 1949, George T. Christopher retired from the company. Hugh Ferry was elected to fill the open post in December, 1949. He would soon try to hire James J. Nance away from General Electric Co. to assume the presidency of Packard. Custom Eights built to 1949 specifications are recognized Milestone Cars. Dick Bachman, PO Box 875, Post Falls, ID 83854

has done extensive personal research on serial numbers, motor numbers, model charts and production totals for 22nd and 23rd Series Packards and is interested in contacting owners of such cars to obtain information that may help refine his charts on these models.

1950 PACKARD
(23rd SERIES)

1950 Packard, Station Sedan, 8-cyl

STANDARD/DELUXE EIGHT — (8-CYL) — SERIES 2301-5 — Beginning on Oct. 1, 1949, the "Golden Anniversary" Packards were re-designated 1950 Models for purposes of registration. At almost the same time, Ultramatic Drive was made available, (as an option) on the low-priced Eights. This was about the only major change, with even retail prices and weights staying the same. Also, a Carter WGD two-barrel carburetor replaced the WDO type as standard equipment. Several new options, including Select-O-Seat spring inserts, (June 14); sedan rear seat draft deflectors (June 21); accelerator pedal wear pads (June 21) and woodgrained tissue dispenser (July 1) were made running additions to the list of available accessories during the summer of 1949. Consequently such items are most commonly seen on 1950 models. Quick identification of Packard's economical products was possible by spotting the "Goddess of Speed" ornament on the hood. Deluxe Eights continued to be distinguished by three inch larger hubcaps than Standard Eights used.

PACKARD I.D. NUMBERS: Packard motor numbers were the most important of three types of manufacturer's codes. They were stamped on a white-painted boss on the upper left-hand side of the cylinder block. A vehicle number was also stamped on a plate attached to the left top side of the cowl and was the same as a Body/Style Number, since it identified the model or style. These numbers correspond to the Body/Style Number in the second column of our charts, with the first two symbols 23 to indicate Twenty-Third series and a suffix -5 to indicate 1950 model year registration. A Body Number was provided and was also stamped on the plate attached to the left top side of the cowl, below the hood. The Body Number does not provide model identification, but seems to represent a production sequence record used mainly for factory purposes. The Body/Style Number appeared as the first four digits of the Packard serial number, followed by the motor number. Motor numbers for the Standard/Deluxe Eights were H-200001 to H-291000 for 1949 (Series 2300) models and continued through H-295000 for 1950 (Series 2300-5) models. Motor numbers for Super Eights were H-400001 to H-416000 for 1949 (Series 2300) models and continued through H-425,000 for 1950 (Series 2300-5) models. Motor numbers for Custom Eights were H-600001 to H-602000 for 1949 (Series 2300) models and continued through H-610000 for 1950 (Series 2300-5) models. According to research by Dick Bachman, engines built after Feb. 8, 1950 also had an F in the suffix to indicate the use of hydraulic valve lifters.

PACKARD EIGHT SERIES

Series Number	Body/Style Number	Body Type & Seating	Factory Price	Shipping Weight	Production Total
2301-5	2392-5	4-dr Sed-6P	2249	3815	Note 1
2301-5	2395-5	2-dr Clb Sed-6P	2224	3740	Note 1
2301-5	2393-5	4-dr Sta Sed-6P	3449	4075	Note 1

DELUXE LINE

PACKARD EIGHT SERIES

Series Number	Body/Style Number	Body Type & Seating	Factory Price	Shipping Weight	Production Total
2301-5	2362-5	4-dr Sed-6P	2383	3840	Note 1
2301-5	2365-5	2-dr Clb Sed-6P	2358	3770	Note 1

NOTE 1: 40,359 Series 2300-5 (1950) Standard/Deluxe Eights built.
NOTE 2: No breakout per body style available.

SUPER/SUPER DELUXE EIGHT — (8 CYL) — SERIES 2302/2322/2332-5 — Supers could be identified by the window molding that stopped at the center of the rear fender, in combination with a sweepspear that touched the taillamp housing. No other line had both features. Super Deluxes had chrome wheel rims and pelican hood ornaments as standard equipment. Hydraulic valve lifters were adopted, as a running production change for Supers on Feb. 8, 1950. For an undetermined reason, standard references sources indicate the weight of the 1950 convertible dropped by 150 pounds. The convertible and Super Deluxes continued to use eggcrate grilles and matching rear beauty panels.

1950 Packard, Super Deluxe four-door sedan, 8-cyl

SUPER SERIES

PACKARD EIGHT SERIES

Series Number	Body/Style Number	Body Type & Seating	Factory Price	Shipping Weight	Production Total
STANDARD LINE					
2302-5	2382-5	4-dr Sed-6P	2633	3870	Note 1
2302-5	2385-5	2-dr Clb Sed-6P	2608	3800	Note 1
DELUXE LINE					
2302-5	2372-5	4-dr Sed-6P	2919	3925	Note 1
2302-5	2375-5	2-dr Clb Sed-6P	2894	3855	Note 1
LONG WHEEL BASE (CLOSED)					
2322-5	2371-5	4-dr Sed-7P	3950	4600	0
2322-5	2370-5	4-dr Limo-7P	4100	4620	0
VICTORIA CONVERTIBLE COUPE					
2332-5	2379-5	2-dr Conv-6P	3350	4110	614

NOTE 1: 4,722 Series 2300-5 (1950) Super Eights built.
NOTE 2: No breakout per body style (except convertibles) is provided.

CUSTOM EIGHT — (8-CYL) — SERIES 2306/2333-5 — Custom Eights continued with eggcrate grilles front and rear; pelican hood ornaments; extra-rich Bedford cloth and leather trims; and extended upper belt moldings that looped around the deck lid. Base price was increased by $225, on both models, to cover the inclusion of Ultramatic transmission as standard equipment. It should be noted that this was the same as the cost of this optional gearbox the previous year, although the 1950 price was lowered to $185 on other series. In other words, Custom Eight buyers were spending $40 more to have this feature, than those who purchased it separately in lower-rung Packards. A Super Deluxe Sedan with automatic transmission would cost $3,104, compared to a Custom Eight sedan at $3,975, though both would be practically the same car with slightly different interiors and power plants.

CUSTOM EIGHT SERIES

PACKARD EIGHT SERIES

Series Number	Body/Style Number	Body Type & Seating	Factory Price	Shipping Weight	Production Total
2306-5	2352-5	4-dr Sed-6P	3975	4310	870
2333-5	2359-5	2-dr Conv-6P	4520	4539	85

ENGINES

(STANDARD/DELUXE EIGHT) Inline. L-head eight. Cast iron block. Displacement: 288 cid. Bore and stroke: 3-1/2 x 3-3/4 inches. Compression ratio: 7.0:1. Brake hp: 135 at 3600 rpm. Five main bearings. Solid valve lifters. Carburetor: Carter Type WGD two-barrel Model 728S or 728SA (Carburetor change took place Oct., 1949 with engine number H-238000. This may have been the starting number for "1950" Series 2300-5 models.

(SUPER EIGHT) Inline. L-head eight. Cast iron block. Displacement: 327 cid. Bore and stroke: 3-1/2 x 4-1/4 inches. Compression ratio: 7.0:1. Brake hp: 150 at 3600 rpm. Solid valve lifters. (Hydraulic lifters after Feb. 8, 1950) Five main bearings. Carburetor: Carter Type WDO two-barrel Model 643SA.

(CUSTOM EIGHT) Inline. L-head eight. Cast iron block. Displacement: 356 cid. Bore and stroke: 3-1/2 x 4-5/8 inches. Compression ratio: 7.0:1. Brake hp: 165 at 3600 rpm. Nine main bearings. Hydraulic valve lifters. Carburetor: Carter Type WDO two-barrel Model 531S or 531SA.

CHASSIS FEATURES: Wheelbase: (2301 Eights) 120 inches; (Super Series 2322) 141 inches; (other Supers and Customs) 127 inches. Overall length: (2301 Eights) 204-11/16 inches; (Super Series 2322) 225-11/16 inches; (other Supers) 211-11/16 inches; (Customs) 213-1/4 inches. Front tread: (Custom) 60-3/32 inches; (Super Convertible) 60 inches; (all others) 59-19/32 inches. Rear tread: (Custom) 60-23/32 inches. Tires: (Station sedan) 7.00 x 15; (other 2301 Eights and closed Super Eights) 7.60 x 15; (Super 8 Deluxe) 8.00 x 15; (Super 8 Convertible) 8.20 x 15; (all Customs) 8.20 x 15.

OPTIONS: Heater and defroster. Six-tube radio. Deluxe eight-tube radio. Roof-mount radio antenna. Cowl-mount radio antenna. Custom sun visor. Traffic light viewfinder. White sidewall tires. Coat hooks. Dual vanity mirrors. Emergency brake alarm. Cormorant hood ornament (unless standard). Rear wheel shrouds (unless standard). Tissue dispenser. Road lamps. Fog lamps. Rear seat draft deflectors on four-door sedans. Cloisonne hubcap medallions (except standard Customs). Vent-Shades. License plate frames. Gasoline filler panel guard. Door edge guards. Spare tire valve extension. Outside rear view mirrors (right and/or left-hand). Plaque with original owner initials. Vacuum type radio antenna. Fuse kit. Trouble light. Exhaust deflector. Wheel blocks. Curb feelers. Underhood light. Spotlight. Wheel trim rings. Rear bumper guard and protection rail. Select-O-Spring seat inserts. Two-tone finish. Ultra-matic trunk logo (standard on cars with Ultramatic Drive). Overdrive ($92). Electronic clutch with overdrive ($128). Ultramatic Drive ($185-225). Oil bath air cleaner ($7; standard on Super and Custom). Available rear axle ratios included: 3.54:1, 3.90:1, 4.09:1, 4.1:1 and 4.36:1.

HISTORICAL FOOTNOTES: Colonel Jesse G. Vincent retired as executive vice-president at the end of the year. He had been with the firm since 1912. Vincent continued service as an engineering consultant and member of the board of directors. Packard obtained several choice military contracts on the verge of war's outbreak in Korea. Model year sales peaked at 106,040 cars. Calendar year production was 72,138 units, giving Packard 16th industry ranking. A new R-11 type overdrive was used on 23rd series cars and was said to provide three extra miles of driving on each gallon of gasoline. On March 2, 1950, Packard adopted

---

14 mm spark plugs for its straight eight engines. Milestone Car status applies to 23rd Series Custom Eights sold as 1950 models. Dick Bachman, PO Box 875, Post Falls, ID 83854 has done extensive personal research on serial numbers, motor numbers, model charts and production totals for 22nd and 23rd Series Packards and is interested in contacting owners of such cars to obtain information that may help refine his charts on these models.

1951 PACKARD
(24th SERIES)

PACKARD 200 — (8 CYL) — SERIES 2401 — Aug. 24, 1950 saw the introduction of an all-new 24th Series Packard line. Styling more contemporary to the 1950s appeared on these cars designed by John Reinhart. According to sales literature, "Packards, for 1951, are only 5-foot 2-1/2 inches high, for in-the-groove roadability with 'hats on' headroom in front and back. New low bonnets (hoods) and high crown fenders give the outlook of a sports car." This was not too great an exaggeration, when compared to the look of the past. The base model range was the Packard 200 line, identified by a single strip of chrome across the front fenders and door and a 'toothless' grille. A low, single-fin hood mascot was seen. The 200 Deluxe was further distinguished by its chrome wheel rings and turn indicators. Standard equipment on all Packards included twin horns; two sun visors; two variable speed windshield wipers; horn blow ring; front and rear bumper guards; jack and tools.

1951 Packard, '200' two-door Club Sedan, 8-cyl

PACKARD I.D. NUMBERS: VIN found on a plate attached to the left front door past. Motor serial numbers were located on a boss at the upper left-hand side of the cylinder block. VINS began with the Body/Style Number suffixed by the motor serial number. Body Style Numbers started with the first two symbols '24' to indicate 24th Series. The second pair of symbols indicated body style. All four symbols conformed to those in the second column of the chart below. Motor serial numbers: [PACKARD 200/200 Deluxe] J-200000 to J-275000; [PACKARD 250] J-400001 to J-425000. [PACKARD 300] J-400001 to J-425000. [PATRICIAN 400] J-60001 to 610000.

PACKARD 200 SERIES

Series Number	Body/Style Number	Body Type & Seating	Factory Price	Shipping Weight	Production Total
STANDARD LINE					
2401	2492	4-dr Sed-6P	2469	3665	Note 1
2401	2495	2-dr Clb Sed-6P	2416	3600	Note 1
2401	2498	2-dr Bus Cpe-3P	2302	3550	Note 1
DELUXE LINE					
2401	2462	4-dr Sed-6P	2616	3660	Note 2
2401	2465	2-dr Clb Sed-6P	2563	3605	Note 2

NOTE 1: 24,310 Packard 200s were built.
NOTE 2: 47,052 Packard 200 Deluxes were built.
NOTE 3: No breakouts per body style are available.

PACKARD 250 — (8 CYL) — SERIES 2401 — The Packard 250 was on the same wheelbase platform as more modestly priced models, but utilized a 327 cid straight eight. Packard's only convertible and first hardtop coupe were included. Trim identification was provided by chrome moldings across the front fender and door plus four 'jet louver' ornaments on the rear fender. A toothy-looking grille insert and pelican hood mascot were seen. Especially colorful and rich upholstery was used for both these sporty cars. Fender skirts were standard on both.

PACKARD 250 SERIES

Series Number	Body/Style Number	Body Type & Seating	Factory Price	Shipping Weight	Production Total
2401	2467	2-dr HT Cpe-6P	3234	3820	Note 1
2401	2469	2-dr Conv-6P	3391	4040	Note 1

NOTE 1: 4,640 Packard 250s were built.
NOTE 2: No breakouts per body style are available.

1951 Packard, '300' four-door sedan, 8-cyl (AA)

PACKARD 300 — (8 CYL) — SERIES 2402 — Identification for the Packard 300 sedan came from a straight chrome molding running across the rear doors, rear fenders and taillights in a horizontal plane. Standard equipment included all Packard 200 features, plus oil bath air cleaner; tilt-type glare proof rearview mirror; chrome plated wheel discs; trunk compartment light; and robe rail. Double lens taillamps were used. A wide variety of interior trims was provided.

PACKARD 300 SERIES

Series Number	Body/Style Number	Body Type & Seating	Factory Price	Shipping Weight	Production Total
2401	2472	4-dr Sed-6P	3034	3875	15,309

1951 Packard, Patrician '400' four-door sedan, 8-cyl (AA)

PATRICIAN 400 — (8 CYL) — SERIES 2406 — The Patrician was the replacement for the fancy Custom Eight. It was identified by wide, vertically ribbed, chrome gravel shields on the lower front region of the rear fender bulge; three 'jet louvers' on the middle of rear fenders; a chrome spear high on front fenders and doors; a second chrome spear running from the gravel shield to the extreme rear of the car; chrome, finned moldings atop rear fenders; and double-lens horizontal taillamps. A wraparound style backlight provided a hardtop roof look. The grille insert had vertical 'teeth' and the tip of the hood had a cormorant. Luxurious 'fashion forum' interiors were featured, with special carpeting and a chrome-plated steering column. All features of the Packard 300 were incorporated, plus cloisonne wheelcover center medallions. This was the model for buyers seeking an elite machine.

PATRICIAN 400 SERIES

Series Number	Body/Style Number	Body Type & Seating	Factory Price	Shipping Weight	Production Total
2406	2452	4-dr Sed-6P	3662	4115	9,001

NOTE 1: Custom Formal Sedans on the Patrician 400 platform were available.

ENGINES

(PACKARD 200/200 DELUXE) Inline. L-head eight. Cast iron block. Displacement: 288 cid. Bore and stroke: 3-1/2 x 3-3/4 inches. Compression ratio: 7.0:1 hp: 135 at 3600 rpm. Solid valve lifters. Five main bearings. Carburetor: Carter Type WGD two-barrel model 784S.

(PACKARD 250/300) InLine. L-head eight. Cast iron block. Displacement: 327 cid. Bore and stroke: 3 1/2 x 4 1/4 inches. Compression ratio: 7.0:1. Brake hp: 150 at 3600 rpm. Five main bearings. Hydraulic valve lifters. Carburetor: Carter Type WGD two-barrel Model 767S.

(PATRICIAN 400) Inline. L-head eight. Cast iron block. Displacement: 327 cid. Bore and stroke: 3-1/2 x 4-1/4 inches. Compression ratio: 7.8:1. Brake hp: 155 at 3600 rpm. Nine main bearings. Hydraulic valve lifters. Carburetor: Carter Type WGD two-barrel Model 767S.

CHASSIS FEATURES: Wheelbase: (Series 2401) 122 inches; (all others) 127 inches. Overall length: (Series 2401) 209-3/8 inches; (all others) 217-3/4 inches. Front tread: (Packard 200) 59-1/2 inches; (Packard 250/300/Patrician 400) 60 inches. Rear tread: (Packard 200) 60-23/32 inches; (Packard 250/300/Patrician 400) 61-7/32 inches. Tires: (Packard 200) 7.60 x 15; (all others) 8.00 x 15.

OPTIONS: Whitewall tires. ($28 exchange). Heater and defroster ($77). Signal-Seeking radio with electric antenna and rear speaker ($125.80). Rear fender shrouds ($21). Cloisonne wheel hub shell covers ($16). Pelican hood ornament ($13). Windshield washer ($9). Foam cushion rear seat ($12). Backup lights and trunk light ($14). Robe cord ($12). Two-tone finish ($20). Genuine leather trim ($153). Rear window wiper. Exterior sunshade. Traffic light view-finder. Visor vanity mirrors. Emergency brake alarm. Tissue dispenser. Road and fog lamps. Vent shades. License plate frame. Gas door guard. Door edge guards. Spare tire valve extension. Extension rear view mirror. Fuse Kit. Trouble light. Exhaust deflector. Wheel blocks. Curb feelers. Spotlight. Underhood lamps. Ultramatic rear fender nameplates (standard on cars with automatic transmission). NOTE: Car collectors have documented several cases where extra 'jet louvers' were added to Patrician 400s (and possibly other models) by company dealers. This was an attempt to bolt-on a little extra prestige by dressing-up the exterior appearance at very small cost. Overdrive transmissions ($100). Ultramatic Drive was standard in Patrician 400s, optional on other models at ($189) extra cost. When equipped with Ultra-

matic, the Packard 300 was delivered with a 7.8:1 high-compression head that increased the hp output to 155. This was still, however, the type of 327 cid motor with five main bearings. (The 327 cid Patrician engine had nine main bearings). Also, when equipped with Ultramatic, the Packard 200/200 Deluxe was delivered with a 7.5:1 high-compression head. It increased output of the 288 cid motor to 138 hp. The 327 cid Packard 300 engine was a ($45) option in lower-priced models. Oil bath air cleaner ($9). Oil filter ($12). The 327 cid Patrician 400 engine could not be made optional in other lines because it was too long to fit comfortably in the shorter wheelbase chassis.

HISTORICAL FOOTNOTES: Introduction of 1951 Packards in the 200, 200 Deluxe, 300 and Patrician 400 series began in August, 1950. The Packard 250 line with the convertible and Mayfair hardtop was added in March, 1951. On Oct. 12, 1950 the Society of Motion Picture Art Directors acclaimed the 24th Series Packard as "the most beautiful car of the year." The midyear two-door hardtop was called the Mayfair. An experimental Phantom II sports car was constructed for Packard design chief Ed Macauley on a highly-modified Club Sedan. It featured a long, wide hood scoop; wide, ribbed bright metal underscores; similarly ribbed fender skirts; Custom concentric circle wheel discs; hardtop coupe styling; and two-place seating. A Packard 200 touring sedan exhibited average fuel consumption of 22.023 mpg while participating in the 1951 Mobilgas Economy Run. This was better than 12 other entries in the same class. A total of 100,132 Packards were supplied to buyers during the 1951 model run. Calendar year totals were counted at 76,075 cars, good for 16th position on industry sales charts. Standard reference sources listing U.S. auto production by body style indicate that Packard built 2,572 convertibles and 3,356 hardtops in calendar year 1953. Milestone Cars include the Patrician 400 sedans.

1952 PACKARD
(25th SERIES)

1952 Packard, '200' two-door sedan, 8-cyl (AA)

PACKARD 200 — (8-CYL) — SERIES 2501 — As indicated previously, annual model year changes were adopted after 1951. Therefore, the 1952 Packards were 25th Series cars. General styling was modestly changed. Packard block lettering, seen along the lower edge of the 1951 hood, was removed this year. A medallion bearing the company crest was set into the middle of the upper grille surround. 'Base level' Packard 200s were identified by single chrome spears across the front fender and door; single-fin "jet plane" hood ornaments; hood edge lettering; and exclusive use of the same toothless grille seen last season. Upholstery trims were in plain-looking quality cloth. Standard equipment was comprised of twin horns; two sun visors; two variable-speed vacuum windshield wipers; horn blow ring; front and back bumper guards; bumper jack; tools; map lights; front door courtesy lights; and front seat armrests. The Packard 200 Deluxe, for 1952, had some additional points of distinction. It was provided with the toothy type grille; three "jet louvers" on the rear quarter of the body and chrome wheel trim rings. It had all Packard 200 features, plus foam rubber front seat cushions; turn indicators; glovebox lamp; and electric clock. Upholstery was in gray or brown pinstriped cloth. The base level 200 business coupe was dropped.

PACKARD I.D. NUMBERS: VIN found on a plate attached to the left front door post. Motor serial numbers were located on a boss at the upper left-hand side of the cylinder block. VINS began with the Body/Style Number suffixed by the motor serial number. Body Style Numbers started with the first two symbols '25' to indicate 25th Series. The second pair of symbols indicated body style. All four symbols conformed to those in the second column of the chart below. Motor serial numbers: [PACKARD 200/200 Deluxe] K-200000 to K-250000; [PACKARD 250/PACKARD 300] K-400001 to K-415000. [PATRICIAN 400] K-600000 to 605000.

PACKARD 200 SERIES

Series Number	Body/Style Number	Body Type & Seating	Factory Price	Shipping Weight	Production Total
STANDARD LINE					
2501	2592	4-dr Sed-6P	2528	3680	Note 1
2501	2595	2-dr Clb Sed-6P	2475	3640	Note 1
DELUXE LINE					
2501	2562	4-dr Sed-6P	2675	3685	Note 2
2501	2565	2-dr Clb Sed-6P	2632	3660	Note 2

NOTE 1: 46,720 Packard 200s were built.
NOTE 2: About 7,000 cars included in 46,720 total were Deluxe models.
NOTE 3: No breakouts per body style are available.

PACKARD 250 — (8-CYL) — SERIES 2531 — The Packard 250 was again on the same platform as more modestly-priced models and used the five main bearing 327 cid straight eight. However, it had separate series coding this year. Trim and ornamentation features included a new pelican hood ornament (with lower wings); chrome wheel discs; rear fender shields; single spear molding on the front fenders and door; unlettered lower hood edge; three 'jet louvers' on rear fendersides and a vertical-tooth type grille. Standard equipment included all 200 Deluxe items, plus hydraulic valve lifters; oil filter; oil bath air cleaner; trunk compartment lamp; tilt type rearview mirror; front and rear wool carpeting; and rear seat

armrests. The Mayfair hardtop was provided with six interior upholstery combinations of ribbed nylon and leather materials, while the convertible had seats covered with a combination of genuine top grain leather and washable woven leather-like plastic.

1952 Packard, Mayfair two-door hardtop Sport Coupe, 8-cyl (AA)

PACKARD 250 SERIES

Series Number	Body/Style Number	Body Type & Seating	Factory Price	Shipping Weight	Production Total
2531	2577	2-dr HT Spt Cpe-6P	3293	3805	Note 1
2531	2579	2-dr Conv-6P	3450	4000	Note 1

NOTE 1: 5,201 Packard 250s were built.
NOTE 2: No breakouts per body style are available.

PACKARD 300 — (8-CYL) — SERIES 2502 — The Packard 300 sedan was on the 127 inch wheelbase again. It could be identified by the straight chrome spear running across the rear doors and fenders, in addition to the spear on the front doors and fenders. The toothy grille; non-lettered hood; low-wing pelican; chrome wheel discs; rear fender shields; and wraparound backlight were among other visual distinctions. Seen again were twin-lens taillamps horizontally positioned behind a flare at the middle edge of rear fenders, plus fin-like bands of chrome atop the fender peak. Standard equipment included all 200 Deluxe items plus glare-proof inside rearview mirror; robe rail and rear seat foam rubber cushions. The interior was trimmed with striped fabric and had embossed, pleated door panels. The numbers '300,' in chrome, appeared at the base of the rear roof pillar.

PACKARD 300 SERIES

Series Number	Body/Style Number	Body Type & Seating	Factory Price	Shipping Weight	Production Total
2402	2572	4-dr Sed-6P	3094	3880	6,705

PATRICIAN 400 — (8-CYL) — SERIES 2506 — Packard called the Patrician 400, "The Most Luxurious Motor Car in the World." It was like a Packard 300 that had won the Kentucky Derby and spent the loot on both appearance and performance improvements. Identification could most easily be made through the rear fender trim treatment. At the bottom of the rear door "pontoon" was a form-fitting gravel deflector which was vertically ribbed at its trailing edge. A strip of chrome molding traced the upper contour of the gravel deflector to the door line break, where it met a straight extension molding that swept along the top of the fender shield to the back bumper. Also, on the upper rear fender tip there was a blade of fin-like chrome that dropped down to the horizontal taillamp. The section of this molding directly above the red lens was embellished with short, horizontal ribbing. At the base of the wrapover roof pillar was placed '400' numbering. Cloisonne type wheel hub shell covers were used. Standard equipment was comprised of all other Packard 300 styling, trim and equipment features, plus hassock foot rests; chrome exhaust extensions; the nine bearing crankshaft engine; Ultra-matic Drive; and four "jet louvers" (three on the fenderside centerline and one on the rear door). Interior appointments included a special steering wheel, Wilton carpeting and color-keyed two-tone Bedford cord upholstery with a pattern of alternating pleated and plain sections.

PATRICIAN 400 SERIES

Series Number	Body/Style Number	Body Type & Seating	Factory Price	Shipping Weight	Production Total
2506	2552	4-dr Sed-6P	3797	4100	3,975

NOTE 1: Packard dealer literature indicates it was possible for a buyer to negotiate the purchase of a Custom Formal Sedan on the Patrician 400 platform.

ENGINES

(PACKARD 200/200 DELUXE) Inline. L-head eight. Cast iron block. Displacement: 288 cid. Bore and stroke: 3-1/2 x 3-3/4 inches. Compression ratio: 7.0:1. Brake hp: 135 at 3600 rpm. Five main bearings. Solid valve lifters. Carter Type WGD two-barrel. Model 784S. (This engine was optionally available with hydraulic lifters, a 7.5:1 high-compression cylinder head and 138 hp at 3600 rpm).

(PACKARD 250/300) Inline. L-head eight. Cast iron block. Displacement: 327 cid. Bore and stroke: 3-1/2 x 4-1/4 inches. Compression ratio: 7.0:1. Brake hp: 150 at 3600 rpm. Five main bearings. Hydraulic valve lifters. Carburetor: Carter Type WGD two-barrel Model 928S. Besides a carburetor model change, this engine featured a new timing chain, new vertical type air cleaner and higher output 45 ampere generator. (This engine was optionally available with a 7.8:1 high-compression cylinder head and 155 hp at 3600 rpm).

(PATRICIAN 400) Inline. L-head eight. Cast iron block. Displacement: 327 cid. Bore and stroke: 3-1/2 x 4-1/4 inches. Compression ratio: 7.8:1. Brake hp: 155 at 3600 rpm. Nine main bearings. Hydraulic valve lifters. Carburetor: Carter Type WGD two-barrel Model 928S. Besides a carburetor model change, this engine featured the new timing chain, new vertical type air cleaner higher output 45 ampere generator. (This engine was optionally available with a 7.0:1 low-compression cylinder head and 150 hp at 3600 rpm.)

1952 Packard, Patrician '400' four-door sedan, 8-cyl (AA)

CHASSIS FEATURES: Wheelbase: (Series 2501 and 2531) 122 inches; (Series 2502 and 2506) 127 inches. Overall length: (Series 2501 and 2531) 212-3/4 inches; (Series 2502 and 2506) 217-3/4 inches. Front tread: (200/200 Deluxe) 59.5 inches; (all other models) 60 inches. Rear tread: (200/200 Deluxe) 60-23/32 inches; (all other models) 61-7/32 inches. Tires: (200/200 Deluxe) 7.60 x 15; (all other models) 8.00 x 15.

OPTIONS: Whitewall tires, when available ($27.60). Genuine leather upholstery ($153). Heater and defroster ($76.50). Two-tone exterior finish ($20). Signal-seeking radio with electric antenna and rear speaker ($125.80). Rear fender shrouds ($21.45). Wheel hub shell covers ($16.35). Pelican hood mascot ($13.45). Robe cord ($12.35). Windshield washer ($9.40). Non-glare rearview mirror ($5.95). Patrician 400 steering wheel ($14.25). Foam rubber rear seat cushions ($12.25). Back-up lights and trunk compartment lamp ($13.85). Solex tinted glass ($45.20). Easamatic power brakes ($39.45). Rear window wipers. Fog lamps. Spotlight. Woodgrained tissue dispenser. Exterior sun shade. Traffic light finder. Visor vanity mirror. Road lamps. Vent-I-Shades. Chrome exhaust deflector. Curb feelers. Gas door guard. Locking gas door. Door edge guards. Spare tire valve extension. Exterior rearview mirror left-hand and/or right-hand. Fuse kit. Trouble light. Underhood lamp. Wheel blocks. Overdrive transmission ($102). Ultramatic Drive standard in Patrician 400, optional on other models at extra cost ($189). When equipped with Ultramatic, changes in relation to use of high-compression cylinder heads were the same detailed under 1951 Packard powertrain options. The 327 cid five main bearing Packard 300 engine was available in Packard 200/200 Deluxes at extra cost ($45). Oil bath air cleaner ($8.70). Oil filter ($11.80). On cars equipped with overdrive transmissions (not available in Patrician 400) a new clutch driven member and tailshaft mounting were used.

HISTORICAL FOOTNOTES: Model year production was 69,921 cars. Calendar year sales were 69,988 cars. Packard was the 16th ranked automaker. In May, 1952, Hugh Ferry announced that James J. Nance would become his successor as president and general manager of Packard Motor Car Corp. The 25th Series was introduced Nov. 14, 1951 on the nationwide television comedy show hosted by Red Skelton. Packard's first special non-production type show car was exhibited this year. It was called the Pan American convertible. Lightly plated 'Korean War' chrome (with reduced nickel content) was used on Packards this year, due to Korean War material restrictions. Such chrome deteriorated much more rapidly than the conventional type, a fact that old car hobbyists usually must deal with in restorations of such models. According to standard reference sources listing U.S. calendar year car production by body styles, Packard built 3,730 hardtops; 1,133 convertibles; and no station wagons in 1952. The Patrician 400 is a Milestone Car.

1953 PACKARD
(26th SERIES)

1953 Packard, Clipper four-door sedan, 8-cyl (AA)

CLIPPER SPECIAL/CLIPPER DELUXE — (8-CYL) — SERIES 2601/2611 — When 1953 Packards were introduced on Nov. 21, 1952, the Clipper was back. It was the base Packard nameplate, in a year marked by model expansions. Changes for the 26th Series were a grille with full-width curved center bar; new hood ornaments; wraparound backlights on all cars; and noticeable trim revisions. The Clipper Special was most like the old styles as plain, rounded rear fenders were retained. A straight chrome molding with barbed tip sat high on the front fenders and doors. A second straight molding was set, just a tad lower, on the rear fenders and back door of the touring sedan. Jet plane hood ornaments and plain cloth interiors appeared. The basic Packard equipment assortment included twin horns; twin visors and wipers; a horn ring; front and back bumper guards; jack; and tools. The Clipper Special added turn signals, a glovebox light and a clock to the list. A fancier Deluxe Clipper seemed to have

the front and rear bodyside moldings linked via a staggered chrome plate. It was actually part of one long, continuous arrangement of chrome strips. The Deluxe had all the same features found on Clipper Specials, plus chrome wheel trim rings and fin-shaped rear fendertop chrome blades Packard called "fishtails." Beginning this year, the relationship between Packards and Clippers was de-emphasized.

PACKARD I.D. NUMBERS: VIN found on a plate attached to the left front door past. Motor serial numbers were located on a boss at the upper left-hand side of the cylinder block. VINS began with the Body/Style Number suffixed by the motor serial number. The Body/Style Number forming the first part of VIN started with the symbols '26' to indicate 26th Series. The next two symbols indicated body style. All four symbols appear in the second column of the charts below. Motor serial numbers for 1953 were: [CLIPPER SPECIAL] L-200000 to L-233778. [CLIPPER DELUXE] L-300000 to L-330920. [CAVALIER/PACKARD 2631] L-400000 to L-418552; [PATRICIAN/EXECUTIVE] L-600000 to L-607829.

PACKARD 200 SERIES

CLIPPER/CLIPPER DELUXE SERIES

Series Number	Body/Style Number	Body Type & Seating	Factory Price	Shipping Weight	Production Total
CLIPPER SPECIAL					
2601	2692	4-dr Sed-6P	2588	3715	23,126
2601	2695	2-dr Clb Sed-6P	2534	3685	6,370
2601	2697	2-dr Sptster-6P	2795	3685	3,671
CLIPPER DELUXE					
2611	2662	4-dr Sed-6P	2735	3745	26,037
2611	2665	2-dr Clb Sed-6P	2681	3705	4,678

1953 Packard, Cavalier four-door sedan, 8-cyl (AA)

CAVALIER/PACKARD 2631 (8-CYL) — SERIES 2602/2631 — The basic Cavalier Series included a sedan which was comparable to the former Packard 300. However, a few more sporty Packards were listed in a Cavalier sub-series. They were the convertible, the Mayfair Sports Coupe and the new semi-custom Caribbean convertible inspired by the Pan American show car of 1952. All three were grouped in the Packard 2631 Series. The Cavalier had horizontal taillights; "fishtail" rear fender treatments; Packard lettering on the rear fenders; and an arrangement of side moldings that somewhat resembled a lightning bolt with a short upper slash on front fenders and a long lower slash from behind the front wheelwell to the rear of the car. The two slashes were connected by a curved, fluted piece of chrome that slanted forward, along the front wheelhousing's rear lip. The Mayfair was trimmed in the same manner as Clipper Deluxes on the outside, but came with rich interiors. The regular convertible also had the Clipper Deluxe (staggered) type molding treatment, but with three "jet louvers" added under the rear fender spear. Both had "fishtail" rear treatments; fender skirts; stylized pelican hood ornaments; chrome wheel discs; tilt-type rearview mirrors; and trunk lights. The Caribbean convertible was a show car brought to life via body modifications by Mitchell-Bently Corp., of Ionia, Mich. Its unique standard features list included a full-leather interior; chrome-plated wire wheels; enlarged wheel openings with flared lips; full-length, full-width front hood scoop; "de-chromed" body look; horizontal taillights; integrated "fishtail" rear fender treatment; chrome wheelwell moldings front and rear; continental tire kit; and Custom finish in one of just four shades of paint; Polaris blue; Gulf green metallic; Matador maroon metallic; or Sahara sand. A Packard script nameplate appeared on the rear mounted spare tire, which was encased in a metal cover. It had a center cutout to show off a wire wheel with a Packard center wheel disc.

1953 Packard, Caribbean convertible, 8-cyl (AA)

CAVALIER 2602/PACKARD 2631 SERIES

Series Number	Body/Style Number	Body Type & Seating	Factory Price	Shipping Weight	Production Total
CAVALIER					
2602	2672	4-dr Sed-6P	3234	3975	10,799
MAYFAIR HARDTOP					
2631	2677	2-dr HT Spt Cpe-6P	3278	3905	5,150
CAVALIER CONVERTIBLE					
2631	2679	2-dr Conv-6P	3234	3960	1,518
CARIBBEAN CUSTOM CONVERTIBLE					
2631	2678	2-dr Cus Conv-6p	5210	4110	750

PATRICIAN/CORPORATE-EXECUTIVE — (8-CYL) — SERIES 2606/2626 — Identification features of 1953 Packard Patricians included the manufacturer's name in script on the rear upper portion of back fenders. They also had the standard pelican/cormorant type hood ornaments; horizontal taillights; and a side molding treatment similar to that seen on Cavaliers, but with chrome gravel shields added. Standard equipment included all found on Clipper Deluxes, plus tilt-type rearview mirror; chrome wheel discs; trunk compartment light; and robe rails. Long-wheelbase models reappeared in the Packard catalog this year and were called Executive Sedans and Corporate Limousines. They were actually built by Henney Motor Co., a maker of professional cars, hearses and ambulances. These eight-passenger jobs used the lightening bolt style arrangement of moldings, with the rear streak extending a very long ways toward the back of the car. The house of Derham, a Custom body firm, also created a limited number of Custom Formal Sedans on the 1953 platform. They carried Patrician style trim.

PATRICIAN/CORPORATE-EXECUTIVE SERIES

Series Number	Body/Style Number	Body Type & Seating	Factory Price	Shipping Weight	Production Total
PATRICIAN					
2606	2652	4-dr Sed-6P	3735	4190	7,456
2606	2653	4-dr Derham Fml Sed-6P	6531	4335	25
HENNEY CORPORATE EXECUTIVES					
2626	2651	4-dr Exec Sed-8P	6900	4650	100
2626	2650	4-dr Corp Limo-8P	7100	4720	50

BASE ENGINES

(CLIPPER SPECIAL) Eight Inline. L-Head. Cast iron block. Displacement: 288.6 cid. Bore and stroke: 3-1/2 x 3-3/4 inches. Compression ratio: 7.7:1. Brake hp: 150 at 4000 rpm. Five main bearings. Solid or hydraulic valve lifters (cars with hydraulic valve lifters had a 'H' suffix on motor number). Carburetor: Carter Type WGD two-barrel model 784S.

(CLIPPER DELUXE) Eight. Inline. L-Head. Cast iron block. Displacement: 327 cid. Bore and stroke: 3-1/2 x 4-1/4 inches. Compression ratio: 8.0:1. Brake hp: 160 at 3600 rpm. Five main bearings. Solid or hydraulic valve lifters (cars with hydraulic valve lifters had an 'H' suffix on motor number). Carburetor: Carter Type WGD two-barrel Model 928S or 2102S.

(CAVALIER/MAYFAIR) Inline. L-head eight. Cast iron block. Displacement: 327 cid. Bore and stroke: 3-1/2 x 4-1/4 inches. Compression ratio: 8.0:1. Brake hp: 180 at 4000 rpm. Five main bearings. Hydraulic valve lifters. Carburetor: Carter Type WCFB four-barrel Model 2084S or Model 985S.

(PATRICIAN/CORPORATE EXECUTIVE) All specifications for this engine were the same as those given for the Cavalier engine, except that a nine main bearing crankshaft was used in the Patrician and Corporate Executive powerplant.

CHASSIS FEATURES: Wheelbase: (Series 2601, 2611 and 2631) 122 inches; (Series 2602 and 2606) 127 inches; (Series 2626) 149 inches. Overall length: (Series 2601, 2611 and 2631) 213-3/32 inches; (Series 2602 and 2606) 218-5/32 inches; (Series 2626) 240-5/32 inches. Front tread: (Clippers) 59-1/2 inches; (all others) 60 inches. Rear tread: (Clippers) 60-23/32 inches; (all others) 61-7 32 inches. Tires: (Clipper) 7.60 x 15; (Executives) 8.20 x 15; (all others) 8.00 x 15.

OPTIONS: Power steering ($195). Easamatic power brakes ($39). Push-button radio with manual antenna ($97); with electric antenna ($109). Signal-seeking radio with manual antenna ($118); with electric antenna ($132). Rear compartment speaker ($16). Power windows and front seat ($153). Windshield washers ($9.40). Back-up lights ($1 1). Size 7.60 x 15 whitewalls, exchange ($30). Size 8.00 x 15 whitewalls, exchange ($33). Two-tone paint ($20). Fresh air heater and defroster ($80). Tinted Solex glass ($45). Overdrive ($110). Ultramatic was standard in Patricians only, optional in other models at extra cost ($199). Available rear axle gear ratios included: (conventional) 3.9:1; (overdrive) 4.0:1 and (Ultramatic) 3.54:1.

HISTORICAL FOOTNOTES: Factory introductions were made Nov. 28, 1952. The model run brought production of 89,730 cars. Calendar year sales hit 81,341 vehicles. Packard was rated number 14th among automakers. Body Style 2697, the Clipper Sportster, used the two-door Club Sedan body with Mayfair trim features including chrome interior roof bows; extra-heavy side window moldings; staggered type side trim, etc., to give the car a pillarless hardtop look. Packard Clipper was lettered above the body side moldings on the upper rear quarters and the "fishtail" type rear fender treatment was seen. The special Caribbean convertible was not introduced until midyear, appearing in January, 1953. A unique Packard Balboa show car was constructed this year and put on exhibit on Aug. 31, 1953. It was based on the Caribbean body with a reverse sloping fiberglass roof and roll-down rear window. Air conditioning, not offered since 1942, was released as a $625 option (for four models) on July 1, 1953. The first two air-conditioners were, however, installed in two White House fleet cars on May 19, 1953. The limousine was introduced on March 14, 1953. The Patrician 400 is a Milestone car.

1954 PACKARD
(54th SERIES)

CLIPPER SPECIAL — (8-CYL) — SERIES 5400 — The 1954 Packard products were introduced to the public on Jan. 15, 1954, with the Clipper Special four-door added on March 29. General styling changes for an expanded line of Clippers included revised sweepspear patterns; redesigned rear fenders; new taillights set into the rear fender tips; and the addition of wraparound chrome plates between the horizontal grille bar extensions and outer edges of the front bumper. The Clipper Special continued with two separate sweepspears. Seen on the rear door or fender was a Clipper nameplate under the spear. In addition, a Clipper Special nameplate was located on the trunk lid. Standard equipment included twin horns; twin sun visors; two variable-speed vacuum windshield wipers; horn blow ring; front and back bumper guards; bumper jack; and tools. These cars were marketed as Clippers, with the Packard tie-in de-emphasized.

PACKARD I.D. NUMBERS: VIN found on a plate attached to the left front door post. Motor serial numbers were located on a boss at the upper left-hand side of the cylinder block. VINS began with the Body/Style Number suffixed by the motor serial number. The Body/Style Number forming the first part of the VIN was revised and no longer used consecutive series numbering. Packard switched to using the last two digits of the calendar year as the first two symbols of the series and model designations. Therefore, the first two symbols used to identify cars, series and models were '54.' The second pair of symbols indicated body style. All four symbols conformed to those in the second column of the charts below. Motor serial numbers:

[CLIPPER SPECIAL] M-200000 to M-202019. [CLIPPER DELUXE] M-300000 to M-321199. [CAVALIER/PACKARD 2631] M-400000 to M-402638; [PATRICIAN/EXECUTIVE] M-600000 to M-605618.

CLIPPER SPECIAL SERIES

Series Number	Body/Style Number	Body Type & Seating	Factory Price	Shipping Weight	Production Total
5400	5482	4-dr Sed-6P	2594	3650	970
5400	5485	2-dr Clb Sed-6P	2544	3585	912

1954 Clipper, Panama two-door hardtop coupe, 8-cyl (AA)

DELUXE CLIPPER/SUPER CLIPPER — (8-CYL) — SERIES 5401/5411 — There were now two extra-fancy, extra-powerful lines of Clippers on the same 122 inch wheelbase as Clipper Specials. They had the bigger 327 cid/165 hp Packard engine under the hood. The Deluxe was trimmed with a continuous sweepspear molding running high on the bodysides from behind the headlights to the bottom of the taillights. Clipper Deluxe lettering appeared on the trunk lid. The Sportster coupe continued, now as a Deluxe. It was actually a pillared club coupe, but had wide exterior window frame moldings that gave it a hardtop appearance. It also had a very sporty interior and chrome headliner bows. Except for the bigger engine, Deluxe equipment features were similar to those of Special Clippers. An all-new line was the Super Clipper series, which was identified with model name lettering on the trunk and added a glovebox light to the features list. It included a sporty business coupe with two separate sweepspears, like Clipper Specials had. This model had a "Panama" script under the forward section of the rear fender spear. It was trimmed about the same as the Deluxe Sportster. Another step up came the Panama Sports Coupe (two-door hardtop) in the Super Clipper line. It used the same roofline as the all-new Packard Pacific and was otherwise similar to Deluxe/Super Clippers outside. Inside was a different story, as very rich appointments were used. In total, over 20 trim combinations (genuine leather, broadcloth, nylon cord and nylon matelasse in a rainbow of colors) were provided for Clippers this year. Packard was pushing the Clipper as a stronger entry in the hot medium-price market, which had a lot to do with its new models and enrichments.

DELUXE/SUPER CLIPPER SERIES

Series Number	Body/Style Number	Body Type & Seating	Factory Price	Shipping Weight	Production Total
DELUXE SERIES					
5401	5492	4-dr Sed-6P	2695	3660	7610
5401	5495	2-dr Clb Sed-6P	2645	3590	1470
5401	5497	2-dr Sptster-6P	2830	3595	1336
SUPER SERIES					
5411	5462	4-dr Sed-6P	2815	3695	6270
5411	5465	2-dr Clb Sed-6P	2765	3610	887
PANAMA SUB-SERIES					
5411	NA	2-dr Bus Cpe-6P	NA	NA	Note 1
5411	5467	2-dr HT Spt Cpe-6P	3125	3805	3618

NOTE 1: The two-door Business Coupe is a Panama. Body/Style Number, factory delivered price and shipping weight data for this model was not provided. The production of Panama business coupes is combined in total for the 5467 model.

CAVALIER — (8-CYL) — SERIES 5402 — The Cavalier was now the lowest-priced true Packard and the only one to utilize the five main bearing engine. Basic Packard styling changes included new "horned" headlamp rims; curvier rear fender "fishtails;" and new side spear treatments. On the Cavalier, the forward spear was placed high on the body and ran from behind the headlamps to a point just below the rear ventipanes. A rear spear was positioned much lower and traveled from the forward edge of the fender pontoon, almost to the rear of the car, passing just above the fender skirts. The area between where the two moldings passed each other was decorated with three short, parallel strips of chrome. A Packard medallion was placed on the base of the rear roof pillar. A Packard script appeared on the rear fendersides. On Packards, but not Clippers, the center horizontal grille bar had vertical fluting on both sides of the center vertical grille post. The taillight clusters were placed halfway up the rear fenders. Standard Cavalier extras included directional signals; tilt-type rearview mirror; chrome-plated wheel discs; trunk compartment light; and robe rail. This model was on the 127 inch wheelbase.

CAVALIER SERIES

Series Number	Body/Style Number	Body Type & Seating	Factory Price	Shipping Weight	Production Total
5402	5472	4-dr Sed-6P	3344	3955	2580

1954 Packard, Caribbean two-door convertible, 8-cyl (AA)

PACKARD LINE — (8-CYL) — SERIES 5431 — To emphasize the difference between Packards and Clippers, the company's three sportiest Packards were provided with the nine main bearing straight eight this year and called the "Packard Line." Included were the Packard convertible; Pacific coupe hardtop; and Caribbean convertible coupe. The new names stressed a luxury tie-in, but still gave each of these attention-getting models a distinct identity. James Nance felt that if all models had their own names they would not be forgotten or confused. The conventional convertible had the same type of side trim featured on the Cavalier, except that the Packard script was moved from the rear fenders to the deck lid. Standard equipment also included a pelican style hood mascot and rear fender shields. The interior was trimmed in a combination of leather and leather-grained plastic. The Pacific looked very much like the ragtop, except that the roof didn't fold away. However, it did have rear fender scripts, as well as medallions near the base of the rear roof pillar. The 1954 Caribbean had the new type headlamp rims; a chrome trim band along the edge of the hood scoop, lower rear wheel cutouts; two-tone finish, color-keyed to interior tones; Caribbean scripts on the sides of the front fenders; sweepspear moldings that began above the split taillamps and ran straight to the front of the fender pontoon, then arched up and into the upper beltline and new, integral taillamps. Standard equipment, on this model only, included power steering; power brakes; windshield washers; white sidewall tires; power windows; power seat; dual heaters and defrosters; three-way radio with electric antenna; continental spare tire; chromed wire wheels; and wide chrome wheelhousing surrounds with body sill and rear quarter panel extensions.

PACKARD 5431 LINE

Series Number	Body/Style Number	Body Type & Seating	Factory Price	Shipping Weight	Production Total
PACKARD PACIFIC					
5431	5477	2-dr HT Cpe-6P	3827	4040	1189
PACKARD					
5431	5479	2-dr Conv-6P	3935	4260	863
CARIBBEAN CUSTOM					
5431	5478	2-dr Cus Conv-6P	6100	4400	400

PACKARD PATRICIAN CUSTOM/HENNEY LINE — (8-CYL) — SERIES 5406/5426 — A staggered (or step-down) type sweepspear molding, connected by ribbed diagonal chrome ornaments, was used on Patrician models and the Henney-built eight-passenger sedans and Limousines. Also on these models, chrome buffer strips appeared on the rocker sills to underscore the stately beauty of the most luxurious Packards. The Packard Patrician had round medallions on the rear roof pillar and many extra-rich appointments.

PACKARD PATRICIAN CUSTOM/HENNEY CUSTOM LINE

Series Number	Body/Style Number	Body Type & Seating	Factory Price	Shipping Weight	Production Total
5426	5451	4-dr-Sed-8P	6900	4650	65
5426	5450	4-dr Limo-8P	7250	4720	35
5426	5472	4-dr Sed-8P	3890	4190	n.a.

NOTE 1: Prices for the Henney-built Executive Sedan and Corporate Limousine were factory delivered prices at Henney Motor Car plant in Freeport, Ill.

1954 Packard, Patrician four-door sedan, 8-cyl (AA)

ENGINES

(CLIPPER SPECIAL) Inline. L-head eight. Cast iron block. Displacement: 288 cid. Bore and stroke: 3-1/2 x 3-3/4 inches. Compression ratio: 7.7:1. Brake hp: 150 at 4000 rpm. Five main bearings. Solid or hydraulic valve lifters. (Cars with hydraulic valve lifters had an 'H' motor number suffix.) Carburetor: Carter Type WGD two-barrel Model 986S.

(DELUXE/SUPER CLIPPER) Inline. L-head eight. Cast iron block. Displacement: 327 cid. Bore and stroke: 3-1/2 x 4-1/4 inches. Compression ratio: 8.0:1. Brake hp: 165 at 3600 rpm. Five main bearings. Hydraulic or solid valve lifters (Cars with hydraulic valve lifters had an 'H' motor number suffix. Carburetor: Carter Type WGD two-barrel Models 2102S.

(CAVALIER) Inline. L-head eight. Cast iron block. Displacement: 327 cid. Bore and stroke: 3-1/2 x 4-1/4 inches. Compression ratio: 8.0:1. Brake hp: 185 at 4000 rpm. Five main bearings. Hydraulic valve lifters. Carburetor: Carter Type WCFB four-barrel model 2103S.

(PACKARD LINES 5431/5406/5426) Inline. L-Head. Eight. Cast iron block. Displacement: 359 cid. Bore and stroke: 3-9/16 x 41/2 inches. Compression ratio: 8.7:1. Brake hp, 212 at 4000 rpm. Nine main bearings. Hydraulic valve lifters. Carburetor: Carter WCFB four-barrel Model 2212S.

CHASSIS FEATURES: Wheelbase: (Series 5400, 5401, 5411 and 5431) 122 inches; (Series 5402 and 5406) 127 inches; (Series 5426) 149 inches. Overall length: (Clippers) 215-1/2 inches; (Cavalier and Patrician) 216-1/2 inches; (Pacific, Packard convertible, Caribbean) 211-1/2 inches; (Henney models) 238-1/2 inches. Front tread: (Clippers) 59-3/4 inches; (all others) 60 inches. Rear tread: (Clippers) 59.9 inches; (Packard) 60.8 inches; (Henney Custom) 60.9 inches. Tires: (Clippers) 7.60 x 15; (Cavalier) 8.00 x 15; (Henney models) 8.20 x 15; (all others) 8.00 x 15.

OPTIONS: Power steering ($177.50). Power brakes ($43). Four-Way power seat ($75). Windshield washer ($16.75). Sun visor ($31.50). Spotlight ($28.50). Pelican ($13.45). Curb signals ($1.75). Hydraulic windows ($153). Standard radio ($102). Three-way tuning radio with electric antenna ($132). Ultramatic ($199). Heater/defroster ($79.50). White sidewall tires ($32.50 exchange). Backing lights ($13). Rear seat speaker ($16.80). Solex glass ($45.20). Molding mirror ($5.10). C.T. carrier ($270). Overdrive ($110). Ultramatic drive was standard in the Caribbean and Patrician, optional on other models at extra cost.

HISTORICAL FOOTNOTES: Factory introductions were held Jan. 15, 1954. Model year sales were 30,965 cars; calendar year sales 27,593 cars. Packard was America's 16th ranked maker again. The Panther-Daytona (or Grey Wolf II) experimental Packard sports car was driven by Dick Rathman at Daytona SpeedWeeks. It hit 110.9 mph (officially) and clocked 131 mph (unofficially) later. Experimentation with supercharged straight eights began in 1953 and continued this season. Packard did a lightning-like conversion of its Conner Ave. plant in the fall of 1954. In just 62 days, this factory was turned into a modern body assembly facility, so that the company could build its own bodies for the first time in many years. On June 22, 1954, after months of preliminary discussion, an agreement to merge Packard with Studebaker was signed by the presidents of these two companies. On Oct. 1, 1954, The Studebaker-Packard Corp. came into official existence, with its headquarters in Detroit. Packard models recognized by the Milestone Car Society include the 1953 Caribbean and Patrician 400 sedan.

1955 PACKARD
(55th SERIES)

CLIPPER DELUXE/SUPER — (V-8) — SERIES 5540 — Everything seemed new this year. There were massive bumpers with bullet-shaped guards. There were full-width grilles with bowed upper bars and "ship's wheel" center medallions. Very fine vertical blades were seen on Clipper grilles. The front fenders were "bent-over" to hood the headlamps. Sweep-around windshields appeared. The fact that this was merely a face-lift of previous bodies showed up only at the rear of the Clipper, where a 1954 look was retained. At the middle of the rear deck was another "ship's wheel" medallion and, on either side, model identification scripts were placed. The left-hand signature said Clipper; the right-hand one said either Deluxe or Super. Side moldings curved down and back from the front ventipane to the rear edge of front doors, then ran straight to the taillamps. With "integrated two-toning," everything above and behind this molding was painted one color, everything else was done in another. Clipper scripts decorated the hood and the fender area above the front bumper's wraparound edges. The only Packard identification was a very small script on the right corner of the trunk. Deluxes had small hubcaps and lacked rocker panel moldings. Supers had chrome wheel discs and bright metal strips on the rockers, along with upgraded nylon and vinyl interiors.

PACKARD I.D. NUMBERS: VIN found on a plate attached to the left front door post. Motor serial numbers were located on a boss at the upper left-hand side of the cylinder block. VINS began with the Body/Style Number suffixed by the motor serial number. The Body/Style Number forming the first part of the VIN was revised and no longer used consecutive series numbering. Packard switched to using the last two digits of the calendar year as the first two symbols of the series and model designations. Therefore, the first two symbols used to identify cars, series and models were '55.' The second pair of symbols indicated body style. All four symbols conformed to those in the second column of the charts below. Motor serial numbers: [CLIPPER DELUXE] 5522-1001 to 5522-9039; [CLIPPER SUPER] 5542-1001 to 5542-8979. [PANAMA HARDTOP] 5547-1001 to 5547-8016. [CLIPPER CUSTOM] 5562-1001 to 5562-9702. [CONSTELLATION] 5567-1001 to 5567-7678. [PATRICIAN] 5582-1001 to 5582-10127. [PACKARD 400 HARDTOP] 5587-1001 to 5587-8206. [CARIBBEAN CONVERTIBLE] 5588-1001 to 5588-1500.

CLIPPER DELUXE/SUPER SERIES

Series Number	Body/Style Number	Body Type & Seating	Factory Price	Shipping Weight	Production Total
DELUXE SERIES					
5540	5522	4-dr Sed-6P	2586	3680	8,309
SUPER SERIES					
5540	5542	4-dr Sed-6P	2686	3670	7,979
PANAMA SUPER SUB-SERIES					
540	5547	2-dr HT Spt Cpe-6P	2776	3700	7,016

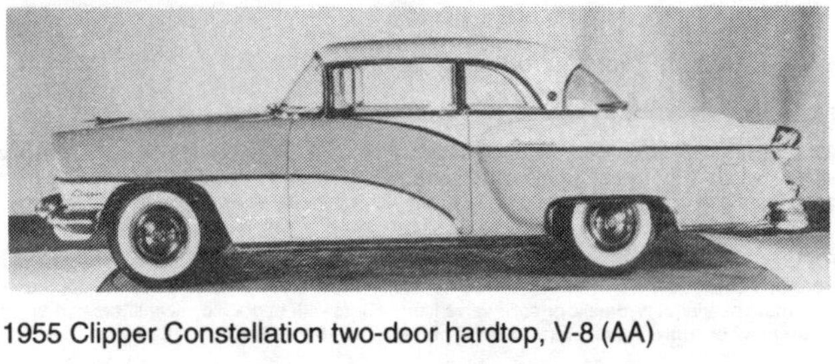

1955 Clipper Constellation two-door hardtop, V-8 (AA)

CLIPPER CUSTOM — (V-8) — SERIES 5560 — Chrome wheel discs; rocker panel moldings; and fender skirts were standard Clipper Custom equipment, except for the Constellation model. This two-door hardtop had no skirts, but featured a chrome molding on the fender openings. A Custom script was placed on the right-hand side of the trunk. Interior materials ranged all the way up to the same genuine leather used in Patricians, although the trim patterns varied between the two cars. Two-tone Constellation hardtops came standard with a side molding treatment that gave a double color sweep effect. This was done by extending the lower front spear (which ran straight from the upper bumper bar to mid-door on other Clippers) in a downward curve towards the rocker molding, near the rear of front doors. Then, the region below this molding was colored to match the roof and the panels above the upper rear side spear. It looked very novel and could be ordered, as an option, on the Clipper Custom touring sedan.

CLIPPER CUSTOM SERIES

Series Number	Body/Style Number	Body Type & Seating	Factory Price	Shipping Weight	Production Total
CLIPPER CUSTOM					
5560	5562	4-dr Sed-6P	2926	3885	8,708
CLIPPER CONSTELLATION					
5560	5567	2-dr HT Spt Cpe-6P	3076	3865	6,672

PACKARD LINE — (V-8) — SERIES 5580 — Senior Packards had the same shape grille opening as Clippers, but used a grid type insert. New features included wraparound parking lamps; sweep-around windshields; Packard rear fenderside scripts; and hood ornaments. All-new rear fenders with cathedral-shaped taillights and a flat, rounded tailfin look were used. At the leading edge were vertical, simulated vent panels finished in chrome. Trim and decoration varied between models. The Four-Hundred was a hardtop. It had Packard block letters on the hood; gold trunk ornaments; a modified pelican hood ornament; roof medallions; and 'Four Hundred' signatures on the deck and front fenders. A straight spear of chrome ran from the corner of the upper grille bar, over the wheel opening, then across the door to the vertical 'vent.' A second spear ran from the back bumper, over the fender skirt, straight to the front wheelhousing. It touched the bottom of the vertical 'vent.' Thus, a rectangular panel was formed where the higher molding passed over the lower one. This allowed three-tone finish with one color on the roof and under the bottom molding; a second within the parallel moldings; and a third on all other areas. The Caribbean convertible had a twin-scoop hood with no ornamentation, except on the front edge of the scoops. An overlapping, fender-within-fender treatment was seen at the rear. The 'shorter' fender was banded with a thin molding that dropped to gas filler door level, then ran straight to the headlamps. The 'long' fender dropped to the bumper exhaust pod, at which level another horizontal spear ran forward to the front wheel housing. To achieve three-tone finish, everything above the upper molding was one color; everything between the moldings (plus the fender extension area) was a second color and all panels below the bottom molding were painted a third color. Except for air conditioning, every choice option including dual outside mirrors and rear antennas was standard. In comparison, Patricians looked elegantly simple. They had one straight molding on the back fender (which hit the vertical 'vent' at right angles) and a separate front molding that ran straight from the upper grille bar edge to the rear of the front door. A split-fin hood ornament was seen and two-toning meant a different color for the roof. However, optional trim was offered to make the Patrician look more like the '400.' With this treatment, the higher molding was simply extended back to the 'vent,' thereby forming a horizontal rectangle which was finished with the same color used on the roof. It had a Patrician script placed inside it. All senior Packards came with rocker moldings, fender skirts, chrome wheel discs and Ultramatic Drive. All Patricians had "tin foil" side trim.

1955 Packard, Caribbean convertible, V-8 (AA)

PACKARD LINE

Series Number	Body/Style Number	Body Type & Seating	Factory Price	Shipping Weight	Production Total
FOUR-HUNDRED					
5580	5587	2-dr HT Cpe-6P	4080	4250	7,206
CARIBBEAN					
5580	5588	2-dr Cus Conv-6P	5932	4755	500
PATRICIAN					
5580	5582	4-dr Sed-6P	4040	4275	9,127

BASE ENGINES

(CLIPPER DELUXE/SUPER) V-8. Overhead valves. Cast iron block. Displacement: 320 cid. Bore and stroke: 3-13/16 x 3-1/2 inches. Compression ratio: 8.5:1. Brake hp: 225 at 4600 rpm. Five main bearings. Hydraulic valve lifters. Carburetor: Carter Type WCFB four-barrel: (with cylinder head No. 440689) Model 2232S; (with cylinder head No. 440854) Model 2284S.

(CLIPPER CUSTOM/PACKARD LINE) V-8. Overhead valves. Cast iron block. Displacement: 352 cid. Bore and stroke: 4 x 31/2 inches. Compression ratio: 8.5:1. Brake hp: 245 at 4600 rpm. Five main bearings. Hydraulic valve lifters. Carburetor: Carter Type WCFB four-barrel Models 2232S or 2284S. Packard line models used the same engine with carburetion changes for higher output. The Patrician and Four-Hundred had a Rochester Type 4GC four-barrel Model 440823 carburetor. It gave 260 hp at 4600 rpm. The Caribbean had two (2) Rochester Type 4GC four-barrel carburetors as follows: (front) Model 476010; (rear) Model 476011. They helped produce 275 horsepower at 4800 rpm.

CHASSIS FEATURES: Wheel base: (Clipper) 122 inches; (Packard) 127 inches. Overall length: (Clipper) 214.8 inches; (Packard) 218.5 inches. Front tread: (Clipper) 59.7 inches; (Packard) 60 inches. Rear tread: (Clipper) 60 inches; (Packard) 60-63/64 inches. Tires: (Clipper) 7.60 x 15 tubeless; (Packard) 8.00 x 15 tubeless. Torsion-Level suspension was

standard on Clipper Custom and Packard, not available on other models, which came with conventional layout. A 12-volt positive ground electrical system was new. Power brakes standard on Caribbean.

1955 Packard, Four-Hundred two-door hardtop, V-8 (AA)

OPTIONS: Radio ($102). Heater ($80). Power steering ($115). Power brakes ($40). Power seat ($70). Power windows ($108). Air conditioning ($647). Power antenna. Tinted glass. Wonderbar radio. Rear window defogger. Roll-up trunk light. Bolt-on wire wheelcovers. Remote spare tire filler. Locking gas cap door. Rain vent shades. Curb feelers. Traffic light viewer. License plate frames. Door edge guards. Lighted vanity mirror. Drink holder and pocket pouch. Snap-in Car-Pet mats. Chrome rocker arm covers. Remote master cylinder filler. Fog lamps. A three-speed manual transmission was standard on all Clippers. Ultramatic Drive was optional on all Clippers at $199. Ultramatic Drive was standard and mandatory on all Packards. Overdrive transmission was optional on Clippers at $110. An oil bath air cleaner was standard with Packard; optional with Clipper. All Packards had dual exhausts with reverse flow mufflers and resonators. Available rear axle gear ratios included: (standard) 3.9:1; (Ultramatic) 3.23:1 and (overdrive) 3.9:1.

HISTORICAL FOOTNOTES: Factory introductions took place Jan. 17, 1955. Model year output was 55,247 cars. Calendar year sales were 69,667 units. Packard was America's 14th ranked automaker. A Patrician ran 25,000 miles at an average speed of 104.737 mph in an AAA-supervised test at the company's Utica Proving Ground in Utica, Mich. The Packard Request show car with a "classic" grille was built this year. Packard supplied V-8 engines and Ultramatic transmission to American Motors Corp. for use in Nash and Hudson Eights. Richard Teague was now chief stylist at Studebaker-Packard Corp.

1956 PACKARD
(56th SERIES)

CLIPPER DELUXE/SUPER — (V-8) — SERIES 5640 — In 1956 the Clipper grille was given fine horizontal blades instead of the short vertical type. A mesh type insert was installed in the front bumper "air scoop" opening. The hood and deck lid were redesigned and wraparound parking lamps were seen. Bumper guards were moved further outward, below the headlights. New chrome trims and horizontal two-toning were adopted. Identifying the Deluxe sedan was a Deluxe script on front fenders and separate side spears front and rear. The front spear ran straight from the upper grille molding to the rear edges of front doors. The second molding was positioned higher on the rear body, running from under the back ventipane to the taillamp cluster. Clipper Supers had model identifying front fender scripts, but now lacked rocker panel moldings. Two full-length rub rail moldings were used on the side of the new body. The first ran straight from mid-headlamp level to the rear of the body. The second ran from the upper grille bar edge straight to the middle of the front door, then dipped to the same level as the top of the rear wheelhousing in a curve. Upon hitting the forward bulge of the rear fender, this molding straightened out again and ran back to the bumper, passing right over the top of the fender skirt. On all Clippers the rear fenders were redone and ended in a V-shaped notch (referred to as a reverse vertical sweep) that housed 'boomerang-shaped' cathedral taillights. A more massive rear bumper was seen.

PACKARD I.D. NUMBERS: VIN found on a plate attached to the left front door post. Motor serial numbers were located on a boss at the upper left-hand side of the cylinder block. VINS began with the Body/Style Number suffixed by the motor serial number. The Body/Style Number forming the first part of the VIN was revised and no longer used consecutive series numbering. Packard again used the last two digits of the calendar year as the first two symbols of the series and model designations. Therefore, the first two symbols used to identify cars, series and models were '56.' The second pair of symbols indicated body style. All four symbols conformed to those in the second column of the charts below. Motor serial numbers: [CLIPPER DELUXE] 5622-1001 to 5622-6715; [CLIPPER SUPER] 5642-1001 to 5642-6715. [PANAMA HARDTOP] 5647-1001 to 5647-4999. [CLIPPER CUSTOM] 5662-1001 to 5662-3130. [CONSTELLATION] 5667-1001 to 5667-2494. [PATRICIAN] 5682-1001 to 5682-4775. [PACKARD 400 HARDTOP] 5687-1001 to 5687-4224. [CARIBBEAN CONVERTIBLE] 5699-1001 to 5699-1276. [CARIBBEAN HARDTOP] 5697-1001 to 5697-1263.

CLIPPER DELUXE/SUPER SERIES

Series Number	Body/Style Number	Body Type & Seating	Factory Price	Shipping Weight	Production Total
DELUXE					
5640	5622	4-dr Del Sed-6P	2731	3955	5,715
SUPER					
5640	5642	4-dr Sup Sed-6P	2866	4010	5,173
SUPER PANAMA					
5640	5647	2-dr Sup HT Cpe-6P	2916	4035	3,999

CLIPPER CUSTOM — (V-8) — SERIES 5660 — Custom scripts on the front fenders and chrome rocker panel moldings can help in spotting Clipper Customs. The balance of trim on these cars was similar to that used on Clipper Supers, including twin rub rails with the lower molding having a curved dip near the rear quarters. Interior appointments were the richest offered on Clippers, the Constellation hardtop having leather trim options available and standard chrome roof bows.

1956 Clipper, Custom four-door sedan, V-8 (AA)

CLIPPER CUSTOM SERIES

Series Number	Body/Style Number	Body Type & Seating	Factory Price	Shipping Weight	Production Total
CLIPPER CUSTOM					
5660	5662	4-dr Cus Sed-6P	3069	4070	2,129
CLIPPER CUSTOM CONSTELLATION					
5660	5667	2-dr Cus HT-6P	3164	4070	1,466

EXECUTIVE LINE — (V-8) SERIES 5670 — The Executive line was introduced on April 9, 1956 as a replacement for the entire Clipper Custom lineup. This car was designed to fill a marketing gap existing between the lowest-priced Packard and the Clipper Deluxe. The Executive had a Packard grille and Packard-inspired side body trim, but was more closely related to Clippers. The 352 cid 1956 Clipper V-8 was used for power and the body was the Clipper type (with reverse vertical sweep fenders and taillights). Body ornamentation had a Packard look. The Executive was trimmed with two straight horizontal rub rails running from behind the headlights to ahead of the taillights. In two-tone color schemes, the area between the parallel moldings was painted to match the roof. There was no vertical simulated 'vent' strip on the rear quarter of this car. Rocker panel moldings were used between the wheel openings only.

EXECUTIVE LINE

Series Number	Body/Style Number	Body Type & Seating	Factory Price	Shipping Weight	Production Total
5670	5672A	4-dr Sed-6P	3465	4185	1,784
5670	5677A	2-dr HT Cpe-6P	3560	4185	1,031

1956 Packard, Four-Hundred two-door hardtop, V-8 (AA)

PACKARD LINE — (V-8) — SERIES 5680 — Changes in the Packard body, from 1955, included a redesigned grille with a mesh type insert having a gridwork of vertical and horizontal chrome bars placed against it. Both the mesh and the grille could also be seen in the 'air scoop' opening under the main horizontal bumper bar. Wraparound parking lamps were seen again, but had rounded rear edges. The headlamp hoods were lowered by one inch. Front fenders were extended on all Packards and Executives. Packard hood letters no longer appeared, being replaced by a centrally mounted crest. Due to the redesigned bumper, the guards were spaced wider apart, placing them directly under the headlights. Included in this series were the Patrician sedan and the Four-Hundred hardtop coupe. Both had vertical 'vents' on the rear fenders and the same arrangement of side trim. This consisted of a wide, ribbed chrome band extending the full length of the car between two horizontal rub rails. The first rail ran from the front edge of the upper grille bar to the rear edge of the back fender; the second was parallel to it, about eight inches lower. Both moldings intersected the vent ornament and outside door courtesy/safety lamps were placed at this spot. Also seen on both cars were model identification scripts, set into the contrast panel, behind the front wheelhousing. In addition, both were highlighted by bright metal body underscores which continued across the fender skirts and had wide, ribbed chrome rear extension panels. The Ultramatic transmission offered an electronic push-button selector mounted on the steering column.

PACKARD LINE

Series Number	Body/Style Number	Body Type & Seating	Factory Price	Shipping Weight	Production Total
PATRICIAN					
5680	5682	4-dr Sed-6P	4160	4255	3,775
FOUR-HUNDRED					
5680	5687	2-dr HT Cpe-6P	4190	4290	3,224

1956 Packard, Caribbean convertible, V-8 (AA)

CARIBBEAN SUB-SERIES — (V-8) — SERIES 5688 — The Caribbean was now a separate Packard sub-series having two models with special styling and engineering. General styling changes from 1955 Caribbeans were minimal. The deeper hooded headlight look was used; the rear edge of parking lamps was rounded; the Caribbean scripts were colored gold; and gridwork in the grille insert was of slightly wider squares so that several divisions were eliminated both horizontally and vertically. In addition, the new Packard 'air scoop' bumper (with the center cutout revealing a portion of the grille insert) was used. This located the bumper guard bullets directly under the headlights. Also, new three-tone color combinations were offered, such as maroon, light blue and ivory white. The hardtop was a new addition and its roof had a pair of lengthwise ribs, one on each side. Use of a dual four-barrel induction system was continued with the 374 cid/310 hp Caribbean V-8. Caribbeans had reversible seat cushions that could be unsnapped and repositioned.

CARIBBEAN SUB-SERIES

Series Number	Body/Style Number	Body Type & Seating	Factory Price	Shipping Weight	Production Total
5688	5697	2-dr Cus HT Cpe-6P	5495	4590	263
5688	5699	2-dr Cus Conv-6P	5995	4960	276

BASE ENGINES

(CLIPPER DELUXE/SUPER) V-8. Overhead valve. Cast iron block. Displacement: 352 cid. Bore and stroke: 4 x 3-1/2 inches. Compression ratio: 9.5:1. Brake hp: 240 at 4600 rpm. Five main bearings. Hydraulic valve lifters. Carburetor: Carter Type WGD two-barrel Model 2393S.

(CLIPPER CUSTOM/EXECUTIVE) V-8. Overhead valve. Cast iron block. Displacement: 352 cid. Bore and stroke: 4 x 3-1/2 inches. Compression ratio: 9.5:1. Brake hp: 275 at 4600 rpm. Five main bearings. Hydraulic valve lifters. Carburetor: Rochester Type 4GC four-barrel carburetor model 6480253.

(PACKARD LINE) V-8. Overhead valves. Cast iron block. Displacement: 374 cid. Bore and stroke: 4-1/8 x 3-1/2 inches. Compression ratio: 10.0:0. Brake hp: 290 at 4600 rpm. Five main bearings. Hydraulic valve lifters. Carburetor: Rochester Type 4GC four-barrel Model 6480253.

(CARIBBEAN) V-8. Overhead valves. Cast iron block. Displacement: 374 cid. Bore and stroke: 4-1/8 x 3-1/2 inches. Compression ratio: 10.0:0. Brake hp: 310 at 4600 rpm. Five main bearings. Hydraulic valve lifters. Carburetion: Two (2) Rochester Type 4GC four-barrel carburetors were used as follows: (front) Model 6489090; (rear) Model 6489091.

CHASSIS FEATURES: Wheelbase, length, tread and tire data for 1956 Packard models was the same as for comparable 1955 models. The new Executive had the same specifications as 1955 Clippers. Electrical ground was changed to negative.

CHASSIS FEATURES: Wheelbase: (Clipper/Executive) 122 inches; (Packard) 127 inches. Overall length: (Clipper/Executive) 215.3 inches; (Packard) 218.6 inches. Front tread: (Clipper/Executive) 59.7 inches; (Packard) 60 inches. Rear tread: (Clipper/Executive) 60 inches; (Packard) 60.8 inches. Tires: (Clipper/Executive) 7.60 x 15 tubeless; (Packard) 8.00 x 15 tubeless.

OPTIONS: Torsion suspension, Clipper ($150, but by the end of the production run, all models had Torsion-Level suspension as standard equipment). Radio with manual antenna ($103). Three-way tuning radio with electric antenna and rear speaker ($135). Front seat heater ($46). Power steering ($115). Power brakes ($40). Four-Way power seat ($70). Electric windows ($70). Air conditioning ($647). Power antenna. Solex glass with filter ($45.20). Whitewall tires ($33 exchange). Hub shells ($15). Dual exhausts ($35). Spotlight with mirror ($28.50). Tilt type mirror ($3.65). Tinted glass. Wonderbar radio. Rear window defogger. Roll-up trunk light. Bolt-on wire wheelcovers. Remote spare tire filler. Locking gas cap door. Rain vent shades. Curb feelers. Traffic light viewer. License plate frames. Door edge guards. Lighted vanity mirror. Drink holder and pocket pouch. Snap-in Car-Pet mats. Chrome rocker arm covers. Remote master cylinder filler. Fog lamps. Three-speed manual transmission was standard on Clippers; not available on Packards (except Clipper-based Executives). Overdrive was optional on Clippers and Executives at $110. Limited-slip differential was optional on all models. Oil bath air cleaner standard on all models. Twin Ultramatic Drive was a mandatory option in Packards, except Clipper/Executive models ($199 extra). Torsion-Level suspension standard on all models by end of year. Available as no-cost option on Deluxe models was conventional suspension. Power brakes were standard on all senior Packards; optional on Clipper and Executive. Electronically-controlled, push-button Ultramatic gear selection was standard in Caribbean, optional on all cars with automatics. Available rear axle gear ratios included: (standard) 3.9:1; (Ultramatic) 3.23:1 and (overdrive) 3.9:1.

HISTORICAL FOOTNOTES: Factory introductions were Nov. 3, 1955 for Clippers and Packards and April 9, 1956 for Executives. The total model run of Packards was a mere 28,835 cars. Calendar year sales dropped to 13,432. Packard slid to the 15th industry ranking. These figures did not combine Packard and Studebaker sales. (Studebaker was ranked 13th.) The 1955-1956 Four-Hundred/Patrician and Caribbean are Milestone Cars. The 1956 Caribbean convertible came with reversible seat upholstery that was brocaded on one side and leather on the other. The futuristic Predictor show car was constructed this year. On July 27, 1956 Studebaker-Packard Corp. entered a joint management agreement with Curtiss-Wright Corp. Shortly thereafter, James Nance resigned as chief executive officer. On Aug. 15, 1956, Packard operations in Detroit were brought to a halt. For 1957 and 1958, a limited range of Packards would be built off of Studebaker platforms at Studebaker's South Bend, Ind. plant. The 1957 models were called Clippers and the 1958 models had Packard nameplates and trim. Both were far different than Packard products of the past.

1957 PACKARD

1957 Packard, Clipper Ctry Sedan four-door station wagon, V-8 (AA)

CLIPPER — (V-8) — SERIES 57L — The 1957 Packard Clipper was a badge-engineered automobile built off a Studebaker President chassis. Packard modifications included finned rear fenders, a special rear wheel panel treatment and more elaborate trim. The Packard name appeared in individual block letters on the front of the hood. A Clipper script was placed on the rear fenders. Packard and Clipper scripts were also affixed to the deck lid or station wagon tailgate. The traditional Clipper "ship's wheel" medallion decorated the grille and the rear of the cars. Side trim distinctive to the Packard Clipper consisted of a wide, grooved bright metal band extending the full length of the car and across the tailgate of the station wagon. Standard equipment included modified 1956 Clipper chrome wheel discs; chrome drip moldings; two-speed electric wipers; turn signals; back-up lights; front bumper guards; padded dashboard; deep-dish steering wheel; electric clock; cigar lighter; glovebox lamp; front and rear carpeting; foam rubber seat cushions; and a rear seat center armrest on the Town Sedan.

CLIPPER SERIES I.D. NUMBERS: The serial number plate was located on the left-hand front door hinge pillar facing. Motor numbers were stamped on a machined pad at the left of the oil filler tube mounting on top of the cylinder block. The first two symbols '57' indicated the model year. The third symbol was an alphabetical series code and was 'L' for all 1957 models. Serial numbers were 57L L-1001 to L-5809. Motor numbers were LS-101 and up. Body/Style Numbers utilized the first three symbols of the above codes, a dash, a letter indicating the model and a number. 57L-Y8 identified the Town Sedan; 57L-P8 identified the Country Sedan station wagon. Only these two styles were offered.

CLIPPER SERIES 57L

Series Number	Body/Style Number	Body Type & Seating	Factory Price	Shipping Weight	Production Total
TOWN SEDAN					
57L	57L-Y8	4-dr Sed-6P	3212	3570	3,940
COUNTRY SEDAN					
57L	57L-P8	4-dr Sta Wag-6P	3384	3650	869

ENGINE

(CLIPPER) V-8. Overhead valves. Cast iron block. Displacement: 289 cid. Bore and stroke: 3-9/16 x 3-5/8 inches. Compression ratio: 7.8:1. Brake hp: 275 at 4800 rpm. Five main bearings. Solid valve lifters. Carburetor: Stromberg WW6121 two-barrel. Included as standard equipment on this engine was a McCulloch Model VS-57S supercharger designed to cut in at 3000 rpm.

CHASSIS FEATURES: Wheelbase: (Town sedan) 120.5 inches; (Country sedan) 116.5 inches. Overall length: (Town sedan) 211.8 inches; (Country sedan) 204.8 inches. Front tread: 56-11/16 inches. Rear Tread: 55-11/16 inches. Tires: 7.60 x 15.

OPTIONS: Tinted glass ($32). White sidewall tires ($28). Power steering ($98). Power brakes ($38). Power windows ($103). Power seat ($45). Dual rear antennas (electric for sedan, manual for station wagon). Pair, front seat belts ($25). Padded sun visors. Country Sedan luggage carrier ($60). Air conditioning, Town sedan only ($325). Rear radio speaker ($13). Flight-O-Matic transmission was standard equipment. Limited-slip differential was optional at extra cost. Conventional suspension was featured, with helper springs on Country Sedan station wagon. Available axle ratios included: (standard) 3.31:1; (optional at no-cost) 3.07: 1 or 3.54: 1.

HISTORICAL FOOTNOTES: The Studebaker-based Packard Clipper was introduced in Jan. 31, 1957. The possibility of a marketing program between Studebaker-Packard and Mercedes-Benz was explored in the spring of 1957. H.D. Churchill was president of Studebaker-Packard in 1957. The corporation lost $43.3 million this year. The supercharger used on the 1957 engine was built by McCulloch Motors, best known as a chain saw manufacturer. While often identified as a Paxton supercharger, it was not until March 1962 that the supercharger branch became the Paxton Products Div. of Studebaker-Packard Corp.

1958 PACKARD

PACKARD — (V-8) — SERIES 58L — The 1958 cars were marketed as a midyear line introduced in January, 1958. The Clipper designation was dropped. Four models were available with a Packard Hawk hardtop and Packard hardtop being added to the line. Only the Packard

Standard Catalog of American Cars

Hawk V-8 was supercharged. General changes from 1957 included new bodies with an unusual "shovel nose." This low, wide air-intake type grille surround was actually a fiberglass bolt-on item. New dual headlamps were on all models, except Hawks. Radical pointed tailfins took the fender-within-fender theme of earlier Caribbeans to the extreme. There were now fins on top of fins, with the top one curving sharply upward. The bottom fin jutted out further at the rear and housed "boomerang-shaped" taillights with integral back-up lights. The lower fin turned into a sweepspear contrast panel that tapered as it ran the full length of the body from above the rear bumper to just below the front fender tip. The cars were fitted with 14 inch wheels to make them lower. A scoop appeared on the hood, along with Packard block lettering. Packard scripts were affixed to the fins and rear deck lid. Styling on the Packard Hawk was distinctive and it is described below, as a separate sub-series. Standard equipment was the same as 1957, except the engine was not supercharged.

1958 Packard, two-door hardtop Sports Coupe, V-8 (AA)

CLIPPER SERIES I.D. NUMBERS: The serial number plate was located on the left-hand front door hinge pillar facing. Motor numbers were stamped on a machined pad at the left of the oil filler tube mounting on top of the cylinder block. The first two symbols '58' indicated the model year. The third symbol was an alphabetical series code and was 'L' for all 1958 models. Serial numbers were 58L-6101 and up. Body/Style Number for the sedan was J8; for the hardtop Y8 and for the station wagon P8. The station wagon was no longer called the Country Sedan. [PACKARD HAWK] The serial numbering system and code locations were the same. Serial Numbers were 58LS-K91001 up. Motor numbers were 58L LS-101 up. The new Body/Style Number for the Packard Hawk was K9.

PACKARD SERIES 58L

Series Number	Body/Style Number	Body Type & Seating	Factory Price	Shipping Weight	Production Total
58L	58L-J8	4-dr Sed-6P	3212	3505	1,200
58L	58L-Y8	2-dr HT Cpe-6P	3262	3480	675
58L	58L-P8	4-dr Sta Wag-6P	3384	3555	159

PACKARD HAWK — (V-8) — SERIES 58LS — The Packard Hawk had the same fiberglass, bolt-on air-intake type grille as other Packards. It was, however, bolted onto the Studebaker Hawk sports car body, a sleek two-door hardtop coupe style car. A number of special extras were included. For example, padded 'armrests' on the outside of the doors; a continental tire impression stamped on the deck lid; genuine leather interior with sports car type instrument board and full instrumentation; simulated and integrated hood scoop; front fender markers; Mylar sweep panel inserts; Packard emblem hubcaps; wide, chromed 'halo' roof band over backlight; tachometer; vacuum gauge; supercharger pressure gauge and 275 hp supercharged engine. The Hawk was lettered and 'scripted' like other Packards, but had a different trim arrangement. A thin band of chrome outlined the concave rear tailfins and a straight spear stretched from the single headlights to almost the rear edge of the door. A flap type vertical air vent door appeared behind the front wheel cutout.

PACKARD HAWK SERIES 58LS

Series Number	Body/Style Number	Body Type & Seating	Factory Price	Shipping Weight	Production Total
58LS	58LS-K9	2-dr HT Spt Cpe-5P	3995	3470	588

ENGINES

(PACKARD) V-8. Overhead valves. Cast iron block. Displacement: 289 cid. Bore and stroke: 3.56 x 3.63 inches. Compression ratio: 8.3:1. Brake hp: 225 at 4500 rpm. Five main bearings. Solid valve lifters. Carburetor: Carter Model 2575S four-barrel. Non-supercharged. (A low-compression 7.0:1 head was optional for this engine.)

(PACKARD HAWK) V-8. Overhead valves. Cast iron block. Displacement: 289 cid. Bore and stroke: 3.56 x 3.63 inches. Compression ratio: 7.8:1. Brake hp: 275 at 4800 rpm. Five main bearings, solid valve lifters. Carburetor: Stromberg WWG-122A two-barrel. Included as standard equipment on this engine was a McCulloch Model VS-57S supercharger designed to cut in at 3000 rpm.

CHASSIS FEATURES: Wheelbase: (Packard Hawk and sedan) 120.5 inches; (Packard hardtop and station wagon) 116.5 inches. Overall length: (Hawk) 205.1 inches; (sedan) 213.2 inches; (hardtop) 209.2 inches and (station wagon) 206.2 inches. Front tread: 56-11/16 inches. Rear tread: 55-11/16 inches. Tires: 8.00 x 14.

1958 Packard Hawk, 2-dr hardtop sports coupe, V-8 (AA)

OPTIONS: Power steering ($68.86). Power brakes ($37.66). Power windows, in two-doors ($54); in four-doors ($102.60). Power seat ($45.19). Oil filter ($21.52). Seven-tube push-button radio ($79.90). Six-tube manual radio ($60.50). Rear speaker ($12.95). Climatizer heater ($71). Whitewall tires ($27.91 exchange). Two-tone paint ($21.50). Tinted glass ($32). Station wagon luggage carrier ($59.95). Hill Holder ($15.06). Dealer-installation air conditioner ($79.80). Trunk installation air conditioner ($275). Pair of front seat safety belts ($24.95). Rideaway Third seat for station wagon ($101.68). Undercoating ($12.75). Flight-O-Matic was 'standard' on all models in that it was considered 'normal' equipment, but it still cost $189 extra. Overdrive was a $110.40 option. Dual exhausts, standard on Packard Hawk; $23.43 on others. Twin-Traction differential was $34.90 extra. An oil bath air cleaner was $8.07. Available rear axle gear ratios were: (standard) 3.92:1 or 4.27:1; (overdrive) 4.09:1 and (Flight-O-Matic) 3.31:1.

HISTORICAL FOOTNOTES: Production of 1958 models stopped July 13, 1958. No Packard automobiles were built thereafter. The name Studebaker-Packard survived until 1962.

STANDARD CATALOG OF
PLYMOUTH
1946-1975

1971 Plymouth, Road Runner 440 Six-Pack two-door hardtop, V-8

With the momentum of its successful first 14 years of production, Plymouth successfully entered the post World War II market with restyled and mechanically refined versions of its 1942 models.

Retaining its 117 inch wheelbase, Plymouth sported a new front grille and rear fenders, as well as a restyled interior and several chassis improvements. Escalating labor and material costs were reflected in higher model prices. No design changes were introduced until the spring of 1949.

The all-new 1949 Plymouths were based on the 'box styling' philosophy of Chrysler chairman K.T. Keller who had succeeded Walter Chrysler in 1940. Emphasizing practicality over beauty, Keller is credited with the efficiency and roominess of the 1949 models. These new models, in DeLuxe and Special DeLuxe versions, sat on a longer wheelbase and were powered by Plymouth's L-head six-cylinder engine. This same year Plymouth also offered a shorter 111 inch wheelbase line with a coupe, sedan and a new all-steel Suburban station wagon.

Although introducing the automatic electric choke and the combination ignition/starter switch to the low-priced field in 1950, Plymouth entered the '50s with no real styling changes. Sales dropped from third to fifth place in the industry by 1954. Plymouth added flow-through fenderlines and a one-piece windshield to its 1953 models, but all were powered by the same L-head Six which was quickly becoming dated and dull.

The two-speed PowerFlite automatic transmission offered by Plymouth in 1954, however, proved popular.

Virgil Exner's all-new styling arrived with 1955 Plymouths and a brand new polyspherical-head V-8 engine brought even more excitement to the new lineup. In addition to new standard features, such as dashboard-controlled PowerFlite automatic transmission, suspended foot pedals and tubeless tires, buyers could now opt for air-conditioning, power windows and power front seats. A total departure from Plymouth's past was the 1955 Belvedere. Called "A great new car for the young at heart," it included a sporty hardtop and convertible, the latter available only with a V-8 engine.

Along with the tailfins of Virgil Exner's 'Forward Look' in 1956 Plymouth introduced an optional Highway H-Fi record player and expanded its Suburban, Belvedere, and Savoy series. Contributing to Plymouth's performance image in 1956 was the new limited-edition Fury hardtop, which was painted white-and-gold and featured a 303 cid V-8 engine with four-barrel carburetion and dual exhausts.

From 1957 through the end of the decade, Plymouths were hailed as being ahead of their time. Daring styling and advanced performance put Plymouth in third place in the industry again in 1957. When Plymouth dropped its Plaza model in 1959, the Fury was elevated to a separate series and the Sport Fury moved in as the new high-performance entry. Also introduced, as an option in 1959, was the new 361

'Golden Commando' wedge head V-8, which delivered 305 hp.

With the exception of the 1954 Plymouth Belmont show car built by Briggs, Chrysler's Virgil Exner and Ghia coachworks of Italy collaborated on most of Plymouth's show cars during the 1950s. They included the XX-500 sedan, the 1954 Explorer grand tourer, the sporty Belmont, the 1956 Plainsman station wagon and the 1958 Cabana wagon.

During the '60s Plymouth's sales plummeted with only sporadic recoveries. The tailfinned Savoy, Belvedere, Fury and Suburban models for 1960 were coolly received by the buying public and, in 1962, the public shunned Plymouth's new, down-sized models for larger Fords and Chevrolets. Only Plymouth's compact Valiant, with its strong slant six engine, was well received. In mid-1964 Plymouth also launched its successful sporty compact the Barracuda. Along with more pleasing styling, Plymouth's success in racing competition spurred a remarkable sales recovery by 1965.

In the '60s, the 426 cid/425 hp Hemi engine was offered as an option on Plymouth's Belvedere II and Satellite models, first in racing tune and then in a street performance edition to qualify it as a production option. The 'Street Hemi' package included heavy-duty suspension and oversized brakes. In factory it qualified for A/Stock and AA/Stock drag racing and NASCAR's shorter circuits in 1966. Richard Petty won both the 1964 Daytona 500 and the 1967 NASCAR championship for Plymouth.

For 1968, Plymouth restyled its intermediates with more rounded lines and introduced its hot Road Runner model available in hardtop and coupe. Identified by special wheels, a hood scoop, Road Runner emblems and cartoon birds on sides and rear, the Road Runner could be had with either the 383 cid V-8 or the 426 Hemi. In addition to the Road runner, Plymouth's GTX model, introduced in 1967, was continued for 1968.

In 1968 and 1969, Plymouth offered big-block models of its popular Barracuda, called the 'Cuda 340 and 'Cuda 383. In 1970, the Barracuda was completely restyled. It shared an all-new body shell with another Chrysler performance compact, the Dodge Challenger. A midyear variation of the Barracuda was the AAR (All-American Race) 'Cuda 340, identifiable by its bold tape stripes. Fewer than 2,900 AAR models were built.

In 1970, Plymouth's Valiant was revived in the form of the Duster coupe and the optional Gold Duster. A high-performance variation, the Duster 340, used options similar to the AAR 'Cuda's to convert an otherwise mild Valiant into a skyrocket. Plymouth's most awesome newcomer in 1970 was the high-performance Superbird, which was part of the Road Runner Series. With its droop-snout front end, sleek body and deck lid carrying a stabilizer wing high above its tail, the Superbird was capable of over 220 mph in racing trim. In street form, the four-barrel 440 cid engine with TorqueFlite automatic transmission was standard. A six-barrel 440 engine, a racing 426 Hemi and four-speed manual transmission were optional. The Superbird accounted for 21 of 38 Chrysler victories on the Grand National circuit. When NASCAR changed its rules in 1971, however, the Superbird's dominance of high-speed ovals was over.

By 1972, the Barracuda series was severely cut and the optional 383, 440 and 426 Hemi engines were eliminated. A competition Hemi could still be had by professional racers, however, on special order. High insurance rates and government pressure for emission controls were contributed to a decline of the performance car market. No longer around was the GTX. Due to sagging sales, it was dropped in 1971. That same year the Sport Fury was cast off in favor of the Gran Fury and all of the senior Plymouths were face-lifted.

In 1973 Plymouth made an exhaust gas recirculation system and an orifice spark advance and electrically-assisted choke standard on all models to reduce air pollution. A new five mph impact-absorbing front bumper was also introduced. By 1974 Plymouth's sales shrunk, hurt by the prior year's Arab Oil Embargo. Most models were carried over from 1973 with minor changes, due to the emphasis on unleaded fuel and other factors restricting power output. Plymouth stopped publishing passenger car horsepower ratings by 1975. This same year Plymouth equipped most models with catalytic converters and an emission control device in the exhaust system requiring engines to use lead-free fuel.

1947 Plymouth, Special Deluxe two-door convertible, 6-cyl

1950 Plymouth, Special Deluxe two-door convertible, 6-cyl

1954 Plymouth, Belvedere two-door convertible, 6-cyl

1957 Plymouth, Belvedere Fury two-door hardtop coupe, V-8

1946 PLYMOUTH

1946 Plymouth, Deluxe two-door business coupe, 6-cyl (TVB)

DELUXE SIX — (6-CYL) — SERIES P-15 — The Deluxe Six was the low-priced Plymouth in 1946. Styling was a carryover of the last prewar designs with a simpler grille bar pattern and a front bumper that wrapped around the corners of the body. The rear fenders were also new and had a lower, smaller wheel opening. Standard equipment was comprised of airplane type shock absorbers; All-Weather ventilation; front-end sway bar; sealed beam headlights; burn resistant exhaust valve seat inserts; scuff proof four-ring aluminum pistons; air-cooled soft-action clutch; calibrated knock-free ignition; floating oil intake; full-pressure lubrication; front coil springs; Hotchkiss drive, metal leaf spring covers; Oilite gas filter; rubber-mounted steering gear; instrument panel starter button; Rubber Poise body mountings; and hyphoid rear axle. Chrome trim consisting of small wheel center covers; heavy rocker sill strips; chrome headlamp rims; 'Mayflower' hood-nose emblem; horizontal bar grille; front fender moldings; hood ornament; and an upper beltline molding running from the forward portion of the hood to the upper rear quarter area. A nameplate reading 'Plymouth Deluxe' was placed on the sides of the hood below the beltline trim. A black rubber windshield frame and rear window surround were used. The deck carried a massive, bright metal latching mechanism and 'Mayflower' emblem with light-up plastic lens.

PLYMOUTH I.D. NUMBERS: Serial number on plate on left front door post (right front door post of very early 1946 models) is the only code used for identification/registration purposes. It consists of a Plymouth prefix 'P' and two-symbol series number (P-15). The four or more symbols following this are the production sequence number starting with 1001 at each factory. Motor number near front upper left side of block between first and second cylinders takes same format as serial number, but may not match. Motor number should not be used for identification. Motor numbers sometimes had suffixes: A=.020 inch cylinder overbore; B=.010 inch undersize journals and diamond-shaped symbol=.008 inch oversize tappet bore. Plymouth factory codes are: M=Detroit, Mich.; LA=Los Angeles, Calif.; E=Evansville, Ind. and SL=San Leandro, Calif. These codes do not appear in serial number. Chrysler did not use body style numbers at this time. Serial numbers for 1946 were as follows: Deluxe Series: (M) 15154001-15206835; (LA) 26000001-36003588 and (E) 22042001-22053039. Special Deluxe Series: (M) 11496001-11643103; (LA) 25000001-25009752 and (E) 20165001-20185186.

DELUXE SIX SERIES

Series Number	Body/Style Number	Body Type & Seating	Factory Price	Shipping Weight	Production Total
P-15	NA	2-dr Cpe-3P	1089	2977	Note 1
P-15	NA	2-dr Clb Cpe-6P	1159	3037	Note 1
P-15	NA	2-dr Sed-6P	1124	3047	Note 1
P-15	NA	4-dr Sed-6P	1164	3082	Note 1

NOTE 1: See 1948 section for 1946-1948 P-15 series production.

SPECIAL DELUXE SIX — (6-CYL) — SERIES P-15 — The Special Deluxe line was the second and higher-priced 1946 Plymouth model range. There were only small visual distinctions between cars in each series. Lettering at the rear corner of the hood, just ahead of the cowl area, carried the words 'Special Deluxe.' Bright metal moldings surrounded the windshield. Standard equipment included extra features like dual windshield wipers and sun visors; glove box lock; rear bumper fender guards; and rear window vents on sedans. The Special Deluxe could be ordered with either pencil stripe broad cloth upholstery or soft pile fabrics. Special Deluxe models were not quite as distinctive as in prewar times and weighed only slightly more than Deluxes. The convertible and wood-bodied station wagon came in the Special Deluxe series only. Both had their own unique interior appointments. The convertible featured genuine leather seats and the station wagon owner sat on leather-like upholstery. The station wagon came only in three-seats-for-eight-passengers format, but the second and third seats were removable to create a large cargo deck. It had white ash wood framing and dark, maple paneling. The top on the convertible coupe was of the blind rear quarter style, carried over from before the war.

SPECIAL DELUXE SIX SERIES

Series Number	Body/Style Number	Body Type & Seating	Factory Price	Shipping Weight	Production Total
P-15	NA	2-dr Cpe-3P	1159	2982	Note 1
P-15	NA	2-dr Clb Cpe-6P	1234	3057	Note 1
P-15	NA	2-dr Conv-5P	1439	3282	Note 1
P-15	NA	2-dr Sed-6P	1199	3062	Note 1
P-15	NA	4-dr Sed-6P	1239	3107	Note 1
P-15	NA	4-dr Sta Wag-8P	1539	3402	Note 1

NOTE 1: See 1948 section for 1946-1948 P-15 series production.

DELUXE SIX SERIES ENGINE: Inline. L-head Six. Cast iron block. Displacement: 217.8 cid. Bore and stroke: 3-1/4 x 4-3/8 inches. Compression ratio: 6.6:1. Brake hp: 95 at 3600 rpm. Four main bearings. Solid valve lifters. Carburetor: Carter Type BB one-barrel Model DGG1.

1946 Plymouth, Special Deluxe four-door sedan, 6-cyl

CHASSIS FEATURES: Wheelbase: 117 inches. Overall length: (station wagon) 195-5/8 inches; (other styles) 196-3/4 inches. Front tread: 57 inches. Rear tread: 60-1/8 inches. Tires: 6.00 x 16.

OPTIONS: Heater and defroster. Radio and antenna. Large hubcaps (nine-inch hubcaps were standard on Deluxe, 10-inch standard on Special Deluxe and optional on Deluxe). Directional signals. Seat covers. White sidewall discs. Wheel trim rings. Fog lamps. Spotlamp. Light-up hood ornament. Dual sun visors on Deluxe Six. Clock in Deluxe Six. Deluxe steering wheel. Deluxe Six. Rear fender molding (early in year only) Glove box lock, in Deluxe Six. Dual windshield wipers, on Deluxe Six. External sunshade visor. Traffic light viewer. Bumper guards. Grille guard. Wing guards. License plate frames. OSRV mirrors. Three-speed manual transmission was standard. Heavy-duty air cleaner was available at extra cost. Available rear axle gear ratios (various).

HISTORICAL FOOTNOTES: The first postwar Plymouths were introduced in February, 1946 and the P-15 Series continued in production through early 1949. Calendar year production peaked at 242,534 units. Calendar year registrations of 211,800 cars were recorded. Plymouth was America's third largest producer of cars and accounted for 11.3 percent of United States auto production. Plymouth's 1946 sales slogan was "Now it's Plymouth: 50 new features and improvements." U.S. Body & Forging Co., of Franfurt, Ind., built wood-crafted bodies for Plymouth station wagons. The P-15 series, which entered production in Feb. 1946, would continue being made for 39 consecutive months with only minor changes. You didn't need a crystal ball to predict what next year's Plymouth was going to look like in the first few years after World War II.

1947 PLYMOUTH

1947 Plymouth, Deluxe four-door taxi sedan, 6-cyl

DELUXE SIX — (6-CYL) — SERIES P-15 — The Deluxe Six for 1947 was identical to the comparable 1946 model. Nomenclature was also the same. Plymouth simply continued with the same series for another year. Cars built after Jan. 1, 1947 were sold as 1947 models. The only way to pinpoint the model year is by reference to serial number codes. Even prices and weights stayed the same during the first part of 1947. The 154th edition of RED BOOK, dated April 1, 1947, reflects this consistency. Later, however, the price changes included in the charts below went into effect. Some models increased at retail, while others declined.

PLYMOUTH I.D. NUMBERS: Serial number on plate on left front door post is the only code used for identification/registration purposes. It consists of a Plymouth prefix 'P' and two-symbol series number (P-15). The four or more symbols following this are the production sequence number starting with 1001 at each factory. Motor number near front upper left side of block between first and second cylinders takes same format as serial number, but may not match. Motor number should not be used for identification. Motor numbers sometimes had suffixes: A=.020 inch cylinder overbore; B=.010 inch undersize journals and diamond-shaped symbol=.008 inch oversize tappet bore. Plymouth factory codes are: M=Detroit, Mich.; LA=Los Angeles, Calif.; E=Evansville, Ind. and SL=San Leandro, Calif. These codes do not appear in serial number. Serial numbers for 1947 were: Deluxe: (M) 15206936-15252278, (LA) 26003589-26010839; (E) 22043040 22063369. Special Deluxe (M) 11643104-11854385; (LA) 25009753-25035585 and (E) 20185186-20233167

DELUXE SIX SERIES

Series Number	Body/Style Number	Body Type & Seating	Factory Price	Shipping Weight	Production Total
P-15	NA	2-dr Cpe-3P	1139	2977	Note 1
P-15	NA	2-dr Clb Cpe-6P	1189	3037	Note 1
P-15	NA	2-dr Sed-6P	1164	3047	Note 1
P-15	NA	4-dr Sed-6P	1214	3082	Note 1

NOTE 1: See 1948 section for 1946-1948 P-15 series production.

1947 Plymouth, Special Deluxe four-door sedan, 6-cyl (TVB)

SPECIAL DELUXE SIX — (6-CYL) — SERIES P-15 — The Special Deluxe Six for 1947 was identical to the comparable 1946 model in appearance, construction and nomenclature. Cars built the P-15 Series, built after Jan. 1, 1947, were simply sold as next year models. Even prices remained unchanged at first, but later increased due to the postwar seller's market and inflationary spiral. Hoodside lettering, bright windshield frames and richer upholstery trims were telltale signs of a Special Deluxe. Serial numbers can be referred to for positive identification of year, but do not include body style coding.

SPECIAL DELUXE SIX SERIES

Series Number	Body/Style Number	Body Type & Seating	Factory Price	Shipping Weight	Production Total
P-15	NA	2-dr Cpe-3P	1209	2982	Note 1
P-15	NA	2-dr Clb Cpe-6P	1264	3057	Note 1
P-15	NA	2-dr Conv-5P	1565	3282	Note 1
P-15	NA	2-dr Sed-6P	1239	3062	Note 1
P-15	NA	4-dr Sed-6P	1289	3107	Note 1
P-15	NA	4-dr Sta Wag-8P	1765	3402	Note 1

NOTE 1: See 1948 section for 1946-1948 P-15 series production.

1947 Plymouth Special Deluxe two-door business coupe, 6-cyl. JL

PLYMOUTH BASE ENGINE: Inline. L-head Six. Cast iron block. Displacement: 217.8 cid. Bore and stroke: 3-1/4 x 4-3/8 inches. Compression ratio: 6.6:1. Brake hp; 95 at 3600 rpm. Four main bearings. Solid valve lifters. Carburetor: Carter Type BB one-barrel Model DGG1.

CHASSIS FEATURES: Wheelbase: (all models) 117 inches. Overall length: (station wagon) 195-5/8 inches; (all other styles) 196-3/4 inches. Front tread: (all models) 57 inches. Rear tread: (all models) 60-1/8 inches. Tires: (all models, early) 6.00 x 16; (all models, late) 6:70 x 15. The switch to 15-inch wheels was made in November and December, 1947, and corresponded with the following serial numbers: Deluxe: (M) 15251917, (LA) 26010991, (E) 22063548. Special Deluxe: (M) 11851594; (LA) 25036148. (1) 20234249

OPTIONS: Heater and defroster. Radio and antenna. Large hubcaps (nine-inch hubcaps were standard on Deluxe, 10-inch standard on Special Deluxe and optional on Deluxe). Directional signals. Seat covers. White sidewall discs. Wheel trim rings. Fog lamps. Spotlamp. Light-up hood ornament. Dual sun visors on Deluxe Six. Clock in Deluxe Six. Deluxe steering wheel. Deluxe Six. Rear fender molding (early in year only) Glove box lock, in Deluxe Six. Dual windshield wipers, on Deluxe Six. External sunshade visor. Traffic light viewer. Bumper guards. Grille guard. Wing guards. License plate frames. OSRV mirrors. Three-speed manual transmission was standard. Heavy-duty air cleaner was available at extra cost. Available rear axle gear ratios (various).

HISTORICAL FOOTNOTES: Plymouths of the P-15 Series built after Dec. 1, 1946 were considered 1947 models and appeared in dealer showrooms after Jan. 1, 1947. Calendar year production peaked at 350,327 units. Calendar year registrations of 313,118 cars were recorded. Plymouth sales jumped 44.6 percent in 1947. The P-15 series ran from its 11th to 22nd consecutive months of production during calendar year 1947. Until late 1947, all models had 16 inch wheels and 16 x 6.00 tires. A full-sized mock-up of a small-car proposal called the Plymouth "Cadet" was completed in 1947. This super-economy model resembled the soon-to-appear 1949 design. Project A-92 was another 1947 Plymouth styling concept for a larger postwar design car.

1948 Plymouth, Deluxe two-door sedan, 6-cyl (TVB)

DELUXE SIX — (6-CYL) — SERIES P-15 — The Plymouth P-15 Series continued into 1948 without change as far as appearance, construction or nomenclature. Cars sold after Jan. 1, 1948 were designated 1948 models. Due to variations in state registration laws, it's possible to find 1947 models titled as 1948s. Some states issued license plates based on the date of sale. Check serial numbers for positive identification of Plymouths built as 1948 models. Prices increased substantially this season. A specifications change was in tire sizes. Fifteen inch diameter types replaced 16 inch size of 1946-1947. (Some sources date the tire size change to late 1947, shortly before the Dec. 1, date designated as the start of 1948 production.) The smaller diameter tires gave the cars a lower look.

PLYMOUTH I.D. NUMBERS: Serial number on plate on left front door post is the only code used for identification/registration purposes. It consists of a Plymouth prefix 'P' and two-symbol series number (P-15). The four or more symbols following this are the production sequence number starting with 1001 at each factory. Motor number near front upper left side of block between first and second cylinders takes same format as serial number, but may not match. Motor number should not be used for identification. Motor numbers sometimes had suffixes: A=.020 inch cylinder overbore; B=.010 inch undersize journals and diamond-shaped symbol=.008 inch oversize tappet bore. Plymouth factory codes are: M=Detroit, Mich.; LA=Los Angeles, Calif.; E=Evansville, Ind. and SL=San Leandro, Calif. These codes do not appear in serial number. Chrysler did not use body style numbers at this time. Serial numbers for 1948 were as follows: Deluxe: (M) 15252279-15284534: (LA) 2601084026017025 and (E) 22063370-22071866. Special Deluxe: (M) 11854386-12066019: (LA) 25035586-25062782: (E) 20233168-20287571.

1948 Plymouth Special Deluxe four-door sedan

DELUXE SIX SERIES

Series Number	Body/Style Number	Body Type & Seating	Factory Price	Shipping Weight	Production Total
P-15	NA	4-dr Sed-6P	1441	3030	120,757
P-15	NA	2-dr Sed-6P	1383	2995	49,918
P-15	NA	2-dr Clb Cpe-6P	1409	3005	10,400
P-15	NA	2-dr Cpe-3P	1346	2955	16,117

NOTE 1: 1946-1948 P-15 series production totals listed above.

NOTE 2: A total of 10 chassis only were also built.

SPECIAL DELUXE SIX — (6-CYL) — SERIES P-15 — Following corporate policy the Special Deluxe Six was carried over into 1948 with no change in appearance, construction or nomenclature. Tire size changed to 15 inch. Prices went up, too. All 1946-1949 (First Series) Plymouths shared a few minor running changes, but none of these were of great significance. As previously mentioned, serial numbers should be referred to for dating and identifying P-15 Series Plymouths, as to model year.

SPECIAL DELUXE SIX SERIES

Series Number	Body/Style Number	Body Type & Seating	Factory Price	Shipping Weight	Production Total
P-15	NA	4-dr Sed-6P	1529	3045	514,986
P-15	NA	2-dr Sed-6P	1471	3030	125,704
P-15	NA	2-dr Clb Cpe-6P	1503	3020	156,629
P-15	NA	2-dr Cpe-3P	1440	2950	31,399
P-15	NA	2-dr Conv-5P	1857	3225	15,295
P-15	NA	4-dr Sta Wag-8P	2068	3320	12,913

NOTE 1: 1946-1948 P-15 series production totals listed above.
NOTE 2: A total of 5,361 chassis only were also built.

1948 Plymouth, Special Deluxe two-door convertible, 6-cyl

ENGINE: Inline. L-head Six. Cast iron block. Displacement: 217.8 cid. Bore and stroke: 3-1/4 x 4-3/8 inches. Compression ratio: 6.6:1. Brake hp; 95 at 3600 rpm. Solid valve lifters. Carburetor: Carter Type BB one-barrel Model DGG1.

CHASSIS FEATURES: Wheelbase: (all models) 117 inches. Overall length: (station wagon) 195-5/8 inches; (all other styles) 196-3/4 inches. Front tread: (all models) 57 inches. Rear tread: (all models) 60-1/8 inches. Tires: (all models) 6.70 x 15.

OPTIONS: Heater and defroster. Radio and antenna. Large hubcaps (nine inch hubcaps were standard on Deluxe, 10-inch standard on Special Deluxe and optional on Deluxe). Directional signals. Seat covers. White sidewall discs. Wheel trim rings. Fog lamps. Spot lamp. Light-up hood ornament. Dual sun visors on Deluxe Six. Clock in Deluxe Six. Deluxe steering wheel. Deluxe Six. Rear fender molding (early in year only) Glove box lock, in Deluxe Six. Dual windshield wipers, on Deluxe Six. External sunshade visor. Traffic light viewer. Bumper guards. Grille guard. Wing guards. License plate frames. OSRV mirrors. Three-speed manual transmission was standard. Heavy-duty air cleaner was available at extra cost. Available rear axle gear ratios (various). White sidewall tires. Two economy packages were offered. One had a smaller capacity carburetor and intake manifold, which reduced hp to 65 at 3000 rpm. and a 3.73:1 rear axle ratio. Along with these changes, the second option also included a throttle stop limiting top speed to 45 mph.

HISTORICAL FOOTNOTES: Plymouths of the P-15 Series built after Dec. 1, 1947 were considered 1948 models and appeared in dealer showrooms after January 1, 1948. Calendar year production peaked at 378,048 units. Calendar year registrations of 347,174 cars were recorded. Plymouth sales rose 9.9 percent in 1948. The P-15 series ran from its 22nd consecutive month, at the beginning of 1948, to its 34th month in December.

1949 PLYMOUTH

(FIRST SERIES)

DELUXE AND SPECIAL DELUXE — (6-CYL) — (FIRST 1949 SERIES) — From January to March, 1949, Plymouth continued to market P-15 Series models built to 1948 model year specifications. These cars were officially built and sold as 1949 automobiles. They were, however, identical to 1948 models and carry approximately the same value to modern day car collectors. All of these cars were manufactured after Dec. 1, 1948 and had the following serial numbers at indicated factories: Deluxe Six: (Detroit) 15284535 to 15292209; (Evansville) 22071867 to 22073646 and (Los Angeles) 26017026 to 26018852. Special Deluxe Six: (Detroit) 12066020 to 12116123; (Evansville) 20287572 to 20299104 and (Los Angeles) 25062783 to 25071430. All of these cars were manufactured to be sold and registered as 1949 models. Owners of remaining examples should refer to the 1948 Plymouth section for information about these cars.

1949 Plymouth, Deluxe two-door Suburban, 6-cyl (PH)

(SECOND SERIES)

DELUXE (SHORT WHEELBASE) SIX — (6-CYL) — SERIES P-17 — Plymouth's first true postwar cars appeared March, 1949. The short wheelbase P-17 Deluxe models were the low-priced offering. Three two-door models — business coupe, Suburban and fastback sedan — were introduced successively. All had boxy lines, reflecting the thinking of Chrysler's president W.T. Keller. They could be identified by their smaller, shorter sheet metal and Deluxe scripts on front fendersides. Frontal decorations consisted of a stylized 'Mayflower' hood ornament; Plymouth block lettering at the nose; chrome headlight rings; and a massive horizontal plate above the grille bearing a 'Mayflower' emblem. The grille cavity was covered by a thick, horizontal bar between the headlights; two similar lower bars extending below the headlights (and housing rectangular parking lights at each outboard end); two thin horizontal moldings placed between the thicker ones (and equalling the top bar in length); plus, three wide-spaced vertical moldings. Bumpers were of a triple-fluted design, with two vertical guards, and wrapped around the body corners. Other trim included a front fenderside molding; Deluxe front fender script: triple-fluted rocker panel strips; upper belting molding; black rubber windshield surround; small hub center caps; trunk ornament/emblem; trunk latch handle; and rear bumper with guards. A rear fenderside spear was optional on early production units, but later became a regular feature. Upholstery was of the Deluxe level.

1949 Plymouth Special Deluxe two-door club coupe, 6-cyl. JL

PLYMOUTH I.D. NUMBERS: Serial number on plate on left front door post is the only code used for identification/registration purposes. It consists of a Plymouth prefix 'P' and two-symbol series number (P-17, P-18, etc.). The four or more symbols following this are the production sequence number starting with 1001 at each factory. Motor number near front upper left side of block between first and second cylinders takes same format as serial number, but may not match. Motor number should not be used for identification. Motor numbers sometimes had suffixes: A=.020 inch cylinder overbore; B=.010 inch undersize journals and diamond-shaped symbol=.008 inch oversize tappet bore. Plymouth factory codes are: M=Detroit, Mich.; LA=Los Angeles, Calif.; E=Evansville, Ind. and SL=San Leandro, Calif. These codes do not appear in serial number. Chrysler did not use body style numbers at this time. Serial numbers for 1949 at each factory were: P-17 Deluxe: (M) 18000101-18040467; (E) 24000001-24011890; (LA) 28000101-28003814 and (SL) 28500101-28503162; P-18 Deluxe: (M) 153000001-15358928; (E) 22080001-222096252; (LA) 26025001-26030100 and (SL) 26500101-26503423. P-18 Special Deluxe (M) 1212000-112383178; (E) 20304001-20366486; (LA) 25075001-25097094 and (SL) 25500101-25510640. Engine Numbers for the three series were P-18-1001 thru P-18-509050. P-17 = short wheelbase Deluxe; P18=long wheelbase Deluxe or Special Deluxe. Production of Plymouths at SanLeandro, California (code SL) began this year.

DELUXE (SHORT WHEELBASE) SIX SERIES

Series Number	Body/Style Number	Body Type & Seating	Factory Price	Shipping Weight	Production Total
P-17	NA	2-dr Sed-6P	1492	2951	28,516
P-17	NA	2-dr Cpe-3P	1371	2825	13,715
P-17	NA	2-dr Sub-5P	1840	3105	19,220
P-17	NA	Chassis only	—	—	4

DELUXE SIX — (6-CYL) SERIES P-18 — Standard wheelbase Plymouths comprised the P-18 line. Two styles — sedan and club coupe — were offered with the basic Deluxe level of trim, equipment and appointments. External identification points for all P-17 and P-18 Deluxes included, black rubber windshield surrounds; the lack of rear fender stone guards; and Deluxe front fender side scripts. The Deluxe level interior had painted finish on the dashboard and window garnish panels and plainer upholstery fabrics. Important features found on all Plymouths this year were woven asbestos clutch facing; wider Safety-Rim wheels; Safe-Guard hydraulic brakes; shock-proof steering; rigid box-type frame; removable fenders; splash-proof distributors; resistor spark plugs; Floating-Power engine mountings; new Sea-Leg shock absorbers; engine splash shields; counter-balanced trunk lid; rotary door latches; rust-proof sheet metal; full-automatic spark control; theft-proof ignition switch; Oilite gasoline filter; and oil bath air cleaner. An electrically-operated automatic choke was one additional technical innovation and a redesigned intake manifold was another.

DELUXE SIX SERIES

Series Number	Body/Style Number	Body Type & Seating	Factory Price	Shipping Weight	Production Total
P-18	NA	4-dr Sed-6P	1551	3059	61,021
P-18	NA	2-dr Clb Cpe-6P	1519	3034	25,687

SPECIAL DELUXE SIX — (6-CYL) — SERIES P-18 — The Special Deluxe Six represented the top level of trim for Plymouth again this year. Standard extras found with cars in this line included bright metal windshield and rear window trim moldings; mahogany grained dashboard and garnish moldings; richer upholstery fabrics; and special Deluxe front fenderside scripts. Only the standard wheelbase (P-18) models came with such trim and two exclusive body types were provided. The convertible had as standard equipment a power operated folding top, convertible top boot and genuine leather upholstery. The Special Deluxe station wagon had three seats with leather-like coverings. The rear two were completely removable. The wood-trimmed bodies (by U.S. Steel & Forging Co.) were constructed with an all-steel roof and steel tailgate with integral spare tire enclosure. The roof pillars and rear upper hatch were of real wood. Station wagon bumpers, taillamps and trim were unique to this particular model. All Plymouths had new "bull's eye" headlight lenses with magnifier spots in the center. Taillights were housed in small fins mounted on top of the rear fenders on all standard wheelbase models except the station wagon.

SPECIAL DELUXE SIX SERIES

Series Number	Body/Style Number	Body Type & Seating	Factory Price	Shipping Weight	Production Total
P-18	NA	4-dr Sed-6P	1629	3079	252,878
P-18	NA	2-dr Clb Cpe-6P	1603	3046	99,059
P-18	NA	2-dr Conv-6P	1982	3323	15,240
P-18	NA	4-dr Sta Wag-8P	2372	3341	3,443
P-18	NA	Chassis only	—	—	981

DELUXE SIX SERIES ENGINE: Inline. L-head Six. Cast iron block. Displacement; 217.8 cid. Bore and stroke 3.25 x 4.375 inches. Compression ratio; 7.0:1. Brake hp; 97 at 3600 rpm. Four main bearings. Solid valve lifters. Carburetor: Carter Type BB one-barrel Model D6H1.

1949 Plymouth, Special Deluxe two-door convertible, 6-cyl.

CHASSIS FEATURES: Wheelbase: (P-17 Series) 111 inches; (P-18 Series) 118.5 inches. Overall length: (P-17 Series) 185-5/16 inches: P-18 Series (191-12) inches. Front tread: (all models) 55 inches. Rear tread: (all models) 56 inches. Tires: (P-17 Series) 6.40 x 15: (P-18 Series) 6.70 x 15.

OPTIONS: Heater and defroster. Radio and antenna. Full disc wheelcovers. Wheel trim rings. White sidewall tires. License plate frames. Bumper guards. Grille guards. Dual windshield wipers, Deluxe. Dual horns, Deluxe. Dual sun visors. Deluxe. Chrome exhaust extension. Spotlight. Fog lamps. Back-up light. OSRV mirrors. Turn signals. Outside sunshade. Traffic light viewer. Seat covers. Stainless steel stone guards. Vent-T-shades. Lockable glove box. Deluxe lockable gas cap. Electric gas cap flipper. Three-speed manual transmission was standard. Heavy-duty air cleaner was optional at extra cost. Available rear axle gear ratios (various).

HISTORICAL FOOTNOTES: The Second Series 1949 Plymouth P-18 models were introduced in March, 1949 and the P-17 models appeared in dealer showrooms April, 1949. Model year production peaked at 508,000 units. Calendar year sales of 574,734 cars were recorded. D S. Eddins was the chief executive officer of the company this year. Plymouth retained its position as America's number three maker and held a 21.1 percent market share. The company was located at 6334 Lynch Road, Detroit, Mich. "The Great New Plymouth" was one of the slogans used to promote sales of the new 1949 postwar design. Production leaped 47.5 percent from 1948 and actually taxed Plymouth's ability to build enough cars. Toward the end of 1949, some cars were built with aluminum brake shoes due to a steel shortage. Some early versions of the all-new car had overly high riding heights. Shorter front coils and flatter rear leaf springs were adopted to lower them one and one-half inches. The Deluxe Suburban was a midyear model released in June 1949 and promoted as "the car with 101 uses." U.S. Body & Forging Co. continued to make the bodies for the "woodie" wagon, which began to decline in popularity.

1950 PLYMOUTH

1950 Plymouth, Deluxe two-door business coupe, 6-cyl (TVB)

DELUXE (SHORT WHEELBASE) SIX — (6-CYL) — SERIES P-19 — Styling changes for 1950 were of the bolt-on type. In addition to trim variations, they included new peaked rear fenders on most cars. This was a sheet metal revision, but one easily accomplished on Plymouths. The company heavily promoted the fact that rear fenders on all of its products were attached with bolts and readily replaceable in case of collision damage. Grille appearances were changed by reducing the number of horizontal blades. The two lower, thick bars remained, but the thin moldings were gone and a bowed upper bar was used. It had a trim molding right above it, with short extensions onto the fender edges. Plymouth lettering, a small

nose emblem and the 'Mayflower' mascot were also seen on the hood. Triple-fluted bumpers were replaced with smoother, plainer ones, but ribbed rocker panel moldings were retained. Horizontal spears decorated both the front and rear fendersides and chrome headlamp rings and vertical bumper guards were seen once more. The side of the front fender carried a Deluxe script. At the rear, smaller trunk emblems, handles and taillights were worn. Deluxe models did not have rear gravel guards and used rubber windshield and rear window surrounds. Rear windows were made slightly larger. In September, 1950, a fancy Special Suburban was offered. It had bright metal gravel guards and window frames, fancier upholstery and Special Suburban front fender scripts. Both Suburbans continued to use 1949 style rear fenders.

PLYMOUTH I.D. NUMBERS: Serial number on plate on left front door post is the only code used for identification/registration purposes. It consists of a Plymouth prefix 'P' and two-symbol series number (P-19, P-20). The four or more symbols following this are the production sequence number starting with 1001 at each factory. Motor number near front upper left side of block between first and second cylinders takes same format as serial number, but may not match. Motor number should not be used for identification. Motor numbers sometimes had suffixes: A=.020 inch cylinder overbore; B=.010 inch undersize journals and diamond-shaped symbol=.008 inch oversize tappet bore. Plymouth factory codes are: M=Detroit, Mich.; LA=Los Angeles, Calif.; E=Evansville, Ind. and SL=San Leandro, Calif. These codes do not appear in serial number. Chrysler did not use body style numbers at this time. Serial numbers for 1950 at each factory were as follows: P19 Deluxe: (M) 18041001-18119094; (E) 24012001-24035538; (LA) 28004001-28009848 and (SL) 28503501-28511177; P20 Deluxe (M) 15359501-15456084; (E) 22097001-22125803; (LA) 26030501-26035870 arid (SL) 26504001-26510569. P20 Special Deluxe: (M) 12384501-12627867 (E) 20367001-22125803; (LA) 26030501-26035870 and (SL) 26504001-26510569. Engine Numbers for the three series were: P20-1001-P204.

1950 Plymouth Deluxe two-door sedan, 6-cyl, JL

DELUXE SIX SERIES

Series Number	Body/Style Number	Body Type & Seating	Factory Price	Shipping Weight	Production Total
P-19	NA	2-dr Sed-6P	1492	2946	67,584
P-19	NA	2-dr Cpe-3P	1371	2872	16,861
P-19	NA	2-dr Sub-5P	1840	3116	34,457

SPECIAL DELUXE

Series Number	Body/Style Number	Body Type & Seating	Factory Price	Shipping Weight	Production Total
P-19	NA	2-dr Sub-5P	1946	31 55	Note 1

NOTE 1: Special Suburban included in the figure of 34,457 Suburbans built.
NOTE 2: One chassis only was also built.

DELUXE SIX — (6-CYL) — SERIES P-20 — Styling changes for 1950 Plymouth P-20 models paralleled those of the lower-priced cars, although some of the parts (such as grille members) were actually larger in size. They looked the same, but were not interchangeable between both series. Two models continued to be offered in the low level Deluxe trim line. Standard features included Deluxe front fender scripts; black rubber windshield and rear window moldings; painted dashboard and garnish moldings; and plainer upholstery fabrics. In base form, no rear fender gravel shields were worn. Unlike many other makers, Plymouth did not use black rubber stone guards on its cheaper models. However, chrome shields could be ordered as an option on all Plymouths. To increase rear vision, the rear window glass area was enlarged and now extended down to the rear deck region. Small hubcaps were standard equipment on Plymouth Deluxe automobiles.

DELUXE SIX SERIES

Series Number	Body/Style Number	Body Type & Seating	Factory Price	Shipping Weight	Production Total
P-20	NA	4-dr Sed-6P	1551	3068	87,871
P-20	NA	2-dr Clb Cpe-6P	1519	3040	53,890

SPECIAL DELUXE — (6-CYL) — SERIES P-20 — The Special Deluxe P-20 Series was Plymouth's high-dollar range. These cars had, as standard equipment, bright metal windshield and rear window frames; richer interior fabric choices; wood-grain finish on metal interior panels; and Special Deluxe front fender scripts. The convertible (officially described as a convertible club coupe) used leather upholstery and a power top riser mechanism and came with a simulated leather snap-on boot. The station wagon had the same features outlined for comparable 1949 models. In fact, its rear fenders and taillights were of the 1949 style. Factory photographs indicate Special Deluxes came with larger hubcaps, but not full wheelcovers. Trim rings are seen on most of these cars. Also, as in 1949, the large cars had slightly bigger tires. Other features found as regular equipment in the Special Deluxe models were armrests on both front doors; cigar lighter and clock.

SPECIAL DELUXE SIX SERIES

Series Number	Body/Style Number	Body Type & Seating	Factory Price	Shipping Weight	Production Total
P-20	NA	4-dr Sed-6P	1629	3072	234,084
P-20	NA	2-dr Clb Cpe-6P	1603	3041	99,361
P-20	NA	2-dr Conv-6P	1982	3295	12,697
P-20	NA	4-dr Sta Wag-8P	2372	3353	2,057
P-20	NA	Chassis only	NA	NA	2,091

DELUXE SIX SERIES ENGINE: Inline. L-head Six. Cast iron block. Displacement; 217.8 cid. Bore and stroke 3.25 x 4.375 inches. Compression ratio; 7.0:1. Brake hp; 97 at 3600 rpm. Four main bearings. Solid valve lifters. Carburetor: Carter Type BB one-barrel Model D6H1.

CHASSIS FEATURES: Wheelbase: (P-19 Series) 111 inches; (P-20 Series) 118-1/2 inches. Overall length: (P-19 Series) 186-1/2 inches, (P-20 Series) 192-5/8 inches. Front tread: (all models) 55-7/16 inches. Rear tread: (all models) 58-7/16 inches. Tires (P-19 Series) 6.40 x 15; (P-20 Series) 6.70 x 15.

OPTIONS: Heater and defroster. Radio and antenna. Full disc wheelcovers. Wheel trim rings. White sidewall tires. License plate frames. Bumper guards. Grille guards. Dual windshield wipers, Deluxe. Dual horns, Deluxe. Dual sun visors. Deluxe. Chrome exhaust extension. Spotlight. Fog lamps. Back-up light. OSRV mirrors. Turn signals. Outside sunshade. Traffic light viewer. Seat covers. Stainless steel stone guards. Vent-T-shades. Lockable glove box. Deluxe. Lockable gas cap. Electric gas cap flipper. Three-speed manual transmission was standard. Heavy-duty air cleaner was available at extra cost. Available rear axle gear ratios (various).

1950 Plymouth, Special Deluxe four-door station wagon, 6-cyl (JL)

HISTORICAL FOOTNOTES: The 1950 Plymouths were introduced Jan. 12, 1950. Model year production peaked at 590.000 units. Calendar year sales of 573,166 cars were recorded. D.S. Eddins was the chief executive officer of the company this year. Plymouth was still America's third largest automaker and held a 15.9 percent market share. Plymouth sales grew less than half a percent as the postwar boom in demand for autos subsided. A 100-day shutdown due to a labor strike didn't help either. The 1950 models were promoted as "The Beautifully New Plymouth." L.L. "Tex" Colbert succeeded K.T. Keller as president of Chrysler Corp. in 1950. Keller became chairman of the board. This would be the last year for Plymouth woodie wagons with bodies by U.S. Body & Forging Co.

1951 PLYMOUTH

CONCORD — (6-CYL) — SERIES P-22 — The new Concord P-22 Series played the same role, in the Plymouth lineup, as the short wheelbase Deluxe had in the past. Styling changes looked more extensive than they actually were. The sheetmetal was nicely re-worked to create a more modern look without major re-tooling. The hood contour was lower, smoother and broader. Front fenders sloped downward at the front. The grille had a full-width, bow-shaped upper bar and a horizontal center blade, which was also slightly bowed. A trio of vertical elements looked more like misplaced bumper guards. Horizontal parking lights were set into vertical extensions of the upper bar. The full wraparound bumper was of more massive design and had two vertical guards. A plate, with the word Plymouth stamped into it, stretched above the grille. 'Mayflower' nose emblems and hood mascots appeared. Additional trim included front and rear fender moldings; rocker sill strips; black rubber windshield frame; new hubcaps; upper beltline trim; and Concord fender scripts. The Concord Suburban was now a two-seat economy station wagon, with spare tire carried inside. The Concord Savoy replaced the Special Deluxe Suburban and came with large hubcaps; chrome gravel guards; bright metal window frames; extra trim moldings; and special two-tone luxury upholstery. Standard equipment for the Concord Savoy included front and rear armrests; rear passenger assist straps; rear seat side storage compartments; and sliding central windows. Savoy nameplates were seen on the front fenders. This was now the company's fanciest station wagon type vehicle, since the 'Woodie' was dropped from the P-23 Series

1951 Plymouth, Concord two-door sedan, 6-cyl

1951 Plymouth Savoy two-door Suburban, 6-cyl, JL

PLYMOUTH I.D. NUMBERS: Serial number on plate on left front door post is the only code used for identification/registration purposes. It consists of a Plymouth prefix 'P' and two-symbol series number (P-22, P-23, etc.). The four or more symbols following this are the production sequence number starting with 1001 at each factory. Motor number near front upper left side of block between first and second cylinders takes same format as serial number, but may not match. Motor number should not be used for identification. Motor numbers sometimes had suffixes: A=.020 inch cylinder overbore; B=.010 inch undersize journals and diamond-shaped symbol=.008 inch oversize tappet bore. Plymouth factory codes are: M=Detroit, Mich.; LA=Los Angeles, Calif.; E=Evansville, Ind. and SL=San Leandro, Calif. These codes do not appear in serial number. Chrysler did not use body style numbers at this time. Serial numbers for 1951 at each factory were as follows: P-22 Deluxe Concord: (M) 18126001-18192309; (E) 24042001-24056628; (LA) 28011001-28015486 and (SL) 28513001-28518903. P23 Deluxe Cambridge: (M) 15460001-15577561; (E) 22132001-22159468; (LA) 26040001-26045476 and (SL) 26512001-26517909. P-23 Special Deluxe Cranbrook: (M) 12635001-12906467; (E) 20435001-20482924; (LA) 25112001-25124987; (SL) 25531001-25545618. Engine Numbers for all three series were P23-1001 and up.

CONCORD SERIES

Series Number	Body/Style Number	Body Type & Seating	Factory Price	Shipping Weight	Production Total
DELUXE TRIM					
P-22	NA	2-dr Sed-6P	1673	2969	49,139
P-22	NA	2-dr Cpe-3P	1537	2919	14,255
P-22	NA	2-dr Sub-5P	2064	3124	76,520
SPECIAL SAVOY' TRIM					
P-22	NA	2-dr Sub-5P	2182	3184	Note 1

NOTE 1: Production of Savoy Special Suburban included in 76,520 Suburbans.
NOTE 2: Totals cover both 1951 and 1952 Series P-22 Plymouths.

1951 Plymouth, Cambridge two-door club coupe, 6-cyl (TVB)

CAMBRIDGE — (6-CYL) — SERIES P-23 — The new Cambridge models played the same role in the Plymouth lineup as the former standard wheelbase Deluxes. Comparable styles were available, too. The word Cambridge appeared on fendersides, above the horizontal trim spear. All 1951 Plymouths came with interior colors selected to match the exterior finish. A completely new dash panel harmonized with other appointments and housed conveniently positioned controls. Outstanding new features included, electric windshield wipers; chair high seats; downdraft carburetors. Synchro-Silent gears, a higher compression six-cylinder engine and Safety-Flow Ride. This latter enhancement claimed to utilize hydraulics to create "cushions of oil", that gave a smooth ride on the roughest roads.

Series Number	Body/Style Number	Body Type & Seating	Factory Price	Shipping Weight	Production Total
P-23	NA	4-dr Sed-6P	1739	3104	179,417
P-23	NA	2-dr Clb Cpe-6P	1703	3059	101,784

NOTE 1: Totals cover both 1951 and 1952 Plymouth P-23 Series.

CRANBROOK — (6-CYL) — SERIES P-23 — The 1951 Cranbrook models played the starring role in the annual Plymouth revue. They replaced the former Special Deluxe line and embodied similar attributes. Block letters spelled out the model designation at the upper, trailing front fender area. A new body style was added in this range. The Belvedere two-door convertible hardtop had the fashionable pillarless 'hardtop convertible' look. It featured a smoothly wrapped around three-piece backlight: wedge shaped rear side windows: cloth and simulated leather upholstery and special Belvedere nameplates on the front fendersides. A convertible was another exclusive offering in Cranbrook level trim, but the station wagon was gone. Plymouth's classiest utility model this season was the Savoy in the short wheelbase P-22 Series.

1951 Plymouth, Belvedere two-door hardtop coupe, 6-cyl (TVB)

CRANBROOK SERIES

Series Number	Body/Style Number	Body Type & Seating	Factory Price	Shipping Weight	Production Total
P-23	NA	4-dr Sed-6P	1826	3109	388,735
P-23	NA	2-dr Clb Cpe-6P	1796	3074	126,725
P-23	NA	2-dr HT Cpe-6P	2114	3182	51,266
P-23	NA	2-dr Conv-6P	2222	3294	15,650
P-23	NA	Chassis Only	NA	NA	4,171

NOTE 1: Totals cover both 1951 and 1952 Plymouth P-23 models.

DELUXE SIX SERIES ENGINE: Inline. L-head Six. Cast iron block. Displacement; 217.8 cid. Bore and stroke 3.25 x 4.375 inches. Compression ratio; 7.0:1. Brake hp: 97 at 3600 rpm. Four main bearings. Solid valve lifters. Carburetor: Carter Type BB one-barrel Model D6H1.

CHASSIS FEATURES: Wheelbase (Concord) 111 inches. (Cambridge, Cranbrook) 118-1/2 inches. Overall length (Concord) 188-1/8 inches. (Cambridge, Cranbrook) 193-7/8 inches. Front tread (all models) 55-7/8 inches Rear tread (all models) 58-7/16 inches. Tires (Concord) 6.40 x 15. (Cambridge, Cranbrook) 6.70 x 15.

OPTIONS: Heater and defroster. Radio and antenna. Wheel trim rings. Full disc wheelcovers. Solex tinted safety glass. Bumper guards, Grille guards. Spotlight. Fog light. Outside rearview mirror. White sidewall tires. External sunshade. Traffic light viewer. Rear fender chrome gravel shields. License plate frames. Seat covers. Rear seat speaker. Glove compartment lock. Electric clock. Special body colors. Mudguard flaps. Three-speed manual transmission was standard. Heavy-duty air cleaner was optional at extra cost. Available rear axle gear ratios (P-22) 3:73:1 or 3.9:1. (P-23) 1 or 4.1:11.

HISTORICAL FOOTNOTES: The 1951 Plymouths were introduced Jan. 12, 1951 and the Belvedere hardtops appeared in dealer showrooms March 31. 1951. Model year production peaked at 576,000 units. Calendar year sales of 620,870 cars were recorded. D.S. Eddins was the chief executive officer of the company this year. On a calendar year basis Plymouth built 11,180 convertibles, 31,360 hardtops and 45,300 station wagons between Jan. 1, 1951 and the same date a year later. These would be very close to model year figures since the model year at this time ran from Jan. 12, 1951 to November, 1951, after which date production of cars built to 1952 specifications ensued. Overdrive transmission was not available in 1951. Plymouth set an all-time production record in 1951 and was the only auto manufacturer to do so that season. The company had an 11.63 percent market share and was responsible for 10.7 percent of all new car registrations. Plymouth's business climbed 8.2 percent in 1951, despite an overall decline in auto sales throughout the industry. Korean War material restrictions limited the supply of some parts. The Ghia-built Plymouth XX-500 dream car was made in Italy this year. It had futuristic features including slab sides, a one-piece curved windshield and fastback roof. It went on the auto show circuit in the mid-'50s. Plymouth also received a government contract to build seaplane hulls for the Grumman Albatross at its Evansville, Ind. plant.

1952 PLYMOUTH

CONCORD — (6-CYL) — SERIES P-22 — Due to the outbreak of war in Korea, Plymouth continued its 1951 models into 1952, with only surface changes. The emblem on the nose of the cars was slightly redesigned. Signature style chrome script plates were used to adorn the front fenders as model identification trim. At the rear the manufacturer's nameplate was repositioned from above the trunk emblem to a relief cut into the top of the emblem. Prices were increased, with permission from government agencies, but the series nomenclature was unchanged. Consequently, output figures for 1951 and 1952 Plymouths are recorded as a single total. Overdrive transmission was a Plymouth technical innovation this season. America's number three maker had not offered this feature on previous postwar models. By the end of the run, nearly 51,670 cars had this option installed. Neither automatic or semi-automatic transmissions were yet available in Plymouth automobiles. The short wheelbase Concord was dropped from production in October, 1952.

1952 Plymouth, Concord two-door business coupe, 6-cyl

PLYMOUTH I.D. NUMBERS: Serial number on plate on left front door post is the only code used for identification/registration purposes. It consists of a Plymouth prefix 'P' and two-symbol series number (P-15, P-17, etc.). The four or more symbols following this are the production sequence number starting with 1001 at each factory. Motor number near front upper left side of block between first and second cylinders takes same format as serial number, but may not match. Motor number should not be used for identification. Motor numbers sometimes had suffixes: A=.020 inch cylinder overbore; B=.010 inch undersize journals and diamond-shaped symbol=.008 inch oversize tappet bore. Plymouth factory codes are: M=Detroit, Mich.; LA=Los Angeles, Calif.; E=Evansville, Ind. and SL=San Leandro, Calif. These codes do not appear in serial number. Chrysler did not use body style numbers at this time. Serial numbers for 1952 at each factory changed as follows: Concord: (M) 18192501-18223600; (E) 24056701-24063833; (LA) 28015701-2801555 and (SL) 28519101-28522352. Cambridge; (MA) 15577801-1566660; (E) 22159601-22181520; (LA) 26045701-26049991 and (SL) 26518201-26523546. Cranbrook: (M) 12906701-13066238: (E) 20485001-20516075; (LA) 25125301-25134190 and (SL) 25546101-25555957. Engine Numbers for all series were P23-1001 and up.

1952 Plymouth, Savoy two-door Suburban, 6-cyl

CONCORD SERIES

Series Number	Body/Style Number	Body Type & Seating	Factory Price	Shipping Weight	Production Total
DELUXE TRIM					
P 22	NA	2-dr Sed-6P	1753	2959	Note 1
P 22	NA	2-dr Cpe-3P	1610	2893	Note 1
P 22	NA	2-dr Sub-5P	2163	3145	Note 1
SPECIAL 'SAVOY' TRIM					
P-22	NA	2-dr Sub-5P	2287	3165	Note 1

NOTE 1: See 1951 Plymouth production totals. Figures for both years are lumped together with no annual breakout available

CAMBRIDGE — (6-CYL) — SERIES P-23 — The 1952 Cambridge was a mildly face-lifted version of the previous comparable model. The only variations between both years were number codes; prices and redesigned nameplates, plus new hood and trunk emblems. It was also hard, to buy a Plymouth equipped with optional whitewall tires this year. Raw material supplies were greatly diminished, due to restrictions imposed during the Korean conflict. Despite National Production Administration (NPA) ceilings on auto manufacturing during the Korean War, Plymouth continued as the output leader among Chrysler Corp. divisions. The company produced approximately 50 percent of all Chrysler automobiles built this year.

CAMBRIDGE SERIES

Series Number	Body/Style Number	Body Type & Seating	Factory Price	Shipping Weight	Production Total
P-23	NA	4-dr Sed-6P	1822	3068	Note 1
P-23	NA	2-dr Clb Cpe-6P	1784	3030	Note 1

NOTE 1: See 1951 Plymouth production totals. Figures for both years are lumped together, with no annual breakout available.

CRANBROOK — (6-CYL) — SERIES P-23 — As is the case with other 1952 Plymouths, the Cranbrook models were merely a continuation of the basic 1951 product for another year The only annual changes were new model identification scripts; redesigned hood mascots and slightly revised trim at the front and rear. Even the P-23 series designation was carried through again. The Belvedere, however, received some extra attention in that its identification badge was repositioned to the rear roof pillar and a different type of two-tone finish was employed. The top color, with this paint scheme, extended onto the rear quarter sheetmetal. While the front and sides of the body were done in one tone, the roof, rear deck lid and deck lid surrounding area were painted a second shade, which contrasted with the main color. Solex tinted glass was a new option available on all 1952 Plymouths.

1952 Plymouth, Cranbrook two-door convertible, 6-cyl

CRANBROOK SERIES

Series Number	Body/Style Number	Body Type & Seating	Factory Price	Shipping Weight	Production Total
P-23	NA	4-dr Sed-6P	1914	3088	Note 1
P-23	NA	2-dr Clb Cpe-6P	1883	3046	Note 1
P-23	NA	2-dr HT Cpe-6P	2216	3105	Note 1
P-23	NA	2-dr Conv-6P	2329	3256	Note 1

NOTE 1: See 1951 Plymouth production totals. Figures for both years are lumped together, with no annual breakout available.

CONCORD SERIES ENGINE: Inline. L head Six. Cast iron block. Displacement: 217.8 cid. Bore and stroke: 3:25 x 4:375 inches. Compression ratio: 7.0:1. Brake hp: 97 at 3600 rpm. Four main bearings Solid valve lifters. Carburetor: Carter Type BB one-barrel Model D6H2.

CHASSIS FEATURES: Wheelbase: (Concord) 111 inches; (Cambridge, Cranbrook) 118112 inches. Overall length: (Concord, Cambridge) 118-1/2 inches; (Cranbrook) 1937/8 inches. Front tread: (all models) 55-7/8 inches. Rear tread: (all models) 58-7/16 inches Tires: (Concord sedan and coupe) 6.40 x 15: (Cranbrook) 6.70 x 1 5.

OPTIONS: Heater and defroster. Radio and antenna. Wheel trim rings. Full disc wheel covers, Solex tinted safety glass. Bumper guards, Grille guards. Spotlight. Fog light Outside rearview mirror. White sidewall tires. External sunshade. Traffic light viewer. Rear fender chrome gravel shields. License plate frames. Seat covers. Rear seat speaker. Glove compartment lock. Electric clock. Special body colors. Mudguard flaps. Three-speed manual transmission was standard. Overdrive transmission ($102). Heavy-duty air cleaner was available at extra cost. Available rear axle gear ratios: (P22) 3.73: 1 or 3.9:1; (P23) 3.9:1 or 4:1.1.

HISTORICAL FOOTNOTES: The 1952 Plymouths were introduced Jan. 4, 1952. Sales went down 23.74 percent, largely due to the outbreak of fighting in Korea. Model year production peaked at 368,000 units. Calendar year sales of 474,836 cars were recorded. D.S. Eddins was the chief executive officer of the company this year. On a calendar year basis, Plymouth manufactured 21,290 Belvederes, 4,269 convertibles and 35,885 Suburbans between Jan. 1, 1952 and the same date a year later. Some of these were 1953 models, which entered production in the fall of 1952, earlier than usual. Overdrive transmission was a new option this year and was installed in 61,710 Plymouths built to 1952 specifications. The 111 inch wheelbase Concord line was dropped in October, 1952. Plymouth bodies were built by Briggs Manufacturing Co. Plymouths were assembled at Detroit, Mich., Evansville, Ind., Los Angeles, and San Leandro, Calif. The Detroit plant had 1,393,497 square feet under one roof and was a one-half mile long. The National Production Administration (NPA) established production quotas this year, based on Korean war materials allotments. Aircraft hulls were constructed, under government contract, in the Evansville factory with the first one delivered late in 1952.

1953 PLYMOUTH

1953 Plymouth, Cambridge two-door business coupe, 6-cyl

CAMBRIDGE — (6-CYL) — SERIES P24-1 — The short wheelbase Concord line was not marketed after 1952. The Cambridge line was the base offering and used 4-1/2 inch shorter stance, shared with all 1953 Plymouths. The company celebrated its 25th anniversary this season by introducing all-new styling. Changes included a more modern body with one-piece windshield. Detachable rear fenders were finally abandoned, with stamped flairs decorating the front and rear quarter panels. The main grille bar and parking lights formed a horizontal V-shape. The 'Mayflower' hood ornament was fully redesigned. A new hood emblem incorpo-

rated the name Plymouth and the glove compartment was placed in the center of the instrument panel. The fuel filler pipe was located below the deck lid on the left side. Cambridge identification features included black rubber windshield frames. Cambridge front tender scripts on passenger cars and Suburban front fender script on station wagons. These cars had no side spears, no gravel shields, no tail ornaments and stationary rear vent windows. Small hubcaps were standard equipment. A new feature was 'one-third/two-third' type front seat. which was used in all two-door models. New equipment features included splay-mounted rear leaf springs: Oriflow shock absorbers, cyclebond brake linings and floating engine oil intake.

PLYMOUTH I.D. NUMBERS: Serial number on plate on left door post. Serial number starts with prefix (P=Plymouth) and three digit series code 24-1; 24-2 followed by sequential production number starting at 1001 at each factory, Factory codes M=Detroit, Mich.; LA=Los Angeles, Calif.; E=Evansville, Ind. and SL=San Leandro, Calif. do not appear in serial number. Motor numbers near front upper left of block between cylinders one and two. Motor number resembles serial number, but may not match. Motor numbers should not be used for identification. Prefix symbols changed to P24-1=Cambridge and P24-2=Cranbrook. Serial Numbers at each factory were: Cambridge: (M) 13070001-13505308; (E) 2052001-20657000, (LA) 25136001-25161846, and (SL) 25560001-25588345. Cranbrook: same number range as Cambridge. Engine Numbers for both Series were P24-1001 through P24-628721.

CAMBRIDGE SERIES

Series Number	Body/Style Number	Body Type & Seating	Factory Price	Shipping Weight	Production Total
P24-1	NA	4-dr Sed-6P	1745	2983	93,585
P24-1	NA	2-dr Clb Cpe-6P	1707	2943	1,050
P24-1	NA	2-dr Bus Cpe-3P	1598	2888	6,975
P24-1	NA	2-dr Sub-6P	2044	3129	43,545
P24-1	NA	2-dr Sed-6P	—	—	56,800

1953 Plymouth, Cranbrook, four-door sedan, 6-cyl

CRANBROOK — (6-CYL) — SERIES P24-2 — Cranbrooks shared all 1953 styling changes such as the new sheet metal and grille design, but had a higher level of trim and appointments. Identification points included chrome windshield moldings; chrome sweep spears on front and rear fenders; chrome gravel shields; chrome 'fishtail' ornaments; operable vent wings in all doors and special front fender nameplates. The signature scripts on passenger cars said Cranbrook or Belvedere, while those on the Suburban station wagon read Savoy. The Belvedere was marketed as a luxury level, two-door pillarless hardtop. Its special features included a band of chrome and medallions on the rear roof pillar, plus higher grade interior trim. The Savoy also had special upholstery and interior appointments to set it apart from the basic Suburban. The convertible, as usual, had leather grained trim; power top riser; special door panels and a new, zip-out pliable plastic rear window. Plymouth introduced Hy-Drive, a three-speed manual transmission with torque converter that eliminated the need to use the clutch except when changing between reverse and forward gears. It was introduced in March, 1953. By June, 3,000 cars per week were being built with this feature. On March 23, 1953, prices on all models were slashed an average of $100. This helped spur an all-time sales record for the model year.

CRANBROOK SERIES

Series Number	Body/Style Number	Body Type & Seating	Factory Price	Shipping Weight	Production Total
P24-2	NA	4-dr Sed-6P	1853	3023	298,976
P24-2	NA	2-dr Clb Cpe-6P	1823	2971	92,102
P24-2	NA	2-dr Belv HT-6P	2044	3027	35,185
P24-2	NA	2-dr Savoy Sub-6P	2187	3170	12,089
P24-2	NA	2-dr Conv Cpe-6P	2200	3193	6,301
P2402	NA	Chassis only	—	—	843

NOTE 1: 2,250 Belvedere sedans built in addition to above.
NOTE 2: 760 Belvedere sport coupes built in addition to above.

1953 Plymouth Cranbrook Belvedere two-door hardtop, 6-cyl. JL.

ENGINE: Inline. L-head Six. Cast iron block. Displacement: 217.8 cid. Bore and stroke: 3.24 x 4.375. Compression ratio: 7.1:1. Brake hp: 100 at 3600 rpm. Four main bearings. Solid valve lifters. Carburetor: Carter Type BB one-barrel Model D6H2.

CHASSIS FEATURES: Wheelbase (all models) 114 inches. Overall length: (all models) 189 1/8 inches. Front tread: (all models) 55 7/8 inches. Rear tread: (all models) 58 7/16 inches. Tires (all models 6.70 x 15.

OPTIONS: Heater and defroster ($45). Radio ($100). Tinted glass ($31). Directional signals ($17). Windshield washer ($11). Back-up lights. Chrome wheel discs. Chrome wire wheels ($293) Painted wire wheels. Wire spoke wheelcovers, set ($99). White sidewall tires. Grille guard. Bumper wing guards. Front fender molding. Cambridge. Rear fender molding, Cambridge. Chrome grille molding. Cambridge. Chrome gravel shields. Chrome exhaust extension. Taxicab package. Wheel trim rings. Outside sunshade. Traffic light viewer. Spotlight. Fog lamps. Seat covers. License plate frames. Three-speed manual transmission was standard. Overdrive transmission ($98). Semi-automatic transmission ($146). Available rear axle gear ratios: (standard) 3.73:1; (overdrive) 4.10:1.

HISTORICAL FOOTNOTES: The 1953 Plymouths were introduced Nov. 20, 1952 and the XX-500 prototype appeared in dealer auto shows March 14-22, 1953. Sales increased 39.5 percent during Plymouth's 25th anniversary year and the eight millionth Plymouth was made in September. Model year production peaked at 636,000 units. Calendar year sales of 662,515 cars were recorded. J.P. Mansfield was the chief executive officer of the Co. this year. Hy-Drive transmission and Sychro Silent Drive were introduced. A total of 600,447 Plymouths were registered in calendar 1953. On March 23, 1953, Plymouth reduced prices on its models by an average $100. The 1953 production totals marked a new, all-time high for Plymouth Div. Chrysler purchased the Briggs Manufacturing Co. on Dec. 29, 1953. Hy-Drive was first introduced in March, 1953. By July, 25 percent of all Plymouths being produced were ordered with Hy-Drive. The Detroit factory accounted for 70 percent of Plymouth's total production. During the calendar year 9,900 Plymouths were built with power steering (most likely all being 1954 models). For the model year, 109,300 Plymouths had overdrive attachments. Plymouth built its last Grumman Albatross.

1954 PLYMOUTH

1954 Plymouth, Belvedere two-door hardtop, 6-cyl

PLAZA — (6-CYL) — SERIES P25-1 — The Plaza line was the base Plymouth series for 1954. Annual styling revisions amounted to a minor facelift over the previous season, although model offerings were substantially rearranged. The word Plymouth now appeared at the center of the main horizontal grille bar, with wraparound chrome moldings on each side. The headlights were given a recessed look by widening the chrome plated surrounds. Circular front parking lamps were used and mounted at the outboard ends of the lower horizontal grille bar. Plaza models used black rubber gravel shields and had Plaza front fender scripts. Power steering was introduced as a new option, but was used in only about 20,000 cars built in this calendar year. Some of these were 1955 models, manufactured in the fall of 1954. On Feb. 26, 1954, fully-automatic PowerFlite transmission was added to the optional equipment list. Plymouth buyers could then order cars with three-speed manual, overdrive, semi-automatic or automatic transmission. A total of about 75,000 of all 1954 Plymouths came with the latter unit attached. The Plaza four-door sedan had stationary rear ventipanes. Two-door styles featured the 'one-third/two-third' type front seat.

PLYMOUTH I.D. NUMBERS: Serial number on plate on left door post. Serial number starts with prefix 'P' for Plymouth and two symbol series code (P25-1=Plaza; P25-2=Savoy and P25-3=Belvedere) followed by sequential production number starting at 1001 at each factory, Factory codes M=Detroit, Mich.; LA=Los Angeles, Calif.; E=Evansville, Ind. and SL=San Leandro, Calif. do not appear in serial number. Motor numbers near front upper left of block between cylinders one and two. Motor number resembles serial number, but may not match. Motor numbers should not be used for identification. Serial numbers at each factory were: (M) 13506001-13829336; (E) 20658001-20739829; (LA) 25163001-25175377; (SL) 25590001-25606284. Engine Numbers P-25-1001 thru P25-243000 were used until Feb. 25, 1954. Engine Numbers past this date were P25-24300L to 454271. The three series were manufactured in mixed production fashion and used the same range of serial and engine numbers.

PLAZA SERIES

Series Number	Body/Style Number	Body Type & Seating	Factory Price	Shipping Weight	Production Total
P25-1	NA	4-dr Sed-6P	1745	3004	43,077
P25-1	NA	2-dr Clb Cpe-6P	1707	2943	27,976
P25-1	NA	2-dr Bus Cpe-3P	1598	2889	5,000
P25-1	NA	2-dr Sub-6P	2044	3122	35,937
P25-1	NA	Chassis only	—	—	1
P25-1	NA	2-dr Clb Cpe-6P			1,275

SAVOY — (6-CYL) — SERIES P25-2 — The Savoy nameplate changed from a model to a series designation this year. It was used to identify Plymouth's middle-priced line and also signified a higher level of trim and appointments. Identification features of the Savoy Included full-length side body moldings; newly designed chrome gravel shields; and Savoy signatures placed on the cowl side area of front fenders. Bright metal windshield frames replaced the black rubber type used with Plazas. The Savoy interior was a bit fancier, too, but most of its extras qualified as exterior trim. The highest grade fabrics and furnishings were reserved for

Belvederes. A surprise was the fact that Suburbans were not normally provided with Savoy level trim, even though the name had been taken from the fancy all-steel station wagon model. However, the Chrysler Historical Archives indicate that a small number of Savoy Suburbans were manufactured,

SAVOY SERIES

Series Number	Body/Style Number	Body Type & Seating	Factory Price	Shipping Weight	Production Total
P25-2	NA	4-dr Sed-6P	1853	3036	139,383
P25-2	NA	2-dr Clb Sed-6P	1815	2986	25,396
P25-2	NA	2-dr Clb Cpe-6P	1823	2982	30,700
P25-2	NA	2-dr Sub	—	—	450
P25-2	NA	Chassis only	—	—	3,588

1954 Plymouth, Belvedere two-door Suburban, 6-cyl JL

BELVEDERE — (6-CYL) — SERIES P25-3 — The Belvedere nameplate no longer identified only the two-door pillarless hardtop. This designation was now used to label a four model lineup including this style, a sedan, a convertible and a fancy all-steel Suburban station wagon. Identification points included all extras found on Savoys, plus full wheel discs; chrome 'fish tall' rear fender top fins; full-length rocker sill moldings; and Belvedere front fender scripts. The hardtop and sedan also featured roof pillar medallions. The convertible had similar medallions behind the gravel shields and the station wagon (Suburban) had fin-less rear fenders, making each model slightly distinctive. Dressier interior furnishings were used on all of these cars. They included richer combinations of fabrics; extra armrests; special dashboard trim; Deluxe steering wheel; clock; and fancier garnish moldings. In the spring, a special trim option was released for Belvedere hardtops and convertibles. It added a narrow fin-shaped chrome molding below the side window openings, with the area above finished in contrasting color. When the production of 1954 Plymouths ended, on Aug. 20, 1954, the Hy-Drive semi-automatic transmission was dropped.

BELVEDERE SERIES

Series Number	Body/Style Number	Body Type & Seating	Factory Price	Shipping Weight	Production Total
P25-3	NA	4-dr Sed-6P	1933	3050	106,601
P25-3	NA	2-dr HT Cpe-6P	2125	3038	25,592
P25-3	NA	2-dr Conv Cpe-6P	2281	3273	6,900
P25-3	NA	2-dr Sub-6P	2268	3186	9,241
P25-3	NA	Chassis only	—	—	2,031

ENGINES:

Inline. L-head Six. Cast iron block. Displacement: 217.8 cid. Bore and stroke: 3.24 x 4.375 inches. Compression ratio: 7.1:1. Brake hp: 100 at 3600 rpm. Four main bearings. Solid valve lifters. Carburetor: Carter Type BB one-barrel Model D6H2.

Inline. L-head Six. Cast iron block. Displacement: 230.2 cid. Bore and stroke: 3.25 x 4.625 inches. Compression ratio: 7.25:1. Brake hp: 110 at 3600 rpm. Four main bearings. Solid valve lifters. Carburetor: Carter Type BB one-barrel Model BB-D6H2. (This 'high head' engine was optional on cars late in 1954.)

CHASSIS FEATURES: Wheelbase: (all models) 114 inches. Overall length: (Suburban) 190-1/4 inches; (passenger cars) 193-1/2 inches. Front tread: (all models) 55-7/8 inches. Rear tread: (all models) 58-7/16 inches. Tires: (all models) 6.70 x 15.

OPTIONS: Power steering ($139.75). Radio ($82.50). Heater ($56.25). Directional signals ($13.30). Whitewall tires, exchange ($26.65). "Egg Cup" electric clock. Wire wheelcovers ($59.15). Full wheel discs ($14). Wire wheels, chrome ($279.50). Wire wheels, painted ($102.15). Two-tone paint. Back-up lights. Bumper wing guards. Grille guard. Wheel trim rings. Seat covers. Vent-A-Shades ($21). Wood weave door trim (convertible and Sport Coupe) ($37.65). Solex tinted glass ($37.65). Continental spare wheel mount ($129). Outside sun visor. Traffic lamp viewer. Deluxe trim, four-door ($108). Custom trim, four-door ($188). Power brakes ($37). Three-speed manual transmission was standard. Overdrive transmission ($97.55). Semi-automatic transmission ($145.80); PowerFlite fully automatic transmission ($189). Six-cylinder 230.2 cid 110 hp 'high head' engine. Available rear axle gear ratios: (standard) 3.73:1; (overdrive) 4.10:1 and (HyDrive) 3.7 3:1.

HISTORICAL FOOTNOTES: The 1954 Plymouths were introduced Oct. 15, 1953 and the Belvedere appeared in dealer showrooms the same date. Model year production peaked at 433,000 units. Calendar year sales of 399,900 cars were recorded. J.P. Mansfield was the chief executive officer of the Co. this year. Robert Anderson, who later became Chrysler Div. head officer, was Plymouth's chief engineer. Chrysler's Chelsea, Mich. proving grounds opened this year. When it was dedicated in June, one of the special cars seen was a Plymouth Belvedere hardtop with a gas turbine engine. On March 15, 1954, power brakes were introduced as a Plymouth option at $36.55. A total of 61,000 1954 models had PowerFlite fully-automatic transmission and 75,000 had Hy-Drive semi-automatic attachments. Hy-Drive was dropped at the end of the 1954 model run. Production of 1954 models stopped on Aug. 13, 1954. Factory dream cars seen this year included the Plymouth-Ghia Explorer.

1955 PLYMOUTH

PLAZA — (6-CYL/V-8) — SERIES P26/P27 — The 1955 Plymouths were completely restyled with new longer, lower bodies. All sheet metal was new and more modern. The upper edge of the body line ran, in a straight line, from front to rear. A sweeping roofline was supported by wraparound glass at both ends. The side panels were slab shaped. Hood and deck were flatter. At the front, the fenders hooded the single headlamps. The grille cavity was highlighted by two wing-shaped, horizontal blades that were joined, at the center, by a ribbed horizontal tie-bar. The Plaza represented the low-priced line, but could be had with either six-cylinder or V-8 power plants. No extraneous trim appeared on this series. Chrome ornamentation was limited to a large signature script, placed ahead of the front wheel opening. A fin shaped hood ornament was used. Windshield framing was in black rubber. Cars with V-8 power had V-shaped emblems attached to the hood and trunk. A Plymouth badge was seen on the hood. At the rear, vertical taillights were set into the backwards pointing fender tips. Buyers were able to order side spear moldings as optional equipment after midyear. These moldings ran from below the taillight to the middle of the front door and then slanted forward, hitting the rocker sill at the door's front lower corner. Sales features included many new items such as tubeless tires; follow-thru starter; push-button door handles and a dashboard mounted automatic gear shift selector. Plainer-looking cloth upholstery was standard in the Plaza, but vinyl combinations were available at slight extra cost. A business coupe was still provided in this model range. It used the two-door sedan body shell with only a front seat and stowage space in the rear compartment. Suspended type control pedals were another 1955 innovation.

1955 Plymouth, Plaza four-door sedan, 6-cyl (AA)

PLYMOUTH I.D. NUMBERS: Serial number on plate on left door post. Serial number starts with prefix (P=Plymouth) and series code (P26=six-cylinder; P27=V-8) followed by sequential production number starting at 1001 at each factory. Factory codes M=Detroit, Mich.; LA=Los Angeles, Calif.; E=Evansville, Ind. and SL=San Leandro, Calif. do not appear in serial number. Six-cylinder motor numbers near front upper left of block between cylinders one and two. V-8 motor numbers on flat surface at front of block between two cylinder heads. Motor number resembles serial number, but may not match. Motor numbers should not be used for identification. Serial Numbers at each factory were kept according to the type of engine and changed as follows: P26 six-cylinder: (M) 13835001-14119261; (E) 20745001-20819358 and (LA) 25180001-25200109. P27 V-8: (M) 15630001-15871476; (E) 22118201-22244749 and (LA) 26524001-26549993 and 26500001-26500290. Engine Numbers were as follows: P26-1001 to 378770, P27-1001 to 60200 and P27-60201 to 298919.

PLAZA SERIES

Series Number	Body/Style Number	Body Type & Seating	Factory Price	Shipping Weight	Production Total
P26/27	NA	4-dr Sed	1756/1859	3129/3246	84,156
P26/27	NA	2-dr Clb Sed-6P	1713/1816	3089/3202	53,610
P26/27	NA	2-dr Bus Cpe-3P	1614	3025	4,882
P26/27	NA	2-dr Sub-6P	2052/2155	3261/3389	31,788
P26/27	NA	4-dr Sub-6P	2133/2237	3282/3408	15,442

NOTE 1: Data above slash for six-cylinder/below for V-8.
NOTE 2: The three-passenger business coupe came only with six-cylinder power.

SAVOY — (6-CYL/V-8) — SERIES P26/P27 — The Savoy was Plymouth's mid-price model range in 1955. Standard equipment included slightly dressier interiors; chrome windshield frames; bright metal roof gutter rail; chrome trim on the rear deck overhang; horizontal sweepspear molding high on front fenders and doors; and Savoy front fender signature scripts. The Sport Tone trim option, previously described on the Plaza is available on the Savoy (after midyear) at slight extra cost. General styling features are the same as these outlined for 1955 Plazas. Cars with V-8 power had V-shaped hood and deck insignia. Sixes of all trim levels were designated as part of the P-26 Series; V-8s were P-27 models.

SAVOY SERIES

Series Number	Body/Style Number	Body Type & Seating	Factory Price	Shipping Weight	Production Total
P26/27	NA	4-dr Sed-6P	1855/1958	3154/3265	162,741
P26/27	NA	2-dr Clb Sed-6P	1812/1915	3109/3224	74,880

NOTE 1: Data above slash for six-cylinder/below for V-8.

1955 Plymouth, Belvedere two-door hardtop coupe, V-8

BELVEDERE — (6-CYL/V-8) — SERIES P26/P27 — The Belvedere was the high-priced Plymouth line. It had the same general styling features described for other models, with richer interior and exterior finish. All body styles had Belvedere front fender scripts; chrome windshield and rear window moldings; chrome trim on the rear deck lid overhang; chrome trim inside the headlight hoods; moldings decorating the taillamps; and bright metal highlights on the rear roof pillar. Sedans and station wagons had full-length chrome sweepspears on their sides. The sport coupe and convertible had special contrasting 'color sweep' panels as standard equipment. The panel was formed by the side molding arrangement and two-tone paint treatment. A horizontal spear ran from the headlamp hood to the mid-door area. A second horizontal spear ran from above the taillamp to the middle of the door. Forward slanting moldings intersected the front spear below the front vent window and below the windshield post. The shorter one (below vent window) also intersected the lower horizontal piece. The longer one dropped to the rocker sill, at the mid-door point. Panels underneath the lower horizontal molding and between the slanting pieces were finished in a contrasting color, usually matching the roof color. A small crest type emblem was placed between the slanting moldings on the door. Belvedere upholstery came in especially rich combinations, such as Jacquard 'Black Magic' Boucle. Deluxe steering wheels; dual ashtrays; armrests; clock; and special courtesy lights were included as regular attributes.

BELVEDERE SERIES

Series Number	Body/Style Number	Body Type & Seating	Factory Price	Shipping Weight	Production Total
P26/27	NA	4-dr Sed-6P	1954/2057	3159/3267	160,984
P26/27	NA	2-dr Clb Sed-6P	1911/2014	3129/3228	41,645
P26/27	NA	2-dr HT Cpe-6P	2088/2192	3149/3261	47,375
P26/27	NA	2-dr Conv-6P	2326	3409	8,473
P26/27	NA	4-dr Sub-6P	2297/2400	3330/3475	18,488

NOTE 1: Data above slash for six/below slash for V-8.
NOTE 2: Belvedere convertible came only as a V-8.
NOTE 3: 786 Belvedere four-door sedans; 100 club coupes; 93 hardtops and 21 Suburban built for Canada.
NOTE 4: Plymouth made 10 Savoy chassis-only and one Belvedere chassis-only.

ENGINES

(SIX) Inline. L-head Six. Cast iron block. Displacement: 230.2 cid. Bore and stroke: 3.25 x 4.625 inches. Compression ratio: 7.4:1. Brake hp: 117 at 3600 rpm. Four main bearings. Solid valves lifters. Carburetor: Carter Type B&B one-barrel Model 2063SA.

(HY-FIRE V-8) V-8. Overhead valves. Cast iron block. Displacement: 241 cid. Bore and stroke: 3.44 x 3.25 inches. Compression ratio: 7.6:1. Brake hp: 157 at 4400 rpm. Five main bearings. Hydraulic (non-adjustable) valve lifters. Carburetion: Carter Type BBD two-barrel Model 2262S.

(OPTIONAL V-8). Overhead valves. Cast iron block. Displacement: 259.2 cid. Bore and stroke: 3.563 x 3.25 inches. Compression ratio: 7.6:1. Brake hp: 167 (opt: 177) at 4400 rpm. Five main bearings. Hydraulic (non-adjustable) valve lifters. Carburetion: Carter Type BBD two-barrel Model 2155S (opt: Carter four-barrel WCFB2253S).

CHASSIS FEATURES: Wheelbase: (all models) 115 inches. Overall length: (all models) 203.8 inches. Front tread: (all models) 58-13/32 inches. Rear tread: (all models) 58112 inches. Tires: (all models) 6.70 x 15.

OPTIONS: Power brakes ($35). Power steering ($90). Air conditioning ($525). Power seat ($42). Power windows ($95). Radio ($83). Standard heater ($45). Deluxe heater ($70). Whitewalls, exchange ($25). Full wheel discs. Wire wheel discs. Grille guard. Seat covers. Dual exhausts. Oil filter. Rear seat speaker. Two-tone paint. Tinted Solex glass. Bumper guards. Variable speed electric wipers. Windshield washer. Three-speed manual transmission was standard. Overdrive transmission ($100). Automatic transmission ($165). V-8 240 cid 157 hp two-barrel engine. V-8 260 cid 167 hp two-barrel engine. V-8 260 cid 177 hp four-barrel engine. Available rear axle gear ratios (standard) 3.73:1; (automatic) 3.54:1; (overdrive) 4.0:1.

HISTORICAL FOOTNOTES: The 1955 Plymouths were introduced Nov. 17, 1954 and the Suburbans appeared in dealer showrooms Dec. 22, 1954. Model year production peaked at 672,100 units. Calendar year sales of 742,991 cars were recorded. J. P. Mansfield was the chief executive officer this year. Plymouth created a new fleet sales department during 1955. The club coupe was dropped. Four-door Suburbans and Belvedere two-door sedans were new Plymouth styles. Detroit area dealers were shown the new models on Nov. 4, 1955, as they had entered actual production during September. Production lines at the Detroit factory were made 67 feet longer because the 1955 models were larger than past Plymouth products. On a calendar year basis, 35,664 Plymouths had power brakes; 33,000 had power steering, 348,771 (46 percent) had automatic transmission, 30,791 had overdrive and 60.8 percent had V-8 engines. The 157 hp V-8 was dropped (except for Canadian and export models) by the end of 1954 so Plymouth could advertise the highest standard horsepower V-8 (167) in the low-price field. Chevy and Ford both offered 162 hp V-8s.

1956 PLYMOUTH

PLAZA/DELUXE SUBURBAN (6-CYL/V-8) P28/P29-1 For 1956, Plymouth face-lifted the body introduced the previous season. Styling changes included fin type rear fenders and a new grille with a grid pattern center piece (decorated with a gold V-shaped emblem on V-8s).

Full-length taillights extended from the tip of the rear fins to the back-up lamp housing. Plymouth block lettering stretched across the edge of the hood. A wide jet airplane type hood mascot was used. The Plaza range included the economy offerings. Identification features included rubber windshield and rear window gaskets; painted taillight trim; Plaza rear fender side scripts; painted back-up light housings; small hubcaps; single, horizontal front tender spears; and painted roof gutter rails. This year the Plymouth Suburbans (station wagons) were actually grouped in their own, separate four-model series. However, the Deluxe Suburban was trimmed in Plaza fashion and will be included as such in this catalog. New technical features for 1956 included a 12-volt electrical system; independent safety handbrake and push-button automatic transmission controls.

PLYMOUTH I.D. NUMBERS: Serial number on plate on left door post. Serial number starts with prefix (P=Plymouth) and series code (P28=six-cylinder; P29=V-8) followed by sequential production number starting at 1001 at each factory, Factory codes M=Detroit, Mich.; LA=Los Angeles, Calif.; E=Evansville, Ind. and SL=San Leandro, Calif. do not appear in serial number. Six-cylinder motor numbers near front upper left of block between cylinders one and two. V-8 number on flat surface near front of block between two cylinder heads. Motor number resembles serial number, but may not match. Motor numbers should not be used for identification. Prefix symbols changed as follows: P28-1 = Plaza Six; P28-2 = Savoy Six; P28-3 = Belvedere Six; P29-1 = Plaza V-8; P29-2 = Savoy V-8 and P29-3 = Belvedere V-8 and P29-3 = Fury. Serial Numbers at each factory were changed as follows: Six-cylinder: (M) 14120001-14272723; (E) 20820001-20857927; (LA) 25202001-25212960. V-8: (M) 15873001-16080450; (E) 2224701-22325907 and (LA) 26552001-26590897. Fury/V-8: (M) 15873001-16080450; (E) 2224701-22325907 and (LA) 26552001-26590897. Engine Numbers were: P28-1001-204591 (Six); P29-40001-8000 (187 hp V-8); P29-250001-274000 (187 hp V-8): P29-1001-40000 (180 hp V-8); P29-80001-250000 (180 hp V-8) and P29-1001-329132 (Fury V-8).

PLAZA SERIES/DELUXE SUBURBAN

Series Number	Body/Style Number	Body Type & Seating	Factory Price	Shipping Weight	Production Total
P28/29-1	NA	4-dr Sed-6P	1868/1971	3145/3275	60,197
P28/29-1	NA	2-dr Clb Sed-6P	1825/1928	3100/3250	43,022
P28/29-1	NA	2-dr Bus Cpe-6P	1726/1829	3030/3170	3,728
P28/29	NA	2-dr DeL Sub-6P	2138/2241	3285/3460	23,866

1956 Plymouth, Savoy two-door hardtop coupe, V-8

SAVOY/CUSTOM SUBURBAN — (6-CYL/V-8) — P28/P29-2 — The Savoy line was the mid-range 1956 Plymouth offering and shared annual styling changes with other models. Standard equipment included front fender horizontal sweepspear molding; chrome taillight molding; chrome headlight trim; painted back-up lamp housing; bright metal windshield and rear window frames; small hubcaps; and Savoy rear fender scripts. Although actually part of a separate series, two custom Suburbans came with Savoy type features and trim, except for the rear fender script, which read Custom Suburban. One of these six-passenger station wagons was a two-door model and the other had four-doors. As usual, the interiors on the mid-priced Plymouths carried a few extra rich appointments. Buyers could also dress-up the exterior of Savoys (and Plazas) with the optional 'Sport Tone' molding treatment (as described for 1955 Plaza models).

SAVOY SERIES/CUSTOM SUBURBAN

Series Number	Body/Style Number	Body Type & Seating	Factory Price	Shipping Weight	Production Total
P28/29-2	NA	4-dr Sed-6P	1967/2070	3160/3295	51,762
P28/29-2	NA	2-dr Clb Sed-6P	1924/2027	3125/3255	57,927
P28/29-2	NA	2-dr Spt Cpe-6P	2071/2174	3155/3275	16,473
P28/29	NA	4-dr Cus Sub-6P	2255/2358	3375/3565	33,333
P28/29	NA	2-dr Cus Sub-6P	2209/2312	3355/3500	9,489

NOTE 1: Data above slash for six/below slash for V-8.

1956 Plymouth, Belvedere four-door hardtop sedan, V-8

BELVEDERE/SPORT SUBURBAN/FURY — (6-CYL/V-8) — SERIES P28/29-3 — The Belvedere was Plymouth's high trim level car again. The four-door Sport Wagon, in the Suburban series, also had Belvedere features. A new body style was the four-door hardtop Sport Sedan. Indentifiers for these models included front door model nameplates; chrome back-up lamp housings; 'Forward Look' medallions; armrests; clock; Deluxe steering wheel; dressier interior trappings and bright metal moldings on the windshield, rear window, headlights, taillights; rear deck lid overhang and front edge of the hood. Belvederes (and sport Suburbans) came standard with 'Sport Tone' side trim of a distinct, angled-back pattern. The Sport Suburban also had 'Forward Look' medallions on the rear fenders and tweed pattern seat cushions and backs, plus a rooftop luggage carrier. Introduced as a midyear model, the Plymouth Fury high-performance sport coupe was actually part of the Belvedere V-8 series. Its custom features included off-white exterior finish; tapering gold anodized aluminum side trim; gold-finished aluminum grille; directional signals; back-up lights; variable-speed wipers;

dual exhaust system with chrome deflectors; windshield washers; dual outside rearview mirrors; prismatic inside rearview mirror; special tires; gold anodized spoke-style wheelcovers and 240 hp V-8. There were Fury rear fender scripts.

1956 Plymouth, Fury two-door hardtop coupe, V-8

BELVEDERE/FURY SERIES/ SPORT SUBURBAN

Series Number	Body/Style Number	Body Type & Seating	Factory Price	Shipping Weight	Production Total
P28/29-3	NA	4-dr Sed-6P	2051/2154	3170/3325	84,218
P28/29-3	NA	4-dr Spt Sed-6P	2223/2326	3270/3415	17,515
P28/29-3	NA	2-dr Clb Sed-6P	2008/2111	3125/3285	19,057
P28/29-3	NA	2-dr Spt Cpe-6P	2155/2258	3165/3320	24,723
P29-3	NA	2-dr Conv-6P	2419	3435	6,735
P28/29	NA	4-dr Spt Sub-6P	2425/2528	3420/3605	15,104

FURY SUB-SERIES

Series Number	Body/Style Number	Body Type & Seating	Factory Price	Shipping Weight	Production Total
P29-3	NA	2-dr Spt Cpe-6P	2807	3650	4,485

NOTE 1: Data above slash for six/below slash for V-8.

BASE ENGINES

(SIX) Inline. L-head Six. Cast iron block. Displacement: 230.2 cid. Bore and stroke: 3.25 x 4.625 inches. Compression ratio: 7.6:1. Brake hp: 125 (opt: 131) at 3600 rpm. Four main bearings. Solid valve lifters. Carter Type B&B one-barrel Model 2063SA (opt: Carter Type BBS two-barrel Model 2293S).

(V-8) V-8. Overhead valves. Cast iron block. Displacement: 268.8 cid. Bore and stroke: 3.63 x 3.256 inches. Compression ratio: 8.0:1. Brake hp: 180 at 4400 rpm. Five main bearings. Hydraulic valve lifters. Carburetor: Carter Type BBD two-barrel Model 2259SB. Base V-8 for all except Fury.

(FURY V-8) V-8. Overhead valves. Cast iron block. Displacement: 303 cid. Bore and stroke: 3.81 x 3.31 inches. Compression ratio: 9.25:1. Brake hp: 240 at 4800 rpm. Five main bearings. Solid valve lifters. Carburetor: Carter Type WCFB four-barrel Model 2442S.

OPTIONAL ENGINE: V-8. Overhead valves. Cast iron block. Displacement: 276.1 cid. Bore and stroke: 3.75 x 3.125 inches. Compression ratio: 8.0:1. Brake hp: 187 at 4400 rpm. Five main bearings. Hydraulic or solid valve lifters. Carburetor: Carter Type BBD two-barrel Model 2407S. NOTE: This is called the '277' engine and came with solid valve lifters when the optional four-barrel 'Power Pack' was installed.

CHASSIS FEATURES: Wheelbase: (all models) 115 inches. Overall length: (all models, 204.8 inches. Front tread: (all models) 58-13/32 inches. Rear tread: (Fury) 58-29/32 inches: (all other models) 58-1/2 inches. Tires: (Fury) 7.10 x 15; (all other models; 6.70 x 15.

OPTIONS: Power brakes ($40). Power steering ($81). Air conditioning, V-8 club sedan/sport coupe/four-door sedan/sport sedan only, ($427). Power windows ($102). Power seat ($45). Standard radio ($90). Deluxe radio ($107). Heater ($75). Full wheel discs. Wheel trim rings. Wire wheelcovers. White sidewall tires. Front safety belts. Rear safety belts. Hi-Way Hi-Fi. Undercoating. Padded dashboard. Outside rearview mirror. 'Sport Tone' moldings. Two-tone paint. Bumper guards. Station wagon roof top luggage rack. Back-up lights. Directional signals. Windshield washer. Solex tinted glass. Three-speed manual transmission was standard. Overdrive transmission ($108). Automatic transmission ($184). V-8 268.8 cid 180 hp two-barrel engine. V-8 276.1 cid 187 hp two-barrel engine. V-8 276.1 cid 200 hp four-barrel engine. V-8 303 cid 240 hp Fury four-barrel engine. Four-barrel carburetor was standard with the Fury V-8 and available as 'Power Pack' equipment on the 276.1 cid V-8 (Carter WCFB2442). Positive traction rear axle. Available rear axle gear ratios (standard) 3.73:1; (automatic) 3.73:1 (overdrive) 4.1:1.

HISTORICAL FOOTNOTES: The 1956 Plymouths were introduced Oct. 21, 1955 and the Fury sport coupe appeared in dealer showrooms Jan. 7, 1956. Model year production peaked at 521,000 units. Calendar year sales of 452,958 cars were recorded. J.P. Mansfield was the chief executive officer this year. Push-button PowerFlite automatic transmission controls were introduced. The Plymouth Plainsman station wagon, a futuristic show car, appeared at the Chicago Auto Show. An experimental turbine-powered Fury sport coupe was also constructed. Optional equipment installed on 1956 Plymouth models, by percentage, included automatic transmission (61.7 percent); power steering (6.1 percent); power brakes (6.0 percent); power seat (0.6 percent); power windows (.6 percent); radio (34.3 percent); heater (94.8 percent); whitewalls (44.9 percent); overdrive (3.3 percent); tinted glass (19.2 percent); windshield washers (19.7 percent); back-up lights (28.9 percent); directional signals (96.9 percent) and V-8 engine (63.7 percent). On Jan. 10, 1956, the new Fury ran the Flying Mile at Daytona Beach, Fla. and hit a speed of 124.01 mph. The Fury was timed at 9.6 seconds for 0-to-60 and 17 seconds for the quarter-mile.

1957 PLYMOUTH

PLAZA/DELUXE SUBURBAN (6-CYL/V-8) SERIES KP30/KP31-1 — The 1957 Plymouths were completely redone. New touches included a wraparound aluminum grid style grille with vertical air slot bumper; tower type tailfin rear fenders; dart shaped body profile and parking lamps set alongside headlights for a quad-lamp effect. Plaza was the low-priced line. The

Deluxe Suburban was part of a separate station wagon series, but had Plaza trim. Identification features included model nameplates on rear fenders; untrimmed body sides; small hubcaps; painted roof gutter rails and V-shaped front fender tip emblems on V-8 models. Tapered 'Sport Tone' side moldings were available at extra cost. Standard equipment included single speed windshield wipers; left-hand sun visor; dual horns; five tubeless tires; bumper jack and tire changing tools. Newly introduced features of the 1957 Plymouths included safety power frame construction and Torsion Air Ride (with torsion bar front suspension).

PLYMOUTH I.D. NUMBERS: Serial number on plate on left door post. Serial number starts with P301 = Plaza Six; P30-2 — Savoy Six; P30-3 — Belvedere Six; P31-1 — Plaza V-8; P31-2 Savoy V-8; P31-3 — Belvedere V-8 and P31 — Fury V-8 followed by sequential production number starting at 1001 at each factory. Factory codes M=Detroit, Mich.; LA=Los Angeles, Calif.; E=Evansville, Ind.; SL=San Leandro, Calif.; and (new) NJ=Newark, N.J. do not appear in serial number. Six-cylinder motor numbers near front upper left of block between cylinders one and two; V-8 on top of block, near front, between cylinder heads. Motor number resembles serial number, but may not match. Motor numbers should not be used for identification. Serial Numbers at each factory changed as follows: Six: (M) 14280001-14410539; (E) 20860001-20891720; (LA) 25215001-25222883 and (Newark, N.J.) 28100001 to 28103737. V-8: (M) 1683001 to 16392956; (E) 223300001 to 22450693; (LA) 26595001-26643618 and (NJ) 28525001-28534683. Fury V-8: (M) 16083001 to 16392956. Engine Numbers were: (Six) P30-1001 thru 177184; (V-8) P31-1001 thru 492995 and (Fury V-8) FP31-1001492995. Furys were assembled only at the Detroit, Mich. factory.

PLAZA SERIES/DELUXE SUBURBAN

Series Number	Body/Style Number	Body Type & Seating	Factory Price	Shipping Weight	Production Total
P30/P31-1NA		4-dr Sed-6P	2030/2130	3260/3405	70,248
P30/P31-1	NA	2-dr Clb Sed-6P	1984/2084	3160/3330	49,137
P30/P31-1	NA	2-dr Bus Cpe-3P	1874/1974	3155/3315	2,874
P30/P31-1	NA	2-dr DeL Sub-6p	2305/2405	3555/3685	20,111
P30/P31-1	NA	4-dr Taxi Spec-6P	2174/2274	3410/3515	NA

NOTE 1: Data above slash for six/below slash for V-8.

SAVOY/CUSTOM SUBURBAN — (6-CYL/V-8) — SERIES KP30/KP31-2 — Savoys and Custom Suburbans shared the same general level of trim and appointments. They were Plymouth's mid-priced lines and had the same basic design changes as Plazas. The amount of standard equipment and decorative items was one step up the scale. The Savoy had all features of the lower-priced car, plus air foam seat cushions; armrests; horn-blowing ring; dual sun visors and a single horizontal side molding running from behind the headlights to just above the back-up lights. Dual, tapering 'Sport Tone' molding treatments were an option available at extra cost. Savoy block lettering was placed on the side of fins on passenger cars, while the comparable Suburban had double nameplates attached at mid-fin height. They read 'Custom' in script and 'Suburban' in block letters. The Suburbans had slightly different rear fenders than other models and also came with contrasting 'Sport Tone' finish, as an option.

1957 Plymouth, Savoy two-door sedan, 6-cyl

SAVOY SERIES/CUSTOM SUBURBAN

Series Number	Body/Style Number	Body Type & Seating	Factory Price	Shipping Weight	Production Total
P30-P31-2NA		4-dr Sed-6P	2169/2269	3265/3415	53,093
P30/P31-2NA		4-dr HT Sed-6P	2292/2392	3375/3480	7,601
P30/P31-2NA		2-dr Clb Sed-6P	2122/2222	3190/3335	55,590
P30/31-2	NA	2-dr HT Cpe-6P	2204/2304	3260/3410	31,373
P30/P31-2NA		4-dr Cus Sub-6P	2469/2569	3665/3840	40,227
P30/P31-2NA		4-dr Cus Sub-9P	2624/2724	NA/NA	9,357
P30/P31-2NA		2-dr Cus Sub	2415/2515	3580/3755	11,196

NOTE 1: Data above slash for six/below slash for V-8.

1957 Plymouth, Belvedere four-door sedan, V-8 (AA)

BELVEDERE/SPORT SUBURBAN/FURY — (6-CYL/V-8) — SERIES KP30/KP313/KP31 — The Belvedere group represented the top Plymouth line. The Sport Suburban was the comparably equipped station wagon and the Fury was a special high-performance model, which had many standard extras. Belvederes had single side moldings as standard equipment and tapering dual side moldings, with 'Sport Tone' contrast panels as a slight extra cost option. Belvedere block letters were positioned at the middle sides of the rear tailfins, just above the moldings. Standard equipment included all items found on Savoys, plus full wheelcovers; rear quarter stone shields; electric clock; lockable glove box; cigarette lighter and oil filter. The Sport Suburban had a special thick pillar roof treatment (also used on four-door Custom Suburbans); upright spare tire and rear-facing third seat. Model nameplates appeared at mid-fin level, above the rear tip of the horizontal side moldings or optional dual 'Sport Tone' moldings. The Fury came only as a two-door hardtop with Fury rear fender nameplates; Sand Dune White finish with gold anodized aluminum 'Sport Tone' trim inserts; upswept front bumper end extensions; safety padded dash; padded sun visors; foam seat front and rear; special clock; back-up lights; directionals; dual outside rearview mirrors; and a 290 hp V-8. The new three-speed TorqueFlite automatic transmission was offered only in the Belvedere and Fury lines.

BELVEDERE SERIES/SPORT SUBURBAN/FURY

Series Number	Body/Style Number	Body Type & Seating	Factory Price	Shipping Weight	Production Total
P30/P31-2NA		4-dr Sed-6P	2285/2385	3270/3475	10,414
P30/P31-3NA		4-dr HT Sed-6P	2394/2494	3350/3505	37,446
P30/P31-3NA		2-dr Clb Sed-6P	2239/2339	3235/3340	55,590
P30/P31-3NA		2-dr HT Cpe-6P	2324/2424	3280/3415	67,268
P31-3	NA	2-dr Conv-6P	2613	3585	9,866
P30/P31-3NA		4-dr Spt Sub-6P	2597/2697	3655/3840	15,444
P30/P31-3NA		4-dr Spt Sub-9P	2752/2852	NA/NA	7,988

FURY SUB-SERIES

Series Number	Body/Style Number	Body Type & Seating	Factory Price	Shipping Weight	Production Total
P31-3	NA	2-dr HT Cpe-6P	2900	3595	7,438

NOTE 1: Data above slash for six/below slash for V-8.
NOTE 2: Belvedere convertible came only with V-8 power.

BASE ENGINES

(SIX) Inline L-head Six. Cast iron block. Displacement: 230.2 cid. Bore and stroke: 3.25 x 4.625 inches. Compression ratio: 8.0:1. Brake hp: 132 at 3600 rpm. Four main bearings. Solid valve lifters. Carburetor: Carter Type BBS one-barrel Model 2567S.

(EIGHT) V-8. Overhead valves. Cast iron block. Displacement: 276.1 cid. Bore and stroke: 3.75 x 3.125 inches. Compression ratio: 8.0:1. Brake hp: 197 at 4400 rpm. Five main bearings. Hydraulic valve lifters. Carburetor: Carter Type BBD two-barrel Model 2407S. NOTE: The Deluxe Suburban used the 299.6 cid '301' V-8 as standard equipment.

(FURY) V-8. Overhead valves. Cast iron block. Displacement: 299.6 cid. Bore and stroke: 3.906 x 3.125 inches. Compression ratio: 8.5:1. Brake hp: 235 at 4400 rpm. Five main bearings. Solid valve lifters. Carburetor: Carter Type WCFB four-barrel Model 2631S.

OPTIONAL ENGINES

V-8. Overhead valves. Cast iron block. Displacement: 299.6 cid. Bore and stroke: 3.906 x 3.125 inches. Compression ratio: 8.5:1. Brake hp: 215 at 9700 rpm. Five main bearings. Solid valve lifters. Carburetor: Carter Type BBD two-barrel Model 2512S. NOTE: This engine is normally referred to as the '301' V-8, although its actual displacement was 299.6 cid. It was standard in all 1957 Suburbans.

(FURY) V-8. Overhead valves. Cast iron block. Displacement: 317.6 cid. Bore and stroke: 3.906 x 3.312 inches. Compression ratio: 9.25:1. Brake hp: 290 at 5400 rpm. Five main bearings. Solid valve lifters. Carburetor: Two (2) Carter Type WCFB four-barrels Model 2631S.

CHASSIS FEATURES: Wheelbase: (all passenger cars) 118 inches; (all Suburbans) 122 inches. Overall length: (Fury) 206.1 inches; (all other passenger cars) 204.6 inches; (all station wagons) 208.6 inches. Front tread: (all models) 60-29/32 inches. Tires: (Fury and nine-passenger Suburbans) 8.00 x 14; (all other models) 7.50 x 14.

OPTIONS: Power brakes ($38). Power steering ($84). Air conditioning ($446). Power windows ($102). Two-Way Power seat ($48). Push-button transistor radio with antenna ($73). Search Tune transistor radio with antenna ($106). Search Tune radio with antenna and Hi-Fi ($187). Rear seat speaker ($12). Heater and defroster ($69). White sidewall tires, exchange ($33). Disc wheelcovers on Plaza or Savoy ($18). 'Sport Tone' Two-tone paint ($20). 'Sport Tone' on Suburbans ($24). Tinted Solex glass ($32). Back-up lights ($8). Suburban Back-up lights ($10). Front and rear bumper guards ($34). Variable speed windshield wipers ($6). Windshield washer ($12). Electric clock on Plaza and Savoy ($14). Padded dashboard and sun visors ($24). Undercoating and hood panel ($13).

POWERTRAIN OPTIONS: Oil filter ($6). Three-speed manual transmission was standard. Overdrive transmission ($108). PowerFlite two-speed automatic transmission ($180). Torque-Flite three-speed automatic transmission was optional with V-8 engines only ($220). Dual exhaust was optional with V-8 engines only ($19.80). V-8 229.6 cid, 215 hp two-barrel engine. V-8 299.6 cid 235 hp four-barrel engine. V-8 317.6 cid 290 hp dual four-barrel engine ($320). Four-barrel carburetor ($39). Positive traction rear axle ($50). Available rear axle gear ratios: (standard) 3.53:1; (overdrive) 3.9:1; (automatic) 3.54: 1 or 3.35:1.

HISTORICAL FOOTNOTES: The 1957 Plymouths were introduced Oct. 25, 1956 and the Fury appeared in dealer showrooms Dec. 18, 1956. Model year production peaked at 762,231 units. Calendar year sales of 655,526 cars were recorded. J.P. Mansfield was the chief executive officer this year. Plymouth retained the third rank in American auto sales. A unique station wagon prototype called the Cabana was built this year. It was based on the experimental Plainsman show car, but failed to reach the production stage. The Savoy sports sedan (four-door pillarless hardtop) was a midyear addition to the 1957 line introduced in March of the calendar year. The famous "Suddenly it's 1960" theme was used to promote the 1957 Plymouths. The Fury was re-introduced in January as a mid-year high-performance model. With the 318 cid/290 hp engine it could do 0-to-60 in 8.6 seconds and cover the quarter-mile in 16.5 seconds.

1958 PLYMOUTH

PLAZA/DELUXE SUBURBAN — (6-CYL/V-8) — SERIES LPI/LP2-L — The Plaza group again represented the base Plymouth model range. The Deluxe Suburban was the counterpart station wagon. General styling revisions for the year included a new, horizontal bar grille below the front bumper; fin type front fendertop ornaments on Belvederes and

Savoys; new taillights; redesigned side trim treatments and four-beam headlamps on all models. Anodized aluminum 'Sport Tone' moldings and inserts were now optional on Belvederes and Sport Suburbans. Plazas (and Deluxe Suburbans) could be identified by their respective rear fender nameplates. Normal side trim consisted of a straight sweepspear molding extending from the rear bumper to nearly across the front door. A molding arrangement forming a bullet-shaped side body cove with contrasting finish, was optional at slight extra cost. Deluxe Suburbans had the same features as Plaza models, except for the rear fenderside nameplates. Basic equipment on the low-priced Plymouths included directional signals; dual headlights; single-speed electric windshield wipers; left-hand sun visor; dual horns; five tubeless tires; bumper jack and wheel lug wrench. Gold V-shaped emblems at the center of the grille were used to identify models with V-8 power.

PLYMOUTH I.D. NUMBERS: Serial number on plate on left door post. Six cylinder motor numbers on front upper left side of block between cylinders one and two. V-8 numbers on flat surface, front top of block, between cylinder heads. Motor number resembles serial number, but may not match. Motor numbers should not be used for identification. VIN: First symbol L=1958; second symbol P=Plymouth. The third symbol designated type of engine as follows: 1=6-cyl; 2=V-8. The fourth symbol designated the assembly plant as follows: Detroit, Michigan (no code used); Los Angeles=L; Evansville, Ind.=E and Delaware=N. The following group of symbols was the sequential unit production number, with series in mixed production according to factory and engine type. Body Style Numbers were not used, but a new method of coding trim levels shows up in the charts below. This code used the first three symbols of the Serial Number, followed by a letter that indicated the level of price and/or trim. These letters were 'L' for low; 'M' for medium; 'H' for high and 'P' for premium. Serial Numbers for 1958 models were as follows: (Six-Cylinder) LPIL-1001 to 6444; LPIN-1001 to 18176; LPIE-1001 to 23101; LPI-1001 to 66871. (V-8) LP2L-1001 to 39675; LP2N-1001 to 36506; LP2EI00I-84801 and LP2-1001. Motor Numbers for 1958 Sixes were LP6-1001 and up or LP230-100001 and up (after March 26, 1958). Motor Numbers for V-8s were LP8-1001 and up.

PLAZA SERIES/DELUXE SUBURBAN

Series Number	Body/Style Number	Body Type & Seating	Factory Price	Shipping Weight	Production Total
LP1/2-L	NA	4-dr Sed-6P	2134/2242	3255/3415	54,194
LP1/2-L	NA	2-dr Clb Sed-6P	2083/2190	3190/3315	39,062
LP1/2-L	NA	2-dr Bus Cpe-3P	1993/2101	3170/3320	1,472
LP1/2-L	NA	4-dr DeL Sub-6P	2451/2558	3580/3740	15,625
LP1/2-L	NA	2-dr DeL Sub-6P	2397/2504	3475/3645	15,535

NOTE 1: Data above slash for six/below slash for V-8.

SAVOY/CUSTOM SUBURBAN — (6-CYL/V-8) — SERIES LPI/LP2-L — The Savoys played their traditional role as mid-priced Plymouth models and the Custom Suburbans were the comparable offerings in the Suburban Series. Equipment for these cars included all Plaza features, plus Air Foam (foam rubber) seat cushions; armrests; horn-blowing steering wheel ring; dual sun visors and slightly enriched upholstery combinations. Identification aids included model nameplates on rear fenders and front fender top ornaments. Standard bodyside trim was a full-length, single horizontal molding running from headlights to taillights. Finger-shaped 'Sport Tone' treatments were a $20 option on passenger car models and $24 extra on station wagons. With this type of trim the molding ran from the rear bumper to nearly the front edge of the front door, then looped back, along the doors and quarters, dropping down to the rocker sill just ahead of the rear wheel opening. The area within the moldings was painted a contrasting color, which usually matched that of the roof. In the Spring, a special Silver Savoy Special was marketed. It was a club sedan with special sport toning; front door and fender spears: metallic silver roof and wheels; turn signals; electric wipers and washers and a price tag that matched the model year. It sold for $1,958.

SAVOY SERIES/CUSTOM SUBURBAN

Series Number	Body/Style Number	Body Type & Seating	Factory Price	Shipping Weight	Production Total
LP1/2-M	NA	4-dr Sed-6P	2270/2378	3220/3400	67,933
LP1/2-M	NA	4-dr HT Sed-6P	2365/2472	3310/3475	5,060
LP1/2-M	NA	2-dr Clb Sed-6P	2219/2327	3220/3360	17,624
LP1/2-M	NA	2-dr HT Cpe-6P	2294/2401	3240/3400	19,500
LP1/2-M	NA	4-dr Cus Sub-6P	2572/2680	3575/3755	38,707
LP1/2-M	NA	4-dr Cus Sub-9P	2712/2820	3685/3840	17,158
LP1/2-M	NA	2-dr Cus Sub-6P	2518/2626	3570/3690	5,925

NOTE 1: Data above slash for six/below slash for V-8.

BELVEDERE/SPORT SUBURBAN/FURY — (6-CYL/V-8) — SERIES LPI/LP2-H — Belvedere represented the top full-line Plymouth series. The Sport Suburban was the comparable station wagon. The Fury was a Belvedere sub-series containing only the special, high-performance sport coupe. Nameplates on the rear fender identified each particular car. The standard type of Belvedere side trim was a single, full-length horizontal molding of slightly distinctive design. Running with a slight downward slant, it moved from headlamp level towards the back fender. About a foot ahead of the taillights, the molding angled up towards the top of the fin. When optional 'Sport Tone' finish was added, a lower molding was added. It ran from above the back bumper and tapered towards the upper molding at the front fender tip. The area inside the moldings was then finished with contrasting colors, usually matching the roof. Belvederes and Sport Suburbans had all Savoy features, plus full wheelcovers; rear fender stone shields; electric clock; lockable glove box; cigar lighter: oil filter and front fendertop ornaments. The Fury was a limited-edition Buckskin Beige two-door hardtop with Fury rear fender nameplates; 'Sport Tone' moldings (with gold anodized aluminum inserts); bumper wing guards; padded interior; front and rear foam seats; back-up lights: dual outside rearview mirrors and special Dual Fury or Golden Commando V-8.

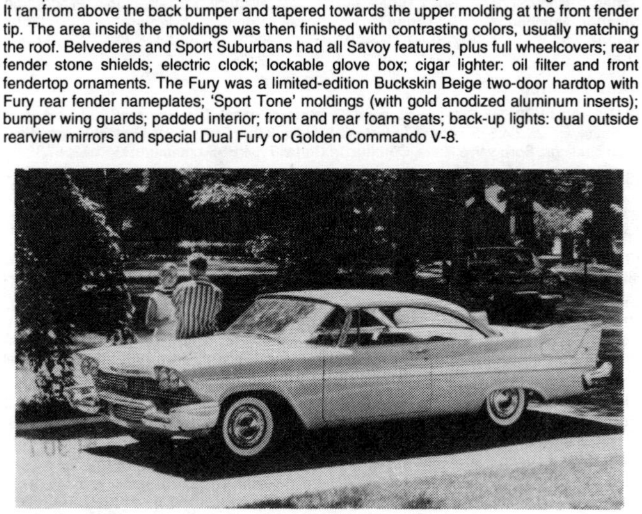

1958 Plymouth, Fury two-door hardtop sport coupe, V-8 (AA)

BELVEDERE SERIES/SPORT SUBURBAN/FURY

Series Number	Body/Style Number	Body Type & Seating	Factory Price	Shipping Weight	Production Total
LP1/2-H	NA	4-dr Sed-6P	2404/2512	3255/3430	49,124
LP1/2-H	NA	4-dr HT Sed-6P	2493/2600	3330/3520	18,194
LP1/2-H	NA	2-dr Clb Sed-6P	2354/2461	3240/3370	4,229
LP1/2-H	NA	2-dr HT Cpe-6P	2422/2529	3250/3410	36,043
LP2-H	NA	2-dr Conv-6P	2727	3545	9,941
LP1/2-H	NA	4-dr Spt Sub-6P	2725/2833	3615/3745	10,785
LP1/2-H	NA	4-dr Spt Sub-9P	2865/2973	3685/3830	12,385
FURY SUB-SERIES					
LP2-H	NA	2-dr HT Cpe-6P	3032	3510	5,303

NOTE 1: Data above slash for six/below slash for V-8.
NOTE 2: The Belvedere convertible and Fury hardtop came only with V-8 power.

BASE ENGINES

(SIX) Inline L-head Six. Cast iron block. Displacement: 230.2 cid. Bore and stroke: 3.25 x 4.625 inches. Compression ratio: 8.0:1. Brake hp: 132 at 3600 rpm. Four main bearings. Solid valve lifters. Carburetor: Carter Type BBS one-barrel Model 2567S.

(EIGHT) V-8. Overhead valves. Cast iron block. Displacement: 317.6 cid. Bore and stroke: 3.906 x 3.312 inches. Compression ratio: 9.0:1: Brake hp: 225 at 4400 rpm. Five main bearings. Solid valve lifters. Carburetor: Carter Type BBS two-barrel Model 2644S.

(FURY) V-8. Overhead valves. Cast iron block. Displacement: 3l7.6 cid. Bore and stroke: 3.906 x 3.312 inches. Compression ratio: 9.25:1. Brake hp: 290 at 5200 rpm. Five main bearings. Solid valve lifters. Carburetor: Two Carter Type WCFB four-barrel Model 2631S.

(GOLDEN COMMANDO OPTION) V-8. Overhead valves. Cast iron block. Displacement: 350 cid. Bore and stroke: 4.062 x 3.375 inches. Compression ratio: 10.0:1. Brake hp: 305 at 5000 rpm. Five main bearings. Hydraulic valve lifters. Carburetion: two Carter four-barrel Model 2631S. (An electronic fuel injection option rated at 315 hp was short-lived.)

1958 Plymouth, Belvedere two-door hardtop sport coupe, V-8

CHASSIS FEATURES: (all passenger cars) 118 inches; (all Suburbans) 122 inches. Overall length: (Fury) 206 inches; (all other passenger cars) 204.6 inches; (all Suburbans) 213.1 inches. Front tread: (all models) 60-29/32 inches. Rear tread: (all models) 59-39/64 inches. Tires: (Fury and nine-passenger Suburban) 8.00 x 14: (all other models) 7.50 x 14.

OPTIONS: Power brakes ($38). Power steering ($77). Air conditioning ($446). Power windows ($102). Two-Way power seat ($48). Push-button transistor radio ($73). Search Tuner transistor radio ($106). Search Tuner radio with HI-FI ($187). Rear seat speaker ($12). Heater and defroster ($69). Four-ply white sidewall tires, exchange ($33). Disc wheelcovers, Plaza and Savoy ($18). 'Sport-Tone' finish, passenger cars ($20). 'Sport-Tone' finish, Suburbans ($24). Solex tinted glass ($32). Back-up lamps, passenger car ($8). Back-up lamps, Suburban ($10). Front and rear outer bumper guards ($34). Air Foam seat ($9). Variable-speed electric windshield wipers ($6). Windshield washers ($12). Electric clock on Plaza and Savoy ($14). Padded panel and sun visors ($24). Undercoating and fiberglass hood pad ($13). Sure-Grip. Three-speed manual transmission was standard. Overdrive transmission ($108). PowerFlite automatic transmission with all but Golden Commando V-8 ($180). TorqueFlite automatic transmission with V-8 only ($220). 318 cid 225 hp two-barrel Fury V-8 'Fury' engine ($107). 318 cid 250 hp four-barrel Fury Super-Pak ($146). V-8 318 cid 290 hp dual four-barrel 'Dual Fury' engine. V-8 350 cid 305 hp 'Golden Commando' engine ($324). V-8 350 cid 315 hp E.F.I. engine ($500). Four-barrel carburetor ($39). Fuel injection ($500). Dual exhausts with V-8 engine only ($19.80). Oil filter ($6). Available rear axle gear ratios 3.54: 1; 3.73: 1; 2.93:1; 3.15:1: 3.31:1; 3.90:1; 4.10:1.

HISTORICAL FOOTNOTES: The 1958 Plymouths were introduced Oct. 16, 1957 and the Fury appeared in dealer showrooms at the same time. Model year production peaked at 443,799 units. Calendar year sales of 367,296 cars were recorded. The term 'Power Pack' applied to cars having a four-barrel carburetor installed as optional equipment. The 'Dual Fury' V-8 came with two (2) Carter WCFB type four-barrel carburetors, 9.25:1 compression and 290 hp at 5200 rpm. The EFI engine utilized a Bendix electronic fuel-injection system. All EFI equipped cars were Furys, which were first built with the 'Dual Fury' induction setup and were then converted to EFI on a special assembly line in the DeSoto factory in Detroit. Cars with this option were later recalled so that most, if not all, could be re-converted to the 'Dual Fury' configuration. Plymouth retained its number three sales rank for the industry as a whole, with a 30.6 percent market share. Furys equipped with the wedge head 350 cid/305 hp big-block V-8 were capable of 0-to-60 mph in 7.7 seconds and could run the quarter-mile in 16.1 seconds.

1959 PLYMOUTH

SAVOY/DELUXE SUBURBAN — (6-CYL/V-8) — SERIES MP1-L/MP2-L — To upgrade its image for 1959, Plymouth discarded the Plaza name and shuffled its series designations one notch. The Plaza became the Savoy; the Savoy the Belvedere; the Belvedere the Fury. The special high-performance range, formerly known as the Fury, was now the Sport Fury Series

and had one new model, a two-door convertible. General styling features included a twin section anodized aluminum eggcrate grille insert; new 'double-barrel' front fenders; longer, outward canted rear tailfins; oval-shaped horizontal taillights and flatter, more sweeping rear deck contours. The Savoy line was now the base series offering, as standard equipment, directional signals; dual headlights; single-speed electric windshield wipers; left-hand sun visor; dual horns; five tubeless tires; bumper jack; and wheel lug wrench. Identification features included Savoy rear fender nameplates; single side spears running from the front wheel opening to the back of the car; and small hubcaps. The Deluxe Suburbans (now available in two or four-door styles) were the station wagon counterparts of Savoys. The two-door wagons had thin, straight roof pillars, while the four-door models had a thicker 'C' pillar and 'flattop' rear roof look. Dual side trim moldings, with aluminum fin-shaped inserts below the 'green house' area, were optional on low-priced Plymouths.

PLYMOUTH I.D. NUMBERS: The vehicle number was located on the left front hinge pillar of Savoys and Belvederes and on the left side of the cowl, below the hood on Furys. Motor Numbers were found at the front of the engine block on the left side of sixes and on the top center of the V-8 block. Vehicle numbers began with a four symbol prefix. The first symbol M=1959. The second symbol designated engine, as follows: I=six and 2=V-8. The third symbol designated series as follows: 3=Savoy; 5=Belvedere; 7=Suburban and 9=Sport Fury. The fourth symbol designated the manufacturing/assembly plant as follows: 1=Detroit; 2=Detroit (Dodge); 5=California; 6=Newark, Del.; 7=St. Louis, Mo. Then came the sequential unit production number, with series in mixed production according to engine and factory. Numbers began with 100001 and up at each factory. Ending Serial Numbers are not provided in standard reference sources. Body Style Numbers were used this year and are shown in the second column of the specifications charts below.

SAVOY SERIES/DELUXE SUBURBAN

Series Number	Body/Style Number	Body Type & Seating	Factory Price	Shipping Weight	Production Total
MP1/2-L	41	4-dr Sed-6P	2283/2402	3275/3425	84,274
MP1/2-L	21	2-dr Clb Sed-6P	2232/2352	3240/3390	46,979
MP1-L	22	2-dr Bus Cpe-3P	2143	3130	1,051
MP1/2-L	45A	4-dr Del Sub-6P	2641/2761	3625/3725	35,086
MP1/2-L	25	2-dr Del Sub-6P	2574/2694	3560/3690	15,074

NOTE 1: Data above slash for six/below slash for V-8.

1959 Plymouth, Deluxe four-door, V-8 (AA)

BELVEDERE/CUSTOM SUBURBAN — (6-CYL/V-8) — SERIES MP1-M/MP2-M — Belvederes and Custom Suburbans represented middle-of-the-line Plymouths for 1959. The side trim moldings on these cars began behind the front wheel opening, flaring into a fin-shaped, tapering dual molding. This arrangement ran from just ahead of the front door, to the extreme rear of the body. Belvedere or Custom Suburban model nameplates appeared near the tops of the fins. Equipment included at regular prices began with all items found on Savoys and added foam seat cushions; armrests; horn ring; and dual sun visors. A special silver anodized insert could be ordered for $18.60 to fill the area between the bodyside moldings. As in the past, the Belvedere convertible was offered only with V-8 power. Many new options appeared for Plymouths this year and several became standard equipment on Sport Furys. Included were swivel type front seats and deck lid tire cover impressions. Due to growth of the station wagon market in the late 1950s, Plymouth again offered three types of Custom Suburbans this season. Six-passenger editions came in two and four-door styles, while the latter model could also be had with a rear-facing third seat. The nine-passenger Custom Suburban and two-door Custom Suburban also came with V-8 power only.

BELVEDERE SERIES/CUSTOM SUBURBAN

Series Number	Body/Style Number	Body Type & Seating	Factory Price	Shipping Weight	Production Total
MP1/2-M	41	4-dr Sed-6P	2440/2559	3275/3430	67,980
MP1/2-M	43	4-dr HT Sed-6P	2525/2644	3275/3475	5,713
MP1/2-M	21	2-dr Clb Sed-6P	2389/2509	3225/3395	13,816
MP1/2-M	23	2-dr HT Spt Cpe-6P	2461/2581	3230/3405	23,469
MP2-M	27	2-dr Conv-6P	2814	3580	5,063
MP1/2-M	45A	4-dr Cus Sub-6P	2762/2881	3625/3730	35,024
MP2-M	45B	4-dr Cus Sub-9P	2991	3775	16,993
MP2-M	25	2-dr Cus Sub-6P	2814	3690	1,852

NOTE 1: Data above slash for six/below slash for V-8.

FURY/SPORT SUBURBAN — (V-8) — SERIES MP2-H — Furys and Sport Suburbans were marketed as higher-level offerings and came only with V-8 attachments. Standard features included all items mentioned for the Belvedere Series, plus disc wheelcovers; rear quarter stone shields; Deluxe steering wheel with horn ring; electric clock; lockable glove compartment; cigar lighter; and oil filter. Fury signature scripts were positioned high on the tailfins. Side chrome was of a dual molding type which began as a single spear behind the headlamps, flared into a double spear behind the front wheel opening and tapered to a point in front of the taillamp wraparound edges. A single molding then continued around the rear body corner and fully across the rear deck lid overhang. A Plymouth signature, in chrome, was placed at the left-hand corner of the deck lid. The rear bumper ran straight across the car and wrapped around the body corners, with a center depression below the license plate holder. All 1959 Plymouths with V-8 power including all Furys and Sport Suburbans had small V-shaped emblems near the Plymouth signature on the rear deck lid.

FURY SERIES/SPORT SUBURBAN

Series Number	Body/Style Number	Body Type & Seating	Factory Price	Shipping Weight	Production Total
MP2-H	41	4-dr Sed-6P	2691	3455	30,149
MP2-H	43	4-dr HT Sed-6P	2771	3505	13,614
MP2-H	23	2-dr HT Cpe-6P	2714	3435	21,494
MP2-H	45A	4-dr Spt Sub-6P	3021	3760	7,224
MP2-H	45B	4-dr Spt Sub-9p	3131	3805	9,549

1959 Plymouth, Sport Fury two-door hardtop sport coupe, V-8 (AA)

SPORT FURY — (V-8) — SERIES MP2-P — The alphabetical suffixes appearing in Plymouth Series codes were L for low-price; M for mid-priced; H for high-priced and P for premium-priced. In past years the limited-edition Fury had been designated an "H" model and was actually a Belvedere. This season the Belvedere moved down a notch and the new top dog was the Sport Fury. Two body styles, sports coupe and convertible, were marketed only with V-8 power. They had several special identification features. For example, the upper branch of the dual side spears curved upward on the rear fenders, to repeat the general contour of the fins. The lower branch wrapped around the rear body corners and ran fully across the deck lid overhang. A silver anodized insert panel was standard and Fury signature scripts were placed inside the dual moldings at the rear. Positioned directly behind the moldings were large, colorful 'Forward Look' medallions. Standard equipment for these cars included all Fury features, plus swivel front seats; sport deck lid tire cover stamping; and custom padded steering wheel. The 'Golden Commando' wedge head V-8 with four-barrel carburetion and 305 hp was optional.

1959 Plymouth Sport Fury convertible, V-8. JL

SPORT FURY SERIES

Series Number	Body/Style Number	Body Type & Seating	Factory Price	Shipping Weight	Production Total
MP2-P	23	2-dr HT Cpe-6P	2927	3475	17,867
MP2-P	27	2-dr Conv-6P	3125	3670	5,990

BASE ENGINES

(SAVOY/BELVEDERE SIX) Inline L-head Six. Cast iron block. Displacement: 230.2 cid. Bore and stroke: 3.25 x 4.625 inches. Compression ratio: 8.0:1. Brake hp: 132 at 3600 rpm. Four main bearings. Solid valve lifters. Carburetor: Carter Type BBS one-barrel Model 2567S.

(SAVOY/BELVEDERE/FURY/WAGON) V-8. Overhead valves. Cast iron block. Displacement: 317.6 cid. Bore and stroke: 3.906 x 3.312 inches. Compression ratio: 9.0:1. Brake hp: 230 at 4400 rpm. Five main bearings. Solid valve lifters. Carburetor: Carter Type BBD two-barrel Model 2824S.

(SPORT FURY) V-8. Overhead valves. Cast iron block. Displacement: 317.6 cid. Bore and stroke: 3.906 x 3.312 inches. Compression ratio: 9.0:1. Brake hp: 260 at 4400 rpm. Five main bearings. Solid valve lifters. Carburetor: Carter Type AFB four-barrel Model 2813S.

(GOLDEN COMMANDO 395) V-8. Overhead valves. Cast iron block. Displacement: 360.8 cid. Bore and stroke: 4.12 x 3.38 inches. Compression ratio: 10.0:1. Brake hp: 305 at 4600 rpm. Five main bearings. Hydraulic valve lifters. Carburetor: Carter Type AFB four-barrel Model 2813S.

CHASSIS FEATURES: Wheelbase: (all passenger cars) 118 inches; (all Suburbans) 122 inches. Overall length: (all passenger cars) 210 inches. (all Suburbans) 214.5 inches. Tires: (nine-passenger Suburban) 8.00 x 14; (all other models) 7.50 x 14.

OPTIONS: Power brakes ($36). Power steering ($63). Air conditioning ($372); for station wagons ($531). Push-button radio ($59). Rear seat speaker ($11). Dual rear antenna ($10). Fresh air heater and defroster ($58). Instant Air gas heater ($86). Tinted glass ($36). Windshield washer ($10). Rear window defogger ($19). Variable speed windshield wipers ($6). Headlight dimmer ($40). Pair, contour floor mats ($8). Pair, regular floor mats ($4). Two-

Way power seat ($40). Power windows ($84). Swivel seat ($57). Constant-Level air suspension ($86). Power tailgate window, standard on 45B ($28). Padded dashboard ($12). Padded sun visor ($6). Padded steering wheel, standard Sport Fury ($12). Clear plastic seat covers ($30). Anti-freeze ($6). Safety belts, each ($13). White sidewall tires ($28). Oversize tires, exchange ($13). Tutone paint ($15). Silver side moldings, standard Fury ($19). Station wagon storage compartment ($24). bumper guards ($12). Front bumper guards ($10). Front bumper end guards ($16). Cigar lighter, standard Fury ($4). wheelcovers, standard Fury ($17). Rear foam seat cushion ($10). Tilt type rearview mirror ($4). Automatic tilt mirror ($14). Left-hand remote control outside rearview mirror ($16). Dual mirrors, left-hand remote control ($23). Undercoating with hood pad ($13). Side view mirror ($6). Group 311, wheelcovers. stone shields, electric clock and glove box lock, standard Fury ($32). Group 312. Back-up lights, windshield washer and variable speed wipers ($24). Group 313, right sun visor; front armrests and front foam cushion, standard Belvedere and Fury ($20). Three-speed manual transmission was standard. PowerFlite automatic transmission was optional with all but Golden Commando V-8 ($189). Overdrive transmission ($84). TorqueFlite automatic transmission ($227). V-8 318 cid 260 hp 'Super Pack' engine ($32). V-8 360.8 cid 305 hp 'Golden Commando' engine ($74). Four-barrel carburetor ($32). Oil filter ($10). Dual exhausts. V-8 only ($23). Available rear axle gear ratios (various).

HISTORICAL FOOTNOTES: The 1959 Plymouths were introduced in October 1958. Plymouth sales leaped 11.6 percent. Model year production peaked at 458,261 units. Calendar year sales of 413,204 cars were recorded. Plymouth again held third rank on industry sales charts, but Rambler was closing the gap. Plymouth's market share was a declining 13.19 percent. Fuel-injection was deleted from the power options list, but new extras included air suspension, swiveling seats for driver and passenger, the "Flite Sweep" rear deck lid with spare tire embossment, an electric headlight dimmer and a self-dimming illuminated rearview mirror. This was Plymouth's 30th anniversary and general manager Harry E. Cheesbrough marked the production of the company's 11th millionth vehicle in 1959. The Golden Commando 395 engine, named for the fact that it developed 395 lbs.-ft. of torque, was optional in all Plymouths except the Savoy business coupe. A Fury four-door hardtop was converted into the latest in a series of Chrysler turbine-engined cars and made a 576-mile cross-country reliability run. Well, it certainly didn't cross the country, but Chrysler's promotional copywriters described the endurance trial that way.

1960 PLYMOUTH

VALIANT V-100 — (6-CYL) — SERIES QX1-L — Chrysler Corp. introduced its compact Valiant as a 1960 model. This all-new car was not yet identified as a Plymouth and was officially considered a distinct brand of car, but a year later, it became a Plymouth. The Valiant was assembled by Dodge Div., but sold mainly by Plymouth dealers. It was an immediate success and enjoyed a high rate of sales. Features included unitized body construction; torsion bar front suspension; seven-dip rust proofing; Lustre-Bond exterior finish; light weight and small, but roomy size; 12-volt electrical system; and large trunk or station wagon cargo capacity (24.9 and 72 cu. ft., respectively). Valiant styling features included a long hood/short rear deck look; high degree of body sculpturing; large wheel cutouts; large trapezoid-shaped radiator grille with Delicate criss-cross pattern insert; dual headlamps; 'cat's eyes' taillights; and rear deck lid tire cover stamping. The low-priced V-100 models had a short, bright metal molding extending forward from the taillights. A new overhead valve 'Slant Six' engine and three-speed manual floor shift transmission were standard equipment. Gray cloth interiors were used for V-100 models.

PLYMOUTH I.D. NUMBERS: VIN on plate attached to left front door pillar. First symbol identifies car-line: 1=Valiant; 2=Plymouth six-cylinder; 3=Plymouth V-8. Second symbol identifies series: 1=V-100/Savoy; 2=Belvedere; 3=V-200/Fury; 5=V-100 wagon/Savoy wagon; 6=Belvedere wagon; 7=V-200 wagon/Fury wagon; 9=taxicab; 0=fleet car. Third symbol 0=1960. Fourth symbol indicates factory: 3=Detroit; 6=Los Angeles; 7=St. Louis; 8=Clairpointe; 0=Canada. Body plate below hood on cowl, inner fenders or radiator support indicates schedule date (SO); sequential body production number; body style number (second symbol in VIN plus numbers and letters in second column of charts below); trim code; and paint code. Six-cylinder motor number stamped on front or rear of left-hand side of block below cylinder head. V-8 motor numbers stamped on flat on top right-hand side of block behind water pump. Engine codes: P-17=170 cid/101 hp six and 170 cid/148 hp 'hyper-pack' six; P-22=225 cid/ 145 hp six; P-318=318 cid/230 hp two-barrel V-8 or 318 cid/260 hp four-barrel V-8; P-36=361 cid/305 hp "Golden Commando" V-8 with four-barrel carb or 361 cid/310 hp "Golden Commando V-8" with dual four-barrel carbs; P-38=383 cid/325 hp V-8 with four-barrel carb and 383 cid/330 hp V-8 with both dual four-barrel carbs and dual fours with Ram-Tuned induction.

VALIANT V-100 SERIES

Series Number	Body/Style Number	Body Type & Seating	Factory Price	Shipping Weight	Production Total
V-100	41	4-dr Sed-6P	2033	2635	52,788
V-100	45A	4-dr Sub-6P	2345	2815	12.018

1960 Valiant, V-200 four-door sedan, 6-cyl

VALIANT V-200 — (6-CYL) — SERIES QX1-H — The high-priced Valiant line was the V-200 Series with bright metal side trim moldings extending from the front wheel opening to the taillight. They curved upwards, below the rear ventipanes, to follow the rear fender contour. Interiors for the high-line cars were available in three choices of color and featured vinyl seat bolsters and Nylon cloth inserts.

VALIANT V-200 SERIES

Series Number	Body/Style Number	Body Type & Seating	Factory Price	Shipping Weight	Production Total
V-200	41	4-dr Sed-6P	2110	2655	106,515
V-200	45A	4-dr Sub-6P	2423	2855	16,368
V-200	45B	4-dr Sub-9P	2546	2860	4,675

ET SPECIAL/SAVOY/DELUXE SUBURBAN — (6-CYL/V-8) — SERIES PP1-L/PP2-L — All 1960 Plymouths had a few common major styling changes. Most obvious was a new grille of close-spaced horizontal blades accented with thin, vertical division bars. The front fenders had a wing-like look, with feature lines wrapping around the body corners to the front wheel openings, creating a sort of a cove just ahead of the wheel cutout. Thin moldings were used to accent the sweep of this unique front fender treatment. Side trim moldings were re-arranged and 'shark fin' rear fender panels appeared. The Savoy was the low-priced line in the regular market, but economy level 'Fleet Special' editions were provided for commercial customers. Standard equipment for the Savoy (and also Deluxe Suburbans) included oil filter; turn signals; dual sun visors; and five tubeless black wall tires. Single sun visors and other deletions characterized the Fleet Specials. Savoys had no model nameplates; straight side trim moldings from the front door back to taillights and single 'Jet Age' missile medallions on the rear fins. Uni-body construction; Safety-Guard door latches; asymmetrical rear leaf springs and the new overhead valve Slant Six were technical innovations for 1960.

SAVOY SERIES/DELUXE SUBURBAN

Series Number	Body/Style Number	Body Type & Seating	Factory Price	Shipping Weight	Production Total
FLEET SPECIAL LEVEL TRIM PASSENGER CAR					
PP1/2-L	41	4-dr Sed-5P	2242/2394	NA	Note 1
PP1/2-L	21	2-dr Sed-5P	2192/2344	NA	Note 1
DELUXE LEVEL TRIM PASSENGER CAR					
PP1/2-L	41	4-dr Sed-6P	2275/2395	3365/3500	51,384
PP1/2-L	21	2-dr Sed-6P	2225/2344	3330/3490	26,820
SUBURBANS					
PP1/2-L	45	4-dr Sta Wag-6P	2623/2753	3740/3890	18,482
PP1/2-L	25	2-dr Sta Wag-6P	2567/2686	3680/3870	5,503

NOTE 1: Data above slash for six/below slash for V-8.

1960 Plymouth, Belvedere two-door hardtop sport coupe, 6-cyl

BELVEDERE/CUSTOM STATION WAGON — (6-CYL/V-8) — SERIES PP1-M/PP2-M — The Belvedere was Plymouth's medium range offering. The Custom station wagon was its utilitarian counterpart. Passenger cars had Belvedere scripts on the front fender "coves" and three shield medallions on the tailfins. Standard equipment included all Savoy features, plus front armrest and cigarette lighter. The station wagons did not carry front fender signatures. The nine-passenger Custom station wagon did, however, come standard with oversized tires and a power tailgate window.

BELVEDERE SERIES/CUSTOM STATION WAGON

Series Number	Body/Style Number	Body Type & Seating	Factory Price	Shipping Weight	Production Total
PASSENGER CARS					
PP1/2-M	41	4-dr Sed-6P	2404/2524	3375/3520	42,130
PP1/2-M	21	2-dr Sed-6P	2354/2473	3340/3505	6,529
PP1/2-M	23	2-dr HT Sed-6P	2426/2545	3370/3505	14,085
SUBURBANS					
PP1/2-M	45A	4-dr Sta Wag-6P	2726/2845	3750/3890	17,308
PP2-M	45B	4-dr Sta Wag-9P	2955	4000	8,116

NOTE 1: Data above slash for six/below slash for V-8s.

1960 Plymouth, Fury two-door convertible, V-8

FURY/SPORT SUBURBAN — (6-CYL/V-8) — PPI/2-H — The Fury was Plymouth's high-level offering. The Sport station wagon was its utilitarian counterpart. These models carried, as standard equipment, all items found on Belvederes, plus electric clock; chrome stone shields; back-up lights, lockable glove box; Fury front fender scripts (passenger cars only); large tailfin medallions of circular shape; wide, horizontally ribbed rocker panel underscores with rear extensions; and upper beltline moldings. The Sport Fury premium line was dropped. As in the lower lines, the Sport station wagon lacked front fender scripts and was equipped, at regular price, with oversize tires and power tailgate window when sold with rear-facing third seat. Plymouth started calling these "station wagons." They were part of a separate Suburban Series, but each wagon compared to the car-line they are grouped with here. The Sport Suburban was comparable to a Fury.

FURY SERIES/SPORT STATION WAGON

Series Number	Body/Style Number	Body Type & Seating	Factory Price	Shipping Weight	Production Total
PASSENGER CARS					
PP1/2-H	41	4-dr Sed-6P	2540/2659	3400/3550	21,292
PP1/2-H	43	4-dr HT Sed-6P	2621/2740	3445/3610	9,036
PP1/2-H	23	2-dr HT Sed-6P	2564/2683	3395/3535	18,079
PP2-H	27	2-dr Conv-6P	2932	3630	7,080
SUBURBANS					
PP2-H	45A	4-dr Sta Wag-6P	2989	3895	3,333
PP2-H	45B	4-dr Sta Wag-9P	3099	4020	4,253

NOTE 1: Data above slashes for six when offered/below slash for V-8.

PLYMOUTH BASE ENGINES

(VALIANT V-100) Inline. Six. Overhead valves. Cast iron block. Displacement: 170.9 cid. Bore and stroke: 3.406 x 3.125 inches. Compression ratio: 8.5:1. Brake hp: 101 at 4400 rpm. Four main bearings. Solid lifters. Carburetor: Carter Ball and Ball Type BBS one-barrel model 2900S. In mid-model year an aluminum cylinder block was adopted.

(SAVOY/BELVEDERE/FURY SIX) Inline. Six. Overhead valves. Cast iron or aluminum block. Displacement: 225.5 cid. Bore and stroke: 3.406 x 4.125 inches. Compression ratio: 8.5:1. Brake hp: 145 at 4000 rpm. Four main bearings. Solid valve lifters. Carburetor: Carter Type BBS one-barrel model 2985S.

(SAVOY/BELVEDERE/FURY/WAGON V-8) V-8. Overhead valves. Cast iron block. Displacement: 317.6 cid. Bore and stroke: 3.906 x 3.312 inches. Compression ratio: 9.0:1. Brake hp: 230 at 4400 rpm. Five main bearings. Solid valve lifters. Carburetor: Carter Type BBD two-barrel model 2921S.

CHASSIS FEATURES: Wheelbase: (Valiant) 106.5 inches. (Suburbans) 122 inches; (Plymouth passenger cars) 118 inches. Overall length: (Valiant 100 passenger cars) 183.7 inches; (Valiant 100 nine-passenger wagon) 184.8 inches; (Valiant 200 nine-passenger wagon) 185.1 inches; (Valiant 200 passenger cars) 184 inches; (Plymouth passenger cars) 209.4 inches; (Plymouth Suburbans) 214.9 inches. Tires: (all Valiants) 6.50 x 13; (Plymouth nine-passenger wagon) 8.00 x 14; (all others) 7.50 x 14.

OPTIONS (VALIANT): Power brakes ($41). Power steering ($73). Basic group ($102). Basic radio group ($160). Appearance group ($63). Convenience group, V-100 only ($16). Anti-freeze ($4). Front and rear bumper guards ($12). Solex safety glass ($37). Deluxe V-200 floor covering ($17). Hot water heater with defroster ($74). Back-up lights ($11). Left-hand outside rearview mirror ($5). Power tailgate window ($33). Push-button radio ($59). Padded dashboard ($13). Station wagon third seat ($61). White sidewall tires ($29). Undercoating with underhood pad ($14). Deluxe wheelcovers ($16). Variable speed windshield wipers ($17). Three-speed manual floor shift transmission was standard. Automatic transmission ($172). Six-cylinder 170 cid 148 hp 'Hyper Pack' engine. Four-barrel carburetor was optional as part of the 'Hyper Pack' option. When so-equipped, the Slant Six had 10.5:1 compression ratio and gave 148 hp at 5200 rpm.

OPTIONS (PLYMOUTH): Power brakes ($43). Power steering ($77). Air conditioning ($446); dual including heater ($640). Front fender sport shield ($14). Heater and defroster ($75). Back-up lights ($11). Prismatic inside mirror ($4). Two-tone paint, except convertible ($17). Sport Tone paint ($21). Sport Tone paint, station wagons ($32). Six-Way power seat ($96). Power windows ($102). Hi-Fi radio ($84). Push-button radio ($59). RCA automatic record player, radio mandatory ($52). Padded dashboard ($14). Sport deck tire cover ($28). Deluxe steering wheel ($11). Rear stone shields, Savoy, Belvedere, Deluxe and Custom ($4). Station wagon stowage compartment and Captive Air tires, 6-P ($62): 9-P ($91). Automatic swivel seats, Fury ($87). Four wheelcovers ($19). Windshield washer ($12). Variable speed windshield wipers ($6). Left-hand remote control outside rearview mirror ($18). Safe-T-Matic power door locks, two-doors ($23): four-doors ($30). Clear Ski-Hi rear window in Belvedere sport coupe ($23). Solex tinted Ski-Hi rear window in Belvedere sport coupe ($66). Electric clock, Savoy, Belvedere, Deluxe and Custom ($16). Three-speed manual transmission was standard. PowerFlite automatic transmission was optional, except with Commando V-8s ($189). TorqueFlite automatic transmission with V-8 engine ($211). TorqueFlite automatic transmission with Sixes only ($192). V-8 318 cid 260 hp 'Super Pack' four-barrel engine ($39). V-8 360.8 cid 305 hp 'Golden Commando' engine ($206). V-8 361 cid 310 hp 'Sonoramic Commando' engine ($389). V-8 383 cid 325 hp four-barrel engine. V-8 383 cid 330 hp 'Sonoramic Commando' engine ($405). Sure-Grip positive traction rear axle ($50). Dual exhaust, when not ordered in 'Super Pack' or standard with Commando V-8s ($27). Available rear axle gear ratios (various ratios). 'Sonoramic' engines used 30-inch tuned tubular intake manifolds with two four-barrel carburetors. See 1960 Dodge section for detailed engine specifications.

HISTORICAL FOOTNOTES: Rambler moved into third rank with higher sales, dropping Plymouth into fourth position, but only by a margin of less than 1,800 units. Plymouth's new fleet sales department helped sell many taxicabs and police cars this year. A 1960 Fury experimental prototype with a gas turbine engine evidenced Chrysler Corp.'s continued interest in this field. The Plymouth XNR sports-experimental dream car appeared this season. A fleet of 'Hyper-Pack' Valiants took the top seven positions in the 10 lap Compact Car Race at Daytona Speedway, Jan. 31, 1960. Three Valiants driven by Marvin Panch, Roy Schecter and Larry Frank then placed, 1-2-3 in the 20 lap main event in front of coast-to-coast television cameras.

1961 PLYMOUTH

VALIANT V-100 — (6-CYL) — SERIES 1100 — Valiants were classified as Plymouths this year. There were very few styling changes. A new look was achieved by blacking-out the delicately patterned grille inserts, while leaving the wider horizontal and vertical blades in chrome finish. This gave an 'eggcrate' grille appearance. Scripts reading Valiant were again seen behind the front wheel opening, but Plymouth signatures now decorated the trunk lid. Once again, a simulated spare tire impression was seen on the deck lid. The Valiant had generous headroom and a spacious front compartment, but rear legroom was cramped for six-footers. The glove compartment was of a bin-type design, but its push-button latching mechanism was difficult to operate. The V-100 models comprised the base offerings. Standard equipment included electric windshield wipers, turn signals, oil filter and five tubeless blackwall tires. In the middle of the 1961 model year, a version of the 225 cid Slant Six was released as a Valiant option. This engine had the same horsepower rating as the 1960 four-barrel 170 cid motor with 'Hyper-Pack' option.

PLYMOUTH I.D. NUMBERS: VIN on plate attached to left front door pillar. First symbol identifies car-line: 1=Valiant; 2=Plymouth six-cylinder; 3=Plymouth V-8. Second symbol identifies series: 1=V-100/Savoy; 2=Belvedere; 3=V-200/Fury; 5=V-100 wagon/Savoy wagon; 6=Belvedere wagon; 7=V-200 wagon/Fury wagon; 8=taxicab; 9=law enforcement special; 0=fleet car. Third symbol 1=1961. Fourth symbol indicates factory: 1=Detroit; 5=Los Angeles; 6=Newark, Del.; 7=St. Louis. Body plate below hood on cowl, inner fenders or radiator support indicates schedule date (SO); sequential body production number; body style number (second symbol in VIN plus numbers and letters in second column of charts below); trim code; and paint code. Six-cylinder motor number stamped on front or rear of left-hand side of block below cylinder head. V-8 motor numbers stamped on flat on top right-hand side of block behind water pump. Engine codes: R-17=170 cid/101 hp six and 170 cid/148 hp "hyper-pack" six; R-R-22=225 cid/145 hp six; R-318=318 cid/230 hp two-barrel V-8 or 318 cid/260 hp four-barrel V-8; R-36=361 cid/305 hp "Golden Commando" V-8 with four-barrel carb; R-38=383 cid/325 hp V-8 with four-barrel carb or 383 cid/330 hp V-8 with dual four-barrel carbs or 383 cis/330 hp V-8 with dual fours with "long-ram" induction or 318 cid/340 hp V-8 with dual fours and "short-ram" induction. R-41=413 cid/350 hp four-barrel V-8 or 413 cid/375 hp V-8 with dual fours and "short ram" induction.

Series Number	Body/Style Number	Body Type & Seating	Factory Price	Shipping Weight	Production Total
1110	41	4-dr Sed-6P	2014	2590	25,695
1110	21	2-dr Sed-6P	1953	2565	22,230
1110	45	4-dr Sta Wag-6P	2327	2745	6,717

1961 Plymouth, Valiant V-200 two-door hardtop coupe, 6-cyl

VALIANT V-200 — (6-CYL) — SERIES 1110 — The higher-priced Valiants were again grouped in the V-200 Series and were immediately perceptible by their bright metal side window trim moldings and extra bodyside brightwork. An upper molding traveled along the front fender feature line and onto the flare on the front door, piercing a large circular medallion positioned below the vent window. The lower body crease had a second strip of stainless steel running from behind the front wheel openings, across the doors and partially up the rear fenders, with a touch of ribbing at the back. As with the base series, a two-door model was added. It was called a two-door sedan though it had no center post. (The new V-100 two-door was of the 'post' style). Standard equipment for V-200s included all baseline items, plus the convenience group features: front door armrests; cigar lighter; right side sun visor; and dual horns. The V-200 also used a lower compression base power plant and, after midyear, could be had with an optional 225 hp engine.

Series Number	Body/Style Number	Body Type & Seating	Factory Price	Shipping Weight	Production Total
V1100	41	4-dr Sed-6P	2110	2600	59,056
V1100	10023	2-dr HT Sed-6P	2137	2605	18,586
V1100	10045	4-dr Sta Wag-6P	2423	2770	10,794

FLEET SPECIAL/SAVOY/DELUXE STATION WAGON — (6-CYL/V-8) — SERIES RPI/RP2-L — Plymouth's sheet metal was drastically and uniquely altered by Virgil Exner's design team. Styling was based on straight lines, supplemented by sculptured curves. This sounds like a contradiction and looked like it, too. A straight beltline ran from the front body corners to the rear, across the deck overhang and continued entirely around to the opposite front corner. This created a flat, shelf-like upper beltline plane into which the hood and deck gently sloped. However, the front fender feature lines had an entirely different look. It was rounded and canted at the same time. They came around the body corner running straight, but then angled into the stamped aluminum 'eggcrate' grille, made an abrupt curve and ran into the dual individual headlights, which sat side-by-side at a slight angle. Below the 'shelf,' the bodysides were a maze of concave and convex shapes, with flat doors thrown in for good measure. The front bumper ran straight across, with a rippled center section. The rear deck had a small, thin dorsal fin and a concave latch panel. Large, missile-shaped taillights were hung on the lower rear bodysides. Sleek flowing rooflines were used on all models — even Suburbans. Standard equipment on base models included oil filter; turn signals; sun visors; electric wipers; front foam cushions; front armrests; glove box lock; and five tubeless blackwall tires. Savoys and Deluxe Suburbans had no trim to speak of. The 'Fleet Specials' had a few standard features Deleted.

SAVOY SERIES/DELUXE SUBURBAN

Series Number	Body/Style Number	Body Type & Seating	Factory Price	Shipping Weight	Production Total
FLEET LEVEL/PASSENGER					
RP1/2-L	41	4-dr Sed-6P	2242/2361	3305/3460	Note 1
RP1/2-L	21	2-dr Sed-6P	2192/2311	3295/3435	Note 1
DELUXE LEVEL/PASSENGER					
RP1/2-L	41	4-dr Sed-6P	2310/2430	3310/3465	44,913
RP1/2-L	21	2-dr Sed-6P	2260/2379	3300/3440	18,729
DELUXE SUBURBAN					
RP1/2-L	45	4-dr Sta Wag-6P	2668/2788	3715/3885	12,980
RP1/2-L	25	2-dr Sta Wag-6P	2602/2721	3675/3845	2,464

NOTE 1: Data above slash for six/below slash for V-8.

1961 Plymouth, Belvedere two-door sedan, 6-cyl

BELVEDERE/CUSTOM STATION WAGON — (6-CYL/V-8) — SERIES RPI/RP2-M — Belvedere level trim included a tapering contrast panel along the beltline from behind the rear most door edge to the rear body corner, with chrome louvers at its forward end. There was also slightly brighter window trim and Belvedere script plates on the left edge of the concave rear deck lid latch panel. Belvederes (and Custom Suburbans) had all Savoy/Deluxe type equipment, plus rear armrests; cigar lighter and, on nine-passengers, a power tailgate window and oversized tires. Plymouth paid quite a bit of attention to interior appointments for 1961. The transmission push buttons (automatic) were larger and rectangular for easier operation. A new, magnetic drive 'thermometer' type speedometer functioned with less noise. The previous system of gears was replaced with a cable-driven 12-pole annular-ceramic magnet with temperature compensator. This early analog gauge was more accurate. Body insulation was also improved. Square steering wheels — said to give a good instrument field of view — were a Belvedere option. Technical innovations included standardization of Ram-Tuned induction manifolding with the 383 cid engine option; the use of a cast iron intake manifold on the Slant Six; lower compression ratios for regular fuel adaptability; alternator electrical systems; and closed crankcase ventilation on all cars built for California sale.

BELVEDERE SERIES/CUSTOM SUBURBAN

Series Number	Body/Style Number	Body Type & Seating	Factory Price	Shipping Weight	Production Total
PASSENGER CARS					
RP1/2-M	41	4-dr Sed-6P	2439/2559	3315/3470	40,090
RP1/2-M	23	2-dr HT Sed-6P	2461/2580	3320/3460	9,591
RP1/2-M	21	2-dr Sed-6P	2389/2508	3300/3450	4,740
SUBURBANS					
RP1/2-M	45A	4-dr Sta Wag-6P	2761/2880	3730/3885	13,553
RP2-M	45B	4-dr Sta Wag-9P	2990	3985	NA

NOTE 1: Data above slash for six if offered/below slash (or no slash) for V-8.

1961 Plymouth, Fury two-door hardtop sport coupe, V-8

FURY/SPORT STATION WAGON — (6-CYL/V-8) — SERIES — RP1/RP2-H — Furys and Sport Suburbans were Plymouth's richest models and the only real flashy cars of the year. They began at the Belvedere/Custom trim level and added upgraded upholstery; bright, full-length beltline trim; Fury or Sport signatures behind the front wheel openings; heavy slanted chrome louvers on the upper bodyside contrast panels (which also had aluminum inserts); a chrome base for the deck lid dorsal fin; full wheel discs; and, on two-door hardtop sedans, a larger 'Sky-Hi' rear window. Standard equipment extras were back-up lights and an electric clock. In addition, the missile-shaped taillight housings were fully chrome-plated. One outstanding performance attribute of all 1961 Plymouths was handling. The cars were extremely stable at all speeds and known, among enthusiasts, for excellent maneuverability. They could really go, too, when equipped with the Golden Commando (305 hp) V-8; Sonoramic Commando Ram-Tuned (330 and 340 hp) 383 cid V-8 or 350 and 375 performance options on a new 413 cid block. The latter choices were midyear additions aimed at increased competition from Pontiac, Ford, and Chevrolet in racing.

FURY SERIES/SPORT SUBURBAN

Series Number	Body/Style Number	Body Type & Seating	Factory Price	Shipping Weight	Production Total
PASSENGER CARS					
RP1/2-H	41	4-dr Sed-6P	2575/2694	3350/3515	22,619
RP1/2-H	43	4-dr HT Sed-6P	2656/2775	3390/3555	8,507
RP1/2-H	23	2-dr HT Sed-6P	2599/2718	33--/3520	16,141
RP2-H	27	2-dr Conv-6P	2967	3535	6,948
SUBURBANS					
RP2-H	45A	4-dr Sta Wag-6P	3024	3890	2,844
RP2-H	45B	4-dr Sta Wag-9P	3134	3995	3,088

NOTE 1: Data above slash for six if offered/below slash (or no slash) for V-8.

BASE ENGINES

(VALIANT V-100/V-200) Inline. Slant Six. Overhead valves. Cast iron block. Displacement: 170.9 cid. Bore and stroke: 3.406 x 3.125 inches. Compression ratio: 8.2:1. Brake hp 101 at 4400 rpm. Four main bearings. Solid lifters. Carburetor: Carter Ball and Ball Type BBS one-barrel model 3093S.

(SAVOY/BELVEDERE/FURY/WAGON SIX) Inline. Slant Six. Overhead valves. Aluminum block. Displacement: 225.5 cid. Bore and stroke: 3.406 x 4.125 inches. Compression ratio: 8.4:1. Brake hp: 145 at 4000 rpm. Four main bearings. Solid valve lifters. Carburetor: Carter Type BBS one-barrel model 3679S.

(SAVOY/BELVEDERE/FURY/WAGON V-8) V-8. Overhead valves. Cast iron block. Displacement: 317.6 cid. Bore and stroke: 3.906 x 3.312 inches. Compression ratio: 9.0:1. Brake hp: 230 at 4400 rpm. Five main bearings. Solid valve lifters. Carburetor: Carter Type BBD two-barrel model 3682S.

CHASSIS FEATURES: Wheelbase (Valiant) 106.5 inches; (Plymouth Suburban) 122 inches. (Plymouth passenger cars) 118 inches. Overall length: (Valiant) 183.7 inches; (Plymouth Suburban) 217.7 inches; (Plymouth passenger cars) 209.5 inches. Front tread: (Valiant) 56 inches; (Plymouth) 60.9 inches. Rear tread: (Valiant) 55.5 inches. (Plymouth) 59.6 inches. Tires: (nine-passenger Suburbans) 8.00 x 14; (other Plymouth V-8) 7.50 x 14; (other Plymouth 6-cyl) 7.00 x 14; (Valiants) 6.50 x 13.

OPTIONS (VALIANT): Power brakes ($41). Power steering ($73). Basic group ($102). Basic radio group ($160). Appearance group ($63). Convenience group, V-100 only ($16). Anti-freeze ($4). Front and rear bumper guards ($12). Solex safety glass ($37). Deluxe V-200 floor covering ($17). Hot water heater with defroster ($74). Back-up lights ($11). Left-hand outside rearview mirror ($5). Power tailgate window ($33). Push-button radio ($59). Padded dashboard ($13). Station wagon third seat ($61). White sidewall tires ($29). Undercoating with underhood pad ($14). Deluxe wheelcovers ($16). Variable speed windshield wipers ($17). Three-speed manual floor shift transmission was standard. Automatic transmission ($172). Six-cylinder 225.5 cid 148 hp Slant Six engine. Positive crankcase ventilation system, mandatory on California cars ($5).

OPTIONS (PLYMOUTH): Power brakes ($43). Power steering ($77). Air conditioning including heater ($446). dual air conditioning with heater ($640). Front bumper grille bar ($14). All solex glass ($43). Headlight trim plate ($18). Heater and defroster ($74). Saf-T-Matic power door locks, two-door ($23); four-door ($30). Locking spare tire compartment, six-passenger wagons ($4). Two-tone paint, except convertible ($17). Six-Way power seat ($96). Power tailgate window, six-passenger wagon ($33). Push-button radio ($59). Hi-fi radio ($84). RCA automatic record player, radio required ($52). Square-shaped Deluxe steering wheel ($11). Four wheelcovers ($19). Left OSRV mirror ($5); same remote control ($14); matching right-hand manual ($5). Inside Prismatic mirror ($4). Safety pad instrument panel ($14). Windshield wipers, variable ($6); washers ($12), both together ($17). Savoy/Deluxe options, clock ($16): cigar lighter ($4). Custom/Sport Wagon. tailgate assist handle ($16). Undercoating and underhood pad ($14). Savoy/Deluxe, Belvedere/Custom Back-up lights ($11). Basic group ($92). Basic radio accessory group ($150). Appearance group ($47). Easy driving group ($98). Three-speed manual transmission was standard. TorqueFlite automatic transmission with standard V-8 ($189). TorqueFlite automatic transmission with V-8 engine options ($211). TorqueFlite automatic transmission with Slant Six ($192). Crankcase vent system, mandatory on California cars ($5). Dual exhausts as optional equipment ($27). V-8 317.6 cid hp four-barrel 'Super Fury' engine ($158). V-8 360.8 cid 305 hp four-barrel Golden Commando engine ($206). V-8 383 cid 325 hp four-barrel engine. V-8 383 cid 330 hp dual four-barrel Sonoramic Commando engine ($405). V-8 383 cid 340 hp dual four-barrel engine. V-8 413.2 cid 350 hp four-barrel engine. V-8 413.2 cid 375 hp dual four-barrel engine. Four-barrel carburetor ($119). All dual four-barrel engines used 'Sonoramic' tuned ram induction intake manifolds. Sure-Grip positive traction rear axle ($50). See 1961 Dodge section for detailed engine specifications.

HISTORICAL FOOTNOTES: The full-sized Plymouths were introduced Sept. 29, 1960 and the Valiant appeared in dealer showrooms the same day. Model year production peaked at 198,444 units for Plymouths and 133,487 Valiants. This compared to 242,725 and 187,808, respectively, in 1960. General manager of the company. this year was C.E. Briggs, who also held the title of Plymouth vice-president and chief executive officer. Chrysler-Plymouth Div. was formed this year, joining together the marketing of the related nameplates. Plymouth sales alone dropped to seventh rank in the American industry. The radical new styling was one factor in this decline. Option installation rates showed the following percentage applications for Plymouths (and Valiants in parenthesis): automatic transmission, 78 (62.1); V-8 engine, 63.7 (NA); radio, 46.1 (34.6); heater, 97.6 (94.6); power steering, 51.7 (10.7); power seat. 0.8 (NA); power brakes, 15.6 (0.8); air conditioning, 4.3 (NA); dual exhausts, 4.8 (NA); tinted glass, 18.3 (4.4) and windshield washers, 33.4 (24.4).

1962 PLYMOUTH

VALIANT V-100 — (6-CYL) — SERIES SV1-L — There were no major changes in 1962 Valiant styling, but minor refinements in appearance were visible from any angle. The inverted, trapezoid shaped grille had a heavier chrome frame which gave a richer look. The area ahead of the hood lip was flattened and had the Valiant name, in block letters, stamped into it. The grille insert consisted of six vertical 'stacks' of short horizontal blades, running top to bottom. They were segmented by means of five vertical division moldings. The center grille emblem was gone, replaced by a small rectangle of chrome at the top of the center divider. Side trim, on base models, was the same as in 1961. It consisted of just a Valiant chrome signature behind the front wheel opening. At the rear, the stamped 'continental tire' impression was gone. The 'cat's eye' taillamps of earlier years were replaced by round units at each lower body corner. A large round chrome ring was placed on the rear deck and pierced by a strip of chrome running up the center. The V-100 Series was the base line. Standard equipment included electric windshield wipers; turn signals; oil filter; front door armrests; cigar lighter; sun visors; dual horns; and five tubeless blackwall tires. Small hubcaps; unaccented window frames; and plain, but durable upholstery trims were seen.

PLYMOUTH I.D. NUMBERS: VIN on plate attached to driver's side front door hinge pillar. First symbol identifies car-line: 1=Valiant; 2=Plymouth six; 3=Plymouth V-8. Second symbol identifies series: 1=Valiant 100/Savoy; 2=Belvedere; 3=Valiant 200/Fury; 4=Valiant Signet/Sport Fury; 5=Valiant 100 wagon/Savoy wagon; 6=Belvedere wagon; 7=Valiant 200/Fury wagon; 8=taxicab; 9=law enforcement special; 0=fleet car. Third symbol indicate model year 2=1962. Fourth symbol identifies assembly plant: 1=Detroit, Mich.; 5=Los Angeles, Calif.; 6=Newark, Del.; 7=St. Louis, Mo. Last six symbols are sequential production number for series at factory. Body Number Plate on inner fenders, cowl or radiator support indicates SO number, body production sequence number, body style code (second column of charts below), trim code and paint code. Motor numbers stamped on right side of block; on six below cylinder head opposite number 1 cylinder; on V-8 below distributor. Engine number indicates

year (S=1962), displacement (17 for 170 cid, etc.), month (1=Jan., etc.) and day (01=Jan. 1). Engine codes: S-17=170 cid/101 hp six; S-22=225 cid/145 hp six; S-318=318 cid/230 hp 2V V-8 or 318 cid/260 hp 4V V-8; S-361=361 cid/305 hp 4V V-8 or 361 cid/310 hp 2x4V V-8; S-38=383 cid/330 hp 4V V-8 or 383 cid/335 hp 2x4V V-8; S-41=413 cid/365 hp 4V V-8 or 413 cid/385 hp 2x4V V-8 or 413 cid/410 hp 2x4V "Ram-Tuned" V-8.

VALIANT V-100 SERIES

Series Number	Body/Style Number	Body Type & Seating	Factory Price	Shipping Weight	Production Total
SV1-L	113	4-dr Sed-6P	1991	2500	33,769
SV1-L	111	2-dr Sed-6P	1930	2480	19,679
SV1-L	156	4-dr Sta Wag-6P	2285	2660	5,932

VALIANT V-200 — (6-CYL) — SERIES SV1-H — The Valiant V-200 lineup continued with three styles that were somewhat better dressed than the lowest-priced cars. They had bright metal side window accents; a bright metal roof gutter rail; chrome taillamp rings; full wheelcovers; and sweepspear side moldings. This trim began behind the front wheel opening and traced the lower body feature line to the rear quarters where three flat black 'dashes' were stamped into the molding. The trim then continued up over the rear wheel housing, across the upper fender line and around the rear upper body corners (short strips were used on all models at this point). The ring-type rear deck emblem, to conceal a body weld at this point, was a bit fancier, too. The V-200 came with all the basic features, plus special upholstery and trim and DeLuxe carpeting. Technical advances for all Valiants included 32,000 mile interval chassis lubrication, a higher torque starting motor and electrical printed circuitry. Unibody construction was continued and was highly publicized. The V-200 two-door hardtop sedan of 1961 was replaced by a conventional (full-pillared) two-door sedan.

1962 Plymouth, Valiant Signet two-door hardtop sport coupe, 6-cyl.

VALIANT V-200 SERIES

Series Number	Body/Style Number	Body Type & Seating	Factory Price	Shipping Weight	Production Total
SV1-H	133	4-dr Sed-6P	2087	2510	55,789
SV1-H	131	2-dr Sed-6P	2026	2500	8,484
SV1-H	176	4-dr Sta Wag-6P	2381	2690	8,055

SIGNET — 200 — (6-CYL) — SV1-P — The Valiant two-door hardtop sedan of 1961 was turned into a separate series one car. It was called the Signet-200 hardtop (the old and incorrect term "sedan" being dropped). This model had an exclusive appearance and unique appointments. The grille and headlight inserts were painted black and a large chrome ring was placed in the center of the grille. Special wheelcovers were seen. A Signet-200 medallion was added behind the front wheel opening at each side. In addition, painted accent stripes highlighted the upper front fender contour. Standard equipment included all V-200 items, plus bucket type front seats and a padded instrument panel. Like the V-200, the Signet was available with the optional 145 hp motor, but it used the same base engine as other lines. The series code SVI-P indicated its premium level status, the 'P' designating a 'premium' type Valiant.

SIGNET-200 SERIES

Series Number	Body/Style Number	Body Type & Seating	Factory Price	Shipping Weight	Production Total
SV1-P	142	2-dr HT Cpe-5P	2230	2515	25,586

FLEET SPECIAL/SAVOY — (6-CYL/V-8) — SERIES SP1-L/SP2-L — The Valiant had proved a relatively successful addition to the Plymouth family so this year the full-sized cars were given a Valiant look and scaled down by two inches in wheelbase and 7-1/2 inches in overall length. However, the rear side feature line stopped short of the Valiant's around-the-wheelhouse sweep. In fact, the back of the cars looked like the outcome of mating a Valiant with a regular 1961 Plymouth. The low, thin center dorsal fin remained atop the rear deck. The grille was not a Valiant inspiration either. It was concave, with a series of concave, vertically segmented fins. Dual horizontal headlamps were seen. The inner lenses were set into the grille and looked smaller than the outer lenses, which were positioned in large, tunneled, circular housings at each corner of the body. Rooflines were a radical departure from the past, most having wraparound backlights and a more formal look. A long bladed/short deck theme was apparent throughout the line. Savoys were the basic models, with their script nameplates high on the front doors and no extraneous trim. Standard equipment included oil filter; turn signals; sun visors; electric wipers; front armrests; glove box lock; five tubeless blackwell tires; and small hubcaps. Fleet Specials were basically Savoys with less standard features.

FLEET SPECIAL/SAVOY SERIES

Series Number	Body/Style Number	Body Type & Seating	Factory Price	Shipping Weight	Production Total
FLEET SPECIAL					
NA	203/303	4-dr Sed-6P	2913/2351	2955/3115	Note 1
NA	201/301	2-dr Sed-6P	2137/2295	2930/3080	Note 1
SAVOY					
SP1/2-L	213/313	4-dr Sed-6P	262/2369	2960/3115	49,777
SP1/2-L	211/311	2-dr Sed-6P	206/2313	2930/3080	18,825
SP1/2-L	256/356	4-dr Sta Wag-6P	2609/2717	3225/3390	12,710

NOTE 1: Fleet Special production included in Savoy.
NOTE 2: Data above slash for six/below slash for V-8.

BELVEDERE — (6-CYL/V-8) — SERIES SP1 /SP2-M — The Belvedere represented Plymouth's mid-priced full-sized nameplate. These cars had a strip of stainless steel running, along the fender feature line, from above the headlamps to mid-door, and ending with a spear tip there. Placed above the molding, on the door, were bright Belvedere signatures. Standard equipment was comprised of the Savoy assortment, plus armrests; front foam seat cushions; cigar lighter; and power tailgate window on nine-passenger station wagons. Like the Valiant, the 1962 Plymouths promoted 32,000 intervals between chassis lubes. They also had

printed electrical circuits; higher torque starters; uni-body construction; and a new aluminum transmission case to brag about. This automatic gearbox was a three-speed TorqueFlite unit, with push-button controls, available only on V-8 attachments. It allowed a lower transmission tunnel hump and shaved a few pounds as well. The year's early V-8 options included the 318 cid/260 hp 'Super Fury' V-8 with four-barrel carburetion, dual exhausts, 10.2:1 compression ratio and hydraulic lifters, plus the 361 cid/305 hp 'Golden Commando' engine with four-barrel induction, dual exhausts, 9.0:1 compression ratio and hydraulic lifters. Other choices were released as running additions to the high-performance equipment list.

BELVEDERE SERIES

Series Number	Body/Style Number	Body Type & Seating	Factory Price	Shipping Weight	Production Total
SP1/2-M	223/323	4-dr Sed-6P	2399/2507	2960/3095	31,263
SP1/2-M	221/321	2-dr Sed-6P	2342/2450	2930/3070	3,128
SP1/2-M	222/322	2-dr HT Sed-6P	2341/2538	2945/3075	5,086
SP1/2-M	266/366	4-dr Sta Wag-6P	2708/2815	3245/3390	9,781
SP2-M	367	4-dr Sta Wag-6P	2917	3440	4,168

NOTE 1: Data above slash for six/below slash for V-8.

1962 Plymouth, Fury four-door hardtop sedan, V-8

FURY — (6-CYL/V-8) — SP1/SP2-H — The Fury's SP1-H or SP2-H designation said a lot. S=1962; P=Plymouth; 1=six-cylinder/2= V-8. But it was the suffix 'H' which told the Fury story. It stood for high-priced. High-level appointments and a high-level of equipment were standard on Furys. Included were all Belvedere items, plus aluminum exterior trim inserts (on rear door/body top edge); back-up lights; electric clock; and power tailgate window operation on nine-passenger station wagons. Also, specially available options like all-vinyl trim in hardtops, rear foam seat cushion and Six-Way power seat. Wheelcovers were optional — not standard. A Fury signature script, quite large in size, was used for identification being placed behind the front wheel opening. The front fender feature line was highlighted with a heavy chrome strip, which was fluted at the forward tip. Thin moldings outlined the front and rear wheel openings, too. Only two styles, sedan and two-door hardtop sedan, were marketed with a six.

FURY SERIES

Series Number	Body/Style Number	Body Type & Seating	Factory Price	Shipping Weight	Production Total
SP1/2-H	233/333	4-dr Sed-6P	2563/2670	2990/3125	17,231
SP1/2-H	232/332	2-dr HT Sed-6P	2585/2693	2960/3105	9,589
SP2-H	334	4-dr HT Sed-6P	2742	3190	5,995
SP2-H	335	2-dr Conv-6P	2924	3210	4,349
SP2-H	377	4-dr Sta Wag-9P	3071	3455	2,411
SP2-H	376	4-dr Sta Wag-6P	2968	3395	2,352

NOTE 1: Data above slash for six/below slash; no slash is for V-8.

1962 Plymouth, Sport Fury two-door convertible, V-8

SPORT FURY — (V-8) — SERIES SP2-P — Announced about four months after the rest of the line, the revived Sport Fury became Plymouth's premium (P suffix) offering. It had such extras as bucket seats; center front console; full wheelcovers; all-vinyl trim; rear foam seat cushions; and Deluxe steering wheel as standard equipment. Even the fanciest 1961 Plymouths looked quite plain. In response to dealer wishes, several tack-on items were added to all Furys and Sport Furys at midyear. They included a third taillamp on each side (total six); beltline trim extensions (full-length); and license plate recess trim. Sport Furys, however, were distinguished by their signature script placement (ahead of front wheel opening); deck lid license plates; and red, white and blue finished trim insert dimples. Also, the grille was given a more strongly segmented appearance by blacking-out the wider division panels. The Sport Fury came as a two-door hardtop or convertible. Special engines were optional. Only V-8s were used in these cars, however. The 1962 Sport Fury convertible is quite a rare machine.

SPORT FURY SERIES

Series Number	Body/Style Number	Body Type & Seating	Factory Price	Shipping Weight	Production Total
SP2-P	342	2-dr HT-5P	2851	3195	4,039
SP2-P	345	2-dr Conv-5P	3082	3295	1,516

BASE ENGINES

(VALIANT V-100/V-200/SIGNET) Inline Six. Overhead valves. Cast-iron block. Displacement: 170.9 cid. Bore and stroke: 3.406 x 3.125 inches. Compression ratio: 8.2:1. Brake hp: 101 at 4400 rpm. Four main bearings. Solid valve lifters. Carburetor: Carter Type BBS one-barrel Model 3462S.

(FEET/SAVOY/BELVEDERE/FURY SIX) Inline Six. Overhead valves. Aluminum block. Displacement: 225 cid. Bore and stroke: 3-13/22 x 4-1/8 inches. Compression ratio: 8.2:1. Brake hp: 145 at 4000 rpm. Four main bearings. Solid valve lifters. Carburetor: Carter Type BBS one-barrel Model 3466S.

(V-8 FLEET/SAVOY/BELVEDERE/FURY) V-8. Overhead valves. Cast iron block. Displacement: 317.6 cid. Bore and stroke: 3-29/32 x 3-15/16 inches. Compression ratio: 9.0:1. Brake hp: 230 at 4400 rpm. Five main bearings. Solid valve lifters. Carburetor: Carter Type BBD two-barrel Model 3472S.

(V-8 SPORT FURY) V-8. Overhead valves. Cast iron block. Displacement: 360.8 cid. Bore and stroke: 4.125 x 3.375. Compression ratio: 9.0:1. Brake hp: 305 at 4800 rpm. Five main bearings. Hydraulic valve lifters. Carburetor: Carter AFB-3252S four-barrel.

(See 1962 Dodge section for complete MoPar engine specifications.)

CHASSIS FEATURES: Wheelbase: (Valiants) 106.5 inches; (Plymouths) 116 inches. Overall length: (Valiants) 184.2 inches; (Plymouth station wagons) 210 inches; (other Plymouths) 202 inches. Front tread: (Valiant) 55.9 inches; (Plymouth) 59.4 inches. Rear tread: (Valiant) 55.6 inches: (Plymouth) 57.5 inches. Tires: (Valiants) 6.50 x 13; (all Plymouth wagons/ V-8s) 7.00 x 14, (other Plymouths) 6.50 x 14.

OPTIONS, VALIANT: Power brakes ($41). Power steering ($73). Air conditioning dealer installation. Anti-freeze ($4). Front and rear bumper guards ($11). Tinted windshield ($14); all tinted windows; Solex ($28). Heater and defroster ($74). Back-up lights ($11). Left-hand outside rearview mirror ($5). Day/Nite inside rearview mirror ($4). Two-tone exterior finish ($16). Radio ($63). Station wagon luggage carrier ($48). Front seat belts ($19). Front foam seat cushions, except Signet ($11). Padded instrument panel ($13). White sidewall tires, size 6.50 x 13 ($29). Vinyl trim, V-200 four-door sedan ($20). Deluxe wheelcovers ($16). Windshield washer ($12). Variable speed windshield wipers ($5). Basic Group, includes: heater, variable speed wipers, left-hand outside rearview mirror, windshield washer and back-up lights ($107). Basic Radio Group, includes: radio, plus Basic Group ($166). Appearance Group, includes: wheelcovers, safety padded instrument panel and white sidewall tires, for V-200 only ($58). Three-speed manual transmission was standard. Six-cylinder 225 cid 145 hp aluminum engine. Crankcase vent system ($5).

OPTIONS, PLYMOUTH: Power brakes ($43). Power steering ($77). Air conditioning including heater ($446). Air-conditioning group ($375). Anti-freeze ($5). Front bumper bar ($14). Savoy options: Cigar lighter ($4); Front foam seat ($11); Clock ($16). Tinted glass, all windows ($43); Windshield only ($22). Heater and defroster, standard with air-conditioning ($75). Back-up lights ($11). Roof luggage rack, wagons ($48). Six-passenger Suburban, left-hand outside rearview mirror ($6). Day/nite inside rearview mirror ($4). Two-tone paint ($17). Six-Way power seat, Fury only ($96). Six-passenger station wagon power tailgate window ($33). Power windows ($102). Standard push-button radio ($59). Deluxe radio ($84). Seat belts ($19). Padded dashboard ($14). Deluxe steering wheel ($11). All-vinyl trim, Fury hardtops ($30). Four wheelcovers, except Sport Fury ($19). Windshield washer ($12). Variable speed windshield wipers ($6). Basic Group, Fury ($104); other models ($114). Basic Radio Group, Fury ($162); other models ($173). Safety Group ($107). Assist Lights Group, nine-passenger wagon ($7); other models ($12). Three-speed manual transmission was standard. TorqueFlite automatic transmission with six-cylinder ($192). Aluminum TorqueFlite automatic transmission with V-8 ($211). 'Super Fury' V-8 317.6 cid 260 hp four-barrel engine ($39). 'Golden Commando' V-8 361 cid 305 hp four-barrel engine ($103). Short ram V-8 413 cid 410 hp dual four-barrel engine ($545). Short ram V-8 413 cid 420 hp dual four-barrel engine ($612). S Sure-Grip positive traction rear axle ($50).

HISTORICAL FOOTNOTES: The full-sized Plymouths were introduced Sept. 28, 1961 and the Valiants appeared in dealer showrooms the same day. Model year production peaked at 172,134 full-sized units. Calendar year sales of 331,079 total cars were recorded. C.E. Briggs was the chief executive officer of the Chrysler-Plymouth Div. this year. Plymouth's model year output included 6,148 exported cars. The compact Valiant's model year output was recorded at 145,353 units of which 28,200 cars were built for export. Total Plymouth-Valiant model year totals were 317,487 assemblies. A total of 4,992 Plymouths and 28,198 Valiants had bucket seats for the model run. This indicates that some Sport Furys were made with bench seats and that some non-Signet Valiants had bucket seats. A total of 98,800 Plymouths used V-8 engines. Two versions of the '413' V-8 with 'short ram' intake manifolds became available in May 1962 and were used mostly for drag racing. Rare Plymouth options (with percentage installation rates in parentheses) include: power seat (0.6); power windows (0.8); back-up lights (5.2); tinted glass (10.8); and air conditioning (5.2); for Valiants, power steering (9.1); power brakes (0.7); seat belts (4.2); and tinted glass (3.0). Plymouth customers were not really options buyers. In August, 1962 a specially-equipped Plymouth attained the fastest speed ever recorded for a stock-bodied auto at this time. Running at the annual Bonneville National Speed Trials, the car roared at 190.073 mph over a one-way run.

1963 PLYMOUTH

1963 Plymouth, Valiant two-door hardtop, 6-cyl (PH)

VALIANT V-100 — (6-CYL) — SERIES TV1-L — A complete and major styling change was the first revamp for Valiants. The compact Plymouth was now two inches longer. It had a wide, flat hood and flat, square rear deck. The roofline was flatter, sharpened in profile and more conventional than in the past. Advances in body structure, many accessories and a new spring-staged choke were promotional highlights. The grille was a variation of the inverted trapezoid shape that characterized contemporary Chryslers, with a fine mesh insert. The upper belt feature line ran from the rear body, in a gentle sweep, to the front fender tip. Here it was 'veed' back and down to the trailing edge of the front fender. A nameplate adorned the hood of all styles and the sides of station wagons (or new convertible in upper level lines). Standard V-100 equipment included electric wipers; turn signals; front door armrests; cigar lighter; dual visors and horns and five black tires. The 170 cid slant six continued as base powerplant. Early in the season the 225 cid, aluminum version was an all-model option. However, it was later discontinued and replaced by a cast iron '225.' New, horizontal taillamps wrapped around the rear fender corners.

PLYMOUTH I.D. NUMBERS: VIN on plate attached to driver's side front door hinge pillar. First symbol identifies car-line: 1=Valiant; 2=Plymouth six; 3=Plymouth V-8. Second symbol identifies series: 1=Valiant 100/Savoy; 2=Belvedere; 3=Valiant 200/Fury; 4=Valiant Signet/Sport Fury; 5=Valiant 100 wagon/Savoy wagon; 6=Belvedere wagon; 7=Valiant 200/Fury wagon; 8=taxicab; 9=law enforcement special; 0=fleet car. Third symbol indicate model year 3=1963. Fourth symbol identifies assembly plant: 1=Detroit, Mich.; 2=Hamtramck, Mich.; 5=Los Angeles, Calif.; 6=Newark, Del.; 7=St. Louis, Mo. Last six symbols are sequential production number for series at factory. Body Number Plate on inner fenders, cowl or radiator support indicates SO number, body production sequence number, body style code (second column of charts below), trim code and paint code. Motor numbers stamped on right side of block; on six below cylinder head opposite number 1 cylinder; on V-8 below distributor. Engine number indicates year (T=1963), displacement (17 for 170 cid, etc.), month (1=Jan., etc.) and day (01=Jan. 1). Engine codes: T-17=170 cid/101 hp six; T-22=225 cid/145 hp six; S-318=318 cid/230 hp 2V V-8; T-361=361 cid/265 hp 2V V-8; T-38=383 cid/330 hp 4V V-8; T-42= Super Stock 426 cid/415 hp "Max Wedge Stage II" or Super Stock 426 cid/425 hp "Max Wedge Stage II" V-8.

VALIANT V-100 SERIES

Series Number	Body/Style Number	Body Type & Seating	Factory Price	Shipping Weight	Production Total
TV1-L	113	4-dr Sed-6P	1973	2535	54,617
TV1-L	111	2-dr Sed-6P	1910	2515	32,761
TV1-L	156	4-dr Sta Wag-6P	2268	2700	11,864

VALIANT V-200 — (6-CYL) — SERIES TV1-H — Again there was no code 'M' (middle level) Valiant Series. The high-priced line was the V-200, with the new styling. These models came with all basic features, plus special upholstery, special trims and Deluxe carpeting. The convertible was a new body style. An extra trim feature was a thin, full-length upper beltline molding. Station wagons had roof pillar nameplates.

VALIANT V-200 SERIES

Series Number	Body/Style Number	Body Type & Seating	Factory Price	Shipping Weight	Production Total
TV1-H	133	4-dr Sed-6P	2097	2555	57,029
TV1-H	131	2-dr Sed-6P	2035	2515	10,605
TV1-H	135	2-dr Conv-5P	2340	2640	7,122
TV1-H	176	4-dr Sta Wag-6P	2392	2715	11,147

VALIANT SIGNET — (6-CYL) — SERIES TV1-P — The Signet was classed as Valiant's 'Premium' range, above high-priced. Price, however, was in the compact car class and not really steep at all. Extra standard equipment on both body styles included bucket type front seats, back-up lights with appliques and full wheelcovers. The convertible came with a manually-operated top. A power top was not on the introductory accessories list, but may have been added during the year to stay competitive. Special Signet nameplates were attached at the front fender tips. On Dec. 1, 1962 an optional vinyl roof became available; the first offered on any Plymouth.

VALIANT SIGNET SERIES

Series Number	Body/Style Number	Body Type & Seating	Factory Price	Shipping Weight	Production Total
TV1-P	142	2-dr HT Cpe-5P	2230	2570	30,857
TV1-P	145	2-dr Conv-5P	2454	2675	9,154

FLEET SPECIAL/SAVOY — (6-CYL/V-8) — SERIES TP1/TP2-L — A return to conventionality and more normal size characterized Plymouth's 1963 styling theme. The cars were three inches longer, an inch wider and had a flat roofline that angled into a flatter rear deck. The front had a square look. Oval parking lamps ran vertically at each body corner. Uniform-sized appearing headlamps were housed, horizontally, within bright metal surrounds on the grille. The grille had a fine textured pattern, with prominent horizontal segments. Plymouth was spelled out, in block letters, across the edge of the head. A stand-up hood ornament was used. The bodyside feature line ran from the upper front fender slanting just slightly downward as it moved to the rear. There it overlapped a square-shaped contour. Savoy features were comprised of oil filter; turn signals; electric wipers; glovebox lock; dual sunvisors and front armrests. The nine-passenger wagon had, in addition, a power rear window and cargo light. Passenger cars came with two-ply tires, wagons with four-ply types of similar size.

FLEET SERIES

Series Number	Body/Style Number	Body Type & Seating	Factory Price	Shipping Weight	Production Total
FLEET SPECIAL					
NA	203/303	4-dr Sed-6P	NA/NA	3015/3215	Note 1
NA	201/301	2-dr Sed-6P	NA/NA	2970/NA	Note 1
SAVOY					
TP1/2-L	213/313	4-dr Sed-6P	2262/2369	3020/3220	56,313
TP1/2-L	211/311	2-dr Sed-6P	2206/2313	2980/3200	20,281
TP1/2-L	257/357	4-dr Sta Wag-9P	2710/2818	3375/3560	4,342
TP1/2-L	256/356	4-dr Sta Wag-6P	2609/2717	3325/3475	12,874

NOTE 1: Production of Fleet Specials not available; probably incl. in Savoy.
NOTE 2: Data above slash for six/below slash for V-8s.

BELVEDERE — (6-CYL/V-8) — SERIES TPI/TP2-M — Belvedere was full-sized Plymouth's middle-priced nameplate. This model had a wide, colored molding along the bodyside feature line. Belvedere signatures replaced Savoy script, at mid-fender behind the front wheel cutout. A short molding was placed on the rear roof pillar. Belvederes could still be ordered with the Slant Six or base V-8 engines. Other equipment included rear armrests, front foam seats, and cigar lighter.

BELVEDERE SERIES

Series Number	Body/Style Number	Body Type & Seating	Factory Price	Shipping Weight	Production Total
TP1/2-M	223/323	4-dr Sed-6P	2399/2507	3020/2335	54,929
TP1/2-M	221/321	2-dr Sed-6P	2342/2450	3000/3215	6,218
TP1/2-M	222/322	2-dr HT Cpe-6P	2431/2538	3025/3190	9,204
TP2-M	367	4-dr Sta Wag-9P	2917	3585	4,012
TP2-M	366	4-dr Sta Wag-6P	2815	3490	10,297

NOTE 1: Data above slash for six/below slash; no slash for V-8.

FURY — (6-CYL/V-8) — SERIES TP1/TP2-H — The Fury was Plymouth's high-level offering. In standard form it came with everything found in Belvederes, plus a padded dashboard, back-up lamps and electric timepiece. Trim features included a distinctive side molding (with color insert) that narrowed ahead of the front door. More window frame moldings were also added. And a rear deck panel beauty strip was applied. Identification was further increased with signatures behind the front wheel cutout; Fury block letters on the trunk and a rectangular emblem set into the right-hand end of the rear beauty panel. Two Furys still came with a Slant Six (cast iron block for most of the year), while V-8s included the '318' Commando; '383' Golden Commando and midyear '426 Commando;' better known to enthusiasts as the 'Super Stock' or 'Max Wedge Stage II' powerhouse. The four-speed gear box came only with V-8s, but another choice was a floor shifted three-speed manual unit with non-synchromesh first gear.

FURY SERIES

Series Number	Body/Style Number	Body Type & Seating	Factory Price	Shipping Weight	Production Total
TP1/2-H	233/333	4-dr Sed-6P	2563/2670	3075/3265	31,891
TP1/2-H	232/332	2-dr HT Cpe-6P	2585/2693	3030/3215	13,832
TP2-H	334	4-dr HT Sed-6P	2742	3295	11,877
TP2-H	335	2-dr Conv-6P	2924	3340	5,221
TP2-H	377	4-dr Sta Wag-9P	3071	3590	3,368
TP2-H	376	4-dr Sta Wag-6P	2968	3545	3,304

NOTE 1: Data above slash for six/below slash or no slash for V-8.

1963 Plymouth, Sport Fury two-door. hardtop, V-8 (PH)

SPORT FURY — (V-8) — SERIES TP2-P — The Sport Fury represented a premium priced Plymouth, easily identified by bright rocker panel strips. The hardtop also had three hash marks on the rear roof pillar. Standard was everything regular Furys came with, plus bucket seats; center console; wheelcovers, all-vinyl upholstery; Deluxe steering wheel and rear foam seat cushions.

SPORT FURY SERIES

Series Number	Body/Style Number	Body Type & Seating	Factory Price	Shipping Weight	Production Total
TP2-P	342	2-dr HT Cpe5P	2851	3235	11,483
TP2-P	345	2-dr Conv-5P	3082	3385	3,836

BASE ENGINES

(VALIANT V-100/V-200/SIGNET SIX) Inline, Six. Overhead valves. Cast iron block. Displacement: 170.9 cid. Bore and stroke: 3.406 x 3.125 inches. Compression ratio: 8.2:1. Brake hp: 101 at 4400 rpm. Four main bearings. Solid valve lifters. Carburetor: Carter Type BBS one-barrel Model 3675S.

(SAVOY/FLEET SIX) Inline, Six. Overhead valves. Aluminum/cast iron block. Displacement: 225.5 cid. Bore and stroke: 3.406 x 4.125 inches. Compression ratio: 8.2:1. Brake hp: 145 at 4000 rpm. Four main bearings. Solid valve lifters. Carburetor: Carter Type BBS one-barrel Model 3466S. NOTE: Due to demand which was too low to justify extra production costs. Plymouth discontinued the cast aluminum Six early in the 1963 model run.

(V-8 SAVOY/BELVEDERE/FURY/FLEET/SPORT FURY) V-8. Overhead valve. Cast iron block. Displacement: 317.6 cid. Bore and stroke: 3.906 x 3.312 inches. Compression ratio: 9.0:1. Brake hp: 230 at 4400 rpm. Five main bearings. Solid valve lifters. Carburetor: Carter Type BBD two-barrel Model 3472S.

(See 1963 Dodge section for complete MoPar engine specifications.)

CHASSIS FEATURES: Wheelbase: (Valiants) 106 inches, (Plymouths) 116 inches. Overall length: (Valiant wagons) 186.8 inches; (other Valiants) 186.2 inches; (Plymouth wagons) 210.1 inches; (other Plymouths) 205 inches. Front tread: (Valiant) 55.9 inches; (Plymouth) 59.4 inches. Rear tread: (Valiant) 55.6 inches; (Plymouth) 57.5 inches. Tires: (Valiants) 6.50 x 13; (Plymouths) 7.00 x 14.

OPTIONS, VALIANT: Power steering ($73). Air conditioning, dealer installation. Front and rear bumper guards ($12). Tinted glass, all windows ($28); windshield ($14). Heater with defroster ($74). Back-up lights. V-100 ($11). Back-up lights, with applique, V-200 ($14). Left-hand OSRV mirror ($5). Day/Nite inside rearview mirror ($4). Two-tone paint ($16). Power tailgate window ($33). Radio ($59). Roof luggage rack ($48). Front seat belts ($18). Front foam seats, except Signet ($11). Padded dash ($16). White sidewall tires ($29). Undercoating with hood pad ($13). Vinyl trim, V-200 four-door styles only ($20). Deluxe wheelcovers ($16). Windshield washer ($12). Variable speed wipers ($5). Basic Group, V-100 ($102); V-200 ($105). Basic Radio Group, V-100 ($165); V-200 ($167). Custom Appearance Group. V-100 ($50); V-200 ($34). Special Signet Group, Signet-200 only ($188). Three-speed manual transmission was standard. Automatic transmission ($172). Six-cylinder 225 cid 145 hp aluminum engine ($47). Six-cylinder 225 cid 145 hp cast iron engine. Heavy-duty 48-amp battery ($8).

OPTIONS, PLYMOUTH: Power brakes ($43). Power steering ($77). Air conditioning ($446); as part of accessory group ($375). Front bumper bar ($14). Rear bumper guards ($14). Savoy options: Cigar lighter ($4); foam seats ($11). Savoy and Belvedere options: Electric clock ($16); padded dash ($14). Rear foam seats, Fury ($11). Tinted glass, all ($40); windshield only ($22). Heater and defroster, without air conditioning ($74). Back-up lights, standard Furys ($11). Left-hand OSRV mirror ($6). Six-way power seat, Fury only ($95). Power windows, Furys only ($102). Standard push-button radio ($59). Deluxe radio ($84). Deluxe steering wheel, standard Sport Fury ($11). All-vinyl Fury hardtop trim, standard Sport Fury ($25). Undercoating with hood pad ($14). Tailgate assist handles with rear wind deflector ($21). Four wheelcovers, standard Sport Fury ($19). Windshield washer ($12). Variable speed wipers ($6). Basic Group. Fury ($104); others ($114). Basic Radio Group, Fury ($162); others ($173). Safety Group, Furys ($94); others ($107). Light Group, nine-passenger wagon ($7); others ($12). 7.50 x 14 tires. Three-speed manual transmission was standard. Automatic transmission with six ($192). Four-speed manual floor shift transmission was available in mid-season. 'Commando' V-8 360.8 cid 265 hp two-barrel 'Wedge' engine ($60). 'Golden Commando' V-8 383 cid 330 hp four-barrel 'Wedge' engine ($122). 'Super Stock' V-8 426 cid 415 hp four-barrel' Max Wedge Stage II' engine (NA). 'Super Stock 'V-8 426 cid 425 hp dual four-barrel 'Max Wedge Stage II' engine (NA). Sure-Grip positive traction rear axle ($50).

HISTORICAL FOOTNOTES: The full-sized Plymouths were introduced Oct. 3, 1962 and the Valiant appeared in dealer showrooms the same day. Model year production peaked at 442,794 units. Calendar year sales of 496,412 cars were recorded. P.N. Buckminster was the chief executive officer of the company this year. The model year production total included 244,395 Plymouths (158,612 with V-8s) and 198,399 Valiants (all sixes). The Belvedere became a 'hot' car this year. In June 1963, Plymouth announced development of its 426 cid "Super-Stock" or "Max Wedge Stage II" V-8 engine for supervised drag racing and stock car racing. Cars with this engine finished first and second in USAC (U.S. Auto Club) competition. Four-speed manual transmissions were made available at about the same time. The power team worked best in the lighter weight cars. The Belvedere was such a machine and even looked good with its new colored body trim. Two versions of the Super-Stock wedge engine with either 415 or 425 hp were available by special order. A total of just 2,130 Chrysler products (all brands) were made with 426 cid wedge engines. Some were Dodges, the rest Plymouths. Rare Plymouth options (percentage rates in parenthesis) included four-speed transmission (1.2); power seat (0.5); power windows (1.0); dual exhaust (4.1); and limited-slip differential (5.1); for Valiants, power steering (10.1); tinted glass (3.2); and air conditioning (1.6). The Satellite convertible, a show car, was seen this year. Many Plymouths went racing.

1964 PLYMOUTH

VALIANT V-100 — (6-CYL) — SERIES VV1-L — For 1964, Plymouth retrimmed the new Valiant body released in 1963. The most obvious styling change was a new grille with a horizontal bar theme. A medallion was placed at the center of the grille where the bars had a flat bulge. At the rear, the taillights were redone. They were now positioned vertically in the ends of the fenders. The ring style rear deck decoration was replaced with a Valiant script, located at the right-hand corner. The V-100 was in the base series. Heater and defroster; vinyl trim; turn signals; courtesy lights; front door armrests; and five tubeless black sidewall tires were listed as standard equipment. A new 273 cid V-8 was optional in all Valiants. However, there was no separate V-8 series. Passenger cars had V-100 identification on the rear roof 'C' pillar, but station wagons had Valiant signatures behind the front wheel housing and small V-100 nameplates on their narrow 'C' pillars.

PLYMOUTH I.D. NUMBERS: VIN on plate attached to driver's side front door hinge pillar. First symbol identifies car-line: V=Valiant V-8; 1=Valiant six; 2=Plymouth six; 3=Plymouth V-8. Second symbol identifies series: 1=Valiant 100/Savoy; 2=Belvedere; 3=Valiant 200/Fury; 4=Valiant Signet/Sport Fury/Barracuda; 5=Valiant 100 wagon/Savoy wagon; 6=Belvedere wagon; 7=Valiant 200/Fury wagon; 8=taxicab; 9=law enforcement special; 0=fleet car. Third symbol indicate model year 4=1964. Fourth symbol identifies assembly plant: 1=Detroit, Mich. (Lynch Rd.); 2=Hamtramck, Mich.; 3=Detroit, Mich. (Jefferson); 5=Los Angeles, Calif.; 6=Newark, Del.; 7=St. Louis, Mo. Last six symbols are sequential production number for series at factory. Body Number Plate on inner fenders, cowl or radiator support indicates SO number, body production sequence number, body style code (second column of charts below), trim code and paint code. Motor numbers stamped on right side of block; on six below cylinder head opposite number 1 cylinder; on V-8 below distributor. Engine number indicates year (V=1964), displacement (17 for 170 cid, etc.), month (1=Jan., etc.) and day (01=Jan. 1). Engine codes: V-17=170 cid/101 hp six; V-22=225 cid/145 hp six; V-273=273cid/180 hp V-8; V-318=318 cid/230 hp 2V V-8; V-36=361 cid/265 hp 2V V-8; V-38=383 cid/350 hp 4V V-8; V-42=426 cid/365 hp "Street Wedge" 4V V-8; V-426=426 cid/415 hp "Max Wedge Stage III" Super-Stock V-8 (2x4V) and V-426+ =426 cid/425 hp "Max Wedge Stage III" Super-Stock V-8 (2x4V); VH-426=426 cid/415 hp "Race Hemi" V-8 (2x4V); VH-426HC=high-compression 426 cid/425 hp "Race Hemi" V-8 (2x4V).

VALIANT V-100 SERIES

Series Number	Body/Style Number	Body Type & Seating	Factory Price	Shipping Weight	Production Total
VV1-L	113	4-dr Sed-6P	1992	2575	44,208
VV1-L	111	2-dr Sed-6P	1921	2540	35,403
VV1-L	156	4-dr Sta Wag-6P	2273	2725	10,759

VALIANT V-200 — (6-CYL) — VV1-H — The V-200 again represented the one-step-up Valiant. Trim distinctions were helpful in spotting these cars. A triangular badge on the deck lid centerline; a latch panel beauty molding; thin beltline moldings; bright metal roof gutter rails; and lower bodyside moldings were a few identifiers. V-200s had all of the basic equipment, plus full wheelcovers; special upholstery; Deluxe carpeting; front and rear armrests; instrument panel beauty moldings; and cigarette lighter. A small plate bearing the series designation was placed under the Valiant signature at the right-hand corner of the deck lid. All 1964 Valiants had a bevelled feature line along the edge of the roof.

VALIANT V-200 SERIES

Series Number	Body/Style Number	Body Type & Seating	Factory Price	Shipping Weight	Production Total
VV1-H	133	4-dr Sed-6P	2112	2570	63,828
VV1-H	131	2-dr Sed-6P	2044	2545	11,013
VV1-H	135	2-dr Conv-5P	2349	2670	5,856
VV1-H	176	4-dr Sta Wag-6P	2388	2730	11,146

VALIANT SIGNET — (6-CYL) — SERIES VV1-P — The Signet for 1964 came with foam rubber front seat cushions and attractively styled wheelcovers. A lower bodyside molding stretched horizontally between the wheelhousings and was complemented by another molding on the lower rear quarter 'projectile' flare. The front fender ahead of the wheelhousing carried a chrome Signet signature and a 200 number plate. Bucket seats were standard. Cars with the optional 273 cid engine came with V-shaped emblems at the sides of the cowl. This engine became available until Jan. 1, 1964.

VALIANT SIGNET 200 SERIES

Series Number	Body/Style Number	Body Type & Seating	Factory Price	Shipping Weight	Production Total
VV1-P	142	2-dr HT Cpe-5P	2256	2600	37,736
VV1-P	145	2-dr Conv-5P	2473	2690	7,636

554 Standard Catalog of American Cars

1964-1/2 Plymouth, Valiant Barracuda two-door fastback coupe, V-8

BARRACUDA — (6-CYL) — SERIES VV1-P — April 1, 1964 was the Barracuda's birthday. The sporty new 'glassback' coupe went head-to-head against Ford's new Mustang, but lost in the sales race. It was an adaptation of Valiant sheet metal to a uniquely styled roof, deck and rear window. The roof received a wrapover look mated to an oversized, curved rear backlight with a fastback shape. The deck lid bulged up to meet the glass. Trim features, front to rear. were distinct for this model. They included a split, negative space grille with center insert and horizontal outer division bars, wide rocker sill panels and a chrome band across the rear window base housing a center medallion. Plymouth block letters decorated the trunk and Barracuda signatures were positioned on the sides of the cowl. Front fenders with a slimmer V-shaped feature line were seen. Standard equipment included bucket front seats; bucket-shaped rear bench seat with folding backrest; special finned wheelcovers with three-bar spinners or slotted wheelcovers with simulated exposed hub and lug nuts; round chrome back-up light housings; and the base Valiant power team. For this year only, Barracudas carried Plymouth, Valiant and Barracuda identification plates.

BARRACUDA SERIES

Series Number	Body/Style Number	Body Type & Seating	Factory Price	Shipping Weight	Production Total
VV1-P	149	2-dr GlsBk HT-5P	2365	2740	23,443

SAVOY — (6-CYL/V-8) — SERIES VP1/VP2-L — Plymouth styling was face-lifted for 1964. A bevelled edge feature line was used for the roofs of sedans, while hardtops had a new, canti-levered type roof pillar. With this design, an extra large, wraparound backlight was employed and the pillars were much wider at the top than the bottom. A full-width grille was seen. It was 'veed' to the horizontal plane and featured an insert with six stacks of short horizontal blades, segmented by vertical division bars. There were wider horizontal blade sections at the outboard ends into which the dual headlamps were placed side-by-side. A more massive front bumper, housing the parking lamps, was used. At the rear, the 1963 look was further refined. Savoys had large, rectangular single taillamps. There was just a hint of a dorsal fin remaining. Plymouth block letters decorated the edge of the trunk. Savoy features were comprised of oil filter; turn signals; electric wipers; glovebox lock; dual sunvisors and front armrests. The nine-passenger wagon had, in addition, a power rear window and cargo light. Passenger cars came with two-ply tires, wagons with four-ply types of similar size. A Savoy identification script was positioned on the sides of front fenders, behind the wheel opening.

SAVOY/SERIES

Series Number	Body/Style Number	Body Type & Seating	Factory Price	Shipping Weight	Production Total
VP1/2-L	213/313	4-dr Sed-6P	2280/2388	3040/3210	51,024
VP1/2-L	211/311	2-dr Sed-6P	2224/2332	2990/3205	21,326
VP1/2-L	257/357	4-dr Sta Wag-9P	2721/2829	3400/3600	3,242
VP1/2-L	256/356	4-dr Sta Wag-6P	2620/2728	3345/3495	12,401

NOTE 1: Data above slash for six/below slash for V-8.

BELVEDERE — (6-CYL/V-8) — SERIES VP1/VP2-M — Plymouth's middle line was called the Belvedere again. This range could be identified by its full-length body side molding that was hook-shaped at the front end. Sedans also carried a horizontal 'C' pillar strip. Equipment feature extras were the same as seen the year before. A Belvedere signature script appeared behind the front wheel openings and on the right-hand side of the deck lid latch panel. However, there were no Plymouth letters on the rear edge of the trunk. The company was striving to give the Belvedere its own strong identity. An increased emphasis on performance was evident, too. However, Belvederes could still be ordered with the Slant Six or base V-8. Other standard equipment included rear armrests, front foam seats, and cigar lighter.

BELVEDERE SERIES

Series Number	Body/Style Number	Body Type & Seating	Factory Price	Shipping Weight	Production Total
VP1/2-M	223/323	4-dr Sed-6P	2417/2524	3065/3225	57,307
VP1/2-M	221/321	2-dr Sed-6P	2359/2466	3000/3210	5,364
VP1/2-M	222/322	2-dr HT Cpe-6P	2444/2551	3010/3190	16,334
VP2-M	367	4-dr Sta Wag-9P	2928	3605	4,207
VP2-M	366	4-dr Sta Wag-6P	2826	3510	10,317

NOTE 1: Data above slash for six/below slash for V-8.

1964 Plymouth, Fury four-door station wagon, V-8 (PH)

FURY — (6-CYL/V-8) — SERIES VP1/VP2-H — Plymouth's high-priced line was the Fury Series. It included four V-8 only models and two cars available with Slant Sixes. In standard form it came with everything found in Belvederes, plus a padded dashboard, back-up lamps and electric timepiece. Furys included wide bodyside moldings with color inserts that tapered to a single spear on the front tenders. Also seen was Fury block lettering on the rear fender sides; Fury script on the right-hand edge of the trunk; rear deck panel 'grille'; dual taillamps; roof pillar medallions on sedans; and upgraded interior trim. Any Plymouth from Savoy up, could be ordered with the optional 'Commando 426-S' engine.

FURY SERIES

Series Number	Body/Style Number	Body Type & Seating	Factory Price	Shipping Weight	Production Total
VP1/2-H	233/333	4-dr Sed-6P	2573/2680	3040/3230	34,901
VP1/2-H	232/332	2-dr HT Cpe-6P	2598/2706	3045/3215	26,303
VP2-H	334	4-dr HT Sed-6P	2752	3300	13,713
VP2-H	335	2-dr Conv-6P	2937	3345	5,173
VP2-H	377	4-dr Sta Wag-9P	3084	3630	4,482
VP2-H	376	4-dr Sta Wag-6P	2981	3530	3,646

NOTE 1: Data above slash for six/below slash for V-8.

1964 Plymouth, Sport Fury two-door hardtop coupe, V-8 (PH)

SPORT FURY — (V-8) — SERIES VP2-P — The Sport Fury was the year's premium offering. Exterior trim was characterized by a wide bodyside feature line molding with color insert and a red, white and blue cowlside decorative panel. Sport Fury lettering and scripts were seen in the normal places. Special wheelcovers with simulated knock-off hubs were used. Bucket seats were standard equipment, as was V-8 power. Cars ordered with the special 426-SS "Max-Wedge Stage III" V-8 had unique external telltale signs. Numbers revealing the displacement were set against a black panel bridging the opening of the stand-up hood ornament. This subtle touch was an understated way to let the world know what kind of beast was lurking below the hood.

SPORT FURY SERIES

Series Number	Body/Style Number	Body Type & Seating	Factory Price	Shipping Weight	Production Total
VP2-P	342	2-dr HT Cpe-5P	2864	3270	23,695
VP2-P	345	2-dr Conv-5P	3095	3405	3,858

NOTE 1: Data above slash for six/below slash for V-8.

BASE ENGINES

(VALIANT SIX) Inline Six. Overhead valves. Cast iron block. Displacement: 170 cid. Bore and stroke' 3.4 x 3.125 inches. Compression ratio: 8.2:1. Brake hp: 101 at 4400 rpm. Four-main bearings. Solid valve lifters. Carburetor: Carter Type BBS one-barrel Model 3462S.

(BARRACUDA/PLYMOUTH SIX) Inline Six. Overhead valves. Cast iron block. Displacement: 225 cid. Bore and stroke: 3.4 x 4.125 inches. Compression ratio: 8.2:1. Brake hp: 145 at 4000 rpm. Four main bearings. Solid valve lifters. Carburetor: Carter Type BBS one-barrel Model 3839S.

(VALIANT/BARRACUDA V-8) V-8. Overhead valves. Cast iron block. Displacement: 273 cid. Bore and stroke: 3.62 x 3.312 inch. Compression ratio: 8.8:1. Brake hp: 180 at 4200 rpm. Five main bearings. Solid valve lifters. Carburetor: Carter Type BBD two-barrel Model 3767S.

(V-8 PLYMOUTH) V-8. Overhead valves. Cast iron block. Displacement: 318 cid. Bore and stroke: 9.0:1. Brake hp: 230 at 4400 rpm. Five main bearings. Solid valve lifters. Carburetor: Carter Type BBD two-barrel Model 3682S.

NOTE: See 1964 Dodge for complete MoPar engine listing.

CHASSIS FEATURES: Wheelbase: (Valiant) 106 inches; (Barracuda) 106 inches; (Plymouth) 116 inches. Overall length: (Valiant station wagon) 188.8 inches; (Valiant car) 188.2 inches; (Barracuda) 188.2 inches; (Plymouth station wagon) 211.5 inches; (Plymouth car) 206.5 inches. Front tread: (Valiant/ Barracuda) 55.9 inches; (Plymouth) 59.5 inches. Rear tread: (Valiant/Barracuda) 55.6 inches. (Plymouth) 59.6 inches. Tires: (Valiant Six) 6.50 x 13; (Valiant V-8) 7.00 x 13, (Plymouth station wagon) 7.50 x 14; (other Plymouths) 7.00 x 14.

OPTIONS, VALIANT: Power brakes ($43). Power steering ($82). Tinted glass, all windows ($29); windshield only ($14). Remote-control outside rearview mirror ($12). Barracuda racing stripes ($31). Special buffed paint, Barracuda/Signet ($17). Two-tone finish, except Barracuda/Signet and convertibles ($16). Power convertible roof ($54). Transaudio radio ($59). Station wagon rooftop luggage rack ($48). Retractable front seat belts ($7). Safety padded instrument panel ($16). Three-spoke steering wheel, except V-100 ($1 7). Heavy-duty shock absorbers and suspension package ($17). Vinyl trim in V-200 four-door styles ($20). Vinyl roof, Signet hardtop only ($77). Custom spinner wheelcovers, Barracuda ($13); V-200 ($28). Bolt-on design sports wheelcovers, Signet/Barracuda ($34); V-200 ($50). Deluxe wheelcovers, V-100 and V-200 ($16). Variable speed wipers and washers ($17). Basic Group, includes: left-hand outside rearview mirror; windshield washer; variable speed wipers and radio ($84). Wagon Group, includes: power tailgate window; wind deflectors and luggage rack ($96). Sport Group, includes: simulated woodgrain three-spoke steering wheel; bolt-on-design wheelcovers; whitewalls ($80-$100). Performance Group, includes: suspension package; 273 cid four-barrel V-8 and power brakes, except wagons ($156). Air conditioning ($364). Three-speed manual transmission was standard. Four-speed manual floor shift transmission ($180). Six-cylinder 225 cid 145 hp two-barrel engine ($47). V-8 273 cid 180 hp two-barrel engine ($131). Heavy-duty 48-amp battery ($8). Sure-Grip positive traction rear axle ($39).

OPTIONS, PLYMOUTH: Power brakes ($43). Power steering, Belvedere ($86); Fury ($97). Dual air-conditioning, Fury station wagon ($550). Auto-Pilot speed control, Fury V-8 with automatic/power brakes ($85). Electric clock, standard Sport Fury ($16). Rear window defogger, Fury ($21). Tinted glass, all windows ($40); windshield only ($22). Padded instrument panel ($19). Back-up lights, standard Sport Fury ($11). Four-way power left-hand bucket seat, Sport Fury only ($78). Four-way power left and right bucket seats, Sport Fury only ($156). Four power windows ($102). Transaudio radio ($59). Transaudio AM/FM radio ($129). Front foam seat cushions ($11). Deluxe steering wheel, Belvedere ($11). Adjustable steering wheel, automatic and power steering required ($46). Deluxe steering wheel, Fury ($15). Tachometer, Sport Fury only ($50). Tailgate assist handles, Belvedere wagons ($21). Vinyl trim sedans and hard tops ($25). Wheelcovers, standard Sport Fury ($19). Bumper guards, front and rear except nine-passenger wagon, Belvedere ($31); Fury ($34). Retractable seat belts front and rear compartments ($30). Rear seat speaker with reverberator, except wagons ($36). Basic Radio Group ($86). Six-passenger station wagon Basic Wagon Group ($91). Air conditioning ($417). Three-speed manual transmission was standard. Automatic transmission ($191-$210). Four-speed manual Hurst floor shift transmission ($188). 'Commando' V-8 361 cid/265 hp two-barrel engine ($59). 'Commando' V-8 383 cid/305 hp two-barrel engine ($71). 'Commando' V-8 383 cid/330 hp four-barrel engine ($122). 'Commando' (Street Wedge) V-8 426 cid/365 hp four-barrel engine ($483). 'Super Stock' (Max-Wedge Stage III) V-8 426 cid/ 415 hp engine ($515). 'Super Stock' (Max-Wedge Stage III) V-8 426 cid/425 hp engine ($545). 'Super Commando' V-8 426/cid 415 hp 'Hemi' engine. ($1,800). 'Super Commando' V-8 426 cid 425 hp 'Hemi' engine ($2,000). Four-barrel carburetor on Commando '383' ($51). Sure-Grip positive traction rear axle ($50). Available rear axle gear ratios: 3.23:1; 3.31:1; 2.93:1; and 2.76:1.

HISTORICAL FOOTNOTES: The 1964 Plymouths and Valiants were introduced Sept. 20, 1963 and the Barracuda appeared in dealer showrooms in May, 1964. Model year production of Plymouths peaked at 274,689 units. Calendar year sales of 330,440 cars were recorded. The Valiant saw model year production of 225,245 units this year and calendar year sales of 190,789 cars. Total calendar year production for Plymouth and Valiant combined was 571,339. P.N. Buckminster was the chief executive officer of the company this year. The 'Super Stock' Max-Wedge Stage III 426 cid (426-R) V-8 was continued as a racing-only option in the $500 price range. Depending on compression ratio, it gave 415 or 425 hp. New was a street-tuned 426-S version of 365 advertised horsepower (about 410 actual horsepower). The 'Super Commando' 426 cid Hemi V-8 was released around Feb. 9, 1964 for competition use. The Hemi's in-the-crate price was approximately $1,800. Published power figures of 415 for the 11.0:1 compression version and 425 hp for the 12.5:1 high-compression version were considered conservative by most enthusiasts. A total of only 6,359 Chrysler products (Dodge and Plymouth) were built with 426 cid engines for model year 1964. Of these, only 271 were "Race Hemis." Rare Plymouth options and their percentage installation rates (in parentheses) included: four-speed gearbox (4.1); power seat (0.6), power windows (1.1); and dual exhausts (8.3); for Valiants, four-speed transmission (6.7); power brakes (0.7); and air conditioning (2.3).

1965 PLYMOUTH

VALIANT V-100/V-200 — (6-CYL) — SERIES VV1-L — The Valiant was only slightly face-lifted. The most obvious styling change was a new grille with more horizontal bars. The V-100 was in the base series. Heater and defroster; vinyl trim; turn signals; courtesy lights; front door armrests; and five tubeless black sidewall tires were listed as standard equipment. A new 273 cid V-8 was optional in all Valiants. However, there was no separate V-8 series. Passenger cars had V-100 identification on the rear roof 'C' pillar, but station wagons had Valiant signatures behind the front wheel housing and small V-100 nameplates on their narrow 'C' pillars.

PLYMOUTH I.D. NUMBERS: VIN on plate attached to driver's side front door hinge pillar. First symbol identifies car-line: V=Barracuda V-8; 1=Barracuda six; 3=Belvedere six; 5=Fury six; P=Fury V-8; R=Belvedere V-8. Second symbol identifies series: 1=Valiant 100/Belvedere I/Fury I; 2=Fury II; 3=Valiant 200/Belvedere II/Fury III; 4=Valiant Signet/Satellite/Sport Fury; 5=Valiant 100 wagon/Belvedere I wagon/Fury I wagon; 6=Fury II wagon; 7=Valiant 200/ Belvedere II wagon; 8=Barracuda; 9=Police special; 0=fleet car. Third symbol indicate model year 5=1965. Fourth symbol identifies assembly plant: 1=Detroit, Mich. (Lynch Rd.); 2=Hamtramck, Mich.; 5=Los Angeles, Calif.; 6=Newark, Del.; 7=St. Louis, Mo. Last six symbols are sequential production number for series at factory. Body Number Plate on inner fenders, cowl or radiator support indicates SO number, body production sequence number, body style code (second column of charts below), trim code and paint code. Motor numbers stamped on right side of block; on six below cylinder head opposite number 1 cylinder; on V-8 below distributor. Engine number indicates year (A=1965), displacement (170 for 170 cid, etc.), month (A=Jan., etc.) and day (A01=Jan. 1). Engine codes: A-170=170 cid/101 hp six; A-225=225 cid/145 hp six; A-273=273cid/180 hp V-8 and 273 cid/235 hp 4V V-8; A-318=318 cid/ 230 hp 2V V-8; A-361=361 cid/265 hp 2V V-8; A-383=383 cid/270 hp 2V V-8 and 383 cid/330 hp 4V V-8; A-426=426 cid/365 hp "Street Wedge" 4V V-8; V-426R=426 cid/415 hp "Max Wedge Stage III" Super-Stock V-8 (2x4V) and A-426S=426 cid/425 hp "Max Wedge Stage III" Super-Stock V-8 (2x4V); AH-426=426 cid/415 hp "Race Hemi" V-8 (2x4V); AH-426HC=high-compression 426 cid/425 hp "Race Hemi" V-8 (2x4V).

VALIANT VIOO/V200 SERIES

Series Number	Body/Style Number	Body Type & Seating	Factory Price	Shipping Weight	Production Total
V100					
AV1/2-L	V13	4-dr Sed-6P	2050/2178	2590/2770	42,857
AV1/2-L	V11	2-dr Sed-6P	1980/2108	2560/2740	40,434
AV1/2-L	V56	4-dr Sta Wag-6P	2330/2458	2750/2930	10,822
V200					
AV1/2-H	V33	4-dr Sed-6P	2167/2295	2605/2795	41,642
AV1/2-H	V31	2-dr Sed-6P	2101/2229	2570/2750	8,919
AV1/2-H	V35	2-dr Conv-5P	2404/2532	2695/2875	2,769
AV1/2-H	V76	4-dr Sta Wag-6P	2442/2570	2755/2935	6,133

NOTE 1: Data above slash for six/below slash for V-8.

1965 Plymouth, Barracuda two-door fastback coupe, V-8 (PH)

VALIANT SIGNET/BARRACUDA — (6-CYL/V-8) — SERIES AV — The bucket seat Signet was the premium level Valiant. Appearance extras included roof pillar trim; wheelhouse moldings; rocker panel moldings; front fender top ornaments and circular medallions on the trunk and grille. Standard equipment was comprised of all V-200 features, plus front foam seat cushions and full wheelcovers. The Barracuda was a second type of premium compact from Plymouth and technically a sub-model in the Signet line. However, a Valiant nameplate no longer appeared on the deck lid's right-hand corner. This was about the only external change from the original. New was an optional 'Formula S' competition package which included a 235 hp edition of the 273 cid V-8 (four-barrel); heavy-duty front torsion bars; heavy-duty rear springs; firm ride shock absorbers; sway bar; rally stripes; extra wide wheel rims; Goodyear Blue Streak wide oval tires; and 'Formula S' medallions ahead of the front wheel openings. Barracuda sales took a big jump this season.

VALIANT SIGNET/BARRACUDA SERIES

Series Number	Body/Style Number	Body Type & Seating	Factory Price	Shipping Weight	Production Total
VALIANT SIGNET					
AV1/2-P	V42	2-dr HT Cpe-5P	2309/2437	2620/2820	10,999
AV1/2-P	V45	2-dr Conv-5P	2526/2654	2725/2905	2,578
BARRACUDA					
AV1/2-P	V89	2-dr Spt HT-5P	2453/2535	2725/2930	64,596

NOTE 1: Data above slash for six/below slash for V-8.

1965 Plymouth, Belvedere Satellite two-door hardtop coupe, V-8

BELVEDERE — (6-CYL/V-8) — SERIES AR — The Belvedere nameplate was no longer used to designate the level of trim and equipment. It was now used to classify intermediate size ranges. Actually, this was the same platform used for all Plymouths just one year earlier. There were three kinds of Belvederes. The low level (L) offerings were in the Belvedere I Series and had, as standard equipment, heater and defroster; front seat belts; oil filter; and five blackwall tires. Trim consisted of a straight, three-quarter length side body molding from the front door edge back and with Belvedere I scripts ahead of it. The high level (H) Belvedere II models had, in addition, carpeting; special trim and upholstery; foam cushions; and back-up lights. Appearance distinctions were wide, full-length slanting horizontal moldings with color insert; Belvedere II signatures behind front wheel openings; and rocker panel strips. The premium level (P) Belvedere Satellite was endowed with a rich and sporty character. It had all equipment of the downscale models, plus front bucket seats; center console; full wheelcovers; and all-vinyl trim on the two-door hardtop. Side trim moldings were deleted, but louvers were seen on the Satellite's rear fenders and rocker panel moldings were used. Wheel opening moldings; Satellite signatures; and a rear horizontal beauty strip were nice accents. The 1965 Belvedere came with 318, 361, 383, and 426-S (wedge head) V-8s. Professional racers could also get the 426 cid Hemi with 425 hp. Styling for these cars was a revamp of the 1964 body with single headlamps and a crossbar grille super-imposed over a rectangular mesh background.

BELVEDERE SERIES

Series Number	Body/Style Number	Body Type & Seating	Factory Price	Shipping Weight	Production Total
BELVEDERE I					
AR1/2-L	R13	4-dr Sed-6P	2236/2330	3105/3200	35,968
AR1/2-L	R11	2-dr Sed-6P	2198/2292	3045/3130	12,536
ARI/2-L	R56	4-dr Sta Wag-6P	2527/2621	3380/3465	8,338
BELVEDERE II					
AR1/2-M	R33	4-dr Sed-6P	2321/2415	3100/3155	41,445
AR1/2-M	R32	2-dr HT Cpe-6P	2347/2441	3075/3170	24,924
AR1/2-M	R35	2-dr Conv-6P	2561/2655	3195/3265	1,921
AR1/2-M	R77	4-dr Sta Wag-9P	2708/2802	3450/3525	3,294
AR1/2-M	R76	4-dr Sta Wag-6P	2612/2706	3385/3465	5,908
BELVEDERE SATELLITE					
AR2-P	R42	2-dr HT Cpe-5P	2612	3220	23,341
AR2-P	R45	2-dr Conv-5P	2827	3325	1,860

NOTE 1: Data above slash for six/below slash for V-8.

1965 Plymouth, Sport Fury two-door convertible, V-8

FURY — (6-CYL/V-8) — SERIES AP — There were four lines of Furys for 1965. The low level (L) Fury I had heater and defroster; front seat belts; oil filter; and five blackwall tires. The Fury II (M) added front foam seats and carpets. The Fury III (H) also had a courtesy light package; electric clock; and back-up lamps. The Sport Fury (P) added bucket seats; console; special wheelcovers; Deluxe Fury steering wheel; and rear fender skirts. All four full-size Plymouths were on a 119 inch wheelbase (121 inch for wagons) and had unique sheetmetal. Features included a long, narrow and high look; hooded, vertically stacked dual headlamps; V-shaped rear fender profile; full-length, rectangular bodyside depression; formal sedan roof treatment or semi-fastback cantilevered roofline on hardtops; and flat rear deck lid with peaked centerline and a cove-like latch panel treatment. Fury I trim consisted of a three-quarter length horizontal molding from front door edge back. They had single taillamps. The Fury II had a full-length body side molding and single taillamps. The Fury III added a color insert to the side molding and had three, short horizontal bars of chrome on the cowl sides at mid-fender level. In addition, a twin taillamp treatment was used. The Sport Fury used two bars on the side of the cowl, with color treatment, and had Sport Fury signatures on front fenders and deck.

FURY SERIES

Series Number	Body/Style Number	Body Type & Seating	Factory Price	Shipping Weight	Production Total
FURY					
AP1/2-L	P13	4-dr Sed-6P	2401/2505	3490/3655	48,575
AP1/2-L	P11	2-dr Sed-6P	2348/2452	3430/3605	17,294
AP1/2-L	P56	4-dr Sta Wag-6P	2740/2844	3940/4120	13,360
FURY II					
AP1/2-M	P23	4-dr Sed-6P	2500/2604	3485/3660	43,350
AP1/2-M	P21	2-dr Sed-6P	2448/2552	3445/3605	4,109
AP2-M	P67	4-dr Sta Wag 9P	3009	4160	6,445
AP2-M	P66	4-dr Sta Wag-6P	2908	4135	12,853
FURY III					
AP1/2-H	P33	4-dr Sed-6P	2649/2754	3505/3685	50,725
AP1/2-H	P32	2-dr HT Cpe-6P	2656/2760	3485/3640	43,251
AP2-H	P34	4-dr HT Sed-6P	2825	3690	21,367
AP2-H	P35	2-dr Conv-6P	3006	3710	5,524
AP2-H	P77	4-dr Sta Wag-9P	3148	4200	9,546
AP2-H	P76	4-dr Sta Wag-6P	3047	4140	8,931
SPORT FURY					
AP2-P	P42	2-dr HT Cpe 5P	2920	3715	38,348
AP2-P	P45	2-dr Conv-5P	3164	3755	6,272

NOTE 1: Data above slash for six/below slash for V-8.

BASE ENGINES

(VALIANT/SIGNET SIX) Inline Six. Overhead valves. Cast iron block. Displacement: 170 cid. Bore and stroke: 3.40 x 3.125 inches. Compression ratio: 8.5:1. Brake hp: 101 at 4400 rpm. Four main bearings. Solid valve lifters. Carburetor: Carter Type BBS one-barrel Model 3833S.

(BARRACUDA/PLYMOUTH SIX) Inline Six. Overhead valves. Cast iron block. Displacement: 225 cid. Bore and stroke: 3.40 x 4.125 inches. Compression ratio: 8.4:1. Brake hp: 145 at 4000 rpm. Four main bearings. Solid valve lifters. Carburetor: Carter Type BBS one-barrel Model 3839S.

(V-8 VALIANT/SIGNET/BARRACUDA) V-8. Overhead valves. Cast iron block. Displacement: 273 cid. Bore and stroke: 3.63 x 3.31 inches. Compression ratio: 8.8:1. Brake hp: 180 at 4200 rpm. Five main bearings. Solid valve lifters. Carburetor: Carter Type BBD two-barrel Model 3767S.

(BARRACUDA 'FORMULA' V-8) Commando 273 V-8. Overhead valves. Cast iron block. Displacement: 273 cid. Bore and stroke: 3.63 x 3.31 inches. Compression ratio: 10.5:1. Brake hp: 235 at 5200 rpm. Five main bearings. Solid valve lifters. Carburetion: Carter AFB four-barrel.

(V-8 PLYMOUTH) V-8. Overhead valves. Cast iron block. Displacement: 318 cid. Bore and stroke: 3.91 x 3.31 inches. Compression ratio: 9.0:1. Brake hp: 230 at 4400 rpm. Five main bearings. Solid valve lifters. Carburetor: Carter Type BBD two-barrel Model 3847S.

NOTE: See 1965 Dodge for complete MoPar engine listings.

CHASSIS FEATURES: Wheelbase: (Valiant) 106 inches; (Barracuda) 106 inches; (Belvedere) 116 inches; (Satellite) 116 inches; (Fury station wagon) 121 inches; (Fury) 119 inches; (Sport Fury) 119 inches. Overall length: (Valiant/Barracuda) 188.2 inches; (Valiant station wagon) 188.8 inches; (Belvedere/Satellite) 203.4 inches; (Belvedere station wagon) 208.5 inches; (Fury/Sport Fury) 209.4 inches; (Fury station wagon) 216.1 inches. Tires: (Valiant/Barracuda Six) 6.50 x 13; (Valiant/Barracuda V-8) 7.00 x 13; (all Plymouth passenger) 7.35 x 14; (Plymouth station wagon) 7.75 x 14 or 8.25 x 14.

OPTIONS, VALIANT: Power brakes ($43). Power steering ($82). Tinted glass, all windows ($29); windshield only ($14). Remote-control outside rearview mirror ($12). Barracuda racing stripes ($31). Special buffed paint, Barracuda/Signet ($17). Two-tone finish, except Barracuda/Signet and convertibles ($16). Power convertible roof ($54). Transaudio radio ($59). Station wagon rooftop luggage rack ($48). Retractable front seat belts ($7). Safety padded instrument panel ($16). Three-spoke steering wheel, except V-100 ($1 7). Heavy-duty shock absorbers and suspension package ($17). Vinyl trim in V-200 four-door styles ($20). Vinyl roof, Signet hardtop only ($77). Custom spinner wheelcovers, Barracuda ($13); V-200 ($28). Bolt-on design sports wheelcovers, Signet/Barracuda ($34); V-200 ($50). Deluxe wheelcovers, V-100 and V-200 ($16). Variable speed wipers and washers ($17). Basic Group, includes: left-hand outside rearview mirror; windshield washer; variable speed wipers and radio ($84). Wagon Group, includes: power tailgate window; wind deflectors and luggage rack ($96). Sport Group, includes: simulated woodgrain three-spoke steering wheel; bolt-on-design wheelcovers; whitewalls ($80-$100). Performance Group, includes: suspension package; 273 cid four-barrel V-8 and power brakes, except wagons ($156). Air conditioning ($364). Three-speed manual transmission was standard. Four-speed manual floor shift transmission ($180). Six-cylinder 225 cid 145 hp two-barrel engine ($47). V-8 273 cid 180 hp two-barrel engine ($131). Heavy-duty 48-amp battery ($8). Sure-Grip positive traction rear axle ($39). Three-speed manual transmission was standard. TorqueFlite automatic transmission, with Six ($172); with V-8 ($181). Four-speed manual floor shift transmission with '170' Six ($179); with V-8 ($179). Four-speed manual transmission with floor shift and '225' Six ($186). Valiant/Signet six-cylinder 225 cid 145 hp one-barrel engine ($46). Barracuda V-8 273 cid 235 hp four-barrel engine ($230). Crankcase vent system, mandatory for California built cars ($5). Sure-Grip positive traction rear axle ($39). Available rear axle gear ratios: (six) 3.23:1; (V-8) 2.93:1.

BARRACUDA OPTION PACKAGES: The Barracuda Formula S package included Commando 273 V-8 engine; rally suspension; heavy-duty shocks; 5.50 x 14 wheels; Goodyear Blue Streak tires; tachometer; 'open wheel' covers.

OPTIONS, PLYMOUTH: Power brakes ($43). Power steering, Belvedere ($86); Fury ($97). Air conditioning ($346). Dual air-conditioning, Fury station wagon ($550). Auto Pilot speed control, Fury V-8 with automatic/power brakes ($85). Electric clock, standard Sport Fury and Fury III ($16). Rear window defogger, Fury ($21). Tinted glass, all windows ($40); windshield only ($22). Padded instrument panel ($19). Back-up lights, standard Sport Fury/Fury III/Satellite ($11). Six-Way power seat, Fury III only ($96). Four-way power left-hand bucket seat, Sport Fury only ($78). Four-way power left and right bucket seats, Sport Fury only ($156). Four power windows, except Belvedere I and Fury I/II ($102). Transaudio radio ($59). Transaudio AM/FM radio ($129). Front foam seat cushions, Fury I/Belvedere I ($11). Fender skirts, except wagons and standard Sport Fury ($19). Deluxe steering wheel, Belvedere ($11). Adjustable steering wheel, automatic and power steering required ($46). Deluxe steering wheel, Fury ($15). Tachometer, Sport Fury/Satellite only ($50). Tailgate assist handles, Belvedere wagons ($21). Vinyl trim, Belvedere II/Fury III sedans and hard tops ($25). Wheelcovers, standard Satellite/Sport Fury ($19). Bumper guards, front and rear except nine-passenger wagon, Belvedere ($31). Fury ($34). Retractable seat belts. front and rear compartments ($30). Rear seat speaker with reverberator, except wagons ($36). Basic Radio Group ($86). Six-passenger station wagon Basic Wagon Group ($91). Three-speed manual transmission was standard. TorqueFlite automatic transmission, with 6-cyl. ($192); with '273' V-8 ($203); with other V-8s ($211). Four-speed manual floor shift transmission with '361' and '383' V-8 ($188). 'Commando' V-8 318 cid 230 hp two-barrel engine ($31). 'Commando' V-8 361 cid 265 hp two-barrel engine ($88). 'Commando' V-8 383 cid 330 hp four-barrel engine ($153). Hemi V-8 426 cid 425 hp dual four-barrel engine ($1800). '426-S' V-8 426 cid 365 hp four-barrel engine ($514). "436-S' V-8 426 cid 365 hp four-barrel engine ($545). "426-R' V-8 Hemi, 426 cid 415 hp dual four barrel engine ($1100). '426-R' Hemi V-8 426 cid 415 hp dual four-barrel engine ($1150). Crankcase vent system, mandatory on California built cars ($5). Sure-Grip positive traction rear axle ($39). Available rear axle gear ratios: (Six) 3.31:1; (V-8) 3.23:1 or 2.93:1. (Race Hemi not available in Fury).

HISTORICAL FOOTNOTES: The full-size Plymouths were introduced Sept. 25, 1964 and the Valiants appeared in dealer showrooms the same day. Model year production peaked at 683,456 units. Calendar year sales of 728,228 cars were recorded. P.N. Buckminster was the chief executive officer of the company this year. A Sport Fury convertible was pace car at the 1965 Indianapolis 500. Plymouth released a special Pace Car drivetrain package. available in any Fury at extra cost. The XP-VIP experimental show car was built this year. The 1965 Fury body introduced the use of curved side window glass on Plymouth products. A total of 6,929 Chrysler Corp. products, including Plymouths had 426 cid V-8s installed this year. Of these, only 360 were "Race Hemis" installed in Plymouths and Dodges. Four-speed transmissions were found in 2.6 percent of all Furys, 4.0 percent of all Belvederes, 19.4 percent of all Barracudas and 1.3 percent of all Valiants. Bucket seats were used in all Barracudas, 16 percent of Furys, 15.9 per cent of Belvederes and 10.8 percent of Valiants. Some '65 Plymouths (and Dodges) had an altered wheelbase "drag package" for NHRA Factory Experimental class drag racing.

1966 PLYMOUTH

VALIANT V-100/V-200 — (6-CYL/V-8) — SERIES BV — The Valiant V-100 was the base series. Standard features included front fender tip series identification badges; chrome band at base of roof pillar; heater and defroster; vinyl interior; turn signals; courtesy lights; front seat belts; front door armrests; and five blackwall tires. The 170 cid/101 hp Slant Six was the base engine in the BV1-L line. The 273 cid/180 hp V-8 was base engine in the BV2-L line. The Valiant V-200 was the one-step-up line. It had all of the above features, plus V-200 identification badges at front fender tips; straight, horizontal beltline molding; special upholstery and trim; Deluxe carpeting; front and rear armrests; and cigar lighter. The V-200 two door sedan and convertible were discontinued. Styling changes for the year included a split grille with fine-patterned insert; new front fenders; new rear fenders on sedans; new bevelled-edge rear deck lid; heavier rear bumper; and new, more formal roofline with large backlight. Station wagons had the new front end treatment, but carryover roof and rear end styling. A lower body feature

line ran at bumper height from the front to the rear quarter. It looped over both wheelhousings. On sedans, this line continued to the rear bumper. On station wagons, it stopped behind the rear wheel opening.

PLYMOUTH I.D. NUMBERS: VIN on plate attached to driver's side front door hinge pillar. First symbol identifies car-line: B=Barracuda; R=Belvedere/Satellite; P=Fury; V=Valiant. Second symbol identifies series: L=Valiant 100/Belvedere I/Fury I; H=Signet/Valiant 200/Belvedere II/Fury III; M=Fury II; P=Barracuda/Satellite/Sport Fury; K=Police; T=taxicab; S=VIP. Third and fourth symbols indicate body style and appear as the last two digits in Body/Style Number in charts below. Fifth symbol identifies engine: A=170 cid six; B=225 cid six; C=special order option six; D=273 cid V-8; E=318 cid V-8; F=361 cid V-8; G=383 cid V-8; H=426 "Street Hemi;" J=440 cid V-8; K=special order option V-8. Sixth symbol indicate model year 6=1966. Seventh symbol identifies assembly plant: 1=Detroit, Mich. (Lynch Rd.); 2=Hamtramck, Mich.; 4=Belvedere, Ill.; 5=Los Angeles, Calif.; 6=Newark, Del.; 7=St. Louis, Mo.; 9=Windsor, Ontario, Canada. Last six symbols are sequential production number for series at factory. Body Number Plate on inner fenders, cowl or radiator support indicates SO number, body production sequence number, body style code (second column of charts below), trim code and paint code. Motor numbers stamped on right side of block; on six below cylinder head opposite number 1 cylinder; on V-8 below distributor. Engine number indicates year (B=1966), displacement (170 for 170 cid, etc.), month (A=Jan., etc.) and day (A01=Jan. 1). Engine codes: A-170=170 cid/101 hp six; B-225=225 cid/145 hp six; B-273=273cid/180 hp V-8 and 273 cid/235 hp 4V V-8; B-318=318 cid/230 hp 2V V-8; B-361=361 cid/265 hp 2V V-8; B-383=383 cid/270 hp 2V V-8, 383 cid/325 hp 4V V-8; BH-426=426 cid/425 hp "Street Hemi" V-8 (2x4V); B-440=440 cid/365 hp 4V V-8.

VALIANT VI00/V200 SERIES

Series Number	Body/Style Number	Body Type & Seating	Factory Price	Shipping Weight	Production Total
V100					
BV1/2-L	VL41	4-dr Sed-6P	2095/2223	2630/2820	36,031
BV1/2-L	VL21	2-dr Sed-6P	2025/2153	2600/2800	35,787
BV1/2-L	VL45	4-dr Sta Wag-6P	2387/2515	2780/2970	6,838
V200					
BV1/2-H	VH41	4-dr Sed-6P	2226/2354	2635/2820	39,392
BV1/2-H	VH45	4-dr Sta Wag-6P	2502/2630	2780/3985	4,537

NOTE 1: Data above slash for six/below slash for V-8.

1966 Plymouth, Valiant Signet two-door hardtop coupe, V-8

VALIANT SIGNET/BARRACUDA — (6-CYL/V-8) — SERIES BV — Standard features of Signets included front fender tip identification plates and scripts; front fender top turn indicators; wheel opening moldings; lower feature line moldings; (with full-length, satin-finish paint treatment below); bucket seats with front foam cushions; and special full wheelcovers. Signet styling changes followed the Valiant pattern set by other lines, as did power teams. The two-door hardtop and convertible continued to be offered. The 1966 Barracuda was redesigned towards the front and largely unchanged at the rear and above the belt. It had the new split Valiant grille opening, but used an insert with a grid style pattern and had a circular medallion on the horizontally ribbed body-colored center panel. Barracuda scripts appeared in front of the forward wheel openings. On cars having the Barracuda 'S' option package, small circular medallions were placed below the scripts. The 225 cid/145 hp Slant Six (optional on other Valiants) was standard in the BV1-P Series Barracuda. The 273 cid two-barrel V-8 was standard in the BV2-P Series Barracuda. Pinstriping now appeared along the Barracuda's beltline and a vinyl top was a new option. Bucket seats; front fender turn indicators; rocker panel moldings; special full wheelcovers; and carpets were among standard items.

1966 Plymouth, Barracuda two-door fastback coupe, V-8

VALIANT SIGNET/BARRACUDA SERIES

Series Number	Body/Style Number	Body Type & Seating	Factory Price	Shipping Weight	Production Total
VALIANT SIGNET					
BV1/2-H	VH23	2-dr HT Cpe-5P	2261/2389	2635/2835	13,045
BV1/2-H	VH27	2-dr Conv-5P	2527/2655	2735/2925	2,507
VALIANT BARRACUDA					
BV1/2-P	VP29	2-dr Spt HT-5P	2556/2637	2800/2930	38,029

NOTE 1: Data above slash for six/below slash for V-8.

1966 Plymouth, Belvedere Satellite two-door hardtop coupe, V-8

BELVEDERE — (6-CYL/V-8) — SERIES BR — The Belvedere received a major restyling in 1966. It had a very square body. The fenders had a slab-like look, but were also gently sculptured forming a full-length rectangular depression panel above bumper top level. The large front wheel opening curved up into the rectangle, but the feature line passed over the rear wheel cutout. In profile, the edge of the front fender thrusted forward into a wide V-shaped form. Sedans had a square-angular roof with thick rear pillars. Hardtops retained the cantilevered roof treatment with a thicker base. This treatment was now seen at the rear of station wagons as well. Standard equipment on the Belvedere I included a Belvedere I nameplate behind front wheelhousing; thin, straight moldings along the lower feature line (from behind front wheel housing to rear bumper); heater and defroster; front seat belts; oil filter; and five blackwall tires. Base power teams were three-speed manual transmission with the 225 cid Slant Six or 273 cid V-8. The Belvedere II Series had its identification nameplate set a bit higher. It was adorned by a wide full-length chrome spear placed above the bodyside centerline. The lower trunk lid panel was satin-finished. Carpeting; upgraded upholstery; front foam cushions; and back-up lights were featured. The Satellite had less side trim than other models, but came with the fancy trunk treatment; rocker panel moldings; bucket seats and console; wheelcovers; and vinyl trims. A new powertrain option was a 'street' version of the 426 cid Hemi V-8 with 425 hp.

BELVEDERE SERIES

Series Number	Body/Style Number	Body Type & Seating	Factory Price	Shipping Weight	Production Total
BELVEDERE I					
BR1/2-L	RL41	4-dr Sed-6P	2315/2409	3040/3210	31,063
BR1/2-L	RL21	2-dr Sed-6P	2277/2371	3015/3175	9,381
BR1/2-L	RL45	4-dr Sta Wag-6P	2605/2699	3470/3575	8,200
BELVEDERE II					
BR1/2-H	RH41	4-dr Sed-6P	2405/2499	3035/3195	49,911
BR1/2-H	RH23	2-dr HT Cpe-6P	2430/2524	3040/3205	36,644
BR1/2-H	RH27	2-dr Conv-6P	2644/2738	3115/3285	2,502
BR1/2-H	RH46	4-dr Sta Wag-9P	2804/2989	3565/3670	8,667
BR1/2-H	RH45	4-dr Sta Wag-6P	2695/2789	3465/3585	4,726
BELVEDERE SATELLITE					
BR2-P	RP23	2-dr HT Cpe-5P	2695	3255	35,399
BR2-P	RP27	2-dr Conv-5P	2910	3320	2,759

NOTE 1: Data above slash for six/below slash for V-8.

1966 Plymouth, Sport Fury two-door hardtop coupe, V-8

FURY — (6-CYL/V-8) — SERIES BP — Plymouth's full-sized models for 1966 were face-lifted. A new split grille with horizontal blades stretched between stacked head lights. The rear quarter panels and bumper were changed on passenger cars. The top face of the bumper had Plymouth block lettering. The deck lid had a flat center depression that carried over the rear panel, splitting it horizontally. The Fury I was the base model range. Equipment included model nameplates; full-length mid-bodyside moldings; heater and defroster; front seat belts; oil filter; and five blackwall tires. The Fury II had all above features, plus front foam seats; carpets; Fury II nameplates; and moldings along the upper feature line. A spring special edition had metallic silver finish; blue vinyl seats; whitewalls; Deluxe wheelcovers; and bright side window accents. It revived an old Plymouth tradition. The Fury III had all features of 'L' and 'M' suffix models, plus the light package; electric clock; back-up lights; oversized tires on convertible; hooked 'candy cane' molding treatment; Fury III nameplates; and louver style cowlside ornaments. The premium offering in this car line was the Sport Fury, which had all above, plus bucket seats; console; Deluxe Fury steering wheel; special finned wheelcovers; fender skirts; and three decorative bars on front doors. A new offering, based on the full-sized sheet metal, was the VIP line. It originally included only a four-door hardtop with VIP identification; special side moldings with woodgrained inserts; fender skirts; center armrest seats; and interior roof pillar reading lamps. After Jan. 1, 1966, a VIP two-door hardtop coupe was available.

FURY SERIES

Series Number	Body/Style Number	Body Type & Seating	Factory Price	Shipping Weight	Production Total
FURY I					
BP1/2-L	PL41	4-dr Sed-6P	2479/2584	3485/3655	39,698
BP1/2-L	PL21	2-dr Sed-6P	2426/2531	3425/3610	12,538
BP1/2-L	PL45	4-dr Sta Wag-6P	2836/2941	3965/4130	9,690

FURY II

BP1/2-M	PM41	4-dr Sed-6P	2579/2684	3480/3665	55,016
BP1/2-M	PM21	2-dr Sed-6P	2526/2631	3430/3630	2,503
BP2-M	PM46	4-dr Sta Wag-9P	3087	4175	5,580
BP2-M	PM45	4-dr Sta Wag-6P	2986	4145	10,718

FURY III

BP1/2-H	PH41	4-dr Sed-6P	2718/2823	3505/3715	46,505
BP1/2-H	PH23	2-dr HT Cpe-6P	2724/2829	3480/3675	41,869
BP2-H	PH23	4-dr HT Sed-6P	2893	3730	33,922
BP2-H	PH27	2-dr Conv-6P	3074	3720	4,326
BP2-H	PH46	4-dr Sta Wag-9P	3216	4165	10,886
BP2-H	PH45	4-dr Sta Wag-6P	3115	4155	9,239

SPORTFURY

BP2-P	PP33	2-dr HT Cpe-5P	3006	3730	32,523
BP2-P	PP27	2-dr Conv-5P	3251	3755	3,418

VIP

BP2-H	PS43	4-dr HT Sed-6P	3133	3780	12,058
BP2-H	PS23	2-dr HT Cpe-6P	3069	3700	Note 1

NOTE 1: VIP two-door hardtop included in totals for Fury III two-door hardtop.
NOTE 2: Data above slash for six/below slash for V-8.

BASE ENGINES

(VALIANT/SIGNET SIX) Inline Six. Overhead valves. Cast iron block. Displacement: 170 cid. Bore and stroke: 3.40 x 3.125 inches. Compression ratio: 8.5:1. Brake hp: 101 at 4400 rpm. Four main bearings. Solid valve lifters. Carburetor: Carter Type BBS one-barrel Model 3833S.

(BARRACUDA/PLYMOUTH SIX) Inline Six. Overhead valves. Cast iron block. Displacement: 225 cid. Bore and stroke: 3.40 x 4.125 inches. Compression ratio: 8.4:1. Brake hp: 145 at 4000 rpm. Four main bearings. Solid valve lifters. Carburetor: Carter Type BBS one-barrel Model 3839S.

(V-8 VALIANT/SIGNET/BARRACUDA/BELVEDERE) V-8. Overhead valves. Cast iron block. Displacement: 273 cid. Bore and stroke: 3.63 x 3.31 inches. Compression ratio: 8.8:1. Brake hp: 180 at 4200 rpm. Five main bearings. Solid valve lifters. Carburetor: Carter Type BBD two-barrel Model 3767S.

(V-8 'FORMULA' BARRACUDA) Commando 273 V-8. Overhead valves. Cast iron block. Displacement: 273 cid. Bore and stroke: 3.63 x 3.31 inches. Compression ratio: 10.5:1. Brake hp: 235 at 5200 rpm. Five main bearings. Solid valve lifters. Carburetion: Carter AFB four-barrel.

(V-8 FURY/VIP) V-8. Overhead valves. Cast iron block. Displacement: 318 cid. Bore and stroke: 3.91 x 3.31 inches. Compression ratio: 9.0:1. Brake hp: 230 at 4400 rpm. Five main bearings. Solid valve lifters. Carburetor: Carter Type BBD two-barrel Model 3847S.

NOTE: See 1966 Dodge for complete MoPar engine listings.

CHASSIS FEATURES: Wheelbase: (Valiant) 106 inches; (Belvedere station wagons) 117 inches; (other Belvederes/Satellite) 116 inches; (Fury station wagon) 121 inches; (other Furys/VIP) 119 inches. Overall length: (Valiant station wagons) 189 inches; (other Valiants/Barracuda) 188.3 inches; (Belvedere station wagons) 270.1 inches; (Belvedere Style 46 station wagon) 208.1 inches; (other Belvederes/Satellite) 200.5 inches; (Fury Style 45 station wagon) 216.1 inches; (Fury Style 46 station wagon) 217.4 inches; (other Furys/VIP) 209.8 inches. Tires: (Barracuda/Valiant Six) 6.50 x 13; (Barracuda/Valiant V-8) 7.00 x 13; (Belvedere sedans/wagons) 6.95 x 14 with Six or 7.35 x 14 with V-8. (Belvedere convertible/Fury Six) 7.35 x 14 or 7.75 x 14 or Style 45/8.25 x 14 on Style 46; (Fury V-8 and VIP) 7.75 x 14 or 8.55 x 14 on all wagons.

OPTIONS: [VALIANT/BARRACUDA] Power brakes ($42). Power steering ($80). Power disc brakes ($82). Air conditioning ($319). Three-speed manual transmission was standard. TorqueFlite automatic transmission, with six ($172); with V-8 ($181). Four-speed manual floor shift transmission with '170' Six ($179); with V-8 ($179). Four-speed manual transmission with floor shift and '225' Six ($186). Valiant/Signet six-cylinder 225 cid/145 hp one-barrel engine ($46). Barracuda V-8 273 cid/235 hp four-barrel engine ($97). Crankcase vent system, mandatory, on California built cars ($5). Sure-Grip positive traction rear axle ($39). Available rear axle gear ratios: (Six) 3.23:1; (V-8) 2.93:1. [FURY] Power brakes ($42). Disc brakes ($110). Power steering, Belvedere/Satellite ($84). Power steering, Fury/VIP ($95). Air conditioning, all ($338). Three-speed manual transmission was standard. Automatic transmission with six ($192); with V-8 ($211). Four-speed manual floor shift transmission with '383' or '440' V-8s. 'Commando' V-8 383/cid 270 two-barrel engine ($71). 'Commando' V-8 383 cid/325 hp four-barrel engine ($120). 'Commando' V-8 440/cid 365 hp four-barrel engine ($234). Crankcase vent system, mandatory on California built cars. ($5). Sure-Grip positive traction rear axle ($50). Available rear axle gear ratios: 3.23:1, 3.55:1; 2.93:1 and 2.94:1. [BELVEDERE] 'Commando' V-8 383 cid 325 hp four-barrel engine ($150). 'Street Hemi' V-8 426 cid 425 hp dual four-barrel engine ($1105). 'Race Hemi' V-8 426 cid 425 hp dual four-barrel engine ($1800). Crankcase vent system, mandatory for California built cars ($5). Sure-Grip positive traction rear axle ($39). Available rear axle gear ratios: 3.23:1; 3.55:1; 2.93:1 and 2.94:1.

HISTORICAL FOOTNOTES: The Fury, Belvedere and Valiant were introduced Sept. 29, 1965 and the Barracuda appeared in dealer showrooms Nov. 25, 1965. Model year production peaked at 656,200 units. Calendar year sales of 687,514 cars were recorded. Robert Anderson was the chief executive officer of the company this year. The legendary Plymouth 'Street Hemi' engine was introduced this year. It had a bore and stroke of 4.25 x 3.75 inches; domed pistons with 10.25:1 compression; and dual four-barrel carburetors. It was conservatively rated for 425 hp at 5000 rpm. A total of 2,729 Street Hemi motors were installed in Dodges and Plymouths. Plymouth installations of the engine included 136 engines in Belvedere I two-door sedans (79 with four-speeds); 531 engines in Belvedere II hardtops (280 with four-speeds); 10 engines in Belvedere II convertibles (four with four-speeds); 817 engines in Belvedere Satellite hardtops (503 with four-speeds) and 27 engines in Belvedere Satellite convertibles, with no transmission break-out available. Richard Petty won the Daytona 500 stock car race with an average speed of 160.627 mph driving a Belvedere hardtop coupe with a de-stroked 404 cid 'Race Hemi.' Petty's engine produced over 550 hp. Industry trade journals indicate a total of 3,629 Chrysler products built with 426 cid V-8s of Wedge and Hemi design this season. Only some of these were Plymouths. Four-speed manual transmission was used in 1.6 percent of all Furys; 4.8 percent of Belvederes; 14.9 percent of Barracudas; and 0.5 percent of Valiants.

VALIANT/SIGNET — (6-CYL/V-8) — SERIES CV — All-new bodies were used on 1967 Valiants. The general styling was very straight and square, although the sides were mildly sculptured. They had a tapering lower feature line that widened toward the rear. The new fenders had a vertical 'slab' look. Features included a two-inch longer wheelbase; curved side glass; single headlamps in square bezels; a split grille that was subdivided horizontally; and vertical taillamps. The V-100 Series was the low line. Standard equipment included all safety features now required by government mandate; front armrests on two-doors (front and rear on four-doors); heater and defroster; five blackwall tires; and small model name bars at mid rear fender height. The trunk and center left-hand horizontal grille divider carried the Plymouth name. The V-200 was dropped, but a '200' decor group option was priced $71.95. It included bodyside moldings; cloth and vinyl trim; Deluxe door panels; ashtray and rear armrest (in two-doors); colored rubber mats; partial horn ring; and '200' nameplates. Valiants came with either the 170 cid Slant Six or 273 cid V-8 as standard, depending upon six or V-8 Series. Horsepower rating for the six was raised to 115 by use of Carter BBS Model 4286S one-barrel carb. The Signet was classed as the high level series and included all above features, plus bright window accents; roof gutter rail moldings; rocker panel strips; fender-mounted turn indicator lamps; Signet rear fender scripts; cologne-grain vinyl seats; carpeting; map, courtesy, trunk, and glove box lamps; cigar lighter; custom padded dash with aluminum trim; padded sun visor; horn ring; and either the 225 cid Slant Six or 274 cid V-8.

PLYMOUTH I.D. NUMBERS: VIN on plate attached to driver's side front door hinge pillar. First symbol identifies car-line: B=Barracuda; R=Belvedere; P=Fury; V=Valiant. Second symbol identifies series: E=Belvedere/Fury I; L=Valiant/Belvedere/Fury II; H=Signet/Belvedere II/Sport Fury; M=Fury III; Road Runner; P=Barracuda/Satellite/VIP; K=Police; T=taxicab; S=GTX/Sport Fury two-door; O=Super Stock. Third and fourth symbols indicate body style and appear as the last two digits in Body/Style Number in charts below. Fifth symbol identifies engine: A=170 cid six; B=225 cid six; C=special order option six; D=273 cid V-8; E=273 cid high-performance V-8 F=318 cid V-8; G=383 cid V-8; H=383 cid 4V high-performance V-8; J=426 cid "Street Hemi;" K=440 cid V-8; L=440 cid 4V high-performance V-8h; M=special order option V-8. Sixth symbol indicate model year 7=1967. Seventh symbol identifies assembly plant: 1=Detroit, Mich. (Lynch Rd.); 2=Hamtramck, Mich.; 4=Belvedere, Ill.; 5=Los Angeles, Calif.; 6=Newark, Del.; 7=St. Louis, Mo.; 8=Export; 9=Windsor, Ontario, Canada. Last six symbols are sequential production number for series at factory. Body Number Plate on inner fenders, cowl or radiator support indicates SO number, body production sequence number, body style code (second column of charts below), trim code and paint code. Motor numbers stamped on right side of block; on six below cylinder head opposite number 1 cylinder; on V-8 below distributor. Engine number indicates year (C=1967), displacement (170 for 170 cid, etc.), month (A=Jan., etc.) and day (A01=Jan. 1). Engine codes: C-170=170 cid/115 hp six; C-225=225 cid/145 hp six; C-273=273cid/180 hp V-8 or 273 cid/235 hp V-8; C-318=318 cid/230 hp 2V V-8; C-383=383 cid/270 hp V-8 or [Barracuda] 383 cid/280 hp V-8 or 383 cid/325 hp 4V V-8; [Road Runner only] C-383=375 hp; C-426=426 cid/425 hp "Street Hemi" V-8 (2x4V); C-440=440 cid/350 hp 4V V-8 and 440 cid/375 hp 4V high-performance V-8.

1967 Plymouth, Valiant Signet four-door sedan, V-8

VALIANT/SIGNET SERIES

Series Number	Body/Style Number	Body Type & Seating	Factory Price	Shipping Weight	Production Total
VALIANT 100					
CV1/2-L	VL41	4-dr Sed-6P	2163/2291	2675/2850	46,638
CV1/2-L	VL21	2-dr Sed-6P	2117/2245	2655/2830	29,093
VALIANT SIGNET					
CV1/2-H	VH41	4-dr Sed-6P	2308/2436	2680/2855	26,395
CV1/2-H	VH21	2-dr Sed-6P	2262/2390	2660/2835	6,843

NOTE 1: Data above slash for six/below slash for V-8.

1967 Plymouth, two-door Sports Barracuda with 'Formula S', V-8

BARRACUDA — (6-CYL/V-8) — SERIES CB — For 1966 the Barracuda shed its link to the Valiant family. It became a separate line with notch back, fastback and convertible available, all with totally new styling. They had curvy flowing features with a bare minimum of extraneous trim. Many magazines of the time compared the new Barracuda look to that of the Buick Riviera, but the two cars were actually world's apart in appearance. Characteristics for the redesigned Plymouth product included single headlights; concave roof pillars (on notch back coupe); curved side glass; a concave rear deck panel; wide wheel openings; and a sleek fastback. The fastback had a flowing, streamlined rear roof treatment and less glass area for rear window. The fastback was called the Sports Barracuda. Standard equipment on these cars included three-speed manual transmission; carpeting; full instrumentation; grille-mounted Rally lights; heater and defroster; left-hand outside rearview mirror; padded dash; rear fold-down seat (fastback); front bucket seats (convertible); all standard safety equipment; power top and glass rear window (convertible); and either the 225 cid Slant Six or 273 cid V-8. The new Barracudas were introduced Nov. 25, 1966, a bit later than other Plymouths.

BARRACUDA SERIES

Series Number	Body/Style Number	Body Type & Seating	Factory Price	Shipping Weight	Production Total
CB1/2-H	BH23	2-dr HT Cpe-5P	2449/2530	2730/2855	28,196
CB1/2-H	BH29	2-dr FsBk Cpe-6P	2639/2720	2815/2940	30,110
CB1/2-H	BH27	2-dr Conv-5P	2779/2860	2840/2965	4,228

NOTE 1: Data above slash for six/below slash for V-8.

1967 Plymouth, Belvedere GTX two-door hardtop coupe, V-8

BELVEDERE/SATELLITE/GTX SERIES

Series Number	Body/Style Number	Body Type & Seating	Factory Price	Shipping Weight	Production Total
BELVEDERE					
CR1/2-E	RE45	4-dr Sta Wag-6P	2579/2673	3455/3575	5,477
BELVEDERE I					
CR1/2-L	RL21	2-dr Sed-6P	2318/2412	3025/3185	4,718
CR1/2-L	RL41	4-dr Sed-6P	2356/2450	3065/3220	13,988
CR1/2-L	RL45	4-dr Sta Wag-6P	2652/2746	3470/3585	3,172
BELVEDERE II					
CR1/2-H	RH23	2-dr HT Cpe-6P	2457/2551	3050/3205	34,550
CR1/2-H	RH41	4-dr Sed-6P	2434/2528	3055/3210	42,694
CR1/2-H	RH27	2-dr Conv-6P	2695/2789	3120/3290	1,552
CR1/2-H	RH45	4-dr Sta Wag-6P	2729/2833	3485/3590	5,583
CR1/2-H	RH46	4-dr Sta Wag-9P	2836/2930	3555/3660	3,968
SATELLITE					
CR2-P	RP23	2-dr HT Cpe-5P	2747	3245	30,328
CR2-P	RP27	2-dr Conv-5P	2986	3335	2,050
GTX A					
CR2-P	RS23	2-dr HT Cpe-5P	3178	3535	Note 1
CR2-P	RS27	2-dr Conv-5P	3418	3615	Note 1

NOTE 1: GTX production included in 1967 Satellite production totals.
NOTE 2: Data above slash/below slash; no slash for V-8.

BELVEDERE/SATELLITE/GTX — (6-CYL/V-8) — SERIES CR — The medium-sized Belvedere and its derivative models were slightly face-lifted. The horizontal grille blades were thinner and housed dual side-by-side headlights with small grille extensions between them. The parking lamps were moved into the bumper. The taillamps were redone. A new economy model was a very plain station wagon, simply called a Belvedere. It was intended to replace the Valiant station wagon in price. Features included seat belts; dual outside rearview mirrors; dual brake system; flashers; energy absorbing steering column; Belvedere nameplates on front fender tips; and no bodyside moldings. Cars in the Belvedere I line included all above features, plus cigar lighter; padded dash; two-speed wipers with washers; back-up lights; front and rear armrests; tailgate filler panel on station wagons; rocker panel moldings; and Belvedere I nameplates. The Belvedere II line had all of the above, plus front foam seats; parking brake warning lamp; wraparound taillights; carpeting; wheel opening moldings; full-length side moldings (along upper feature line); and Belvedere II nameplates. Three-seat wagons in this series had all-vinyl seats; power tailgate window; two dome lamps; rear bumper step; and wall-to-wall carpeting. Convertibles had glass rear windows. The Satellite models had additional extras including front bucket seats with console (or center armrest seat); Deluxe wheelcovers; glove box light; fender top turn signals; upper body accent stripe; courtesy lights; and aluma-plate full-length lower body trim panels. The high-performance GTX had all this and more, including a "Pit-Stop" gas cap; Red Streak tires; dual hood scoops; dual sports stripes; heavy-duty three-speed TorqueFlite, brakes, suspension, and battery; and a standard 440 cid four-barrel V-8 engine.

1967 Plymouth, Sports Fury two-door hardtop coupe, V-8

FURY/VIP — (6-CYL/V-8) — SERIES CP — Completely new styling characterized full-sized Plymouths. Features included larger, slab-sided bodies; 'coke-bottle' profiles; horizontally segmented grilles with fine pattern inserts and thin center division bar; stacked dual headlamps; and front fenders with a 'fanned-out' look. The cantilevered hardtop roofline was gone, replaced by a semi-fastback on some styles and a 'Fast Top' formal look on others. Standard on Fury I was carpeting; armrests; vinyl headliner; heater/defroster; glove box lock; dual brake system; brake warning light; left-hand outside rearview mirror; back-up lights; inside mirror; energy absorbing steering column; two-speed wipers and washers; flasher; toggle/roller type panel; panel dash and visors; seat belts; and all-vinyl seats on wagons. Fury IIs also had vinyl and cloth sedan interiors; foam seats; bright window accents; bodyside moldings; and special nine-passenger wagon equipment. To all of this, the Fury IIIs added Deluxe cloth and vinyl interiors; electric clock; brake warning lamp; trunk light; glove box light; torsion bar front suspension; Flow-Through ventilation (four-door hardtop); light group; glass rear window; and all-vinyl interior in convertible. Extras on the Sport Furys were bucket seats; Deluxe 15 inch wheels; armrest seat cushion center unit (or console); Deluxe steering wheel; body accent stripes; sport wheelcovers; fender-mounted turn signals; and, on 'Fast Top' models, light group and Flow-Through ventilation. The VIP had all Fury III items, plus simulated walnut paneling; Deluxe gold-fleck upholstery with vinyl trim; Deluxe wheelcovers; lounge/sofa type seats; center armrests; Deluxe 15 inch wheels; light group; and Flow-Through ventilation.

FURY/VIP SERIES

Series Number	Body/Style Number	Body Type & Seating	Factory Price	Shipping Weight	Production Total
FURY I					
CP1/2-E	PE21	2-dr Sed-6P	2473/2578	3435/3535	6,647
CP1/20E	PE41	4-dr Sed-6P	2517/2622	3490/3590	29,354
CP1/2-E	PE45	4-dr Sta Wag-6P	2884/2989	3945/4055	6,067
FURY II					
CP1/2-L	PL21	2-dr Sed-6P	2571/2676	3435/3540	2,783
CP1/2-L	PL41	4-dr Sed-6P	2614/2719	3470/3595	45,673
CP2-L	PL45	4-dr Sta Wag-6P	3021	4060	10,736
CP2-L	PL46	4-dr Sta Wag-9P	3122	4100	5,649
FURY III					
CP1/2-M	PM23	2-dr HT Cpe-6P	2767/2872	3475/3605	37,448
CP1/2-M	PM41	4-dr Sed-6P	2746/2851	3515/3615	52,690
CP2-M	PM43	4-dr HT Sed-6P	2922	3668	43,614
CP2-M	PM27	2-dr Conv-6P	3118	367	4,523
CP2-M	PM45	4-dr Sta Wag-6P	3144	4080	9,270
CP2-M	PM46	4-dr Sta Wag-9P	3245	4125	12,533
SPORT FURY					
CP2-H	PH23	2-dr HT Cpe-5P	3033	3625	28,448
CP2-H	PH23	2-dr FsTp Cpe-5P	3062	3620	Note I
CP2-H	PH27	2-dr Conv-5P	3279	3705	3,133
VIP					
CP2-P	PP23	2-dr HT Cpe-6P	3117	3630	7,912
CP2-P	PP43	4-dr HT Sed6P	3182	3705	10,830

NOTE 1: Sport Fury two-door hardtop coupe/two-door Fast Top totals combined.
NOTE 2: Data above slash for six/below slash; no slash for V-8.

BASE ENGINES

(VALIANT 100 SIX) Inline Six. Overhead valves. Cast iron block. Displacement: 170 cid. Bore and stroke: 3.40 x 3.125 inches. Compression ratio: 8.5:1. Brake hp: 115 at 4400 rpm. Four main bearings. Solid valve lifters. Carburetor: Carter Type BBS one-barrel Model 4286S.

(SIGNET/BARRACUDA/PLYMOUTH SIX) Inline Six. Overhead valves. Cast iron block. Displacement: 225 cid. Bore and stroke: 3.40 x 4.125 inches. Compression ratio: 8.4:1. Brake hp: 145 at 4000 rpm. Four main bearings. Solid valve lifters. Carburetor: Carter Type BBS one-barrel Model 3839S.

(V-8 VALIANT/SIGNET/BARRACUDA/BELVEDERE) V-8. Overhead valves. Cast iron block. Displacement: 273 cid. Bore and stroke: 3.63 x 3.31 inches. Compression ratio: 8.8:1. Brake hp: 180 at 4200 rpm. Five main bearings. Solid valve lifters. Carburetor: Carter Type BBD two-barrel Model 3767S.

(V-8 'FORMULA' BARRACUDA/BELVEDERE) Commando 273 V-8. Overhead valves. Cast iron block. Displacement: 273 cid. Bore and stroke: 3.63 x 3.31 inches. Compression ratio: 10.5:1. Brake hp: 235 at 5200 rpm. Five main bearings. Solid valve lifters. Carburetion: Carter AFB four-barrel.

(V-8 FURY/VIP) V-8. Overhead valves. Cast iron block. Displacement: 318 cid. Bore and stroke: 3.91 x 3.31 inches. Compression ratio: 9.0:1. Brake hp: 230 at 4400 rpm. Five main bearings. Solid valve lifters. Carburetor: Carter Type BBD two-barrel Model 3847S.

(GTX ENGINE) V-8. Overhead valves. Cast iron block. Displacement: 440 cid. Bore and stroke: 4.32 x 3.75 inches. Compression ratio: 10.1:1. Brake hp: 375 at 4600 rpm. Five main bearings. Hydraulic valve lifters. Carburetor: Carter Type AFB four- barrel Model 4326S.

NOTE: See 1966 Dodge for complete MoPar engine listings.

CHASSIS FEATURES: Wheelbase: (Valiant/Barracuda) 108 inches; (Belvedere station wagon) 117 inches; (Belvedere passenger cars) 116 inches; (Fury station wagon) 122 inches; (Fury passenger cars) 119 inches. Overall length: (Valiant) 188.4 inches; (Belvedere six-

passenger wagon) 207.1 inches; (Belvedere nine-passenger wagon) 208.1 inches; (Belvedere/Satellite/GTX) 200.5 inches; (Fury six-passenger wagon) 216 inches; (Fury nine-passenger wagon) 217.3 inches; (Fury/Sport Fury/VIP) 213.1 inches;. Front tread: (Valiant) 57.4 inches; (Belvedere) 59.5 inches; (Fury) 62.0 inches. Rear tread: (Valiant) 55.6 inches; (Belvedere) 58.5 inches; (Fury) 60.7 inches. Tires: (Valiant/Barracuda Six) 6.50 x 13; (Valiant/ Barracuda V-8) 7.00 x 13; (Belvederes/Satellite/GTX) 7.35 x 14; 7.75 x 14; 8.25 x 14; (Fury/ Sport Fury/VIP) 7.75 x 14.

OPTIONS, BARRACUDA/VALIANT: Power brakes ($42). Power steering ($80). Air conditioning ($319). Front and rear bumper guards ($22). Tinted glass, all windows ($28); windshield only ($14). Remote control outside rearview mirror ($7). Special buffed paint ($17). Two-tone paint ($19). Transaudio AM radio ($57). Signet, vinyl bucket seat interior ($75). Twin front shoulder belts ($26). Fast manual steering ($13). Deluxe steering wheel with full ring on V-100 ($11); on other models ($5). Signet, Deluxe woodgrained wheel ($26). Vinyl roof on Signet ($75). Vinyl trim in Signet ($23). Bolt-on design 14 inch wheels, Signet ($51). Deluxe 13 inch wheels ($18). Deluxe 14 inch wheels ($21). Heavy-Duty suspension package ($14). Valiant 200 decor group package ($72). Basic group includes AM radio, wheelcovers, power steering and variable speed windshield wipers, with 13 inch wheels ($161); with 14 inch wheels ($164). Disc brakes. Three-speed manual transmission was standard. Automatic transmission, with six ($172); with V-8 ($181). Four-speed manual floor shift transmission, with V-8 only ($179). Valiant six-cylinder 225.5 cid/145 hp one-barrel engine ($46). Valiant V-8 273 cid/180 hp two-barrel engine ($97). Barracuda V-8 273 cid/235 hp four barrel engine. Barracuda V-8 383 cid/280 hp four-barrel engine. Heavy-duty battery 70-amp/hour ($8). Sure-Grip positive traction rear axle ($39). Available rear axle gear ratios: 3.23:1; 2.93:1 and various options.

OPTIONS, BELVEDERE/SATELLITE: Power brakes ($42). Power steering ($90). Front and rear bumper guards ($31). Cigar lighter, Belvedere wagon ($4). Cleaner Air package with six ($18); with V-8 ($25). Electric clock ($15). GTX console in Satellite ($53). Disc brakes with V-8 ($70). Tinted glass, all windows ($40); windshield only ($21). Headrests with bucket or individual bench seats, pair ($42). Station wagon rooftop luggage rack ($47). Two-tone paint, except convertible ($22). Special buffed paint ($21). Power windows, two-door ($100). Transaudio AM radio ($57). Transaudio AM/FM radio ($127). GTX front seat with folding center armrest, standard Satellite ($53). Heavy-duty shock absorbers, standard in GTX ($4). Twin front shoulder belts ($26). GTX Sport stripes ($31). Full horn ring Deluxe steering wheel, except wagon ($5). Woodgrained Deluxe steering wheel, except wagon ($26). Heavy-duty suspension package, except wagon ($22). Satellite and GTX Tachometer ($49). Vinyl roof, except wagons and convertibles ($75). Belvedere II vinyl trim ($24). Satellite 'Road Wheels' ($77). Satellite 14 inch sport wheelcovers ($18). Variable-speed wipers ($5). Three-speed manual transmission was standard. TorqueFlite automatic transmission with six ($188); with '273' V-8 ($202); with other V-8s ($206). Four-speed manual floor shift transmission, all except GTX ($188). Note: Four-speed manual gearbox not available with six or '273' and '318' V-8s. Commando V-8 318 cid/230 hp two-barrel engine ($30). Commando V-8 383 cid/270 hp two-barrel engine ($100). Commando V-8 383 cid/325 hp four-barrel engine ($150). 'Street Hemi' V-8 426 cid/425 hp dual four-barrel engine ($564). 'Super Commando' V-8 440 cid/375 hp four-barrel engine (standard in GTX). Heavy-duty alternator ($11). Heavy-duty battery ($21). Heavy-duty Sure-Grip axle, GTX ($139). Sure-Grip positive traction rear axle ($38). Available rear axle gear ratios: 3.23:1; 3.55:1; 2.93:1, and other options. Note: The only optional V-8 in the GTX was the 426 cid 'Street Hemi.'

OPTIONS, FURY/VIP CONVENIENCE: Power brakes ($42). Power steering ($95). Air conditioning ($338); dual system in Fury wagons ($538). Auto Pilot ($83). Sport Fury center console (no charge). Rear window defogger ($20). Front disc brakes ($70). Sport Fury/VIP headrests, left ($21). Power door locks, four-door ($54); two-door ($36). Six-Way power bench seat ($94). Left-hand Six-Way power bucket seat ($90). Power windows, VIP/Fury III/Sport Fury ($100) VIP two-door reclining passenger cloth/vinyl seat ($97). VIP four-door reclining passenger cloth/vinyl seat ($104). Bench seat leather trim, VIP only ($104). Tilt-A-Scope steering wheel ($87). Deluxe steering wheel, standard Sport Fury ($89). Tailgate assist handles, Fury wagons ($16). Vinyl roof on hardtops ($75). Vinyl trim in Fury III hardtops and sedans ($24). Deluxe 15 inch wheels, standard VIP and Sport Fury ($21). Sport-type 14 inch wheels, standard Sport Fury ($40). Deep dish 14 inch wheels, Sport Fury only ($18). VIP 'Road Wheels' ($76). 'Road Wheels' on Fury I, Fury II, Fury III ($97). 'Road Wheels' on Sport Fury ($58). Three-speed windshield wipers ($5). Three-speed manual transmission was standard. TorqueFlite automatic transmission, with six ($188); with '318' V-8 ($206); others ($216). Four-speed manual floor shift transmission; with '383' or '440' V-8 ($188). Commando V-8 383 cid 270 hp two-barrel engine ($70). Commando V-8 383 cid 325 hp four-barrel engine ($120). Station wagon V-8 440 cid 350 hp four-barrel engine ($234). Passenger car V-8 440 cid 375 hp four-barrel engine ($268). Heavy-duty alternator ($11). Heavy-duty battery ($21). Heavy-duty Sure-Grip axle ($139). Sure-Grip positive traction rear axle ($49). Available rear axle gear ratios: 3.23: 1; 3.55: 1; 2.93:1 and other options.

HISTORICAL FOOTNOTES: The Plymouths and Valiants were introduced Sept. 29, 1966 and the Barracuda appeared in dealer showrooms Nov. 25, 1966. Calendar year sales of 638,075 cars were recorded. Robert Anderson was the chief executive officer of the company this year. Plymouth factory installations of the "Street Hemi" in 1967 models included two in Satellite hardtops (both four-speeds); one in a Satellite convertible (four-speed equipped); 55 engines in Belvedere II hardtops (no transmission attachment data for this model); and 720 in Belvedere GTX hardtops and convertibles (312 with four-speeds).

1968 PLYMOUTH

VALIANT/SIGNET — (6-CYL/V-8) — SERIES DV — Minor styling changes were seen on 1968 Valiants. The horizontal division bar was removed from the grille. A fine pattern cross-hatched insert was used and was framed by a segmented chrome surround. A Plymouth nameplate was placed on the left-hand grille insert. Vertical taillights were seen. They, too, were segmented and had a 'fanned-out' look. Model nameplates were moved from the rear fender to the front fender, ahead of the wheel opening. Standard equipment on the base V-100 models included five 7.00 x 13 blackwall tires; seat belts; dual brake system with warning lamp; emergency flashers; back-up lights; turn signals; heater and defroster; padded dash and visors; left-hand outside rearview mirror; inside day/nite mirror; energy-absorbing steering column; armrests; side marker lamps; windshield wipers and washers; and Safety-Rim wheels. Cars in the Signet series had all of these items, plus body and wheel opening moldings; rocker moldings with front and rear extensions; cloth and vinyl interiors; cigar lighter; dual horns; carpeting; rear deck lid horizontal beauty panel; and Signet front fender signature scripts. A 230 hp 318 cid V-8 was a Valiant option for the first time.

1968 Plymouth, Valiant Signet four-door sedan, 6-cyl

PLYMOUTH I.D. NUMBERS: VIN on plate attached to driver's side front door hinge pillar. First symbol identifies car-line: B=Barracuda; R=Belvedere; P=Fury; V=Valiant. Second symbol identifies series: E=Belvedere/Fury I; L=Valiant/Belvedere/Fury II; H=Signet/Satellite/ Sport Fury; M=Fury III; Road Runner; P=Barracuda/Sport Satellite/VIP; K=Police; T=taxicab; S=GTX/Sport Fury Fast Top; O=Super Stock; X=Fury III two-door Fast Top. Third and fourth symbols indicate body style and appear as the last two digits in Body/Style Number in charts below. Fifth symbol identifies engine: A=170 cid six; B=225 cid six; C=special order option six; D=273 cid V-8; F=318 cid V-8; G=383 cid V-8; H=383 cid 4V high-performance V-8; J=426 cid "Street Hemi;" K=440 cid V-8; L=440 cid 4V high-performance V-8; M=special order option V-8; P=340 cid V-8. Sixth symbol indicates model year 8=1968. Seventh symbol identifies assembly plant: A=Detroit, Mich. (Lynch Rd.); B=Hamtramck, Mich.; D=Belvedere, Ill.; E=Los Angeles, Calif.; F=Newark, Del.; G=St. Louis, Mo.; G=Windsor, Ontario, Canada. Last six symbols are sequential production number for series at factory. Body Number Plate on inner fenders, cowl or radiator support indicates SO number, body production sequence number, body style code (second column of charts below), trim code and paint code. Motor numbers stamped on right side of block; on six below cylinder head opposite number 1 cylinder; on V-8 below distributor. Engine number indicates year (PT=1968), displacement (170 for 170 cid, etc.), month (A=Jan., etc.) and day (A01=Jan. 1). Engine codes: PT-170=170 cid/115 hp six; PT-225=225 cid/145 hp six; PT-273=273cid/190 hp V-8; PT-318=318 cid/230 hp 2V V-8; PT-383=383 cid/290 hp 2V V-8, 383 cid/300 hp 4V V-8, 383 cid/330 hp 4V V-8, [Road Runner only] 383 cid/335 hp 4V high-performance V-8; PT-426=426 cid/425 hp "Street Hemi" V-8 (2x4V); PT-440=440 cid/350 hp 4V V-8 and 440 cid/375 hp 4V high-performance V-8.

VALIANT SIGNET SERIES

Series Number	Body/Style Number	Body Type & Seating	Factory Price	Shipping Weight	Production Total
VALIANT 100					
DV1/2-L	VL41	4-dr Sed-6P	2275/2456	2695/2895	49,446
DV1/2-L	VL21	2-dr Sed-6P	2228/2409	2675/2875	31,178
VALIANT SERIES					
DV1/2-H	VH41	4-dr Sed-6P	2421/2602	2695/2895	23,906
DV1/2-H	VH21	2-dr Sed-6P	2374/2555	2675/2875	6,265

NOTE 1: Data above slash for sixes/below slash for V-8.

1968 Plymouth, Barracuda Formula 'S' two-door hardtop coupe, V-8

BARRACUDA — (6-CYL/V-8) — SERIES DB — The big news for Barracuda this year was the release of four new engine options. Buyers could now have 318, 340 or 383 cubic inches of V-8 below the hood and a special '383-S' engine was a Barracuda exclusive. Nameplates and scripts (plus engine identification badges) were moved to the cowlside front fender region. A vertical blade grille replaced the former cross-hatch mesh type. The word Plymouth appeared in block letters on the left-hand hood lip. Taillights were slightly changed and the rear deck panel received a black-out treatment. Standard equipment included either the 225 cid six or 318 cid V-8; three-speed manual transmission; carpeting; chromed hood louvers; full instrumentation; Rally lights; power top and glass window on convertible; heater and defroster; left-hand outside rearview mirror; energy absorbing steering column; dual brake system with warning lamp; emergency flasher; inside day/night mirror; front and rear seat belts; padded sun visors; two-speed wipers with washers; padded dash; cleaner air package; fold-down rear seat (in fastback); front bucket seats (in convertible); and Deluxe wheelcovers. The Formula 'S' package came in two forms, with both including high-performance V-8; four-speed manual transmission with heavy-duty clutch or special automatic; wide wheels; heavy-duty suspension; white or red stripe wide oval tires; dual exhausts; sill moldings; and special instrumentation.

BARRACUDA SERIES

Series Number	Body/Style Number	Body Type & Seating	Factory Price	Shipping Weight	Production Total
DB1/2-H	BH23	2-dr HT Cpe-5P	2579/2685	2715/2910	19,997
DB1/2-H	BH29	2-dr FsBk Cpe-5P	2736/2842	2810/3005	22,575
DB1/2-H	BH27	2-dr Conv-5P	2907/3013	2870/3070	2,840

NOTE 1: Data above slash for sixes/below slash for V-8.

1968 Plymouth, Road Runner two-door hardtop coupe, V-8

PLYMOUTH INTERMEDIATES — (6-CYL/V-8) — SERIES DR — The Plymouth/Belvedere intermediate lines were restyled this season. The model lineup was re-arranged and expanded. too. The economy wagon was deleted. A new medium-priced high-performance entry was the Road Runner. It came between Belvedere and Satellite, in terms of price and features, except that its base engine was a 383 cid four-barrel job. The Belvedere I designation was no longer used for low-priced cars, since the Belvedere II and Belvedere III nameplates disappeared entirely. The Satellite was now the high-priced line and a Sport Satellite Series was one rung higher. Then came the Satellite Sport Suburban Series. Top offerings bore GTX identification and were considered "special" level cars. General styling changes centered around a sleek new body for all intermediate models. The square look was gone. These cars had smooth-flowing lines that emphasized lowness and width. A 'coke bottle' image was evident. The grille was basically a low, horizontal opening with canted rectangles at each end housing dual headlights. Grille insert patterning differed with each line. The taillamps were housed in sculptured fender extensions with a sideways 'U-shaped' appearance. The rear deck lid was somewhat high and slightly 'veed' along its horizontal plane. Exterior trim was kept to a minimum on all models. The Belvedere grille was used on Belvederes, Satellites and Satellite wagons. It had two horizontal rows of oval-rectangular openings framed in chrome. A narrow rocker panel molding appeared. Standard equipment included side marker lights; folding seatback latches (two-doors); padded dash; recessed controls; energy absorbing seatbacks and steering column; safety armrests; left-hand outside rearview mirror; Safety-Rim wheels; dual brake system with warning lamp; flashers; day/night inside mirror; seat belts; padded visor; two-speed washer/wipers; turn signals; horn ring; and carpeting. The Satellites had all of the above, plus wider rocker moldings on wagons; upper belt moldings; chrome window frames and gutter rails; Satellite fender scripts; vinyl door panels; armrests with ashtrays; and dual horns. The Sport Satellite had a blacked-out horizontal blade grille; foam seat cushions; base '318' V-8; and body accent stripes, plus wide rocker moldings like Satellite wagons. The Road Runner had all Belvedere features, plus base '383' four- barrel V-8; heavy-duty suspension and shocks; four-speed manual gear box; F70-14 white streak tires; chrome roof drip rails; armrests with ashtrays; special 'Beep-Beep' dual horns; simulated air scoop hood; wider rim wheels; Road Runner identification and cartoon emblems; and the Sport Satellite type grille. The GTX was equipped like a Sport Satellite (with the same grille), but had many standard extras. They included the '440 Super Commando' V-8; heavy-duty brakes, suspension, battery and shocks; dual scoop hood; and GTX identification. Station wagons had Belvedere features, plus ashtray armrests and, on Satellite Sport Wagons, Satellite Sport trim and woodgrained exterior paneling.

PLYMOUTH INTERMEDIATE-SIZE SERIES

Series Number	Body/Style Number	Body Type & Seating	Factory Price	Shipping Weight	Production Total
BELVEDERE					
DR1/2-L	RL41	4-dr Sed-6P	2457/2551	3010/3190	17,214
DR1/2-L	RL21	2-dr Cpe-6P	2418/2512	2975/3160	15,702
DR1/2-L	RL45	4-dr Sta Wag-6P	2747/2841	3450/3580	8,982
SATELLITE					
DR1/2-H	RH41	4-dr Sed-6P	2546/2640	3010/3195	42,309
DR1/2-H	RH23	2-dr HT Cpe-6P	2568/2662	2995/3180	46,539
DR1/2-H	RH27	2-dr Conv-6P	2824/2918	3075/3260	1,771
DR1/2-H	RH46	4-dr Sta Wag-9P	2972/3006	3525/3660	10,883
DRI/2-H	RH45	4-dr Sta Wag-6P	2865/2959	3445/3580	12,097
ROAD RUNNER					
DR2-M	RM21	2-dr Cpe-6P	2870	3405	29,240
DR2-M	RM23	2-dr HT Cpe-6P	3034	3400	15,359
SPORT SATELLITE					
DR2-P	RP23	2-dr HT Cpe-5P	2796	3225	21,014
DR2-P	RP27	2-dr Conv-5P	3036	3290	1,523
SATELLITE SPORT WAGON					
DR2-P	RP46	4-dr Sta Wag-9P	3213	3660	Note 2
DR2-P	RP45	4-dr Sta Wag-6P	3105	3580	Note 2
GTX					
DR2-S	RS23	2-dr HT Cpe-5P	3329	3520	17,914
DR2-S	RS27	2-dr Conv-5P	3590	3620	1,026

NOTE 1: Chrysler records show 39,488 Belvedere two-door sedans built in 1968.
NOTE 2: Style Number RH46/RH45 totals include Satellite Sport station wagons.
NOTE 3: Data above slash for six/below slash; no slash for V-8.

1968 Plymouth, Fury III four-door hardtop sedan, V-8

PLYMOUTH FULL-SIZED — (6-CYL/V-8) — SERIES DP — Except in the case of station wagons, full-sized Plymouths for 1968 received new rear end sheetmetal including deck lids, quarter panels and rear doors of four-door styles. The deck now ran straight across, with horizontal taillamps. It had a crisper and slimmer look. At the front, the basic elements of the 1967 design were retained, but grille surround moldings were repositioned in line with the new Plymouth theme of slim, horizontal shapes. Gone were the stand-up hood ornaments of the past. Standard equipment on Fury I models included untrimmed bodysides; front fender side nameplates; small rectangular taillights; Plymouth block lettering across concave rear panel; cloth/vinyl seats; foam padded cushions; front armrests; rear armrests with ashtrays; carpets; bright windshield frames; bright rear window moldings; back-up lights; cigar lighter; glove box lock; dome and side marker lamps; padded dash; energy absorbing front seatbacks; left outside rearview mirror; dual brake system with warning light; emergency flasher; inside day/night mirror; seat belts; padded visor; two-speed wipers with washers and Safety-Rim wheels. The Fury II had all above items, plus full-length mid-bodyside molding; Fury II nameplates; roof gutter moldings and rear deck moldings with satin aluminum insert area; and Plymouth block letters across edge of deck lid. The Fury III models had all of the above, plus wheel opening moldings; dual taillamps; bright upper door moldings (on four-door sedan); electric clock; lights in the glove box and trunk; and a Fury III badge in the center of the satin aluminum rear insert. The Sport Furys had all Fury III items, plus front grille with Sport Fury designation; bucket seats; all-vinyl interior; choice of console or center armrest bench seat; sport wheelcovers; rocker panel moldings; fender-mounted turn signals; bright pedal moldings; combination map and courtesy lights; ignition switch lamp with time delay shutoff; and Sport Fury front fenderside nameplates. The VIP came with most Sport Fury equipment (except bucket seats) and added the following extras: front grille with VIP designation; Deluxe cloth and vinyl interiors with front seat center armrest; nylon carpeting; and rear pillar courtesy lamps. The basic Suburban was equipped in the manner of the Fury I. The Custom Suburban added '318' V-8; electric tailgate window and assist strap; full-length bodyside molding; wheel opening moldings; bright upper door moldings; rear center dome light; and Custom Suburban fenderside nameplates. The Sport Suburban had all this equipment, plus all-vinyl seats with individual seatbacks; nylon carpeting; woodgrained bodyside paneling; electric clock; glove box lamp; and, on three-seat models, rear bumper guards and step pads.

PLYMOUTH FULL SIZE SERIES

Series Number	Body/Style Number	Body Type & Seating	Factory Price	Shipping Weight	Production Total
FURY I					
DP1/2-E	PE41	4-dr Sed-6P	2634/2739	3465/3605	23,208
DP1/2-E	PE21	2-dr Sed-6P	2591/2696	3410/3545	5,788
FURY II					
DP1/2-L	PL41	4-dr Sed-6P	2731/2836	3470/3605	49,423
DP1/2-L	PL21	2-dr Sed-6P	2689/2794	3425/3565	3,112
DP1/2-E	PE45	4-dr Sta Wag-6P	3022/3127	3950/4080	6,749
FURY III					
DP1/2-M	PM41	4-dr Sed-6P	2864/2969	3490/3625	57,899
DP1/2-M	PM23	2-dr HT Cpe-6P	2886/2991	3480/3680	60,472
DP1/2-M	PX23	2-dr FsTp Cpe-6P	2906/3011	3480/3620	NA
DP2-M	PM43	4-dr HT Sed-6P	3041	3670	45,147
DP2-M	PM27	2-dr Conv-6P	3236	3685	4,483
DD2-L	PL46	4-dr Sta Wag-9P	3327	4125	9,954
DP2-L	PL45	4-dr Sta Wag-6P	3226	4085	17,078
SPORT FURY					
DP2-H	PH-23	2-dr HT Cpe-5P	3180	3645	6,642
DP2-H	PS23	2-dr FT Cpe-5P	3199	3645	17,073
DP2-H	PH27	2-dr Conv-5P	3425	3700	2,489
VIP					
DP2-P	PP43	4-dr HT Sed-6P	3300	3720	10,745
DP2-P	PP23	2-dr FsTp Cpe-6P	3234	3630	6,768
DP2-M	PM46	4-dr Sta Wag-9P	3517	4150	13,224
DP2-M	PM45	4-dr Sta Wag-6P	3416	4105	9,203

NOTE 1: Data above slash for six/below slash; no slash is V-8.
NOTE 2: Total for Fury III 'Fast Top' combined with the two-door hardtop total.

CHASSIS FEATURES: Wheelbase: (Valiant/Barracuda) 108 inches; (Belvedere/Satellite wagons) 117 inches; (Belvedere/Satellite/GTX/Road Runner) 116 inches; (Fury/VIP wagons) 122 inches; (Fury/VIP) 119 inches. Overall length: (Valiant) 188.4 inches; (Barracuda) 192.8 inches; (Belvedere/Satellite wagons) 208 inches; (Belvedere/Satellite/GTX/Road Runner) 202.7 inches; (Fury/VIP nine-passenger wagon) 217 inches; (Fury/VIP six-passenger wagon) 216 inches; (Fury/VIP) 213 inches. Front tread: (Valiant) 58.4 inches; (Belvedere) 59.5 inches; (Satellite) 59.5 inches; (Fury) 62.0 inches. Rear tread: (Valiant) 55.6 inches; (Belvedere) 59.5 inches; (Satellite) 59.2 inches; (Fury) 60.7 inches. Tires: (Valiant six) 6.50 x 13; (Barracuda/Valiant V-8) 6.95 x 14; (Barracuda six) 7.00 x 13; (Belvedere six) 7.35 x 14; (Belvedere wagons, all engines) 8.25 x 14; (Fury, all engines) 8.25 x 14; (Fury wagon, all engines) 8.55 x 14; (Belvedere/Satellite/GTX/Road Runner V-8) F70-14: (Belvedere 'RL' V-8) 7.35 x 14.

OPTIONS, VALIANT: Power brakes ($44). Power steering ($84). Air conditioning ($335). Front and rear seat belts ($11). Pair of shoulder belts ($28). Signet vinyl bucket seats with paint stripe ($78). Front disc brakes, 14 inch tires mandatory ($73). Front and rear bumper guards ($23). Rear window defogger ($21). Tinted glass, all windows ($30); windshield only ($15). Pair of head restraints ($44). Deluxe 13 inch wheelcovers ($19). Deluxe 14 inch wheelcovers ($22). Bolt on design 14 inch wheelcovers ($45). Wire wheelcovers, 14 inch only ($67). Basic Group: includes AM radio; Deluxe wheelcovers; remote-control left outside rearview mirror; foam front seat cushion, with 13 inch wheels and bench seats ($97); with 13 inch wheels and bucket seats ($89); with 14 inch wheels and bucket seats ($92); with 14 inch wheels and bench seat ($101). Valiant 200 Decor Group: includes three-spoke steering wheel with partial horn ring; color-keyed floor mats; cigar lighter; dual horns; body side molding; Valiant 200 nameplate, with cloth and vinyl ($76); with all-vinyl trim ($100). AM radio ($60). Vinyl roof, hardtop ($79). Fast manual steering ($14). Sport simulated woodgrained steering wheel, with 200 group ($33). Three-speed manual transmission was standard. Automatic transmission, with six ($180); with '273' V-8 ($190); with '318' V-8 ($194). Four-speed manual floor shift transmission, with V-8 only ($188). Six-cylinder 225 cid 145 hp one-barrel engine ($49). V-8 318 cid 230 hp two-barrel engine ($32). Heavy-duty battery ($8). Heavy-duty alternator, with air ($11); without ($15). Positive traction rear axle ($45).

OPTIONS, BARRACUDA: Power brakes ($44). Power steering ($84). Air conditioning ($335). Front disc brakes ($73). Bumper guards ($23). Console, with bucket seats, except three-speed ($51). Custom sill moldings ($21). Paint accent stripes ($15). Sport paint stripes ($20). Special buffed paint ($18). Wheelhouse liners, except convertible ($47). Deluxe wiper and washer package ($10). Undercoating with hood pad ($16). Vinyl roof, hardtop ($79). Fast manual steering ($14). Full horn ring steering wheel ($9). Woodgrained sport steering wheel ($27). Tachometer, V-8 only ($51). Performance gauge cluster, without clock or tachometer ($16). Deluxe wheelcovers ($22). Bolt-on design wheelcovers ($45). Wire wheelcovers ($67). AM radio ($60). Basic Group: includes AM radio; power steering; remote-control outside rearview mirror; variable-speed wipers and electric washers, with '383' V-8 ($80); without '383' V-8 ($164). Rally Cluster: includes trip odometer; 150 mph speedometer and woodgrained dash trim ($6). Formula 'S' Group, as described in text, with '340' engine ($212); with 383 engine ($251). Three-speed manual transmission was standard. Automatic transmission, with six ($199); with '318' V-8 ($212); with other V-8s ($227). Four-speed manual floor shift transmission, with V-8s only ($188). Formula' S' V-8 383 cid/300 hp four-barrel engine ($251).

562 Standard Catalog of American Cars

Heavy-duty battery ($6). Heavy-duty alternator ($11 or $15). Positive traction rear axle ($45). Transmissions available with 383 cid engine were four-speed manual or high-performance TorqueFlite with high-speed governor.

OPTIONS, PLYMOUTH INTERMEDIATES: Power brakes ($44). Power steering ($94). Air conditioning ($355). Automatic speed control ($53). Armrest with ashtray ($8). Bumper guards front and rear, except wagons ($14). Electric clock ($16). Rear window defogger ($21). Tinted glass, all windows ($42); windshield ($22). Left and right head restraints ($44). Station wagon luggage rack ($49). Remote control left outside rearview mirror ($9). Right manual outside rearview mirror ($7). Road Runner, Satellite, Sport wagon custom sill molding ($21). Upper belt moldings, two-door coupe and hardtop ($18). Two-tone paint, except convertible ($15). Road Runner body accent stripes ($15). Special buffed paint ($22). Road Runner and GTX performance black-out hood finish ($18). Solid state AM radio with stereo tape ($195). Solid state AM radio ($60). Firm Ride shocks, standard Road Runner and GTX ($4). Tachometer, V-8 only ($51). Vinyl roof, except station wagons ($79). Power windows, hardtop/convertibles only ($105). Vinyl trim, Belvedere sedan and wagon ($26). Vinyl trim, Satellite sedan and hardtop ($26). Road wheels, except with 'Street Hemi' ($102). Deluxe wheelcovers, 14 inch ($22); 15 inch ($26). Sport style wheelcovers, except 'Street Hemi' ($38). Three-speed manual transmission was standard. Automatic transmission in Road Runner only ($39). Automatic transmission, with six ($299); with '273' V-8 ($217); with other V-8s ($227). Four-speed manual floor shift transmission, with '383' or '426' only ($198). Four-speed manual transmission with floor shift, standard in Road Runner and no charge in GTX. Optional V-8 318 cid/230 hp two-barrel engine ($32). Optional V-8 383 cid/290 hp two-barrel engine ($105). Sport Satellite V-8 383 cid/290 hp two-barrel engine ($73). Optional V-8 383 cid/330 hp four-barrel engine ($176). Sport Satellite V-8 383 cid/330 hp four-barrel engine ($144). Road Runner V-8 426 cid/425 hp 'Street Hemi' dual four-barrel engine ($714). GTX V-8 426 cid/425 hp 'Street Hemi' four-barrel engine ($605). Heavy-duty Sure-Grip axle, Road Runner and GTX only ($146). Sure-Grip positive traction rear axle ($45). Note: Some V-8s listed above were standard in certain models; not available in others. Prices varied from one attachment to another. Some engines required specific transmission attachments.

OPTIONS, FULL-SIZED PLYMOUTH: Power brakes ($44). Power steering ($94). Air conditioning ($355). Dual Suburban air-conditioning ($565). Single Auto Temp air-conditioning, V-8 only ($434). Dual Auto Temp air-conditioning, wagon only ($644). Front and rear bumper guards ($35). Electric clock, standard Fury II/FuryIII/Sport/VIP ($16). Console, Sport Fury only, substitution (no charge). Rear window defogger ($21). Fender skirts, Fury III/Sport Fury/VIP only ($28). Tinted glass, all windows ($42); windshield ($22). Station wagon luggage rack ($66). Solid state AM radio ($60). Solid state AM with stereo tape ($195). Solid state AM/FM radio ($140). Rear seat speaker ($15). Vinyl roof, Fury III/Sport Fury/VIP only ($79). Cloth and vinyl split bench seat, VIP four-door only ($109). Cloth and vinyl bucket seat, VIP two-door only ($102). Six-Way power bucket or split bench, Sport Fury/VIP only ($95). Six-Way power bench seat, Fury III/VIP/Sport Wagon only ($98). Leather-trimmed bench seat, VIP only ($109). Power windows: Fury III/Sport Fury/VIP/Sport Wagon only ($105). Road wheels, VIP ($80); Sport Fury ($61); other models ($102). Deluxe 14 inch wheelcovers, standard VIP ($22). Deluxe 15 inch wheelcovers, standard Sport Fury/VIP ($26). Sport style 14 inch wheelcovers, VIP ($16); others ($38). Deep-dish 14 inch wheelcovers, VIP ($30); Sport Fury ($11); others ($52). Three-speed windshield wipers ($5). Three-speed manual transmission was standard. Automatic transmission, with six ($199); with '383' ($217); with other V-8 ($227). Four-speed manual floor shift transmission, except wagons or cars with six or '318' V-8 ($198). Commando V-8 383 cid/290 hp two-barrel engine ($73). Commando V-8 383 cid/330 hp four-barrel engine ($144). Suburban V-8 440 cid/350 hp four-barrel engine ($245). Super Commando V-8 440 cid/375 hp four-barrel engine ($281). Heavy-duty alternator ($11). Heavy-duty battery ($8). Heavy-duty Sure-Grip ($146). Positive traction rear axle ($51).

HISTORICAL FOOTNOTES: The full-sized Plymouths were introduced Sept. 14, 1967 and the compacts appeared in dealer showrooms the same date. Model year production peaked at 682,193 units. Calendar years sales of 683,678 cars were recorded. G.E. White was the chief executive officer of the company this year. Chrysler-Plymouth Div. retail sales hit an all-time high this year. Plymouth was America's fourth largest automaker. The company held an 8.1 percent market share. Only 2,502 Chrysler products were sold with 426 cid 'Street Hemis' this season. Plymouth installations included 1,019 engines in Road Runner hardtops and coupes (576 with four-speeds) and 450 in Belvedere GTX hardtops and convertibles (234 four-speeds). A handful of Barracudas were also fitted with the 426 cid/425 hp Hemi V-8 for professional drag racing. With fiberglass hoods and front fenders and light steel doors these cars were capable of quarter-mile times under 11 seconds at top speeds over 130 mph.The rarest options for each line were four-speed transmission in Furys (only 0.2 percent installation rate); speed control in Belvederes (only 0.4 percent); disc brakes in Barracudas (6.1 percent) and four-speed manual gear box in Valiant (0.2 per cent).

1969 PLYMOUTH

VALIANT/SIGNET — (6-CYL/V-8) — SERIES EV — A new grille, new taillights and trim and a straight element rear window were featured in the 1969 Valiant 100 and Signet Series. Standard engines were unchanged, although refinements in the Chrysler "Cleaner Air System" were said to produce better operating economy from the Slant Sixes. Improved brake adjusters, a more efficient power steering pump and improvements to the optional Sure-Grip differential were highlighted by the maker. The Valiant 100 was the base car-line and came with all safety features; vinyl interior; three-spoke steering wheel; a new horizontal bar grille, (with satin-finished surround); cowlside fender nameplates; small hubcaps; and new, lower prices. The Signet also had rear window, deck lid, and ribbed rocker panel moldings; cigar lighter; front armrests; rear armrest with ashtray (in four-door sedan); carpets; dual horns; inverted 'V' shaped grille center badge; and Signet front fender scripts.

PLYMOUTH I.D. NUMBERS: VIN on plate attached to driver's side front door hinge pillar. First symbol identifies car-line: B=Barracuda; R=Belvedere; P=Fury; V=Valiant. Second symbol identifies series: E=Fury I; L=Valiant/Belvedere/Fury II; H=Signet/Satellite/Sport Fury; M=Fury III; Road Runner; P=Barracuda/Sport Satellite/VIP; K=Police; T=taxicab; S=GTX; O=Super Stock. Third and fourth symbols indicate body style and appear as the last two digits in Body/Style Number in charts below. Fifth symbol identifies engine: A=170 cid six; B=225 cid six; C=special order option six; D=273 cid V-8; F=318 cid V-8; G=383 cid V-8; H=383 cid 4V high-performance V-8; J=426 cid "Street Hemi;" K=440 cid V-8; L=440 cid 4V high-performance V-8; M=440 cid "Six-Pak;" P=340 cid V-8. Sixth symbol indicate model year 9=1969. Seventh symbol identifies assembly plant: A=Detroit, Mich. (Lynch Rd.); B=Hamtramck, Mich.; C=Detroit (Jefferson); D=Belvedere, Ill.; E=Los Angeles, Calif.; F=Newark, Del.; G=St. Louis, Mo. Last six symbols are sequential production number for series at factory. Body Number Plate on inner fenders, cowl or radiator support indicates SO number, body production sequence number, body style code (second column of charts below), trim code and paint code. Motor numbers stamped on right side of block; on six below cylinder head opposite number 1 cylinder; on V-8 below distributor. Engine number indicates year (PT=1969), displacement (170 for 170 cid, etc.), month (A=Jan., etc.) and day (A01=Jan. 1). Engine codes: PT-170=170 cid/115 hp six; PT-225=225 cid/145 hp six; PT-273=273cid/190 hp V-8; PT-318=318 cid/230 hp 2V V-8; [Barracuda only] PT-340=340 cid/275 hp 4V V-8 PT-383=383 cid/290 hp 2V V-8, [Barracuda only] 383 cid/300 hp 4V V-8, 383 cid/330 hp 4V V-8, [Road Runner only] 383 cid/335 hp 4V high-performance V-8; [Barracuda Super Stock/Road Runner/GTX only] PT-426=426 cid/425 hp "Street Hemi" V-8 (2x4V); PT-440=440 cid/350 hp 4V V-8, 440 cid/375 hp 4V high-performance V-8, and [Road Runner/GTX only] 440 cid/390 hp "Six-Pak" high-performance V-8.

VALIANT/SIGNET SERIES

Series Number	Body/Style Number	Body Type & Seating	Factory Price	Shipping Weight	Production Total
VALIANT 100					
EV1/2-L	VL41	4-dr Sed-6P	2354/2465	2676/2844	49,409
EV1/2-L	VL21	2-dr Sed-6P	2307/2418	2656/2824	29,672
VALIANT SIGNET					
EV1/2-H	VH41	4-dr Sed-6P	2500/2611	2676/2844	21,492
EV1/2-H	VH21	2-dr Sed-6P	2453/2564	2656/2824	6,645

NOTE 1: Data above slash for six/below slash for V-8.

1969 Plymouth, Barracuda '383-S' two-door hardtop coupe, V-8

BARRACUDA — (6-CYL/V-8) — SERIES EB — The 'Cuda 340 was the new, high-performance 'option-model' in the Barracuda line, with either fastback or hardtop styling. These styles, plus the convertible, also came as regular Barracudas. The 'Cuda line of option-created-models included four-speed manual transmission; sport tires; and heavy-duty suspension and brakes. The hardtop was available with an optional yellow flowered vinyl roof. Base Barracuda V-8 engine was the '318,' with 383 and 340 cid motors available. The Barracuda six came with the tried and true 225 cid Slant Six. Installed on the basic models was all standard (government required) safety equipment; all-vinyl interior; bucket seats; `Pit Stop` gas cap; rally lights; front shoulder belts (except convertible); beltline molding on fastback; red or white stripe tires (with V-8 engines); and aluminized horizontal rear deck panel with Barracuda block lettering. An easy way to tell a 1969 model from a 1968 edition is by the new side marker lamps, which are now rectangular. Few other obvious differences are seen. The hoods and grilles were face-lifted slightly, however.

BARRACUDA SERIES

Series Number	Body/Style Number	Body Type & Seating	Factory Price	Shipping Weight	Production Total
EB1/2-H	BH23	2-dr HT-5P	2674/2780	2731/2899	12,757
EF1/2-H	BH29	2-dr FsBk-5P	2707/2813	2816/2987	17,788
EB1/2-H	BH27	2-dr Conv-5P	2976/3082	2846/3034	1,442

NOTE 1: Data above slash for six/below slash for V-8.

1969 Plymouth, GTX two-door hardtop coupe, V-8

PLYMOUTH INTERMEDIATES — (6-CYL/V-8) — SERIES ER — Two new models, the Sport Satellite four-door sedan and the Road Runner convertible were added to the intermediate Belvedere line for 1969. The GTX could be optionally equipped with an all-new cold-air induction package fed through functional hood scoops. All 18 models sported new grilles and new rear styling. The optional flowered vinyl roof and matching 'mod' interior were available for the Satellite two-door hardtop. Belvederes had the safety group; heater/defroster; lockable glove box; nylon and vinyl trim (all-vinyl in coupe) and front shoulder belts. They had a twin-level horizontal bar grille. Satellites added rear ashtray armrests; dual horns; roof drip and lower body (rocker) moldings; all-vinyl convertible trim; and vertical center grille divider. Sport Satellites also had 'B' pillar and wheel opening moldings; accent striping; front foam seats; (convertible) bucket seats; and chrome door frames on sedans. The Road Runner had all this, plus heavy-duty suspension, brakes and shocks; dash nameplate; deck lid nameplate; door nameplates; top opening hood scoops; chrome engine parts; unsilenced air cleaner; Hemi-orange paint treatment; red or white streak tires; four-speed with Hurst shifter; fake walnut shift knob; reverse lamp; and (except coupe) Deluxe steering wheel. The GTX featured all these items, plus heavy-duty battery; exhaust trumpets; red or white reflective stripes; twin hood scoops; foam bucket seats; performance cam; big valves and ports; all-vinyl trim; heavy-duty TorqueFlite; and heavy-duty underpinnings. Wagons followed the car trim levels, with exterior wood paneling on Sport Satellite wagons.

PLYMOUTH INTERMEDIATE SERIES

Series Number	Body/Style Number	Body Type & Seating	Factory Price	Shipping Weight	Production Total
BELVEDERE (225/318)					
ER1/2-L	RL41	4-dr Sed-6P	2548/2638	3008/3156	12,914
ER1/2-H	RL21	2-dr Cpe-6P	2509/2599	2978/3126	7,063
ER1/20L	RL45	4-dr Sta Wag-6P	2879/2969	3488/3591	7,038
ROAD RUNNER (383)					
ER2-M	RM21	2-dr Cpe-6P	2945	3435	33,743
ER2-M	RM23	2-dr HT Cpe-6P	3083	3450	48,549
ER2-M	RM27	2-dr Conv-5P	3313	3790	2,128
SATELLITE (225/318)					
ER1/2-H	RH41	4-dr Sed-6P	2635/2725	3013/3161	35,296
ER1/2-H	RH23	2-dr HT Cpe-6P	2659/2749	3008/3151	38,323
ER1/2-H	RH27	2-dr Conv-6P	2875/2965	3123/3276	1,137
ER1/2-H	RH46	4-dr Sta Wag-9P	3106/3196	3568/3656	4,730
ER1/2-H	RH45	4-dr Sta Wag-6P	2997/3087	3493/3586	5,837
SPORT SATELLITE (318)					
ER2-P	RP41	4-dr Sed-6P	2911	3196	5,836
ER2-P	RP23	2-dr HT Cpe-6P	2883	3156	15,807
ER2-P	RP27	2-dr Conv-5P	3081	3276	818
ER2-P	RP46	4-dr Sta Wag-9P	3350	3666	3,152
ER2-P	RP45	4-dr Sta Wag-6P	3241	3596	3,221
GTX (440)					
ER2-S	RS23	2-dr HT Cpe-5P	3416	3465	14,902
ER2-S	RS27	2-dr Conv-5P	3635	3590	700

NOTE 1: Data above slash for six/below slash for V-8.

1969 Plymouth, Fury III four-door hardtop sedan, V-8

PLYMOUTH FULL-SIZED — (6-CYL/V-8) — SERIES EP — With all-new sheet metal for 1969, the Fury came in 17 models and five series. They were named Fury I, Fury II, Fury III, Sport Fury and VIP. The cars were 1-1/2 inches longer and almost two inches wider than pervious models. Engine choices included the '225' Slant Six or '318' V-8, with the '383' and '440' V-8s optional. Horizontal twin headlamps; a one-tier horizontal grille; and rectangular side markers were car spotter aids. The Fury I came with all standard safety features; glove box lock; heater/defroster; front fenderside nameplates; and no side trim. The Fury II also had full-length bodyside moldings; bright roof side moldings and, on the coupe, frameless front door glass. The Fury III had all above items, plus vinyl/nylon foam padded bench seat; carpeting; concealed wipers; clock; and Deluxe steering wheel. The Sport Fury had all safety features; concealed wipers; sport wheelcovers; dual paint stripes; red, white and blue body side markers; all-vinyl front bucket seats with console (or bench seat with fold-down armrest); Custom sill moldings; and upper door frame moldings. The VIP had all safety equipment, plus Deluxe wheelcovers, fender skirts; concealed wipers; die-cast grille; bench seats with fold-down center armrest; Safe-Flight dash; clock; front foam cushions; and Deluxe steering wheel. Wagons had two-way tailgates; all-vinyl and trim; equipment and trim matching next step-up passenger cars and integral rear roof deflector.

PLYMOUTH FULL-SIZED SERIES

Series Number	Body/Style Number	Body Type & Seating	Factory Price	Shipping Weight	Production Total
FURY I					
PE1/2-E	PE41	4-dr Sed-6P	2744/2849	3488/3578	18.771
PE1/2-E	PE21	2-dr Sed-6P	2701/2806	3458/3548	4,971
PE1/2-E	PE45	4-dr Sta Wag-6P	3231/3336	4008/4103	6,424
FURY II					
PE1/2-L	PL41	4-dr Sed-6P	2841/2946	3488/3583	41,047
PE1/2-L	PL21	2-dr Cpe-6P	2813/2918	3458/3553	3,268
PE2-L	PL46	4-dr Sta Wag-9P	3527	4148	10,216
PE2-L	PL45	4-dr Sta Wag-6P	3436	4103	15,976
FURY III					
PE1/2-M	PM41	4-dr Sed-6P	2979/3084	3493/3588	72,747
PE1/2-M	PM23	2-dr HT Cpe-6P	3000/3105	3468/3563	44,168
PE1/2-M	PM29	2-dr FsTp Cpe-6P	3020/3125	3548/3653	22,738
PE2-M	PM43	4-dr HT Sed-6P	3155	3643	68,818
PE2-M	PM27	2-dr Conv-6P	3324	3704	4,129
PE2-M	PM46	4-dr Sta Wag-9P	3718	4173	13,502
PE2-M	PM45	4-dr Sta Wag-6P	3651	4123	8,201
SPORT FURY					
EP2-H	PH23	2-dr HT Cpe-5P	3283	3603	14,120
EP2-H	PH29	2-dr FsTp Cpe-5P	3303	3678	2,169
EP2-H	PH27	2-dr Conv-5P	3502	3729	1,579
VIP					
EP2-P	PP43	4-dr HT Sed-6P	3433	3663	7,982
EP2-P	PP23	2-dr HT Cpe-6P	3382	3583	4,740
EP2-P	PP29	2-dr FsTp Cpe-6P	3382	3668	1,059

NOTE 1: Data above slash is for six/below slash; no slash for V-8.

BASE ENGINES

(VALIANT V-100 SIX) Inline six. Overhead valves. Cast iron block. Displacement: 170.9 cid. Bore and stroke: 3.406 x 3.125 inches. Compression ratio: 8.5:1. Brake hp: 115 at 4400 rpm. Four main bearings. Solid valve lifters. Carburetor: Ball & Ball Type BBS model 4601S.

(SIGNET/BARRACUDA/PLYMOUTH SIX) Inline six. Overhead valves. Cast iron block. Displacement: 225.5 cid. Bore and stroke: 3.406 x 4.125 inches. Compression ratio: 8.4:1. Brake hp: 145 at 4000 rpm. Four main bearings. Solid valve lifters. Carburetor: Holley Type R one-barrel Model 4163A.

(V-8 VALIANT/BARRACUDA/BELVEDERE) V-8. Overhead valves. Cast iron block. Displacement: 273.5 cid. Bore and stroke: 3.63 x 3.312 inches. Compression ratio: 9.0:1. Brake hp: 190 at 4400 rpm. Four main bearings. Solid valve lifters. Carburetor: Carter BBD 4607S.

(V-8 SATELLITE/FURY/SPORT FURY) V-8. Overhead valves. Cast iron block. Displacement: 318 cid. Bore and stroke: 3.906 x 3.312 inches. Compression ratio: 9.2:1. Brake hp: 230 at 4400 rpm. Five main bearings. Hydraulic valve lifter. Carburetor: Carter Type BBD two-barrel Model 4607S.

(V-8 ROAD RUNNER) V-8. Overhead valves. Cast iron block. Displacement: 383 cid. Bore and stroke: 4.25 x 3.375 inches. Compression ratio: 10.0:1. Brake hp: 335 at 5200 rpm. Five main bearings. Hydraulic valve lifters. Carburetor: Carter Type AVS four-barrel Model 4615S.

(V-8 GTX) V-8. Overhead valves. Cast iron block. Displacement: 440.7 cid. Bore and stroke: 4.325 x 3.75 inches. Compression ratio: 10.1:1. Brake hp: 375 at 4600 rpm. Five main bearings. Hydraulic valve lifters. Carburetor: Carter Type AVS four-barrel Model 4617S.

CHASSIS FEATURES: Wheelbase: (Valiant/Barracuda) 108 inches; (Belvedere wagons) 117 inches; (Belvedere passenger cars) 116 inches; (Fury wagons) 122 inches; (Fury passenger cars) 120 inches. Overall length: (Valiant) 188.4 inches; (Barracuda) 192.8 inches; (Belvedere wagons) 208 inches; (other Belvederes) 202.7 inches; (Fury wagons) 219.1 inches; (other Furys) 214.5 inches. Tires: (Valiant six) 6.50 x 13; (Barracuda six/V-8) 6.95 x 14; (Valiant V-8) 7.00 x 13; (Belvedere six/V-8) 7.35 x 14; (Fury six/V-8) 7.75 x 14; (Fury wagon) 8.55 x 15; (Road Runner) 8.25 x 15; (GTX) 8.85 x 15.

OPTIONS: Air conditioning, Belvedere ($358); Fury ($365); Valiant ($361). Air grabber scoop, with Road Runner and GTX ($55). Auto speed control, Belvedere ($58); Fury ($61). Disc front brakes, Belvedere, Fury and Valiant/Barracuda ($49). Bumper guards, front and rear, Belvedere ($32); Fury ($34); Valiant ($24). Color-keyed carpet mats, Belvedere and Fury ($14); Valiant ($11). Console with bucket seats, Road Runner/Sport Satellite ($54); Barracuda ($53). Fold-down rear seat, Barracuda fastback ($65). All-tinted glass, Belvedere ($41); Fury ($42); Valiant ($33). Tinted windshield, Belvedere ($26); Fury ($26); Valiant ($21). Dual head rests, all models ($27). Note: Headrests standard after Jan. 1, 1969. Headlights-on signal, Belvedere and Fury ($7). Cornering lamps, Fury Series ($36). Station wagon roofrack, Belvedere type ($52); Fury type ($63). Power steering, Belvedere and Fury ($100); Valiant ($85). Performance hood paint, Road Runner/GTX ($18). Code N96 'Air Grabber' hood scoop. Road Runner/GTX ($55). Sport stripes paint treatment, Road Runner ($27); Barracuda ($26). Performance gauges, Barracuda without clock or tachometer ($17). Power brakes, all models ($43). Solid state AM radio ($62). Solid state AM/FM in Belvedere/Barracuda only ($135). Solid state AM with tape, Belvedere/Fury only ($196). Tilt adjustment steering wheel. Fury only ($47). Tachometer, Belvedere V-8/Fury I/Fury II/Barracuda V-8 ($50). Leather bench seats, VIP ($104). Floral roof treatment, Barracuda hardtop ($96). Floral interior, Barracuda hardtop, with buckets and 'Cuda ($113). Chrome styled wheels, 14 inch, Belvedere except Hemi ($100). Formula 'S' option package. Barracuda '383' ($222). Formula 'S' package, Barracuda '383' convertible ($198). Valiant '200' decor trim package with vinyl bench seats ($102). Turnpike package, Belvedere except Road Runner/GTX ($243). Turnpike package, Fury Series, with Basic Group ($246). Super performance axle package, GTX, with Hemi ($242). Track Pack option, Road Runner/GTX, required with four-speed ($143). Super Track Pack, Road Runner/GTX, with '440' or '426' and four-speed ($256). Rally gauge cluster, Barracuda ($6). Barracuda Sport Group, except cars with 'Cuda package ($51). Interior Decor Group, including fold-down rear seat (on fast back): wood-grained door and quarter panel trim; door map pouches; bright pedal trim: rear compartment carpet (required fastback); luxury vinyl bucket seats; rear armrests; ashtrays; and wheelhouse carpets (fastback), on fastback ($181). 'Cuda 340 package, includes four-speed manual transmission; hood scoops; hood tape stripe; lower black body stripes; dual exhausts with chrome tips; heavy-duty suspension; firm-ride shocks; E70-14 red stripe "Wide-Boot" tires; 14 x 5-1/2 inch wheel rims; black grille; vinyl bench seat and 340 cid V-8 ($309.35. 'Cuda 383 package, includes four-speed manual transmission; hood scoops; hood tape stripe; lower black body stripes; dual exhausts with chrome tips; heavy-duty suspension; firm-ride shocks; E70-14 red stripe "Wide-Boot" tires; 14 x 5-1/2 inch wheel rims; black grille; vinyl bench seat and 383 cid V-8 ($344.75). Powertrain options were about the same as in 1968, at the same or slightly higher prices, except that the '318' V-8 replaced the '273' as base powerplant in the Barracuda V-8 Series. After midyear, the 440 cid/375 hp V-8 became available in limited quantities in the Barracuda. On cars with the 'Cuda option, the '340' V-8 was standard. This powerplant, first used in 1968, had a 4.04 x 3.312 bore and stroke, 10.5:1 compression and 275 hp at 5000 rpm. The 'Street Hemi' was again provided as an $813.45 power option for the Road Runner and a $700.90 power option in the GTX.

HISTORICAL FOOTNOTES: The full-sized Plymouths were introduced Sept. 19, 1968 and the Valiants appeared in dealer showrooms the same day. Model year production peaked at 645,130 units. Calendar year sales of 651,124 cars were recorded. G.E. White was the chief executive officer of the company this year. Domestic production of full-sized models in the Fury line was declining, as this car was now being built in greater quantities in Canada. This was a result of the U.S. Canada Auto Trade Agreement of 1965. Over 100,000 Furys were made in Canada in 1968 and exported to the U. S. A total of 1,702 "Street Hemi" engines were installed in MoPars this year. Plymouth installations of the engine included 422 Road Runner hardtops (234 with four-speed); 356 Road Runner coupes (194 with four-speed); 10 Road Runner convertibles (four with four-speed); 198 Belvedere GTX hardtops (99 with four-speed) and 11 Belvedere GTX convertibles (five four-speeds).

1970 PLYMOUTH

VALIANT/VALIANT DUSTER — (6-CYL/V-8) — SERIES FV/FS — The Plymouth Valiant was carried over with minor detail changes. They included a different grille for 1970. Grille elements were about the same, but had a refined look. The central portion bulged out and the horizontal bars were wider and finished in black-out style. New was the Valiant Duster, built off the same platform with the same front end sheetmetal, but different from the cowl back. The Duster came only as a two-door coupe and bridged the gap between compact economy car and performance machine. Standard engine was a new 198 cid six, but selections ranged to the '340' V-8. Standard equipment on the Valiant included turn signals; taillights; front

armrests; the new six; and 6.95-14 blackwall tires. The Duster came comparably equipped in basic form. Regular equipment on the youth-market Duster 340 included the 340 cid V-8; three-speed manual transmission with floor shift; special instrument panel; road wheels; performance stripes; high-rate torsion bars; heavy-duty springs and shocks; front anti-sway bar and disc brakes; and E70-14 fiberglass-belted black sidewall tires with raised white letters. Duster sales were extremely impressive and helped by the fact that some other makers put stress on big cars this year. The special 'Gold Duster' appeared as a midyear 'package model.' It included the 225 cid six or 318 cid V-8; dual horns; whitewall tires; specific wheelcovers; bright scalp rails; Argent Silver grille finish; golden tape stripes sides and rear; front bucket seats; and cigarette lighter. No separate 'Gold Duster' production total is available.

1970 Plymouth, Duster '340' two-door hardtop sport coupe, V-8

PLYMOUTH I.D. NUMBERS: VIN on top left of dash. First symbol identifies marque: B=Barracuda; V=Valiant; R=Belvedere/Satellite; P=Fury. Second symbol indicates car-line price class: E=economy; L=low; M=Medium; H=High; P=Premium; S=Special; K=Police; T=Taxicab. Third and fourth symbols indicate body style. (First four symbols appear in second column of charts below). Fifth symbol indicates engine: B=198/125 hp six; C=225 cid/145 hp six; E=special order six; G=318 cid/230 hp V-8; H=340 cid/275 hp high-performance V-8; [AAR 'Cuda only] J=340 cid/290 hp "Six Pack" V-8; L=383 cid/290 hp V-8; N=383 cid/330 hp high-performance V-8; R=426 cid/425 hp "Street Hemi" V-8; T=440 cid/350 hp V-8; U=440 cid/375 hp high-performance V-8; V=440 cid/390 hp "Six-Pack" V-8; Z=Special Order V-8. The sixth symbol designated model year (0=1970). The seventh symbol indicated assembly plant; A=Lynch Rd., Detroit; B=Hamtrack, Mich.; C=Jefferson Ave., Detroit; D=Belvedere, Ill.; F=Newark, Del.; G=St. Louis, Mo.; P=Wyoming Ave., Detroit and R=Windsor, Canada). The last six symbols were the sequential unit production number. Number PH29G0C100050 would, therefore, indicate a Plymouth Sport Fury two-door Formal Top hardtop with base 230 hp 318 cid V-8 built in 1970 at the Jefferson factory, in Detroit, Mich. as the 50th car off the line at that plant.

VALIANT/VALIANT DUSTER

Series Number	Body/Style Number	Body Type & Seating	Factory Price	Shipping Weight	Production Total
VALIANT VL					
FV1/2	VL41	4-dr Sed-6P	2250/2361	2795/2875	50,810
VALIANT DUSTER VL					
FV1/2	VL29	2-dr Cpe-6P	2172/2283	2790/2865	192,375
DUSTER 340 VS					
FV2	VS29	2-dr Cpe-5P	2547	3110	24,817

NOTE 1: Data above slash for sixes/below slash for V-8s.

1970 Plymouth, 'Cuda two-door hardtop coupe, V-8

BARRACUDA/CUDA/GRAN COUPE — (6-CYL/V-8) — SERIES FB — Totally redesigned, the Barracuda line for 1970 offered buyers a wider choice of models and engines. Three styles were available with a total of nine engines. Stress was placed on extending the racy image of long hoods/short decks and rakish windshields. The specialty/performance class 'Cuda offered an innovative 'shaker' hood option. A classy Gran Coupe was the top of the line. Even the 426 cid 'Street Hemi' was now offered in special Barracudas, built in limited numbers. Standard equipment in Barracudas included high-back buckets with all-vinyl trim; integral headrests; molded door and quarter trim panels; flood-lighted instrument panel; three-spoke wood grain steering wheel; floor shift; carpeting; 225 cid six; and E78-15 fiberglass-belted tires. The Gran Coupe had all Barracuda items, plus body sill, wheel lip, and beltline moldings; Gran Coupe emblems; leather bucket seats and consolette in Knit Jersey (hardtop only); molded headliner; and, in covertible, leather bucket seats. DeLuxe vinyl or cloth and vinyl trims were available at lowered cost. The 'Cuda carried all Gran Coupe equipment, plus the four-barrel 383 V-8; heavy-duty suspension and drum brakes; 'Cuda ornamentation; and F70-14 white-letter tires. The 'Street Hemi' came as an $871.45 extra in TorqueFlite equipped 'Cudas. Few were ordered. The AAR 'Cuda was offered in the spring of 1970 with special performance features for the Trans AM racing circuit, including an exclusive 290 hp version of the 340 V-8 with triple two-barrel carburetors, G60 x 15 rear tires and E60 x 15 front tires on 7 x 15 wheels. Production of 2,800 units was programmed, but the exact number of AAR 'Cudas built is unknown.

BARRACUDA/GRAN COUPE/'CUDA

Series Number	Body/Style Number	Body Type & Seating	Factory Price	Shipping Weight	Production Total
BARRACUDA SERIES					
FB1/2	BH23	2-dr HT Cpe-5P	2764/2865	2790/3025	25,651
FB1/2	BH27	2-dr Conv-5P	3034/3135	3045/3100	1,554
GRAN COUPE SERIES					
FB1/2	BP23	2-dr HT Cpe-5P	2934/3035	2990/3040	8,183
FB1/2	BP27	2-dr Conv-5P	3160/3260	3065/3115	596
'CUDA SERIES					
FB2	BS23	2-dr HT Cpe-5P	3164	3395	18,880
FB2	BS27	2-dr Conv-5P	3433	3480	635

NOTE 1: Data above slash for sixes/below slash; no slash for V-8s.

1970 Plymouth, Road Runner Super Bird two-door hardtop coupe, V-8

PLYMOUTH INTERMEDIATES — (6 CYL/V-8) — SERIES FR — Redesigned grilles, hoods, and fenders characterized Plymouth's 16 model intermediate-sized lineup. Also new was a full-width rear panel housing arrow-shaped taillamps. The grille had a sort of 'telephone receiver' shape with integral dual headlamps at each end. Round park and back-up lamps graced the central bumper region front and rear. Belvederes had color-keyed floor mats; front armrests; rear ashtray/armrests/cigar lighter; glove box lock; sill moldings; all-vinyl two-door coupe interior (cloth-and-vinyl in sedan); heavy-duty brakes (on wagon); and 225 cid six or 318 cid V-8. The Road Runner featured three-on-the-floor; heavy-duty goodies including suspension and brakes; carpets; dual exhausts; all-vinyl trim; front and rear armrests; cigar lighter; glove box light; 'Beep-Beep' horn; performance hood; front bumper guards; 150 mph speedometer; cartoon emblems; F70-14 wide tires; safety wheel rims; three-speed wipers; roof drip rails and upper door frame moldings; plus special shocks. The Superbird was a sub-series of the Road Runner featuring an aerodynamic extended nose; concealed headlights; and a tall stabilizer wing on the rear. It was designed for NASCAR SuperSpeedway racing. To qualify for NASCAR, Plymouth built Superbirds on the basis of one for every two dealerships. The standard engine was the 440 cid V-8 with single four-barrel. Satellites had all Belvedere items, plus DeLuxe cloth and vinyl trim (all-vinyl in convertible); carpets; roof drip and wheel-house moldings; swing-away day/night inside mirror; dual horns; and, on wagons, heavy-duty brakes and rocker panel sill moldings. The Sport Satellite added DeLuxe wheelcovers; DeLuxe all-vinyl interior (or cloth and vinyl sedan bench seat); bodyside pinstripes; wheel opening, 'B' pillar, upper door and quarter window moldings; custom rocker sill trim; scalp moldings; and 318 cid V-8. Sport Satellite hardtops also had foam-cushioned front bucket seats, while wagons had bigger brakes and comparable exterior trim (except for lack of custom sill moldings). Finally, the GTX took up where the Road Runner left off, adding extras to the basic performance package. They included heavy-duty TorqueFlite transmission; DeLuxe vinyl interior with foam-cushioned bucket seats; reflective bodyside tape accent treatment; side markers; dual horns; 70-ampere battery; bright exhaust trumpets; and big-block 440 cid 'Super-Commando' V-8 engine. In all, eight engines could be chosen for the full line of Plymouth intermediates, including a 390 hp job with 'Six-Pack' carburetion ($250 in Road Runner/$119 in GTX) and dual four-barrel 425 hp 'Street Hemi' ($841 in Road Runner/$711 in GTX). The performance V-8s were not available with three-speed manual transmission, air conditioning, automatic speed control, or trailer towing attachments.

PLYMOUTH INTERMEDIATES

Series Number	Body/Style Number	Body Type & Seating	Factory Price	Shipping Weight	Production Total
BELVEDERE					
FR1/2	RL41	4-dr Sed-6P	2641/2731	3085/3180	13,945
FR1/2	RL21	2-dr Cpe-6P	2603/2693	3050/3140	4,717
FR1/2	RL45	4-dr Sta Wag-6P	2985/3075	3610/3655	5,584
ROAD RUNNER					
FR2	RM21	2-dr Cpe-6P	2896	3450	15,716
FR2	RM23	2-dr HT Cpe-6P	3034	3475	24,944
FR2	RM23	2-dr Superbird-6P	4298	3785	1,920
FR2	RM27	2-dr Conv-6P	3289	3550	824
SATELLITE					
FR1/2	RH41	4-dr Sed-6P	2741/2831	3075/3175	30,377
FR1/2	RH23	2-dr HT Cpe-6P	2765/2855	3055/3155	28,200
FR1/2	RH27	2-dr Conv-6P	3006/3096	3175/3260	701
FR1/2	RH46	4-dr Sta Wag-9P	3211/3301	3685/3730	3,277
FR1/2	RH45	4-dr Sta Wag-6P	3101/3191	3615/3660	4,204
SPORT SATELLITE					
FR2	RP41	4-dr Sed-6P	3017	3205	3,010
FR2	RP23	2-dr HT Cpe-5P	2988	3170	8,749
FR2	RP46	4-dr Sta Wag-9P	3455	3750	2,161
FR2	RP45	4-dr Sta Wag-6P	3345	3675	1,975
SATELLITE GTX					
FR2	RS23	2-dr HT Cpe-5P	3535	3515	7,748

NOTE 1: Data above slash for sixes/below slash; no slash for V-8s.

1970 Plymouth, Fury GT, two-door hardtop sports coupe, V-8

PLYMOUTH FULL-SIZED/FURY — (6-CYL/V-8) — SERIES FP — Integrated loop bumpers; non-wraparound horizontal taillamps; increased length; widened rear tread; new four-door styles; and generally more massive appearances were the elements of change in the big Plymouths this year. Several sporty option-created 'models' debuted during the year. Fury Is had a loop front bumper; dual headlights; hubcaps; OSRV mirror; gauges (but, oil pressure lamp); panel light dimmer; electric wiper/washers; padded dash and steering wheel and visors; crank-out vertipanes; and blackwall tires. Fury II had the same, plus integral back-up lamps and taillights in rear bumper; 120 mph speedometer; heater control; and carpets. Fury III had all of this (except no ventipanes on hardtop coupe), plus vinyl bodyside moldings; side markers: DeLuxe steering wheel; ashtray and trunk lights; door frame trim; larger tires; and, on convertible, upper belt molding and pocket panel light. Sport Fury added concealed headlights; red, white and blue grille ornament; deck medallion; glove box light; and wheelhouse moldings, but had no vent windows or trunk light. The basic Suburban had a two-way tailgate; torsion bar suspension; integral rear wind deflector; power tailgate window; larger tires; and '318' V-8. Custom wagons had upper door frame trim; bigger brakes; and carpets on nine-passenger job. The Sport Wagon had woodgrain exterior paneling; hidden headlights; DeLuxe steering wheel; and special grille. All models included regulation safety features. The Fury S-23 came with hood stripes; front anti-sway bar; Rally road wheels and 'Strobe Stripe' reflective tone treatment. The Fury GT came with 'Strobe Stripe' tape treatment; Rally road wheels; H70-15 fiberglass belted tires; a Super Commando 440 cid four-barrel V-8; chrome exhaust trumpets; heavy-duty suspension; heavy-duty brakes; 3.23:1 rear axle and hood striping.

PLYMOUTH FULL-SIZED/FURY

Series Number	Body/Style Number	Body Type & Seating	Factory Price	Shipping Weight	Production Total
FURY I SERIES					
FP1/2	PE41	4-dr Sed-6P	2825/2930	3625/3655	14,813
FP1/2	PE21	2-dr Sed-6P	2790/2895	3575/3630	2,353
FURY II SERIES					
FP1/2	PL41	4-dr Sed-6P	2922/3027	3615/3650	27,694
FPI/2	PL21	2-dr Sed-6P	2903/3008	3565/3620	21,316
FP2	PL46	4-dr Sta Wag-9P	3518	4205	2,250
FP1/2	PL45	4-dr Sta Wag-6P	3303/3408	4090/4160	5,300
FURY GRAN COUPE (*)					
FP2	PL21 W/AC	2-dr Sed-6P	4216	3978	Note 2
FP2	PL21	2-dr Sed-6P	3833	3864	Note 2
FURY III SERIES					
FP1/2	PM41	4-dr Sed-6P	3069/3174	3625/3655	50,876
FP1/2	PM22	2-dr HT Cpe-6P	3091/3196	3600/3620	21,373
FP2	PM43	4-dr HT Sed-6P	3246	3690	47,879
FP2	PM29	2-dr FsTp Cpe-6P	3217	3615	12,367
FP2	PM27	2-dr Conv-6P	3415	3770	1,952
FP2	PM46	4-dr Sta Wag-9P	3603	4215	6,792
FP2	PM45	4-dr Sta Wag-6P	3527	4155	8,898
SPORT FURY SERIES					
FP2	PH41	4-dr Sed-6P	3291	3680	5,135
FP2	PH43	4-dr HT Sed-6P	3363	3705	6,854
FP2	PH23	2-dr HT Cpe-6P	3313	3630	8,018
FP2	PH29	2-dr FsTp Cpe-6P	3333	3645	5,688
FP2	PH46	4-dr Sta Wag-9P	3804	4260	9,170
FP2	PH45	4-dr Sta Wag-6P	3725	4200	4,403
S-23 (*)					
FP2	PS23	2-dr HT Cpe-5P	3379	3660	Note 3
FURY GT (*)					
FP2	PP23	2-dr HT Cpe-5P	3898	3925	Note 4

NOTE 1: (*) Option-created-models with Fury Body codes, but specific options.
NOTE 2: Total for Fury Gran Coupe included with Fury II two-door sedan.
NOTE 3: Total for Fury S-23 hardtop included with Sport Fury two-door hardtop.
NOTE 4: Total for Fury GT Coupe included with Sport Fury two-door hardtop.
NOTE 5: Data above slash for sixes/below slash; no slash for V-8s.

BASE ENGINES

(VALIANT/DUSTER SIX) Inline. Six. Overhead valves. Cast iron block. Displacement: 198 cid. Bore and stroke: 3.4 x 3.64 inches. Compression ratio: 8.4:1. Brake hp: 125 at 4400 rpm. Four main bearings. Solid valve lifters. Carburetor: Ball and Ball Type BBS one-barrel Model 4715S.

(V-8 VALIANT/DUSTER/BARRACUDA/FURY/SATELLITE) V-8. Overhead valves. Cast iron block. Displacement: 318 cid. Bore and stroke: 3.91 x 3.31 inches. Compression ratio: 8.8:1. Brake hp: 230 at 4400 rpm. Five main bearings. Hydraulic valve lifters. Carburetor: Carter Type BBD two-barrel Model 4721S.

(V-8 DUSTER 340) V-8. Overhead valves. Cast iron block. Displacement: 340 cid. Bore and stroke: 4.04 x 3.31 inches. Compression ratio: 10.5:1. Brake hp: 275 at 5000 rpm. Five main bearings. Hydraulic valve lifters. Carburetor: Carter Type AVS four-barrel Model 4933S.

BARRACUDA/GRAN COUPE/'CUDA SERIES ENGINE DATA

(BARRACUDA/FURY/SATELLITE SIX) Inline. six. Overhead valves. Cast iron block. Displacement: 225 cid. Bore and stroke: 3.4 x 4.12 inches. Compression ratio: 8.4:1. Brake hp: 145 at 4000 rpm. Four main bearings. Solid valve litters. Carburetor: Holley one-barrel Model 1920-R4352A.

(V-8 STANDARD 'CUDA HIGH-PERFORMANCE/ROAD RUNNER) V-8. Overhead valves. Cast iron block. Displacement: 383 cid. Bore and stroke: 4.25 x 3.38 inches. Compression ratio: 9.5:1. Brake hp: 335 at 5200 rpm. Five main bearings. Hydraulic valve lifters. Carburetor: Carter Type BBD four-barrel Model 4725S.

(V-8 SUPERBIRD/GTX/FURY GT) V-8. Overhead valves. Cast iron block. Displacement: 440 cid. Bore and stroke: 4.32 x 3.75 inches. Compression ratio: 9.7:1. Brake hp: 375 at 4400 rpm. Five main bearings. Hydraulic valve lifters. Carburetor: Carter Type AVS four-barrel Model 4737S. NOTE: The GTX engine produced 375 hp at 4600 rpm.

CHASSIS FEATURES: Wheelbase: (Valiant/Duster/Barracuda) 108 inches; (Belvedere wagons) 117 inches; (Belvedere passenger) 116 inches; (Fury wagons) 122 inches; (Fury passenger) 120 inches. Overall length: (Valiant/Duster) 188.4 inches; (Barracuda) 186.7 inches; (Belvedere wagons) 209.1 inches; (Belvedere passenger) 204 inches; (Fury Wagon) 220.6 inches; (Fury passenger) 215.3 inches. Tires: (Valiant/Duster six.) C78 x 14, (Barracuda V-8/six) E78 x 14; ('Cuda/Fury GT/Superbird/GTX) F70 x 14; (Duster '340') E60 x 15; (Belvedere/Fury) F78 x 14; (Belvedere/Fury wagon) G78 x 14; (Sport Fury) H70 x 15.

POPULAR CONVENIENCE OPTIONS: Power brakes ($43). Power steering, Valiant group ($85); Barracuda group ($90); Fury/Belvedere ($105). Air conditioning, Belvedere/Barracuda ($357); Fury ($365); Valiant ($347). Dual air conditioning, Fury wagons ($581); or as part of option package ($217). Auto-Temp air conditioning, Fury car ($440); Dual type in Fury wagons ($663). 'Air Grabber' hood scoop, Road Runner and GTX, standard with Hemi ($66). Barracuda black air scoop, quarter panel and lower body paint ($36). Automatic speed control, Fury V-8 ($61); Belvedere/Barracuda V-8 ($58). Heavy-duty brakes, Belvedere ($23); Fury ($22); Barracuda ($23). Front disc brakes, Valiant/Belvedere ($28); Fury, standard model with '440' ($28). Rear window defogger, all except convertibles and wagons ($27). Road Runner bright exhaust trumpets, standard with Hemi and GTX ($21). Headlight time delay warning signal, all except Fury III/Fury wagons ($18). Hood hold-down pins, Road Runner and GTX only ($15). Racing mirrors, left-hand remote control, on Barracudas ($11). Left OSRV mirror, remote control, Valiant/Belvedere/Fury ($10). Color-keyed racing mirrors, left-hand remote control, on Barracudas ($26). Performance hood, Road Runner/GTX ($18). Sport striping, 'Cuda without side molding vinyl insert ($26). "Dust Trail" tape stripes, on Road Runner ($16). Power convertible top, on Barracuda ($53). Power windows, Belvedere convertible and hardtop/Fury/Barracuda ($105). Power bench seat, in Furys ($100). Power left-hand bucket seat, or left split bench, Fury III/Sport Fury/Sport Wagon ($93). Power door locks, Fury two-doors ($45); Fury four-doors ($69). Solid state AM radio, all models ($62). Solid state AM/FM radio, Belvederes ($135). Solid state AM radio with stereo tape, all except Valiant ($196). Multiplex AM/FM stereo system, Fury and Barracuda ($214). Bench seat, cloth and vinyl with center armrest GTX/Sport Satellite (no charge). Vinyl bench seat with armrest and folding cushion, Barracudas ($17). Four-place style vinyl bench seats, Duster/Standard Duster '340' ($13). Bucket seat with vinyl trim, Road Runner ($100); Sport Satellite four-door sedan (no charge); Sport Satellite wagon with center armrest and folding cushion ($103); Fury III two-door hardtop ($125); Sport Fury and Fury III convertible ($100), also standard in Sport Satellite and GTX. Leather bucket seat with consolette, Barracuda, also standard in Gran Coupe ($119). Leather bucket seat, in Barracuda convertible ($65). Center cushion and folding armrest, Road Runner/Sport Satellite/GTX ($54). Shaker hood fresh air package, 'Cuda only, standard with 'Hemi' ($97). Tilt adjustment steering wheel, Fury group only ($53). Tachometer, Duster '340'/Belvedere V-8 except Road Runner and GTX ($50). Tachometer, including clock, in Road Runner and GTX ($68). Floral vinyl roof, Barracuda group, except Gran Coupe ($96). Vinyl roof, passenger cars, Fury group ($106); Belvedere ($96); Valiant ($84). Duster vinyl and cloth trim, includes carpets, DeLuxe and '340' models ($39). Valiant/Duster vinyl and cloth trim, standard models ($52). DeLuxe wheelcovers, as option, on Belvedere/Fury/Valiant/Barracuda ($16). Sport wheelcovers, as option, Fury without basic group ($28); with basic group ($12). Wire wheelcovers. Belvedere except Sport Satellite/Barracuda/Valiant [except Duster 340] ($50). Rally Road wheels; Belvedere/Barracuda/Valiant ($33); Belvedere ($17); Fury ($41). Chrome Road wheels: Belvedere ($67); Fury ($75); Sport Fury ($34); Barracuda ($50). Fury Brougham package, includes: luxury style bucket seats and other luxury equipment ($118). Super Track Pak racing equipment package/Road Runner/GTX/'Cuda ($236). Three-speed manual transmission was standard; with floor shift in some models ($14). TorqueFlite automatic transmission, with six ($175-$190); with V-8 ($191-$227). Four-speed manual floor shift transmission, prices vary with model and engine ($188-$197). Six-cylinder 225 cid/145 hp Valiant engine ($25). Commando V-8 383 cid/290 hp in Belvedere/Fury/Barracuda ($70). Commando V-8 383 cid 330/335 hp in Belvedere/Fury/Barracuda ($138). Street Hemi V-8 426 cid/425 hp in Road Runner ($841). Street Hemi V-8 426 cid/425 hp engine in 'Cuda ($871). Street Hemi V-8 426 cid/425 hp in GTX ($711). Commando V-8 440 cid/350 hp in Fury ($234). Commando V-8 440 cid/350 hp Fury w/air engine ($164). "Six-Pack" V-8 440 cid/390 hp in Road Runner ($250). "Six Pack" V-8 440 cid/390 hp engine in GTX ($119). "Six Pack" V-8 440 cid/390 hp 'Cuda engine ($250). Commando V-8 440 cid/350 hp 'Cuda engine ($131). Heavy-duty, 70-ampere Valiant battery ($13). Heavy-duty, 59-ampere Valiant battery ($13). Heavy-duty. 50-ampere Valiant alternator ($11-$15). Sure-Grip positive traction rear axle, in specific Belvederes/Valiants ($42); Furys ($49). Evaporative emissions control system ($38). Available rear axle gear ratios: 2.76 or 3.55 optional ($10).

HISTORICAL FOOTNOTES: The 1970 Plymouths were introduced Sept. 23, 1969 and the Valiant line appeared in dealer showrooms the same day. Model year production peaked at 725,600 units. Calendar year sales of 699,031 cars were recorded. This was the last year for convertibles in the Satellite and Fury lines. L.A. Townsend was the chief executive officer of the company this year. R.D. McLaughlin was General Sales Manager. Of all Chrysler products built this model year, only 1,543 had 426 cid 'Street Hemi' engines and only a portion of these went into Plymouths. The cars that received these engines included 75 Belvedere Road Runner hardtops (59 with four-speeds); 74 Road Runner coupes (44 with four-speeds); three Road Runner convertibles (one with the four-speed); 135 Road Runner Super Birds (58 with four-speed); 72 Belvedere GTX hardtops (43 with four-speeds); 652 'Cuda hardtops (284 with four-speeds); and 14 'Cuda convertibles (five with four-speeds). Besides Hemi 'Cudas, Plymouth put the following performance engine/transmission combinations in specific versions of its sports compact: ['Cuda 340 convertible] 19 three-speeds; 88 four-speeds and 155 automatics. ['Cuda 340 coupe] 1,872 three-speeds; 3,492 four-speeds; 3,392 automatics. ['Cuda 383 convertible] nine three-speeds; 63 four-speeds; 137 automatics; ['Cuda 383 coupe] 150 three-speeds; 1,905 four-speeds; 2,540 automatics; ['Cuda 440 four-barrel convertible] six four-speeds and 28 automatics; ['Cuda 440 four-barrel coupe] 334 four-speeds and 618 automatics. ['Cuda 440 Six-Pack convertible] 17 four-speeds and 12 automatics. ['Cuda 440 Six-Pack coupe] 903 four-speeds and 852 automatics. [AAR 'Cuda coupe] 1,120 four-speeds and 1,604 automatics. Rare options for Fury group models and their percentage installation rates (in parentheses) were: six-cylinder engine (1.3); stereo tape (1.9); power door locks (1.5); Styled Road wheels (1.2); and movable steering column (1.4). Rare Belvedere options and their percentage installation rates (in parentheses) were: power side windows (0.5) and speed control (0.4). Eighty-three percent of all Barracudas had bucket seats and 18.5 percent had four-speed manual transmission. The rarest Valiant option was power drum brakes, used in just 1.6 percent of all Valiants built.

1971 PLYMOUTH

1971 Plymouth, Valiant Scamp two-door hardtop sports coupe, V-8

PLYMOUTH CRICKET — (4-CYL) — MODEL 4B21 — The sub-compact Plymouth Cricket was a new entry in the company's model lineup this year. This $1,915 four-door sedan was essentially a badge engineered vehicle made by Chrysler United Kingdom, Ltd., the English subsidiary which used to be Rootes Motors. The car was sold in Great Britain as the Hillman Avenger and the American market version was changed mainly in the design of nameplates used on the body. Since THE STANDARD CATALOG of AMERICAN CARS 1946-1975 is primarily concerned with vehicles produced in the United States, the Cricket will not be covered in detail.

VALIANT GROUP — (6-CYL/V-8) — SERIES GV — The Valiant Group now included three different types of cars with totally different sheet metal, Valiant, Duster and Scamp. The basic Valiant was virtually unchanged. Small revisions included removal of the center grille emblem and a new kind of finish treatment on the grille surround. It now had a blacked-out look, instead of Satin Silver treatment. Regulation safety features were used on all Plymouth products. Valiants also had color-keyed door armrests (rear on four-door sedan only); clean air system; concealed spare tire; directionals with lane change; anti-theft lock and ignition buzzer; and two-speed electric wipers. New grilles and rear end appearances and 18 exterior colors gave the strong selling Duster a new look for 1971. It no longer carried Valiant nameplates and had the same cowl-back distinctions seen the previous year. Standard equipment began with all Valiant features, plus swing-out rear quarter windows; ventless side glass; twin stacked horizontal slat taillights; and Duster emblems. The Duster '340' also had floor shift manual transmission; unique vertically segmented grille; tape accent stripes; cigar lighter; roof drip rail moldings; special instrument panel; heavy-duty suspension; and the 340 cid V-8 with dual exhausts and twin snorkel air cleaner. A number of optional packages including DeLuxe trim, Sports trim and the mid-season 'Twister' group allowed tailoring to individual taste. The Scamp was built off the Dodge Swinger platform with Dodge Dart sheet metal and a Valiant grille. It was larger and longer, but otherwise came with Valiant equipment features and identification. Both Dusters and Scamps used Valiant front end sheet metal, but were different types of vehicles from the cowl back.

PLYMOUTH I.D. NUMBERS: VIN on top left of dash. First symbol identifies marque: B=Barracuda; V=Valiant; R=Belvedere/Satellite; P=Fury. Second symbol indicates car-line price class: E=Economy; L=low; M=Medium; H=High; P=Premium; S=Special; K=Police; T=Taxicab. Third and fourth symbols indicate body style. (First four symbols appear in second column of charts below). Fifth symbol indicates engine: B=198/125 hp cid six; C=225 cid/145 hp six; E=special order six; G=318 cid/230 hp V-8; H=340 cid/275 hp V-8; [AAR 'Cuda only] J=340 cid/290 hp "Six Pack" V-8; K=360 cid V-8; L=383 cid/275 hp V-8; N=383 cid/300 hp high-performance V-8; R=426 cid/425 hp "Street Hemi" V-8; T=440 cid/335 hp V-8; U=440 cid/370 hp high-performance V-8; V=440 cid/385 hp "Six-Pack" V-8; Z=Special Order V-8=440 V-8. The sixth symbol designated model year (1=1971). The seventh symbol indicated assembly plant; A=Lynch Rd., Detroit; B=Hamtramck, Mich.; C=Jefferson Ave., Detroit; D=Belvedere, Ill.; F=Newark, Del.; G=St. Louis, Mo.; and R= Windsor, Canada. The last six symbols were the sequential unit production number.

VALIANT GROUP

Series Number	Body/Style Number	Body Type & Seating	Factory Price	Shipping Weight	Production Total
VALIANT					
GV1/2	VL41	4-dr Sed-6P	2392/2516	2835/2925	42,660
DUSTER					
GV1/2	VL29	2-dr Cpe-6P	2313/2437	2825/2920	173,592
DUSTER '340'					
GV2	VS29	2-dr Cpe-6P	2703	3140	12,886
SCAMP					
GV1/2	VH23	2-dr HT Cpe-6P	2561/2685	2900/2985	48,253

NOTE 1: Data above slash for six/below slash; no slash for V-8s.

BARRACUDA GROUP — (6-CYL/V-8) — SERIES GB — The Barracuda was again related to the Valiant, but listed as an entirely different series catering to the sports/compact market. New grilles and rear lamps highlighted styling detail changes. Elastometric bumpers in a choice of colors were optionally available. Equipment for base models consisted of dual headlamps and horns; hubcaps; day/night inside mirror; brake warning light; left OSRV mirror; fuel, temperature and ammeter gauges; bucket seats; cigar lighter; heater and defroster; and two-speed wipers. The base coupe came with the Valiant six-cylinder engine, while other Barracuda sixes used the Plymouth 225 cid job. A new grille with recessed, vertically divided segments was used on all lines. Taillamps and back-up lights were now individual units. The second-step-up Barracuda was the Gran Coupe, which came with all features above, plus

overhead consolette; pedal trim: leather bucket seats; formed headliner; wheel lip moldings; belt moldings; Gran Coupe ornamentation; and a V-8. The high-performance 'Cuda was the flagship of the fleet and had all the above items, plus chrome rocker sill moldings; special 'performance' hood (with integral scoops); color-keyed grille; black-finished rear deck panel; heavy-duty suspension and brakes; 'Cuda ornamentation; whitewall tires; and the 383 cid four-barrel V-8. The 'Street Hemi' engine was an $884 option requiring the four-speed gearbox and other mandatory extra-cost equipment.

1971 Plymouth, 'Cuda '340' two-door hardtop coupe, V-8

BARRACUDA GROUP

Series Number	Body/Style Number	Body Type & Seating	Factory Price	Shipping Weight	Production Total
BARRACUDA					
GB1/2	BH21	2-dr Cpe-5P	2654/2780	3010/3070	Note 2
GB1/2	BH23	2-dr HT Cpe-5P	2766/2867	3035/3090	9,459
GB1/2	BH27	2-dr Conv-5P	3023/3124	3115/3165	1,014
BARRACUDA GRAN COUPE					
GB2	BP23	2-dr HT Cpe-5P	3029	3105	1,615
'CUDA					
GB2	BS23	2-dr HT Cpe-5P	3156	3475	6,228
GB2	BS27	2-dr Conv-5P	3412	3550	374

NOTE 1: Data above slash for six/below slash; no slash for V-8s.
NOTE 2: Total for Style BH21 is included in the total for Style Number BH23.

1971 Plymouth, Road Runner two-door hardtop coupe, V-8

SATELLITE GROUP — (6-CYL/V-8) — SERIES GR — The so-called 'fuselage' body design was the hit of 1971 at Plymouth and different variations were seen on two-door and four-door models. Not a single panel of sheet metal interchanged on the two different basic types of cars. They looked different, too. The coupes and hardtop coupes seemed futuristic with their integral bumper/grilles, down-swooping curved panels and blending sail panel treatments. Styling feature lines gave the impression of the mid body wrapping over the lower body. On sedans and wagons the look was completely different. It almost seemed if someone had squashed down one of the old slab sided cars until that the body bulged out at the sides. In design lingo, this is called increasing the amount of 'tumble-home.' The four-doors were much more conventional looking, with their regular type grilles and slimmer horizontal taillamps. Many model names were changed and the model listings were confused by the practice of breaking cars out by body type, instead of the traditional series designations: L = Low; M = Medium; H = High; P = Premium; and S = Special. The base for the line was simply called Satellite and had all-vinyl trim; color-keyed rubber floor coverings; dome light; transistorized voltage regulator; hubcaps; clean air system; heater/defroster; and (except in coupes) cigar lighter and day/night inside rearview mirror. Coded as an 'RM' model ('R' for Belvedere; 'M' for medium-priced) was the Road Runner, which had all above equipment, plus floor-shift; heavy-duty suspension; 'Beep-Beep' horn; Rally gauge cluster; deep pile carpets; performance hood; low-restriction dual exhausts; front foam seat cushions; drip rail moldings; heavy-duty shocks; and 383 cid high-performance V-8. The Satellite Sebring was the high-priced Belvedere two-door and came with the basic Satellite equipment assortment, plus dual conventional horns; drip rail accents; sill moldings; wheelhouse trim; and front foam cushions. Satellite Customs represented high-priced Satellites in four-door form and matched the regular Sebring in standard features. For premium-price marketing, extra equipment (but not the same items) were added to each of the above cars. Then, each body style in each level was given an identifiable name. Thus, there was the Sebring-Plus hardtop; the Satellite Brougham sedan; the Satellite Regent wagon (with two or three seats) and the 'RS' coded ('R' for Belvedere; 'S' for specialty) high-performance GTX. The Sebring-Plus came with vinyl bucket seats (or center armrest seat with cloth and vinyl trim); front foam cushions; DeLuxe wheelcovers; and, if desired, wheel trim rings at no extra cost. Sebring Brougham sedans had the same thing (with center armrest seat mandatory); bright armrest bases; similar rear seat armrests; and bright upper door frame moldings. The Regent station wagon had all of this, plus heavy-duty brakes and carpets, but used a vinyl bench seat instead of the bucket or armrest types. Unlike the Sebring-Plus and Satellite Brougham (and Road Runner, as well) the Regents did not come with whitewall tires. Last, but not least, was the GTX: a Road Runner with extra features. They included the 440 cid 'Super Commando' V-8; TorqueFlite transmission; bucket seats; low-restriction dual exhausts with chrome trumpets; dual horns; vinyl trim (cloth and vinyl no charge); 70 ampere battery; custom sill moldings; wheel opening accents; drip rail trim; extra-heavy-duty suspension; and raised white-letter tires. GTX buyers could have a cloth and vinyl center armrest seat, white sidewall tires or floor-mounted manual three-speed transmission as equipment substitutions with no change in price. Of course, in

addition to all these different body styles, trim levels and nameplates, there was a host of individual options or pre-packaged accessory groups, including 'Air Grabber' hood scoops; louvered backlight (except in Pennsylvania); performance hood paint treatment; 'Strobe Stripes;' and aerodynamic spoiler.

SATELLITE GROUP

Series Number	Body/Style Number	Body Type & Seating	Factory Price	Shipping Weight	Production Total
SATELLITE					
GR1/2	RL41	4-dr Sed-6P	2734/2829	3240/3340	11,059
GR1/2	RL21	2-dr Cpe-6P	2663/2758	3185/3295	Note 2
GR1/2	RL45	4-dr Sta Wag-6P	3058/3153	3725/3790	7,138
SATELLITE SEBRING					
GR1/2	RH23	2-dr HT Cpe-6P	2931/3026	3210/3320	46,807
SATELLITE CUSTOM					
GR1/2	RH41	4-dr Sed-6P	2908/3003	3240/3340	30,773
GR1/2	RH46	4-dr Sta Wag-9P	3315/3410	3800/3865	3,865
GR1/2	RH45	4-dr Sta Wag-6P	3235/3330	3730/3795	5,045
ROAD RUNNER					
GR2	RM23	2-dr HT Cpe-5P	3147	3640	14,218
SATELLITE SEBRING-PLUS					
GR2	RP23	2-dr HT Cpe-5P	3179	3330	16,253
SATELLITE BROUGHAM					
GR2	RP41	4-dr Sed-6P	3189	3300	3,020
SATELLITE REGENT WAGON					
GR2	RP46	4-dr Sta Wag-9P	3638	3885	2,985
GR2	RP45	4-dr Sta Wag-6P	3558	3815	2,161
GTX					
GR2	RS23	2-dr HT Cpe-5P	3733	3675	2,942

NOTE 1: Data above slash for six/below slash; no slash for V-8s.
NOTE 2: Total for Style RL21 is included in the total for Style RH23.

1971 Plymouth, Sport Fury two-door hardtop sports coupe, V-8

FURY GROUP — (6-CYL/V-8) — SERIES GP — At the beginning of the model year standard-sized Plymouths came in 19 models grouped into five series: Fury I, Fury II, Fury III, Sport Fury and Sport Fury GT. Around May, 1971, TorqueFlite automatic transmission became standard in all full-sized Plymouths. Prices were increased to cover this change and a well-equipped (but 'economy' coded) Fury Custom Series was announced. Highlights for the season included a new Fury II two-door hardtop; new front and rear appearances; ventless side window glass; more luxurious interiors; and new cassette tape and sun roof options. Major technical improvements included Torsion-Quiet Ride formerly available only on more expensive Chryslers and Imperials. A new isolation system was designed to cut vibrations and noise and there was an optional regular-fuel 360 cid V-8. Sport Furys were available with color-keyed polyurethane rear inserts, while wagons came with translucent woodgrain trim that permitted the body color to show through. Standard Fury I equipment included loop type front bumpers; dual headlights; hubcaps; brake warning light; left OSRV mirror; fuel-temperature gauges; ammeter-oil pressure warning lights; interior lights with panel dimmer; inside day/night mirror; front and rear armrests; non-glare flood-lighted instrumentation; two-speed electric wiper/washers; cigar lighter; glove box lock; three-spoke steering wheel with integral horn button; dome lamp; courtesy lamp door switches; front and rear ashtrays; bright drip rail moldings; concealed Wipers; side cowl ventilation; and fresh air heater/defroster. The Fury II also had deep-pile carpets and full-length bodyside moldings. The Fury III had all of this, plus color-keyed vinyl molding inserts; ashtray and trunk lights; wheel lip moldings; wood-grained door panel inserts and dash pad; woodgrained dash panel trim; glove box light; wood-look steering wheel; bright metal armrest bases; and upper door frame accent moldings. The Sport Fury added door pull straps; lower door carpet panels; pull-down center armrest with integral headrest; sill molding; concealed headlamps; Sport Fury nameplates, ornaments and medallions; belt moldings (on all except the four-door sedan); and dome lamp rear courtesy switches on four-door sedan only. The Sport Fury GT had all features found on the lower level cars, plus hood stripes; heavy-duty suspension; 70 ampere battery; 3.23:1 rear axle gear ratio; dual exhausts; power front disc brakes; Rally Road Wheels; white letter tires; and the 'Super Commando' V-8. A side and rear 'Strobe Stripe' tape treatment replaced upper beltline moldings on the 'GT' and TorqueFlite transmission was standard in this model all year long. Interestingly, its price still increased in May, but not as much as the window stickers on other models. Fury Suburbans had the basic Fury I equipment, plus three-way tailgate; torsion bar suspension; rear integral wind deflector; power tailgate window; and heavy-duty brakes. Custom Suburbans added front foam seat cushions; carpets; and bright upper door frame, rocker sill and wheelhouse moldings. Sport Suburbans also had vinyl trim over a center armrest bench seat and woodgrained side body panels. The Fury Custom, which was mentioned earlier, came standard with DeLuxe wheelcovers; two-tone paint; vinyl side moldings; woodgrained dash appliques; Custom bodyside nameplates; paisley pattern vinyl bench seats; extra-long front armrests with bright bases; and special Fury deck lid cover. This model was priced between Fury I and Fury II.

FURY GROUP

Series Number	Body/Style Number	Body Type & Seating	Factory Price	Shipping Weight	Production Total
FURY I					
GP1/2	PE41	4-dr Sed-6P	3146/3256	3705/3780	16,395
GP1/2	PE21	2-dr Sed-6P	3113/3223	3670/3750	5,152
FURY CUSTOM					
GP1/2	PE41	4-dr Sed-6P	3241/3351	3705/3780	Note 2
GP1/2	PE21	2-dr Sed-6P	3208/3318	3670/3750	Note 2
FURY II					
GP1/2	PL41	4-dr Sed-6P	3262/3372	3710/3785	20,098
GP1/2	PL23	2-dr HT Cpe-6P	3283/3393	3675/3750	7,859
GP2	PL46	4-dr Sta Wag-9P	3869	4290	2,662
GP2	PL45	4-dr Sta Wag-6P	3758	4245	4,877
FURY III					
GP1/2	PM41	4-dr Sed-6P	3437/3547	3715/3790	44,244
GP1/2	PM23	2-dr HT Cpe-6P	3458/3568	3680/3755	21,319
GP2	PM43	4-dr HT Sed-6P	3612	3820	55,356
GP2	PM29	2-dr FsTp Cpe-6P	3600	3750	24,465
GP2	PM46	4-dr Cus Sub-9P	3930	4300	11,702
GP2	PM45	4-dr Cus Sub-6P	3854	4240	10,874
SPORT FURY					
GP2	PH41	4-dr Sed-6P	3656	3845	2,823
GP2	PH43	4-dr HT Sed-6P	3724	3865	55,356
GP2	PH29	2-dr FsTp Cpe-6P	3710	3810	3,957
GP2	PH23	2-dr HT Cpe-6P	3677	3805	3,912
GP2	PH46	4-dr Spt Sub-9P	4146	4370	13,021
GP2	PH45	4-dr Spt Sub-6P	4071	4090	5,103
SPORT FURY 'GT'					
GP2	PP23	2-dr HT Cpe-6P	4111	4090	375

NOTE 1: Data above slash for six/below slash; no slash for V-8s.
NOTE 2: Production of Fury Customs included with same Fury I body style.
NOTE 3: 700 Fury IIs and 200 Fury IIIs built with six-cylinder engines.

BASE ENGINES

(VALIANT/DUSTER SIX) Inline. six. Overhead valves. Cast iron block. Displacement: 198 cid. Bore and stroke: 3.4 x 3.64 inches. Compression ratio: 8.4:1. Brake hp: 125 at 4000 rpm. Four main bearings. Solid valve lifters. Carburetor: one-barrel.

(BARRACUDA/BELVEDERE/FURY/SATELLITE SIX) Inline. six. Overhead valves. Cast iron block. Displacement: 225 cid. Bore and stroke: 3.4 x 4.125 inches. Compression ratio: 8.4:1. Brake hp: 145 at 4000 rpm. Four main bearings. Solid valve lifters. Carburetor: Carter Type BBS two-barrel.

(V-8 VALIANT/DUSTER/BARRACUDA/BELVEDERE/FURY) V-8. Overhead valves. Cast iron block. Displacement: 318 cid. Bore and stroke: 3.91 x 3.31 inches. Compression ratio: 8.8:1. Brake hp: 230 at 4400 rpm. Five main bearings. Hydraulic valve lifters. Carburetor: two-barrel.

(BASE DUSTER '340' ENGINE) V-8. Overhead valves. Cast iron block. Displacement: 340 cid. Bore and stroke: 4.04 x 3.31 inches. Brake hp: 275 at 5600 rpm. Compression ratio: 10.3:1. Five main bearings. Hydraulic valve lifters. Carburetor: four-barrel.

(BASE 'CUDA/ROAD RUNNER ENGINE) V-8. Overhead valves. Cast iron block. Displacement: 383 cid. Bore and stroke: 4.25 x 3.375 inches. Compression ratio: 9.5:1. Brake hp: 335 at 4800 rpm. Carburetor: Carter four-barrel.

(BASE GTX/FURY GT V-8) V-8. Overhead valves. Cast iron block. Displacement: 440 cid. Bore and stroke: 4.32 x 3.75 inches. Compression ratio: 9.7:1. Brake hp: 375 at 4800 rpm. Five main bearings. Hydraulic valve lifters. Carburetor: four-barrel.

CHASSIS FEATURES: Wheelbase: (Valiant/Duster/Barracuda) 108 inches; (Scamp) 111 inches; (Satellite two-door) 115 inches; (Satellite four-door) 117 inches; (Fury Suburban) 122 inches; (Fury Group) 120 inches. Overall length: (Valiant/Duster) 188.4 inches; (Scamp) 193 inches; (Barracuda Group) 186.6 inches; (Satellite two-door) 203.2 inches; (Satellite wagon) 210.9 inches; (Satellite four-door) 204.6 inches; (Fury Suburban) 220.2 inches; (Fury Group) 215.1 inches. Tires: (Satellite) E78 x 14; (Satellite wagons) H78 x 14; (Brougham) F78 x 14; (Fury) F78 x 15; (Fury Suburbans) J78 x 15; (Fury GT) H70 x 15; (Valiant) 6.95 x 14; (Duster) 6.45 x 14; (Barracuda) 7.35x 14; ('Cuda/GTX) F70 x 14.

OPTIONS: Air conditioning, Valiant ($384); Barracuda, except '198' six and '426' or '440' V-8s ($370); Satellite ($383); Fury ($391). Dual air conditioning, all Suburbans and wagons with automatic transmission ($608). 'Air Grabber' hood scoop for Road Runner or GTX ($67). Assist handles, in wagons ($19). Automatic locking tailgate ($27). Heavy-duty front and rear brakes, standard on wagons; on Valiant ($21); on Satellite ($23); on Barracuda ($23). Front disc brakes, Valiant ($32); on Satellite with power brakes ($24); on Barracuda with power brakes ($23). Front and rear bumper guards, Valiant ($25); Satellite, except wagons, ($34). Carpeted wagon cargo compartment ($22). Electric clock, Barracuda ($16); Road Runner/Sebring-Plus center console ($58). Decorative exhaust tips on Road Runner, standard in GTX, but not available in California ($22). Hood pins; Barracuda, standard on 'Cuda ($15); Valiant, except sedan ($15); Road Runner/GTX ($17). Backlight louvers, Satellite Group except Brougham and wagon and cars for Pennsylvania sale ($68). Dual outside racing mirrors, left remote-control and both color-keyed, on Valiants ($26); Barracuda ($26); Satellite ($28). Performance hood paint treatment, Duster coupe ($18); Duster '340' with engine 'call-out' designation ($21). Paint treatment, rear fender 'Strobe' and C-pillar stripes ($34). Paint treatment, 'Strobe Stripes' on Fury III/Sport Fury two-door/Sport Fury Formal hardtop ($28). Rear tape stripe for Duster coupe, standard with Duster '340' ($13). Bodyside tape stripe on Barracuda sedan ($29); on Gran Coupe, replaces paint stripe ($14); on Duster coupe, standard with Duster '340' ($26); on GTX, not available with 'Air Grabber' hood scoop or Hemi V-8 ($23). Paint treatment, rear quarter panel 'Sport Stripe,' on 'Cuda without vinyl side moldings ($38). Performance hood, Barracuda Group, except standard with 'Cuda ($20). Front disc brakes, power type on Fury Group ($70). Power deck lid release on Fury, except wagons ($16). Power door locks, two-door ($47); four-door ($73). Power steering, Valiant ($100), Barracuda ($97); others ($111). Barracuda power lift convertible top ($49). Power side windows, Satellite ($110); Fury ($120); Barracuda ($101). Inside hood release, Satellites ($11). Microphone tape recorder, Valiants ($21); Barracuda ($11); Satellite and Fury ($12). AM/FM radio with stereo and tape, Barracuda ($337); Satellite and Fury ($366). Vinyl roof, Barracuda ($82); Satellites, except wagons ($96); Furys, except wagons ($106). Canopy style vinyl roof, Road Runner and Sebring-Plus ($67). Three-speed manual transmission was standard, except as indicated in text. Automatic transmission was standard in many models after midyear. Automatic transmission, in Valiant ($183); Barracuda Coupe ($209); V-8 Valiant ($191). Automatic transmission, in Satellite/Fury six ($216); Satellite/Fury V-8 ($216-$238). Three-speed manual floor shift transmission, in Satellite ($14); Valiant ($13). Four-speed manual floor shift transmission, in Barracuda ($198). Four-speed manual transmission with floor shift, in Satellite ($206). Four-speed manual transmission with floor shift, in Road Runner ($206). Valiant six-cylinder 225 cid/145 hp one-barrel engine ($39). Barracuda Coupe six-cylinder 225 cid/145 hp one-barrel engine ($39). 'Cuda V-8 340 cid/275 hp four-barrel engine ($44). Road Runner and Fury V-8 440 cid/370 hp four-barrel engine ($46). Fury V-8 360 cid/255 hp two-barrel engine ($46). Satellite/Sport Fury V-8 383 cid/275 hp two-barrel engine ($73). Satellite/Fury V-8 383 cid/300 hp four-barrel engine ($145). 'Cuda/Road Runner V-8 426 cid/425 hp 'Street Hemi' engine ($884). GTX V-8 426 cid/425 hp 'Street Hemi' engine ($747). Fury V-8 440 cid/330 hp 'Six-Pack' engine ($253). Road Runner V-8 440 cid/385 hp

'Six-Pack' engine ($262). GTX V-8 440 cid/385 hp 'Six-Pack' engine ($125). Fury Suburban V-8 440 cid/370 hp four-barrel engine ($198). Barracuda V-8 383 cid/275 hp two-barrel engine ($7 1). Barracuda 383 cid V-8/300 hp four-barrel engine ($140). Sure-Grip axle ($42-$49). Available rear axle gear ratios: 2.76: 1; 3.23:1, 3.55:1.

HISTORICAL FOOTNOTES: The full-sized Plymouths were introduced Oct. 6, 1970 and the Valiant line appeared in dealer showrooms Sept. 15, 1970. Model year production peaked at 625,812 units. Calendar year production of 636,592 cars was recorded. L.A. Townsend was the chief executive officer of Chrysler Corp. this year. F.G. Hazelroth was General Sales Manager of Chrysler Plymouth Div. A total of 20,260 Crickets were marketed in the United States. This was the last year for the Barracuda convertible. Richard Petty continued to campaign a Hemi-powered Road Runner in NASCAR stock car racing this year. His brilliant blue Number 43 Plymouth helped him achieve his third Grand National championship. This was the last season for the offering of the "Street Hemi" and it was installed in just 356 MoPars. They included 55 Road Runners (28 with four-speeds); 30 Belvedere GTXs (11 with four-speeds); 107 'Cuda hardtops (59 with four-speeds); and seven 'Cuda convertibles (two with four-speeds). The rest of the Hemi engines went into Dodges. In the 'Cuda series, the following additional engine/transmission attachments were made: ['Cuda 340 convertible] eight with three-speeds; 30 with four-speeds and 102 with automatic. ['Cuda 340 coupe] 51 with three-speeds; 1,141 with four-speeds and 2,008 with automatic. ['Cuda 383 convertible] eight with three-speed; 33 with four-speeds and 87 with automatics. ['Cuda 383 coupe] 75 with three-speeds; 501 with four-speeds and 1,163 with automatic. ['Cuda 440 "Six-Pack" convertible] five with four-speed and 12 automatic. ['Cuda 440 "Six-Pack" coupe] 108 with four-speed and 129 with automatic.

1972 PLYMOUTH

VALIANT GROUP — (6-CYL/V-8) — SERIES HV — The 1971 Valiant set sales records with 256,930 calendar year deliveries, so there was little motivation to change it. Only details of the taillights and grille were altered. The front side marker was a little slimmer and longer. This was the fifth year of the same basic four-door sedan body. The Dodge Dart-based Scamp was also little changed. New was a Scamp signature at the right-hand corner of the deck lid, just below the Plymouth block lettering. The base Duster models followed the pattern of minor revision, but the rear side marker lamps were moved an inch or two higher above the lower rear feature line. In addition, a nameplate was added to the sides of front fenders above the lower feature line and behind the wheel opening. This identification was not used on units with optional body striping packages, which had Duster decals at the front fender tip. The Twister included a stripe with a cartoon tornado at the rear tip and cartoon style "Twister" lettering, plus special hood paint treatment. Other ingredients included: dual racing mirrors (left remote-control); drip rail moldings; wheel lip moldings; bodyside tape stripe; and lower deck tape. The Twister package was $98.20. 'Gold Duster' packages included a gold reptile-grain canopy style vinyl top and special front fenderside decals. The Gold Duster package also included harmonizing exterior; gold bodyside stripes; gold rear deck tape; whitewalls; wider wheels; special wheelcovers; bright drip moldings; and special interior trim. It was a mid-year option. Price not available.The high-performance Duster 340 had a beltline tape stripe treatment and '340' rear fender lettering. Base Duster equipment included ventless side windows, concealed spare tire and two-speed wipers. The base Valiant added front and rear door armrests that were color-keyed to match the interior. The Scamp hardtop had the base Duster items, plus color-keyed front door armrests; interior Decor Group trim; and cigar lighter. The Duster 340 added lower deck tape stripe; bodyside tape stripe; three-speed manual floor-shift; optional axle ratio; locking glove box: heavy-duty suspension; a unique grille; dual snorkel air cleaner; roof drip rail moldings; cigar lighter; wide tires; and the 340 cid V-8 with dual exhausts. The 225 cid six was optional in all models, except the Duster '340.' The 340 cid V-8 was also extra in the other models.

PLYMOUTH I.D. NUMBERS: VIN on top left of dash. First symbol identifies marque: B=Barracuda; V=Valiant; R=Satellite; P=Fury. Second symbol indicates car-line price class: L=low; M=Medium; H=High; P=Premium; S=Special; K=Police; T=Taxicab. Third and fourth symbols indicate body style. (First four symbols appear in second column of charts below). Fifth symbol indicates engine: B=198/100 nhp cid six; C=225 cid/110 nhp six; E=special order six; G=318 cid/150 nhp V-8; H=340 cid/240 nhp V-8; K=360 cid/175 nhp V-8; M=400 cid/190 nhp two-barrel V-8; P=400 cid/255 nhp high-performance V-8; T=440 cid/225 nhp four-barrel V-8; U=440 cid/280 nhp high-performance V-8; V=440 cid/330 hp "Six-Pack" V-8; Z=Special Order V-8=440 V-8. The sixth symbol designated model year (2=1972). The seventh symbol indicated assembly plant: A=Lynch Rd., Detroit; B=Hamtramck, Mich.; C=Jefferson Ave., Detroit; D=Belvedere, Ill.; F=Newark, Del.; G=St. Louis, Mo.; and R= Windsor, Canada). The last six symbols were the sequential unit production number.

1972 Plymouth, Duster two-door coupe, 6-cyl

VALIANT GROUP

Model Number	Body/Style Number	Body Type & Seating	Factory Price	Shipping Weight	Production Total
VALIANT					
HV1/2	VL41	4-dr Sed-6P	2355/2483	2800/2900	52,911
DUSTER					
HV1/2	VL29	2-dr Spt Cpe-6P	2287/2407	2780/2875	212,311
SCAMP					
HV1/2	VH23	2-dr HT Cpe-6P	2528/2648	2825/2915	49,470
DUSTER '340'					
HV2	VS29	2-dr Spt Cpe-6P	2728	3100	15,681

NOTE 1: Data above slash is for six/below slash for V-8.

1972 Plymouth, 'Cuda '340' two-door hardtop coupe, V-8

BARRACUDA GROUP — (6-CYL/V-8) — SERIES HB — Popularity of the Barracuda was on the decline as government and insurance company pressures combined to assault the pony car market with restrictive regulations or unbearable insurance rates. Deliveries had dropped 20,000 units in 1971. This season the Barracuda convertible disappeared and styling changes were limited to face-lifting and repositioning of trim and equipment details. A split grille with louvered center divider and single headlamps was seen. Rectangular front parking lamps were moved towards the center on either side of the below-the-bumper license plate holder. Dual round taillamps appeared at each corner of the rear deck latch panel. The high-powered 'Cuda received a new twin scoop performance hood treatment and had a blacked-out rear panel (with 'Cuda lettering on the left side) and dual rectangular exhaust exits in the lower gravel pan, under the bumper. The model count was cut from nine to three. Standard equipment on the base coupe Included all regulation safety devices; dual headlamps and horns; hub caps: inside day/night mirror; brake warning lamp: left outside rearview mirror; bucket seats; cigar lighter; fuel, temperature and ammeter gauges; black sidewall tires; and either the 225 cid six or 318 cid V-8. The 'Cuda had all of these items, plus chrome wheel lip and body sill moldings; performance hood; color-keyed grille; black-out rear deck panel; heavy-duty suspension and brakes; electronic ignition; wide profile tires with white sidewalls; and the 318 cid two-barrel V-8. New options included an electrically-operated sun roof and Sport Decor Group trim package. The only Barracuda engine option was the 340 V-8 with four-barrel carburetion. Anything else was practically uninsurable and that included the famed 'Street Hemi.' The Hemi 'Cuda was a thing of the past.

BARRACUDA GROUP

Series Number	Body/Style Number	Body Type & Seating	Factory Price	Shipping Weight	Production Total
BARRACUDA					
HB1/2	BH23	2-dr HT Cpe-4P	2710/2808	3040/3090	10,622
'CUDA					
HB2	BS23	2-dr HT Cpe-4P	2953	3330	7,828

1972 Plymouth, Satellite Sebring two-door hardtop coupe, V-8

SATELLITE GROUP — (6-CYL/V-8) — SERIES HR — Plymouth's intermediate-sized line for 1972 included one two-door coupe and three two-door hardtops on the 115 inch wheelbase platform, plus two sedans and six wagons on a two inch longer stance. Body restylings were minor. Engineering improvements were comprised of such things as a new 400 cid V-8; electronic ignition system; better alternator; improved transmissions; a solid stainless steel antenna; three-point safety belt system; better body sealing;. stronger seats; reusable litter bag; and safer disc brakes. Wagons featured a three-way tailgate that opened in a door-like manner without having to lower the window. A flatter style grille insert was used on the lower-priced models and their side body nameplates were moved from in back of the front wheel opening to ahead of the rear opening. Standard features were a glovebox lock; dome light; hubcaps; soft coat hooks; inside day/night mirror (except coupe); color-keyed rubber floor covering; all-vinyl interior; cigar lighter (except coupe); and 225 cid six or 318 cid V-8. The Sebring had the same equipment, but without the vinyl upholstery, plus dual horns; front foam seat cushions; a solid stainless steel covered rear bench seat; DeLuxe wheelcovers; bodyside moldings along the lower feature line (with Argent Silver finish below the molding); and standard V-8 power. The Satellite Custom began with all Sebring items and added front armrests and rear armrests with ashtrays, both with bright metal bases. The Sebring-Plus hardtop also had vinyl bucket seats up front; vinyl covered rear bench seat; DeLuxe wheelcovers; bodyside moldings for the drip rails, body sills and wheel cutouts, with carpeting used on the floor. In addition, the Sebring-Plus buyer could add wheel trim rings, at no extra cost, and substitute a cloth vinyl front seat with center armrest, in place of front buckets. Then

came the Road Runner hardtop. It had all standard Satellite features, plus the following additions or substitutions: three-speed floor shift transmission; heavy-duty suspension and brakes; front and rear sway bars; deep-pile carpets; performance hood; low-restriction dual exhausts; 'Beep-Beep' horn; Rally instrument cluster; 150 mph speedometer; special deep recess split grille with Argent Silver inset; Road Runner front end medallion (with special lettering); specific inside and outside trim; rear deck cartoon decal; F70 x 14 white sidewall tires; and a 400 cid four-barrel V-8. On Satellite, Custom and Road Runner models, the side body nameplates were re-positioned. They were still just ahead of the rear wheel opening, but were on the lower body feature line (instead of at mid-body height as on Sebring and Sebring-Plus). The base Satellite wagon had bright upper door frame moldings; vinyl trimmed bench seats; front foam seat cushions; inside day/night mirror; cigar lighter; hubcaps; color-keyed rubber floor coverings; and the new three-way tailgate. Drip rail, wheel opening and custom sill moldings were added to the Custom wagon, which also had a thin full-length mid-body molding and an Argent Silver finished horizontal band across the tailgate. The top-of-the-line Regent wagon had full wheelcovers (except in some early factory photos) and wood-grained side paneling below a full-length molding that arched over each wheelhousing.

SATELLITE GROUP

Series Number	Body/Style Number	Body Type & Seating	Factory Price	Shipping Weight	Production Total
SATELLITE					
HRI/2	RL41	4-dr Sed-6P	2678/2770	3350/3345	12,794
HRI/2	RL21	2-dr Cpe-6P	2609/2701	3240/3300	10,507
HR2	RL45	4-dr Sta Wag-6P	3152	3785	7,377
SATELLITE SEBRING					
HR1/2	RH23	2-dr HT Cpe-6P	2871/2963	3250/3315	34,353
SATELLITE CUSTOM					
HR1/2	RH41	4-dr Sed-6P	2848/2940	3285/3350	34,973
RH2	RH45	4-dr Sta Wag-6P	3325	3780	5,485
HR2	RH46	4-dr Sta Wag-9P	3403	3825	5,637
REGENT WAGON					
HR2	RP45	4-dr Sta Wag-6P	3547	3790	1,893
HR2	RP46	4-dr Sta Wag-9P	3625	3830	2,907
SEBRING-PLUS					
HR2	RP23	2-dr HT Cpe-5P	3112	3320	21,399
ROAD RUNNER					
HR2	RM23	2-dr HT Cpe-6P	3080	3495	7.628

NOTE 1: Data above slash for six/below slash; no slash for V-8.

1972 Plymouth, Fury Gran two-door hardtop sports coupe, V-8

FURY GROUP — (6-CYL/V-8) SERIES HP — Sixteen models made up the Fury line of full-sized cars for 1972. The high-priced offerings were the Gran Coupe and Gran Sedan. All-new styling was evident in the sheetmetal; bumpers; grilles; lamps and ornamentation. On base models a more massive grille with larger body corner wraparounds was seen. It was divided into two individual openings, right and left, each of which housed dual headlamps with a horizontal bar between the headlights and wide center divider. The rear featured horizontal, rectangular taillights set into the bumper with the bumper having Plymouth lettering across its upper face bar. More expensive models had the two grille openings completely filled with fine vertical-blade inserts. There were hidden headlamps on these cars and larger taillamps with vertical segmentation. Rectangular nameplate badges were carried ahead of the front side markers and at the right-hand corner of the deck lid. Standard equipment on Fury I models included automatic transmission; all-vinyl bench seats with adjustable head restraints; power steering; ventless side glass; left outside rearview mirror; inside day/night mirror; front and rear armrests; two-speed electric wipers; electric washers; glove box lock; front and rear side marker lamps; front and rear ashtrays; concealed wipers; front door courtesy light switches; brake warning light; keyless door locking; cigar lighter; bias-belted blackwall tires; and inside hood release. A 318 cid two-barrel V-8 was the base engine. Fury II models had all the above, plus deep-pile carpeting and bright, full-length side body moldings. The Fury II models added color-keyed vinyl insert type side moldings; trunk light; upper door frame moldings on four-doors; wheel opening moldings; wood-grained dash and door panels; glove box light; dual-sized taillamps with bright ornamentation; bright metal armrest bases; and carpeting. The Gran Coupe/Sedan was a Fury III with certain extras, including door-pull straps; carpeted lower door panels; folding center armrest seat; body sill and beltline moldings; color-keyed vinyl rear bumper pads; rear door courtesy light switches on sedans; and concealed headlamps. The base wagon was comparable to the Fury I and also had a three-way tailgate; integral roof top air deflector; power tailgate window; and heavy-duty brakes. The next-step-up Custom Suburban added front foam seat cushions; carpets; bright upper door frames; and wheel opening moldings. The Sport Suburban also had a vinyl trim bench seat with center armrest and woodgrained bodyside paneling. The Fury GT, like most other members of the Plymouth 'Rapid Transit System,' had bit the dust. It was obvious that the high-performance era was dying and the day of the fully-equipped (and expensive) base model car had arrived. Buyers who wanted a cheap, economical Plymouth, with hardly any extras, would have to settle for a Cricket. This car was still around, but does not fit into the scope of a catalog covering American-built postwar cars.

FURY GROUP

Series Number	Body/Style Number	Body Type & Seating	Factory Price	Shipping Weight	Production Total
FURY I					
HP2	PL41	4-dr Sed-6P	3448	3840	14,006
FURY II					
HP2	PM41	4-dr Sed-6P	3567	3830	20,051
HP2	PM23	2-dr HT Cpe-6P	3589	3790	7,515
FURY III					
HP2	PH41	4-dr Sed-6P	3747	3830	46,713
HP2	PH43	4-dr HT Sed-6P	3813	3865	48,618
HP2	PH23	2-dr HT Cpe-6P	2769	3790	21,204
HP2	PH29	2-dr FsTp Cpe-6P	3802	3790	9,036
FURY GRAN COUPE/SEDAN					
HP2	PP43	4-dr HT Sed-6P	3971	3865	17,551
HP2	PP23	2-dr HT Cpe-6P	3925	3735	15,840
HP2	PP29	2-dr FsTp Cpe-6P	3958	3805	8,509
SUBURBANS					
HP2	PM45	4-dr Sta Wag-6P	3964	4315	5,368
HP2	PM46	4-dr Sta Wag-9P	4079	4360	2,773
HP2	PH45	4-dr Cus Wag-6P	4063	4315	11,067
HP2	PH46	4-dr Cus Wag-9P	4141	4365	14,041
HP2	PP45	4-dr Spt Wag-6P	4329	4335	4,971
HP2	PP46	4-dr Spt Wag-9P	4406	4395	15,928

NOTE 1: Data above slash for six/below slash; no slash for V-8.

BASE ENGINES

(VALIANT/DUSTER SIX) Inline six. Overhead valves. Cast iron block. Displacement: 198 cid. Bore and stroke: 3.4 x 3.64 inches. Compression ratio: 8.4:1. SAE Net hp: 100. Four main bearings. Solid valve lifters. Carburetor: one-barrel.

(BARRACUDA/SATELLITE SIX) Inline six. Overhead valves. Cast iron block. Displacement: 225 cid. Bore and stroke: 3.4 x 4.12 inches. Compression ratio: 8.4:1. (SAE Net) hp: 100. Four main bearings. Solid valve lifters. Carburetor: one-barrel.

(V-8 VALIANT/DUSTER/BARRACUDA/SATELLITE/FURY) V-8. Overhead valves. Cast iron block. Displacement: 318 cid. Bore and stroke: 3.91 x 3.31 inches. Compression ratio: 8.6:1. SAE Net hp: 150. Five main bearings. Hydraulic valve lifters. Carburetor: two-barrel.

(DUSTER '340' BASE ENGINE) V-8. Overhead valves. Cast iron block. Displacement: 340 cid. Bore and stroke: 4.04 x 3.31 inches. Compression ratio: 8.5:1. SAE Net hp: 240. Five main bearings. Hydraulic valve lifters. Carburetor: four-barrel.

(BASE ROAD RUNNER ENGINE) V-8. Overhead valves. Cast iron block. Displacement: 400 cid. Bore and stroke: 4.34 x 3.38 inches. Compression ratio: 8.2:1. SAE Net hp: 255. Five main bearings. Hydraulic valve lifters. Carburetor: four-barrel.

CHASSIS FEATURES: Wheelbase: (Valiant/Duster) 108 inches; (Scamp) 111 inches; (Barracuda/'Cuda) 108 inches: (Satellite two-door) 115 inches; (Satellite four-door) 117 inches; (Fury Suburban) 122 inches; (Fury) 120 inches. Overall length: (Valiant/Duster) 188.4 inches; (Scamp) 192.1 inches; (Barracuda/'Cuda) 186.6 inches; (Satellite two-door) 203.2 inches; (Satellite wagon) 210.9 inches; (Satellite four-door) 204.6 inches; (Fury Suburban) 222 inches; (Fury) 217.2 inches.

OPTIONS: Power brakes, in Valiant only ($40). Power steering, in Valiant ($92); Satellite ($114); Barracuda ($104). Air conditioning, in Valiant ($353); in Barracuda ($365); in Satellite ($378); in Fury ($386). Automatic lock tailgate, in all station wagons ($27). DeLuxe Dual air conditioning, in Fury station wagons ($598). Front end and rear bumper guards; Valiant ($24); Barracuda ($27); Satellite ($33); Fury ($38). Carpets, in base models as optional equipment ($19). Carpeted cargo compartment, all wagons ($21). Electric clock, in Satellites without tachometer ($18); in Fury ($17). Center console, in Barracuda ($52); in Fury Gran Coupe/Sedan (no charge); in Satellite ($56). Rear window defogger, Valiant ($26); Barracuda ($28); others ($31). Engine block heater, Furys ($15). Decorative exhaust tips, on Satellites, except wagons ($21). Luggage roof rack, Satellite wagons ($56); Fury wagons ($67). Accessory floor mats, Fury and Satellite ($14). Left-hand remote-control racing type outside rearview mirror, Satellite two-doors ($16). Rear fender skirts, Furys without deep-dish wheelcovers ($32). Road Runner C-pillar 'Strobe Stripe' ($33). Valiant performance hood paint treatment ($17). Valiant/Duster bodyside tape stripe ($25). Road Runner hood/fender tape stripe ($22). Hood or deck tape treatment on Satellite two-doors, each ($22). Power disc brakes, on Valiant ($62); on Fury/Satellite ($68); on Barracuda ($68). Power deck lid release, Furys ($15). Power door locks, Fury four-door sedan and wagon. ($71). Power bench seat, Fury ($103). Power seat, bucket type or left-hand unit of 50/50 bench type ($91). Power windows, on Satellite, except coupe ($119); on Fury ($125). AM radio, Fury/Satellite ($65); Valiant ($59); Barracuda ($59). AM/FM radio, Fury ($71); Valiant ($125 or $136). AM radio with stereo tape cassette, Fury/Satellite ($214); Barracuda ($196). Rooftop air deflector, Satellite wagon ($20). Vinyl roof, Valiant ($75); Barracuda ($80); Satellite ($94); Fury ($106). Vinyl roof, Fury station wagons only ($139). Vinyl canopy roof, Satellite group ($66). Vinyl bucket seats, Valiant including carpets ($120); Fury Gran Sport ($103). Center cushion armrest seat, Road Runner/Sebring ($56). 'Cuda performance hood paint treatment ($17). Rim-blow steering wheel, Fury ($26). Tilt steering with rim-blow, Satellite/Fury ($55). 'Tuff' steering wheel, in Scamp ($28); in other Valiants ($18). 'Tuff' Rally steering wheel, Satellite/Road Runner ($20-$30). Sun roof, on Valiant with 6.95 x 14 or larger tires mandatory ($223). Vinyl roof with sun roof, Satellite with full vinyl top ($475); with canopy ($446). Barracuda Rally gauge package ($75-$85). Tachometer ($52). Deep-dish wheelcovers, Fury ($31-58). Wire wheelcovers, Satellite ($42-69). Chrome styled Road wheels, Satellite/Fury ($62-$101). Rally Road wheels, Valiant/Sebring/Regent ($29-$58). Barracuda bodyside tape stripe ($28). Barracuda chrome styled Road wheels ($81). Barracuda Rally type Road wheels ($28-$53). Barracuda vinyl roof ($80). Barracuda power sun roof with vinyl top covering ($434). Barracuda performance hood, standard with 'Cuda ($20). Three-speed manual transmission was standard. Automatic transmission was standard in Fury. Automatic transmission, in Barracuda ($203-$223); in Valiant ($178-$208); in Satellite ($211-$231). Three-speed manual floor shift transmission; Valiant ($24). Four-speed manual floor shift transmission ($184-$201). Base Valiant six-cylinder 225 cid/100 hp one-barrel engine ($38). Road Runner V-8 340 cid/240 hp four-barrel engine ($64). Fury Group V-8 360 cid/175 hp two-barrel engine ($45). Fury/Satellite V-8 400 cid/190 hp two-barrel engine ($84). Satellite V-8 400 cid/225 hp four-barrel engine ($186). Fury V-8 400 cid/225 hp four-barrel engine ($193). Road Runner V-8 440 cid/280 hp four-barrel engine ($153). Road Runner V-8 440 cid/330 hp 'Six-Pack' V-8. 'Cuda V-8 340 cid/240 hp four-barrel engine ($210). Barracuda V-8 340 cid/240 hp four-barrel engine ($277). 'Air Grabber' air induction package, Road Runner only ($67). Positive traction rear axle ($41-$48). Available rear axle gear ratios: 2.76:1; 3.23:1; 3.55:1.

HISTORICAL FOOTNOTES: The full-sized Plymouths were introduced Sept. 28, 1971 and the Valiant appeared in dealer showrooms the same day. Model year production peaked at 708,587 units. Calendar year sales of 733,124 cars were recorded. F.G. Hazelroth was general sales manager this year. Many options and accessories were offered. The Satellite Brougham package included cloth and vinyl bench seat with headrests and folding center armrest and woodstone lower door panels at ($120). The Fury Brougham package included the same features, plus a 50/50 bench seat with the left unit of the adjustable recliner type. It was priced at $159 on Fury Gran Coupe/Sedan and Sport Suburban models and $184 on Custom Suburbans. Plymouth marketed a large variety of safety, convenience and perfor-

mance features as individual groups, (at special package prices). In addition, it was also possible to select an 'Easy Order Package' for Satellite and Fury models, which provided an assortment of popular groups as an all-inclusive package at prices in the $500-$550 range.

and by the same twin-scoop performance hood of the year before. With the exceptions noted above standard equipment was a carryover from 1972, too.

1973 PLYMOUTH

1973 Plymouth, Barracuda two-door coupe, V-8

BARRACUDA GROUP

Series Number	Body/Style Number	Body Type & Seating	Factory Price	Shipping Weight	Production Total
BARRACUDA (V-8)					
JB1/2	BH23	2-dr HT Cpe-5P	2935	3140	11,587
'CUDA					
J82	BS23	2-dr HT Cpe-5P	3120	3235	10.626

1973 Plymouth, Valiant four-door sedan, 6-cyl

VALIANT GROUP — (6-CYL/V-8) — SERIES JV — For 1973, Valiants continued to be marketed in three forms including Duster two-door coupes, Scamp two-door hardtops and Valiant sedans. New front and rear end treatments on all models gave the cars a fresh appearance. Interiors were considerably upgraded. Major improvements included an optional fold-down rear seat on the Duster; optional electrically heated window defogger; the inclusion of front and rear bumper guards as standard equipment; ventless side glass on Valiant Group hardtops; standard disc brakes on V-8 models; and an improved, quieter ride on all. New low-back style seats were standard in Scamp and an option for Dusters and Valiants. With the above changes, the standard equipment distinctions were the same as in 1972. A new grille made the styling of the 1973 Valiant different than the previous year. It had single headlamps housed in square-shaped bezels at each end. Next to the headlamps were three oblong openings with vertical segmentation housing the rectangular parking lamps. Below the nose of the car were three larger oblong openings which 'Veed' from the centerline and also had vertical segmentations. Above them was placed a chrome header bearing the word Plymouth in stamped block letters. A Valiant script remained on the sides of the cowl. The Duster also had the same new grille and front safety bumper with rubber-faced guards flanking the license plate recess. Large single-lens taillamps replaced the former slat type. 'Gold Duster' and 'Twister' packages were available again. The Gold Duster option package was priced $161. The Duster 340 had a wide tape stripe running the full length of the car along the beltline and bold '340' lettering on the rear fender edge. The Scamp was changed at the front by addition of the new Valiant style grille. The only rear end alteration was a pair of more massive, rubber-faced bumper guards. The Scamp's ventless glass emphasized its hardtop look. The Duster '340' came standard with the 340 cid V-8. The '198' six or '318' V-8 were the base motors for the other Valiant Group entries. The only option this season was the '225' six, available only in base sixes, of course.

PLYMOUTH I.D. NUMBERS: VIN on plate attached to upper left-hand top of dash, viewable through windshield. First symbol indicate make: B=Barracuda; P=Fury; R=Satellite/Sebring; V=Valiant/Duster. Second symbol indicates price class: L=low; M=medium; H=high; G=Grand; P=premium; S=Special; T=taxicab; K=police car. Third and fourth symbols indicate body style. (First four symbols appear in Body/Style Number column of charts below). Fifth symbol indicates engine: B=198 .nhp six; C=225 cid/105 nhp six; E=special order six; G=318 cid/150 nhp two-barrel V-8; H=340 cid/240 nhp four-barrel high-performance V-8; K=360 cid/170 nhp two-barrel V-8; M=400 cid/175 nhp two-barrel V-8; P=400 cid/260 hp four-barrel high-performance V-8; T=440 cid/220 nhp four-barrel V-8; U=440 cid/280 four-barrel TNT V-8. Z=Special order V-8. Sixth symbol indicates model year: (3=1973). The seventh symbol indicated assembly plant; A=Lynch Rd., Detroit; B=Hamtramck, Mich.; C=Jefferson Ave., Detroit; D=Belvedere, Ill.; F=Newark, Del.; G=St. Louis, Mo.; and R=Windsor, Canada. The last six symbols were the sequential unit production number.

VALIANT GROUP

Series Number	Body/Style Number	Body Type & Seating	Factory Price	Shipping Weight	Production Total
VALIANT					
JV1/2	VL41	4-dr Sed-6P	2447/2564	2865/2980	61,826
DUSTER					
JV1/2	VL29	2-dr Spt Cpe-6P	2346/2493	2830/2950	249,243
SCAMP					
JV1/2	VH23	2-dr HT Cpe-6P	2617/2734	2885/3000	53,792
DUSTER '340' (V-8)					
JV2	VS29	2-dr Spt Cpe-6P	2822	3175	15,731

NOTE 1: Data above slash for six/below slash; no slash for V-8.

BARRACUDA GROUP — (V-8) — SERIES JB — The Barracuda and 'Cuda were now referred to as "specialty compacts" to downplay the high-performance image. Still, they continued to exhibit their previous sporty flavor. The six-cylinder engine was no longer available in either line. The 318 cid V-8, now including electronic ignition was standard. The '340' V-8 was optional. Another new standard feature was manual disc brakes. Full-volume urethane foam- cushioned bucket seats were used. A host of performance packages and decor packages were offered including sway bars, sport hoods and bodyside tape stripes. Revisions in appearance were seen mainly in bumper design. Rubber-faced guards were standard. The front side marker lamps were also moved to the side body feature line, instead of slightly below it. Cowlside signature scripts on base models were positioned slightly lower than before. 'Cudas were identified by bold model letters on the left-hand side of the rear panel

1973 Plymouth, Satellite Custom four-door sedan, V-8

SATELLITE GROUP — (6-CYL/V-8) — SERIES JR — Styling of the two-door Satellite models was more conservative and de-emphasized the high-performance image in favor of a rich, luxury look. Standard equipment began with all items listed for 1972 models, plus electronic ignition and manual disc brakes (with power discs standard in wagons). Basic sheet metal was a carryover from the 1971-1972 design, again with different wheelbases for two- and four-door cars. Details of the grille designs varied, helping car spotters in telling the different lines apart. On all models, the loop type grille was gone. Satellites and Sebrings substituted a double-deck grid patterned insert. It stretched between quad headlights set into bright metal, rectangular housings. Satellite Custom and Regent station wagons had their quad headlamps set into Argent Silver finished housings. A recessed rectangle in the center housed a gridwork of chrome bars with square, honeycomb-like inserts. On these models the portion of the bumper face bar between the bumper guards had an upward curve. Road Runners combined the Satellite/Sebring type grille with a hood having a wide center 'power bulge.' Taillights on all models were still rectangular. They were fatter, but not as long as the previous season. Engine availability included the 225 cid six and five V-8s up to the emasculated '440.' On all models (even the Road Runner) a 318 cid V-8 was standard equipment. 'Six-Pack' induction was no longer available. All 1973 Plymouth motors featured a new EGR (exhaust gas recirculation) system, electric choke and orifice spark advance. The new bumpers on all models were intended to meet federal impact standards and steel beam door construction was adopted at midyear. Plymouths couldn't go as fast as before, but they were safer and cleaner and more sophisticated with more sophisticated pricing, as well.

SATELLITE GROUP

Series Number	Body/Style Number	Body Type & Seating	Factory Price	Shipping Weight	Production Total
SATELLITE					
JR1/2	RL41	4-dr Sed-6P	2824/2936	3450/3515	14,716
JR1/2	RL21	2-dr Cpe-6P	2755/2867	3375/3440	13,570
SATELLITE CUSTOM					
JR1/2	RH41	4-dr Sed-6P	2974/3086	3445/3510	46,748
SATELLITE SEBRING					
JR1/2	RH23	2-dr HT Cpe-6P	2997/3109	3390/3460	51,575
SATELLITE-PLUS					
JR2	RP23	2-dr HT Cpe-5P	3258	3455	43,628
ROAD RUNNER					
JR2	RM23	2-dr HT Cpe-6P	3115	3525	19,056
SATELLITE WAGONS					
JR2	RL45	4-dr Sta Wag-6P	3272	3950	6,906
JR2	RH46	4-dr Cus Wag-9P	3518	3990	7,705
JR2	RH45	4-dr Cus Wag-6P	3400	3945	6,733
JR2	RP46	4-dr Spt Wag-9P	3740	4010	4,786
JR2	RH46	4-dr Spt Wag-6P	3621	3950	2,781

NOTE 1: Data above slash for six/below slash; no slash for V-8.

1973 Plymouth, Fury Gran two-door sports coupe, V-8

FURY GROUP — (V-8) — SERIES JP — Retaining the basic design configuration of 1972, the Fury Group had an altered frontal appearance with a new grille, new hood, bolt-on fender extensions and energy-absorbing bumper. Quad headlamps were now set into individual square-shaped bezels in the fender extension panels. A massive rectangular grille featured thin horizontal blades and a Plymouth nameplate at the left-hand side. The bumper bar ran across the face of the grille and the blade-pattern insert showed underneath. This lower grille was split into two rectangles, one on either side of the license plate holder. Rear styling featured a massive bumper that was formed to dip under the taillamps at each end. High in the center, a rectangular depression with Plymouth lettering was seen. Integral, rubber-faced rear bumper guards were spaced wide apart, flanking the license plate recess on both sides. The vertical taillamps had the shape of a tall, thin triangle with rounded corners. They were deeply recessed into the fender extension caps and trimmed with chrome moldings on the outside and ribbed bands of bright metal around the inner lip. As the car-line's level of trim and appointments increased, full-length horizontal side moldings were added and Fury Gran Sports also had front fender turn indicators, stand-up hood ornaments, body sill moldings and a small crest at the right side of the deck lid. The Fury Brougham package was priced $160. Suburbans had wraparound horizontal taillamps with tailgate beauty bands and woodgrained side paneling on Sport models. Automatic transmission, V-8 engines, power disc brakes and electric ignition were standard, with the remaining equipment distinctions for each line following the 1972 pattern. A four-door hardtop was added to the Fury III Series and new options for this season included steel-belted radial tires and vent windows on four-door models. The '318' V-8 was standard in passenger cars; the '360' in Suburbans. A special option-created model appearing this season was the Fury Special. It's standard extras included Chestnut metallic brown paint; a parchment textured vinyl top, color coordinated vinyl side molding inserts; rocker panel moldings; stand-up hood ornament; all-vinyl interior, tapestry cloth seat insert panels and special carpeting.

FURY GROUP

Series Number	Body/Style Number	Body Type & Seating	Factory Price	Shipping Weight	Production Total
FURY I					
JP2	PL41	4-dr Sed-6P	3575	3865	17,365
FURY II					
JP2	PM41	4-dr Sed-6P	3694	3845	21,646
FURY III					
JP2	PH41	4-dr Sed-6P	3866	3860	51,742
JP2	PH43	4-dr HT Sed-6P	3932	3880	51,215
JP2	PH23	2-dr HT Cpe-6P	3883	3815	34,963
GRAN FURY					
JP2	PP43	4-dr HT Sed-6P	4110	3890	14,852
JP2	PP23	2-dr HT Cpe-6P	4064	3845	18,127
SUBURBANS					
JP2	PM45	4-dr Sta Wag-6P	4150	4410	5,206
JP2	PH46	4-dr Cus Wag-9P	4354	4465	15,671
JP2	PH45	4-dr Cus Wag-6P	4246	4420	9,888
JP2	PP46	4-dr Spt Wag-9P	4599	4495	15,680
JP2	PP45	4-dr Spt Wag-6P	4497	4435	4,832

NOTE 1: 3,176 Fury II two-door hardtops were made, probably for Canadian sale.

Note: See 1973 Dodge for complete MoPar engine data.

CHASSIS FEATURES: Wheelbase: (Valiant/Duster) 108 inches; (Scamp) 111 inches; (Satellite two-door) 115 inches; (Satellite four-door) 117 inches; (Fury Suburban) 122 inches; (Fury) 120 inches; (Barracuda) 108 inches. Overall length: (Valiant/Duster) 195.8 inches: (Scamp) 199.6 inches; (Satellite wagon) 216-1 inches: (Satellite two-door) 210.8 inches. (Satellite four-door) 213.3 inches (Fury wagon) 227.5 inches@ (Fury) 223.4 inches. (Barracuda) 193 inches; (Road Runner) 210.8 inches. Tires: See 1972 tire data.

OPTIONS: Barracuda vinyl top ($81). Barracuda air conditioning ($369). Barracuda Rally wheels ($53). Barracuda AM/FM radio ($194). Barracuda electric sun roof ($434). Barracuda power disc brakes, standard in 'Cuda ($65). Valiant disc brakes ($65). Duster, electric sun roof ($223). Valiant air conditioning ($358). Valiant vinyl top ($76). Satellite Group sun roof ($171). Satellite Group, vinyl top ($101). Satellite Group, AM/FM stereo ($212). Satellite Group, AM/FM stereo with tape ($363). Fury Group, vinyl top ($108). Fury Group, electric sun roof ($480). Fury Group, DeLuxe Dual Suburban air conditioning ($598). Fury Group, AM/FM stereo ($212), Fury Group, AM/FM stereo with tape ($363). Three-speed manual transmission was standard. Automatic transmission was standard on Fury Group models. Automatic transmission, Valiant six 225 cid one-barrel engine ($45). Valiant six 225 cid/ 235 hp two-barrel engine ($90). 'Cuda V-8 340 cid/235 hp two-barrel engine ($85). Satellite Group V-8 400 cid/ 175 hp two-barrel engine. Satellite Group 400 cid/260 hp four-barrel engine. Road Runner V-8 400 cid/260 hp four-barrel engine. Road Runner V-8 440 cid/280 hp four-barrel engine. Fury Group V-8 360 cid/170 hp two-barrel engine. Fury Group V-8 400 cid/185 hp two-barrel engine. Fury Group V-8 440 cid/220 hp four-barrel engine. Positive traction rear axle.

HISTORICAL FOOTNOTES: The full-sized 1973 Plymouths were introduced Sept. 26, 1972 and the Valiant Group appeared in dealer showrooms the same day. Model year production peaked at 746,821 units. Calendar year production of 742,957 cars was recorded. F.G. Hazelroth was the general sales manager this year. Plymouth Div. held a 7.69 percent share of the total U.S. auto market and was America's sixth largest producer of automobiles.

1974 PLYMOUTH

VALIANT GROUP — (6-CYL/V-8) — SERIES 4V — For the Valiant Group the year's only styling changes were directly related to engineering revisions. They included a larger Valiant sedan and a new rear end treatment for Scamps. Otherwise, the only appearance variations were new decals, tape stripes and options packages. In most cases, not even grilles or taillights were redesigned. The four-door Valiant's sheet metal was adopted to the 111 inch Scamp wheelbase, with the extra inches showing behind the doors. The larger size resulted in thicker roof pillars and new rear fender contours. The front treatment was unchanged in any way, except for slimmer bumper guards, although even these became optional again. The basic Duster was also untouched, save for the new, optional bumper guards. Slightly different arrangements of decals and stripes were used with each of the cosmetic packages like 'Twister,' 'Gold Duster' or 'Space Duster' groupings. The regular Duster 'Twister' package cost $124.05 and included lower deck and bodyside tape stripes; Rally wheels; front sway bar; dual racing mirrors; drip rail and wheel lip moldings; and 'Twister' decal. The Duster 'Gold Duster' package cost $187.25 and included canopy vinyl top; DeLuxe insulation; rear deck and bodyside tape stripes, DeLuxe wheelcovers; 'Gold Duster' decal; and 6.95 x 14 white sidewall tires. The 'Gold Duster/Twister' combination cost $234.60 and included all 'Gold Duster' extras, plus wheel lip moldings; Rally road wheels; dual racing mirrors; front sway bar; and wheel trim rings. The 'Space Duster' package cost $88.80 and included folding rear seatback; carpeted cargo area; and security panel. The Duster 340 was replaced by the Duster 360 with a 245 net hp four-barrel V-8 of 360 cid capacity. This car had the same stripes as the '340,' but lacked the rear fender engine call-out decals. The Duster had a shelf-like, energy-absorbing rear bumper and new taillights to go with it. They wrapped around the back corners of the body and flanked a center beauty panel bearing Plymouth lettering. The midyear Valiant Brougham option included luxury appointments. It came either on the new four-door model or what was really a Scamp hardtop body with Valiant nameplates. Standard equipment for the base Valiant included all regulation safety features: two-speed wipers; ventless side windows; concealed spare; rubber floor mats; three-speed manual transmission: '198' six or '318' two-barrel V-8; and 6.95 x 14 blackwall tires. The Scamp had all of the above, plus carpets; dual horns; cigar lighter; DeLuxe steering wheel; interior decor group; wheel opening and drip moldings; and front door color-keyed armrests. The base Duster was equipped like a Valiant, while the Duster 360 had all the basics, plus floor shift controls; lower deck and bodyside tape stripes; heavy-duty suspension; power front disc brakes; electronic ignition; drip moldings; cigar lighter; locking glove box; optional axle ratios; E70 x 14 black sidewall tires; and the 360 cid V-8.

PLYMOUTH I.D. NUMBERS: VIN on plate attached to upper left-hand top of dash, viewable through windshield. First symbol indicate make: B=Barracuda; P=Fury; R=Satellite/Sebring; V=Valiant/Duster. Second symbol indicates price class: L=low; M=medium; H=high; P=premium; S=Special; T=taxicab; K=police car. Third and fourth symbols indicate body style. (First four symbols appear in Body/Style Number column of charts below). Fifth symbol indicates engine: B=198 cid/95 nhp six; C=225 cid/105 nhp six; E=special order six; G=318 cid/150 nhp two-barrel V-8; H=360 cid/245 nhp four-barrel high-performance V-8; J=360 cid/ 200 nhp four-barrel V-8; K=360 cid/180 nhp two-barrel V-8; L= 360 cid high-performance four-barrel V-8; M=400 cid/175 nhp two-barrel V-8; N=400 cid/205 nhp four-barrel V-8; P=400 cid/ 250 hp four-barrel high-performance V-8; T=440 cid/230 nhp four-barrel V-8; U=440 cid/275 four-barrel TNT V-8. Z=Special order V-8. The sixth symbol indicates model year, 4=1974. The seventh symbol indicates assembly plant: A=Lynch Rd., Detroit, Mich.; B=Hamtramck, Mich.; C=Jefferson Ave., Detroit, Mich.; D=Belvedere, Ill.; F=Newark, Del.; G=St. Louis, Mo.; R=Windsor, Ontario, Canada. The last six symbols are the production sequence number starting at 100001 at each factory.

1974 Plymouth, Duster '360' two-door coupe, V-8

VALIANT GROUP

Series Number	Body/Style Number	Body Type & Seating	Factory Price	Shipping Weight	Production Total
VALIANT					
4V1/2	VL41	4-dr Sed-6P	2942/3093	3035/3135	127,430
DUSTER					
4V1/2	VL29	2-dr Spt Cpe-6P	2829/2980	2975/3010	277,409
SCAMP					
4V1/2	VH23	2-dr HT Cpe-6P	3077/3228	3010/3110	51,699
VALIANT BROUGHAM					
4V1/2	VP23	2-dr HT Cpe-6P	794/3880	3180/3270	13,766
4V1/2	VP41	4-dr Sed-6P	3819/3905	3195/3285	2,545
DUSTER '360' (V-8)					
4V2	VS20	2-dr Spt Cpe-6P	3288	3315	3,969

NOTE 1: Data above slash for six/below slash for V-8.

BARRACUDA GROUP — (V-8) — SERIES 4B — This was to be the final season of Barracuda production, as sales slid to the lowest level in the history of this nameplate. There were no styling changes from 1973. Even the tape stripe treatments stayed basically the same, although there may have been a few new color combinations. Standard equipment for the Barracuda included all regulation safety features; dual horns; hubcaps; inside day/night mirror; brake warning light; left outside rearview mirror; vinyl bucket seats; cigar lighter; fuel, temperature and ammeter gauges; carpets; concealed windshield wipers; three-speed manual transmission with floor shift; 7.35 x 14 blackwall tires; and the 318 cid two-barrel V-8. The specialty 'Cuda also had power front disc brakes; performance hood; heavy-duty suspension; electronic ignition; wheel lip moldings: color-keyed grille; black-out finished rear deck panel; and F70 x 15 white sidewall tires. The sole engine option was the four-barrel '360' claiming a 245 hp SAE net output rating. There weren't even many options packages left for the sporty compact. The Basic Group option package included AM radio; chrome-plated remote-control left outside rearview mirror; day/night inside mirror; three-speed wipers with electric washers; and DeLuxe wheelcovers (same as Valiant Basic Group package), plus power steering (Barracuda only) at $196. Buyers could also add the Code A51 Sport Decor Group with body sill and wheel lip moldings; bodyside tape stripe; and Sport hood for $49.85 with the 360 cid V-8 or $70.55 with the 318 cid V-8. This was the same features the 'Cuda included in its regular equipment. A little more exciting was the Rally Instrument Panel Group, Code J97, which included tachometer; oil pressure gauge; trip odometer; 150 mph speedometer; three-speed wipers; and electric clock. It went for $89.45 in cars without basic options and $78.65 in those which also had the Basic Group. For the few remaining speed freaks who could afford the insurance rates, there was the Code A36 Performance Axle Package with Sure-Grip differential; high-performance radiator; and heavy-duty 3.55:1 rear axle ratio for $62.85 on Barracudas with the '360' V-8.

1974 Plymouth, 'Cuda '360' two-door hardtop coupe, V-8

BARRACUDA

Series Number	Body/Style Number	Body Type & Seating	Factory Price	Shipping Weight	Production Total
BARRACUDA V-8)					
4B2	BH23	2-dr HT Cpe-5P	3067	3210	6,745
'CUDA (V-8)					
4B2	BS23	2-dr HT Cpe-5P	3252	3300	4,989

1974 Plymouth, Road Runner two-door hardtop coupe, V-8

SATELLITE GROUP — (6-CYL/V-8) — SERIES 4R — Despite its 'Space Age' name, the Satellite was a 'Race Age' machine and the performance age had ended. This would be the final season for it. The intermediate line was carried over into 1974 with only minor change. The grille had a more subdued look than the previous design. There were dual headlamps in large, rectangular bright metal housings at each corner of the front. Between them was grillework that emphasized negative space in the twin rectangular openings. Elements were stacked upon each other, with a horizontal center bar and an upright badge at the center. The more luxurious models substituted double-deck grid-patterned inserts in each of the main openings. Rear styling seemed unchanged, although the bumper was now of the energy-absorbing type with shock absorber mountings. Lower level models carried nameplates on the trailing edge of the front fender, just above the feature line. On other models they were moved onto or below the rear roof pillar. The Road Runner had cartoon bird emblems at the center of this pillar. Standard features for the Satellite were all regulation safety items; locking glove box; dome lamp; hubcaps; vinyl interior trim; cigar lighter (except coupe); color-keyed rubber floor coverings; E78 x 14 belted blackwall tires; and the '225' six or '318' two-barrel V-8. Wagons also had power front disc brakes; two-way tailgate; concealed storage compartment; and H78 x 14 belted tires. Sebrings had all the above, plus dual horns; drip rail and wheel lip moldings; cigar lighter; front foam cushions; carpets; and E78 x 14 bias-belted tires. The Sebring-Plus added a vinyl interior with bucket seats. Cloth and vinyl armrest type seats were optional. DeLuxe wheelcovers (no charge for trim rings) and side body moldings also came on the Sebring-Plus. Satellite Customs had the same features as regular Sebrings, plus Custom interior appointments and body sill moldings. The Regent was essentially a Satellite wagon with DeLuxe wheelcovers; three-way tailgate; wood-grain exterior paneling and vinyl

bench seat. The Road Runner offered buyers certain extras above base Satellite equipment. They included dual horns; floor shift three-speed manual transmission; heavy-duty suspension and brakes; front and rear sway bars; carpets; three-speed wipers; performance hood; Rally instrument cluster; dual exhausts; and F70 x 14 white letter tires.

SATELLITE GROUP

Series Number	Body/Style Number	Body Type & Seating	Factory Price	Shipping Weight	Production Total
SATELLITE					
4R1/2	RL21	2-dr Cpe-6P	3155/3271	3435/3510	10,634
4R1/2	RL41	4-dr Sed-6P	3226/3342	3520/3590	12,726
SATELLITE CUSTOM					
4R1/2	RH41	4-dr Sed-6P	3329/3445	3515/3585	45,863
SATELLITE SEBRING					
4R1/2	RH23	2-dr HT Cpe-6P	3353/3468	3455/3530	31,980
SEBRING-PLUS (V-8)					
4R2	RP23	2-dr HT Cpe-5P	3621	3555	18,480
ROAD RUNNER (V-8)					
4R2	RM21	2-dr Cpe-6P	3545	3616	11,555
STATION WAGONS (V-8)					
4R2	RL45	4-dr Sta Wag-6P	3655	4065	4,622
4R2	RH45	4-dr Custom-6P	3839	4065	4,354
4R2	RH46	4-dr Custom-9P	4152	4110	5,591
4R2	RP45	4-dr Regent-6P	4066	4065	2,026
4R2	RP46	4-dr Regent-9P	4381	4130	3,132
TAXICAB					
4R1/2	RL41	4-dr Sed-8P	NA	NA	2,631
POLICE CAR					
4R1/2	RL41	4-dr Sed-6P	NA	NA	4,274

NOTE 1: Data above slash six/below slash for V-8.

1974 Plymouth, Fury Gran four-door hardtop sedan, V-8

FURY GROUP — (V-8) — SERIES 4P — The full-sized Plymouths were totally restyled and re-engineered for 1974. Two-door and four-door styles were now built off different wheelbase platforms. The new front bumper was a shelf-type, energy-absorbing design. Above it, dual headlamps were still housed in square bright metal bezels. However, they seemed more an integral part of the overall grille design, since the segmented styling motif was dropped. The new, multi-blade grille had a slimmer appearance, because horizontal lines were emphasized overall. However, it really wasn't much different in total area than the 1973 design and it still showed through the slots in the lower part of the bumper. The front bumper guards were moved closer together and nearer the center of the car. The front fenders had a more sweeping, downward slope, while the back fenders had an angular kick-up at the upper rear quarter and also had a crisper, straight-line look at their trailing edge. The rear featured massive, horizontal taillamps with Plymouth lettering on the body-color panel between them. The bumper was also more massive and ran almost straight across, without the previous taillight dip. In mid-season, an opera window roof treatment became available for the Fury Gran Coupe. Fury I equipment included all-vinyl bench seats; automatic transmission; power steering; power front disc brakes; G78 x 14 blackwall tires; left outside rearview mirror; inside day/night mirror; front and rear armrests; two-speed wipers; lockable glove box; front and rear side marker lights; concealed wipers; cigar lighter; inside hood release; brake warning light; and '360' two-barrel V-8. The Fury II had the same, plus carpets and cloth and vinyl bench seats. The Fury III also had a three-spoke steering wheel with wood-grain inserts; glove box, ashtray and trunk lights; bright armrest bases; body sill moldings; upper door frame moldings (on sedan); and front foam seat. The Gran Coupe/Sedan had all Fury III features, plus DeLuxe wheelcovers; electric clock; vinyl center armrest seat; door-pull straps; carpeted lower door panels; rear door dome light switches (sedan); beltline moldings; stand-up hood ornament; and concealed headlights. The base Suburban had Fury I equipment, plus three-way tailgate; rear air deflector; power tailgate window; and heavy-duty brakes with J78-15 tires on two-seat jobs and L78-15s on three-seaters. Custom wagons had carpets; foam seat cushions; and wheel opening moldings. Sport Suburbans also had sill moldings; vinyl center armrest bench seats; woodgrain bodyside and surround panels; electric clock; DeLuxe wheelcovers; and concealed headlights. All nine-passenger wagons also had bright upper door frame moldings. A Brougham package was available for Fury Gran Coupe/Sedans, Custom Suburbans and Sport Suburbans at prices between $154.55 and $193.15. It included a cloth and vinyl trimmed 50/50 Comfort Seat with adjustable left unit and folding center armrest; 'D' pillar Brougham nameplate on wagons; deck lid nameplates on passenger cars; reclining front passenger seat backrest; and, in Gran Coupes only, cloth and vinyl bucket seats with armrest type center cushion. It was also possible to purchase an all-inclusive Luxury Equipment Package (Code A08) for just about any Fury. It included all options that could possibly be installed on one car; everything from air conditioning and power windows, to speed control and a digital clock. The cost ran from $1,257.95 on the three-seat station wagon to $1,498.45 on the Fury III sedan with '400' or '440' cid V-8.

FURY GROUP

Series Number	Body/Style Number	Body Type & Seating	Factory Price	Shipping Weight	Production Total
FURY I (V-8)					
4P2	PL41	4-dr Sed-6P	4101	4185	8,162

FURY II (V-8)					
4P2	PM41	4-dr Sed-6P	4223	4165	11,649
FURY III (V-8)					
4P2	PH41	4-dr Sed-6P	4400	4180	27,965
4P2	PH23	2-dr HT Cpe-6P	4418	4125	14,167
4P2	PH43	4-dr HT Sed-6P	4468	4205	18,778
GRAN FURY (V-8)					
4P2	PP23	2-dr HT Cpe-5P	4627	4300	9,617
4P2	PP43	4-dr HT Sed-6P	4675	4370	8,191
SUBURBANS (V-8					
4P2	PM45	4-dr Std-6P	4669	4745	2,490
4P2	PH45	4-dr Custom-6P	4767	4755	3,887
4P2	PH46	4-dr Custom-9P	4878	4800	5,628
4P2	PP45	4-dr Sport-6P	5025	4795	1,712
4P2	PP46	4-dr Sport-9P	5130	3850	6,047
POLICE EMERGENCY WAGON (V-8)					
4P2	PM45	4-dr Std-6P	NA	NA	285
EXPORT (FURY II)					
4P2	PM23	2-dr HT Cpe-6P	NA	NA	1,826

BASE ENGINES

(VALIANT/DUSTER SIX) Inline. Overhead valve. Cast iron block. Displacement: 198 cid. Bore and stroke: 3.4 x 3.64 inches. Compression ratio: 8.4:1. SAE net hp: 95 at 4400 rpm. Four main bearings. Carburetor: one-barrel.

(SATELLITE SIX) Inline. Overhead valves. Cast iron block. Displacement: 225 cid. Bore and stroke: 3.41 x 4.13 inches. Compression ratio: 8.4:1. SAE net hp: 105 at 4000 rpm. Four main bearings. Solid valve lifters. Carburetion: one-barrel.

(V-8 BARRACUDA/DUSTER/VALIANT/SATELLITE/ROAD RUNNER) V-8. Overhead valves. Cast iron block. Displacement: 318 cid. Bore and stroke: 3.91 x 3.31 inches. Compression ratio: 8.6:1. SAE net hp: 150 at 4000 rpm. Hydraulic valve lifters. Carburetion: two-barrel.

(V-8 FURY) V-8. Overhead valves. Cast iron block. Displacement: 360 cid. Bore and stroke: 4 x 3.58 inches. Compression ratio: 8.4:1. SAE Net hp: 170. Five main bearings. Hydraulic valve lifters. Carburetor: two-barrel.

NOTE: For complete MoPar engine data see 1974 Dodge section of catalog.

CHASSIS FEATURES: Wheelbase: (Valiant/Scamp) 111 inches, (Duster/Barracuda) 108 inches; (Satellite two-door) 115 inches; (Satellite four-door) 117 inches; (Fury I and II) 120 inches; (Fury III/Gran Fury) 122 inches; (Fury Suburban) 124 inches. Overall length: (Valiant/Scamp) 197.6 inches; (Duster) 194.1 inches; (Barracuda) 195.6 inches; (Satellite two-door) 212.4 inches; (Satellite four-door) 208.9 inches; (Satellite wagon) 217.1 inches; (Road Runner) 212.4 inches; (Sebring) 210.8 inches; (Fury I/Fury II) 223.4 inches; (Fury III/Gran Fury) 219.9 inches; (Suburbans) 223.3 inches. Tires: See tire data in text.

OPTIONS: Air conditioning, Barracuda ($384); Fury ($406); Satellite ($398); Valiant ($384). Air conditioning, with automatic temperature control, Fury only ($484). Bumper guards, front and rear, Fury ($40); Satellite two-door ($17); Valiant ($31). Carpets, Valiant except Scamp ($18); Satellite/Road Runner/Fury I ($20). Electric clock, Barracuda ($17); Satellite ($19); Fury Group ($18). Digital electronic clock, Fury I/II/III ($40); Gran Fury/Suburban ($22). Console, bucket seats required, Road Runner/Sebring-Plus ($59). Console, bucket-seats required, Duster/Barracuda ($54). Front manual disc brakes, Valiant except Duster 360 ($23). Engine block heater, Fury Group ($16). Gauges, temperature and oil pressure, Fury Group ($18). Tinted glass, all windows, Fury ($52); Satellite ($45); others ($37). Hood tie-down pins, Road Runner only ($17). Barracuda Sport Hood, standard with 'Cuda hardtop ($21). Left outside rearview mirror, remote control, Barracuda ($15); Satellite ($17). Remote-control, dual outside rearview mirrors, Fury ($40). Performance hood paint treatment, Duster and '360' ($18). Hood and fender stripes, Road Runner only ($23). Duster lower deck stripes, standard Duster '360' ($13). Bodyside tape stripes, Barracuda ($29). Standard Duster ($26). Power front disc brakes; Valiant six ($66). Valiant V-8 ($43). Satellite ($46). Remote control trunk release, Fury ($16). Power door locks, two-door Fury ($49); four-door Fury ($75). Power steering, Valiant/Barracuda ($107); Satellite ($120). Power Six-Way bench seat, Fury Group ($108). Power left-hand bucket seat, Gran Coupe/Sedan/Sport Wagons ($96). Power left-hand bucket seat, Fury III except Style PH23 ($96). Automatic locking tailgate, all wagons ($28). Power windows, Satellite Group ($125); Fury Group ($131). Power tailgate window, Satellite wagons ($36). AM/FM stereo radio, average price for all models ($202). AM/FM stereo radio with tape, average price for all Furys ($397). Vinyl top, compact-intermediate ($84-$99). Vinyl top, Fury Group, except wagons ($112). Vinyl canopy top, Satellite two-door ($69); Dusters ($63). Duster, vinyl trim bucket seats and carpets ($127). Vinyl trim split-bench seat with center armrest, Valiant Group ($78). Vinyl trim 50/50 split- bench seat, Fury III four-door ($138). Cloth and vinyl bucket seat with center armrest, Sebring-Plus ($96). Security alarm system, Fury Group ($104). Automatic speed control, Fury and Satellite with TorqueFlite ($67). Tilt-A-Scope steering wheel, standard trim Furys ($92). 'Tuff' steering wheel, Valiant/Satellite/Road Runner Groups ($11-$31). Tachometer, Sebring-Plus/Road Runner models ($54). DeLuxe wheelcovers ($26-$28). Premier style wheelcovers, Satellite ($51); Fury ($33-$61). Chrome styled Road wheels, average price ($80). Rally Road wheels, Valiant/Barracuda/Satellite, average price ($56). Manual vent windows, Fury Group four-doors ($35). Three-speed electric wipers and washers, ($6-$11). DeLuxe windshield wipers, Fury Group ($12). Code A06 Sebring 'Easy Order' package included AM radio; Light Group; power disc brakes; TorqueFlite; power steering; vinyl roof: left remote-control outside rearview mirror; whitewalls; three-speed wipers; wagon luggage rack; DeLuxe wheelcovers; bright bumper guards; inside hood release; and undercoating with hood pad at prices from $396 to $745. Salon package was available for Fury III four-door models and the Custom Suburban after the middle of the year. It was priced at an average of $230. Three-speed manual transmission was standard in Valiant/Barracuda/Satellite Groups. Automatic transmission was standard in Fury Group; optional on others at various prices. Three-speed manual floor transmission, optional Valiant ($27). Four-speed manual floor shift transmission, optional ($195-$235). Valiant six-cylinder 225 cid 105 hp one-barrel engine ($39). Satellite V-8 360 cid/245 hp four-barrel engine ($86). Fury I/II/III V-8 360 cid/245 hp four-barrel engine ($39). Barracuda V-8 360 cid/245 hp four-barrel engine ($259). 'Cuda V-8 360 cid/245 hp four-barrel engine ($189). Road Runner V-8 360 cid/245 hp four-barrel engine ($161). Fury I/Satellite V-8 400 cid/205 hp four-barrel engine ($117). Fury I/II V-8 400 cid/205 hp four-barrel engine ($80). Gran Fury/Suburban V-8 400 cid/205 hp four-barrel ($39). Satellite Coupe V-8 400 cid/250 hp four-barrel dual-exhaust engine ($183). Road Runner V-8 400 cid/250 hp four-barrel dual exhaust engine ($127). Fury I/II/III V-8 440 cid/230 hp four-barrel engine ($156). Gran Fury/Suburban V-8 440 cid/230 hp four-barrel engine ($115). Road Runner V-8 440 cid/275 hp four-barrel dual exhaust engine ($255). Satellite V-8 360 cid/180 hp two-barrel engine ($47). Positive traction rear axle. Fury Group ($50); Satellite ($47); Valiant/Barracuda ($43). Available rear axle gear ratios: 3.2 1: 1; 3.23:1 ($13-$14 extra per Group).

HISTORICAL FOOTNOTES: The full-sized Plymouths were introduced Sept. 25, 1973 and the Valiant line appeared in dealer showrooms the same day. Model year U.S. dealer sales peaked at 651,586 units. Calendar year production of 609,385 cars was recorded. R.K. Brown was the Group vice-president for U.S. sales this year. After a lapse of many years, Plymouth re-entered the commercial vehicle market with a line of van type trucks bearing a new Voyager nameplate.

1975 PLYMOUTH

VALIANT GROUP — (6-CYL/V-8) — SERIES 5V — The Valiant lineup was expanded this year, and for good reason. One out of every four compact cars sold in 1974 was a member of Plymouth's Valiant Group. Improvements in styling and engineering details could be detected throughout the line. The Valiant Brougham returned and was the plushest edition yet. The popular Dusters and Scamps were carried over with minor revisions. On the technical side, several new items became available to buyers with increasing interest in fuel economy. Radial tires, a unique Fuel Pacer system, lower gear ratios and a lighter torque convertor were designed specifically for gas savings. There were new, 50,000 mile spark plugs and batteries and a 'Clincher' warranty that covered everything on the car except tires for 12 months with no mileage restrictions. Added to the former line of six sedans and coupes, was a high-level Duster Custom sport coupe and Valiant Custom sedan. The coupes were on the 108 inch wheelbase, with sedans and hardtops having a three inch longer stance. The Duster 360 had an engine which matched the call-out part of its name, while other models offered, as base equipment, the '225' six or '318' V-8. Styling distinctions were limited to a new cross-hatched grille insert with stand-up Valiant identification badge in its center, a de-chromed wraparound taillight treatment on the Scamp-based bodies and, on the new Customs, full-length mid-bodyside moldings, a wide selection of upholstery and seat designs, rocker sill moldings and loop-pile floor carpeting. Standard equipment for the carryover models followed the specifications outlined in the 1974 section, except for the Duster 360. This car again had heavy-duty suspension; special shock absorbers; front and rear sway bar; and dual exhausts. But, now it also featured a new rear panel and beltline tape stripe treatment and automatic transmission as standard equipment. The same tape stripes were optional on other Dusters and consisted of a thin full-length stripe and a separate, wide upper rear fender tape panel.

1975 Plymouth, Valiant Brougham four-door sedan, V-8

PLYMOUTH I.D. NUMBERS: VIN on plate attached to upper left-hand top of dash, viewable through windshield. First symbol indicate make: P= Gran Fury; R=Fury; V=Valiant; =Volare. Second symbol indicates price class: L=low; M=medium; H=high; P=premium; S=Special; K=police car. Third and fourth symbols indicate body style. (First four symbols appear in Body/Style Number column of charts below). Fifth symbol indicates engine: C=225 cid/105 nhp six; E=special order six; G=318 cid two-barrel V-8; J=360 cid four-barrel V-8; K=360 cid two-barrel V-8; L=360 cid four-barrel high-performance V-8; M=400 cid two-barrel V-8; N=400 cid four-barrel V-8; P=400 cid/260 hp four-barrel high-performance V-8; T=440 cid/220 nhp four-barrel V-8; U=440 cid/280 four-barrel TNT V-8. Z=Special order V-8. The sixth symbol indicates model year, 5=1975. The seventh symbol indicates assembly plant: A=Lynch Rd., Detroit, Mich.; B=Hamtramck, Mich.; C=Jefferson Ave., Detroit, Mich.; D=Belvedere, Ill.; F=Newark, Del.; G=St. Louis, Mo.; R=Windsor, Ontario, Canada. The last six symbols are the production sequence number starting at 100001 at each factory.

VALIANT GROUP

Series Number	Body/Style Number	Body Type & Seating	Factory Price	Shipping Weight	Production Total
VALIANT					
5V1/2	VL41	4-dr Sed-6P	3247/3369	3040/3185	44,471
5V1/2	VH41	4-dr Cus Sed-6P	3422/3544	3040/3185	56,258
5V1/2	VP41	4-dr Brgm Sed-6P	4139/4236	3250/3340	17,803
DUSTER					
5V1/2	VL29	2-dr Cpe-6P	3243/3364	3115/3115	79,884
5V1/2	VH29	2-dr Cus Cpe-6P	3418/3539	2970/3115	38,826
5V2	VS29	2-dr'360'Cpe-6P	3979	3315	1,421
SCAMP					
5V1/2	VH23	2-dr HT Cpe-6P	3518/3640	3020/3165	23,581
5V1/2	VP23	2-dr Brgm HT-6P	4232/4328	3240/3325	5,781
EXPORT VALIANT					
5V1/2	VL23	2-dr HT Cpe-6P	NA	NA	1,302
VALIANT TAXICAB					
5V1/2	VE41	4-dr Sed-6P	NA	NA	123

NOTE 1: Data above slash for six/below slash for V-8.
NOTE 2: The export Valiant two-door hardtop probably a Canadian market model.

FURY GROUP — (6-CYL/V-8) — SERIES 5R — For 1975, the intermediate-sized Plymouths took the Fury name and the Satellite designation was dropped. (The standard-sized models were then called Gran Furys). The mid-sized cars were completely redesigned, although the overall styling was still related to that seen previously on Satellites. The cars came on two different wheelbases. There were 115 inches between the hub centers of two-door hardtops and a 118 inch stance for sedans and wagons. The only nameplate carried over from the past was Road Runner, which model was distinguished by a blacked-out grille treatment and a beltline tape stripe running from the front fender tip to the leading edge of the rear roof pillar and, from that point, up over the roof. The Road Runner came with heavy-duty suspension; dual exhausts and a choice of five V-8s ranging from the base 318 cid two-barrel job, to a 400 cid four-barrel high-output type. A unique new Road Runner option was a rear deck graphics

decor package spelling the model name out boldly on back of the car. The appearance of the mid-sized Furys was characterized by the use of large expanses of glass and a more tailored styling theme, which had some of the flair of Chrysler's new Cordoba. The two and four-door models had the same look at the front, but used entirely different rear treatments. Two-door cars featured canted, vertical taillights and an angular center deck lid bulge with a trapezoid-shaped rear face that was mirrored in the bumper contours. Four-door cars had a Duster-like rear image, with a totally different bumper housing three-segment horizontal taillamps. The front end featured single headlights mounted in individual square bezels. The grille opening was of a round-cornered rectangular shape divided into 12 segments by vertical, bright metal bars. The outer segments housed vertical parking lamps and all of the segments were filled with a grid patterned insert which, on Road Runners, was finished in black (bright-finished on other models). The bumper was a straight-across affair with integral bumper guards and no air slots or lower openings. A sleek, wrapover roof pillar treatment was seen on two-door models.

1975 Plymouth, Fury Sport two-door hardtop coupe, V-8

FURY GROUP

Series Number	Body/Style Number	Body Type & Seating	Factory Price	Shipping Weight	Production Total
FURY CUSTOM/SPORT LINE					
5R1/2	R221	2-dr HT Cpe-6P	3542/3672	3555/3670	8,398
5R1/2	RH23	2-dr Cus HT-6P	3711/3840	3635/3750	27,486
5R2	RP23	2-dr Spt HT-6P	4105	3790	17,782
5R1/2	R241	4-dr Sed-6P	3591/3720	3585/3585	11,432
5R1/2	RH41	4-dr Cus Sed-6P	3704/3834	3635/3750	31,080
ROAD RUNNER LINE					
5R2	RM21	2-dr HT Cpe-6P	3973	3760	7,183
SUBURBAN LINE					
5R2	R245	4-dr Std Wag-6P	4309	4180	4,468
5R2	RH45	4-dr Cus Wag-6P	4512	4230	3,890
5R2	RH46	4-dr Cus Wag-9P	4632	4285	4,285
5R2	RP45	4-dr Spt Wag-6P	4770	4230	1,851
5R2	RP46	4-dr Spt Wag-9P	4867	4295	3,107
TAXICAB					
5R2/2	RE41	4-dr Sed-6P	NA	NA	1,627
POLICE SPECIAL					
5R1/2	R241	4-dr Sed-6P	NA	NA	6,877

NOTE 1: Data above slash for six/below slash; no slash for V-8.

1975 Plymouth, Gran Fury Custom, four-door hardtop sedan, V-8

GRAN FURY GROUP — (V-8) — SERIES 5P — The Gran Fury designation, which had formerly been used to identify two high-level offerings, was now applied to all full-sized Plymouths. The Gran Fury Series supplied 111 inch wheelbase sedans and hardtops, plus 124 inch wheelbase Suburban station wagons. At the top of the line were the Gran Fury-Broughams and comparable Sport Suburbans. All of these cars used the same basic body with new grille and rear end treatments, which were different for each line. The Custom style grilles and taillamps had only minor changes from the previous year. At the front a horizontal center divider ran across the middle of the grille insert and carried an upright identification badge at its center. At the rear, the bumper guards were shorter and fatter. The standard Gran Furys had a bright metal mid-bodyside molding that was broken by the wheel opening contours. Custom models had a similar molding with color-keyed vinyl inserts, bright wheel lip opening trim and rocker sill moldings. Broughams had no side trim, except for cowlside signature scripts and rocker sill moldings, but featured a distinctive grille design. On the Brougham, single headlamps and vertical parking lamps were housed in a segmented, rectangular surround with bright metal finish. The central grille insert was set into a separate, round-cornered rectangular opening and had a square-grid pattern look. There was a stand-up hood ornament and Plymouth lettering across the lip of the hood. The front bumper was similar to the 1974 style, with slots on either side of the bumper guards allowing the grillework to show through. However, black vinyl protective strips were added. They moved, horizontally, from below the headlamps to around the corners of the bumper. A formal roof treatment, complete with opera style rear quarter windows, was standard on two-door Broughams. The standard engine for all Gran Furys was the '318' V-8, with options including the 360, 400 and 440 cid

V-8s. Radial tires and wiper-mounted windshield washers were standard for Broughams. Other equipment variations between the various lines followed the pattern outlined for 1974 Plymouths, with models comparable to Fury II: Customs to Fury III and Brougham to the former Gran Coupe/Sedan.

GRAN FURY GROUP

Series Number	Body/Style Number	Body Type & Seating	Factory Price	Shipping Weight	Production Total
GRAN FURY					
5P2	PM41	4-dr Sed-6P	4565	4260	8,185
5P2	PH41	4-dr Cus Sed-6P	4761	4260	19,043
5P2	PH43	4-dr Cus HT Sed-6P	4837	4290	11,292
5P2	PH23	2-dr Cus HT Cpe-6P	4781	4205	6,041
5P2	PP29	2-dr Brgm HT Cpe 6P	5146	4310	6,521
5P2	PP43	4-dr Brgm HT Sed 6P	5067	4400	5,521
SUBURBANS					
5P2	PM45	4-dr Std Wag-6P	5067	4855	2,295
5P2	PH45	4-dr Cus Wag-6P	5176	4870	3,155
5P2	PH46	4-dr Cus Wag-9P	5294	4915	4,500
5P2	PP45	4-dr Spt Wag-6P	5455	4885	1,508
5P2	PP46	4-dr Spt Wag-9P	5573	4930	4,740
TAXICAB					
5P2	PE41	4-dr Sed-6P	NA	NA	742
POLICE SPECIAL					
5P2	PS41	4-dr Sed-6P	NA	NA	4,208
GRAN FURY EXPORT					
5P2	P123	2-dr HT Cpe-6P	NA	NA	1,433

BASE ENGINES

(VALIANT/DUSTER/FURY SIX) Inline six. Overhead valves. Cast iron block. Displacement: 225 cid. Bore and stroke: 3.4 x 4.12 inches. SAE Net hp: 95. Four main bearings. Solid valve lifters. Carburetor: one-barrel.

BASE V-8

(V-8 VALIANT/DUSTER/FURY/ROAD RUNNER) V-8. Overhead valves. Cast iron block. Displacement: 318 cid. Bore and stroke: 3.91 x 3.31 inches. SAE Net hp: 145. Five main bearings. Hydraulic valve lifters. Carburetor: two-barrel.

(V-8 DUSTER '360') V-8. Overhead valves. Cast iron block. Displacement: 360 cid. Bore and stroke: 4 x 3.58 inches. SAE Net hp: 230. Five main bearings. Hydraulic valve lifters. Carburetor: four-barrel.

(V-8 GRAN FURY/CUSTOM) V-8. Overhead valves. Cast iron block. Displacement: 360 cid. Bore and stroke: 4 x 3.58 inches. SAE Net hp: 180. Five main bearings. Hydraulic valve lifters. Carburetor: two-barrel.

(V-8 SUBURBAN/BROUGHAM) V-8. Overhead valves. Cast iron block. Displacement: 400 cid. Bore and stroke: 4.34 x 3.38 inches. SAE Net hp: 175. Five main bearings. Hydraulic valve lifters. Carburetor: two-barrel.

CHASSIS FEATURES: Wheelbase: (Valiant Group Sedan/hardtop) 111 inches; (Duster Coupe) 108 inches; (Fury two-door) 115 inches; (Fury four-door/wagon) 117.5 inches; (Road Runner) 115 inches; (Gran Fury Suburban) 124 inches; (Gran Fury passenger) 121.5 inches. Overall length: (Valiant/Scamp) 200 inches; (Duster) 197 inches; (Fury two-door) 213.8 inches; (Fury four-door) 217.9 inches; (Road Runner) 213.8 inches; (Gran Fury Suburban) 219.9 inches; (Gran Fury passenger) 223.3 inches. Tires: (Valiant Group Cpe) 6.95 x 14; (other Valiants) D78-14; (Road Runner) G70-14; (Fury wagons) H78 x 14; (other Furys) F78 x 14; (Gran Fury wagons) 2R 78-15; (Brougham) HR78-15; (other Gran Furys) GR78-15.

OPTIONS: [VALIANT] Bucket seats ($83); Gold Duster package ($181). Electric rear window defroster ($67). Tinted glass, all windows ($44). Power disc brakes, average price ($65). Duster 'Decorator Special' package ($272). Power steering standard in Valiant Brougham. Power brakes standard on Duster 360. Factory air conditioning ($407). [FURY] Exterior Decor package ($116). Electric rear window defroster ($73). Power disc brakes, standard on station wagon; other models ($58). Station wagon luggage rack ($67). Sun roof ($296). AM/FM stereo with tape ($397). Power windows ($138). Power bench seats ($117). AM/FM stereo ($254). Saloon package ($230). Exterior Decor package ($116). Electric rear window defroster ($73). Power disc brakes, standard on station wagon; other models ($58). Station wagon luggage rack ($67). Sun roof ($296). AM/FM stereo with tape ($397). Power windows ($138). Power bench seats ($117). AM/FM stereo ($254). [GRAN FURY] Reclining seat with special interior trim ($174). Sure-Grip axle ($52). Electric rear window defroster ($73). Security Alarm system ($112). Station wagon luggage rack ($79). Sun roof ($634). Automatic height control ($99). Vinyl top ($117). AM/FM stereo with tape ($397). Power seats ($117). AM/FM stereo ($254). Power brakes (standard). TorqueFlite automatic transmission was standard on all Gran Furys; mid-sized Fury station wagons; Valiant Broughams and the Duster 360. Three-speed manual transmission was standard with all other models in base trim. The 230 hp 360 cid V-8 with four-barrel carburetor was optional in the Valiant Group. A 180 hp 360 cid V-8 was optional in mid-sized Furys. A 200 hp 360 cid V-8 was also optional in mid-sized Furys. A 135 hp 318 cid economy V-8 was also optional in mid-sized Furys (the 145 hp 318 cid V-8 was standard). Four versions of the 400 cid V-8 with 175, 185, 190, or 235 net hp were also available in specific mid-sized Furys. The standard Gran Fury/Custom V-8 was optional in Broughams and Suburbans, while the standard Brougham/Suburban V-8 was optional in Gran Fury/Custom models. Also available in specific applications were a 190 hp 360 cid V-8 and 200 hp 400 cid V-8. Other options for full-sized cars included a 175 hp 400 cid V-8 and a 215 hp 440 cid V-8. In some cases, a certain engine may have superseded another during the model year. In different cases, certain engines were available only in federally certified cars; others only in cars certified for sale in the state of California or designated high-altitude counties. The 360 cid four-barrel V-8 was a $202 option in Road Runners and Furys. The 400 cid two-barrel V-8 was a $93 option in Furys. The 400 cid two-barrel V-8 was a $44 option in Gran Furys. The 400 cid four-barrel V-8 was a $122 option in Furys. The 400 cid four-barrel V-8 was an $84 option in Gran Fury. These are the only prices available for 1975 Plymouth.

HISTORICAL FOOTNOTES: The full-sized Plymouths were introduced Oct. 1, 1974 and the compact line appeared in dealer showrooms the same day. Model year dealer sales peaked at 403,169 units. Calendar year production of 447,403 cars was recorded. R.B. McCurry, Jr. was the Group Vice-President for U.S. Automotive Sales at Chrysler-Plymouth Div. this year. United States dealers sold a total of 12,330 Voyager vans and trucks during the 1975 model year. Production for the model year, including Voyagers, was 507,338 cars and trucks. In mid-model year the Plymouth Arrow, a car built in Japan by Mitsubishi Industries, was added to the product line as an imported subcompact model. Also available, as part of the Voyager line, were two-wheel-drive and four-wheel-drive Trail Duster pickup/utility trucks.

1955 Pontiac, Custom Star Chief two-door Catalina hardtop, V-8

Ever since its introduction in 1926, Pontiac's basic premise for success was to give the Pontiac owner much of the luxury, comfort and fine detail of expensive cars at a price just higher than the low-priced lines. By 1941, this premise had brought Pontiac sales to fifth rank in the American industry. And it was this policy, little altered, that characterized the company's early postwar products as well.

The 1946-1948 Pontiacs were reincarnations of the 1942 models in terms of both styling and engineering. They were as reliable and value-packed as the cars offered before World War II, but just as predictable, too. These flathead sixes and eights slowly, but surely, gained a reputation as middle-of-the-road cars best-suited for middle class, middle-age buyers in the middle price bracket. In its struggle to market a reliable product at the lowest possible price, Pontiac found itself stuck on a plateau that was out of step with the sporty car boom of the postwar period.

Reaction to the growing youth market came slowly at Pontiac, because there was a reluctance to upset the apple cart in quest of modernization. Although old-fashioned, Pontiacs were still selling better than ever through the end of 1953. Hydra-Matic transmission was introduced in 1948 and gained immediate popularity. Newly redesigned bodies with lower lines and integral rear fenders were the hit of 1949. An attractive Catalina two-door hardtop made the scene in 1950 and rear fender humps, somewhat resembling Cadillac tailfins, were adopted for 1953. The following year, the top Pontiac line featured up-dated bodies with an extended deck that emphasized the extra luxury associated with the nameplate. But there was still an inline flathead eight below the hood. Unfortunately, this type power plant was too much of a throwback to earlier days. Sales took a tumble and a need for change seemed more than crystal clear.

Work on a V-8 engine for Pontiac had begun as early as 1949, under longtime general manager Harry J. Klinger. Development proceeded slowly at first. In 1951, the conservative Klinger became vice president of vehicle production for GM. Arnold Lenz took over Pontiac, hoping to institute rapid change. When Lenz died in a car/train crash the following year, the V-8 program was set back. R.M. Critchfield succeeded Lenz and slowly got the modernization program rolling again. It was 1955 before the new Pontiac engine hit the market and, when it did, sales took an immediate jump to 554,000 units in the model year.

A new era started for Pontiac in 1956 when Semon E. (Bunkie) Knudsen took over the reins as general manager. Knudsen, son of former GM president William S. Knudsen, was the youngest GM general manager at age 43. He proceeded, without fanfare, to make over the Pontiac image.

With a new engineering group headed by E.M. (Pete) Estes and John Z. Delorean, a line of new cars with true performance potential was methodically developed. To highlight a move into a competition and factory racing program, an 'extra horsepower' engine option with dual four-barrel carbu-

retors and a full-race camshaft was crafted by staff motor engineer Malcolm R. 'Mac' McKellar. It was released in mid-1956 and became the first in a series of so-called NASCAR and Super-Duty Pontiac V-8s.

Starting with 1959 models, the image of a sporty, youthful car with appeal across the spectrum of new car buyers emerged at Pontiac. The result was six straight years of low-slung, Wide-Track, full-size performance machines that out-ran the majority of competitors in both sales and racing. In the fall of 1960, following intensive research, development and testing, Pontiac expanded the bottom of its line with a completely innovative compact model called the Tempest.

When Knudsen moved to Chevrolet in 1961, Estes took over at Pontiac. Under his able direction the division continued to grow in sales volume and facilities. The Tempest moved the company into third place in U.S. sales in 1961. Traditionally the 'hot spot' of the auto market, Pontiac was able to dominate the third rung during the 1960s.

Pontiac performance reached a peak in 1963 and racing activities were officially curtailed shortly afterwards due to a corporate ban. To maintain its edge in the youth car market, the company skirted another GM policy by dropping its most popular big car engine (the 389 cid V-8) into medium-sized Tempest bodies in true hot rod fashion. The result was the first Pontiac GTO. A year later, John Z. DeLorean was made manager.

With introductions of 1966 models, Pontiac announced a completely new overhead camshaft six-cylinder engine as standard equipment in Tempests. In the middle of the 1967 model year, the Firebird sports/personal car was unveiled. It was offered in a range of model-options from the ohc six to a new 400 cid V-8. Ram Air induction was optional. A milestone was achieved in 1968 when an all-time high of 940,000 cars left the factory. It was also the first time that sales of Pontiac speciality models like Tempests, Grand Prixs and Firebirds, exceeded the sales of traditional lines.

The hit of 1969 was a restyled Grand Prix with neo-classical appearances. A few months later, the most exciting of all Firebirds was introduced as the semi-race-ready Trans Am. Conceived as a factory sedan-racer, the Trans Am had a motor that was too big to qualify for track competition, but just right for stoplight performance. By this time the government was starting to crack down on factory hot rods of the late 1960s, but the Trans Am passed as a sports car and thereby kept the performance image alive for a few more years.

In February, 1969, F. James McDonald became Pontiac general manager. He replaced DeLorean who moved to Chevrolet in the same capacity. The division's new 300,000 square foot, ultra-modern administration building opened early the next year. This was a critical stage for car development programs, due to pressures from the government and insurance companies alike. High-performance was continually de-emphasized in favor of safety and fuel economy gains combined with engine emissions reductions.

During the 1971 calendar year, Pontiac captured third place in U.S. auto sales for the 10th time in 11 years, but the division's image was loosing impact at the same time. The low-priced Ventura II compact hit the market; a new, less powerful 1972 Trans Am appeared; and the nearest thing to a full-sized performance car available was the luxurious Bonneville with a massive 455 cid V-8.

On Oct. 1, 1972, Martin J. Caserio became general manager of Pontiac Motor Div. Under him a new regular fuel Super-Duty V-8 evolved and became an instant collector's item when ultimately released in late 1973 Trans Ams and Formula Firebirds. Under Caserio the GTO disappeared and the Firebird came close to meeting a similar fate.

The 1973 Pontiac lineup was highlighted by a totally redesigned intermediate series, topped by the stunning Grand Am. This car was rendered in the image of a European road tourer with a slotted, slanting `soft' nose fashioned of flexible urethane rubber. Calendar year sales of 854,343 cars were the second best in company history, but like 20 years earlier, future trends did not favor Pontiac. The 1974 models featured new engineering and radial-tuned suspension, while 1975 brought the sub-compact Astre, a more luxurious Grandville Brougham line and the demise — at least temporarily — of convertibles with Pontiac nameplates.

Today, postwar Pontiac models seem to be coming into their stride as collector cars. There is a clear emphasis on restoring and preserving the more specialized models and the cars that have optional high-performance equipment. Without a doubt, the earliest Bonneville models, the most powerful GTOs and Trans Ams with sport equipment combinations are the cars most desirable to enthusiasts right now. But almost as popular, are early Catalinas, all 1955-1957 styles (especially Starchief Custom Safaris), Grand Prixs, Grand Ams, Catalina 2 + 2s and the rare Catalina Super-Duty factory experimental drag racing cars.

1948 Pontiac, Torpedo two-door convertible, 8-cyl

1953 Pontiac, Chieftain Custom Catalina two-door hardtop, 8-cyl

1946 PONTIAC

1946 Pontiac Torpedo two-door sedan

1946 Pontiac, Streamliner four-door sedan, 8-cyl

TORPEDO SERIES — (SIX) SERIES 25/(EIGHT) SERIES 27 — Torpedos comprised Pontiac's short wheelbase (A-Body) line. Buyers could order any Torpedo on either the six or eight-cylinder chassis ($27-30 extra for Eights). There was no difference in Series 25 or Series 27 features, except for engine identifying trim. Styling highlights of all Pontiacs were: wraparound bumpers, a massive 14-blade grille, new nameplates and concealed safe-light parking lamps. An Indian head mascot with upward curved feathers, short moldings atop front fenders, absence of belt moldings and painted pinstripes on the fender "speedline" ribs distinguished Torpedos. Lettering on hood emblems and badges placed forward of the "speedlines" identified eights. Closed-body Torpedos came with grey tan cloth trims and convertibles were done in cloth combined with black, tan, green, blue or red leather.

PONTIAC I.D. NUMBERS: VIN located on left side of firewall under hood. First symbol indicated the assembly plant: P=Pontiac, Mich.; C=California (Southgate); L=Linden, N.J.; K=Kansas City, Kan. Second symbol indicated engine type: 6=six-cylinder; 8=eight-cylinder. Next two symbols were series code appearing as last two characters in first column of charts below. Following this came the sequential production number, which began with 1001 at each assembly plant. Engine serial number on raised pad on front left side of block. VINs matched the engine serial number. The 1946 numbers for each series were: [TORPEDO SIXES]: (Mich.) P6LA-1001 to P6LA-17381; (Calif.) C6LA-1001 to C6LA-3314; (Kan.) K6LA-1001 to K6LA-2520; (N.J.) L6LA-1001 to L6LA4721. [TORPEDO EIGHTS] (Mich.) P8LA-1001 to P8LA-13652; (Calif.) C8LA-1001 to C8LA-2786; (Kan.) K8LA-1001 to K8LA-2520; (N.J.) L8LA-1001 to L8LA-3738. [STREAMLINER SIXES]: (Mich.) P6LB-1001 to P6LB35238; (Calif.) C6LB-1001 to C6 LB3696; (Kan.) K6LB-1001 to K6LB-2299; (N.J.) L6LB-1001 to L6LB-5357. [STREAMLINER EIGHTS]: (Mich.) P8LB-1001 to P8LB-39764; (Calif.) C8LB-1001 to C8LB-4257; (Kans.) K8LB-1001 to K8LB-2590; (N.J.) L8LB-1001 to L8LB-6618. Another code located on the firewall tag on Pontiacs is the Fisher Body/Style Number. It consists of a prefix indicating model year (46=1946) and suffix indicating series number and body type. These numbers appear in the second column of the charts below. Pontiac parts suppliers use these numbers to aid proper parts applications so they are very important.

TORPEDO SIXES

Model Number	Body/Style Number	Body Type & Seating	Factory Price	Shipping Weight	Production Total
25LA	46-2527B	2-dr Cpe-3P	1307	3261	NA
25LA	46-2507	2-dr Sed Cpe-5P	1399	3326	NA
25LA	46-2527	2-dr Spt Cpe-5P	1353	3311	NA
5LA	46-2567	2-dr Conv-5P	1631	3591	NA
25LA	46-2511	2-dr Sed-5P	1368	3326	NA
25LA	46-2519	4-dr Sed-5P	1427	3361	NA

NOTE 1: 26,636 Torpedo sixes built; no body style breakouts available.

TORPEDO EIGHTS

Model Number	Body/Style Number	Body Type & Seating	Factory Price	Shipping Weight	Production Total
27LA	46-2727B	2-dr Cpe-3P	1335	3331	NA
27LA	46-2707	2-dr Sed Cpe-5P	1428	3391	NA
27LA	46-2727	2-dr Spt Cpe-5P	1381	3376	NA
27LA	46-2767	2-dr Conv-5P	1658	3651	NA
27LA	46-2711	2-dr Sed-5P	1395	3396	NA
27LA	46-2719	4-dr Sed-5P	1455	3436	NA

NOTE 1: 18,273 Torpedo eights built; no body style breakouts available.

STREAMLINER SERIES — (SIX) SERIES 26 (EIGHT) SERIES 28 — Streamliners represented Pontiac's B-Body line. The first postwar Pontiac available (Sept. 13, 1945) was the Streamliner sedan-coupe, which remained the sole product for a time. Streamliners could be identified by straight-back Indian head hood ornaments, chrome beltline moldings and bright moldings on the "speedline" fender ribs. They also had longer front fender crown moldings and were generally larger in size. Interior trims on passenger cars were in grey striped cloth. Station wagons had three seats in standard trim; two seats in Deluxe trim and used imitation leather upholstery and passenger car style interior hardware.

STREAMLINER SIXES

Model Number	Body/Style Number	Body Type & Seating	Factory Price	Shipping Weight	Production Total
26LB	46-2607	2-dr Sed Cpe-5P	1438	3435	NA
26LB	46-2609	4-dr Sed-5P	1510	3490	NA
26LB	46-Sta Wag	4-dr Std Sta Wag-8P	1942	3790	NA
26LB	46-Sta Wag	4-dr Del Sta Wag-6P	2019	3735	NA

NOTE 1: 43,430 Streamliner sixes built; no body style breakouts available.

STREAMLINER EIGHTS

Model Number	Body/Style Number	Body Type & Seating	Factory Price	Shipping Weight	Production Total
28LB	46-2807	2-dr Sed Cpe-5P	1468	3495	NA
28LB	46-2809	4-dr Sed-5P	1538	3550	NA
28LB	46-Sta Wag	4-dr Std Sta Wag-8P	1970	3870	NA
28LB	46-Sta Wag	4-dr Del Sta Wag-6P	2047	3805	NA

NOTE 1: 49,301 Streamliner eights built; no body style breakouts.

ENGINES

(SIX) Six-cylinder: L-head. Cast iron block. Displacement: 239.2 cid. Bore and stroke: 3-9/16 x 4 inches. Compression ratio: (standard) 6.5:1, (optional) 7.5:1. Brake hp: 90 at 3200 rpm. Four main bearings. Solid valve lifters. Carburetor: Carter WAI-537-S one-barrel.

(EIGHT) Eight-Cylinder: L-head. Cast iron block. Displacement: 248.9 cid. Bore and stroke: 3-1/4 x 3-3/4 inches. Compression ratio: See Torpedo six. Brake hp: 103 at 3500 rpm. Five main bearings. Solid valve lifters. Carburetor: Carter WDO548-S two-barrel.

CHASSIS FEATURES: [TORPEDO] Wheelbase: 119 inches. Overall length: 204.5 inches. Front tread: 58 inches. Rear tread: 61-1/2 inches. Tire size: 6.00 x 16. [STREAMLINER] Wheelbase: 122 inches. Overall length: (passenger cars) 210-1/4 inches, (wagons) 215-5/8 inches. Front tread: 58 inches. Rear tread: 61-1/2 inches. Tires: 6.50 x 16.

OPTIONS: Rear windshield wiper. Windshield washer. White sidewall discs. Fog lights. Safety light. Weather Chief heater (dash type). Defroster (dash type). Venti-Heat underseat heater and defroster. Five-tube Master radio. Seven-tube Air Mate radio. Eight-tube Air King radio. Mast antenna. Rear fender panels (Torpedo). Rear fender panels with moldings (Streamliner). Sponge rubber cushions (per body style). Kool Kushin. Luggage compartment light. Lock package. Electric visor vanity mirror. E-Z-I non-glare rearview mirror. Non-electric visor vanity mirror. Hand brake lamp. Umbrella holder. Santoy seat covers (per body style). Bumper guards, wheel rim rings, electric clock, exhaust deflector and various lights available in standard accessory packages. All 1946 Pontiacs had three-speed manual transmission with column shifting. Performance options were limited to 3.9:1 (economy) and 4.55:1 (mountain) rear axle gear ratios, a 7.5:1 "high-compression" cylinder head and automatic No-Rol device.

HISTORICAL FOOTNOTES: The first postwar Pontiac was built Sept. 13, 1945. The full model line was back in production by June 10, 1946. Calendar year production was 131,538 cars. Model year production was 137,640 cars. Harry J. Klinger was general manager of Pontiac Motor Div. (PMD). George Delaney became the company's chief engineer this season, replacing Ben Anibal, who worked on the development of the first 1926 Pontiacs. The three-passenger coupe was called a business coupe. The convertible was called a convertible sedan-coupe. General Motors two-door fastbacks were also referred to as "Sport Dynamic" coupes. The early postwar Pontiacs sometimes had the words "Silver Streak" on the hoods, but the proper model names are Streamliner and Torpedo. Silver Streak is not an official model name.

1947 PONTIAC

TORPED0 SERIES — (SIX) SERIES 25 — (EIGHT) SERIES 27 — The Torpedos comprised the same line as in 1946. A "Silver Streak" styling theme was continued, now with five bands of chrome on hoods. All Pontiacs had new grilles with four broad, gently bowed horizontal bars. Hoods and fenders were protected by an inverted steer's horn-shaped bar incorporating a die-cast plate with Indian head relief. Torpedos carried no beltline or speedline moldings and had short strips of chrome on the front fender crowns. All 1947 Pontiacs had identical hood ornaments. Interiors were similar to 1946, but due to material shortages some convertibles were built with red, blue or black imitation leather upholstery in combination with tan Bedford cloth. Only the Torpedo sedan-coupe had fastback styling with individual-loop chrome moldings on the side windows.

PONTIAC I.D. NUMBERS: VIN located on left side of firewall under hood. First symbol indicated the assembly plant: P=Pontiac, Mich.; C=California (Southgate); L=Linden, N.J.; W=Wilmington, Del.; K=Kansas City, Kans.; A=Atlanta, Ga. Second symbol indicated engine type: 6=six-cylinder; 8=eight-cylinder. Next two symbols were series code appearing as last two characters in first column of charts below. Following this came the sequential production number, which began with 1001 at each assembly plant. Engine serial number on raised pad on front left side of block. VINs matched the engine serial number. The 1947 numbers for each series were: [TORPEDO SIXES]: (Mich.) P6MA-1001 to P6MA-37322; (N.J.) L6MA-1001 to L6MA-13895; (Kan.) K6MA-1001 to K6MA-8096; (Del.) W6MA-1001 to W6MA-1850; (Calif.) C6MA-1001 to C6MA-7794. [TORPEDO EIGHTS] (Mich.) P8MA-1001 to P8MA-22682; (N.J.) L8MA-1001 to L8MA-7387; (Kan.) K8MA-1001 to K8MA-4165; (Dela.) W8MA-1001 to W8MA-1431; (Calif.) C8MA-1001 to C8MA-4150. [STREAMLINER SIXES] (Mich.) P6MB-1001 to P6MB-27844; (N.J.) L6MB-1001 to L6MB-7877; (Kan.) K6MB-1001 to K6MB-4569; (Dela.) W6MB-1001 to W6MB-3976; (Calif.) C6MB-1001 to C6-MB-3976; (Ga.) A6MB-1001 to A6MB-1080. [STREAMLINER EIGHTS] (Mich.) P8MB-1001 to P8MB-56382; (N.J.) L8MB-1001 to L8MB-15246; (Kans.) K8MB-1001 to K8MB-9184; (Dela.) W8MB-1001 to W8MB-1954; (Calif.) C8MB-1001 to C8MB-8197; (Ga.) A8MB-1001 to A8MB-1145. Another code located

on the firewall tag on Pontiacs is the Fisher Body/Style Number. It consists of a prefix indicating model year (47=1947) and suffix indicating series number and body type. These numbers appear in the second column of the charts below. Pontiac parts suppliers use these numbers to aid proper parts applications so they are very important.

TORPEDO SIXES

Model Number	Body/Style Number	Body Type & Seating	Factory Price	Shipping Weight	Production Total
25MA	47-2527B	2-dr Cpe3P	1217	3245	NA
25MA	47-2507	2-dr Sed Cpe-5P	1305	3300	NA
25MA	47-2527	2-dr Spt Cpe-5P	1261	3295	NA
25MA	47-2567	2-dr Conv-5P	1595	3560	NA
25MA	47-2511	2-dr Sed-5P	1275	3295	NA
25MA	47-2519	4-dr Sed-5P	1331	3320	NA

NOTE 1: 67,125 Torpedo sixes built; no body style breakouts available.

TORPEDO EIGHTS

Model Number	Body/Style Number	Body Type & Seating	Factory Price	Shipping Weight	Production Total
27MA	47-2727B	2-dr Cpe-3P	1262	3310	NA
27MA	47-2707	2-dr Sed Cpe-5P	1350	3370	NA
27MA	47-2727	2-dr Spt Cpe-5P	1306	3360	NA
27MA	47-2767	2-dr Conv-5P	1640	3635	NA
27MA	47-2711	2-dr Sed-5P	1320	3370	NA
27MA	47-2719	4-dr Sed-5P	1376	3405	NA

NOTE 1: 34,815 Torpedo eights built; no breakouts per body style.

1947 Pontiac, Streamliner station wagon, 8-cyl

STREAMLINER SERIES — (SIX) SERIES 26 — (EIGHT) SERIES 28 — Streamliners also stayed basically the same as 1946, except for grille and trim variations. Interiors for coupes and sedans were redesigned with Berwick beige panels for dashboard and windows. Windshield, door and garnish moldings were finished in Autumn brown with dado-stripe border moldings. All coupes and sedans in this series were fastbacks with full-loop-around window moldings.

STREAMLINER SIXES

Model Number	Body/Style Number	Body Type & Seating	Factory Price	Shipping Weight	Production Total
26MB	47-2607	2-dr Sed Cpe-5P	1359	3400	NA
26MB	47-2609	4-dr Sed-5P	1407	3405	NA
26MB	47-Sta Wag	4-dr Std Sta Wag-8P	1992	3775	NA
26MB	47-Sta Wag	4-dr DeL Sta Wag-6P	2066	3715	NA

NOTE 1: 42,336 Streamliner sixes built; no body style breakouts available.

STREAMLINER EIGHTS

Model Number	Body/Style Number	Body Type & Seating	Factory Price	Shipping Weight	Production Total
28MB	47-2807	2-dr Sed Cpe-5P	1404	3455	NA
28MB	47-2809	4-dr Sed-5p	1452	3515	NA
28MB	47-Sta Wag	4-dr Std Sta Wag-8P	2037	3845	NA
28MB	47-Sta Wag	4-dr DeL Sta Wag-6P	2111	3790	NA

NOTE 1: 86,324 Streamliner eights built; no body style breakouts available.

ENGINES

(SIX) Six-cylinder: L-head. Cast iron block. Displacement: 239.2 cid. Bore and stroke: 3-9/16 x 4 inches. Compression ratio: (standard) 6.5:1, (optional) 7.5:1. Brake hp: 90 at 3200 rpm. Four main bearings. Solid valve lifters. Carburetor: Carter WAI-537-S one-barrel.

(EIGHT) Eight-Cylinder: L-head. Cast iron block. Displacement: 248.9 cid. Bore and stroke: 3-1/4 x 3-3/4 inches. Compression ratio: See Torpedo six. Brake hp: 103 at 3500 rpm. Five main bearings. Solid valve lifters. Carburetor: Carter WCD two-barrel models 630S or 630SB.

CHASSIS FEATURES:
[TORPEDO] Wheelbase: 119 inches. Overall length: 204.5 inches. Front tread: 58 inches. Rear tread: 61-1/2 inches. Tire size: 6.00 x 16. [STREAMLINER] Wheelbase: 122 inches. Overall length: (passenger cars) 210-1/4 inches, (wagons) 215-5/8 inches. Front tread: 58 inches. Rear tread: 61-1/2 inches. Tires: 6.50 x 16.

OPTIONS:
Rear windshield wiper. Windshield washer. White sidewall discs. Fog lights. Safety light. Weather Chief heater (dash type). Defroster (dash type). Venti-Heat underseat heater and defroster. Five-tube Master radio. Seven-tube Air Mate radio. Eight-tube Air King radio. Mast antenna. Rear fender panels (Torpedo). Rear fender panels with moldings (Streamliner). Sponge rubber cushions (per body style). Kool Kushin. Luggage compartment light. Lock package. Electric visor vanity mirror. E-Z-I non-glare rearview mirror. Non-electric visor vanity mirror. Hand brake lamp. Umbrella holder. Santoy seat covers (per body style). Bumper guards, wheel rim rings, electric clock, exhaust deflector and various lights available in standard accessory packages. All 1946 Pontiacs had three-speed manual transmission with column shifting. Performance options were limited to 3.9:1 (economy) and 4.55:1 (mountain) rear axle gear ratios, a 7.5:1 "high-compression" cylinder head and automatic No-Rol device.

HISTORICAL FOOTNOTES:
Production of 1947 Pontiacs began Dec. 19, 1946. Calendar year output came to 223,015 units. Model year assemblies totaled 230,600 cars. A Pontiac prototype with a rear-mounted straight eight-cylinder engine was constructed in 1947. Aluminum replacement fenders for 1942-1948 models were made available later and at least one modern collector has discovered such fenders on his car. Body styles 47-2567 and 47-

2767 were now called convertible coupes. Body styles 47-2507; 47-2707; 47-2607 and 47-2807 were Sport Dynamic coupes and are commonly known as fastbacks today. Body styles 47-2609 and 47-2809 were Sport Dynamic four-door sedans, also with fastback styling.

1948 PONTIAC

1948 Pontiac, Torpedo Deluxe four-door sedan, 6-cyl

TORPEDO SERIES — (SIX) SERIES 25 — (EIGHT) SERIES 27 — There were no radical appearance changes in Torpedos, except for adoption of new Pontiac styling including triple "Silver Streaks," a horizontal grille theme with vertical shafts, and round taillights. The word "Silver Streak" was carried on the sides of the hood with eights having an "8" placed between the two words. The model lineup was expanded by offering several body styles with Deluxe trims. Characterizing standard models were plain fenders and rubber gravel guards. Deluxes had fender moldings, bright metal gravel guards and chrome-plated wheel discs. Grey tan cloth continued as trim on standard Torpedos, but Deluxe types with closed bodies used tan and dark blue pattern cloth combinations. Convertibles came with genuine Colonial grain leather or imitation leather upholstery and had instrument boards lacquered in body color.

PONTIAC I.D. NUMBERS: VIN located on left side of firewall under hood. Serial numbers took the form ( )[ ]P{ }-1001 to ( )[ ]P{ }-ending number. First symbol ( ) indicated the assembly plant: P=Pontiac, Mich.; C=California (Southgate); L=Linden, N.J.; W=Wilmington, Del.; K=Kansas City, Kan.; A=Atlanta, Ga.; F=Framingham, Mass. Second symbol [ ] indicated engine type: 6=inline six-cylinder; 8=inline eight-cylinder. Third symbol indicated model year: P=1948. Fourth symbol { } contains a letter indicating series: A=Torpedo; B=Streamliner. Remaining symbols are the sequential unit production number for each car-line at each assembly plant. Beginning number at each plant is 1001. Ending numbers for 1948 were: [TORPEDO SIX] (Mich.) 25366; (Calif.) 5150; (N.J.) 5301; (Dela.) 4375; (Kan.) 5303; (Ga.) 3429 and (Mass.) 3454. [TORPEDO EIGHT] (Mich.) 18933; (Calif.) 4368; (N.J.) 5471; (Dela.) 3854; (Kan.) 4134; (Ga.) 2820; (Mass.) 2720. [STREAMLINER SIX] (Mich.) 18146; (Calif.) 4765; (N.J.) 4350; (Dela.) 3772; (Kan.) 5556; (Ga.) 2926 and (Mass.) 2951. [STREAMLINER EIGHT] (Mich.) 61682; (Calif.) 13302; (N.J.) 12359; (Dela.) 10616; (Kan.) 16561; (Ga.) 7603 and (Mass.) 7776. Engine serial number on raised pad on front left side of block. VINs matched the engine serial number. Fisher Body/Style Number on plate under hood on left of firewall can be very helpful for identification of model and ordering parts. A prefix to the main number indicates model year, 48=1948. The first two symbols in the main number indicate series 25, 26, 27 or 28. The next two symbols indicate the body style. Some numbers have an alphabetical suffix indicating trim level, such as D=Deluxe. These numbers appear in Body/Style Number column of charts below adjacent to corresponding body style listing.

TORPEDO SIXES

Model Number	Body/Style Number	Body Type & Seating	Factory Price	Shipping Weight	Production Total
6PA	48-2527B	2-dr Bus Cpe-3P	1500	3230	NA
6PA	48-2527(D)	2-dr Spt Cpe-5P	1552/1641	3220/3230	NA
6PA	48-2507(D)	2-dr Sed Cpe-5P	1614/1704	3275/3275	NA
6PA	48-2567(D)	2-dr Conv-5P	1935/2025	3525/3530	NA
6PA	48-2511	2-dr Sed-5P	1583	3280	NA
6PA	48-2519(D)	4-dr Sed-5P	1641/1731	3320/3340	NA

NOTE 1: 25,325 Torpedo sixes with Hydra-Matic built
NOTE 2: 13,937 Torpedo sixes with Synchromesh built
NOTE 3: 49,262 total Torpedo sixes built; no body style breakouts available.

1948 Pontiac, Torpedo Deluxe two-door convertible, 8-cyl

TORPEDO EIGHTS

Model Number	Body/Style Number	Body Type & Seating	Factory Price	Shipping Weight	Production Total
8PA	48-2727B	2-dr Bus Cpe-3P	1548	3296	NA
8PA	48-2727(D)	2-dr Spt Cpe-5P	1599/1689	3295/3305	NA
8PA	48-2707(D)	2-dr Sed Cpe-5P	1661/1751	3340/3340	NA
8PA	48-2767(D)	2-dr Conv-5P	1982/2072	3595/3600	NA
8PA	48-2711	2-dr Sed-5P	1630	3360	NA
8PA	48-2719(D)	4-dr Sed-5P	1689/1778	3395/3395	NA

NOTE 1: 24,294 Torpedo eights with Hydra-Matic built.
NOTE 2: 11,006 Torpedo eights with Synchromesh built.
NOTE 3: 35,360 total Torpedo eights built; no body style breakouts available.
NOTE 4: "D" suffix indicates car came as both standard and Deluxe.
NOTE 5: Data above slash for standard/below slash for Deluxe.
NOTE 6: Factory info conflicts (i.e. standard convertible probably not made.)

STREAMLINER SERIES — (SIX) SERIES 36) — (EIGHT) SERIES 28 — Streamliners were again larger and more expensive. All Streamliners, two-door and four-door fastbacks (B-Body) and the station wagon, now came standard or Deluxe. As on Torpedos, Deluxe models were distinguished by spear moldings on front fenders, bright gravel guards and chrome plated wheel discs on all cars except wagons. Deluxe interiors had two-tone trims with pillow-and-tuft seatbacks, quarter-sawed mahogany dash and window trim, electric glovebox door clocks, Deluxe steering wheels and other rich appointments. Standard wagons had tan imitation leather seats and Deluxe wagons had red upholstery of the same type.

STREAMLINER SIXES

Model Number	Body/Style Number	Body Type & Seating	Factory Price	Shipping Weight	Production Total
6PB	48-2607(D)	2-dr Sed Cpe-5P	1677/1766	3365/3370	NA
6PB	48-2609(D)	4-dr Sed-5P	1727/1817	3450/3455	NA
6PB	Sta Wag(D)	4-dr Sta Wag-6/8P	2364/2442	3755/3695	NA

NOTE 1: 23,858 Streamliner sixes with Hydra-Matic built.
NOTE 2: 13,834 Streamliner sixes with Synchromesh built.
NOTE 3: 37,742 total Streamliner sixes built; no body style breakouts.

STREAMLINER EIGHTS

Model Number	Body/Style Number	Body Type & Seating	Factory Price	Shipping Weight	Production Total
8PB	48-2807(D)	2-dr Sed Cpe-5P	1724/1814	3425/3455	NA
8PB	48-2809(D)	4-dr Sed-5P	1755/1864	3525/3530	NA
8PB	Sta Wag(D)	4-dr Sta Wag-6/8P	2412/2490	3820/3765	NA

NOTE 1: 98,469 Streamliner eights built with Hydra-Matic.
NOTE 2: 24,646 Streamliner eights built with Synchromesh.
NOTE 3: 123,115 total Streamliner eights built; no breakouts per body style.
NOTE 4: "D" suffix indicates car came as both standard and Deluxe sub-series.
NOTE 5: Data above slash for standard/below slash for Deluxe.
NOTE 6: Station wagon seating: Deluxe=6-passenger; Standard=8-passenger.

ENGINES

(SIX) Six-cylinder. L-head. Cast iron block. Displacement: 239.2 cid. Bore and stroke: 3-9/16 x 4 inches. Compression ratio: (standard) 6.5:1, (optional) 7.5:1. Brake hp: (standard) 90 at 3400 rpm, (optional) 93 at 3400 rpm. Four main bearings. Solid valve lifters. Carburetor: Carter WA1-537-S one-barrel.

(EIGHT) Eight-cylinder. L-head. Cast iron block. Displacement: 248.9 cid. Bore and stroke: 3-1/4 x 3-3/4 inches. Compression ratio: Same as on six-cylinder. Brake hp: (standard head) 104 at 3800 rpm, (optional 'high head') 106 at 3800 rpm. Five main bearings. Solid valve lifters. Carburetor: Carter WCD-630-S two-barrel.

CHASSIS FEATURES: [TORPEDO] Wheelbase: 119 inches. Overall length: 204.5 inches. Front tread: 58 inches. Rear tread: 61-1/2 inches. Tire size: 6.00 x 16 tube type. [STREAM-LINER] Wheelbase: 122 inches. Overall length: (cars) 204.5 inches, (wagons) 215-5/8 inches. Front tread: 58 inches. Rear tread: 61-1/2 inches. Tire size: 6.50 x 16 tube type.

OPTIONS: Rear windshield wiper. Windshield washer. White sidewall discs. Fog lights. Safety light. Weather Chief heater (dash type). Defroster (dash type). Venti-Heat underseat heater and defroster. Five-tube Master radio. Seven-tube Air Mate radio. Eight-tube Air King radio. Mast antenna. Rear fender panels (Torpedo). Rear fender panels with moldings (Streamliner). Sponge rubber cushions (per body style). Kool Kushin. Luggage compartment light. Lock package. Electric visor vanity mirror. E-Z-I non-glare rearview mirror. Non-electric visor vanity mirror. Hand brake lamp. Umbrella holder. Santoy seat covers (per body style). Bumper guards, wheel rim rings, electric clock, exhaust deflector and various lights available in standard accessory packages. All 1948 Pontiacs had three-speed manual transmission with column shifting as standard equipment. A new option was Hydra-Matic Drive ($185). Performance options were limited to 3.9:1 (economy) and 4.55:1 (mountain) rear axle gear ratios, a 7.5:1 "high-compression" cylinder head and automatic No-Rol device.

HISTORICAL FOOTNOTES: The 1948 Pontiacs entered production on Dec. 29, 1947. Model year output came to 245,419 cars, which gave Pontiac a 6.56 percent share of the domestic automobile marketplace. Calendar year production peaked at 253,469 cars, making Pontiac America's fifth ranked automaker.

1949 PONTIAC

STREAMLINER LINE — (SIX) SERIES 25 — (EIGHT) SERIES 27 — The 1949 Pontiacs featured low, sleek envelope bodies. Streamliner coupes and sedans utilized the fastback B-body shell. Station wagons were also incorporated in this line. All these cars came as standards or Deluxes. All station wagons and other standard models had small hubcaps. Standard coupes, sedans and wagons were characterized by an absence of beltline trim along with use of rubber gravel guards and painted headlight rims. Deluxes had belt moldings, chrome gravel guards and bright plated headlight doors. Silver Streak styling was seen again. Silver Streak lettering was placed above front fender spears on Deluxes and high on the fenders of standards. Eights had the number '8' between the two words. Most standard models had grey striped pattern cloth upholstery. Most Deluxes used dark grey broadcloth trims. Convertibles and wagons were trimmed as before, except imitation leather was used only on standard wagons.

PONTIAC I.D. NUMBERS: VIN located on tag on left front door post. Matching engine serial number located on raised pad on front left side of cylinder block. Serial numbers took the form ( )-[ ]R{ }-1001 to ( )-[ ]P{ }-ending number. First symbol ( ) indicated the assembly plant: P=Pontiac, Mich.; C=California (Southgate); L=Linden, N.J.; W=Wilmington, Del.; K=Kansas City, Kan.; A=Atlanta, Ga.; F=Framingham, Mass. Second symbol [ ] indicated engine type: 6=inline six-cylinder; 8=inline eight-cylinder. Third symbol indicated model year: R=1949. Fourth symbol { } changed to a letter indicating type of transmission: S=synchromesh; H=Hydra-Matic. Remaining symbols are the sequential unit production number for each car-line at each assembly plant. Beginning number at each plant is 1001. Ending numbers for 1949 were: [SERIES 25 SIX with synchromesh] (Mich.) 17919; (Calif.) 4767; (N.J.) 4657; (Dela.) 4077; (Kan.) 7406; (Ga.) 3404 and (Mass.) 3613. [SERIES 25 SIX with/Hydra-Matic] (Mich.) 12320; (Calif.) 4142; (N.J.) 3998; (Dela.) 3425; (Kan.) 5887; (Ga.) 2903; (Mass.) 3012. [SERIES 27 EIGHT with synchromesh] (Mich.) 26054; (Calif.) 7209; (N.J.) 7398; (Dela.) 6200; (Kan.) 10608; (Ga.) 4975 and (Mass.) 5188. [SERIES 27 EIGHT with Hydra-Matic] (Mich.) 68436; (Calif.) 19959; (N.J.) 19989; (Dela.) 16062; (Kan.) 30890; (Ga.) 12657 and (Mass.) 13336. Fisher Body/Style Number on plate under hood on left of firewall can be very helpful for identification of model and ordering parts. A prefix to the main number indicates model year, 49=1949. The first two symbols in the main number indicate series 25 or 27. The next two symbols indicate the body style. Some numbers have an alphabetical suffix indicating trim level, such as D=Deluxe. These numbers appear in Body/Style Number column of charts below adjacent to corresponding body style listing.

STREAMLINER SIXES

Model Number	Body/Style Number	Body Type & Seating	Factory Price	Shipping Weight	Production Total
6R	2508(D)	4-dr Sed-5P	1740/1835	3385/3415	NA
6R	2507(D)	2-dr Sed Cpe-5P	1689/1784	3360/3375	NA
6R	2561(D)	4-dr Wood Wag-8P/6P	2543/2622	3745/3730	NA
6R	2562(D)	4-dr Metal Wag-8/6P	2543/2622	3650/3580	NA

NOTE 1: See Historical Footnotes for series production total.
NOTE 2: Data above slash for standard/below slash for Deluxe.

STREAMLINER EIGHTS

Model Number	Body/Style Number	Body Type & Seating	Factory Price	Shipping Weight	Production Total
8R	2508(D)	4-dr Sed-5P	1808/1903	3470/3500	NA
8R	2507(D)	2-dr Sed Cpe-5P	1758/1853	3435/3445	NA
8R	2561(D)	4-dr Wood Wag-8P/6P	2611/2690	3835/3800	NA
8R	2562(D)	4-dr Metal Wag-8/6P	2611/2690	3690/3640	NA

NOTE 1: See Historical Footnotes for series production total.
NOTE 2: Data above slash for standard/below slash for Deluxe.
NOTE 3: See STANDARD CATALOG of LIGHT-DUTY AMERICAN TRUCKS for sedan delivery.

1949 Pontiac, Chieftain Deluxe two-door convertible, 8-cyl

CHIEFTAIN LINE — (SIX) SERIES 25 — (EIGHT) SERIES 27 — Chieftains were characterized by notch back body styling and all models in the line were used the General Motors A-body shell. The only dimensional difference between the new Streamliners and Chieftains was that the latter were approximately 3/4-inch higher than comparable B-body styles. Lengths and widths were identical for all models in both lines, except station wagons. Trim variations between sixes and eights or standards and Deluxes were the same as on Streamliners.

CHIEFTAIN SIXES

Model Number	Body/Style Number	Body Type & Seating	Factory Price	Shipping Weight	Production Total
6R	2569(D)	4-dr Sed-5P	1761/1856	3385/3415	NA
6R	2511(D)	2-dr Sed-5P	1710/1805	3355/3360	NA
6R	2527(D)	2-dr Sed Cpe-5P	1710/1805	3330/3345	NA
6R	2527B	2-dr Bus Cpe-3P	1587	3280	NA
6R	2567DTX	2-dr Del Conv-5P	2183	3600	NA

NOTE 1: See Historical Footnotes for series production total.
NOTE 2: Data above slash for standard/below slash for Deluxe.

Model Number	Body/Style Number	Body Type & Seating	Factory Price	Shipping Weight	Production Total
8R	2569(D)	4-dr Sed-5P	1829/1924	3475/3480	NA
8R	2511(D)	2-dr Sed-5P	1779/1874	3430/3430	NA
8R	2527(D)	2-dr Sed Cpe-5P	1779/1874	3390/3415	NA
8R	2427B	2-dr Bus Cpe-3P	1656	3355	NA
8R	2567DTX	2-dr Del Conv-5P	2206	3670	NA

NOTE 1: See Historical Footnotes for series production total.
NOTE 2: Data above slash for standard/below slash for Deluxe.

ENGINES

(SIX) Six-cylinder. L-head. Cast iron block. Displacement: 239.2 cid. Bore and stroke: 3-9/16 x 4. Compression ratio: (standard) 6.5:1 (optional) 7.5:1. Brake hp: (standard) 90 at 3400 rpm (optional) 93 at 3400 rpm. Four main bearings. Solid valve lifters. Carburetor: Carter WA1-537-S one-barrel.

(EIGHT) Eight-cylinder. L-head. Cast iron block. Displacement: 248.9 cid. Bore and stroke: 4-1/4 x 4-3/4 inches. Compression ratios: Same as sixes. Brake hp: (standard) 103 at 3800 rpm, (optional) 106 at 3800 rpm. Five main bearings. Solid valve lifters. Carburetor: Carter WCD two-barrel model 6305B.

CHASSIS FEATURES: Wheelbase: 120 inches all lines. Overall length: (all cars) 202-1/2 inches; (wagons) 203.8 inches. Front tread: 58 inches. Rear tread: 59 inches. Tires: (standard) 7.10 x 15 (special equipment) 7.60 x 15. Tube type.

OPTIONS: Seven-tube Chieftain radio. Mast antenna. No-Blo wind deflectors. Car cushions. Venti-Seat underseat heater. Venti-Shades. Windshield Sun Visor. Traffic light viewer. Polaroid visor. Rear fender panels (skirts). License frames. Illuminated hood ornament. Wheel trim rings. Steel wheel discs. White sidewall discs. Deluxe steering wheel. Remington Auto-Home shaver. Visor vanity mirror. Tissue dispenser. Compass. Rear window wiper. Windshield washers. Deluxe electric clock. Glove compartment light. Leather utility pocket. Luggage compartment light. Seat covers. Safti-Jack, Outside rearview mirror. Back-up lights. Safety spotlight. Fog lights. No-Rol. Bumper guards. Exhaust deflector. Venetian blinds. No-Mar gas filler trim. Fuel door lock. Scuff pads. Multi-purpose lamp. Underhood trouble lamp. Jack bag. Tool kit. A three-speed Synchromesh gearbox with column shift was standard on all models. Hydra-Matic four-speed automatic transmission was available at $159 extra. Rear axle ratios: (standard) 4.1:1, (economy) 3.9:1, (mountain) 4.3:1, (Hydra-Matic) 3.63:1.

HISTORICAL FOOTNOTES: Calendar year production was 333,957 cars. Model year production was 304,819 cars. The latter included a total of 69,654 Streamliner and Chieftain sixes (29,515 with Hydra-Matic and 40,139 with synchromesh) and 235,165 Streamliner and Chieftain eights (174,449 with Hydra-Matic and 60,716 with synchromesh.) Pontiac sold 21.2 percent of the U.S. cars in its price class. Hydra-Matic Drive was installed in 78 percent of all Pontiacs made for the year. During 1949, the company built the 3 millionth Pontiac made since the marque was introduced in 1926. Prototypes of a new "Catalina" two-door hardtop Sports Coupe were seen this year. Note that Pontiac Motor Div. now kept production records by chassis series (six or eight), without regard to car-line (Streamliner or Chieftain). This practice was followed through 1954 and there are no breakouts by car-line of body style available until model year 1955. Standard station wagons continued to feature eight-passenger seating, while Deluxe wagons came with six-passenger seating. Body styles 2527 and 2527D are often called Club Coupes and feature direct-action (non-cranking) rear quarter window operation. These styles resemble the two-door sedan, but have shorter roofs and longer rear decks.

1950 PONTIAC

STREAMLINER LINE — (SIX) SERIES 25 — (EIGHT) SERIES 27 — The 1950 Pontiacs utilized the popular 1949 envelope bodies with revisions to trim and appointments. The horizontal center grille bar now wrapped around the corners of the body. Deluxes had a chrome body strip, chrome wheel rings, chrome headlight rings and stainless steel gravel guards. Eights had an '8' between the words `Silver Streak' on fenders. Streamliners, except wagons (and sedan delivery trucks) had sloping fastback styling.

PONTIAC I.D. NUMBERS: VIN located on tag on left front door post. Matching engine serial number located on raised pad on front left side of cylinder block. Serial numbers took the form ( )-[ ]T{ }-1001 to ( )-[ ]T{ }-ending number. First symbol ( ) indicated the assembly plant: P=Pontiac, Mich.; C=California (Southgate), L=Linden, N.J.; W=Wilmington, Del.; K=Kansas City, Kan.; A=Atlanta, Ga.; F=Framingham, Mass. Second symbol [ ] indicated engine type: 6=inline six-cylinder; 8=inline eight-cylinder. Third symbol indicated model year: T=1950. Fourth symbol { } changed to a letter indicating type of transmission: S=synchromesh; H=Hydra-Matic. Remaining symbols are the sequential unit production number for each car-line at each assembly plant. Beginning number at each plant is 1001. Ending numbers for 1950 were: [SERIES 25 SIX with synchromesh] (Mich.) 47948; (Calif.) 5571; (N.J.) 8011; (Dela.) 74745; (Kan.) 14626; (Ga.) 4925 and (Mass.) 8048. [SERIES 25 SIX with/Hydra-Matic] (Mich.) 15001; (Calif.) 2553; (N.J.) 2999; (Dela.) 2534; (Kan.) 3696; (Ga.) 1960; (Mass.) 2575. [SERIES 27 EIGHT with synchromesh] (Mich.) 3815; (Calif.) 4746; (N.J.) 4619; (Dela.) 5558; (Kan.) 11497; (Ga.) 5257 and (Mass.) 4070. [SERIES 27 EIGHT with Hydra-Matic] (Mich.) 128647; (Calif.) 29630; (N.J.) 19058; (Dela.) 17360; (Kan.) 42698; (Ga.) 14851 and (Mass.) 117242. Fisher Body/Style Number on plate under hood on left of firewall can be very helpful for identification and ordering parts. A prefix to the main number indicates model year, 50=1950. The first two symbols in the main number indicate series 25 or 27. The next two symbols indicate the body style. Some numbers have an alphabetical suffix indicating trim level, such as B=Business and D=Deluxe. These numbers appear in Body/Style Number column of charts below adjacent to corresponding body style listing.

STREAMLINER SIXES

Model Number	Body/Style Number	Body Type & Seating	Factory Price	Shipping Weight	Production Total
6T	2508(D)	4-dr Sed-6P	1724/1745	3414/3499	NA
6T	2507(D)	2-dr Sed Cpe-6P	1673/1768	3379/3399	NA
6T	2562(D)	4-dr Metal Wag-8/6P	2264/2343	3714/3649	NA

NOTE 1: See Historical Footnotes for series production total.
NOTE 2: Data above slash for standard/below slash for Deluxe.

STREAMLINER EIGHTS

Model Number	Body/Style Number	Body Type & Seating	Factory Price	Shipping Weight	Production Total
8T	2508(D)	4-dr Sed-6P	1792/1887	3499/3509	NA
8T	2507(D)	2-dr Sed Cpe-6P	1742/1837	3464/3469	NA
8T	2562(D)	4-dr Metal Wag-8/6P	2332/2411	3799/3739	NA

NOTE 1: See Historical Footnotes for series production total.
NOTE 2: Data above slash for standard/below slash for Deluxe.

1950 Pontiac, Chieftain Super Deluxe Catalina, 8-cyl

CHIEFTAIN LINE — (SIX) SERIES 25 — (EIGHT) SERIES 27 — Chieftains were built off the A-body shell with trim distinctions for Deluxes and eights the same as on Streamliners. A new Chieftain body style was the Catalina two-door hardtop coupe, classified as a Super Deluxe model within the Deluxe sub-series. It came finished only in San Pedro ivory, Sierra rust or two-tone combinations of these colors. The interior was done in rust and ivory leather combinations.

CHIEFTAIN SIXES

Model Number	Body/Style Number	Body Type & Seating	Factory Price	Shipping Weight	Production Total
6T	2569(D)	4-dr Sed-6P	1745/1840	3409/3414	NA
6T	2511(D)	2-dr Sed-6P	1694/1789	3384/3389	NA
6T	2527(D)	2-dr Sed Cpe-6P	1694/1789	3359/3364	NA
6T	2537SD	2-dr Cat HT-6P	2000	3469	NA
6T	2567DTX	2-dr Conv-6P	2122	3624	NA
6T	2527B	2-dr Bus Cpe-3P	1571	3319	NA

NOTE 1: See Historical Footnotes for series production total.
NOTE 2: Data above slash for standard/below slash for Deluxe.

CHIEFTAIN EIGHTS

Model Number	Body/Style Number	Body Type & Seating	Factory Price	Shipping Weight	Production Total
8T	2569(D)	4-dr Sed-6P	1813/1908	3494/3499	NA
8T	2511(D)	2-dr Sed-6P	1763/1858	3454/3464	NA
8T	2527(D)	2-dr Sed Cpe-6P	1763/1858	3444/3454	NA
8T	2537SD	2-dr Cat Cpe-6P	2069	3549	NA
8T	2567DTX	2-dr Conv-6P	2190	3704	NA

NOTE 1: See Historical Footnotes for series production total.
NOTE 2: Data above slash for standard/below slash for Deluxe.

ENGINES

(SIX) Six-cylinder. L-head. Cast iron block. Displacement: 239.2 cid. Bore and stroke: 3-9/16 x 4. Compression ratio: (standard) 6.5:1; (optional) 7.5:1. Brake hp: (standard) 90 at 3400 rpm; (optional) 93 at 3400 rpm. Four main bearings. Solid valve lifters. Carburetor: Carter WA1-719-S one-barrel.

(EIGHT) Eight-cylinder. L-head. Cast iron block. Displacement: 268.2 cid. Bore and stroke: 3-3/8 x 3-3/4 inches. Compression ratio: (standard) 6.5:1 (optional) 7.5:1. Brake hp: (standard) 108 at 3600 rpm; (optional) 113 at 3600 rpm. Five main bearings. Solid valve lifters. Carburetor: Carter WCD-719-S two barrel.

CHASSIS FEATURES: Wheelbase: 120 inches all lines. Overall length: (all cars) 202-1/2 inches; (wagons) 203.8 inches. Front tread: 58 inches. Rear tread: 59 inches. Tires: (standard) 7.10 x 15 (special equipment) 7.60 x 15. Tube type.

OPTIONS: Seven-tube Chieftain radio. Mast antenna. No-Blo wind deflectors. Car cushions. Venti-Seat underseat heater. Venti-Shades. Windshield Sun Visor. Traffic light viewer. Polaroid visor. Rear fender panels (skirts). License frames. Illuminated hood ornament. Wheel trim rings. Steel wheel discs. White sidewall discs. Deluxe steering wheel. Remington Auto-Home shaver. Visor vanity mirror. Tissue dispenser. Direction signals. Compass. Rear window wiper. Windshield washers. Deluxe electric clock. Glove compartment light. Leather utility pocket. Luggage compartment light. Seat covers. Safti-Jack, Outside rearview mirror. Back-up lights. Safety spotlight. Fog lights. No-Rol. Bumper guards. Grill guard. Exhaust deflector. Venetian blinds. No-Mar gas filler trim. Fuel door lock. Scuff pads. Multi-purpose lamp. Underhood trouble lamp. Jack bag. Tool kit. A three-speed Synchromesh gearbox with column shift was standard on all models. Hydra-Matic four-speed automatic transmission was available at $159 extra. Rear axle ratios: (standard) 4.1:1, (economy) 3.9:1, (mountain) 4.3:1, (Hydra-Matic) 3.63:1.

HISTORICAL FOOTNOTES: Production of 1950 Pontiacs began Nov. 10, 1949. Calendar year assemblies were a strong 467,950 units. Model year output was also very strong, at 446,426 cars. The latter included a total of 115,542 Streamliner and Chieftain sixes (24,930 with Hydra-Matic and 90,612 with synchromesh) and a total of 330,887 Streamliner and Chieftain eights (263,188 with Hydra-Matic and 67,699 with synchromesh).

1951 PONTIAC

STREAMLINER LINE — (SIX) SERIES 25 — (EIGHT) — SERIES 27 — The 1951 "Silver Anniversary" Pontiacs reflected 25 years of advanced engineering. A wing-shaped grille was seen and a `Silver Streak' theme continued. Streamliners again used the B-body shell with sloping fastbacks on coupes. Deluxes had chrome body strips, bright gravel guards and headlight rings. Beltline moldings on all Deluxe cars, but not station wagons, had a dip behind the doors. Standard belt moldings were straight. A script plate reading `Pontiac' was used on Series 25 sixes and on Series 27 eights a different script read `Pontiac eight.'

PONTIAC I.D. NUMBERS: VIN located on tag on left front door post. Matching engine serial number located on raised pad on front left side of cylinder block. Serial numbers took the form ( )-[ ]U{ }-1001 to ( )-[ ]U{ }-ending number. First symbol ( ) indicated the assembly plant: P=Pontiac, Mich.; C=California (Southgate); L=Linden, N.J.; W=Wilmington, Del.; K=Kansas City, Kan.; A=Atlanta, Ga.; F=Framingham, Mass. Second symbol [ ] indicated engine type: 6=inline six-cylinder; 8=inline eight-cylinder. Third symbol indicated model year: U=1951. Fourth symbol { } changed to a letter indicating type of transmission: S=synchromesh; H=Hydra-Matic. Remaining symbols are the sequential unit production number for each car-line at each assembly plant. Beginning number at each plant is 1001. Ending numbers for 1951 were: [SERIES 25 SIX with synchromesh] (Mich.) 24016; (Calif.) 3519; (N.J.) 4133; (Dela.) 4175; (Kan.) 6567; (Ga.) 3282 and (Mass.) 3181. [SERIES 25 SIX with/Hydra-Matic] (Mich.) 6543; (Calif.) 1473; (N.J.) 1592; (Dela.) 1562; (Kan.) 1954; (Ga.) 1416; (Mass.) 1323. [SERIES 27 EIGHT with synchromesh] (Mich.) 31777; (Calif.) 6224; (N.J.) 5984; (Dela.) 6068; (Kan.) 11644; (Ga.) 5406 and (Mass.) 4177. [SERIES 27 EIGHT with Hydra-Matic] (Mich.) 119780; (Calif.) 20125; (N.J.) 22197; (Dela.) 23140; (Kan.) 40060; (Ga.) 18117 and (Mass.) 14080. Fisher Body/Style Number on plate under hood on left of firewall can be very helpful for identification of model and ordering parts. A prefix to the main number indicates model year, 51=1951. The first two symbols in the main number indicate series 25 or 27. The next two symbols indicate the body style. Some numbers have an alphabetical suffix indicating trim level, such as B=Business; D=Deluxe; and SD=Super Deluxe. These numbers appear in Body/Style Number column of charts below adjacent to corresponding body style listings.

STREAMLINER SIXES

Model Number	Body/Style Number	Body Type & Seating	Factory Price	Shipping Weight	Production Total
6U	2407(D)	2-dr Sed Cpe-6P	1824/1927	3248/3263	NA
6U	2562(D)	4-dr Sta Wag-8/6P	2470/2556	3603/3523	NA

NOTE 1: See Historical Footnotes for series production total.
NOTE 2: Data above slash for standard/below slash for Deluxe.

STREAMLINER EIGHTS

Model Number	Body/Style Number	Body Type & Seating	Factory Price	Shipping Weight	Production Total
8U	2507(D)	2-dr Sed Cpe-6P	1900/2003	3343/3348	NA
8U	2562(D)	4-dr Sta Wag-8/6P	2544/2629	3698/3628	NA

NOTE 1: See Historical Footnotes for series production total.
NOTE 2: Data above slash for standard/below slash for Deluxe.

1951 Pontiac, Chieftain two-door coupe sedan, 6-cyl

CHIEFTAIN LINE — (SIX) SERIES 25 — (EIGHT) SERIES 27 — Chieftains had notch back A-body styling. Trim variations distinguishing standards and Deluxes or sixes and eights were the same as with Streamliners. Convertibles came as Deluxes only. Catalina Coupes came only as Deluxes or Super Deluxes, the latter forming a separate `Super' sub-series. Deluxe Catalinas (style 2537D) had interiors similar to other Deluxes, but the interior trim on Super Deluxe Catalinas (style 2537SD) came in a blue and ivory leather/cloth combination or optional all-leather (in the same colors). Super Deluxe Catalina can be distinguished externally by horizontally grooved trim plates on their rear roof pillars. The three-passenger business coupe was available only in standard trim.

Model Number	Body/Style Number	Body Type & Seating	Factory Price	Shipping Weight	Production Total
CHIEFTAIN/CHIEFTAIN DELUXE SIX					
6U	2569(D)	4-dr Sed-6P	1903/2006	73	NA
6U	2511(D)	2-dr Sed-6P	848/1951	43	NA
6U	2527(D)	2-dr Sed Cpe-6P	1848/1951	28	NA
6U	2527B	2-dr Bus Cpe-3P	1713	3193	NA
6U	2537D	2-dr Del Cat HT-6P	2182	3343	NA
6U	2567DTX	2-dr Del Conv-6P	2314	3488	NA
CHIEFTAIN SUPER DELUXE SIX					
6U	2537SD	2-dr Sup Del Cat HT-6P	2244	3353	NA

NOTE 1: See Historical Footnotes for series production total.
NOTE 2: Data above slash/below slash for Deluxe.

CHIEFTAIN EIGHTS

Model Number	Body/Style Number	Body Type & Seating	Factory Price	Shipping Weight	Production Total
CHIEFTAIN/CHIEFTAIN DELUXE EIGHT					
8U	2569(D)	4-dr Sed-6P	977/2081	3363/3373	NA
8U	2511(D)	2-dr Sed-6P	1922/2026	3328/3333	NA
8U	2527(D)	2-dr Sed Cpe-6p	1922/2026	3303/3318	NA
8U	2527B	2-dr Bus Cpe-3P	1787	3273	NA
8U	2537D	2-dr Del Cat HT-6P	2257	3428	NA
8U	2567DTX	2-dr Del Conv-6P	2388	3568	NA
CHIEFTAIN SUPER DELUXE EIGHT					
8U	2537SD	2-dr Sup Del Cat HT-6P	2320	3433	NA

NOTE 1: See Historical Footnotes for series production total.
NOTE 2: Data above slash for standard/below slash for Deluxe.

1951 Pontiac, Chieftain Deluxe four-door station wagon, 8-cyl

ENGINES

(SIX) Six-cylinder. L-head. Cast iron block. Displacement: 239.2 cid. Bore and stroke: 3-9/16 x 4 inches. Compression ratio: (standard) 6.5:1; (optional) 7.5:1. Brake hp: (standard) 96 at 3400 rpm; (optional) 100 at 3400 rpm. Four main bearings. Solid valve lifters. Carburetor: Rochester BC one-barrel.

(EIGHT) Eight cylinder. L-head. Cast iron block. Displacement: 268.4 cid. Bore and stroke: 3-3/8 x 3-3/4 inches. Compression ratio: (standard) 6.5:1; (optional) 7.5:1. Brake hp: (standard) 116 at 3600 rpm; (optional) 120 at 3600 rpm. Five main bearings. Solid valve lifters. Carburetor: (synchromesh) Carter WCD 719S or WCD 719SA; (Hydra-Matic) Carter WCD 720S or WCD 720SA.

CHASSIS FEATURES: Wheelbase: 120 inches all lines. Overall length: (all cars) 202-1/2 inches; (wagons) 203.8 inches. Front tread: 58 inches. Rear tread: 59 inches. Tires: (standard) 7.10 x 15 (special equipment) 7.60 x 15. Tube type.

OPTIONS: Seven-tube Chieftain radio. Mast antenna. No-Blo wind deflectors. Car cushions. Venti-Seat underseat heater. Venti-Shades. Windshield Sun Visor. Traffic light viewer. Polaroid visor. Rear fender panels (skirts). License frames. Illuminated hood ornament. Wheel trim rings. Steel wheel discs. White sidewall discs. Deluxe steering wheel. Remington Auto-Home shaver. Visor vanity mirror. Tissue dispenser. Direction signals. Compass. Rear window wiper. Windshield washers. Deluxe electric clock. Glove compartment light. Leather utility pocket. Luggage compartment light. Seat covers. Safti-Jack. Outside rearview mirror. Back-up lights. Safety spotlight. Fog lights. No-Rol. Bumper guards. Grill guard. Exhaust deflector. Venetian blinds. No-Mar gas filler trim. Fuel door lock. Scuff pads. Multi-purpose lamp. Underhood trouble lamp. Jack bag. Tool kit. A three-speed Synchromesh gearbox with column shift was standard on all models. Hydra-Matic four-speed automatic transmission was available at $159 extra. Rear axle ratios: (standard) 4.1:1, (economy) 3.9:1, (mountain) 4.3:1, (Hydra-Matic) 3.63:1.

HISTORICAL FOOTNOTES: Production start-up took place Nov. 27, 1950. The 1951 models were introduced Dec. 11, 1950 and commemorated the company's 25th anniversary year. Arnold Lenz became the general manager of Pontiac Motor Div., but his tenure would be cut short by a tragic accident in 1952. Pontiac made 343,795 cars during the calendar year. Model year production came to 343,795 units. This included a total of 53,748 Streamliner and Chieftain sixes (10,195 with Hydra-Matic and 43,553 with synchromesh) and a total of 316,411 Streamliner and Chieftain eights (251,987 with Hydra-Matic and 64,424 with synchromesh). On an industrywide basis, for the calendar year, Pontiac built 6.7 percent of America's convertibles; 9.6 percent of domestic hardtops; and 4.7 percent of domestic station wagons. The company also produced the amphibious Otter, a continuous-track military vehicle used in the Korean War. Body Styles 2507 and 2507D. Streamliner sedan coupes, were discontinued in April, 1951.

1952 PONTIAC

CHIEFTAIN LINE — (SIX) SERIES 25 — (EIGHT) SERIES 27 — The fastback Streamliner line was discontinued and station wagons joined the A-body notch back styles in the Chieftain line. Grilles were similar to 1951, but all models had four black, oblong indentations in the upper grille blade, under a new Pontiac nameplate. Dual `sweepspear' body moldings, stainless steel gravel guards and chrome wheel and headlight rings characterized Deluxes. Standards were upholstered in dark grey check pattern cloth doors and solid grey wool cloth seats. Deluxes were trimmed in rich wool diamond-pattern cloth with a button-deuk look. Convertibles and Deluxe Catalinas had leather and cloth trims. Super Deluxe Catalinas had two-tone green top grain cowhide seats with leather-and-cloth optional. The Super Deluxe Catalina hardtop coupe also carried special horizontally grooved trim plates on the rear roof pillar for outward identification. Standard station wagons featured seats in rust imitation leather. Deluxe station wagons offered a choice of grey Bedford cord cloth with genuine leather in tan, red, green, blue or black.

PONTIAC I.D. NUMBERS: VIN located on tag on left front door post. Matching engine serial number located on raised pad on front left side of cylinder block. Serial numbers took the form ( )-[ ]W{ }-1001 to ( )-[ ]W{ }-ending number. First symbol ( ) indicated the assembly plant: P=Pontiac, Mich.; C=California (Southgate); L=Linden, N.J.; W=Wilmington, Del.; K=Kansas City, Kan.; A=Atlanta, Ga.; F=Framingham, Mass. Second symbol [ ] indicated engine type: 6=inline six-cylinder; 8=inline eight-cylinder. Third symbol indicated model year: W=1952. Fourth symbol { } is a letter indicating type of transmission: S=synchromesh; H=Hydra-Matic. Remaining symbols are the sequential unit production number for each car-line at each assembly plant. Beginning number at each plant is 1001. Ending numbers for 1951 were: [SERIES 25 SIX with synchromesh] (Mich.) 10041; (Calif.) 1723; (N.J.) 1986; (Dela.) 1967; (Kan.) 2745; (Ga.) 1669 and (Mass.) 1551. [SERIES 25 SIX with/Hydra-Matic] (Mich.) 3457; (Calif.) 1883; (N.J.) 1210; (Dela.) 1223; (Kan.) 1406; (Ga.) 1165; (Mass.) 1103. [SERIES 27 EIGHT with synchromesh] (Mich.) 16833; (Calif.) 3440; (N.J.) 3920; (Dela.) 3736; (Kan.) 6109; (Ga.) 3444 and (Mass.) 2312. [SERIES 27 EIGHT with Hydra-Matic] (Mich.) 89530; (Calif.) 20083; (N.J.) 23732; (Dela.) 22776; (Kan.) 39194; (Ga.) 18358 and (Mass.) 10897. Fisher Body/Style Number on plate under hood on left of firewall can be very helpful for identification of model and ordering parts. A prefix to the main number indicates model year, 52=1952. The first two symbols in the main number indicate series 25 or 27. The next two symbols indicate

the body style. Some numbers have an alphabetical suffix indicating trim level, such as D=Deluxe and SD=Super Deluxe. These numbers appear in Body/Style Number column of charts below adjacent to corresponding body style listings.

CHIEFTAIN/CHIEFTAIN DELUXE SIX

Model Number	Body/Style Number	Body Type & Seating	Factory Price	Shipping Weight	Production Total
6W	2569(D)	4-dr Sed-6P	2014/2119	3278/3278	NA
6W	2511(D)	2-dr Sed-6P	1956/2060	3253/3253	NA
6W	2563(D)	4-dr Sta Wag-8/6P	2615/2699	3593/3528	NA
6W	2537D	2-dr Del Cat HT-6P	2304	3358	NA
6W	2567DTX	2-dr Del Conv-6P	2444	3478	NA

CHIEFTAIN SUPER DELUXE SIX

Model Number	Body/Style Number	Body Type & Seating	Factory Price	Shipping Weight	Production Total
6W	2537SD	2-dr Sup Del Cat HT-6P	2370	3368	NA

NOTE 1: See Historical Footnotes for series production total.
NOTE 2: Data above slash for standard/below slash for Deluxe.

1952 Pontiac, Chieftain Deluxe four-door station wagon, 8-cyl

CHIEFTAIN EIGHT

Model Number	Body/Style Number	Body Type & Seating	Factory Price	Shipping Weight	Production Total
8W	2569(D)	4-dr Sed-6P	2090/2194	3378/3378	NA
8W	2511(D)	2-dr Sed-6P	2031/2136	3333/3333	NA
8W	2562(D)	4-dr Sta Wag-8/6P	2689/2772	2688/3633	NA
8W	2537D	2-dr Del Cat HT-6P	2380	3443	NA
8W	2567DTX	2-dr Del Conv-6P	2518	3558	NA

CHIEFTAIN SUPER EIGHT

Model Number	Body/Style Number	Body Type & Seating	Factory Price	Shipping Weight	Production Total
8W	2537SD	2-dr Sup Del Cat HT-6P	2446	3448	NA

NOTE 1: See Historical Footnotes for series production total.
NOTE 2: Data above slash for standard/below slash for Deluxe.
NOTE 3: When (D) appears came in both standard and Deluxe.

ENGINES

(SIX) Six-cylinder. L-head. Cast iron block. Displacement: 239.2 cid. Bore and stroke: 3-9/16 x 4 inches. Compression ratio: (synchromesh) 6.8:1; (Hydra-Matic) 7.7:1. Brake hp: (synchromesh) 100 at 3400 rpm; (Hydra-Matic) 102 at 3400 rpm. Four main bearings. Solid valve lifters. Carburetor: Rochester BC one-barrel.

(EIGHT) Eight-cylinder. L-head. Cast iron block. Displacement: 268.4 cid. Bore and stroke: 3-3/8 x 3-3 4 inches. Compression ratios: (synchromesh) 6.8:1; (Hydra-Matic) 7.7:1. Brake hp: (synchromesh) 118 at 3600 rpm; (Hydra-Matic) 122 at 3600 rpm. Five main bearings. Solid valve lifters. Carburetor: Carter WCD 720S or WCD 720SA two-barrel.

CHASSIS FEATURES: Wheelbase: 120 inches. Overall length: (cars) 202.5 inches (station wagons) 203.9 inches. Front tread: 58 inches. Rear tread: 59 inches. Tires: (standard) 7.10 x 15 (special equipment) 7.60 x 15. Tube type.

OPTIONS: Seven-tube Chieftain radio. Mast antenna. No-Blo wind deflectors. Car cushions. Venti-Seat underseat heater. Venti-Shades. Windshield Sun Visor. Traffic light viewer. Polaroid visor. Rear fender panels (skirts). License frames. Illuminated hood ornament. Wheel trim rings. Steel wheel discs. White sidewall discs. Deluxe steering wheel. Remington Auto-Home shaver. Visor vanity mirror. Tissue dispenser. Direction signals. Compass. Rear window wiper. Windshield washers. Deluxe electric clock. Glove compartment light. Leather utility pocket. Luggage compartment light. Seat covers. Safti-Jack. Outside rearview mirror. Back-up lights. Safety spotlight. Fog lights. No-Rol. Bumper guards. Grill guard. Exhaust deflector. Venetian blinds. No-Mar gas filler trim. Fuel door lock. Scuff pads. Multi-purpose lamp. Underhood trouble lamp. Jack bag. Tool kit. A three-speed Synchromesh gearbox with column shift was standard on all models. Hydra-Matic four-speed automatic transmission was available at $159 extra. Rear axle ratios: (standard) 4.1:1, (economy) 3.9:1, (mountain) 4.3:1, (Hydra-Matic) 3.08:1.

HISTORICAL FOOTNOTES: Introduced Dec. 3, 1951. Production was 277,156 cars for the calendar year, giving Pontiac fifth rank in the American auto industry. Model year production included a total of 19,809 Series 25 Chieftain sixes (15,582 with Hydra-Matic and 4,227 with synchromesh) and a total of 251,564 Series 27 Chieftain eights (218,602 with Hydra-Matic and 32,962 with synchromesh). Combined model year assemblies were 271,373. Arnold Lenz was killed in a car-train crash at a Lapeer, Mich. railroad crossing. MOTOR TREND road tested the 1952 Pontiac Chieftain Deluxe sedan recording a 21 second quarter-mile run and top speed of 95.24 mph. Fuel economy was 16.4 mpg in overall driving.

1953 PONTIAC

CHIEFTAIN LINE — (SIX) SERIES 25 — (EIGHT) SERIES 27 — The 1953 Pontiacs were new from bumper-to-bumper. Changes included one-piece windshields; wraparound rear windows; new hood ornaments; ignition key starting; stepped-up rear fenders; more massive

chrome headlight doors on all models; new grille styling that encircled parking lamps; and `panorama view' instrument panels. Standard models were now called Specials and came with small hubcaps, rubber gravel guards, straight upper beltline trim and short arrow-shaped side trim. Deluxe Chieftains had long `dual streak' body moldings, stainless steel gravel guards with rear fender extensions, dipping belt moldings and chrome full wheel discs. Eights had an '8' emblem between twin `Silver Streaks' on deck lids. Cars finished in Caravan blue, Spruce green, Marathon grey and black had red Pontiac nameplates in front, while those in other colors had black nameplates. The Custom Catalina Coupe, was outwardly distinguished by horizontally grooved decorative trim plates at the rear roof pillar edge. This car was available only in Laurel green, Milano ivory or two-tone combinations of these hues. A nylon and leather interior of harmonizing tones was featured and an all-leather option was available and frequently ordered.

PONTIAC I.D. NUMBERS: VIN located on tag on left front door post. Matching engine serial number located on raised pad on front left side of cylinder block. Serial numbers took the form ( )-[ ]X{ }-1001 to ( )-[ ]X{ }-ending number. First symbol ( ) indicated the assembly plant: P=Pontiac, Mich.; C=California (Southgate); L=Linden, N.J.; W=Wilmington, Del.; K=Kansas City, Kan.; A=Atlanta, Ga.; F=Framingham, Mass. Second symbol [ ] indicated engine type: 6=inline six-cylinder; 8=inline eight-cylinder. Third symbol indicated model year: X=1953. Fourth symbol { } is a letter indicating type of transmission: S=synchromesh; H=Hydra-Matic; P=Powerglide. Remaining symbols are the sequential unit production number for each car-line at each assembly plant. Beginning number at each plant is 1001. Ending numbers for 1953 were: [SERIES 25 SIX with synchromesh] (Mich.) 18925; (Calif.) 3115; (N.J.) 3799; (Dela.) 3496; (Kan.) 4543; (Ga.) 2888 and (Mass.) 2691. [SERIES 25 SIX with Hydra-Matic] (Mich.) 3872; (Calif.) 1227; (N.J.) 1163; (Dela.) 1180; (Kan.) 1305; (Ga.) 1138; (Mass.) 1058. [SERIES 25 SIX with Powerglide] (Mich.) 1384. [SERIES 27 EIGHT with synchromesh] (Mich.) 35914; (Calif.) 4469; (N.J.) 8264; (Dela.) 6368; (Kan.) 9013; (Ga.) 6391 and (Mass.) 5041. [SERIES 27 EIGHT with Hydra-Matic] (Mich.) 117860; (Calif.) 28700; (N.J.) 30873; (Dela.) 28720; (Kan.) 48580; (Ga.) 25799 and (Mass.) 19391. [SERIES 27 EIGHT with Power-glide] (Mich.) 9950. Fisher Body/Style Number on plate under hood on left of firewall can be very helpful for identification of model and ordering parts. A prefix to the main number indicates model year, 53=1953. The first two symbols in the main number indicate series 25 or 27. The next two symbols indicate the body style. Some numbers have an alphabetical suffix indicating trim level, such as D=Deluxe and SD=Super Deluxe. These numbers appear in Body/Style Number column of charts below adjacent to corresponding body style listings.

CHIEFTAIN SIX

CHIEFTAIN SPECIAL/CHIEFTAIN DELUXE SIX

Model Number	Body/Style Number	Body Type & Seating	Factory Price	Shipping Weight	Production Total*
6X	2569W(D)	4-dr Sed-6P	2015/2119	3391/3396	NA
6X	2511W(D)	2-dr Sed-6P	1956/2060	3341/3356	NA
6X	2537D	2-dr Del Cat HT-6P	2304	3416	NA
6X	2567DTX	2-dr Del Conv-6P	2444	3546	NA
6X	2563DF	4-dr Del Sta Wag-6P	2590	3636	NA
6X	2562(F)	4-dr Spl Sta Wag-8/6P	2450/2505	3633/3606	NA

CHIEFTAIN CUSTOM SIX

Model Number	Body/Style Number	Body Type & Seating	Factory Price	Shipping Weight	Production Total*
6X	2537SD	2-dr Cus Cat HT-6P	2370	3416	NA

NOTE 1: See Historical Footnotes for series production total.
NOTE 2: Data above slash for standard/below slash for Deluxe.

CHIEFTAIN EIGHT

CHIEFTAIN SPECIAL/CHIEFTAIN DELUXE EIGHT

Model Number	Body/Style Number	Body Type & Seating	Factory Price	Shipping Weight	Production Total
8X	2569W(D)	4-dr Sed-6P	2090/2194	3456/3471	NA
8X	2511W(D)	2-dr Sed-6P	2031/2136	3421/3436	NA
8X	2537D	2-dr Del Cat HT-6P	2380	3496	NA
8X	2567DTX	2-dr Del Conv-6P	2515	3626	NA
8X	2562DF	4-Del Sta Wag-6P	2664	3716	NA
8X	2562(F)	4-dr Spl Sta Wag-8/6P	2525/2580	3713/3686	NA

CHIEFTAIN CUSTOM EIGHT

Model Number	Body/Style Number	Body Type & Seating	Factory Price	Shipping Weight	Production Total
8X	2537SD	2-dr Cus Cat HT-6P	2446	3496	NA

NOTE 1: See Historical Footnotes for series production total.
NOTE 2: Data above slash for standard/below slash for Deluxe.
NOTE 3: (D) indicates available in both Special and Deluxe sub-series.

1953 Pontiac, Chieftain Deluxe four-door sedan, 8-cyl

ENGINES

(SIX) Six-cylinder. L-head. Cast iron block. Displacement: 239.2 cid. Bore and stroke: 3-9/16 x 4 inches. Compression ratio: (synchromesh) 7.0:1; (Hydra-Matic) 7.7:1. Brake hp: (synchromesh) 115 at 3800 rpm; (Hydra-Matic) 118 at 3800 rpm. Four main bearings. Solid valve lifters. Carburetor: Carter WCD-2010-S two-barrel.

(EIGHT) Eight-cylinder. L-head. Cast iron block. Displacement: 268.4 cid. Bore and stroke: 3-3/8 x 3-3/4 inches. Compression ratios: (synchromesh) 6.8:1; (Hydra-Matic) 7.7:1. Brake hp: (synchromesh) 118 at 3600 rpm; (Hydra-Matic) 122 at 3600 rpm. Five main bearings. Solid valve lifters. Carburetors: (synchromesh) Carter WCD 719S or 719SA; (Hydra-Matic) Carter WCD 720S or 720SA two-barrel.

CHASSIS FEATURES: Wheelbase: 122 inches. Overall length: (passenger cars) 202-11/16 inches; (station wagons) 205.3 inches. Front tread: 58.5 inches. Rear tread: 59.05 inches. Tires: (passenger cars) 7.10 x 15 4-ply; (regular equipment station wagons and sedan deliveries/optional passenger cars) 7.10 x 15 6-ply; (optional passenger cars only) 7.60 x 15 4-ply. Pontiac promoted new `Tru-Arc' safety steering and `Curve Control' front suspension in 1953.

OPTIONS: Power steering ($134). Woodgrain Di-Noc exterior trim ($80 all station wagons). Venti-heat underseat heater and defroster. Chieftain 7-tube radio. Directional signals. Autronic Eye. Back-up lamps. Non-glare rearview mirror. Rear fender panels (skirts came with steel underscore on Deluxes). Exhaust deflector. No-Mar fuel guard door trim. Deluxe steering wheel (standard on Deluxes). Illuminated hood ornament. Windshield sun visor. Traffic light viewer. Latex foam seat cushions. Windshield washers. Outside rearview mirror. Visor vanity mirror. Glovebox lamp. Trunk lamp. Underhood lamp. Lighted ash tray. Hand brake signal. Grille guard. Wing guards. E-Z-Eye glass. Dual fog lamps. Rear seat speaker. Electric antenna. Safety spot lamp. Chrome trim rings. Safti-jack. Oil bath air cleaner. (Dealer installed options): Seat covers. Hand spot lamp. Venti-shades. Fold-away umbrella. Draft deflectors; Rear window wiper. Tissue dispenser. Magna Tray. Fuel door lock. Illuminated compass. Color tipon. Road reflector flares. Thermaster bottle. Thermaster refrigerator. Auto-Home Remington electric shaver. Continental tire extension. Simulated wire wheel discs. A three-speed synchromesh gearbox with column-mounted gearshift was standard on all models. Dual-Range four-speed Hydra-Matic drive was available at $178 extra. Two-speed Power-glide automatic transmission (by Chevrolet) was installed in Pontiacs built at Pontiac, Mich. from Sept. 8, 1953 to Nov. 19, 1953 after an Aug. 12 fire at GM's Livonia, Mich. Hydra-Matic factory. Rear axle ratios: (six) 4.1:1; (Eight) 3.9:1; (six/mountain) 4.3:1, (eight/mountain) 4.1:1; (Hydra-Matic) 3.08:1'. The high-compression Hydra-Matic cylinder head was available, as an option, on cars with synchromesh.

HISTORICAL FOOTNOTES: A total of 38,914 Chieftain sixes were built. Of these, 33,705 had synchromesh; 4,507 had Hydra-Matic and 702 had Powerglide attachments. A total of 379,705 Chieftain eights were built. Of these, 68,565 had synchromesh; 293,343 had Hydra-Matic and 17,797 had Powerglide attachments. Production lines started cranking out 1953 Pontiacs on Nov. 17 of the previous year and they were introduced to the public Dec. 6, 1952. Model year output came to 418,619 units. The calendar year counted production of 414,011 cars. This maintained Pontiac's rank as the fifth largest American automaker another season. After the devastating Aug. 12 at the Hydra-Matic transmission plant in Livonia, Mich., cars were made for a time, at the Pontiac, Mich. factory, with Chevrolet Powerglide transmissions installed. Following the untimely passing of Arnold Lenz, Robert Critchfield became general manager of Pontiac Motor Div. Plans to install V-8s in 1953 Pontiacs were set back by Lenz's fatal accident and flathead straight eights continued to be used. However, the 1953 Pontiac chassis is designed to accommodate the 1955-style V-8. Body Style suffix 'SD' indicates 'Super Deluxe' trim. The term 'Catalina' was Pontiac's nomenclature for pillarless hardtop styling. Body Style 2562, the Special station wagon, came standard with three seats. Body style 2562F was the Special station wagon with two seats, the second of the folding type. Body style 2537SD, T Body Style numbers were embossed on the firewall data plate and preceeded by the prefix '53' to designate the model year.

1954 PONTIAC

1954 Pontiac, Chieftain Deluxe four-door sedan, 8-cyl

CHIEFTAIN LINE — (SIX) SERIES 25 (EIGHT) SERIES 27 — In 1954 the Chieftains represented Pontiac's least costly line of A-body models on a 122 inch wheelbase and had styling changes common to all Pontiacs. Included were a grille with an oval centerpiece; new hood ornament and nameplate; and thinner `Silver Streaks.' Chieftain Specials had straight upper beltline moldings; small stainless steel gravel guards; four `Silver Streaks' on the deck lid; and short front fender spears. Chieftain Deluxes had broad, full-length `sweepspears' that blended into the gravel guards; the gravel guards had rear fender, extensions and the upper beltline trim "dipped" down. There were also four deck lid streaks. The Chieftain Custom series included the `Super Deluxe' Catalina Coupe, which was outwardly distinguished by decorative edge plates on the roof pillars. Custom Catalina hardtops also have special plated interior roof bows. Interior trims ranged from two-tone pattern cloth-and-elascofab combinations on standard models to all-leather options on Catalinas, convertibles and Deluxe station wagons. A new B-O-P assembly plant in Arlington, Tex. began operations this year.

PONTIAC I.D. NUMBERS: VIN located on tag on left front door post. Matching engine serial number located on raised pad on front left side of cylinder block. Serial numbers took the form ( )-[ ]X( )-1001 to ( )-[ ]X( )-ending number. First symbol ( ) indicated the assembly plant: P=Pontiac, Mich.; C=California (Southgate); L=Linden, N.J.; W=Wilmington, Del.; K=Kansas City, Kan.; A=Atlanta, Ga.; F=Framingham, Mass.; T=Arlington, Texas. Second symbol [ ] indicated engine type: 6=inline six-cylinder; 8=inline eight-cylinder. Third symbol indicated model year: Z=1954. Fourth symbol { } is a letter indicating type of transmission: S=synchromesh; H=Hydra-Matic or (Star Chief only) C=conventional (synchromesh); A=automatic (Hydra-Matic). Remaining symbols are the sequential unit production number for each car-line at each assembly plant. Beginning number at each plant is 1001. Ending numbers for 1954 were: [SERIES 25 SIX with synchromesh] (Mich.) 12141; (Calif.) 1799; (N.J.) 2429; (Dela.) 2233; (Kan.) 2622; (Ga.) 1866 and (Mass.) 2033; (Texas) 1399. [SERIES 25 SIX with/Hydra-Matic] (Mich.) 2858; (Calif.) 1076; (N.J.) 1090; (Dela.) 1096; (Kan.) 1117;

(Ga.) 1067; (Mass.) 1053.; (Texas) 1023. [SERIES 27 EIGHT with synchromesh] (Mich.) 16612; (Calif.) 2351; (N.J.) 3471; (Dela.) 3032; (Kan.) 3890; (Ga.) 3265; (Mass.) 3146; (Texas) 2043. [SERIES 27 EIGHT with Hydra-Matic] (Mich.) 60891; (Calif.) 8698; (N.J.) 16002; (Dela.) 10002; (Kan.) 12490; (Ga.) 7477; (Mass.) 7854; (Texas) 4330. [SERIES 28 with synchromesh] (Mich.) 1371; (Calif.) 1015; (N.J.) 1046; (Dela.) 1049; (Kan.) 1036; (Ga.) 1010; (Mass.) 1035; (Texas) 1008. [SERIES 28 with Hydra-Matic] (Mich.) 60543; (Calif.) 8165; (N.J.) 13680; (Dela.) 8629; (Kan.) 12117; (Ga.) 8076; (Mass.) 6382; (Texas) 4925. Fisher Body/Style Number on plate under hood on left of firewall can be very helpful for identification of model and ordering parts. A prefix to the main number indicates model year, 54=1954. The first two symbols in the main number indicate series 25, 27 or 28 Star Chief. The next two symbols indicate the body style. Some numbers have an alphabetical suffix indicating trim level, such as D=Deluxe and SD=Super Deluxe. These numbers appear in Body/Style Number column of charts below adjacent to corresponding body style listings.

CHIEFTAIN SIX

Model Number	Body/Style Number	Body Type & Seating	Factory Price	Shipping Weight	Production Total
CHIEFTAIN SIX SPECIAL/DELUXE					
6Z	2569W(D)	4-dr Sed-6P	2027/2131	3391/3406	NA
6Z	2511W(D)	2-dr Sed-6P	1968/2072	3331/3351	NA
6Z	2537D	2-dr Del Cat HT-6P	2316	3421	NA
6Z	2562DF	4-dr Del Sta Wag-6P	2504	3646	NA
6Z	2562(F)	4-dr Spl Sta Wag-8/6P	2364/2419	3691/3601	NA
CHIEFTAIN CUSTOM SIX					
6Z	2537SD	2-dr Cus Cat HT-6P	2582	3421	NA

NOTE 1: See Historical Footnotes for series production total.
NOTE 2: Data above slash for standard/below slash for Deluxe.

CHIEFTAIN EIGHT

Model Number	Body/Style Number	Body Type & Seating	Factory Price	Shipping Weight	Production Total
CHIEFTAIN EIGHT SPECIAL/DELUXE					
8Z	2569W(D)	4-dr Sed-6P	2102/2206	3451/3466	NA
8Z	2511W(D)	2-dr Sed-6P	2043/2148	3396/3416	NA
8Z	2537D	2-dr Del Cat HT-6P	2392	3491	NA
8Z	2562DF	4-dr Del Sta Wag-6P	2579	3716	NA
8Z	2562(F)	4-dr Spl Sta Wag-8/6P	2439/2494	3771/3676	NA
CHIEFTAIN CUSTOM EIGHT					
8Z	2537SD	2-dr Cus Cat HT-6P	2458	3491	NA

NOTE 1: See Historical Footnotes for series production total.
NOTE 2: Data above slash for standard/below slash for Deluxe.
NOTE 3: (D) indicates model is available in Special and Deluxe sub-series.
NOTE 4: (F) indicates folding second seat in station wagons.

1954 Pontiac, Custom Star Chief four-door sedan, 8-cyl

STAR CHIEF LINE — (EIGHT) SERIES 28 — A brand new long wheelbase Star Chief line was created by adding an 11-inch frame extension towards the rear of the GM A-body platform and fitting longer rear sheet metal. Two `28' sub-series, Deluxe and Custom, were provided. Both came only with eight-cylinder power. All Star Chiefs had five `Silver Streaks' on the deck lid, special visored taillight doors with rear fender extensions, longer `sweepspears' and three small stylized stars on rear fender fins. Deluxe trims were regular equipment, but the `Super Deluxe' Custom Sedan and Custom Catalina were further distinguished by extra-rich cloth-and-leather upholstery inside and distinctive trim outside. The Star Chief Custom Catalina hardtops also have special plated interior roof bows.

Model Number	Body/Style Number	Body Type & Seating	Factory Price	Shipping Weight	Production Total
STAR CHIEF DELUXE					
8Z	2869WD	4-dr Sed-6P	2301	3536	NA
8Z	2867DTX	2-dr Conv-6P	2630	3776	NA
STAR CHIEF CUSTOM					
8Z	2869WSD	4-dr Sed-6P	2394	3526	NA
8Z	2837SD	2-dr Cus Cat HT-6P	2557	3551	NA

ENGINES

(SIX) Six-cylinder. L-head. Cast iron block. Displacement: 239.2 cid. Bore and stroke: 3-9/16 x 4 inches. Compression ratio: (synchromesh) 7.0:1; (Hydra-Matic) 7.7:1. Brake hp: (synchromesh) 115 at 3800 rpm; (Hydra-Matic) 118 at 3800 rpm. Four main bearings. Solid valve lifters. Carburetor: Carter WCD-2010-S two-barrel.

(EIGHT) Eight-cylinder. L-head. Cast iron block. Displacement: 268.4 cid. Bore and stroke: 3-3/8 x 3-3/4 inches. Compression ratios: (synchromesh) 6.8:1; (Hydra-Matic) 7.7:1. Brake hp: (synchromesh) 122 at 3800 rpm; (Hydra-Matic) 127 at 3800 rpm. Five main bearings. Solid valve lifters. Carburetors: (synchromesh) Carter WCD 719SA used in early production; WCD 720SA used on most; (Hydra-Matic) Carter WCD 2122S.

CHASSIS FEATURES: Wheelbase: (Chieftains) 122 inches. (Star Chiefs) 124 inches. Overall length: (Chieftain passenger cars) 202-11/16 inches; (Chieftain station wagons) 205.3 inches. (Star Chiefs) 213.7 inches. Front tread: (All) 58.5 inches. Rear Tread: (All) 59.05 inches. Tires: (passenger cars) 7.10 x 15 4-ply; (station wagons) 7. 10 x 15 6-ply; (optional passenger cars only) 7.60 x 15 4-ply.

OPTIONS: Power steering ($134). Woodgrain Di-Noc exterior trim ($80 all station wagons). Venti-heat underseat heater and defroster. Chieftain 7-tube radio. Directional signals. Autronic Eye. Back-up lamps. Non-glare rearview mirror. Rear fender panels (skirts came with steel underscore on Deluxes). Exhaust deflector. No-Mar fuel guard door trim. Deluxe steering wheel (standard on Deluxes). Illuminated hood ornament. Windshield sun visor. Traffic light viewer. Latex foam seat cushions. Windshield washers. Outside rearview mirror. Visor vanity mirror. Glovebox lamp. Trunk lamp. Underhood lamp. Lighted ash tray. Hand brake signal. Grille guard. Wing guards. E-Z-Eye glass. Dual fog lamps. Rear seat speaker. Electric antenna. Safety spot lamp. Chrome trim rings. Safti-jack. Oil bath air cleaner. (Dealer installed options): Seat covers. Hand spot lamp. Venti-shades. Fold-away umbrella. Draft deflectors; Rear window wiper. Tissue dispenser. Magna Tray. Fuel door lock. Illuminated compass. Color tipon. Road reflector flares. Thermaster refrigerator. Thermaster bottle. Auto-Home Remington electric shaver. Continental tire extension. Simulated wire wheel discs. Power brakes ($36). Air-conditioning. Electric window lifts. Padded dashboard. Door edge guards. Door handle guards. Arctic windshield wipers. Dash panel courtesy lamps. Wide brake pedals. Reduced ratio power steering. Grille bug screen. Comfort-Control 300-position manual seat. Remote control outside mirrors. Deluxe steering wheel for Special station wagons. A three-speed synchromesh gearbox with column-mounted gearshift was standard on all models. Dual-Range four-speed Hydra-Matic drive was available at $178 extra. Rear axle ratios: (six) 4.1:1; (eight) 3.9:1; (Star Chief with Hydra-Matic) 3.23:1 (six/mountain) 4.3:1, (eight/mountain) 4.1:1; (Hydra-Matic) 3.08:1. The high-compression Hydra-Matic cylinder head was available, as an option, on cars with synchromesh.

HISTORICAL FOOTNOTES: Production began Dec. 1, 1953. The 1954 models were introduced Dec. 18, 1953. Calendar year production was 370,887. Model year production was 287,744. The only model year production breakouts available are: [CHIEFTAIN] A total of 22,670 Chieftain sixes were built. Of these 19,666 had synchromesh and 3,004 had Hydra-Matic attachments. A total of 149,986 Chieftain eights were built. Of these, 29,906 had synchromesh and 120,080, had Hydra-Matic attachments. [STAR CHIEF] A total of 115,088 Star Chiefs were built. Of these, 571 had synchromesh and 114,517 had Hydra-Matic attachments. The new Buick-Olds-Pontiac (BOP) assembly plant in Arlington, Texas opened on June 3, 1953. A Catalina hardtop built on June 18, 1954 was the company's 5 millionth automobile produced. The sedan delivery was not cataloged this year although rumors persist that four were built in early production.

1955 PONTIAC

1955 Pontiac, Chieftain '860' Colony two-door station wagon, V-8

CHIEFTAIN LINE — (V-8) — SERIES 27 — Completely new bodies and chassis were featured on all 1955 Pontiacs. Changes from 1954 included a massive, divided bumper grille; revised body moldings; split `Silver Streak' bands; twin streaks atop rear fenders; swept style front wheel cutouts; and wraparound windshields. Chieftains were divided into three sub-series. One was a unique station wagon. This Custom Safari had two-door hardtop styling and Star Chief trim and appointments on the smaller Series 27 chassis. The two-door Custom Safari was announced Jan. 31, 1955. It is one of a few Pontiacs recognized as Milestone Cars. These Safaris feature two-door hardtop styling with slanting tailgates, width-wise grooved roofs, Pontiac rear fenders and luxury interior appointments. Except for this offering, which was really considered a Star Chief, Chieftains featured constant width slanting vertical slash moldings. Chieftain 860s had small hubcaps; painted taillight housings; and no upper beltline moldings. Chieftain 870s had full wheel discs; chrome taillight rings; and upper beltline trim.

PONTIAC I.D. NUMBERS: VIN located on left front door hinge pillar. Matching engine serial number on pad on front of right-hand cylinder bank. Serial numbers took the form ( )-[ ]55{ }-1001 to ( )-[ ]55{ }-ending number. The first symbol ( ) was a letter indicating assembly plant: P=Pontiac, Mich.; T=Arlington, Texas; A=Atlanta, Ga.; F=Framingham, Mass; K=Kansas City, Kan.; L=Linden, N.J.; C=South Gate, Calif.; W=Wilmington, Dela. The second symbol [ ] indicated series: 7=Series 27; 8=Series 28. The third and fourth symbols indicated model year: 55=1955. The fifth symbol indicated transmission: S=synchromesh; H=Hydra-Matic. The following symbols were the sequential unit production number starting at 1001 for each series at each assembly plant. Ending numbers for 1955 were: [SERIES 27 with synchromesh] (Mich.) 26879; (Texas) 3331; (Ga.) 6802; (Mass.) 4714; (Kan.) 5868; (N.J.) 6536; (Calif.) 4572; (Dela.) 5564. [SERIES 27 with Hydra-Matic] (Mich.) 126714; (Texas) 14339; (Ga.) 26027; (Mass.) 15847; (Kan.) 30873; (N.J.) 33154; (Calif.) 31707; (Dela.) 24851. [SERIES 28 with synchromesh] (Mich.) 1696; (Texas) 1026; (Ga.) 1018; (Mass.) 1085; (Kan.) 1061; (N.J.) 1134; (Calif.) 1061; (Dela.) 1075. [SERIES 28 with Hydra-Matic] (Mich.) 85247; (Texas) 10511; (Ga.) 17315; (Mass.) 10484; (Kan.) 20584; (N.J.) 24173; (Calif.) 20372; (Dela.) 17278. Fisher Body/Style Number on plate under hood on left of firewall can be very helpful for identification of model and ordering parts. A prefix to the main number indicates model year, 55=1955. The first two symbols in the main number indicate series 27 or 28 Star Chief. The next two symbols indicate the body style. Some numbers have an alphabetical suffix indicating trim level, such as D=Deluxe and SD=Super Deluxe. These numbers appear in Body/Style Number column of charts below adjacent to corresponding body style listings.

CHIEFTAIN 860 (SPECIAL)

Model Number	Body/Style Number	Body Type & Seating	Factory Price	Shipping Weight	Production Total
860-27	2519	4-dr Sed-6P	2164	3621	65,155
860-27	2511	2-dr Sed-6P	2105	3586	58,654
860-27	2562	4-dr Sed-6P	2518	3736	6,091
860-27	2563F	2-dr Sta Wag-6P	2434	3736	8,618
CHIEFTAIN 870 (Deluxe)					
870-27	2519D	4-dr Sed-6P	2268	3621	91,187
870-27	2511D	2-dr Sed-6P	2209	3586	28,950
870-27	2537D	2-dr Del Cat HT-6P	2335	3631	72,608
870-27	2563DF	4-dr Wagon-6P	2603	3786	19,439
STAR CHIEF CUSTOM (SERIES 27)					
27	2764DF	2-dr Safari-6P	2962	3746	3,760

NOTE 1: 354,466 Chieftain 860s and 870s were built.
NOTE 2: 57,730 had synchromesh and 296,736 had Hydra-Matic.
NOTE 3: The two-door Star Chief Custom Safari is included in these totals.
NOTE 4: Two Series 27 chassis were converted into hearses or ambulances.

1955 Pontiac Star Chief two-door convertible V-8

STAR CHIEF LINE — (V-8) — SERIES 28 — Completely new A-body styling with an 11-inch rear frame extension characterized the 1955 Star Chiefs. All models featured tapered slanting vertical slash moldings, which were also used on the Series 27 two-door Star Chief Custom Safari. Star Chiefs, including the Safari, also had three stylized star emblems on front fenders and doors. The Catalina coupe and the convertible had wide fluted lower rear fender extensions. The Custom four-door sedan had stainless steel moldings encircling the side windows. Full wheel discs were regular equipment on all Star Chiefs.

STAR CHIEF (SERIES 28)

Model Number	Body/Style Number	Body Type & Seating	Factory Price	Shipping Weight	Production Total
28	2819D	4-dr Sed-6P	2362	3666	44,800
28	2867DTX	2-dr Conv-6P	2691	3901	19,762
STAR CHIEF CUSTOM (SERIES 28)					
28	2819SD	4-dr Sed-6P	2455	3666	35,153
28	2837SD	2-dr Cat HT-6P	2499	3676	99,929

NOTE 1: 199,624 Series 28 Star Chiefs were built.
NOTE 2: 1,156 had synchromesh and 198,468 had Hydra-Matic.
NOTE 3: This does not include two-door Star Chief Custom Safari production.
NOTE 4: 280 Series 28 chassis were converted into hearses or ambulances.

BASE ENGINE: V-8: Overhead valves. Cast Iron block. Displacement: 287.2 cid. Bore and stroke: 3-3 /4 x 3-1 /4 Inches. Compression ratio: (synchromesh) 7.4:1; (Hydra-Matic) 8.0:1. Brake hp: (synchromesh) 173 at 4400 rpm; (Hydra-Matic) 180 at 4600 rpm. Five main bearings. Hydraulic valve lifters. Carburetors: Carter WGD models 2182S, 2182SA, 2182SB, 2207S or 2207SB two-barrel. Also, Rochester 2GC two-barrel.

CHASSIS FEATURES: Wheelbase: (Series 27) 122 inches; (Series 28) 124 inches. Overall length: (Series 27 passenger cars) 203.2 inches; (Series 27 station wagons) 202.9 inches; (Series 28) 210.2 inches. Front tread: (All) 58.66 inches. Rear tread: (All) 59.05 inches. Tires: (passenger cars) 7.10 x 15; (station wagons 7.60 x 15, tubeless type. The use of 7.60 x 15 tires was recommended for Star Chiefs.

OPTIONS: Power steering ($108). Power brakes ($36). Fender skirts ($11). Power windows ($97). Four-Way power seat ($40). Venti-heat underseat heater and defroster. Chieftain 7-tube radio. Directional signals. Autronic Eye. Back-up lamps. Non-glare rearview mirror. Exhaust deflector. No-Mar fuel guard door trim. Deluxe steering wheel (standard on Deluxes). Illuminated hood ornament. Windshield sun visor. Traffic light viewer. Latex foam seat cushions. Windshield washers. Outside rearview mirror. Visor vanity mirror. Glovebox lamp. Trunk lamp. Underhood lamp. Lighted ash tray. Hand brake signal. Grille guard. Wing guards. E-Z-Eye glass. Dual fog lamps. Rear seat speaker. Electric antenna. Safety spot lamp. Chrome trim rings. Safti-jack. Oil bath air cleaner. (Dealer installed options): Seat covers. Hand spot lamp. Venti-shades. Fold-away umbrella. Draft deflectors; Rear window wiper. Tissue dispenser. Magna Tray. Fuel door lock. Illuminated compass. Color tipon. Road reflector flares. Thermaster refrigerator. Thermaster bottle. Auto-Home Remington electric shaver. Continental tire extension. Simulated wire wheel discs. Power brakes ($36). Air-conditioning. Electric window lifts. Padded dashboard. Door edge guards. Door handle guards. Arctic windshield wipers. Dash panel courtesy lamps. Wide brake pedals. Reduced ratio power steering. Grille bug screen. Comfort-Control 300-position manual seat. Remote control outside mirrors. Deluxe steering wheel for Special station wagons. A three-speed synchromesh gearbox with column-mounted gearshift was standard on all models. Dual-Range four-speed Hydra-Matic drive was available at $178 extra. Available after March 1, 1955 for $35 was an optional engine "power-pack." It consisted of a Rochester 4GC four-barrel carburetor providing a boost of 20 hp over standard V-8s or a maximum of 200 hp on Hydra-Matic equipped cars. Carter WCFB model 2268S and 2283S four-barrel carburetors were also used on some 1955 Pontiacs as optional equipment. A variety of rear axle gear ratios was available.

HISTORICAL FOOTNOTES: Production of 1955 Pontiacs started Oct. 4, 1954. They were introduced to the public 15 days later, with the Star Chief Custom two-door Safari bowing the following Jan. 31. Calendar year production of 581,860 cars made Pontiac America's sixth ranked manufacturer. Hydra-Matic transmission was in 90.6 percent of these cars. Model year

production was 554,090 units. The new engine introduced in 1955 was Pontiac's FIRST overhead valve V-8, although it was the SECOND V-8 for the company, as the first had been used in 1932 models. An all-time monthly production record was recorded in December, 1955. Chieftain station wagons for 1955 utilized Chevrolet station wagon rear fender styling. Styles number 2562 and 2562DF had distinctive rear ventipanes. The two-door Chieftain station wagon, style number 2563F, was sometimes called the `Colony' wagon.

1956 PONTIAC

1956 Pontiac, Chieftain 870 four-door station wagon, V-8

CHIEFTAIN LINE — (V-8) — SERIES 27 — New Pontiac styling for 1956 featured combination bumper grilles with enclosed circular parking lights and round, bomb-type bumper guards. All models had reversed vertically slanting slash accent moldings and `sweepspear' body rub trim. On Chieftains the slash accents were of constant width. There were reflectorized oval embossments on rear fenders with gull-wing and circle medallions on the deck lid. Special level Chieftain 860s lacked upper belt moldings, wore small hubcaps and had plain taillight rings. Deluxe level Chieftain 870 models, (except station wagons), had visored taillight rings, full wheel discs and upper beltline trim. The two-door Custom Safari was continued as a Star Chief on the Chieftain chassis, now with the base four-barrel Star Chief engine. An 860 Catalina Coupe was new as were 860 and 870 four-door hardtops, the latter pair designated as Catalina sedans. In some factory literature Chieftain 870s are called Super Chiefs.

PONTIAC I.D. NUMBERS: VIN located on left front door hinge pillar. Matching engine serial number on pad on front of right-hand cylinder bank. Serial numbers took the form ( )-[ ]56{ }-1001 to ( )-[ ]56{ }-ending number. The first symbol ( ) was a letter indicating assembly plant: P=Pontiac, Mich.; T=Arlington, Texas; A=Atlanta, Ga.; F=Framingham, Mass; K=Kansas City, Kan.; L=Linden, N.J.; C=South Gate, Calif.; W=Wilmington, Dela. The second symbol [ ] indicated series: 7=Series 27; 8=Series 28. The third and fourth symbols indicated model year: 56=1956. The fifth symbol indicated transmission: S=synchromesh; H=Hydra-Matic. The following symbols were the sequential unit production number starting at 1001 for each series at each assembly plant. Ending numbers for 1956 were: [SERIES 27 with synchromesh] (Mich.) 12447; (Texas) 2383; (Ga.) 3633; (Mass.) 3050; (Kan.) 3526; (N.J.) 3089; (Calif.) 3117; (Dela.) 3139. [SERIES 27 with Hydra-Matic] (Mich.) 97877; (Texas) 14815; (Ga.) 22073; (Mass.) 13307; (Kan.) 27978; (N.J.) 26487; (Calif.) 33138; (Dela.) 26575. [SERIES 28 with synchromesh] (Mich.) 1259; (Texas) 1016; (Ga.) 1013; (Mass.) 1038; (Kan.) 1022; (N.J.) 1052; (Calif.) 1014; (Dela.) 1026. [SERIES 28 with Hydra-Matic] (Mich.) 47697; (Texas) 8896; (Ga.) 11452; (Mass.) 6999; (Kan.) 13124; (N.J.) 13766; (Calif.) 15590; (Dela.) 13092. Fisher Body/Style Number on plate under hood on left of firewall can be very helpful for identification of model and ordering parts. A prefix to the main number indicates model year, 56=1956. The first two symbols in the main number indicate series 27 or 28 Star Chief. The next two symbols indicate the body style. Some numbers have an alphabetical suffix indicating trim level, such as D=Deluxe and SD=Super Deluxe. These numbers appear in Body/Style Number column of charts below adjacent to corresponding body style listings.

Model Number	Body/Style Number	Body Type & Seating	Factory Price	Shipping Weight	Production Total
CHIEFTAIN 860 (SPECIAL)					
860-27	2719	4-dr Sed-6P	2294	3617	41,987
860-27	2739	4-dr Cat HT-6P	2439	3682	35,201
860-27	2711	2-dr Sed-6P	2236	3557	41,908
860-27	2737	2-dr Cat HT-6P	2366	3617	46,335
860-27	2763	2-dr Sta Wag-6P	2564	3717	6,099
860-27	2762FC	4-dr Sta Wag-6P	2648	3812	12,702
CHIEFTAIN 870 (Deluxe)					
870-27	2719D	4-dr Sed-6P	2409	3617	22,082
870-27	2739D	4-dr Cat HT-6P	2530	3682	25,372
870-27	2737D	2-dr Cat HT-6P	2476	3617	24,744
870-27	2763DF	4-dr Sta Wag-6P	2744	3762	21,674
STAR CHIEF CUSTOM (SERIES 27)					
27	2764DF	2-dr Sta Wag-6P	3124	3762	4,042

NOTE 1: 184,232 Chieftain 860s were built.
NOTE 2: 24,117 Chieftain 860s had synchromesh and 160,115 had Hydra-Matic.
NOTE 3: 93,872 Chieftain 870s (or Super Chiefs) were built.
NOTE 4: 3,289 Chieftain 870s had synchromesh and 90,583 had Hydra-Matic.
NOTE 5: 10 Custom Safaris had synchromesh and 4,032 had Hydra-Matic.

1956 Pontiac, Custom Star Chief Catalina four-door hardtop, V-8

STAR CHIEF LINE — (V-8) — SERIES 28 — All Star Chiefs were distinguished by tapered diagonal accent slash moldings on front doors and three stylized star emblems on front fenders and doors. Catalinas and convertibles had wide fluted lower rear fender extensions. The Custom Catalina sedan had stainless steel window surround moldings and all Custom Star Chiefs used hooded taillight rings.

Model Number	Body/Style Number	Body Type & Seating	Factory Price	Shipping Weight	Production Total
STAR CHIEF (SERIES 28)					
28	2819D	4-dr Sed-6P	2523	3697	18,346
28	2867DTX	2-dr Conv-6P	2853	3917	13,510
STAR CHIEF CUSTOM (SERIES 28)					
28	2839SD	4-dr Cat HT-6P	2731	3767	48,035
28	2837SD	2-dr Cat HT-6P	2661	3687	43,392

NOTE 1: 123,584 Series 28 Star Chiefs were built.
NOTE 2: 440 had synchromesh and 123,144 had Hydra-Matic.
NOTE 3: Does not include two-door Star Chief Custom Safari.
NOTE 4: is 301 vehicles converted into professional vehicles.

CHIEFTAIN ENGINES: V-8: Overhead valves. Cast iron block. Displacement: 316.6 cid. Bore and stroke: 3.94 x 3.25 inches. Compression ratio: (synchromesh) 7.9:1; (Hydra-Matic) 8.9:1. Brake hp: (synchromesh) 192 at 4400 rpm; (Hydra-Matic) 205 at 4800 rpm. Five main bearings. Hydraulic valve lifters. Carburetor: (synchromesh) Rochester 2GC two-barrel with black tag number 8696; (Hydra-Matic) Rochester 2GC two-barrel with brass tag number 8695. The two-door Custom Safari came standard with a Star Chief four-barrel V-8.

STAR CHIEF ENGINES: V-8: Overhead valve. Cast iron block. Displacement: 316.6 inches. Bore and stroke: 3.94 x 3.25 inches. Compression ratio: (synchromesh) 7.9:1. (Hydra-Matic) 8.9:1. Brake hp: (synchromesh) 216 at 4800 rpm; (Hydra-Matic) 227 at 4800 rpm. Five main bearings. Hydraulic valve lifters. Carburetors: (synchromesh) Rochester 4GC four-barrel with black tag number 7900; (Hydra-Matic) Rochester 4GC four-barrel with brass tag number 8697. Some cars were also equipped -with Carter WCFB model 2364S four-barrels.

CHASSIS FEATURES: Wheelbase: (Series 27) 122 inches; (Series 28) 124 inches. Overall length: (Series 27 passenger cars) 205.6 inches; (Series 27 Chieftain station wagons) 206 inches; (Series 27 Safari) 206.7 inches; (Series 28) 212.6 inches. Front,# tread: (All) 58.66 inches. Rear tread: (All) 59.05 inches. Tires: (Passenger cars) 7.10 x 15; (station wagons) 7.60 x 15, tubeless.

CONVENIENCE OPTIONS: Power brakes ($38). Power windows ($97). Power steering ($108). 6-Way power seat ($93). Radios ($90 or $118). Seat belts ($11 per passenger). Air-conditioning ($43 1). Hydra-Matic attachments were now considered 'standard', but cost extra. The D-56 Dual-Range type ($188) was used In Chieftains in both the 860 and 870 sub-series. A new Strato-Flight Hydra-Matic ($205) was employed in two-door Star Chief Custom Safaris and all Series 28 models. A three-speed synchromesh gearbox with column-mounted shift was the base price transmission. In March 1956, an `extra hp' V-8 was released. It also displaced 317 cid, but came with 10.0:1 compression heads, dual four-barrel Rochester carburetors (part no. 7009820) and additional high-performance components. The output of this engine was rated 285 hp at 5100 rpm. Pontiac experts have estimated that 200 cars were equipped with this motor. Standard rear axle gear ratios were as follows: (synchromesh) 3.64:1; (Hydra-Matic) 3.23:1. Additional ratios were also available. Dual exhausts were optional on all Pontiacs except the Chieftain 860 three-seat station wagon (not available) and cars with `extra hp' V-8s (standard). Four-barrel carburetion was optional for Chieftain 860 and 870 models.

HISTORICAL FOOTNOTES: Production of 1956 models started Oct. 3, 1955. They were introduced Oct. 21, 1955. Calendar year output was 332,268 cars. Model year output was 405,730 cars. Pontiac remained the sixth largest American automaker. On Aug. 3, 1956, the six millionth Pontiac was built. Semon "Bunkie" Knudsen took over as Pontiac general manager on July 1, 1956. The 1956 Star Chief two-door Custom Safari is recognized as a "Milestone Car" by the Milestone Car Society. The 227 hp 1956 Star Chief four-door sedan was good for 0 to 60 in 11.4 seconds and an 18.1 second quarter-mile.

1957 PONTIAC

CHIEFTAIN LINE — (V-8) — SERIES 27 — Pontiac introduced new `Star Flight' styling. General features were missile-shaped side trim; flatter tailfins; extended rear fenders with V-shaped tips; lower hoods; a more massive bumper grille; longer horizontal taillights; and 14-inch wheels. The budget-priced line was now called the Chieftain. The Super Chief name totally replaced the old Chieftain 870 designation for cars on the small wheelbase with Deluxe trim. The two-door Star Chief Custom Safari remained on the Series 27 platform and again had a four-barrel V-8 as base engine. Chieftains had small hubcaps; three stars on rear fenders; and Chieftain front fender scripts. Super Chiefs had full wheel discs; upper belt moldings; three stars on rear fenders; and Super Chief front fender scripts. The distinctive Custom Safari had Star Chief trims and a companion four-door Custom Safari Transcontinental station wagon was announced in late December, 1956.

1957 Pontiac, Chieftain two-door sedan, V-8

PONTIAC I.D. NUMBERS: VIN located on left front door hinge pillar. Matching engine serial number on pad on front of right-hand cylinder bank. Serial numbers took the form ( )-[ ]57{ }-1001 to ( )-[ ]57{ }-ending number. The first symbol ( ) was a letter indicating assembly plant: P=Pontiac, Mich.; T=Arlington, Texas; A=Atlanta, Ga.; F=Framingham, Mass; K=Kansas City, Kan.; L=Linden, N.J.; C=South Gate, Calif.; W=Wilmington, Dela. The second symbol [ ] indicated series: 7=Series 27; 8=Series 28. The third and fourth symbols indicated model year: 57=1957. The fifth symbol indicated transmission: S=synchromesh; H=Hydra-Matic. The following symbols were the sequential unit production number starting at 1001 for each series at each assembly plant. Ending numbers for 1957 were: [SERIES 27 with synchromesh] (Mich.) 7722; (Texas) 1656; (Ga.) 2041; (Mass.) 2040; (Kan.) 2301; (N.J.) 2223; (Calif.) 1765; (Dela.) 1970. [SERIES 27 with Hydra-Matic] (Mich.) 94357; (Texas) 10608; (Ga.) 18541; (Mass.) 11045; (Kan.) 24194; (N.J.) 21243; (Calif.) 22055; (Dela.) 22332. [SERIES 28 with synchromesh] (Mich.) 1212; (Texas) 1004; (Ga.) 1005; (Mass.) 1010; (Kan.) 1019; (N.J.) 1028; (Calif.) 1016; (Dela.) 1015. [SERIES 28 with Hydra-Matic] (Mich.) 45497; (Texas) 6679; (Ga.) 9462; (Mass.) 5007; (Kan.) 11022; (N.J.) 11067; (Calif.) 11387; (Dela.) 10558. Fisher Body/Style Number on plate under hood on left of firewall can be very helpful for identification of model and ordering parts. A prefix to the main number indicates model year, 57=1957. The first two symbols in the main number indicate series 27 or 28 Star Chief. The next two symbols indicate the body style. Some numbers have an alphabetical suffix indicating trim level, such as D=Deluxe and SD=Super Deluxe. These numbers appear in Body/Style Number column of charts below adjacent to corresponding body style listings.

Model Number	Body/Style Number	Body Type & Seating	Factory Price	Shipping Weight	Production Total
CHIEFTAIN					
27	2719	4-dr Sed-6P	2527	3670	35,671
27	2739	4-dr Cat HT-6P	2614	3745	40,074
27	2711	2-dr Sed-6P	2463	3625	21,343
27	2737	2-dr Cat HT-6P	2529	3665	51,017
27	2762FC	4-dr Sta Wag-9P	2898	3945	11,536
27	2763F	2-dr Sta Wag-6P	2841	3800	2,934
SUPER CHIEF					
27	2719D	4-dr Sed-6P	2664	3695	15,153
27	2739D	4-dr Cat HT-6P	2793	3750	19,758
27	2737D	2-dr Cat HT-6P	2735	3680	15,494
27	2762DF	4-dr Sta Wag-6P	3021	3875	14,095
STAR CHIEF CUSTOM (SERIES 27)					
27	2764DF	2-dr Sta Wag-6P	3636	3955	1,292
27	2762SDF	4-dr Sta Wag-6P	3481	3860	1,894

NOTE 1: All Pontiac station wagons used Safari name starting in 1957.
NOTE 2: 162,575 Chieftains were built.
NOTE 3: 12,867 Chieftains had synchromesh and 149,708 had Hydra-Matic.
NOTE 4: 64,692 Super Chiefs were built.
NOTE 5: 1,063 had Super Chiefs had synchromesh and 63,629 had Hydra-Matic.
NOTE 6: 3,186 Star Chief Custom Safaris were built.
NOTE 7: Four Custom Safaris had synchromesh and 3,182 had Hydra-Matic.
NOTE 8: 192 Super Chiefs were used for hearse and ambulance conversions.

1957 Pontiac, Super Chief Catalina two-door hardtop, V-8

STAR CHIEF LINE — (V-8) — SERIES 28 — Star Chiefs were identified by suitable front fender scripts, four stars on rear fenders, chrome semi-cylindrical trim at the back of missile-shaped inserts and full wheel discs. The Custom (Super Deluxe) sedan was reinstated and distinguished by off-shoulder interior styling patterns. A unique, limited-edition Custom Bonneville Convertible was announced in early December, 1956 and released on Jan. 11, 1957. This car was in the Custom Star Chief sub-series. Released only one-to-a-dealer, Bonneville availability was limited to 630 production examples and two (2) prototypes. The pre-production prototypes had four bucket seats and small trim differences. A fuel-injected V-8 was used in all of these cars.

Model Number	Body/Style Number	Body Type & Seating	Factory Price	Shipping Weight	Production Total
STAR CHIEF (SERIES 28)					
28	2819D	4-dr Sed-6P	2839	3740	3,774
28	2867DTX	2-dr Conv-6P	3105	3970	12,789
STAR CHIEF CUSTOM (SERIES 28)					
28	2819SD	4-dr Sed-6P	2896	3755	8,874
28	2839SD	4-dr Cat HT Sed-6P	2975	3820	44,283
28	2837S	2-dr Cat HT-6P	2901	3750	32,862
28	2867SDX	2-dr Bonn Conv-6P	5782	4285	630

NOTE 1: 103,588 Series 28 Star Chiefs were built.
NOTE 2: 309 Star Chiefs had synchromesh and 103,279 had Hydra-Matic.
NOTE 3: Totals do not include Series 27 two- or four-door Custom Safaris.
NOTE 4: 376 Star Chief chassis were built for professional car conversions.

1957 Pontiac, Star Chief Custom Bonneville two-door convertible, V-8

ENGINES

(CHIEFTAIN) V-8; Overhead valves. Cast iron block. Displacement: 347 cid. Bore and stroke: 3.94 x 3.56 inches. Compression ratio: (synchromesh) 8.5:1; (Hydra-Matic) 10.0:1. Brake hp: (synchromesh) 227 at 4600 rpm; (Hydra-Matic) 252 at 4600 rpm. Five main bearings. Hydraulic valve lifters. Carburetor: Rochester 2GC two-barrel.

(CUSTOM SAFARI/SUPER CHIEF/STAR CHIEF) V-8: Overhead valves. Cast iron block. Displacement: 347 cid. Bore and stroke: 3.94 x 3.56 inches. Compression ratio: (synchromesh) 8.5:1; (Hydra-Matic) 10.0:1. Brake hp: (synchromesh) 244 at 4800 rpm: (Hydra-Matic) 270 at 4800 rpm. Five main bearings. Hydraulic valve lifters. Carburetor: (Early production) Rochester 4GC four-barrel; (Late production) A Carter AFB four-barrel was used in mixed production with the Rochester 4GC type.

(BONNEVILLE) V-8: Overhead valves. Cast iron block. Displacement: 347 cid. Bore and stroke: 3.94 x 3.56 inches. Compression ratio: 10.25:1. Brake hp: (estimated) 315 at 4800 rpm. Five main bearings. Hydraulic valve lifters. Induction: Rocnester mechanical fuel-injection.

(NASCAR/TRI-POWER) In December, 1956 three different triple two-barrel engines were released. The first was an option for the standard Hydra-Matic V-8. The others were options for the `extra horsepower' (NASCAR-certified) V-8 with either synchromesh or Hydra-Matic attachment. Specifications were as follows: (1) Standard V-8. 347 cid. 10.0:1 compression. 290 hp at 5000 rpm. Hydraulic valve lifters. 3 x 2V Rochester carburetors. Single-breaker ignition with Hydra-Matic only. (2) (Extra-Horsepower V-8/synchromesh) 347 cid. 10.0:1 compression. 317 hp at 5200 rpm. Hydraulic valve lifters. 3 x 2V Rochester carburetors. Dual-breaker ignition. (3) (Extra-Horsepower V-8/Hydra-Matic) 347 cid. 10.0:1 compression. 317 hp at 5200 rpm. Hydraulic valve lifters. 3 x 2V Rochester carburetors. Single-breaker ignition.

CHASSIS FEATURES: Wheelbase: (Series 27) 122 inches; (Series 28) 124 inches. Overall length: (Series 27 passenger cars) 206.8 inches; (Series 27 station wagons) 207.7 inches; (Series 28) 213.8 inches. Front tread: 59.0 inches. Rear tread: 59.4 inches. Tires: (Chieftain with synchromesh) 7.50 x 14; (station wagons and Bonneville) 8.50 x 14; (others) 8.00 x 14.

OPTIONS: Power steering ($108). Power brakes ($39). Eight-way power seat ($97). Six-way manual seat ($41). Power windows ($102). Radios ($99 and $125). Heater and defroster ($91). Air conditioning ($431). Tinted glass ($34) Lamp group ($23.10). Mirror group ($12.35). Power Sweep Contour electric wiper/washer ($25.25). Deluxe steering wheel and padded dash ($31.70). Electric clock ($10.50). Whitewalls ($58.70). Deluxe carpet floor mat ($11). Cowl vent chrome trim and Custom wheel discs ($21.80). Deluxe basic group ($255.50). Hydra-Matic attachments were again considered `standard,' but cost extra. Strato-Flight Hydra-Matic ($231) was used in all lines. A three-speed synchromesh gearbox with column-shift was the base price transmission. Four-barrel carburetion was optional in Chieftains. Dual exhausts were $24 extra. Rear axle ratios: (synchromesh) 3.42:1; (Hydra-Matic) 3.08:1. In December, 1956, a 3.23:1 axle was made standard for Hydra-Matic equipped cars and the 3.08:1 axle was made a plains ratio option for all cars except Safari models.

HISTORIC FOOTNOTES: Production of 1957 models started Oct. 17, 1956. They were introduced Nov. 19, 1956. Model year output was 334,041 cars. Calendar year output was 343,298 cars. Pontiac held a 5.4 percent share of the U.S. market and was ranked the sixth largest automaker. First news of the Bonneville convertible was released Dec. 2, 1956, the same day the Tri-Power carburetor options were announced. The four-door Custom Star Chief Safari Transcontinental wagon and the Bonneville convertible were both introduced on Jan. 11, 1957. E.M. "Pete" Estes became the chief engineer of Pontiac this year. The 1957 Pontiac Super Chief two-door sedan with the 290 hp V-8 was capable of doing 0 to 60 in 8.5 seconds and the quarter-mile in 16.8 seconds. The 1957 Star Chief two-door Custom Safari is a Milestone Car.

1958 PONTIAC

CHIEFTAIN LINE — (V-8) — SERIES 25 AND SERIES 27 — The 1958 Pontiacs featured all new styling and chassis engineering which was hailed as a bold advance over the past. General appearance characteristics included honeycomb grilles, a longer, lower silhouette, quad headlamps and taillamps, recessed floors and concave rear fender panels. Chieftains could be identified by the script model nameplates at the front of concave insert panels on the rear doors or fenders and three stars on the rear fenders. Small hubcaps were standard on all

Standard Catalog of American Cars

Chieftains, but many were sold with optional full wheel discs. Taillamps without trim rings were seen on Chieftains, except the convertible. The rag-top was in a separate series sharing a unique ribbed rear deck lid with the Bonneville convertible. Princess pattern Lustrex upholstery with Morrokide imitation leather trim was seen inside Chieftains, except the convertible, which had special Seville-finish Morrokide seats in 'off shoulder' combination patterns.

1958 Pontiac, Chieftain two-door sedan, V-8

PONTIAC I.D. NUMBERS: VIN located on left front door hinge pillar. Matching engine serial number on pad on front of right-hand cylinder bank. Serial numbers took the form ( )-[ ]58{ }-1001 to ( )-[ ]58{ }-ending number. The first symbol ( ) was a letter indicating assembly plant. P=Pontiac, Mich.; T=Arlington, Texas; A=Atlanta, Ga.; F=Framingham, Mass; K=Kansas City, Kan.; L=Linden, N.J.; C=South Gate, Calif.; W=Wilmington, Dela. The second symbol [ ] indicated series: 7=Series 27; 8=Series 28; 5=Series 25 Bonneville. The third and fourth symbols indicated model year: 58=1958. The fifth symbol indicated transmission. S=synchromesh; H=Hydra-Matic. The following symbols were the sequential unit production number starting at 1001 for each series at each assembly plant. Ending numbers for 1957 were: [SERIES 27 with synchromesh] (Mich.) 4036; (Texas) 1429; (Ga.) 1508; (Mass.) 1296; (Kan.) 2003; (N.J.) 1568; (Calif.) 1592; (Dela.) 1427. [SERIES 27 with Hydra-Matic] (Mich.) 43381; (Texas) 7317; (Ga.) 11942; (Mass.) 6113; (Kan.) 17504; (N.J.) 14411; (Calif.) 12585; (Dela.) 12574. [SERIES 28 with synchromesh] (Mich.) 1159; (Texas) 1006; (Ga.) 1008; (Mass.) 1011; (Kan.) 1016; (N.J.) 1026; (Calif.) 1018; (Dela.) 1015. [SERIES 28 with Hydra-Matic] (Mich.) 25986; (Texas) 5695; (Ga.) 8672; (Mass.) 4130; (Kan.) 10785; (N.J.) 8446; (Calif.) 8168; (Dela.) 8157. [BONNEVILLE SERIES 25 with synchromesh] (Ga.) 1003; (Calif.) 1021; (Mass.) 1005; (Kan.) 1023; (N.J.) 1020; (Mich.) 1163; (Dela.) 1015. [BONNEVILLE SERIES 25 with Hydra-Matic] (Ga.) 2543; (Calif.) 3324; (Mass.) 1969; (Kan.) 2640; (N.J.) 3180; (Mich.) 9141; (Texas) 1677; (Dela.) 2858. Fisher Body/Style Number on plate under hood on left of firewall can be very helpful for identification of model and ordering parts. A prefix to the main number indicates model year, 58=1958. The first two symbols in the main number indicate series 27 or 28 Star Chief or 25 Bonneville. The next two symbols indicate the body style. Some numbers have an alphabetical suffix indicating trim level, such as D=Deluxe and SD=Super Deluxe. These numbers appear in Body/Style Number column of charts below adjacent to corresponding body style listings.

CHIEFTAIN (SERIES 27)

Model Number	Body/Style Number	Body Type & Seating	Factory Price	Shipping Weight	Production Total
27	2749	4-dr Sed-6P	2638	3815	44,999
27	2739	4-dr Cat HT-6P	2792	3900	17,946
27	2741	2-dr Sed-6P	2573	3755	17,394
27	2731	2-dr Cat HT-6P	2707	3765	26,003
27	2793	4-dr Sta Wag-6P	3019	4140	9,701
27	2794	2-dr Sta Wag-9P	3088	4185	5,417

CHIEFTAIN (SERIES 25)

Model Number	Body/Style Number	Body Type & Seating	Factory Price	Shipping Weight	Production Total
25	2567	2-dr Conv-5P	3019	3965	7,359

SUPER CHIEF LINE — (V-8) — SERIES 28 — In 1958 the Super Chief nameplate was used to designate three cars on the long wheelbase (Star Chief) chassis with two-barrel (Chieftain) V-8s as base engines. Identification features included full wheel discs, taillamps with chrome rings and rear fender coves decorated with Super Chief script and four stars. Deluxe steering wheels were used. The four-door sedan was upholstered in a blend of Palisades pattern Lustrex with Plaza pattern bolsters. Catalina buyers could choose either all-Morrokide or Morrokide and Lustrex trims at the same price.

SUPER CHIEF (SERIES 28 Deluxe)

Model Number	Body/Style Number	Body Type & Seating	Factory Price	Shipping Weight	Production Total
28	2849D	4-dr Sed-6P	2834	3865	12,006
28	2839D	4-dr Cat HT-6P	2961	3925	7,886
28	2831D	2-dr Cat HT-6P	2880	3805	7,236

STAR CHIEF LINE — (V-8) — SERIES 27 AND SERIES 28 — Pontiac's "something really special" cars were four 'Super Deluxe' level Star Chiefs. A distinctive four-door Custom Safari station wagon was on the shorter Chieftain platform, while other models had the 124-inch wheelbase shared with Super Chiefs. Identification features included Star Chief front fenders script plates, four stars within the concave insert panels, taillamp trim rings and funnel-shaped decorative scoops at the front of the insert panels. These scoops were embellished with golden rectangular 'V' badges and triple wind-split moldings. Chrome wheel discs were regular equipment outside, while a Deluxe steering wheel and electric clock were found inside. Upholstery trims were tridimensional Prado pattern Lustrex in the Catalina sedan, with all-leather optional at no extra cost on both Catalinas. A roof rack, horizontal tailgate moldings and distinct Safari gate scripts were featured on the Custom Safari and all Star Chiefs boasted 'stardust' carpeting. Jeweltone Lucite acrylic lacquer paint finish was standard and exclusive on Star Chiefs and Bonnevilles.

1958 Pontiac, Star Chief Catalina four-door hardtop, V-8

Model Number	Body/Style Number	Body Type & Seating	Factory Price	Shipping Weight	Production Total
STAR CHIEF (SERIES 28 SUPER DELUXE)					
28	2849SD	4-dr Cus Sed-6P	3071	3915	10,547
28	2839SD	4-dr Cat HT-6P	3210	3965	21,455
28	2831SD	2-dr Cat HT-6P	3122	3850	13,888
STAR CHIEF CUSTOM SAFARI					
27	2793SD	4-dr Cus Sta Wag-6P	3350	4180	2,905

BONNEVILLE LINE — (V-8) — SERIES 25 — Bonneville became a line name instead of a single model designation in 1958. A convertible and sport coupe were offered. Base powerplants in Bonnevilles were the Star Chief V-8s and both cars were on the Chieftain wheelbase, but with the same longer, ribbed rear deck lid used on the Series 25 Chieftain convertible. This made the bodies slightly longer than Series 27 types. Identification features included Bonneville front fender scripts, Bonneville block letters on hoods and decks, four bright metal chevrons on the lower front fendersides, four stars on the rear fender panels and rocket-shaped, ribbed semi-cylindrical moldings at the front of the concave inserts. Standard equipment included Deluxe steering wheel, chrome wheel discs and special upholstery.

1958 Pontiac, Bonneville Custom Sport Coupe, V-8

Model Number	Body/Style Number	Body Type & Seating	Factory Price	Shipping Weight	Production Total
BONNEVILLE (SERIES 25 SUPER DELUXE)					
25	2547SD	Cus Spt Cpe-5P	3481	3825	9,144
25	2567SD	Cus Conv-5P	3586	4040	3,096

ENGINES

(CHIEFTAIN/SUPER CHIEF) Base V-8s: Overhead valves. Cast iron block. Displacement: 370 cid. Bore and stroke: 4.06 x 3.56 inches. Compression ratio: (synchromesh) 8.6:1; (Hydra-Matic) 10.0:1. Brake hp: (synchromesh) 240 at 4500 rpm; (Hydra-Matic) 270 at 4600 rpm. Five main bearings. Hydraulic valve lifters. Carburetor: (early) Rochester 2GC two-barrel; (late) same with air bypass idle.

(STAR CHIEF/BONNEVILLE) Base V-8s: Overhead Valves. Cast iron block. Displacement: 370 cid. Bore and stroke: 4.06 x 3.56 inches. Compression ratio: (synchromesh) 8.6:1; (Hydra-Matic) 10.0:1. Brake hp: (synchromesh) 255 at 4500 rpm; (Hydra-Matic) 285 at 4600 rpm. Five main bearings. Hydraulic valve lifters. Carburetor: (Regular production) Carter AFB four-barrel; (Special) 500 cars were built with Rochester 4GC four-barrel carburetors late in the year. These were available only in four sales zones and were likely 'PM' optioned cars assembled for NASCAR certification.

CHASSIS FEATURES: Wheelbase: (Series 25 and 27) 122 inches; (Series 28) 124 inches. Overall length: (Series 25) 211.7 inches; (Series 27) 210.5 inches; (Series 28) 124 inches. Front tread: 58.8 inches. Rear tread: 59.4 inches. Tires: (coupes and sedans) 8.00 x 14; (station wagons and all w/air-conditioning) 8.50 x 14.

OPTIONS: Power steering ($108). Power brakes ($38). Power windows ($108). Power seat ($77). Deluxe radio ($102). Deluxe Electromatic radio ($161). Power antenna ($30). Rear seat speaker $13.75, $18.90 and $21 on Safari/Bonneville, Star Chief and Chieftain/Super Chief respectively. Heater and defroster ($96). Dual exhaust ($31). White sidewall tires 8.00 x 14, 4-ply ($65). Two-tone paint in standard colors ($27). E-Z Eye Glass ($38). Electric clock ($20). Windshield washer ($14). Electric contour wipers ($14). Oil filter ($10). Padded dash ($19). Foam seat ($13). Deluxe steering wheel ($14). Outside rearview mirror ($7). Wheel discs ($18). Brake-on light ($6). Air-conditioning ($430). Air suspension ($175). Bonneville bucket seats ($84). Transmission and Axle Options: A three-speed synchromesh gear box with column mounted gear shift was the base price transmission. Four-speed Strato-Flight Hydra-Matic was $231.34 extra. In late production a Borg-Warner heavy-duty police gear box was optional. At least one car, built for racing at Daytona Beach, left the factory with a floor mounted four-speed manual transmission. Transmission attachment date was now recorded by series. A total of 19,599 cars were built in Series 25. Of these, 210 had synchromesh and 19,389 had Hydra-Matic attachments. A total of 124,685 cars were built in Series 27. Of these, 6,943 had synchromesh and 117,742 had HydraMatic attachments. A total of 73,019 cars

were built in Series 28. Of these, 258 had synchromesh and 72,761 and Hydra-Matic attachments. The difference between output of individual models and total series production was 321 cars, which indicates the approximate number of Pontiac chassis delivered for professional car conversions this year. Of these, 320 were Series 27 chassis and one (1) was a Series 28 chassis. Rear axle options included Safe-T-Track differential and the following gear ratios: (HydraMatic) 3.23:1; (Optional Hydra-Matic) 3.08:1; (synchromesh) 3.42:1; (Optional synchromesh) 3.64:1; (dealer installed) 3.90:1 and 4.10:1. Powerplant Options: The four-barrel V-8 could be installed as an option in Chieftains and Super Chiefs. Tri-Power carburetion on standard blocks was $84 for these lines and $93.50 on Star Chiefs and Bonnevilles. This 'standard' Tri-Power setup used three two-barrel Rochester carburetors, 10.5:1 cylinder heads, high-lift camshaft and gave 300 hp at 4600 rpm. Rochester fuel-injection was a $500 option on any 1958 Pontiac and this package included 10.5:1 cylinder heads and gave 310 hp at 4800 rpm. Pontiac experts believe that 200 Bonnevilles carried this option. In Mar. 1958, two NASCAR-certified 'extra hp (Tempest 395-A) V-8s were released. The 'PK' option was $254 on Chieftains or Super Chiefs and $233 on Star Chiefs or Bonnevilles. It included a four-barrel carburetor, 10.5:1 cylinder heads, higher-lift camshaft, low-restriction dual exhausts and other special components good for 315 hp at 5000 rpm. The 'PM' option was $331 on lower-priced lines and $320 on upper lines and included the special features with Tri-Power induction for 330 hp at 5200 rpm. Both displaced 370 cid.

HISTORICAL FOOTNOTES: Model year production was 217,303 units for a 5.1 percent share of market. Calendar year output was 219,823 cars. To celebrate General Motors' 50th anniversary, a special "Golden Jubilee" trim and paint scheme was announced in November. This color was coded `Z' with DuPont stock number 2865L. Special "Golden Jubilee" ornamentation was applied to a limited number of cars, all of which are believed to have been Star Chief Custom four-door sedans. The number made is not known. Cars with optional fuel-injection had fuel-injection call-out on the front fenders. Cars with Tri-Power engines had a different type of front fender call-out. A Tri-Power Bonneville convertible was selected as the Official Pace Car for the Indianapolis 500 Mile Race in May, 1958. The 1958 Bonneville hardtop with the 300 hp motor was road tested by a magazine. Zero-to-60 mph took 7.6 seconds and the quarter-mile took 16 seconds.

1959 PONTIAC

CATALINA SERIES — (V-8) — SERIES 21 — Major styling changes for 1959 Pontiacs included lower, longer bodies with more interior room; new twin grille theme; twin-fin rear fenders; 'V' contour hoods; increased glass area; and flat, rear over-hanging roofs on four-door Vista hardtops. The old Chieftain line was renamed, adopting the term Catalina as a new series name. Identification features included Catalina script on rear fins; plain deck lids; and bodysides trimmed by clean 'Sweepspear' moldings with undecorated projectile flares. Standard equipment included directional signals; electric wipers; dual sun visors; dome lamps; cigarette lighter; dual headlamps; front and rear ashtrays; coat hooks; instrument panel Snak Bar; dual horns'; tubeless tires; bumper jack; and wheel lug wrench.

PONTIAC I.D. NUMBERS: VIN located on left front door hinge pillar. Matching engine serial number on pad on front of right-hand cylinder bank. Assembly plant codes: P=Pontiac, Mich.; T=Arlington, Texas; A=Atlanta, Ga.; F=Framingham, Mass; K=Kansas City, Kan.; L=Linden, N.J.; C=South Gate, Calif.; W=Wilmington, Dela. [CATALINA] Serial numbers took the following form — 159WI001 and up. The first character (1) indicating Series 21; the second and third characters (59) indicating model year; the fourth character (W) indicating factory. Serial numbers at each factory began with 1001 and transmission type was no longer indicated. [STAR CHIEF] Serial numbers took the same general form as Catalina I. D. numbers, but with a '4' as the first character to designate Series 24. [BONNEVILLE CUSTOM] Serial numbers for Bonneville passenger cars began with an '8' and for Custom Safaris with a '7' representing the series the cars were in.

CATALINA

Model Number	Body/Style Number	Body Type & Seating	Factory Price	Shipping Weight	Production Total
21	2119	4-dr Sed-6P	2704	3955	72,377
21	2139	4-dr Vista HT-6P	2844	4005	45,012
21	2111	2-dr Spt Sed-6P	2633	3870	26,102
21	2137	2-dr HT-6P	2768	3900	38,309
21	2167	2-dr Conv-5P	3080	3970	14,515
21	2135	4-dr Sta Wag-6P	3101	4345	21,162
21	2145	4-dr Sta Wag-9P	3209	4405	14,084

NOTE 1: 231,561 Catalinas were built.
NOTE 2: 9,939 Catalinas had synchromesh and 221,622 had Hydra-Matic.

1959 Pontiac, Star Chief two-door Sport Sedan, V-8

CUSTOM STAR CHIEF SERIES (V-8) — SERIES 24 — The Super Chief disappeared and 1959 Custom Star Chiefs were large-sized Pontiacs utilizing the base Catalina engines. There were Star Chief emblems on the fins, four stylized stars on the projectile flares, `sweepspear' body side moldings and a narrow deck lid ornament to aid with identification. Regular equipment included all standard Catalina features, plus two-speed electric wipers, Deluxe steering wheel, electric clock, Deluxe chrome wheel covers and loop-pile Lurex-flexed carpeting.

CUSTOM STAR CHIEF

Model Number	Body/Style Number	Body Type & Seating	Factory Price	Shipping Weight	Production Total
24	2419	4-dr Sed-6P	3005	4005	27,872
24	2439	4-dr Vista HT-6P	3138	4035	30,689
24	2411	2-dr Spt Sed-6P	2934	3930	10,254

NOTE 1: 68,815 Custom Star Chiefs were built.
NOTE 2: 333 Custom Star Chiefs had synchromesh and 68,482 had Hydra-Matic.

1959 Pontiac, Bonneville two-door convertible, V-8

BONNEVILLE CUSTOM LINE — (V-8) — SERIES 27 AND SERIES 28 — The Bonneville Customs were the prestige offering. They were big, powerful Pontiacs with high level trim and appointments and four-barrel V-8s. Bonnevilles were set apart by golden scripts on the right-hand grille, rear fins and deck lid; four groups of short, horizontal louvers on the projectile-shaped rear fender flares; and crest medallions on the deck lid and doors. Regular equipment included all Star Chief features, plus padded dashboard, inside door safety reflectors, rear seat foam cushions, dash courtesy lights and padded assist rails for passengers.

Model Number	Body/Style Number	Body Type & Seating	Factory Price	Shipping Weight	Production Total
27	2735	4-dr Sta Wag-6P	3532	4370	4,673
BONNEVILLE CUSTOM (SERIES 28)					
28	2839	4-dr Vista HT-6P	3333	4085	38,696
28	2837	2-dr HT-6P	3257	3985	27,769
28	2867	2-dr Conv-6P	3478	4070	11,426

NOTE 1: 4,673 Bonneville Custom Safari station wagons (Series 27) were built.
NOTE 2: 16 Custom Safaris had synchromesh and 4,657 had Hydra-Matic.
NOTE 3: 78,271 Bonnevilles (Series 28) were built.
NOTE 4: 673 Bonneville Customs (Series 28) w/synchromesh and 77,596 w/HMT.
NOTE 5: 380 (124-inch wheelbase cars) used for hearse/ambulance conversions.

BASE ENGINES

(CATALINA/CUSTOM STAR CHIEF) V-8s: Overhead valves. Cast iron block. Displacement: 389 cid. Bore and stroke: 4.06 x 3.75 inches. Compression ratio: (synchromesh) 8.6:1; (Hydra-Matic) 10.0:1. Brake hp: (synchromesh) 245 at 4200 rpm; (Hydra-Matic) 280 at 4400 rpm. Five main bearings. Hydraulic valve lifters. Carburetor: (synchromesh) Rochester model no. 7015910 two-barrel; (Hydra-Matic) Rochester model no. 7015909 two-barrel.

(BONNEVILLE CUSTOM) V-8: Overhead valves. Cast iron block. Displacement: 389 cid. Bore and stroke: 4.06 x 3.75 inches. Compression ratio: (synchromesh) 8.6:1; (Hydra-Matic) 10.0:1. Brake hp: (synchromesh) 260 at 4200 rpm; (Hydra-Matic) 300 at 4600 rpm. Five main bearings. Hydraulic valve lifters. Carburetor: (synchromesh) Carter AFB-2820S (no. 532301) four-barrel; (Hydra-Matic) Carter AFB-2820S (no. 532302) four-barrel.

CHASSIS FEATURES: Wheelbase: (Series 21 and 27) 122 inches; (Series 24 and 28) 124 inches. Overall length: (Catalina passenger cars) 213.7 Inches; (Star Chief and Bonneville-passenger cars) 220.7 inches; (All station wagons) 214.3 inches. Front tread: 63.7 inches. Rear tread: 64 inches. Pontiac promoted `Wide Track Drive' for the first time this year. Tires: (passenger cars) 8.00 x 14; (Station wagons and all w/airconditioning) 8.50 x 14.

OPTIONS: Push-button radio ($74). Wonderbar radio ($100). Sportable radio ($104). Electric antenna ($20). Rear seat speaker ($11). Fresh air heater and defroster ($74). Air-conditioning ($355). Tinted glass ($35). Back-up lights ($9). Windshield washers ($11). Deluxe steering wheel in Catalina ($12). Parking brake signal ($4). Padded dash ($16). Two-speed power brakes ($35). Power windows (4-dr) $85; (2-dr) $48. Power tailgate window ($27). Six-way power seat ($81). Ever-Level air ride ($155). Oil filter ($8). Heavy-duty air cleaner ($6). Clear plastic seat covers ($30). Whitewall 8.00 x 14 tires ($34). Whitewall 8.50 x 14 tires ($37). Two-tone paint ($11). Front foam seat cushion ($9). Bonneville convertible bucket seats ($84). Catalina decor trim ($45). Lamp group ($23). Safety group ($34). Mirror group ($10). Custom wheel covers ($26). Full wheel discs on Catalina ($14). Outside rearview mirror ($5). Tilt mirror ($4). Undercoating ($15). Anti-freeze ($7). Tissue dispenser ($6). Safety belts ($12). A three-speed manual gearbox with column-mounted gearshift was standard on all models. Four-speed Super Hydra-Matic (Strato-Flight) transmission was $180 extra. Rear axle ratios were approximately the same as 1958. SafeT-Track non-slip differential was $42 extra. A number of optional V-8s were offered, all on the 389 cid block. The Tempest 420E option was available as a super-economy offering, for no extra charge, in any Pontiac. It had an especially fuel efficient camshaft, model no. 7015958 Rochester two-barrel carburetor and 8.6:1 compression ratio for 215 hp at 3600 rpm. The four-barrel Bonneville V-8 was available in Catalinas and Star Chiefs at $20 extra. Tri-Power on the standard Hydra-Matic block (10.0:1 compression ratio) was $73 for Bonnevilles and $81 for other series. This engine produced 315 hp at 4600 rpm. Extra-hp options included four-barrel and Tri-Power induction on the special heavy-duty NASCAR-certified block, both with 10.5:1 compression ratio. Brake horsepower ratings were 330 and 345 respectively, with both peaking at 4800 rpm. Dual exhausts, normally a $26 option, were standard with these engines.

HISTORICAL FOOTNOTES: Production start-up took place Sept. 11, 1958. Introductions were made one month later. Model year output was 383,320 units for a 6.9 percent market share. Calendar year production included 388,856 cars for fourth place in the industry. One or two "El Camino" type car-based pickup trucks were built from the 1959 Catalina chassis as prototypes. One of these vehicles was used as a "yard car" at the Pontiac factory in Pontiac, Mich. for many years. Reports of a second "El Catalina" in the west have surfaced from time

to time. Pontiac introduced its famous eight-lug aluminum wheels on Aug. 27, 1959, though it's likely that they were intended for 1960 sale. MOTOR TREND magazine selected the 1959 Pontiac as its "Car of the Year." Pontiac's were victorious in many 1959 stock car races, including the Daytona 500 and Darlington 500, with drivers such as Fireball Roberts behind the wheel. The hot "Wide-Tracks" also captured the National Hot Rod Association's "Top Eliminator" title and won the checkered flag at Pikes Peak. The 280 hp 1959 Catalina two-door hardtop (or Sport Coupe) was tested at 8.8 seconds for 0-to-60 and 16.9 seconds for the quarter-mile. Catalina was no longer a body style designation. Vista was now Pontiac's nomenclature for pillarless hardtop styling. The Sport Coupe was a two-door hardtop. The Sport Sedan was the two-door pillared sedan. Nine-passenger station wagons now used a rear-facing third seat of fold-away design. Station wagons were still called Safaris and all Safaris had four-door bodies. Taillamps used on all station wagons and Catalinas were short horizontal-oval types without trim rings. Taillamps used on Custom Star Chiefs and Bonneville Customs were long horizontal types with dual trim rings. The 1959 Bonneville Custom was picked as `Best Buy in the $2,000-$3,000 Class' by CAR LIFE magazine.

1960 PONTIAC

1960 Pontiac, Catalina four-door Safari, V-8

CATALINA SERIES — (V-8) — SERIES 21 — Pontiac's major styling changes for 1960 included undivided-horizontal bar grilles, straight full-length side trim moldings and a new deck lid which was nearly flush with the tops of the fenders. Catalinas had plain beltline moldings, Catalina front fender scripts, and Pontiac block letters on the belt latch panel. Standard features included turn signals, oil filter, five tubeless tires and courtesy lamps on convertibles.

PONTIAC I.D. NUMBERS: The VIN is located on a plate attached to left front door post. First symbol identifies series: 21=Catalina; 23=Ventura; 24=Star Chief; 27=Bonneville Safari; 28=Bonneville. Second and third symbols indicate model year: 60=1960. Fourth symbol identifies assembly plant: P=Pontiac, Mich.; S=South Gate, Calif.; L=Linden, N.J.; W=Wilmington, Dela.; K=Kansas City, Kan.; D=Doraville, Ga.; A=Arlington, Texas; E-Euclid, Ohio. Remaining symbols are the unit's sequential production number starting with 1001 at each factory. Body/Style Number plate on left side of cowl below hood indicates manufacturer and various codes. Body/Style Number prefixed by model year code (60=1960). First two symbols in main Body/Style Number are the series code, last two symbols are the body style code. These four numbers appear in second column of charts below. Trim, paint and some accessory codes may also be shown on the Body/Style Number plate. Pontiac engines are stamped with a production code and motor serial number matching the VIN. Production code on pad on front of right-hand cylinder bank has an alpha-numerical stamping identifying the engine. All 1960 V-8s were 389 cid. Engine codes included: A1 (283 hp); A2 (215 hp); B1 (303 hp); B2 (281 hp); C1 (318 hp/Tri-Power); C4 (318 hp/Tri-Power); E3 (215 hp); F1 (330 hp); F4 (330 hp); M1 (345 hp/Tri-Power); M4 (345 hp/Tri-Power).

CATALINA

Model Number	Body/Style Number	Body Type & Seating	Factory Price	Shipping Weight	Production Total
21	2119	4-dr Sed-6P	2702	3935	72,650
21	2139	4-dr Vista HT-6P	2842	3990	32,710
21	2111	2-dr Spt Sed-6P	2631	3850	25,504
21	2137	2-dr HT-6P	2766	3835	27,496
21	2167	2-dr Conv-6P	3078	3940	17,172
21	2145	4-dr Sta Wag-9P	3207	4365	14,149
21	2135	4-dr Sta Wag-6P	3099	4310	21,253

NOTE 1: 210,934 Catalinas were built.
NOTE 2: 10,831 Catalinas had synchromesh and 200,101 had Hydra-Matic.
NOTE 3: Some 'AmbleWagons' on the standard Safari chassis may have been sold.

VENTURA SERIES — (V-8) — SERIES 23 — The Ventura was a Custom trim level Pontiac on the short wheelbase. Identifying cars in this series were plain belt moldings, Ventura front fender scripts and the model name, in block letters, on the trunk latch panel. Venturas had all Catalina features plus custom steering wheel, electric clock, Deluxe wheel discs, full carpeting, triple-tone Morrokide seats, right-hand ash trays and special decor moldings.

VENTURA

Model Number	Body/Style Number	Body Type & Seating	Factory Price	Shipping Weight	Production Total
23	2339	4-dr Vista HT-6P	3047	3990	28,700
23	2337	2-dr HT-6P	2971	3865	27,577

NOTE 1: 56,277 Ventura were built.
NOTE 2: 2,381 Venturas had synchromesh and 53,896 had Hydra-Matic.

STAR CHIEF SERIES — (V-8) SERIES 24 — Built off the long wheelbase with the Catalina two-barrel V-8 for base power, Star Chiefs had the same regular equipment as Venturas, plus dual-speed wipers. Distinguishing touches included Star Chief front fender scripts and four stylized stars at the rear of the lower beltline moldings.

1960 Pontiac, Star Chief two-door Sport Sedan, V-8

STAR CHIEF

Model Number	Body/Style Number	Body Type & Seating	Factory Price	Shipping Weight	Production Total
24	2419	4-dr Sed-6P	3003	3995	23,038
24	2439	4-dr Vista HT-6P	3136	4040	14,856
24	2411	2-dr Spt Sed-6P	2932	3910	5,797

NOTE 1: 43,691 Star Chiefs were built.
NOTE 2: 166 Star Chiefs had synchromesh and 43,525 had Hydra-Matic.

1960 Pontiac, Bonneville two-door hardtop sport coupe, V-8

BONNEVILLE LINE — (V-8) SERIES 27 AND SERIES 28 — Pontiac's top line could be told by distinctive front fender scripts, Bonneville lettering on the deck latch panel, beltline moldings ending in three dashes of chrome at the rear and a V-shaped crest on the lower front fenders. Bonnevilles incorporated rear foam seat cushions, padded dashboards with walnut inserts, courtesy lamps, and four-barrel V-8s in addition to everything found in lower-priced Pontiacs. All- Morrokide seats were standard and genuine cowhide leather was available as an option.

BONNEVILLE CUSTOM (SERIES 27)

Model Number	Body/Style Number	Body Type & Seating	Factory Price	Shipping Weight	Production Total
27	2735	4-dr Sta Wag-6p	3532	4370	5,163

BONNEVILLE (SERIES 28)

Model Number	Body/Style Number	Body Type & Seating	Factory Price	Shipping Weight	Production Total
28	2839	4-dr Vista HT-6P	3333	4085	39,037
28	2837	2-dr HT-6P	3257	3985	24,015
28	2867	2-dr Conv-5P	3478	4070	17,062

NOTE 1: 5,163 Bonneville Custom Safaris were built.
NOTE 2: 12 Safaris had synchromesh and 5,151 had Hydra-Matic.
NOTE 3: 80,651 Series 28 Bonnevilles were built.
NOTE 4: 1,111 Series 28 Bonnevilles had synchromesh; 79,540 had Hydra-Matic.
NOTE 5: 537 Bonneville chassis were sold to hearse/ambulance makers.

ENGINES

(CATALINA/VENTURA/STAR CHIEF) V-8: Overhead valves. Cast iron block. Displacement: 389 cid. Bore and stroke: 4.05 x 3.75 inches. Compression ratio: (synchromesh) 8.6:1; (Hydra-Matic) 10.25:1. Brake hp: (synchromesh) 215 at 3600 RPM; (Hydra-Matic) 283 at 4400 rpm. Five main bearings. Hydraulic valve lifters. Carburetor: Rochester 2GC two-barrel.

(BONNEVILLE) V-8: Overhead valves. Cast iron block. Displacement: 389 cid. Bore and stroke: 4.06 x 3.75 inches. Compression ratio: (synchromesh) 8.6:1; (Hydra-Matic) 10.25:1. Brake hp: (synchromesh) 281 at 4400 rpm; (Hydra-Matic) 303 at 4600 rpm. Five main bearings. Hydraulic valve lifters. Carburetor: Carter AFB four-barrel.

CHASSIS FEATURES: Wheelbase: (Series 21, 23 and 27) 123 inches; (Series 24 and 28) 124 inches. Overall length: (Catalina, Ventura and Bonneville Custom Safari) 213.7 inches; (All others) 220.7 inches. Front tread: 63.7 inches. Rear tread: 64 inches. Tires: (Passenger cars) 8.00 x 14; (Station wagons and all with air conditioning) 8.50 x 14.

OPTIONS: Air conditioning ($430). Electric antenna ($30) Aluminum hubs and drums ($107). E-Z-Eye Glass ($43). CircL-Aire heater defroster ($43 Direct Aire heater defroster ($94). Sportable radio ($129). Wonder Bar radio ($125). Super Deluxe radio ($89). Rear seat speaker ($14). Luggage carrier ($19). Padded dash ($19). Bucket seats ($100). Safeguard speedometer ($15). Magi-Cruise ($13). Custom wheel discs ($17-32); Deluxe wheel discs ($16). Windshield washer ($13). Continental spare tire and cover ($258). Underhood utility lamp ($7). Remote control mirror ($12). Power windows ($58 or $106). Power steering ($108). Power brakes ($43). Custom steering wheel ($15). A column-shift three-speed manual transmission was standard. Super Hydra-Matic (Strato-Flight) transmission was $231.34 extra. A four-speed manual floor mounted transmission became available in mid-year, though not as a regular production option (RPO). Most went into professionally-driven NASCAR racers. The unit was basically the same one used by Corvettes and Chevrolets and retailed for $188.30 from Chevrolet. The Pontiac price is probably the same. A variety of rear axle ratios were

available. Safe-T-Track differential was $43 extra and optional dual exhausts cost $31. The Tempest 66E option or '425E' two-barrel 215 hp economy engine was optional on all models at no extra cost, but only with Hydra-Matic. The Bonneville four-barrel carburetor was $23.94 extra in other lines. Tri-Power on the standard (10.5:1 compression) block produced 315 hp on cars with synchromesh and 318 hp on Hydra-Matic equipped units, both at 4600 rpm. Price for this option was $89/$99/$132/$142 depending on the engine/transmission combination. (Note: High-performance engine prices also varied by series and transmission, with lowest cost on high-trim models with Hydra-Matic.) Tri-Power on the Tempest 425 block (NASCAR motor with 10.75:1 compression) gave 348 hp at 4600 rpm and prices for the option were $316/$326/$359/$369. Four-barrel induction on the Tempest 425 V-8 gave 333 hp at 4600 rpm and prices were $230/$251/$273/$294.

HISTORICAL FOOTNOTES: Production began Aug. 31, 1959. Introductions were Oct. 1, 1959. Calendar year output was 450,206 (including early 1961 Tempests) for 6.6 percent market share. Model year production was 396,716. Four NASCAR Grand Nationals and three other stock car races were won by Pontiacs. Jim Wangers drove a 1960 Pontiac to the NHRA "Top Eliminator" title. Mickey Thompson installed four Pontiac engines in his Challenger I World Land Speed Record car and drove it 363.67 mph. The 333 hp Catalina two-door hardtop was timed at 7.8 seconds for 0-to-60 and 16 seconds for the quarter-mile. Safari remained Pontiac's nomenclature for a station wagon. All 1960 Safaris were four-door types and nine-passenger (three-seat) versions had power tailgate windows and rear-facing folding seats. The term Vista meant four-door pillarless hardtop. The term Sport Sedan meant two-door pillared coupe. Safaris had distinctive single taillamps and rear decor trim. Starlight two-toning was $40 in regular colors or $52 in special colors. AmbleWagons were low-cost professional cars built off a standard Pontiac station wagon chassis by the Automotive Conversion Corp., Troy, Mich.

1961 PONTIAC

CATALINA SERIES — (V-8) — SERIES 23 — Down-sizing was seen at Pontiac this year. Thanks to a new perimeter frame design the bodies on standard sized cars were smaller and lighter in weight. A radically new compact named the Tempest was introduced as a Pontiac entry in the growing small car market. Major design differences included a return to the twin grille styling theme, sculptured side panels, taller rooflines and squared-off bodies with small tail fins added. Standard equipment on Catalinas included turn signals, oil filter, cigarette lighter, sun visors, electric windshield wipers and five tubeless blackwall tires.

PONTIAC I.D. NUMBERS: VIN on left front door post. First symbol tells series: 21=Tempest; 23=Catalina; 25=Ventura; 26=Star Chief; 27=Bonneville Safari; 28=Bonneville. Second and third symbols tell year: 61=1961. Fourth symbol tells assembly plant: P=Pontiac, Mich.; S=South Gate, Calif.; L=Linden, N.J.; W=Wilmington, Dela.; K=Kansas City, Kan.; D=Doraville, Ga.; A=Arlington, Texas; E=Euclid, Ohio. Fifth through last symbols are the sequential number starting at 1001 for each assembly plant. Body/Style Number plate under hood tells manufacturer, Fisher style number, assembly plant, trim code, paint code, accessory codes. Style number consists of 61 (for 1961) prefix and four symbols that appear in second column of charts below. First two symbols indicate series; second two symbols indicate body type. VIN appears on front of engine at right-hand cylinder bank along with an alpha-numerical engine production code. Engine production codes included: [195 cid/110 hp four] DA/DS; [195 cid/120 hp four] OSY; [195 cid/155 hp four] XS/YS/XA; [195 cid/140 hp four] OA; [215 cid/155 hp aluminum V-8] YA. [389 cid/215 hp V-8] A2/G4; [389 cid/230 hp V-8] E3/ W3/E7/W7/; [389 cid/235 hp V-8] P4/B4/H4 [389 cid/267 hp V-8] S1/S5; [389 cid/287 hp V-8] A1/A5; [389 cid/303 hp V-8] B1/T1/PO/B5/T5/. [389 cid/318 hp H.O. Tri-Power V-8] C4/RC4/ CO/RCO/I9/R19; [389 cid/333 hp V-8] F4/FO/RMO/U9; [389 cid/348 hp H.O. Tri-Power V-8] M4/RM4/MO/V9; [389 cid/363 hp Super-Duty Tri-Power V-8] RMP. [421 cid/373 hp Super-Duty V-8] 11-5.

CATALINA

Model Number	Body/Style Number	Body Type & Seating	Factory Price	Shipping Weight	Production Total
23	2369	4-dr Sed-6P	2702	3725	38,638
23	2339	4-dr Vista HT-6P	2842	3785	17,589
23	2311	2-dr Spt Sed-6P	2631	3650	9,846
23	2337	2-dr HT-6P	2766	3680	14,524
23	2367	2-dr Conv-5P	3078	3805	12,379
23	2345	4-dr Sta Wag-9P	3207	4175	7,783
23	2335	4-dr Sta Wag-6P	3099	4135	12,595

NOTE 1: 113,354 Catalinas were built.
NOTE 2: 6,337 had Synchromesh and 107,017 had Hydra-Matic.

VENTURA SERIES — (V-8) — SERIES 25 — The Ventura continued as a Catalina-sized car with Custom level interior and out. Identification included chrome outline moldings for side spears, Ventura script inside the spear on the door and bright metal roof drip moldings. Unlike the Catalinas with horizontal-oval taillamps and small hubcaps, Venturas carried two round taillamps and full Deluxe wheel discs. Interiors were trimmed in three-tone Jeweltone Morrokide. Standard equipment included custom steering wheel, electric clock and right-hand ashtray, plus all features seen on Catalinas.

VENTURA

Model Number	Body/Style Number	Body Type & Seating	Factory Price	Shipping Weight	Production Total
25	2539	4-dr Vista HT-6P	3047	3795	13,912
25	2537	2-dr HT-6P	2971	3685	13,297

NOTE 1: 27,209 Venturas were built.
NOTE 2: 1,940 had Synchromesh and 25,269 had Hydra-Matic.

STAR CHIEF SERIES — (V-8) — SERIES 26 — Star Chiefs could be outwardly identified by chrome outline moldings on the concave portion of the side spears which encircled a Star Chief script on the front door, thin horizontal moldings on the convex section of the spear, three chrome stars stacked on the side of the fins and triple taillights on each side. Standard equipment was comprised of all found in Venturas, plus two-speed wipers. Interiors were furnished in Jacquard woven cloth with metallic highlights accented by Jeweltone Morrokide.

STAR CHIEF

Model Number	Body/Style Number	Body Type & Seating	Factory Price	Shipping Weight	Production Total
26	2669	4-dr Sed-6P	3003	3840	16,024
26	2639	4-dr Vista HT-6P	3136	3870	13,557

NOTE 1: 29,581 Star Chief chassis were made.
NOTE 2: 130 had Synchromesh and 29,451 had Hydra-Matic.

BONNEVILLE SERIES — (V-8) — SERIES 28 — Cars in Pontiac's top series were distinguished by golden Bonneville nameplates on the left-hand grille, bright metal moldings on side spears, Bonneville block letters on the convex portion of the spears where front fenders and doors met and triple taillamps set into bright metal housings. Everything included on Star Chiefs was considered standard. Upholstery ranged from nylon and Morrokide combinations on closed cars to all-Morrokide on convertibles, with full genuine leather trims optional.

BONNEVILLE

Model Number	Body/Style Number	Body Type & Seating	Factory Price	Shipping Weight	Production Total
28	2839	4-dr Vista HT-6P	3331	3895	30,830
28	2837	2-dr HT-6P	3255	3810	16,906
28	2867	2-dr Conv-5P	3476	3905	18,264

NOTE 1: A total of 66,385 Bonnevilles were built.
NOTE 2: 1,480 had Synchromesh and 64,905 had Hydra-Matic.
NOTE 3: About 385 Bonneville chassis went to professional car makers.

BONNEVILLE CUSTOM SERIES — (V-8) — SERIES 27 — Comprising a separate series by itself was the Bonneville Custom Safari, which was built off the Catalina platform with Bonneville power and appointments. The majority of trim and equipment was similar to other Bonnevilles, but the four-door station wagon had unique Safari rear fender scripts, vertical taillamps and a circular keyhole ornament on the tailgate.

BONNEVILLE CUSTOM

Model Number	Body/Style Number	Body Type & Seating	Factory Price	Shipping Weight	Production Total
27	2735	4-dr Sta Wag-6P	3530	4185	3,323

NOTE 1: 3,323 Custom Safaris were built.
NOTE 2: 18 had Synchromesh and 3,305 had Hydra-Matic.

1961 Pontiac, Tempest four-door sedan, 4-cyl

TEMPEST — (4-CYL) — SERIES 21 — In appearance the Tempest was pure Pontiac with twin grilles, sculptured body panels, V-contour hood and bodyside windsplits. It was technically innovative featuring an integral body and frame, flexible "rope" driveshaft, torque tube drive, independent rear suspension, rear-mounted transaxle and a four-cylinder base powerplant created by cutting a 389 cid V-8 in half. Standard equipment included electric wipers, turn signals, dual sun visors and five tubeless blackwall tires. A four-door sedan and Safari station wagon were first to appear, but were joined by a pair of two-door hardtop Sport Coupes later in the year. One of these was a Deluxe model with bucket seats, named the LeMans.

TEMPEST

Model Number	Body/Style Number	Body Type & Seating	Factory Price	Shipping Weight	Production Total
21	2119	4-dr Sed-6P	2702	2800	22,557
21	2127	2-dr HT-6P	2113	2785	7,432
21	2135	4-dr Sta Wag-6P	2438	2980	7,404

TEMPEST (WITH CUSTOM TRIM PACKAGE)

Model Number	Body/Style Number	Body Type & Seating	Factory Price	Shipping Weight	Production Total
21	2119	4-dr Sed-6P	2884	2800	40,082
21	2127	2-dr LeMans HT-6P	2297	2795	7,455
21	2135	4-dr Sta Wag-6P	2611	2980	15,853

NOTE 1: 98,779 Tempest with four-cylinder engines were built.
NOTE 2: 26,737 Tempest fours had Synchromesh and 72,042 had Hydra-Matic.
NOTE 3: 2,004 Tempests were built with optional (Buick) aluminum V-8s.
NOTE 4: Three Tempest V-8s had Synchromesh and 2,001 had Hydra-Matic.

BASE ENGINES

(CATALINA/VENTURA/STAR CHIEF) Base V-8s: Overhead valves. Cast iron block. Displacement: 389 cid. Bore and stroke: 4.06 x 3.75 inches. Compression ratio: (Synchromesh) 8.6:1; (Hydra-Matic) 10.25:1. Brake hp: 215 at 3600 R.P.M.; (Hydra-Matic) 267 at 4200 rpm. Five main bearings. Hydraulic valve lifters. Carburetor: Rochester Number 7019060 two-barrel. 4400 rpm.

(BONNEVILLE/BONNEVILLE CUSTOM) Base V-8s: Overhead Valves. Cast iron block. Displacement: 389 cid. Bore and stroke: 4.06 x 3.75 inches. Compression ratios: (Synchromesh) 8.6:1; (HydraMatic) 10.25:1. Brake hp: (Synchromesh) 235 at 3600 rpm.; (Hydra-Matic) 303 at 4600 rpm. Five main bearings. Hydraulic valve lifters. Carburetor: Carter AFB3123S four-barrel.

(TEMPEST "INDY FOUR") Inline. Four-cylinder. Overhead valves. Cast iron block. Displacement: 194.5 cid. Bore and stroke: 4.06 x 3.75 inches. Compression ratios: (Synchromesh) 8.6: 1; (Hydra-Matic) 10.25:1. Brake hp: (Synchromesh) 110 at 3800 rpm; (Hydra-Matic) 120 at 3800 rpm. Five main bearings. Hydraulic valve lifters. Carburetor: Rochester Number 7019061 two-barrel.

OPTIONAL PONTIAC V-8 ENGINES

215 cid. Compression ratio: 8.8. Carburetion: two-barrel. Brake hp: 155 at 4600 rpm. (optional in Tempest)

389 cid. Compression ratio: 8.6. Carburetion: two-barrel. Brake hp: 230 at 4000 rpm. (optional all models with Hydra-Matic)

389 cubic inch. Compression ratio: 8.6. Carburetion: four-barrel. Brake hp: 235 at 3600 rpm. (standard in Bonneville; optional all others with synchromesh)

389 cid. Compression ratio: 10.25. Carburetion: two-barrel. Brake hp: 267 at 4200 rpm. (optional in Catalina and Ventura with Hydra-Matic).

389 cid. Compression ratio: 10.25. Carburetion: two-barrel. Brake hp: 283 at 4400 rpm. (optional in Star Chief with Hydra-Matic).

389 cid. Compression ratio: 10.25. Carburetion: four-barrel. Brake hp: 303 at 4600 rpm. (optional in Bonneville with Hydra-Matic).

389 cid. Compression ratio: 10.25. Carburetion: four-barrel. Brake hp: 287 at 4400 rpm. (optional in Catalina with Hydra-Matic)

389 cid. Compression ratio: 10.75. Carburetion: three two-barrels. Brake hp: 318 at 4600 rpm. (optional in all models with any transmission)

389 cid. Compression ratio: 10.75. Carburetion: four-barrel. Brake hp: 333 at 4800 rpm. (optional all models with any transmission)

389 cid. Compression ratio: 10.75. Carburetion: three two-barrels. Brake hp: 348 at 4800 rpm. (optional all models with any transmission)

421 cid. Compression ratio: 11. Carburetion: two four-barrels. Brake hp: 405 at 5600 rpm. (Super-Duty: available only in Catalina two-door; off-road use only)

CHASSIS FEATURES: Wheelbase: (Series 23, 25 and 27) 119 inches; (Series 26 and 28) 123 inches; (Series 21) 112 inches. Overall length: (Series 23 and 25) 210 inches; (Series 27 and Series 23 Safaris) 209.7 inches; (Series 26 and 28) 217 inches; (Tempest) 189.3 inches. Front tread: (Pontiac) 62.5; (Tempest) 56.8. Rear tread (Pontiac) 62.5; (Tempest) 56.8. Tires: (Pontiac) 8.00 x 14; (Pontiac Safaris) 8.50 x 14; (Tempests) 6.00 x 15.

OPTIONS

[PONTIAC] Air conditioning ($430). Electric antenna ($30). Guide-Matic headlamp control ($43). Power brakes ($43). Six-way power seat ($97). Power windows ($104). Safeguard speedometer ($19). Magic-Cruise ($16) Aluminum hubs and drums ($107). Bucket seats ($116). Heavy-duty springs ($19) E-Z Eye glass ($43). Luggage carrier ($99) Power tailgate ($32) and more. A three-speed manual transmission was standard. Four-speed Super Hydra-Matic was $231.34 extra. A four-speed manual gearbox with floor shift was $306.66 extra on full-sized cars. Rear axle ratios: (Synchromesh) 3.23:1; (Hydra-Matic) 2.87:1. Other ratios were available. Safe-T-Track differential was $43 extra. The four-barrel induction system was $24 extra on all cars except Bonnevilles. Tri-Power induction was priced $110 to $168 depending upon model and transmission. The four-barrel Tempest '425A' high-performance engine was priced $230 to $293 depending upon model and transmission. The Tri-Power Tempest '425A' high-performance engine was priced $338 to $396 depending upon model and transmission.

[TEMPEST] Basic group ($167-172); Power tailgate window ($54). Deluxe wheel discs ($16) Windshield washer ($13) Power steering ($75). Bumper guards ($16). Back-up lights ($11-12). Cool-Pack air-conditioner ($318). Interior decor group ($70-75). Lower exterior decor group ($13). Upper exterior decor group ($40). Protection group ($40-42). A three-speed manual transmission was standard. A two-speed Tempes-Torque automatic transmission with dashboard-mounted 'spoon' lever control was $172 extra. Engine options included a high-output one-barrel edition of the four with 140 hp at 4400 rpm.; a four-barrel edition of the four with 155 hp at 4800 rpm and a 215 215 cid Buick V-8 with 8.8:1 compression, two-barrel carburetor and 155 hp at 4600 rpm. ($216 extra).

HISTORICAL FOOTNOTES: Production start-up: Sept. 1, 1960. Introduction: Oct. 6, 1960. Model year assemblies were 340,635. Calendar year output was 360,336 Pontiacs and Tempests. Pontiac had a 6.3 percent market share. The term Vista means four-door hardtop. The term Sport Sedan means two-door pillared coupe. The term Safari means station wagon. Bucket seats available only in body style 2867. Pontiac took 21 of 52 NASCAR Grand Nationals. Bunkie Knudsen was the general manager of PMD. Two road tests were done on Pontiacs with the 348 hp V-8. The first featured a Ventura hardtop that went 0-to-60 in 8.2 seconds and did the quarter-mile in 15.5 seconds. The second featured a Catalina S/S drag racing car based on the two-door hardtop. It went from 0-to-60 in 4.6 seconds and did the quarter-mile in 13.7 seconds.

1962 PONTIAC

1962 Pontiac, Catalina four-door Vista hardtop, V-8

CATALINA SERIES — (V-8) — SERIES 23 — Standard Pontiacs grew about an inch-and-a-half for 1962. Styling revisions included a V-shaped twin grille, full-length side sculpturing and new rear end styling with curved taillamps. Vista sedans no longer sported the 'flat-top' look and Sport Coupes had multi-plated roofs with a "convertible-like" appearance. Ventura trim became an add-on package for two Catalinas. Regular equipment on Catalinas included turn signals, oil filter, cigarette lighter, sun visors, heater and defroster, windshield wiper and five tubeless tires. Nine-passenger Catalina Safaris had power tailgate windows. Outwardly the cars came with small hubcaps, unaccented side spears and Catalina front fender scripts.

PONTIAC I.D. NUMBERS: VIN on left front door post. First symbol tells series: 21=Tempest; 23=Catalina; 26=Star Chief; 27=Bonneville Safari; 28=Bonneville; 29=Grand Prix. Second and third symbols tell year: 62=1962. Fourth symbol tells assembly plant: P=Pontiac, Mich.;

S=South Gate, Calif.; L=Linden, N.J.; W=Wilmington, Dela.; K=Kansas City, Kan.; D=Doraville, Ga.; A=Arlington, Texas. The remaining symbols in VIN are the sequential production number beginning at 1001 for each factory. Body/Style Number plate under hood tells manufacturer, Fisher style number, assembly plant, trim code, paint code, accessory codes. Style number consists of 62 (for 1962) prefix and four symbols that appear in second column of charts below. First two symbols indicate series; second two symbols indicate body type. VIN appears on front of engine at right-hand cylinder bank along with an alpha-numerical engine production code. Engine production codes included: [195 cid/110 hp four] 89Z/85Z; [195 cid/115 hp four] 79Y; [195 cid/120 hp four] 86Z; [195 cid/140 hp four] 76Y; [195 cid/166 hp four] 77Y/87Z; [215 cid/185 hp aluminum V-8] 91Z/97Z. [389 cid/215 hp V-8] O1A/O3B. [389 cid/230 hp V-8] 20L/21L/40R/41R. [389 cid/235 hp V-8] O2B. [389 cid/267 hp V-8] 15H/17H. [389 cid/283 hp V-8] 35M/37M. [389 cid/303 hp V-8] 16J/16K/18K/39N/36P/38P. [389 cid/318 hp H.O. Tri-Power V-8] 10B/27J/49N. [389 cid/333 hp V-8] O8B/25/47NJ. [389 cid/348 hp H.O. Tri-Power V-8] 11B/28J/50N. [421 cid/405 hp Super-Duty V-8] 12-5.

CATALINA

Model Number	Body/Style Number	Body Type & Seating	Factory Price	Shipping Weight	Production Total
23	2389	4-dr Sed-6P	2796	3765	68,124
23	2389	4-dr Vista HT-6P	2936	3825	29,251
23	2311	2-dr Sed-6P	2725	3705	14,263
23	2347	2-dr HT-6P	2860	3730	46,024
23	2367	2-dr Conv-5P	3172	3855	16,877
23	2345	4-dr Sta Wag-9P	3301	4220	10,716
23	2335	4-dr Sta Wag-6P	3193	4180	19,399

NOTE 1: 204,654 Catalinas were built.
NOTE 2: 13,104 had Synchromesh and 191.550 had Hydra-Matic.

1962 Pontiac, Bonneville two-door hardtop sport coupe, V-8

STAR CHIEF SERIES — (V-8) — SERIES 26 — Star Chiefs were distinguished by full-length body rub moldings and three slanting stars on the rear fins. Standard equipment included all Catalina features, plus custom steering wheel; electric clock; Deluxe wheel discs; right-hand ashtray and decor molding; dual speed wipers; and special upholstery. Interior trims included Pyramid Pattern cloth and Morrokide combinations or all-Morrokide.

STAR CHIEF

Model Number	Body/Style Number	Body Type & Seating	Factory Price	Shipping Weight	Production Total
26	2669	4-dr Sed-6P	3097	3875	27,760
26	2639	4-dr Vista HT-6P	3230	3925	13,882

NOTE 1: A total of 41,642 Star Chiefs were built.
NOTE 2: 196 had Synchromesh and 41,446 had Hydra-Matic.

BONNEVILLE SERIES — (V-8) — SERIES 28 — Trim on Bonneville included chrome side spear moldings with ribbed bands in the concave portion, elongated V-shaped rear fender medallions, ribbed trim moldings on the deck lid latch panel, Bonneville block letters on the front fenders and deck lid latch panel and series identification on the left-hand radiator grille. Standard equipment included all items found on Star Chiefs plus rear foam cushions, padded dashes and courtesy lamps. Upholstery was of fine woven Morrokide or optional all-leather. High-wing bucket seats were optional in convertibles.

BONNEVILLE

Model Number	Body/Style Number	Body Type & Seating	Factory Price	Shipping Weight	Production Total
28	2839	4-dr Vista HT-6P	3425	4005	44,015
28	2847	2-dr HT-6P	3349	3900	31,629
28	2867	2-dr Conv-5P	3570	4005	21,582

NOTE 1: 97,772 Series 28 Bonnevilles were built.
NOTE 2: 1,874 Series 28 Bonnevilles had synchromesh; 95,848 had Hydra-Matic.
NOTE 3: 496 Series 28 chassis were provided to professional car builders.

BONNEVILLE CUSTOM SERIES — (V-8) — SERIES 27 — The Custom Safari again formed a separate series. It was the heaviest and most expensive Pontiac. Pleated Morrokide upholstery in two-tones was featured, as well as a concealed luggage locker.

BONNEVILLE CUSTOM

Model Number	Body/Style Number	Body Type & Seating	Factory Price	Shipping Weight	Production Total
27	2735	4-dr Sta Wag-6P	3624	4255	4,527

NOTE 1: 4,527 Series 27 Bonneville Custom station wagons were built.
NOTE 2: 35 had synchromesh and 4,492 had Hydra-Matic.

GRAND PRIX SERIES — (V-8) SERIES 29 — The new Grand Prix replaced the Ventura model, although Ventura-Catalinas were still available as a trim option. The "GP" was identified by clean side styling with a checkered flag badge in the concave section of side spears, rocker panel molding, an anodized grille insert and nose piece and special rear end styling. The from-the-factory equipment list included all Bonneville features (except courtesy lamps), plus solid color Morrokide upholstery, bucket seats and center console with tachometer.

GRAND PRIX

Model Number	Body/Style Number	Body Type & Seating	Factory Price	Shipping Weight	Production Total
29	2947	2-dr HT-5P	3490	3835	30,195

NOTE 1: 30,195 GPs were built.
NOTE 2: 3,939 had Synchromesh and 26,556 had Hydra-Matic.

1962 Pontiac, Grand Prix two-door hardtop, V-8

TEMPEST — (4-CYL) — SERIES 21 — Styling changes for Tempests included a new wider-spaced split grille theme with a third grille section (incorporating a V-shaped emblem) placed in the center and the addition of bolt-in bright metal fins at the rear. There were five basic models, but two were called Customs and could be optioned with the LeMans trim package. Standard equipment included heater and defroster, electric wipers, turn signals, left-hand visors and five tubeless blackwall tires. Those delivered in Custom trim level had twin sun visors, cigarette lighters, Deluxe steering wheel, custom upholstery and special exterior trim. The Custom Convertible sported courtesy lamps.

TEMPEST

Model Number	Body/Style Number	Body Type & Seating	Factory Price	Shipping Weight	Production Total
21	2119	4-dr Sed-6P	2240	2815	16,057 (21,373)
21	2127	2-dr Cpe-6P	2186	2785	15,473
21	2117	2-dr HT-6P	2294	2800	12,319
21	2167	2-dr Conv-5P	2564	2955	5,076
21	2135	4-dr Sta Wag-6P	2511	2995	6,504 (11,170)

TEMPEST CUSTOM (LEMANS OPTION)

Model Number	Body/Style Number	Body Type & Seating	Factory Price	Shipping Weight	Production Total
21	2117	2-dr HT-6P	2418	N/A	39,662
21	2167	2-dr Conv-5P	2742	N/A	15,599

NOTE 1: 141,535 Tempest fours were built.
NOTE 2: 28,867 Tempest fours had synchromesh; 112,668 had Tempes-Torque.
NOTE 3: 1,658 Tempest V-8s were built.
NOTE 4: 86 Tempest V-8s had synchromesh and 1,572 had Tempes-Torque automatic.
NOTE 5: Figures in parenthesis are production of Tempests with Deluxe package.
NOTE 6: Sport Coupe and convertible came Custom-only; no Deluxe option.

BASE ENGINES

(CATALINA) V-8. Overhead valves. Cast iron block. Displacement: 389 cid. Bore and stroke: 4.06 x 3.75 inches. Compression ratio: (Synchromesh) 8.6:1; (Hydra-Matic) 10.25:1. Brake hp: (Synchromesh) 215 at 3600 rpm; (Hydra-Matic) 267 at 4200 rpm. Five main bearings. Hydraulic lifters. Carburetor: Rochester two-barrel.

(STAR CHIEF) V-8s for Star Chiefs were the same as listed for Catalinas, except the Star Chief Hydra-Matic engine had a slightly higher output of 283 hp at 4400 rpm due to the use of a different Rochester two-barrel carburetor.

(BONNEVILLE/GRAND PRIX) V-8. Overhead valves. Cast iron block. Displacement: 389 cid. Bore and stroke: 4.06 x 3.75 inches. Compression ratio: (Synchromesh) 8.6:1; (Hydra-Matic) 10.25:1. Brake hp: (Synchromesh) 235 at 3600 rpm; (Hydra-Matic) 303 at 4600 rpm. Five main bearings. Hydraulic valve lifters. Carburetor: Carter AFB four-barrel.

(TEMPEST "INDY FOUR") Inline. Four-cylinder. Overhead valves. Cast iron block. Displacement: 194.5 cid. Bore and stroke: 4.06 x 3.75. Compression ratio: (Synchromesh) 8.6:1; (Tempest-Torque) 10.25:1. Brake hp: (Synchromesh) 110 at 3800 rpm; (Tempest-Torque) 120 at 3800 rpm. Carburetor: Rochester one-barrel.

OPTIONAL V-8 ENGINES

215 cid. Compression ratio: 11. Carburetion: four-barrel. Brake hp: 190 at 4800 rpm. (optional in Tempest)

389 cid. Compression ratio: 8.6. Carburetion: two-barrel. Brake hp: 215 at 3600 rpm. (standard in Catalina and Star Chief with synchromesh).

389 cid. Compression ratio: 8.6. Carburetion: four-barrel. Brake hp: 235 at 3600 rpm. (standard on Bonneville with manual, optional all others)

389 cid. Compression ratio: 8.6. Carburetion: two-barrel. Brake hp: 230 at 4000 rpm. (optional all models with automatic)

389 cid. Compression ratio: 10.25. Carburetion: two-barrel. Brake hp: 267 at 4200 rpm. (optional on Catalina with automatic)

389 cid. Compression ratio: 10.25. Carburetion: two-barrel. Brake hp: 283 at 4400 rpm. (optional on Star Chief with automatic)

389 cid. Compression ratio: 10.25. Carburetion: two-barrel. Brake hp: 305 at 4600 rpm. (standard on Bonneville & Grand Prix with automatic, optional on Catalina & Star Chief with automatic)

389 cid. Compression ratio: 10.75. Carburetion: three two-barrels. Brake hp: 318 at 4600. (optional all models with any transmission)

389 cid. Compression ratio: 10.75. Carburetion: four-barrel. Brake hp: 333 at 4800. (optional all models, any transmission)

389 cid. Compression ratio: 10.75. Carburetion: three two-barrels. Brake hp: 348 at 4800 rpm. (optional all models, any transmission) 389 cid. Compression ratio: 10.75. Carburetion: four-barrel. Brake hp: 385 at 5200 rpm. (Super Duty-optional on Catalina two-door only)

421 cid. Compression ratio: 11.0:1. Carburetion: two four-barrels. Brake hp: 405 at 5600 rpm. (Super-Duty, optional on Catalina two-door only)

CHASSIS FEATURES: Wheelbase: (Series 23 Safari and Series 27) 119 inches; (Series 23 and 29) 120 inches; (Series 26 and 28) 123 inches; (Series 21) 112 inches. Overall length: (Series 23 and Safari and Series 27) 212.3 inches; (Series 23 and 29) 211.6 inches; (Series 26 and 28) 218.6 inches. Front tread: (Pontiac) 62.5 inches; (Tempest) 56.8 inches. Rear tread: (Pontiac) 62.5 inches; (Tempest) 56.8 inches. Tires: (Pontiac) 8.00 x 14; (Tempest) 6.00 x 15.

OPTIONS

[PONTIAC] Guidematic headlamp control ($43). Bucket seats for Body Style 2867 ($116). Console for Body Style 2867 w/bucket seats ($161). Padded dash ($16). Power bench seat ($97). Power bucket seat ($28). Power brakes ($43). Power steering ($108). Magi-Cruise ($16). Ventura trim for Body Styles 2339 and 2347 ($118.) Aluminum hubs and drums ($108-122). Two-speed wipers ($5). Windshield washers ($13). Power tailgate window ($31). Power windows ($18). Split-back Safari seat ($116). A three-speed manual transmission was standard. Super Hydra-Matic was $231.34 extra. Four-speed Synchromesh with floor shift was $231.34 extra. Dual exhausts were standard with the Trophy '425A' V-8s and $30.88 extra on others. Safe-T-Track differential was $42 extra. Four-barrel carburetion was standard on Bonneville and Grand Prix and $24 extra on others. Tri-Power induction was $116-174 extra depending on model and transmission. The four-barrel '425A' V-8 was $199-294 extra depending on model and transmission. The Tri-Power '425A' V-8 was $312-401 extra depending on model and transmission. Approximately 1,514 cars were built with 421 cid Super-Duty V-8s. This motor represented a stroked version of the Trophy V-8 block with two four-barrel carburetors. Such engines developed 405 hp at 5600 rpm and cost $2,250 extra. Seven rear axle gear ratios were provided the 3.64:1 and 3.90:1 on special order only.

[TEMPEST] Air conditioner ($319). Back-up lights ($11-13). Bumper guards ($16). Electric clock ($16). Tinted windshield ($20). Padded dash ($4). Remote control mirror ($12). Power steering ($75). Power tailgate window ($54). Manual radio ($54). Push-button radio ($62). Upper decor group ($19-34). Lower decor group ($34). Interior decor group ($70-75). Exterior decor group combo ($54-67). Code 088 LeMans option group: (Custom Convertible) $178; (Custom Sports Coupe) $124. A three-speed manual transmission was standard. Two-speed Tempes-Torque automatic or four-speed Synchromesh were $172.80 extra. Four-barrel carburetion on the 'Indy Four' (166 hp at 4800 rpm) was $38.74 extra. The two-barrel aluminum Buick V-8 (185 hp at 4800 rpm) was $261.36 extra. A 3.55:1 rear axle was standard and 3.31:1 was optional.

HISTORICAL FOOTNOTES: Production started Aug. 15, 1961. Introductions took place Sept. 21, 1961. The model year saw 521,933 assemblies. In the calendar year, 547,350 cars were made, putting Pontiac in third place in vehicle production in the U.S. Pontiacs took 14 of 18 United States Auto Club stock car races and 22 of 53 NASCAR events. Joe Weatherly won the driving championship in a Pontiac. Bunkie Knudsen moved to Chevrolet and E.M. "Pete" Estes took over as the new general manager of PMD. Jim Wanger's 1962 Catalina Super-Duty hardtop was tested in a car buff magazine. The 405 hp "Poncho" went from 0-to-60 in 5.4 seconds and did the quarter-mile in 13.9 at 107 mph. A Catalina with a special 370 hp "Royal Bobcat" package from Royal Pontiac (Royal Oak, Mich.) ran 0-to-60 in 6.5 seconds and did the quarter-mile in 14.5. Carol Cox took the NHRA Winternationals with a 13.06 quarter-mile performance in a Catalina S/SA drag car. Vista means four-door hardtop. Safari means station wagon. Body Styles 2117 and 2167 came only as Tempest Custom or Tempest Custom with LeMans option. Bucket seats, center console and floor mounted gearshift control were standard on Body Style 2947.

1963 PONTIAC

1963 Pontiac, Catalina four-door sedan, V-8

CATALINA — (V-8) — SERIES 23 — Styling and luxury were emphasized by Pontiac in 1963 and GM banned factory competition efforts. Styling was totally new with clean, square lines, angled roofs, upward curving taillamps, recessed split grilles and non-panoramic windshields. Catalinas wore small hubcaps, plain full-length body moldings and Catalina front fender scripts. Turn signals, oil filters, cigarette lighter, sun visors, heater and defroster, electric wipers and five tubeless tires were standard equipment. Safaris had oversize 8.50 x 14 tires and the nine-passenger job had a power tailgate window.

PONTIAC I.D. NUMBERS: VIN on left front door post. First symbol tells series: 21=Tempest; 22=LeMans; 23=Catalina; 26=Star Chief; 28=Bonneville; 29=Grand Prix. Second and third symbols tell year: 63=1963. Fourth symbol tells assembly plant: P=Pontiac, Mich.; S=South Gate, Calif.; L=Linden, N.J.; W=Wilmington, Dela.; K=Kansas City, Kan.; D=Doraville, Ga.; A=Arlington, Texas. Following symbols are sequential production number starting with 1001 at each assembly plant. Body/Style Number plate under hood tells manufacturer, Fisher style number, assembly plant, trim code, paint code, accessory codes. Style number consists of 63 (for 1963) prefix and four symbols that appear in second column of charts below. First two symbols indicate series; second two symbols indicate body type. VIN appears on front of engine at right-hand cylinder bank along with an alpha-numerical engine production code. Engine production codes included: [195 cid/115 hp four] 89Z/85Z/79Y. [195 cid/120 hp four] 86Z/83Z. [195 cid/140 hp four] 76Y. [195 cid/166 hp four] 77Y/84Z/87Z. [326 cid/260 hp V-8] 68X/71X/60O/69O. [326 cid/280 hp V-8] 70X/59O. [389 cid/215 hp V-8] O1A/O3B. [389 cid/230 hp V-8] 20L/21L/40R/41R. [389 cid/235 hp V-8] O2B/O4B. [389 cid/267 hp V-8] 15H/17H. [389 cid/283 hp V-8] 35M/37M. [389 cid/303 hp V-8] O6B/16K/18K/36P/38P. [389 cid/313 hp H.O. Tri-Power V-8] O7B/48N/26G. [421 cid/320 hp V-8] 22B/43N/34J. [421 cid/353 hp V-8] O8B/47Q/25G. [421 cid/370 hp H.O. Tri-Power V-8] 11B/28G/50Q. [421 cid/405 hp Super-Duty V-8] 12-5. [421 cid/420 hp Super-Duty V-8] 13-5.

CATALINA

Model Number	Body/Style Number	Body Type & Seating	Factory Price	Shipping Weight	Production Total
23	2311	2-dr Sed-6P	2725	3685	14,091
23	2369	4-dr Sed-6P	2795	3755	79,961
23	2347	2-dr HT-6P	2859	3725	60,795
23	2339	4-dr Vista HT-6P	2935	3815	31,256
23	2367	2-dr Conv-5P	3300	3835	18,249
23	2335	4-dr Sta Wag-6P	3171	4175	18,446
23	2345	4-dr Sta Wag-9P	3193	4230	11,751

NOTE 1: 234,549 Catalinas were built.
NOTE 2: 16,811 had Synchromesh and 217,738 had Hydra-Matic.

STAR CHIEF — V-8 — SERIES 26 — Star Chiefs had full-length body moldings, Deluxe wheel discs, star emblems on the rear roof pillar and Star Chief front fender scripts. Rocker panel moldings were also seen. Standard equipment included all Catalina features plus custom steering wheel, electric clock, dual-speed wipers and special upholstery.

STAR CHIEF

Model Number	Body/Style Number	Body Type & Seating	Factory Price	Shipping Weight	Production Total
26	2669	4-dr Sed-6P	3096	3885	28,309
26	2639	4-dr Vista HT-6P	3229	3915	12,448

NOTE 1: 40,757 Star Chiefs were built.
NOTE 2: 175 had synchromesh and 40,582 had Hydra-Matic.

1963 Bonneville two-door convertible, V-8

BONNEVILLE — (V-8) — SERIES 28 — Bonnevilles came with all Star Chief features, plus rear foam cushions, padded instrument panels and courtesy lamps. They were outwardly identified by broad, ribbed moldings on the front fenders and doors, rear fin badges, left-hand grille nameplates, rocker panel moldings and block-lettered horizontal decor panels on the deck lid latch panel which carried the Bonneville name.

BONNEVILLE

Model Number	Body/Style Number	Body Type & Seating	Factory Price	Shipping Weight	Production Total
28	2847	2-dr HT-6P	3348	3895	30,995
28	2839	4-dr Vista HT-6P	3423	3985	49,929
28	2867	2-dr Conv-5P	3568	3970	23,459
28	2835	4-dr Safari-6P	3623	4245	5,156

NOTE 1: 110,316 Bonnevilles were built.
NOTE 2: 1,819 had synchromesh and 108,497 had Hydra-Matic attachments.
NOTE 3: 777 Bonneville chassis were provided for professional car builders.

1963 Grand Prix two-door hardtop Sports Coupe.

GRAND PRIX — (V-8) — SERIES 29 — The GP was restyled from bumper to bumper. It had a clean look with no side trim, a grille emphasizing negative space with bright accents and enclosed parking lamps, grilled-over taillamps mounted on the deck lid and a concave rear window treatment. Standard equipment included the full list of Bonneville items, plus special solid color Morrokide upholstery, woodgrained steering wheel and dash trim, bucket type front seats and a center console with a vacuum gauge. The Grand Prix badges were now mounted on the sides of the rear fenders and rocker panel moldings were employed.

GRAND PRIX

Model Number	Body/Style Number	Body Type & Seating	Factory Price	Shipping Weight	Production Total
29	2957	2-dr HT-5P	3490	3915	72,959

NOTE 1: 72,959 GPs were built.
NOTE 2: 5,157 had synchromesh and 67,802 had Hydra-Matic.

TEMPEST — (4-CYL) — SERIES 21 — The term "senior compact" was often used to describe the new Tempests. They had the same wheelbase and technical features as earlier Tempests, but they were two inches wider and five inches longer. Design changes included a slight "coke bottle" shape, more angular rooflines, creased side panels, longer trunks, split grille styling, wider wheel openings and dual vertically-stacked taillamps. Standard equipment included heater and defroster, electric wipers, turn signals, left-hand sun visors and five black tubeless tires. Oversize 6.50 x 15 tires were uses on V-8 equipped Tempests and Safaris.

TEMPEST

Model Number	Body/Style Number	Body Type & Seating	Factory Price	Shipping Weight	Production Total
21	2127	2-dr Coupe-6P	2188	2810	13,307
21	2117	2-dr HT-6P	2294	2820	(13,157)
21	2119	4-dr Sed-6P	2241	2815	12,808
					(15,413)
21	2167	2-dr Cus Conv-5P	2554	2955	5,012
21	2135	4-dr Sta Wag-6P	2512	2995	4,203
					(5,932)

NOTE 1: 69,831 Series 21 Tempests were built.
NOTE 2: 16,657 had synchromesh and 53,174 had Tempest-Torque.
NOTE 3: Figures in parenthesis are Tempests with optional Deluxe trim.
NOTE 4: Production of Body Style 2117 is not broken out separately.

TEMPEST LEMANS — (V-8) — SERIES 22 — The LeMans nameplate was listed as a separate series. Standard equipment on LeMans included dual sun visors, Deluxe steering wheel, custom interior, bucket seats, console and power convertible top. Identification features included model badges on front fenders, partially blacked-out grilles, horizontal taillights and a horizontal decor panel on the deck latch panel.

TEMPEST LEMANS

Model Number	Body/Style Number	Body Type & Seating	Factory Price	Shipping Weight	Production Total
22	2217	2-dr HT-6P	2418	2865	45,701
22	2267	2-dr Cus Conv-5P	2742	3035	15,957

NOTE 1: 61,659 LeMans were built.
NOTE 2: 18,034 had synchromesh and 43,625 had Tempest-Torque.
NOTE 3: 23,227 Sport Coupes and 8,744 convertibles were four-cylinders.
NOTE 4: All other LeMans were V-8 powered.

BASE ENGINES

(CATALINA) V-8: Overhead valves. Cast iron block. Displacement: 389 cid. Bore and stroke: 4.06 x 3.75 inches. Compression ratio: 8.6:1 (synchromesh); (Hydra-Matic) 10.25:1. Brake hp: (synchromesh) 215 at 3600 rpm.; (Hydra-Matic) 267 at 4200 rpm. Five main bearings. Hydraulic lifters. Carburetor: Rochester two-barrel (synchromesh) model 7023066; (Hydra-Matic) 7023066.

(STAR CHIEF) V-8s on Star Chiefs had the same specifications as listed for Catalinas except the Star Chief Hydra-Matic engine had a more powerful 283 hp rating.

(BONNEVILLE/GRAND PRIX) V-8: Overhead valves. Cast iron block. Displacement: 389 cid. Bore and stroke: 4.06 x 3.75 inches. Compression ratio: (synchromesh) 8.6:1; (Hydra-Matic) 10.25:1. Brake hp: (synchromesh) 235 at 3600 rpm; (Hydra-Matic) 303 at 4600 rpm. Five main bearings. Hydraulic valve lifters. Carburetor: Carter AFB four-barrel.

(TEMPEST/LEMANS "INDY FOUR") Inline. Four-cylinder. Overhead valves. Cast iron block. Displacement: 194.5 cid. Bore and stroke: 4.06 x 3.75. Compression ratio: (synchromesh) 8.6:1; (automatic) 10.25:1. Brake hp: (synchromesh) 115 at 4000 rpm; (automatic) 120 at 3800 rpm. Five main bearings. Hydraulic valve lifters. Carburetor: Rochester one-barrel.

OPTIONAL V-8 ENGINES

(TEMPEST)

326 cid. Compression ratio: 10.25. Carburetion: two-barrel. Brake hp: 260 at 4800 rpm. (optional Tempest and LeMans)

(PONTIAC)

389 cid. Compression ratio: 8.6. Carburetion: two-barrel. Brake hp: 215 at 3600 rpm. (standard on Star Chief and Catalina with manual transmission)

389 cid. Compression ratio: 8.6. Carburetion: four-barrel. Brake hp: 235 at 3600 rpm. (standard Bonneville with manual; optional all others)

389 cid. Compression ratio: 8.6. Carburetion: two-barrel. Brake hp: 230 at 4000 rpm. (optional all models with automatic)

389 cid. Compression ratio: 10.25. Carburetion: two-barrel. Brake hp: 267 at 4200 rpm. (standard on Catalina with automatic)

389 cid. Compression ratio: 10.25. Carburetion: two-barrel. Brake hp: 283 at 4400 rpm. (standard on Star Chief with automatic)

389 cid. Compression ratio: 10.25. Carburetion: three two-barrels. Brake hp: 313 at 4600 rpm. (optional all models)

421 cid H.O. Compression ratio: 10.75. Carburetion: four-barrel. Brake hp: 353 at 5000 rpm. (optional all "B-body" models with any transmission)

421 cid H.O. Compression ratio: 10.75. Carburetion: three two-barrels. Brake hp: 370 at 5200 rpm. (optional on all "B-body" models with any transmission)

421 cid. Compression ratio: 12.0:1. Carburetion: four-barrel. Brake hp: 390 at 5800 rpm. (Super Duty-optional in Catalina two-door only)

421 cid. Compression ratio: 12.0:1. Carburetion: two four-barrels. Brake hp: 405 at 5600 rpm. (Super Duty-optional in Catalina two-door only)

421 cid. Compression ratio: 13.0:1. Carburetion: two four-barrels. Brake hp: 410 at 5600 rpm. (Super Duty-optional in Catalina two-door only)

CHASSIS FEATURES: Wheelbase: (All Pontiac Safaris) 119 inches; (Series 23 and 29) 120 inches; (Series 26 and 28) 123 inches; (Tempests) 112 inches. Overall length: (All Pontiac Safaris) 212.8 inches; (Series 23 and 29) 211.9 inches; (Series 26 and 28) 218.9 inches; (All Tempests) 194.3 inches. Front tread: (Pontiac) 64 inches; (Tempest) 57.3 inches. Rear tread: (Pontiac) 64 inches; (Tempest) 58 inches. Standard tires: (Pontiac) 8.00 x 14; (Tempest) 6.00 x 15.

OPTIONS

[PONTIAC] Air conditioning ($430). Console including tachometer ($161). Instrument gage cluster ($21-59). Luggage carrier ($94). Remote control mirror ($12). Power brakes ($57). Power seat ($96). Power tilt left-hand bucket seat ($71). Tachometer ($54). Cordova top ($86). Ventura trim on body styles 2339, 2347 and 2369 ($118). Sports wheelcovers ($30-46). Aluminum hubs and drums ($122-138). A three-speed manual transmission was standard. A heavy-duty three-speed manual gearbox was $48 extra on Catalinas and Bonnevilles. A four-speed manual gearbox with floor shift was $231 extra. Super Hydra-Matic was also $231 extra. Dual exhausts were standard with '425A' V-8s and $31 extra on others. Safe-T-Track differential was $43 more. Four-barrel carburetion was standard on Bonneville and Grand Prix and $35 extra on others. Tri-Power induction was $126 on Catalinas and Star Chiefs and $116 on Grand Prixs and Bonnevilles. This engine, with 10.25:1 compression, now gave 313 hp at 4600 rpm. The '421' engines, with 10.75:1 compression heads, were now called H.O. motors. The four-barrel edition was priced $291-343 extra depending upon model and transmission.

It produced 353 hp at 5000 rpm. The Tri-Power 421 H.O. engine was priced $404-445 extra depending on model and transmission. It produced 370 hp at 5200 rpm. A variety of axle ratios were available.

[TEMPEST] Air conditioner ($319). LeMans console shift ($48). Padded dash ($16). Power Convertible top ($54). Power tilt left bucket seat ($67). Power steering ($75). Power tailgate window ($54). Push-button radio ($62). Bucket seats ($134). Custom steering wheel ($6-9). Deluxe steering wheel with ring ($4). Tachometer ($54). Cordova top ($75). Two-speed wipers and washer ($17). A three-speed manual transmission was standard. Two-speed Tempest-Torque automatic was $173 extra. A four-speed manual gearbox with floor shift was priced $189. Four-barrel carburetion on the 'Indy Four' was $39 extra. A new V-8 was available at $167 over base price. Based on a standard Pontiac V-8 with bore size reduced, this engine displaced 326 cid (5.3 liters). Bore and stroke measured 3.72 x 3.75 inches. With a two-barrel carburetor and 10.25:1 compression it produced 260 hp at 4800 rpm. A heavy-duty clutch was available for the one-barrel and four-barrel versions of the 'Indy Four' at prices of $27 and $66 respectively. Standard axle ratio for Tempests was 3.55:1 and optional is 3.31:1.

HISTORICAL FOOTNOTES: Production began Sept. 4, 1962. Introductions were on Oct. 4, 1962. Model year output was 590,071 for an 8.9 percent share of market. Calendar year output was 625,268, making Pontiac the third largest auto producer. Pontiac had four NASCAR wins and startled the drag racing world with the release of "Swiss Cheese" Catalina factory lightweight racing cars. The name came from the fact that their frames were drilled to decrease the weight. The 370 hp 1963 Grand Prix was good for 0-to-60 mph in 6.6 seconds and did the quarter-mile in 15.1 seconds. Vista means four-door hardtop. Safari means station wagon. Vista means four-door hardtop. Safari means station wagon. Sports Sedan was sometimes used to identify two-door pillared coupes. Body style 2957 had a distinctive roofline not shared with other lines. Bucket seats now available for Catalina coupes and convertibles, plus Bonnevilles including the Custom Safari station wagon. The following "Super-Duty 421" vehicles were built in 1963: 13 Catalina and Grand Prix four-barrels; 59 Catalinas and Grand Prixs with two four-barrel carburetors; five unspecified models (believed to be Catalinas with aluminum front ends) with dual four-barrel induction; and 11 Tempests with the dual-quad engine.

1964 PONTIAC

1964 Pontiac, Catalina 2+2 two-door hardtop, V-8

CATALINA — (V-8) — SERIES 23 — Full-size Pontiacs were face-lifted for 1964. They looked shorter, but were about an inch longer overall. Trim identification features seen on Catalinas included three-quarter length side moldings running from the front wheel opening back, Catalina front fender scripts and series medallions on the rear fender. Standard equipment was about the same as a year earlier. Full wheel discs and rocker moldings were options seen on many Catalinas. The Catalina 2 + 2 option package was available an style numbers 2347 and 2367 at approximately $291. The Ventura trim package was available as an interior decor option for Catalina style numbers 2339, 2347 and 2367 at approximately $118.

PONTIAC I.D. NUMBERS: VIN on left front door post. First symbol tells engine type: 6=six-cylinder; 8=V-8. Second symbol indicates series: 0=Tempest; 1=Tempest Custom; 2=LeMans; 3=Catalina; 6=Star Chief; 8=Bonneville; 9=Grand Prix. Third symbol tells year: 64=1964. Fourth symbol tells assembly plant: P=Pontiac, Mich.; S=South Gate, Calif.; L=Linden, N.J.; K=Kansas City, Kan. GMAD plant; D=Doraville, Ga.; A=Arlington, Texas; F=Fremont, Ohio; B=Baltimore, Md.; M=Kansas City, Kan. Chevrolet assembly plant. Following symbols are sequential production number starting with 1001 at each assembly plant. Body/Style Number plate under hood tells manufacturer, Fisher style number, assembly plant, trim code, paint code, accessory codes. Style number consists of 64 (for 1964) prefix and four symbols that appear in second column of charts below. First two symbols indicate series; second two symbols indicate body type. VIN appears on front of engine at right-hand cylinder bank along with an alpha-numerical engine production code. Engine production codes included: [215 cid/140 hp six] 80Z/81Z/85Z/83Y/88Y/89Y. [326 cid/250 hp V-8] 92X/96O. [326 cid/280 hp V-8] 94X/97O. [389 cid/215 hp V-8] O1A/O2B/O3B. [389 cid/230 hp V-8] O4L/O5L/O8R/O9R. [389 cid/239 hp V-8] O3B/O4B. [389 cid/235 hp] 22B. [389 cid/240 hp V-8] 13H. [389 cid/257 hp V-8] 19M. [389 cid/267 hp V-8] 11H/12H. [389 cid/276 hp V-8] 30P. [389 cid/283 hp V-8] 10A/17M/18M. [389 cid/303 hp V-8] 25K/26K/27P/28P. [389 cid/306 hp V-8] 23B/29N/ [389 cid/330 hp H.O. Tri-Power V-8] 32B/33G/34N. [421 cid/320 hp V-8] 35B/38S/43N. [421 cid/350 hp H.O. Tri-Power V-8] 44B/47S/49N. [421 cid/370 hp H.O. Tri-Power V-8] 45B/46G/50Q. [389 cid/325 hp four-barrel GTO V-8] 78X with synchromesh; 79J with Hydra-Matic. [389 cid/348 hp GTO Tri-Power V-8] 76X with synchromesh; 77J with Hydra-Matic. (Note: Some marque experts claim a few GTOs were built with factory-installed and/or dealer-installed 421 V-8s.)

CATALINA

Model Number	Body/Style Number	Body Type & Seating	Factory Price	Shipping Weight	Production Total
23	2369	4-dr Sed-6P	2806	3770	84,457
23	2339	4-dr HT-6P	2945	3835	33,849
23	2311	2-dr Sed-6P	2735	3695	12,480
23	2347	2-dr HT-6P	2869	3750	74,793
23	2367	2-dr Conv-5P	3181	3825	18,693
23	2345	4-dr Sta Wag-9P	3311	4235	13,140
23	2335	4-dr Sta Wag-6P	3203	4190	20,356

NOTE 1: 257,768 Catalinas were built.
NOTE 2: 15,194 had synchromesh and 242,574 had Hydra-Matic.
NOTE 3: 7,998 cars had the 2 + 2 option package.

STAR CHIEF — (V-8) — SERIES 26 — Star Chiefs had Deluxe steering wheels and wheel-covers as standard equipment, as well at two-speed wipers and electric clocks. Trim features included Catalina-like side spears, front fender model scripts and three stylized stars stacked on rear fenders.

STAR CHIEF

Model Number	Body/Style Number	Body Type & Seating	Factory Price	Shipping Weight	Production Total
26	2669	4-dr Sed-6P	3107	3885	26,453
26	2639	4-dr HT-6P	3239	3945	11,200

NOTE 1: 37,653 Star Chiefs were built.
NOTE 2: 132 had synchromesh and 37,521 had Hydra-Matic.

1964 Pontiac, Bonneville two-door convertible, V-8

BONNEVILLE — (V-8) — SERIES 28 — Bonnevilles had no bodyside moldings. Identifiers included V-shaped front fender badges, ribbed lower body beauty moldings (on rocker panels) with front and rear fender extensions and Bonneville block lettering on the rear fendersides. Courtesy lamps, padded dashboards and rear foam seat cushions were standard, plus all items found on the Star Chief equipment list. A Bonneville Brougham trim package was available for Style Number 2839 and included special interior trim and roof pillar nameplates.

BONNEVILLE

Model Number	Body/Style Number	Body Type & Seating	Factory Price	Shipping Weight	Production Total
28	2839	4-dr HT-6P	3433	3995	57,630
28	2847	2-dr HT-6P	3358	3920	34,769
28	2867	2-dr Conv-5P	3578	3985	22,016
28	2835	4-dr Sta Wag-6P	3633	4275	5,844

NOTE 1: 115,060 Bonnevilles (123 inch wheelbase) were built.
NOTE 2: 1,470 cars (123 inch) had synchromesh and 113,590 had Hydra-Matic.
NOTE 3: 5,844 Bonneville (119 inch wheelbase) were built.
NOTE 4: 42 cars (119 inch) had synchromesh and 5,802 had Hydra-Matic.
NOTE 5: 645 Bonneville (123 inch) chassis provided for conversions.

GRAND PRIX — (V-8) — SERIES 29 — Grand Prixs were identified by model lettering and badges behind the front wheel cutout, rectangular front parking lamps, more deeply recessed grilles and GP lettering on the left-hand grille. Concave rear window treatments, grilled-over taillamps and woodgrained trim for dashboards and steering wheels were seen. Standard equipment included dual exhausts, bucket seats, center console and front foam seat cushions.

GRAND PRIX

Model Number	Body/Style Number	Body Type & Seating	Factory Price	Shipping Weight	Production Total
29	2957	2-dr HT-5P	3499	3930	63,810

NOTE 1: 63,810 Grand Prixs were built.
NOTE 2: 3,124 had synchromesh and 60,686 had Hydra-Matic.

TEMPEST — (6-CYL) — SERIES 20 — Tempests were enlarged again and had separate frame construction with conventional drivetrain engineering. A six-cylinder engine, assembled by PMD from Chevrolet-produced components, was the base powerplant. There were three lines. Identifying Series 20 base Tempests were small hubcaps, the absence of upper beltline moldings and triple windsplits behind front wheel openings. Cars with optional V-8 power were dressed with front fender badges

TEMPEST

Model Number	Body/Style Number	Body Type & Seating	Factory Price	Shipping Weight	Production Total
20	2069	4-dr Sed-6P	2313	2970	15,516 (3,911)
20	2027	2-dr HT-6P	2259	2930	17,169 (4,596)
20	2035	4-dr Sta Wag-6P	2605	3245	4,597 (2,237)

NOTE 1: No brackets=Tempest six production; brackets=Tempest V-8 production.

TEMPEST CUSTOM — (6 CYL) — SERIES 21 — Tempest Customs had the same general styling features as base Tempests, but could be easily identified by the bright upper beltline moldings accenting the `Coke bottle' shape. There were also Tempest Custom nameplates on the rear fenders. Extra standard equipment included carpeting, Deluxe steering wheel and courtesy lamps on convertibles.

TEMPEST CUSTOM

Model Number	Body/Style Number	Body Type & Seating	Factory Price	Shipping Weight	Production Total
21	2169	4-dr Sed-6P	2399	2990	15,851 (14,097)
21	2167	2-dr Conv-5P	2641	3075	4,465 (3,522)
21	2127	2-dr HT-6P	2345	2955	12,598 (13,235)
21	2135	4-dr Sta Wag-6P	2691	3260	4,254 (6,442)

NOTE 1: No brackets=Tempest six production; brackets=Tempest V-8 production.

1964 LeMans GTO two-door hardtop Sports Coupe (V-8).

TEMPEST LEMANS — (6-CYL) — SERIES 22 — LeMans series Tempests had distinct styling touches such as LeMans nameplates on the rear fendersides, ribbed decor plates for the deck lid latch panel, model badges on the deck lid, simulated slanting louvers ahead of rear wheel cutouts and LeMans script plates for the dashboard. Bucket seats were standard on all models. The famous Grand Turismo Omologato (GTO) option package was released for LeMans models this year. The idea behind this package was to circumvent a corporate high-performance ban by providing the 389 cid V-8 as an option in the most luxurious Pontiac intermediate. GTOs featured special appearance items in place of some regular LeMans styling touches.

TEMPEST LEMANS

Model Number	Body/Style Number	Body Type & Seating	Factory Price	Shipping Weight	Production Total
22	2227	2-dr Cpe-5P	2491	2975	11,136 (20,181)
22	2237	2-dr HT-5P	2556	2995	7,409 (23,901)
22	2267	2-dr Conv-5P	2796	3125	5,786 (11,773)

NOTE 1: No brackets=Tempest six production; brackets=Tempest V-8 production.

TEMPEST LEMANS (WITH GTO OPTION)

Model Number	Body/Style Number	Body Type & Seating	Factory Price	Shipping Weight	Production Total
22	2227	2-dr Cpe-5P	2852	3106	7,384
22	2237	2-dr HT-5P	2963	3126	18,422
22	2267	2-dr Conv-5P	3081	3360	6,644

1964 Pontiac, LeMans GTO two-door convertible, V-8

BASE ENGINES

(CATALINA) V-8. Overhead valves. Cast iron block. Displacement: 389 cid. Bore and stroke: 4 x 3.75 inches. Compression ratio: (synchromesh) 8.6:1; (Hydra-Matic) 10.5:1. Brake hp: (synchromesh) 235 at 4000 rpm; (Hydra-Matic) 267 at 4200 rpm. Five main bearings. Hydraulic valve lifters. Carburetor: Rochester two-barrel model 7023066.

(STAR CHIEF) V-8. Overhead valves. Cast iron block. Displacement: 389 cid. Bore and stroke: 4 x 3.75 inches. Compression ratio: (synchromesh) 8.6:1; (Hydra-Matic) 10.5:1. Brake hp: (synchromesh) 235 at 4000 rpm; (Hydra-Matic) 283 at 4400 rpm. Five main bearings. Hydraulic valve lifters. Carburetor: Rochester two-barrel model 7023066.

(BONNEVILLE) V-8. Overhead valves. Cast iron block. Displacement: 389 cid. Bore and stroke: 4.06 x 3.75 inches. Compression ratio: (synchromesh) 8.6:1; (Hydra-Matic) 10.25:1. Brake hp: (synchromesh) 255 at 4000 rpm; (Hydra-Matic) 306 at 4600 rpm. Five main bearings. Hydraulic valve lifters. Carburetor: Carter AFB model 3647S four-barrel.

(GRAND PRIX) Base V-8s for Grand Prixs were the same used on Bonnevilles. Horsepower ratings were slightly lower in the case of the Hydra-Matic attachments (303 hp), since a type HM 61-10 ("Slim Jim") transmission was used.

(TEMPEST) Six-cylinder. Inline. Overhead valves. Cast iron block. Displacement: 215 cid. Bore and stroke: 3.75 x 3.25 inches. Compression ratio: 8.6:1. Brake hp: 140 at 4200 rpm. Seven main bearings. Hydraulic valve lifters. Carburetor: Rochester one-barrel.

OPTIONAL V-8 ENGINES

[TEMPEST]

326 cid. Basically the same as 1963, except two-barrel engine was now 250 hp at 4600 rpm and a four-barrel 326 was added. It had 280 hp at 4800 rpm. (both engines optional in Tempest and LeMans)

389 cid. Compression ratio: 10.75. Carburetion: four-barrel. Brake hp: 325 at 4800 rpm. (standard on GTO only)

389 cid. Compression ratio: 10.75. Carburetion: three two-barrels. Brake hp: 348 at 4900 rpm. (optional on GTO only)

[PONTIAC]

389 cid. Compression ratio: 8.6. Carburetion: two-barrel. Brake hp: 230 at 4000 rpm. (optional all models with automatic)

389 cid. Compression ratio: 8.6. Carburetion: two-barrel. Brake hp: 235 at 4000 rpm. (standard on Catalina and Star Chief with synchromesh)

389 cid. Compression ratio: 8.6. Carburetion: four-barrel. Brake hp: 255 at 4000 rpm. (standard on Bonneville with synchromesh, optional on all other models)

389 cid. Compression ratio: 10.5. Carburetion: four-barrel. Brake hp: 306 at 4800 rpm. (optional on all B-body models)

389 cid. Compression ratio: 10.5. Carburetion: two-barrel. Brake hp: 267 at 4200 rpm. (standard on Catalina with synchromesh)

389 cid. Compression ratio: 10.5. Carburetion: four-barrel. Brake hp: 303 at 4600 rpm. (standard on Bonneville and Grand Prix with automatic)

389 cid. Compression ratio: 10.75. Carburetion: three two-barrels. Brake hp: 330 at 4600 rpm. (optional on all B-body models)

421 cid. Compression ratio: 10.5. Carburetion: four-barrel. Brake hp: 320 at 4400 rpm. (optional in all B-body models)

421 cid. Compression ratio: 10.75. Carburetion: three two-barrels. Brake hp: 370 at 5200 rpm. (optional in all B-body models)

421 cid. Compression ratio: 10.75. Carburetion: three two-barrels. Brake hp: 350 at 4600 rpm. (optional all B-body models)

CHASSIS FEATURES: Wheelbase: (All Pontiac Safaris) 119 inches; (Series 23 and 29 passenger cars) 120 inches; (Series 26 and 28 passenger cars) 123 inches; (All Tempests) 115 inches. Overall length: (All Pontiac Safaris) 213.8 inches; (Series 23 and 29 passenger cars) 213 inches; (Series 26 and 28 passenger cars) 220 inches; (All Tempests) 203 inches. Front track: (Pontiac) 62.5 inches (Tempest) 58 inches. Rear track: (Pontiac) 64 inches; (Tempest) 58 inches. Standard tires: (Pontiac) 8.00 x 14; (Tempest) 6.50 x 14.

OPTIONS

[PONTIAC] Air conditioning ($430). Console including tachometer ($161). Instrument gage cluster ($21-59). Luggage carrier ($94). Remote control mirror ($12). Power brakes ($57). Power seat ($96). Power tilt left-hand bucket seat ($71). Tachometer ($54). Cordova top ($86). Ventura trim on body styles 2339, 2347 and 2369 ($118). Sports wheelcovers ($30-46). Aluminum hubs and drums ($122-138). Three-speed manual transmission was standard. Hydra-Matic was optional. A four-speed manual transmission with floor shift was optional. The four-barrel V-8 was optional in Catalinas and Star Chiefs. The economy version of the 389 cid V-8 was a no cost option giving 230 hp at 4000 rpm with Hydra-Matic on1y. Tri-Power on the 389 V-8 was available with 10.75:1 compression heads in two forms. The first gave 330 hp at 4600 rpm; the second gave 348 hp at 4900 rpm. Tri-Power 421 cid V-8s, also with 10.75:1 heads, came in two variations. The first gave 350 hp at 4600 rpm; the second gave 370 hp at 3800 rpm.

[TEMPEST] Air conditioner ($319). LeMans console shift ($48). Padded dash ($16). Power Convertible top ($54). Power tilt left bucket seat ($67). Power steering ($75). Power tailgate window ($54). Push-button radio ($62). Bucket seats ($134). Custom steering wheel ($6-9). Deluxe steering wheel with ring ($4). Tachometer ($54). Cordova top ($75). Two-speed wipers and washer ($17). Three-speed manual transmission was standard. Automatic transmission was optional. A four-speed manual transmission was optional. A 326 cubic V-8 was optional in Tempest, Tempest Custom and Tempest LeMans lines for cars without the GTO option. With synchromesh and 8.6:1 heads this motor gave 250 hp at 4600 rpm. With Hydra-Matic and 10.5:1 heads this motor gave 280 hp at 4800 rpm. The 389 cid V-8 was available exclusively in the GTO. It came with 10.75:1 compression and two different induction setups. The standard version had four-barrel carburetion and gave 325 hp at 4,800 rpm. Tri-Power was optional on the same block and produced 348 hp at 4900 rpm. The GTO could also be ordered with a heavy-duty three-speed manual gearbox or a Muncie close-ratio four-speed manual box with Hurst linkage. GTO option package: included 389 cid high-performance V-8; special GTO nameplates for the grille, fenders, deck lid and glovebox door; simulated engine-turned aluminum dash panel inserts; and dual simulated air scoops on the hood. Many special GTO accessories were available.

HISTORICAL FOOTNOTES: Production started Sept. 3, 1963. Pontiac introductions were held Oct. 3, 1963. Model year output of 715,261 cars was good for a 9.1 percent share of market. Calendar year output of 693,634 vehicles maintained PMD`s third rank in the industry. The Catalina 2+2 and GTO options were introduced for performance buyers this season. Victor Borge and the Smothers Brothers were among famous people who helped promote Pontiac sales. Pete Estes remained general manager of the division. At least three high-performance Pontiacs were road tested by contemporary magazines. The 325 hp GTO convertible went 0-to-60 in 7.7 seconds and did the quarter-mile in 15.8 seconds at 93 mph. It's top speed was 115 mph. The 348 hp GTO hardtop went 0-to-60 in 6.6 seconds and did the quarter-mile in 14.8 seconds. The 1964 Catalina 2+2 with the 370 hp Tri-Power "421" did 0-to-60 in 7.2 seconds and covered the quarter-mile in 16.1 seconds. The term Sport Coupe was now commonly used to identify the pillarless two-door hardtop body. The term Vista was phased out and Safari nomenclature was still used to identify station wagons.

Standard Catalog of American Cars

1965 PONTIAC

1965 Pontiac Catalina 2+2 two-door hardtop, V-8

CATALINA — (V-8) — **SERIES 252** — Styling changes for full-size 1965 Pontiacs included larger bodies; twin air-slot grilles; vertically stacked barrel-shaped headlamps visored by cut-back front fenders; V-shaped hoods with a prominent center bulge; curved side glass; and symmetrical Venturi contours with fin-shaped creases along the lower bodysides. Catalinas had thin moldings along the lower body crease, V-shaped front fender badges and Catalina rear fender scripts. Coupes and convertibles with the optional 2 + 2 Sports package were trimmed with "421" engine badges on front fenders, 2 + 2 numbering on rear fenders and deck lid, and simulated louvers behind the front wheel cutouts. Catalinas with the Ventura package also had special trims. Standard equipment for all Catalinas included turn signals; oil filter; cigarette lighter; front foam seat cushions; sun visors; heater and defroster; electric windshield wipers; front seat belt; and five tubeless blackwall tires. Safaris came standard with oversized 8.55 x 14 tires. The nine-passenger Safari had a power tailgate window.

PONTIAC I.D. NUMBERS: VIN on left front door post. First symbol indicates GM division: 2=Pontiac. Second and third symbols indicate series: 33=Tempest; 35=Tempest Custom; 37=LeMans; 52=Catalina; 56=Star Chief; 62=Bonneville; 66=Grand Prix. Fourth and fifth symbols indicate body style and appear as last two symbols in Body/Style Number column of charts below. Sixth symbol indicates model year: 5=1965. Seventh symbol tells assembly plant: P=Pontiac, Mich.; C=South Gate, Calif.; E=Linden, N.J.; X=Kansas City, Kan.; D=Doraville, Ga.; R=Arlington, Texas; Z=Fremont, Calif; B=Baltimore, Md.; K=Kansas City, Mo.; U=Lordstown, Ohio. Following symbols are sequential production number starting with 100001 at each assembly plant. Body/Style Number plate under hood tells manufacturer, Fisher style number, assembly plant, trim code, paint code, accessory codes. Style number consists of 65 (for 1965) prefix and four symbols that appear in second column of charts below. First two symbols indicate series; second two symbols indicate body type. VIN appears on front of engine at right-hand cylinder bank along with an alpha-numerical engine production codes included:[215 cid/125 hp six] ZD/ZE. [215 cid/140 hp six ZK/ZL/ZM/ZN/ZR/ZS. [326 cid/250 hp V-8] WP/YN6O. [326 cid/285 hp V-8] WR/YP. [389 cid/256 hp V-8] WA/WB/YA/YB. [389 cid/250 hp V-8] XA/XB. [389 cid/276 hp V-8] WDB/O4B. [389 cid/290 hp V-8] WC/YC/YD. [389 cid/293 hp V-8] XC. [389 cid/325 hp V-8] YE/YF. [389 cid/333 hp V-8] WE. [389 cid/338 hp Tri-Power V-8] WF/YG. [421 cid/338 hp V-8] WG/YH. [421 cid/356 hp Tri-Power V-8] YJ/WH. [421 cid/376 hp Tri-Power V-8] WJ/YK. [389 cid/335 hp four-barrel GTO V-8] WT with synchromesh; YS with Hydra-Matic. [389 cid/360 hp GTO Tri-Power V-8] WS with synchromesh; YR with Hydra-Matic.

CATALINA (SERIES 252)

Model Number	Body/Style Number	Body Type & Seating	Factory Price	Shipping Weight	Production Total
252	25269	4-dr Sed-6P	2748	3772	78,853
252	25239	4-dr HT-6P	2885	3843	34,814
252	25211	2-dr Sed-6P	2678	3702	9,526
252	25237	2-dr HT-6P	2809	3748	92,009
252	25267	2-dr Conv-6P	3103	3795	18,347
252	25245	4-dr Sta Wag-9P	3241	4244	15,110
252	25235	4-dr Sta Wag-6P	3136	4211	22,399

NOTE 1: 271,058 Catalinas were built.
NOTE 2: 14,817 had synchromesh and 256,241 had Hydramatic.
NOTE 3: Figures include 11,521 cars with W51 Catalina 2 + 2 option.
NOTE 4: 5,316 Catalina 2+2 had synchromesh and 6,205 had Hydra-Matic.
NOTE 5: No body style breakouts are available for the 2 + 2 option.
NOTE 6: No record of the number of Ventura options sold.

STAR CHIEF — (V-8) — **SERIES 256** — External decorations on Star Chief included stylized stars on the rear roof pillar, Star Chief script on the rear fender and wider chrome moldings along the fin-shaped body crease. All features found in Catalinas were standard equipment and extras included Deluxe wheel discs and steering wheels, electric clock, dual-speed wipers and special upholstery.

STAR CHIEF (SERIES 256)

Model Number	Body/Style Number	Body Type & Seating	Factory Price	Shipping Weight	Production Total
256	25669	4-dr Sed-6P	3042	3858	22,183
256	25639	4-dr HT-6p	3171	3917	9,132

NOTE 1: 31,315 Star Chiefs were built.
NOTE 2: 97 had synchromesh and 31,214 had Hydra-Matic.

BONNEVILLE — (V-8) — **SERIES 262** — Bonneville identification features included Bonneville lettering on the left-hand side of the hood and on the rear fenders, elongated V-shaped badges behind front wheel cutouts, and wide stainless steel accent panels along the lower body under the fin-shaped crease. Standard equipment was everything found on Star Chief plus padded instrument panel, front and rear armrests, padded assist grip, courtesy lamps and cloth and vinyl upholstery combinations. An undetermined number of four-door hardtops had the Brougham option package which included Ponchartrain cloth and Morrokide upholstery, a cordova top and `Brougham by Fisher' roof pillar badges. Bonneville passenger cars wore fender skirts.

BONNEVILLE (SERIES 262)

Model Number	Body/Style Number	Body Type & Seating	Factory Price	Shipping Weight	Production Total
262	26239	4-dr HT-6P	3362	3993	62,480
262	26237	2-dr HT-6P	3288	3909	44,030
262	26267	2-dr Conv-6P	3520	3935	21,050
262	26235	4-dr Sta Wag-6P	3557	4282	6,460

1965 Pontiac, Bonneville two-door convertible, V-8

NOTE 1: 134,663 Bonnevilles and Bonneville station wagons were built.
NOTE 2: 1,449 had synchromesh and 133,214 had Hydra-Matic.
NOTE 3: 643 Bonnevilles chassis were provided for conversions.

GRAND PRIX — (V-8) — **SERIES 266** — The Grand Prix hardtop sports coupe was the most distinctive of all 1965 full-sized Pontiacs. For special identification it had an air slot grille with a unique, vertically divided, aluminized insert which incorporated rectangular parking lamps. The fin-shaped crease along the lower body was trimmed with a wide stainless steel molding. The letters `GP' appeared on the left-hand lip of the hood and Grand Prix lettering was placed on the front fenders behind the wheel opening. A badge for further identification was placed on the sides of the rear fenders. As on Bonneville passenger cars, the Grand Prix wore fender skirts. Standard equipment included all features found on Bonneville, plus monotone Morrokide upholstery. Buyers had a choice of special front bench seats or bucket seats with a console and tachometer. A glovebox lamp was also included.

GRAND PRIX (SERIES 266)

Model Number	Body/Style Number	Body Type & Seating	Factory Price	Shipping Weight	Production Total
266	26657	2-dr HT Cpe-5P	3426	4282	57,881

NOTE 1: 57, 881 Grand Prixs were built.
NOTE 2: 1,973 had synchromesh and 55,908 had Hydra-Matic attachments.

TEMPEST — (6-CYL) — **SERIES 233** — Design refinements characterized the three Tempest lines for 1965 and included vertically stacked headlamps, larger wheel openings, crisper side body sculpturing and more deeply recessed grilles. Base models in the 233 Series were identified by the absence of upper beltline moldings and plainer interior trims. Vinyl rubber floor mats were used. Standard equipment included heater and defroster, electric wipers, seat belts, turn signals and five black tubeless tires. Safari station wagons came with 7.35 x 14 oversized tires as regular equipment.

TEMPEST (SERIES 233)

Model Number	Body/Style Number	Body Type & Seating	Factory Price	Shipping Weight	Production Total
233	23369	4-dr Sed-6P	2263	2963	15,705
233	23327	2-dr Cpe-6P	2211	2943	18,198
233	23335	4-dr Sta Wag-6P	2549	3237	5,622

1965 Pontiac Grand Prix two-door hardtop sport coupe V-8

NOTE 1: 39,525 Tempests were built.
NOTE 2: 9,255 had synchromesh and 30,270 had automatic attachments.

TEMPEST CUSTOM — (6-CYL) — **SERIES 235** — Tempest Custom models had bright upper beltline moldings to accent the Venturi shaped body styling. Standard extras included carpeting and Deluxe steering wheel. The Custom convertible had courtesy lamps.

TEMPEST CUSTOM (SERIES 235)

Model Number	Body/Style Number	Body Type & Seating	Factory Price	Shipping Weight	Production Total
235	23569	4-dr Sed-6P	2496	3021	25,242
235	23527	2-dr Cpe-6P	2295	2965	18,367
235	23537	2-dr HT-6P	2359	2983	21,906
235	23567	2-dr Conv-6P	2584	3064	8,346
235	23535	4-dr Sta Wag-6P	2633	3250	10,792

NOTE 1: 84,653 Tempest Customs were built.
NOTE 2: 10,630 had synchromesh and 74,023 had automatic attachments.

TEMPEST LEMANS — (6-CYL) — **SERIES 237** — Special identifying features seen on the Tempest LeMans models included grilled-over taillamps, LeMans front fender nameplates, LeMans lettering on the sides of rear fenders and simulated louvers behind front wheel cutouts (two-door models only). All features found on Tempest Customs were considered standard equipment, as well as vinyl interior trim, custom foam front seat cushions, front bucket seats

on two-door styles and power-operated folding tops on LeMans convertibles. Cars equipped with GTO equipment had standard V-8 power. The GTO was not yet a separate series, although special identification features on GTOs replaced some items regularly seen on LeMans Tempests. This included GTO lettering for the left-hand grille, rear fendersides and deck lid; a single hood scoop and elongated V-shaped badges behind the front wheel openings.

TEMPEST LEMANS (SERIES 237)

Model Number	Body/Style Number	Body Type & Seating	Factory Price	Shipping Weight	Production Total
237	23769	4-dr Sed-6P	2496	3021	14,227
237	23727	2-dr Cpe-5P	2437	2996	18,881
237	23737	2-dr HT-5P	2501	3014	60,548
237	23767	2-dr Conv-5P	2736	3107	13,897

TEMPEST LEMANS (SERIES 237 WITH GTO OPTION)

Model Number	Body/Style Number	Body Type & Seating	Factory Price	Shipping Weight	Production Total
237	23727	2-dr Cpe-5P	2787	3478	8,319
237	23737	2-dr HT-5P	2855	3478	55,722
237	23767	2-dr Conv-5P	3093	3700	11,311

NOTE 1: 182,905 LeMans Tempests were built including cars with the GTO option.
NOTE 2: 75,756 had synchromesh attachments and 107,149 had automatic.
NOTE 3: 75,352 GTOs are included in these totals.
NOTE 4: 56,378 had synchromesh and 18,974 had automatic.
NOTE 5: Four-speed gearboxes were installed in 18.8 percent of all 1965 Tempests.

1965 Pontiac, LeMans two-door convertible (with GTO option), V-8

BASE ENGINES

(CATALINA) V-8: Overhead valves. Cast iron block. Displacement: 389 cid. Bore and stroke: 4.06 x 3.75 inches. Compression ratio: (synchromesh) 8.6:1; (Hydra-Matic) 10.5:1. Brake hp: (synchromesh) 256 at 4600 rpm.; (Hydra-Matic) 290 at 4600 rpm. Five main bearings. Hydraulic valve lifters. Carburetor: Rochester two-barrel.

(BONNEVILLE/GRAND PRIX) V-8: Overhead valves. Cast iron block. Displacement: 389 cid. Bore and stroke: 4.06 x 3.75 inches. Compression ratio: (synchromesh) 8.6:1; (Hydra-Matic) 10.5:1. Brake hp: (synchromesh) 333 at 5000 rpm.; (Hydra-Matic) 325 at 4800 rpm. Five main bearings. Hydraulic valve lifters. Carburetor: Carter AFB four-barrel.

(TEMPEST/TEMPEST CUSTOM) Inline six. Overhead valves. Cast iron block. Displacement: 215 cid. Bore and stroke: 3.75 x 3.25 inches. Compression ratio: 8.6:1. Brake hp: 140 at 4200 rpm. Seven main bearings. Hydraulic valve lifters. Carburetor: Rochester one-barrel.

CHASSIS FEATURES: Wheelbase: (All Pontiac Safaris) 121 inches; (Series 252 and 266 passenger cars) 121 inches; (Series 256 and 262 passenger cars) 124 inches; (All Tempests) 115 inches. Overall length: (All Pontiac Safaris) 217.9 inches; (Series 252 and 266 passenger cars) 214.6 inches; (Series 256 and 262 passenger cars) 221.7 inches; (Tempest Safaris) 204.4 inches; (Tempest passenger cars) 206.2 inches. Front tread: (Pontiacs) 62.5 inches; (Tempests) 58 inches. Rear tread: (Pontiacs) 64 inches. (Tempests) 58 inches. Standard tires: (Pontiacs) 8.25 x 14; (Tempest) 6.95 x 14; (GTO) 7.75 x 14.

OPTIONS

[PONTIAC] Bonneville Brougham option for Style Number 26239 ($161). Front bucket seats or Bonneville style numbers 26237 and 26267 ($116). Console ($108). Remote control deck lid ($11). Electro Cruise and fuel warning ($96). Tinted glass ($43). Tinted windshield ($29). Instrument gage cluster ($21-38) Safari luggage carrier ($86). Glareproof tilt mirror ($4). Remote control rearview mirror ($12). Power brakes ($43). Power door locks ($46-70). Six-way power seat ($97). Power windows ($106). Power tilt bucket seats L.H. ($71). AM/FM manual. radio ($151). Push-button AM radio ($89). Split-back Safari seat ($38). Front bucket seats for Catalina two-door hardtop and convertible with special trims ($204). Super-Lift shock absorbers ($40). Sports option 2 + 2 package for Style Number 25237 ($419). Sports option 2 + 2 package for Style Number 25267 ($397). Tachometer, except on cars with four-speed and console ($54). Cordova top ($97-108). Safari cordova top ($135). Ventura trim package for style numbers 25237, 25239 and 25269 ($118). Wire wheel discs ($20-71). Aluminum hubs and drums ($120-138). A three-speed manual transmission was standard. Turbo-Hydra-matic transmission and four-speed manual transmission were $231 extra. A heavy-duty clutch was $9 extra on Catalinas with certain engines. Safe-T-Track differential was $43 extra. Dual exhausts were $31 extra, but standard on Grand Prix. The four-barrel V-8 with heavy-duty clutch was $44 extra for Catalinas and Star Chiefs. A Tri-Power 389 cid V-8 with 10.75:1 compression and 338 hp at 4800 rpm was $134-174 extra depending on model and transmission. A four-barrel 421 cid V-8 with 10.5:1 compression and 338 hp at 4600 rpm was $108-174 extra depending on model and was standard in cars with the 2 + 2 Sports Option. A Tri-Power 421 cid V-8 with 10.75:1 compression and 356 hp at 4800 rpm was $241-307 extra depending upon model. The Tri-Power H.O. V-8 of 421 cid with 10.75:1 compression was $344-410 extra depending on model. It produced 376 hp at 5500 rpm. A two-barrel premium fuel version of the 389 cid V-8 was $21 extra in Catalinas and Star Chiefs with three-speed manual transmission. Transistor ignition was $75 extra on air-conditioned cars and $65 extra on others. A transistorized regulator was $11 extra. Various rear axle ratios were available.

[TEMPEST] Air conditioner ($346). Carpets ($19). Electric clock ($19). Remote control deck lid ($11). GTO option for Style Numbers 23727, 23737. 23767 ($296). Handling & Ride package ($16). Parking brake signal ($3). Safari luggage carrier ($65). Panel cluster and tachometer Rally Gage ($86). AM/FM push-button radio ($137). Safeguard speedometer ($16). Super-Life shock absorbers ($40). Custom sports steering wheel ($39-43). Tilt steering with power assist only ($43). Power steering ($97). Power brakes ($43). Cordova tops ($72-86). Wire wheel discs ($54-71). Custom wheel discs ($20-37). Rally wheels ($36-53). Two-speed wipers and washers ($17) and much more. A three-speed manual transmission was standard. A four-speed manual transmission was $188 extra. Two different two-speed automatic gearboxes were available. With six-cylinder power the first automatic was $188 extra; with V-8s the second was $199 extra. Transistor ignition was priced the same as on full-sized cars. Dual exhausts were standard with the GTO option and $31 extra on other cars. Safe-T-Grip differential was $38 extra. A two-barrel 326 cid V-8 with 9.2 compression and 250 hp at 4600 rpm was $108 extra on all Tempests. With four-barrel induction and 10.5:1 compression heads, this engine produced 285 hp at 5500 rpm and was $173 extra on all Tempests. A four-barrel 389 cid V-8 with 335 hp at 5000 rpm. was standard with the GTO option. A Tri-Power 389 cid V-8 with 10.75:1 compression and 360 hp at 5200 rpm was $116 extra in GTOs only. A variety of rear axle ratios were available.

HISTORICAL FOOTNOTES: Production started Aug. 24, 1964. Introductions were done on Sept. 24, 1964. The one-millionth Tempest was built late in the year. Calendar year output was 860,652. Model year output was 802,000. On April 13, 1965 the 10 millionth Pontiac was made. It was a gold Catalina. The 335 hp GTO convertible went 0-to-60 in 7.2 seconds and did the quarter-mile in 16.1 seconds. The 1965 Catalina 2+2 hardtop with the 338 hp "421" did 0-to-60 in 7.4 seconds and the quarter-mile in 15.8 seconds. The 1965 Catalina 2+2 hardtop with the 376 hp "421" was even faster. It could do 0-to-60 in 7.2 seconds and the quarter-miles took 15.5. Pontiac fans could get a GTO record and poster for 25-cents which is a collector's item today. Pete Estes moved to Chevrolet and John Z. DeLorean became the general manager of Pontiac Motor Div. The term Safari was used to denote station wagons. In the Tempest series a Sport Coupe was a pillared two-door sedan.

1966 PONTIAC

CATALINA — (V-8) — SERIES 252 — Styling changes for full-sized 1966 Pontiacs were subtle ones. New plastic grilles were adopted and headlamp extension caps gave a more integrated frontal appearance. Catalinas now had thin full-length horizontal belt moldings, instead of body crease trim. An identifying script was placed on the front fenders behind the wheel openings. A rear fender badge was also seen. Standard equipment was the same as the previous year. Cars with the Ventura option had special upholstery and fender lettering.

PONTIAC I.D. NUMBERS: VIN on left front door post. First symbol indicates GM division: 2=Pontiac. Second and third symbols indicate series: 33=Tempest; 35=Tempest Custom; 37=LeMans; 52=Catalina; 56=Star Chief; 62=Bonneville; 66=Grand Prix. Fourth and fifth symbols indicate body style and appear as last two symbols in Body/Style Number column of charts below. Sixth symbol indicates model year: 6=1966. Seventh symbol tells assembly plant: P=Pontiac, Mich.; C=South Gate, Calif.; E=Linden, N.J.; X=Kansas City, Kan.; D=Doraville, Ga.; R=Arlington, Texas; Z=Fremont, Calif; B=Baltimore, Md.; K=Kansas City, Mo.; U=Lordstown, Ohio. Following symbols are sequential production number starting with 100001 at each assembly plant. Body/Style Number plate under hood tells manufacturer, Fisher style number, assembly plant, trim code, paint code, accessory codes. Style number consists of 66 (for 1966) prefix and four symbols that appear in second column of charts below. First two symbols indicate series; second two symbols indicate body type. VIN appears on front of engine at right-hand cylinder bank along with an alpha-numerical engine production code. Engine production codes included:[230 cid/155 hp ohc six] ZF/ZG; [230 cid/165 hp ohc six] ZK/ZS/ZN/ZM. [230 cid/207 hp ohc six] ZD/ZE. [326 cid/250 hp V-8] WP/WX/YN/XF. [326 cid/285 hp V-8] WR/YP/XG. [389 cid/256 hp V-8] WA/WB/YA. [389 cid/260 hp V-8] XA/XB. [389 cid/290 hp] WC/YC/YD/YU/YV. [389 cid/293 hp V-8] XC. [389 cid/325 hp V-8] YE/YF/YL/YW/YX. [389 cid/333 hp V-8] WE. [421 cid/338 hp V-8] WK/YZ/YT/WG/YH. [421 cid/356 hp Tri-Power V-8] YJ/YM/WH. [421 cid/376 hp Tri-Power V-8] WJ/YK. [389 cid/335 hp four-barrel GTO V-8] WT/WW with synchromesh; YS/XE with Hydra-Matic. [389 cid/360 hp GTO Tri-Power V-8] WS/WV with synchromesh; XS/YR with Hydra-Matic.

CATALINA (SERIES 252)

Model Number	Body/Style Number	Body Type & Seating	Factory Price	Shipping Weight	Production Total
252	25269	4-dr Sed-6P	2831	3785	80,483
252	25239	4-dr HT-6P	2968	3910	38,005
252	25211	2-dr Sed-6P	2762	3715	7,925
252	25237	2-dr HT-6P	2893	3835	79,013
252	25267	2-dr Conv-6P	3219	3860	14,837
252	25245	4-dr Sta Wag-9P	3338	4315	12,965
252	25235	4-dr Sta Wag-6P	3217	4250	21,082

NOTE 1: 247,927 Catalinas were built.
NOTE 2: 5,003 Catalinas had synchromesh and 242,924 had Hydra-Matic.

CATALINA 2+2 — (V-8) — SERIES 254 — The Catalina 2+2 models were in a separate series for 1966. They could be easily identified by appearance items such as a twin lens taillamp treatment, 2+2 badges on the deck lid and rear fenders, vertical air slots behind the doors and 'Pontiac 421' front fender emblems. Standard equipment included a four-barrel 421 cid V-8 with 338 hp, low-restriction exhausts, chromed air cleaner and valve covers and three-speed Hurst linkage transmission. Heavy-duty suspension, carpeting, bucket seats, Sports Custom steering wheel and non-glare inside rearview mirror were standard. Available axle ratios included 3.08, 3.23 and 3.42.

CATALINA 2+2 (SERIES 254)

Model Number	Body/Style Number	Body Type & Seating	Factory Price	Shipping Weight	Production Total
254	25437	2-dr HT-5P	3298	4005	N/A
254	25467	2-dr Conv-5P	3602	4030	N/A

NOTE 1: 6,383 Catalina 2+2s were built.
NOTE 2: 2,208 Catalina 2+2s had synchromesh and 4,175 had Hydra-Matic.
NOTE 3: Body style breakouts were not recorded for this series.

STAR CHIEF EXECUTIVE — (V-8) — SERIES 256 — For identification, models in the 256 Series had "Executive" lettering behind front wheel openings. They wore thin horizontal body rub moldings, stylized rear fender stars and Jeweltone monochromatic Morrokide upholstery. Star Chief Executives incorporated all Catalina equipment, plus deluxe wheel discs and steering wheel, electric clock and dual-speed wipers.

STAR CHIEF EXECUTIVE (SERIES 256)

Model Number	Body/Style Number	Body Type & Seating	Factory Price	Shipping Weight	Production Total
256	25669	4-dr Sed-6P	3114	3920	24,489
256	25639	4-dr HT-6P	3244	3980	10,583
256	25637	2-dr HT-6P	3170	3920	10,140

NOTE 1: 45,212 Star Chief Executives were built.
NOTE 2: 134 Star Chief Executives had Synchromesh and 45,078 had Hydra-Matic.

1966 Pontiac, Catalina Vista Sedan four-door hardtop, V-8

1966 Pontiac, Bonneville two-door convertible, V-8

BONNEVILLE — (V-8) — SERIES 262 — Bonnevilles could easily be distinguished by their broad accent panels below the lower body crease, Bonneville block lettering on the left-hand grille and behind the front wheel openings and by their standard fender skirts. Regular equipment on closed cars included cloth upholstery, padded dashboards and front rear armrests. The convertible had deeply piped Morrokide covered seats. The Brougham option package added tufted Plaza pattern cloth upholstery and model identification badges for the rear roof pillars, but cordova tops were optional, even on Broughams.

BONNEVILLE (SERIES 262)

Model Number	Body/Style Number	Body Type & Seating	Factory Price	Shipping Weight	Production Total
262	26239	4-dr HT-6P	3428	4070	68,646
262	26237	2-dr HT-6P	3354	4020	42,004
262	26267	2-dr Conv-6P	3586	4015	16,229
262	26245	4-dr Sta Wag-9P	3747	4390	8,452

NOTE 1: 135,954 Bonnevilles were built.
NOTE 2: 729 Bonnevilles had synchromesh and 139,225 had Hydra-Matic.
NOTE 3: 553 Bonnevilles chassis were provided for conversions.

1966 Pontiac, Grand Prix, two-door hardtop coupe, V-8

GRAND PRIX (V-8) — SERIES 266 — Grand Prixs were distinguished by wire mesh grilles enclosing rectangular parking lamps GP identification on front fenders and elongated V-shaped emblems on the ribbed lower beauty panels. A monochromatic interior of deeply piped Morrokide was featured. Standard equipment was the same as in 1965, except Strato Bucket seats were new. Fender skirts were seen again.

GRAND PRIX (SERIES 266)

Model Number	Body/Style Number	Body Type & Seating	Factory Price	Shipping Weight	Production Total
266	26657	2-dr HT-5P	3492	4015	36,757

NOTE 1: 36,757 Grand Prixs were built.
NOTE 2: 917 Grand Prixs had synchromesh and 35,840 had Hydra-Matic.

STANDARD TEMPEST — (6-CYL) — SERIES 233 — Tempests were completely restyled with smoother bodies, rounder contours, wider wheel openings, recessed split grilles and stacked headlamps. Each of four series now had completely distinctive ornamentation. An undetermined amount of cars in each series were built with a sporty-looking Sprint option package. The really big news was under the hood, where a unique overhead camshaft six-

cylinder engine was now employed as the base power plant for all models, except GTOs. Standard Tempest trim appointments included, windsplit moldings behind front wheel openings, Tempest rear fender scripts and nylon-faced fabric upholstery with Jeweltone Morrokide accents.

STANDARD TEMPEST (SERIES 233)

Model Number	Body/Style Number	Body Type & Seating	Factory Price	Shipping Weight	Production Total
233	23369	4-dr Sed-6P	2331	3075	17,392
233	233307	2-dr Cpe-6P	2278	3040	22,266
233	23335	4-dr Sta Wag-6P	2624	3340	4,095

NOTE 1: 43,753 standard Tempests were built.
NOTE 2: 10,610 had standard Tempests synchromesh and 33,143 had automatic.

TEMPEST CUSTOM — (6-CYL) — SERIES 235 — Tempest Custom trimmings included thin moldings accenting the smooth new `Coke bottle' shape and Tempest Custom script/badge identification on the rear fenders. Deluxe steering wheels and carpets were extra standard features. Convertibles sported courtesy lamps and Morrokide trims.

TEMPEST CUSTOM (SERIES 235)

Model Number	Body/Style Number	Body Type & Seating	Factory Price	Shipping Weight	Production Total
235	23569	4-dr Sed-6P	2415	3100	23,988
235	23539	4-dr HT-6P	2547	3195	10,996
235	23507	2-dr Cpe-6P	2362	3060	17,182
235	23517	2-dr HT-6P	2426	3075	31,322
235	23567	2-dr Conv-6P	2655	3170	5,557
235	23535	4-dr Sta Wag-6p	2709	3355	7,614

NOTE 1: 96,659 Tempest Customs were built.
NOTE 2: 13,566 Tempest Customs had synchromesh and 83,093 had automatic.

1966 Pontiac, Tempest Custom two-door Sprint Coupe, OHC-6

TEMPEST LEMANS — (6-CYL) — SERIES 237 — LeMans models had special trim features that set them apart. They included simulated louvers on the forward edge of front fenders, elongated V-shaped emblems behind front wheel openings and LeMans lettering on the rear fendersides. A new `shadow box' roofline was seen on the two-door hardtop coupe. Standard equipment included Morrokide-and-cloth trim combinations in four-door hardtops and all-Morrokide in others. Convertibles, hardtops and Sport Coupes (two-door sedans) came with the choice of bucket or notch back front seats with folding armrest. All LeMans had carpeting; front foam seat cushions; lamps for ashtray; cigarette lighter and glovebox; and a power top on convertibles.

TEMPEST LEMANS (SERIES 237)

Model Number	Body/Style Number	Body Type & Seating	Factory Price	Shipping Weight	Production Total
237	23739	4-dr HT-6P	2701	3195	13,897
237	23707	2-dr Cpe-6p	2505	3090	16,654
237	23717	2-dr HT-6P	2568	3125	78,109
237	23767	2-dr Conv-6P	2806	3220	13,080

NOTE 1: 121,740 LeMans were built.
NOTE 2: 22,862 LeMans had synchromesh and 98,878 had automatic attachments.

TEMPEST GTO — (V-8) — SERIES 242 — GTO line was now a separate series with distinctive trim on the new Tempest sheet metal. A wire mesh grille insert without horizontal divider bars was used. The grille incorporated rectangular parking lamps and a GTO nameplate on the left-hand side. A single scoop appeared on the hood, elongated V-shaped badges were mounted behind the front wheel openings, GTO lettering appeared on the deck lid and rear fenders, the upper beltline contour was pin striped and horizontal twin-slot taillamps were used. Standard equipment included all LeMans items, plus a special 389 cid four-barrel V-8; walnut grain dash panel inserts; dual exhausts; heavy-duty shock absorbers, springs and stabilizer bar; and 7.75 x 14 redline or whitewall tires.

TEMPEST GTO (SERIES 242)

Model Number	Body/Style Number	Body Type & Seating	Factory Price	Shipping Weight	Production Total
242	24207	2-dr Cpe-5	2783	3445	10,363
242	24217	2-dr HT-5P	2847	3465	73,785
242	24267	2-dr Conv-5P	3082	3555	12,798

BASE ENGINES

(CATALINA/STAR CHIEF EXECUTIVE) V-8: Overhead valves. Cast iron block. Displacement: 389 cid. Bore and stroke: 4.06 x 3.75 inches. Compression ratio: (synchromesh) 8.6:1; (Hydra-Matic) 10.5:1. Brake hp: (synchromesh) 256 at 4600 rpm.; (Hydra-Matic) 290 at 4600 rpm. Five main bearings. Hydraulic valve lifters. Carburetor: Rochester two-barrel model 7026066.

(CATALINA 2 + 2) V-8. Overhead valves. Cast iron block. Displacement: 421 cid. Bore and stroke: 4.094 x 4.00. Compression ratio: 10.5:1. Brake hp: 338 at 4600 rpm. Five main bearings. Hydraulic valve lifters. Carburetor: Carter AFB model 4033S.

(BONNEVILLE) V-8: Overhead valves. Cast iron block. Displacement: 389 cid. Bore and stroke: 4.06 x 3.75 inches. Compression ratio: (synchromesh) 8.6:1; (Hydra-Matic) 10.5:1. Brake hp: (synchromesh) 333 at 5000 rpm.; (Hydra-Matic) 325 at 4800 rpm. Five main bearings. Hydraulic valve lifters. Carburetor: Carter AFB four-barrel model 4033S.

(GRAND PRIX) V-8: Overhead valves. Cast iron block. Displacement: 389 cid. Bore and stroke: 4.06 x 3.75 inches. Compression ratio: (synchromesh) 8.6:1; (Hydra-Matic) 10.5:1. Brake hp: (synchromesh) 333 at 4600 rpm.; (Hydra-Matic) 325 at 4800 rpm. Five main bearings. Hydraulic valve lifters. Carburetor: Carter AFB four-barrel model 4033S.

(TEMPEST/TEMPEST CUSTOM) OHC-Six: Overhead valves. Cast iron block. Displacement: 230 cid. Bore and stroke: 3.87 x 3.25 inches. Compression ratio: 9.0:1. Brake hp: 165 at 4700 rpm. Seven main bearings. Hydraulic lifters. Carburetor: Rochester one-barrel.

(GTO) V-8: Overhead valves. Cast iron block. Displacement: 389 cid. Bore and stroke: 4.06 x 3.75 inches. Compression ratio: 10.75:1. Brake hp: 335 at 5000 rpm. Five main bearings. Hydraulic valve lifters. Carburetor: Carter AFB four-barrel model 4033S.

CHASSIS FEATURES: Wheelbase: (Pontiac Safaris) 121 inches; (series 252 and 266, passenger cars) 121 inches; (series 256 and 262 passenger cars) 124 inches; (Tempests) 115 inches. Overall length: (Pontiac Safaris) 218.1 inches; (series 252 and 266 passenger cars) 214.8 inches; (series 256 and 262 passenger cars) 221.8 inches; (2 + 2) 214.8 inches; (Tempest Safari) 203.6 inches; (Tempest and GTO passenger cars) 206.4 inches. Front tread: (Pontiacs) 63 inches; (Tempests) 58 inches. Rear tread: (Pontiacs) 64 inches; (Tempests) 58 inches. Standard tires: (Pontiac) 8.25 x 14; (Tempest convertible and hardtop) 7.35 x 14; (other Tempests) 6.95 x 14. Oversized tires for all Safaris are noted above.

OPTIONS

[PONTIAC] Options were about the same availability and price as 1965, with following variations noted: Whitewall tires ($29). Bucket seats ($105). Tilt steering wheel ($43); Power steering ($97). Air-conditioning ($30). Power brakes ($43). Super Hydra-Matic transmission ($230). Heavy-duty suspension ($16). Manual AM radio ($89). [TEMPEST] Power steering ($95). Air-conditioning ($343). Sprint option package ($127). Standard whitewalls ($41). Ride and Handling package ($16). Rally wheel rims ($40). Custom steering wheel ($29). Safe-T-Track ($37). The 338 hp version of the 389 cid V-8 with 10.75:1 compression and Tri-Power was dropped. The GTO and GTO V-8 options were the same as in 1965. The new overhead camshaft six-cylinder Tempest engine was the only significantly changed power train option. This engine came in two forms. Specifications for the base 165 hp job are given above under standard Tempest engines. An optional choice was the 'Sprint' version with 10.5:1 compression, four-barrel Rochester carburetor and 207 hp at 5200 rpm.

HISTORICAL FOOTNOTES: Production began Sept. 13, 1965 and model introductions took place Oct. 7, 1965. Model year output was 831,331 units. Calendar year production was 866,385 units. The big news of the year was introduction of the overhead cam six. Also, Pontiac earned an over 10 percent share of market for the first time ever. In magazine road tests, the 335 hp GTO coupe was found to go 0-to-60 in 6.8 seconds and down the quarter-mile in 15.4 seconds. The 360 hp GTO convertible had the same 0-to-60 time and did the quarter-mile in 15.5 seconds at 93 mph. The 207 hp Tempest Sprint could go 0-to-60 in 8.2 seconds and do the quarter-mile in 16.7 seconds at 82 mph. The new Safari and station wagon were synonymous. Style number 26657 had distinct roofline styling. The Brougham option was available for Bonneville four-door hardtops. The term Vista was sometimes used to describe full-sized four-door hardtops. The Ventura option was available for Catalina hardtops, convertibles and Vistas. The term Sport Coupe was used to describe two-door Tempest pillared sedans, not hardtops. In this edition, we have changed the description of these models to "Cpe" to avoid confusion. Two-door Tempests with the Sprint option had horizontal racing stripes between the wheel openings.

1967 PONTIAC

1967 Pontiac, Catalina two-door hardtop (with Ventura option), V-8

CATALINA — (V-8) — SERIES 252 — Integral bumper-grilles, `wasp waist' body styling, angular wedge-shaped front fender tips and recessed windshield wipers characterized full-sized Pontiacs for 1967. A crisp horizontal beltline crease and flare sculpturing between the doors and rear wheel openings were other new design traits. All standard GM safety features were found in Catalinas, plus woodgrain trimmed dashboards and nylon blend carpeting. Small hubcaps were regular equipment and there were Pontiac letters on the left-hand grille and the word Catalina on the sides of fenders. Taillamps were mainly horizontal with a single long lens that curved downwards at each side. Cars with Ventura or 2+2 options were trimmed differently.

PONTIAC I.D. NUMBERS: VIN on left front door post. First symbol indicates GM division: 2=Pontiac. Second and third symbols indicate series: 23=Firebird; 33=Tempest; 35=Tempest Custom; 37=LeMans; 39=Tempest Safari; 42=GTO; 52=Catalina; 56=Star Chief; 62=Bonneville; 66=Grand Prix. Fourth and fifth symbols indicate body style and appear as last two symbols in Body/Style Number column of charts below. Sixth symbol indicates model year: 7=1967. Seventh symbol tells assembly plant: P=Pontiac, Mich.; C=South Gate, Calif.; E=Linden, N.J.; X=Kansas City, Kan.; R=Arlington, Texas; Z=Fremont, Calif; B=Baltimore, Md.; K=Kansas City, Mo.; U=Framingham, Mass.; V=Lordstown, Ohio. Following symbols are sequential production number starting with 100001 at each assembly plant. Body/Style Number plate under hood tells manufacturer, Fisher style number, assembly plant, trim code, paint code, accessory codes. Style number consists of 67 (for 1967) prefix and four symbols that appear in second column of charts below. First two symbols indicate series; second two

symbols indicate body type. VIN appears on front of engine at right-hand cylinder bank along with an alpha-numerical engine production code. Engine production codes included:[230 cid/ 155 hp ohc six] ZF/ZG; [230 cid/165 hp ohc six] ZK/ZS/ZN/ZM. [230 cid/215 hp ohc six] ZD/ ZE/ZR/ZL. [326 cid/250 hp V-8] WP/WX/YN/XF/WH/WC/YJ/XL. [326 cid/285 hp V-8] WK/ WOWR/YM/YP/XG/XO/XR. [400 cid/260 hp V-8] YB. [400 cid/265 hp V-8] WA/YA/YB/WB. [400 cid/290 hp] YC/YD. [400 cid/293 hp V-8] XC. [400 cid/325 hp V-8] YE/YF/YT/WI/WQ/WU/ WU/XN. [400 cid/333 hp V-8] WE/WD/XZ/XY/XH. [400 cid/350 hp] XZ/XY/XJ. [428 cid/360 hp V-8] WG/WK/XD/Y2/YH/YY/YZ/YT. [428 cid/376 hp V-8] WJ/WL/XK/YK. [400 cid/255 hp two-barrel GTO V-8; automatic only] XL/XM. [400 cid/335 hp four-barrel special GTO V-8] WT/WW with synchromesh; YS with Turbo Hydramatic. [400 cid/360 hp GTO special V-8] WS/WV with synchromesh; XP/XS/YR/YZ with Hydra-Matic.

CATALINA (SERIES 252)

Model Number	Body/Style Number	Body Type & Seating	Factory Price	Shipping Weight	Production Total
252	25269	4-dr Sed-6P	2866	3825	80,551
252	25239	4-dr HT-6	3020	3960	37,256
252	25211	2-dr Sed-6P	2807	3735	5,633
252	25287	2-dr HT Cpe-6P	2951	3860	77,932
252	25267	2-dr Conv-6P	3276	3910	10,033
252	25245	4-dr Sta Wag-9P	3374	4340	11,040
252	25235	4-dr Sta Wag-6P	3252	4275	18,305

NOTE 1: 211,405 Catalinas were built.
NOTE 2: 3,653 had synchromesh and 207,752 had Turbo Hydramatic.
NOTE 3: 1,768 Catalinas had 2+2 option with no body style breakout available.

EXECUTIVE — (V-8) — SERIES 256 — The Star Chief name was dropped. Executives had the same equipment as Catalinas, plus electric clocks, deluxe wheelcovers, deluxe steering wheels, decor moldings and special ornamentation. Trim features included V-shaped deck lid emblems and Executive front fenderside lettering. Only wagons with external woodgrained paneling were called Safaris and the Executive Safari was born.

EXECUTIVE (SERIES 256)

Model Number	Body/Style Number	Body Type & Seating	Factory Price	Shipping Weight	Production Total
256	25669	4-dr Sed-6P	3165	3955	19,861
256	25639	4-dr HT-6P	3296	4020	8,699
256	25687	2-dr HT Cpe-6P	3227	3925	6,931
256	25645	4-dr Sta Wag-9P	3722	4370	5,593
256	25635	4-dr Sta Wag-6P	3600	4290	5,903

NOTE 1: 35,491 Executive passenger cars were built.
NOTE 2: 84 Executive passenger cars had synchromesh; 35,407 Turbo-Hydramatic.
NOTE 3: 11,496 Executive station wagons were also built.
NOTE 4: 38 Executive wagons had synchromesh and 11,458 had Turbo-Hydramatic.

BONNEVILLE — (V-8) — SERIES 262 — As usual, the word Bonneville appeared on the left-hand grille on cars in Pontiac's luxury class series. Similar lettering was on the rear fender below the beltline crease. Taillamps were of the same overall shape as on Catalinas and Executives, but three individual lenses were seen. Fender skirts were featured along with rocker panel and rear panel accent moldings. Standard equipment included all items found on Executives plus notch back front seats with center armrests, burl style dashboard trim and a four-barrel V-8. Station wagons had rear folding seats, courtesy lamps, power tailgate windows and load area carpeting.

BONNEVILLE (SERIES 262)

Model Number	Body/Style Number	Body Type & Seating	Factory Price	Shipping Weight	Production Total
262	26239	4-dr HT-6P	3517	4110	56,307
262	26287	2-dr HT Cpe-6P	3227	3925	31,016
262	26267	2-dr Conv-6P	3680	4010	8,902
262	26245	4-dr Sta Wag-9P	3819	4415	6,771

NOTE 1: 96,708 Bonneville passenger cars were built.
NOTE 2: 278 Bonneville passenger cars had synchromesh; 96,430 Turbo-Hydramatic.
NOTE 3: 6,771 Bonneville station wagons were built.
NOTE 4: 29 Bonneville wagons had synchromesh and 6,742 had Turbo-Hydramatic.
NOTE 5: 483 Bonneville chassis sold to professional car converters.

GRAND PRIX — (V-8) — SERIES 266 — The Grand Prix was set apart this year by distinct styling touches and a new convertible body style. For identification there were GP letters on the left-hand grille, Grand Prix rear fender lettering, hide-away headlights, front parking lamps hidden behind slits in the fender and straight horizontal twin-slot taillamps. Fender skirts and lower body accent moldings were seen as well. Grand Prixs featured all standard GM safety equipment, plus a 350 hp V-8, front Strato Bucket seats and a console. The hardtop coupe did not have vent windows. convertibles had GP initials leaded into the vent window glass.

GRAND PRIX (SERIES 266)

Model Number	Body/Style Number	Body Type & Seating	Factory Price	Shipping Weight	Production Total
266	26657	2-dr HT Cpe-5P	3549	4005	37,125
266	26667	2-dr Conv-5P	3813	4040	5,856

NOTE 1: A total of 42,981 Grand Prixs were built.
NOTE 2: 760 Grand Prixs had synchromesh and 42,221 had Turbo-Hydramatic.

1967 Pontiac, Grand Prix two-door convertible, V-8

TEMPEST — (6-CYL) — SERIES 233 — All Tempests were mildly face-lifted with grille and rear panel treatments varying by series. The base models had new molded plastic grille bars arranged vertically, in groups of four, with wide spaces between them. Three block-shaped taillamp lenses set into rectangular frames were seen. The Tempest name appeared behind the front wheel and the rear fender had three horizontal slits on the side which housed side markers. All GM safety features were standard, plus vinyl floor mats, cigar lighters, armrests, heater and defroster, five blackwall tubeless tires and standard type steering wheel.

STANDARD TEMPEST (SERIES 233)

Model Number	Body/Style Number	Body Type & Seating	Factory Price	Shipping Weight	Production Total
233	23369	4-dr Sed-6P	2388	3140	13,136
233	23307	2-dr Cpe-6P	2341	3110	17,978
233	23335	4-dr Sta Wag-6P	2666	3370	3,495

NOTE 1: A total of 34,609 standard Tempests were built.
NOTE 2: 7,154 standard Tempests had synchromesh; 27,455 had automatic.

TEMPEST CUSTOM — (6-CYL) — SERIES 235 — Standard equipment on Tempest Custom models included special interior trim, carpeting, Deluxe steering wheel and courtesy lamps on convertibles. There were no horizontal slits on the rear fendersides and the nameplate behind the front wheel opening carried Tempest Custom lettering. Upper beltline and wheel opening decor moldings were used.

TEMPEST CUSTOM (SERIES 235)

Model Number	Body/Style Number	Body Type & Seating	Factory Price	Shipping Weight	Production Total
235	23569	4-dr Sed-6P	2482	3145	17,445
235	23539	4-dr HT-6P	2608	3240	5,493
235	23507	2-dr Cpe-6P	2434	3130	12,469
235	23517	2-dr HT Cpe-6P	2494	3140	30,512
235	23567	2-dr Conv-6P	2723	3240	4,082
235	23535	4-dr Sta Wag-6P	2760	3370	5,324

NOTE 1: A total of 75,325 Tempest Customs were built.
NOTE 2: 8,302 Tempest Customs had synchromesh and 67,023 had automatic.

TEMPEST LEMANS — (6-CYL) — SERIES 237 and 239 — When the name LeMans appeared on the back fenders Tempest buyers got carpeting, front foam seat cushions and lamps for the ashtray, cigar lighter and glovebox as standard equipment. Buyers of two-door models in this line found three vertical air slots on rear fenders and had a choice of bucket or notch back bench seats with armrests. The four-door hardtop came with cloth-and-Morrokide trim and short slanting chrome slashes on the rear roof pillar. Other styles had all-Morrokide upholstery. A special station wagon with woodgrained exterior paneling was called the Series 239 Tempest Safari and was generally finished in LeMans level-trim appointments.

TEMPEST LEMANS (SERIES 237)

Model Number	Body/Style Number	Body Type & Seating	Factory Price	Shipping Weight	Production Total
237	23739	4-dr HT -6P	2771	3265	8,424
237	23707	2-dr Cpe-5P	2586	3155	10,693
237	23717	2-dr HT Cpe-5P	2648	3155	75,965
237	23767	2-dr Conv-5P	2881	3250	9,820

TEMPEST SAFARI (SERIES 239)

Model Number	Body/Style Number	Body Type & Seating	Factory Price	Shipping Weight	Production Total
239	23935	4-dr Sta Wag-6P	2936	3390	4,511

NOTE 1: 104,902 LeMans passenger cars were built.
NOTE 2: 14,770 LeMans passenger cars had synchromesh and 90,132 had automatic.
NOTE 3: 4,511 Tempest Safari wagons were built.
NOTE 4: 129 Tempest Safari wagons had synchromesh and 4,382 had automatic.

1967 Pontiac, GTO two-door hardtop, V-8

TEMPEST GTO — (V-8) — SERIES 242 — On GTOs the trim along the center grille divider now went from one side of the car to the other, with a dip around the center divider. V-shaped fender badges behind the front wheel opening were eliminated. Like the Grand Prix, the GTO had twin pinstripes along the upper beltline region. Bodyside accent moldings were slightly revised. Rectangular front grille parking lights were still used in front and the taillights now took the form of four thin rectangles at each side. All LeMans features were standard, plus walnut grain dash inserts, heavy-duty shocks, springs and stabilizer bars, redline or whitewall tires, dual exhausts and a 335 hp four-barrel 400 cid V-8.

TEMPEST GTO (SERIES 242)

Model Number	Body/Style Number	Body Type & Seating	Factory Price	Shipping Weight	Production Total
242	24207	2-dr Cpe-5P	2871	3425	7,029
242	24217	2-dr HT Cpe-5P	2935	3430	65,176
242	24267	2-dr Conv-5P	3165	3515	9,517

NOTE 1: 81,722 GTOs were built.
NOTE 2: 39,128 GTOs had synchromesh and 42,594 had automatic.

1967 Pontiac, Firebird two-door convertible, V-8

FIREBIRD — (6-CYL) — SERIES 223 — The first Firebird was made at Lordstown, Ohio in early January, 1967. The new car-line was officially released Feb. 23, 1967. External features included sculptured body styling, twin grilles of a bumper-integral design, front vent windows, and three vertical air slots on the leading edge of rear body panels. Bucket seats were standard. Two body styles were offered and came with any of the Tempest or GTO power trains. However, the two body styles were marketed in five "model-options" created by adding regular production options (RPOs) in specific combinations. Production records were not kept according to the RPO packages, but by the number of sixes and V-8s built with standard or deluxe appointments. The model-option such as Sprint, HO and 400 are described in the optional equipment section above.

FIREBIRD (SERIES 223)

Model Number	Body/Style Number	Body Type & Seating	Factory Price	Shipping Weight	Production Total
223	22337	2-dr HT Cpe-5P	2666	2955	67,032
223	22367	2-dr Conv-5P	2903	3247	15,528

Note 1: Prices/weights for base Firebird with 165 hp ohc six and synchromesh.

PRODUCTION NOTES:

standard ohc six Firebirds	(synchromesh)	5,258	(automatic)	5,597	(Total)	10,855
standard V-8 Firebirds	(synchromesh)	8,224	(automatic)	15,301	(Total)	23,525
deluxe ohc six Firebirds	(synchromesh)	2,963	(automatic)	3,846	(Total)	6,809
deluxe V-8 Firebirds	(synchromesh)	11,526	(automatic)	29,845	(Total)	41,371
		27,971	(automatic)	54,589		82,560

BASE ENGINES

(CATALINA/EXECUTIVE) Base V-8: Overhead valves. Cast iron block. Displacement: 400 cid. Bore and stroke: 4.125 x 3.746. Compression ratio: (synchromesh) 8.6:1; (Turbo-Hydra-matic) 10.5:1. Brake hp: (synchromesh) 265 at 4600 rpm.; (Turbo-Hydramatic) 290 at 4600 rpm. Five main bearings. Hydraulic valve lifters. Carburetor: Rochester model 7027066 two-barrel.

(BONNEVILLE) Base V-8s: Overhead valves. Cast iron block. Displacement: 400 cid. Bore and stroke: 4.125 x 3.746. Compression ratio: (synchromesh) 8.6:1; (Turbo-Hydramatic) 10.5:1. Brake hp: (synchromesh) 333 at 5000 rpm.; (Turbo-Hydramatic) 325 at 4800 rpm. Five main bearings. Hydraulic valve lifters. Carburetor: Carter AFB model 4243S four-barrel.

(GRAND PRIX) Base V-8: Same general specifications as on Bonneville Turbo-Hydra-matic V-8, except that a high lift camshaft giving 350 hp at 5000 rpm was used on the Grand Prix.

(TEMPEST/TEMPEST CUSTOM/FIREBIRD) OHC-Six: Overhead valves. Cast iron block. Displacement: 230 cid. Bore and stroke: 3.87 x 3.25 inches. Compression ratio: 9.0:1. Brake hp: 165 at 4700 rpm. Seven main bearings. Hydraulic lifters. Carburetor: Rochester one-barrel.

(GTO) Base V-8: Overhead valves. Cast iron block. Displacement: 400 cid. Bore and stroke: 4.125 x 3.746. Compression ratio: 10.75:1. Brake hp:335 at 5000 rpm. Five main bearings. Hydraulic valve lifters. Carburetor: Rochester model 7027263 Quadra-Jet four-barrel. (Note: The two-barrel V-8 was a delete-option, not the base engine.)

CHASSIS FEATURES: Wheelbase: (Pontiac station wagons) 121 inches; (Series 252 and 266 passenger cars) 121 inches; (Series 256 and 262 passenger cars) 124 inches; (Tempests) 115 inches; (Firebirds) 108 inches. Overall length: (Pontiac station wagons) 218.4 inches; (Series 252 and 266 passenger cars) 215.6 inches; (Series 256 and 262 passenger cars) 222.6 inches; (Tempest station wagons) 203.4 inches; (Tempest and GTO passenger cars) 206.6 inches; (Firebirds) 188.4 inches. Front tread: (Pontiac) 63 inches; (Tempest) 58 inches; (Firebird) 60 inches. Rear tread: (Pontiac) 64 inches; (Tempest) 59 inches; (Firebird) 60 inches. Standard tires: (two-door and four-door Catalina sedans) 8.25 x 14; (other full-size Pontiacs) 8.55 x 14; (Tempest) 7.75 x 14; (Firebird) E70 x 14; (GTO) F70 x 14.

OPTIONS

[PONTIAC] Custom air conditioner ($421). Air injector exhaust control ($44). Console ($105). Cruise control ($63). Front disc brakes ($105). Rear window defogger ($21). Headrests ($42-52). Capacitor ignition ($104-115). Cornering lamps ($34). Low-fuel lamp ($6). Custom gage panel cluster ($21-36). Power antenna ($29). Power steering ($95-105). AM/FM Stereo ($239). Safeguard speedometer ($16). Reclining right-hand seat ($84). Super-Lift shock absorbers ($40). Front shoulder belts ($23-26). Fender skirts ($26). Ride & Handling package ($9). Strato Bucket seats on Bonneville coupe and convertible only ($114). Cordo top ($105-132). Turbo-Hydramatic ($226). Four-speed manual transmission ($226). Three-speed manual transmission with floor shift ($42). Ventura Custom option with bench seats ($134). Ventura Custom convertible option with bucket seats ($206). Ventura Custom hardtop option with bucket seats ($248). Aluminum hubs and drums ($118-135). Rally II wheels ($65-73). 2+2 Sport Option ($389-410). (Note: The 2+2 Sport Option included deluxe wheel discs and steering wheel, decor moldings, bucket seats, four-barrel 428 cid V-8, three-speed manual floor shift, dual exhausts and heavy-duty stabilizer bar. Lower 2+2 price applies to Catalina convertible; higher price to hardtop coupe.) The 265 hp Catalina V-8 was a no-cost economy option in other full-sized lines. Base Bonneville V-8s were $35-44 extra in Catalinas or Executives with prices depending upon model and transmission. The 428 cid V-8 with 10.5:1 compression and four-barrel carburetor was optional in all full-sized Pontiacs at $79-114 extra, with prices depending upon model, transmission and use of air injector exhaust control. A 428 cid HO (high-output) V-8 was available in all full-sized Pontiacs for $119-263 extra, with prices depending upon model, transmission and use of air injector exhaust control.

[TEMPEST/FIREBIRD] Dual-stage air cleaner ($9). Custom air conditioner ($343). Carpeting ($19). GTO console ($68). Cruise control ($53). Remote control deck lid ($13). GTO tailpipe extensions ($21). Head rests ($42). Station wagon luggage carrier ($63). Remote control outside mirror ($7). Rally gage cluster ($84). Power antenna ($29). AM/FM Radio ($134). Reclining right-hand bucket seat ($84). Stereo tape player ($128). Tilt steering ($42). Three-speed manual transmission w/floor shift ($42). Three-speed manual transmission w/full-

synchromesh ($84). Four-speed manual transmission ($184). Automatic transmission with base OHC-6 ($226). Automatic transmission with 326 cid V-8 ($195). Turbo-Hydramatic in GTO only ($226). Wire wheel discs ($53-70). Rally I wheels ($40-57). Rally II wheels ($56-72). Integral hubs and drums ($83-100). Sprint package ($106-127). (Sprint package includes heavy-duty stabilizer shaft, ohc six with four-barrel carburetor, three-speed manual transmission with floor shift, sport type shocks, front fender emblems, wheel opening moldings on Tempests and Tempest Customs and Sprint side stripes on coupes and convertibles). The 326 cid V-8 with 9.2:1 compression, two-barrel carburetion and 250 hp at 4600 rpm was $95 extra in Tempests. The Sprint OHC-6 with 10.5:1 compression, four-barrel carburetion and 207 hp at 5200 rpm. was $58 extra in Tempests. The 326 cid V-8 with 10.5:1 compression, four-barrel carburetion and 285 hp at 5000 rpm was $159 extra in Tempests, except station wagons. (Note: Above options not available in GTOS). [GTO] The 255 hp 400 cid V-8 with 8.6:1 compression and 255 hp at 4400 rpm was a no cost GTO economy option. A second option in this series was the RAM AIR 400 cid V-8 with the same specifications as base GTO engines. It also gave 360 hp, but at a higher peak of 5400 rpm.

[FIREBIRD "MODEL-OPTION" PACKAGES]

FIREBIRD SPRINT: Sprint models featured a 215 hp ohc six with four-barrel carburetion. A floor-mounted three speed manual gearbox and heavy-duty suspension was standard. Body still moldings with "3.8 Litre Overhead Cam" emblems were seen. Bodyside racing stripes were an option. The Firebird Sprint convertible was priced $3,019 and the Firebird Sprint coupe was $2,782. The additional weight over respective base models was 55 pounds.

FIREBIRD 326: Firebird 326s featured a 250 hp version of the base Tempest V-8 with two-barrel carburetion. The Firebird 326 convertible was priced $2,998 and weighed 3,415 pounds. The Firebird 326 coupe was priced $2,761 and weighed 3,123 pounds.

FIREBIRD 326-HO: Firebird 326-HOs used a 285 hp version of the base Tempest V-8 with 10.5:1 compression and four-barrel carburetion. Three-speed manual transmission with column shift, dual exhausts, HO side stripes, heavy-duty battery and F70 x 14 wide oval tires were standard. The Firebird 326-HO convertible was priced $3,062 and the Firebird 326-HO coupe was priced $2,825.

FIREBIRD 400: Firebird 400s used a 325 hp version of the GTO V-8 with four-barrel carburetion. Standard equipment included dual scoop hood, chrome engine parts, three-speed heavy-duty floor shift and sport type suspension. The letters `400' appeared on the right-hand side of the deck lid. The Firebird 400 convertible was priced $3,177 and the Firebird 400 coupe was priced $2,777. Options included a RAM AIR induction setup that gave 325 hp at a higher rpm peak and cost over $600 extra.

HISTORICAL FOOTNOTES: Pontiacs were introduced in the fall of 1966 and the Firebird debuted Feb. 23, 1967. Calendar year production was 857,171 units. This was the only year that a Grand Prix convertible was ever offered. Interesting conversions of 1967 Pontiacs include the George Barris-built "Monkeemobile" GTO phaeton (made for the TV show) and the "Fitchbird," a performance-oriented package for Firebirds marketed by race car builder/driver John Fitch. New features included 400 cid and 428 cid V-8s and the so-called "His-And-Her" transmission that allowed conventional shifting of the automatic gear selector. In magazine road tests, the '67 Firebird Sprint hardtop with 215 hp did 0-to-60 in 10 seconds and the quarter-mile in 17.5 seconds. With the 325 hp Firebird 400 option, the numbers went down to 6.4 and 14.3 respectively. The Firebird 400 hardtop with the 325 hp motor was clocked by a second test driver at 14.7 seconds and 98 mph in the quarter-mile. A total of 7,724 Catalina 2+2s with the standard 428 cid/360 hp V-8 were built. Another 1,405 full-size Pontiacs had the 428 HO/376 hp engine. The term Safari was used only for station wagons with woodgrained trim. The term Sports Coupe was used to describe Tempest and GTO two-door pillared coupes (See Cpe in charts). The Bonneville Brougham package, available for four-door sedans and hardtops only, was $273 extra and included front foam seat cushions, power windows and Strato Bench seats.

1968 PONTIAC

CATALINA — (V-8) — SERIES 252 — New styling features for full-sized 1968 Pontiacs included peripheral front bumpers, pointed noses, split grilles new interiors, revised instrument panels and redesigned taillamps. Standard equipment for Catalinas included GM safety features; cigar lighter, glovebox and ashtray lamps, woodgrained dash trim, carpeting, concealed two-speed wipers and a two-barrel V-8. Convertibles and station wagons had Morrokide seats and the nine-passenger wagon had a power tailgate window. Code 554 Ventura Custom trim option available on style numbers 25287 and 25267 with bucket seats ($178-219) and all other Catalinas, except two-door sedan, with bench seats ($105). Ventura Custom option includes special interior trim and Ventura fender lettering. Catalina lettering appeared on the front fender tip, except cars with the Ventura package carried the Ventura name instead.

PONTIAC I.D. NUMBERS: VIN on left front door post. First symbol indicates GM division: 2=Pontiac. Second and third symbols indicate series: 23=Firebird; 33=Tempest; 35=Tempest Custom; 37=LeMans; 39=Tempest Safari; 42=GTO; 52=Catalina; 56=Star Chief; 62=Bonneville; 66=Grand Prix. Fourth and fifth symbols indicate body style and appear as last two symbols in Body/Style Number column of charts below. Sixth symbol indicates model year: 8=1968. Seventh symbol tells assembly plant: L=Van Nuys, Calif.; 1=Oshawa, Ontario, Canada; P=Pontiac, Mich.; C=South Gate, Calif.; E=Linden, N.J.; X=Kansas City, Kan.; R=Arlington, Texas; Z=Fremont, Calif; B=Baltimore, Md.; K=Kansas City, Mo.; G=Framingham, Mass.; V=Lordstown, Ohio. Following symbols are sequential production number starting with 100001 at each assembly plant. Body/Style Number plate under hood tells manufacturer, Fisher style number, assembly plant, trim code, paint code, accessory codes. Style number consists of 68 (for 1968) prefix and four symbols that appear in second column of charts below. First two symbols indicate series; second two symbols indicate body type. VIN appears on front of engine at right-hand cylinder bank along with an alpha-numerical engine production code. Engine production codes included: [230 cid/175 hp ohc six] ZK/ZN. [230 cid/215 hp ohc six] ZD/ZE/ZO. [350 cid/265 hp V-8] WP/YN/WD/WC/YJ. [350 cid/320 hp V-8] WR/YM/YP/WK. [400 cid/265 hp V-8] XM/YA. [400 cid/290 hp] WA/WB/YC. [400 cid/330 hp V-8] WZ/YT; [400 cid/335 hp] WQ/WI/YW/XN. [400 cid/340 hp] WE/YE. [400 cid/350 hp] XZ/XH. [428 cid/375 hp V-8] WG/YH. [428 cid/390 hp V-8] WJ/YK. [400 cid/265 hp two-barrel GTO V-8; automatic only] XM. [400 cid/335 hp four-barrel special GTO V-8] WT/WW with synchromesh; YS with Turbo Hydra-matic. [400 cid/350 hp GTO special V-8] WT manual transmission only. [400 cid/360 hp special GTO V-8] WS/XS with synchromesh; YZ/XP Hydra-Matic.

CATALINA (SERIES 252)

Model Number	Body/Style Number	Body Type & Seating	Factory Price	Shipping Weight	Production Total
252	25269	4-dr HT-6P	3004	3888	94,441
252	25239	4-dr HT-6P	3158	4012	41,727
252	25211	2-dr Sed-6p	2945	3839	5,247
252	25287	2-dr HT-6P	3089	3943	92,217
252	25267	2-dr Conv-6P	3391	3980	7,339
252	25245	4-dr Sta Wag-9P	3537	4408	13,363
252	25235	4-dr Sta Wag-6P	3390	4327	21,848

NOTE 1: 240,971 Catalina passenger cars were built.
NOTE 2: 2,257 had Catalina passenger cars had synchromesh; 238,714 automatic.
NOTE 3: 35,211 Catalina station wagons were built.
NOTE 4: 289 Catalina station wagons had synchromesh and 34,922 had automatic.

EXECUTIVE — (V-8) — SERIES 256 — Executives had all Catalina equipment, plus Deluxe steering wheel, decor moldings, Deluxe wheel discs and map, courtesy and trunk lamps. Executive lettering appeared behind front wheel openings.

EXECUTIVE (SERIES 256)

Model Number	Body/Style Number	Body Type & Seating	Factory Price	Shipping Weight	Production Total
256	25669	4-dr Sed-6P	3309	4022	18,869
256	25639	4-dr HT-6P	3439	4077	7,848
256	25687	2-dr HT-6P	3371	3975	5,880
256	25645	4-dr Sta Wag-6P	3890	4453	5,843
256	25635	4-dr Sta Wag-6P	3744	4378	6,195

NOTE 1: 32,597 Executive passenger cars were built.
NOTE 2: 47 had Executive passenger cars synchromesh; 32,550 had automatic.
NOTE 3: 12,038 Executive station wagons were built.
NOTE 4: 23 Executive station wagons had synchromesh and 12,015 had automatic.

BONNEVILLE — (V-8) — SERIES 262 — Bonnevilles had all Executive features, plus fender skirts, carpeted lower door trim, elm burl vinyl dash trim and a 340 hp V-8. Convertibles had leather and Morrokide interiors. Wagons had notch back front seats with folding armrest, folding third seat, courtesy lamps, power tailgate window and carpeted load area. The Bonneville name, in block letters, appeared behind the front wheel opening and on the deck lid latch panel. Bonneville taillights were of the same shape used a year earlier, but were now of a single design, the lens being longer than used on Catalinas and Executives. The code 511 Bonneville Brougham trim option was available on style numbers 26239 and 26287 ($273) and 26267 ($316). It includes front foam cushions, spare tire cover, power windows and Strato bench seat.

1968 Pontiac, Executive four-door hardtop sedan, V-8

BONNEVILLE (SERIES 262)

Model Number	Body/Style Number	Body Type & Seating	Factory Price	Shipping Weight	Production Total
262	26239	4-dr HT-6P	3660	4171	57,055
262	26287	2-dr HT-6P	3592	4054	29,598
262	26267	2-dr Conv-6P	3800	4090	7,358
262	26245	4-dr Sta Wag-6P	3987	4485	6,926
262	26269	4-dr Sed-6P	3530	4122	3,499

NOTE 1: 98,005 Bonneville passenger cars were built.
NOTE 2: 208 Bonneville passenger cars had synchromesh; 97,797 had automatic.
NOTE 3: 6,926 Bonneville station wagons were built.
NOTE 4: Nine Bonneville station wagons had synchromesh; 6,917 had automatic.
NOTE 5: 495 Bonnevilles were provided for conversions.

1968 Pontiac, Grand Prix two-door hardtop coupe, V-8

GRAND PRIX — (V-8) — SERIES 266 — Only the Grand Prix coupe was back for 1968. Standard were all GM safety features, plus deluxe wheel discs, fender skirts, dual exhausts, padded bucket seats with contoured backs and armrests, center console and a 400 cid/350 hp four-barrel V-8 with three-speed manual attachment. New styling included a peripheral bumper, extra-long horizontal taillamps integrated into bumper, downswept rear deck, redesigned dash panel and hidden headlights. A 'GP' badge appeared on the left-hand grille and right-hand corner of the deck lid with engine displacement badges on rocker panel moldings.

GRAND PRIX (SERIES 266)

Model Number	Body/Style Number	Body Type & Seating	Factory Price	Shipping Weight	Production Total
266	26657	2-dr HT Cpe-6P	3697	4075	31,711

NOTE 1: 31,711 GPs were built.
NOTE 2: 306 GPs had synchromesh and 31,405 had automatic.

TEMPEST — (6-CYL) — SERIES 233 — Tempests now had long hood/short deck styling. Two and four-door models were built with different wheelbases. A peripheral bumper grille was used and taillights were placed in the bumper. Regular equipment on standard Tempests included GM safety features, heater and defroster, door armrests and an overhead cam six-cylinder engine. Cars with the base engine had ohc six lettering on rocker panels. Tempest Sprint package available at prices of $106-126 depending on series and body style. Tempest Sprint package includes four-barrel ohc six, heavy-duty stabilizer shaft, three-speed manual transmission, sport type shocks, ohc six rocker panel molding emblems and (on some models) wheel opening moldings and Sprint side stripes.

TEMPEST (SERIES 233)

Model Number	Body/Style Number	Body Type & Seating	Factory Price	Shipping Weight	Production Total
233	23369	4-dr Sed-6P	2509	3307	11,590
233	23327	2-dr Cpe-6p	2461	3242	19,991

NOTE 1: 31,581 standard Tempests were built.
NOTE 2: 5,876 had synchromesh and 25,705 had automatic.

TEMPEST CUSTOM — (6-CYL) — SERIES 235 — Tempest Customs had all features found on series 233 models, plus special interior and exterior trim, carpeting, Deluxe steering wheel, armrests with ashtrays, cigarette lighter, ignition buzzer alarm, front and rear bodyside marker lights and dual horns. Station wagons and convertibles had all-Morrokide seats and carpeting, with panel courtesy lamps on convertibles. Tempest lettering along with custom badges appeared at tips of front fenders.

TEMPEST CUSTOM (SERIES 235)

Model Number	Body/Style Number	Body Type & Seating	Factory Price	Shipping Weight	Production Total
235	23569	4-dr Sed-6P	2602	3297	17,304
235	23539	4-dr HT-6P	2728	3382	6,147
235	23527	2-dr Cpe-6P	2554	3252	10,634
235	23537	2-dr HT Cpe-6P	2614	3277	40,574
235	23567	2-dr Conv-6P	2839	3337	3,518
235	23535	4-dr Sta Wag-6P	2906	3667	8,253

NOTE 1: 75,325 Custom Tempests were built.
NOTE 2: 8,302 had synchromesh and 67,023 had automatic.

1968 Pontiac, LeMans four-door hardtop sedan, 6-cyl

TEMPEST LEMANS — (6-CYL) — SERIES 237 AND SERIES 239 — Standard in LeMans were all GM safety features, plus disappearing wipers, dual horns and Morrokide interior. Two-door models came with a choice of bucket or notch back armrest seats. The four-door hardtop had cloth and Morrokide upholstery and a choice of notch back or bench seats. Deluxe steering wheel, carpeting, cigar lighter, armrests and ashtrays, ignition alarm, panel courtesy lamps, ashtray and glovebox lamps were also featured. The LeMans convertible had a power top and special courtesy lights. The series 239 Safari was generally appointed in LeMans level trim with woodgrained interior and exterior paneling. The word LeMans was on the rear fender of each LeMans. The word Safari was on front of wood-trimmed station wagons.

TEMPEST LEMANS (SERIES 237)

Model Number	Body/Style Number	Body Type & Seating	Factory Price	Shipping Weight	Production Total
237	23739	4-dr HT-6P	2916	3407	9,002
237	23727	2-dr Cpe-6P	2724	3287	8,439
237	23737	2-dr HT Cpe-6P	2786	3302	110,036
237	23767	2-dr Conv-6P	3015	3377	8,820

TEMPEST SAFARI (SERIES 239)

Model Number	Body/Style Number	Body Type & Seating	Factory Price	Shipping Weight	Production Total
239	23935	4-dr Sta Wag-6P	3017	3677	4,414

NOTE 1: 136,297 LeMans cars were built.
NOTE 2: 12,233 LeMans cars had synchromesh and 124,074 had automatic.
NOTE 3: 4,414 LeMans Safari station wagons were built.
NOTE 4: 122 LeMans Safaris had synchromesh and 4,292 had automatic.

GTO — (V-8) — SERIES 242 — Standard in GTOs were all GM safety features, dual exhausts, three-speed manual transmission with Hurst shifter, sports type springs and shock absorbers, fastback redline tires, bucket or notch back armrest seats, cigar lighter, carpeting,

---

ignition alarm, disappearing wipers, panel courtesy, ashtray and glovebox lamps, deluxe steering wheel and 350 hp 400 cid four-barrel V-8 (or two-barrel 400 cid regular fuel V-8). GTOs had hidden headlights; a steel-reinforced 'Endura' rubber front bumpers; twin scoop hoods; GTO lettering on left-hand grille and right-hand deck lid; V-shaped badge behind front wheel opening; V-shaped nose emblems; and distinct taillamps.

GTO (SERIES 242)

Model Number	Body/Style Number	Body Type & Seating	Factory Price	Shipping Weight	Production Total
242	24237	2-dr HT Cpe-5P	3101	3506	77,704
242	24267	2-dr Conv-5P	2996	3346	9,980

NOTE 1: 87,684 GTOs were built.
NOTE 2: 36,299 had synchromesh and 51,385 had automatic.

FIREBIRD — (6-CYL) — SERIES 223 — Base Firebird equipment included the standard GM safety features, front bucket seats, vinyl upholstery, simulated burl woodgrain dashboard, outside mirror, side marker lights, E70 x 14 black sidewall wide-oval tires with Space Saver spare and 175 hp overhead cam six-cylinder engine. Styling was nearly identical to 1967-1/2 Firebirds except that vent windows were replaced with one-piece side door glass. Technical changes included bias-mounted rear shock absorbers and multi-leaf rear springs.

BASE FIREBIRD (SERIES 233)

Model Number	Body/Style Number	Body Type & Seating	Factory Price	Shipping Weight	Production Total
223	22337	2-dr HT Cpe-5P	2781	3061	90,152
223	22367	2-dr Conv-5P	2996	3346	16,960

FIREBIRD PRODUCTION NOTES

Model No.	Engine/Trim	Synchro.	Auto.	Total
Model 223	standard ohc six	7,528	8,441	15,969
Model 224	Standard V-8	16,632	39,250	55,882
Model 225	deluxe ohc six	1,216	1,309	2,525
Model 226	deluxe V-8	7,534	25,202	32,736
		32,910	74,202	107,112

BASE ENGINES

(CATALINA/EXECUTIVE) V-8. Overhead valves. Cast iron block. Displacement: 400 cid. Bore and stroke: 4.13 x 3.75 inches. Compression ratio: (synchromesh) 8.6:1; (Turbo-Hydra-matic) 10.5:1. Brake hp: (synchromesh) 265 at 4600 rpm; (Turbo-Turbo-Hydramatic) 290 hp at 4600 rpm. Five main bearings. Hydraulic valve lifters. Carburetor: Rochester two-barrel. (Note: the 290 hp V-8 was considered standard for 1968 Catalinas.)

(BONNEVILLE) Turbo-Hydramatic was considered standard on Bonnevilles and came attached to a 400 cid V-8 with 10.5:1 compression, a Rochester four-barrel carburetor and 340 hp at 4800 rpm. Bonnevilles with synchromesh utilized the same 8.6:1 compression V-8 used in other lines.

(TEMPEST/TEMPEST CUSTOM/LEMANS/FIREBIRD) Base OHC-Six. Overhead valves. Cast iron block. Displacement: 250 cid. Bore and stroke: 3.88 x 3.53 inches. Compression ratio: 9.0:1. Brake hp: 175 at 4800 rpm. Seven main bearings. Hydraulic valve lifters. Carburetor: Rochester one-barrel.

(GTO/GRAND PRIX) Base V-8: Overhead valves. Cast iron block. Displacement: 400 cid. Bore and stroke: 4.12 x 3.75 inches. Compression ratio: 10.75:1. Brake hp: 350 at 5000 rpm. Five main bearings. Hydraulic valve lifters. Carburetor: Rochester four-barrel.

HIGH PERFORMANCE ENGINES

400 cid. Compression ratio: 10.75. Carburetion: four-barrel. Brake hp: 330 at 4800 rpm (standard in Firebird Formula 400)

400 cid. Compression ratio: 10.5. Carburetion: four-barrel. Brake hp: 340 at 4800 rpm (standard in Bonneville, optional in other B-body models) 400 cid. Compression ratio: 10.5. Carburetion: four-barrel. Brake hp: 350 at 5000 rpm (standard in Grand Prix)

400 cid. Compression ratio: 10.75. Carburetion: four-barrel. Brake hp: 350 at 5000 rpm (standard in GTO)

400 cid. Compression ratio: 10.75. Carburetion: four-barrel. Brake hp: 335 at 5000 rpm (optional in Firebird Formula 400)

400 cid. Compression ratio: 10.75. Carburetion: four-barrel. Brake hp: 360 at 5100 rpm (optional in GTO)

400 cid. Compression ratio: 10.75. Carburetion: four-barrel. Brake hp: 366 at 5400 rpm (optional in GTO)

428 cid. Compression ratio: 10.5. Carburetion: four-barrel. Brake hp: 375 at 4800 rpm (optional in Catalina, Executive, Bonneville and Grand Prix)

428 cid. Compression ratio: 10.75. Carburetion: four-barrel. Brake hp: 390 at 5200 rpm (optional in Catalina, Executive, Bonneville and Grand Prix)

1968 Pontiac, Firebird 350 HO hardtop coupe, V-8

CHASSIS FEATURES: Wheelbase: (Series 252, 266 and all Pontiac station wagons) 21 inches; (Series 256 and 262) 124 inches; (Tempest two-door) 112 inches; (Tempest four-door) 116 inches; (Firebird) 108 inches. Overall length: (All Pontiac station wagons) 217.8 inches; (Series 252 and 266) 216.5 inches; (Series 256 and 262) 223.5 inches; (Tempest station wagons) 211 inches; (Tempest two-door) 200.7 inches; (Tempest four-door) 204.7 inches; (Firebird) 188.8 inches. Front tread: (Pontiac) 63 inches; (Tempest and Firebird) 60 inches. Rear tread: (Pontiac) 64 inches; (Tempest and Firebird) 60 inches.

OPTIONS

[PONTIAC] Custom air-conditioner ($421). Auxiliary gage panel ($21-37). Console ($105). Remote-control deck lid ($14). Rear window defogger ($21). Door guards ($6-10). Electric clock ($16). Head restraints ($42-53). Custom gear shift knob ($4). Underhood utility lamp ($7). Visor vanity mirror ($2-4). Power brakes ($42). Power antenna ($30). Left power bucket seat ($69). Power steering ($105-116). Power windows ($104). Power vent windows ($53). AM/FM Stereo ($239). Split back station wagon second seat ($37). Hood-mounted tachometer ($63). Strato bucket seats ($114). Wire wheel discs ($53-74). Heavy-duty 15 inch wheels ($11). Aluminum hubs and drums ($126-147). Rally II wheels ($63-84). Transmission options included Turbo-Hydramatic ($237) Four-speed manual ($226); Close-ratio three-speed manual with floorshift ($42) and close-ratio four-speed manual ($226). The 265 hp two-barrel 400 cid V-8 was $9 extra on Catalinas and Executives with three-speed manual transmission. The 350 hp four-barrel 400 cid V-8 was $35-44 extra on the same models. The 375 hp four-barrel 428 cid V-8 was $79-114 extras on all Pontiacs with price depending on transmission. The 390 hp four-barrel 428 cid V-8 was $199-263 extra on all Pontiacs with price depending on model and transmission. Dual exhausts were $31 extra. Safe-T-Track differential was $42 extra. A variety of axle ratios were available.

[TEMPEST/GTO/FIREBIRD] Custom air conditioner ($360). Custom carpets ($19). Console ($51-68). Cruise control ($53). Front disc brakes ($63). Auxiliary gage cluster ($32). Rally gage cluster ($51). Rally gage cluster with tachometer ($84). Tinted windows ($35). Tinted windshield ($26). Right reclining bucket seat head restraint ($84). Dual horns ($4). Station wagon luggage carrier ($63). Four-way power seat ($70). Power brakes ($42). Power steering ($69). Left four-way power bucket seat ($70). AM/FM radio ($134). Rally stripes on GTO ($11). Rally stripes for Firebirds except 350 HO ($15). Safeguard speedometer ($16). Super-Lift shocks for Tempest/GTO ($42). Adjustable front and rear shocks for Firebird ($42). Hood-mounted tachometer ($63). Cordova top ($84-95). Wire wheel discs ($53-74). Rally I wheels ($40-61). Rally II wheels ($84). Transmission options included two-speed automatic ($195); four-speed manual ($184) and heavy-duty three-speed manual with floor shift ($84). The 265 hp two-barrel regular fuel 350 cid V-8 was $106 extra. The 320 hp four-barrel HO 350 V-8 was $170 extra. Dual exhausts were $31 extra. Safe-T-Track differential was $42 extra. GTO Transmission options included Turbo-Hydramatic ($237) and close-ratio four-speed manual with floor shift ($184). The 366 hp four-barrel HO 400 cid V-8 was $631.12 extra. Dual exhausts were standard. Heavy-duty Safe-T-Track differential was $63 extra. Firebird transmission options included all offered for Tempests and GTOS. Firebird engine options are listed in Firebird RPO packages section below.

FIREBIRD RPO PACKAGES

FIREBIRD SPRINT PACKAGE: Included three-speed manual transmission with floor shift, ohc six Sprint emblems, body sill moldings and four F70 x 14 tires. Engine: 250 cid ohc six with 10.5:1 compression, Rochester four-barrel carburetor and 215 hp at 5200 rpm. Price: $116 over base model cost.

FIREBIRD 350 PACKAGE: included three-speed manual transmission with column shift and F70 x 14 tires. Engine: 350 cid (3.88 x 3.75 bore and stroke) V-8 with 9.2:1 compression, Rochester two-barrel carburetor and 265 hp at 4600 rpm. Price: $106 over base model cost.

FIREBIRD 350-HO PACKAGE: Included three-speed manual transmission with column shift, dual exhausts, HO side stripes, heavy-duty battery and four F70 x 14 tires. Engine: 350 cid V-8 with 10.5:1 compression, Rochester four-barrel carburetor and 320 hp at 5100 rpm. Price: $181 over base model cost.

FIREBIRD 400 PACKAGE: Included three-speed manual transmission with floor shift, chrome air cleaner, chrome rocker covers, chrome oil cap, sports type springs and shock absorbers, heavy-duty battery, dual exhausts, hood emblem and dual scoop hood, F70 x 14 red stripe or whitewall tires and 'Power Flex' variable pitch cooling fan. Engine: 400 cid V-8 with 10.75:1 compression, Rochester four-barrel carburetor and 330 hp at 4800 rpm. Price: $351-435 depending on transmission. Lower price applies to cars with Turbo-Hydramatic four-speed manual transmissions.

FIREBIRD RAM AIR 400 PACKAGE: Same inclusions as above, except for addition of de-clutching fan and twin functional hood scoops. Engine: 400 cid V-8 with 10-75:1 compression, Rochester four-barrel carburetor and 335 hp at 5000 rpm. Price: $616 over base model cost.

HISTORICAL FOOTNOTES: Production started Aug. 21, 1967. The model introductions were Sept. 21, 1967. Model year output was 910,977 cars. Calendar year output was 943,253 cars. The GTO Endura nose was a popular new option. This was the first year for two wheelbases in the Tempest series, with four-doors on the longer chassis. The 1968 Firebird 400 with the 335 hp option was capable of 0-to-60 in 7.6 seconds and the quarter-mile in 15.4 seconds. The 360 hp GTO hardtop did 0-to-60 in 6.6 seconds and the quarter-mile took 15.5 seconds. There were 6252 standard 428 V-8 engines installed and 453 full-size 428 HO Pontiacs were built.

1969 PONTIAC

CATALINA — (V-8) — SERIES 252 — New styling features for full-sized 1969 Pontiacs included split bumpers, revised rooflines and ventless windows. Wheelbases increased one inch. Catalinas had all GM Safety features, carpeting, peripheral front bumpers with Endura rubber center inserts, `pulse' windshield wipers with concealed blades, front foam seat cushions, upper level ventilation systems and a choice of low-compression (regular fuel) two-barrel V-8s or a 290 hp 400 cid V-8. Station wagons had woodgrained dashboards and new two-way tailgates with power rear windows on nine-passenger styles. The Ventura trim package was offered for closed cars only.

PONTIAC I.D. NUMBERS: VIN on left top of instrument panel, visible through windshield. First symbol indicates GM division: 2=Pontiac. Second and third symbols indicate series: 23=Firebird; 33=Tempest; 35=Tempest Custom; 37=LeMans; 39=Tempest Safari; 42=GTO; 52=Catalina; 56=Star Chief; 62=Bonneville; 76=Grand Prix. Fourth and fifth symbols indicate body style and appear as last two symbols in Body/Style Number column of charts below. Sixth symbol indicates model year: 9=1969. Seventh symbol tells assembly plant: A=Atlanta, Ga.; L=Van Nuys, Calif.; 1=Oshawa, Ontario, Canada; P=Pontiac, Mich.; C=South Gate, Calif.; E=Linden, N.J.; X=Kansas City, Kan.; R=Arlington, Texas; Z=Fremont, Calif; B=Baltimore, Md.; K=Kansas City, Mo.; G=Framingham, Mass.; V=Lordstown, Ohio. Following symbols are sequential production number starting with 100001 at each assembly plant. Body/Style Number plate under hood tells manufacturer, Fisher style number, assembly plant, trim code, paint code, accessory codes. Style number consists of 69 (for 1969) prefix and four symbols that appear in second column of charts below. First two symbols indicate series; second two symbols indicate body type. VIN appears on front of engine at right-hand cylinder bank along with an alpha-numerical engine production code. Engine production codes included: [250 cid/175 hp six] ZC/ZF/ZK/ZN. [250 cid/215 hp six] ZL/ZE. [250 cid/230 hp six] ZH/ZD. [350 cid/265 hp V-8] WU/YU/XS/XR/YN/WP/WM YE XB/WC XL YJ. [350 CID/

325 HP v-8] WN/XG/[350 cid/330 hp V-8] WV/XU. [400 cid/265 hp V-8] XM/XX/YA/YB/YF. [400 cid/290 hp] WD/WE/YD/WA/WB. [400 cid/330 hp] WZ/YT. [400 cid/335 hp] WQ/YW. [400 cid/345 hp] WH/XN. [400 cid/350 hp] WX/XH/Wt. [400 cid/350 hp] WT/YS. [400 cid/366 hp] WS/WW/YZ. [428 cid/340 hp] WG; [428 cid/360 hp] WG/YH/XJ/YL/XE. [428 cid/370 hp] XK/WF/XF. [428 cid/390 hp] WJ/YK/WL/XG.

CATALINA (SERIES 252)

Model Number	Body/Style Number	Body Type & Seating	Factory Price	Shipping Weight	Production Total
252	25269	4-dr Sed-6P	3090	3945	48,590
252	25239	4-dr HT-6P	3244	4005	38,819
252	25237	2-dr HT-6P	3174	2935	84,006
252	25267	2-dr Conv-6P	3476	2985	5,436
252	25246	4-dr Sta Wag-9P	3664	4520	13,393
252	25236	4-dr Sta Wag-6P	3519	4455	20,352

NOTE 1: 212,851 Catalina passenger cars were built.
NOTE 2: 837 Catalina passenger cars had synchromesh and 212,014 had automatic.
NOTE 3: 33,745 Catalina station wagons were built.
NOTE 4: 170 Catalina station wagons had synchromesh and 33,575 had automatic.

1969 Pontiac, Bonneville two-door convertible, V-8

EXECUTIVE — (V-8) — SERIES 256 — Standard equipment on Executive included everything found on Catalinas, plus deluxe wheelcovers, three-spoke padded vinyl steering wheel, simulated elm burl dash trim, rear foam seat cushions, electric clock and Morrokide upholstery. Executive Safaris also had woodgrained exterior paneling with simulated teakwood molding trim, vinyl floor mats and a concealed cargo locker.

EXECUTIVE (SERIES 256)

Model Number	Body/Style Number	Body Type & Seating	Factory Price	Shipping Weight	Production Total
256	25669	4-dr Sed-6P	3394	4045	14,831
256	25639	4-dr HT-6P	3525	4065	6,522
256	25637	2-dr HT-6P	3456	2970	4,492
256	25646	4-dr Sta Wag-9P	4017	4545	6,805
256	25636	4-dr Sta Wag-6P	3872	4475	6,411

NOTE 1: 25,845 Executive passenger cars were built.
NOTE 2: 25 Executive passenger cars had synchromesh and 25,820 had automatic.
NOTE 3: 13,216 Executive station wagons were built.
NOTE 4: 14 Executive station wagons had synchromesh and 13,202 had automatic.

BONNEVILLE — (V-8) — SERIES 262 — Bonnevilles had all features found on Executives, plus a die-cast grille, choice of several Bonneville Custom interiors, extra-thick foam seat padding, front center fold-down armrest, fender skirts, carpeted lower door panels and a 360 hp four-barrel V-8. The convertible had an all-Morrokide upholstery with leather accents. Station wagons featured a notch back front seat with folding armrest, a folding third seat and courtesy lamps. Bonneville lettering appeared on the left-hand grille, the rocker panel moldings and the center edge of the deck lid. The Brougham option was again available, but for coupes and convertibles only.

BONNEVILLE (SERIES 262)

Model Number	Body/Style Number	Body Type & Seating	Factory Price	Shipping Weight	Production Total
262	26269	4-dr Sed-6P	3626	4180	4,859
262	26239	4-dr HT-6P	3756	4180	40,841
262	26237	2-dr HT-6P	3688	4080	27,773
262	26267	2-dr Conv-6P	3896	4130	5,438
262	26246	4-dr Sta Wag-9P	4104	4600	7,428

NOTE 1: 89,334 Bonneville passenger cars were built.
NOTE 2: 44 Bonneville passenger cars had synchromesh and 89,290 had automatic.
NOTE 3: 7,428 Bonneville station wagons were built.
NOTE 4: Seven (7) Bonneville wagons had synchromesh and 7,421 had automatic.
NOTE 5: 447 Bonneville chassis were provided for conversions.

1969 Pontiac, Grand Prix 'J' hardtop coupe, V-8

GRAND PRIX — (V-8) — SERIES 276 — An all-new Grand Prix on an exclusive 118 inch platform was a popular offering this year. Styling highlights were a V-shaped grille, square headlamp surrounds, an aircraft inspired interior and the longest hood of any production car in history. Standard equipment included dual exhaust, Strato Bucket seats, padded integral console with floor shift, hidden radio antenna, carpeted lower door panels, upper level ventilation system and `pulse' type recessed windshield wipers. An `SJ' option package was available. A 350 hp V-8 was standard.

GRAND PRIX (SERIES 276)

Model Number	Body/Style Number	Body Type & Seating	Factory Price	Shipping Weight	Production Total
276	27657	2-dr HT Coupe-5P	3866	3715	112,486

NOTE 1: 112,486 GPs were built.
NOTE 2: 1,014 GPs had synchromesh and 111,472 had automatic.
NOTE 3: Approximately 676 cars above had four-speed manual transmission.

TEMPEST — (6-CYL) — SERIES 233 — Tempests were mildly face-lifted with new grille and taillight treatments. Two-door hardtops and convertibles now had ventless side window styling. Standard equipment on base models included all GM safety features, carpets, Morrokide accented upholstery trims and the ohc six. A Tempest script was placed on the leading edge of front fenders.

TEMPEST (SERIES 233)

Model Number	Body/Style Number	Body Type & Seating	Factory Price	Shipping Weight	Production Total
233	23369	4-dr Sed-6P	2557	3250	9,741
233	23327	2-dr Cpe-6P	2510	3180	17,181

NOTE 1: 26,922 standard Tempest were built.
NOTE 2: 4,450 had synchromesh and 22,472 had automatic.

TEMPEST CUSTOM — (6-CYL) — SERIES 235 — This was now called the Custom 'S' series and front fender scripts carried this designation. Standard equipment included all Tempest features, plus all-Morrokide upholstery, concealed windshield wipers, dual horns, ignition buzzer and panel courtesy lamps on convertibles. Cars with six-cylinder engines had ohc six badges on the body sill moldings. Small hubcaps were a regular feature.

TEMPEST CUSTOM 'S' (SERIES 235)

Model Number	Body/Style Number	Body Type & Seating	Factory Price	Shipping Weight	Production Total
235	23569	4-dr Sed-6P	2651	3235	16,532
235	23539	4-dr HT-6P	2777	3315	3,918
235	23527	2-dr Cpe-6P	2603	3210	7,912
235	23537	2-dr HT-6P	2663	3220	46,886
235	23567	2-dr Conv-6P	2888	3265	2,379
235	23535	4-dr Sta Wag-6P	2956	5696	6,963

NOTE 1: 84,590 Tempest Custom 'S' models were built.
NOTE 2: 4,045 Tempest `S' had synchromesh and 80,545 had automatic.

TEMPEST LEMANS — (6-CYL) — SERIES 237 AND 239 — LeMans, models incorporated all Custom `S' equipment, plus a 3.23:1 rear axle, deluxe three-spoke steering wheel, `pulse' wipers, lamp packages and several seating arrangement choices. Two-door models were available with bucket or notch back seats; four-door hardtop buyers had a choice of bench or notch back seats with center armrests. LeMans convertibles had power tops and Safaris had woodgrained exterior panelling and concealed headlamps. The Sprint option was available for all six-cylinder Tempests, except station wagons. LeMans block lettering appeared on the front fender tips and there were bright metal window and wheel opening moldings. Wood-trimmed station wagons had Safari fender scripts. The Safari was not a LeMans, but was close to it in overall level of trim.

TEMPEST LEMANS (SERIES 237)

Model Number	Body/Style Number	Body Type & Seating	Factory Price	Shipping Weight	Production Total
237	23769	4-dr HT-6P	2965	3360	6,475
237	23727	2-dr Cpe-6P	2773	3225	5,033
237	23737	2-dr HT-6P	2835	3245	82,817
237	23767	2-dr Conv-6P	3064	3290	5,676
TEMPEST SAFARI (SERIES 239)					
239	23936	4-dr Sta Wag-6P	3198	3690	4,115

NOTE 1: 100,001 LeMans passenger were built.
NOTE 2: 6,303 LeMans passenger cars had synchromesh and 93,698 had automatic.
NOTE 3: 4,115 Tempest Safaris were built.
NOTE 4: 86 Tempest Safaris had synchromesh and 4,029 had automatic.

1969 Pontiac, GTO two-door hardtop coupe, V-8

GTO — (V-8) — SERIES 242 — GTOs were based on LeMans with additional standard equipment features including a 400 cid/350 hp V-8, dual exhausts, 3.55:1 rear axle ratio, heavy-duty clutch, three-speed gearbox with floor shifter, Power-Flex cooling fan, sports type springs and shock absorbers, redline wide-oval tires, carpeting, Deluxe steering wheel and choice of bucket or notch back seats. A cross-hatched grille insert with horizontal divider bars appeared and hidden headlights were standard. GTO lettering was seen, on the left-hand grille, right-hand side of deck lid and behind the front wheel openings. Taillamps were no longer completely surrounded by bumpers and carried lenses with bright metal trim moldings. Side marker lights were of a distinctive rectangular shape, instead of the triangular type used on other Tempests. A special high-performance `The Judge' option was released Dec. 19, 1968. It included one of two available RAM AIR V-8s as standard equipment as well as many other `muscle car' features. Though more expensive than base GTOS, a 'The Judge' was the least expensive of several cars now on the market with comparable equipment.

GTO (SERIES 242)

Model Number	Body/Style Number	Body Type & Seating	Factory Price	Shipping Weight	Production Total
242	24237	2-dr HT-5P	2831	3080	58,126
242	24267	2-dr Conv-5P	3382	3553	7,328
242	2437	2-dr Judge HT-5P	3161	NA	6,725
242	24267	2-dr Judge Conv-5P	4212	NA	108

NOTE 1: 72,287 GTOs and `The Judge' optioned GTOs were built.
NOTE 2: 31,433 GTOs and Judges had synchromesh and 40,854 had automatic.
NOTE 3: 8,491 GTOs and Judges (including 362 convertibles) had RAM AIR III V-8s.
NOTE 4: RAM AIR III engines were coded `YZ' or `WS.'
NOTE 5: 759 GTOS and Judges (including 59 convertibles) had RAM AIR IV V-8s.
NOTE 6: RAM AIR IV engines were coded `XP' (automatic) or `WW' (synchromesh).

1969 Pontiac, Firebird Trans Am two-door hardtop, V-8

FIREBIRD — (6-CYL) — SERIES 223 — Firebirds were restyled very late in 1968 to incorporate revisions similar to those planned for the Chevrolet Camaro. Design changes included flatter wheel openings, front fender windsplits, new rooflines and a creased lower beltline. The gas filler was moved behind the rear license plate and a boxier split bumper grille was used. Headlamps were set into square body-colored Endura bezels. The high-performance Trans Am was introduced Mar. 8, 1969. This was the most highly refined "model-option" to come from Pontiac up to this point in time. Because of slow sales and late introductions of next-year-models, 1969 Firebirds left in stock were carried over and sold through the following fall. Standard equipment for base Firebirds included vinyl bucket seats, grained dashboards, carpeting, outside mirrors, side marker lamps and E70 x 14 tires. "Model-options" included Firebird Sprint, Firebird 350 and 350 HO, Firebird 400 and 400 HO and Firebird RAM AIR 400, in addition to the midyear Trans Am.

FIREBIRD (SERIES 223)

Model Number	Body/Style Number	Body Type & Seating	Factory Price	Shipping Weight	Production Total
223	22337	2-dr HT 5P	2831	3080	75,362
223	22367	2-dr Conv-5P	3045	3330	11,649
TRANS AM					
223	22337	2-dr HT-5P	3556	N/A	689
223	22367	2-dr Conv-5P	3770	N/A	8

NOTE 1: 87,709 Firebirds and Trans Ams were built.
NOTE 2: 20,840 Firebirds and Trans Ams had synchromesh; 66,868 had automatic.
NOTE 3: 114 Trans Ams had the L-74 RAM AIR III V-8 and Turbo-Hydramatic.
NOTE 4: 520 Trans Ams had the L-74 RAM AIR V-8 and synchromesh.
NOTE 5: All eight Trans Am convertibles were L-74s; four had manual gearboxes.
NOTE 6: Nine (9) Trans Ams had the L-67 RAM AIR IV motor and Turbo-Hydramatic.
NOTE 7: 46 Ams Ams had the L-67 RAM AIR IV motor and synchromesh.

BASE ENGINES

(CATALINA/EXECUTIVE) V-8. Overhead valves. Cast iron block. Displacement: 400 cid. Bore and stroke: 4.13 x 3.75 inches. Compression ratio: 10.5:1. Brake hp: 290 at 4600 rpm. Five main bearings. Hydraulic valve lifters. Carburetor: Rochester two-barrel. (Note: The 265 hp regular fuel V-8 was a no-cost option on cars with three-speed manual transmission only).

(BONNEVILLE) V-8. Overhead valves. Cast iron block. Displacement: 400 cid. Bore and stroke: 4.13 x 3.75 cid. Compression ratio: 10.5:1. Brake hp: 360 at 4600 rpm. Five main bearings. Hydraulic valve lifters. Carburetor: Rochester four-barrel.

(TEMPEST/CUSTOM 'S/FIREBIRD') Ohc six. Overhead valves. Cast iron block. Displacement: 250 cid. Bore and stroke: 3.88 x 3.53 inches. Compression ratio: 9.0:1. Brake hp: 175 at 4800 rpm. Seven main bearings. Hydraulic valve lifters. Carburetor: Rochester one-barrel.

(GTO) V-8. Overhead valves. Cast iron block. Displacement: 400 cid. Bore and stroke: 4.13 x 3.75 inches. Compression ratio: 10.75:1. Brake hp: 350 at 5000 rpm. Five main bearings. Hydraulic valve lifters. Carburetor: Rochester four-barrel.

CHASSIS FEATURES: Wheelbase: (Series 252 and all Pontiac station wagons) 122 inches; (Series 256 and 262) 125 inches; (Series 276) 118 inches; (Tempest two-door) 112 inches; (Tempest four-door) 116 inches; (Firebird) 108 inches. Overall length: (All Pontiac station wagons) 220.5 inches; (Series 252) 217.5 inches; (Series 256 and 262) 223.5 inches; (Series 276) 210.2 inches; (All Tempest station wagons) 211 inches; (Tempest two-door) 201.5 inches; (Tempest four-door) 205.5 inches; (Firebird) 191.1 inches. Front tread; (Pontiac) 63 inches; (Others) 60 inches. Rear tread: (Pontiac) 64 inches; (Others) 60 inches.

OPTIONS

[PONTIAC/TEMPEST] Heavy-duty aluminum front brake drums ($72). Load floor carpeting ($53). Console ($56). Cruise control ($58). GTO type exhaust extensions ($21). Instant air heater ($16). Luggage carrier for station wagons ($63-84). Power rear antenna ($32). Power disc front brakes ($64-74). Power door locks ($4568). Wonder Touch steering ($100-105). GTO Rally Stripes ($14). GTO retractable headlight covers ($53). Custom Sport steering wheel ($34-50). Tilt wheel with power steering ($45). Hood mounted tachometer ($63). Cordova top ($100-142). Rally II wheel ($64-84). Arctic wiper blades ($6). Station wagon rear window deflector ($26). Recessed wipers on base Tempest ($19). Leather GP trim ($199). Three speed manual transmissions were provided at base prices, including a heavy-duty type in Grand Prix. Turbo-Hydramatic $227 extra. Grand Prix buyers had two other options, close or wide-ratio four-speed manual gearboxes, both at $185. The regular fuel V-8 was a no charge option in any line. The Bonneville four-barrel was $38 extra on lower lines. The 375 hp four-barrel 428 cid V-8 was $67-105 extra on all Pontiacs (except Catalina and Executive station wagons) with price depending on series and transmission. The 390 hp four-barrel 428 cid HO V-8 was $150-255 extra with the same qualifications. Dual exhaust and Safe-T-Track differential were priced as in 1968. (GTO) Transmission options included Turbo-Hydramatic/

Turbo-Hydramatic/Hydramatic ($227) and wide or close-ratio four-speed manual ($185). The 366 hp and 370 hp RAM AIR V-8s were available with the price of RAM AIR IV set at $558. Dual exhausts were standard. Heavy-duty Safe-T-Track was again $63.

[FIREBIRD] Custom air conditioner ($376). Heavy-duty battery ($4). Brake pedal trim package ($5). Electric clock ($16). Console ($54.) Cruise control ($58). Remote control deck lid ($15). Rally gage cluster with tachometer ($84). Rally gage cluster with clock ($47). Tinted windows ($33). Tinted windshield ($22). Custom stick-shift knob ($5). Leather and Morrokide trim ($199). Remote control outside mirror ($11). Power brakes ($42). Power steering ($105). Left power bucket seat ($74). Power convertible top ($53). Power windows ($105). Wire wheel discs ($53-74). Rally II wheels ($63-84). Turnpike cruise option package ($177). Transmission options included two-speed automatic ($174-185); Turbo-Hydramatic ($195-227); Three-speed manual with floor shift ($42); Heavy-duty three-speed manual with floor shift ($84) and wide or close-ratio four-speed manual ($185 each). The Sprint option package (Code 342) was $111-132 and included the 215 hp ohc six, which was not offered separately. The 265 hp two-barrel regular fuel 350 cid V-8 was $11 extra. The 330 hp four-barrel 350 cid HO V-8 was $175 extra. Dual exhausts and Safe-T-Track were priced as in 1968. (FIREBIRD) Transmission options included all offered for Tempests and GTOS. Engine options are listed in Firebird RPO Packages section below.

FIREBIRD RPO PACKAGES

FIREBIRD SPRINT PACKAGE: Included three-speed manual transmission with floor shift, ohc six emblems and four F70 x 14 tires (no Sprint stripes). Engine: 250 cid ohc six with 10.5:1 compression, Rochester four-barrel carburetor and 230 hp at 5400 rpm. Price: $121 over base model cost.

FIREBIRD 350 PACKAGE: option Code 343. Engine Code L-30. Included three-speed manual transmission with column shift and F70 x 14 tires. Engine: 350 cid V-8 with 9.2:1 compression, Rochester two-barrel carburetor and 265 hp at 4600 rpm. Price: $111 over base model cost.

FIREBIRD 350-HO PACKAGE: option Code 344. Engine Code L-76. Included three-speed manual transmission with column shift, dual exhausts and heavy-duty battery. Engine: 350 cid V-8 with 10.5:1 compression, Rochester four-barrel carburetor and 325 hp at 5100 rpm. Price $186 over base model cost.

FIREBIRD 400 PACKAGE: option code 345. Engine code W-S6. Included chrome engine parts, dual exhausts, heavy-duty battery, three-speed manual transmission with floor shift, F70 x 14 red stripe or whitewall tires and variable pitch cooling fan. Engine: 400 cid V-8 with 10.75:1 compression, Rochester four-barrel carburetor and 330 hp at 4800 rpm. Special hood is used with non-functional scoops. Ride and handling package required. Price: $275-358 over base model cost depending on transmission.

FIREBIRD RAM AIR 400 PACKAGE: option Code 348. Engine Code L-74. Same inclusions as above, except for addition of de-clutching fan and twin functional hood scoops with operating mechanism. Engine: Same as 1968. Price: $351-435 over base model cost depending on transmission attachment.

FIREBIRD RAM AIR IV PACKAGE: option Code 347. Engine Code L-67. Same equipment inclusions as above, plus special hood scoop emblems. Engine: 400 cid V-8 with special camshaft and valve train, 10.75:1 compression, Rochester four-barrel carburetor and 345 hp at 5400 rpm. Price: $832 over base model cost. Specific transmissions required.

TRANS AM PACKAGE: Code 322 UPC WS-4. Engine Code L-74. Included heavy-duty three-speed manual gearbox with floor shifter: 3.55:1 axle; fiberglass-belted tires; heavy-duty shocks and springs; one-inch stabilizer bar; power front disc brakes; variable ratio power steering; engine air exhaust louvers; rear deck air foil; black textured grille; full-length body stripes; white and blue finish; leather covered steering wheel and special identification decals. Base engine specifications: See 1968 Firebird RAM AIR 400 Package listing optional engine package. Price for standard Trans Am: $725 over base model cost.

HISTORICAL FOOTNOTES: Production began Aug. 26, 1968. Introductions took place a month later, except for the Trans Am. It was introduced on March 8, 1969. Calendar year assemblies came to 772,104 cars for a 10.3 percent share of market. This was to be Pontiac's last year as America's third-ranking automaker. The 370 hp GTO Judge hardtop could do 0-to-60 in 6.2 seconds and the quarter-mile in 14.5 seconds. Bonneville Brougham trim group (Code 522) available for convertible ($316) and coupe ($273). Grand Prix 'SJ' option ($316). Rally Group option ($153-195). Turnpike Cruise package included tilt steering and 4-way bench or bucket seat ($177-208). Ventura package available on all Catalinas except convertible ($105.) A short stroke 303 cid tunnel-port V-8 Trans Am engine was used in a small number of Firebirds used exclusively for SCCA Trans Am racing. There were 26,049 full-size. Pontiacs with the standard 428 cid engine (360 hp). Also, there were 1,820 full-size Pontiacs with the 428 HO engine (390 hp).

1970 PONTIAC

CATALINA — (V-8) — SERIES 252 — Radiator grilles inspired by Grand Prixs, taillights set into bumpers, hoods with wider and flatter center bulges, hidden radio antennas and wrapover front fender tips characterized 1970 Pontiacs. Catalinas had plain body sill moldings, Catalina or Ventura lettering behind front wheel openings, untrimmed taillights, the word 'Pontiac' centered on edge of rear deck, horizontal blade grilles and no fender skirts. Standard in Catalinas were carpeting, upper level ventilation, Endura side moldings, walnut-grained vinyl inserts, padded dashboards and fiberglass blackwall tires. Station wagons had Morrokide upholstery with power tailgate windows included on nine-passenger styles. The Ventura Custom option was available on all Catalinas except convertibles at $105 extra.

PONTIAC I.D. NUMBERS: VIN on top of dash at left, viewable through windshield. First symbol tell GM division: 2=Pontiac. Second and third symbols tell series: 23=Firebird; 24=Espirit; 26=Formula 400; 28=Trans Am; 33=Tempest/T-37; 35=LeMans;37=LeMans Sport; 42=GTO; 52=Catalina; 56=Executive; 62=Bonneville; 76=Grand Prix. Fourth and fifth symbols indicate body style and appear as last two digits of Body/Style Number in charts below. Sixth symbol indicates model year: 0=1970. Seventh symbol indicates assembly plant: A=Atlanta, Ga.; B=Baltimore, Md.; C=Southgate, Calif.; E=Linden, N.J.; G=Framingham, Mass.; L=Van Nuys, Calif.; N=Norwood, Ohio; P=Pontiac, Mich.; R=Arlington, Texas; X=Kansas City, Kan.; Z=Fremont, Calif.; 1=Oshawa, Ontario, Canada; 2=St. Therese, Quebec, Canada. Remaining symbols are sequential unit production number at factory, starting with 100001. Fisher Body plate on cowl tells style number: (model year prefix 70, plus number in second column of charts below), body number, trim code, paint code and other data. Six-cylinder engine code stamped on distributor mounting on right side of block. V-8 engine code on front of block below right cylinder head. Engine production codes for 1970 were: [250 cid/155 hp six] CG/RF/ZB/ZG. [350 cid/255 hp V-8] WU/YU/W7/X7. [400 cid/265 hp V-8] XX/YB. [400 cid/290 hp V-8] WE/YD. [400 cid/330 hp V-8] WT/YS/XV/XZ. [400 cid/345 hp V-8] WS/YZ. [400 cid/350 hp V-8] WT/WX/YS/YH. [400 cid/366 hp V-8] WS/YZ. [400 cid/370 hp V-8] WW/WH/XP/XN. [455 cid/360 hp V-8] YH. [455 cid/370 hp V-8] WA/WG/YC/YA/XF.

CATALINA (SERIES 252)

Model Number	Body/Style Number	Body Type & Seating	Factory Price	Shipping Weight	Production Total
252	25269	4-dr Sed-6P	3164	3997	84,795
252	25239	4-dr HT-6P	3319	4042	35,155
252	25237	2-dr HT-6P	3249	3952	70,350
252	25267	2-dr Conv-6P	3604	4027	3,686
252	25246	4-dr Sta Wag-9P	3791	4607	12,450
252	25236	4-dr Sta Wag-6P	3646	4517	16,944

NOTE 1: 193,986 Catalina passenger cars were built.
NOTE 2: 579 Catalina passenger cars had synchromesh; 193,407 had automatic.
NOTE 3: 29,394 Catalina station wagons were built.
NOTE 4: 113 Catalina station wagons had synchromesh and 29,281 had automatic.

EXECUTIVE (V-8) — SERIES 256 — Executives featured all Catalina equipment plus Deluxe wheelcovers, walnut-grained dash and door trim, Morrokide or cloth and Morrokide interiors, rear seat armrests, electric clock and convenience lights. Executive lettering appeared behind the front wheel openings. Station wagons in this line included such extras as woodgrained exterior panelling and full carpeting. The balance of regular trim and equipment features was similar to that seen on Catalinas.

EXECUTIVE (SERIES 256)

Model Number	Body/Style Number	Body Type & Seating	Factory Price	Shipping Weight	Production Total
256	25669	4-dr Sed-6	3538	4087	13,061
256	25639	4-dr HT-6	3669	4132	5,376
256	25637	2-dr HT-6	3600	4042	3,499
256	25646	4-dr Sta Wag-9	4160	4632	5,629
256	25636	4-dr Sta Wag-6	4015	4552	4,861

NOTE 1: 21,936 Executive passenger cars were built.
NOTE 2: Six (6) Executive passenger cars had synchromesh; 21,930 automatic.
NOTE 3: 10,490 Executive station wagons were built.
NOTE 4: Eight (8) Executive wagons had synchromesh and 10,482 had automatic.

BONNEVILLE — (V-8) — SERIES 262 — Die-cast cross-hatched grille inserts and horn ports, creased body still moldings with rear fender extensions, Bonneville front fender lettering, decorative taillight accents and right-hand deck lid edge nameplates characterized Series 262 models outwardly. Standard equipment included all items found on Executives, plus extra-heavy padded bench seats, special interior trims, illuminated wiper and headlamp switches, fold down front seat armrests, rear armrests with ashtrays and larger tires. Bonneville station wagons did not have standard exterior panelling, but notch back front seats, folding third seats, courtesy lamps and load area carpeting were included at base price. Brougham trim was optionally available on hardtops and convertibles. The Bonneville Brougham package was available on style numbers 26237 and 26239 and included front foam cushions, power windows, visor vanity mirror, remote control mirror, electric clock, remote control deck lid and heavy-duty air cleaner.

BONNEVILLE (SERIES 262)

Model Number	Body/Style Number	Body Type & Seating	Factory Price	Shipping Weight	Production Total
262	26269	4-dr Sed-6P	3770	4181	3,802
262	26239	4-dr HT-6P	3900	4226	44,241
262	26237	2-dr HT-6P	3832	4111	23,418
262	26267	2-dr Conv-6P	4040	4161	3,537
262	26246	4-dr Sta Wag-9P	4247	4686	7,033

NOTE 1: 75,348 Bonneville passenger cars were built.
NOTE 2: 28 had Bonneville passenger cars had synchromesh; 75,320 automatic.
NOTE 3: 7,033 Bonneville station wagons were built.
NOTE 4: Six (6) Bonneville wagons used synchromesh and 7,027 had automatic.

1970 Pontiac, Grand Prix "SJ" hardtop coupe, V-8

GRAND PRIX — (V-8) — SERIES 276 — A minimum of styling changes, such as taillamp revisions and recessed door handles, appeared on 1970 GPs. Series script replaced chrome slash moldings on the rear roof pillar. Standard equipment included dual exhaust, aircraft inspired interiors, front Strato Bucket seats, integral console with floor shift, carpeted lower door panels and trim panels, chrome body decor moldings and special upholstery trims. The 'SJ' option was available again at $223-244 extra and included 'SJ' badges, lamp group, larger tires and the 4555 cubic inch V-8.

GRAND PRIX (SERIES 276)

Model Number	Body/Style Number	Body Type & Seating	Factory Price	Shipping Weight	Production Total
276	27657	2-dr HT Cpe-5P	3985	3784	65,750

NOTE 1: A total of 65,750 Grand Prixs were built.
NOTE 2: 500 Grand Prixs had synchromesh and 65,250 had automatic.
NOTE 3: Of the cars with synchromesh, 329 had four-speed manual gearboxes.

TEMPEST — (6-CYL) — SERIES 233 — Tempests were given new Firebird-look bumper grilles, wraparound front parking and taillights, crease sculptured side styling and body color nose panels. Standard equipment included front door armrests; panel, ashtray and cigar lighter lamps; 37-amp Delcotrons; dome lamps; automatic interior lamp switches; in-the-windshield hidden antennas; wraparound side reflex markers; cloth and Morrokide interiors; fiberglass belted blackwall tires; and side guard door beams. Tempest lettering was carried behind front wheel openings. In February, 1970, the cut-price Tempest T-37 hardtop coupe was introduced. This move was followed by the appearance of a pair of economy type high-performance cars, the GT-37 V-8 coupe and GT-37 hardtop coupe.

TEMPEST (SERIES 233)

Model Number	Body/Style Number	Body Type & Seating	Factory Price	Shipping Weight	Production Total
233	23369	4-dr Sed-6P	2670	3295	9,187
233	23337	2-dr HT-6P	2750	3360	
233	23327	2-dr Cpe-6P	2623	3225	11,977

TEMPEST (MIDYEAR ADDITIONS TO SERIES 233)

Model Number	Body/Style Number	Body Type & Seating	Factory Price	Shipping Weight	Production Total
T-37	23337	2-dr HT Cpe-6P	2683	3250	20,883
GT-37	23337	2-dr HT Cpe-6P	2920	3360	
GT-37	23327	2-dr Cpe-6P	2907	3300	

NOTE 1: 42,047 Series 233 Tempests were built.
NOTE 2: 5,148 had synchromesh and 36,899 had automatic.
NOTE 3: Totals for similar body styles listed above are combined.
NOTE 4: 1,419 GT-37 coupes and hardtops (combined) were built.

LEMANS — (6-CYL) — SERIES 235 — LeMans nameplates were now attached to the mid-priced Tempests, which were formerly called Custom models. Added extras included loop pile carpets, Morrokide seats and sides, day/night rearview mirrors and rear armrests with ashtrays. Styling included body decor moldings, LeMans rear fender lettering, four short horizontal chrome slashes behind front wheel openings and LeMans block letters on the right-hand edge of the deck lid.

LEMANS (SERIES 235)

Model Number	Body/Style Number	Body Type & Seating	Factory Price	Shipping Weight	Production Total
235	23569	4-dr Sed-6P	2782	3315	15,255
235	23539	4-dr HT-6P	2921	3385	3,872
235	23527	2-dr Cpe-6P	2735	3240	5,656
235	23537	2-dr HT-6P	2795	3265	52,304
235	23535	4-dr Sta Wag-6P	3092	3585	7,165

NOTE 1: 84,252 LeMans were made.
NOTE 2: 2,315 LeMans had synchromesh and 81,937 had automatic.

LEMANS SPORT — (6-CYL) — SERIES 237 — The 'high rung' Tempest line was now identified as the LeMans Sport series and had a 'Sport' script below the rear fender model lettering. Standard equipment included all LeMans features plus glove compartment and ashtray lamps, front foam cushions, knit and expanded Morrokide trim and padded woodgrained dashboards. Four-door hardtops had notch back seats; hardtop coupes and convertibles had bucket seats or notch back bench seats. The LeMans Sport Safari had exterior wood trim.

LEMANS SPORT (SERIES 237)

Model Number	Body/Style Number	Body Type & Seating	Factory Price	Shipping Weight	Production Total
237	23739	4-dr HT-6P	3083	3405	3,657
237	23727	2-dr Cpe-6P	2891	3265	1,673
237	23737	2-dr HT-6P	2953	3290	58,356
237	23767	2-dr Conv-6P	3182	3330	4,670
237	23736	4-dr Sta Wag-6P	3328	3775	3,872

NOTE 1: 72,179 LeMans Sports were built.
NOTE 2: 3,413 LeMans Sports had synchromesh and 68,766 had automatic.

GTO — (V-8) — SERIES 242 — The GTOs utilized Tempest sheet metal combined with a standard Endura rubber nose. Twin oval cavities housed recessed grilles with GTO letters on the left-hand insert. There was also GTO lettering behind the front wheel openings and flared, crease-sculptured fenders. Standard equipment included bucket seats; vinyl trimmed padded dashboard; twin scoops; heavy-duty clutch; sports type springs and shock absorbers; carpeting; glovebox, ashtray and panel courtesy lamps; dual exhausts; Deluxe steering wheel; three-speed manual floor shift; and G78 x 14 blackwall fiberglass tires. A Code 332-WT1 "The Judge" option was again available at $337 over base model price. It included the 400 cid RAM AIR V-8; Rally II wheels less trim rings; G70 x 14 fiberglass blackwall tires; rear deck air foil; side stripes; Judge stripes and decals; black textured grilles; and T-handle shifters (on cars with manual gearboxes).

1970 Pontiac, GTO two-door hardtop coupe, V-8

GTO (SERIES 242)

Model Number	Body/Style Number	Body Type & Seating	Factory Price	Shipping Weight	Production Total
242	24237	2-dr HT-5P	3267	3641	32,737
242	24267	2-dr Conv-5P	3492	3691	3,615

GTO (SERIES 242 with WT-1 'THE JUDGE' OPTION)

Model Number	Body/Style Number	Body Type & Seating	Factory Price	Shipping Weight	Production Total
242	24237	2-dr HT-5P	3604	N/A	3,629
242	24267	2-dr Conv-5P	3829	N/A	168

NOTE 1: 40,149 GTOs and Judges were built in 1970.
NOTE 2: 16,033 GTOs and Judges had synchromesh and 24,116 had automatic.
NOTE 3: 366 hp RAM AIR V-8s in 4,356 GTO/Judge hardtops; 288 convertibles.
NOTE 4: 370 hp RAM AIR IV V-8s in 767 GTO/Judge hardtops and 37 convertibles.

BASE FIREBIRD — (6-CYL) — SERIES 223 — Standard equipment on base Firebirds included a 250 cid/155 hp six, E78 -14 black fiberglass tires, front and rear bucket type seats, vinyl upholstery, woodgrained dashboard, carpeting, outside rearview mirror, manual front disc brakes, 6-inch wheel rims and door storage pockets. Styling changes included Endura rubber front ends with dual recessed grilles, single headlights, split side marker lamps, enlarged wheel openings, flush door handles and smooth, clean, curvy body panels. Firebird lettering and engine badges appeared behind front wheel cutouts.

BASE FIREBIRD (SERIES 223)

Model Number	Body/Style Number	Body Type & Seating	Factory Price	Shipping Weight	Production Total
223	22387	2-dr HT-4P	2875	3140	18,874

NOTE 1: 18,874 base Firebirds were built.
NOTE 2: 2,899 base Firebirds had synchromesh and 15,975 had automatic.
NOTE 3: 3,134 Firebirds were built with six-cylinder power.

FIREBIRD ESPIRIT — (V-8) — SERIES 224 — The Espirit was outwardly identified by model script on the rear roof pillar, bright roof rail and wheel opening moldings, V-8 displacement badges under front fender Firebird lettering and bird emblems above the grille. Standard equipment included all found on base models, plus knit vinyl upholstery, vinyl-covered Deluxe steering wheel, dual body-color outside sport mirrors, concealed windshield wipers and antenna, trunk floor mats, wheel trim rings, custom trim, decor moldings and a 350 cid two-barrel V-8 with 8.8:1 compression and 255 hp at 4600 rpm. A three-speed manual gearbox with floor-mounted shift lever was regular equipment.

FIREBIRD ESPIRIT (SERIES 224)

Model Number	Body/Style Number	Body Type & Seating	Factory Price	Shipping Weight	Production Total
224	22487	2-dr HT-4P	3241	3435	18,961

NOTE 1: A total of 18,961 Firebird Espirits were built.
NOTE 2: 2,104 had synchromesh and 16,857 had automatic.

FIREBIRD FORMULA 400 — (V-8) — SERIES 226 — Standard equipment on Formula 400s included all GM safety features, 1-1/8 inch front and 5/8-inch rear stabilizer bars, high-rate springs, wind-up rear axle controls, F70 x 14 bias-belted blackwall tires, 7-inch wheel rims, manual front disc brakes and rear drums, carpets, vinyl interiors, front and rear bucket type seats, dual outside sport mirrors, concealed wipers and antennas and deluxe steering wheel. Power came from a 400 cid four-barrel V-8 with 10.25:1 compression and 265 hp at 4600 rpm, which was linked to a three-speed Hurst floor shift. External distinctions included extra-long, twin hood scoops and Formula 400 nameplates.

FIREBIRD FORMULA 400 (SERIES 226)

Model Number	Body/Style Number	Body Type & Seating	Factory Price	Shipping Weight	Production Total
226	22687	2-dr HT-4P	3370	3470	7,708

NOTE 1: 7,708 Firebird Formula 400s were built.
NOTE 2: 2,777 had synchromesh and 4,931 had automatic.

1970 Pontiac, Firebird Formula 400 two-door hardtop, V-8

TRANS AM — (V-8) — SERIES 228 — Trans Am had all GM safety features, plus front air dams; front and rear spoilers; shaker hood; side air extractors; rear end spoilers; aerodynamically styled outside mirrors with left-hand remote control type; front and rear stabilizers; heavy-duty shock absorbers and springs; engine-turned dash inserts; Rally gage cluster; concealed wipers; bucket seats; carpets; vinyl upholstery; power brakes and steering; 11-inch wide 15-inch diameter Rally rims; and F60-15 white letter tires. Standard V-8 in the Trans Am was a 335 hp RAM AIR engine. The factory called this the RAM AIR HO. The 400 cid four-barrel V-8 was coded as the L74 engine. It had 10.5:1 compression heads and developed peak power at 5000 rpm. The base transmission was a wide-ratio four-speed manual gearbox with Hurst floor shift. Trans Ams had white or blue finish with contrasting racing stripes.

TRANS AM (SERIES 228)

Model Number	Body/Style Number	Body Type & Seating	Factory Price	Shipping Weight	Production Total
228	22887	2-dr HT-5P	4305	3550	3,196

NOTE 1: 3,196 Trans Ams were built.
NOTE 2: 1,769 had synchromesh and 1,398 had automatic.
NOTE 3: 3,108 Trans Ams were L74s (1,339 with automatic; 1,769 with manual).
NOTE 4: 88 Trans Ams were LS1s (59 with automatic; 29 with manual).

BASE ENGINES

(CATALINA/EXECUTIVE) V-8. (convertible and station wagon) 400 cid V-8 with two-barrel carburetor, 10.0:1 compression and 290 hp at 4600 rpm. (Other Styles) 350 cid V-8 with two-barrel carburetor, 8.8:1 compression and 255 hp at 4600 rpm.

(BONNEVILLE) Base V-8s: (Station wagon) 455 cid V-8 with four-barrel carburetor, 10.75:1 compression and 370 hp at 4600 rpm. (Other Styles) 455 cid V-8 with four-barrel carburetor, 10.0:1 compression and 360 hp at 4300 rpm. This engine had overhead valves, cast iron block, 4.15 x 4.21 inch bore and stroke, five main bearings and hydraulic valve lifters.

(GRAND PRIX) Base V-8. A 400-cid V-8 with four-barrel carburetor, 10.25:1 compression and 350 hp at 5000 rpm. was standard in Grand Prixs. A 455 cid V-8 with four-barrel carburetor, 10.25:1 compression and 370 hp at 466 rpm was base V-8 on 'SJ' optioned cars.

(TEMPEST/LEMANS/FIREBIRD) Base six-cylinder: A Chevrolet manufactured 250 cid six with 8.5:1 compression and 135 hp at 4600 rpm was standard in all Tempests, but not GTOs. This engine had overhead valves, cast iron block, 3.88 x 3.53 bore and stroke, seven main bearings, hydraulic valve lifters and a Rochester Model M or Model MV one-barrel carburetor.

(GTO) V-8. The standard engine in GTOs was the 400 cid four-barrel V-8 with 10.25:1 compression and 350 hp at 5000 rpm.

CHASSIS FEATURES: Wheelbase: (series 252 and all Pontiac station wagons) 122 inches; (series 256 and 262) 125 inches; (series 276) 118 inches; (Tempest two-door) 112 inches; (Tempest four-door) 116 inches; (Firebird) 108 inches. Overall length: (all Pontiac station wagons 220.9 inches; (series 252) 217.9 inches; (series 256 and 262) 223.9 inches; (series 276) 210.2 inches; (Tempest station wagons) 210.6 inches; (Tempest two-door) 202.5 inches; (Tempest four-door) 206.5 inches; (GTO) 202.9 inches; (Firebird) 191.6 inches. Front tread: (Pontiac) 63 inches (others) 60 inches. Rear tread: (Pontiac) 64 inches; (others) 60 inches.

OPTIONS

[PONTIAC/GRAND PRIX/TEMPEST] Tempest air conditioning ($376). Pontiac air conditioning ($422). Automatic level control ($79. Auxiliary panel gages $21-79). Cruise control ($63). Rear window defroster ($53). Driver-controlled GTO exhausts ($63). Tinted windshield ($22-30). Tempest Instant Air ($16). Luggage carrier for station wagons ($63-84). Left remote-control outside mirror ($11). Tempest wheelhouse moldings ($16). Power brakes ($42-64). Remote-control deck lid ($15). Power front bucket seat for Tempest and Grand Prix ($73). AM/FM stereo ($239). Rally gage cluster with tachometer for Tempest and Grand Prix ($84). Safeguard speedometer ($16). Catalina passenger car fender skirts ($37). Grand Prix leather trim ($199). Rally II wheel rims for passenger cars and Tempest station wagons ($63-84). Base Tempest recessed wipers ($19). Bonneville Brougham trim ($378). Grand Prix 'SJ' group ($223-244). GTO Judge package ($337). Turnpike Cruise package ($177-208). Three-speed manual transmissions were provided at base prices, including a heavy-duty type in Grand Prix. Turbo-Hydramatic was $227 extra. Grand Prixs had two other options, close- or wide-ratio four-speed manual gearboxes, both at $227 extra. The 400 cid two-barrel regular fuel V-8 (265 hp) was $53 extra in Catalinas with Turbo-Hydramatic. The four-barrel Bonneville V-8 was $47 more in Catalina station wagons, Catalina convertibles or Executives and $100 extra in other Catalinas. The two-barrel premium fuel 400 cid V-8 was $53 extra in Catalina coupes and hardtops. The 455 cid four-barrel V-8 with 10.0:1 compression and 360 hp at 4300 rpm was $150-169 extra in Catalinas and Executives with price depending upon transmission. The 455 cid four-barrel high-performance V-8 with 10.25:1 compression and 370 hp at 4600 rpm was $200-253 extra in Catalina and Executives, $95 extra in Bonnevilles and $58 extra in Grand Prixs without decor packages. (TEMPEST) Transmission options included two-speed automatic on cars with six-cylinder power ($164-174); Turbo-Hydramatic on V-8s ($227); three-speed manual with heavy-duty floor shift ($84) and wide-ratio four-speed manual ($185). The 255 hp regular fuel 350 cid V-8 with 8.8:1 compression was $111 extra. The 265 hp regular fuel two-barrel 400 cid V-8 with 8.8:1 compression was $53-163 extra in Tempests, with price depending upon model and transmission. The 400 cid four-barrel V-8 with 10.0:1 compression and 330 hp at 4800 rpm was $210 extra. Dual exhausts were $31 extra and Safe-T-Track differential was $42-63 extra. (GTO) Transmission options included Turbo-Hydramatic ($227) and wide- or close-ratio four-speed manual gearboxes ($185). The 366 hp HO V-8 was $169 extra on cars without 'The Judge' options. The 370 hp RAM AIR IV engine was $390 extra with 'The Judge' and $558 extra on other GTOs. In midyear the 360 hp 455 cid V-8 was added as a third GTO power option. Dual exhausts were standard. Heavy-duty Safe-T-Track was again $63.

[FIREBIRD] Air conditioning ($376). Electric clock ($16). Rally gage cluster ($47). Rally gage cluster with tachometer ($95). Cruise control ($58). Rear window defogger ($26). Electric rear window defroster ($53). Tinted glass, all windows ($33). Tinted windshield ($26). Dual horns ($4). Convenience lamps ($12). Dual outside mirrors in body color with left-hand remote-controlled ($26). Decor moldings ($47). Wonder Touch power brakes ($42). Power door locks ($45) Power door and seat back locks ($68). Variable ratio power steering ($105). Stereo tape player ($105). AM/FM push-button radio ($134). AM/FM stereo ($239). Cordova top ($74-90). Deluxe steering wheel ($16). Formula steering wheel ($42-58). Tilt steering wheel ($45). Wire wheel discs ($53-74). Rally II rims ($63-84). Transmission options included all offered for Tempests and GTOs. The 350 cid two-barrel V-8 was $111 extra in base Firebirds. The two-barrel regular fuel 400 cid V-8 was $53 extra in Espirits. The L74 RAM AIR V-8 was $169 extra in Formula Firebirds. A mountain ratio performance axle was $17 extra. Safe-T-Track differential was $42 extra.

HISTORICAL FOOTNOTES: Pontiacs were introduced Sept. 18, 1970 and the all-new second-generation Firebird bowed Feb. 26, 1971. Calendar year output was 422,212 units for sixth place in the sales rankings. The totals were pulled down by a painful UAW strike. James McDonald became the new general manager of PMD, replacing John Z. DeLorean, who moved to Chevrolet. The 1970 GTO with the 400 cid/366 hp V-8 was capable of 0-to-60 in six seconds flat. It did the quarter-mile in 14.6 seconds. The 455 cid/360 hp GTO hardtop registered 6.6 seconds 0-to-60 and a 14.8 second quarter-mile. The Firebird 400 with 330 hp did 0-to-60 in 6.4 seconds and covered the quarter-mile in 14.9 seconds. The W55 Turnpike Cruise option included cruise control, tilt steering wheel and power seats.

1971 PONTIAC

CATALINA — (V-8) — SERIES 252 — Full-size Pontiacs had all-new styling with 'fuselage' bodies, more massive V-shaped split radiator grilles, and dual headlamps set high into the hood line with horizontal grilles below. Standard equipment on Catalinas included integral molded foam front seat cushion and solid foam back, loop-pile carpeting, cloth and Morrokide upholstery on hardtops and sedans and all-Morrokide on convertibles, woodgrained dash accents, Deluxe steering wheel, center flow ventilation, glovebox lamp, dual-action parallel sweep concealed wipers, bright rocker panel moldings, hood rear edge moldings, hub caps, roof drip moldings on hardtops, blackwall tires, power front disc brakes and rear drums. Convertibles had rear quarter interior courtesy lamps. Catalina Safaris had all-Morrokide upholstery, ashtray lamps, vinyl cargo covering, right-hand outside mirror, power tailgate window, disappearing tailgate and L78-15 tires. Nine-passenger styles had forward facing third seats and split back second seats.

PONTIAC I.D. NUMBERS: VIN on top of dash at left, viewable through windshield. First symbol tell GM division: 2=Pontiac. Second and third symbols tell series: 13=Ventura II; 23=Firebird; 24=Espirit; 26=Formula 400; 28=Trans Am; 33=Tempest/T-37; 35=LeMans;37=LeMans Sport; 42=GTO; 52=Catalina; 58=Catalina Brougham; 62=Bonneville; 68=Grand Ville; 76=Grand Prix. Fourth and fifth symbols indicate body style and appear as last two digits of Body/Style Number in charts below. Sixth symbol indicates model year: 1=1971. Seventh symbol indicates assembly plant: A=Atlanta, Ga.; B=Baltimore, Md.; C=Southgate, Calif.; D=Doraville, Ga.; E=Linden, N.J.; L=Van Nuys, Calif.; N=Norwood, Ohio; P=Pontiac, Mich.; R=Arlington, Texas; X=Kansas City, Kan.; Z=Fremont, Calif.; 1=Oshawa, Ontario, Canada; 2=St. Therese, Quebec, Canada. Remaining symbols are sequential unit production number at factory, starting with 100001. Fisher Body plate on cowl tells style number: (model year prefix 71, plus number in second column of charts below), body number, trim code, paint code and other data. Six-cylinder engine code stamped on distributor mounting on right side of block. V-8 engine code on front of block below right cylinder head. Engine production codes for 1971 were: [250 cid/155 hp six] ZB/CAA/ZG/CAB. [307 cid/200 hp V-8] CCA/CCC. [350 cid/250 hp V-8] WR/WU/XU/XR/WN/WP/YN/YP. [400 cid/265 hp V-8] WS/WX/XX/YX. [400 cid/300 hp V-8] WT/WK/YS. [455 cid/280 hp V-8] WG/YG. [455 cid/325 hp V-8] WJ/YC/WL/WC/YE/YA.

1971 Pontiac, Catalina two-door hardtop, V-8

CATALINA (SERIES 252)

Model Number	Body/Style Number	Body Type & Seating	Factory Price	Shipping Weight	Production Total
252	25269	4-dr Sed-6P	3421/3770	4033/4077	59,355
252	25239	4-dr HT-6P	3590/3939	4063/4170	22,333
252	25257	2-dr HT-6P	3521/3870	3998/4042	46,257
252	25267	2-dr Conv-6P	3807/4156	4065/4161	2,036
252	25235	4-dr Sta Wag-6P	3892/4315	4735/4815	10,322
252	25245	4-dr Sta Wag-9P	4039/4462	4820/4905	9,283

NOTE 1: Automatic transmission became standard equipment in March 1971.
NOTE 2: Data above slash applied in fall 1970/below slash, after March.
NOTE 3: 129,983 Catalina passenger cars were built.
NOTE 4: 144 Catalina passenger cars had synchromesh and 129,893 had automatic.
NOTE 5: 19,616 Catalina station wagons were built.
NOTE 6: 30 Catalina station wagons had synchromesh and 19,586 had automatic.

CATALINA BROUGHAM — (V-8) — SERIES 258 — Cars in this entirely new series had the same basic equipment as Catalinas, plus special luxury upholstery, electric clock, Castillian leather appearance instrument panel inserts, ashtray lamps, wheel opening moldings, Deluxe wheelcovers, bright roof drip moldings and rear foam-padded seats on four-door sedans. A Brougham script was placed on the rear roof pillar.

CATALINA BROUGHAM (SERIES 258)

Model Number	Body/Style Number	Body Type & Seating	Factory Price	Shipping Weight	Production Total
258	25869	4-dr Sed-6P	3629/4000	4098/4149	6,069
258	25839	4-dr HT-6P	3783/4154	4128/4179	9,001
258	25857	2-dr HT-6P	3713/4084	4068/4119	8,823

NOTE 1: Automatic transmission became standard equipment in March 1971.
NOTE 2: Data above slash applied in fall 1970/below slash, after March.
NOTE 3: 23,892 Catalina Broughams were built.
NOTE 4: Six (6) Catalina Broughams had synchromesh and 23,886 had automatic.

BONNEVILLE AND GRAND SAFARI — (V-8) — SERIES 262 — Bonnevilles were no longer top line Pontiacs, as a new Grand Ville series was placed even higher and had more standard features. Station wagons in Series 262 used a nameplate that was a mixture of both lines. They were called Grand Safaris. The wagons, however, used the Bonneville engines and series code. Identifying features of Bonnevilles include model nameplates on the left-hand grille and behind the front wheelwells and slanting vertical slashes on the body sill moldings. Bonnevilles had the same basic equipment as Catalinas, plus ashtray, panel courtesy and trunk lamps, pedal trim plates; custom cushion steering wheel; electric clock; wheel well moldings; bright roof drip moldings; H78-15 tires and power steering. The four-door sedan also had foam rear seat padding and side window reveal moldings. Grand Safaris had the same equipment as Catalina station wagons plus fold-down front seat center armrests, carpeted load area, dash panel courtesy lamps, pedal trim plates, electric clocks, custom cushion steering wheels, side window reveal moldings, wheel opening moldings, roof drip moldings, power steering and Deluxe wheelcovers. There were Grand Safari nameplates on the left-hand grille and behind the front wheel cutouts. Woodgrained exterior panelling was optional.

BONNEVILLE AND GRAND SAFARI (SERIES 262)

Model Number	Body/Style Number	Body Type & Seating	Factory Price	Shipping Weight	Production Total
262	26269	4-dr Sed-6P	3968/4210	4188/4213	6,513
262	26239	4-dr HT-6P	4098/4340	4248/4273	16,393
262	26257	2-dr HT-6P	4030/4272	4163/4188	8,778
262	26235	4-dr Sta Wag-6P	4401/4643	4843/4855	3,613
262	26245	4-dr Sta Wag-9P	4548/4790	4913/4970	5,972

NOTE 1: Automatic transmission became standard equipment in March 1971.
NOTE 2: Data above slash applied in fall 1970/below slash, after March.
NOTE 3: 31,879 Bonnevilles were built.
NOTE 4: Four (4) had synchromesh and 31,875 had automatic.
NOTE 5: All Grand Safaris had automatic.

GRAND VILLE — (V-8) — SERIES 268 — Standard equipment on cars in Series 268 was the same as on Bonnevilles, plus Carpathian Elm burl vinyl instrument panel trim, rear door dome lamp switches, roof rail assist grips, formal roofline, belt reveal moldings and four-barrel V-8 power. The convertible and the hardtop coupe had notch back bench seats and the former model also featured two rear quarter interior lamps. Several appearance distinctions such as cross-hatched grille inserts and dual stacked horizontal taillights were shared with Bonnevilles. Grand Villes, however, did not have slash louvers on body sill moldings and used "Grand Ville" lettering on the left-hand grille and behind front fender cutouts.

GRAND VILLE (SERIES 268)

Model Number	Body/Style Number	Body Type & Seating	Factory Price	Shipping Weight	Production Total
268	26849	4-dr HT-6P	4324/4566	4278/4303	30,524
268	26847	2-dr HT-6P	4255/4497	4198/4223	14,017
268	26867	2-dr Conv-6P	4464/4706	4240/4266	1,784

NOTE 1: Automatic transmission became standard equipment in March 1971.
NOTE 2: Data above slash applied in fall 1970/below slash, after March.
NOTE 3: 46,330 Grand Villes were built.
NOTE 4: Two (2) had synchromesh and 46,328 had automatic.
NOTE 5: 194 Grand Ville chassis were supplied to professional car makers.

1971 Pontiac, Grand Prix two-door hardtop, V-8

GRAND PRIX — (V-8) — SERIES 276 — Grand Prixs now had single headlamps (still in square housings), a bumper running across the grille and an attractive looking semi-boattail rear end. Model script plates decorated the left-hand front panel, the roof pillars and the right-hand edge of the deck lid. Buyers had a choice of notch back bench or bucket seats at the same price. Standard equipment included right-hand front door armrest ashtray; carpeted lower door panels; safety armrests with ashtrays; loop-pile carpets; foam seat padding; pedal trim plates; custom cushion steering wheel; Castillian leather appearance dash trim; upper level ventilation; courtesy and glovebox lamps; concealed wipers; wheel opening, roof drip, belt reveal and hood rear edge moldings; Deluxe wheelcovers; power flex cooling fan; power steering; power brakes (with front disc); 7-inch wide safety wheel rims; G78-14 blackwall tires and center console on cars with bucket seats. The 'SJ' option package was priced $195 extra. This option (code 324) included 455 cid four-barrel V-8, Rally Gage cluster, luggage lamp, body color outside mirrors (left-hand remote control), vinyl pin stripes, `SJ' emblems and Delco X battery. A limited-edition Hurst SSJ Grand Prix was marketed.

GRAND PRIX (SERIES 276)

Model Number	Body/Style Number	Body Type & Seating	Factory Price	Shipping Weight	Production Total
276	27657	2-dr HT-5P	4314/4557	3838/3863	58,325

NOTE 1: Automatic transmission became standard equipment in March 1971.
NOTE 2: Data above slash applied in fall 1970/below slash, after March.
NOTE 3: 58,325 Grand Prixs were built.
NOTE 4: 116 had synchromesh and 58,208 had automatic.

1971 Pontiac, LeMans two-door hardtop (with GT-37 option), V-8

LEMANS T-37 — (6 CYL) — SERIES 233 — Revisions to Pontiac intermediates included new model names, new series designations, redesigned grilles and reworked GTO nose and hood. Pontiac T-37 lettering was seen behind the front wheelwells of the lowest priced models. Standard equipment included cloth and Morrokide bench seats, vinyl floor covering, Deluxe steering wheel, upper level ventilation in hardtops, black grained instrument panel, door operated dome lamp switches, woodgrained roof moldings, windshield and rear window reveal moldings, dual-action parallel sweep wipers, front disc brakes and E78-14 black wall tires. Pillared coupes and sedans also had chrome edged ventiplanes. The GT-37 was available again and was advertised as "The GTO For Kids Under 30." This option (code 334) was offered in just two hardtop versions. It included vinyl accent stripes, Rally II wheels (less trim rings), G70-14 tires (white-lettered), dual exhausts with chrome extensions, heavy-duty three-speed manual transmission with floor shift, body-colored outside mirrors (left-hand remote control), hood locking pins, and GT-37 nameplates. It was designed to provide buyers with a low-cost high-performance option.

T-37 (SERIES 233)

Model Number	Body/Style Number	Body Type & Seating	Factory Price	Shipping Weight	Production Total
233	23327	2-dr Sed-6P	2747/2868	3189/3445	7,184
233	23369	4-dr Sed-6P	2795/2916	3219/3475	8,336
233	23337	2-dr HT-6P	2807/2928	3194/3450	29,466

NOTE 1: Data above slash for six/below slash for V-8.
NOTE 2: 44,986 T-37s were built.
NOTE 3: 5,525 T-37s had synchromesh and 39,461 had automatic.
NOTE 4: A combined total of 5,802 GT-37s built as 1971 and 1971-1/2 models.

LEMANS (6-CYL) — SERIES 235 — LeMans models had the word "Pontiac" on the left-hand grille and carried vertical slash louvers behind the wheelwells and LeMans lettering under the rear fender crease lines. Extra features on LeMans included richer upholstery, loop-pile carpets, safety rear armrests with integral ashtrays, woodgrained dash, concealed wipers, rocker panel moldings, hood rear edge moldings, side window reveals on coupes and vent windows on four-door styles. Station wagons had two-way tailgates and power front disc brakes.

LEMANS (SERIES 235)

Model Number	Body/Style Number	Body Type & Seating	Factory Price	Shipping Weight	Production Total
235	23527	2-dr Sed-6P	2877/2998	3199/3455	2,734
235	23569	4-dr Sed-6P	2025/3046	3229/3485	11,979
235	23559	4-dr HT-6P	3064/3185	3314/3570	3,186
235	23537	2-dr HT-6P	2938/3059	3199/3455	40,966
235	23536	4-dr Sta Wag-6P	3353/3474	3765/3995	6,311
235	23546	4-dr Sta Wag-9P	3465/3586	3825/4045	4,363

NOTE 1: Data above slash for six/below slash for V-8.
NOTE 2: 69,179 LeMans were built.
NOTE 3: 1,231 LeMans had synchromesh and 67,948 had automatic.

LEMANS SPORT — (6-CYL) — SERIES 237 — Standard equipment in LeMans Sport models included all items found in LeMans models plus dual horns, pedal trim plates, ashtray and glovebox lamps, courtesy lamps on convertibles, carpeted lower door panels, custom cushion steering wheel and wheelwell moldings. Buyers of two-door hardtops and convertibles had a choice of knit vinyl bucket seats or notch bench seats and the four-door hardtop used knit vinyl bench seats. LeMans Sport model nameplates were seen on the sides of rear fenders. GTO type Endura rubber noses were a $74 styling option for all LeMans Sport models including station wagons. This front end was also marketed as part of the code 602 LeMans Sport Endura styling option including GTO hood, GTO Endura bumper and GTO headlamp assembly.

LEMANS SPORT (SERIES 237)

Model Number	Body/Style Number	Body Type & Seating	Factory Price	Shipping Weight	Production Total
237	23739	4-dr Spt HT-6P	3255/3376	3314/3570	2,451
237	23737	2-dr Spt HT-6P	3125/3246	3199/3455	34,625
237	23767	2-dr Spt Conv-6P	3359/3480	3289/3545	3,865

NOTE 1: Data above slash for six/below slash for V-8
NOTE 2: 40,941 LeMans Sports were built.
NOTE 3: 1,229 had synchromesh and 39,712 had automatic.

GTO — (V-8) — SERIES 242 — A new Endura nose piece identified the 1971 GTO. It had larger twin grille cavities, round parking lamps and integral body colored bumpers. Other characteristics included twin air slots at the front of the hood and GTO lettering on left-hand grille, front fendersides and right-hand edge of the deck lid. Standard equipment included all items found on LeMans models plus engine-turned aluminum dash inserts, dual exhausts with extensions through valance panel, power-flex cooling fan, heavy-duty stabilizer bars, shock absorbers and springs and G70-14 blackwall tires. For $395 extra the `Judge' option was available. This option (code 332) included 455 cid four-barrel HO V-8, Rally II wheels (less trim rings), hood air inlet system, T-handle gear shift control (with manual transmission), rear deck lid air foil, specific side stripes, 'The Judge' decals, RAM AIR decals, and black-textured grille.

GTO (SERIES 242)

Model Number	Body/Style Number	Body Type & Seating	Factory Price	Shipping Weight	Production Total
242	24237	2-dr HT-5P	3446	3619	9,497
242	24267	2-dr Conv-5P	3676	3664	661

GTO (WITH 'THE JUDGE' OPTION)

242	24237	2-dr HT-5P	3,840	N/A	357
242	24267	2-dr Conv-5P	4070	N/A	17

NOTE 1: A total of 10,532 GTOs were built.
NOTE 2: 2,287 had synchromesh and 7,945 had automatic.

BASE FIREBIRD — (6-CYL) — SERIES 223 — Styling changes for 1971 Firebirds were of the minor variety. High-back seats were used, new wheelcovers appeared and all models, except Trans Ams, had simulated louvers behind the front wheel cutouts. Standard equipment on the basic Firebird included vinyl bucket seats, woodgrained dash, deluxe steering wheel, Endura front bumper, bright grille moldings, standard hubcaps, narrow rocker panel moldings, front disc brakes and E78-14 tires. Base engine was the 145 hp 250 cid six.

BASE FIREBIRD (SERIES 223)

Model Number	Body/Style Number	Body Type & Seating	Factory Price	Shipping Weight	Production Total
223	22387	2-dr HT-4P	3047	3164	23,021

NOTE 1: 23,022 base Firebirds were built.
NOTE 2: 2,778 base Firebirds had synchromesh and 20,244 had automatic.
NOTE 3: 2,975 base Firebirds were built with six-cylinder powerplants.

FIREBIRD ESPIRIT — (V-8) — SERIES 224 — Espirits included custom trim features with knit vinyl upholstery, custom cushion steering wheel, trunk mat, bright roof drip moldings, wheel opening moldings, concealed wipers, twin body-colored outside mirrors, wheel trim rings and dual horns as standard extras. Power was supplied by the two-barrel 350 cid V-8 with 8.0:1 compression and 250 hp at 4400 rpm. A floor-mounted three-speed manual transmission was the standard gearbox.

FIREBIRD ESPIRIT (SERIES 224)

Model Number	Body/Style Number	Body Type & Seating	Factory Price	Shipping Weight	Production Total
224	22487	2-dr HT-4P	3416	3423	20,185

NOTE 1: 20,185 Firebird Espirits were built.
NOTE 2: 947 Firebird Espirits had synchromesh and 19,238 had automatic.

FIREBIRD FORMULA — (V-8) — SERIES 226 — Standard equipment on Formula Firebirds included vinyl bucket seats, custom cushion steering wheel, flame chestnut woodgrain appearance dash panel, right and left body-colored outside mirrors, (left-hand remote-controlled), Endura rubber front bumper, fiberglass hood with simulated twin air scoops, black-textured grille insert, bright grille moldings, dual horns, front disc brakes, handling package, dual exhausts with chrome extensions and the heavy-duty three-speed manual transmission. Also featured were standard hubcaps, F70-14 blackwall tires and Formula 350 or 400 or 455 identification numbering. Engine choices were the two-barrel 350 cid V-8, the four-barrel 400 cid V-8 and the four-barrel 455 cid V-8.

FIREBIRD FORMULA (SERIES 226)

Model Number	Body/Style Number	Body Type & Seating	Factory Price	Shipping Weight	Production Total
226	22687	2-dr HT-4P	3445	3473	7,802

NOTE 1: 7,802 Formula Firebirds were built.
NOTE 2: 1,860 Formula Firebirds had synchromesh and 5,942 had automatic.
NOTE 3: Data shown for "Formula 350."
NOTE 4: "Formula 400" was $100 extra; "Formula 455" was $158 extra.

Standard Catalog of American Cars

1971 Pontiac, Trans Am two-door hardtop sports coupe, V-8

TRANS AM — (V-8) — SERIES 228 — Standard equipment on Trans Ams included vinyl bucket seats, Rally gages (with clock and tachometer), Endura front bumper, Formula steering wheel, twin body-color outside mirrors (left-hand remote control), special honeycomb wheels, functional front fender air extractors, rear deck lid spoiler, black textured grille insert, bright grille moldings, front and rear wheel opening air spoilers, concealed wipers, Trans Am identification markings, performance dual exhausts with extensions, special air cleaner with rear-facing cold air intake on hood controlled by throttle, power flex cooling fan, power steering, Safe-T-Track differential, handling package, dual horns, power brakes with discs in front and drums at rear and F60-15 white lettered tires. The RPO LS5 455 HO engine with four-barrel carburetion, 8.4:1 compression and 335 hp at 4800 rpm was standard in all Trans Ams, as was a heavy-duty three-speed manual gearbox with floor shifter.

TRANS AM SERIES 228)

Model Number	Body/Style Number	Body Type & Seating	Factory Price	Shipping Weight	Production Total
228	22887	2-dr HT-4	4594	3578	2,116

NOTE 1: 2,116 Trans Ams were built.
NOTE 2: 885 Trans Ams had synchromesh and 1,231 had automatic.

VENTURA II — (6 CYL) — SERIES 213 — The Ventura II line was introduced on March 11, 1970 as an addition to the Pontiac family. It was based on the compact-sized Chevy II Nova with wider taillamp lenses and split, twin-slot type grille. Standard equipment included all required safety features plus heater and defroster, outside rearview mirror, cloth and Morrokide upholstery, foam front seat padding, woodgrained dashboard accents, padded Morrokide door panels with woodgrained trim inserts and E78 x 14 tires. The 250 cid six-cylinder 145 hp engine was base power plant. The Ventura Sprint option 9code 322) included three-speed manual transmission with floor shift, wheel trim rings, left-hand remote control color-keyed mirrors, custom carpets, custom sport steering wheel, blacked-out grille, side striping, 14 x 6 inch rims and THR E78-14 whitewall tires.

VENTURA II (SERIES 213)

Model Number	Body/Style Number	Body Type & Seating	Factory Price	Shipping Weight	Production Total
213	21327	2-dr Cpe-5P	2458	2934	34,681
213	21369	4-dr Sed-5P	2488	2983	13,803

NOTE 1: 48,484 Ventura IIs were built.
NOTE 2: 8,542 Ventura IIs had synchromesh and 39,942 had automatic.

BASE ENGINES

(CATALINA) Base engine for all Catalinas was the 350 cid two-barrel V-8 with 8.0:1 compression and 250 hp at 4400 rpm.

(CATALINA SAFARI/CATALINA BROUGHAM) Base engine for all Catalina Broughams was the 400 cid two-barrel V-8 with 8.2:1 compression and 265 hp at 4400 rpm.

(BONNEVILLE/GRAND SAFARI) Base V-8 for cars and station wagons in Series 262 was the 455 cid V-8 with 8.2:1 compression and 280 hp at 4400 rpm.

(GRAND VILLE) Base engine for Grand Villes was the 455 cid four-barrel V-8 with 8.2:1 compression and 325 hp at 4400 rpm. This was the only Grand Ville engine.

(GRAND PRIX) Base engine for Grand Prixs was the 400 cid four-barrel V-8 with 8.2:1 compression and 300 hp at 4800 rpm. The 455 cid V-8 used in Grand Villes was standard in the Grand Prix 'SJ' and optional on base GPs.

(T-37/LEMANS/LEMANS SPORT/FIREBIRD/VENTURA II SIX) Base engine for six-cylinder T-37s was the 250 cid Chevrolet-built powerplant with a one-barrel carburetor, 8.5:1 compression and 145 hp at 4200 rpm.

(T-37/LEMANS/LEMANS SPORT/FIREBIRD V-8) Base engines for eight-cylinder T-37s was the 350 cid V-8 with a two-barrel carburetor, 8.0:1 compression and 250 hp at 4400 rpm.

(GTO) Base V-8 on GTOs was the four-barrel, 400 cid engine with 8.2:1 compression and 300 hp at 4800 rpm.

(GTO "THE JUDGE") The 335 hp four-barrel 455 cid HO V-8 was standard on cars with 'The Judge' option.

OPTIONAL V-8 ENGINES

350 cid. Compression ratio: 8. Carburetion: two-barrel. Brake hp: 250 at 4400 rpm. (standard in Firebird Esprit and Catalina; optional in LeMans)

400 cid. Compression ratio: 8.2. Carburetion: four-barrel. Brake hp: 300 at 4800 rpm. (standard in GTO)

400 cid. Compression ratio: 8.2. Carburetion: four-barrel. Brake hp: 300 at 4800 rpm. (standard in Grand Prix/Firebird Formula 400; optional in LeMans/Catalina)

455 cid. Compression ratio: 8.2. Carburetion: two-barrel. Brake hp: 280 at 4400 rpm. (standard in Bonneville; optional in Catalina)

455 cid. Compression ratio: 8.2. Carburetion: four-barrel. Brake hp: 325 at 4400 rpm. (standard in Grand Ville; optional in Firebird Formula 455/LeMans/GTO/Catalina/Bonneville)

455 cid. Compression ratio: 8.4. Carburetion: four-barrel. Brake hp: 335 at 4800 rpm. (standard on Trans Am; optional in GTO/LeMans)

CHASSIS FEATURES: Wheelbase: (All Pontiac station wagons) 127 inches; (Series 252 and 258) 123.5 inches; (Series 262 and 268) 126 inches; (Grand Prix) 118 inches; (Ventura) 111 inches; (Others) Same as 1970. Overall length: (All Pontiac station wagons): 230.2 inches; (Series 252 and 258) 220.2 inches; (Series 262 and 268) 224.2 inches; (Grand Prix) 212.9 inches; (Tempest station wagons) 210.9 inches; (Tempest two-doors) 202.3 inches; (Tempest four-doors) 206.8 inches; (Firebird) 191.6 inches; (Ventura) 194.5 inches.

OPTIONS

[PONTIAC/GRAND PRIX]: Automatic air conditioning ($521). Automatic level control ($79). Luggage carrier ($84). Electric clock ($18). Cruise control ($68). All tinted glass ($51). Tinted windshield ($36). Bumper guards ($16). Cornering lights ($37). Grand Prix power bucket seats ($79). 60/40 Bench seat with Six-Way power adjustments ($79). AM/FM stereo and tape system ($373). Grand Prix Rally Gage cluster with tachometer and clock ($84). Pontiac station wagon and GP cordova tops ($142). Cordova top on other Pontiacs ($119). Grand Prix wire wheel discs ($58). Rally II wheels ($63-90). Custom Grand Ville trim group ($132-237). Grand Prix 'SJ' option ($195).

[TEMPEST/FIREBIRD]: Manual air conditioning ($408). T-37 custom carpets ($21). Firebird rear console ($26). Firebird, GTO and LeMans Sport front seat console ($60-61). Cruise control ($63). All tinted glass ($38). Tinted windshield ($31). Bumper guards ($16). Formula and GTO air inlet hood ($84). Body-colored mirrors with left-hand remote controlled ($26). Firebird power brakes ($47). LeMans front disc brakes ($70). Wonder Touch brakes ($47). Tape player and stereo cassette ($134). Firebird Rally Gage cluster with tachometer and clock ($95). Firebird Formula rear deck spoiler ($33). Vinyl side stripes for two-door LeMans or GP ($31-63). Tilt steering wheel with power steering required ($45). Formula steering wheel ($42). Hood-mounted tachometer on LeMans ($63). Firebird cordova top ($74-90). LeMans cordova top ($100). Firebird and LeMans wire wheel discs ($84). Rally II wheels ($90). Honeycomb styled wheels on T-37 ($63); on other LeMans and Firebirds ($100-126). LeMans Sport Endura styling option ($74). T-37 hardtop coupe 'GT' option ($237). 'The Judge' option ($395). Code 331 Firebird Ride & Handling package ($205) included honeycomb wheels, F60-15 white-lettered fiberglass tires, Trans Am front and rear stabilizer bars and Trans Am rear springs.

[VENTURA II]: Manual air conditioner ($392). Custom carpets ($21). Front seat console ($59). Rear window defogger ($32). Left-hand remote control mirror ($26). Disc front brakes ($70). Wonder Touch brakes ($47). Power steering ($103). Custom cushion steering wheel ($16). Sun Roof ($184). Rally II wheels ($63). Chrome wheel trim rings ($26). Custom bucket seat group ($242). Sprint option package ($233-254).

[MIXED POWER TRAIN OPTIONS]: The 350 cid two-barrel V-8 was $121 extra in base Firebirds, T-37s and LeMans. The 400 cid two-barrel V-8 was $53 extra in Espirits and Catalinas and $174 extra in T-37 and LeMans. The 400 cid four-barrel V-8 was $100 extra in Formulas and Catalinas, $221 extra in all T-37s and LeMans (except standard in GTO) and $47 extra in Catalina Broughams. The 455 cid two-barrel V-8 was $58 extra in Catalina Broughams and $111 extra in Catalinas. The 455 cid four-barrel V-8 was $47 extra in Bonnevilles, $58 extra in GTO and Grand Prix, $105 extra in Catalina Broughams and $158 extra in Catalinas. The 455 cid HO engine was standard in Trans Ams and 'The Judge', $137 extra in other GTOs, $237 extra in Formula Firebirds and $358 extra in T-37 and LeMans coupes and convertibles. In most cases, specific transmission were required with the above power train options. Dual exhausts were $41 extra. Safe-T-Track differential was $46 extra. Heavy-duty Safe-T-Track differential was $67 extra. Special order, performance and economy rear axles were each $11 extra. Heavy-duty batteries were $11 extra and Delco X maintenance free batteries were $26 extra. Optional in Ventura was a 307 cid Chevrolet V-8 with two-barrel carburetion, 8.5:1 compression and 200 hp at 4600 rpm.

HISTORICAL FOOTNOTES: Production of the 1971 models started Aug. 10, 1970 and the Ventura II was added to the line March 11, 1971. Model year production was 586,856 cars. Calendar year output was 728,615 cars for a 7.4 percent market share and number three ranking in the industry. A special Hurst SSJ Grand Prix was marketed this year. These cars were built in conjunction with Hurst Performance Products Co. Pontiac opened a 48,000 sq. ft. emissions and testing laboratory and did a 100,000 sq. ft. assembly plant expansion.

1972 PONTIAC

CATALINA — (V-8) — SERIES 2L — New energy-absorbing bumpers, redesigned radiator styled grilles, and revised taillamp treatments characterized full-size Pontiacs for 1972. Catalinas featured front fender model lettering, horizontal blade grilles and single deck taillamps with chrome outlined quadrants. Standard equipment included solid foam front seat cushions with integral springs, solid foam front seat backs, nylon carpets, center-flow ventilation, front ashtrays, teakwood dash trim, ashtray and glovebox lamps, trunk mat, concealed wipers and windshield radio antennas. Other features included bright roof gutter moldings (on most models), hood rear edge moldings, power steering, power brakes with front discs and G78-15 blackwall tires. Closed body styles were upholstered in cloth and Morrokide. Convertibles featured all-Morrokide trims, twin rear quarter interior lamps and power tops with glass rear windows. Catalina Safaris also had all-Morrokide seats, Deluxe steering wheel, vinyl load floor coverings, L78-15 tires and power tailgate windows on nine-passenger jobs. All full-size Pontiacs had V-8 power and Turbo-Hydramatic transmission.

PONTIAC I.D. NUMBERS: The serial numbering system was changed slightly this year' The first symbol was again the GM divisional code, using a '2' for Pontiacs. The second symbol was alphabetical, using letters to indicate series as follows: (Y) for Ventura; (S) for basic Firebird; (T) for Firebird Espirit; (U) for Formula Firebird; (V) for Trans Am; (D) for LeMans; (G) for Luxury LeMans; (L) for Catalina; (M) for Catalina Brougham; (N) for Bonneville; (P) for Grand Ville and (K) for Grand Prix. The third and fourth symbols indicated the body style. The fifth symbol was a new numerical engine code as follows: VIN on top of dash at left, viewable through windshield. First symbol tells GM division: 2=Pontiac. Second symbol tells series: Y=Ventura II; S=Firebird; T=Espirit; U=Formula 400; V=Trans Am; D=LeMans; G=Luxury Lemans; K=Grand Prix; L=Catalina; M=Catalina Brougham; N=Bonneville; P=Grand Ville. Third and fourth symbols indicate body style and appear as last two letters of Body/Style Number in charts below. Fifth symbol indicates engine (See chart at beginning of "Engines" section below.) Sixth symbol indicates model year: 2=1972. Seventh symbol indicates assembly plant: A=Atlanta, Ga.; C=Southgate, Calif.; D=Doraville, Ga.; G=Framingham, Mass.; L=Van Nuys, Calif.; N=Norwood, Ohio; P=Pontiac, Mich.; W=Willow Run, Mich.; X=Kansas City, Kan.; Z=Fremont, Calif.; 2=St. Therese, Quebec, Canada. Remaining symbols are sequential unit production number at factory, starting with 100001. Fisher Body plate on cowl tells style number: (model year prefix 72, plus (this year only) 1971 type Body/Style Number codes, body number, trim code, paint code and other data. Six-cylinder engine code stamped on distributor mounting on right side of block. V-8 engine code on front of block below right cylinder head. Engine production codes for 1972 were: [250 cid/110 nhp six] W6/CBJ/Y6/CBG/CBA/CBC [307 cid/130 nhp V-8] CKG/CAY/CKH/CAZ/CTK/CMA. [350 cid/160 nhp V-8] WR/YU/YV/YR. [400 cid/180 nhp V-8] YX/ZX. [400 cid/200 nhp] WS/WK/YS/ZS. [400 cid/250 nhp] YY. [455 cid/190 nhp] YH/ZH. [455 cid/220 nhp] YC/YA. [455 cid/300 nhp] YB/YE. [455 cid/210 nhp] n.a. [455 cid/240 nhp] n.a. [455 cid/200 nhp] U.

CATALINA (2L SERIES)

Model Number	Body/Style Number	Body Type & Seating	Factory Price	Shipping Weight	Production Total
2L	2L69	4-dr Sed-6p	3713	4154	83,004
2L	2L39	4-dr HT-6P	3874	4179	28,010
2L	2L57	2-dr HT-6P	3808	4129	60,233
2L	2L67	2-dr Conv-6P	4080	4204	2,399
2L	2L35	4-dr Sta Wag-6P	4232	4743	14,536
21	2L45	4-dr Sta-Wag-9P	4472	4818	12,766

CATALINA BROUGHAM — (V-8) — SERIES 2M — Broughams had the same features as L Series Catalinas plus special interior trim, carpeted lower door panels, custom cushion steering wheel, electric clock, Deluxe wheelcovers and door handles with body-color inserts. Chrome signatures were seen on the roof pillar to identify Broughams externally. They used the same horizontal blade grille and single deck taillamps as Catalinas.

CATALINA BROUGHAM (2M SERIES)

Model Number	Body/Style Number	Body Type & Seating	Factory Price	Shipping Weight	Production Total
2M	2M69	4-dr Sed-6p	3916	4188	8,007
2M	2M39	4-dr HT-6P	4062	4238	8,762
2M	2M57	2-dr HT Cpe-6P	3996	4158	10,545

BONNEVILLE (V-8) — SERIES 2N — Bonnevilles had single deck taillights with chrome outline quadrants like Catalinas, but cross-hatched grille inserts like Grand Villes. Bonneville lettering appeared on the left-hand grille, behind the front wheel openings and between the taillights. The standard equipment list was the same as the Catalina Brougham's, plus dash panel courtesy and trunk lamps, trunk compartment sidewall panels, formal roofline, bright metal window reveal moldings on four-door Sedan and H78-15 blackwall tires. Bonneville Grand Safaris had the same equipment as Catalina station wagons, plus bench seats with center armrests, carpeted lower door panels and cargo area, custom cushion steering wheel, electric clock, dash panel courtesy lamps and Deluxe wheelcovers.

BONNEVILLE (2N SERIES)

Model Number	Body/Style Number	Body Type & Seating	Factory Price	Shipping Weight	Production Total
2N	2N69	4-dr Sed-6P	4169	4288	9,704
2N	2N39	4-dr HT-6P	4293	4388	15,806
2N	2N57	2-dr HT Cpe-6P	4228	4238	10,568
2N	2N35	4-dr Sta Wag-6p	4581	4918	5,675
2N	2N45	4-dr Sta Wag-9P	4721	4938	8,540

GRAND VILLE — (V-8) — SERIES 2P — Grand Villes featured Bonneville type cross-hatched grilles and distinctive twin-deck slotted taillights. There was model identification lettering on the left-hand grille, behind the front wheel openings and between the taillights. Standard equipment consisted of all items found on Bonnevilles, plus bench seats with folding center armrests (or notch back bench seats with center armrests) and, on convertibles, two rear quarter interior lamps and power operated tops with glass windows.

GRAND VILLE (2P SERIES)

Model Number	Body/Style Number	Body Type & Seating	Factory Price	Shipping Weight	Production Total
2P	2P49	4-dr HT-6P	4507	4378	41,346
2P	2P47	2-dr HT Cpe-6P	4442	4263	19,852
2P	2P67	2-dr Conv-6P	4640	4333	2,213

1972 Pontiac, Grand Prix two-door hardtop coupe, V-8

GRAND PRIX — (V-8) — SERIES 2K — Grand Prixs featured high-intensity single headlamps, new cross-hatched grilles, model identification signature scripts and semi-boattail rear deck styling with triple-lens horizontal taillights. Buyers had a choice of bucket or notch back front bench seats. Standard equipment included carpeting; carpeted lower door panels; a console and floor shift (with bucket seats); custom cushion steering wheel; upper level ventilation; electric clock; front ashtrays; teakwood dash trim; ashtray, dash panel and courtesy lamps; trunk compartment side panels; Deluxe wheelcovers; concealed wipers; windshield antenna; and moldings for roof gutters, windshield, rear window, window sills, hood rear edge, wheel openings and rocker panels. Other regular features included power steering, power brakes with front discs, power-flex cooling fan, dual exhausts and G78-14 blackwall tires. The `SJ' option package was again available and included a big V-8, body color outside mirrors, vinyl pinstripes, luggage and door courtesy lamps, and a Rally Gage cluster. All Grand Prixs had automatic transmission. The code 332 Grand Prix 'SJ' option included the 455 cid four-barrel V-8, body-color outside mirrors (left-hand remote control), vinyl accent stripes, luggage and door courtesy lamps, Delco X battery and Rally Gage cluster.

GRAND PRIX (SERIES 2K)

Model Number	Body/Style Number	Body Type & Seating	Factory Price	Shipping Weight	Production Total
2K	2K57	2-dr HT-5P	4472	3898	91,961

BASE LEMANS — (6-CYL) — SERIES 2D — Standard equipment included bench seats with cloth and Morrokide trim; front and rear foam seats; rear ashtrays in armrests (except coupe); loop-pile carpets (except coupe); Deluxe steering wheel; upper level ventilation (hardtop coupe); teakwood dash accents; windshield radio antenna; concealed wipers (except coupe); ventipanes (except hardtop coupe); chrome valance panel; and bright moldings on the roof gutters, windshield, rear window and body sills of most styles. Station wagons had all-Morrokide seats, under floor cargo compartments, vinyl cargo floor coverings, two-way

tailgates with built-in steps, power brakes with front discs and power tailgate windows on nine-passenger jobs. Standard tires were H78-14 size on Safaris and F78-14 size on other styles. The WW-4 option was available on LeMans Style Numbers 2027 and 2037 and included a 400 cid four-barrel V-8, four-speed manual transmission with floor shift, heavy-duty Safe-T-Track differential, front power disc brakes, custom carpets (coupe only) and the Ride and Handling package. The WW-5 option was available on LeMans style numbers 2027 and 2037 and included Turbo-Hydramatic or close-ratio four-speed manual transmission, 455 cid four-barrel HO V-8, body-color outside mirrors (left-hand remote control), Formula steering wheel, roof drip moldings and carpets (coupe only), Rally Gage cluster with tachometer, Ride & Handling package, RAM AIR hood and unitized ignition system.

BASE LEMANS (20 SERIES)

Model Number	Body/Style Number	Body Type & Seating	Factory Price	Shipping Weight	Production Total
2D	2D27	2-dr Cpe-6P	2722/2840	3294/3510	6,855
2D	2D36	4-dr Sta Wag-6P	3271/3389	3799/4015	8,332
2D	2D37	2-dr HT-6P	2851/2969	3234/3450	80,383
2D	2D46	4-dr Sta Wag-9	3378/3496	3839/4055	5,266
2D	2D69	4-dr Sed-6P	2814/2932	3269/3485	19,463

NOTE 1: Data above slash for six/below slash for V-8.
NOTE 2: A total of 120,299 LeMans were built.
NOTE 3: 9,601 LeMans had synchromesh and 110,698 had automatic.

LEMANS SPORT (6-CYL) — SERIES D67 — The LeMans Convertible was considered a separate sub-series called the LeMans Sport line. This model carried special `Sport' signature scripts and had standard bucket seats. Many sources list this style with the LeMans series, but the factory broke it out separately in calculating production totals. The code 332 Lemans `GT' package was available on style numbers 2D37 and 2D67 and included three-speed heavy-duty manual transmission, G70 x 14 white-letter tires, body-color mirrors, Rally II wheels (less trim rings), vinyl tape stripes, dual exhausts with side splitters and `GT' decals. The code 734 LeMans Sport option was available on style number 2D37 and included bucket seats, custom console and rear quarter trim, custom rear seat and special front fender nameplate.

LEMANS SPORT (2D SUB-SERIES)

Model Number	Body/Style Number	Body Type & Seating	Factory Price	Shipping Weight	Production Total
2D	2D67	2-dr Spt Conv-5P	3228/3346	3284/3500	3,438

NOTE 1: Data above slash for six/below slash for V-8.
NOTE 2: 3,438 LeMans Sport "Sport convertibles" were built.
NOTE 3: 317 LeMans Sport `Sport convertibles' w/synchromesh; 3,121 automatic.

1972 Pontiac, Luxury LeMans two-door hardtop, V-8

LUXURY LEMANS — (V-8) — SERIES 2G — A distinctive grille treatment with twin cavities divided by bright horizontal blades was used on Luxury LeMans models. Twin-ribbed full-length bodyside moldings, fender skirts and roof pillar letter badges were additional external distinctions. The standard equipment list was the same as for LeMans styles, plus all-Morrokide bucket seats in hardtop coupes or notch back bench seats in any body style. Interior trim included all-Morrokide or cloth and Morrokide upholstery combinations, carpeted lower door panels with reflectors, custom cushion steering wheel, pedal trim plates, front door assist straps, bright armrest accents and ashtray and glovebox lamps.

LUXURY LEMANS (2G SERIES)

Model Number	Body/Style Number	Body Type & Seating	Factory Price	Shipping Weight	Production Total
2G	2G37	2-dr HT-5P	3196	3488	8,641
2G	2639	4-dr HT-6P	3319	3638	37,615

NOTE 1: 46,256 Luxury LeMans models were built.
NOTE 2: 269 Luxury LeMans had synchromesh and 45,987 had automatic.

GTO — (V-8) — SERIES D OPTION — The GTO was no longer a separate series. There was a code 334 GTO option package available for the style number 2D37 LeMans hardtop coupe and the 2D27 LeMans two-door coupe. It included the Code T engine, three-speed heavy-duty manual floor shift transmission, G70-14 blackwall tires, body-color mirrors, Endura styling option, special twin air slot hood, front fender air extractors, firm shock absorbers, front and rear stabilizer bars and GTO identification at a price of $344 over base model cost. The code X and code Y engines were optional. Only 5,807 GTOs left the factory and body style breakouts are not available. (Note: These cars are included in the LeMans production totals given above).

BASE FIREBIRD — (6-CYL) — SERIES 2S — The possibility of dropping the Firebird was raised this year and styling changes were minimal. There was a new honeycomb mesh grille insert, new interior trims and redesigned hubcaps and wheelcovers. Standard equipment in the basic model included front and rear bucket type seats with all-vinyl trim, solid foam seat cushions with integral springs, loop-pile carpets, Deluxe steering wheel, upper-level ventilation, woodgrained dash accents, ashtray light, Endura front bumper, small full-width front air dam, hubcaps, windshield radio antenna, bright moldings on windshield, rear window and grille, thin body sill moldings, front disc brakes, three-speed manual column shift transmission and E78-14 blackwall tires.

Standard Catalog of American Cars

BASE FIREBIRD (2S SERIES)

Model Number	Body/Style Number	Body Type & Seating	Factory Price	Shipping Weight	Production Total
2S	2S87	2-dr HT-4P	2838/2956	3357/3359	12,000

NOTE 1: Data above slash for six/below slash for V-8.
NOTE 2: 12,001 basic Firebirds were built.
NOTE 3: 1,263 Firebirds had synchromesh and 10,738 had automatic.

FIREBIRD ESPIRIT — (V-8) — SERIES 2T — The Espirit had model signature script moldings on the roof pillar. Standard equipment was the same as in basic Firebirds, plus custom cloth and Morrokide trim, distinctive door trim panels, perforated headliner, added sound insulation, custom cushion steering wheel, rear armrest ashtrays, trunk mat, dash assist grip, wheel trim rings, body-color mirrors (left-hand remote-controlled), body-color door handle inserts, concealed wipers, bright roof rail trim, window sill moldings, rear hood edge accents, wheel opening moldings and wide rocker panel accent strips. Three-speed manual floor shift transmission was also included.

FIREBIRD ESPIRIT (2T SERIES)

Model Number	Body/Style Number	Body Type & Seating	Factory Price	Shipping Weight	Production Total
2T	2T87	2-dr HT-4P	3194	3359	11,415

NOTE 1: 11,415 Firebirds Espirits were built.
NOTE 2: 504 Firebird Espirits had synchromesh and 10,911 had automatic.

FIREBIRD FORMULA — (V-8) — SERIES 2U — Formula Firebirds had the same equipment features as Espirits, plus a fiberglass hood with forward-mounted twin air scoops, special Formula identification, 1-1/8 inch front stabilizer bars, firm control shock absorbers, dual exhausts with chrome extensions and F70-14 tires.

FORMULA FIREBIRD (2U SERIES)

Model Number	Body/Style Number	Body Type & Seating	Factory Price	Shipping Weight	Production Total
2U	2U87	2-dr HT-4P	3221	3424	5,250

NOTE 1: 5,249 Formula Firebirds were built.
NOTE 2: 1,082 Formula Firebirds had synchromesh and 4,167 had automatic.

FIREBIRD TRANS AM — (V-8) — SERIES 2V — Trans Ams had the same standard features as Firebirds, plus a Formula steering wheel, engine-turned dash trim, Rally Gage cluster with clock and tachometer, front air dam, front and rear wheel opening flares, full-width rear deck spoiler, engine air extractors, shaker hood, 15-inch Rally II rims with trim rings, black-textured grille inserts, fast-rate power steering, power brakes with front discs, 1-1/4 inch stabilizer bars, 7/8 rear stabilizer bars, special high-rate rear springs, Safe-T-Track differential, air cleaner with rear-facing cold air induction system, power-flex cooling fan, four-speed close-ratio manual transmission with floor shift (or Turbo-Hydramatic) and F60-15 white lettered tires.

FIREBIRD TRANS AM (2V SERIES)

Model Number	Body/Style Number	Body Type & Seating	Factory Price	Shipping Weight	Production Total
2V	2V87	2-dr HT-4P	4256	3564	1,286

NOTE 1: 1,286 Trans Ams were built.
NOTE 2: 458 Trans Ams had synchromesh and 828 had automatic.

1972 Pontiac, Ventura II two-door coupe (with Sprint option), V-8

VENTURA II — (6-CYL) — SERIES 2Y — There were virtually no changes in the 1972 Ventura II. Minor alterations included variations in fender lettering, interior trim modifications and a new steering wheel. Standard equipment included bench seats with cloth and Morrokide trim, front seat foam cushions, vinyl covered floor mats, rear ashtrays in armrests, deluxe steering wheel, woodgrained vinyl dash trim, hubcaps, front door vent windows, bright moldings on windshield and rear window, E78-14 blackwall tires and three-speed manual column shift transmission. Two specialty "model-options" were the Ventura `SD' and the Sprint. The code 332 Ventura (coupe) Sprint option included three-speed manual floor shift transmission, E78 x 14 whitewalls, body-colored mirrors (left-hand remote control), custom sport steering wheel, chrome wheel trim rings, custom carpets, blacked-out grille, side striping, 14 x 16 inch rims and Sprint I decals. The Ventura 'SD' (for 'Sport Deluxe') was a limited-edition package offered only in cars built at Van Nuys, Calif. It was introduced in midyear and a production run of 500 units was predicted.

VENTURA II (SERIES 2Y)

Model Number	Body/Style Number	Body Type & Seating	Factory Price	Shipping Weight	Production Total
2Y	2Y69	4-dr Sed-5P	2454/2544	2979/3129	21,584
2Y	2Y27	2-dr Cpe-5P	2426/2516	2944/3094	51,203

NOTE 1: Data above slash for six/below slash for V-8.
NOTE 2: 72,787 Ventura IIs were built.
NOTE 3: 6,421 Ventura IIs had synchromesh and 26,644 had automatic.

ENGINES

Code *	Type	CID	Carb.	Comp. Ratio	Net H.P. at RPM
D	6-cyl	250	1-V	8.5:1	110@4200
F	V-8	307	2-V	8.5:1	140@4000
M	V-8	350	2-V	8.0:1	160@4400
N	V-8	350	2-V	8.0:1	175 @ 4400**
R	V-8	400	2-V	8.2:1	175@4000
P	V-8	400	2-V	8.2:1	200 @ 4000**
S	V-8	400	4-V	8.2:1	200@4000
T	V-8	400	4-V	8.2:1	250 @ 4000**
V	V-8	455	2-V	8.2:1	185@4000
U	V-8	455	2-V	8.2:1	200 @ 4000**
W	V-8	455	4-V	8.2:1	220@3600
Y	V-8	455	4-V	8.2:1	250 @ 3600**
X	V-8	455	4-V	8.4:1	300 @ 4000**

* VIN engine code; not engine production code.

** dual exhaust.

(CATALINA) Base V-8 in Catalinas was the code N engine. The base V-8 in Catalina Safaris was the code R engine. code S, V, Y, W, T and U engines were optional.

(CATALINA BROUGHAM) Base V-8 in Catalina Broughams was the code R engine. Code S/V/Y/W/T/U engines were optional.

(BONNEVILLE) Base V-8 in Bonnevilles was the code V engine. Code T/W/U engines were optional.

(GRAND VILLE) Base V-8 in Grand Ville was the code W engine. The only available option was the code Y engine.

(GRAND PRIX) Base V-8 in Grand Prixs was the code S engine. Options were the code T/Y engines, with the latter included in the `SJ' option package as regular equipment.

(LEMANS) Base six-cylinder power plant in LeMans was the code D engine. Base V-8 was the code M engine. Codes R/S/T/W/Y/X engines were other options.

(LUXURY LEMANS) Base V-8 in Luxury LeMans models was the code M engine. Code R/S/W/Y engines were additional options.

(BASE FIREBIRD) Base six-cylinder power plant in Firebirds was the code D engine. Base V-8 was the code M engine and the code N engine was optional.

(FIREBIRD ESPIRIT) Base V-8 in Firebirds Espirits was the code M engine. Options included code N and code R power plants.

(FORMULA FIREBIRD) Base V-8 in Formula Firebirds was the code M engine. Options included the code N, T and X power plants. Depending on engines, cars were identified as Formula 350s, Formula 400s or Formula 455s.

(TRANS AM) The code X engine was the only Trans Am power plant this year.

(VENTURA II) Base six-cylinder power plant in Ventura IIs was the code D engine. The code F engine was optional, except for cars registered in California, where the code M engine was used as the approved V-8.

CHASSIS FEATURES: Wheelbase: Wheelbases for all lines were the same as 1971. Overall length: For Venturas, Firebirds and base LeMans overall lengths were the same as for comparable body styles in 1971. Luxury LeMans models were 202.8 inches long; all Pontiac Safaris were now 228 inches long; Catalinas were 222.4 inches long; Bonneville/Grand Villes were 226.2 inches long and Grand Prixs were 213.6 inches long.

OPTIONS: Pontiac automatic air conditioning ($507). Firebird and LeMans air conditioning ($397). Formula or LeMans rear deck spoiler ($32-46). Pontiac automatic level control ($77). Firebird rear seat console ($26). Ventura and Firebird front seat console ($57). LeMans two-door hardtop and Sport convertible console ($59). Cruise Control ($62-67). Deck lid remote control ($14). Electric rear window defroster ($62). Base LeMans Endura styling option ($41). All-windows Soft-Ray glass ($39-49). Soft-Ray windshield ($30-35). Auxiliary gage panel for Catalina ($38). Bumper guards ($5-15). Warning lamps ($21). Auxiliary lamp group ($18). Convenience lamp group ($11). Safari luggage carrier ($62-82). Front disc brakes ($46-68). Wonder Touch brakes ($44-46). Power bench seats ($67-77-103). Power left bucket seat ($77). Ventura power steering ($100). Variable ratio power steering for LeMans and Firebirds ($113). AM/FM Stereo and 8-Track ($363). Rally Gage cluster with clock and tachometer ($92). Honeycomb wheels ($62-123). Rally II wheel rims ($56-87). woodgrained Safari exterior panelling ($154). LeMans 'GT' package ($23). Grand Ville Custom trim group ($231). Ventura sun roof ($179). LeMans Sport option ($164). Ventura Sprint option ($190). LeMans WW-4 performance option ($510-796). LeMans WW5 RAM AIR option ($982-995). Dual exhausts ($40). Performance or economy ratio rear axles ($10). Safe-T-Track differential was $45 extra and heavy-duty Safe-T-Track was $66 extra. Heavy-duty batteries were $10-$15 extra and a Delco X battery was $26 extra. Functional air inlet hoods for Formulas and specially-equipped LeMans models were $56 extra.

HISTORICAL FOOTNOTES: Production start-up date was Aug. 12, 1971. Factory introductions were held Sept. 23, 1971. Model year output was 707,017 cars. Calendar year totals of 702,571 assemblies gave PMD fifth place. On Oct. 1, 1972, Martin J. Caserio became Pontiac's general manager. The 1972 GTO hardtop with 300 net horsepower was tested at 7.1 seconds 0-to-60 and 15.4 seconds in the quarter-mile. The 1972 Firebird Espirit did 0-to-60 in 9.9 seconds and the quarter-mile in 17.6 seconds. The GTO returned to option status this year and Pontiac made Turbo-Hydramatic and disc brakes standard on all models.

1973 PONTIAC

CATALINA — (V-8) — SERIES 2L — Catalina front end styling was new and was characterized by full-width grilles having thin horizontal blades. Catalina lettering was seen behind the front wheel openings. Standard equipment was similar to the previous model year with small hubcaps, untrimmed wheel cutouts and thin body sill moldings. Taillamp treatments were simpler than on other lines. The Catalina convertible and Catalina Brougham series were deleted. Base Catalinas came with a 350 cid two-barrel V-8, Turbo-Hydramatic and variable-ratio power steering.

1973 Pontiac, Catalina two-door hardtop, V-8

1973 Pontiac, Grand Prix, two-door hardtop, V-8

PONTIAC I.D. NUMBERS: VIN on top of dash at left, viewable through windshield. First symbol tells GM division: 2=Pontiac. Second symbol tells series: Y=Ventura; Z=Ventura Custom; S=Firebird; T=Esprit; U=Formula 400; V=Trans Am; D=LeMans; F=LeMans Sport; G=Luxury Lemans; H=Grand Am; K=Grand Prix; L=Catalina; N=Bonneville; P=Grand Ville. Third and fourth symbols indicate body style and appear as last two digits of Body/Style Number in charts below. Fifth symbol indicates engine (See chart at beginning of "Engines" section below.) Sixth symbol indicates model year: 3=1973. Seventh symbol indicates assembly plant: A=Atlanta, Ga.; C=Southgate, Calif.; D=Doraville, Ga.; G=Framingham, Mass.; L=Van Nuys, Calif.; N=Norwood, Ohio; P=Pontiac, Mich.; Z=Fremont, Calif. Remaining symbols are sequential unit production number at factory, starting with 100001. Fisher Body plate on cowl tells style number: (model year prefix 73, plus new type Body/Style Number codes (i.e. 2L69 for Catalina four-door sedan), body number, trim code, paint code and other data. Six-cylinder engine code stamped on distributor mounting on right side of block. V-8 engine code on front of block below right cylinder head. Engine production codes for 1972 were: [250 cid/100 nhp six] CCC/CCD/CCA/CCB/CDR/CDS/CAW. [350 cid/150 nhp V-8] YL/ Y2/YR/Y7/YV/YL/XR/XV/ZR/ZV/XC. [350 cid/175 nhp V-8] WV/ZB/ZD/WD/XC/X2/WF/WA/ XF/WC/WL/WN/YW. [400 cid/170 nhp V-8] YP/Y4/YX/Y1/ZX/ZK/YZ. [400 cid/185 nhp V-8] P. [400 cid/200 nhp V-8] S. [400 cid/230 nhp V-8] WK/WS/WP/YS/Y3/YN/YT. [400 cid/250 nhp V-8] X4/X1/X3/XH/W5/Y6/YF/YG/XN/XX/X5/XZ/XK. [455 cid/215 nhp V-8] W. [455 cid/250 nhp V-8] WW/WT/YC/YA/ZC/ZZ/ZE/XE/XA/XJ/XL/XO/XT/X7/XY/XM. [455 cid/310 nhp Super-Duty V-8] ZJ/XD/W8/Y8.

CATALINA (2L SERIES)

Model Number	Body/Style Number	Body Type & Seating	Factory Price	Shipping Weight	Production Total
2L	L69	4-dr Sed-6P	3770	4234	100,592
2L	L39	4-dr HT-6P	3938	4270	31,663
2L	L57	2-dr HT-6P	3869	4190	74,394
2L	L45	4-dr Sta Wag-9P	4457	4873	14,654
2L	L35	4-dr Sta Wag-6P	4311	4791	15,762

BONNEVILLE — (V-8) — SERIES 2N — Bonnevilles had a new `eggcrate' mesh grille running from side to side. Double twin-deck taillamps were used along with wide body sill moldings having rear panel extensions. Bonneville lettering appeared on the left side of the grille, behind front wheel openings and between the taillamps. Bonnevilles were now the same as Catalinas, but had higher levels of interior and exterior trim including Deluxe wheelcovers, decor moldings and custom upholstery combinations. Fender skirts were no longer standard equipment, but other features were about the same as in 1972. A special RTS handling package was introduced for the hardtop. This "Bonneville RTS coupe" was priced $4,225 and included radial tires and heavy-duty underpinnings at this cost. Bonneville Safaris were moved to the Grand Ville series.

BONNEVILLE (2N SERIES)

Model Number	Body/Style Number	Body Type & Seating	Factory Price	Shipping Weight	Production Total
2N	N69	4-dr Sed-6P	4163	4333	15,830
2N	N39	4-dr HT-6P	4292	4369	17,202
2N	N57	2-dr HT-6P	4225	4292	13,866

GRAND VILLE — (V-8) — SERIES 2P — Grand Ville passenger cars were now the same as other full-size Pontiacs. The new grille on this line was similar to the Bonneville type except that a signature script model badge was placed above the left-hand grille instead of on it. Stacked, horizontally-slit taillamps were an exclusive feature. Full wheel discs, wide body sill moldings, roof pillar nameplates (except convertible) and fender skirts were additional identification aids. Standard equipment was about the same as in 1972. The Bonneville Safaris became Grand Ville Safaris. The big wagons were on a three-inch longer wheelbase than other Pontiacs. Safari features were about the same as those seen on 1972 Bonneville station wagons.

GRAND VILLE (2P SERIES)

Model Number	Body/Style Number	Body Type & Seating	Factory Price	Shipping Weight	Production Total
2P	P49	4-dr HT-6P	4592	4376	44,092
2P	P47	2-dr HT-6P	4524	4321	23,963
2P	P67	2-dr Conv-6P	4766	4339	4,447
2P	P45	4-dr Sta Wag-9P	4821	4925	10,776
2P	P35	4-dr Sta Wag-6P	4674	4823	6,894

GRAND PRIX — (V-8) — SERIES 2K — The Grand Prix retained a link to previous styling themes, with several refinements. A new type of wide grille design was used and opera windows were an available styling option. The GP was on a shorter wheelbase and looked trimmer, even though overall size was increased. V-shaped hood styling was emphasized again. A new feature was African crossfire mahogany accents for the instrument panel. A custom cushion steering wheel and all-Morrokide trims were available this year. The general level of trim, appointments and standard equipment was the same as in 1972. The `SJ' option was offered again, with production counted separately for the first time. It included firm shock absorbers, front stabilizer bar, Rally RTS suspension and the 250 hp V-8.

GRAND PRIX (2K SERIES)

Model Number	Body/Style Number	Body Type & Seating	Factory Price	Shipping Weight	Production Total
2K	K57	2-dr HT-5P	4583	4025	133,150
2K	K57	'SJ' HT-5P	4962	4400	20,749

LEMANS — (6-CYL) — SERIES 2D AND SERIES 2AF — Pontiac's A-body intermediate line had highly revised "Buck Rogers" styling this season. Design characteristics included V-shaped hoods, split rectangular grilles, single headlamps mounted in square housings, highly sculptured fenders and "Colonnade" style rooflines. The Colonnade styling provided heavier roof pillars to meet federal rollover standards with large window openings cut deep into the beltline in limousine style. LeMans lettering appeared behind the front wheel opening and thin body sill moldings were used. The LeMans Sport convertible was discontinued and replaced by the Series 2AF LeMans Sport sport coupe. This model constituted a separate sub-series and came standard with bucket seats and louvered rear quarter window styling. Station wagons were officially called `Safaris' again. Available options on the LeMans or LeMans Sport Coupes included the `GT' and `GTO' packages. Base models had a uniform vertical blade grille insert, with flat textured finish on the GTO. The GTO option also included the 400 cid four-barrel V-8, dual air scoop hood, wide oval tires, dual exhausts, floor mounted three-speed manual gearbox, rear sway bars, baby moon hubcaps, 5 x 7 inch wheel rims, specific body striping and suitable model identification trim.

LEMANS (2AD SERIES)

Model Number	Body/Style Number	Body Type & Seating	Factory Price	Shipping Weight	Production Total
2AD	D29	4-dr HT-6P	2918/3036	3605/3821	26,554
2AD	D37	2-dr HT-6P	2920/3038	3579/3795	68,230
2AD	D45	4-dr Sta Wag-9P	3429/3547	3993/4209	6,127
2AD	D35	4-dr Sta Wag-6P	3296/3414	3956/4172	10,446

LEMANS SPORT (2AF SERIES)

Model Number	Body/Style Number	Body Type & Seating	Factory Price	Shipping Weight	Production Total
2AF	F37	2-dr HT-5P	3008/3126	3594/3810	50,999

NOTE 1: Data above slash for six/below slash for V-8.
NOTE 2: 4,806 LeMans/LeMans Sport two-door Colonade hardtops had GTO option.

LUXURY LEMANS — (V-8) — SERIES 2AG — Luxury LeMans models also featured Colonnade styling, but with higher level interior and exterior appointments, plus standard V-8 power. Styling features included wide beauty moldings running the full-width of the body at about mid-wheel height; fender skirts with chrome edge moldings; rear deck beauty panels between the taillights; vertical blade grilles with vertical chrome division moldings; Deluxe wheelcovers; and `Luxury' signatures above the LeMans fender lettering. Luxury LeMans upholstery combinations were patterned after those seen in Grand Villes.

LUXURY LEMANS (2AG SERIES)

Model Number	Body/Style Number	Body Type & Seating	Factory Price	Shipping Weight	Production Total
2AG	G29	4-dr HT-6P	3344	3867	9,377
2AG	G37	2-dr HT-6P	3274	3799	33,916

1973 Pontiac, Grand Am Colonnade two-door hardtop, V-8

GRAND AM — (V-8) — SERIES 2AH — One of the most distinctive cars offered in the sales sweepstakes this model year was the Pontiac Grand Am. This A-body intermediate had an international flavor. Standard equipment included a sloping three-piece nose section of body-color injection-molded urethane plastic; twin sloping vertical-slot triple quadrant grilles; bucket seats with adjustable lumbar support; 14 inch custom cushion steering wheel; African crossfire mahogany dash trim; 10 inch diameter power front disc brakes; Grand Prix style dashboard; full-instrumentation with Rally Gage cluster; variable- ratio power steering; heavy-duty suspension; steel-belted wide-base G70-15 radial tires on 15 x 7 inch wheels; Pliacell shock absorbers; thick front and rear stabilizer bars; specific trim stripes; and special nameplates. Upholstery options included cloth with corduroy insert panels or perforated, leather-like Morrokide. A V-8 engine was also standard.

GRAND AM (2AH SERIES)

Model Number	Body/Style Number	Body Type & Seating	Factory Price	Shipping Weight	Production Total
2AH	H29	4-dr HT-6P	4353	4018	8,691
2AH	H37	2-dr HT-6P	4264	3992	34,445

BASE FIREBIRD — (6-CYL) — SERIES 2F2
Base Firebirds had a new 'eggcrate' grille insert. Styling was not greatly changed from 1972, but the Endura nose had been substantially improved to meet U.S. government crash standards. Standard equipment was basically similar to that offered in 1972 models.

BASE FIREBIRD (SERIES 2FS)

Model Number	Body/Style Number	Body Type & Seating	Factory Price	Shipping Weight	Production Total
2FS	S87	2-dr HT-4P	2895/3013	3159/3380	14,096

NOTE 1: Data above slash for six/below slash for V-8.
NOTE 2: 1,370 cars were built with six-cylinder power.

FIREBIRD ESPIRIT — (V-8) — SERIES 2FT
The Firebird Espirit could be most easily identified by the model signature scripts on the roof pillars. Also considered standard equipment were a custom interior, concealed windshield wipers, twin body-color mirrors (left-hand remote-controlled) and African crossfire mahogany dash and console accent panels.

FIREBIRD ESPIRIT (SERIES 2FT)

Model Number	Body/Style Number	Body Type & Seating	Factory Price	Shipping Weight	Production Total
2FT	T87	2-dr HT-4P	3249	3309	17,249

FIREBIRD FORMULA — (V-8) — SERIES 2FU
Formula Firebirds could again be identified by the special twin-scoop hoods. Other features included a custom cushion steering wheel, heavy-duty suspension, black textured grille, dual exhausts and F70-14 tires plus all items include on lower priced lines.

FIREBIRD FORMULA (SERIES 2FU)

Model Number	Body/Style Number	Body Type & Seating	Factory Price	Shipping Weight	Production Total
2FU	U87	2-dr HT-4P	3276	3318	10,166

1973 Pontiac, Trans Am two-door hardtop coupe, V-8

FIREBIRD TRANS AM — (V-8) — SERIES 2FV
The most significant change to Firebird Trans Ams this season was the addition of the "chicken" graphics treatment for the hood. Stylist John Schinella created this modernized rendition of the legendary Indian symbol. Standard equipment included Formula steering wheel, Rally Gage cluster with clock and tachometer, full-width rear deck spoiler, power steering and front disc brakes, Safe-T-Track differential, wheel opening flares, front fender air extractors, dual exhausts with chrome extensions, heavy-duty underpinnings, Rally II wheels with trim rings, dual body-color mirrors (left-hand remote-controlled), F60-15 white-lettered tires and a choice of Turbo-Hydramatic or four-speed manual transmission.

FIREBIRD TRANS AM (SERIES 2FV)

Model Number	Body/Style Number	Body Type & Seating	Factory Price	Shipping Weight	Production Total
2FV	V87	2-dr HT-4P	4204	3504	4,802

VENTURA — (6-CYL) — SERIES 2Y
The name Ventura II was shortened to Ventura and cars in the Y Series had several styling refinements. A 'double-decker' twin slot grille was continued in use on cars with base level trim. Standard equipment included Deluxe steering wheel, bench seats with cloth and Morrokide trim, front and rear armrests, high/low ventilation system, rubber floor mats and hubcaps. A Sprint package including custom cushion steering wheel, custom carpeting, body color outside mirrors, custom striping, model identification trim and 14x6 inch wheel rims was available on two-door models. There were now a pair of two-door styles available, the notch back coupe and the hatchback coupe, along with a four-door notch back sedan. Cars with the Sprint package wore a Firebird style twin rectangular grille.

VENTURA (SERIES 2Y)

Model Number	Body/Style Number	Body Type & Seating	Factory Price	Shipping Weight	Production Total
2Y	Y69	4-dr Sed-5P	2481/2599	3124/3336	21,012
2Y	Y27	2-dr Cpe-5P	2452/2570	3064/3276	49,153
2Y	Y17	2-dr Hatch-5P	2603/2721	3170/3382	26,335

NOTE 1: Data above slash for six/below slash for V-8.
NOTE 2: Totals include base Venturas, Customs and Sprints of same body style.

1973 Pontiac, Ventura two-door hatchback coupe, 6-cyl

VENTURA CUSTOM — (6-CYL) — SERIES 2Z
Ventura Customs included a choice of cloth or all-Morrokide upholstery, custom cushion steering wheel, bright metal front seat side panels, glovebox lamp, nylon carpeting, Deluxe wheelcovers, pedal trim plates, body decor moldings and body sill beauty strips. The hatchback coupe include load area carpeting and dome lamp, fold-down rear seat and a Space Saver spare tire. As on base models Ventura block letters were seen behind the front wheel openings, but additional identification was provided by signature scripts reading `Custom' positioned on the rear roof pillars.

VENTURA CUSTOM (SERIES 2Z)

Model Number	Body/Style Number	Body Type & Seating	Factory Price	Shipping Weight	Production Total
2Z	Z69	4-dr Sed-5P	2638/2756	3157/3369	(Note 2)
2Z	Z27	2-dr Coupe-5P	2609/2727	3097/3309	(Note 2)
2Z	Z17	2-dr Hatch-5P	2759/2877	3203/3415	(Note 2)

NOTE 1: Data above slash for six/below slash for V-8.
NOTE 2: Ventura Custom totals included in base Ventura chart above.

ENGINES

Code	Type	CID	Carb.	Comp. Ratio	Net HP at RPM
D	6-cyl	250	1-V	8.25:1	100@3600
F	V-8	307	2-V	8.5:1	130 @ 4000*
M	V-8	350	2-V	7.6:1	150@4000
N	V-8	350	2-V	7.6:1	175 @ 4400**
R	V-8	400	2-V	8.0:1	170@3600
P	V-8	400	2-V	8.0:1	185 @ 4000**
S	V-8	400	4-V	8.0:1	200@4000
T	V-8	400	4-V	8.0:1	250 @ 4400**
W	V-8	455	4-V	8.0:1	215@3600
Y	V-8	455	4-V	8.0:1	250 @ 4000**
X	V-8	455	4-V	8.4:1	310 @ 4000**

* Canada only.
** Dual exhausts.

(CATALINA) The base Catalina V-8 was the code M engine. Codes R/P/S/T/W/Y engines were optional. The code R engine was standard in Catalina Safaris.

(BONNEVILLE) The base Bonneville V-8 was the code R engine. Code P/S/T/W/Y engines were optional.

(GRAND VILLE) The base Grand Ville V-8 was the code W engine. The code Y engine was optional.

(GRAND PRIX) The base Grand Prix V-8 was the code T engine. The code Y/X engines were optional.

(LEMANS/VENTURA) Base six-cylinder power plant in LeMans models was the code D engine. Base V-8 in LeMans passenger cars was the code R engine. Code P/S/T/W/Y engines were optional in passenger cars. The code R engine was standard in Safari V-8s with code S/W engines as options. The code T engine was standard in cars with the GTO package.

(LUXURY LEMANS) Base V-8 power plant in Luxury LeMans models was the code M engine. code R/S/Y engines were optional.

(GRAND AM) Base V-8 power plant in Grand Ams was the code R engine. Code S/Y/X engines were optional.

(BASE FIREBIRD) Standard six-cylinder power plant in basic Firebirds was the code D engine. Base V-8 was the code M engine. No other options were listed.

(FIREBIRD ESPIRIT) Base V-8 power plant in Espirits was the code M engine. The only option was also a V-8, the code R engine.

(FIREBIRD FORMULA) Base V-8 power plant in the Formula Firebird series was the code M engine. Code R/Y/X engines were optional V-8s.

(FIREBIRD TRANS AM) Base V-8 power plant in Trans Ams was the code Y engine. The code X engine was the only power train option.

OPTIONAL V-8 ENGINES

350 cid. Compression ratio: 7.6. Carburetion: two-barrel. Brake hp: 150 at 4000 rpm. (standard in Catalina, Luxury LeMans, Firebird Espirit; optional in Ventura/LeMans/Firebird)

350 cid. Compression ratio: 7.6. Carburetion: two-barrel. Brake hp: 175 at 4400 rpm. (optional in Ventura/LeMans/Catalina; standard in Firebird Formula 350)

400 cid. Compression ratio: 8. Carburetion: two-barrel. Brake hp: 170 at 3600 rpm. (standard in Grand Am, Safari, Bonneville; optional in LeMans/Catalina/Firebird Espirit)

400 cid. Compression ratio: 8. Carburetion: two-barrel. Brake hp: 185 at 4000 rpm. (optional in LeMans/Grand Am/Catalina)

400 cid. Compression ratio: 8. Carburetion: four-barrel. Brake hp: 200 at 4000 rpm. (standard in Grand Safari; optional in Catalina/Bonneville)

400 cid. Compression ratio: 8. Carburetion: four-barrel. Brake hp: 230 at 4400 rpm. (standard in GTO, Grand Prix; optional in LeMans/Grand Am/Formula 400/Catalina/Bonneville)

455 cid. Compression ratio: 8. Carburetion: four-barrel. Brake hp: 215 at 3600 rpm. (standard in Grand Ville; optional in Catalina/Bonneville)

455 cid. Compression ratio: 8. Carburetion: four-barrel. Brake hp: 250 at 4000 rpm. (standard in Trans Am; optional in Grand Prix/Grand Ville/Catalina/Bonneville/GTO/LeMans/Formula 455)

455 cid. Compression ratio: 8. Carburetion: four-barrel. Brake hp: 290 at: 4000 rpm. (optional in Trans Am/Formula 455)

CHASSIS FEATURES: Wheelbase: (All Pontiac Safaris) 127 inches; (All Pontiac passenger cars) 124 inches; (A-body two-doors) 112 inches; (A-body four-doors) 116 inches; (Grand Prix) 116 inches; (Firebird) 108 inches; (Ventura) 111 inches. Overall length: (All Pontiac Safaris) 228.8 inches; (All Pontiac passenger cars) 224.8 inches; (Grand Am two-door) 208.6 inches; (Grand Am four-door) 212.6 inches; (Grand Prix) 216.6 inches; (Other A-body two-doors) 207.4; (Other A-body four-doors) 211.4; (A-body Safaris) 213.3 inches. (Firebird) 192.1 inches; (Ventura) 197.5 inches.

OPTIONS: Custom Safari option package ($317). GTO LeMans option package ($368). LeMans Ride & Handling package ($188). LeMans GT option ($237). Grand Prix 'SJ' option ($379). Electric sun roof for A-body models ($325) Ventura sun roof ($179). Grand Prix electric sun roof ($325). Ventura vinyl top ($82) Firebird AM/FM stereo ($233); with tape deck $363. Firebird power windows ($75). LeMans vinyl top ($97). LeMans AM /FM stereo ($233); with tape deck ($363). LeMans power windows ($103). LeMans Rally II wheels ($87). Pontiac six way power seat ($103). Pontiac power windows ($129). Pontiac AM/ FM stereo ($233); with tape deck ($363). Safari 60/40 bench seats ($77). Grand Prix vinyl roof ($116). Grand Prix power windows ($75).

HISTORICAL FOOTNOTES: Model year production was 919,872, the highest ever for Pontiac Motor Div. Calendar year output of 866,598 cars was also recorded for a 9.5 percent market share. On Nov. 27, 1972 a blue Catalina sedan became the 16th millionth Pontiac ever made. The SD-455 Trans Am was capable of 0-to-60 in 7.3 seconds and the quarter-mile in 15 seconds. The 250 nhp Grand Am traveled from 0-to-60 in 7.9 seconds and made it down the dragstrip in 15.7. Production of SD-455 Trans Ams totaled 252 cars, of which 180 had automatic transmission and 72 had manual transmission. Fifty Formula Firebirds also had the SD-455 muscle-engine.

1974 PONTIAC

CATALINA — (V-8) — SERIES 2BL — The front and rear of 1974 Catalinas was restyled and some body styles also had new rooflines. A radiator grille was used again. It had a chrome shell with a broad vertical center bar forming two openings. Each was filled with a cross-hatched grille accented by five bright horizontal division bars. Two-piece rectangular parking lamps were set into the front panel below the headlamps and above the bumper. Pontiac lettering appeared on the left front panel. Catalina lettering and engine displacement numbers were placed behind front wheel openings. Twin rectangular taillights were used at each side in the rear. Hardtop coupes featured Colonnade type rooflines. All full-sized Pontiacs had the following as standard equipment: woodgrained dash trim; high/low ventilation; windshield radio antenna; front and rear energy-absorbing bumpers; ashtrays; glovebox lamp; inside hood release; nylon carpeting; safety belt warning system; windshield, roof drip, hood rear edge and rear window moldings (except Grand Prixs and Safaris); power steering; power brakes with front discs; Turbo-Hydramatic transmission; and V-8 engines. Catalinas also had a two-spoke steering wheel, cloth and Morrokide front bench seat, trunk mat and G78-15 blackwall tires. Catalina Safaris had all-Morrokide upholstery, storage compartments, Glide-Away tailgates, power tailgate windows, right-hand outside mirror, tailgate vertical rub stripes, rear quarter and tailgate window moldings and L78-15 tires. The nine-passenger model came with a split-back second seat and rear-facing third seat.

PONTIAC I.D. NUMBERS: VIN on top of dash at left, viewable through windshield. First symbol tells GM division: 2=Pontiac. Second symbol tells series: Y=Ventura; Z=Ventura Custom; S=Firebird; T=Espirit; U=Formula 400; V=Trans Am; D=LeMans; F=LeMans Sport; G=Luxury Lemans; H=Grand Am; K=Grand Prix; L=Catalina; N=Bonneville; P=Grand Ville. Third and fourth symbols indicate body style and appear as last two digits of Body/Style Number in charts below. Fifth symbol indicates engine (See chart at beginning of "Engines" section below). Sixth symbol indicates model year: 4=1974. Seventh symbol indicates assembly plant: A=Atlanta, Ga.; C=Southgate, Calif.; D=Doraville, Ga.; G=Framingham, Mass.; L=Van Nuys, Calif.; N=Norwood, Ohio; P=Pontiac, Mich.; W=Williow Run, Mich.; X=Kansas City, Kan.; Z=Fremont, Calif.; 1=Oshawa, Canada. Remaining symbols are sequential unit production number at factory, starting with 100001. Fisher Body plate on cowl tells style number (model year prefix 74, plus "2" for Pontiac and Body/Style Number from charts below), plus body number, trim code, paint code and other data. Six-cylinder engine code stamped on distributor mounting on right side of block. V-8 engine code on front of block below right cylinder head. Engine production codes for 1974 were: [250 cid/100 nhp six] CCR/ CCX/CCW. [350 cid/155 nhp V-8] WA/WB/YA/YB/YC/AA/ZA/ZB. [350 cid/170 nhp V-8] WN/ WP/YN/YP/YS/ZP. [400 cid/175 nhp V-8] YH/YJ/AH/ZH/ZJ. [400 cid/200 nhp V-8] WT/YT/AT/ ZT/YZ. [455 cid/215 nhp V-8] YY/YU/YX/AU/ZU/ZX/YW/ZW/YR. [455 cid/310 nhp Super-Duty V-8] W8/Y8.

CATALINA (SERIES 2BL)

Model Number	Body/Style Number	Body Type & Seating	Factory Price	Shipping Weight	Production Total
2BL	L69	4-dr Sed-6P	4190	4294	46,025
2BL	L39	4-dr HT-6P	4347	4352	11,769
2BL	L57	2-dr HT-6	4278	4279	40,657
2BL	L45	4-dr Sta Wag-9P	4834	5037	6,486
2BL	L35	4-dr Sta Wag-6P	4692	4973	5,662

BONNEVILLE — (V-8) — SERIES 2BN — Bonnevilles featured `eggcrate' style grille inserts and one-piece horizontal parking lamps. Bonneville lettering was seen on the left-hand front body panel and behind the front wheel openings, as well as on the rear deck. Taillights were similar to the Catalina type, but accented with a deck latch panel beauty strip. Standard equipment Included all Items found on Catalinas, plus a choice of cloth and Morrokide or all-Morrokide upholstery, custom cushion steering wheel, electric clock, rear door light switches (on four-doors), dash courtesy lamps, pedal trim plates, trunk mat with side panels, Deluxe wheelcovers, decor moldings at wheelwells, wide body sill moldings with rear extensions, luggage lamp, rubber bumper strips and H78-15 blackwall tires.

BONNEVILLE (SERIES 2BN)

Model Number	Body/Style Number	Body Type & Seating	Factory Price	Shipping Weight	Production Total
2BN	N69	4-dr Sed-6P	4510	4384	6,770
2BN	N39	4-dr HT-6P	4639	4444	6,151
2BN	N57	2-dr HT-6P	4572	4356	7,639

1974 Pontiac, Grand Ville four-door hardtop sedan, V-8

GRAND VILLE AND GRAND SAFARI — (V-8) — SERIES 2BP

Model Number	Body/Style Number	Body Type & Seating	Factory Price	Shipping Weight	Production Total
2BP	P49	4-dr HT-6P	4939	4515	21,714
2BP	P47	2-dr HT-6P	4871	4432	11,631
2BP	P67	2-dr Conv-6P	5113	4476	3,000
2BP	P45	4-dr Sta Wag-9P	5256	5112	5,255
2BP	P35	4-dr Sta Wag-6P	5109	5011	2,894

1974 Pontiac, Grand Prix two-door hardtop coupe, V-8

GRAND PRIX — (V-8) — SERIES 2GK — Grand Prix styling changes included a shorter grille that did not drop below the bumper line, thinner and more rectangular parking lamps, twin vertical taillights and a crease sculptured contour line behind the front wheel opening. Standard equipment was the same as in Bonnevilles, plus carpeted lower door panels, black custom cushion steering wheel, cigar lighter and courtesy lamps, lateral restraint front bucket seats or notch back front bench seat, aircraft style wraparound instrument panel with integrated console (except with bench seats), rear quarter opera window styling, windowsill and wide body sill moldings, floor shift (bucket seats only), dual exhausts and G78-15 tires. Approximately 92 percent of all Grand Prixs had bucket seats and the `SJ' option package, which collectors consider a separate model, was available again.

GRAND PRIX (SERIES 2GK)

Model Number	Body/Style Number	Body Type & Seating	Factory Price	Shipping Weight	Production Total
GRAND PRIX J					
2GK	K57	2-dr HT-6P	4936	4096	85,976
GRAND PRIX SJ					
2GK	K57	2-dr HT-5	5321	4300	13,841

LEMANS AND LEMANS SPORT — (6-CYL) — SERIES 2AD/2AF — LeMans models had new front bumpers with rubber-faced protective guards, more angular front fender corner sections, twin rectangular grilles accented by bright horizontal division bars and vertically curved taillights with new rear bumpers. Standard equipment in all A-body cars included woodgrained dash trim; deluxe two-spoke steering wheel; safety belt warning system; high/ low ventilation; nylon carpeting; inside hood release; concealed wipers; windshield radio antenna; new energy-absorbing bumpers; hubcaps; manual front disc brakes; windshield, roof drip, body sill, rear and rear quarter window moldings; and F78-14 blackwall tires. Base models had cloth-and-Morrokide front bench seats. The LeMans Sport coupe featured a notch back armrest front seat, woodgrained glovebox trim and louvered rear quarter window treatment.

1974 Pontiac, LeMans GT two-door hardtop, V-8

LEMANS (SERIES 2AD)

Model Number	Body/Style Number	Body Type & Seating	Factory Price	Shipping Weight	Production Total
2AD	D29	4-dr HT-6P	3236/3361	3628/3844	17,266
2AD	D37	2-dr HT-6P	3216/3341	3552/3768	37,061
2AD	D45	4-dr Sta Wag-9P	4186	4371	4,743
2AD	D35	4-dr Sta Wag-6P	4052	4333	3,004
LEMANS SPORT (SERIES 2AF)					
2AF	F37	2-dr HT-6P	3300/3425	3580/3796	37,955

NOTE 1: Data above slash for six/below; no slash for V-8.

LUXURY LEMANS — (V-8) — SERIES 2AG — Luxury LeMans models had special vertically-segmented grille inserts; wide body sill moldings with front and rear extensions; distinctive curved vertical taillamps accented with chrome moldings; a deck latch panel beauty strip; luxury scripts behind the front wheel openings; and fender skirts. Standard equipment included deluxe wheelcovers; custom cushion steering wheel; and V-8 power. The Luxury LeMans hardtop provided buyers with a choice of front bucket seats or a notch back type with armrest. This model also incorporated ashtray and glovebox lamps, cloth-and-Morrokide or all-Morrokide trims; door-pull straps; pedal trim plates; dual horns; decor moldings; and

special taillight styling. The Luxury LeMans Safari came with woodgrained dash trim; all-Morrokide seats; under-floor storage compartment; liftgate; textured steel cargo floor; tailgate vertical rub strips; power front disc brakes; and all other base LeMans station wagon features. The nine-passenger jobs had a rear-facing third seat, electric tailgate release and swing-out rear quarter ventipanes.

LUXURY LEMANS (SERIES 2AG)

Model Number	Body/Style Number	Body Type & Seating	Factory Price	Shipping Weight	Production Total
2AG	G29	4-dr HT-6P	3759	3904	4,513
2AG	G37	2-dr HT-6P	3703	3808	25,882
2AG	G45	4-dr Sta Wag-9P	4459	4401	1,178
2AG	G35	4-dr Sta Wag-6P	4326	4363	952

GRAND AM — (V-8) — SERIES 2AH — Standard equipment for all Grand Ams was based on the Luxury LeMans list, with the following variations: courtesy lamps; custom sport steering wheel; mahogany dash trim; electric clock; turn stalk headlight dimmer switch; integrated console with mahogany trim; floor-mounted gear shift lever; lateral-restraint bucket seats with adjustable lumbar support; custom finned wheelcovers; Endura bumper protective strips; power brakes with front discs; Rally Gages with trip odometer; power steering; Turbo-Hydra-matic transmission; and radial-tuned suspension with GR70-15 tires. Styling distinctions included a special vertically segmented polyurethane nose panel, exclusive taillight design and specific striping and badge ornamentation.

GRAND AM (SERIES 2AH)

Model Number	Body/Style Number	Body Type & Seating	Factory Price	Shipping Weight	Production Total
2AH	H29	4-dr HT-5P	4623	4073	3,122
2AH	H37	2-dr HT-5P	4534	3992	13,961

BASE FIREBIRD — (6-CYL) — SERIES — 2FS — New Firebird styling changes included a shovel-nosed Endura front end, a horizontal slotted taillamp treatment, lowered rear fender line and twin horizontal-rectangular grille inserts with vertical blades. All Firebird models had ashtray lamps, nylon carpeting, high/low ventilation, Endura styling and windshield radio antenna. The basic Firebird also featured a Deluxe two-spoke steering wheel, single-buckle seat and shoulder belt arrangement, narrow rocker panel moldings and E78-14 tires.

FIREBIRD (SERIES 2FS)

Model Number	Body/Style Number	Body Type & Seating	Factory Price	Shipping Weight	Production Total
2FS	S87	2-dr HT-4	3335/3460	3283/3504	26,372

NOTE 1: Data above slash for six/below slash for V-8.
NOTE 2: 7,063 base Firebirds had six-cylinder engines.

FIREBIRD ESPIRIT — (V-8) — SERIES 2FT — As usual, a model badge on the rear roof pillar was a trait of Espirit models. Standard extras in this line included custom cushion steering wheel, custom interior package, body-color door handle inserts, concealed wipers with articulated left arm, Deluxe wheelcovers, dual horns, dual outside mirrors (left-hand remote-controlled), roof drip and wheel opening moldings, wide body sill moldings, window sill and rear hood edge moldings, three-speed manual floor shift (with base engine only), safety belt warning system and E78-14 tires.

FIREBIRD ESPIRIT (SERIES 2FT)

Model Number	Body/Style Number	Body Type & Seating	Factory Price	Shipping Weight	Production Total
2FT	T87	2-dr HT-4	3687	35440	22,583

FORMULA FIREBIRD — (V-8) — SERIES 2FU — In addition to equipment standard in Espirits, Formula Firebirds featured hubcaps, dual-scoop fiberglass hoods, special heavy-duty suspension, black-textured grilles, dual exhausts and F70-14 tires. Available model options included Formula 350, Formula 400 and Formula 455.

FORMULA FIREBIRD (SERIES 2FU)

Model Number	Body/Style Number	Body Type & Seating	Factory Price	Shipping Weight	Production Total
2FU	U87	2-dr HT-4	3659	3548	14,519

1974 Pontiac, Trans Am two-door hardtop coupe, V-8

FIREBIRD TRANS AM — (V-8) — SERIES 2FV — Standard equipment on Trans Am included formula steering wheel, Rally Gages with clock and dash panel tachometer, swirl grain dash trim, full-width rear deck lid spoiler, power steering and front disc brakes, limited-slip differential, wheel opening air deflectors (flares), front fender air extractors, dual exhausts with chrome extensions, Rally II wheels with trim rings, special heavy-duty suspension, four-speed manual transmission (or M40 Turbo-Hydramatic), dual outside racing mirrors and F60-15 white-lettered tires.

FIREBIRD TRANS AM (SERIES 2FV)

Model Number	Body/Style Number	Body Type & Seating	Factory Price	Shipping Weight	Production Total
2FV	V87	2-dr HT-4P	4446	3655	10,255

1974 Pontiac, Ventura two-door sedan (with GTO option), V-8

VENTURA — (6-CYL) — SERIES 2XY — The Firebird style grille seen on 1973 Ventura Sprints was now used on all models in this line. There were minimal styling changes otherwise. Standard equipment included Deluxe two-spoke steering wheel, bench front seat with cloth and Morrokide trim, woodgrained door inserts, front and rear armrests, high/low ventilation, rubber floor covering, hubcaps, vent windowless styling and E78-14 tires. Cars with the Sprint option package (two-doors only) had black-textured grilles. The most interesting option was the GTO package, which was now available exclusively for Ventura coupes.

VENTURA (SERIES 2XY)

Model Number	Body/Style Number	Body Type & Seating	Factory Price	Shipping Weight	Production Total
2XY	Y69	4-dr Sed-5P	2921/3046	3169/3398	21,012
2XY	Y27	2-dr Cpe-5P	2892/3017	3184/3376	49,153
2XY	Y17	2-dr Hatch-5P	3018/3134	3257/3486	26,335

VENTURA WITH GTO OPTION

Model Number	Body/Style Number	Body Type & Seating	Factory Price	Shipping Weight	Production Total
2XY	Y27	2-dr Cpe-5P	3212	3400	(7,058)

NOTE 1: Data above slash for six/below slash for V-8.
NOTE 2: GTO option total (in parenthesis) included in Ventura coupe total.

VENTURA CUSTOM — (6-CYL) — SERIES 2XZ — Ventura Customs had all features found on base models plus a choice of cloth or all-Morrokide trim, custom cushion steering wheel, bright metal front seat side panels, glovebox lamp, nylon carpeting, pedal trim plates, right-hand door jamb switch, deluxe wheelcovers and drip, scalp and rocker panel moldings. Hatchback coupes also had load floor carpeting, fold-down seats, Space Saver spare tires, cargo area dome lights and trimmed sidewalls.

VENTURA CUSTOM (SERIES 2XZ)

Model Number	Body/Style Number	Body Type & Seating	Factory Price	Shipping Weight	Production Total
2XZ	Z69	4-dr Sed-5P	3080/3205	3208/3398	(Note 2)
2XZ	Z27	2-dr Cpe-5P	3051/3176	3184/3413	(Note 2)
2XZ	Z17	2-dr Hatch-5P	3176/3301	2362/3491	(Note 2)

VENTURA CUSTOM W/GTO OPTION

Model Number	Body/Style Number	Body Type & Seating	Factory Price	Shipping Weight	Production Total
2XZ	Z27	2-dr Cpe-5P	3371	3437	(Note 3)

NOTE 1: Data above slash for six/below slash for V-8.
NOTE 2: Ventura/Ventura Custom combined by body style; see Ventura chart.
NOTE 3: Ventura/Ventura Custom GTO production combined; see Ventura chart.

ENGINES

Code	Type	CID	Carb.	C. R.	H.P. at rpm.
D	6-Cyl	250	1-V	8.2:1	100 @ 3600
M	V-8	350	2-V	7.6:1	155 @ 4000
N	V-8	350	2-V	7.6:1	170 @ 4000 **
J	V-8	350	4-V	7.6:1	185 @ 4000
K	V-8	350	4-V	7.6:1	200 @ 4000 **
R	V-8	400	2-V	7.6:1	175 @ 3600
P	V-8	400	2-V	8.0:1	190 @ 4000
S	V-8	400	4-V	8.0:1	200 @ 4000
T	V-8	400	4-V	8.0:1	225 @ 4000 **
W	V-8	455	4-V	8.0:1	215 @ 3600
Y	V-8	455	4-V	8.0:1	250 @ 4000 **
X	V-8	455	4-V	8.4:1	290 @ 4000

NOTE: Dual exhausts are indicated by symbol (**)

(CATALINA) Base V-8 in Catalina was the code R engine. Code P/S/T/W/Y engines were optional in federally certified cars. Code S and code T engines were not available for cars sold in California.

(BONNEVILLE) Base V-8 in Bonnevilles was the code R engine. Code P/S/T/W/Y engines were optional in federally certified cars. Code S and T engines were not available for cars sold in California.

(GRAND VILLE/GRAND SAFARI) Base V-8 in Grand Villes and Grand Safaris was the code W engine. The code Y engine was optional only in passenger cars.

(GRAND PRIX) Base V-8 in Grand Prixs was the code T engine. The code Y power plant was optional and was also part of the 'SJ' option package.

(LEMANS/LEMANS SPORT) Base six-cylinder power plant for passenger cars in both series was the code D engine. Base V-8 for Safaris and passenger cars was the code M engine. Code J/R/T/Y engines were optional in federally certified cars. Code R/P/S/T/W engines were optional in federally certified Safaris. Code J and code S engines were not available in any cars sold in California. Code M and code T engines were not available in Safari station wagons sold in California.

(LUXURY LEMANS) Base V-8 in Luxury LeMans passenger cars was the code M engine. Code J/R/T/Y engines were optional in federally certified passenger cars. Base V-8 in Luxury LeMans Safaris (with federal certification) was the code M engine. Base V-8 in Luxury LeMans

Safaris sold in California was the code R engine. Additional Safari options included code P/S/T/W engines. The code J engine was not available in passenger cars sold in California. The code S and code T engines were not available in Safaris sold in California.

(GRAND AM) Base V-8 in Grand AMs was the code P engine. Code T and code Y engines were optional. The code X Super-Duty 455 cid V-8, which had been listed as optional in 1973, but never issued, was no longer listed in 1974.

(BASE FIREBIRD) The standard six-cylinder power plant in the basic Firebird was the code D engine. The base V-8 was the code M engine. There were no other options.

(FIREBIRD ESPIRIT) Base V-8 in Firebird Espirits was the code M engine. The code R engine was the only option in this line.

(FORMULA FIREBIRD) Base V-8 in Formula Firebirds was the code M engine. Code R/T/Y/X engines were optional. All Firebirds built for sale in California were required to have automatic transmission.

(FIREBIRD TRANS AM) Base V-8 in Trans Ams was the code T engine. Code Y and code X engines were optional. The latter power plant (SD-455) was officially called the LS2 option and was installed in 731 cars with Turbo-Hydramatic and 212 cars with synchromesh attachment.

(VENTURA) The base six-cylinder power plant for Venturas was the code D engine. The base V-8 for Venturas was the code M engine. The code J engine was included in the Ventura GTO option package and was a separate option in federally certified cars, but not in cars built for California sale.

(VENTURA CUSTOM) The base six-cylinder power plant for Venturas was the code D engine. The base V-8 for Venturas was the code M engine. The code J engine was included in the Ventura GTO option package and was a separate option in federally certified cars, but not in cars built for California sale.

CHASSIS FEATURES: Wheelbase: (B-body passenger cars) 124 inches; (B-body Safaris) 127 inches; (G-Body) 116 inches; (A-body two-doors) 112 inches; (A-body four-doors) 116 inches; (F-Body) 108 inches; (X-Body) 111 inches. Overall length: (B-body passenger cars) 226 inches; (B-body Safaris) 231.3 inches; (G-Body) 217.5 inches; (Grand Am two-door) 210.9 inches; (Grand Am four-door) 214.9 inches; (A-body two-door) 208.8 inches; (A-body Safaris) 216 inches; (A-body four-doors) 212.8 inches; (F-Body) 196 inches; (X-Body) 199.4 inches. (Note: GM body nomenclature such as A-body now corresponds to first letter in Body/Style Number).

OPTIONS: Pontiac and Grand Am air conditioning ($488-522). Ventura air conditioning ($396). Firebird air conditioning ($412). Clock and Rally Gage cluster ($29-49). Clock tachometer and Rally Gage cluster ($51-100); with trip odometer on GP ($51-90). Firebird rear seat console ($26). Ventura and Firebird front seat console ($58). Cruise control ($69-70). Rear window defogger ($33-38). LeMans air scoop hood ($87). LeMans D37 and Trans Am hood decals ($55). Formula Firebird RAR AIR hood ($56). Rear quarter windowless louver styling option on LeMans Sport ($35). Safari remote tailgate release ($14). Grand Prix reclining bucket seats ($112). Ventura bucket seats ($132). Grand Prix notch back seat ($50 credit since bucket seats were standard). Grand Am and Grand Prix accent stripes ($31). LeMans and Grand Prix electric sunroof ($325); manual sun roof ($275). Firebird radial tuned suspension with FR78-14 whitewall tires ($107-145); same on Formula ($24-36). Ventura radial tuned suspension ($113-170); same with Sprint package ($91). Custom finned wheel-covers on LeMans and Firebird ($24-50). Honeycomb wheels on Grand Prix, Grand Am and Firebird ($54-123). Rally II rims ($37-87). Transmission options included three-speed manual with column shift standard in Ventura and LeMans. Three-speed manual with floor shift in Venturas was $26 extra. Heavy-duty three-speed manual with floor shift was $82 extra in certain LeMans hardtops. Four-speed manual was $197 extra in LeMans; $207 in Venturas and Firebirds and a $45 delete option in Grand Ams. M38 Turbo-Hydramatic was $221 extra in base Firebirds and certain LeMans; $206 extra in Venturas and $221 extra in Espirits, Formulas and Luxury LeMans. M40 Turbo-Hydramatic was standard in Grand Am; a no-charge option in Trans Ams; $21 extra in LeMans Safaris and $242 extra in LeMans, Espirit and Formulas. Full-sized Pontiacs and Grand Prixs had standard Turbo-Hydramatic.

OPTION PACKAGES: A code 308 custom trim package was available on Style Numbers FU87 and FV87 and included pedal trim, custom appointments, door handle decor inserts, Deluxe front bucket and custom rear seats and fitted trunk mat. A code 342 LeMans GT option package was available at $202-246 and included Rally II wheels less trim rings, G70 x 14 tires, dual exhausts with chrome extensions, specific accent stripes, dual sport mirrors (left-hand remote control), wheel opening moldings and three-speed manual transmission with floor shift. The code 342 Grand Prix 'SJ' option sold for $354-385 and included the 455 cid four-barrel V-8, body color mirrors (left-hand remote control), custom wheelcovers, accent stripes, Delco 'X' battery, Rally Gage cluster with trip odometer, GR70 x 15 steel-belted tires, special shock absorbers and heavy-duty stabilizer bars. The code 341 Ventura Sprint option sold for $88-168 and included specific front end styling, body-color sport mirrors, custom cushion steering wheel, custom carpets, cargo area carpeting, vinyl accent stripes, Rally 11 wheels less trim rings and a deck lid Sprint decal. The Ventura GTO option package sold for $195 and included a 350 cid four-barrel V-8, front and rear stabilizer bars, radial-tuned suspension, Pliacell shock absorbers, power steering, front and rear drum brakes, E78-14 tires, heavy-duty three-speed manual gearbox, dual exhausts with splitter extensions, 3.08:1 ratio axle; Rally II rims less trim rings, special grille driving lights, rear-facing 'shaker' air scoop and computer selected high-rate rear springs. This was the eleventh and last GTO.

HISTORICAL FOOTNOTES: The 1974 Pontiacs were introduced on Sept. 20, 1973. Model year production of 580, 748 cars was registered and included LeMans models made in Canada. Calendar year production was 502,083 units. A total of 212 Firebirds were built with LS2 SD-455 engines. This was the last year for a GTO (so far).

1975 PONTIAC

CATALINA — (V-8) — SERIES 2BL — Full-sized Pontiacs were redesigned for 1975, with most models featuring new roofline treatments. Catalinas had a distinctive radiator grille with a wide vertical center divider and chrome accent moldings forming three stacked rectangles on either side. Triple-stacked taillights were also used, which were shorter than those seen on other lines. The two-door notch back hardtop had an exclusive roofline featuring wide rear quarter windows, thin C-pillars and a large backlight. Standard equipment was about the same as on 1974 Catalinas, except that a new Efficiency System and radial-tuned suspension became regular features.

PONTIAC I.D. NUMBERS: VIN on top of dash at left, viewable through windshield. First symbol tells GM division: 2=Pontiac. Second symbol tells series: X=Astre; B=Ventura SJ; S=Firebird; T=Espirit; U=Formula 400; V=Trans Am; D=LeMans; F=LeMans Sport; G=Luxury Lemans; H=Grand Am; K=Grand Prix; L=Catalina; P=Bonneville Grand Safari; R=Grand Ville Brougham. Third and fourth symbols indicate body style and appear as last two digits of Body/Style Number in charts below. Fifth symbol indicates engine (See chart at beginning of "Engines" section below.) Sixth symbol indicates model year: 5=1975. Seventh symbol indicates assembly plant: A=Atlanta, Ga.; C=Southgate, Calif.; G=Framingham, Mass.; L=Van Nuys, Calif.; N=Norwood, Ohio; P=Pontiac, Mich.; T=Tarrytown, N.Y.; U=Lordstown, Ohio; W=Willow Run, Mich.; X=Kansas City, Kan.; 1=Oshawa, Canada. Remaining symbols are sequential unit production number at factory, starting with 100001. Fisher Body plate on cowl tells style number: (model year prefix 75, plus division code and Body/Style Number code (i.e. 2L69 for Catalina four-door sedan), body number, trim code, paint code and other data. Six-cylinder engine code stamped on distributor mounting on right side of block. V-8 engine code on front of block below right cylinder head. Engine production codes for 1975 were: [140 cid/78 nhp four-cylinder] BB/BC. [140 cid/87 hp four-cylinder] AM/AS/AR/AT/CAM/CAW/CBB/CBD/CAR/CAU. [140 cid/80 nhp four-cylinder] CAS/CAT. [250 cid/105 nhp six-cylinder] JU/JT/JL. [260 cid/110 nhp V-8] QA/QD/QE/QJ/TE/TJ. [350 cid/145 hp V-8] RI/RS. [350 cid/155 hp V-8] YA/YB. [350 cid/165 nhp V-8] RW/RX. [350 cid/175 nhp V-8] WN/YN/ZP/RN/RO. [400 cid/170 nhp V-8] YH. [400 cid/185 nhp V-8] YT/YM/YS/WT/ZT. [455 cid/200 nhp V-8] YW/YU/ZW/ZU/WX.

CATALINA (SERIES 2BL)

Model Number	Body/Style Number	Body Type & Seating	Factory Price	Shipping Weight	Production Total
2BL	L69	4-dr Sed-6P	4612	4347	40,398
2BL	L57	2-dr HT-6P	4700	4334	40,657
2BL	L45	4-dr Sta Wag-9P	5295	5000	4,992
2BL	L35	4-dr Sta Wag-6P	5149	4933	3,964

1975 Pontiac, Grand Safari four-door station wagon, V-8

BONNEVILLE — (V-8) — SERIES 2BP — The N Series was dropped and Bonnevilles moved to the P Series (formerly Grand Ville) with Grand Safaris included. A radiator grille with criss-crossed dividers and 'eggcrate' inserts was seen. Headlamps were mounted in rectangular housings with square parking lamps on the outside wrapping around the corners of the fenders. New rear quarter window treatments were employed. Taillights were wider than the Catalina type and wrapped around the corners of the rear fenders. Standard equipment was about the same as on 1975 Bonnevilles with the addition of the High-Efficiency ignition system and radial-tuned suspension.

BONNEVILLE (SERIES 2BP)

Model Number	Body/Style Number	Body Type & Seating	Factory Price	Shipping Weight	Production Total
2BP	P49	4-dr HT-6P	5153	4503	12,641
2BP	P47	2-dr HT-6P	5085	4370	7,854
2BP	P45	4-dr Sta Wag-9P	5580	5090	4,752
2BP	P35	4-dr Sta Wag-6P	5433	5035	2,568

GRAND VILLE BROUGHAM — (V-8) — SERIES 2BR — Grand Ville Broughams were essentially Bonnevilles with a slightly higher level of interior and exterior appointments. Identifying features included wide body sill accent moldings with rear extensions, fender skirts and Grand Ville Brougham signature scripts behind the front wheelhousings.

GRAND VILLE BROUGHAM (SERIES 2BR)

Model Number	Body/Style Number	Body Type & Seating	Factory Price	Shipping Weight	Production Total
2BR	R49	4-dr HT-6P	5896	4558	15,686
2BR	R47	2-dr HT-6)	5729	4404	7,447
2BR	R67	2-dr Conv-6P	5858	5035	4,519

1975 Pontiac, Grand Prix two-door hardtop coupe, V-8

GRAND PRIX — (V-8) — SERIES 2GK — Styling refinements were seen in the grille, taillight design and decorative trim of 1975 Grand Prixs. Both the grille and taillights were segmented to produce a more strongly vertical look. The sports-oriented 'SJ' package returned and a new luxury-image 'U' option group was introduced. Modern collectors consider these to be separate models. So did Pontiac, and individual production totals are available for all three types of GPs. Standard equipment was a near match for that featured the year before, except for ignition and suspension systems, which received the same improvements seen on full-size lines. The style number K57 coupe was available with the 'U' package including distinctive two-tone paint finish, Deluxe wheelcovers, outside mirrors, custom interior trim and Cordova top. All Grand Prixs now had speedometers calibrated in kilometers and headlight dimmer switches built into the turn signal stalk.

GRAND PRIX (SERIES 2GK)

Model Number	Body/Style Number	Body Type & Seating	Factory Price	Shipping Weight	Production Total
GRAND PRIX J					
2GK	K57	2-dr HT-5P	5296	4032	64,581
GRAND PRIX SJ					
2GK	K57	2-dr HT-5P	5573	N/A	7,146
GRAND PRIX LJ					
2GK	K57	2-dr HT-5P	5995	N/A	14,855

LEMANS/LEMANS SPORT — (6-CYL) — SERIES 2AD/2AF — The 1975 base LeMans and LeMans Sport series were basically unchanged from the previous year except for a new 'eggcrate' grille insert and some minor trim variations. An available styling option on two-door hardtop coupes was a louvered rear quarter window treatment, which was also standard on Series 2AF LeMans Sport sport coupes.

LEMANS (SERIES 2AD)

Model Number	Body/Style Number	Body Type & Seating	Factory Price	Shipping Weight	Production Total
2AD	D29	4-dr HT-6P	3612/3742	3729/3948	15,065
2AD	D37	2-dr HT-6P	3590/3720	3656/3875	20,636
2AD	D45	4-dr Sta Wag-9P	4688	4500	2,393
2AD	D35	4-dr Sta Wag-6P	4555	4401	3,898

LEMANS SPORT (SERIES 2AF)

Model Number	Body/Style Number	Body Type & Seating	Factory Price	Shipping Weight	Production Total
2AF	F37	2-dr HT-5P	3708/3838	3688/3907	23,817

NOTE 1: Data above slash for six/below slash or no slash for V-8.

GRAND AM — (V-8) — SERIES 2AH — The Grand Am continued to feature a unique vertically segmented polyurethane nose and louvered rear quarter windows on coupes. Little was changed except for some pinstriping and grille insert details. The standard equipment list was about the same as in 1974 with the addition of the High-Efficiency ignition system. At the end of the 1975 run this nameplate was temporarily dropped.

1975 Pontiac, Grand Am Colonnade four-door hardtop, V-8

GRAND AM (SERIES 2AHO

Model Number	Body/Style Number	Body Type & Seating	Factory Price	Shipping Weight	Production Total
2AH	H29	4-dr HT-5P	4976	4055	1,893
2AH	H37	2-dr HT-5P	4887	4008	8,786

GRAND LEMANS — (V-8) — SERIES 2AG — The Luxury LeMans became the Grand LeMans this year. There was a distinctive grille design with six groupings of vertical blades arranged three on each side of the center divider. Stand-up hood ornaments appeared and fender skirts were used as standard equipment on all models, except Grand LeMans Safaris.

GRAND LEMANS (SERIES 2AG)

Model Number	Body/Style Number	Body Type & Seating	Factory Price	Shipping Weight	Production Total
2AG	G29	4-dr HT-6P	4157/4287	3786/3905	4,906
2AG	G37	2-dr HT-6P	4101/4231	3723/3942	19,310
2AG	G45	4-dr Sta Wag-9P	4882	4500	1,501
2AG	G35	4-dr Sta Wag-6P	4749	4462	1,393

NOTE 1: Data above slash for six/below slash or no slash for V-8.

1975 Pontiac, Formula Firebird two-door hardtop coupe, V-8

FIREBIRDS — (6-CYL) — SERIES 2FS (BASE)/2FT/(ESPIRIT)/2FU (FORMULA)/2FV (TRANS AM) — Firebirds continued to look much the same as in 1974, except for a new roofline with a wraparound backlight. High-Efficiency ignition and radial-tuned suspension systems were added to the equipment list. As usual, base models had conventional wipers and minimal trim. Espirits had concealed wipers, decor moldings, door handle inserts and roof pillar signature scripts. Formulas featured heavy-duty chassis components and a distinctive

twin scoop hood. The Trans Am had flares, spoilers, extractors, shaker hood scoop and Firebird decals. There were some changes in a technical sense. The base power plant in Espirit was now the Chevy-built six. At the beginning of the year, the biggest engine for Trans Am was the 400 cid job. At midyear, the code Y engine (455 cid) was reinstated, but only with single exhausts and a catalytic convertor. Due to the decrease in brute horsepower, the M38 Turbo-Hydramatic was the only automatic transmission used. In addition, all Firebirds certified for sale in California were required to use this transmission.

FIREBIRDS (MODEL CODE INDICATES SERIES)

Model Number	Body/Style Number	Body Type & Seating	Factory Price	Shipping Weight	Production Total
FIREBIRD					
2FS	S87	2-dr HT-4P	3713/3843	3386/3610	22,293
ESPIRIT					
2FT	T87	2-dr HT-4P	3958/4088	3431/3655	20,826
FORMULA					
2FU	U87	2-dr HT-4P	4349	3631	13,670
TRANS AM					
2FV	V87	2-dr HT-4P	4740	3716	27,274

NOTE 1: Data above slash for six/below slash or no slash for V-8.
NOTE 2: 8,314 Firebirds were six-cylinders.
NOTE 3: 26,417 Trans Am had the 400 cid four-barrel (L78) engine.
NOTE 4: 20,277 L78 Trans Ams had Turbo-automatic and 6,140 had synchromesh.
NOTE 5: 857 Trans Am were built with the 455 cid four-barrel (L75) engine.
NOTE 6: All L75 Trans Ams had synchromesh.

1975 Pontiac, Ventura two-door hatchback coupe, V-8

VENTURA — (6-CYL) — SERIES 2XE (VENTURA S)/SERIES 2XY (VENTURA)/SERIES 2XZ (VENTURA CUSTOM)/SERIES 2XB (VENTURA SJ) — Venturas were completely restyled. The new 1975 frontal treatment featured distinctive grille ports with integral parking lights and an energy-absorbing front bumper. Rooflines were made somewhat slimmer with lower beltlines and more glass area than before. The Ventura was the basic model at the beginning of the year, with features about the same as 1974 base models. The GM Efficiency System was made standard equipment, but on Venturas did not include radial tires. The next-step-up line was the Custom series with such things as custom interior trim, body decor moldings and custom cushion steering wheel. Equipment variations over base models were again about the same as in 1974. A Ventura 'SJ' series was new. Features included custom finned wheelcovers, custom steering wheel, Grand Prix style instrument cluster, extra acoustical insulation, cigar lighter, rocker panel moldings and decor trim for wheel openings, rear end, roof and side windows. Interior trims were similar to the Grand AM type and Ventura 'SJ' lettering appeared behind the front wheelhousings. In the middle of the model run a Ventura with less equipment than the base model was introduced as the Ventura 'S.'

VENTURA S (SERIES 2XE)

Model Number	Body/Style Number	Body Type & Seating	Factory Price	Shipping Weight	Production Total
2XE	E27	2-dr Cpe-5P	3162/3292	3276/3443	(Note 2)
VENTURA (SERIES 2XY)					
2XY	Y69	4-dr Sed-5P	3304/3434	3335/3502	20,619
2XY	Y27	2-dr Coupe-5P	3293/3423	3299/3466	28,473
2XY	Y17	2-dr Hatch-5P	3432/3562	3383/3550	8,841
VENTURA CUSTOM (SERIES 2XZ)					
2XZ	Z69	4-dr Sed-5P	3464/3594	3378/3545	(Note 3)
2XZ	Z27	2-dr Cpe-5P	3449/3579	3338/3505	(Note 3)
2XZ	Z17	2-dr Hatch-5P	3593/3565	3398/3565	(Note 3)
VENTURA SJ (SERIES 2XB)					
2XB	B69	4-dr Sed-5P	3846/3976	3370/3537	1,449
2XB	B27	2-dr Cpe-5P	3829/3959	3340/3507	2,571
2XB	B17	2-dr Hatch-5P	3961/4091	3400/3567	1,622

NOTE 1: Data above slash for six/below slash for V-8.
NOTE 2: Ventura `S' production included with base Ventura totals.
NOTE 3: Ventura Custom production included with base Ventura/Ventura S totals.
NOTE 4: Approximately 63 percent of all Venturas were built with V-8s.

ASTRE — (4-CYL) — SERIES 2HC (ASTRE 'S')/SERIES 2HV (BASE ASTRE)/SERIES 2HX (ASTRE 'SJ') — Pontiac's entry in the 1975 sub-compact wars was the Astre. It was initially offered in hatchback coupe and Safari body styles, both of which came with base or 'SJ' trim. The Astre 'S' economy series was introduced at midyear and included the two original body styles, plus an exclusive notch back coupe. Standard equipment included all GM safety, anti-theft, convenience and emissions control features, three-speed manual floor shift transmission, manual steering, manual brakes with front discs, heater and defroster, front bucket seats, carpeting and A78-13 bias ply tires. The 'SJ' models came standard with special upholstery, custom carpets, custom steering wheel, woodgrain dash inserts, Rally Gage cluster with tachometer and clock, Rally III wheels and four-speed manual transmission. Also available was an Astre 'GT' option package which added the two-jet induction system, front and rear stabilizer bars, Rally wheels, body-color sport mirrors and radial-tuned suspension. A limited number of Astre-based panel delivery trucks were built in the U.S. for the Canadian market.

ASTRE S (SERIES 2HC)

Model Number	Body/Style Number	Body Type & Seating	Factory Price	Shipping Weight	Production Total
2HC	C11	2-dr Cpe-4P	2841	2416	8,339
2HC	C77	2-dr Hatch-4P	2954	2487	40,809
2HC	C15	2-dr Sta Wag-4P	3071	2539	15,322

BASE ASTRE (SERIES 2HV)

2HV	V77	2-dr Hatch-4P	3079	2499	(Note 2)
2HV	V15	2-dr Sta Wag-4P	3175	2545	(Note 2)
2HV	N/A	2-dr Panel-2P	N/A	N/A	131

ASTRE 'SJ' (SERIES 2HX)

2HX	X77	2-dr Hatch-4P	3610	2558	(Note 3)
2HX	X15	2-dr Sta Wag-4P	3686	2602	(Note 3)

NOTE 1: Astre output was broken out by body styles, but not by series.
NOTE 2: Base Astre production included with totals for same Astre 'S' model.
NOTE 3: Astre 'SJ' output included with totals for same Astre 'S' model.

ENGINES

Code	Type	CID	Carb.	Comp. Ratio	Net H.P. at rpm.
A	4-cyl	140	1-V	8.0:1	78 @ 4200(C)
B	4-cyl	140	2-V	8.0:1	87 @ 4400(C)
D	6-cyl	250	1-V	8.25:1	105 @ 3800(C)
E	V-8	350	2-V	8.0:1	145 @ 3200(B)
H	V-8	350	4-V	8.0:1	165 @ 3800(B)
F	V-8	260	2-V	8.0:1	110 @ 3400(0)
M	V-8	350	2-V	7.6:1	155 @ 4000
J	V-8	350	4-V	7.6:1	175 @ 4400
R	V-8	400	2-V	7.6:1	170 @ 4000
S	V-8	400	4-V	7.6:1	185 @ 3600
Y	V-8	455	4-V	7.6:1	200 @ 3500

Letters after the horsepower rating for engines in the chart above indicate manufacture by Chevrolet (C); Buick (B) or Oldsmobile (0) divisions. Catalytic convertors were required on all engines and dual exhausts were not available.

(CATALINA) Base V-8 for federally certified Catalinas was the code R engine. Base V-8 for 'California' Catalinas and federally certified Catalina Safaris was the code S engine. Base V-8 in 'California' Safaris was the code Y engine, which was also optional in federally certified passenger cars.

(BONNEVILLE) Bonneville engine offerings were the same used in Catalinas.

GRAND VILLE BROUGHAM ENGINES

Base V-8 for Grand Ville Broughams was the code S engine. The code Y engine was optional. Both V-8s were certified for federal and California sale.

(GRAND PRIX) Base V-8 in Grand Prixs was the code S engine. The code R engine was optional in federally certified cars only and the code Y engine was optional in all and was also part of the 'SJ' package.

(LEMANS/LEMANS SPORT/GRAND LEMANS) Base six-cylinder power plant for passenger cars in both series was the code D engine. The code M engine was the base V-8 for federally certified passenger cars. The code J engine was the base V-8 for 'California' cars and the code S engine was optional in all passenger cars. The code R engine was base power plant for federally certified Safaris. The code S engine was base V-8 for 'California' Safaris and optional in others.

(GRAND AM) Base V-8 in federally certified Grand AMs was the code R engine. The code S engine was base V-8 in cars built for California sale. The code Y engine was optional in all Grand AMs.

(FIREBIRD) Base Firebirds and Espirits had the same engine offerings. For these models the code D six-cylinder power plant was standard equipment. The code M engine was the base V-8 for non-California sale. The code J engine was the base V-8 for 'California' cars and optional in all others. This was also the base engine in Formulas. The code S engine was optional in Formulas and standard in Trans AMs. The code Y engine was released as a midyear option for Trans AMs.

(VENTURA) Base six-cylinder power plant for all Venturas was the code D engine. Base V-8 for all Venturas was the code F engine. The code H and J engines were optional in all Ventura series.

(ASTRE) Standard four-cylinder engine on coupes was the code A power plant. The code B engine was standard in 'SJ' and optional in other series.

CHASSIS FEATURES: Wheelbase: (B-body Safari) 127 inches; (B-body passenger car) 123.4 inches; (Grand Prix) 116 inches; (A-body two-door) 112 inches; (A-body four-door) 116 inches; (Ventura) 111.1 inches; (Firebird) 108.1 inches; (Astre) 97 inches. Overall length: (B-body Safari) 231.3 inches; (B-body passenger car) 226 inches; (Grand Prix) 212.7 inches; (Grand AM four-door) 215 inches; (Grand AM two-door) 211 inches; (A-body Safaris) 215.4 inches; (LeMans four-door) 212 inches; (LeMans two-door) 208 inches; (Firebird) 196 inches; (Ventura) 199.6 inches; (Astre) 175.4 inches.

OPTIONS: Astre vinyl roof ($79). Astre air conditioning ($398). Astre Safari luggage rack ($50). Astre AM/FM stereo ($213). Code B engine ($50). Ventura vinyl top ($87). Ventura tape deck ($215). Ventura, LeMans and Firebird AM/FM stereo ($233). LeMans and Firebird vinyl top ($99). LeMans Safari luggage rack ($68). LeMans and Grand Prix power seats 17). LeMans and Pontiac AM/FM stereo with tape ($363). Firebird tape deck ($130). Pontiac 6-way power seat ($117). Pontiac 60/40 seats ($81). Pontiac Safari luggage rack ($89). Grand Prix vinyl top ($119). Grand Prix power windows ($91). Grand Prix sun roof ($350). Grand Prix custom trim ($120). Ventura and LeMans power brakes ($47); with front discs ($70).

HISTORICAL FOOTNOTES: The 1974 Pontiacs appeared in showrooms on Sept. 27, 1974. Calendar year output was 523,469 cars. A new sales promotion tool was a program of price rebates on compact models. Road testers found the 1975 Trans Am with the 185 nhp V-8 capable of 0-to60 in 9.8 seconds and the quarter-mile in 16.8 seconds.

STUDEBAKER

1946-1966

By VJ Day in 1945, the Studebaker company would look back over 93-1/2 years of producing road vehicles. Because of the successful Champion, which was introduced in 1939, and cost-plus war contracts, the Studebaker Corp. emerged from World War II in the best financial state it had been in since 1929. The company, proud of its heritage, looked forward to the postwar years with great anticipation.

By Fred K. Fox

Anticipation and hope had always been the hallmark of the Studebaker organization. Two brothers, Henry and Clement Studebaker, set the company in motion in February, 1852, when they opened a small blacksmith shop in South Bend, Ind. At first they only produced a few horse drawn farm wagons, but with hard work and capital, and help from a third brother John M. (who made a bundle building wheelbarrows for the goldminers of California) they propelled the company to international prominence. Not long after younger brothers Peter and Jacob joined the family organization, the Studebaker Brothers Manufacturing Co. proclaimed that it was the largest producer of horse drawn vehicles in the world.

Studebaker produced its first salable automobile, an electric, in 1902. It entered the gasoline automobile business in 1904. In late 1910, Studebaker merged with EMF Corp. to form Studebaker Corp. In 1915, the first non-family member,

Albert R. Erskine, became president of the corporation. During this period, Studebaker was, except for Ford, among the largest producers of automobiles in the country. Sales increases continued at a steady clip until the stock market crash in 1929.

Erskine felt that the Depression would be short lived, so he continued to distribute large dividends. Erskine's misjudgement led Studebaker into receivership in 1933. Two resourceful Studebaker executives, Paul G. Hoffman and Harold S. Vance, pulled things together and saved the company. Hoffman and Vance guided the corporation through the depression and introduced the successful Champion model. They were still directing the company in 1945, when automobile production resumed.

Hoffman was president. Vance acted as chairman of the board. Both men were responsible for Studebaker becoming the first established American automobile company to introduce a new postwar styling. A striking new car and a healthy seller's market helped Studebaker establish new sales and profit records during the late '40s.

Although Studebaker's image seemed rosy, it was during this period that the seeds of the company's eventual undoing were taking root. A pampered work force and many outdated buildings resulted in poor productivity and high overhead. When the seller's market switched to a buyer's market, in the early 1950s, these problems started to eat away at the profits. If the company had fed more profits back into plant improve-

ments and taken a hard labor strike, things would have been much better. By 1953, the automobile division was operating in the red. Hoffman, who had left in 1948 to take a government position, returned in 1953. Neither he nor Vance could stop the flow of red ink.

Low-slung new styling in 1953, a takeover by Packard in 1954, and help from Curtiss-Wright in 1956, just prolonged what most insiders felt was a hopeless cause. The formation of the Studebaker-Packard Corp. brought in James Nance as chief executive officer. Two years later, under the guidance of Curtiss-Wright, Harold Churchill was selected as Studebaker-Packard's new president. This was a wise choice. Churchill, an engineer, was a loyal Studebaker man who had been with the corporation since 1926. He was determined to see that the company survived.

In late 1958, Churchill introduced the Lark. This compact car proved to be a big success during its first year. Churchill wanted to use 1959 profits to keep Studebaker in the forefront of small car development. However, the board of directors preferred using most of the profits for diversification. This difference of opinion resulted in the early 1961 replacement of Churchill with Sherwood Egbert.

Egbert, working within the constrictions of the board, also hoped to save the automotive division. His efforts fostered the creation of the Gran Turismo Hawk and the Avanti. Egbert's achievements, although commendable, did not help

Studebaker's position. It was again on the negative side of the profit scale. The Packard name was dropped in 1962.

In late 1963, Egbert stepped down because of failing health. Studebaker's directors voted to close most of the South Bend, Ind. facility. Production was then centralized at the Hamilton plant, in Ontario, Canada. President of the Hamilton division was Gordon Grundy. He tried his best to operate the Canadian facility in the black. He did manage to make small profits, but not enough to satisfy the board of directors. Because of the board's dissatisfaction, the Canadian plant was closed in March 1966.

By early 1966, the corporation's other diversified holdings, including STP, represented a majority of Studebaker's sales. These other companies kept Studebaker going. In mid-1967, the Studebaker Corp. purchased the Wagner Electric Corp. and in November 1967 Studebaker combined with the Worthington Corp. to form Studebaker-Worthington. In the fall of 1979, the Studebaker-Worthington Corp. was absorbed by the smaller McGraw-Edison Co. of Illinois. Cooper Industries took over McGraw-Edison in 1985.

Nathan Altman and Leo Newman, two South Bend businessmen, revived the Avanti after Studebaker left town. In 1965, they created the Avanti Motor Corp. Avanti has been sold several times since, but is still producing today. (Note: The Avanti II is covered, separately, in the second main section of The Standard Catalog of American Cars 1946-1975).

1946 Studebaker, Skyway Champion four-door sedan, 6-cyl

1953 Studebaker, Commander Regal Starliner two-door hardtop, V-8

1948 Studebaker, Commander Regal two-door convertible, 6-cyl

1955 Studebaker, Commander Deluxe two-door coupe, V-8

1946 STUDEBAKER

SKYWAY CHAMPION — MODEL 5G — The Champion, which had been Studebaker's lowest priced model from 1939 to 1942, was the only Studebaker series produced for the 1946 model year. Production only lasted from December 1945 to March 1946. It was used as a filler between the end of World War II and the introduction of Studebaker's dramatic new 1947 models. Skyway trim, which was limited to Commanders and Presidents in 1942, was made standard on 1946 Champions. The main Skyway Champion styling features were clean sides combined with wide horizontally grooved moldings on the rocker panels and the lower edges of the front and rear fenders. These moldings were not used on 1942 Champions. Two-tone options were listed in early literature, but current knowledge indicates that only a few prototypes were painted two-tone. A model identification script was located in the center of the instrument panel.

STUDEBAKER I.D. NUMBERS: Serial number on left front door lock pillar post. Motor number on top left side of front corner of cylinder block. The serial numbers for the 1946 Skyway Champion were G-193001 to G-212279. The motor numbers were 216501 to 235776. All were produced in the South Bend, Ind. plant.

SKYWAY CHAMPION SERIES

Model Number	Body/Style Number	Body Type & Seating	Factory Price	Shipping Weight	Production Total
5G	W7	4-dr Sed-6P	1097	2566	10,525
5G	F7	2-dr Sed-5P	1046	2541	5,000
5G	Q10	2-dr Cpe-5P	1044	2491	1,285
5G	Q8	2-dr Cpe-3P	1002	2456	2,465

ENGINE: Six-cylinder. L-head. Cast iron block. Displacement: 169.6 cid. Bore and stroke: 3 x 4 inches. Compression ratio: 6.5:1. Brake hp: 80 at 4000 rpm. Four main bearings. Solid valve lifters. Carburetor: Carter model WE-532S one-barrel.

CHASSIS FEATURES: Wheelbase: 110 inches. Overall length: 197.8 inches. Front tread: 56.25 inches. Rear tread: 57 inches. Tires: 5.50 x 16 tube type.

OPTIONS: Hill Holder. Directional signals. Fender lamps. Skyway 8-tube push-button radio or Liberator 6-tube manual tuning radio. Internally controlled cowl radio antenna. Front and rear Winguards (bumper extensions). Fog lights. Spotlight. Package compartment light. Underhood light. Climatizer heater/defroster. Two-tone Mattex seat covers. Cigar lighters. Electric clock. Locking gas tank cap. Plastic whitewall wheel discs. Stainless steel wheel trim rings. Chrome license plate frames. Exhaust extensions. Front gravel deflectors. Rear fender pebble deflectors. Automatic windshield cleaner. Glare-proof interior rearview mirror. Exterior rearview mirror. Visor vanity mirror. Transparent plastic grille cover (for cold weather). Tire chains. Wet oil bath air cleaner. Fram oil filter. A three-speed manual gearbox with column-mounted gearshift was standard. Overdrive was available at $54.67 extra. A 7.0:1 compression ratio was optional.

HISTORICAL FOOTNOTES: Body style W7 was called a Cruising Sedan. Body style F7 was called a Club Sedan. Body style Q10 was called a Double Dater. Body style Q8 was a business coupe.

1947 STUDEBAKER

1947 Studebaker, Champion two-door convertible, 6-cyl (AA)

CHAMPION — MODEL 6G — The Deluxe Champion was Studebaker's low price model. The Regal Deluxe trim version featured stainless steel windshield trim and stainless steel rocker panel moldings. The Deluxe version did not feature these items. The Champion's stainless steel grille was suspended in the radiator opening. The horizontal taillights were divided into two sections. A model identification script was located in the center of the instrument panel. All-new styling by Raymond Loewy and Virgil Exner featured front fenders flush with body. The 1947 Champion was introduced in May 1946.

STUDEBAKER I.D. NUMBERS: Serial number on left front door lock pillar post. Motor number on top left side of front corner of cylinder block. [CHAMPION] The serial numbers for the 1947 Champions were G-212501 to G-314500 (South Bend) and G-824001 to G-827300 (Los Angeles). Champion motor numbers were 236001 to 342000 for both plants. [COMMANDER]: The serial numbers for the 1947 Commanders were 4232501 to 4287000 (South Bend) and 4818501 to 4820500 (Los Angeles). The Commander motor numbers were H-182001 to 239000 for both plants.

CHAMPION SERIES

Model Number	Body/Style Number	Body Type & Seating	Factory Price	Shipping Weight	Production Total
DELUXE LINE					
6G	W3	4-dr Sed-6P	1478	2735	23,958
6G	F3	2-dr Sed-6P	1446	2685	10,860
6G	Q1	2-dr Cpe-3P	1378	2600	5,221
6G	C3	2-dr Cpe-5P	1472	2670	7,670
REGAL DELUXE LINE					
6G	W5	4-dr Sed	1551	2760	30,000
6G	F5	2-dr Sed	1520	2710	12,697
6G	Q2	2-dr Cpe-3P	1451	2620	3,379
6G	C5	2-dr Cpe-5P	1546	2690	9,061
6G	S2	2-dr Conv-5P	1902	2875	2,251

1947 Studebaker, Commander two-door sedan, 6-cyl

COMMANDER — MODEL 14A — For 1947 the Commander was Studebaker's top line model. The President, which had been Studebaker's prewar prestige model, was not returned to production until 1955. Regal Deluxe and Deluxe exterior trim variations were the same as on Champions. Except for the Land Cruiser, all basic bodies were the same as Champions from the cowl back. The long wheelbase Land Cruiser, like the convertible, came only with Regal Deluxe trim. The Commander's stainless steel grille sections were set into a painted steel stamping. Taillights were divided into four sections. "Black light" instrument illumination was standard on all Commanders and Champions. Model identifications were located on the front edge of the hood and the right side of the instrument panel.

COMMANDER SERIES

Model Number	Body/Style Number	Body Type & Seating	Factory Price	Shipping Weight	Production Total
DELUXE LINE					
14A	Q1	2-dr Cpe-3P	1661	3140	301
14A	C3	2-dr Cpe-5P	1755	3210	2,742
14A	W3	4-dr Sed-6P	1761	3265	3,485
14A	F3	2-dr Sed-6P	1729	3230	548
REGAL DELUXE LINE					
14A	W5	4-dr Sed-6P	1882	3280	13,539
14A	F5	2-dr Sed-6P	1850	3245	2,159
14A	Q2	2-dr Cpe-3P	1781	3155	1,046
14A	C5	2-dr Cpe-5P	1876	3225	10,557
14A	S2	2-dr Conv-5P	2236	3420	1,503
LAND CRUISER (123" W.B.)					
14A	Y5	4-dr Sed-6P	2043	3340	20,519

ENGINES

(CHAMPION) Six-cylinder. L-head. Cast iron block. Displacement: 169.6 cid. Bore and stroke: 3 x 4 inches. Compression ratio: 6.5:1. Brake hp: 80 at 4000 rpm. Four main bearings. Solid valve lifters. Carburetor: Carter model WE-532S one-barrel.

(COMMANDER) Six-cylinder. L-head. Cast iron block. Displacement: 226.2 cid. Bore and stroke: 3-5/16 x 4-3/8 inches. Compression ratio: 6.5:1. Brake hp: 94 at 3600 rpm. Four main bearings. Solid valve lifters. Carburetor: Stromberg model BXOV-26 one-barrel.

CHASSIS FEATURES: Wheelbase: (Champion) 112 inches; (Commander except Land Cruiser) 119 inches; (Land Cruiser) 123 inches. Overall length: (Champion) 192.7 inches; (Commander except Land Cruiser) 204.4 inches; (Land Cruiser) 208.4 inches. Front tread: (Champion) 56.25 inches; (Commander) 55 inches. Rear tread: (Champion and Commander) 54 inches. Tires: (Champion) 5.50 x 15 tube type; (Commander) 6.50 x 15 tube type.

OPTIONS: Hill Holder. Directional signals. White sidewall tires. Skyway 8-tube push button radio or Liberator 6-tube manual tuning radio. Internally controlled cowl radio antenna. Climatizer heater/defroster or economy Quad-Duty heater. Champion hood ornament. Front fender ornaments. Strat-O-Lined or Universal exterior rearview mirror. Champion front and rear winguards (bumper extensions). Commander rear winguards (front winguards standard on Commander). Plastic whitewall wheel discs or stainless steel wheel trim rings. Chrome license plate frames. Exhaust extension. Fog lights. Spotlight. Underhood light. Champion Deluxe luggage compartment light. Champion package compartment light. Electric clock. Glare-proof interior rearview mirror. Visor vanity mirror. Two-tone Mattex seat covers. Automatic windshield washer. Champion vacuum windshield wiper booster (standard on Commander). Locking gas cap. Rear ash receivers for Champion Deluxe two and four-door sedans. Regal steering wheel for Deluxe trim models. Fram oil filter for Champions. Wet oil bath air cleaner. Tire chains. A three-speed manual gear box with column mounted gear shift was standard on all models. Overdrive was available for $84.75 extra on Champions and $90.85 extra on Commanders. A 7.0:1 compression ratio was optional on both engines.

HISTORICAL FOOTNOTES: Body style Q was a business coupe. Starting in 1949, body style C was called a Starlight. The Starlight name is now applied retroactively to 1947 C bodies. The Y body (Land Cruiser) was a stretched W body. The Land Cruiser had vent windows in the rear doors.

1948 STUDEBAKER

1948 Studebaker, Champion two-door convertible, 6-cyl (AA)

CHAMPION — MODEL 7G — The 1948 Champion continued with the same body style and trim offerings as in 1947. A single, full width, horizontal stainless steel bar was added to the grille. A Champion script was affixed to the left front edge of the hood. Standard one-piece curved windshields on convertibles and five-passenger coupes were continued from 1947. All others had flat two-piece windshields.

STUDEBAKER I.D. NUMBERS: Serial number on left front door lock pillar post. Motor number on top left side of front corner of cylinder block. [CHAMPION] The serial numbers for the 1948 Champions were G-314501 to G-399772 (South Bend); G-827301 to G-839550 (Los Angeles) and G-700,001 and up (Canada). Motor numbers were 342001 to 439798 (South Bend and Los Angeles) and C1001 and up Canada. [COMMANDER] The serial numbers for the 1948 Commanders were 4287001 to 4360743 (South Bend) and 4820501 to 4832598 (Los Angeles). The motor numbers were H-239001 to H-324981 for both South Bend and Los Angeles plants.

CHAMPION SERIES

Model Number	Body/Style Number	Body Type & Seating	Factory Price	Shipping Weight	Production Total
DELUXE LINE					
7G	W3	4-dr Sed-6P	1635	2720	21,436
7G	F3	2-dr Sed-6P	1604	2675	10,203
7G	Q1	2-dr Cpe-3P	1535	2590	3,783
7G	C3	2-dr Cpe-5P	1630	2670	5,499
REGAL DELUXE LINE					
7G	W5	4-dr Sed-6P	1709	2725	30,494
7G	F5	2-dr Sed-6P	1677	2685	9,471
7G	Q2	2-dr Cpe-3P	1609	2615	823
7G	C5	2-dr Cpe-5P	1704	2690	8,982
7G	S2	2-dr Conv-5P	2059	2865	9,996

1948 Studebaker, Commander Regal Deluxe convertible, 6-cyl

COMMANDER — MODEL — 15A — The 1948 Commander continued with the same body style and trim offerings as in 1947, although production records indicate only one three-passenger coupe was produced. A wide horizontal trim strip was added to the front edge of the hood. Nylon upholstery was introduced as a standard feature on the Land Cruiser. The Land Cruiser, like the Champion/Commander five-passenger coupe and convertible, continued with a one-piece curved windshield. A gradual attempt was made to promote the Land Cruiser as a separate model.

COMMANDER SERIES

Model Number	Body/Style Number	Body Type & Seating	Factory Price	Shipping Weight	Production Total
DELUXE LINE					
15A	Q1	2-dr Cpe-3P	1856	—	0
15A	W3	4-dr Sed-6P	1956	3195	8,898
15A	F3	2-dr Sed-6P	1925	3165	1,440
15A	C3	2-dr Cpe-5P	1951	3150	2,913

REGAL DELUXE LINE

Model Number	Body/Style Number	Body Type & Seating	Factory Price	Shipping Weight	Production Total
15A	W5	4-dr Sed-6P	2077	3215	15,685
15A	F5	2-dr Sed-6P	2045	3175	1,661
15A	Q2	2-dr Cpe-3P	1977	—	1
15A	C5	2-dr Cpe-5P	2072	3165	11,528
15A	S2	2-dr Conv-5P	2431	3385	7,982

LAND CRUISER (123" W.B.)

Model Number	Body/Style Number	Body Type & Seating	Factory Price	Shipping Weight	Production Total
15A	Y5	4-dr Sed-6P	2265	3280	35,731

ENGINES

(CHAMPION) Six-cylinder. L-head. Cast iron block. Displacement: 169.6 cid. Bore and stroke: 3 x 4 inches. Compression ratio: 6.5:1. Brake hp: 80 at 4000 rpm. Four main bearings. Solid valve lifters. Carburetor: Carter model WE-532S or WE-661S one-barrel.

(COMMANDER) Six-cylinder. L-head. Cast iron block. Displacement: 226.2 cid. Bore and stroke: 3-5/16 x 4-3/8 inches. Compression ratio: 6.5:1. Brake hp: 94 at 3600 rpm. Four main bearings. Solid valve lifters. Carburetor: Stromberg model BXOV-26 one-barrel.

CHASSIS FEATURES: Wheelbase: (Champion) 112 inches; (Commander except Land Cruiser) 119 inches; (Land Cruiser) 123 inches. Overall length: (Champion) 190.7 inches; (Commander except Land Cruiser) 204.2 inches; (Land Cruiser) 208.2 inches. Front tread: (Champion) 56.25 inches; (Commander) 55 inches. Rear tread (Champion and Commander) 54 inches. Tires: (Champion) 5.50 x 15 tube type; (Commander) 6.50 x 15 tube type.

CONVENIENCE OPTIONS: Hill Holder. Directional signals. White sidewall tires. Skyway 8-tube push-button radio or Starline 6-tube push-button radio. Internally controlled cowl radio antenna. Climatizer heater/defroster or economy Quad-Duty heater. Front fender ornaments. Strat-O-Lined or Universal exterior rearview mirror. License plate frames. Plastic wheel discs or stainless wheel trim rings. Commander stainless wheel discs. Front and rear winguards (bumper extensions). Grille and truck guards. Rear fender skirts. Exhaust deflector. Locking gas cap. Plastic top cover for convertibles. Regal steering wheel for Deluxe models. Horn ring for Commander Deluxe models. Fog lights. Spotlight (internal or external control). Back-up light. Service light. Under hood light. Champion Deluxe luggage compartment light. Champion package compartment light. Cigarette lighter and front ashtray Tell-Tale lights. Fabric, Mattex or plastic seat covers. armrest covers. Door scuff pads. Select-O-Seat cushion springs. Exterior windshield sun visor. Noblo window deflector for rear doors. Door window awnings. Venetian shades. Breez-Bye Wind Rejector for convertibles. Rubber floor mats. Electric clock (standard on Land Cruiser). Glare-proof interior rearview mirror. Visor vanity mirror. Rear ash receivers for Champion Deluxe two and four-door sedans. Automatic windshield washer. Studebaker Auto-Serv Kleenex dispenser. Custom luggage. Champion vacuum windshield wiper booster. Fram oil filter for Champions. Hydraulic bumper jack. Undercoating. Tire chains. A three-speed manual gear box with column mounted gear shift was standard on all models. Overdrive was available for $84.75 extra on Champions and $90.85 extra on Commanders. A 7.0:1 compression ratio was optional on both engines.

HISTORICAL FOOTNOTES: Body style Q was a business coupe. Starting in 1949, body style C was called a Starlight. The Starlight name is now applied retroactively to 1948 C bodies. The Y body (Land Cruiser) was a stretched W body. The Land Cruise had vent windows in the rear doors.

1949 STUDEBAKER

CHAMPION — MODEL 8G — The Champion continued as Studebaker's low price model. Body style and trim selections were the same as 1947 and 1948. Standard wraparound front and rear bumpers were introduced on all models. A second full width horizontal stainless steel bar was added to the grille. The five-passenger (C body) coupe was christened the Starlight.

STUDEBAKER I.D. NUMBERS: [CHAMPION] The serial numbers for the 1949 Champions were G-400501 to G-467959 (South Bend), G-839701 to G-851669 (Los Angeles) and G-703101 and up (Canada). The engine numbers were 441001 to 520550 (South Bend and Los Angeles) and C-4101 and up in Canada. [COMMANDER] The serial numbers for the 1949 Commanders were 4361001 to 4398473 (South Bend) and 4832701 to 4838950 (Los Angeles). The engine numbers were H-326001 to 369772 for both South Bend and Los Angeles plants.

CHAMPION SERIES

Model Number	Body/Style Number	Body Type & Seating	Factory Price	Shipping Weight	Production Total
DELUXE LINE					
8G	Q1	2-dr Cpe-3P	1588	2645	1,642
8G	C3	2-dr Starlight Cpe-5P	1683	2705	5,917
8G	W3	4-dr Sed-6P	1688	2745	20,134
8G	F3	2-dr Sed-6P	1657	2720	10,359
REGAL DELUXE LINE					
8G	W5	4-dr Sed-6P	1762	2750	24,328
8G	F5	2-dr Sed-6P	1730	2725	5,618
8G	Q2	2-dr Cpe-3P	1662	2650	718
8G	C5	2-dr Starlight Cpe-5P	1757	2725	9,829
8G	S2	2-dr Conv-5P	2086	2895	7,035

COMMANDER — MODEL 16A — The Commander continued as Studebaker's top line series. Except for the discontinuance of the Commander three-passenger business coupe (Q body), the body styles and trim selections were the same as 1947-48. Wraparound bumpers were made standard. Chrome and stainless steel overlays were added to the grille to cover up the painted areas. For the first time since 1938, the displacement of the Commander engine was increased.

COMMANDER SERIES

Model Number	Body/Style Number	Body Type & Seating	Factory Price	Shipping Weight	Production Total
DELUXE LINE					
16A	W3	4-dr Sed-6P	2019	3240	6,280
16A	F3	2-dr Sed-6P	1988	3215	1,418
16A	C3	2-dr Starlight Cpe-5P	2014	3200	2,712

REGAL DELUXE LINE

16A	W5	4-dr Sed	2140	3245	10,005
16A	F5	2-dr Sed	2109	3220	934
16A	C5	2-dr Starlight Cpe-5P	2135	3205	6,278
16A	S2	2-dr Conv-5P	2467	3415	1,702

LAND CRUISER (124" W.B.)

16A	Y5	4-dr Sed-6P	2328	3325	14,390

1949 Studebaker, Commander two-door Starlight coupe, 6-cyl

ENGINES

(CHAMPION) Six-cylinder. L-head. Cast iron block. Displacement: 169.6 cid. Bore and stroke: 3 x 4 inches. Compression ratio: 6.5:1. Brake hp: 80 at 4000 rpm. Four main bearings. Solid valve lifters. Carburetor: Carter Model WE-715S one-barrel.

(COMMANDER) Six-cylinder. L-head. Cast iron block. Displacement: 245.6 cid. Bore and stroke: 3-5/16 x 4-3/4 inches. Compression ratio: 6.5:1. Brake hp: 100 at 3400 rpm. Four main bearings. Solid valve lifters. Carburetor: Stromberg model BXOV-26 one-barrel.

CHASSIS FEATURES: Wheelbase: (Champion) 112 inches; (Commander except Land Cruiser) 119 inches; (Land Cruiser) 123 inches. Overall length: (Champion) 191.9 inches; (Commander except Land Cruiser) 205.4 inches; (Land Cruiser) 209.4 inches. Front tread: (Champion) 56.25 inches; (Commander) 55 inches. Rear tread: (Champion and Commander) 54 inches. Tires: (Champion) 6.40 x 15 tube type; (Commander) 6.50 x 15 tube type.

OPTIONS: Hill Holder. Directional signals. White sidewall tires. Skyway 8-tube push-button radio or Starline 6-tube push-button radio. Internally controlled vacuum powered front fender radio antenna or internally controlled reel-type cowl radio antenna. Climatizer heater/defroster or economy Quad-Duty heater. Champion front fender ornaments. Start-O-Vu, Strat-O-Lined, Universal or Dor-Top exterior rearview mirror. License plate frames. Plastic wheel discs, stainless wheel discs or stainless wheel trim rings. Grille and trunk guards. Rear fender skirts. Exhaust deflector. Locking gas cap. Grease fitting Lubri-Caps. Door scuff pads. Rubber splashguards. Rubber floor mats. Regal horn ring for Deluxe models. Plastic top cover for convertibles. Fabric, Mattex or plastic seat covers. Select-O-Seat cushion springs. armrest covers. Fog lights. Spotlight (internal or external control). Back-up light. Champion package compartment light. Underhood light. Champion Deluxe luggage compartment light. Service light. Cigarette lighter and front ashtray Tell-Tale lights. Exterior windshield sun visor. Breez-Bye Wind Rejector for convertibles. Noblo wind deflector. Door window awnings. Venetian shades. Electric clock (standard on Land Cruiser). Glare-proof interior rearview mirror. Visor vanity mirror. Rear ash receivers for Champion Deluxe two and four-door sedans. Robe rail for all models except Land Cruiser (standard on Land Cruiser). Safety child-proof rear door locks for four-door sedans. Automatic windshield washer. Champion vacuum windshield wiper booster. Kleenex dispenser. Custom luggage. Fram oil filter for Champions. Hydraulic jack. Headbolt engine heater. Tire chains. Undercoating. A three-speed manual gear box with column mounted gear shift was standard on all models. Overdrive was available for $91.55 extra on Champion and $97.85 extra on Commander. A 7.0:1 compression ratio was optional on both engines.

HISTORICAL FOOTNOTES: Body style Q was a business coupe. The Y body (Land Cruiser) was a stretched W body. The Land Cruiser had vent windows in the rear doors.

1950 STUDEBAKER

CHAMPION — MODEL 9G — A "bullet-nose" front end and rear fenders that supported vertical taillights were new for 1950. The central body section was unchanged. The model identification was on the front fenders. Small headlight trim rings were used on Champions. Starting in midyear, these rings were chrome plated on Deluxe and Regal Deluxe trim lines. A low-priced Custom model was introduced at midyear. A new Automatic Drive was introduced as an option during midyear. A growing buyers' market reduced prices from 1949 and during the year they were reduced again. Available body types were the same as 1949. There was no hood ornament on Custom models. Stainless steel rocker panel moldings were standard on Regal Deluxe models.

STUDEBAKER I.D. NUMBERS: Serial number on left front door lock pillar post. Motor number on top left side of front corner of cylinder block. [CHAMPION] The serial numbers for the 1950 Champions were G-468101 to G-686431 (South Bend), G-851801 to G-889014 (Los Angeles) and G-709401 and up (Canada). The beginning engine numbers were 521001 (South Bend and Los Angeles) and C-10501 in Canada. [COMMANDER] The beginning serial numbers for the 1950 Commanders were 4398601 to 4461853 (South Bend) and 4839001 to 4848311 (Los Angeles). The beginning engine number was H-370001 for both South Bend and Los Angeles plants.

1950 Studebaker, Champion two-door convertible, 6-cyl

CHAMPION SERIES

Model Number	Body/Style Number	Body Type & Seating	Factory Price	Shipping Weight	Production Total
CUSTOM LINE					
9G	W1	4-dr Sed-6P	1519	2730	16,000
9G	F1	2-dr Sed-6P	1487	2695	19,593
9G	Q4	2-dr Cpe-3P	1419	2620	1,562
9G	C1	2-dr Starlight Cpe-5P	1514	2690	3,583
DELUXE LINE					
9G	W3	4-dr Sed-6P	1597	2750	46,027
9G	F3	2-dr Sed-6P	1565	2720	45,280
9G	Q1	2-dr Cpe-3P	1497	2635	2,082
9G	C3	2-dr Starlight Cpe-5P	1592	2705	19,028
REGAL DELUXE LINE					
9G	W5	4-dr Sed	1676	2755	55,296
9G	F5	2-dr Sed	1644	2725	21,976
9G	Q2	2-dr Cpe-3P	1576	2640	849
9G	C5	2-dr Starlight Cpe-5P	1671	2715	29,966
9G	S2	2-dr Conv-5p	1981	2900	9,362

1950 Studebaker, Land Cruiser four-door sedan, 6-cyl (AA)

COMMANDER — MODEL 17A — The 1950 Commander's "bullet-nose" and rear fenders were the same as on Champions, while the front fenders and headlight trim rings were much larger. The bullet-nose piece was fully chrome plated on both Commanders and Champions. The model identification was on the front fenders. A Land Cruiser script was adjacent to the rear deck lid on that model. Body style and trim offerings were the same as in 1949. Standard chrome headlight trim rings and optional Automatic Drive were introduced as a running change. Prices were also reduced at midyear. On both Commanders and Champions a coil spring and A-arm arrangement replaced the former planar cross leaf spring independent front suspension system.

COMMANDER SERIES

Model Number	Body/Style Number	Body Type & Seating	Factory Price	Shipping Weight	Production Total
DELUXE LINE					
17A	W3	4-dr Sed-6P	1902	3255	11,440
17A	F3	2-dr Sed-6P	1871	3215	4,588
17A	C3	2-dr Starlight Cpe-5P	1897	3215	4,383
REGAL DELUXE LINE					
17A	W5	4-dr Sed-6P	2024	3265	14,832
17A	F5	2-dr Sed-6P	1992	3220	2,363
17A	C5	2-dr Starlight Cpe-5P	2018	3220	7,375
17A	S2	2-dr Conv-5P	2328	3375	2,867
LAND CRUISER (124" W.B.)					
17A	Y5	4-dr Sed-6P	2187	3355	24,712

ENGINES

(CHAMPION) Six-cylinder. L-head. Cast iron block, Displacement: 169.6 cid. Bore and stroke: 3 x 4 inches. Compression ratio: 7.0:1. Brake hp: 85 at 4000 rpm. Four main bearings. Solid valve lifters. Carburetor: Carter model WE-715S one-barrel.

(COMMANDER) Six-cylinder. L-head. Cast Iron block. Displacement: 245.6 cid. Bore and stroke: 3-5/16 x 4-3/8 inches. Compression ratio: 7.0:1. Brake hp: 102 at 3200 rpm. Four main bearings. Solid valve lifters. Carburetor: Stromberg model BXOV-26 one-barrel or Carter model WE-627SA one-barrel.

CHASSIS FEATURES: Wheelbase (Champion) 113 inches; (Commander except Land Cruiser) 120 inches; (Land Cruiser) 124 inches. Overall length: (Champion) 197.25 inches; (Commander except Land Cruiser) 207.9 inches; (Land Cruiser)-211.9. Front tread: (Champion) 56.4 inches; (Commander) 55.5 inches. Rear tread: (Champion and Commander) 54 inches. Tires: (Champion) 6.40 x 15 tube type; (Commander) 7.60 x 15 tube type.

OPTIONS: Hill Holder. Directional signals. White sidewall tires. Stratoline 8-tube push-button radio, Starline 6-tube push-button radio or Starline 6-tube manual tuning radio. Internally controlled vacuum powered front fender radio antenna or internally controlled reel-type cowl radio antenna. Climatizer heater/defroster. Champion front fender ornaments. Strat-O-Vu, Stratoline, Universal or Dor-Top exterior rearview mirror. Stratoline or Deluxe exhaust deflector. Rear fender skirts. License plate frames. Full chrome wheelcovers or stainless wheel trim rings. Fabric or plastic seat covers. armrest covers. Exterior windshield sun visor. Noblo wind deflector. Rubber floor mats (two types). Select-O-Seat cushion springs. Robe cord for all models except Land Cruiser. Grille and trunk guards. Plastic top cover for convertibles. Grease fitting Lubri-Caps. Door scuff pads. Rubber front fender splash guards. Locking gas cap. Trunk compartment mat for all models except Land Cruiser. Accelerator pedal cover and wear pad. Back-up lights. Fog lights. Spotlight (internal or external control). Parking brake warning light. Service light. Underhood light. Champion Custom/Deluxe luggage compartment light. Champion package compartment light. Standard or Drawmatic cigarette lighter. Cigarette lighter and front ash receiver Tell-Tale light. Electric clock (standard on Land Cruiser). Glare-proof interior rearview mirror. Deluxe or standard vanity mirror. Kleenex dispenser. Windshield washer. Safety child-proof rear door locks. Rear ash receivers for Champion Custom/Deluxe two and four-door sedans. Custom luggage. Electro-Vac wiper booster for Champions. Fram oil filter for Champions. Headbolt engine heater. Winter transparent plastic grille cover. Cold weather Battery Vitalizer. Tire chains. Hydraulic jack. Undercoating. Pastel Sparkel Spray exterior finish treatment. Accessories specifically for the Champion Custom: Extra interior sun visor, front door armrest, rear armrests (two and four-door sedans), extra horn, hood ornament and interior courtesy light. A three-speed manual gear box with column mounted gear shift was standard on all models. Overdrive was available for $92 extra on Champions and $98 extra on Commanders. Automatic Drive, starting in mid-year, was available for $201 extra on all models. A 7.5:1 compression ratio was optional on both engines.

HISTORICAL FOOTNOTES: Body style Q was a business coupe. The Y body (Land Cruiser) was a stretched W body. The Land Cruiser had vent windows in the rear doors. The Land Cruiser continued with Regal Deluxe trim.

1951 STUDEBAKER

CHAMPION — MODEL 10G — The Champion was continued as Studebaker's low priced series. The outer edge of the "bullet-nose" section was painted body color and the center piece was made of plastic. One-piece curved windshields were standard on all body styles. The former two-piece rear window on two and four-door sedans was replaced by a one-piece unit. The "Deluxe" term was deleted from the Regal Deluxe trim name. Painted headlight and taillight trim rings were used only on Custom models. Deluxe models had chrome headlight and taillight trim rings, but lacked the stainless steel rocker panel moldings that were standard on Regal models. The Champion and Commander wheelbases were identical. All fender and body panels were the same on Champions and Commanders for corresponding bodies. The model Identification was located on the left front edge of the hood.

1951 Studebaker, Champion two-door sedan, 6-cyl (AA)

STUDEBAKER I.D. NUMBERS: Serial numbers were located on the front door lock pillar post. Champion engine numbers were located on top left side front corner of cylinder block. Commander engine numbers were located on the top of the rear of the cylinder block next to the distributor. [CHAMPION] The serial numbers for 1951 were G-1000001 to G-1115017 (South Bend), G-889101 to G-907190 (Los Angeles) and G-724501 and up (Canada). The beginning engine numbers were 778001 and up (South Bend and Los Angeles) and C-25,501 and up in Canada. [COMMANDER] The serial numbers for the 1951 Commanders were 8110001 to 8216497 (South Bend), 8800001 to 8815942 (Los Angeles) and 8952001 and up (Canada). The beginning engine numbers were V-101 (South Bend and Los Angeles) and VC-101 (Canada).

CHAMPION SERIES

Model Number	Body/Style Number	Body Type & Seating	Factory Price	Shipping Weight	Production Total
CUSTOM LINE					
10G	W1	4-dr Sed-6P	1571	2690	9,972
10G	F1	2-dr Sed-6P	1540	2670	10,689
10G	Q4	2-dr Cpe-3P	1471	2585	2,429
10G	C1	2-dr Starlight Cpe-5P	1566	2650	2,781
DELUXE LINE					
10G	W3	4-dr Sed-6P	1649	2715	26,019
10G	F3	2-dr Sed-6P	1618	2690	18,591
10G	Q1	2-dr Cpe-3P	1549	2610	961
10G	C3	2-dr Starlight Cpe-5P	1644	2675	9,444

REGAL LINE

10G	W5	4-dr Sed-6P	1728	2715	35,201
10G	F5	2-dr Sed-6P	1697	2690	8,931
10G	Q2	2-dr Cpe-3P	1628	2615	373
10G	C5	2-dr Starlight Cpe-5P	1723	2675	14,103
10G	S2	2-dr Conv-5P-5P	2034	2890	4,742

1951 Studebaker, Land Cruiser four-door sedan, V-8 (AA)

COMMANDER — MODEL H — New for Commanders in 1951 was a V-8 overhead valve engine. The Deluxe trim name was discontinued and the Regal Deluxe became just the Regal. A new State name was used for top line models. State models came standard with fender ornaments. Body selections were the same as in 1951, except that the Los Angeles plant produced one Commander business coupe. Bullet-nose, windshield and rear window changes were the same as on Champions. The grille on both Commanders and Champions was increased in size and moved forward so it was flush with the front sheet metal. The Commander and Champions had larger taillight lenses than in 1950. The model identification was located on the left front edge of the hood. The Land Cruiser name remained on the front fenders.

COMMANDER SERIES

Model Number	Body/Style Number	Body Type & Seating	Factory Price	Shipping Weight	Production Total
REGAL LINE					
H	W3	4-dr Sed-6P	1839	3070	29,603
H	F3	2-dr Sed-6P	1807	3050	8,034
H	Q1	2-dr Cpe-3P	—	—	1
H	C3	2-dr Starlight Cpe-5P	1833	3025	8,192
STATE LINE					
H	W5	4-dr Sed-6P	1939	3070	21,134
H	F5	2-dr Sed-6P	1907	3050	3,903
H	C5	2-dr Starlight Cpe-5P	1933	3025	11,637
H	S2	2-dr Conv-5P	2244	3245	3,770
LAND CRUISER (119" W.B.)					
H	Y5	4-dr Sed-6P	2071	3165	38,055

ENGINES

(CHAMPION) Six-cylinder. L-head. Cast iron block. Displacement: 169.6 cid. Bore and stroke: 3 x 4 inches. Compression ratio: 7.0:1. Brake hp: 85 at 4000 rpm. Four main bearings. Solid lifters. Carburetor: Carter model WE-715S one-barrel.

(COMMANDER) V-8. Overhead valve. Cast iron block. Displacement: 232.6 cid. Bore and stroke: 3-3/8 x 3-1/4 inches. Compression ratio: 7.0:1. Brake hp: 120 at 4000 rpm. Five main bearings. Solid valve lifters. Carburetor: Stromberg model AAUVB-26 two-barrel.

CHASSIS FEATURES: Wheelbase: (Champion and Commander except Land Cruiser) 115 inches; (Land Cruiser) 119 inches. Overall length: (Champion and Commander except Land Cruiser) 197.5 inches; (Land Cruiser) 201.5 inches. Front tread: 56.5 inches. Rear tread: 54 inches. Tires: (Champion) 6.40 x 15 tube type; (Commander) 7. 10 x 15 tube type.

OPTIONS: Hill Holder. Directional signals. White sidewall tires. Stratoline 8-tube push-button radio. Starline 6-tube push-button radio. Starline 6-tube manual tuning radio. Internally controlled vacuum powered front fender radio antenna or internally controlled reel-type cowl radio antenna. Climatizer heater/defroster. Champion and Regal Commander front fender ornaments. Strat-O-Vu, Stratoline or Universal exterior rearview mirror. Exhaust deflector. Rear fender skirts. Gas door guard. License plate frames. Full chrome wheelcovers or stainless wheel trim rings. Fabric or plastic seat covers. Exterior windshield sun visor. Side window ventshades. No-Blo wind deflector. Venetian shields. Select-O-Seat cushion springs. Robe cord for all models except Land Cruiser (standard on Land Cruise). Grille and trunk guards. Plastic top cover for convertibles. Spark plug weather proofing kit. Rubber front fender splashguards. Door scuff pads. Locking gas cap. Rubber floor mats (two types). Accelerator pedal cover and wear pad. Back-up lights. Spotlight. Fog lights. Parking brake warning light. Underhood light. Glove compartment light. Service light. Luggage compartment light for all models except Land Cruiser (standard on Land Cruiser). Electric clock (standard on Land Cruiser). Standard or Drawmatic cigarette lighter. Glare-proof interior rearview mirror. Kleenex dispenser. Standard or illuminated vanity mirror. Safety child-proof rear door locks. Windshield washer. Rear ash receivers for Champion Custom/Deluxe two and four-door sedans. Custom luggage. Electric windshield wipers for Champions. Fram oil filter for all models except Land Cruiser (standard on Land Cruiser). Headbolt engine heater. Cold weather Battery Vitalizer. Tire chains. Hydraulic jack. Undercoating. Plastel Sparkel Spray exterior finish treatment. Accessories specifically for the Champion Custom: Extra interior sun visor, front door armrests, rear armrests (two and four-door sedans), extra horn, hood ornament an interior courtesy light. A three-speed manual gear box with column mounted gear shift was standard on all models. Overdrive was available for $92 extra on Champions and $98 extra on Commanders. Automatic Drive was available for $201 extra on all models. A 7.5:1 compression ratio was optional on the Champion engine.

HISTORICAL FOOTNOTES: Body style Q was a business coupe. The Y body (Land Cruiser) was a stretched W body. The Land Cruiser had vent windows in the rear doors. The Land Cruiser featured State trim.

1952 STUDEBAKER

1952 Studebaker, Champion Regal two-door hardtop, 6-cyl (AA)

CHAMPION — MODEL 12G — The Champion body style and trim selections were the same as 1951, except that the business coupe (Q) was discontinued and a new two-door hardtop (K) was added. The bullet-nose front end design was dropped and a horizontal grille, slightly like the upcoming 1953 design was adopted. The grille molding bent down to form a 'V' in the center of the grille. Six vertical bars sloped back into the grille. Champions had an oblong emblem above the grille molding. The top one-third of each taillight was hooded. The central body sections, discounting the new hardtop, continued with the basic 1947 design. Rear fenders were unchanged from 1950-1951. The model identification was located on the left front edge of the hood. Two-tones were available on hardtops.

STUDEBAKER I.D. NUMBERS: Serial numbers were located on the front door lock pillar post. Effective with Champion serial number 8266501 and Commander serial number G-1160245 the location was moved to a plate attached to the left front door hinge pillar facing. Champion engine numbers were located on top left side front corner of cylinder block. Commander engine numbers were located on the top of the rear of the cylinder block next to the distributor. [CHAMPION] The serial numbers for the 1952 Champions were G-1115501 to 1197180 (South Bend), G-907301 to 917641 (Los Angeles) and G-735701 and up (Canada). The motor numbers were 911501 to 1000639 (South Bend and Los Angeles) and C36722 and up for Canada. [COMMANDER] The serial numbers for the 1952 Commanders were 8217001 to 8289877 (South Bend), 8816001 to 8826703 (Los Angeles) and 8954001 and up (Canada). The engine numbers were V-123001 to V-206512 (South Bend and Los Angeles) and VC-2036 and up for Canada.

CHAMPION SERIES

Model Number	Body/Style Number	Body Type & Seating	Factory Price	Shipping Weight	Production Total
CUSTOM LINE					
12G	W1	4-dr Sed-6P	1769	2695	6,400
12G	F1	2-dr Sed-6P	1735	2655	4,310
12G	C1	2-dr Starlight Cpe-5P	1763	2660	1,096
DELUXE LINE					
12G	W3	4-dr Sed-6P	1862	2720	24,542
12G	F3	2-dr Sed-6P	1828	2685	12,989
12G	C3	2-dr Starlight Cpe-5P	1856	2675	6,075
REGAL LINE					
12G	F5	2-dr Sed-6P	1913	2690	5,534
12G	W5	4-dr Sed-6P	1946	2725	20,566
12G	C5	2-dr Starlight Cpe-5P	1941	2695	6,183
12G	K2	2-dr Starliner HT-P	2220	2860	12,119
12G	S2	2-dr Conv-5P	2273	2870	1,575

1952 Studebaker, Commander State five-passenger coupe, V-8

COMMANDER — MODEL 3H — The Commander styling changes were essentially the same as those for the Champion. A two-door hardtop was also added to Commander lineup. Commanders had the same basic new grille as Champions, but a V-shaped Studebaker crest was mounted above the grille molding. Commander and Champion instrument panels were different. Since 1950 the Champion's instruments had been enclosed in a single enclosure, while the Commander's, since 1947, were held in three round dials. The model identification

was located on the left front edge of the hood and-on the deck lid. The Land Cruiser name was moved from the front fender to the deck lid. Front fender ornaments were standard on State models. Nineteen fifty-two marked the last year the 1947 body styling was used. It was also the last year Studebaker used suicide rear doors on four-door sedans.

COMMANDER SERIES

Model Number	Body/Style Number	Body Type & Seating	Factory Price	Shipping Weight	Production Total
REGAL LINE					
3H	W3	4-dr Sed-6P	2121	3085	22,037
3H	F3	2-dr Sed-6P	2086	3040	5,995
3H	C3	2-dr Starlight Cpe-5P	2115	3030	5,127
STATE LINE					
3H	W5	4-dr Sed-6P	2208	3075	9,998
3H	F5	2-dr Sed-6P	2172	3055	1,529
3H	C5	2-dr Starlight Cpe-5P	2202	3025	3,784
3H	K2	2-dr Starliner-5P	2488	3220	14,548
3H	S2	2-dr Conv-5P	2548	3230	1,715
LAND CRUISER (119" W.B.)					
3H	Y5	4-dr Sed-6P	2365	3155	20,117

ENGINES

(CHAMPION) Six-cylinder. L-head. Cast iron block. Displacement: 169.6 cid. Bore and stroke: 3 x 4 inches. Compression ratio: 7.0:1. Brake hp: 85 at 4000 rpm. Four main bearings. Solid valve lifters. Carburetor: Carter model WE-715S one-barrel.

(COMMANDER) V-8. Overhead valve. Cast iron block. Displacement: 232.6 cid. Bore and stroke: 3-3/8 x 3-1/4 inches. Compression ratio: 7.0:1. Brake hp: 120 at 4000 rpm. Five main bearings. Solid valve lifters. Carburetor: Stromberg model AAUVB-26 two-barrel.

CHASSIS FEATURES: Wheelbase: (Champion and Commander except Land Cruiser) 115 inches; (Land Cruiser) 119 inches. Overall length: (Champion and Commander except Land Cruiser) 197.5 inches; (Land Cruiser) 201.5 inches. Front tread: 56.5 inches. Rear tread: 54 inches. Tires: (Champion) 6.40 x 15 tube type; (Commander) 7.10 x 15 tube type.

OPTIONS: Hill Holder. Directional signals. White sidewall tires. Stratoline 8-tube push-button radio. Starline 6-tube manual tuning radio. Internally controlled vacuum powered front fender radio antenna or internally controlled reel-type cowl radio antenna. Climatizer heater/defroster. Fabric or plastic seat covers. Champion and Regal Commander front fender ornaments. Rear fender ornaments. Exhaust deflector. Starliner medallion. Rear fender skirts. "Automatic Drive" name plate. Deluxe steering wheel. Full wheelcovers or stainless wheel trim rings. Stra-O-Vu, Stratoline or Universal exterior rearview mirror. Gas door guard. License plate frames. Grille and trunk guards. Rubber floor mats. Plastic top cover for convertibles. Rubber front splashguards. Accelerator pedal cover and wear pad. Locking gas cap. Back-up lights. Spotlight. Fog lights. Parking brake warning light. Glove compartment light. Underhood light. Luggage compartment light for all models except Land Cruiser (standard on Land Cruiser). Electric clock (standard on Land Cruiser). Glare-proof interior rearview mirror. Kleenex dispenser. Cigarette lighter. Windshield washer. Standard or illuminated vanity mirror. Safety child-proof rear door locks. Exterior windshield sunvisor. Side window ventshades. Noblo wind deflector. Venetian shades. Select-O-Seat cushion springs. Custom luggage. Rear ash receiver for Champion Custom/Deluxe two and four-door sedans. Sav-A-Battery caps. Fram oil filter for all models except Land Cruiser (standard on Land Cruiser). Electric windshield wipers for Champions. Fram radiator water filter. Headbolt engine heater. Cold weather Battery Vitalizer. Snow chains. Hydraulic jack. Undercoating. Accessories specifically for the Champion Custom: Extra interior sun visor, front door armrests, rear armrests (two- and four-door sedans), extra horn, hood ornament and interior courtesy light. A three-speed manual gear box with column mounted gear shift was standard on all models. Overdrive was available for $105 extra on Champions and $118 extra on Commanders. Automatic Drive was available for $231 extra on Champions and $243 extra on Commanders. A 7.5:1 compression ratio was optional on both engines.

HISTORICAL FOOTNOTES: The Y body (Land Cruiser) was a stretched W body. The Land Cruiser had vent windows in the rear doors. The Land Cruiser featured State trim. The Starliner hardtop (K body) was based on the convertible (S) styling.

1953 STUDEBAKER

CHAMPION — MODEL 14G — Studebaker introduced all new bodies for 1953. The new sedans were shorter (except the Land Cruiser) and higher than the sporty Starliner hardtop (K) and Starlight coupe (C). The Starlight no longer featured the large wraparound four-piece rear window. The Starliner featured a single-piece rear window instead of the three-piece style used in 1952. The convertible was discontinued. Custom models continued with painted headlight and taillight trim rings. The Deluxe versions featured narrow stainless steel windshield moldings, while the Regal style had very wide stainless steel windshield moldings. The instrument panel featured three circular instrument clusters covered by a single glass. Plastic taillight lenses replaced the former glass ones. The grille had two front openings located above the bumper. They ran the full width of the cars, with a horizontal bar "floating" in each scoop-like opening. Parking lamps and directionals were mounted at each end. Model identification was on the left grille bar. Champions also had a hood ornament supplemented by the symbol 'S.' The Champion continued as the low priced series.

1953 Studebaker, Champion Regal two-door Starlight coupe, 6-cyl

STUDEBAKER I.D. NUMBERS: Serial numbers were located on the front door lock pillar post. Effective with Champion serial number 8266501 and Commander serial number G-1160245 the location was moved to a plate attached to the left front door hinge pillar facing. Champion engine numbers were located on top left side front corner of cylinder block. Commander engine numbers were located on the top of the front of the cylinder block next to the oil filler tube mounting. [CHAMPION] Serial numbers for the 1953 Champions were G-1197501 to G-1270324 (South Bend), G-917701 to G-927156 (Los Angeles) and G-745101 and up (Canada). Engine numbers were G-1004001 and up (South Bend and Los Angeles) and C-46501 and up for Canada. [COMMANDER] Serial numbers for the 1953 Commanders were 8290001 to 8353332 (South Bend), 8826801 to 8836505 (Los Angeles) and 8955401 and up (Canada). The beginning engine numbers were V-207001 (South Bend and Los Angeles) and VC-3501 (Canada).

CHAMPION SERIES

Model Number	Body/Style Number	Body Type & Seating	Factory Price	Shipping Weight	Production Total
CUSTOM					
14G	W1	4-dr Sed-6P	1767	2710	5,496
14G	F1	2-dr Sed-6P	1735	2690	3,983
DELUXE					
14G	W3	4-dr Sed-6P	1863	2735	17,180
14G	F3	2-dr Sed-6P	1831	2700	7,564
14G	C3	2-dr Starlight Cpe-5P	1868	2695	9,422
REGAL					
14G	W5	4-dr Sed-6P	1949	2745	17,897
14G	F5	2-dr Sed-6P	1917	2715	2,968
14G	C5	2-dr Starlight Cpe-5P	1995	2700	16,066
14G	K5	2-dr Starliner HT-5P	2116	2760	13,058

1953 Studebaker, Land Cruiser four-door sedan, V-8 (AA)

COMMANDER — MODEL 4H — Commanders, like Champions, received new 1953 bodies. For a given body type, the Champion and Commander bodies were identical. The State name was dropped and the Commander Deluxe identification was returned. Deluxe and Regal variations were the same as on Champions. The grille had two front openings located above the bumper. They ran the full width of the cars, with a horizontal fin "floating" in each scoop-like opening. Parking lamps and directionals were mounted at each end. Model identification was on the left grille bar. Champions also had a hood ornament supplemented by the symbol '8' as one of several V-8 emblems. During midyear, the tri-star emblems used on the hood and deck lid of early Commanders and Champions were replaced by large "V" emblems. The new instrument panel featured four hooded instrument pods. Model identification was on the left grille bar and on the deck lid of some, but not all examples.

COMMANDER SERIES

Model Number	Body/Style Number	Body Type & Seating	Factory Price	Shipping Weight	Production Total
DELUXE					
4H	W3	4-dr Sed-6P	2121	3075	10,065
4H	F3	2-dr Sed-6P	2089	3055	2,371
4H	C3	2-dr Starlight Cpe-5P	2127	3040	6,106
REGAL					
4H	W5	4-dr Sed-6P	2208	3095	7,454
4H	C5	2-dr Starlight Cpe-5P	2213	3040	14,752
4H	K5	2-dr Starliner HT-5P	2374	3120	19,236
LAND CRUISER					
4H	Y5	4-dr Sed-6P	2316	3180	15,981

ENGINES

(CHAMPION) Six-cylinder. L-head. Cast iron block. Displacement: 169.6 cid. Bore and stroke: 3 x 4 inches. Compression ratio: 7.0:1. Brake hp: 85 at 4000 rpm. Four main bearings. Solid valve lifters. Carburetor: Carter model WE-989SA one-barrel.

(COMMANDER) V8. Overhead valve. Cast iron block. Displacement: 232.6 cid. Bore and stroke: 3-3/8 x 3-1/4 inches. Compression ratio: 7.0:1. Brake hp: 120 at 4000 rpm. Five main bearings. Solid valve lifters. Carburetor: Stromberg model WWUVL-26 two-barrel.

CHASSIS FEATURES: Wheelbase: (Sedans except Land Cruiser) 116.5 inches; (Land Cruiser coupes and hardtops) 120.5 inches. Overall length: (Sedans except Land Cruiser) 198.6 inches; (Land Cruiser) 202.6 inches; (coupes and hardtops) 201.9 inches. Front tread: 56.5 inches. Rear tread: 55.5 inches. Tires: (Champion) 6.40 x 15 tube type; (Commander) 7.10 x 15 tube type.

OPTIONS: Hill Holder. Hydraulic power steering ($134). (Mechanical power steering was mentioned in early publicity, but it was never put into production.) Directional signals. White sidewall tires. Stratoline 8-tube push-button radio. Starline 6-tube manual tuning radio. Internally controlled reel-type cowl radio antenna. Auxiliary rear seat radio speaker. Climatizer heater/defroster. Fabric or plastic seat covers. Deluxe or Strat-O-Styled hood ornament. Front fender ornaments. Exhaust deflector. License plate frames (two styles). Gas door guard. "Automatic Drive" nameplate. Strat-O-Styled, Strat-O-Vu or Universal exterior rearview mirror. Rear fender skirts. Full wheelcovers or wire wheel type wheelcovers. Front and rear winguards (bumper extensions). Rubber floor mats. Rubber front splash guards. Accelerator pedal cover and wear pad. Locking gas cap. Fog light bumperettes with or without the fog lights. Spotlight (with built-in rear mirror). Back-up lights. Parking brake warning light. Glove compartment light. Underhood light. Trunk light for all models except Land Cruiser (standard on Land Cruiser). Electric clock. Safety child-proof rear door locks. Glareproof rearview mirror. Kleenex dispenser. Cigarette lighter. Vanity mirror. Windshield washer. Exterior windshield sun visor. Side window vent shades. Custom luggage. Rear window defroster. Headbolt engine heater. Tire chains. Artic wiper blades. Undercoating. Electric windshield wipers for Champions. Rear ash receiver for Champion Custom/Deluxe sedans. Fram oil filter for all models except Land Cruiser (standard on Land Cruiser). Fram radiator water filter. Crankcase ventilator. Accessories specifically for the Champion Custom: extra interior sun visor, front door armrests, rear armrests and rear seat ashtray. A three-speed manual gear box with column mounted gear shift was standard on all models. Overdrive was available for $105 extra on Champions and $118 extra on Commanders. Automatic Drive was available for $231 extra on Champions and $243 extra on Commanders. A 7.5:1 compression ration was optional on both engines.

HISTORICAL FOOTNOTES: The Y body (Land Cruiser) was a stretched W body. The Land Cruiser had vent windows in the rear doors. The Land Cruiser featured Regal trim.

1954 STUDEBAKER

1954 Studebaker, Champion four-door sedan, 6-cyl (AA)

CHAMPION — MODEL 15G — Except for the addition of a new Conestoga two-door station wagon (D body), the body style offerings and trim identifications were the same as in 1953. Main exterior trim differences between Custom, Deluxe and Regal models remained unchanged. The addition of 10 vertical "teeth" in the grille and new flat-faced front bumper guards were the main exterior styling changes for 1954. Deluxes had chrome window trim. Regals had a rub molding extending from the front door panel to the rear fender. All Regal and Deluxe sedans and station wagons featured a standard "air scoop" hood ornament. All new interior fabrics were color keyed to the exterior paint scheme. The model identification remained on the left horizontal grille bar and for 1954 it was also placed on the deck lid handle of all body styles except the station wagon. Two-tones were available on all models except the Custom line.

STUDEBAKER I.D. NUMBERS: VIN on left front door pillar. Champion motor number on top of left front corner of block. Commander motor number top front of cylinder block near oil filler tube mounting. [CHAMPION] Serial numbers for the 1954 Champions were G-1274001 to G-1315831 (South Bend), G-927401 to G-932286 (Los Angeles) and G-753301 and up (Canada). The beginning engine numbers were 1090001 (South Bend and Los Angeles) and C-55782 (Canada). [COMMANDER] The beginning serial numbers for the 1954 Commanders were 8354901 to 8380448 (South Bend), 8836801 to 8841029 (Los Angeles) and 8956751 and up (Canada). The beginning engine numbers were V-282501 (South Bend and Los Angeles) and VC-4941 (Canada).

CHAMPION SERIES

Model Number	Body/Style Number	Body Type & Seating	Factory Price	Shipping Weight	Production Total
CUSTOM					
15G	W1	4-dr Sed-6P	1801	2735	2,860
15G	F1	2-dr Sed-6P	1758	2705	2,653
DELUXE					
15G	F3	2-dr Sed-6P	1875	2730	4,449
15G	W3	4-dr Sed-6P	1918	2765	9,668
15G	C3	2-dr Starlight Cpe-5P	1972	2740	7,042
15G	D3	2-dr Sta Wag-6P	2187	2930	3,910

REGAL

Model Number	Body/Style Number	Body Type & Seating	Factory Price	Shipping Weight	Production Total
15G	W5	4-dr Sed-6P	2026	2780	7,286
15G	F5	2-dr Sed-6P	1983	2745	1,066
15G	C5	2-dr Starlight Cpe-5P	2080	2750	5,125
15G	K5	2-dr Starliner HT-5P	2241	2825	4,302
15G	D5	2-dr Sta Wag-6P	2295	2950	3,074

1954 Studebaker, Commander two-door Conestoga wagon, V-8 (AA)

COMMANDER — MODEL 5H — For a given body type and trim line, the Commander exterior styling features were the same as on 1954 Champions. On the inside a single instrument visor replaced the four separate units used in 1953. A Commander Conestoga two-door station wagon was also introduced. Deluxes had chrome window trim. Regals had a rub molding extending from the front door panel to the rear fender. Land Cruisers had a folding rear seat armrest.

COMMANDER SERIES

Model Number	Body/Style Number	Body Type & Seating	Factory Price	Shipping Weight	Production Total
DELUXE					
5H	W3	4-dr Sed-6P	2179	3105	4,615
5H	F3	2-dr Sed-6P	2136	3075	1,086
5H	C3	2-dr Starlight Cpe-5P	2233	3085	2,868
5H	D3	2-dr Sta Wag-6P	2448	3265	1,912
REGAL					
5H	W5	4-dr Sed-6P	2287	3120	2,571
5H	C5	2-dr Starlight Cpe-5P	2341	3095	3,151
5H	K5	2-dr Starliner HT-5P	2502	3175	5,040
5H	D5	2-dr Sta Wag-6P	2556	3265	2,878
LAND CRUISER					
5H	Y5	4-dr Sed-6P	2438	3180	6,383

ENGINES

(CHAMPION) Six-cylinder. L-head. Cast iron block. Displacement: 169.6 cid. Bore and stroke: 3 x 4 inches. Compression ratio: 7.5:1. Brake hp: 85 at 4000 rpm. Four main bearings. Solid valve lifters. Carburetor: Carter model WE-989SA, WE-2018S or WE-2190S one barrel.

(COMMANDER) V-8. Overhead valve. Cast iron block. Displacement: 232.6 cid. Bore and stroke: 3-3/8 x 3-1/4 inches. Compression ratio: 7.5:1. Brake hp: 127 at 4000 rpm. Five main bearings. Solid valve lifters. Carburetor: Stromberg model WWUVL-26 two-barrel.

CHASSIS FEATURES: Wheelbase: (wagons and sedans except Land Cruiser) 116.5 inches; (Land Cruiser, coupes and hardtops) 120.5 inches. Overall length: (sedans except Land Cruiser) 198.6 inches; (Land Cruiser) 202.6 inches; (coupes and hardtops) 202.2 inches; (station wagons) 195.6 inches. Front tread: 56.5 inches. Rear tread: 55.5 inches. Tires: (Champion except station wagon) 6.40 x 15 tube type; (Champion station wagon) 6.70 x 15 tube type; (Commander) 7.10 x 15 tube type.

OPTIONS: Hill Holder. Hydraulic power steering ($134). Directional signals. White sidewall tires. Stratoline 8-tube push-button radio. Starline 6-tube manual tuning radio. Internally controlled reel-type cowl radio antenna. Auxiliary rear seat speaker. Climatizer heater/ defroster. Fabric or plastic seat covers. Front fender ornaments. Strat-O-Styled hood ornament for models without standard hood ornament. Exterior rearview mirror. Rear fender skirts. Full wheelcovers, wire wheel type wheelcovers, wide stainless wheel trim rings or white painted metal trim rings. Imitation knock-off Sportster hubs. License plate frames. Gas door guard. Front and rear wing guards (bumper extensions). Grille guard. Fog light bumperettes with or without the fog lights. Rubber floor mats. Rubber front splashguards. Accelerator pedal cover and wear pad. Locking gas cap. Spotlight (with built-in rearview mirror). Back-up lights. Parking brake warning light. Glove compartment light. Underhood light. Trunk light for all models except Land Cruiser and station wagons (standard on Land Cruiser). Electric clock (standard on Land Cruiser). Kleenex dispenser. Vanity mirror. Exterior windshield sun visor. Side window vent shades. Glare-proof interior rearview mirror. Cigarette lighter. Safety child- proof rear door locks. Windshield washer. Custom luggage. Rear window defroster. Artic wiper blades. Tire chains. Undercoating. Electric windshield wipers for Champions. Rear ash receiver for Champion Custom/ Deluxe sedans. Fram oil filter (standard on Land Cruiser). Fram radiator water filter. Crankcase ventilator. Accessories specifically for the Champion Custom: Extra interior sun visor, front door armrests, rear armrests and rear seat ashtrays. A three-speed manual gear box with column mounted gear shift was standard on all models. Overdrive was available for $105 extra on Champions and $118 extra on Commanders. Automatic Drive was available for $216 extra on Champions and $227 extra on Commanders.

HISTORICAL FOOTNOTES: The Y body (Land Cruiser) was a stretched W body. The Land Cruiser had vent windows in the rear doors. The Land Cruiser featured Regal trim. A $60 ambulance conversion for the station wagon was introduced during midyear. Called the "Ambulet," it was available as a Champion or Commander with Deluxe (D7) or Regal (D9) trim. Numerous options, including a siren, red beacon light and cot, were available for the Ambulet.

1955 STUDEBAKER

CHAMPION — MODEL 16G6 — The low priced Champion series continued with the same body style and trim lines as in 1954, except for the deletion of the Regal two-door sedan. After Jan. 1, 1955, wraparound windshields were introduced on sedans and station wagons. Basic exterior trim differences between Custom, Deluxe and Regal models remained unchanged from 1954, except for the addition of wide "butter knife" side trim on Regal sedans, coupes and hardtops. A massive horizontal chrome grille replaced the delicate 1953-54 style. A hood ornament was standard on all models. Exterior model identification was limited to the deck lid handle. Starliner and Starlight names were discontinued. The Conestoga station wagon was still only available in two-door form.

STUDEBAKER I.D. NUMBERS: VIN on left front door pillar. Champion motor number on top of left front corner of block. Commander motor number top front of cylinder block near oil filler tube mounting. [CHAMPION] Serial numbers were G-1316501 to 1357374 (South Bend), G-932501 to G-936679 (Los Angeles) and G-758-201 and up (Canada). The beginning engine numbers were 1138001 (South Bend and early Los Angeles), L-101 (late Los Angeles) and C-60,501 for Canada. [COMMANDER] The serial numbers for the 1955 Commanders with 224.3 cid engines were 8380601 to 8397200 (South Bend), 8841201 to 8843000 (Los Angeles) and 8957601 and up (Canada). The engine numbers for cars with the 224 cid engine were V-312701 up (South Bend and Los Angeles) and VC-5701 up (Canada). The serial numbers for the 1955 Commanders with 259.2 cid engines were 8397201 to 8429407 (South Bend), 8843001 to 8849083 (Los Angeles) and 8958101 up (Canada). The engine numbers for cars with the 259 cid engine were V-331101 up (South Bend), VL-101 up (Los Angeles) and VC-6201 up (Canada). [PRESIDENT] The serial numbers for the 1955 Presidents were 7150001 to 7170827 (South Bend), 7805001 to 7808480 (Los Angeles) and 7900001 up (Canada). The beginning engine numbers were P-101 (South Bend and early Los Angeles), PL-101 (late Los Angeles) and PC-101 (Canada).

CHAMPION SERIES

Model Number	Body/Style Number	Body Type & Seating	Factory Price	Shipping Weight	Production Total
CUSTOM					
16G6	W1,2	4-dr Sed-6P	1783	2790	3,290
16G6	F1,2	2-dr Sed-6P	1741	2740	2,801
DELUXE					
16G6	W3,4	4-dr Sed-6P	1885	2805	13,621
16G6	F3,4	2-dr Sed-6P	1841	2780	7,666
16G6	C3	2-dr Cpe-5P	1875	2790	5,572
16G6	D3,4	2-dr Sta Wag-6P	2141	2980	3,517
REGAL					
16G6	W5,6	4-dr Sed-6P	1993	2815	7,406
16G6	C5	2-dr Cpe-5P	1975	2795	2,721
16G6	K5	2-dr HT-5P	2129	2865	2,408
16G6	D5,6	2-dr Sta Wag-6P	2312	2985	1,372

1955 Studebaker, Commander four-door sedan (late-year), V-8 (AA)

COMMANDER — MODEL 16G8 — The mid range Commander series offered the same body styles and trim lines as the 1955 Champions. After Jan. 1, 1955, wraparound windshields were introduced on sedans and station wagons. As in the Champion line, Regal and State models had a belt molding extending from the headlamps to taillamps, widening at the edge of the rear door. Series designations were "Commander" or "President" in script on the rear fenders. Exterior model identification was also on the deck lid handle.

COMMANDER SERIES

Model Number	Body/Style Number	Body Type & Seating	Factory Price	Shipping Weight	Production Total
CUSTOM					
16G8	W1,2	4-dr Sed-6P	1919	3065	2,082
16G8	F1,2	2-dr Sed-6P	1873	3005	1,413
DELUXE					
16G8	W3,4	4-dr Sed-6P	2014	3075	16,768
16G8	F3,4	2-dr Sed-6P	1969	3045	6,834
16G8	D3,4	2-dr Sta Wag-6P	2274	3265	4,280
16G8	C3	2-dr Cpe-5P	1989	3065	6,975
REGAL					
16G8	C5	2-dr Cpe-5P	2094	3065	4,639
16G8	K5	2-dr HT-5P	2282	3150	3,296
16G8	D5,6	2-dr Sta Wag-6P	2445	3275	2,516
16G8	W5,6	4-dr Sed-6P	2127	3080	9,985

1955 Studebaker, President Speedster two-door hardtop coupe, V-8

PRESIDENT — MODEL 6H — After an absence of 13 years, the top line President series was returned. Basic President styling was the same as 1955 Champions and Commanders. The tri-level painted President Speedster hardtop was introduced in January 1955. State and Speedster styles featured the "butter-knife" side trim. Instrument panels were shared by all Champions, Commanders and Presidents (except the Speedster). The Speedster had an engine turned instrument panel. Almost every conceivable option was standard on the Speedster. After Jan. 1, 1955, wraparound windshields were introduced on sedans. The President State four-door sedan replaced the Land Cruiser. Model identification was on the deck lid handle and rear quarter panels. South Bend built Speedsters had only "Speedster" on quarter panels, while Los Angeles ones had both "President" and "Speedster" on these panels.

PRESIDENT SERIES

Model Number	Body/Style Number	Body Type & Seating	Factory Price	Shipping Weight	Production Total
DELUXE					
6H	Y3/Y4	4-dr Sed-6P	2311	3165	1,021
STATE					
6H	Y5/Y6	4-dr Sed-6P	2381	3220	14,634
6H	C5	2-dr Cpe-5P	2270	3110	3,327
6H	K5	2-dr HT-5P	2456	3175	3,468
6H	K7	2-dr Spds HT-5P	3253	3301	2,215

ENGINES

(CHAMPION) Six-cylinder. L-head. Cast iron block. Displacement: 185.6 cid. Bore and stroke: 3 x 4-3/8 inches. Compression ratio: 7.5:1. Brake hp: 101 at 4000 rpm. Four main bearings. Solid valve lifters. Carburetor: Carter model WE-21085 one-barrel.

(COMMANDER) Early V-8. Overhead valve. Cast iron block. Displacement: 224.3 cid. Bore and stroke: 3-9/16 x 2-13/16 inches. Compression ratio: 7.5:1. Brake hp: 140 at 4500 rpm. Five main bearings. Solid valve lifters. Carburetor: Stromberg model WW two-barrel. Late V-8. Overhead valve. Cast iron block. Displacement: 259.2 cid. Bore and stroke: 3-9/16 x 3-1/4 inches. Compression ratio: 7.5:1. Brake hp: 162 at 4500 rpm. Five main bearings. Solid valve lifters. Carburetor: Stromberg model WW two-barrel.

(PRESIDENT) V-8. Overhead valve. Cast iron block. Displacement: 259.2 cid. Bore and stroke: 3-9/16 x 3-1/4 inches. Compression ratio: 7.5:1. Brake hp: 175 (early) and 185 (late) at 4500 rpm. Five main bearings. Solid valve lifters. Carburetor: Carter model WCFB four-barrel.

CHASSIS FEATURES: Wheelbase: (Wagons and sedans except President) 116.5 inches; (President four-door sedans, coupes and hardtops) 120.5 inches. Overall length: (Sedans except President) 202.2 inches; (President four-door sedans) 206.2 inches; (Coupes and hardtops) 204.4 inches; (Station wagons) 197.7 inches. Front tread: 56.7 inches. Rear tread: 55.7 inches. Tires: (Champion except station wagon) 6.40 x 15 tubeless; (Champion station wagon and all Commanders) 6.70 x 15 tubeless; (President) 7.10 x 15 tubeless.

OPTIONS: Hill Holder. Power steering ($108). Power brakes. Air conditioning for V-8 powered sedans (A $567 midyear option). Power seats (midyear option). Power windows (midyear option). Directional signals. White sidewall tires. Stratoline 8-tube push-button radio or Starline 6-tube manual tuning radio. Internally controlled reel-type cowl antenna. Auxiliary rear seat speaker. Climatizer heater/defroster. Fabric or plastic seat covers. Cushion toppers. Fender ornaments for models without standard fender ornaments. Exhaust deflectors (two styles). Exterior rearview mirror(s) (three styles). License plate frames. Door handle guards. Rear fender skirts. Gas door guard. Full wheelcovers. Wire wheel type wheelcovers, or wide stainless wheel trim rings. Imitation knock-off Sportster hubs. Grille guard. Fog light bumperettes. Rubber floor mats. Front wheel splash guards. Accelerator pedal cover and wear pad. Locking gas cap. Spotlight (with built in rearview mirror). Back-up lights. Glove compartment light. Underhood light. Trunk light (standard on President State sedan). Electric clock (standard on Presidents). Kleenex dispenser. Custom luggage. Vanity mirror. Exterior windshield sun visor. Side door vent shades. Glare-proof interior rearview mirror. Safety child-proof rear door locks. Windshield washer. 3-D Booster horn. Rear window defroster. Artic wiper blades. Tire chains. Undercoating. Electric windshield wipers for Champions. Rear ash receivers for models not fitted with them. Fram oil filter (standard on Presidents). Fram radiator water filter. Accessories specifically for the Champion/Commander Custom: Front door armrests and rear armrests. A three-speed manual gear box with column mounted gear shift was standard on all models except the Speedster. Automatic Drive or overdrive was standard on the Speedster. Overdrive was available for $115 extra on Champions and $118 on Commanders and Presidents. Automatic Drive was available for $216 extra on Champions and $227 extra on Commanders and Presidents. A power kit which featured a four-barrel carburetor (Carter WCFB) and dual exhausts was available for Commanders. The kit raised the 224 engine's power to 160 hp at 4500 rpm. and the 259 engine's power to 182 hp at 4500 rpm.

HISTORICAL FOOTNOTES: The President four-door sedans (Y bodies) were stretched W bodies. The Y bodies had vent windows (fixed on President Deluxe) in the rear doors. An ambulance/emergency vehicle conversion for the station wagon was available. Called the Ambulet, it was available as a Champion or Commander with Deluxe (D7/D8) or Regal (D9/D10) trim Numerous options, including a siren, red beacon light and cot, were available for the Ambulet. Early model sedans and wagons with non-wraparound windshields used odd (1, 3, 5, 7, 9), trim number identifications. Late model (after Jan. 1, 1955) sedans and wagons with wraparound windshields used even (2,4,6,8, 10) trim number identifications.

1956 Studebaker, Champion two-door sedan, 6-cyl (AA)

CHAMPION AND FLIGHT HAWK — SERIES 56G — The front and rear sections of all Studebaker sedans were greatly restyled in 1956. The station wagons, which had front ends like the sedans, were fitted with small fiberglass fins on the rear quarter panels. The coupes and hardtops were named Hawks and featured a square shaped grille and flat-backed deck lid. Custom sedan models, which included the two-door sedanet, had horizontal side trim along the front two-thirds of the car. Regular sedans had full length side trim. The rare Regal model, which was built mainly for sales outside the United States, had dual full length side moldings. A new "Cyclops Eye" speedometer was introduced on sedans and station wagons. All models were switched from 6-volt to 12-volt electrical systems.

STUDEBAKER I.D. NUMBERS: VIN on left front door pillar. Champion motor number on top of left front corner of block. Commander motor number top front of cylinder block near oil filler tube mounting. [CHAMPION/FLIGHT HAWK] Serial numbers were G-1357501 to G-1379117 (South Bend), G-936701 to G-938796 (Los Angeles) and G-763701 up (Canada). The engine numbers were 1180251 up (South Bend), L-3201 up (Los Angeles) and C-66001 up for Canada. [COMMANDER/POWER HAWK] The serial numbers for the 1956 Commanders and Power Hawks were 8429601 to 8454060 (South Bend), 8849101 to 8852866 (Los Angeles) and 8960001 up (Canada). The beginning engine numbers were V-363-751 and up (South Bend), VL-6301 up (Los Angeles) and VC-8101 up for Canada. [PRESIDENT AND SKY HAWK] The serial numbers for the 1956 President and Sky Hawk were 7171001 to 7188817 (South Bend), 7808501 to 7811699 (Los Angeles) and 7900601 up (Canada). The beginning engine numbers were P-22001 (South Bend), PL-2701 (Los Angeles) and PC-601 for Canada. [GOLDEN HAWK] The serial numbers for the 1956 Golden Hawks were 6030001 to 6033472 (South Bend) and 6800001 to 6800601 (Los Angeles). The beginning engine numbers were K-1001 (with overdrive) and S-1001 (with Twin Ultramatic).

CHAMPION/FLIGHT HAWK SERIES

Model Number	Body/Style Number	Body Type & Seating	Factory Price	Shipping Weight	Production Total
DELUXE					
CUSTOM					
56G	W2	4-dr Sed-6P	1717	—	1,170
DELUXE					
56G	W4	4-dr Sed-6P	1996	2835	11,983
56G	F2	2-dr S'net-6P	1844	2780	3,097
56G	F4	2-dr Sed-6P	1946	2800	4,301
REGAL					
56G	W6	4-dr Sed-6P	—	—	1,180
FLIGHT HAWK					
56G	C3	2-dr Cpe-5P	1986	2780	4,389
56G	K7	2-dr HT-5P	—	—	560
PELHAM					
56G	D4	2-dr Sta Wag-6P	2232	3000	2,236

1956 Studebaker, Commander Parkview station wagon, V-8

COMMANDER AND POWER HAWK — SERIES 56B — Styling changes were the same as those made on the Champions. Exterior trim variations were also the same as on Champions. The model identification was located on the front fenders of sedans and station wagons and all deck lids. The Commander continued as Studebaker's mid-range offering. The Power Hawk, like the Flight Hawk coupe, was based on the original 1953 Starlight.

COMMANDER/POWER HAWK SERIES

Model Number	Body/Style Number	Body Type & Seating	Factory Price	Shipping Weight	Production Total
DELUXE					
56B	W4	4-dr Sed-6P	2125	3140	14,700
56B	F2	2-dr S'net-6P	1974	3085	1,523
56B	F4	2-dr Sed-6P	2076	3110	3,663
CUSTOM					
56B	W2	4-dr Sed-6P	1829	—	335
POWER HAWK					
56B	C3	2-dr Cpe-5P	2101	3095	7,095
PARKVIEW					
56B	D4	2-dr Sta Wag-6P	2354	3300	3,333

1956 Studebaker, Power Hawk two-door coupe, V-8 (AA)

1956 Studebaker, President Classic four-door sedan, V-8 (AA)

PRESIDENT AND SKY HAWK — SERIES 56H — The President series was limited to the top line trim which featured dual side trim moldings on sedans and station wagons. The President Classic had wide grooved horizontal moldings just above the rocker panels. The model identification locations were the same as on Commanders and Champions. Except for the Golden Hawk model, the President series continued as Studebaker's top line offering.

PRESIDENT/SKY HAWK SERIES

Model Number	Body/Style Number	Body Type & Seating	Factory Price	Shipping Weight	Production Total
PRESIDENT					
56H	W6	4-dr Sed-6P	2235	3210	6,822
56H	F6	2-dr Sed-6P	2188	3180	1,914
PRESIDENT CLASSIC					
56H	Y6	4-dr Sed-6P	2489	3295	8,507
SKY HAWK					
56H	K7	2-dr HT-5P	2477	3215	3,050
PINEHURST					
56H	D6	2-dr Sta Wag-6P	2529	3395	1,522

GOLDEN HAWK — MODEL 56J — The Golden Hawk, like the Sky Hawk and Flight Hawk hardtops, was based on the original 1953 Starliner body. Small upright fiberglass fins on the top of the rear fenders were a Golden Hawk exclusive among the four 1956 Hawk models. Like the President Classic, the Golden Hawk had wide grooved horizontal moldings just above the rocker panels.

GOLDEN HAWK SERIES

Model Number	Body/Style Number	Body Type & Seating	Factory Price	Shipping Weight	Production Total
56J	K7	2-dr Gold Hawk HT-5P	3061	3360	4,071

ENGINES

(CHAMPION AND FLIGHT HAWK ENGINE) Six-cylinder. L-head. Cast iron block. Displacement: 185.6 cid. Bore and stroke: 3 x 4-3/8 inches. Compression ratio: 7.8:1. Brake hp: 101 at 4000 rpm. Four main bearings. Solid valve lifters. Carburetor: Carter model WE-2108S or WE-2417S one-barrel.

(COMMANDER AND POWER HAWK ENGINE) V-8. Overhead valve. Cast iron block. Displacement: 259.2 cid. Bore and stroke: 3-9/16 x 3-1/4 inches. Compression ratio: 7.8:1. Brake hp: 170 at 4500 rpm. Five main bearings. Solid valve lifters. Carburetor: Stromberg model WW two-barrel.

(PRESIDENT AND SKY HAWK ENGINE) V-8. Overhead valve. Cast iron block. Displacement: 289 cid. Bore and stroke: 3-9/16 x 3-5/8 inches. Compression ratio: 7.8:1. Brake hp: 210 at 4500 rpm. on Classic and Sky Hawk; 190 at 4500 rpm. on others. Five main bearings. Solid valve lifters. Carburetor: Carter model WCFB four-barrel on Classic and Sky Hawk. Stromberg model WW two-barrel on all others.

(GOLDEN HAWK ENGINE) Packard V-8. Overhead valve. Cast iron block. Displacement: 352 cid. Bore and stroke: 4 x 3-1/2 inches. Compression ratio: 9.5:1. Brake hp: 275 at 4600 rpm. Five main bearings. Hydraulic valve lifters. Carburetor: Carter model WCFB-23945 four-barrel.

1956 Studebaker, Golden Hawk two-door hardtop coupe, V-8 (AA)

CHASSIS FEATURES: Wheelbase: (wagons and Sedans except President Classic) 116.5 inches; (President Classic and Hawks) 120.5 inches. Overall length: (Sedans except President Classic) 200.7 inches; (President Classic) 204.7 inches; (Hawks) 203.9 inches; (Station wagons) 196.7 inches. Front tread: 56.7 inches. Rear tread: 55.7 inches. Tires: 56G (except station wagons) 6.40 x 15 tubeless; (Champion wagon, 56B and 56H except Classic) 6.70 x 15 tubeless; (President Classic and Golden Hawk) 7.10 x 15 tubeless.

OPTIONS: Hill Holder. Power steering ($108). Power brakes. Air conditioning for V-8 powered sedans. Power sedans. Power windows. Direction signals. White sidewall tires. Stratoline push-button radio. Starline manual tuning radio. Internally controlled reel-type cowl antenna or dual rear mounted antenna. Rear seat speaker. Regular full wheelcovers or imitation spoke (not wire) wheelcovers. Regal or Deluxe license plate frames. Imitation dual exhaust extension for sedan models with single exhaust. Exhaust extension for Hawks and station wagons. Rear bumper guards for sedans. Gas door guard. Door handle guards. Curb signals. Rubber floor mats. Rubber splash guards. Accelerator pedal cover and wear pad. Locking gas cap. Exterior rearview mirror. Glare-proof interior rearview mirror. Brake fluid safety reservoir. Windshield washer. Climatizer heater/defroster. Door mounted front safety belts. Spotlight. Parking brake warning light. Glove compartment light (standard on Classic and Golden Hawk). Trunk and utility light. Underhood light. Back-up lights. Electric clock for models it was not standard on. Compass. Traffic light viewer. Cigarette lighter. Automatic transmission Anti Creep. Station wagon luggage carrier. Cushion toppers. Vanity mirror. Kleenex dispenser. Custom luggage. Station wagon air mattress. Fram oil filter for Champions and Commanders (standard on all others). Undercoating. A three-speed gear box with column mounted gear shift was standard on all models except the Golden Hawk. Overdrive or Packard's Twin Ultra-matic ($100 extra) was standard on the Golden Hawk. Overdrive was available for $108 extra on 56G, 56B and Sky Hawk models. It was $118 extra on other President models. Flightomatic was available for $189 extra on all models except the Golden Hawk. An optional four-barrel carburetor (Carter model WCFB) was available on Commanders, Power Hawks and W, F and D bodied Presidents. It increased the 259 cid V-8's power to 185 hp at 4500 rpm. and the President's to 210 hp at 4500 rpm. The optional four-barrel carburetor was part of a power kit option that included dual exhausts. A 8.3:1 compression ratio was optional on Studebaker V-8 engines. A special order Commander Custom four-door Police Car was available with a 289 cid President engine.

HISTORICAL FOOTNOTES: The President Classic four-door sedan (Y body) was a stretched W body. The Classic had vent windows in the rear doors. An ambulance/emergency vehicle conversion for the station wagons was available. Called the Ambulet, it was available as a 56G-D8 and a 56B-D8. Numerous options, including siren, red beacon lights and cot, were available for the Ambulet. The Custom four-door sedan (W2) was limited to police, taxi and export/Canadian sales. Except for one car, the Champion Regal (President trim) four-door sedan (56G-E6) was limited to export/Canadian sales. The Flight Hawk hardtop with Sky Hawk trim (56G-K7) was, e1957 Studebaker.

1957 STUDEBAKER

CHAMPION AND SILVER HAWK SIX — SERIES 57G — A new wraparound grille and larger taillights were the obvious changes for 1957 on sedans and wagons. A four-door station wagon was introduced. Hawks were fitted with large canted metal fins on the rear fenders. Custom models had rubber moldings around the windshield and rear windows and single side trim moldings on the front two-thirds of the car. Deluxe versions featured bright metal moldings around the windshield and rear window and full length side trim. Regal models (built only for sales outside the United States) had double side trim moldings on the rear quarter panels and single pieces on the front. A low priced plain-Jane Scotsman line was introduced during midyear. The Scotsman had painted hubcaps and grille and no side trim moldings. The Scotsman was introduced as a Champion, but it was eventually referred to as a separate model like the Silver Hawk six. Except for the Scotsman and Silver Hawk, the model identification was on the front fenders. The Scotsman had no model identification and the Silver Hawk's nameplate was on the deck lid. In 1957, directional signals were made standard on all models.

1957 Studebaker, Champion two-door sedan, 6-cyl

STUDEBAKER I.D. NUMBERS: VIN on left front door pillar. Champion motor number on top of left front corner of block. Commander motor number top front of cylinder block near oil filler tube mounting. [CHAMPION/SILVER HAWK SIX] Serial numbers were G-1379201 to G-1405239 (South Bend) and G-769101 up (Canada). The beginning engine numbers were 1202101 (South Bend) and C-71401 (Canada). The Los Angeles plant was closed. [SCOTSMAN] Scotsman serial numbers were G-1393130 to G-1405239 and motor numbers began at 1213263 and up. [COMMANDER/SILVER HAWK 259] The serial numbers for the 1957 Commander and Silver Hawk 259s were 8454101 to 8471491 (South Bend) and 8962601 and up for Canada. The beginning engine numbers were V-390001 (South Bend) and VC-10,701 for Canada. [PRESIDENT/SILVER HAWK 289] The serial numbers for the 1957 President and Silver Hawk 289s were 7188901 to 7209836 (South Bend) and 7901501 up for Canada. The beginning engine numbers for 1957 Presidents and Silver Hawk 289s were P-39601 up (South Bend) and PC-1501 up for Canada. [GOLDEN HAWK] The serial number for the 1957 Golden Hawk were 6100001 to 6104354 (South Bend). The beginning engine number for the 1957 Golden Hawks was PS-1001.

CHAMPION/SILVER HAWK SIX SERIES

Model Number	Body/Style Number	Body Type & Seating	Factory Price	Shipping Weight	Production Total
SCOTSMAN					
57G	W1	4-dr Sed-6P	1826	2725	3,005
57G	F1	2-dr Sed-6P	1776	2680	2,943
57G	D1	2-dr Sta Wag-6P	1995	2875	3,400
CUSTOM					
57G	W2	4-dr Sed-6P	2049	2785	2,106
57G	F2	2-dr Sed-6P	2001	2755	1,751
57G	P2	4-dr Sta Wag-6P	—	—	25
DELUXE					
57G	W4	4-dr Sed-6P	2171	2810	8,313
57G	F4	2-dr Sed-6P	2123	2780	1,950
67G	P4	4-dr Sta Wag-6P	—	—	1
PELHAM					
57G	D4	2-dr Sta Wag-6P	2382	3015	1,120
REGAL					
57G	W6	4-dr Sed-6P	—	—	247
SILVER HAWK					
57G	C3	2-dr Cpe-5P	2142	2790	4,163
57G	K3	2-dr HT-5P	—	—	120

1957 Studebaker, Commander two-door sedan, V-8

COMMANDER AND SILVER HAWK 259 — SERIES 57B — Styling changes and trim differences were the same as on Champions. Hawk models continued with the engine turned instrument panel concept introduced on the 1955 Speedster. Model identifications were in the same locations as on Champions. The Flight Hawk, Power Hawk and Sky Hawk models of 1956 were replaced by the various 1957 Silver Hawk models. Certain Silver Hawk models were limited to sales outside the U.S. For instance, the Silver Hawk V-8 sold in the United States came with a 289 engine, while the Canadian version was fitted with a 259 engine.

COMMANDER/SILVER HAWK 259 SERIES

Model Number	Body/Style Number	Body Type & Seating	Factory Price	Shipping Weight	Production Total
CUSTOM					
57B	W2	4-dr Sed-6P	2173	3015	828
57B	F2	2-dr Sed-6P	2124	3075	530
DELUXE					
57B	W4	4-dr Sed-6P	2295	3140	10,285
57B	F4	2-dr Sed-6P	2246	3100	2,072

Model Number	Body/Style Number	Body Type & Seating	Factory Price	Shipping Weight	Production Total
STATION WAGON					
57B	D4	2-dr Park Sta Wag-6P	2505	3310	738
57B	P4	4-dr Prov Sta Wag-6P	2561	3355	3,995
SILVER HAWK					
57B	C3	2-dr Cpe-5P	—	—	1,180
57B	K3	2-dr HT HT-5P	—	—	248

1957 Studebaker, Golden Hawk two-door hardtop coupe, V-8

PRESIDENT/SILVER HAWK 289/GOLDEN HAWK — SERIES 57H — Styling changes and trim differences were the same as on Champions. The Silver Hawk 289 came only as a pillared coupe. The Golden Hawk came only as a hardtop. Standard on the Golden Hawk was a belt-driven supercharger. Model identifications were in the same locations as on Champions.

1957 Studebaker, President Broadmoor four-door station wagon, V-8

PRESIDENT/SILVER HAWK 289/GOLDEN HAWK SERIES

Model Number	Body/Style Number	Body Type & Seating	Factory Price	Shipping Weight	Production Total
CUSTOM					
57H	W2	4-dr Sed-6P	—	—	74
57H	F2	2-dr Sed-6P	—	—	62
57H	P2	4-dr Wag-6P	—	—	6
DELUXE					
57H	W4	4-dr Sed-6P	—	—	33
57H	F4	2-dr Sed-6P	—	—	8
47H	D4	2-dr Sta Wag-6P	—	—	8
REGAL					
57H	W6	4-dr Sed-6P	2407	3205	3,127
57H	F6	2-dr Sed-6P	2358	3170	836
CLASSIC					
57H	Y6	4-dr Sed-6P	2539	3270	6,063
BROADMOOR STATION WAGON					
57H	P6	4-dr Sta Wag-6P	2666	3415	1,530
SILVER HAWK					
57H	C3	2-dr Cpe-5P	2263	3185	9,607
GOLDEN HAWK					
57H	K7	2-dr HT-5P	3182	3400	4,356

ENGINES

(CHAMPION/SILVER HAWK) Six-cylinder. L-head. Cast iron block. Displacement: 185.6 cid. Bore and stroke: 3 x 4-3/8 inches. Compression ratio: 7.8:1. Brake hp: 101 at 4000 rpm. Four main bearings. Solid valve lifters. Carburetor: Carter model WE or BBR1 one-barrel.

(COMMANDER/SILVER HAWK 259) V-8. Overhead valve. Cast iron block. Displacement: 259.2 cid. Bore and stroke: 3-9/16 x 3-1/4 inches. Compression ratio: 8.3:1. Brake hp: 180 at 4500 rpm. Five main bearings. Solid valve lifters. Carburetor: Stromberg model WW two-barrel.

(PRESIDENT/SILVER HAWK 289) V-8. Overhead valve. Cast iron block. Displacement: 289 cid. Bore and stroke: 3-9/16 x 3-5/8 inches. Compression ratio: 8.3:1. Brake hp: 225 at 4500 rpm. on Classic; 210 at 4500 rpm. on all others. Five main bearings. Solid valve lifters. Carburetor: Carter model WCFB four-barrel on Classic. Stromberg model WW two-barrel on all others.

(GOLDEN HAWK) V-8. Overhead valve. Cast block. Displacement: 289 cid. Bore and stroke: 39/16 x 3-5/8 inches. Compression ratio: 7.8:1. Brake hp: 275 at 4800 rpm. Five main bearings. Solid valve lifters. Carburetor: Stromberg model WW two-barrel.

CHASSIS FEATURES: Wheelbase: (wagons and sedans except President and Classic) 116.5 inches; (President Classic and Hawks) 120.5 inches. Overall length: (wagons and sedans except President Classic) 202.4 inches; (President Classic) 206.4 inches; (Hawks) 204 inches. Front tread: 56.7 inches. Rear tread: 55.7 inches. Tires: 57G (except station wagon) 6.40 x 15 tubeless; (Champion wagon, 57B and 57H except Classic and Golden Hawk) 6.70 x 15 tubeless; (President Classic and Golden Hawk) 7.10 x 15 tubeless.

OPTIONS: [SCOTSMAN] Hill Holder. Rear-facing third seat for station wagons. Electric windshield wipers. Extra interior sun visor. Door armrests. A simple heater/defroster was standard on the Scotsman. A radio was not a listed option for Scotsmans. [OTHER MODELS] Power steering ($98). Hill Holder. Power brakes. Air conditioning for V-8 powered sedans. Power seats. Power windows. Rear-facing third seat for station wagons (midyear option; when third seat was ordered, Captive-Air tires were fitted since there was no room for a spare tire and wheel.) White sidewall tires. Stratoline push-button radio. Starline manual tuning radio. Internally controlled reel-type cowl antenna or dual rear mounted antenna. Rear seat speaker. Regular full wheelcovers or imitation spoke (not wire) wheelcovers. License plate frames. Exhaust extensions or Stratoline exhaust deflectors. Exterior rearview mirrors (three types). Door edge guards. Gas door guard. Door handle guard. Front bumper guards. Locking gas cap. Curb signals. Rubber floor mats or carpet toppers. Rubber splashguards. Accelerator pedal cover and wear pad. Automatic transmission Anti Creep. Brake fluid safety reservoir. Rear door safety locks. Windshield washer. Door mounted front safety belts. Climatizer heater/defroster. Spotlight. Parking brake warning light. Glove compartment light (standard on Classic and Golden Hawk). Trunk and utility light. Underhood light. Back-up light. Seat toppers. Electric clock. Auto compass. Traffic light viewer. Cigarette lighter (standard on Presidents and Golden Hawks). Vanity mirror (illuminated or not). Kleenex dispenser. Custom luggage. Roof luggage carrier for sedans and wagons. Station wagon air mattress. Tripod jack. Fram oil filter (standard on 289 V-8s.) Undercoating. A three-speed manual gear box with column-mounted gear shift was standard on all models except the Golden Hawk. Overdrive or Flightomatic were ($119 extra); standard on the Golden Hawk. Overdrive was available for $100 extra on all other models. Flightomatic was available for $189 extra on all models other than the Golden Hawk and Scotsman. Flightomatic was not available on the Scotsman. An optional power kit that included a four-barrel carburetor (Carter model WCFB) and dual exhausts was available on 57B (259 V-8) models and W, F, C, D and P 57H (289 V-8) models. The kit increased the 259 V-8's power to 195 hp at 4500 rpm and the 289 V-8's power to 225 hp at 4500 rpm. A Twin Traction limited slip differential was optional on all models. This type of differential was pioneered on Packard cars and light Studebaker trucks in 1956. Larger tire sizes were optional on most models.

HISTORICAL FOOTNOTES: The President Classic four-door sedan (Y body) was a stretched W body. The Classic had vent windows in the rear doors. Except for the Scotsman, two-door sedans were called Club Sedans. An ambulance conversion for station wagons was available. Called the Ambulet, it was available as a 57G-D8, a 57B-D8 and 57H-D8. Heavy-duty two-door and four-door sedans and wagons with Custom or Deluxe trim were utilized for emergency service vehicle use. They were available with 185 six or 259 V-8 engines. Special Commander Police Cruisers with standard 289 V-8s were built. They were available as two-door or four-door sedans or wagons with Custom or Deluxe trim. They were identified as 57Hs, so they are included in the President production figures. The following were limited to export/Canadian sales: 57GW6, 57G-P2, 57B-C3 and 57B-K3. A few heavy-duty sedans with special "breathable Naugahyde" upholstery were sold as taxis.

1958 STUDEBAKER

CHAMPION AND SILVER HAWK SIX — SERIES 58G — Canted metal rear quarter panel fins on regular Champion (not Scotsman) sedans and wagons, plus dual headlight pods (with optional dual headlights) on the same body type were the main 1958 additions. Scotsman models had restyled round taillights, Studebaker lettering on the left rear quarter panel and a square mesh radiator grille. The Silver Hawk had new grille mesh in the side grille openings and small dual fins on the front fender mounted parking lights. A large round Hawk emblem was placed in the lower center of the central Hawk grille. A long wheelbase Scotsman four-door sedan called the "Econ-O-Miler" was introduced. Model identification was on the rear fins, except on the Silver Hawk and Scotsman. The Scotsman had no model identification and the Silver Hawk nameplate was on the deck lid.

1958 Studebaker, Silver Hawk two-door coupe, V-8

STUDEBAKER I.D. NUMBERS: VIN on left front door pillar. Champion motor number on top of left front corner of block. Commander motor number top front of cylinder block near oil filler tube mounting. [CHAMPION/SILVER HAWK SIX] The beginning serial numbers for the 1958 Champions and Silver Hawk Sixes were G-1405401 (South Bend) and G-772301 (Canadian). The beginning engine numbers were 1228401 (South Bend) and C-74,701 (Canada). [COMMANDER AND SILVER HAWK 259] The beginning serial numbers for the 1958 Commander and Silver Hawk 259s were 8471601 (South Bend) and 8965101 (Canada). The beginning engine numbers were V-407501 (South Bend) and VC-13301 (Canada). [PRESIDENT/SILVER HAWK 289/GOLDEN HAWK] The beginning serial numbers for the 1958 Presidents (including Marshals) and Silver Hawk 289s were 7210001 (South Bend) and 7902001 (Canada). The beginning serial number for the 1958 Golden Hawks was 6104501

(South Bend). The beginning engines for 1958 Presidents (including Marshals) and Silver Hawk 289s were P-60701 (South Bend) and PC-2001 (Canada). The beginning engine number for 1958 Golden Hawks was PS-5501 (South Bend).

CHAMPION/SILVER HAWK SERIES

Model Number	Body/Style Number	Body Type & Seating	Factory Price	Shipping Weight	Production Total
SCOTSMAN					
58G	F1	2-dr Sed-6P	1795	2695	5,538
58G	W1	4-dr Sed-6P	1874	2740	7,654
58G	D1	2-dr Wag-6P	2055	2870	7,680
SCOTSMAN ECON-O-MILER					
58G	Y1	4-dr Sed-6P	—	3030	1,118
CHAMPION					
58G	W4	4-dr Sed-6P	2253	2835	5,178
58G	F4	2-dr Sed-6P	2189	2795	1,455
58G	J4	2-dr HT Sed-6P	—	—	120
CHAMPION DELUXE					
58G	P4	4-dr Sta Wag-6P	—	—	12
SILVER HAWK					
58G	C3	2-dr Cpe-5P	2219	2810	2,442

COMMANDER AND SILVER HAWK 259 — SERIES 58B — Styling changes and trim differences were basically the same as on Champions, except that regular Commander sedans and wagons came with standard dual headlights. A new two-door "sedan-sized hardtop" was introduced in 1958. It was called a Starlight in most publicity announcements. Model identifications were in the same location as in Champions.

COMMANDER/SILVER HAWK 259 SERIES

Model Number	Body/Style Number	Body Type & Seating	Factory Price	Shipping Weight	Production Total
SCOTSMAN					
58B	W1	4-dr Sed-6P	—	—	37
58B	F1	2-dr Sed-6P	—	—	44
58B	D1	2-dr Sta Wag-6P	—	—	7
COMMANDER					
58B	W4	4-dr Sed-6P	2378	3185	6,771
58B	J4	2-dr HT Sed-6P	2493	3270	2,555
58B	P4	4-dr Prov Sta Wag-6P	2644	3420	2,412
SILVER HAWK					
58B	C3	2-dr Cpe-5P	—	—	367
58B	K3	2-dr HT-5P	—	—	56

1958 Studebaker, President two-door hardtop coupe, V-8

PRESIDENT, SILVER HAWK 289 AND GOLDEN HAWK — SERIES 58H — Styling changes were the same as on Commanders. Special President-powered Scotsman police cars, called Marshals, were introduced. A belt driven supercharger was standard on the Golden Hawk. Model identifications were in the same locations as on Commanders.

PRESIDENT/SILVER HAWK/GOLDEN HAWK SERIES

Model Number	Body/Style Number	Body Type & Seating	Factory Price	Shipping Weight	Production Total
MARSHAL (POLICE)					
58H	W1	4-dr Sed-6P	—	3162	115
58H	F1	2-dr Sed-6P	—	—	152
58H	D1	2-dr Sta Wag-6P	—	—	70
PRESIDENT					
59H	J6	2-dr HT Sed-6P	2695	3355	1,171
58H	P4	4-dr Del Sta Wag-6P	—	—	1
58H	Y6	4-dr Sed-6P	2639	3365	3,570
SILVER HAWK					
58H	C3	2-dr Cpe-6P	2352	3210	4,485
GOLDEN HAWK					
58H	K7	2-dr HT-5P	3282	3470	878

ENGINES

(CHAMPION/SILVER HAWK SIX) Six-cylinder. L-head. Cast iron block. Displacement: 185.6 cid. Bore and stroke: 3 x 4-3/8 inches. Compression ratio: 7.8:1. Brake hp: 101 at 4000 rpm. Four main bearings. Solid valve lifters. Carburetor: Carter model WE or BBR1 one-barrel.

(COMMANDER/SILVER HAWK 259) V-8. Overhead valve. Cast iron block. Displacement: 259.2 cid. Bore and stroke: 3-9/16 x 3-1/4 inches. Compression ratio: 8.3:1. Brake hp: 180 at 4500 rpm. Five main bearings. Solid valve lifters. Carburetor: Stromberg model WW two-barrel.

(PRESIDENT/SILVER HAWK 289) V-8. Overhead valve. Cast iron block. Displacement: 289 cid. Bore and stroke: 3-9/16 x 3-5/8 inches. Compression ratio: 8.3:1. Brake hp: 225 at 4500 rpm. on President J6 and Y6; 210 at 4500 rpm. on all others. Five main bearings. Solid valve lifters. Carburetor: Carter model WCFB four-barrel on President J6 and Y6. Stromberg model WW two-barrel on all others.

(GOLDEN HAWK ENGINE) Supercharged V-8. Overhead valve. Cast iron block. Displacement: 289 cid. Bore and stroke: 3-9/16 x 3-5/8 inches. Compression ratio: 7.8:1. Brake hp: 275 at 4800 rpm. Five main bearings. Solid valve lifters. Carburetor: Stromberg model WW two-barrel.

CHASSIS FEATURES: Wheelbase: (wagons and sedans except Y bodies) 116.5 inches; (Y bodies and Hawks) 120.5 inches. Overall length: (wagons and sedans except Y bodies) 202.4 inches; (President Y6 sedan and Econ-O-Miler Y1 sedan) 206.4 inches; (Hawks) 204 inches. Front tread: (with 15-inch wheels) 57.2 Inches; (with 14-inch wheels) 57.1 inches. Rear tread: (with 15-inch wheels) 56.2 inches; (with 14-inch wheels) 56.1 inches. Tires: 57G (except station wagons and Econ-O-Miler) 6.40 x 15 tubeless; (Champion wagon, Econ-O-Miler and 57B-H with WI, FI and DI bodies) 6.70 x 15 tubeless; (Provincial, Golden Hawk and President Y6 sedan) 8.00 x 14 tubeless; (all others) 7.50 x 14 tubeless.

OPTIONS: [SCOTSMAN] Hill Holder ($15). Rear-facing third seat for station wagons ($102). Electric windshield wipers ($12). Chrome hubcaps. Side moldings. Chrome headlamp rims. Chrome back-up lamps. Extra sun visor. Door armrests. Gas door guard. Door handle guards. Door edge guards. [OTHER MODELS] Power steering ($69). Hill Holder ($15). Power brakes ($38). Power windows ($102). Power seats ($45). Air conditioning ($325). Rear facing third seat for station wagons ($102). When this "Hideaway" third seat was ordered, Captive-Air tires were fitted since there was no room for a spare tire and wheel. White sidewall tires ($28). Transistor push-button Signal Seeker radio. Seven tube transistor push-button radio ($80). Manual six-tube tuning tube radio ($61). Electric cowl antenna. Reel-type internally controlled antenna. Single deck lid antenna. Dual rear antenna. Rear seat speaker ($13). Regular full wheelcovers ($17). Imitation spoke (not wire) wheelcovers (15 inch only). License plate frames. Imitation deck lid continental spare tire cover. Exterior rearview mirrors (two types). Front bumper guards. Locking gas cap. Curb signals. Gas door guards. Door handle guards. Door edge guards. Rubber floor mats or carpet toppers. Rubber splash-guards. Accelerator pedal cover and wear pad. Automatic transmission Anti Creep. Brake fluid safety reservoir. Windshield washer ($12). Rear door safety locks. Seat belts ($25). Spotlight. Back-up lights ($8). Trunk and utility light. Parking brake warning light. Glove compartment light (standard on regular Presidents and Golden Hawks). Electric clock ($16). Auto compass. Traffic light viewer. Vanity mirror (two types). Cigarette lighter (standard on regular Presidents and Golden Hawks). Roof luggage carrier for sedans and wagons ($60). Seat toppers. Kleenex dispenser. Tripod jack. Gasoline fired Mini-Heat engine coolant heater. Fram oil filter (standard on 289 V-8s). Undercoating. A three-speed manual gear box with column mounted gear shift was standard on all models except the Golden Hawk. Overdrive or Flightomatic ($78 extra) was standard on the Golden Hawk. Overdrive was available for $110 extra on all other models except the Econ-O-Miler taxi. Flightomatic was available for $189 extra on all models except the Econ-O-Miler and Scotsman 58G-WI, FI, DI models. A heavy-duty water-cooled automatic was optional on the Econ-O-Miler taxi. An optional power kit, that included a four-barrel carburetor (Carter model WCFB) and dual exhaust, was available on 58B (259 V-8) models and W, F, C and D 58H (289 V-8) models. The kit increased the 259 V-8's power to 196 hp at 4500 rpm. and the 289 V-8's to 225 hp at 4500 rpm. Twin-Traction was optional on all models at $35-44. Optional tire and wheel sizes were available on most models.

HISTORICAL FOOTNOTES: The President Y6 and Econ-O-Miler Y1 four-door sedans were stretched W bodies. They had vent windows (fixed on Econ-O-Miler) in the rear doors. Most all Econ-O-Milers were sold for taxi use. A kit was sold to convert Scotsman two-door station wagons into Panel-wagons. A special Scotsman two-door sedan with no rear seat was produced. It was called the Utility Sedan. The following were limited to export/Canadian sales: 58G-J4, 58G-P4, 58B-WI, 48B-FI, 58B-C3, 58B-K3, 58B-D 1.

1959 STUDEBAKER

1959 Studebaker, Lark two-door hardtop coupe, 6-cyl

LARK VI AND SILVER HAWK SIX — SERIES 59S — All-new Lark compact models were introduced in 1959. Except for the Silver Hawk coupe, all of the former designs were discontinued. The 1959 Econ-O-Miler long wheelbase four-door sedan was based on the Lark. The central body section of the Lark was basically the 1958 Studebaker body, but the front and back sections were drastically shortened. Deluxe models had painted headlight moldings, no grille moldings and lacked padded instrument panels. Regal Larks had chrome moldings around the grille and headlights and a padded instrument panel. On sedans and station wagons the former "Cyclops-Eye" speedometer was replaced by a normal speedometer, although the central glovebox was retained. On Silver Hawk models the parking lights were relocated in the side grille. Lark model identification was below the deck lid on sedans and on the tailgate of station wagons. The Silver Hawk identification was on the rear fins. All models were available with only single headlights. The two-tone paint option was discontinued on everything except fleet cars.

STUDEBAKER I.D. NUMBERS: VINS were on left front door hinge pillar. Six-cylinder motor numbers on pad at upper part of left-hand side of engine block. V-8 motor numbers on pad at upper left front of cylinder block. [LARK IV/SILVER HAWK SIX] The beginning serial numbers for the 1959 Lark VIs and Silver Hawk Sixes were 59S-1001 (South Bend) and 59SC-1001 (Canada). The beginning engine numbers were S-10001 (South Bend) and SC-10001 (Canada). [LARK VIII/SILVER HAWK V-8] The beginning serial numbers were 59V-1001 (South Bend) and 59VC-1001 (Canada). The beginning engine numbers were V-418701 (South Bend) and VC-14701 (Canada). Engines were stamped with a prefix followed by a production sequence number. Prefixes identified the engine as follows: S=six-cylinder; V=259 cid V-8; P=289 cid V-8.

LARK VI/SILVER HAWK SIX SERIES

Model Number	Body/Style Number	Body Type & Seating	Factory Price	Shipping Weight	Production Total
ECON-O-MILER					
59S	Y1	4-dr Sed-6P	—	2870	1,033
DELUXE					
59S	D4	2-dr Sta Wag-6P	2295	2805	13,227
59S	F4	2-dr Sed-6P	1925	2577	33,259
59S	W4	4-dr Sed-6P	1995	2605	26,566
REGAL					
59S	W6	4-dr Sed-6P	2175	2600	11,898
59S	J6	2-dr HT-6P	2275	2710	7,075
59S	D6	2-dr Sta Wag-6P	2455	2815	5,685
SILVER HAWK					
59S	C6	2-dr Cpe-6P	2360	2795	2,417

1959 Studebaker, Silver Hawk two-door coupe, V-8

LARK VIII AND SILVER HAWK V-8 SERIES 59B — Body style offerings and trim differences were the same as 59S models. Model identifications were also in the same locations. The 59V Deluxe models were limited to special order sales, Marshal sales, fleet sales and sales outside the United States. Both Lark VI and VIII models featured a black background Hawk emblem in the grille and on the tailgate of station wagons.

LARK VIII AND SILVER HAWK V-8 SERIES

Model Number	Body/Style Number	Body Type & Seating	Factory Price	Shipping Weight	Production Total
ECON-O-MILER					
59V	Y1	4-dr Sed-6P	—	3225	92
DELUXE					
59V	W4	4-dr Sed-6P	—	2925	1,367
59V	F4	2-dr Sed-6P	—	2899	550
59V	D4	2-dr Sta Wag-6P	—	3138	378
REGAL					
59V	W6	4-dr Sed-6P	2310	2924	14,530
59V	J6	2-dr HT-6P	2410	3034	7,996
59V	D6	2-dr Sta Wag-6P	2590	3148	7,419
SILVER HAWK					
59V	C6	2-dr Cpe-6P	2495	3140	5,371

ENGINES

(LARK VI/SILVER HAWK SIX) Six-cylinder. L-head. Cast iron block. Displacement: 169.6 cid. Bore and stroke: 3 x 4 inches. Compression ratio: 8.3:1. Brake hp: 90 at 4000 rpm. Four main bearings. Solid valve lifters. Carburetor: Carter model AS one-barrel.

(LARK VIII/SILVER HAWK V-8) V-8. Overhead valve. Cast iron block. Displacement: 259.2 cid. Bore and stroke: 3-9/16 x 2-1/4 inches. Compression ratio: 8.8:1. Brake hp: 180 at 4500 rpm. Five main bearings. Solid valve lifters. Carburetor: Stromberg model WW two-barrel.

CHASSIS FEATURES: Wheelbase: (Hardtop and sedans except Y1) 108.5 inches; (station wagons and Econ-O-Miler Y1) 113 inches; (Silver Hawk) 120.5 inches. Overall length: (Hardtop and sedans except Y1) 175 inches; (station wagons) 184.5 inches; (Econ-O-Miler Y1) 179 inches; (Silver Hawk) 204 inches. Front tread: 57.4 inches. Rear tread: 56.6 inches. Tires: (Lark VI) 5.90 x 15 tubeless; (Lark VIII Silver Hawk 6 and Econ-O-Miler 6) 6.40 x 15 tubeless; (Silver Hawk V-8 and Econ-O-Miler V-8) 6.70 x 15 tubeless.

CONVENIENCE OPTIONS: Power steering for 59V models ($74). Air conditioning ($325). Power brakes ($38). Hill Holder ($15). Full reclining front seats ($26-38). Rear-facing third seat for station wagons ($124). When the "Hideaway" seat was ordered, Captive-Air tires were fitted, since there was no room for a spare tire and wheel white sidewall tires. Tinted glass ($32). Transistor push-button Signal Seeking radio ($101). Transistor push-button radio ($80). Manual tuning tube radio ($61). Internally controlled reel-type crown antenna ($10). Single deck lid antenna ($9). Dual rear antenna ($17). Rear seat speaker ($13). Imitation deck lid continental spare tire cover. Exterior rearview mirrors (three types) ($5 up). License plate frames. Bumper guards ($10). Gas door guards. Door handle guards. Locking gas cap. Rubber splash guards. Rubber front floor mats. Accelerator pedal cover and wear pad. Regular full wheelcovers ($17). Imitation spoke (not wire) wheelcovers. Windshield washer, manual ($9); electric ($12). Seat belts. Rear door safety locks. Compressed CO2 can for fire fighting or tire inflation. Back-up lights. Spotlight. Glove compartment light. Electric clock. tachometer for Silver Hawk V-8. Vanity mirror. Traffic light viewer. Cigarette lighter. Kleenex dispenser. Touch-up paint applicator. Station wagon luggage carrier ($31). Tripod jack. Ice scraper and squeegee. Clear plastic seat covers. Climatizer heater/defroster. Under-

Standard Catalog of American Cars

coating. Oil filter. Special options for Deluxe models: Rear armrests. Second sun visor. Two-tone steering wheel with horn ring. Padded instrument panel. A Regal exterior trim kit was available for the Econ-O-Miler. A three-speed manual gear box with column mounted gear shift was standard on all models. Overdrive was available for $110 extra on all models except the Econ-O-Miler taxi. Flightomatic was available for $200 extra on all models except the Econ-O-Miler. A heavy-duty water cooled automatic was optional on the Econ-O-Miler taxi at $220. An optional power kit, that included a four-barrel carburetor (Carter model WCFB) and dual exhaust, was available on all V-8s at $48 extra. The kit increased the 259 V-8's power to 195 hp at 4500 rpm. Twin Traction was optional on all models at $35. Other tire sizes were optional. Lower compression ratios were available for exported cars.

HISTORICAL FOOTNOTES: The Econ-O-Miler Y1 four-door sedan was a stretched W body. It had non-functional rear door vent windows. Most were sold as taxis, although some were sold outside the United States for private use. A kit was sold to convert Lark station wagons to Panel Wagons. A special Lark two-door sedan without a rear seat was offered. It was called the Utility Sedan.

1960 STUDEBAKER

1960 Studebaker, Lark VI two-door hardtop coupe, 6-cyl

LARK VI AND HAWK SIX — SERIES 60S — The Lark styling was only slightly changed from 1959. A Lark emblem with a red background replaced the Hawk emblem used in the grille and on the station wagon tailgate. Mesh, instead of horizontal bars, was used in the small side grilles. Exterior trim differences between DeLuxe and Regal models were basically the same as 1959. New in 1960 was a Lark convertible and a Lark four-door station wagon. The Econ-O-Miler was continued as a long wheelbase heavy-duty four-door sedan with Lark styling. The "Silver" name was dropped from the Hawk's title. Hawks had imitation louvers on the front edge of the fins and red background Hawk emblems. The Hawk six was sold only outside North America. Lark model identification was on the back and also on the front fenders. The Hawk nameplate was on the rear fins.

STUDEBAKER I.D. NUMBERS: VIN stamped on plate on left front door pillar. First two symbols indicated model year: 60=1960. Third symbol indicated engine: S=six-cylinder (170 cid); V=V-8 (259 cid); P=V-8 (289 cid). Fourth symbol (used on Canadian-built cars only) was a C for Canada. Following symbols indicated the production sequence at the assembly plant. Six-cylinder engine number on pad at upper left-hand front side of block. V-8 engine numbers on pad at upper left-hand front side of block. Engine numbers carried the engine codes as a prefix, followed by production sequence number. [LARK VI/HAWK SIX] Starting serial number: 60S-1001 (South Bend) and 60SC-1001 (Canada). The beginning engine numbers were S-106001 (South Bend) and SC-15501 for Canada. [LARK VIII/HAWK V-8] Starting serial numbers for the 1960 Lark VIIs and Hawk V-8s were 60V-1001 (South Bend) and 60VC-1001 (Canada). The beginning 259 cid engine numbers were V-454701 (South Bend) and VC16701 (Canada). The beginning 289 cid engine numbers were P-70501 (South Bend) and PC-2201 (Canada). Studebaker also attached a Body Number Plate to the cowl below the hood. It carried the company name, VIN (serial number), series code (first column of charts below) the Body/Style Number (second column of charts below), plus one of many interior trim codes too numerous to list here.

LARK VI/HAWK SIX SERIES

Model Number	Body/Style Number	Body Type & Seating	Factory Price	Shipping Weight	Production Total
ECON-O-MILER					
60S	Y1	4-dr Sed-6P	2393	2930	1,096
DELUXE					
6OS	F4	2-dr Sed-6P	1976	2588	24,605
6OS	W4	4-dr Sed-6P	2046	2592	22,534
6OS	D4	2-dr Sta Wag-6P	2366	2763	3,497
6OS	P4	4-dr Sta Wag-6P	2441	2792	5,420
REGAL					
6OS	P6	4-dr Sta Wag-6P	2591	2836	1,925
6OS	L6	2-dr Conv-6P	2621	2961	3,107
6OS	J6	2-dr HT-6P	2296	2697	2,829
HAWK					
6OS	C6	2-dr Cpe-6P	2383	2770	227

LARK VIII AND HAWK V-8 — SERIES 60V — Body style offerings and trim differences were the same as on 60S models. Model identifications were in the same locations. The Hawk V-8 came standard with a 289 cid engine in the United States and Canada. For other countries it came standard with a 259 cid engine. The 289 was optional in most of these countries on Hawk models.

1960 Studebaker, Hawk two-door coupe, V-8

LARK VIII/HAWK V-8 SERIES

Model Number	Body/Style Number	Body Type & Seating	Factory Price	Shipping Weight	Production Total
ECON-O-MILER					
60V	Y1	4-dr Sed-6P	30	3225	215
DELUXE					
6OV	F4	2-dr Sed-6P	2111	2921	8,102
6OV	W4	4-dr Sed-6P	2181	2941	14,231
6OV	D4	2-dr Sta Wag-6P	2501	3138	1,734
6OV	P4	4-dr Sta Wag-6P	2576	3161	5,711
REGAL					
6OV	W6	4-dr Sed-6P	2331	2966	11,410
6OV	J6	2-dr HT-6P	2431	3033	4,565
6OV	P6	4-dr Sta Wag-6P	2726	3183	5,741
6OV	L6	2-dr Conv-6P	2756	3315	5,464
HAWK					
6OV	C6	2-dr Cpe-6P	2650	3207	4,280

ENGINES

(LARK VI/HAWK) Six-Cylinder. L-head. Cast iron block. Displacement: 169.6 cid. Bore and stroke: 3 x 4 inches. Compression ratio: 8.3:1. Brake hp: 90 at 4000 rpm. Four main bearings. Solid valve lifters. Carburetor: Carter model AS one-barrel.

(LARK VIII/HAWK 259) V-8. Overhead valve. Cast iron block. Displacement: 259.2 cid. Bore and stroke. 3-9/16 x 3-1/4 inches. Compression ratio: 8.8:1. Brake hp: 180 at 4500 rpm. Five main bearings. Solid valve lifters. Carburetor: Stromberg model WW two-barrel.

(HAWK 289 V-8) V-8. Overhead valve. Cast iron block. Displacement: 289 cid. Bore and stroke: 3-9/16 x 3-5/8 inches. Compression ratio: 8.8:1. Brake hp: 210 at 4500 rpm. Five main bearings. Solid valve lifters. Carburetor: Stromberg model WW two-barrel.

CHASSIS FEATURES: Wheelbase: (hardtop, convertible and sedans except Y1) 108.5 inches; (Station wagons and Econ-O-Miler Y1) 113 inches; (Hawk) 120.5 inches. Overall length: (hardtop, convertibles and sedans except Y1) 175 inches; (station wagons) 184.5 inches; (Econ-O-Miler) 179 inches; (Hawk) 204 inches. Front tread: 57.4 inches. Rear tread: 56.6 inches. Tires: (Lark VI except convertible) 5.90 x 15 tubeless; (Lark VIII except convertible, Lark VI convertible and Econ-O-Miler six) 6.40 x 15 tubeless; (Hawk V-8, Lark VIII convertible and Econ-O-Miler V-8) 6.70 x 15 tubeless.

OPTIONS: Power steering for 60V models ($75). Air conditioning ($325). Power brakes ($38). Hill Holder ($15). Full reclining front seats ($26-$38). Headrests for reclining seats ($12). Individually adjustable front seats ($15). Rear-facing third seat for station wagons ($124). When the Hideaway third seat was ordered, Captive-Air tires were fitted since there was no room for a spare tire and wheel. White sidewall tires ($28-$48). Tinted glass ($32). Transistor push-button radio ($64). Manual tuning tube radio ($57). Internally controlled reel-type cowl antenna ($10). Rear seat speaker ($13). Lark hood ornament. Bumper guards ($10). License plate frames. Station wagon cargo mat. Rubber splashguards. Exhaust deflector. Locking gas cap. Door handle guards. Regular full wheelcovers ($16). Imitation spoke (not wire) wheelcovers. Exterior rearview mirror (two types). Rubber front floor mats. Windshield washer (manual or electric) ($11). Front and rear seat belts. Rear door safety locks. Back-up lights. glovebox light. Spotlight. Electric clock. Tachometer for Hawk V-8 ($38). Station wagon luggage carrier ($54). Cigarette lighter ($4). Kleenex dispenser. Cushion toppers. Clear plastic seat covers. Touch-up paint applicators. Climatizer heater/defroster ($71). Lark oil filter (standard on Hawk V-8) ($10). Gas line filter. Padded sun visors. Undercoating ($20). Special options for Deluxe models: Rear armrests. Second sun visor. ($8). Padded instrument panel ($15). Two-tone steering wheel with horn ring. ($7). Regal exterior trim kit (also available for Econ-O-Miler) ($36). A three-speed manual gearbox with column-mounted gearshift was standard on all models. Overdrive was available for $110 extra on all models except the Econ-O-Miler taxi. Except for the Econ-O-Miler taxi, Flightomatic was available for $179 extra on six-cylinder models and $200 extra on eight-cylinder models. A heavy-duty water-cooled automatic was optional on the Econ-O-Miler taxi and Marshals. An optional power kit, that included a four-barrel carburetor (Carter WCFB) and dual exhausts (except for the Hawk 289 V-8 which came standard with dual exhausts), was available on all V-8s for $44.95 extra. The kit increased the 259 V-8's power to 195 hp at 4500 rpm and the 289 V-8's to 225 hp at 4500 rpm. Twin Traction was optional on all models. Other tire sizes were optional on most models. Lower compression ratios were available for exported cars. A few Larks, mainly police Marshals, were special ordered with 289 cid V-8s.

HISTORICAL FOOTNOTES: The Econ-O-Miler Y1 four-door sedan was a stretched W body. It had nonfunctional rear door vent windows. Most were sold as taxis, although some were sold outside the United States for private use. A kit was sold for $34.97 to convert two-door Lark station wagons to Panel Wagons. A special Lark two-door sedan with no rear seat was offered. It was called the Utility Sedan. Six cylinder and V-8 Lark Marshals were available with W, F, Y, D and P bodies.

Standard Catalog of American Cars

1961 STUDEBAKER

LARK VI AND HAWK SIX — SERIES 61S — The Lark was slightly restyled in 1961. Regal models had standard dual headlights. Single headlights were standard on Deluxe models, although duals were an option. Rocker panel moldings were standard on Regal models. Rubber windshield and rear window moldings were standard on Deluxe models, although Regal stainless steel moldings were optional. Side trim on all Lark related models, except the regular Y1 (heavy-duty long-wheelbase four-door sedan) ran above the natural front fender contour line. The Y1 did not have side moldings as standard, although they were an option. A new Regal version of the Y body was introduced. It was called the Lark Cruiser and was marketed for private ownership. The six-cylinder Cruiser was only marketed outside North America. An extra fin type trim molding and color band was added to the Hawk. The Hawk Six was also sold only outside of North America. Lark model identification was on the back and also on the front fenders. The Hawk nameplate was on the rear fins. The six-cylinder engine was converted to overhead valves.

1961 Studebaker, Lark VIII four-door Cruiser sedan, V-8 (AA)

LARK VIII AND HAWK V-8 — SERIES 61V — Body type and exterior trim selections were the same as the 61S. Model identifications were also in the same location. All Larks had a new instrument panel with the glove compartment on the far right. All left-hand drive Larks had swing brake and clutch (if fitted) pedals. The Hawk V-8 came standard with a 289 cid engine in the United States and Canada. For other countries it came standard with a 259 cid engine. The 289 was optional in most of these countries.

1961 Studebaker, Lark VI Skytop four-door sedan, 6-cyl (AA)

STUDEBAKER I.D. NUMBERS: VIN stamped on plate on left front door pillar. First two symbols indicated model year: 61=1961. Third symbol indicated engine: S=six-cylinder (170 cid); V=V-8 (259 cid); P=V-8 (289 cid). Fourth symbol (used on Canadian-built cars only) was a C for Canada. Following symbols indicated the production sequence at the assembly plant. Six-cylinder engine number on pad at upper left-hand front side of block. V-8 engine numbers on pad at upper left-hand front side of block. Engine numbers carried the engine codes as a prefix, followed by production sequence number. [LARK VI/HAWK SIX] Starting serial number: 61S-1001 (South Bend) and 61SC-1001 (Canada). The beginning engine numbers were S-172601 (South Bend) and SC-20101 for Canada. [LARK VIII/HAWK V-8] Starting serial numbers for the 1960 Lark VIIIs and Hawk V-8s were 61V-1001 (South Bend) and 61VC-1001 (Canada). The beginning 259 cid engine numbers were V-510401 (South Bend) and VC18501 (Canada). The beginning 289 cid engine numbers were P-74701 (South Bend) and PC-2501 (Canada). Studebaker also attached a Body Number Plate to the cowl below the hood. It carried the company name, VIN (serial number), series code (first colm of charts below) the Body/Style Number (second column of charts below), plus one of many interior trim codes too numerous to list here.

1961 Studebaker, Hawk two-door coupe, V-8 (AA)

LARK VI/HAWK SIX SERIES

Model Number	Body/Style Number	Body Type & Seating	Factory Price	Shipping Weight	Production Total
HEAVY-DUTY					
61S	Y1	4-dr Sed-6P	2252	2943	1,108
DELUXE					
61S	F4	2-dr Sed-6P	1935	2661	12,571
61S	W4	4-dr Sed-6P	2005	2665	15,891
61S	D4	2-dr Sta Wag-6P	2290	2836	1,210
61S	P4	4-dr Sta Wag-6P	2370	2865	2,924
REGAL					
61S	W6	4-dr Sed-6P	2155	2692	3,802
61S	J6	2-dr HT-6P	2243	2770	1,870
61S	P6	4-dr Sta Wag-6P	2520	2870	693
61S	L6	2-dr Conv-6P	2554	3034	979
61S	Y6	4-dr Cruiser Sed-6P	—	—	24
HAWK					
61S	C6	2-dr Cpe-6P	—	—	266

LARK VIII/HAWK V-8 SERIES

Model Number	Body/Style Number	Body Type & Seating	Factory Price	Shipping Weight	Production Total
HEAVY-DUTY					
61V	Y1	4-dr Sed-6P	2389	3225	222
DELUXE					
61V	F4	2-dr Sed-6P	2070	2921	2,003
61V	W4	4-dr Sed-6P	2140	2941	7,343
61V	D4	2-dr Sta Wag-6P	2425	3112	1,177
61V	P4	4-dr Sta Wag-6P	2505	3161	1,815
REGAL					
61V	W6	4-dr Sed-6P	2290	2966	3,202
61V	J6	2-dr HT-6P	2378	3034	1,666
61V	P6	4-dr Sta Wag-6P	2655	3166	1,851
61V	L6	2-dr Conv-6P	2689	3315	1,002
61V	Y6	4-dr Cruiser-6P	2458	3001	5,232
HAWK					
61V	C6	2-dr Cpe-6P	2650	3207	3,663

ENGINES

(LARK VI/HAWK SIX) Six-Cylinder. Overhead valve. Cast iron block. Displacement: 169.6 cid. Bore and stroke: 3 x 4 inches. Compression ratio: 8.5:1. Brake hp: 112 at 4500 rpm. Four main bearings. Solid valve lifters. Carburetor: Carter model AS one-barrel.

(LARK VIII/HAWK 259 V-8) V-8. Overhead valve. Cast iron block. Displacement: 259.2 cid. Bore and stroke: 3-9/16 x 3-1/4 inches. Compression ratio: 8.8:1. Brake hp: 180 at 4500 rpm. Five main bearings. Solid valve lifters. Carburetor: Stromberg model WW two-barrel.

(LARK/PURSUIT MARSHAL/HAWK 289 V-8) V-8. Overhead valve. Cast iron block. Displacement: 289 cid. Bore and stroke: 3-9/16 x 3-5/8 inches. Compression ratio: 8.8:1. Brake hp: 210 at 4500 rpm. Five main bearings. Solid valve lifters. Carburetor: Stromberg model WW two-barrel.

CHASSIS FEATURES: Wheelbase: (hardtop, convertible and sedans except Y) 108.5 inches; (station wagons and Y bodies) 113 inches; (Hawk) 120.5 inches. Overall length: (hardtop, convertible and sedans except Y) 175 inches; (station wagons) 184.5 inches; (Y bodies (Cruiser and Heavy-Duty sedan) 179 inches; (Hawk) 204 inches. Front tread: 57.4 inches. Rear Tread: 56.6 inches. Tires: (Lark VI except convertible) 6.00 x 15 tubeless; (Lark VIII except convertible, Lark VI convertible, Hawk six and Heavy-Duty sedan six) 6.50 x 15 tubeless; (Hawk V-8, Lark VIII convertible and Heavy-Duty sedan V-8) 6.70 x 15 tubeless.

OPTIONS: Power steering ($75). Air conditioning ($278- $325). Skytop sun roof ($185). Power brakes ($38). Hill Holder ($15). Full reclining front seats ($25-$47). Headrests for reclining seats ($12). Individually adjusted front seats (standard on North American Hawks) ($13-$35). Rear-facing third seat for station wagons ($124 including Captive-Air tires and no spare). White sidewall tires ($28-$49). Tinted glass ($32). Transistor push-button radio ($64-$66). Manual tuning radio ($59). Internally controlled reel-type cowl antenna (now included with higher radio price). Rear seat speaker ($13). Lark hood ornament. Bumper guards ($10). Exterior rearview mirror (two types) ($5). Rubber splashguards. Exhaust deflectors. Locking gas cap. Rubber station wagon cargo mat. Rubber floor mats. License plate frames. Regular full wheelcovers ($16). Imitation spoke (not wire) wheelcover. Front and rear seat belts ($13). Rear door safety locks. Windshield washer ($12). No-creep for automatic transmission. Cushion toppers. Clear plastic seat covers. Kleenex dispenser. Station wagon luggage rack

($54). Cigarette lighter (standard on Regal models) ($4). Electric clock (standard on Cruiser) ($16). Tachometer for Hawk V-8 ($54). Back-up lights. Glove compartment light. Spotlight. Climatizer heater/defroster ($71). Oil filter ($4 on some 289 V-8s; $10 on other V-8 models). Gas line filter. Touch-up paint applicators. Padded sun visors. Undercoating. Special options for Deluxe models: Regal windshield and rear window moldings ($20-$33). Dual headlights ($24). Rear ashtray. Second sun visor. Rear armrests. A Regal exterior trim kit was optional on Heavy-Duty sedans ($150). A three-speed manual gearbox with column-mounted gearshift was standard on all models. Overdrive was available for $110 extra on all models except the Heavy-Duty sedan. Except for the Heavy-Duty sedan and Marshal, Flightomatic was available for $165 extra on six-cylinder models and $200 extra on eight-cylinder models. A heavy-duty water cooled automatic was optional on the Heavy-Duty sedan and Marshal. A new four-speed gearbox with floor-mounted gearshift was optional on the Hawk V-8 at $188 extra. An optional four-barrel carburetor (Carter WCFB) was available for all V-8s at $21.52. The four-barrel increased the 259 V-8's power to 195 hp at 4500 rpm. and the 289 V-8's to 225 hp at 4500 rpm. The 259 V-8 dual exhaust kit was a separate $23.43 option. Dual exhausts were standard on 289 V-8 models. The 289 V-8 was optional on the Cruiser. The "Cruiser" package included the 289 cid V-8. No. 44 axle, finned brake drums, heavy-duty radiator, oil filter and dual exhausts. Twin Traction was optional on all models at $38.93. Other tire sizes were optional on most models. Lower compression ratios were available for export cars.

HISTORICAL FOOTNOTES: The Heavy-Duty sedan, (Y1) and Lark Cruiser (Y6) featured stretched W bodies. They had rear door vent windows (not functional on Y1). Most domestic Heavy-Duty sedans were sold as taxis, although some were sold outside the United States for private use. A kit was sold, for $34.97, to convert two-door Lark station wagons to Panel Wagons. A special Lark two-door sedan with no rear seat was offered. It was called the Utility Sedanette. Six-cylinder and V-8 Lark Marshals were available with W, F, Y, D and P bodies. The six-cylinder model was the City Marshal, the 259 V-8 was the Patrol Marshal and the 289 V-8 was the Pursuit Marshal.

1962 STUDEBAKER

1962 Studebaker, Lark two-door hardtop coupe, V-8 (AA)

LARK SIX AND GRAN TURISMO HAWK SIX — SERIES 62S — The Lark models were again re-styled. Dual headlights were made standard on all Lark type vehicles. Larks had round taillights. Regular Deluxe models had only rubber moldings around the windshield and rear windows. Regal models had stainless steel windshield and rear window moldings. The new Daytona hardtop and convertible models had special wide side moldings with the name Daytona on them. All four-door sedans used the long wheelbase Y body, although the Cruiser was the only one with rear. door vent windows Heavy-Duty Lark police and severe service four-door sedan, two-door sedan and four-door wagon models were given their own model identifications. The two-door station wagon was discontinued. The new Gran Turismo Hawk had a squared roofline, no fins and rocker panel moldings. The six-cylinder Gran Turismo Hawk and six-cylinder Cruiser were only sold outside North America. Lark and Cruiser nameplates were on the front fenders. On Hawks, the "Hawk" name was on the deck lid and the "Gran Turismo" script was on the doors.

STUDEBAKER I.D. NUMBERS: VIN stamped on plate on left front door pillar. First two symbols indicated model year: 62=1962. Third symbol indicated engine: S=six-cylinder (170 cid); V=V-8 (259 cid); P=V-8 (289 cid). Fourth symbol (used on Canadian-built cars only) was a C for Canada. Following symbols indicated the production sequence at the assembly plant. Six-cylinder engine number on pad at upper left-hand front side of block. V-8 engine numbers on pad at upper left-hand front side of block. Engine numbers carried the engine codes as a prefix, followed by production sequence number. [LARK SIX/GT HAWK SIX] Starting serial number: 62S-1001 (South Bend) and 62SC-1001 (Canada). The beginning engine numbers were S-210901 (South Bend) and SC-24301 for Canada. [LARK -8/GT HAWK V-8] Starting serial numbers for 1962 were 62V-1001 (South Bend) and 62VF-1001 (Canada). The beginning 259 cid engine numbers were V-534910 (South Bend) and VC-19601 (Canada). The beginning 289 cid engine numbers were P-79801 (South Bend) and PC-2801 (Canada). Studebaker also attached a Body Number Plate to the cowl below the hood. It carried the company name, VIN (serial number), series code (first column of charts below) the Body/Style Number (second column of charts below), plus one of many interior trim codes too numerous to list here.

LARK/GRAN TURISMO HAWK SIXES

Model Number	Body/Style Number	Body Type & Seating	Factory Price	Shipping Weight	Production Total
TAXI					
62S	Y1	4-dr Taxi-6P	—	2970	Note 1
HEAVY-DUTY					
62S	F3	2-dr Sed-6P		2765	Note 1
62S	Y3	4-dr Sed-6P		2830	Note 1
62S	P3	4-dr Sta Wag-6P		2935	Note 1

Model Number	Body/Style Number	Body Type & Seating	Factory Price	Shipping Weight	Production Total
DELUXE					
62S	Y4	4-dr Sed-6P	2040	2765	Note 1
62S	F4	2-dr Sed-6P	1935	2655	Note 1
62S	P4	4-dr Sta Wag-6P	2405	3000	Note 1
REGAL					
62S	Y6	4-dr Sed-6P	2190	2765	Note 1
62S	J6	2-dr HT-6P	2218	2765	Note 1
62S	P6	4-dr Sta Wag-6P	2555	3000	Note 1
62S	L6	2-dr Conv-6P	2589	3075	Note 1
DAYTONA					
62S	J8	2-dr HT-5P	2308	2765	Note 1
62S	L8	2-dr Conv-5P	2679	3075	Note 1
62S	Y8	4-dr Cruiser-6P	—	—	Note 1
GRAN TURISMO HAWK					
62S	K6	2-dr HT-5P	—	—	Note 1

NOTE 1: Complete production total breakouts are not available. The following figures are for both six-cylinder and V-8 models: (four-door sedans, except taxi) 49,961; (Style F two-door sedans) 19,196; (Style K Gran Turismo Hawk) 9,335; (Style J two-door hardtop coupe) 8,480; (Style P four-door station wagons) 10,522; (Style L convertibles) 2,681 and (Style Y1 taxicab) 2,212.

LARK V-8 AND GRAN TURISMO HAWK V-8 — SERIES 62V — Body type and exterior trim selections were the same as for the 62S. Eight-cylinder Lark sedans, hardtops and convertibles had V-8 emblems on the rear deck lid. Other model identifications were' the same as on the 62S models. The Gran Turismo Hawk V-8 came standard with a 289 cid engine in the United States and Canada. For most other countries it came standard with a 259 cid engine. The 289 was optional in many of these countries.

1962 Studebaker, Lark Daytona two-door convertible, V-8 (IMS)

LARK/GRAN TURISMO HAWK V-8S

Model Number	Body/Style Number	Body Type & Seating	Factory Price	Shipping Weight	Production Total
TAXI					
62V	Y1	4-dr Taxi-6P	—	3170	Note 1
HEAVY-DUTY					
62V	F3	2-dr Sed-6P	—	3005	Note 1
62V	Y3	4-dr Sed-6P	—	3070	Note 1
62V	P3	4-dr Sta Wag-6P	—	3175	Note 1
DELUXE					
62V	F4	2-dr Sed-6P	2070	2925	Note 1
62V	Y4	4-dr Sed-6P	2175	3020	Note 1
62V	P4	4-dr Sta Wag-6p	2540	3130	Note 1
REGAL					
62V	Y6	4-dr Sed-6P	2325	3020	Note 1
62V	J6	2-dr HT-6P	2353	3015	Note 1
62V	P6	4-dr Sta Wag-6P	2690	3130	Note 1
62V	L6	2-dr Conv-6P	2724	3305	Note 1
LARK DAYTONA					
62V	J8	2-dr HT-5P	2443	3015	Note 1
62V	L8	2-dr Conv-5P	2814	3305	Note 1
62V	Y8	4-dr Cruiser-6P	2493	3030	Note 1
GRAN TURISMO HAWK					
62V	K6	2-dr GT HT-5P	3095	3280	Note 1

NOTE 1: See Lark/Gran Turismo Hawk six production note.

ENGINES

(LARK/GRAN TURISMO HAWK SIX) Six-Cylinder. Overhead valve. Cast iron block. Displacement: 169.6 cid. Bore and stroke: 3 x 4 inches. Compression ratio: 8.25:1. Brake hp: 112 at 4500 rpm. Four main bearings. Solid valve lifters. Carburetor: Carter model AS one-barrel.

(LARK/GRAN TURISMO HAWK 259 V-8) V-8. Overhead valve. Cast iron block. Displacement: 259.2 cid. Bore and stroke: 3-9/16 x 3-1/4 inches. Compression ratio: 8.5:1. Brake hp: 180 at 4500 rpm. Five main bearings. Carburetor: Stromberg model WW two-barrel.

(GRAN TURISMO HAWK/LARK PURSUIT MARSHAL 289 V-8) Cast iron block. Displacement: 289 cid. Bore and stroke: 3-9/16 x 3-5/8 inches. Compression ratio: 8.5:1. Brake hp: 210 at 4500 rpm. Five main bearings. Solid valve lifters. Carburetor: Stromberg model WW two-barrel.

CHASSIS FEATURES: Wheelbase: (Lark hardtop, convertible and two-door sedans) 109 inches; (Station wagons and four-door sedans) 113 inches; (Gran Turismo Hawk) 120.5 inches; Overall length: (Lark hardtop, convertible and two-door sedans) 184 inches; (four-door sedans) 188 inches; (Station wagons) 187 inches; (Gran Turismo Hawk) 204 inches. Front tread: 57.4 inches. Rear tread: 56.6 inches. Tires: (Lark six except convertible) 6.00 x 5 tubeless; (Lark V8 except convertible; Lark six convertible, GT Hawk six and taxi six) 6.50 x 15 tubeless; (GT Hawk V8, Lark V8 convertible and taxi V8) 6.70 x 15 tubeless.

1962 Studebaker, Gran Turismo Hawk two-door hardtop coupe, V-8

1963 Studebaker, Lark Regal two-door sedan, 6-cyl (AA)

OPTIONS: Power steering ($77). Air conditioning ($278-325). Skytop sun roof ($185). Power brakes ($42). Hill Holder (as in all years, available only for standard transmission with or without overdrive) ($15). Full reclining front seats ($26-38). Head rests for reclining seats. Individually adjusted front seats (standard on North American GT Hawks and Lark Daytonas). Rear-facing third seat for station wagons (including Captive-Air tires and no spare) ($124). White sidewall tires ($29-49). Tinted glass ($32). All transistor push-button radio ($65-69). Transistor manual tuning radio ($57-62). Internally controlled reel-type cowl antenna (radio prices include antenna options). Rear seat speaker ($13). Lark Winguards (bumper extensions). Bumper guards (front and rear on Lark; front only on Hawk) ($10 each pair). Full wheelcovers ($16). Rubber splash guards. Electric clock ($16). Exterior rearview mirror (two types) ($5). License plate frames. Locking gas cap. Door handle guards. Rubber front floor mats. Exhaust deflector. Seat belts ($12 each). Windshield washer ($12). Automatic transmission No-creep. Rear door safety locks. Lark cushion toppers. Lark clear plastic seat covers. Padded sun visors ($5-8). Cigarette lighter for Deluxe models ($4). Tissue dispenser. Visor vanity mirror. Door utility packet (regular Lark models). Station wagon luggage rack ($40). Station wagon cargo mat. Station wagon rear deck cushion. Spotlight. Glove compartment light. Underhood light. Trunk light. Back-up lights for Deluxe models ($7). Climatizer heater/defroster. Oil filter (standard on 289 V8 models) ($10). Fuel line filter. Touch-up paint applicators. Undercoating ($24). Regal trim kits for Deluxe, Heavy-Duty and taxi models. Special options for the Gran Turismo Hawk: Rear deck lid radio antenna ($59 with manual radio; $67 with push-button radio). Air-Flo or Aero strut wheelcovers. Tachometer for V-8 models ($54). A three-speed manual gearbox with column-mounted gearshift was standard on all models. Overdrive was available for $110 extra on all models except the taxi. Except for the taxi and Marshals, Flightomatic was available for $172 extra on six-cylinder models and $200 extra on eight-cylinder models. A heavy-duty water cooled automatic was optional on the taxi and Marshal models. A four-speed gearbox with floor-mounted gearshift was optional on the Hawk V-8 and Lark Daytona V-8 for $188 extra. An optional four-barrel carburetor (Carter WCFB) was available for all V-8s at $22 extra. The four-barrel increased the 259 V-8's power to 195 hp at 4500 rpm and the 289 V-8's to 225 hp at 4500 rpm. The 259 V-8 dual exhaust kit was a separate option at $23. Dual exhausts were standard on 289 V-8 models. The 289 V-8 was optional on all Lark 62V models. Twin Traction was optional on all models at $39. Other tire sizes were optional on most models. Lower compression ratios were available for export cars.

HISTORICAL FOOTNOTES: Special Heavy-Duty W3, Y3 and P3 models were available for rural route mail carriers. Called the Rural Route Lark they offered some interesting options such as right-hand drive and Signal-Stat warning lights. The Lark Marshals were also based on the Heavy-Duty W3, Y3 and P3 models. The six-cylinder model was called the City Marshal, the 259 V-8 model the Patrol Marshal and the 289 V-8 model the Pursuit Marshal.

1963 STUDEBAKER

SIX-CYLINDER — SERIES 63S — in 1963 the Lark type Studebakers were only slightly restyled, but some major changes were made in their model identification. To give the Cruiser more identity, it was no longer classified as a Lark. The Regal, which for years had been a top line model, was dropped down a notch. The Custom, which was once a low priced trim offering, took over the former Regal position. The Daytona line was expanded to include the highest priced version of the new sliding roof Wagonaire four-door station wagon. Then, in midyear, a bare bones Studebaker line called the Standard was introduced as Studebaker's new low price offering. The Standard had no side moldings. The Regal had one narrow molding per side. The Custom had check mark side moldings similar to what was used on 1962 Daytonas. The 1963 Daytona had side moldings that widened out at the back of the car. The 'Daytona' script was attached to the wide part of the molding. Cruiser side trim was the same as the Daytona, except it was fitted with a Cruiser script. All 1963 Lark related models had a new, non-wraparound windshield and narrow window posts on sedans and wagons. Changes on 1963 Gran Turismo Hawks were limited to trim alterations. Larger lettering on the deck lid overlay and closed-in center grilles were the most obvious. Daytona, Regal, Custom and Heavy-Duty models had Lark block lettering on the front fenders. The Standard had a Studebaker script in the same position. Gran Turismo model identifications were the same as in 1962. The Custom Wagonaire, the Cruiser six and the six-cylinder Gran Turismo Hawk were not available for domestic sales.

STUDEBAKER I.D. NUMBERS: VIN stamped on plate on left front door pillar of Studebakers and top of right frame side member on Avantis. First two symbols indicated model year: 63=1963. Third symbol or group of symbols indicated engine: S=six-cylinder (170 cid); V=V-8 (259 cid); P=V-8 (289 cid); R=Avanti non-supercharged R1 V-8 (289 cid); RS=Avanti supercharged R2 V-8 (289 cid); R3S=Avanti supercharged R3 V-8 (304.5 cid). Extra symbol (used on Canadian-built cars only) was a C for Canada. Remaining symbols indicated the production sequence at the assembly plant. Six-cylinder engine number on pad at upper left-hand front side of block. V-8 engine numbers on pad at upper left-hand front side of block. Engine numbers carried the engine codes or Avanti R-RS-R3S codes as a prefix, followed by production sequence number. [LARK SIX/GT HAWK SIX] Starting serial number: 63S-1001 (South Bend) and 63SC-1001 (Canada). The beginning engine numbers were S-261201 (South Bend) and SC-29701 for Canada. [LARK 8/GT HAWK V-8] Starting serial numbers for 1963 were 63V-1001 (South Bend) and 63VF-1001 (Canada). The beginning 259 cid engine

numbers were V-556601 (South Bend) and VC-21401 (Canada). The beginning 289 cid engine numbers were P-93601 (South Bend) and PC-3401 for Canada. [AVANTI] The beginning serial number for the 1963 Avanti was R-1001. The beginning unsupercharged (R1) engine number was R-1001. The beginning engine number for the optional supercharged (R2) engine was RS-1001. Studebaker also attached a Body Number Plate to the cowl below the hood. It carried the company name, VIN (serial number), series code (first column of charts below) the Body/Style Number (second column of charts below), plus one of many interior trim codes too numerous to list here.

SIX-CYLINDER SERIES — ALL LINES

Model Number	Body/Style Number	Body Type & Seating	Factory Price	Shipping Weight	Production Total
TAXICAB					
63S	Y1	4-dr Taxi-6P	2328	2970	Note 1
STANDARD LINE					
63S	F2	2-dr Sed-6P	1935	2610	Note 1
63S	Y2	4-dr Sed-6P	2040	2735	Note 1
63S	P2	4-dr Sta Wag-6P	2430	2945	Note 1
HEAVY-DUTY LINE					
63S	F3	2-dr Sed-6P	2096	2765	Note 1
63S	Y3	4-dr Sed-6P	2201	2830	Note 1
63S	P3	4-dr Sta Wag-6P	2591	2935	Note 1
REGAL LINE					
63S	F4	2-dr Sed-6P	2055	2610	Note 1
63S	Y4	4-dr Sed-6P	2160	2750	Note 1
63S	P4	4-dr Sta Wag-6P	2550	3200	Note 1
CUSTOM LINE					
63S	Y6	4-dr Sed-6P	2285	2750	Note 1
63S	F6	2-dr Sed-6P	2180	2610	Note 1
63S	P6	4-dr Sta Wag-6P	—	13200	Note 1
LARK DAYTONA					
63S	J8	2-dr HT-5P	2308	2775	Note 1
63S	P8	4-dr Sta Wag-6P	2700	3245	Note 1
63S	L8	2-dr Conv-5P	2679	3020	Note 1
63S	Y8	4-dr Cruiser-6P	—	—	Note 1
GRAN TURISMO HAWK					
63S	K6	2-dr GT HT-5P	—	—	Note 1

NOTE 1: Complete production total breakouts are not available. The following figures are for both six-cylinder and V-8 models: (four-door sedans, except taxi) 40,113; (two-door Style F sedans) 17,401; (Style K Grand Turismo Hawk) 4,634; (Style J two-door hardtop coupe) 3,763; (Style P four-door station wagon) 11,915; (Style L convertibles) 1,015 and (Style Y1 taxicab) 1,170.

1963 Studebaker, Lark Daytona two-door hardtop coupe, V-8

EIGHT-CYLINDER — SERIES 63V — Body type and exterior trim selections were the same as for the 63S. Most Lark related models had V-8 emblems in the grille and on the rear deck lid. The Domestic Gran Turismo Hawks and Cruisers came standard with 289 cid V-8s, but in most other countries they came with 259 cid V-8s. The Custom Wagonaire was not available for domestic sales.

1963 Studebaker, Grand Turismo Hawk two-door hardtop coupe, V-8

EIGHT-CYLINDER SERIES — ALL LINES

Model Number	Body/Style Number	Body Type & Seating	Factory Price	Shipping Weight	Production Total
TAXICAB LINE					
63V	Y1	4-dr Taxi-6P	2465	3170	Note 1
STANDARD LINE					
63V	F2	2-dr Sed-6P	2070	2875	Note 1
63V	Y2	4-dr Sed-6P	2175	2935	Note 1
63V	P2	4-dr Sta Wag-6P	2565	3195	Note 1
HEAVY-DUTY LINE					
63V	F3	2-dr Sed-6P	2231	3005	Note 1
63V	Y3	4-dr Sed-6P	2336	3070	Note 1
63V	P3	4-dr Sta Wag-6P	2726	3175	Note 1
REGAL LINE					
63V	F4	2-dr Sed-6P	2190	2875	Note 1
63V	Y4	4-dr Sed-6P	2295	2970	Note 1
63V	P4	4-dr Wag-6P	2685	3450	Note 1
CUSTOM LINE					
63V	F6	2-dr Sed-6P	2315	2875	Note 1
63V	Y6	4-dr Sed-6P	2420	2970	Note 1
63V	P6	4-dr Sta Wag-6P	—	3450	Note 1
LARK DAYTONA/CRUISER					
63V	J8	2-dr HT-5P	2443	2975	Note 1
63V	P8	4-dr Sta Wag-6P	2835	3490	Note 1
63V	L8	2-dr Conv-5P	2814	3240	Note 1
63V	Y8	4-dr Cruiser-6P	2595	3030	Note 1
GRAN TURISMO HAWK					
63V	K6	2-dr GT HT-5P	3095	3230	Note 1

NOTE 1: See six-cylinder production total note.

1963 Studebaker, Avanti two-door hardtop coupe, V-8 (AA)

AVANTI — MODEL 63R — The Avanti was Studebaker's fiberglass bodied sports coupe. It was the first completely new body styling Studebaker had introduced since 1953. Smooth lines, an under-the-bumper radiator air intake and a wedge-shaped design were the Avanti's hallmarks. Model identification was on the front, just to the left of the right headlight. A Studebaker script was on the deck lid. Supercharged versions had a "supercharged" name tag on each front fender. The Avanti body sat on a modified Lark Daytona convertible chassis. All 1963 Avantis had round headlight enclosures.

AVANTI SERIES

Model Number	Body/Style Number	Body Type & Seating	Factory Price	Shipping Weight	Production Total
R	Q	2-dr Spt Cpe-5P	4445	3148	3,834

ENGINES

(63S SIX) Six-Cylinder. Overhead valve. Cast iron block. Displacement: 169.6 cid. Bore and stroke: 3 x 4 inches. Compression ratio: 8.25:1 Brake hp: 112 at 4500 rpm. Four main bearings. Solid valve lifters. Carburetor: Carter model RBS or AS one-barrel.

(63V 259 V-8) V-8. Overhead valve. Cast iron block. Displacement: 259.2 cid. Bore and stroke: 2-9/16 x 3-1/4 inches. Compression ratio: 8.5:1. Brake hp: 180 at 4500 rpm. Five main bearings. Solid valve lifters. Carburetor: Stromberg model WW two-barrel.

(HAWK/CRUISER/MARSHAL 289 V-8) V-8. Overhead valve. Cast iron block. Displacement: 289 cid. Bore and stroke: 3-9/16 x 3-5/8 inches. Compression ratio: 8.5:1 Brake hp: 210 at 4500 rpm. Five main bearings. Solid valve lifters. Carburetor: Stromberg model WW two-barrel.

(AVANTI R1 ENGINE) V-8. Overhead valve. Cast iron block. Displacement: 289 cid. Bore and stroke: 3-9/16 x 3-5/8 inches. Compression ratio: 10.25: 1. Brake hp: 240. Five main bearings. Solid valve lifters. Carburetor: Carter model AFB four-barrel. (The Avanti V-8 was a $73 option on Cruiser sedans; a $157 option on Hawks and a $208 option on other V-8 models).

(AVANTI SUPERCHARGED R2 ENGINE) V-8. Overhead valve. Cast iron block. Displacement: 289 cid. Bore and stroke: 3-9/16 x 3-5/8 inches. Compression ratio: 9.0:1. Brake hp: 289. Five main bearings. Solid valve lifters. Carburetor: Carter model AFB four-barrel. (The Supercharger was a separate $210 option on Avantis and other Studebakers with the Avanti V-8).

CHASSIS FEATURES: Wheelbase: (two-door sedans, Daytona hardtop, Daytona convertible and Avanti) 109 inches; (four-door sedans and station wagons) 113 inches; (Gran Turismo Hawk) 120-1/2 inches. Overall length: (two-door Sedans, Daytona hardtop and Daytona convertible) 184 inches; (four-door Sedans) 188 inches; (Station wagons) 187 inches; (Gran Turismo Hawk) 204 inches; (Avanti) 192 inches. Front tread: 57.4 inches. Rear tread: 56.6 inches. Tires: (All 63S except convertible and station wagon) 6.00 x 15 tubeless; (All 63V except Cruiser, convertible, station wagon and GT Hawk plus 63S convertible and station wagon) 6.50 x 15 tubeless; (Cruiser, GT Hawk, Avanti, 63V convertible and station wagon) 6.70 x 15 tubeless.

OPTIONS: Power brakes ($45). Skytop sun roof (hardtops and sedans only) ($185). Headrests. Reclining seats. Individually adjusted front seats (standard on some models). All transistor manual tuning radio ($57-62). Internally controlled reel-type cowl antenna (antenna options included in various radio package prices). Wing guards for models without wraparound bumpers. Full wheelcovers ($16). Rubber splash guards. Stratoline exterior rearview mirror. Bumper guards. Electric clock ($16). Tachometer for GT Hawk and Avanti Lark type cars ($54). Exhaust deflector. Safety rear door locks. Clear plastic seat covers or cushion toppers for Lark type vehicles. Padded sun visors. Tissue dispenser. Cigarette lighter for low priced models. Spotlight. Day-Night interior rearview mirror. Auto compass. Back-up lights for low priced models ($8). Glovebox light. Trunk light. Climatizer heater/defroster ($80-88). Fuel line filter. Undercoating. Special station wagon options: Luggage rack ($43). Car-Go-Pak. Power rear window ($33). Cargo mat. Tailgate step. Rear-facing third seat (including Captive-Air tires and no spare). Rear deck cushions. Special options for the Gran Turismo Hawk: Rear deck lid radio antenna. Air-Flo or Aero Strut wheelcovers. Door handle guards. Visor vanity mirror. A convenience group and side moldings were available for low priced models. (Note: Some options were slightly lower-priced for Avantis). Power Holder ($15). Air conditioning (not available with R2 engines) sidewall tires ($32-49). Tinted glass ($32). All transistor push AM-FM push-button transistor radio (added midyear). Rear seat speaker (the only speaker on most GT Hawks) ($13). Strato-vue rearview mirror. License plate frames. Locking gas cap. Rubber floor mats. Seat belts ($10). Automatic transmission No-creep. Windshield washer ($14). Underhood light. Touch-up paint applicators. Power door windows were also optional on the Avanti ($75). A three-speed manual gearbox with column-mounted gearshift was standard on all models except the Avanti. The Avanti came standard with a three-speed manual gearbox with floor-mounted gearshift. Overdrive was available for $110 extra on all models except the taxi, Avanti and Avanti powered 63V models. Except for the Avanti, taxi, Heavy-Duty and Avanti powered 63Vs, Flightomatic was available for $180 extra on six-cylinder models and $210 extra on eight-cylinder models. A heavy-duty water cooled automatic was optional on the taxi and Heavy-Duty models. A floor shift operated Power-Shift automatic was optional on most V-8 models. A four-speed manual gearbox with floor mounted gearshift was optional on all V-8 models except the taxi and Standard. Avanti R1 and R2 engines were optional on all 63V models except the Standard and taxi. The regular 289 V-8 was optional on all 63Vs that it was not standard on, except the Standard. A four-barrel carburetor (Carter AFB) was optional on all regular V-8s at $21.52. The four-barrel increased the 259 V-8's power to 195 hp at 4500 rpm and the 289 V-8's to 225 hp at 4500 rpm. During midyear, R1 and R2 Super Hawk and Super Lark packages were introduced. They included numerous Avanti suspension and powertrain features. Twin Traction was $39 optional on all models. Disc brakes, standard on the Avanti, were optional on all other models at $102. Other tire sizes were optional on most models. Lower compression ratios were available for export cars.

HISTORICAL FOOTNOTES: Special Heavy-Duty W3, Y3 and P3 models were available for rural route mail carriers. Called the Rural Route Lark, they offered interesting options, such as right-hand drive and Signal-stat warning lights. The Lark Marshals were also based on the Heavy-Duty W3, Y3 and P3 models. The six-cylinder model was called the City Marshal, the 259 cid V-8 model the Patrol Marshal and the 289 cid V-8 model, the Pursuit Marshal. The midyear Standard was sold for private use, but its main market was fleet sales. A fixed roof option was available on the Standard Wagonaires and certain export Wagonaires.

1964 STUDEBAKER

SIX-CYLINDER — SERIES 63S/SERIES S — In 1964 the Lark name was de-emphasized and was actually only being used in connection with the early Challenger and Commander models. Several new model names and a squared-up design were the major changes for 1964. The Challenger, which was only sold domestically, replaced the 1963 Standard line. The Challenger had no side moldings and single headlights (duals were optional). Challenger sedans had Lark emblems on the upper rear quarter panels. The Commander replaced the 1963 Regal line. The Commander had narrow side moldings and single headlights (duals optional). Commander sedans had circled "S" emblems on the upper rear quarter panels. The 1964 Daytona line was expanded to include a four-door sedan. The Daytona and Cruiser had wide side moldings and standard dual headlights. The Cruiser had very wide metal moldings across the back of the deck lid. Taxi and Heavy-Duty models were similar to Challengers in exterior trim. The Gran Turismo Hawk had a new smooth deck lid and slightly restyled imitation side grilles. All models, except the Challenger, taxi and Heavy-Duty, had a standard circled "S" hood ornament. Challenger, Commander, Daytona and Cruiser models had model identifications on the front fenders. Taxis and Heavy-Duty models had Studebaker on the front fenders. Gran Turismo Hawk model identifications were the same as 1962-1963. The 1964 model year was like two years in one. The "first" part revolved around cars built before the South Bend plant was closed down in December 1963. The second part evolved when all production was centralized in Canada after Jan. 2, 1964. After the South Bend plant was closed, taxicabs, Challengers, Heavy-Duty models, Gran Turismo Hawks, Avantis and Studebaker trucks were discontinued. A new Special Commander two-door sedan and Canadian Cruiser were introduced in January 1964. During the early period, the six-cylinder Gran Turismo Hawk, Cruiser and Daytona models were limited to sales in certain countries outside the United States. After Jan. 1, 1964, the Cruiser six was still not available in North America.

STUDEBAKER I.D. NUMBERS: VIN stamped on plate on left front door pillar on Studebaker and top of right frame side member on Avanti. First two symbols indicated model year: 64=1964. Following symbol or group of symbols indicated engine: S=six-cylinder (170 cid); V=V-8 (259 cid); P=V-8 (289 cid); R=Avanti V-8 (289 cid/240 hp); RS=Avanti supercharged V-8 (289 cid/289 hp); R3S=Avanti R3 supercharged V-8 (304.5 cid/335 hp). An extra symbol used on Canadian-built cars only was a C for Canada. Remaining symbols indicated the production sequence at the assembly plant. Six-cylinder engine number on pad at upper left-hand front side of block. V-8 engine number on pad at upper left front side of block. Motor numbers carried the engine codes as a prefix. All 1964 engine numbers were based on a complex formula that took into account the type of engine and date of manufacture. Studebaker shop manuals and parts catalogs explain the formula. [64S FIRST SERIES] Starting serial numbers for early-1964 six-cylinder powered Studebakers were 64S-1001 (South Bend) and 64SC-1001 for Canada. [SC-10 SECOND SERIES] The beginning serial number for late-1964 (starting Jan. 2, 1964) six-cylinder powered Studebaker was C-100001 and all were made in Canada. [64V FIRST SERIES] The beginning serial numbers for early-1964 V-8 powered Studebakers were 64V-1001 (South Bend) and 64VC-1001 for Canada. [VC-50 SECOND SERIES] The beginning serial number for late-1964 (starting Jan. 2, 1964) V-8 powered Studebakers was C-500001 and all were made in Canada. [AVANTI] The beginning serial number for 1964 Avantis was R-4835 and Avantis were all built in South Bend early in the model year. Studebaker also attached a Body Number Plate to the cowl below the hood. It carried the company name, VIN (serial number), series code (first column of charts below) the Body/Style Number (second column of charts below), plus one of many interior trim codes too numerous to list here.

1964 "FIRST SERIES" 64S SIX-CYLINDER

Model Number	Body/Style Number	Body Type & Seating	Factory Price	Shipping Weight	Production Total
TAXI					
64S	Y1	4-dr Taxi 6P	—	3060	428
CHALLENGER					
64S	F2	2-dr Sed-6P	1935	2660	2,122
64S	Y2	4-dr Sed-6P	2040	2780	2,546
64S	P2	4-dr Sta Wag-6P	2430	3230	453
HEAVY-DUTY					
64S	F3	2-dr Sed-6P	—	2755	7
64S	Y3	4-dr Sed-6P	—	2850	18
64S	P3	4-dr Sta Wag-6P	2700	3295	9
COMMANDER					
64S	F4	2-dr Sed-6P	2055	2695	4,374
64S	Y4	4-dr Sed-6P	2160	2815	7,102
64S	P4	4-dr Sta Wag-6P	2550	3265	1,206
DAYTONA					
64S	Y8	4-dr Sed-6P	2310	2825	1,036
64S	P8	4-dr Sta Wag-6P	2700	3305	116
64S	L8	2-dr Conv-6P	2662	3090	55
GRAN TURISMO HAWK					
64S	K6	2-dr GT HT-5P	2958	3280	224

1964 Studebaker, Lark Daytona four-door sedan, V-8

1964 "SECOND SERIES" SC-10 SIX-CYLINDER

Model Number	Body/Style Number	Body Type & Seating	Factory Price	Shipping Weight	Production Total
COMMANDER					
S	F4	2-dr Sed-6P	2055	2695	Note 1
S	P4	4-dr Sta Wag-6P	2550	3265	Note 1
S	Y4	4-dr Sed-6P	2160	2815	Note 1
COMMANDER SPECIAL					
S	F4 Sp.	2-dr Sed-6P	2185	2720	Note 1
DAYTONA					
S	Y8	4-dr Sed-6P	2310	2825	Note 1
S	P8	4-dr Sta Wag-6P	2700	3305	Note 1
S	L8	2-dr Conv-6P	2662	3090	Note 1

NOTE 1: Production totals in top chart for 64S and SC-10 series combined

EIGHT-CYLINDER MODELS — SERIES 64V — Styling and model identifications were the same as for the 1964 six-cylinder models. Most V-8 models had "8" emblems on the front fenders. Daytona sedans and hardtops had crossed checkered flag V-8 emblems on the upper rear quarter panels. Domestic Cruisers and Gran Turismo Hawks came standard with 289 V-8s.

1964 Studebaker, Gran Turismo Hawk two-door hardtop coupe, V-8

1964 "FIRST SERIES" 64V (V-8)

Model Number	Body/Style Number	Body Type & Seating	Factory Price	Shipping Weight	Production Total
TAXI					
64V	Y1	4-dr Taxi-6P	—	3270	27
CHALLENGER					
64V	F2	2-dr Sed-6P	2070	2910	274
64V	Y2	4-dr Sed-6P	2175	3010	594
64V	P2	4-dr Wag-6P	2565	3480	286
HEAVY-DUTY					
64V	F3	2-dr Sed-6P	—	2955	153
64V	Y3	4-dr Sed-6P	—	3060	80
64V	P3	4-dr Sta Wag-6P	—	3505	13
COMMANDER					
64V	F4	2-dr Sed-6P	2190	2945	1,553
64V	Y4	4-dr Sed-6P	2295	3045	6,753
64V	P4	4-dr Sta Wag-6P	2685	3515	1,605
DAYTONA					
64V	Y8	4-dr Sed-6P	2445	3055	5,390
64V	J8	2-dr HT-6P	2443	3060	2,414
64V	P8	4-dr Sta Wag-6P	2835	3555	1,543
64V	L8	2-dr Conv-6P	2797	3320	647
CRUISER					
64V	Y9	4-dr Sed-6P	2595	3120	5,023
HAWK					
64V	K6	2-dr GT HT-5P	2958	3280	1,548

1964 "SECOND SERIES" 64VC (V-8)

Model Number	Body/Style Number	Body Type & Seating	Factory Price	Shipping Weight	Production Total
COMMANDER					
V	F4	2-dr Sed-6P	2190	2945	Note 1
V	Y4	4-dr Sed-6P	2295	3045	Note 1
V	P4	4-dr Sta Wag-6P	2685	3515	Note 1
COMMANDER SPECIAL					
V	F4 Sp.	2-dr Sed-6P	2320	2970	Note 1
DAYTONA					
V	Y8	4-dr Sed-6P	2445	3055	Note 1
V	J8	2-dr HT-6P	2443	3060	Note 1
V	P8	4-dr Sta Wag-6P	2835	3555	Note 1
V	L8	2-dr Conv-6P	2797	3320	Note 1
CRUISER					
V	Y9	4-dr Sed-6P	2595	3120	Note 1

NOTE 1: Production totals in top chart for 64V and VC-10 series combined.

AVANTI — Studebaker made no effort to make a definite break between 1963 and 1964 Avantis. Most 1964s had round knobs on the console heater/defroster/vent levers. Early 1964s had round headlight enclosures, but about 750 of the 809 cars produced in 1964 had square headlight enclosures. All 1964 Avantis had woodgrained consoles, instrument panels and steering wheels. The basic body styling was the same as 1963. The last Studebaker Avanti was built in December 1963.

AVANTI SERIES

Model Number	Body/Style Number	Body Type & Seating	Factory Price	Shipping Weight	Production Total
R	Q	2-dr Spts Cpe-5P	4445	3195	809

ENGINES

(64S and S) Six-Cylinder. Overhead valve. Cast iron block. Displacement: 169.6 cid. Bore and stroke: 3 x 4 inches. Compression ratio: 8.25:1. Brake hp: 112 at 4500 rpm. Four main bearings. Solid valve lifters. Carburetor: Carter model RBS or AS one-barrel.

(64V 259 V-8) V8. Overhead valve. Cast iron block. Displacement: 259.2 cid. Bore and stroke: 3-9/16 x 3-1/4 inches. Compression ratio: 8.5:1. Brake hp: 180 at 4500 rpm. Five main bearings. Solid valve lifters. Carburetor: Stromberg model WW two-barrel.

(HAWK/CRUISER/MARSHAL 289 V-8) V-8. Overhead valve. Cast iron block. Displacement: 289 cid. Bore and stroke: 3-9/16 x 3-5/8 inches. Compression ratio: 8.5:1. Brake hp: 210 at 4500 rpm. Five main bearings. Solid valve lifters. Carburetor: Stromberg model WW two-barrel.

(R1 UNSUPERCHARGED) V-8. Overhead valve. Cast iron block. Displacement: 289 cid. Bore and stroke: 3-9/16 x 3-5/8 inches. Compression ratio: 10.25:1. Brake hp: 240. Five main bearings. Solid valve lifters. Carburetor: Carter model AFB four-barrel.

(R2 SUPERCHARGED) V-8. Overhead valve. Cast iron block. Displacement: 289 cid. Bore and stroke: 3-9/16 x 3-5/8 inches. Compression ratio: 9.0:1. Brake hp: 289. Five main bearings. Solid valve lifters. Carburetor: Carter model AFB four-barrel. (This powerplant was optional at extra-cost).

1964 Studebaker, Avanti two-door hardtop coupe, V-8 (AA)

CHASSIS FEATURES: Wheelbase: (two-door sedans, Daytona hardtop, Daytona convertible and Avanti) 109 inches; (four-door sedans and station wagons) 113 inches; (Gran Turismo Hawk) 120.5 inches. Overall length: (two-door sedans, Daytona hardtop and Daytona convertible) 190 inches; (four-door sedans) 194 inches; (station wagons) 193 inches; (Gran Turismo Hawk) 204 inches; (Avanti) 192. Front tread: 57.4 inches. Rear tread: 56.6 inches. Tires: (All 64S except convertibles and station wagons) 6.00 x 15 tubeless; (All 64V except Cruiser, convertible, station wagon and GT Hawk, plus 64S convertible and station wagon) 6.50 x 15 tubeless; (Cruiser, GT Hawk, Avanti, 64V convertible and station wagon) 6.70 x 15 tubeless.

OPTIONS: Only the options printed in bold face type were available on the Avanti. Power brakes. Headrests. Reclining seats. Individually adjusted front seats (standard on some models). Climatizer heater/defroster. Transistor AM manual tuning radio. The rear seat speaker only type available on GT Hawks — as in the past, the rear seat speaker was not available on convertibles or station wagons. Bumper guards. Regular full wheelcovers. V-8 engine dress-up kit. Rear fender stone shields (standard on Cruiser). Front fender splashguards. Stratoline exterior rearview mirror. Electric clock. Tachometer for Avanti-powered GT Hawks and Lark type vehicles. Exhaust deflectors. Rear door safety locks. Day-Night interior rearview mirror. Clear plastic seat covers or cushion toppers for Lark type vehicles. Padded sun visors. Cigarette lighter. Auto compass. Tissue dispenser. Back-up lights for low-priced models. Glove compartment light. Trunk light. Spotlight. Fuel line filter. Undercoating. Trim kits for low-priced models. Special station wagon options: rear-facing third seat (including Captive-Air tires and no spare). Car-Go-Pak. Luggage rack. Cargo mat. Safety Sta-Bar kit. Tailgate step. Cargo cover. Rear deck cushions. Special options for the Gran Turismo Hawk: Rear deck lid radio antenna. Aero Strut wheelcovers. Door handle guards. Visor vanity mirror. Partial vinyl roof. Power steering. Hill Holder. Air conditioning (not available with R2/R3 engines). White sidewall tires. Tinted glass. Transistor AM-FM push-button radio. Transistor AM push-button radio. Rear seat speaker. Strato-Vue rearview mirror. License plate frames. Rubber floor mats. Locking gas cap. Seat belts. Windshield washer. Adjustable shock absorbers. Underhood light. Touch-up paint applicators. Special Avanti options: Tilt steering wheel. Power door windows. Wire spoke wheel discs. A three-speed manual gearbox with column-mounted gearshift was standard on all models except the Avanti. The Avanti came standard with a three-speed manual gearbox with floor mounted gearshift. Overdrive was available for $111 extra on all models except the taxi, Avanti and Avanti powered 64V models. Except for the Avanti, taxi, Heavy-Duty and Avanti powered 64Vs, Flightomatic was available for $185 extra on six-cylinder models and $210 extra on eight-cylinder models. A heavy-duty water-cooled automatic was optional on the taxi and Heavy-Duty models. A floor shift operated Power-Shift automatic or four-speed manual gearbox was optional on most V-8 models. Except for the taxi, Avanti engines were optional on all 64V models. The regular 289 V-8 was optional on all 64Vs on which it was not standard. A four-barrel carburetor was optional on all regular V-8s. The four-barrel increased the 259 V-8's power to 195 hp at 4500 rpm and the 289 V-8's to 225 hp at 4500 rpm. Twin Traction was optional on all models. Disc brakes, standard on the Avanti, were optional on all other models. Other tire sizes were optional on most models. Lower compression ratios were available for export cars. Special extra-cost 304.5 cid Avanti engines were introduced late in 1963. The supercharged R3 engine produced 335 hp. The unsupercharged R4 version, which had two four-barrel carburetors, produced 280 hp.

HISTORICAL FOOTNOTES: Special Heavy-Duty W3, Y3 and P3 models were available for rural route mail carriers. Called the Rural Router, they offered many options, including right-hand drive. The Marshals were also based on the Heavy-Duty W3, Y3 and P3 models. The six-cylinder model was called the City Marshal, the 259 V-8 model the Patrol Marshal, and the 289 V-8 model the Pursuit Marshal. A fixed roof option was available on all Wagonaire station wagons. Only 10 saleable new cars (nine Avantis and one Commander two-door sedan) were fitted at the factory with R3 engines. Only one saleable new car, a Daytona hardtop, was fitted at the factory with an R4 engine.

1965 STUDEBAKER

SIX-CYLINDER COMMANDER/CRUISER — SERIES S ("C-11") — The 1965 stylings were almost Identical to the late 1964 offerings. The major change was the switch to heavy-duty Canadian-built engines. These General Motors-McKinnon motors were based on Chevrolet designs. Dual headlights were standard on all 1965 Studebakers. The wide moldings on the back of the deck lid on Cruisers were discontinued. A new horizontal molding on Daytona Sedans and Cruisers was added below the deck lid opening. The six-cylinder Cruiser was now available in North America. Commanders continued with narrow side moldings, while Cruisers had wide moldings. The model identifications were on the front fenders and also on the back of Cruisers and Daytonas. A six-cylinder Daytona was not offered In 1965.

STUDEBAKER I.D. NUMBERS: VIN on left front pillar post of Studebakers. First two symbols indicate engine: 06=six-cylinder with standard transmission; 66=six-cylinder with automatic; 20=V-8 with standard transmission; 80=V-8 with automatic. Third symbol indicates model year: 5=1965. Last six symbols are the sequential production number at the Canadian

factory starting at 110001 and up for six-cylinder cars and 510001 and up for V-8s. [SIX-CYLINDER] The beginning serial number for the 1965 S models was C-110001 (Canada). The beginning engine numbers were 06510001 with standard transmission and 66510001 with automatic transmission. [V-8]: The beginning serial number for the 1965 models was C-510001 (Canada). The beginning engine numbers were 205420001 with standard transmission and 805420001 with automatic transmission.

1965 Studebaker, Commander two-door sedan, 6-cyl (AA)

COMMANDER/CRUISER SIX SERIES

Model Number	Body/Style Number	Body Type & Seating	Factory Price	Shipping Weight	Production Total
COMMANDER					
S	F4	2-dr Sed-6P	2125	2695	3,067
S	Y4	4-dr Sed-6P	2230	2815	4,319
S	P4	4-dr Sta Wag-6P	2620	3246	564
CRUISER					
S	Y9	4-dr Sed-6P	2470	2815	791

1965 Studebaker, Daytona four-door Wagonaire station wagon, V-8

EIGHT-CYLINDER COMMANDER/DAYTONA/CRUISER. SERIES V ("C-51") — The Daytona was only available as a V-8 in 1965. The Daytona side trim was like that on the Cruiser. A new Daytona Sport Sedan, with standard vinyl roof, replaced the Daytona hardtop. Commander and Cruiser trim was like that on the six-cylinder. models. Model Identifications were in the same locations as on the 'S' models. The 1964 type "8" fender nameplates were continued.

COMMANDER/DAYTONA/CRUISER V-8 SERIES

Model Number	Body/Style Number	Body Type & Seating	Factory Price	Shipping Weight	Production Total
COMMANDER					
V	F4	2-dr Sed-6P	2265	2891	571
V	Y4	4-dr Sed-6P	2370	2991	4,344
V	P4	4-dr Sta Wag-6P	2760	3461	534
DAYTONA					
V	F8	2-dr Spt Cpe-5P	2565	3006	1,626
V	P8	4-dr Sta Wag-6P	2890	3501	723
CRUISER					
V	Y9	4-dr Sed-6P	2610	3006	2,901

1965 Studebaker, four-door Cruiser sedan, V-8 (AA)

BASE ENGINES

(COMMANDER/CRUISER SIX) Six-Cylinder. Overhead valve. Cast iron block. Displacement: 194 cid. Bore and stroke: 3-9/16 x 3-1/4 inches. Compression ratio: 8.5:1. Brake hp: 120 at 4400 rpm. Seven main bearings. Hydraulic valve lifters. Carburetor: Rochester model BV one-barrel.

(COMMANDER/DAYTONA/CRUISER EIGHT) V-8. Overhead valve. Cast iron block. Displacement: 283 cid. Bore and stroke: 3-7/8 x 3 inches. Compression ratio: 9.25:1. Brake hp: 195 at 4800 rpm. Five main bearings. Hydraulic valve lifters. Carburetor: Rochester model 2GV two-barrel.

CHASSIS FEATURES: Wheelbase: (two-door sedans) 109 inches; (four-door sedans and wagons) 113 inches. Overall length: (two-door sedans) 190 inches; (four-door sedans) 194 inches; (Station wagons) 193 inches. Front tread: 57.4 inches. Rear tread: 56.6 inches. Tires: 7.35 x 15 tubeless.

OPTIONS: Hill Holder. V-8 power steering. V-8 power drum brakes. Individual reclining seats. Whitewall tires. Horn ring for Commander models. Tinted glass. Climatizer heater/defroster. Commander back-up lights. Electric clock (standard on Cruiser). Seat belts. Engine block heater. Vanity tray. Transistor push-button AM-FM radio. Transistor AM push-button radio. Transistor AM manual tuning radio. Rear seat speaker. Air conditioning. Exterior rearview mirror (two types). License plate frames. Rubber floor mats. Locking gas cap. Exhaust deflector. Rear door safety locks. Padded sun visors. Day-Night interior rearview mirror. Windshield washer (standard on top-line models). Rear fender stone shield (standard on Cruiser). Regular or wire wheelcovers. Front fender splashguards. Head rests. Auto Compass. Spotlight. Vanity tray light. Trunk light. Underhood light. Undercoating. Special station wagon options: Power rear window. Cargo mat. Cargo cover. Rear deck cushions. Luggage rack. Tailgate step. Safety Sta-Bar kit. A three-speed manual gearbox with column-mounted gearshift was standard on all models. Overdrive was available for $110 extra. Automatic was available for $172 extra on six-cylinder and $200 extra on eight-cylinder models. Twin Traction ($39); Disc brakes, and transistor ignition (made standard on Daytona Sport Sedan) optional on all models. 7.25 x 15 tires were optional on all models.

HISTORICAL FOOTNOTES: A midyear heavy-duty version of the Commander six-cylinder four-door sedan (S-Y4) was promoted for taxi, Police and Fleet car sales. It was listed as an option package instead of a separate model. The Wagonaire station wagon was only available with a sliding top during 1965.

1966 STUDEBAKER

SIX CYLINDER — SERIES S ("C-13") — Standard single headlights, a new grille and very low side moldings were the main styling changes made by Studebaker during its last year of automotive production. "Refreshaire" vents above the taillights on sedans were Studebaker's last engineering achievement. Six-cylinder Daytonas were again offered. The Wagonaire was made a model of its own. Cruisers and Daytonas had wide side moldings, while Commanders and Wagonaires had narrow side moldings. Engine displacement nameplates were placed on the front fenders. Model identifications, except for the Wagonaire, were on the front fender and also below the deck lid on Cruisers and Daytonas. The Wagonaire had a Studebaker script on the front fenders and Wagonaire script on the tailgate.

STUDEBAKER I.D. NUMBERS: VIN on left front hinge pillar post of Studebakers. First two symbols indicate engine: 06=six-cylinder with standard transmission; 66=six-cylinder with automatic; 20=V-8 with standard transmission; 80=V-8 with automatic. Third symbol indicates model year: 6=1966. Last six symbols are the sequential production number at the Canadian factory starting at C-130001 and up for six-cylinder cars and C-530001 and up for V-8s. [SIX-CYLINDER] The beginning serial number for the 1966 S models was C-130001 (Canada). The beginning 194 cid engine numbers were 01610001 with standard transmission and 61610001 with automatic transmission. The beginning 230 cid engine number was 656100001. [V-8] The beginning serial number for the 1966 V series was C-530001 (Canada). The beginning engine numbers were 176400001 with standard transmission and 776400001 with automatic transmission.

1966 Studebaker, Wagonaire four-door station wagon, V-8

SIX-CYLINDER SERIES S

Model Number	Body/Style Number	Body Type & Seating	Factory Price	Shipping Weight	Production Total
COMMANDER					
S	Y4	4-dr Sed-6P	2319	2815	Note 1
S	F4	2-dr Sed-6P	2215	2695	Note 1
DAYTONA/WAGONAIRE					
S	F8	2-dr Spt Sed-5P	2443	2755	Note 1
S	P8	4-dr Sta Wag-6P	2664	3246	Note 1
CRUISER					
S	Y9	4-dr Sed-6P	2544	2815	Note 1

1966 Studebaker, Daytona two-door sedan, V-8

EIGHT CYLINDER SERIES V ("C-53") — The V body style and trim offerings were the same as for the six-cylinder models. Model identifications were in the same locations as on S models.

1966 Studebaker, four-door Cruiser sedan, V-8 (AA)

EIGHT-CYLINDER SERIES V

Model Number	Body/Style Number	Body Type & Seating	Factory Price	Shipping Weight	Production Total
COMMANDER					
V	Y4	4-dr Sed-6P	2456	2991	1,368
V	F4	2-dr Sed-6P	2352	2891	198
DAYTONA/WAGONAIRE					
V	F8	2-dr Spt Sed-5P	2581	3006	620
V	P8	4-dr Sta Wag-6P	2802	3501	618
CRUISER					
V	Y9	4-dr Sed-6P	2682	3066	1,844

BASE ENGINES

(S SERIES SIX) Six-Cylinder. Overhead valve. Cast iron block. Displacement: 194 cid. Bore and stroke: 3-9/16 x 3-1/4 inches. Compression ratio: 8.5:1. Brake hp: 120 at 4400 rpm. Seven main bearings. Hydraulic valve lifters. Carburetor: Rochester model BV one-barrel.

(V SERIES EIGHT) V-8. Overhead valve. Cast iron block. Displacement: 283 cid. Bore and stroke: 3-7/8 x 3 inches. Compression ratio: 9.25:1. Brake hp: 195 at 4800 rpm. Five main bearings. Hydraulic valve lifters. Carburetor: Rochester model 2GV two-barrel.

CHASSIS FEATURES: Wheelbase (two-door sedans) 109 inches; (four-door sedans and wagons) 113 inches. Overall length: (two-door sedans) 190 inches; (four-door sedans) 194 inches; (station wagons) 193 inches. Front tread: 57.4 inches. Rear tread: 56.6 inches. Tires: 7.35 x 15 tubeless.

OPTIONS: Hill Holder. V-8 power steering. Air conditioning. Reclining seats. Bucket seats for Cruiser and Wagonaire. White sidewall tires. Vinyl roof for Cruiser. Vanity tray. Horn ring for Commander and Wagonaire models. Tinted glass. Climatizer heater/defroster. Commander and Wagonaire Back-up lights. Electric clock (standard on Cruiser). Transistor AM-FM push-button radio. Transistor AM manual tuning radio. Rear seat speaker. Rubber floor mats. Seat belts. Front fender splashguards. Rear fender stone shields (standard on Cruiser). Regular or wire wheelcovers. Auto compass. Padded sun visors. Exterior rearview mirror (two types). Exhaust deflector. Rear door safety locks. Day-Night interior rearview mirror. Bumper guards (standard on Cruiser). Underhood light. Trunk light. Vanity tray light. Locking gas cap. Commander chrome gas cap. Spotlight. Special station wagon options: Power rear window. Tailgate step. Cargo mat. Luggage rack. Rear deck cushions. Cargo cover. Safety StaBar kit. A three-speed manual gearbox with column-mounted gearshift was standard on all models. Overdrive was available for $113 extra. Automatic was available for $192 extra on six-cylinder models and $225 extra on eight-cylinder models. A larger 230 cid six-cylinder engine with an 8.5:1 compression ratio and 140 hp at 4400 rpm was originally optional on S series cars with automatic transmissions. It was later made optional on all S series cars. Twin Traction, disc brakes and transistor ignition (standard on Daytona Sport Sedan) optional on all models. 7.75 x 15 tires were optional on all models.

HISTORICAL FOOTNOTES: A heavy-duty taxi option kit for the Commander four-door sedan was available. These converted models were called S-Y4T. A fixed top option was available for the Wagonaire station wagon during 1966.

STANDARD CATALOG OF
WILLYS
1946-1955

1949 Willys-Overland, two-door Jeepster, 6-cyl

Willys-Overland, of Toledo, Ohio, had a long history of making small cars prior to outbreak of World War II. When production of automobiles resumed, in 1945, the company temporarily abandoned the passenger car market, electing to sell civilian versions of its famous military Jeep instead.

By John R. Smith

A wide choice of Jeep-based vehicles was offered, ranging from those specially-equipped for agricultural use to fire trucks. Most were marketed as commercial vehicles, although the dual-purpose station wagon was often used as a passenger car by buyers preferring utility to style.

Willys had plans to return to the passenger car business, but not until the early 1950s. During the interim, the company decided to develop a totally new type of product that combined car and Jeep features. It was called the Jeepster.

Production of the Jeepster began in May of 1948. It was, essentially, a four-passenger open car using the same chassis as the Jeep station wagon. Industrial Designer Brooks Stevens was commissioned to do the overall styling, which incorporated a sporty look. Features included a Jeep-like frontal treatment; angular front fenders (as used on front of the station wagon); double-angled rear fenders and a body reflecting a number of European sports car traits, such as doors with cut-down upper edges. Standard equipment

included bright front and rear bumpers with guards; dual sun visors; Deluxe steering wheel (with horn ring); luxury upholstery; chrome wheel trim rings; and manual transmission with overdrive.

The Jeepster was strictly a two-wheel-drive vehicle and sold for about $1,600 with a four-cylinder engine, manual folding top and plastic windowed side curtains. Beginning in 1949, a six was offered as optional equipment. Slight styling changes were adopted for model year 1950, including the addition of five, bright, horizontal bars in the grille. Production of the Jeepster ended around June, 1950, although sales seem to have gone on with reduced prices for about another year. After the model was gone, it caught on as a used car and was later revived, by Kaiser-Jeep Corp., in 1967.

One reason the Jeepster was dropped was due to Willys' re-entry into the passenger car field with the Aero sedan series of 1952. It consisted of a spartan two-door sedan named the Lark (with a 75 hp L-head six); plus the Wing and the Ace (same body style in richer trim) and the top-of-the-line Eagle two-door hardtop. The latter three cars were powered by a 90 hp version of the same motor, the extra output coming from a higher compression ratio and F-head engine. The F-head had overhead intake valves, but exhaust valves inside the block.

Kaiser took over Willys-Overland on April 28, 1953. The new line of cars was expanded by adding a four-door sedan in the Lark series and a next-step-up Falcon in two- or four-

door form. Both Larks and Falcons used the L-head six, which was in its last year. It's also interesting to note that both of these names were used, years later, on compact models made by other companies. This was Willys' Golden Anniversary year. To commemorate the occasion, the wheel cover centers were finished in red and a gold 'W' was added to the grille.

For 1954, the Willys compact car line continued to grow with over 20 different varieties offered. Even a taxicab model was included. It's likely not all of these cars were produced concurrently, as midyear changes and model additions were quite common in the industry at this time. There was a new series of cars equipped with Kaiser's "Hurricane" (Continental Red Seal) six-cylinder engine. A handful of prototypes were even built with supercharged versions of this power plant and a one-off convertible (which still exists today) was made by Derham Body Co.

The last year for production of the Aero Willys was 1955, as Kaiser Industries was planning to abandon the U.S. passenger car market for good. Three nameplates were marketed this season, the Ace, Custom and Bermuda being advertised as "value leaders for 1955." MOTOR TREND magazine highlighted some of the new styling features like toothier grilles; two-tone color treatments; more fashionable interiors; and padded dashboards.

At this point in time, Kaiser-Willys Div. was selling about every Jeep it could make, but customers were not flocking to either brand's showrooms for passenger cars. The company operated on an international basis, however. It was involved in a diverse number of fields ranging from shipbuilding to aluminum mining. Management decided that the same cars could be produced and successfully marketed by branches of Kaiser Industries in South American countries.

By mid-1955, the Willys body dies were shipped to Brazil where a car very close to the Aero Ace four-door was produced through 1962 as the Aero Willys 2600. A modernized version, bearing Aero Willys nameplates, was also sold in Brazil from 1963 to 1971. In character and size, this Itamaraty (President) model was the same type of car as the original with a trim upgrade by Brooks Stevens. It was even stretched into a limousine, the Itamaraty Executive.

The Itamaraty was the first Latin American car ever displayed at the Paris Auto Show (1963). In 1967, Willys-Overlad de Brazil was sold to Ford. The Willys two- and four-door station wagon was also produced in Brazil and sold there by Ford through 1976. There was even a four-door variant, also designed by Brooks Stevens. Neither Brazilian model, however, should be confused with another called the Willys Interlagos Berlinette (1965-1967), which was actually a Renault marketed under the popular Willys badge. Only about a dozen Itamaraty models have been brought into the United States.

1952 Willys, Aero Wing, two-door sedan, 6-cyl

1949 Willys, two-door Station Sedan, 6-cyl

1951 Willys, two-door Station Sedan, 6-cyl

1953 Willys, Aero Custom Ace, two-door sedan, 6-cyl

1946 WILLYS

WILLYS — (STATION WAGON) — For 1946, Willys introduced an all-steel, truck-like station wagon with a 134 cid four-cylinder engine. It used the same basic 104 inch wheelbase chassis as the prewar Willys American. It was significant in that it was the first true all-steel station wagon, though it was considered more truck than car. It was the only Willys civilian vehicle for the years 1946 and 1947. At first, all of these station wagons came with the front sheet metal painted maroon. The body was painted to resemble birch and mahogany paneling.

1946 Willys, two-door station wagon, 4-cyl (TVB)

WILLYS I.D. NUMBERS: VIN same as serial number. VIN locations: on plate at the left of the driver's seat on the floor riser; on left door sill; on frame front crossmember ahead of front spring hanger; on front frame crossmember at center; on right side of cowl below hood; on inside of frame on left. Serial Numbers for 1946 were 10001 to 16534. The motor number was the same as the serial number and was located on the top of the water pump boss; at the right front upper corner of the engine block.

WILLYS STATION WAGON SERIES

Model Number	Body/Style Number	Body Type & Seating	Factory Price	Shipping Weight	Production Total
446	46	3-dr Sta Wag-6P	1495	2898	6,533

NOTE 1: Price increased to $1,549 late in 1946.

ENGINE: Inline. L-head. Four-cylinder. Cast iron block. Displacement: 134.2 cid. Bore and stroke: 3.13 x 4.38 inches. Compression ratio: 6.48:1. Brake hp: 63 at 4000 rpm. Carburetion: Carter WAI-613S one-barrel. Three main bearings. Solid valve lifters.

CHASSIS FEATURES: Wheelbase: 104 inches. Overall length: 174 Inches. Tires: 6.00 x 15 tube-type blackwall.

OPTIONS: Wheel trim rings. Front bumper guards. Rear bumper guards. Spot light. Fog lamps. Three-speed manual transmission with overdrive was standard. Heavy-duty air cleaner.

HISTORICAL FOOTNOTES: The 1946 Willys were introduced in July, 1946. Model year production peaked at 6,533 units. Calendar year sales of 6,533 cars were recorded. W.M. Canaday was the chief executive officer of Willys-Overland. Civilian Jeep production began in 1945. Station wagons and panel delivery trucks were added to the line during 1946. The four-wheel-drive Jeeps and two-wheel-drive panel trucks are considered commercial vehicles. Information about these model will be found in the STANDARD CATALOG of LIGHT-DUTY AMERICAN TRUCKS by Krause Publications. A total of 71,455 Jeeps and one prototype model were assembled in calendar 1946.

1947 WILLYS

WILLYS — (STATION WAGON) — 1947 Willys station wagons were identical to the 1946 models except for the smallest details.

WILLYS I.D. NUMBERS: VIN same as serial number. VIN locations: on plate at the left of the driver's seat on the floor riser; on left door sill; on frame front crossmember ahead of front spring hanger; on front frame crossmember at center; on right side of cowl below hood; on inside of frame on left. Serial numbers for 1946 were 16535 to 44045. The motor number was the same as the serial number and was located on the top of the water pump boss; at the right front upper corner of the engine block.

WILLYS STATION WAGON SERIES

Model Number	Body/Style Number	Body Type & Seating	Factory Price	Shipping Weight	Production Total
447	463	2-dr Sta Wag-5P	1616	2898	33,214

ENGINE: Inline. L-head. Four-cylinder. Cast iron block. Displacement: 134.2 cid. Bore and stroke: 3.13 x 4.38 inches. Compression ratio: 6.48:1. Brake hp: 63 at 4000 rpm. Carburetion: Carter WA1-613S single-barrel. Three main bearings. Solid valve lifters.

CHASSIS FEATURES: Wheelbase: 104 inches. Overall length: 174 Inches. Tires: 6.00 x 15 tube-type blackwall.

OPTIONS: Wheel trim rings. Front bumper guards. Rear bumper guards. Spot light. Fog lamps. Three-speed manual transmission with overdrive was standard. Heavy-duty air cleaner.

1947 Willys, two-door station wagon, 4-cyl (TVB)

HISTORICAL FOOTNOTES: The 1947 Willys models were introduced January, 1947. Model year production peaked at 33,214 units. Calendar year sales of 33,214 cars were recorded this year. Two-wheel drive and four-wheel drive trucks appeared this season. Willys-Overland Motors, Inc. was headquartered at Toledo, Ohio.

1948 WILLYS

1948 Willys, two-door Jeepster phaeton, 4-cyl

WILLYS — (ALL MODELS) — Production of 1948 Willys station wagons started in November, 1947 and vehicles in this series were sold as both 1948 and 1949 models. As in 1946 and 1947, the 1948 wagon utilized a grille with a vertical center divider and four vertical slots on either side of the center bar. The upscale Station Sedan was added in January, 1948. On May 3, 1948, the Jeepster phaeton was introduced. The station wagon was little changed. The six-cylinder Station Sedan featured a fancier grille with a vertical molding and wider seats. A circular medallion was placed above the grille and a chrome molding graced the front center portion of the hood. On this model, the small upper bodyside panels just under the lower window frames were embossed with a basketweave trim pattern and painted a straw-like color. The Jeepster was an open touring car designed during World War II by Brooks Stevens. Its lines were borrowed from the Jeep. It had an open compartment behind the cowl and a mechanically-operated soft top. The Jeepster and the Station Sedan helped to keep Willys-Overland in business. The station wagon came with two-tone finish that gave the look of a "woodie."

WILLYS I.D. NUMBERS: VIN same as serial number. VIN locations: on plate at the left of the driver's seat on the floor riser; on left door sill; on frame front crossmember ahead of front spring hanger; on front frame crossmember at center; on right side of cowl below hood; on inside of frame on left. Serial numbers for early-series 1948 models were: Series 463 station wagon: 44046 to 79715. Series 663 station sedan: 10001 to 13118. Series VJ2 Jeepster: 65199 to 79715. The motor number was the same as the serial number and was located on the top of the water pump boss; at the right front upper corner of the engine block.

WILLYS SERIES

Model Number	Body/Style Number	Body Type & Seating	Factory Price	Shipping Weight	Production Total
STATION WAGON					
463	463	2-dr Sta Wag-5P	1645	2895	Note 1
STATION SEDAN					
663	663	2-dr Sta Wag-5P	1890	2900	Note 1
JEEPSTER					
463	VJ2	2-dr Phae-4P	1765	2468	10,326

NOTE 1: 22,309 station wagons and station sedans built.
NOTE 2: No break-outs.

ENGINES

(FOUR) Inline. L-head. Four-cylinder. Cast iron block. Displacement: 134.2 cid. Bore and stroke: 3.13 x 4.38 inches. Compression ratio: 6.48:1. Brake hp: 63 at 4000 rpm. Carburetion: Carter WA1-613S single-barrel. Three main bearings. Solid valve lifters.

(SIX) Inline. L-head. Six-cylinder. Cast iron block. Displacement: 148.5 cid. Bore and stroke: 3.00 x 3.50 inches. Compression ratio: 6.42:1. Brake hp: 72 at 4000 rpm. Carburetion: Carter WAI-645S single-barrel. Four main bearings. Solid valve lifters.

CHASSIS FEATURES: Wheelbase: (All models) 104 inches. Overall length: (station wagon) 174 inches; (station sedan) 175.8 inches; (Jeepster) 174.8 inches. Front tread: (All models) 55 inches. Rear tread: (All models) 57 inches. Tires: (Nov. 1948 station wagon series) 15 x 6.70; (Station Sedan and later station wagons) 6.00 x 15; (Jeepster phaeton) 5.90 x 15.

OPTIONS: Front bumper guards. Rear bumper guards. Front grille guard. Wheel trim rings. Large wheel discs. Radio and antenna. License plate frames. White sidewall tires. Three-speed manual transmission with overdrive was standard. High-compression 7.0:1 cylinder head. Heavy-duty air cleaner was optional.

HISTORICAL FOOTNOTES: The 1948 Willys station wagon was introduced in Nov. 1947. The Station Sedan six-cylinder models were introduced in January, 1948. The four-cylinder Jeepster phaeton was added on May 3, 1948. Calendar year production of 32,635 cars was recorded. W.M. Canaday was the chief executive officer again this year. The most important event of the year was the introduction of the Jeepster phaeton. Willys also produced 104,632 non-passenger type commercial vehicles this year. They included 63,170 Jeeps and 41,462 trucks. Willys was ranked as America's 18th largest automaker. The four-cylinder F-head engine was called the "Hurricane Four." The six-cylinder L-head engine was called the "Lightning Six."

1949 WILLYS

1949 Willys, two-door Jeepster phaeton, 4-cyl

WILLYS — (ALL MODELS) — For 1949, Willys offered a new four-wheel-drive station wagon with a 104.5 inch wheelbase at midyear (July 1949). The regular wagon and two versions of the Jeepster rounded out the four-cylinder line. The second Jeepster was introduced in January of 1948 and featured Willys first F-head engine. Willys continued to sell the six-cylinder Station Sedan and station wagon and introduced a new six-cylinder Jeepster.

WILLYS I.D. NUMBERS: VIN same as serial number. VIN locations: on plate at the left of the driver's seat on the floor riser; on left door sill; on frame front crossmember ahead of front spring hanger; on front frame crossmember at center; on right side of cowl below hood; on inside of frame on left. Serial numbers for the cars in the late 1948/early 1949 styles were: (463 station wagon) 79716 to 10654; (663 Station Sedan) 13119 to 22769; (463 Jeepster) 79716 to 10654. Serial numbers for the vehicles introduced in July 1949 were: (four-cylinder wagon) 10001 to 13186; (four-cylinder Jeepster) 10001 to 12698; (six-cylinder Jeepster) 10001 to 10654. The motor number was the same as the serial number and was located on the top of the water pump boss; at the right front upper corner of the engine block.

WILLYS SERIES

Model Number	Body/Style Number	Body Type & Seating	Factory Price	Shipping Weight	Production Total
SERIES STARTING NOV. 1948					
(FOUR-CYLINDER)					
463	NA	2-dr Sta Wag-5P	1595	2895	Note 1
463	NA	2-dr Jeepster-4P	1495	2468	Note 1
(SIX-CYLINDER)					
633	NA	2-dr Sta Wag-5P	1695	2890	Note 1
633	NA	2-dr Sta Sed-5P	1745	2890	Note 1
SERIES STARTING JULY 1949					
(FOUR-CYLINDER)					
4x463	NA	2-dr 4WD Wag-5P	1895	3136	Note 1
VJ3	NA	2-dr Jeepster-4P	1495	2468	Notes 1/3
(SIX-CYLINDER)					
VJ3	NA	2-dr Jeepster-4P	1530	2392	Note 1

NOTE 1: 32,928 units were built for the 1949 calendar year.
NOTE 2: Includes 29,290 station wagons and station sedans; 3,638 Jeepsters.
NOTE 3: Model 463 Jeepster replaced by VJ-3 Jeepster four on Jan. 10, 1949.

ENGINES

(FOUR) Inline. L-head. Cast iron block. Displacement: 134.2 cid. Bore and stroke: 3.13 x 4.38 inches. Compression ratio: 6.48:1. Brake hp: 63 at 4000 rpm. Carburetor: Carter WA1-613S single-barrel. Three main bearings. Solid valve lifters.

(SIX) Inline. L-head. Cast iron block. Displacement: 148.5 cid. Bore and stroke: 3.00 x 3.50 inches. Compression ratio: 6.42:1 Brake hp: 72 at 4000 rpm. Carburetor: Carter WA1-645S one-barrel. Four main bearings. Solid valve lifters.

CHASSIS FEATURES: Wheelbase: (Series 4x463 station wagon) 104.5 inches; (All other models) 104 inches. Overall length: (all models) 174.8 inches. Front tread: (Model 463) 55 inches; (All other models) 56 inches. Rear tread: (All models) 57 inches. Tires: (early Jeepster four) 5.90 x 15; (early series/others) 6.70 x 15; (late Jeepster four) 6.40 x 15; (others six and four) 6.70 x 15; (late 4x4 station wagon) 6.50 x 15.

OPTIONS: Front bumper guards. Rear bumper guards. Front grille guard. License plate frames. Large wheel discs. White sidewall tires. Wheel trim rings. Radio and antenna. Oversize tires. Special paint. Spotlights. Fog lights. Heater and defroster. Three-speed manual transmission was standard on Jeepsters. Overdrive transmission was standard on all models, except Jeepster. Four-cylinder. 134.2 cid 7.0:1 compression engine (no cost). Heavy-duty air cleaner was optional at extra cost.

HISTORICAL FOOTNOTES: The 1949 Willys-Overlands were introduced November, 1948; the VJ3-4 Jeepster bowed Jan. 10, 1949; and the VJ3-6 and 4x463 appeared in dealer showrooms July, 1949. Model year production peaked at 32,928 units. Calendar year registrations of 28,576 cars were recorded. W.M. Canaday was the chief executive officer of Willys. The Jeepster continued to be sold with snap-on side curtains for weather protection. Roll-up side windows were not provided. The Milestone Car Society recognizes 1948 through 1951 Jeepsters as Milestone Cars. Willys-Overland also manufactured 31,595 civilian Jeeps and 18,342 other types of commercial vehicles during calendar 1949.

1950 WILLYS

1950 Willys, two-door four-wheel-drive station wagon, 4-cyl

WILLYS — (ALL MODELS) — For 1950, Willys models were very slightly restyled in the grille, with the vertical grille bars now being more pointed and divided by five horizontal bars. There was a new center-gage dashboard design and new wraparound rear bumper. The remainder of the body styling was unchanged from the previous year. Certain equipment formerly provided on both fours and sixes was now used with sixes only. This included dual wipers; front bumper guards and rails; wheel trim rings; rearview mirrors; cigar lighter and white sidewall tires.

WILLYS I.D. NUMBERS: VIN same as serial number. VIN locations: on plate at the left of the driver's seat on the floor riser; on left door sill; on frame front crossmember ahead of front spring hanger; on front frame crossmember at center; on right side of cowl below hood; on inside of frame on left. Series 463 station wagons began at 106504 and went up to 112425; 4X463 station wagons began at 13186 and went up 17167; the series 4-VJ3 Jeepsters began at 12698 and went up to 13190; the 6-VJ3-6 Jeepsters began at 10654 and went up to 11001; the series 6-663 station sedans began at 22769 and went up to 27786; and the 4-473 station wagons and Jeepsters and the 4-4x473 four-wheel-drive station wagons began at 10001 and went up to 12045 in mixed production. 6-673 station wagons and Jeepsters began at 10001 and went up to 17,456 in mixed production. The motor number was the same as the serial number and was located on the top of the water pump boss; at the right front upper corner of the engine block.

WILLYS SERIES

Model Number	Body/Style Number	Body Type & Seating	Factory Price	Shipping Weight	Production Total
FIRST SERIES FOUR-CYLINDER					
450	463	2-dr Sta Wag-6P	1595	2895	Note 1
450	463x4	2-dr 4WD Sta Wag-6P	1895	3136	Note 1
450	4-VJ3	2-dr Jeepster-5P	1495	2468	Note 1
SECOND SERIES FOUR-CYLINDER					
450	473	2-dr Jeepster-5P	1390	2459	Note 1
450	473SW	2-dr Sta Wag-6P	1495	2818	Note 1
450	473X4	2-dr 4WD Sta Wag-6P	1990	3174	Note 1
FIRST SERIES SIX-CYLINDER					
650	663	2-dr Sta Wag-6P	1695	2895	Note 1
650	VJ3-6	2-dr Jeepster-5P	1530	2392	Note 1
SECOND SERIES SIX-CYLINDER					
650	673SW	2-dr Sta Wag-6P	1575	2831	Note 1
650	673VJ	2-dr Jeepster-5P	1490	2485	Note 1

NOTE 1: 38,052 units built in calendar year.
NOTE 2: 5,834 Jeepsters and 32,218 station wagons in Note 1 total.

WILLYS ENGINES

(FIRST SERIES 463/463x4/VJ-3) Inline. L-head. Four-cylinder. Cast iron block. Displacement: 134.2 cid. Bore and stroke: 3.13 x 4.38 inches. Compression ratio: 6.48:1. Brake hp: 63 at 4000 rpm. Carburetion: Carter WAl-613S single-barrel. Three main bearings. Solid valve lifters.

(FIRST SERIES 663/VJ3-6) Inline. L-head. Six-cylinder. Cast iron block. Displacement: 148.5 cid. Bore and stroke: 3 x 3.5 inches. Compression ratio: 6.42:1. Brake hp: 72 at 4000 rpm. Carburetion: Carter WAl-645S single-barrel. Four main bearings. Solid valve lifters.

(SECOND SERIES 473/473x4) Inline. F-head. Four-cylinder. Cast iron block. Exhaust valves in engine block and intake valves in the cylinder head. Displacement: 134.2 cid. Bore and stroke: 3.13 x 4.38 inches. Compression ratio: 7.4:1. Brake hp: 72 at 4000 rpm. Carburetion: Carter WAl-613S single-barrel. Three main bearings. Solid valve lifters.

(SECOND SERIES 673) Inline. L-head. Six-cylinder. Cast iron block. Displacement: 161 cid. Bore and stroke: 3-1/8 x 3-1/2 inches. Compression ratio: 6.9:1. Brake hp: 75 at 4000 rpm. Carburetion: Carter WAl-645S single-barrel. Four main bearings. Solid valve lifters.

1950 Willys, two-door Jeepster phaeton, 6-cyl

CHASSIS FEATURES: Wheelbase: (Four-wheel-drive models) 104.5 inches; (conventional models) 104 inches. Overall length: (station wagon) 176.25 inches; (Jeepster) first series: 176.25 inches; second series 175.75 inches; (station sedan) 175.8 inches. Front tread: (all models) 55 inches. Rear tread: (all models) 57 inches. Tires: (Jeepster) first series: 5.90 x 15; second series: 6.40 x 15; (station wagon) 6.70 x 15;

OPTIONS: Front bumper guards. Rear bumper guards. Front grille guard. License frames. Large wheel discs. Wheel trim rings. White sidewall tires. Dual wipers on Fours. Cigar lighter in Fours. Special paint. Radio and antenna. Overdrive in Jeepster. Inside rearview mirror. Outside rearview mirror. Three-speed manual transmission was standard on Jeepsters. Overdrive transmission was standard, except on Jeepsters. Four-cylinder 134.2 cid 7.8:1 high-compression engine (no cost). Heavy-duty air cleaner was optional at extra cost.

HISTORICAL FOOTNOTES: The 1950 Willys models were introduced in October, 1949 and an expanded model range appeared in dealer showrooms after April, 1950. Model year production peaked at 38,052 units. Calendar year registrations of 33,926 cars were recorded. W.M. Canaday was the chief executive officer of the company this year. Total output of the Milestone Jeepster was 5,834 units including 4,066 four-cylinder models and 1,778 six-cylinder jobs. Even with the 653 six-cylinder Jeepsters of 1949 thrown in, the total production of Jeepster sixes was below 2,500 cars. Willys-Overland Motors, Inc. also manufactured 26,624 civilian Jeeps and 22,282 other types of commercial vehicles this year. It was the last season for assemblies of Jeepster phaetons, although some such units built in calendar 1950 were sold as 1951 automobiles. Production of military Jeeps resumed this year. In calendar 1950, Willys built 2.8 percent (5,834) of all U.S. convertibles and 21.3 percent (32,218) of all station wagons made in the U.S.

1951 WILLYS

WILLYS — (ALL MODELS) — 1951 Willys were identical to the second series 1950 models, which were introduced in April, 1950.

WILLYS I.D. NUMBERS: VIN same as serial number. VIN locations: on plate at the left of the driver's seat on the floor riser; on left door sill; on frame front crossmember ahead of front spring hanger; on front frame crossmember at center; on right side of cowl below hood; on inside of frame on left. Serial numbers took the format 473-SW-451-AA1-10001. First symbol indicates type of engine: 4=four-cylinder; 6=six-cylinder, except four-wheel-drive models have the prefix 4x to indicate 4x4 system (i.e. 4x473). Next two symbols (73) indicate series. Next two symbols indicate body type: SW=station wagon; VJ=Jeepster. Next symbol indicates engine type again, followed by a pair of symbols indicating model year: 51=1951. Next group of symbols is an alpha-numerical code: AA1=4x2 station wagon; FA1=4x4 station wagon; BA1=4x2 Jeepster. Beginning and ending serial numbers according to model were: (473-SW) 451-AA1-10001 to 451-AA1-25906; (4x473-SW) 451-FA1-10001 to 451-FA1-21854; (473-VJ) 451-BA1-10001 to 451-BA1-14066; (673-SW) 651-AA1-10001 to 651-AA1-18470; (673-VJ) 651-BA1-10001 to 651-BA1-11779. The motor number was the same as the serial number and was located on the top of the water pump boss; at the right front upper corner of the engine block.

WILLYS SERIES

Model Number	Body/Style Number	Body Type & Seating	Factory Price	Shipping Weight	Production Total
FOUR-CYLINDER					
451	473SW	2-dr Sta Wag-6P	1758	2818	Note 1
451	4X473	2-dr 2WD Wag-6P	2180	3174	Note 1
451	473VJ	2-dr Jeepster-5P	1426	2459	Note 3

1951 Willys, two-door Jeepster phaeton, 6-cyl (AA)

SIX-CYLINDER

651	673SW	2-dr Sta Wag-6P	1841	2831	Note 1
651	673VJ	2-dr Jeepster-5P	1529	2485	Note 3

NOTE 1: Total calendar year output was 28,226 units.
NOTE 2: Note 1 total includes 25,316 station wagons and 2,900 Aero Willys.
NOTE 3: No Jeepsters were built in 151 calendar year; leftovers were sold.

1951 Willys, two-door station wagon, 4-cyl

WILLYS ENGINES

(FOUR) Inline. F-head. Four-cylinder. Cast iron block. Exhaust valves in engine block and intake valves in the cylinder head. Displacement: 134.2 cid. Bore and stroke: 3.13 x 4.38 inches. Compression ratio: 7.4:1. Brake hp: 72 at 4000 rpm. Carburetion: Carter YF-768S single-barrel. Three main bearings. Solid valve lifters.

(SIX) Inline. L-head. Six-cylinder. Cast iron block. Displacement: 161.1 cid. Bore and stroke: 3.13 x 3.50 inches. Compression ratio: 6.9:1. Brake hp: 75 at 4000 rpm. Carburetion: Zenith 39 single-barrel. Four main bearings. Solid valve lifters.

CHASSIS FEATURES: Wheelbase: (four-wheel-drive models) 104.5 inches; (conventional models) 104 inches. Overall length: (station wagon) 176.25 inches; (Jeepster) 176.25 inches; (four-wheel-drive) 175.8 inches. Front tread: (all models) 55 inches. Rear tread: (all models) 57 inches. Tires: (Jeepsters) 6.40 x 15; (4x2 station wagons) 6.70 x 15; (4x4 station wagon) 7.00 x 15.

OPTIONS: Front bumper guards. Rear bumper guards. Front grille guard. License frames. Large wheel discs. Wheel trim rings. White sidewall tires. Dual wipers on Fours. Cigar lighter in Fours. Special paint. Radio and antenna. Overdrive in Jeepster. Inside rearview mirror. Outside rearview mirror. Three-speed manual transmission was standard on Jeepsters. Overdrive transmission was standard, except on Jeepsters. Four-cylinder 134.2 cid 7.8:1 high-compression engine (no cost). Heavy-duty air cleaner was optional at extra cost.

HISTORICAL FOOTNOTES: The 1951 Willys models were introduced in November, 1950. Model year production peaked at 28,266 units. Calendar year registrations of 26,049 cars were recorded. W.M. Canaday was the chief executive officer of the company this year. The Jeepster was discontinued, although some leftover 1950-built units were sold as 1951 models. Willys-Overland Motors also built 76,571 civilian Jeeps and 20,244 other types of commercial vehicles in calendar 1951. The company made 24,627 station wagons in the calendar year, which was 12.7 percent of the industry total. Overdrive was installed in 16,581 vehicles made in calendar 1951.

1952 WILLYS

WILLYS — (ALL MODELS) — The big news for 1952 was the introduction of the Aero Willys line of passenger cars. The Aero was styled by designer Phil Wright and engineered by Clyde Paton. Frame-unitized welded chassis and body construction was featured. It had a clean design and provided good comfort and handling. Four separate models were offered in the Aero line. The Aero-Lark was the base trim level and used the old 161 cid/75 hp six-cylinder flathead engine. The Aero-Wing, Aero-Ace and Aero-Eagle hardtop used the overhead valve six-cylinder engine. Again there were two series of station wagons in 1952. The first series was a continuation of the 1951 edition. In April, the 475/685 series was introduced. The station wagons continued basically unchanged for 1952, except for a new chrome trim molding available for the sides of the hood. The little Jeepster phaeton was discontinued after the 1951 model year and would not return until the early '60s.

1952 Willys, Aero Lark two-door sedan, 6-cyl

WILLYS I.D. NUMBERS: VIN same as serial number. VIN locations: on plate at the left of the driver's seat on the floor riser; on left door sill; on frame front crossmember ahead of front spring hanger; on front frame crossmember at center; on right side of cowl below hood; on inside of frame on left. Serial numbers took the format 452-AA1-10001. First symbol indicates type of engine: 4=four-cylinder; 6=six-cylinder. Second and third symbols indicate model year: 52=1952. Next group of symbols is an alpha-numerical code: KA2=Aero-Lark; LA1=Aero-Wing; MA1=Aero-Ace; MC1=Aero Eagle; AA1=first series 4x2 station wagon; FA1=first series 4x4 station wagon; AA2=second series 4x2 station wagon; FA2=second series 4x4 station wagon. Beginning and ending serial numbers according to model were: (473-SW) 452-AA1-10001 to 451-AA1-10920; (673-SW) 652-AA1-10001 to 652-AA1-10652; (475) 452-AA2-10001 to 452-AA2-14277; (4x475) 452-FA2-10001 to 452-FA2-15683; (685) 652-AA2-10001 to 652-AA2-13709. (Lark) 652-KA2-1001 to 652-KA2-17561; (Wing) 652-LA1-1001 to 652-LA1-22820; (Ace) 652-MA1-1001 to 652-MA1-18706; (Eagle) 652-MC1-1001 to 652-MC1-11537. The motor number was the same as the serial number and was located on the top of the water pump boss; at the right front upper corner of the engine block.

1952 Willys, Aero Wing two-door sedan, 6-cyl

WILLYS SERIES

Model Number	Body/Style Number	Body Type & Seating	Factory Price	Shipping Weight	Production Total
FIRST SERIES FOUR-CYLINDER					
452	473SW	2-dr Sta Wag-6P	1631	2818	Note 1
452	4X473	2-dr 4X4 Sta Wag	2092	3174	Note 1
FIRST SERIES SIX-CYLINDER					
652	673SW	2-dr Sta Wag-6P	1708	2831	Note 1
SECOND SERIES FOUR-CYLINDER					
652	475SW	2-dr Sta Wag-6P	1705	2818	Note 1
652	4X475	2-dr 4X4 Sta Wag	2134	3174	Note 1
SECOND SERIES SIX-CYLINDER					
652	685	2-dr Sta Wag-6P	1786	2850	Note 1
AERO LARK SIX-CYLINDER					
652	675	2-dr Del Sed-5P	1588	2487	7,474
AERO WING SIX-CYLINDER					
652	685	2-dr Sup Del Sed-5P	1825	2570	12,819
AERO ACE SIX-CYLINDER					
652	685	2-dr Cus Sed-5P	1904	2584	8,706
AERO EAGLE SIX-CYLINDER					
652	685	2-dr Cus HT-5P	1979	2575	2,364

NOTE 1: 48,845 Aero Willys and wagons built in calendar year 1952.
NOTE 2: 12,890 station wagons built in calendar year 1952.
NOTE 3: 17,482 station wagons built in model year. (Non-verifiable total).

ENGINES

(473-SW/4x473-SW/475-SW/4x475-SW) Inline. F-head. Four-cylinder. Cast iron block. Exhaust valves in the engine block and intake valves in the cylinder head. Displacement: 134.2 cid. Bore and stroke: 3.13 x 4.38 inches. Compression ratio: 7.4:1. Brake hp: 72 at 4000 rpm. Carburetion: Carter YF-768S single-barrel. Three main bearings. Solid valve lifters.

(675 AERO LARK/673-SW) Inline. L-head. Six-cylinder. Cast iron block. Displacement: 161.1 cid. Bore and stroke: 3.13 x 3.50 inches. Compression ratio: 6.9:1. Brake hp: 75 at 4000 rpm. Carburetion: Carter YS-924S single-barrel. Four main bearings. Solid valve lifters.

(685 WAGON AND 685 AERO WING-ACE-EAGLE) Inline. F-head. Six-cylinder. Cast iron block. Exhaust valves in the engine block and intake valves in the cylinder head. Displacement: 161.1 cid. Bore and stroke: 3.13 x 3.50 inches. Compression ratio: 7.6:1. Brake hp: 90 at 4200 rpm. Carburetion: Carter YS-924S single-barrel. Four main bearings. Solid valve lifters.

CHASSIS FEATURES: [STATION WAGON] Wheelbase: 104 inches; (4x473/4x475 station wagons) 104.5 inches. Overall length: 176.3 inches; (4x473/4X475 station wagons) 178 inches. Tires: (4x2) 6.70 x 15 tube-type blackwall; (4x4) 7.00 x 15. [AEROS] Wheelbase: 108 inches. Overall length: 180.8 inches. Tires: 5.90 x 15 tube-type blackwall.

OPTIONS: [STATION WAGON] Front bumper guards. Rear bumper guards. Front grille guard. License frames. Large wheel discs. Wheel trim rings. White sidewall tires. Dual wipers on fours. Cigar lighter in fours. Special paint. Radio and antenna. Inside rearview mirror. Outside rearview mirror. Three-speed manual overdrive transmission was standard. Four-cylinder 134.2 cid 7.8:1 high-compression engine (no cost). Heavy-duty air cleaner was optional at extra cost. [AERO MODELS] Overdrive ($86.08). Electric clock. Cigar lighter. Hood ornament. Locking gas cap. Radio. Turn signals ($16.68). Windshield washers. Back-up lights. White sidewall tires. Radio ($76.54). Heater ($67.58). Continental kit ($149.95). Fender skirts ($24.95). Oil filter ($8.38). Airfoam seat cushion-per seat ($8.50). Full wheel discs ($16.14) and two-tone paint ($16.68).

HISTORICAL FOOTNOTES: The 1952 Willys-Aero line was announced on Jan. 18, 1952. The Aero-Ace was introduced March 5, 1952 and the Aero-Lark on March 21. The 1952 second series Willys station wagons were introduced April 14, 1952. On March 19, the 1,000,000th Jeep was assembled. Annual registrations peaked at 41,016 units. Calendar year sales totals included 48,845 Aero-Ace passenger cars and 12,890 station wagons for the private market. In addition, 119,371 Jeep trucks and 88,098 purpose-built Jeep commercial vehicles were made. Willys-Overland was ranked as America's 17th largest manufacturer of passenger cars this season, but was also the nation's fifth largest producer of motor vehicles. Approximately 36,000 Aero type passenger cars were built to 1952 model specifications. Willys installed 29,268 optional overdrive transmissions this year. W.M. Canaday was president and board chairman of the firm, while the famed D.G. 'Barney' Roos was first vice president. The Willys passenger cars were capable of up to 35 mpg fuel economy. The rear window on Aero-Ace models was larger than on other styles. The Aero-Ace with the F-head engine took second place among all cars in MOTOR TREND magazine's 1952 Engineering Achievement Award.

1953 WILLYS

1953 Willys, Aero Ace four-door sedan, 6-cyl

WILLYS — (ALL MODELS) — Willys-Overland expanded the Aero line in 1953 and made only minor appearance changes from the 1952 models. They included red-painted wheelcover emblems and a gold-plated 'W' in the center of the grille symbolizing the firm's 50th anniversary. The Aero-Wing was replaced with the Aero-Falcon and a new four-door sedan was developed for the Lark, Falcon and Ace lines. The Eagle two-door hardtop continued to be the flagship of the line. The Lark Series was the base trim level and included the word Lark on the trunk lid; the L-head four-cylinder engine; and rubber moldings around its two-piece windshield. The Falcon was the intermediate trim level and included the word Falcon on the trunk lid, the L-head four-cylinder engine; and chrome moldings around its two-piece windshield. The Ace was the top trim level and included the words Custom Ace on the trunk lid; the F-head four-cylinder engine; chrome moldings surrounding its one-piece windshield; and a wraparound rear window. As in previous years, the Willys station wagons continued unchanged from the previous models. On April 28, 1953, Willys-Overland, Inc., was acquired by the Henry J. Kaiser Co. for approximately $60 million. The name was then changed to Willys Motors, Inc. The Toledo, Ohio based Kaiser-Willys Sales Corp. sold the Kaiser-Frazer plant at Willow Run to General Motors. All production was shifted to the plant at Toledo.

WILLYS I.D. NUMBERS: VIN same as serial number. VIN locations: on plate at the left of the driver's seat on the floor riser; on left door sill; on frame front crossmember ahead of front spring hanger; on front frame crossmember at center; on right side of cowl below hood; on inside of frame on left. Serial numbers took the format 453-AA2-10001. First symbol indicates type of engine: 4=four-cylinder; 6=six-cylinder. Second and third symbols indicate model year: 53=1953. Next group of symbols is a series code: RBJ=Heavy-Duty Aero; KB1=Lark Deluxe four-door; KA1=Lark Deluxe two-door; PB1=Falcon Super Deluxe four-door; PA1=Falcon Super two-door; MB1=Ace Custom four-door; MA1=Ace Custom two-door; MC1=Eagle two-door hardtop; AA2=4x2 station wagon; FA2=second series 4x4 station wagon. Beginning and ending serial numbers according to model were: (Aero Heavy-Duty) 653-RBJ-10001 to 653-RBJ-10187; (Aero Lark Deluxe four-door) 653-KB1-10001 to 653-KB1-17691; Aero Lark Deluxe two-door 653-KA1-10001 to 653-KA1-18205; (Aero Falcon Super Deluxe four-door) 653-PBI-10001 to 653-PB1-1347; Aero Falcon Super Deluxe two-door 653-PA1-10001 to 653-PA1-13054; (Aero Ace Custom four-door) 653-MBI-10001 to 653-MB1-17475; (Aero Ace Custom two-door) 653-MAI-10001 to 653-MA1-14988. The Aero Eagle two-door hardtop began at 653-MCI-1001 and went up to 653-MC1-17018. Model 475 station wagon models began at 453-AA2-10001 and went up to 453-AA2-14747. Model 4X475 station wagons began at 453-FA2-10001 and went up to 453-FA2-20631. Model 685 Deluxe station wagons

began at 653-AA2-10001 and went up to 685-AA2-17548. The motor number was the same as the serial number and was located on the top of the water pump boss; at the right front upper corner of the engine block.

WILLYS SERIES

Model Number	Body/Style Number	Body Type & Seating	Factory Price	Shipping Weight	Production Total
FOUR-CYLINDER STATION WAGON					
475SW	AA2	2-dr Sta Wag-6P	1750	2818	4764
4x475	FA2	2-dr 4X4 Sta Wag	2134	3174	10,630
SIX-CYLINDER STATION WAGON					
685	AA2	2-dr Sta Wag-6P	1786	2850	7547

WILLYS-AERO SERIES

AERO HEAVY-DUTY LINE

Model Number	Body/Style Number	Body Type & Seating	Factory Price	Shipping Weight	Production Total
675	RBJ	4-dr Sed-5P	1680	2511	186
AERO LARK Deluxe					
675	KB1	4-dr Sed-5P	1580	2509	7,691
675	KB2	2-dr Sed-5P	1500	2487	8,205
AERO FALCON SUPER Deluxe					
675	PB1	4-dr Sed-5P	1700	2529	3,116
675	PB2	2-dr Sed-6P	1640	2507	3,054
AERO ACE CUSTOM					
685	MB1	4-dr Sed-5P	1870	2735	7,475
685	MB2	2-dr Sed-5P	1800	2585	4,958
AERO EAGLE					
685	MC1	2-dr HT Sed-5P	1979	2575	7,018

NOTE 1: 35,128 Aeros and 5,417 station wagons built in calendar year.
NOTE 2: 41,703 Aeros and 22,941 station wagons built in model year.

ENGINES

(475/4x475) Inline. F-head. Four-cylinder. Cast iron block. Exhaust valves in the engine block and intake valves in the cylinder head. Displacement: 134.2 cid. Bore and stroke: 3.13 x 4.38 inches. Compression ratio:- 7.4:1. Brake hp: 72 at 4000 rpm. Carburetion: Carter YF-924S single-barrel. Three main bearings. Solid valve lifters.

(HEAVY-DUTY AND AERO LARK 675) Inline. L-head. Six-cylinder. Cast iron block. Displacement: 161.1 cid. Bore and stroke: 3.13 x 3.50 inches. Compression ratio: 6.9:1. Brake hp: 75 at 4000 rpm. Carburetion: Carter YS-924S single-barrel. Four main bearings. Solid valve lifters.

(AERO ACE/WING/EAGLE 685/685 STATION WAGON) Inline. F-head. Six-cylinder. Cast iron block. Exhaust valves in the engine block and intake valves in the cylinder head. Displacement: 161.1 cid. Bore and stroke: 3.13 x 3.50 inches. Compression ratio: 7.6:1. Brake hp: 90 at 4400 rpm. Carburetion: Carter YS-924S single-barrel. Four main bearings. Solid valve lifters.

CHASSIS FEATURES: Wheelbase: (4X475 station wagons) 104.5 inches; (other models) 104 inches. Overall length: (station wagons) 176.25 inches; (other models) 180-7/8 inches. Tires: (4X475 station wagons) 7.00 x 15 inches; (4x2 station wagons) 6.70 x 15; (Lark) 5.90 x 15; (Wing/Ace/Eagle) 6.40 x 15.

OPTIONS: [STATION WAGON] Front bumper guards. Rear bumper guards. Front grille guard. License frames. Large wheel discs. Wheel trim rings. White sidewall tires. Dual wipers on fours. Cigar lighter in fours. Special paint. Radio and antenna. Inside rearview mirror. Outside rearview mirror. Three-speed manual overdrive transmission was standard. Four-cylinder 134.2 cid 7.8:1 high-compression engine (no cost). Heavy-duty air cleaner was optional at extra cost. [AERO MODELS] Overdrive ($86.08). Electric clock. Cigar lighter. Hood ornament. Locking gas cap. Radio. Turn signals ($16.68). Windshield washers. Backup lights. White sidewall tires. Radio ($76.54). Heater ($67.58). Continental kit ($149.95). Fender skirts ($24.95). Oil filter ($8.38). Airfoam seat cushion-per seat ($8.50). Full wheel discs ($16.14) and two-tone paint ($16.68).

HISTORICAL FOOTNOTES: The 1953 Willys Aero-Eagle and Aero-Lark were introduced on Dec. 15, 1952; Aero-Falcon on Jan. 15, 1953 and the Aero-Ace on Feb. 15, 1953. The Aero models were advertised as being "fresh out of the future." Willy's golden anniversary was celebrated Feb. 12, 1953. The company became a subsidiary of Kaiser Industries on April 28-29, 1953. Registrations of Willys models in 1953 peaked at 42,433 units. Calendar year sales of 40,563 cars were recorded, which included 35,146 Aeros and 5,417 Jeep station wagons. Nearly 18,000 vehicles, 4,703 hardtops and 13,260 station wagons, were built in California. Edgar F. Kaiser was the chief executive officer this year. Vice-president Barney Roos was gone. The new Aero Eagle hardtop coupe featured pillarless side window styling. MOTOR TREND magazine road tested a 1953 Willys Aero Ace with overdrive, an $80 option that was installed on 23,816 cars for the calendar year. The car covered the quarter mile in 21.1 seconds during acceleration testing, which was slightly faster than average for cars in the under $2,050 price class. The Ace was found to have a top speed of 82.6 mph and gave 24.9 mpg fuel economy. The operating, cost per mile was estimated at 9.3 cents, which was slightly higher than the Chevrolet Two-Ten and Cadillac Sixty-Two. This figure included the cost of typical repairs on each model, but Willys lovers may have difficulty accepting the published results. AUTO AGE magazine test drove a 90 hp Lark Aero-Wing in Feb. 1953, recording a 0-to-60 time of 13 seconds and top speed of 90 mph. It delivered 23 mpg. A Borg-Warner strike, starting May 20, 1953, had a devastating effect on Willys sales and prompted the company, on July 15, to announce availability of a new type of gear box — General Motors' Hydra-Matic — in many Willys models. On July 29, the Kaiser-Willys Sales Division was formed. Willys' sales placed it ninth in the American industry this season.

1954 WILLYS

WILLYS — (ALL MODELS) — At first glance, the 1954 Aero models appeared to be mostly the same as the 1953 models with larger taillights and revised interiors. The dash was more practical and less austere with vertical slots containing "airplane type" levers for the controls. There was a new windshield wiper system with both arms moving in the same direction to overlap and eliminate a blind spot in the center. In March, 1954, the Kaiser 226 cid L-head was made available, as an option, for the Ace and Eagle models. With the Kaiser engine the Aero was clocked at 85 mph by one magazine. It wasn`t as much a high-top-end motor as one geared for good acceleration. Zero-to-60 mph was in the 13 second range. As an experiment, a few cars were fitted with the 140 hp, Kaiser Manhattan engine featuring a Paxton centrifugal supercharger. With the supercharged engine, acceleration was comparable to that of a contemporary V-8 engine. The 1954 Aero models also handled much better than before, with the introduction of a new front suspension. It utilized threaded trunions, which were adjustable for wear. The kingpins and coil springs were longer, shock absorbers and A-arms were stronger and the steering idler arm was lengthened. A crossmember connected left and right front suspension components to eliminate lateral torque and reduce toe-in variations. The Aero-Willys was one of the best combinations of ride and handling offered by a domestic manufacturer in the 1950s. The Lark Series was the base trim level Aero model for 1954 and included rubber moldings around the windshield and rear window; standard headlight trim; and the six-cylinder F-head engine. The Ace was the top trim level of the Aero models and included all Lark trim, plus hooded headlight bezels; chrome windshield moldings; chrome rear window moldings; chrome trim around the top of the grille; and the big six-cylinder L-head. engine. The top line Eagle hardtop featured all the Ace trim, plus 'W' medallions mounted on stainless steel rear window moldings. The Custom models include a continental spare tire mount as standard equipment. All models of the Aero line included new bumper guards; aluminum scuff plates; taillight assemblies; and chrome wheelcovers as additions to the standard equipment listed in 1953. Once again, the Willys station wagon was largely unchanged from the previous year. New features included different two-tone paint treatments and a revised grille, with three horizontal bars instead of five. The Kaiser 6-226 engine became an option.

1954 Willys, Ace Deluxe four-door sedan, 6-cyl

WILLYS I.D. NUMBERS: VIN same as serial number. VIN locations: on plate at the left of the driver's seat on the floor riser; on left door sill; on frame front crossmember ahead of front spring hanger; on front frame crossmember at center; on right side of cowl below hood; on inside of frame on left. Serial numbers took the format 454-FA2-10001. First symbol indicates type of engine: 4=four-cylinder; 6=six-cylinder. Second and third symbols indicate model year: 54=1954. Next group of symbols is a series code: KB3=Lark Deluxe four-door; KA3=Lark Deluxe two-door; MB2=Aero Ace four-door; MA2=Aero Ace two-door; MC3=Aero Eagle two-door hardtop; MB1=Aero Ace Deluxe "226" four-door sedan; MA1=Aero Ace Deluxe "226" two-door sedan; MC1=Aero Eagle Deluxe "226" two-door hardtop; MC2=Aero Eagle Custom "226" two-door hardtop. FA2=4x2 station wagon; AA2= 4x4 station wagon. Beginning and ending serial numbers according to model were: (Aero Lark Deluxe four-door) 654-KB3-10001 to 654-KB3-11482; Aero Lark Deluxe two-door 654-KA3-10001 to 654-KA3-11482; (Aero Ace four-door) 654-MB2-10001 to 654-MB2-11482; (Aero Ace two-door) 654-MA2-10001 to 654-MA2-11482; (Aero Eagle) 654-MC3-10001 to 654-MC3-11482; (four-cylinder 4x2 station wagon) 454-FA2-10001 to 5047; (4x2 station wagon with Willys six-cylinder) AA2-10001 to AA2-10945; (4x2 station wagon with Kaiser six-cylinder) 6-226-FA2-10001 to 6-226-FA2-12645. The motor number was the same as the serial number and was located on the top of the water pump boss; at the right front upper corner of the engine block.

WILLYS SERIES

Model Number	Body/Style Number	Body Type & Seating	Factory Price	Shipping Weight	Production Total
454	FA2	2-dr Sta Wag-6P	2134	3115	Note 1
654	AA2	2-dr Sta Wag-6P	1808	2381	Note 1
6-226	FA2	2-dr Del 4X4 Sta Wag-6P	2223	3278	Note 1

WILLYS-AERO SERIES

Model Number	Body/Style Number	Body Type & Seating	Factory Price	Shipping Weight	Production Total
AERO LARK LINE					
654	KB3	4-dr Sed-5P	1670	2661	1,370
654	KA3	2-dr Sed-5P	1590	2623	1,482
AERO ACE LINE					
654	MB2	4-dr Sed-5P	1806	2709	1,195
654	MA2	2-dr Sed-5P	1735	2682	1,380
AERO EAGLE LINE					
654	MC3	2-dr HT-5P	1991	2778	84
AERO ACE Deluxe '226' LINE					
6-226	MB14-dr Sed-5P	1857	2778	586	
6-226	MA1	2-dr Sed-5P	1786	2751	611
AERO EAGLE Deluxe '226' LINE					
6-226	MA1	2-dr HT-5P	2042	2847	660
AERO EAGLE CUSTOM '226' LINE					
6-226	MC2	2-dr HT-5P	2217	2904	499

NOTE 1: Calendar year output was 9,344 Aeros and 1,597 station wagons.

ENGINES

(454) Inline. F-head. Four-cylinder. Cast iron block. Exhaust valves in the engine block and intake valves in the cylinder head. Displacement: 134.2 cid. Bore and stroke: 3.13 x 4.38 inches. Compression ratio:- 7.4:1. Brake hp: 72 at 4000 rpm. Carburetion: Carter YF-924S single-barrel. Three main bearings. Solid valve lifters.

(654) Inline. L-head. Six-cylinder. Cast iron block. Displacement: 161.1 cid. Bore and stroke: 3.13 x 3.50 inches. Compression ratio: 7.6:1. Brake hp: 90 at 4200 rpm. Carburetion: Carter YF-924S single-barrel. Four main bearings. Solid valve lifters.

(6-226) L-head. Six-cylinder. Cast iron block. Exhaust valves in the engine block and intake valves in the cylinder head. Displacement: 226.2 cid. Bore and stroke: 3.31 x 4.38 inches. Compression ratio: 7.3:1. Brake hp: 115 at 3650 rpm. Carburetion: Carter WBD two-barrel. Four main bearings. Solid valve lifters.

CHASSIS FEATURES: [STATION WAGON] Wheelbase: (654 four-wheel drive station wagon) 104.5 inches; (other models) 104 inches. Overall length: (654 four-wheel drive station wagon) 176.25 inches; (other models) 176.25 inches. Tires: (four-wheel drive station wagons) 7.00 x 15; (other models) 6.70 x 15 tube-type blackwall. [AERO WILLYS] Wheelbase: 108 inches. Overall length: (with continental kit) 189.75 inches. Tires: (Eagles) 5.90 x 15 tube-type blackwall; (other models) 6.40 x 15 tube-type blackwall.

OPTIONS: [STATION WAGON] Front bumper guards. Rear bumper guards. Front grille guard. License frames. Large wheel discs. Wheel trim rings. White sidewall tires. Dual wipers on fours. Cigar lighter in fours. Special paint. Radio and antenna. Inside rearview mirror. Outside rearview mirror. Three-speed manual overdrive transmission was standard. Four-cylinder 134.2 cid 7.8:1 high-compression engine (no cost). Heavy-duty air cleaner was optional at extra cost. [AERO WILLYS] Overdrive ($86). Hydra-Matic automatic transmission ($179). Power steering. Electric clock. Radio ($71). Heater ($63). Cigar lighter. Turn signals. Windshield washers. White sidewall tires, exchange price ($18).

HISTORICAL FOOTNOTES: The Aero Series Willys models were introduced in February, 1954. The Willys Aero Ace Deluxe, Eagle Custom and the Deluxe six station wagon appeared in dealer showrooms March 17, 1954. Registrations for 1954 peaked at just 17,002 units. Calendar year sales of 10,941 vehicles, including 9,344 passenger cars and 1,597 station wagons were recorded. Model year production of passenger car styles was approximately 8,220 units. Calendar year output included 1,619 two-door hardtops. Records show that 659 cars built in calendar 1953 and 1,751 cars built in calendar 1954 were equipped with Hydra-Matic transmission. This option was available, for the first time, in cars built to 1954 model specifications. MOTOR TREND magazine road tested a Willys Aero Ace in its July, 1954 issue. This car, equipped with the '226' Kaiser engine, accelerated from 0-to 60-mph in 17.2 seconds and covered the standing start quarter mile in 20.3 seconds with a terminal speed of 65 mph. It gave 17.7 mpg for the overall test. On April 14, 1954, Willys workers agreed to take a pay cut to help the firm in its attempt to stay competitive in the market. However, not even drastic steps like closings of the Dowagiac, Mich. and Maywood assembly plants were enough to maintain Willys passenger cars past early 1955. An interesting feature of the Aero models was aircraft type, push-pull dashboard control levers.

1955 WILLYS

1955 Willys, Ace Deluxe four-door sedan, 6-cyl

WILLYS — (ALL MODELS) — By early 1955, Kaiser-Willys had decided to stop building passenger cars, but not before selling about 6,500 1955 models. No longer called Aeros, the line was divided into the Custom two- and four-door sedans and the Bermuda hardtop (as well as 659 Ace sedans). Engine options included the 161 cid and 226 cid six-cylinder engines. Prices were cut drastically in an effort to spark sales and the Bermuda was advertised as the nation's lowest-priced hardtop, but only 2,215 were built. Most were powered by the 226 cid Kaiser engine. Styling was much busier than in previous years, and no single designer takes credit for it. New features included full-width grilles; chrome headlamp visors; chrome hood side moldings of a novel design; new two-tone color treatments; and an especially wide selection of upholstery trims. The grille was an assembly of concave vertical chrome bars, rather than the simple unit used in previous models. A nicely styled hardtop station wagon was planned and the entire model line was scheduled for a very sleek restyling for 1956, but neither plan was realized. As before, the Willys station wagon remained unchanged.

WILLYS I.D. NUMBERS — (ALL MODELS) — VIN same as serial number. VIN locations: on plate at the left of the driver's seat on the floor riser; on left door sill; on frame front cross-member ahead of front spring hanger; on front frame crossmember at center; on right side of cowl below hood; on inside of frame on left. Serial numbers were: (Custom two-door) 52467-

1955 Willys, Bermuda two-door hardtop, 6-cyl (rear view)

10001 52467-10288; (Custom four-door) 52367-10001 to 52467-10288; (Bermuda two-door hardtop) 52567-10001 to 52567-12156; (6-226 station wagon) 54168-5001 to 54168-16513; (685 station wagon) 54727-1001 to 54727-11092. The motor number was the same as the serial number and was located on the top of the water pump boss; at the right front upper corner of the engine block.

WILLYS SERIES

Model Number	Body/Style Number	Body Type & Seating	Factory Price	Shipping Weight	Production Total
685	NA	2-dr Sta Wag-6P	1997	2831	Note 1
6-226	NA	2-dr 4WD Sta Wag-6P	2420	3278	Note 1
CUSTOM SERIES					
6226	NA	2-dr Sed-5P	1663	2751	288
6226	NA	4-dr Sed-5P	1725	2778	2,882
BERMUDA					
6226	NA	2-dr HT	1795	2847	2,156
ACE					
6226	NA	2-dr Sed-5P	1856	2709	659

NOTE 1: Calendar 1955 production of station wagons was 12,240 units.
NOTE 2: Model year production of Aero Willys totaled 5,986 units.
NOTE 3: Calendar 1955 production of Aero Willys totaled 4,778 units.
NOTE 4: Calendar year production included 1,740 two-door hardtops.

1955 Willys, Custom four-door sedan, 6-cyl

ENGINES

(454) Inline. F-head. Four-cylinder. Cast iron block. Exhaust valves in the engine block and intake valves in the cylinder head. Displacement: 134.2 cid. Bore and stroke: 3.13 x 4.38 inches. Compression ratio:- 7.4:1. Brake hp: 72 at 4000 rpm. Carburetion: Carter YF-924S single-barrel. Three main bearings. Solid valve lifters.

(6-226) L-head. Six-cylinder. Cast iron block. Exhaust valves in the engine block and intake valves in the cylinder head. Displacement: 226.2 cid. Bore and stroke: 3.31 x 4.38 inches. Compression ratio: 7.3:1. Brake hp: 115 at 3650 rpm. Carburetion: Carter WBD two-barrel. Four main bearings. Solid valve lifters.

CHASSIS FEATURES: [STATION WAGON] Wheelbase: (Model 6-226) 104.5 inches; (685 models) 104 inches. Overall length: 176.3 inches. Tires: (Model 6-226 station wagons) 6.40 x 15 tube-type blackwall; (other models) 6.70 x 15 tube-type blackwall. [AERO WILLYS] Wheelbase: 108 inches. Overall length: 189.8 inches with continental kit. Tires: 6.40 x 15 tube-type blackwall.

OPTIONS: [STATION WAGON] Front bumper guards. Rear bumper guards. Front grille guard. License frames. Large wheel discs. Wheel trim rings. White sidewall tires. Dual wipers on fours. Cigar lighter in fours. Special paint. Radio and antenna. Inside rearview mirror. Outside rearview mirror. Three-speed manual overdrive transmission was standard. Four-cylinder 134.2 cid 7.8:1 high-compression engine (no cost). Heavy-duty air cleaner was optional at extra cost. [AERO WILLYS] Overdrive ($85). Dual-Range Hydra-Matic ($179). Electric clock. Radio. Heater. Cigar lighter. Turn signals. Windshield washers. White sidewall tires.

HISTORICAL FOOTNOTES: Kaiser-Willys withdrew as a car maker in mid-1955, immediately after completing an order for 1,021 Kaisers for the Argentine market. The first 1955 Willys passenger car was assembled Nov. 2, 1954. The Bermuda hardtop and Custom four-door were introduced Jan. 6, 1954 and the two-door sedan was added to the line Feb. 16, 1954. Only 4,778 units were made between Jan. 1, 1954 and April, when auto production ceased. Edgar F. Kaiser was the chief executive officer of the firm again. The Aero did get a new lease on life in South America. Its dies were eventually shipped to the former Kaiser subsidiary, Willys de Brasil, where a cleaned-up 1955 model (without the busy side moldings) was built with Willys F-head power. Production continued through 1962. In all, the Aero actually lasted over 10 years, which attests to its basically good design.

1955 Willys, Bermuda two-door hardtop, 6-cyl (front view

STANDARD CATALOG OF
ALTERNATIVE CARS
1946-1975

A station wagon configuration was used in Brook Steven's 'Auto Familia', a 1963 design concept for Studebaker's Wagonaire. A compact photo-electric fuel cell or gas turbine engine were two alternative power sources considered for this type of vehicle.

The specifications that you will find in the 'Alternative Car' section of THE STANDARD CATALOG OF AMERICAN CARS 1946-1975 are for lesser known American made cars. In the majority of cases, these are models built inside the borders of the United States and within the subject time frame. However, a handful of makes that were built by Americans in other countries, but primarily for the U.S. market, are covered.

By R. Perry Zavitz

A few of these marques were produced in rather large quantities, which totaled several thousands of units. This includes those created as alternative lines of major manufacturers (i.e. Henry J/Allstate), as well as brands like Crosley, Excalibur and Avanti II, which operated as independent companies. Of course, there are others built in substantially smaller numbers.

Some alternative postwar cars may have never gotten beyond the prototype stage. However, we have tried, as much as possible, to limit the inclusion of prototypes to those vehicles that were intended as 'pilots' for a production model. In other words, models that the maker intended to have appear more than once.

Cars not included in this section are those built solely for racing and competition purposes; cars made exclusively for experimental purposes; cars available only as do-it-yourself kits and small, motorized vehicles built only for juvenile use. In all these instances there are, of course, those 'grey' areas where the original intent of the inventor has, simply, never been made clear. For example, was the Bocar intended only for racing? Was the Centaur an experiment or an attempt to interest a financial backer in new production ideas? Did Glasspar sell fully-assembled vehicles? And, how about the Eshelman ... wasn't it really just a kiddie car?

Yes, some cars in this section could, possibly, be considered experimental. We included them because the builders seem to have intended to get into series production themselves, or interest some other manufacturer to do so. We have also incorporated some cars normally thought of as kit cars. In each of these cases, however, there is evidence that the factory did completely assemble some examples. For kiddie-type or racing cars, we tried to determine the manner in which the cars were promoted and advertised in contemporary catalogs, literature and ads. And we applied our guidelines as loosely as possible, to avoid forsaking important new knowledge in the name of strict protocol. Obviously, including too much information about such cars is the lesser of two evils.

Unfortunately, complete technical specifications are not available for many of these little-known, alternative cars. Sometimes, available information is contradictory. We have tried our best to make the following data as complete and accurate as possible, in order that it be informative and useful to restorers and historians alike.

Skorpion Sports Roadster

1947 AIRSCOOT

AIRSCOOT — The Airscoot was a very unusual car designed to fit a common need, but failed to gain hardly any headway. It was a fold-up car intended for carrying aboard private planes. It was a very light conveyance which, when opened up, could to be used for commuting to and from the airport. It had two seats and a luggage rack in front for two suitcases. Although it was capable of 60 mpg, the fuel tank would only hold 3/10ths of a gallon.

I.D. NUMBERS: Not available.

AIRSCOOT

Model Number	Body/Style Number	Body Type & Seating	Factory Price	Shipping Weight	Production Total
NA	NA	Open-2P	NA	72	NA

ENGINE: One-cylinder. Air-cooled. Brake hp: 2.6.

CHASSIS: Overall length: 37 inches.

MANUFACTURER: Aircraft Products, Wichita, Kan.

1949-1950 AIRWAY

AIRWAY — The Airway was a small light car, which was designed by T.P. Hall and Everett Miller. Mr. Hall made several attempts to build a flying car, however, this car was not intended to take to the air, despite the impression its name and lightweight construction would seem to indicate. Styling was quite pleasant looking for both the fastback sedan and the notch back coupe. The tiny wheels gave the illusion that the Airway was larger than it really was. These cars used a great deal of aluminum and plastic in the body. The Town Traveler coupe was to be available with an optional rear seat to increase passenger capacity from two to five.

1948 Airway, coupe, 2-cyl (NAHC)

AIRWAY

Model Number	Body/Style Number	Body Type & Seating	Factory Price	Shipping Weight	Production Total
NA	NA	2-dr Sed-3P	750	800	1
NA	NA	2-dr Cpe-2P	750	775	1

NOTE 1: The two-door coupe was called the Town Traveler.

ENGINE: Air-cooled. Aluminum block. Rear-mounted. Brake hp: 10.

POWERTRAIN: Fluid-drive. (Chain drive).

CHASSIS: Wheelbase: 100 inches. Overall length: 158 inches. Front tread: 50 inches. Rear tread: 50 inches. Tire size: 4.50 x 12.

MANUFACTURER: T.P. Hall Engineering Corp., San Diego, Calif.

1952 ALLSTATE

ALLSTATE — The Allstate was a thinly disguised version of the Henry J. It was built by the Kaiser-Frazer Corp. for sale in a few selected Sears, Roebuck and Co. department stores in the South and Southwest. Styling differences from the Henry J were done by designer Alex Tremulis. Only two-door sedans were offered. In the Henry J grille cavity were two horizontal chrome bars. Sears brand 'Allstate' batteries, tires, etc. were featured, of course. The interiors were usually finished with a unique upholstery material. The fabric was tightly twisted strands of paper, coated with vinyl and woven in colorful plaids. It was extremely durable and eliminated the need for seat covers. Two lines were offered: A-230 and A-240. These were powered by the Willys engine that Kaiser-Willys used in Henry Js; four-cylinder and six-cylinder, respectively. The A-230 came in basic, standard and deluxe trim versions, while the A-240 offered only the basic and deluxe editions.

I.D. NUMBERS: A230-1,000,001 to A230-1,000,942. Engine numbers start at 1001 and continue through 1953.

1952 Allstate, two-door sedan, 6-cyl

SERIES A-230

Model Number	Body/Style Number	Body Type & Seating	Factory Price	Shipping Weight	Production Total
A-230	110	2-dr Bas Sed-5P	1395	2293	200
A-230	111	2-dr Std Sed-5P	1486	2300	500
A-230	113	2-dr Del Sed-5P	1539	2300	200

NOTE 1: Production totals are estimates.
NOTE 2: Serial numbers indicate 942 produced.
NOTE 3: Add 40 lbs. for overdrive.

ENGINE: (A-230 FOUR) Henry J four-cylinder. L-head. Cast iron block. Displacement: 134.2 cid. Bore and stroke: 3-1/8 x 4-3/8 inches. Compression ratio: 7.0:1. Brake hp: 68 at 4000 rpm. Three main bearings. Solid valve lifters. Carburetor: Carter model 820SB.

I.D. NUMBERS: A240-1,000,001 to A240-1,000,602. Engine numbers start at 1001 and continue through 1953.

SERIES A-240

Model Number	Body/Style Number	Body Type & Seating	Factory Price	Shipping Weight	Production Total
A-240	114	2-dr Bas Sed-5P	1594	2325	136
A-240	115	2-dr Del Sed-5P	1693	2325	466

NOTE 1: Serial numbers indicate 602 built.
NOTE 2: Add 40 lbs. for overdrive.

ENGINE: (A-240 SIX) Henry J six-cylinder. L-head. Cast iron block. Displacement: 161 cid. Bore and stroke: 3-1/8 x 3-1/2 inches. Compression ratio: 7.0:1. Brake hp: 80 at 3800 rpm. Four main bearings. Solid valve lifters. Carburetor: Carter model 833SB.

POWERTRAIN: Three-speed manual transmission.

CHASSIS: Wheelbase: 100 inches. Overall length: 176-5/8 inches. Front tread: 54 inches. Rear tread: 54 inches. Tire size: 6.40 x 15.

OPTIONS: Overdrive ($104).

HISTORICAL FOOTNOTE: Introduced Dec. 20, 1951.

1953 ALLSTATE

ALLSTATE — Virtually no styling changes were made to the 1953 Allstate from the previous year. Basic trim versions were not offered. This left a choice of standard and deluxe trim models in the A-330 four-cylinder series and A-340 six-cylinder series.

I.D. NUMBERS: A330-1,000,001 to A330-1,000,425. Engine numbers continued from 1953, with ending number 2,472.

SERIES A-330

Model Number	Body/Style Number	Body Type & Seating	Factory Price	Shipping Weight	Production Total
A330	210	2-dr Std Sed-5P	1499	2385	200
A330	213	2-dr Del Sed-5P	1589	2405	225

NOTE 1: Serial numbers confirm 425 built.
NOTE 2: Add 40 lbs. for overdrive.

ENGINE: (SERIES A-330) Henry J. four-cylinder. L-head. Cast iron block. Displacement: 134.2 cid. Bore and stroke: 3-1/8 x 4-1/8 inches. Compression ratio: 7.0:1. Brake hp: 68 at 4000 rpm. Three main bearings. Carburetor: Carter model 820SB.

I.D. NUMBERS: A340-1,000,001 to A340-1,000,372. Engine numbers continued from 1952, with ending number 6,459.

SERIES A-340

Model Number	Body/Style Number	Body Type & Seating	Factory Price	Shipping Weight	Production Total
A340	215	2-dr Del Sed-5P	1686	2415	372

NOTE 1: Serial numbers confirm 372 built.
NOTE 2: Add 40 lbs. for overdrive.

ENGINE: (Series A-340) Henry J six-cylinder. L-head. Cast iron block. Displacement: 161 cubic -inches. Bore and stroke: 3-1/8 x 3-1/2 inches. Compression ratio: 7.0:1. Brake hp: 80 at 3800 rpm. Four main bearings. Carburetor: Carter model 833SB.

POWERTRAIN: Three-speed manual transmission.

CHASSIS: Wheelbase: 100 inches. Overall length: (A-330 with continental kit) 181-3/4-5/8 inches; (A-340 with continental kit) 182-1/8 inches. Front tread: 54 inches. Rear tread: 54 inches. Tire size: 5.90 x 15.

OPTIONS: Overdrive ($106.55).

HISTORICAL FOOTNOTES: Introduced Oct. 17, 1952. Discontinued July, 1953.

MANUFACTURER: Kaiser-Frazer Corp., Willow Run, Mich.

1955 AMERICAN BUCKBOARD

AMERICAN BUCKBOARD — Most cars have four wheels, some three, but this small two-passenger car had five. The fifth wheel was located right at the back and was the drive wheel. The small motorcycle engine which drove the extra wheel was conveniently located at the back, too. The roadster body was made of fiberglass. The name American Buckboard gives the impression of little more than a motorized board, which this car was not. Perhaps that is one reason the name was changed. It appeared the next year as the Bearcat.

1955 American Buckboard Roadster

I.D. NUMBERS: Not available.

AMERICAN BUCKBOARD

Model Number	Body/Style Number	Body Type & Seating	Factory Price	Shipping Weight	Production Total
NA	NA	2-dr Rds-2P	under 3000	NA	NA

ENGINE: Motorcycle. Two-cylinders. Air-cooled. Rear-mounted. Brake hp: 25.

CHASSIS: Wheelbase: 70 inches (excluding the fifth wheel). Overall length: 120 inches.

POWERTRAIN: Chain-drive to fifth wheel at the rear.

MANUFACTURER: American Buckboard Corp., Los Angeles, Calif.

1966 APACHE

APACHE — This car was claimed to be of European size in engine displacement, steering capacity and overall dimensions. The most unusual feature was its roof, which would quickly convert the car from a fastback coupe to an open model. John G. Zullo was president of the company, which had ambitious, but unrealized plans to produce the Apache.

I.D. NUMBERS: Not available.

APACHE

Model Number	Body/Style Number	Body Type & Seating	Factory Price	Shipping Weight	Production Total
NA	NA	2-dr Conv-2P	2500	NA	NA

MANUFACTURER: Interco Development Corp., New York, N.Y.

1962 APOLLO

APOLLO — The Apollo was a sleek, fastback GT launched by Newt Davis and Milt Brown. The aluminum body, designed by Ron Plescia and Franco Scaglione, was built in Italy by Frank Reisner's Carrozzeria Intermeccanica. Final assembly took place in California using a specially designed ladder-type tubular steel frame. A stock Buick Special V-8 engine powered the Apollo. A single model called the GT was offered.

1962 Apollo '3500'-GT coupe, V-8 (PZ)

I.D. NUMBERS: Not available.

GT

Model Number	Body/Style Number	Body Type & Seating	Factory Price	Shipping Weight	Production Total
NA	NA	2-dr Cpe-2P	6597	2470	Note

ENGINE: Buick. V-8. Overhead valves. Aluminum block. Displacement: 215.5 cid. Bore and stroke: 3.5 x 2.8 inches. Compression ratio: 9.0:1. Brake hp: 190 at 5000 rpm. Carburetor: Rochester model 2GC two-barrel.

POWERTRAIN: Three-speed manual transmission.

CHASSIS: Wheelbase: 97 inches. Overall length: 178 inches. Front tread: 56 inches. Rear tread: 56 inches. Tire size: 185 x 400.

OPTIONS: Borg-Warner four-speed manual transmission. Hydra-Matic transmission.

1963 APOLLO

APOLLO — There was very little in the way of styling or mechanical changes to differentiate the 1963 Apollo from the previous year's model. Again only one model was offered.

I.D. NUMBERS: Not available.

GT

Model Number	Body/Style Number	Body Type & Seating	Factory Price	Shipping Weight	Production Total
NA	NA	2-dr Cpe-2P	6597	2470	Note

ENGINE: Buick. V-8. Overhead valves. Aluminum block. Displacement: 215.5 cid. Bore and stroke: 3.5 x 2.8 inches. Compression ratio: 11.0:1. Brake hp: 200 at 5000 rpm. Carburetor: Carter four-barrel.

POWERTRAIN: Three-speed manual transmission.

CHASSIS: Wheelbase: 97 inches. Overall length: 178 inches. Front tread: 56 inches. Rear tread: 56 inches. Tire size: 185 x 400.

OPTIONS: Borg-Warner four-speed manual transmission. Hydra-Matic transmission.

1964-1965 APOLLO

APOLLO — Because Buick deleted its small aluminum V-8, Apollo switched to a larger and more powerful Buick V-8. The addition of a convertible was an important change for 1964. The 1965 models, virtually unchanged, were the last for Apollo, although the Vetta Ventura was its reincarnation.

I.D. NUMBERS: Not available.

GT

Model Number	Body/Style Number	Body Type & Seating	Factory Price	Shipping Weight	Production Total
5000	NA	2-dr Cpe-2P	7965	NA	Note
5000	NA	2-dr Conv-2P	9865	NA	11

ENGINE: Buick V-8. Overhead valve. Cast iron block. Displacement: 300.4 cid. Bore and stroke: 3.7 5 x 3.40 inches. Compression ratio: 11.0:1. Brake hp: 250 at 4800 rpm. Five main bearings. Carburetor: Rochester model 2GC twin barrel.

POWERTRAIN: Three-speed manual transmission.

CHASSIS: Wheelbase: 97 inches. Overall length: 178 inches. Front tread: 56 inches. Rear tread: 56 inches. Tire size: 185 x 400.

OPTIONS: Borg-Warner four-speed manual transmission. Hydra-Matic transmission. Borrani wire wheels. Air conditioning ($450).

MANUFACTURER: International Motors Inc., Oakland, Calif. (1962-1964). Apollo International Corp., Pasadena, Calif. (1965).

1959 ARGONAUT

1959 Argonaut, coupe, V-8 (WLB)

ARGONAUT — Plans for this ultra luxury car were made by a Cleveland company. A range of seven different models, with Italian-made aluminum bodies was proposed. They were to use tubular chassis ranging from 126-1/2 to 154 inches in wheelbase. The motor was to be an air-cooled, aluminum block, overhead cam V-12, capable of speeds up to 240 mph. Prices were to be in the $17,000 to $30,000 range. In reality, however, only one prototype is believed to have been built and it was only a chassis — not a complete car.

I.D. NUMBERS: Not available.

ARGONAUT

Model Number	Body/Style Number	Body Type & Seating	Factory Price	Shipping Weight	Production Total
NA	NA	Chassis only	NA	NA	1

ENGINE: Chrysler. Some sources say a 7.5-liter engine was installed in the prototype chassis, but Chrysler made no automotive engine that large at that time.

CHASSIS: Wheelbase: 126-1/2 inches.

MANUFACTURER: Argonaut Motor Machine Co., Cleveland, Ohio.

1953-1954 ARNOLT

1954 Arnolt, Continental Sportster convertible, 4-cyl (PZ)

ARNOLT — The Arnolt was conceived by the Midwest British car distributor S.H. "Wacky" Arnolt. His not so wacky car was a rebodied MG. It featured an MG-like grille. Styling was done by Bertone of Italy. The car's appearance was much more acceptable to American tastes than most European cars. (Actually its styling was closely copied a few years later by the British Alvis). The mostly aluminum body, in coupe and convertible versions, was made by Bertone.

I.D. NUMBERS: Not available.

ARNOLT

Model Number	Body/Style Number	Body Type & Seating	Factory Price	Shipping Weight	Production Total
NA	MG	2-dr Cpe-4P	3585	2049	65
NA	MG	2-dr Conv-4P	3585	2029	35

ENGINE: MG. Four-cylinder. Overhead valves. Cast iron block. Displacement: 76.3 inches. Bore and stroke: 2.62 x 3.54 inches. Compression ratio: 8.0:1. Brake hp: 57 at 5500 rpm. Three main bearings. Carburetor: Twin S.U.

POWERTRAIN: Four-speed manual transmission.

CHASSIS: Wheelbase: 94 inches. Overall length: 150 inches. Tire size: 5.50 x 15.

OPTIONS: Wire wheels with knock-off hubs. Radio. Heater. Twin badge bars.

MANUFACTURER: S.H. Arnolt, Inc., Chicago, Ill.

1955-1963 ARNOLT-BRISTOL

ARNOLT-BRISTOL — The Arnolt-Bristol was not at all related to the Arnolt MG in styling or mechanics, although the concept was quite similar. It was a special bodied car using British power. The Bristol was so named because of the Bristol racing engine it used. Its competition-type light steel body was designed and built in Italy by Bertone. The curved windshield was made of plexiglass. Only three coupes, referred to as Mark II, were made. All the others were roadsters, which were offered in Bolide and Deluxe versions.

1954 Arnolt-Bristol roadster (OCW)

I.D. NUMBERS: Not available.

ARNOLT-BRISTOL

Model Number	Body/Style Number	Body Type & Seating	Factory Price	Shipping Weight	Production Total
NA	NA	2-dr Mark II Cpe-2P	NA	NA	3
NA	NA	2-dr Bolide Rds-2P	3995/4250	1396	127
NA	NA	2-dr Del Rds-2P	4996	NA	127
NA	NA	2-dr Cpe-2P	6390	-	-

ENGINE: Bristol. Six-cylinder. Overhead valves. Cast chrome-iron block, with nickel alloy steel dry cylinder liners, and aluminum alloy cylinder head. Displacement: 120.2 cid. Bore and stroke: 2.60 x 3.78 inches. Compression ratio: 9.0.1. Brake hp: 130 at 5500 rpm. Four main bearings. Carburetor: Three multi-jet Solex model 32 B.I.

POWERTRAIN: Four-speed manual transmission.

CHASSIS: Wheelbase: 96-1/4 inches. Overall length: 167 inches. Front tread: 51.86 inches. Rear tread: 54 inches. Tire size: 5.50 x 15.

OPTIONS: Custom type bumpers. Light alloy knock-off hub wheels. Racing screen.

MANUFACTURER: S.H. Arnolt Inc., Chicago, Ill.

1959 ASARDO

1959 Asardo, Type 1500 AR-S coupe, 4-cyl (NAHC)

ASARDO — The Asardo is an acronym of the name of a company which attempted to build this car. It was an aerodynamically styled sports coupe with a short, but somewhat bulky looking rear end. A multi-tubular space frame was used. The fiberglass body had gull-wing doors. An aluminum underpan reduced wind resistance. The engine was a modified Alfa Romeo. Alfa Romeo transmission, rear suspension and other components were used.

I.D. NUMBERS: Not available.

ASARDO

Model Number	Body/Style Number	Body Type & Seating	Factory Price	Shipping Weight	Production Total
1500	AR-SNA	2-dr Cpe-2P	5875	1350	NA

ASARDO ENGINE: Alfa Romeo (modified). Four-cylinder. Double overhead cam. Light alloy block. Cast iron cylinder liners. Displacement: 91.3 cid. Bore and stroke: 3.13 x 2.95 inches. Compression ratio: 11.5:1. Brake hp: 135 at 6800 rpm. Five main bearings. Carburetor: (2) Weber two-barrel.

POWERTRAIN: Four-speed manual transmission (Alfa Romeo).

CHASSIS: Wheelbase: 88 inches. Overall length: 150 inches. Front tread: 51 inches. Rear tread: 50 inches. Tire size: 5.90 x 15.

MANUFACTURER: American Special Automotive Research & Design Organization, North Bergen, N.J.

1955 ASTRA

1955 ASTRA

ASTRA — A custom built hardtop was planned for series production. Evidently, only one prototype was built. A hand-formed aluminum body was fitted over an original tubular frame. The sleek lines of the body were overshadowed by the very prominent headlight hoods (like those of the 1955 Mercury) and its rear fender fins. The hood was so low the radiator had to be located at the back.

1955 Astra, coupe, V-8 (NAHC)

I.D. NUMBERS: Not available.

ASTRA

Model Number	Body/Style Number	Body Type & Seating	Factory Price	Shipping Weight	Production Total
NA	NA	2-dr HT-2P	NA	NA	1

ENGINE: Oldsmobile V-8 (modified).

POWERTRAIN: Lincoln. Three-speed manual transmission, with overdrive.

CHASSIS: Wheelbase: 102 inches.

MANUFACTURER: Jay Everett, Los Angeles, Calif.

1967-1970 AUBURN

AUBURN — Before the 1964-1966 Cord Replica came to a halt, its originator, Glenn Pray, had left the operation. He was off starting another comeback for himself with another classic car replica. It was a copy of the 1935 Auburn boattail speedster. A large, modified Ford V-8 was used in a fiberglass body. This effort was quite successful. Pray stayed in business many years, despite many other Auburn boattail speedster replicars coming on the market.

I.D. NUMBERS: Not available.

AUBURN

Model Number	Body/Style Number	Body Type & Seating	Factory Price	Shipping Weight	Production Total
866	NA	2-dr Rds-2P	8450	2950	NA

NOTE 1: The factory price given above is for the 1967 Auburn.

ENGINE: Ford (modified). V-8. Overhead valves. Cast iron block. Displacement: 428 cid. Bore and stroke: 4.13 x 3.98 inches. Compression ratio: 10.5:1. Brake hp: 365 at 4600 rpm. Five main bearings. Hydraulic valve lifters. Carburetor: Holley 4V.

POWERTRAIN OPTIONS: Four-speed manual transmission.

CHASSIS: Wheelbase: 127 inches. Overall length: 205 inches. Front tread: 62 inches. Rear tread: 62 inches. Tire size: H70-15.

1971-1975 AUBURN

1972 Auburn, '866' Speedster, V-8

AUBURN — Very little styling change from the previous years. A switch to Ford's 429 V-8 was made, because the 428 was no longer being produced. In 1975 a four-door boattail phaeton was also produced.

I.D. NUMBERS: Not available.

AUBURN

Model Number	Body/Style Number	Body Type & Seating	Factory Price	Shipping Weight	Production Total
866	NA	2-dr Rds-2P	16,500	2950	NA
NA	NA	4-dr Phae-4P	NA	NA	NA

NOTE 1: Price above is for 1971 model.

AUBURN ENGINE: Ford. V-8. Overhead valves. Cast iron block. Displacement: 429 cid. Bore and stroke: 4.36 x 3.59 inches. Compression ratio: 10.5:1. Brake hp: 360 at 4600 rpm. Five main bearings. Hydraulic valve lifters. Carburetor: Autolite model 9510 DOOF four-barrel.

POWERTRAIN: Automatic transmission.

CHASSIS: Wheelbase: 127 inches.

MANUFACTURER: Auburn-Cord-Duesenberg Co., Tulsa, Okla.

1973 AUBURN

AUBURN — The survival rate among newcomers to the auto industry is extremely low, so it is unthinkable to start making a car almost the same as what another manufacturer already has on the market. Yet that is what a Buffalo firm did. They began making a 1935 Auburn boattail speedster. Like the other Auburn replicas, it had a fiberglass body and a Ford engine. Its engine was smaller than its competitor, but it offered a larger optional motor.

I.D. NUMBERS: Not available.

AUBURN

Model Number	Body/Style Number	Body Type & Seating	Factory Price	Shipping Weight	Production Total
NA	NA	2-dr Rds-2P	NA	NA	NA

ENGINES

(STANDARD) 1971 Ford V-8. Overhead valve. Cast iron block. Displacement: 351 cid. Bore and stroke: 4.00 x 3.50 inches. Compression ratio: 9.0:1. Brake hp: 240 at 4600 rpm. Five main bearings. Hydraulic valve lifters. Carburetor: Autolite model D1AF-FA two-barrel.

(OPTIONAL) Modified Ford V-8. Overhead valve. Cast iron block. Displacement: 400 at cid. Bore and stroke: 4.00 x 4.00 inches. Brake hp: 260. Five main bearings.

POWERTRAIN: Ford SelectShift Cruise-O-Matic automatic transmission.

CHASSIS: Front tread: 63.3 inches. Rear tread: 64.3 inches. Tire size: 8.20 x 15.

OPTIONS: Four-speed manual transmission. Power front disc brakes. Power steering. Tilt steering wheel. Air conditioning. Tinted glass. Tonneau cover.

MANUFACTURER: Auburn Speedsters Co., Buffalo, N.Y.

1974-1975 AUBURN

AUBURN — In 1973, rights to the 1967-1970 style Auburn Speedster replica were bought by F.P. Pro, president of Glassic Industries, of West Palm Beach, Fla. Pro`s company had been building a fiberglass-bodied replica of the Model A Ford. The new owner made few changes from the Auburn Speedster produced by previous owners of the company. Manufacturing was transferred to Florida (For additional information see 1966-1975 Glassic).

I.D. NUMBERS: Not available.

AUBURN

Model Number	Body/Style Number	Body Type & Seating	Factory Price	Shipping Weight	Production Total
NA	NA	2-dr Rds-2P	NA	NA	35

NOTE 1: Production total given above is for the 1974 model year.

ENGINE: Ford. V-8. Overhead valve. Cast iron block. Displacement: 351 cid. Bore and stroke: 4.00 x 3.50 inches. Compression ratio: 9.0:1. Brake hp: 240 at 4600 rpm. Five main bearings. Hydraulic valve lifters. Carburetor: Autolite model D1AF-FA two-barrel.

POWERTRAIN: Ford SelectShift Cruise-O-Matic automatic transmission.

CHASSIS: Front tread: 63.3 inches. Rear tread: 64.3 inches. Tire size: 8.20 x 15.

OPTIONAL: Air conditioning.

MANUFACTURER: Auburn Motor Car Corp., West Palm Beach, Fla.

1956 AUTO CUB

AUTO CUB -The Auto Cub was little more than an open box on wheels. The body was made of plywood and had flat sides. The buyer had a choice of any color he wanted as long as it was red. Steering was controlled by a tiller. The Auto Cub was about as simple as any form of powered transportation could be and that was reflected in its price.

1956 Auto-Cub, midget roadster, one-cyl. (PZ)

I.D. NUMBERS: Not available.

AUTO CUB

Model Number	Body/Style Number	Body Type & Seating	Factory Price	Shipping Weight	Production Total
NA	NA	Midget Rds-1P	170	115	NA

ENGINES: Briggs & Stratton or Clinton one-cylinder gasoline engine. (Buyer had no choice of engine manufacturer). Brake hp: 1.6.

CHASSIS: Overall length: 51 inches.

MANUFACTURER: Randall Products, Hampton, N.H.

1952-1957 AUTOETTE

AUTOETTE — The Autoette was little more than a golf cart. It was a three-wheel electric runabout. The single wheel was in front. Three models were offered. They varied in wheelbase and overall length, depending on the carrying capacity desired.

I.D. NUMBERS: Not available.

AUTOETTE

Model Number	Body/Style Number	Body Type & Seating	Factory Price	Shipping Weight	Production Total
800	NA	Rbt-2P	773	NA	NA
850	NA	Rbt-2P	NA	NA	NA
875	NA	Rbt-2P	948	NA	NA

1952 Autoette, '850' roadster, (electric motor) (PZ)

AUTOETTE ENGINE: Electric. 24-volt DC motor. Four heavy-duty 17-plate 6-volt batteries. Range between battery charges: 35 to 40 miles.

CHASSIS: Tire size: 4.00 x 8 (5.00 x 8 optional).

MANUFACTURER: Autoette Electric Car Co., Long Beach, Calif.

1965 AVANTI II

AVANTI II — When Studebaker terminated car production in South Bend, Ind., the end of the Avanti seemed certain. There were no plans to build it in Canada, where the regular passenger car production was consolidated. Long-time South Bend Studebaker-Packard dealers Nathanial Altman and Leo Newman tried to interest other auto makers to continue the Avanti. No one was interested, so they bought part of the vacated Studebaker factory and all dies, parts and rights to the Avanti and built it themselves. It was little changed from the Studebaker model. The fiberglass body was supplied by Molded Fiber-Glass of Ashtabula, Ohio (which makes the Corvette body). They selected the Corvette engine to power their car. Because of a different engine size, the front of the car had to be tilted up slightly. A choice of 700 interior upholsteries, colors and styles was offered the buyer.

I.D. NUMBERS: Not available.

AVANTI II

Model Number	Body Style Number	Body Type & Seating	Factory Price	Shipping Weight	Production Total
NA	NA	2-dr Spt Cpe-4P	NA	3181	45

ENGINE: Chevrolet Corvette. V-8. Overhead valve. Cast iron block. Displacement: 327 cid. Bore and stroke: 4.00 x 3.25 inches. Compression ratio: 10.5:1. Brake hp: 300 at 5000 rpm. Five main bearings. Hydraulic valve lifters. Carburetor: Carter model 3846247 four-barrel.

POWERTRAIN: Choice of three-speed automatic, or Borg-Warner four-speed manual transmissions.

CHASSIS: Wheelbase: 109 inches. Overall length: 192-1/2 inches. Front tread: 57-3/8 inches. Rear tread: 56-9/16 inches. Tire size: 7.75 x 15.

1966 AVANTI II

AVANTI II — Very little styling or mechanical change from the previous year.

I.D. NUMBERS: Not available.

AVANTI II

Model Number	Body/Style Number	Body Type & Seating	Factory Price	Shipping Weight	Production Total
NA	NA	2-dr Spt Cpe-4P	6041	3181	59

ENGINE: Chevrolet Corvette. V-8. Overhead valves. Cast iron block. Displacement: 327 cid. Bore and stroke: 4.00 x 3.25 inches. Compression ratio: 10.5:1. Brake hp: 300 at 5000 rpm. Five main bearings. Hydraulic valve lifters. Carburetor: Holley model 3884505 four-barrel.

POWERTRAIN: Choice of three-speed automatic, or Borg-Warner four-speed manual transmissions.

CHASSIS: Wheelbase: 109 inches. Overall length: 192-1/2 inches. Front tread: 57-3/8 inches. Rear tread: 56-9/16 inches. Tire size: 7.75 x 15.

1966 Avanti II, two-door sports coupe, V-8 (AA)

OPTIONS: Automatic transmission. Four-speed manual transmissions. Power steering. Tilt steering wheel. Electric windows. Rear window defogger. AM/FM stereo. Magnum 500 chrome wheels.

1967 AVANTI II

1967 Avanti II, two-door sports coupe, V-8 (AA)

AVANTI II — Very little styling or mechanical change from the previous year.

I.D. NUMBERS: Not available.

AVANTI II

Model Number	Body/Style Number	Body Type & Seating	Factory Price	Shipping Weight	Production Total
NA	NA	2-dr Spt Cpe-4P	6041	3181	66

ENGINE: Chevrolet Corvette. V-8. Overhead valves. Cast iron block. Displacement: 327 cid. Bore and stroke: 4.00 x 3.25 inches. Compression ratio: 10.5:1. Brake hp: 300 at 5000 rpm. Five main bearings. Hydraulic valve lifters. Carburetor: Rochester model 3096631 four-barrel.

POWERTRAIN: Four-speed manual transmission.

CHASSIS: Wheelbase: 109 inches. Overall length: 192-1/2 inches. Front tread: 57-3/8 inches. Rear tread: 56-9/16 inches. Tire size: 7.75 x 15.

OPTIONS: Borg-Warner three-speed automatic transmission. Power steering. Tilt steering wheel. Electric windows. Rear window defogger. AM/FM stereo. Magnum 500 chrome wheels.

1968 AVANTI II

AVANTI II — Very little styling or mechanical change from the previous year.

I.D. NUMBERS: Not available.

AVANTI II

Model Number	Body/Style Number	Body Type & Seating	Factory Price	Shipping Weight	Production Total
NA	NA	2-dr Spt Cpe-4P	6645	3181	100

1968 Avanti II, two-door sports coupe, V-8 (AA)

ENGINE: Chevrolet Corvette. V-8. Overhead valve. Cast iron block. Displacement: 327 cid. Bore and stroke: 4.00 x 3.25 inches. Compression ratio: 10.5:1. Brake hp: 300 at 5000 rpm. Five main bearings. Hydraulic valve lifters. Carburetor: Rochester model 7028207 four-barrel.

CHASSIS: Wheelbase: 109 inches. Overall length: 192-1/2 inches. Front tread: 57-3/8 inches. Rear tread: 56-9/16 inches. Tire size: 7.75 x 15.

OPTIONS: Hurst four-speed manual transmission ($250). Air conditioning ($425). Electric windows ($100). Rear window defogger ($25). Twin traction differential ($100). Tilt steering wheel ($100). AM/FM stereo, four speakers ($240). Eppe fog lights ($60). Magnum 500 chrome wheels ($250). Michelin radial whitewall tires.

1969 AVANTI II

AVANTI II — Very little styling or mechanical change from the previous year. However, a new option was a larger displacement engine, with the same horsepower.

I.D. NUMBERS: Not available.

1969 Avanti II, two-door sports coupe, V-8

AVANTI II

Model Number	Body/Style Number	Body Type & Seating	Factory Price	Shipping Weight	Production Total
NA	NA	2-dr Spt Cpe-4P	7145	3100	92

ENGINES

(BASE) Chevrolet Corvette. V-8. Overhead valve. Cast iron block. Displacement: 327 cid. Bore and stroke: 4.00 x 3.25 inches. Compression ratio: 10.5:1. Brake hp: 300 at 5000 rpm. Five main bearings. Hydraulic valve lifters. Carburetor: Holley model 3906631 four-barrel.

(OPTIONAL) Chevrolet Corvette. V-8. Overhead valve. Cast iron block. Displacement: 350 cid. Bore and stroke: 4.00 x 3.48 inches. Compression ratio: 10.5:1. Brake hp: 300 at 4800 rpm. Five main bearings. Hydraulic valve lifters. Carburetor: Rochester model 7929203 four-barrel.

POWERTRAIN: Four-speed manual transmission.

CHASSIS: Wheelbase: 109 inches. Overall length: 192-1/2 inches. Front tread: 57-3/8 inches. Rear tread: 56-9/16 inches. Tire size: 7.75 x 15.

OPTIONAL: Borg-Warner three-speed automatic torque converter transmission (with manual option). Air conditioning. Electric windows. Rear window defogger.

1970 AVANTI II

AVANTI II — Very little styling change from the previous year.

I.D. NUMBERS: Not available.

1970 Avanti II, two-door sports coupe, V-8 (AA)

AVANTI II

Model Number	Body/Style Number	Body Type & Seating	Factory Price	Shipping Weight	Production Total
NA	NA	2-dr Spt Cpe-4P	7145	3217	117

ENGINES

(BASE) Chevrolet Corvette. V-8. Overhead valve. Cast iron block. Displacement: 327 cid. Bore and stroke: 4.00 x 3.25 inches. Compression ratio: 10.5:1. Brake hp: 300 at 5000 rpm. Five main bearings. Hydraulic valve lifters. Carburetor: Holley model 3906631 four-barrel.

(OPTIONAL) Displacement: 350 cid. Bore and stroke: 4.00 x 3.48 inches. Compression ratio: 10.25:1. Brake hp: 300 at 5000 rpm. Five main bearings. Hydraulic valve lifters. Carburetor: Rochester model 7029203 four-barrel.

POWERTRAIN: Three-speed 'Power Shift' automatic (with manual selection).

CHASSIS: Wheelbase: 109 inches. Overall length: 192-1/2 inches. Front tread: 57-3/8 inches. Rear tread: 56-9/16 inches. Tire size: 7.75 x 15.

OPTIONS: Hurst four-speed manual transmission (no extra cost). Air conditioning. Electric windows. Rear window defogger. Twin traction differential. Tilt steering wheel. Blaupunkt AM/FM stereo with four speakers. Eppe fog lights. Magnum 500 chrome wheels. Michelin radial whitewall tires.

1971 AVANTI II

1971 Avanti II, two-door sports coupe, V-8

AVANTI II — Very little styling and mechanical change from the previous year. No optional engine this year.

I.D. NUMBERS: Not available.

AVANTI II

Model Number	Body/Style Number	Body Type & Seating	Factory Price	Shipping Weight	Production Total
NA	NA	2-dr Spt Cpe-4P	7645	3217	107

ENGINE: Chevrolet Corvette. V-8. Overhead valves. Cast iron block. Displacement: 350 cid. Bore and stroke: 4.00 x 3.48 inches. Compression ratio: 10.25:1. Brake hp: 270 at 4800 rpm. Five main bearings. Hydraulic valve lifters. Carburetor: Rochester model 7041213 four-barrel.

POWERTRAIN: Three-speed 'Power Shift' automatic (with manual selection).

CHASSIS: Wheelbase: 109 inches. Overall length: 192-1/2 inches. Front tread: 57-3/8 inches. Rear tread: 56-5/16 inches. Tire size: F78 x 15.

OPTIONS: Hurst four-speed transmission (no extra cost). Air conditioning. Electric windows. Rear window defogger. Twin traction differential. Tilt steering wheel. Blaupunkt AM/FM stereo with four speakers. Eppe fog lights. Magnum 500 chrome wheels. Michelin radial whitewall tires.

1972 AVANTI II

1972 Avanti II, two-door sports coupe, V-8 (AA)

AVANTI II — Very little styling or mechanical change from the previous year.

I.D. NUMBERS: Not available.

AVANTI II

Model Number	Body/Style Number	Body Type & Seating	Factory Price	Shipping Weight	Production Total
NA	NA	2-dr Spt Cpe-4P	8145	3217	127

ENGINE: Chevrolet Corvette. V-8. Overhead valve. Cast iron block. Displacement: 350 cid. Bore and stroke: 4.00 x 3.48 inches. Compression ratio: 10.25:1. Brake hp: 270 at 4800 rpm. Five main bearings. Hydraulic valve lifters. Carburetor: Rochester model 7042205 four-barrel.

POWERTRAIN: Three-speed Turbo-Hydramatic transmission.

CHASSIS: Wheelbase: 109 inches. Overall length: 192-1/2 inches. Front tread: 57-3/8 inches. Rear tread: 56-9/16 inches. Tire size: F75 x 15.

OPTIONS: Hurst four-speed manual transmission. Air conditioning. Tinted side windows. Electric windows. Rear window defogger. Twin traction differential. Cruise control. Tilt steering wheel. AM/FM stereo. Electric sunroof. Cibie fog lights. Borrani wire wheels with knock-off hubs. Premium radial whitewall tires.

1973 AVANTI II

AVANTI II — Slight visual differences to the front bumper were the result of the government order to equip cars with five mph test bumpers. A larger engine marked the switch from Corvette power to a less exotic General Motors engine.

I.D. NUMBERS: Not available.

AVANTI II

Model Number	Body/Style Number	Body Type & Seating	Factory Price	Shipping Weight	Production Total
RQ-B	NA	2-dr Spt Cpe-4P	8145	3250	106

1973 Avanti II, two-door sports coupe, V-8 (AA)

ENGINE: General Motors. V-8. Overhead valves. Cast iron block. Displacement: 400 cid. Bore and stroke: 4.13 x 3.75 inches. Compression: 8.5:1. Brake hp: 245 at 4400 rpm. Five main bearings. Hydraulic valve lifters. Carburetor: Rochester four-barrel.

POWERTRAIN: Three-speed Turbo-Hydramatic automatic.

CHASSIS: Wheelbase: 109 inches. Overall length: 192-1/2 inches. Front tread: 57-3.8 inches. Rear tread: 56-9/16 inches. Tire size: F75 x 15.

OPTIONS: Hurst four-speed manual transmission ($100). Air conditioning ($425). Tinted side windows ($25). Electric windows ($100). Rear window defogger ($25). Twin traction differential ($100). Cruise control ($85). Tilt steering wheel ($100). AM/FM four-speaker stereo ($250). Electric sunroof ($695). Cibie fog lights ($60). Borrani wire wheels with knock-off hubs ($795). Premium radial whitewall tires ($250).

1974 AVANTI II

1974 Avanti II, two-door sports coupe, V-8 (AA)

AVANTI II — Very little styling or mechanical change from the previous year.

I.D. NUMBERS: Not available.

AVANTI II

Model Number	Body/Style Number	Body Type & Seating	Factory Price	Shipping Weight	Production Total
NA	NA	2-dr Spt Cpe-4P	8645	3250	123

ENGINE: General Motors. V-8. Overhead valves. Cast iron block. Displacement: 400 cid. Bore and stroke: 4.13 x 3.75 inches. Compression ratio: 8.5:1 Brake hp: 180 at 3800 rpm. Five main bearings. Hydraulic valve lifters. Carburetor: Rochester Model 7044526 four-barrel.

POWERTRAIN: Three-speed Turbo-Hydramatic transmission.

CHASSIS: Wheelbase: 109 inches. Overall length: 192.5 inches. Front tread: 57-3/8 inches. Rear tread: 56-9/16 inches. Tire size: F75 x 15.

OPTIONS: Hurst four-speed manual transmission. Air conditioning. Tinted side windows. Electric windows. Rear window defogger. Twin traction differential. Cruise control. Tilt steering wheel. Blaupunkt AM/FM stereo. Electric sunroof. Cibie fog lights. Borrani wire wheels with knock-off hubs. Premium radial whitewall tires.

1975 AVANTI II

AVANTI II — Very little change in styling or mechanics from the previous year.

I.D. NUMBERS: Not available.

AVANTI II

Model Number	Body/Style Number	Body Type & Seating	Factory Price	Shipping Weight	Production Total
NA	NA	2-dr Spt Cpe-4P	9945	3250	125

ENGINE: General Motors. V-8. Overhead valves. Cast iron block. Displacement: 400 cid. Bore and stroke: 4.13 x 3.75 inches. Compression ratio: 8.18:1. Brake hp: 180 at 3800 rpm. Five main bearings. Hydraulic valve lifters. Carburetor: Rochester model 7044526.

POWERTRAIN: Three-speed Turbo-Hydramatic transmission.

CHASSIS: Wheelbase: 109 inches. Overall length: 192.44 inches. Front tread: 57-3/8 inches. Rear tread: 56-9/16 inches. Tire size: F78 x 15.

OPTIONS: Hurst four-speed manual transmission. Air conditioning. Tinted side windows. Electric windows. Rear window defogger. Twin traction differential. Cruise control. Tilt steering wheel. AM/FM stereo. Electric sun roof. Cibie fog lights. Borrani wire with knock-off hubs. Premium radial whitewall tires.

MANUFACTURER: Avanti Motor Corp. South Bend, Ind.

1955 BANGERT

1955 Bangert, two-door sports roadster, 4-cyl (CG)

BANGERT SERIES — (V-8) — The Bangert was a fiberglass kit. The rear fenders had a rounded shape like the contemporary Corvette. Frontal styling was more unique. A scooped-out area from the cowlside to the front created large wheel wells. Its upper feature line rounded the body corner, then dipped low to form a panel with oval-shaped radiator intake. This gave the upper fenders a wing-like look in front view. Also provided, at extra cost, was a 2x3 box tubular frame. Incorporating a roll bar, it was designed for early Ford suspension, but later coil springs would fit. The body accommodated everything from import fours to the Cadillac V-8.

I.D. NUMBERS: Not available or not used.

BANGERT SPORTS CAR

Model Number	Body/Style Number	Body Type & Seating	Factory Price	Shipping Weight	Production Total
NA	NA	2-dr Rds-2P	$495	2,000	NA

NOTE 1: Kit price included body, mounting brackets and hood.
NOTE 2: Dry weight just under 2,000 lbs. with Ford chassis and Cadillac V-8.

ENGINE (TYPICAL): Cadillac V-8. Overhead valves. Cast iron block. Displacement: 331 cid. Bore and stroke: 3-13/16 x 3-5/8 inches. Compression ratio: 9.0:1. hp: 250 at 4600 rpm. Five main bearings. Hydraulic valve lifters. Carburetor: four-barrel.

CHASSIS: Wheelbase: Designed for a 96 inch to 104 inch wheelbase. Adaptable to any 83 inch to 96 inch wheelbase. Transverse rear springs.

POWERTRAIN OPTIONS: Builder's option.

CONVENIENCE OPTIONS: 2x3 box tubular frame ($195). Windshield. Headlights.

HISTORICAL FOOTNOTES: Marketed by Bangert Enterprises, 3515 Cahuenga Blvd., Hollywood, Calif.

BANNER BOY

BANNER BOY BUCKBOARD — Claimed to be a virtual copy of the 1914-1928 Flyer/Auto Red Bug juvenile autos built by A.O. Smith, Briggs & Stratton, and Automotive Electric Service Corp. The tiny vehicle was supposedly the only replica accepted for class judging in Antique Automobile Club of America events. There were detail differences, but it came close. Major change was in the use of a Briggs & Stratton engine mounted on the frame, instead of the powered "Motor Wheel" (fifth-wheel) of the originals. Drive was via centrifugal clutch and V-belts to the right rear wheel. Original type brakes consisted of pads inside and attached to the front tips of the rear fenders, which pressed against the tires. Kits came unassembled and unfinished, though all holes were drilled and paint and varnish were furnished. Top speed was 20 mph.

I.D. NUMBERS: Not available.

BANNER BOY BUCKBOARD

Model Number	Body/Style Number	Body Type & Seating	Factory Price	Shipping Weight	Production Total
NA	NA	Buckboard 2P	399.50	NA	NA

ENGINE: Briggs & Stratton one-cylinder, air-cooled, 2-3/4 hp, rope start.

1958 Banner Boy Buckboard, two-passenger, one-cylinder

CHASSIS: 6 springy boards did triple duty as body, frame, and suspension. Heavy-duty 20 inch bicycle wheels and tires, fenders. 62 inch wheelbase, 30 inch tread, 38 inch overall height.

MANUFACTURER: Banner Welder, Inc., Milwaukee Wis.

1956 BASSON'S STAR

BASSON'S STAR — A very stylish fiberglass open body distinguished the Basson's Star from any other car. Gil D'Andrea, director of design for the manufacturer, was mainly responsible for seeing this economy car become a reality, though few were made. It was a three-wheel car, with the lone wheel at the front.

I.D. NUMBERS: Not available.

1956 Basson's Star, three-wheel runabout, one-cyl.

BASSON'S STAR

Model Number	Body/Style Number	Body Type & Seating	Factory Price	Shipping Weight	Production Total
NA	NA	3-Wheel Rbt-2P	999	NA	NA

ENGINE: One-cylinder. Two-cycle. Brake hp: 10.

CHASSIS: Overall length: approximately 126 inches.

MANUFACTURER: Basson's Industries Corp. Bronx, N.Y.

1956 BEARCAT

BEARCAT — This is nothing more than the American Buckboard chassis with a fiberglass body and a different name. The styling was unchanged and the same small rear-mounted motor was used. The unusual fifth wheel at the back, to drive the car, was retained.

I.D. NUMBERS: Not available.

BEARCAT

Model Number	Body/Style Number	Body Type & Seating	Factory Price	Shipping Weight	Production Total
NA	NA	2-dr Rds-2P	under 1000	NA	NA

1956 Bearcat miniature roadster, two-cyl.

ENGINE: Motorcycle. Two-cylinder. Air-cooled. Brake hp: 25. Rear-mounted.

CHASSIS FEATURE: Wheelbase: 70 inches (excluding fifth wheel). Overall length: 120 inches.

POWERTRAIN OPTIONS: Chain-drive to fifth wheel (located at the rear).

MANUFACTURER: American Buckboard Corp., Los Angeles, Calif.

1946 BEECHCRAFT

BEECHCRAFT — This was a car built and proposed for production by the Beech aircraft company. It was quite unorthodox in many ways. An aircraft engine drove an electric generator which powered four electric motors — one for each wheel. Reversing the polarity of the motors augmented the conventional hydraulic brakes as a fail-safe stopping system. Not surprising from an aircraft maker was the aluminum body. The doors curved up into the roof. The Plainsman a fastback sedan. It looked a bit back-heavy, due to a lack of side windows behind the back doors. An aluminum frame and air suspension were two more unusual features. Series production did not materialize, largely because the projected price was far too high to expect success.

1946 Beechcraft Plainsman, four-door sedan, 4-cyl.

I.D. NUMBERS: Not available.

Model Number	Body/Style Number	Body Type & Seating	Factory Price	Shipping Weight	Production Total
NA	NA	4-dr Sed-6P	5000	2200	2

ENGINE: Franklin (aircraft type). Air-cooled. Four-cylinder. Horizontally-opposed. Brake hp: 100.

CHASSIS: Not available.

MANUFACTURER: Beech Aircraft Co., Wichita, Kan.

1959 BLOOMQUIST

BLOOMQUIST SPORTS CAR — **(SIX)** — Little is known about this fiberglass car. Apparently it was a kit built off a modified Kaiser frame. Styling was like a smooth-sided Austin-Healey with a unique front end. Headlights were mounted in an oval housing a bar grille. A large hood scoop with a V-notch was seen. The windshield was a two-piece, Veed type. An external rear spare was used. The doors opened in 'suicide' fashion.

I.D. NUMBERS: Not available or not used.

BLOOMQUIST SPORTS CAR

Model Number	Body/Style Number	Body Type & Seating	Factory Price	Shipping Weight	Production Total
NA	NA	2-dr Rds-2P	1100	NA	NA

NOTE 1: The price was the cost of building the one and only prototype.

1959 Bloomquist, two-door roadster (CG)

ENGINE: Kaiser six. (See Kaiser section for specifications).

CHASSIS: Shortened Kaiser running gear.

OPTIONS: Not applicable.

HISTORICAL FOOTNOTES: Built by Gordon Bloomquist, Jamestown, N.Y.

1952 BMC

BMC — The letters B, M, and C were the initials of a small California car maker. There was no connection with the British Motor Corp. of about the same period. This car was a re-bodied Singer 1500. Its fiberglass body was much more American in style than the very British Singer body.

I.D. NUMBERS: Not available.

BMC

Model Number	Body/Style Number	Body Type & Seating	Factory Price	Shipping Weight	Production Total
NA	NA	2-dr Rds-2P	3000	NA	NA

1952 BMC, two-door sport-roadster, 4-cyl.

ENGINE: Singer 1500. Four-cylinders. Overhead valves. Cast iron block. Displacement: 91.3 cid. Bore and stroke: 2.85 x 3.49 inches. Compression ratio: 7.0:1. Brake hp: 58 at 4600 rpm. Carburetor: Two Solex.

CHASSIS: Not available.

MANUFACTURER: British Motor Car Co., San Francisco, Calif.

1948 BOARDMAN

BOARDMAN — When the 1947 Studebaker hit the streets its styling was sensational. A Georgia firm tried to produce and market a variation of the Commander business coupe. They turned it into a roadster with cut down doors. Slight re-shaping was done to the rear deck.

I.D. NUMBERS: Not available.

1948 Boardman two-door convertible-roadster, 6-cyl.

BOARDMAN

Model Number	Body/Style Number	Body Type & Seating	Factory Price	Shipping Weight	Production Total
NA	NA	2-dr Rds-3P	NA	NA	1

ENGINE: Studebaker Commander. Six-cylinder. L-head. Cast iron block. Displacement: 226.2 cid. Bore and stroke: 3-5/16 x 4-3/8 inches. Compression ratio: 6.5:1. Brake hp: 94 at 3600 rpm. Four main bearings. Solid valve lifters. Carburetor: BXOV-26 one-barrel.

POWERTRAIN: Three-speed manual transmission.

CHASSIS: Wheelbase: 119 inches. Overall length: 204-1/8 inches. Tire size: 6.50 x 15.

MANUFACTURER: Boardman Motors, Augusta, Ga.

1945-1947 BOBBI-KAR

BOBBI-KAR — Begun by S.A. Williams, the Bobbi-Kar was an economy car which came in coupe, sedan and station wagon body types. Bodies were made of fiberglass, although the coupe had a removable steel top, and the station wagon used some real wood panels. The coupe had its engine mounted in the rear, but the other models had their engines in the front. Torsilastic suspension was featured. Developed by B.F. Goodrich, it used torsion bars bonded in rubber. Legal problems regarding financing in California prompted the company to relocate in Alabama. Shortly, thereafter, the company was reorganized and the car became the Keller.

I.D. NUMBERS: Not available.

1946 Bobbi-Kar, two-door station wagon, 2-cyl

BOBBI-KAR

Model Number	Body/Style Number	Body Type & Seating	Factory Price	Shipping Weight	Production Total
NA	NA	2-dr Cpe-2P	NA	NA	NA
NA	NA	2-dr Sed-2P	400-500	1200	NA
NA	NA	2-dr Sta Wag-4P	NA	NA	NA

ENGINE: Four-cylinder. Water-cooled. Rear-mounted in coupe only. L-head. Cast iron block. Displacement: 64.9 cid. Bore and stroke: 2-5/8 x 3 inches. Brake hp: 25. Three main bearings. Carburetor: one-barrel.

POWERTRAIN: Three-speed manual transmission.

CHASSIS: Wheelbase: (coupe and sedan) 80 inches; (station wagon) 100 inches. Overall length: (coupe and sedan) 132 inches; (station wagon) 161.5 inches. Front tread: (all models) 45 inches. Rear tread: (all models) 46 inches. Tire size: (coupe and sedan) 4.50 x 12 inches; (station wagon) 5.00 x 12.

MANUFACTURER: Bobbi Motor Car Corp., San Diego, Calif. (1945-1946). Dixie Motor Car Corp., Birmingham, Ala. (1947).

1958 BOCAR

BOCAR — Bob Carnes made a short big splash in the car making business by building some high-performance cars. His Bocar (short for Bob Carnes) used the fiberglass sports body on a tubular frame. The first model, XP-4, was powered by a Chevrolet Corvette engine. A larger Pontiac V-8 was available as an option.

I.D. NUMBERS: Not available.

BOCAR (XP-4)

Model Number	Body/Style Number	Body Type & Seating	Factory Price	Shipping Weight	Production Total
XP-4	NA	2-dr Rds-2P	NA	1641	NA

ENGINES

(BASE) Chevrolet Corvette. V-8. Overhead valves. Cast iron block. Displacement: 283 cid. Bore and stroke: 3.88 x 3.00 inches. Five main bearings.

(OPTIONAL) Pontiac. V-8. Overhead valve. Cast iron block. Displacement: 370 cid. Bore and stroke: 4.06 x 3.56 inches.

CHASSIS: Wheelbase: 90 inches.

1959 BOCAR

BOCAR — A more potent model called the XP-5 followed the XP-4. It had a Corvette engine modified to produce much more power than the stock Corvette offered up to this point in time. Top speed was around 120 mph.

I.D. NUMBERS: Not available.

BOCAR (XP-5)

Model Number	Body/Style Number	Body Type & Seating	Factory Price	Shipping Weight	Production Total
XP-5	NA	2-dr Rds-2P	8700	1775	NA

ENGINE: Chevrolet Corvette. V-8. Overhead valve. Cast iron block. Displacement: 283 cid. Bore and stroke: 3.88 x 3.00 inches. Brake hp: 315. Five main bearings.

1959 Bocar, two-door roadster, V-8 (CG)

CHASSIS: Wheelbase: 91 inches.

1960 BOCAR

BOCAR — For its last year in business, Bocar continued making the XP-5, but added the XP-6. It was a bit longer than previous models, but otherwise rather similar. It used the 283 Corvette engine with a supercharger, which raised the horsepower to unprecedented heights for a production car.

I.D. NUMBERS: Not available.

BOCAR (XP-6)

Model Number	Body/Style Number	Body Type & Seating	Factory Price	Shipping Weight	Production Total
XP-6	NA	2-dr Rds-2P	11,700	2290	NA

Bocar, competition roadster

ENGINE: Chevrolet Corvette (modified). V-8. Overhead valve. Cast iron block. Displacement: 283 cid. Bore and stroke: 3.88 x 3.00 inches. Brake hp: 400 at 6200 rpm. Five main bearings. GMC 4-71 supercharger.

CHASSIS: Wheelbase: 104 inches; overall length 170 inches; front tread 54 inches; rear tread 52 inches; tire size 6.00 x 16 front; 6.50 x 15 rear.

MANUFACTURER: Bocar Manufacturing Co. (or Racing Cars Inc.), Denver, Co.

1970 BOLIDE

BOLIDE — Two very different cars bore the name of Bolide, which incidently had no connection with the Arnolt-Bristol Bolide. A competition type of car for street use was a mid-engined sports roadster named Cam Am. It had a molded plastic body. Near the opposite end of the automotive spectrum was a four-wheel-drive sports utility model, which could be used for off-road service. President of the company which built these cars was Andrew J. Griffith Jr., who built the Griffith car a few years earlier.

I.D. NUMBERS: Not available.

CAN AM I MODEL

Model Number	Body/Style Number	Body Type & Seating	Factory Price	Shipping Weight	Production Total
NA	NA	Rds-2P	3500	1500	NA

ENGINE: Ford V-8. Mounted amidships. Overhead valve. Cast iron block. Displacement: 351 cid. Bore and stroke: 4.00 x 3.50 inches. Five main bearings. Hydraulic valve lifters. Carburetor: Autolite model C9ZF-9510-A two-barrel.

CHASSIS: Wheelbase: 90 inches. Overall length: 173 inches. Front tread: 55 inches. Rear tread: 57 inches.

I.D. NUMBERS: Not available.

SPORTS UTILITY MODEL

Model Number	Body/Style Number	Body Type & Seating	Factory Price	Shipping Weight	Production Total
XJ002	NA	Utl-2P	NA	NA	NA

ENGINE: Jeep V-6. Overhead valve. Aluminum block. Displacement: 225 cid. Bore and stroke: 3.75 x 3.40. Compression ratio: 9.0:1. Brake hp: 160 at 4200 rpm. Hydraulic valve lifters.

CHASSIS: Not available.

MANUFACTURER: Bolide Motor Car Corp., Huntington, N.Y.

1955 BOSLEY

1955 Bosley, two-door sports-coupe, V-8

BOSLEY — (V-8) — Bosley built a sleek, fiberglass-bodied sports coupe. They were made by Richard W. Bosley, an enthusiast with a degree in horticulture from Ohio State University. Features included a smoothly curved fenderline; extremely low, fastback roof; single, fender-mounted headlights; hood scoop and oval grille with Ferrari-like cross-hatch insert. A unique touch was a competition fuel filler in the left rear roof. The front end, ahead of the cowl, was forward hinged to open in flip-up fashion. Apparently, just one car was built, although limited production was envisioned. In 1955, the Bosley was featured in several national magazines and drew much attention.

I.D. NUMBERS: Not applicable.

BOSLEY SPORTS CAR

Model Number	Body/Style Number	Body Type & Seating	Factory Price	Shipping Weight	Production Total
NA	NA	2-dr Spt Cpe-2P	NA	3360	1

NOTE 1: Richard Bosley described the cost of his car as "far more dollars than I ever imagined!"

ENGINE: 1952 Chrysler FirePower V-8. Overhead valves. Cast iron block. Displacement: 331.1 cid. Bore and stroke: 3-13/16 x 3-5/8. Compression ratio: unknown. Brake hp: unknown. Hydraulic valve lifters. Five main bearings. Induction: Dual four-barrel on Cunningham manifold with Magspark ignition. Dual fuel delivery system with mechanical and electric fuel pumps.

CHASSIS: Wheelbase: 102 inches. Overall length: 168 inches. Front tread: 58 inches. Rear tread: 60 inches. Pirelli tires. Halibrand slotted wheels with knock-off style hubs. Handcrafted frame of four inch diameter 16-gauge tubular steel welded to 1950 Ford front crossmember. Mercury front spindles. Lincoln brakes. Oriflow shock absorbers. Fifty-five gallon gas tank. Modified 'C' Jaguar rear suspension.

POWERTRAIN OPTIONS: Five-speed transmission.

CONVENIENCE OPTIONS: Stewart-Warner full instrumentation. Leather upholstery.

HISTORICAL FOOTNOTES: Built by Richard W. Bosley, Mentor, Ohio. Work on the Bosley prototype started in September, 1952. Top speed was estimated to be 160 mph. The car appeared in ROAD & TRACK (August, 1955); Hot Rod (October, 1955) and other contemporary automotive magazines.

1946-1948 BROGAN

BROGAN — A varied series of small three-wheel cars were built by an Ohio company shortly after World War II. They had the single wheel in front. In the back was a small air-cooled two-cylinder engine. These two-passenger cars were sometimes called B & B.

1947 Brogan runabout, one-cyl. (OCW)

I.D. NUMBERS: Not available.

1948 Brogan Package Car, one-cyl. (OCW)

BROGAN

Model Number	Body/Style Number	Body Type & Seating	Factory Price	Shipping Weight	Production Total
NA	NA	Rbt-2P	600	450	30

ENGINE: Onan. Two-cylinders. Air-cooled. Rear-mounted. Brake horsepower: 10.

CHASSIS FEATURES: Wheelbase: 60 inches.

1949-1950 BROGAN

BROGAN — Although previous Brogans were two-passenger cars, the company did make a four-passenger called the Broganette. It was a three-wheeler like its predecessors. Presumably, the single wheel was at the rear. Little information about the Broganette has survived the years.

I.D. NUMBERS: Not available.

1950 Brogan, Broganette roadster, one-cyl. (CG)

BROGANETTE

Model Number	Body/Style Number	Body Type & Seating	Factory Price	Shipping Weight	Production Total
NA	NA	2-dr Rbt-4P	NA	NA	NA

ENGINE: Onan. Two-cylinder. Air cooled. Rear-mounted. Brake hp: 10.

CHASSIS FEATURES: Wheelbase: 120 inches.

MANUFACTURER: B & B Speciality Co., Rossmoyne, Ohio.

1957 BUCKAROO

BUCKAROO — Reports persist of a tiny car made in Cleveland in 1957. It had a one-cylinder, air-cooled engine. Since its top speed was only 20 mph and it was priced at just $400, it seems quite obvious that this car could be nothing more than very basic transportation. Further details have not been uncovered.

MANUFACTURER: (unidentified), Cleveland, Ohio.

1956 BUCKBOARD

BUCKBOARD — Donald S. Bruce designed a rather strange car called the Buckboard. It may have been known as the Bruce or Bruce Buckboard. The car was not what is normally considered a buckboard. It was an open two-passenger car with a mahogany-finished body. The wheels had very abbreviated, chrome cycle fenders. The headlights turned in the direction the wheels were steered. Taillights were mounted high above the body on rods. Renault 4CV steering and four-wheel independent suspension was used. However, the motor was an Ariel motorcycle engine, mounted ahead of the rear axle.

I.D. NUMBERS: Not available.

1956 Buckboard open two-passenger (OCW).

BUCKBOARD

Model Number	Body/Style Number	Body Type & Seating	Factory Price	Shipping Weight	Production Total
NA	NA	Open-2P	NA	800	1

ENGINE: Ariel Square-4. Mounted amidships. Brake horsepower: 43 at 6200 rpm.

CHASSIS FEATURES: Wheelbase: 94 inches. Overall length: 143 inches.

MANUFACTURER: Automotive Associates Co., White Plains, N.Y.

1968 BUGETTA

BUGETTA — This two or four-passenger sports car had a one-piece fiberglass body. The top was fiberglass or cloth. It was powered by a contemporary Ford V-8 engine mounted amidships. The same manufacturer also made off-road utility vehicles.

I.D. NUMBERS: Not available.

BUGETTA

Model Number	Body/Style Number	Body Type & Seating	Factory Price	Shipping Weight	Production Total
NA	NA	Open-2P	NA	NA	NA
NA	NA	Open-4P	NA	NA	NA

ENGINE: Ford. V-8. Overhead valve. Cast iron block. Mounted amidships. Displacement: 302 cubic inches. Bore and stroke: 4.00 x 3.00 inches. Compression ratio: 9.0:1. Brake horsepower: 210 at 4600 rpm. Five main bearings. Hydraulic valve lifters. Carburetor: Autolite model 95l0-C8AF-AK two-barrel.

CHASSIS FEATURES: Not available.

MANUFACTURER: Bugetta Inc., Costa Mesa, Calif.

1950 CENTAUR

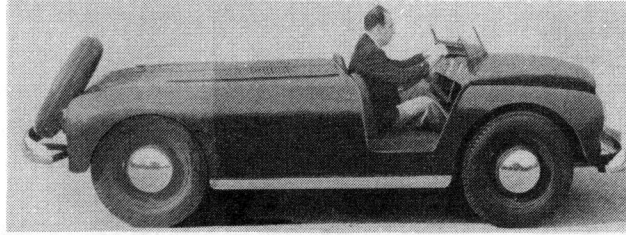

1950 Centaur, two-door roadster, 4-cyl (CG)

CENTAUR — (FOUR) — The Centaur, built by John Palermo, was said to have been a big hit at the 1953 World Motor Sports Show in New York City. It was a rear-engined doorless roadster, the front being reworked from the contemporary Nash Rambler and power coming from a modified 1942 Ford light truck engine. Technical features included four-wheel independent torsion-bar suspension that was adjustable for ride control. The engine had a higher-than-stock compression ratio and one carburetor for every two cylinders. The Centaur was very short up front and extremely long at the rear. What looked like accessory Chevrolet pickup truck bumpers were used, along with an enclosed continental spare tire.

I.D. NUMBERS: Not applicable.

CENTAUR

Model Number	Body/Style Number	Body Type & Seating	Factory Price	Shipping Weight	Production Total
NA	NA	2-dr Rds-2P	2200	NA	NA

NOTE 1: Price is the cost of building a prototype; probably the only example.

ENGINE: Inline Four. (1942 Ford Truck type). L-head. Displacement: 120 cubic inches. Bore and stroke: 3.187 x 3.75 inches. Compression was raised from 6.5:1 to 7.5:1 and horsepower from 36 to 45. Twin carburetors.

CHASSIS FEATURES: Four-wheel independent torsion bar system, adjustable for ride control. Height: 35 inches less windshield. Extremely large tires were used.

POWERTRAIN OPTIONS: Not available.

CONVENIENCE OPTIONS: Not available.

HISTORICAL FOOTNOTES: A top speed of 80 mph was claimed.

1960 CHADWICK

1960 Chadwick, Model '300' two-door roadster, one-cyl. (PZ)

CHADWICK — Although sometimes considered a golf cart, the Chadwick was somewhat more substantial looking than normally expected on the greens. It had two headlights and a taillight. The open body was fiberglass. A BMW motorcycle engine and transmission were used.

I.D. NUMBERS: Not available.

CHADWICK

Model Number	Body/Style Number	Body Type & Seating	Factory Price	Shipping Weight	Production Total
300	NA	Open-2P	NA	680	NA

ENGINE: BMW motorcycle. One-cylinder. Air-cooled. Overhead valve. Four cycle. Rear-mounted. Displacement: 17.6 cubic inches. Bore and stroke: 2.83 x 2.87 inches. Brake horsepower: 13. Solid valve lifters.

POWERTRAIN: BMW. Four-speed manual transmission.

CHASSIS FEATURES: Wheelbase: 58 inches. Overall length: 87 inches. Front tread: 47.2 inches. Rear tread: 20.4 inches. Tire size: 4.80 x 10.

OPTIONS: Automatic clutch. Radio. Surrey top. Fixed windshield and top.

MANUFACTURER: Chadwick Engineering Works, Pottstown, Pa.

1958-1959 CHARLES

1959 Charles Town-About two-door hardtop (OCW)

CHARLES — The dream of Dr. Charles H. Graves, vice-president of Stinson Aircraft, was this good-looking electric car. It was good-looking, because its fiberglass body closely resembled the Volkswagen Karmann-Ghia with 1957 style DeSoto taillights. It was mounted over a tubular aluminum frame. Two electric motors were used. One motor drove each rear wheel. A commercial model called the Charles Van-About was planned. Actually, it was not a van but a pickup. It had a box in the back of its coupe body in the tradition of the coupe-express models of the 1930's. Interestingly, the Van-About seemed to have the styling spirit embodied in the Chevrolet El Camino of 1970s.

I.D. NUMBERS: Not available.

TOWN-ABOUT

Model Number	Body/Style Number	Body Type & Seating	Factory Price	Shipping Weight	Production Total
NA	NA	2-dr HT-4P	2895	3000	NA

MOTORS: Electric. Two motors, one for each rear wheel. Brake horsepower: 3.2 each. Range between battery charges: 75 to 80 miles.

CHASSIS FEATURES: Wheelbase: 94-1/2 inches. Overall length: 164 inches.

MANUFACTURER: Stinson Aircraft Tool & Engineering Corp., San Diego, Calif.

1952-1954 CHICAGOAN

1952 Chicagoan, two-door sports-roadster (OCW)

CHICAGOAN — A fiberglass sports car of pleasant contemporary design, the Chicagoan was offered first in kit form. Later a few examples were factory assembled. The Willys L-head six-cylinder engine was used. In 1954 this car was succeeded by the Triplex.

I.D. NUMBERS: Not available.

CHICAGOAN SIX

Model Number	Body/Style Number	Body Type & Seating	Factory Price	Shipping Weight	Production Total
NA	NA	2-dr Rds-2P	2500	2100	15

NOTE 1: Also offered as a kit for $1500.
NOTE 2: Buyer's could choose a contemporary V-8 engine instead.

ENGINE: Willys. Six-cylinder. L-head. Cast iron block. Displacement: 161 cubic inches. Bore and stroke: 3-1/8 x 3-1/2 inches. Brake horsepower: 75 at 4000 rpm. Four main bearings. Solid valve lifters. Carburetor: Carter YF-937S one-barrel.

CHASSIS FEATURES: Overall length: 174 inches.

MANUFACTURER: Triplex Industries Ltd., Blue Island, Ill.

1974 CITICAR

CITICAR — The most successful electric car from the standpoint of production quantity has been the CitiCar. It was (is?) built in Florida. The small, two-passenger car had rather strange styling, which has now become typical of many small electrics. Made of Cycolac plastic, the CitiCar is quite boxy, but with a flat slope from the front bumper to the roof. This car has a range of up to 50 miles between battery charges. The batteries can be fully recharged 400 to 600 times.

I.D. NUMBERS: Not available.

CITICAR

Model Number	Body/Style Number	Body Type & Seating	Factory Price	Shipping Weight	Production Total
NA	NA	2-dr Cpe-2P	2988	1300	608*

ENGINE: Electric. General Electric. Series wound. Eight, 6-volt, lead-acid batteries. Brake horsepower: 6.

POWERTRAIN: Automatic direct gear drive.

CHASSIS FEATURES: Wheelbase: 65.5 inches. Overall length: 94 inches. Front tread: 43-1/4 inches. Rear tread: 44-1/2 inches. Tire size: 4.80 x 12.

OPTIONS: Rally stripes. Tinted hatchback window. Tinted glass. Right sideview mirror. AM or AM/FM radio. Jack. Spare tire and wheel. Tire inflator. Michelin ZX radial 125 SR 12 tires. Right-hand drive.

1974 CitiCar (Sebring Vangard), two-door coupe, electric motor (PZ)

1975 CITICAR

CITICAR — Very little styling or mechanical change from the previous year.

I.D. NUMBERS: Not available.

CITICAR

Model Number	Body/Style Number	Body Type & Seating	Factory Price	Shipping Weight	Production Total
NA	NA	2-dr Cpe-2P	NA	1300	1193*

ENGINE: Electric. General Electric. Series wound. Eight, 6-volt, lead-acid batteries. Brake horsepower: 6.

POWERTRAIN: Automatic direct gear drive.

CHASSIS FEATURES: Wheelbase: 65.5 inches. Overall length: 94 inches. Front tread: 43-1/4 inches. Rear tread: 44-1/2 inches. Tire size: 4.80 x 12.

OPTIONS: Rally stripes. Tinted hatchback window. Tinted glass. Right sideview mirror. AM or AM/FM radio. Jack. Spare tire and wheel. Tire inflator. Michelin ZX radial 125 SR 12 tires. Right-hand drive.

MANUFACTURER: Sebring Vanguard, Inc., Sebring, Fla.

1958 COLT

COLT — A tiny two-passenger economy car, the Colt claimed up to 60 mpg. Its fiberglass body sported modest fins. Very few details seem to be available about the car or its manufacturer.

Standard Catalog of American Cars

1958 Colt, two-door coupe, one-cyl.

I.D. NUMBERS: Not available.

COLT

Model Number	Body/Style Number	Body Type & Seating	Factory Price	Shipping Weight	Production Total
NA	NA	2-dr Cpe-2P	995	700	NA

ENGINE: Wisconsin. One-cylinder. Four cycle. Air-cooled. Rear-mounted. Displacement: 23 cid.

POWERTRAIN: Automatic transmission.

CHASSIS FEATURES: Wheelbase: 77 inches. Overall length: 120 inches.

MANUFACTURER: Colt Motors Corp., Boston, Mass.

NOTE 1: Manufacturer could also have been Colt Mfg. Co. Milwaukee, Wis.

1946-1948 COMET

1946 Comet two-passenger runabout (OCW)

COMET — The first of several postwar cars to use the Comet name was a small two-passenger doorless open car. It had three wire spoke wheels. The single wheel was in the front. The frame was tubular steel and the body was plastic. An economy car claiming up to 100 mpg, it had a surprisingly large closable cargo compartment over the rear wheels.

I.D. NUMBERS: Not available.

COMET

Model Number	Body/Style Number	Body Type & Seating	Factory Price	Shipping Weight	Production Total
NA	NA	Runabout-2P	500	175	NA

NOTE 1: Available in knock-down form for $350.

ENGINE: Air-cooled. Rear-mounted. Brake horsepower: 4-1/2.

CHASSIS FEATURES: Overall length: 114 inches.

MANUFACTURER: General Developing Co., Ridgewood, L.I., N.Y.

1947 COMET

COMET — Designed by Frank Kurtis, this Comet was actually a sleek convertible body built to be installed on the contemporary Ford chassis. Made of aluminum as well as steel, the body was light for its size. The price shown here is for the body installed at the factory on a chassis brought there by the buyer.

I.D. NUMBERS: Not available.

COMET

Model Number	Body/Style Number	Body Type & Seating	Factory Price	Shipping Weight	Production Total
NA	NA	Rds Conv-2P	$3450	NA	NA

ENGINE: Ford flathead V-8 or inline six-cylinder.

MANUFACTURER: Comet Co., Los Angeles, Calif.

1947 Comet two-passenger convertible (OCW)

1951 COMET

COMET — This Comet was the product of a company which primarily built tiny race cars. For a short time, though, they did offer a roadster model for street use. A sleek two-seater capable of 40 mph and 60 mpg, it was offered fully assembled or as a do-it-yourself kit.

I.D. NUMBERS: Not available.

COMET

Model Number	Body/Style Number	Body Type & Seating	Factory Price	Shipping Weight	Production Total
NA	NA	2-dr Rds-2P	NA	NA	NA

ENGINE: Brake horsepower: 6.

MANUFACTURER: Comet Mfg. Co., Sacramento, Calif.

1964-1966 CORD

CORD — The long-lasting and strong interest in the 1936-1937 Cord prompted Oklahoma school teacher Glenn Pray to produce a car very similar to that classic. Gordon Buehrig styled this car, as he had done in the case of the original. This one was about 80 percent of the size of the former, which led to the model designation of 8/10 for the replica. Offered only as a convertible, it was called the Sportsman. The body was made of Royalex — a durable plastic material developed by Uniroyal. In the Cord tradition, Pray's replica had front-wheel-drive. The car was driven by a front mounted Corvair engine. After 91 cars had been built the operation was halted for several reasons, not the least of which was financial. It also seemed that the market for such a car had been saturated. However, several further attempts to continue the Cord followed.

I.D. NUMBERS: Not available.

8/10 SPORTSMAN

Model Number	Body/Style Number	Body Type & Seating	Factory Price	Shipping Weight	Production Total
8/10	NA	2-dr Conv-2P	4000	NA	91

NOTE 1: Price in 1964; by the time production ended the price was $6,0000.

ENGINES

(BASE) Chevrolet Corvair. Front-mounted. Six-cylinder. Horizontally-opposed. Overhead valves. Cast aluminum alloy block. Displacement: 164 cid. Bore and stroke: 3.44 x 2.94 inches. Compression ratio: 8.25:1. Brake horsepower: 110 at 4400 rpm. Four main bearings. Hydraulic valve lifters. Carburetor: (not available).

(OPTIONAL) (1965-1966): Chevrolet Corvair Corsa (modified). Front-mounted. Six-cylinder. Horizontally-opposed. Overhead valve. Cast aluminum alloy block. Displacement: 164 cid. Bore and stroke: 3.44 x 2.94 inches. Compression ratio: 9.25:1. Brake horsepower: 150 at 4000 rpm. Four main bearings. Hydraulic valve lifters. Carburetor: (not available).

POWERTRAIN: Four-speed manual transmission. Front-wheel drive.

CHASSIS FEATURES: Wheelbase: 100 inches. Overall length: 167.25 inches. Front tread: 62 inches. Rear tread: 60 inches. Tire size: 7.00 x 13.

OPTIONS: Hardtop. Air conditioning.

MANUFACTURER: Cord Automobile Co., Tulsa, Okla.

1968-1970 CORD

1970 Cord, two-door convertible, V-8 (PZ)

CORD — Following the demise of the Cord Automobile Co. of Oklahoma, Elfman Motors of Philadelphia, Pa. took over. It does not appear that any cars were produced by Elfman. In 1968, another Oklahoma company took over the revised Cord operation and they did build a few cars. The firm's name was Sports Automobile Manufacturing Co. It was called Samco. The Samco Cords were altered extensively. The wheelbase was lengthened to 108 and 113 inches for the two models offered. A shorter model called the Warrior used a Ford V-8 engine. The longer, Royal model was powered by a Chrysler Magnum V-8. Both models had rear-wheel-drive. They also had exposed headlights. This not only broke with Cord tradition, but spoiled the front appearance.

WARRIOR I.D. NUMBERS: Not available.

WARRIOR

Model Number	Body/Style Number	Body Type & Seating	Factory Price	Shipping Weight	Production Total
NA	NA	2-dr Conv-2P	7300	NA	NA

WARRIOR ENGINE: Ford. V-8. Overhead valve. Cast iron block. Displacement: 302 cid. Bore and stroke: 4.00 x 3.00 inches. Compression ratio: 9.0:1. Brake horsepower: 220 at 4600 rpm. (210 at 4400 rpm. in 1968). Five main bearings. Hydraulic tappets. Carburetor: Autolite model 95l0-C8AF-AK (in 1968), 95l0-C8AF-BD (in 1969), 9510 DOAF (in 1970) two-barrel.

CHASSIS FEATURES: Wheelbase: 108 inches.

ROYAL I.D. NUMBERS: Not available.

ROYAL

Model Number	Body/Style Number	Body Type & Seating	Factory Price	Shipping Weight	Production Total
NA	NA	2-dr Conv-4P	NA	NA	NA

ROYAL ENGINE: Chrysler Magnum 440. V-8. Overhead valve. Cast iron block. Displacement: 440 cid. Bore and stroke: 4.32 x 3.75 inches. Compression ratio: 10.10:1. Brake horsepower: 350 at 4400 rpm. Five main bearings. Hydraulic valve lifters. Carburetor: Holley model R-4166 (R-3918 A in 1968) four-barrel.

CHASSIS FEATURES: Wheelbase: (Warrior) 108 inches; (Royal) 113 inches.

MANUFACTURER: Sports Automobile Manufacturing Co. (SAMCO), Manford, Okla.

1959-1961 CROFTON

CROFTON — When the Crosley was laid to rest in 1952 it did not stay buried. A California company headed by W.B. Crofton, a well-established GMC and Detroit Diesel dealer, acquired the rights to the amazing little Crosley engine and manufactured it for sale as a small stationary engine. In addition, Crofton produced a utility vehicle called the Bug. Designed by Robert W. Jones, it was a slightly changed version of the Crosley Farm-O-Road, a midget-size Jeep-like vehicle. A Crofton truck model was called the Tug.

1959-1961 Crofton Bug, utility, four-cylinder.

I.D. NUMBERS: Not available

BUG

Model Number	Body/Style Number	Body Type & Seating	Factory Price	Shipping Weight	Production Total
NA	NA	2-dr Utl-4P	1350	1100	200

BUG ENGINE: Crosley (modified). Four-cylinder. Overhead cam. Cast iron block. Displacement: 44 cid. Bore and stroke: 2-1/2 x 2-1/4 inches. Compression: 9.0:1. Brake horsepower: 35 at 5200 rpm. Five main bearings. Carburetor: (not available).

POWERTRAIN: Not available.

CHASSIS FEATURES: Wheelbase: 63 inches (same as Crosley Farm-O-Road). Overall length: 106 inches. Front tread: 40 inches. Rear tread: 40 inches. Tire size: 5.30 x 9 (6.00 x 9 or 6.00 x 13 optional).

OPTIONS: Brawny kit ($450). This consisted of six-speed manual transmission, PowerLok differential, crash pan, Deluxe seats, and 9.00 x 10 tires.

MANUFACTURER: Crofton Marine Engine Co., San Diego, Calif.

1946 CROSLEY

CROSLEY — (4-CYL) — SERIES CC — Powel Crosley, Jr. first ventured into automaking in 1907. He had little success. Four years later, he tried again, with a cyclecar. He met the same results. The Cincinnati businessman did, however, have better luck selling radios and refrigerators during the mid-1930s. In the appliance field, Crosley amassed a fortune, obtaining a popular radio station and a share of the Red Legs baseball team in the process. Still, he clung to his dream of marketing a basic, low-cost economy car that nearly anyone could afford to buy. The result, appearing first in 1939, was an open car with an 80 inch wheelbase and 12 horsepower air-cooled motor that could achieve 50 mph. It sold for under $300 and 4,757 copies were built before World War II broke out. During the conflict, a lucrative contract to build the famous COBRA industrial-type engine and other machines for military use put Crosley Motors on firm financial ground. Shortly after the end of fighting, Crosley obtained government-approval to build 16,000 cars from July 1945 to March, 1946. It took until the summer of 1947 to sell all the cars (and 637 more), at which time the postwar seller's market had helped the company realize a tidy profit. Of these cars, 4,999 were considered 1946 models, including a dozen convertibles. The balance were two-door sedans. These cars continued on the 80 inch wheelbase and were more than a foot shorter than Volkswagen Beetles. Power came from the unique 44 cid COBRA Four which was constructed of sheet metal. It put out 26.5 horsepower. These cars were slab-sided. They had full-length, oval-shaped fenderlines, a protruding nose and headlamps housed by pods that blended into the fenders. There was a small, split radiator grille.

1946 Crosley, two-door sedan, 4-cyl

I.D. NUMBERS: The Crosley serial number (or body number) was located in the center, near the top of the bulkhead or on the engine side of the dash panel, below the hood. Motor numbers were stamped on the left front side of the crankcase. Serial numbers CC46-100 to CC46-5205 were used on 1946 models built from June, 1946 to December, 1946. Motor Numbers CC46-100 to CC46-5586 were used.

CROSLEY CC SERIES

Model Number	Body/Style Number	Body Type & Seating	Factory Price	Shipping Weight	Production Total
CC	NA	2-dr Sed-4P	905	1155	4,087
CC	NA	2-dr Conv-4P	949	1150	12

NOTE 1: Price given for convertible based on 1947; 1946s were prototypes.

ENGINE: Inline. Four. Sheet metal block. Displacement: 44.2 cid. Bore and stroke: 2-1/2 x 2-1/4 inches. Compression ratio: 7.5:1. Brake horsepower: 28 at 5200 rpm. Five main bearings. Overhead valves. Carburetor: Tillotson one-barrel model DY-9B.

CHASSIS FEATURES: Wheelbase: 80 inches. Overall length: 145 inches. Tires: 4.50 x 12 blackwall.

POWERTRAIN OPTIONS: A three-speed manual non-synchromesh transmission was used.

CONVENIENCE OPTIONS: Radio. Antenna. Heater. Bumper guards. Seat covers.

1947 CROSLEY

CROSLEY — (4-CYL) — SERIES CC — For the most part, the 1947 Crosley offerings were a continuation of the 1946 models, with one exception. A station wagon was added to the line. It featured simulated wood-paneled siding on its rear quarters and soon became slightly higher-priced than the passenger cars. The wagon's extra room and trim made it popular and, even today, collector's love the wagons. Like other Crosleys, the station wagon was claimed to be outstanding in the area of fuel economy and provide 35-50 mpg

I.D. NUMBERS: The Crosley serial number (or body number) was located in the center, near the top of the bulkhead or on the engine side of the dash panel, below the hood. Motor numbers were stamped on the left front side of the crankcase. Serial numbers on 1947 models (built from January, 1947 to October 1947) were CC47-10000 to CC47-26999. Body serial numbers on 1947 models built from November, 1947 to December, 1947 were CC-27000 to CC-31999. Motor numbers used for the first series 1947 models were CE7-5587 to CD7-21999. Motor numbers for the second series 1947 models were 22000 to 28803.

CROSLEY CC SERIES

Model Number	Body/Style Number	Body Type & Seating	Factory Price	Shipping Weight	Production Total
CC	NA	2-dr Sed-4P	888	1155	14,090
CC	NA	2-dr Conv-4P	949	1150	4,005
CC	BA	2-dr Sta Wag-4P	929	1305	1,249

CROSLEY ENGINE: Inline. Four. Sheet metal block. Displacement: 44 cid. Bore and stroke: 2-1/2 x 2-1/4 inches. Compression ratio: 7.5:1. Brake horsepower: 26.5 at 5400 rpm. Five main bearings. Carburetor: Tillotson one-barrel Model DV-9B.

CHASSIS FEATURES: Wheelbase: 80 inches. Overall length: 145 inches. Tires: 4.50 x 12 blackwall.

POWERTRAIN OPTIONS: A three-speed manual non-synchromesh transmission was used. After 1949, a cast iron engine was made available and could be retroactively installed in the earlier models.

CONVENIENCE OPTIONS: Radio. Antenna. Heater. Bumper guards. Seat covers.

HISTORICAL FOOTNOTES: "Uncle Tom" McCahill road tested a Crosley in the July, 1947 issue of MECHANIX ILLUSTRATED magazine and raved about its high-speed engine. Many Crosley buyers, however, found holes developing in the cylinders of the sheet metal block, due to electrolysis. The company soon introduced a cast iron block motor, along with a program to refit the early postwar models with the new engine. Many cars were modified this way.

1948 CROSLEY

CROSLEY (4-CYL) — SERIES CC — This was Crosley Motor's best sales year. The postwar buyers were anxious to purchase any new cars and even a miniature model would do. A new model was created by removing the rear seat from the sedan and adding the strip of chrome beltline molding also used on station wagons and convertibles. This created a model called the two-passenger Sport Utility.

I.D. NUMBERS: The Crosley serial number (or body number) was located in the center, near the top of the bulkhead or on the engine side of the dash panel, below the hood. Motor numbers were stamped on the left front side of the crankcase. Cars built from January, 1948 through the same month in 1949 had body serial numbers CC-32000 to 61256. Motor numbers 28804 and up were used.

CROSLEY CC SERIES

Model Number	Body/Style Number	Body Type & Seating	Factory Price	Shipping Weight	Production Total
CC	NA	2-dr Sed-6P	869	1280	Note 1
CC	NA	2-dr Spt Utl-2P	799	1160	Note 1
CC	NA	2-dr Conv-4P	899	1210	2,845
CC	NA	2-dr Sta Wag-4P	929	1305	23,489

NOTE 1: Production for similar body styles (Sed and Sport Utility) combined.
NOTE 2: 2,750 of both models combined were built.

ENGINE: Inline. Four. Sheet metal block. Displacement: 44 cid. Bore and stroke: 2-1/2 x 2-1/4 inches. Compression ratio: 7.5:1. Brake horsepower: 26.5 at 5400 rpm. Overhead valves. Five main bearings. Carburetor: Tillotson one-barrel.

CHASSIS FEATURES: Wheelbase: 80 inches. Overall length: 145 inches. Tires: 4.50 x 12 blackwalls.

POWERTRAIN OPTIONS: A three-speed manual non-synchromesh transmission was used. After 1949, a cast iron engine was made available and could be retroactively installed in the earlier models.

CONVENIENCE OPTIONS: Radio. Antenna. Bumper guards. Seat covers.

HISTORICAL FOOTNOTES: Some people referred to the Crosley as the Crosmobile, in order to avoid confusion with the British-built Crossley. The company also produced commercial vehicle versions including a pickup truck ($839) and chassis and cab ($819) in 1946. Crosley added a panel truck ($899) and front fenders with cowl chassis ($791) in 1947-1948. For additional information see THE STANDARD CATALOG of LIGHT-DUTY AMERICAN TRUCKS by Krause Publications.

1949 CROSLEY

1949 Crosley, two-door station wagon, 4-cyl (AA)

CROSLEY — (FOUR) — SERIES CD — Crosley Motors introduced its restyled 1949 cars in November, 1948. All of the cars had new front end sheet metal. The hood had a broader, flared appearance and its forward edge extended down to the top of a new radiator grille with horizontal blades that ran across the front of the car. A Crosley shield medallion decorated the nose along with a new type of hood mascot. The front fenders took on a revised shape with the headlights integrated into the forward end. The wheel openings were reshaped. A feature line curved forward to upper grille bar level and then ran horizontally to the door break line. Chrome ornaments were placed atop the fenders. At the rear, a new wheel opening shape was also seen and a feature line was used to more clearly define the fender shape, except on station wagons. The wagon had the new frontal look, combined with the old rear end styling. On other body styles, the former slantback design was replaced with a notch back look. New wraparound bumpers were seen at the front and rear. As In the past, the sedan-convertible (also called a Club convertible in 1949) featured a roll-back top arrangement in which the side window frames remained stationary, giving excellent wind protection. The license plate holder was now positioned at the center of the deck lid, instead of at the left-hand side. In July, 1949, the two-seat Crosley Hot Shot sports car was introduced. It was a doorless model with exposed, 'bug-eye' style headlights; a flat one-piece windscreen; rear deck-mounted spare tire; bucket seats and a hatch at the center of the hood, that provides access to cast iron CIBA four-cylinder engine. This motor was based on the specifications of the COBRA four, but was more durable. After January, 1949, it was used in other models and was frequently retro-fitted to earlier Crosley, as well.

I.D. NUMBERS: The Crosley serial number (or body number) was located in the center, near the top of the bulkhead or on the engine side of the dash panel, below the hood. Motor numbers were stamped on the left front side of the crankcase. Body serial numbers VC-10000 to 10727 were used on Hot Shots. Body serial numbers CD-100001 to 108628 were used on other models. Engine numbers were continued from 1948.

CROSLEY SERIES

Model Number	Body/Style Number	Body Type & Seating	Factory Price	Shipping Weight	Production Total
CD	NA	2-dr Del Sed-4P	866	1363	2,231
CD	NA	2-dr Conv-4P	866	1320	645
CD	NA	2-dr Sta Wag-4P	894	1403	3,803

HOT SHOT SERIES

Model Number	Body/Style Number	Body Type & Seating	Factory Price	Shipping Weight	Production Total
VC	NA	2-dr Rds-2P	849	1175	752

ENGINES

(COBRA FOUR) Inline. Four-cylinder. Sheet metal block. Displacement: 44 cid. Bore and stroke: 2.50 x 2.25 inches. Compression ratio: 7.8:1. Brake horsepower: 26.5 at 5400 rpm. Five main bearings. Overhead valves. Carburetor: Tillotson one-barrel Model DY-9C.

(CIBA FOUR) Inline. Four-cylinder. Cast iron block. Displacement: 44 cid. Bore and stroke: 2.50 x 2.25 inches. Compression ratio: 7.8:1. Brake horsepower: 26.5 at 5400 rpm. Five main bearings. Overhead valve. Carburetor: Tillotson one-barrel Model DY-9C.

CHASSIS FEATURES: Wheelbase: (Hot Shot) 85 inches; (other models) 80 inches. Overall length: (Hot Shot) 137 inches; (other models) 145 inches. Tires: 4.50 x 12.

POWERTRAIN OPTIONS: Three-speed manual, non-synchromesh transmission standard in all models. COBRA four standard in sedan, convertible and wagon. CIBA four standard in Hot Shot, optional in other models through Jan.1, 1949; standard equipment thereafter. Some reference sources indicate that a high-compression version of the COBRA four was also an option.

CONVENIENCE OPTIONS: Crosley radio. Antenna. Bumper guards. Seat covers. Heater and defroster. Turn indicator signals.

HISTORICAL FOOTNOTES: Model year production totaled 7,431 units. The Crosley pickup ($825) and panel delivery ($856) were available for commercial vehicle buyers this year. With racing modifications, the Hot Shot could deliver 60 to 70 hp at 10,000 rpm and was capable of speeds in excess of 100 mph.

1950 CROSLEY

CROSLEY (FOUR) — SERIES CD — The nosedive in Crosley's 1949 sales was due to a winding down of the postwar seller's market. In that year, the larger manufacturers had introduced new styling and returned to full-scale production, thereby cutting Crosley's market share. With the downturn in business, little change was seen for 1950, with the exception of the new Super Hot Shot model. Originally priced under $1,000, the Super Hot Shot was distinguished by its use of low doors on either side of the passenger compartment, plus chrome Super scripts alongside of the cowl. Like the Hot Shot, it featured the cast iron CIBA engine and 'Hydra-disc' brakes. Remote-control door handles; sealed-beam headlights and standard turn signals on sedans and convertibles were new this year.

I.D. NUMBERS: The Crosley serial number (or body number) was located in the center, near the top of the bulkhead or on the engine side of the dash panel, below the hood. Motor numbers were stamped on the left front side of the crankcase. Body serial numbers VC-20001 to 20835 were used on Hot Shots. Body serial numbers CD-200001 to 206685 were used on other models. Engine numbers continued from 1949.

CROSLEY SERIES

Model Number	Body/Style Number	Body Type & Seating	Factory Price	Shipping Weight	Production Total
STANDARD					
CD	NA	2-dr Sed-4P	882	1363	Note 1
CD	NA	2-dr Conv-4P	882	1320	Note 1
CD	NA	2-dr Sta Wag-4P	916	1403	Note 1
SUPER					
CD	NA	2-dr Sed-4P	951	1363	Note 1
CD	NA	2-dr Conv-4P	954	1320	Note 1
CD	NA	2-dr Sta Wag-4P	984	1403	Note 1
HOT SHOT SERIES					
VC	NA	2-dr Rds-2P	872	1175	Note 1
VC	NA	2-dr Sup Rds-2	925	1175	Note 1

NOTE 1: Model year production totaled 6792 vehicles.
NOTE 2: Includes 742 Hot Shots; 1,367 sedans; 4,205 wagons; 478 convertibles.
NOTE 3: Standard and Super models use same bodies; no breakouts by trim level.

ENGINE: Inline. Four-cylinder. Cast iron block. Displacement: 44 cid. Bore and stroke: 2.50 x 2.25 inches. Compression ratio: 7.8:1. Brake horsepower: 26.5 at 5400 rpm. Five main bearings. Overhead valves. Carburetor: Tillotson one-barrel Model DY-9C.

CHASSIS FEATURES: Wheelbase: (Hot Shot) 85 inches; (other models) 80 inches. Overall length: (Hot Shot) 137 inches; (other models) 145 inches. Tires: 4.50 x 12.

POWERTRAIN OPTIONS: Three-speed manual, non-synchromesh transmission standard in all models. Cibra type cast iron Four standard in all models. Some reference sources indicate that a high-compression engine was available as an option.

CONVENIENCE OPTIONS: Crosley radio. Antenna. Bumper guards. Seat covers. Heater and defroster. Turn indicator signals.

HISTORICAL FOOTNOTES: Total model year production was 6,792 units. In August, 1950, Crosley Motors introduced the Farm-O-Road, a Jeep-like vehicle designed for the agricultural market. It came in two models, pickup and dump truck, both of which were priced $835. For an extra $150, both could be fitted with a hydraulically-operated drawbar and front and rear power-take-off. In addition, the conventional Crosley pickup and panel delivery were available at the same prices in effect during 1949.

1951 CROSLEY

1951 Crosley, two-door sedan, 4-cyl (AA)

CROSLEY (FOUR) — SERIES CD — Although the model lineup was basically unchanged for, 1951, the Crosleys of this vintage received a more dressed-up appearance. A new frontal design featured a grille with two ribbed horizontal bars and a spinner in the center. Turn indicators were standard equipment on sedans and convertibles again. A new V-shaped bumper treatment added some 3-1/4 inches to overall length. A horizontal bodyside molding was used on Supers. It now stretched from the curve of the front feature line, back across the

fenders and front doors. A larger bird-shaped hood mascot was mounted atop the nose along with a more massive Crosley medallion. The Super Hot Shot became the Super Sport. The standard convertible was dropped and the sedan became a two-passenger business coupe.

I.D. NUMBERS: The Crosley serial number or body number was located in the center, near the top of the bulkhead or on the engine side of the dash panel below the hood. Motor numbers were stamped on the left front side of the crankcase. Body serial numbers VC-300001 to VC-30670 were used on sports car models. Body serial numbers CD-300001 to CD-306958 were use on other Crosleys. Engine numbers continued consecutively.

CROSLEY SERIES

Model Number	Body/Style Number	Body Type & Seating	Factory Price	Shipping Weight	Production Total
STANDARD LINE					
CD	NA	2-dr Bus Cpe-2P	943	1355	Note 1
CD	NA	2-dr Sta Wag-4P	1002	2420	Note 1
SUPER LINE					
CD	NA	2-dr Sed-4P	1033	1370	Note 1
CD	NA	2-dr Conv-4P	1035	1310	Note 1
CD	NA	2-dr Sta Wag-4P	1077	1450	Note 1
HOTSHOT					
VC	NA	2-dr Rds-2P	952	1180	Note 1
SUPER SPORTS					
VC	NA	2-dr Rds-2P	1029	1180	Note 1

NOTE 1: Model year output totaled 6,614 vehicles.
NOTE 2: 646 Rds; 1,077 Sed/Bus Cpe; 4,500 Sta Wag and 391 Conv.
NOTE 3: Standards/Supers with same body counted together; no trim breakouts.

ENGINE: Inline. Four-cylinder. Cast iron block. Displacement: 44 cid. Bore and stroke: 2.50 x 2.25 Inches. Compression ratio: 8.0:1. Brake horsepower: 26.5 at 5400 rpm. Five main bearings. Overhead valves. Carburetor: Tillotson one-barrel Model DY-9C.

CHASSIS FEATURES: Wheelbase: (Hot Shot) 85 inches; (other models) 80 inches. Overall length: (Hot Shot) 137 inches; (other models) 148-1/4 inches. Tires: 4.50 x 12.

POWERTRAIN OPTIONS: Three-speed manual, non-synchromesh transmission standard in all models. High-compression 10:0:1 head standard In Super Sport, optional in other models.

CONVENIENCE OPTIONS: Crosley radio. Antenna. Bumper guards. Seat covers. Directional signals. Heater and defroster.

HISTORICAL FOOTNOTES: Total model year production was 6,614 units. Powell Crosley sent a Super Sport model to France to compete in the LeMans 24 Hour Race. Tom McCahill road tested a specially-prepared Super Sport for MECHANIX ILLUSTRATED. Tuned for racing by Bill Frick and Phil Walters, the car moved from 0 to 60 mph in just 19.7 seconds.

1952 CROSLEY

CROSLEY — (FOUR) — SERIES CD — In 1952 the Crosley was advertised as "America's Most Needed Car," but it seemed that fewer Americans needed one. By July Powell Crosley was ready to throw in the towel. Production, at Crosley's Marion, Ind. plant ended on July 3, 1952. The last Crosley line had been introduced on Nov. 26, 1951 and was mainly unchanged in features or styling. A close inspection below the hood (or engine hatch on sports car models) would reveal a new Carter carburetor and almost no other updates. Even series coding and prices were the same as for 1951, although body serial numbers were altered to indicate that the CD Series was in its fourth year. On March 28, 1953 Crosley Motors merged with Aerojet Engineering Co. of Azusa, Calif., with both firms becoming members of the General Tire and Rubber Co. corporate family.

I.D. NUMBERS: Body serial numbers for 1952 Crosleys were located on the engine side of the dash, just below the hood. Motor numbers were also repositioned, to a point and behind the distributor. Body serial numbers for sports models were VC-400001 and up. Body serial numbers for other Crosleys were CD-400001 and up. Engine numbers continued consecutively from 1951.

CROSLEY SERIES

Model Number	Body/Style Number	Body Type & Seating	Factory Price	Shipping Weight	Production Total
STANDARD LINE					
CD	CD-H	2-dr Bus Cpe-2P	943	1355	Note 1
CD	CD-D3	2-dr Sta Wag-4P	1002	1430	Note 1
SUPER LINE					
CD	CD-A	2-dr Sed-4P	1033	1400	Note 1
CD	CD-C	2-dr Conv-4P	1035	1400	Note 1
CD	CD-D4	2-dr Sta Wag-4P	1077	1480	Note 1
HOTSHOT					
VC	VC-A	2-dr Rds-2P	952	1240	Note 1
SUPER SHOT					
VC	VC-B	2-dr Rds-2P	1029	1240	Note 1

NOTE 1: Model year output totaled 2,075 vehicles.
NOTE 2: Includes 358 Rds; 216 Sed/Bus Cpe; 1,355 Sta Wag; 146 Conv.
NOTE 3: Standards/Supers with same body counted together; no trim breakouts.

ENGINE: Inline. Four-cylinder. Cast iron block. Displacement: 44 cid. Bore and stroke: 2.50 x 2.25 inches. Compression ratio: 8.0:1. Brake horsepower: 25.5 at 5200 rpm. Five main bearings. Overhead valves. Carburetor: Carter one-barrel Model WO-870S.

CHASSIS FEATURES: Wheelbase: (Hot Shot) 85 inches; (other models) 80 inches. Overall length: (Hot Shot) 137 inches; (other models) 148-1/2 inches. Tires: 4.50 x 12.

POWERTRAIN OPTIONS: Three-speed manual, non-synchromesh transmission standard in all models. High-compression 10.0:1 head standard in Super Sport, optional in other models.

CONVENIENCE OPTIONS: Crosley radio. Antenna. Bumper guards. Seat covers. Directional signals. Heater and defroster.

HISTORICAL FOOTNOTES: Total model year production was 2,075 units. General Tire and Rubber Co. owned 72 percent of Crosley and 86 percent of Aerojet Engineering. Rights to the Crosley engine were later obtained by Fageol Co., of Kent, Ohio and the motor was converted to marine use as a low-priced inboard boat engine. Rights to the power plant were later transferred to the Crofton Diesel Engine Co., the Homelite Corp. and Fisher-Pierce, Co.

1951 CUNNINGHAM

CUNNINGHAM — Briggs S. Cunningham, whose middle name was Swift, made a spectacular effort to live up to his name. He entered the LeMans 24 hour endurance race several times, attempting to bring the checkered flag to the United States. He never quite did that, but did bring honors home. His first try was in 1950 using a highly modified Cadillac. The next year he built his own car to race at LeMans. Called the C-2 model, it looked like the raciest thing out of Italy, but it was powered by the new Chrysler Hemi V-8 in stock form. The car finished 18th at the 1951 LeMans, but several copies of it were built and sold.

I.D. NUMBERS: Not available.

CUNNINGHAM (C-2)

Model Number	Body/Style Number	Body Type & Seating	Factory Price	Shipping Weight	Production Total
C-2	NA	2-dr Rds-2P	NA	3450	NA

ENGINE: Chrysler. V-8. Overhead valve. Cast iron block. Displacement: 331.1 cid. Bore and stroke: 3-13/16 x 3-5/8 inches. Compression ratio: 7.5:1. Brake horsepower: 180 at 4000 rpm. Five main bearings. Solid valve lifters. Carburetor: Zenith.

POWERTRAIN: Three-speed manual transmission.

CHASSIS FEATURES: Wheelbase: 105 inches. Overall length: 171 inches. Front tread: 58 inches. Rear tread: 58 inches. Tire size: 7.00 x 16.

CHASSIS FEATURES: Wheelbase: 105 inches. Overall length: 171 inches. Front tread: 58 inches. Rear tread: 58 inches. Tire size: 7.00 x 16.

OPTIONS: Overdrive 7.50 x 16 tires.

1952 CUNNINGHAM

CUNNINGHAM — For his next LeMans try, Cunningham developed another car and gave it the C-4R designation. It looked more menacing than the former and evidently it was. Three were raced. Although two had to drop out, the remaining car came in fourth. The C-4R was more than half a ton lighter than the previous car and was powered by a highly modified Chrysler V-8 engine.

I.D. NUMBERS: Not available.

CUNNINGHAM (C-4R)

Model Number	Body/Style Number	Body Type & Seating	Factory Price	Shipping Weight	Production Total
C-4R	NA	2-dr Rds-2P	NA	2410	NA

ENGINE: Chrysler (modified). V-8. Overhead valve. Cat iron block. Displacement: 331.1 cid. Bore and stroke: 3-13/16 x3-5/8 inches. Compression ratio: 7.5:1. Brake horsepower: 300 at 5200 rpm. Five main bearings. Solid valve lifters. Carburetor: Zenith four-barrel.

POWERTRAIN: Five-speed manual transmission.

CHASSIS FEATURES: Wheelbase: 100 inches. Front tread: 54 inches. Rear tread: 54 inches. Tire size: 7.00 x 16.

1953 CUNNINGHAM

1953 Cunningham, C-3 Continental coupe by Vignale, V-8 (HAC)

CUNNINGHAM — The only passenger car Cunningham built was called the Continental. Its aluminum, fastback, hardtop body was designed and built in Italy by Carrozzeria Vignale. The oval grille was soon adopted by 1954 Nash designers. The Continental used a Chrysler Hemi V-8. The engine was modified, but not as extensively as the one in the C-4R.

I.D. NUMBERS: Not available.

1953 Cunningham, two-door roadster, V-8 (CG)

CONTINENTAL

Model Number	Body/Style Number	Body Type & Seating	Factory Price	Shipping Weight	Production Total
C-3	NA	2-dr HT-2P	9000	2800	Note 1

NOTE 1: Total Continental production for 1953 and 1954 was 26.

C-3 ENGINE: Chrysler (modified). V-8. Overhead valves. Cast iron block. Displacement: 331.1 cid. Bore and stroke: 3-13/16 x 3-5/8 inches. Compression ratio: 7.5:1. Brake horsepower: 220 at 4000 rpm. Five main bearings. Solid valve lifters. Carburetor: Zenith four-barrel.

POWERTRAIN: Three-speed manual transmission.

CHASSIS FEATURES: Wheelbase: 105 inches. Overall length: 171 inches. Front tread: 58 inches. Rear tread: 58 inches. Tire size: 7.00 x 16.

OPTIONS: Semi-automatic torque converter transmission. Radio. Heater and defroster.

1954 CUNNINGHAM

1954 Cunningham, two-door roadster, V-8 (CG)

CUNNINGHAM — The next car in the line of racing Cunninghams was the C-5R, which bore little visual resemblance to any of its predecessors. It had a long sloping tail. Under the hood was another wildly modified Chrysler Hemi V-8. A Siata transmission was fitted.

I.D. NUMBERS: Not available.

CUNNINGHAM (C-5R)

Model Number	Body/Style Number	Body Type & Seating	Factory Price	Shipping Weight	Production Total
C-5R	NA	2-dr Rds-2P	9000	2800	Note 1

NOTE 1: C-5R production not available.

ENGINE: Chrysler (modified). V-8. Overhead valve. Cast iron block. Displacement: 331.1 cid. Bore and stroke: 3-13/16 x 3-5/8 inches. Compression ratio: 9.0:1. Brake horsepower: 310 at 5200 rpm. Five main bearings. Solid valve lifters. Carburetor: (not available).

POWERTRAIN: Siata. Five-speed manual transmission.

CHASSIS FEATURES: Wheelbase: 100 inches. Tire size: 7.00 x 16.

CUNNINGHAM — Virtually no styling or mechanical differences in the Continental from the previous year.

I.D. NUMBERS: Not available

CONTINENTAL

Model Number	Body/Style Number	Body Type & Seating	Factory Price	Shipping Weight	Production Total
C-3	NA	2-dr HT-2P	10,120	2800	Note 1

NOTE 1: Total Continental production for 1953 and 1954 was 26.

ENGINE: Chrysler (modified). V-8. Overhead valve. Cast iron block. Displacement: 331.1 cid. Bore and stroke: 3-13/16 x 3-5/8 inches. Compression: 9.0:1. Brake horsepower: 220 at 4000 rpm. Five main bearings. Solid valve lifters. Carburetor: Zenith four-barrel.

POWERTRAIN: Three-speed transmission.

CHASSIS FEATURES: Wheelbase: 105 inches. Overall length: 171 inches. Front tread: 58 Inches. Rear tread: 58 inches. Tire size: 7.00 x 16.

OPTIONS: Semi-automatic torque converter transmission. Radio. Heater and defroster.

1955 CUNNINGHAM

CUNNINGHAM — The final Cunningham built for and raced at LeMans was a completely restyled car. That is not surprising, because it was the Cunningham habit to completely revise the styling each year. The surprise was the engine in the C-6R. Not a souped-up Chrysler V-8, this was a four cylinder Meyer-Drake motor. The C-6R did not finish at LeMans, but the company was finished building cars. A fortune had been poured into making and racing well-designed cars, but all good things must come to an end.

I.D. NUMBERS: Not available

C-6R

Model Number	Body/Style Number	Body Type & Seating	Factory Price	Shipping Weight	Production Total
C-6R	NA	2-dr Rds-2P	NA	1904	NA

C-6R ENGINE: Meyer-Drake. Four-cylinder. Overhead valve. Cast iron block. Displacement: 179.5 cid. Bore and stroke: 3.90 x 3.59 inches. Brake horsepower: 272 at 7000 rpm.

POWERTRAIN: ZF. Four-speed manual transmission.

CHASSIS FEATURES: Wheelbase: 100 inches. Front tread: 52 inches. Rear tread: 52 inches.

MANUFACTURER: B.S. Cunningham Co., West Palm Beach, Fla.

1953-1960 CUSTER

CUSTER — This Ohio company began making cars before the turn of the century. That effort was short lived, but a second involvement, begun in 1920, continued through World War II. The postwar Custer was a buckboard type of vehicle, available with either gasoline or electric power. The gasoline model had two forward speeds with a top speed of 40 mph. The electric, called the Custer special, had two forward and two reverse speeds. Its top speed was a modest 18 mph. Custer also made motorized vehicles for the handicapped.

1954 Custer, two-passenger buckboard.

I.D. NUMBERS: Not available

CUSTER

Model Number	Body/Style Number	Body Type & Seating	Factory Price	Shipping Weight	Production Total
NA	NA	Buckboard-2P	695	NA	NA

CUSTER ENGINE: Four-cycle. Brake horsepower: 6

I.D. NUMBERS: Not available

SPECIAL

Model Number	Body/Style Number	Body Type & Seating	Factory Price	Shipping Weight	Production Total
NA	NA	Buckboard-2P	NA	NA	NA

SPECIAL ENGINE: Electric. Range between battery charges: 20 miles.

POWERTRAIN: Two-speed manual transmission.

CHASSIS FEATURES: Wheelbase: 70 inches. Overall length: 92 inches.

MANUFACTURER: Custer Speciality Co., Dayton, Ohio.

1946 DARRIN

DARRIN — The famous car stylist Howard 'Dutch' Darrin designed the cars that the Kaiser-Frazer Company began building shortly after World War II. Still, Darrin hoped to get into car production himself. His car was different from the Kaiser-Frazer cars, though the front end styling bore a strong relationship to the 1947 Frazer. The Darrin was a convertible and had what was, possibly, the first fiberglass auto body. There were only four body panels — front, back and (two) doors. The whole front end, including fenders, tilted forward for access to the engine compartment. A Continental six-cylinder engine was used. It was smaller that those used in the Kaisers and Frazers, although it was the same motor that had earlier been considered for the Kaiser (when plans called for Kaiser to be slightly smaller than the Frazer).

I.D. NUMBERS: Not available.

DARRIN

Model Number	Body/Style Number	Body Type & Seating	Factory Price	Shipping Weight	Production Total
NA	NA	2-dr Conv-5P	1950	2400	1

ENGINE: Continental. Six-cylinder. L-head. Cast iron block. Displacement: 187 cid. Bore and stroke: 3-1/4 x 3-3/4 inches. Brake horsepower: 90 at 3700 rpm. Four main bearings. Solid valve lifters. Carburetor: NA.

POWERTRAIN: Three-speed manual transmission.

CHASSIS FEATURES: Wheelbase: 115 inches. Overall length: 185 inches. Front tread: 54 inches. Rear tread: 54 inches. Tire size: 6.00 x 15.

MANUFACTURER: Darrin Motor Car Co., Los Angeles, Calif.

1955 DARRIN

DARRIN — During his association with the Kaiser-Frazer organization, Howard Darrin designed the Kaiser-Darrin sports car. Its life was cut short when Kaiser gave up United States production. However, Darrin himself gave the car a sort of reprieve. He acquired some of the Kaiser-Darrin fiberglass bodies (which had a unique sliding door feature) and stuffed Cadillac Eldorado engines under the hood. The potential performance of these Darrins was exciting. The main visible difference between the Kaiser-Darrin and the Darrin was the fixed fiberglass hardtop on the latter.

I.D. NUMBERS: NA

DARRIN

Model Number	Body/Style Number	Body Type & Seating	Factory Price	Shipping Weight	Production Total
NA	NA	2-dr HT Cpe-2P	3760	NA	Note 1

NOTE 1: Total 1955-1958 production was 50 units.

ENGINE: Cadillac Eldorado. V-8. Overhead valve. Cast iron block. Displacement: 331.1 cid. Bore and stroke: 3-13/16 x 3-5/8 inches. Compression: 9.0:1. Brake horsepower: 270 at 4600 rpm. Five main bearings. Hydraulic valve lifters. Carburetor: Two (2) Carter model WCFB four-barrel.

CHASSIS FEATURES: Wheelbase: 100 inches (Henry J. chassis). Overall length: 184.1 inches. Front tread: 54 inches. Rear tread: 54 inches.

1956 DARRIN

DARRIN — The 1956 Darrin had virtually no styling changes from the previous year. The only mechanical change was the use of the 1956 Cadillac Eldorado engine.

I.D. NUMBERS: Not available.

DARRIN

Model Number	Body/Style Number	Body Type & Seating	Factory Price	Shipping Weight	Production Total
NA	NA	2-dr HT Spt Cpe-2P	NA	NA	Note 1

NOTE 1: Total 1955-1958 production was 50 units.

ENGINE: Cadillac Eldorado. V-8. Overhead valve. Cast iron block. Displacement: 365 cid. Bore and stroke: 4.00 x 3.63 inches. Compression: 9.75:1. Brake horsepower: 305 at 4700 rpm. Five main bearings. Hydraulic valve lifters. Carburetor: Two (2) Carter model WCFB four-barrel.

CHASSIS FEATURES: Wheelbase: 100 inches (Henry J. chassis). Overall length: 184.1 inches. Front tread: 54 inches. Rear tread: 54 inches.

1957 DARRIN

DARRIN — Virtually no styling change from the previous year. The only mechanical change was the use of the 1957 Cadillac Eldorado engine.

I.D. NUMBERS: Not available.

DARRIN

Model Number	Body/Style Number	Body Type & Seating	Factory Price	Shipping Weight	Production Total
NA	NA	2-dr HT Spt Cpe-2P	NA	NA	Note 1

NOTE 1: Total 1955-1958 production was 50 units.

DARRIN ENGINE: Cadillac Eldorado. V-8. Overhead valve. Cast iron block. Displacement: 365 cid. Bore and stroke: 4.00 x 3.63 inches. Compression: 10.0:1. Brake horsepower: 325 at 4800 rpm. Five main bearings. Hydraulic valve lifters. Carburetor: Carter Model 2479S four-barrel.

CHASSIS FEATURES: Wheelbase: 100 inches (Henry J. chassis). Overall length: 184.1 inches. Front tread: 54 inches. Rear tread: 54 inches.

1958 DARRIN

DARRIN — Virtually no styling change from the previous year. The only mechanical change was the use of the 1958 Cadillac Eldorado engine. This was the final Darrin model.

I.D. NUMBERS: Not available.

DARRIN

Model Number	Body/Style Number	Body Type & Seating	Factory Price	Shipping Weight	Production Total
NA	NA	2-dr HT-5P	4350	NA	Note 1

NOTE 1: Total 1955-1958 production was 50 units.

ENGINE: Cadillac Eldorado. V-8. Overhead valve. Cast iron block. Displacement: 365 cid. Bore and stroke: 4.00 3.63 inches. Compression: 10.25:1. Brake horsepower: 335 at 4800 rpm. Five man bearings. Hydraulic valve lifters. Carburetor: Three (3) Rochester model 26C two-barrel.

CHASSIS FEATURES: Wheelbase: 100 inches (Henry J. chassis). Overall length: 184.1 inches. Front tread: 54 inches. Rear tread: 54 inches.

NOTE 1: Total production for 1955 through 1958 was fifty cars. Darrin purchased exactly this many bodies from Kaiser-Frazer and is reported to have sold them all.

MANUFACTURER: Howard A. Darrin, Hollywood, Calif.

1947-1949 DAVIS

DAVIS — Some proposed cars seem to get a good share of publicity, while others go unnoticed. Davis is a good example of the former, being one of the best publicized newcomers to the automotive world. Its sleek aerodynamic aluminum body had a striking appearance helped by the fact that it was a three-wheeler. The sharply rounded nose, hidden headlights, push-button doors and deeply curved windshield indicated the aircraft background of its designers. Of the few cars and military versions built (the latter earned high marks in testing at Aberdeen Proving Grounds), the first ones were powered by Hercules engines. These were replaced in later units by Continental motors. Company president, Glenn Gordon 'Gary' Davis demonstrated phenomenal tight-fast maneuvers the Davis could make. However, it proved somewhat tippy with a high, forward center-of-gravity on the single front wheel. It was claimed the cars could be thrown through full-lock turns (13-ft. radius) at 55 mph. In fact, speeds exceeding 15 mph could cause the inside drive wheel to lift and spin, explaining such high speedometer readings. Claims of 116 mph and 35 mpg were also exaggerated. The best performance actually achieved was on the order of 65 mph and 28 mpg in an overdrive-equipped example. Davis was convicted of fraud regarding his company's finances, though he steadfastly maintained his innocence to the end.

1948 Davis three-wheeler coupe (front view)

1948 Davis three-wheeler coupe (rear view)

I.D. NUMBERS: Consecutive numbers beginning with following engine numbers for each type of engine: IXB3 (Herc.) F4162 (Cont.)

DAVIS

Model Number	Body/Style Number	Body Type & Seating	Factory Price	Shipping Weight	Production Total
482A	D-2	2-dr HT Cpe-4P	995	2400	17
484X	NA	1/4-Ton Jeep-5P	NA	2280	2(?)

DAVIS ENGINES: (early production): Hercules four-cylinder. IXB3, L-head. Displacement: 132.7 cid. Bore and stroke: 3-1/4 x 4 inches. Brake horsepower: 46 at 3000 rpm (late production): Continental four-cylinder. F4162, L-head. Displacement: 162 cid. Bore and stroke: 3-7/16 x 4-3/8 inches. Brake horsepower: 57.6 at 3000 rpm.

POWERTRAIN: Borg-Warner three-speed manual transmission. (early production) torque (late production) Hotchkiss. Spicer rear axle.

CHASSIS FEATURES: Wheelbase: (early) 108 inches; (late) 109-1/2 inches. Overall length: 185.5 inches. Rear tread: 57 inches. Tire size: 5.50 x 15. Brakes: (early) Kinmont clutch-type disc; (late) Bendix drums. Suspension: [Front] (early and late) coil/leading arm yoke and half-fork. [Rear] (early) coil. (Late) semi-elliptic.

OPTIONS: Had production been realized, options included overdrive, slide-out radio with powerpack for remote operation, interchangeable snap-in upholstery, heater, choice of engines.

MANUFACTURER: Davis Motorcar Co., Van Nuys, Calif.

1956 DAYTONA

DAYTONA — This miniature, doorless runabout had a body made of Formica. The sides were flat, but the front and back were rounded. The Daytona was a luxury model compared to the Auto Cub, made by the same New Hampshire company. The Daytona's top speed was 18 mph.

I.D. NUMBERS: Not available.

DAYTONA

Model Number	Body/Style Number	Body Type & Seating	Factory Price	Shipping Weight	Production Total
NA	NA	Rbt-2P	495	235	NA

ENGINE: Briggs & Stratton. Brake horsepower: 2.

CHASSIS FEATURES: Overall length: 72 inches.

MANUFACTURER: Randall Products, Hampton, N.H.

1956 Daytona Minicar, two-door roadster, one-cyl. (PZ)

1947 DELCAR

1947 DelCar station wagon, 4-cyl.

1947 DelCar delivery van, 4-cyl.

DELCAR — This manufacturer had no connection with American Motors Corp. despite the name similarity. Most DelCars were small, box-like delivery vans, but at least one wood-paneled station wagon was also made. There was no hood for the front-mounted engine. This gave an appearance quite different from that seen on vans today. In spite of its short length, there was room for six passengers inside the Delcar.

I.D. NUMBERS: Not available.

DELCAR

Model Number	Body/Style Number	Body Type & Seating	Factory Price	Shipping Weight	Production Total
NA	NA	2-dr Sta Wag-6P	NA	NA	1

ENGINE: Four-cylinder. Brake horsepower: 25.

CHASSIS FEATURES: Wheelbase: 60 inches. Overall length: 102 inches.

MANUFACTURER: American Motors Inc., Troy, N.Y.

1949 DEL MAR

1949 Del Mar, two-door convertible, 4-cyl. (front view)

1949 Del Mar, two-door convertible, 4-cyl. (rear view)

DEL MAR — The Del Mar was a clean-looking convertible. It resembled the contemporary British-made Hillman. Ford transverse springs were used, front and rear. Fuel consumption of 30 mpg was claimed. Only a few prototypes of this aluminum-bodied car were ever produced.

I.D. NUMBERS: Not available.

Model Number	Body/Style Number	Body Type & Seating	Factory Price	Shipping Weight	Production Total
NA	NA	2-dr Conv-5P	1200	NA	NA

ENGINE: Continental. Four-cylinder. L-head. Displacement: 162 cid. Bore and stroke: 3-7/16 x 4-3/8 inches. Brake horsepower: 63. Carburetor: Stromberg.

POWERTRAIN: Warner. Three-speed manual transmission.

CHASSIS FEATURES: Wheelbase: 100 to 104 inches (varied on different prototypes). Front tread: 58 inches. Rear tread: 58 inches. Tire size: 6.00 x 12.

MANUFACTURER: Del Mar Motors Inc., San Diego, Calif.

1957 DETRICK

DETRICK — The lure of steam power inspired Forrest R. Detrick to build such a car in the hopes of getting it into series production. His was a two-cylinder engine, but wasn't too efficient. It consumed fuel oil at the rate of one gallon every seven-and-a-half miles and a gallon of water every seven miles. The car's top speed was 60 mph. Only a single prototype was built and it did not have a body, though a fiberglass body was planned.

1957 Detrick Steamer, two-passenger chassis, 2-cyl.

I.D. NUMBERS: Not available.

DETRICK

Model Number	Body/Style Number	Body Type & Seating	Factory Price	Shipping Weight	Production Total
NA	NA	Chassis-2P	NA	3500	1

DETRICK ENGINE: Steam. Two-cylinder. Displacement: 125.7 cid. Bore and stroke: 4.00 x 5.00 inches.

CHASSIS FEATURES: Wheelbase: 127 inches (modified Ford 1/2 ton truck chassis).

MANUFACTURER: Forrest R. Detrick, Worthington, Ohio.

1953 DETROITER

DETROITER — Raymond Russell, after building the Gadabout and the Russell, designed another car. This one was not at all like his earlier efforts. A very low convertible, the Detroiter had a fiberglass body. At the rear, there was no bumper, as such. The uncovered spare was mounted in a continental tire manner. Many components were of contemporary Ford origin, including the engine.

I.D. NUMBERS: Not available.

1953 Detroiter, two-door convertible, V-8

DETROITER

Model Number	Body/Style Number	Body Type & Seating	Factory Price	Shipping Weight	Production Total
NA	NJ	2-dr Conv-2P	NA	NA	NA

ENGINE: Ford. V-8. L-head. Cast iron block. Displacement: 239.4 cid. Bore and stroke: 3.19 x 3.75 inches. Compression: 7.2:1. Brake horsepower: 110 at 3800 rpm. Three main bearings. Solid valve lifters. Carburetor: Ford model EAB-9510-C.

CHASSIS FEATURES: Wheelbase: 115 inches (Ford chassis, also modified Cadillac chassis).

MANUFACTURER: Detroit Accessories Co., St. Clair Shores, Mich.

1955-1958 DEVIN

DEVIN — Devin is primarily known for its sleek fiberglass bodies. They were built for the do-it-yourselfer to put a chassis of his own choice under. However, Devin did complete assemblies of some cars. The most sensational was the Super Sports, also called the 'SS.' Its Irish-built chassis used three inch steel tubes. A Corvette engine provided exciting performance. It could make 0 to 60 in 4.8 seconds and had a top speed of 140 mph. The high price for the 'SS' probably limited the car's sales success.

1955 Devin, Model 'C' Panhard two-door roadster, 2-cyl (CG)

I.D. NUMBERS: Not available.

SUPER SPORTS

Model Number	Body/Style Number	Body Type & Seating	Factory Price	Shipping Weight	Production Total
NA	NA	2-dr Rds-2P	5950*	2550	15

NOTE 1: The price shot up to around $10,000 by 1961.

ENGINE: Chevrolet Corvette (1957). V-8. Overhead valve. Cast iron block. Displacement: 283 cid. Bore and stroke: 3.88 x 3.00 inches. Compression: 9.5:1. Brake horsepower: 220 at 4800 rpm. Five main bearings. Carburetor: Carter model WCFB 2366SA (or WCFB 2355-S) four-barrel.

POWERTRAIN: Borg-Warner T-10 four-speed manual transmission.

CHASSIS FEATURES: Wheelbase: 92 inches. Overall length: 164 inches. Front tread: 52 inches. Rear tread: 55 inches. Tire size: 6.40 x 15.

1959-1961 DEVIN

DEVIN — After the slow selling 'SS' model got on the market, Devin offered a completely assembled Model D. This small, sleek sports car used a Volkswagen chassis. The Volkswagen engine was also normally used, but some were Porsche -powered.

I.D. NUMBERS: Not available.

'D'

Model Number	Body/Style Number	Body Type & Seating	Factory Price	Shipping Weight	Production Total
D	NA	2-dr Rds-2P	2950	1670	NA

NOTE 1: Also available in kit form for $1,495.

1959 Devin, Model 'D' two-door roadster, 4-cyl (PZ)

ENGINE: Volkswagen. Four-cylinder. Air-cooled. Overhead valve. Cast iron block. Displacement: 72.7 cid. Bore and stroke: 3.03 x 2.52 inches. Compression: 6.6:1. Brake horsepower: 36 at 3700 rpm. Three main bearings. Solid valve lifters. Carburetor: one-barrel.

OPTIONAL ENGINE: Porsche. Four-cylinder. Air-cooled. Overhead valve. Light alloy block. Displacement: 96.8 cid. Bore and stroke: 3.25 x 2.91 inches. Compression: 7.5:1. Brake horsepower: 70 at 4500 rpm. Three main bearings. Carburetor: two (2) Zenith model 32NDIX one-barrel.

POWERTRAIN: Four-speed manual transmission.

CHASSIS FEATURES: Wheelbase: 82 inches. Overall length: 153 inches. Front tread: 51.4 inches. Rear tread: 49.2 inches. Tire size: 5.60 x 15.

1961-1964 DEVIN

DEVIN — Devin expanded its range of fully assembled models by using a Corvair engine in the 'D' body. The result was called the model 'C.'

I.D. NUMBERS: Not available.

DEVIN 'C'

Model Number	Body/Style Number	Body Type & Seating	Factory Price	Shipping Weight	Production Total
C	NA	2-dr Rds-2P	NA	NA	NA

ENGINE: Chevrolet Corvair. Six-cylinder. Horizontally-opposed. Air-cooled. Overhead valve. Cast-aluminum alloy block. Displacement: 145 cid. Bore and stroke: 3.44 x 2.60 inches. Compression: 8.0:1. Brake horsepower: 80 at 4400 rpm. Four main bearings. Hydraulic valve lifters. Carburetor: Two Rochester model 7019101 one-barrels.

CHASSIS FEATURES: Wheelbase: 82 inches. Overall length: 153 inches. Front tread: 51.4 inches. Rear tread: 49.2 inches. Tire size: 5.60 x 15.

MANUFACTURER: Devin Enterprises, El Monte, Calif.

1961 DIEHLMOBILE

DIEHLMOBILE — (ONE-CYLINDER) — This lightweight three-wheeler was marketed in standard or Deluxe forms. It was designed as a runabout that could be easily disassembled and carried in the trunk of a car. Three self-locking screws and quarter-turn aircraft fasteners were used to hold the assembled unit together. The vehicle was based on a girder-type frame and had a definite homemade look to it. There was no body. The single wheel was mounted, airplane-style, at the front. Smaller wheels, with cycle fenders, were employed at the rear. Steering was via a tubular, tiller-type handle. The motor was mounted at the left rear of the frame and drove the left wheel via chain-drive mechanism. Features included a wide, three-passenger seat, folding surrey top (with fringe) and braking via a long lever at the operator's left.

I.D. NUMBERS: Not available or not used.

DIEHLMOBILE

Model Number	Body/Style Number	Body Type & Seating	Factory Price	Shipping Weight	Production Total
STD	NA	Runabout-3P	300	NA	NA
DEL	NA	Del Runabout-3P	380	NA	NA

ENGINE: One-cylinder. Three horsepower.

CHASSIS FEATURES: Steel 1-beam girder frame. Chain-drive transmission.

POWERTRAIN OPTIONS: Not available.

CONVENIENCE OPTIONS: Surrey top on Deluxe ($80).

HISTORICAL FOOTNOTES: Built and marketed from H.L. Diehl, Co., South Willington, Ct. The manufacturer claimed a top speed of 18 mph and that the vehicle could be put together in less than five minutes, using a half-dollar as a tool. The seat could also be used as a lawn chair or boat deck chair.

1961 Diehlmobile, two-door runabout, one-cyl. (CG)

1950 DORAY

DORAY — The Willys Jeepster chassis was the base for this sports car. Its steel body was fitted to, and around, the Jeepster cowl, windshield and doors. However, the hood was fiberglass and was styled like that of the 1936-1937 Cord. The fenders nearly scraped the wheels. To give the front wheels freedom to steer, an ingenious hinge system was devised, whereby the front sections moved in the direction the car was steered.

1950 Doray, two-door sports-convertible, 6-cyl.

I.D. NUMBERS: Not available.

DORAY

Model Number	Body/Style Number	Body Type & Seating	Factory Price	Shipping Weight	Production Total
NA	NA	2-dr Rds-3P	NA	NA	NA

ENGINE: Willys. (Whether the F-head or the L-head Six engine was used is not certain).

CHASSIS FEATURES: Wheelbase: (Willys Jeepster chassis) 104 inches. Front tread: 55112 inches. Rear tread: 57 inches.

MANUFACTURER: Doray Inc., Miami Springs, Fla.

1960 DTL

DTL — Former Detroit Edison research chief, Douglas Dow, designed an electric runabout. It normally had a 30 mile range between battery charges. Longer distances could be reached with an optional one wheel trailer, which carried a gasoline engine to drive the generator. This car may have also been called the Dow Electric.

I.D. NUMBERS: Not available.

DTL

Model Number	Body/Style Number	Body Type & Seating	Factory Price	Shipping Weight	Production Total
NA	NA	Runabout-2P	500-800	447	NA

DTL ENGINE: Electric. Two (2) one-third horsepower motors. Three (3) 12-volt batteries. Four (4) 2-volt batteries. Range between battery charges: 30 miles.

CHASSIS FEATURES: Wheelbase: 47 inches. Overall length: 74 inches.

OPTIONS: One wheel trailer, with 2-1/2 brake horsepower gasoline engine to drive generator for long trips ($150).

MANUFACTURER: Detroit Testing Laboratories, Detroit, Mich.

1956-1962 DUAL-GHIA

1957 Dual-Ghia, two-door convertible, V-8 ("The Auction")

DUAL-GHIA — Gene Casaroll, owner of Automobile Shippers Inc., of Detroit, was so impressed with the 1953 Dodge Firearrow show car that he obtained the rights to produce it. The body was built, in Italy, by Carrozzeria Ghia, who built the original. Only a few styling changes were made for the production model. A modified Dodge chassis was used, along with high-performance Dodge engines. All, but two, Dual-Ghias were convertibles. Those two were hardtops with a fiberglass roof. An entirely redesigned second generation series was built in the early 1960's, but they were entirely Italian built.

DUAL-GHIA I.D. NUMBERS: Not available.

DUAL-GHIA

Model Number	Body/Style Number	Body Type & Seating	Factory Price	Shipping Weight	Production Total
NA	NA	2-dr HT-5P	NA	NA	2*
NA	NA	2-dr Conv-5P	7646	NA	102

NOTE 1: In addition 13 prototypes were built.

1958 Dual-Ghia two-door hardtop, V-8 (LL)

DUAL-GHIA ENGINES: Dodge (1956) D-500. V-8. Overhead valve. Cast iron block. Displacement: 315 cid. Bore and stroke: 3.63 x 3.80 inches. Compression ratio: 8.0:1. Brake horsepower: 230 at 4300 rpm. Five main bearings. Carburetor: Carter four-barrel.

OPTIONAL ENGINE: Dodge D-500-1 ($100 extra). V-8. Overhead. valve. Cast iron block. Displacement: 325 cid. Bore and stroke: 3-11/16 x 3-51/64 inches. Compression: 8.5:1. Brake horsepower: 260 at 4000 rpm. Five main bearings. Carburetor: Carter model WCFB-2532S four-barrel.

POWERTRAIN: Chrysler. Powerflite torque converter.

CHASSIS FEATURES: Wheelbase: 115 inches. Overall length: 203-1/2 inches. Front tread: 58.9 inches. Rear tread: 59.2 inches. Tire size: 6.70 x 15.

OPTIONS: Power brakes ($40). Power steering ($95).

MANUFACTURER: Dual Motors Corp., Detroit, Mich.

1962 Dual-Ghia two-door hardtop, V-8 ("The Auction")

1959 DUESENBERG

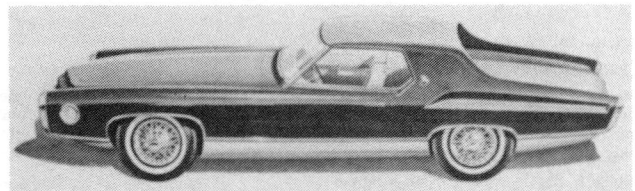

1959 Duesenberg, two-door coupe, V-8 (CG)

DUESENBERG — A car with the character of Duesenberg could not just die in 1937 and then be forgotten forever. Mike Kollins built a steel and aluminum roadster on a modified Packard chassis, then put a souped-up Duesenberg engine in it. Evidently, one prototype was completed.

I.D. NUMBERS: Not available.

DUESENBERG

Model Number	Body/Style Number	Body Type & Seating	Factory Price	Shipping Weight	Production Total
NA	NA	2-dr Rds-2P	NA	NA	1

ENGINE: Duesenberg (modified). Eight-cylinder (inline). Double overhead cams. Cast iron block. Displacement: 435 cid. Bore and stroke: 3.81 x 4.75 inches. Brake horsepower: 400.

CHASSIS FEATURES: Modified 1950 Packard chassis.

MANUFACTURER: Mike Kollins, Detroit, Mich.

1966 DUESENBERG

1966 Duesenberg, four-door sedan, V-8 (CG)

DUESENBERG — Fred 'Fritz' Duesenberg, son of August and nephew of Fred who built the original Duesenberg, undertook to re-establish his family name in the auto industry. The car was modern, but expressed superlative qualities as the original had. The car was styled by Chrysler's former vice-president of styling, Virgil Exner. Built by Ghia in Italy, the body was modern, with a classic flavor. It did not closely resemble any Chrysler styling. As might be expected, this automobile was big, luxurious and expensive. Its engine was a modified Chrysler V-8. After one prototype sedan was built, nothing further developed from the attempted revival.

I.D. NUMBERS: Not available.

DUESENBERG

Model Number	Body/Style Number	Body Type & Seating	Factory Price	Shipping Weight	Production Total
NA	NA	4-dr Sed-6P	19,500	5700	1

ENGINE: Chrysler (modified). V-8. Overhead valves. Cast iron block. Displacement: 440 cid. Bore and stroke: 4.32 x 3.75 inches. Brake horsepower: 425 at 5000 rpm. Hydraulic valve lifters. Five main bearings. Carburetor: (not available).

POWERTRAIN: Three-speed automatic transmission.

CHASSIS FEATURES: Wheelbase: 137.5 inches. Overall length: 244.7 inches. Front tread: 61.8 inches. Rear tread: 62.36 inches. Tire size: 8.90 x 15.

MANUFACTURER: Duesenberg Corp., Indianapolis, Ind.

1970-1973 DUESENBERG

DUESENBERG — The most successful revival of the Duesenberg name was a car which was deliberately intended to resemble the original SSJ roadster. It used a Dodge truck chassis. A Chrysler V-8 engine powered this car and, in the Duesenberg image, it was supercharged.

I.D. NUMBERS: Not available.

DUESENBERG

Model Number	Body/Style Number	Body Type & Seating	Factory Price	Shipping Weight	Production Total
SSJ	NA	2-dr Rds-2P	24,500	3600	NA

ENGINE: Chrysler (modified). V-8. Overhead valve. Cast iron block. Supercharged (Paxton). Displacement: 383 cid. Bore and stroke: 4.25 x 3.38 inches. Brake horsepower: 504 at 4800 rpm. Hydraulic valve lifters. Five main bearings. Carburetor: NA.

POWERTRAIN: Chrysler Loadflite. Three-speed automatic transmission.

CHASSIS FEATURES: Wheelbase: 128 inches. Overall length: 166.5 inches. Front tread: 64.58 inches. Rear tread: 63.3 inches. Tire size: 7.00 x 18 or 7.50 x 18.

OPTIONS: Four-speed manual transmission. Air conditioning.

1974-1975 DUESENBERG

DUESENBERG — Little or no styling change in styling from previous years. However, a switch was made in engine power. A larger, but unsupercharged, Chrysler V-8 was installed.

I.D. NUMBERS: Not available.

DUESENBERG

Model Number	Body/Style Number	Body Type & Seating	Factory Price	Shipping Weight	Production Total
SSJ	NA	2-dr Rds-2P	41,500	3600	NA

NOTE 1: The Factory Price given above is for the 1975 model year.

ENGINE: Chrysler (modified). V-8. Overhead valve. Cast iron block. Displacement: 440 cid. Bore and stroke: 4.32 x 3.75 inches. Brake horsepower: 215 at 4000 rpm. Hydraulic valve lifters. Five main bearings. Carburetor: Carter model TQ-9009S (TQ9010S in California) four-barrel.

POWERTRAIN: Chrysler TorqueFlite. Three-speed automatic transmission.

CHASSIS FEATURES: Wheelbase: 128 inches. Overall length: 166.5 inches. Front tread: 64.58 inches. Rear tread: 63.3 inches. Tire size: 7.00 x 18 or 7.50 x 18.

OPTIONS: Air conditioning.

MANUFACTURER: Duesenberg Corp., (1970-1973) Gardena, Calif.; (1974-1975) Inglewood, Calif.

1954 EDWARDS

EDWARDS — Sterling H. Edwards built only about a half a dozen cars, but they caught the attention of the motoring press across the country, and consequently, the public. Actually his first cars were built in the late 1940s and early 1950s and were entered in various West Coast racing events. Around the mid-1950s production began on cars for public sale. The Edwards was not a sports car by any means. It was large, heavy and luxurious by sports car standards. Yet, it was attractive to America's taste. It was a forerunner of what has since developed into the personal/luxury class automobile. The Edwards was a fiberglass convertible, but some had a detachable hardtop. The only external component borrowed from production cars was the 1952-1953 Mercury taillights. Lincoln and Cadillac engines were used, with Hydra-Matic transmission attachments.

1954 Edwards, America two-door coupe, V-8 (PZ)

I.D. NUMBERS: Not available.

EDWARDS

Model Number	Body/Style Number	Body Type & Seating	Factory Price	Shipping Weight	Production Total
NA	NA	2-dr Conv-5P	4995	2800	2

NOTE 1: Does not include one Oldsmobile powered prototype.

ENGINE: Lincoln. V-8. Overhead valve. Cast iron block. Displacement: 317 cid. Bore and stroke: 3.68 x 3.50 inches. Compression ratio: 8.0:1. Brake horsepower: 205 at 4200 rpm. Five main bearings. Carburetor: Holley model 2140 four-barrel. Transmission was GM Hydra-Matic.

CHASSIS FEATURES: Wheelbase: 107 inches. Overall length: 179 inches. Front tread: 56 inches. Rear tread: 56 inches. Tire size: 8.20 x 15.

1955 EDWARDS

EDWARDS — No significant changes were made in Edwards styling for 1955, but underneath, a Cadillac engine replaced the former Lincoln powerplant.

I.D. NUMBERS: Not available.

EDWARDS

Model Number	Body/Style Number	Body Type & Seating	Factory Price	Shipping Weight	Production Total
NA	NA	2-dr Conv-5P	7800	2800	3

ENGINE: Cadillac. V-8. Overhead valve. Cast iron block. Displacement: 331.1 cid. Bore and stroke: 3-13/16 x 3-5/8 inches. Compression ratio: 9.0:1. Brake horsepower: 250 at 4600 rpm. Five main bearings. Carburetor: Carter model WCFB-2185S.

POWERTRAIN: GM Hydra-Matic.

CHASSIS FEATURES: Wheelbase: 107 inches. Overall length: 179 inches. Front tread: 56 inches. Rear tread: 56 inches. Tire size: 8.20 x 15.

MANUFACTURER: Edwards Engineering Co., South San Francisco, Calif.

1974 ELECTRA

ELECTRA — The least expensive, and probably easiest, way to make an electric car is to use the body of a production car. The Electra was an example of this approach. Using the 1972 Fiat Spider, the conventional gasoline power was replaced with electric power, by way of three electric motors.

I.D. NUMBERS: Not available.

ELECTRA

Model Number	Body/Style Number	Body Type & Seating	Factory Price	Shipping Weight	Production Total
NA	NA	2-dr Rds-2P	NA	2850	NA -

ENGINE: Electric. Three motors. Brake horsepower: 3.2 (each). Range between battery charges: 35 to 40 miles.

CHASSIS FEATURES: Wheelbase: 77.8 inches (Fiat 850 Spider). Overall length: 155.55 inches. Front tread: 46.06 inches. rear tread: 46.06 inches. Tire Size: 150 x 13 or 155 x 13.

MANUFACTURER: Die Mesh Corp., Pelham, N.Y.

1961-1966 ELECTRA-KING

ELECTRA KING — A number of two-passenger electric cars have been produced steadily by this California firm. Boxy-looking fiberglass bodies were used for these three-wheel machines; the third wheel being at the front. A four-passenger model was also offered. It had open sides, a surrey style top and a rear facing second seat.

I.D. NUMBERS: Not available.

ELECTRA KING

Model Number	Body/Style Number	Body Type & Seating	Factory Price	Shipping Weight	Production Total
PI00	NA	2-dr Cpe-2P	NA	675	NA
NA	NA	2-dr Cpe-4P	NA	NA	NA

ENGINE: Electric. NE one horsepower, series-wound DC motor. Five six-volt 130 or 170 ampere batteries. Range between battery charges: up to 45 miles.

POWERTRAIN: Three-speed transmission.

CHASSIS FEATURES: Overall length: 101 inches (coupe). Tire size: 400 x 8.

1967-1971 ELECTRA-KING

ELECTRA KING — Not much change was made to the Electra King over the years, but a four-wheel model was added to the line.

I.D. NUMBERS: Not available.

ELECTRA KING

Model Number	Body/Style Number	Body Type & Seating	Factory Price	Shipping Weight	Production Total
PF100	NA	2-dr Cpe-2P (3W)	NA	750	NA
PF100	NA	2-dr Cpe-2P (4W)	NA	850	NA

ENGINE: Electric. Twenty-four-volt DC series wound motor. Four or five six-volt lead-acid batteries. Range between battery charges: up to 40 miles.

CHASSIS FEATURES: Wheelbase: (three-wheel model) 68-1/2 inches; (other models) 65 inches. Overall length: 99 inches. Front tread: 32-1/2 inches. Rear tread: 35 inches.

POWERTRAIN: Chain-drive to one rear wheel.

ELECTRA KING — A slight change in body styling came with full height doors. Consequently, the former plastic side curtains were no longer supplied.

I.D. NUMBERS: Not available.

ELECTRA KING

Model Number	Body/Style Number	Body Type & Seating	Factory Price	Shipping Weight	Production Total
PFS100	NA	2-dr Cpe-2P (3W)	NA	990	NA
PFS110	NA	2-dr Cpe-2P (4W)	NA	1090	NA

ENGINE: Electric. GE. 36-volt DC series wound motor. Six 6-volt lead-acid batteries. Brake horsepower: 1-1/2. Range between battery charges: 25 miles.

OPTIONAL ENGINES: NE. Brake horsepower: 1; GE. Brake horsepower: 2 ($25); GE. Brake horsepower: 3-1/2 ($50).

CHASSIS FEATURES: Wheelbase: (three-wheel model) 68-1/2 inches; (other model) 65 inches. Overall length: 99 inches. Front tread: 32-1/2 inches. Rear tread: 35 inches.

POWERTRAIN: Chain-drive to one rear wheel.

OPTIONS: 217 ampere hour batteries ($70). Double set 217 ampere hours batteries ($500). Bucket seats ($100). Electric heater with fan ($75). AM radio ($75).

1974-1975 ELECTRA-KING

ELECTRA KING — A slight change in headlight styling was made for 1974. The King of Electric Cars, to quote the company's slogan, offered an interesting variety of combinations. Buyers could get three- or four-wheel models, tiller or wheel steering, and foot or hand controls. The doorless surrey-topped four-passenger model continued to be available.

I.D. NUMBERS: Not available.

ELECTRA KING

Model Number	Body/Style Number	Body Type & Seating	Factory Price	Shipping Weight	Production Total
PFS121	3W TH	2-dr Cpe-2P	2275	990	NA
PFS122	3W TF	2-dr Cpe-2P	2270	990	NA
PFS123	3W SF	2-dr Cpe-2P	2395	990	NA
PFS124	3W SH	2-dr Cpe-2P	2400	1090	NA
PFS125	4W SF	2-dr Cpe-2P	2895	1090	NA
PFS126	4W SH	2-dr Cpe-2P	2900	1090	NA
PFS127	4W TF	2-dr Cpe-2P	2755	1090	NA
PFS128	4W TH	2-dr Cpe-2P	2760	1090	NA
S120	NA	2-dr Cpe-4P	NA	NA	NA

1974 Electra King, PFS-123 two-door coupe, electric motor (PZ)

1974 Electra King, PFS 125, two-door coupe, electric motor (PZ)

ENGINES

(BASE) Electric. GE. 36-volt DC Series wound motor. Six 6-volt lead-acid batteries. Brake horsepower: 1-1/2. Range between battery charges: 25 miles.

(OPTIONAL) NE. Brake horsepower: 1; GE. Brake horsepower: 2 ($25); GE. Brake horsepower: 3-1/2 ($50).

CHASSIS FEATURES: Wheelbase: (three-wheel models) 68-1/2 inches; (other models) 65 inches. Overall length: 101 inches. Front tread: 32-1/2 inches. Rear tread: 35 inches.

POWERTRAIN: Chain-drive to one rear wheel.

OPTIONS: 217 ampere hour batteries ($70). Double set of 217 ampere hour batteries ($500). Bucket seats ($100). Electric heater with fan ($75). AM radio ($75).

MANUFACTURER: B & Z Electric Car Co., Long Beach, Calif.

1950-1966 ELECTRICAR

ELECTRICAR — A range of small, fiberglass-bodied electric cars was produced during the 1950s and, at least, partially into the mid-1960s. They were offered in several different models. Each had different power, depending on the number of electric motors used. This car may have been initially known as BMW. That was the manufacturer's initials, but led to confusion with the famous German maker, with which there was no connection.

I.D. NUMBERS: Not available.

ELECTRICAR

Model Number	Body/Style Number	Body Type & Seating	Factory Price	Shipping Weight	Production Total
CUTIE JUNIOR					
NA	NA	2-dr Rds-2P	NA	NA	NA
CUTIE					
NA	NA	Rds-1P	NA	NA	NA
BOULEVARD					
NA	NA	Rds-1P	350	NA	NA

ENGINE: Electric. 24-volt battery system. Brake horsepower: 1/6th. One motor for the Cutie Junior; Two motors in the Cutie (one drove a front wheel and one drove a rear wheel) and four motors in the Boulevard (one to drive each wheel).

CHASSIS FEATURES: Overall length: 106 inches (Boulevard).

MANUFACTURER: Boulevard Machine Works, Hollywood, Calif.

1952-1962 ELECTRIC SHOPPER

ELECTRIC SHOPPER — For shopping errands, this car was a small, open runabout, about which few details seem to be available. It was a three-wheeler with steel or fiberglass body.

ELECTRIC SHOPPER

Model Number	Body/Style Number	Body Type & Seating	Factory Price	Shipping Weight	Production Total
NA	NA	Rbt-2p	750	NA	NA

NOTE 1: A fiberglass-bodied model was also available at $950.

1960 Electric Shopper, two-door coupe, electric motor (CG)

ENGINE: Electric. 24-volt, traction type, series wound DC motor. Brake horsepower: 1-1/2. Range between battery charges: 30 to 35 miles.

CHASSIS FEATURES: Wheelbase: 61 inches. Overall length: 86 inches.

MANUFACTURER: Electric Shopper, Long Beach, Calif.

1962-1964 ELECTRO-MASTER

ELECTRO MASTER -This was another California built electric shopper type of car. Its fiberglass body accommodated only two passengers.

I.D. NUMBERS: Not available.

ELECTRO MASTER

Model Number	Body/Style Number	Body Type & Seating	Factory Price	Shipping Weight	Production Total
NA	NA	2-dr Rbt-2P	NA	680	NA

ENGINE: Electric. Two (2) horsepower. Six 6-volt batteries. Range between battery charges: 40 miles.

MANUFACTURER: Nepa Manufacturing Co., Pasadena, Calif.

1974 ELECTROMOTION

ELECTROMOTION — (ELECTRIC MOTOR) — Although vehicles built strictly for commercial purposes are not the subject of this catalog, the 1/3-ton Electromotion van may well fit into that crossover area that only narrowly separates certain cars and trucks. Since the mid-1970s, with the down-sizing of vehicles to make them more fuel efficient, it seems that the design of some passenger car models and some types of commercial vehicles are growing increasingly similar in overall concept. And with passenger vehicles growing ever-smaller, there seems to be a very good chance that the station wagon of the future may have to adopt van-like styling in order to provide the traditional utility associated with this type of car. If so, the Electromotion would fit right in. This car-sized truck (the manufacturer termed it a 'delivery van') utilized Saab components made in Sweden, but was built, here, in America. In overall styling, it surely looked like a delivery truck, but its size made it seem more like a car. It was constructed very solidly and even included a rubber-faced, full-width, energy-absorbing type bumper. The Electromotion incorporated a front-wheel-drive powertrain, powerful batteries with a two-year service life and a motor designed to provide trouble-free driving for at least 400,000 miles. It featured a squarish body with a large, slanting-back flat windshield; single headlamps; dual high-back bucket seats; dual windshield wipers and hub caps. The price of this vehicle was an eye-popping $7,000.

I.D. NUMBERS: Not available.

1974 Electromotion, 1/3-ton van, electric motor

ELECTROMOTION

Model Number	Body Style Number	Body Type & Seating	Factory Price	Shipping Weight	Production Total
NA	NA	2-dr Van-2P	7000	NA	NA

ENGINE: Battery-powered electric motor.

CHASSIS FEATURES: Not available.

POWERTRAIN OPTIONS: Not available.

CONVENIENCE OPTIONS: Not available.

HISTORICAL FOOTNOTES: The Electromotion met all federal Safety standards. Approximately 20 dealerships across the country were set up to handle sales.

678

1955 ELECTRONIC

ELECTRONIC — An effort was made, in Utah, to produce an ingenious electric car. Although sedans, station wagons and, even, parcel trucks were proposed, only a sports model called LaSaetta was actually made. A conventional gasoline or diesel engine provided the power to an 80-cell battery pack. That, in turn, drove the Dual-Torque engine located within the rear axle. The Electro-Magnetic Differential provided the car with the electric counterpart of a limited-slip differential. The fiberglass body, built in Oxford, Mich., was to be offered in a convertible model, with a detachable hardtop optional.

I.D. NUMBERS: Not available.

LA SAETTA

Model Number	Body/Style Number	Body Type & Seating	Factory Price	Shipping Weight	Production Total
NA	NA	2-dr Rds-2P	2995	NA	1

ENGINE: Gasoline or diesel engine supplied power to 'turbo electric' 80-cell battery system. Dual-Torque electric motor within the rear axle incorporated Electro-Magnetic Differential. Dynamic braking was featured (which turns the motor into a generator during coasting or braking to save power).

CHASSIS FEATURES: Wheelbase: 110 inches. Overall length: 210 inches.

MANUFACTURER: Electronic Motor Car Co., Salt Lake City, Utah.

1956 EL MOROCCO

EL MOROCCO — A simple and inexpensive idea came into being when a small Detroit firm altered new Chevrolet hardtops and convertibles to look much like contemporary Cadillac Eldorados. Their prices, amazingly, were the same as stock Chevrolets.

I.D. NUMBERS: Not available.

EL MOROCCO

Model Number	Body/Style Number	Body Type & Seating	Factory Price	Shipping Weight	Production Total
NA	NA	2-dr HT-6P	2594	NA	Note 1
NA	NA	4-dr HT-6P	2648	NA	Note 1
NA	NA	2-dr Conv-6P	2762	NA	Note 1

NOTE 1: Total production for all models was 27 cars.

ENGINE: Chevrolet. V-8. Overhead valve. Cast iron block. Displacement: 265 cid. Bore and stroke: 3.75 x 3.00 inches. Compression ratio: 8.0:1. Brake horsepower: 170 at 4400 rpm. Five main bearings. Hydraulic valve lifters. Carburetor: Rochester Model 7008287 two-barrel. It should be noted that any engine offered by Chevrolet was available in the El Morocco.

POWERTRAIN: Chevrolet. Powerglide torque converter.

CHASSIS FEATURES: Wheelbase: 115 inches. Front tread: 58 inches. Rear tread: 58.9 inches. Tire size: 6.70 x 15.

1957 EL MOROCCO

1957 El Morocco, two-door hardtop sports coupe, V-8

1957 El Morocco, two-door hardtop sports coupe, V-8 (rear view)

EL MOROCCO — The basic concept of revising the appearance of Chevrolet hardtops and convertibles to resemble Cadillac Eldorados continued. The only changes for the 1957 models were to approximate the 1957 Eldorado's styling.

I.D. NUMBERS: Not available.

EL MOROCCO

Model Number	Body/Style Number	Body Type & Seating	Factory Price	Shipping Weight	Production Total
NA	NA	2-dr HT-6P	2735	NA	Note 1
NA	NA	4-dr HT-6P	2800	NA	Note 1
NA	NA	2-dr Conv-6P	2947	NA	Note 1

NOTE 1: Total production for all models was 10 cars.

ENGINE: Chevrolet. V-8. Overhead valve. Cast iron block. Displacement: 283 cid. Bore and stroke: 3.88 x 3.00 inches. Compression ratio: 9.5:1. Brake horsepower: 220 at 4800 rpm. Five main bearings. Hydraulic valve lifters. Carburetor: Carter Model WCFB-2655-S four-barrel.

POWERTRAIN: Chevrolet. Powerglide torque convertor.

CHASSIS FEATURES: Wheelbase: 115 inches. Front tread: 57 inches. Rear tread: 59 inches. Tire size: 7.50 x 14.

MANUFACTURER: Ruben Allender, Detroit, Mich.

1953-1958 ESHELMAN

ESHELMAN — This manufacturer produced a trickle of tiny cars of varying designs for a number of years. The first, called a Sportabout, was a very amateurish looking vehicle that was made even weirder-looking by its relatively high top. An air-cooled, one-cylinder engine provided economical transportation for one person only.

I.D. NUMBERS: Not available.

1953 Eshelman, two-door coupe, one-cyl.

SPORTABOUT

Model Number	Body/Style Number	Body Type & Seating	Factory Price	Shipping Weight	Production Total
NA	NA	2-dr Cpe-1P	800	675	NA

ENGINE: Briggs and Stratton. One-cylinder. Air-cooled. Brake horsepower: 8.4.

CHASSIS FEATURES: Overall length: 72 inches.

1955-1960 ESHELMAN

1955 Eshelman Sport Car, roadster, one-cyl. (PZ)

ESHELMAN — A much different midget car was built by Eshelman in the later 1950s. It was almost the same as their children's powered car, but accommodated just one adult and had a more powerful single-cylinder engine. Yet, it was promoted as capable of 70 mpg.

I.D. NUMBERS: Not available.

ESHELMAN

Model Number	Body/Style Number	Body Type & Seating	Factory Price	Shipping Weight	Production Total
NA	NA	Open-1P	395	250	NA

ENGINE: Briggs & Stratton number 8. One-cylinder. Air-cooled. Brake horsepower: 3.

POWERTRAIN: Automatic clutch.

CHASSIS FEATURES: Overall length: 54 inches.

OPTIONS: Hauling cart ($69.96). Lawn mower, with 19 inch reel ($49.95). Leaf and lawn sweeper ($49.95).

MANUFACTURER: Chester L. Eshelman Co., Baltimore, Md.

1960 ESTATE CARRIAGE

ESTATE CARRIAGE — Essentially a Cadillac station wagon conversion, this car had a handcrafted English body. The interior, particularly the cargo area, featured Formica with simulated woodgrain finish.

I.D. NUMBER: Same as Cadillac style.

ESTATE CARRIAGE

Model Number	Body/Style Number	Body Type & Seating	Factory Price	Shipping Weight	Production Total
NA	NA	4-dr Sta Wag-6P	14,000	NA	NA

ENGINE: Cadillac. V-8. Overhead valve. Cast iron block. Displacement: 390 cid. Bore and stroke: 4.00 x 3.88 inches. Compression ratio: 10.5:1. Brake horsepower: 325 a 4800 rpm. Five main bearings. Hydraulic valve lifters. Carburetor: Carter model 2814S four-barrel.

CHASSIS FEATURES: Wheelbase: 130 inches (Cadillac chassis). Overall length: 225 inches.

MANUFACTURER: Peter Stengel, Hollywood, Calif.

1952 EXCALIBUR J

EXCALIBUR J — A two-passenger sports car using the Henry J chassis was created by industrial designer Brooks Stevens. The unique frontal appearance of this aluminum-bodied car featured a protruding rectangular nose for air intake. Cycle type front fenders and free standing, chrome, headlights were used. There was no series connection between this competition car and the production-type Excalibur, which was built by Brooks Stevens beginning in the mid-1960s, and by other owners later on.

I.D. NUMBERS: Not available.

Model Number	Body/Style Number	Body Type & Seating	Factory Price	Shipping Weight	Production Total
J	NA	2-dr Rds-6P	2500	1500	4

1952 Excalibur J, two-door roadster, 4-cyl (Driver: Bob Gary. Others l. to r.: Hal Ullrich, Roland Raabe, David Stevens and Brooks Stevens)

1952 Excalibur J, two-door roadster, 4-cyl. (David Stevens driving)

ENGINES: Willys (modified). Six-cylinder. F-head. Cast Iron block. Displacement: 161 cid. Bore and stroke: 3.13 x 4.38 inches. Brake horsepower: 125-130. Four main bearings. Solid valve lifters. Carburetor: Carter YU sidedraft or Stromberg S.U.

CHASSIS FEATURES: Wheelbase: 100 inches (Henry J chassis).

MANUFACTURER: (Bodies 1 and 2) Beassie Engineering Co., Milwaukee, Wis.; (Body 3) Ullrich Auto Engr., Evanston, Ill.; (Body 4) Bob Webb, Minneapolis, Minn.

1965 EXCALIBUR

EXCALIBUR — Industrial designer Brooks Stevens, who was associated with Studebaker during its last years at South Bend, Ind., conceived the idea of building a modern car in the image of a sports classic of the past. The result was a car resembling the 1928 Mercedes-Benz. It was based on the Studebaker convertible chassis and was to be Studebaker-powered. However, Studebaker's decision to halt all American production caused Stevens to use Chevrolet Corvette engines.

I.D. NUMBERS: Not available.

EXCALIBUR

Model Number	Body/Style Number	Body Type & Seating	Factory Price	Shipping Weight	Production Total
SSK	NA	2-dr Rds-2P	7250	2100	NA

ENGINE: Chevrolet Corvette. V-8. Overhead valve. Cast iron block. Displacement: 327 cid. Bore and stroke: 4.00 x 3.25 inches. Compression ratio: 10.5:1. Brake horsepower: 300 at 5000 rpm. Five main bearings. Hydraulic valve lifters. Carburetor: Carter model 3846247 four-barrel.

POWERTRAIN: Four-speed manual transmission.

CHASSIS FEATURES: Wheelbase: 109 inches. (Studebaker convertible chassis). Overall length: 167.52 inches. Front tread: 57.4 inches. Rear tread: 56.6 inches. Tire size: 7.00 x 15.

OPTIONS: Chevrolet Powerglide torque converter. Four wheel disc brakes.

1965-1969 Excalibur, two-door roadster, Brooks Stevens aboard

1966 EXCALIBUR

EXCALIBUR — The 1966 Excalibur had very little change from the previous model. However, a Deluxe roadster was added. It had long sloping front fenders, running boards and larger rear fenders.

I.D. NUMBERS: Not available.

EXCALIBUR

Model Number	Body/Style Number	Body Type & Seating	Factory Price	Shipping Weight	Production Total
SSK	NA	2-dr Rds-2P	7250	2100	Note 1
SS	NA	2-dr Del Rds-2P	8000	2500	Note 1

NOTE 1: Production total for all models was 88 cars.

ENGINE: Chevrolet Corvette. V-8. Overhead valve. Cast iron block. Displacement: 327 cid. Bore and stroke: 4.00 x 3.25 inches. Compression ratio: 10.5:1. Brake horsepower: 300 at 5000 rpm. Five main bearings. Hydraulic valve lifters. Carburetor: Holley model 3884505 four-barrel.

POWERTRAIN: Four-speed manual transmission.

CHASSIS FEATURES: Wheelbase: 109 inches. (Studebaker convertible chassis). Overall length: 167.52 inches. Front tread: 57.4 inches. Rear tread: 56.6 inches. Tire size: 7.00 x 15.

OPTIONS: Chevrolet Powerglide torque converter. Four wheel disc brakes.

1967 EXCALIBUR

EXCALIBUR — Very little styling or mechanical change from the previous year. An optional supercharged engine was made available. Another model was offered. Called the Phaeton, it was a four-passenger version.

I.D. NUMBERS: Not available.

EXCALIBUR

Model Number	Body/Style Number	Body Type & Seating	Factory Price	Shipping Weight	Production Total
SSK	NA	2-dr Rds-2P	7750	2300	Note 1
SS	NA	2-dr Del Rds-2P	8250	2500	Note 1
SS	NA	2-dr Phae-4P	8950	2600	Note 1

NOTE 1: Production total for all models was 87 cars.

ENGINES

(BASE) Chevrolet Corvette. V-8. Overhead valve. Cast iron block. Displacement: 327 cid. Bore and stroke: 4.00 x 3.25 inches. Compression ratio: 10.0:1. Brake horsepower: 300 at 5000 rpm. Five main bearings. Hydraulic valve lifters. Carburetor: Holley Model 3906631 four-barrel.

(OPTIONAL) Chevrolet Corvette (modified). V-8. Overhead valves. Cast iron block. Displacement: 327 cid. Bore and stroke: 4.00 x 3.25 inches. Supercharged. Brake horsepower: 400. Five main bearings. Hydraulic valve lifters. Carburetor: (not available).

POWERTRAIN: Four-speed manual transmission.

CHASSIS FEATURES: Wheelbase: 109 inches. (Studebaker convertible chassis). Overall length: 167.52 inches. Front tread: 57.4 inches. Rear tread: 56.6 inches. Tire size: 7.00 x 15.

OPTIONS: Chevrolet Powerglide torque converter ($200). Luggage rack ($60). Tonneau cover, for roadster ($60); for phaeton ($100). Center driving light ($75). AM/FM radio ($200).

1968 EXCALIBUR

EXCALIBUR — Very little styling or mechanical change from the previous year.

I.D. NUMBERS: Not available.

EXCALIBUR

Model Number	Body/Style Number	Body Type & Seating	Factory Price	Shipping Weight	Production Total
SSK	NA	2-dr Rds-2P	9000	2300	Note 1
SS	NA	2-dr Rds-2P	9000	2500	Note 1
SS	NA	2-dr Phae-4P	10,000	2600	Note 1

NOTE 1: Total production for all models was 95 cars.

ENGINES

(BASE) Chevrolet Corvette. V-8. Overhead valve. Cast iron block. Displacement: 327 cid. Bore and stroke: 4.00 x 3.25 inches. Compression ratio: 10.0:1. Brake horsepower: 300 at 5000 rpm. Five main bearings. Hydraulic valve lifters. Carburetor: Rochester model 7828207 four-barrel.

(OPTIONAL) Chevrolet Corvette (modified). V-8. Overhead valve. Cast iron block. Displacement: 327 cid. Bore and stroke: 4.00 x 3.25 inches. Supercharged. Brake horsepower: 435. Five main bearings. Hydraulic valve lifters. Carburetor: NA.

1965-1969 Excalibur two-door roadster, V-8 (rear view)

POWERTRAIN: Four-speed manual transmission.

CHASSIS FEATURES: Wheelbase: 109 inches (Studebaker convertible chassis). Overall length: 167.52 inches. Front tread: 57.4 inches. Rear tread: 56.6 inches. Tire size: 7.00 x 15.

OPTIONS: Automatic transmission. Luggage rack. Tonneau cover. Center driving light. AM/FM radio.

1969 EXCALIBUR

EXCALIBUR — Very little styling or mechanical change from the previous year.

I.D. NUMBERS: Not available.

EXCALIBUR

Model Number	Body/Style Number	Body Type & Seating	Factory Price	Shipping Weight	Production Total
SSK	NA	2-dr Rds-2P	10,000	2400	NA
SS	NA	2-dr Rds-2P	10,000	2550	NA
SS	NA	2-dr Phae-4P	11,000	2650	NA

ENGINES

(BASE) Chevrolet Corvette. V-8. Overhead valves. Cast iron block. Displacement: 327 cid. Bore and stroke: 4.00 x 3.25 inches. Compression ratio: 10.0:1. Brake horsepower: 300 at 5000 rpm. Five main bearings. Hydraulic valve lifters. Carburetor: Rochester: four-barrel.

(OPTIONAL) Chevrolet Corvette (modified). V-8. Overhead valve. Cast iron block. Displacement: 327 cid. Bore and stroke: 4.00 x 3.25 inches. Compression ratio: 11.1:1. Supercharged. Brake horsepower: 435. Five main bearings. Hydraulic valve lifters. Carburetor: (not available).

POWERTRAIN: Four-speed manual transmission.

CHASSIS FEATURES: Wheelbase: 109 inches (Studebaker convertible chassis). Overall length: (phaeton) 175 inches; (other models) 166 inches. Front tread: 57.4 inches. Rear tread: 56.6 inches. Tire size: 8.25 x 15.

OPTIONS: Automatic transmission. Luggage rack. Tonneau cover. Center driving light. AM/FM radio.

1970 EXCALIBUR SERIES II

EXCALIBUR SERIES II — Very little styling change was evident from the previous year. However, there was a change in chassis, which made the wheelbase a couple of inches longer. The optional supercharged engine was not offered. The standard engine had a slightly longer stroke. Despite the greater displacement, there was no change in the brake horsepower rating. Starting with the 1970 models, Excaliburs were given a Series II designation.

I.D. NUMBERS: Not available.

EXCALIBUR SERIES II

Model Number	Body/Style Number	Body Type & Seating	Factory Price	Shipping Weight	Production Total
SS	NA	2-dr Rds-2P	11,500	2750	Note 1
SS	NA	2-dr Rds-2P	11,500	2900	Note 1
SS	NA	2-dr Phae-4P	12,500	3000	Note 1

NOTE 1: Production total for all models was 70 cars.

ENGINE: Chevrolet Corvette. V-8. Overhead valve. Cast iron block. Displacement: 350 cid. Bore and stroke: 4.00 x 3.48 inches. Compression ratio: 10.5:1. Brake horsepower: 300 at 5000 rpm. Five main bearings. Hydraulic valve lifters. Carburetor: Rochester model 7040203 four-barrel.

POWERTRAIN: Four-speed manual transmission.

1970-1975 Excalibur Series II, two-roadster, V-8

CHASSIS FEATURES: Wheelbase: 111 inches. Overall length: (phaeton) 174 inches; (other models) 170 inches. Front tread: 62.5 inches. Rear tread: 62.5 inches. Tire size: 8.15 x 15.

OPTIONS: Three-speed Turbo-Hydramatic transmission. Air conditioning. Hardtop.

1971 EXCALIBUR SERIES II

EXCALIBUR SERIES II — Very little styling change or mechanical change from the previous year.

I.D. NUMBERS: Not available.

EXCALIBUR SERIES II

Model Number	Body/Style Number	Body Type & Seating	Factory Price	Shipping Weight	Production Total
SSK	NA	2-dr Rds-2P	12,000	2750	Note 1
SS	NA	2-dr Rds-2P	12,000	2900	Note 1
SS	NA	2-dr Phae-4P	12,900	3000	Note 1

NOTE 1: Production total for all models was 75 cars.

ENGINE: Chevrolet Corvette. V-8. Overhead valve. Cast iron block. Displacement: 350 cid. Bore and stroke: 4.00 x 3.48 inches. Compression ratio: 10.5:1. Brake horsepower: 300 at 5000 rpm. Five main bearings. Hydraulic valve lifters. Carburetor: Rochester four-barrel.

POWERTRAIN: Four-speed manual transmission.

CHASSIS FEATURES: Wheelbase: 111 inches. Overall length: (phaeton) 174 inches; (other models) 170 inches. Front tread: 62.5 inches. Rear tread: 62.5 inches. Tire size: G70 x 15.

OPTIONS: Three-speed Turbo-Hydramatic transmission. Air conditioning. Hardtop.

1972 EXCALIBUR SERIES II

EXCALIBUR SERIES II — Very little styling change from the previous year. However, a change to the biggest, most powerful Corvette engine was made.

I.D. NUMBERS: Not available.

EXCALIBUR SERIES II

Model Number	Body/Style Number	Body Type & Seating	Factory Price	Shipping Weight	Production Total
SSK	NA	2-dr Rds-2P	12,000	2750	Note 1
SS	NA	2-dr Rds-2P	12,000	2900	Note 1
SS	NA	2-dr Phae-4P	12,900	3000	Note 1

NOTE 1: Production total for all models was 75 cars.

ENGINE: Chevrolet Corvette. V-8. Overhead valves. Cast iron block. Displacement: 454 cid. Bore and stroke: 4.25 x 4.00 inches. Compression ratio: 8.3:1. Brake horsepower: 365 at 4800 rpm. Five main bearings. Hydraulic valve lifters. Carburetor: Rochester model 7041205 four-barrel.

POWERTRAIN: Four-speed manual transmission.

CHASSIS FEATURES: Wheelbase: 111 inches. Overall length: (phaeton) 174 inches; (other models) 170 inches. Front tread: 62.5 inches. Rear tread: 62.5 inches. Tire size: G70 x 15.

OPTIONS: Three-speed Turbo-Hydramatic transmission. Air conditioning. Hardtop.

1973 EXCALIBUR SERIES II

1973 Excalibur Series II, two-door roadster, V-8 (CG)

EXCALIBUR SERIES II — Very little styling or mechanical change from the previous year.

I.D. NUMBERS: Not available.

EXCALIBUR SERIES II

Model Number	Body/Style Number	Body Type & Seating	Factory Price	Shipping Weight	Production Total
SSK	NA	2-dr Rds-2P	12,500	3750	Note 1
SS	NA	2-dr Rds-2P	12,500	3800	Note 1
SS	NA	2-dr Phae-4P	13,500	4000	Note 1

NOTE 1: Production total for all models was 125 cars.

ENGINE: Chevrolet Corvette. V-8. Overhead valves. Cast iron block. Displacement: 454 cid. Bore and stroke: 4.25 x 4.00 inches. Compression ratio: 8.5:1. Brake horsepower: 270 at 4000 rpm. Five main bearings. Hydraulic valve lifters. Carburetor: Rochester Model 7042205 four-barrel.

POWERTRAIN: Four-speed manual transmission.

CHASSIS FEATURES: Wheelbase: 112 inches. Overall length: (phaeton) 174 inches; (other models) 170 inches. Front tread: 62.5 inches. Rear tread: 62.5 inches. Tire size: G70 x 15.

OPTIONS: Turbo-Hydramatic 400 torque converter transmission (n/c). Limited-slip differential. Hardtop. Tonneau cover.

1974 EXCALIBUR SERIES II

EXCALIBUR SERIES II — Very little styling or mechanical change from the previous year. The SSK roadster was no longer available. The remaining roadster and the phaeton were offered at a common, but higher price.

I.D. NUMBERS: Not available.

EXCALIBUR SERIES II

Model Number	Body/Style Number	Body Type & Seating	Factory Price	Shipping Weight	Production Total
SS	NA	2-dr Rds-2P	16,000	3800	Note 1
SS	NA	2-dr Phae-4P	16,000	4000	Note 1

NOTE 1: Production total for all models was 144 cars.

ENGINE: Chevrolet Corvette. V-8. Overhead valve. Cast iron block. Displacement: 454 cid. Bore and stroke: 4.25 x 4.00 inches. Compression ratio: 8.0:1. Brake horsepower: 275 at 4400 rpm. Five main bearings. Hydraulic valve lifters. Carburetor: Rochester Model 7043201 four-barrel.

POWERTRAIN: Four-speed manual transmission.

CHASSIS FEATURES: Wheelbase: 112 inches. Overall length: (phaeton) 174 inches; (other models) 170 inches. Front tread: 62.5 inches. Rear tread: 62.5 inches. Tire size: G70 x 15.

OPTIONS: Turbo-Hydramatic 400 torque converter transmission (no charge). Limited-slip differential. Hardtop. Tonneau cover.

1975 EXCALIBUR SERIES II

EXCALIBUR SERIES II — Very little styling or mechanical change from the previous year.

I.D. NUMBERS: Not available.

EXCALIBUR SERIES II

Model Number	Body/Style Number	Body Type & Seating	Factory Price	Shipping Weight	Production Total
SS	NA	2-dr Rds-2P	18,900	3800	Note 1
SS	NA	2-dr Phae-4P	18,900	4000	Note 1

NOTE 1: Production total for all models was 150 cars.

ENGINE: Chevrolet Corvette. V-8. Overhead valve. Cast iron block. Displacement: 454 cid. Bore and stroke: 4.25 x 4.00 inches. Compression ratio: 7.9:1. Brake horsepower: 215 at 4000 rpm. Five main bearings. Hydraulic valve lifters. Carburetor: Rochester Model 7045200 four-barrel.

POWERTRAIN: Turbo-Hydramatic torque converter.

CHASSIS FEATURES: Wheelbase: 112 inches. Overall length: (phaeton) 174 inches; (other models) 170 inches. Front tread: 62.5 inches. Rear tread: 62.5 inches. Tire size: G70 x 15.

OPTIONS: Limited-slip differential. Hardtop. Tonneau cover.

MANUFACTURER: SS Automobiles Inc., Milwaukee, Wis.

1948 FAGEOL

FAGEOL — A big, powerful, sleek, luxurious car was built by the bus manufacturer Twin Coach. With a long hood, a long sloping back and enclosed wheels, the car's styling was rather reminiscent of the prewar Phantom Corsair. The large overhead cam engine could run on gasoline or liquid propane. Top speed of the Fageol was 135 mph. Called the Supersonic, this car was built for company president Louis Fageol.

I.D. NUMBERS: Not available.

SUPERSONIC

Model Number	Body/Style Number	Body Type & Seating	Factory Price	Shipping Weight	Production Total
NA	NA	4-dr Sed-6P	NA	3250	NA

ENGINE: Single overhead cam. Displacement: 404 cid. Compression ratio: 10.0:1. Brake horsepower: 180 (with gasoline) or 275 with liquid propane.

CHASSIS FEATURES: Wheelbase: 124 inches. Overall length: 210 inches.

MANUFACTURER: Twin Coach Company, Kent, Ohio.

1949 FERGUS

FERGUS — This company was an importer of British cars, although they had built the Fergus car in the 1915 to 1922 era. They intended to build another car after World War II. It was a sports car based on the British made Austin A40 Sports. The A40 engine was used. The Fergus styling was distinguishable at the front by protruding headlights and an open, oval grille, but no bumper.

1949 Fergus, two-door convertible, 4-cyl.

I.D. NUMBERS: Not available.

FERGUS

Model Number	Body/Style Number	Body Type & Seating	Factory Price	Shipping Weight	Production Total
NA	NA	2-dr Rds-2P	NA	NA	1

ENGINE: Austin A40. Four-cylinder. Overhead valve. Cast iron block. Displacement: 73.1 cid. Bore and stroke: 3.578 x 3.50 inches. Compression ratio: 7.2:1. Brake horsepower: 40 at 4300 rpm. Solid valve lifters. Carburetor: Zenith Model 30VM5 one-barrel.

CHASSIS FEATURES: Not available.

MANUFACTURER: Fergus Motors Inc., New York, N.Y.

1966 FERRER

FERRER — This manufacturer produced a sensational-looking fiberglass body for the Volkswagen chassis, either as a kit or completely assembled. The GT type body had a very low front with clear aerodynamic covers for the headlights. There was a built-in spoiler on the tail, much like the spoiler used on the yet-to-be-introduced Chevrolet Carmaro or Pontiac Firebird Trans Am. The body's highest point was only three-and-a-half-feet above the ground. Top speed was 90 mph. The Ferrer was called GT.

1966 Ferrer GT, two-door sport coupe, 4-cyl (PZ)

I.D. NUMBERS: Not available.

GT

Model Number	Body/Style Number	Body Type & Seating	Factory Price	Shipping Weight	Production Total
NA	NA	2-dr Cpe-2P	3400	1400	NA

NOTE 1: Also sold as a basic kit for $990, or Deluxe kit for $1800.

ENGINE: Volkswagen. Four-cylinder. Horizontally opposed. Overhead valves. Rear mounted. Cast iron block. Displacement: 78.4 cid. Bore and stroke: 3.03 x 2.72 inches. Compression ratio: 7.3:1. Brake horsepower: 50 at 4600 rpm. Solid valve lifters. Three main bearings. Carburetor: Solex Model 28 PICT two-barrel.

CHASSIS FEATURES: Wheelbase: 94.5 inches (Volkswagen chassis). Overall length: 158 inches. Front tread: 51.4 inches. Rear tread: 51.2 inches.

MANUFACTURER: Ferrer Motors Corp., Miami, Fla.

1953-1954 FIBERSPORT

FIBERSPORT — This fiberglass sports car was made for the Crosley Hot Shot chassis, even though Crosley had stopped production. The Fibersport was available as a fully-assembled car or a do-it-yourself kit. Headlights were mounted inside the rather open grillework. A highly modified Crosley engine was capable of giving this car a top speed in excess of 100 mph. Towards the end of the Fibersport's short life, an original tubular frame was offered as an option.

I.D. NUMBERS: Not available.

FIBERSPORT

Model Number	Body/Style Number	Body Type & Seating	Factory Price	Shipping Weight	Production Total
NA	NA	2-dr Rds-2P	2850	1100	NA

NOTE 1: Also sold as a kit: $650 (4-ply fiberglass); $750 (5-ply fiberglass).

ENGINE: Crosley (modified). Four-cylinder. Overhead cam.

POWERTRAIN: Morris Minor. Four-speed manual transmission.

CHASSIS FEATURES: Wheelbase: 85 inches (Crosley chassis, though some were tubular frames originated by the manufacturer). Front tread: 40 inches. Rear tread: 40 inches.

MANUFACTURER: Fibersport Inc., Bloomington, Ill.

1953 Fibersport, two-door roadster, 4-cyl.

1954 Fibersport, two-door roadster, 4-cyl.

1953-1955 FINA SPORT

FINA-SPORT — Perry Fina, a New York importer of European automobiles, attempted to produce a car of his own car. It was a blend of American and European parts. A modified Ford chassis with Cadillac engine was the basis for an aluminum body fashioned by Vignale, of Italy. The most impressive styling feature of the front was the chrome-plated, floating, U-shaped bar in the grille opening. The car's high price was quite impressive too.

I.D. NUMBERS: Not available.

FINA-SPORT

Model Number	Body/Style Number	Body Type & Seating	Factory Price	Shipping Weight	Production Total
NA	NA	2-dr HT-5P	9800	NA	NA

ENGINES

(STANDARD) Cadillac. V-8. Overhead valve. Cast iron block. Displacement: 331.1 cid. Bore and stroke: 3-13/16 x 3-5/8 inches. Compression ratio: 8.25:1. Brake horsepower: 210 at 4150 rpm. Five main bearings. Hydraulic valve lifters. Carburetor: Carter Model WCFB-2605S.

(OPTIONAL) Cadillac (modified). V-8. Overhead valve. Cast iron block. Brake horsepower: 300. (Other American V-8 engines available if requested by the buyer).

POWERTRAIN: Dual-Range Hydra-Matic transmission.

1954 Fina-Sport, two-door coupe, V-8

CHASSIS FEATURES: Wheelbase: 115 inches (modified Ford chassis). Overall length: 188 inches.

MANUFACTURER: Fina Imported Motor Car Co., New York, N.Y.

1961 FISHER

FISHER — (ELECTRIC) — Try to imagine a plastic turtle crossing the road and you have a good idea of how Allen Fisher's electric-powered prototype car looked. Basically a fiberglass shell mounted on a Crosley frame, this miniature roadster had a wide-skirted, scoop-nosed frontal appearance and "bug-eyed" headlight design. It sat quite high off the ground and had very small front and rear wheel cutouts. On the other hand, the steering wheel was quite large for the size of the machine. Under a hatch in the center of the rear deck lid 36 two-volt batteries were stored. They were arranged to provide 36-volt, 260-amp.-hr. capacity and powered a four-horsepower electric motor. To accomplish speed control and shifting the operator varied voltage through a foot pedal that controlled the resistance in series with the motor. The car was very small, but quite fully-equipped. It had doors with handles; a two-piece windscreen; windshield wipers; bumpers; gauges; headlights; taillamps; two homemade bucket seats; a dashboard mounted rearview mirror; bumpers and bumper guards; and hubcaps. It was likely a one-off effort, as no indication of volume production was given. Inventor Fisher, of West Covina, Calif., claimed a top speed of 30 mph could be achieved, but his travel range, on a single battery charge, was limited to just 30 miles.

I.D. NUMBERS: Not available or not used.

FISHER ELECTRIC

Model Number	Body/Style Number	Body Type & Seating	Factory Price	Shipping Weight	Production Total
NA	NA	2-dr Rds-2P	NA	NA	1

ENGINE: Four-horsepower electric motor with voltage-regulated speed control. Batteries: 36 two-volt. Voltage: 36 volts. Battery capacity: 260 ampere-hours.

1961 Fisher, two-door roadster, electric engine (CG)

CHASSIS FEATURES: Crosley chassis. Wheelbase: 80 inches. Overall length: approximately 150 inches. Tires: 4.50 x 12 inch black sidewall. Transverse leaf springs front and rear.

POWERTRAIN OPTIONS: None.

CONVENIENCE OPTIONS: Bumpers and guards. Hubcaps. Windshield and wipers.

HISTORICAL FOOTNOTES: Built by Allen Fisher, West Covina, Calif. A top speed or 30 mph with a 30 mile driving range was claimed. The Crosley, upon which Fisher's car was based, became a popular source of chassis, drivetrain and body components for many sports customs, homebuilt vehicles and small maker prototypes over the years.

1949-1951 FITCH

1950 Fitch, two-door roadster, V-8

FITCH — Race driver John Fitch designed and built a car for sport driving or out-and-out racing. It had a hopped-up Ford-60 V-8 engine mounted in a Fiat 1000 chassis. It was covered by a much modified Crosley Hot Shot body. With 0-to-60 mph acceleration of just 6.3 seconds and a top speed of 120 mph, Fitch himself drove one of these Type B cars to a second place class finish at the 1950 Watkins Glen Grand Prix. During the 1960s, John Fitch made some interesting "Sprint" conversions of the Chevrolet Corvair. His inexpensive, but effective modifications altered performance, handling and appearance. In addition, kits were offered for dealer or owner installation. Fitch made modifications to Pontiac Firebirds (for $1,000 plus the car), too. His Toronado Phantom was based on the Oldsmobile Toronado. Fitch's most spectacular offering, which never got beyond the prototype stage, was called the Phoenix.

I.D. NUMBERS: Not available.

FITCH TYPE B

Model Number	Body/Style Number	Body Type & Seating	Factory Price	Shipping Weight	Production Total
B	NA	2-dr Rds-2P	2850	1520	NA

ENGINE: Ford (modified '60'). V-8. L-head. Cast iron block. Aluminum heads. Displacement: 136 cid. Bore and stroke: 2.6 x 3.2 inches. Compression ratio: 6.6:1. Brake horsepower: 105 at 5300 rpm. Three main bearings. Solid valve lifters. Carburetor: NA.

POWERTRAIN: Four-speed manual transmission.

CHASSIS FEATURES: Wheelbase: 95 inches (Fiat 1000 chassis). Overall length: 140 inches. Front tread: 49.3 inches. Rear tread: 48 inches. Tire size: 5.25 x 16 (5.50 x 16 optional).

MANUFACTURER: Sports & Utility Motors Inc., White Plains, N.Y.

FITCH-PHOENIX — Ever involved with exciting automobiles in some way, John Fitch planned to build cars once again. He had built the Fitch around 1950. His second car was called the Fitch-Phoenix. It was based on the Chevrolet Corvair. It had a sensationally beautiful body built in Italy by Intermeccanica. A roll bar was built into the top. The rear window would open and close electrically. The roof panel was removable and stowable in the trunk. With the roof open, the car had a landau look. Bulges in the front fenders hid the two spare tires. (Front and rear tires were different sizes). The rear-mounted Corvair engine was modified to produce more power than normal. A top speed in excess of 130 mph was claimed. Only one prototype was built. When it was learned what government regulations had to be met for safety and emission standards, Fitch, unfortunately, decided against going any further. The prototype

was actually the Fitch-Phoenix II. A standard Fitch-Phoenix had been planned, which would have had a stock Corvair motor. It would not have had front disc brakes and a few other features found on the Fitch-Phoenix II.

I.D. NUMBERS: Not available.

FITCH-PHOENIX II

Model Number	Body/Style Number	Body Type & Seating	Factory Price	Shipping Weight	Production Total
II	NA	2-dr Conv-2P	8700	2150*	1

* Dry weight.

ENGINE: Chevrolet Corvair. Six-cylinder. Horizontally opposed. Air-cooled. Overhead valve. Aluminum block. Displacement: 164 cid. Bore and stroke: 3.44 x 2.94 inches. Compression ratio: 9.25:1. Brake horsepower: 170 at 5200 rpm. Four main bearings. Solid valve lifters. Carburetor: Weber Model 36 DCLD two-barrel.

POWERTRAIN: Four-speed manual transmission.

CHASSIS FEATURES: Wheelbase: 95 inches. Overall length: 174 inches. Front tread: 55 inches. Rear tread: 57.2 inches. Tire size: 175 x 14 (front), 185 x 14 (rear).

OPTIONS: AM/FM radio ($110). Automatic transmission.

MANUFACTURER: John Fitch & Co., Falls Village, Ct.

1955 FLAJOLE FORERUNNER

FLAJOLE FORERUNNER — William Flajole built an unusual car. The marque name was his own. The model name was Forerunner. His car was not intended for production, but rather to demonstrate that some new design concepts could be practical in a full-scale car. Contemporary magazines outlined the cars construction on a modified Jaguar XK-120 chassis. They do not mention that a plexiglass roof panel filtered out ultra-violet and infra-red rays. The panel could be slid into the car's sloping back to let in all the sunlight. Mr. Flajole was an industrial designer who did some work for Nash and American Motors. He designed the experimental NXI, which became the Nash Metropolitan. MOTOR LIFE magazine noted that Flajole spent $8,000 of his own money and 7,000 hours of staff time producing the car. The Flajole Forerunner still exists and was sold, not long ago, by Ed Fallon, of Minneapolis, Minn.

I.D. NUMBERS: Not available.

1955 Flajole, Forerunner two-door sports coupe, V-8 (Ed Fallon)

FORERUNNER

Model Number	Body/Style Number	Body Type & Seating	Factory Price	Shipping Weight	Production Total
NA	NA	2-dr Conv-2P	NA	2100	1

ENGINE: Jaguar. Six-cylinder. Double overhead cam. Cast iron block. Displacement: 210 cid. Bore and stroke: 3.27 x 4.17 inches. Compression ratio: 8.0:1. Brake horsepower: 190 at 5500 rpm. Seven main bearings. Carburetor: (2) S.U.

POWERTRAIN: Four-speed manual transmission.

CHASSIS FEATURES: Wheelbase: 100 inches (modified Jaguar XK-140 chassis).

MANUFACTURER: William Flajole, Detroit, Mich.

1957 FLINTRIDGE-DARRIN

FLINTRIDGE-DARRIN — Another car that Howard A. ("Dutch") Darrin was much involved with was the Flintridge-Darrin, sometimes known as the Flintridge Darrin-DWK or just the Flintridge. It used the German made DKW sedan as its base. A Darrin designed fiberglass two-door body replaced the original steel DKW body. The car was a hardtop and the Deluxe model had a detachable roof. The DKW interior was reupholstered. The novel three-cylinder, two-stroke, seven-moving-parts, DKW engine with its front wheel drive was retained. Darrin assembled the cars for the manufacturer. Problems in getting sufficient fiberglass bodies brought about the car's early demise.

I.D. NUMBERS: Not available.

STANDARD

Model Number	Body/Style Number	Body Type & Seating	Factory Price	Shipping Weight	Production Total
NA	NA	2-dr HT-2P	2995	1870	Note

NOTE 1: A total of about 25 cars were built.

DELUXE

Model Number	Body/Style Number	Body Type & Seating	Factory Price	Shipping Weight	Production Total
NA	NA	2-dr Conv-2P	3295	1870	Note

NOTE 1: A total of about 25 cars were built.

ENGINE: DKW. Three-cylinder. Cast iron block. Displacement: 54.8 cid. Bore and stroke: 2.8 x 2.99 inches. Compression ratio: 7.1:1. Brake horsepower: 45 at 4250 rpm. Four main bearings. Carburetor: Solex one-barrel.

1957 Flintridge, Deluxe two-door sports roadster, 3-cyl.

1958 Flintridge, Deluxe two-door sports roadster, 3-cyl.

POWERTRAIN: Four-speed manual transmission.

CHASSIS FEATURES: Wheelbase: 92 inches (DKW chassis). Overall length: 180 inches. Front tread: 49 inches. Rear tread: 49 inches.

MANUFACTURER: Flintridge Motor Mfg. Corp., Los Angeles, Calif.

1961 FRANCE JET

FRANCE JET — This small roadster was very miserly with gas. It got up to 65 mpg with the standard one-cylinder engine. An optional two-cylinder engine was capable of an excellent 55 mpg. This fiberglass-bodied car had a turning radius of just 18 feet. It had two horns — one for city and one for highway use.

I.D. NUMBERS: Not available.

FRANCE JET

Model Number	Body/Style Number	Body Type & Seating	Factory Price	Shipping Weight	Production Total
NA	NA	2-dr Rds-2P	1595	780	NA

NOTE 1: With optional engine, weight was 780 pounds.

ENGINE:

(STANDARD) AMC. One-cylinder. Four cycle. Air-cooled. Displacement: 17 cid.

(OPTIONAL) Two-cylinder. Four-cycle. Air-cooled. Displacement: 66 cid. Brake horsepower: 40. ($250).

CHASSIS FEATURES: Wheelbase: 74 inches; (optional engine) 82 inches. Overall length: 130 inches; (optional engine) 130 inches.

MANUFACTURER: France Jet Motors Ltd., New York, N.Y.

1951-1962 FRAZEN

FRAZEN — This fiberglass-bodied sports roadster used the Henry J chassis and engine. The body styling was rather attractive with rounded, flowing fenders. But the grille, looked like an upside down bird cage. It spoiled the frontal appearance. Cloth or fiberglass tops were a buyer's choice. The Frazen was offered either as a fully assembled car or as a body kit.

1951 Frazen, two-door sports roadster, 6-cyl. (front)

1951 Frazen, two-door sports roadster, 6-cyl. (rear)

I.D. NUMBERS: Not available.

FRAZEN

Model Number	Body/Style Number	Body Type & Seating	Factory Price	Shipping Weight	Production Total
NA	NA	2-dr Rds-2P	2795	NA	NA

NOTE 1: Body kit available at $650.

FRAZEN ENGINE: Henry J. Six-cylinder. L-head. Cast iron block. Displacement: 161 cid. Bore and stroke: 3-1/8 x 3-1/2 inches. Compression ratio: 7.0:1. Brake horsepower: 80 at 3300 rpm. Four main bearings. Solid valve lifters. Carburetor: Carter model 833-S one-barrel.

CHASSIS FEATURES: Wheelbase: 100 inches (Henry J chassis). Front tread: 54 inches. Rear tread: 54 inches.

MANUFACTURER: Ray Greene Co., Toledo, Ohio.

1955 FRICK

FRICK — After Bill Frick had shoe-horned quite a few Cadillac engines into Fords, Allards and Studebakers, he decided to go a little more original and produce his own car. His Ferrari-like coupe was made in Italy by Vignale. As almost anyone would guess, a contemporary Cadillac motor was used.

I.D. NUMBERS: Not available.

FRICK

Model Number	Body/Style Number	Body Type & Seating	Factory Price	Shipping Weight	Production Total
NA	NA	2-dr Cpe	NA	3000	NA

ENGINE: Cadillac. V-8. Overhead valve. Cast iron block. Displacement: 331.1 cid. Bore and stroke: 3-13/16 x 3-5/8 inches. Compression ratio: 9.0:1. Brake horsepower: 250 at 4600 rpm. Five main bearings. Hydraulic valve lifters. Carburetor: Carter Model WCFB-2901S four-barrel.

OPTIONAL ENGINE: Supercharged version of the standard engine.

POWERTRAIN: Dual-Range Hydra-Matic transmission.

CHASSIS FEATURES: Wheelbase: 110 inches.

MANUFACTURER: Bill Frick Motors, Rockville Centre, L.I., N.Y.

1946 GADABOUT

1946 Gadabout, two-door roadster, 4-cyl. (PZ)

GADABOUT — Detroit industrial designer Ray Russel fielded two cars about the same time. The Gadabout was quite different from the other car, called the Russel. This one was a small, sleekly-styled three-passenger roadster, with a duraluminum body. It was mounted on a modified MG chassis, which probably accounts for the car's right-hand drive. An economy vehicle, it got up to 40 mpg.

I.D. NUMBERS: Not available.

GADABOUT

Model Number	Body/Style Number	Body Type & Seating	Factory Price	Shipping Weight	Production Total
NA	NA	2-dr Rds-3P	NA	1100	NA

ENGINE: MG. Four-cylinder. Overhead valve. Cast Iron block. Displacement: 76.3 cid. Bore and stroke: 2.62 x 3.44 Inches. Compression ratio: 7.25:1. Brake horsepower: 54.5 at 5200 rpm. Three main bearings. Solid valve lifters. Carburetor: two (2) Solex.

CHASSIS FEATURES: Wheelbase: 80 inches (modified MG chassis).

MANUFACTURER: Ray Russel, Grosse Pointe Park, Mich.

1960-1961 GASLIGHT

GASLIGHT — The 1902 Rambler provided the pattern for this replicar, which was actually the continuation of another replicar called the Rambler 1902. Styling was patterned after the original antique model, which was a most popular collector car at this time.

I.D. DATA: Not available.

GASLIGHT

Model Number	Body/Style Number	Body Type & Seating	Factory Price	Shipping Weight	Production Total
NA	NA	Rbt-2P	1495	640	NA

ENGINE One-cylinder. Four cycle. Air-cooled. Brake horsepower: 4.

CHASSIS FEATURES: Wheelbase: 77 inches.

MANUFACTURER: Gaslight Motors Corp., Detroit, Mich.

1955 GAYLORD

GAYLORD — The Gaylord was a spectacularly distinctive car conceived by James and Edward Gaylord, sons of the bobby-pin inventor. Brooks Stevens was commissioned to style the car, which he did with great flair. Jim Gaylord designed the hefty chromemolybdenum tubular chassis. The body, with a strong chassis influence, was built in West Germany by Spohn. Some advanced ideas were featured on the Gaylord. Its hide-away steel roof predated the Ford retractable by two years. Power was originally a Chrysler 300 engine.

1955 Gaylord, two-door Sport Coupe, V-8 (front)

1955 Gaylord, two-door Sport Coupe, V-8 (rear)

I.D. NUMBERS: Not available.

GAYLORD

Model Number	Body/Style Number	Body Type & Seating	Factory Price	Shipping Weight	Production Total
NA	NA	2-dr Cpe-4P	10,000	3985	1

ENGINE: Chrysler 300. V-8. Overhead valve. Cast iron block. Displacement: 331.1 cid. Bore and stroke: 3-13/16 x 3-5/8 inches. Compression ratio: 8.5:1. Brake horsepower: 300 at 5200 rpm. Five main bearings. Solid valve lifters. Carburetor: two (2) Carter four-barrel.

POWERTRAIN: Four-speed automatic transmission with optional manual control.

CHASSIS FEATURES: Wheelbase: 100 inches. Overall length: 180 inches. Front tread: 53.7 inches. Rear tread: 55.5 inches. Tire size: 7.10 x 15.

1956 GAYLORD

1956 Gaylord, two-door Sport Coupe, V-8 (OC)

GAYLORD — Little change was seen, stylewise, after the first Gaylord was made. However, the changes that were made seemed a great improvement. The huge hideous Lucas headlights were replaced by quadrabeams. Gaylord was a year ahead of Detroit's first introduction of four headlights. Gaylord's price rose to dizzying heights.

I.D. NUMBERS: Not available.

GAYLORD

Model Number	Body/Style Number	Body Type & Seating	Factory Price	Shipping Weight	Production Total
NA	NA	2-dr Cpe-4P	17,500	3985	2

ENGINE: Cadillac Eldorado. V-8. Overhead valve. Cast iron block. Displacement: 365 cid. Bore and stroke: 4.00 x 3.63 inches. Brake horsepower: 305 at 4700 rpm. Five main bearings. Hydraulic valve lifters. Carburetor: Carter models 2317S and 2372S four-barrel.

POWERTRAIN: Four-speed automatic transmission with optional manual control.

CHASSIS FEATURES: Wheelbase: 100 inches. Overall length: 180 inches. Front tread: 53.7 inches. Rear tread: 55.5 inches. Tire size: 7.10 x 15.

OPTIONS: Air conditioning. Highway passing horn. Emergency lamp over each wheel for night tire changes. Tinted glass. Tonneau cover.

MANUFACTURER: Gaylord Cars Ltd., Chicago, Ill.

1956 GLASCAR

1956 Glascar, two-door roadster, V-8

GLASCAR — This sports car had a body made of only five fiberglass panels. They were adapted from the Chevrolet Corvette. The grille was a 1956 Corvette grille, modified to incorporate the Glascar headlights. Instead of the wraparound Corvette windshield, a regular V-type windshield was used. At the rear, the taillights and dual exhausts were switched from their usual locations. The exhausts came out through the modest fins.

I.D. NUMBERS: Not available.

GLASCAR

Model Number	Body/Style Number	Body Type & Seating	Factory Price	Shipping Weight	Production Total
NA	NA	2-dr Rds-2P	2500	NA	1

ENGINE: The prototype used an Oldsmobile V-8 engine, but plans for production models were to use Ford V-8 flathead engines modified to develop up to 200 brake horsepower.

CHASSIS FEATURES: Wheelbase: 100 inches.

MANUFACTURER: Bob Tucker, Richmond, Ind.

1966-1967 GLASSIC

1966 Glassic, two-door phaeton, 4-cyl (PZ)

GLASSIC — With the replicar craze well established, it was no surprise to see the Ford Model A reincarnated. Jack Faircloth and his son Joel did it in the modern idiom. They put a fiberglass body on an existing chassis. They chose the International Harvester Scout as the base. Its wheelbase and four-cylinder power provided the easiest way to approximate the Model A from contemporary production components. Initially only a roadster was available.

I.D. NUMBERS: Not available.

GLASSIC

Model Number	Body/Style Number	Body Type & Seating	Factory Price	Shipping Weight	Production Total
NA	NA	2-dr Rds-2P	3800	2350	Note 1

NOTE 1: Total production from 1966-1971 was about 300 units.

ENGINE: International Harvester Scout. Four-cylinder (one-half V-8). Overhead valve. Cast iron block. Displacement: 151.8 cid. Bore and stroke: 3-7/8 x 3-7/32. Brake horsepower: 93.4 at 4400 rpm. Five main bearings. Carburetor: Holley one-barrel.

POWERTRAIN: Three-speed manual transmission. Four-speed manual transmission, (optional).

CHASSIS FEATURES: Wheelbase: 100 inches (international Scout chassis). Front tread: 55.17 inches. Rear tread: 55.17 inches. Tire size: 7.35 x 15.

1968 GLASSIC

GLASSIC — Very little styling or mechanical change from the previous year. However, a second model was offered. The new phaeton provided four-passenger accommodation, making it roomier than the roadster, which was also continued.

I.D. NUMBERS: Not available.

GLASSIC

Model Number	Body/Style Number	Body Type & Seating	Factory Price	Shipping Weight	Production Total
NA	NA	2-dr Rds-2P	NA	2350	Note 1
NA	NA	2-dr Phae-2P	NA	NA	Note 1

NOTE 1: Total production from 1966-1971 was about 300 units.

ENGINE: International Harvester Scout. Four-cylinder (one-half V-8). Overhead valves. Cast iron block. Displacement: 151.8 cid. Bore and stroke: 3-7/8 x 3-7/32. Brake horsepower: 93.5 at 4400 rpm. Five main bearings. Carburetor: Holley one-barrel.

1968 Glassic, two-door Phaeton, 4-cyl.

POWERTRAIN: Three-speed manual transmission. Four-speed manual transmission, (optional).

CHASSIS FEATURES: Wheelbase: 100 inches (international Scout chassis). Front tread: 55.17 inches. Rear tread: 55.17 inches. Tire size: 7.35 x 15.

1969 GLASSIC

GLASSIC — Very little styling change from the previous year. The Scout engine, however, was enlarged slightly to give it a bit more power.

I.D. NUMBERS: Not available.

GLASSIC

Model Number	Body/Style Number	Body Type & Seating	Factory Price	Shipping Weight	Production Total
NA	NA	2-dr-Rds-2P	NA	NA	Note 1
NA	NA	2-dr Phae-4P	NA	NA	Note 1

NOTE 1: Total production from 1966 to 1971 was approximately 300 units.
NOTE 2: About 50 cars were built in 1969.

ENGINE: International Harvester Scout. Four-cylinder (one-half V-8). Overhead valves. Cast iron block. Displacement: 195.4 cid. Bore and stroke: 4.13 x 3.56 inches. Brake horsepower: 111 at 4000 rpm. Five main bearings. Carburetor: Holley one-barrel.

POWERTRAIN: Three-speed manual transmission. Four-speed manual transmission, (optional).

CHASSIS FEATURES: Wheelbase: 100 inches (international Harvester Scout chassis). Front tread: 55.17 inches. Rear tread: 55.17 inches. Tire size: 7.35 x 15.

1970 GLASSIC

GLASSIC — Very little styling or mechanical change from the previous year.

I.D. NUMBER: Not available.

GLASSIC

Model Number	Body/Style Number	Body Type & Seating	Factory Price	Shipping Weight	Production Total
NA	NA	2-dr Rds-2P	4150	NA	Note 1
NA	NA	2-dr Phae-4P	NA	NA	Note 1

NOTE 1: Total production from 1966 to 1971 was approximately 300 units.

ENGINE: International Harvester Scout. Four-cylinder (one-half V-8). Overhead valves. Cast iron block. Displacement: 195.4 cid. Bore and stroke: 4.13 x 3.66. Brake horsepower: 111 at 4000 rpm. Five main bearings. Carburetor: Holley one-barrel.

POWERTRAIN: Three-speed manual transmission.

CHASSIS FEATURES: Wheelbase: 100 inches (International Harvester Scout chassis). Front tread: 55.17 inches. Rear tread: 55.17 inches. Tire size: 7.35 x 15.

1971 GLASSIC

GLASSIC — Very little styling or mechanical change from the previous year.

I.D. NUMBERS: Not available.

GLASSIC

Model Number	Body/Style Number	Body Type & Seating	Factory Price	Shipping Weight	Production Total
NA	NA	2-dr Rds-2P	5995	NA	Note
NA	NA	2-dr Phae-4P	5995	NA	Note

ENGINE: International Harvester Scout. Four-cylinder (one-half V-8). Overhead valves. Cast iron block. Displacement: 195.4 cid. Bore and stroke: 4.13 x 3.66 inches. Brake horsepower: 111 at 4000 rpm. Five main bearings. Carburetor: Holley one-barrel.

POWERTRAIN: Three-speed manual transmission.

CHASSIS FEATURES: Wheelbase: 100 inches (international Harvester Scout chassis). Front tread: 55.17 inches. Rear tread: 55.17 inches. Tire size: 7.35 x 15.

MANUFACTURER (1966-1971): Glassic Industries Inc., West Palm Beach, Fla.

1972 GLASSIC

GLASSIC — In 1972, Glassic Industries was sold to Fred Pro. He made some fundamental changes to the car, not all of which were in keeping with the spirit of the original Model A. An engine switch was made to a Ford 302 cid V-8. The big engine, like some of the options now offered, were quite out of character for a Model A pretender.

I.D. NUMBERS: Not available.

GLASSIC

Model Number	Body/Style Number	Body Type & Seating	Factory Price	Shipping Weight	Production Total
NA	NA	2-dr Rds-2P	6595	2485	NA
NA	NA	2-dr Phae-4P	6595	NA	NA

ENGINE: Ford (1971). V-8. Overhead valve. Cast iron block. Displacement: 302 cid. Bore and stroke: 4.00 x 3.00. Compression ratio: 9.0:1. Brake horsepower: 210 at 4600 rpm. Five main bearings. Hydraulic valve lifters. Carburetor: Autolite model D10F-ABA two-barrel.

POWERTRAIN: Three-speed manual transmission.

CHASSIS FEATURES: Wheelbase: 102 inches. Overall length: 156 inches. Front tread: 54 inches. Rear tread: 56-1/2 inches. Tire size: 7.35 x 15.

OPTIONS: SelectShift automatic transmission.

1973 GLASSIC

GLASSIC — Very little styling or mechanical change from the previous year.

I.D. NUMBERS: Not available.

GLASSIC

Model Number	Body/Style Number	Body Type & Seating	Factory Price	Shipping Weight	Production Total
NA	NA	2-dr Rds-2P	6995	2485	NA
NA	NA	2-dr Phae-4P	6995	NA	NA

ENGINE: Ford (1971). V-8. Overhead valve. Cast iron block. Displacement: 302 cid. Bore and stroke: 4.00 x 3.00 inches. Compression ratio: 9.1:1. Brake horsepower: 210 at 4600 rpm. Five main bearings. Hydraulic valve lifters. Carburetor: Autolite Model D1OF-ABA two-barrel.

POWERTRAIN: Three-speed manual transmission.

CHASSIS FEATURES: Wheelbase: 102 inches. Overall length: 156 inches. Front tread: 54 inches. Rear tread: 56-1/2 inches. Tire size: E75 x 15.

OPTIONS: SelectShift automatic transmission.

1974 GLASSIC

GLASSIC — Very little styling or mechanical change from the previous year.

I.D. NUMBERS: Not available.

GLASSIC

Model Number	Body/Style Number	Body Type & Seating	Factory Price	Shipping Weight	Production Total
NA	NA	2-dr Rds-2P	7595	2485	NA
NA	NA	2-dr Phae-6P	7595	NA	NA

GLASSIC ENGINE: Ford (1971). V-8. Overhead valve. Cast iron block. Displacement: 302 cid. Bore and stroke: 4.00 x 3.00. Compression ratio: 9.1:1. Brake horsepower: 210 at 4600 rpm. Five main bearings. Hydraulic valve lifters. Carburetor: Autolite model D10F-ABA two-barrel.

POWER TRAIN: Three-speed Select-Shift automatic transmission.

CHASSIS FEATURES: Wheelbase: 102 inches. Overall length: 156 inches. Front tread: 54 inches. Rear tread: 56-1/2 inches. Tire size: E78 x 14.

OPTIONS: Air conditioning ($450). AM /FM stereo radio and tape player ($350).

1975 GLASSIC

GLASSIC — Very little styling change from previous year. The engine was an updated version of the Ford 302 V-8, with its accompanying air pollution control accounterments and lower net horsepower ratings.

I.D. NUMBERS: Not available.

GLASSIC

Model Number	Body/Style Number	Body Type & Seating	Factory Price	Shipping Weight	Production Total
NA	NA	2-dr Rds-2P	8900	2485	NA
NA	NA	2-dr Phae-4P	8900	NA	NA

ENGINE: Ford (1973). V-8. Overhead valve. Cast iron block. Displacement: 302 cid. Bore and stroke: 4.00 x 3.00. Compression ratio: 8.0:1. Brake horsepower: 138 at 4,000 rpm. Five main bearings. Hydraulic valve lifters. Carburetor: Rawsonville Model 9510 D3GF-BB (9510 DEGF-AF for California) two-barrel.

POWERTRAIN: Three-speed SelectShift automatic transmission.

CHASSIS FEATURES: Wheelbase: 102 inches. Overall length: 153 inches. Front tread: 54 inches. Rear tread: 56-1/2 inches. Tire size: E78 x 14.

OPTIONS: Air conditioning.

MANUFACTURER (1972-1975): Glassic Motor Car Co., Palm Beach, Fla.

1975 GLASSIC/ROMULUS

GLASSIC — Glassic added a totally different replicar to their line for 1975. It was a reproduction of the 1935 Auburn Speedster, even though there were other Auburn Speedster replicas on the market. This was probably a continuation of the third Auburn replicar listed earlier in this section. It used the same Ford engine as the Model A type Glassics.

I.D. NUMBERS: Not available.

ROMULUS

Model Number	Body/Style Number	Body Type & Seating	Factory Price	Shipping Weight	Production Total
NA	NA	2-dr Rds-2P	19,000	3200	NA

ENGINE: Ford. V-8. Overhead valve. Cast iron block. Displacement: 302 cid. Bore and stroke: 4.00 x 3.00 Compression ratio: 8.5:1. Brake horsepower: 138 at 4000 rpm. Five main bearings. Hydraulic valve lifters. Carburetor: Rawsonville Model 9510 D3GFBB (9510 D3GF-AF in California) two-barrel.

POWERTRAIN: Three-speed Cruise-O-Matic automatic transmission.

CHASSIS FEATURES: Wheelbase: 127 inches. Overall length: 205 inches. Front tread: 64 inches. Rear tread: 64 inches. Tire size: H78 x 15.

MANUFACTURER: Glassic Motor Car Co., Palm Beach, Fla.

1950-1954 GLASSPAR

1954 Glasspar, two-door roadster, V-8 (CG)

GLASSPAR — (V-8) — SERIES G-2 — Along with three partners, Bill Tritt formed Glasspar in 1950. They built fiberglass sports car bodies. A pioneer in the use of glass reinforced plastics at the Green Dolphin Boat Works, Tritt designed a Jaguar-like body for attachment to the chassis of a Jeep owned by the wife of a friend, Major Kenneth Brooks. The resulting light green sports custom became the Brooks Boxer and was later called the Alembic I. The name change took place when Naugatuck Chemical Div. of U.S. Rubber Co. purchased the car to promote its new Naugahyde seat surfacing material. In February, 1952, Glasspar began advertising body kits for $650. The ads brought a commission to build 100 modified bodies for Woody Woodill's sports car called the Wildfire. In 1953, Glasspar contracted to make Kaiser-Darrin bodies, too. At about this time, the firm began marketing a steel tubular frame designed to combine its kit bodies with flathead Ford or Mercury V-8 running gear. Apparently, some were sold as fully-build units. In 1955, Glasspar, returned to the sole manufacture of kits. A new model called the Ascot was provided.

I.D. NUMBERS: Not available.

GLASSPAR G-2

Model Number	Body/Style Number	Body Type & Seating	Factory Price	Shipping Weight	Production Total
G-2	NA	2-dr Spts Rds-2P	950	NA	200

NOTE 1: Price is estimated cost of Glasspar body and tubular frame.
NOTE 2: Price does not include Ford or Mercury running gear.
NOTE 3: Production is an estimate and may include kits and assembled vehicles.

ENGINE: Ford or Mercury V-8 of 1940-1949 type. Refer to Ford and Mercury sections for typical specifications.

CHASSIS FEATURES: Estimated wheelbase: 100 inches. Estimated length: 180 inches. Tires: (Ford) 6.00 x 16; (Mercury) 6.00 x 15. Front and rear transverse leaf springs. Front tread: 56 inches. Rear tread: 56 inches.

POWERTRAIN OPTIONS: Builder's choice.

CONVENIENCE OPTIONS: Windshield. Bumpers. Fiberglass hardtop. Side curtains.

HISTORICAL FOOTNOTES: Built by Glasspar Company, Santa Ana, Calif.

ASCOT — The Glasspar Company built countless fiberglass bodies and kits which appeared under the names of many different small-time car builders. However, for a short while in 1955, Glasspar assembled its own car called the Ascot. Naturally, the body was fiberglass. Its styling was contemporary, but with pleasant 1930-style overtones. The tubular chassis was of Glasspar's own design. Engines could be the buyer's choice, but most were Ford four-cylinder industrial motors. The Studebaker six was also a popular choice.

I.D. NUMBERS: Not available.

ASCOT

Model Number	Body/Style Number	Body Type & Seating	Factory Price	Shipping Weight	Production Total
NA	NA	2-dr Rds-2P	2400	1770	NA

ENGINE: Ford (industrial). Displacement: 172 cid.

CHASSIS FEATURES: Wheelbase: 94 inches. Overall length: 126 inches. Front tread: 52 inches. Rear tread: 54 inches.

MANUFACTURER: Glasspar Co., Santa Ana, Calif.

1956 GOFF

GOFF — A fiberglass bodied sports, Goff was rather unique in its class for more than one reason. It used a large quantity of prewar Ford components. It was roomy for a sports car, having five-passenger capacity. The fiberglass top was removable.

I.D. NUMBERS: Not available.

GOFF

Model Number	Body/Style Number	Body Type & Seating	Factory Price	Shipping Weight	Production Total
NA	NA	2-dr Rds-5P	1500	NA	NA

NOTE 1: A body kit only was available for $650.

ENGINES

(STANDARD) Ford (1939). V-8. L-head. Cast iron block. Displacement: 221 cid. Bore and stroke: 3-1/16 x 3-3.4 inches. Compression ratio: 6.15:1. Brake horsepower: 90 at 3800 rpm. Three main bearings. Solid valve lifters. Carburetor: Chandler-Grove Model AA1 one-barrel.

(OPTIONAL) Buyer's choice (extra cost).

CHASSIS FEATURES: Modified 1939 Ford chassis.

1956 Goff, two-door roadster, V-8 (PZ)

1947 GORDON

1947 Gordon-Diamond, two-door sedan, V-8 (HAC)

GORDON-DIAMOND — The Gordon-Diamond was a very unusual car designed for smooth riding and easy maneuverability. The key to these qualities was the diamond pattern of the wheel locations. One wheel situated at the front, one at the back, and one midway along either side. Little wonder the car's model name was Diamond. Both the front and rear wheels were steerable. Consequently, the car's effective wheelbase was one half the actual measurement. Turning radius was only 12 feet, which was less than its apparent stance. A bulky-looking aluminum body was used over a tubular steel frame. A Ford truck engine, mounted amidships, powered this rather large car to a reported 95 mph top speed. The side wheels were the drive wheels.

I.D. NUMBERS: Not available.

DIAMOND

Model Number	Body/Style Number	Body Type & Seating	Factory Price	Shipping Weight	Production Total
NA	NA	2-dr Sed-6P	NA	3750	1

ENGINE: Ford (truck). V-8. (Mounted amidships). L-head. Cast iron block. Displacement: 239 cid. Bore and stroke: 3.19 x 3.75 inches. Brake horsepower: 100 at 3800 rpm.

POWERTRAIN: Three-speed manual transmission.

CHASSIS FEATURES: Wheelbase: 156 inches (between front and rear wheels). Overall length: 214 inches.

MANUFACTURER: H. Gordon Hansen. San Lorenzo, Calif.

1948 GREGORY

GREGORY — Ben F. Gregory was a life-long advocate of front-wheel-drive cars. His first attempt at building such a car occurred around 1920. He made another attempt around 1948. This car somewhat predicted the styling introduced on the Renault Dauphine a few years later. Like the Dauphine, it had its engine in the rear. That made the Gregory quite unusual for its time. The rear engine and front drive required a drive shaft.

I.D. NUMBERS: Not available.

GREGORY

Model Number	Body/Style Number	Body Type & Seating	Factory Price	Shipping Weight	Production Total
NA	NA	2-dr Sedan-4P	NA	1900	1

ENGINE: Continental. Four-cylinder. Horizontally-opposed. Air-cooled. Rear mounted. L-head. Displacement: 119.1; cid. Bore and stroke: 3.19 x 3.75 inches. Brake horsepower: 40 at 3000 rpm.

POWERTRAIN: Borg-Warner. Three-speed manual transmission.

CHASSIS FEATURES: Wheelbase: 94 inches. Overall length: 153 inches.

MANUFACTURER: Ben F. Gregory, Kansas City, Mo.

1948 Gregory, two-door sedan, 4-cyl.

1956 GREGORY

1956 Gregory, two-door roadster, 4-cyl.

GREGORY — Another front-wheel-drive car from Ben Gregory appeared in the mid-1950s. It was an aluminum-bodied sports car, which used Porsche chassis and engine. The chassis was said to have been turned around for the Gregory, which is probably a true, but over-simplified description of the actual situation. Just turning the Porsche chassis around would make the Gregory go backwards! Only in reverse would it go forward. The Gregory's top speed was 95 to 100 mph, so some compensation was obviously made to cause the car to go in the right direction. At least this front drive Gregory had its engine up front and needed no driveshaft.

I.D. NUMBERS: Not available.

GREGORY

Model Number	Body/Style Number	Body Type & Seating	Factory Price	Shipping Weight	Production Total
NA	NA	2-dr Rds-2P	5000	1925	1

ENGINE: Porsche. Four-cylinder. Front mounted. Overhead valve. Displacement: 97 cid. Bore and stroke: 3.25 x 2.92 inches. Compression ratio: 7.5:1. Brake horsepower: 70 at 4500 rpm.

POWERTRAIN: Porsche. Four-speed manual transmission.

CHASSIS FEATURES: Wheelbase: 90 inches (modified Porsche chassis). Front tread: 53 inches. Rear tread: 53 inches. Tire size: 5.50 x 15.

MANUFACTURER: Gregory Front Drive Cars. Kansas City, Mo.

1964 GRIFFITH

GRIFFITH — A former Ford dealer designed a tubular chassis. He installed a stock Ford V-8 engine with a four-speed stick shift. Then he added a two passenger GT coupe body from the British made TVR. The result was a car that could accelerate from 0 to 60 mph in less than four seconds. It was given the Series 200 designation.

I.D. NUMBERS: Not available.

GRIFFITH

Model Number	Body/Style Number	Body Type & Seating	Factory Price	Shipping Weight	Production Total
SERIES 200					
200	NA	2-dr Cpe-2P	3995	1450	Note 1

NOTE 1: Approximately 285 cars were built in 1964 and 1965.

ENGINES

(STANDARD) Ford. V-8. Overhead valve. Cast iron block. Displacement: 289 cid. Bore and stroke: 4.00 x 2.88 inches. Compression ratio: 9.0:1. Brake horsepower: 195 at 4400 rpm. Five main bearings. Hydraulic valve lifters. Carburetor: Ford model C3AF-9510B two-barrel.

(OPTIONAL) Ford. V-8. Overhead valve. Cast iron block. Displacement: 289 cid. Bore and stroke: 4.00 x 2.88 inches. Compression ratio: 10.5:1. Brake horsepower: 271 at 6000 rpm. Five main bearings. Carburetor: Ford Model C30F-9410AJ four-barrel. ($495)

POWERTRAIN: Ford. Four-speed manual transmission.

CHASSIS FEATURES: Wheelbase: 85-1/2 inches. Overall length: 138 inches. Front tread: 52-1/2 inches. Rear tread: 54 inches. Tire size: 185 x 15.

OPTIONS: Heater and defroster ($62). Luggage rack ($37). Seat belts ($14).

1965 GRIFFITH

1965 Griffith, Series 200 two-door coupe, V-8 (PZ)

GRIFFITH — Very little styling or mechanical change from the previous year. There were some differences in the option list, however.

GRIFFITH

Model Number	Body/Style Number	Body Type & Seating	Factory Price	Shipping Weight	Production Total
SERIES 200					
200	NA	2-dr Cpe-2P	4800	1850	Note 1

NOTE 1: Approximately 285 cars were built in 1964 and 1965.

ENGINES

(STANDARD) Ford. V-8. Overhead valve. Cast iron block. Displacement: 289 cid. Bore and stroke: 4.00 x 2.88 inches. Compression ratio: 9.3:1. Brake horsepower: 200 at 4400 rpm. Five main bearings. Hydraulic valve lifters. Carburetor: Ford model C5AF-9510A two-barrel.

(OPTIONAL) Ford. V-8. Overhead valve. Cast iron block. Displacement: 28 cid. Bore and stroke: 4.00 x 2.88 inches. Compression ratio: 10.5:1. Brake horsepower: 271 at 6000 rpm. Five main bearings. Carburetor: Ford Model C40F-9510-AL four-barrel. ($285)

POWERTRAIN: Ford. Three-speed manual transmission.

CHASSIS FEATURES: Wheelbase: 85-1/2 inches. Overall length: 138 inches. Front tread: 52-1/2 Inches. Rear tread: 54 Inches. Tire size: 185 x 15.

OPTIONS: Ford four-speed manual transmission ($188). Dunlop wire wheels and 185 x 15 tires ($267). Heater and defroster ($62). Luggage rack ($37).

1966 GRIFFITH

1966 Griffith, two-door coupe, V-8 (PZ)

GRIFFITH — When the supply of bodies from TVR appeared to be in jeopardy, Jack Griffith changed his car entirely. He obtained a supply of steel bodies from Intermeccanica in Italy. They were sleeker than the former ones and befitting a car with 130 mph top speed. A switch in power was also made to a hot Plymouth engine. After 1966, this car became the Omega.

I.D. NUMBERS: Not available.

GRIFFITH

Model Number	Body/Style Number	Body Type & Seating	Factory Price	Shipping Weight	Production Total
NA	NA	2-dr Cpe-2P	6095	2540	NA

ENGINE: Plymouth. V-8. Overhead valve. Cast iron block. Displacement: 273 cid. Bore and stroke: 3.63 x 3.31 Inches. Compression ratio: 10.5:1. Brake horsepower: 235 at 5200 rpm. Five main bearings. Solid valve lifters. Carburetor: Carter Model AFB3853S four-barrel.

POWERTRAIN: Chrysler. Three-speed Torque-Flite automatic transmission.

CHASSIS FEATURES: Wheelbase: 94-1/2 inches. Overall length: 175-1/2 inches. Front tread: 56 Inches. Rear tread: 56 inches. Tire size: 7.35 x 14.

OPTIONS: Four-speed manual transmission. Radio. Heater and defroster. Air conditioning. Leather upholstery. Removable hardtop.

MANUFACTURER: Griffith Motors, Syosset, New York (1964). Griffith Motor Car Co., White Plains, N.Y. (1965). Griffith Motors Inc., Plainview, N.Y.

1960-1964 HENNEY

1960 Henney Kilowatt, four-door sedan, electric motor (PZ)

HENNEY — The Henney was long in the automotive field. It is probably best remembered for hearse, ambulance and station wagon conversions on the Packard chassis. However, this car was not at all like the extinct Packards, nor was it an attempt to revive the Packard name or spirit. It was an electric. Conventional gasoline power was replaced by electric power In a French made Renault Dauphine that was otherwise little changed. Top speed was 40 mph, but cruising speed was around 30 mph. Its model name was Kilowatt, appropriately enough.

I.D. NUMBERS: Not available.

KILOWATT

Model Number	Body/Style Number	Body Type & Seating	Factory Price	Shipping Weight	Production Total
NA	NA	4-dr Sed-4P	3600	2245	Note 1

NOTE 1: Total production is uncertain. It was reported that 100 Dauphine bodies were ordered.

ENGINE: Electric. 7.2 horsepower motor, powered by 12 six-volt batteries. Range between battery charges: Approximately 40 miles.

CHASSIS FEATURES: Wheelbase: 89 inches (Renault Dauphine chassis). Overall length: 155 inches. Front tread: 49 inches. Rear tread: 48 inches. Tire size: 5.50 x 15.

MANUFACTURER: Henney Motor Co. (changed, about 1962, to Eureka Williams Co.), Bloomington, Ill.

1951 HENRY J

HENRY J — (FOUR/SIX) — SERIES 513/514 — The Henry J was a low-priced economy car of compact size. It was introduced by Kaiser-Frazer in 1951 as an effort to buoy their falling sales. Henry J. Kaiser mistakenly envisioned a mass market for a basic transportation vehicle that could be sold on price alone. Designer Howard 'Dutch' Darrin originally suggested a car based on the styling of the company's full-size lines. The stubborn head of Kaiser Industries wanted something totally different. He had American Metal Products, of Detroit, create a prototype. Darrin later modified this with a few of his personal styling traits. It became the Henry J, named after Mr. Kaiser and aimed at the same class of buyers that Model T Fords had once appealed to. General styling characteristics included a fastback two-door sedan body with forward-thrusting front fenders and modern-looking rear fenders that projected from the back of the car like smooth, rounded taillfins. Perched on a short 100 inch wheelbase, the rather cute little car offered customers a choice of four- or six-cylinder power plants supplied by Willys-Overland. Identification features of the 1951 models included a grille consisting of one horizontal chrome bar, with parking lamps at either end; a heavily-chromed, vertical grille center ornament; chrome molding encircling the complete grille; Henry J script on the left front of hood (above upper grille molding); and a non-opening deck lid. Interior trim included plaid seat surfaces over the miniature bench seats, which were claimed to hold five adults. The rear seat was designed to fold-down, thus providing up to 51 cubic feet of cargo space.

1951 Henry J, two-door sedan, 6-cyl

I.D. NUMBERS: Serial Numbers on both four and six-cylinder Henry Js were located on the left front door pillar post. Motor Numbers on fours were stamped on a pad on the top face of the cylinder block, at the front; on sixes, stamped on a pad on the upper front right-hand side of the cylinder block and, also, (both engines) on a serial number plate mounted at the right-hand side of the cylinder block. Serial numbers for fours built at Willow Run, Mich. were K513-001001 to K513-040876. Serial numbers for sixes built at Willow Run, Mich. were K514-001001 to K514-046029. Cars built at other Kaiser assembly plants had the following serial number prefixes: Long Beach, Calif (A); Jackson, Mich. (B) and Portland, Ore. (C). Four-cylinder motor numbers began at 3500000 and continued into 1952. Six-cylinder motor numbers began at 3000001 and continued into 1952.

HENRY J

Model Number	Body/Style Number	Body Type & Seating	Factory Price	Shipping Weight	Production Total
STANDARD (FOUR)					
51	513	2-dr Sed-5P	1363	2293	38,500
DELUXE (SIX)					
51	514	2-dr Sed-5P	1499	2341	43,400

NOTE 1: Production totals are estimates based on serial numbering data.

ENGINES

Inline. Four. Valves in block. Cast iron block. Displacement: 134.2 cid. Bore and stroke: 3.13 x 4.38 inches. Compression ratio: 7.0:1. Brake horsepower: 68 at 4000 rpm. Three main bearings. Solid valve lifters. Carburetor: Carter Type YF one-barrel Model 832S.

Inline. Six. Valves in block. Displacement: 161.04 inches. Bore and stroke: 3.12 x 3.50 inches. Compression ratio: 7.0:1. Brake horsepower: 80 at 3800 rpm. Four main bearings. Solid valve filters. Carburetor: Carter Type YF one-barrel Model 814S.

CHASSIS FEATURES: Wheelbase: 100 inches. Overall length: 181-3/4 inches. Front tread: 54 inches. Rear tread: 54 inches. Tires: 5.90 x 15 tube-type blackwalls.

POWERTRAIN OPTIONS: Three-speed manual transmission with column lever control was standard equipment. Overdrive transmission ($98).

CONVENIENCE OPTIONS: Radio. Antenna. Taillights. Directional signals. Front and rear bumper guards. Wheel trim rings. Full wheel covers. Heater and defroster. Opening deck lid cover.

1952 HENRY J

VAGABOND/CORSAIR — (FOUR) — SERIES 523/524 — Beginning in December, 1951, the Henry J was marketed as the Vagabond. This car featured carryover styling, except that a spare tire and wheel unit was mounted, externally, between the rear bumper and the trunk lid. The Vagabond four was the base or standard offering, characterized by black rubber moldings around the windshield. In February, 1952, a new model called the Corsair replaced the Vagabond, although dealers with leftover units often sold both 1952 models concurrently. Corsair identification features included a double bar grille; a grille molding that curved downwards, at either side, to meet the horizontal bar; a bronze 'K' medallion at the center of the grille; built-in parking lights; series designation script on front fenders; and a slightly more V-shaped bumper. In addition, the taillamps were seen in a different location and new interior trims appeared.

I.D. NUMBERS: The numbering system and code locations were the same as on previous models. Vagabond fours built at Willow Run, Mich. had serial numbers K23-1.001,001 to K23-1,207,062. Those built at other factories had the same prefixes used in 1951, the prefix letter being placed directly ahead of the last seven numbers after the dash. Corsair fours were manufactured at Willow Run only and had serial numbers K524-1,200,000 to K524-1,209,094. Motor numbers for both models were a continuation of the 1951 sequence.

STANDARD FOUR

Model Number	Body/Style Number	Body Type & Seating	Factory Price	Shipping Weight	Production Total
VAGABOND					
52	523	2-dr Sed-5P	1407	2365	3,000
CORSAIR					
52	524	2-dr Sed-5P	1517	2370	7,600

NOTE 1: Production totals in chart are estimates based on serial number data.

ENGINE: Inline. Four. Valves in block. Cast iron block. Displacement: 134.2 cid. Bore and stroke: 3.13 x 4.38 inches. Compression ratio: 7.0:1. Brake horsepower: 68 at 4000 rpm. Three main bearings. Solid valve lifters. Carburetor: Carter Type YF one-barrel Model 832S.

1952 Henry J, two-door Vagabond sedan, 6-cyl

VAGABOND DELUXE/CORSAIR DELUXE — (SIX) — SERIES 524 — Bright moldings framing the windshield were one way to tell Deluxe models apart from the standard fours without lifting the hood. The Vagabond six was sold from Dec. 15, 1951, until being replaced by the Corsair six the following February 26. Styling differences between the early and late 1952 six-cylinder cars following the same pattern as on the fours.

I.D. NUMBERS: The numbering system and code locations were the same as on previous models. Vagabond sixes built at Willow Run, Mich. had serial numbers K524-1,001,001 to K524-1,209,094. Those built at other factories had the same prefixes used in 1951, with the prefix letter being placed directly ahead of the last seven numbers, after the dash. Corsair sixes were manufactured at Willow Run only and had serial numbers K24-1,200,000 to K524-1,209,094. Motor numbers for both models were a continuation of the 1951 sequence.

DELUXE SIX

Model Number	Body/Style Number	Body Type & Seating	Factory Price	Shipping Weight	Production Total
VAGABOND					
52	524	2-dr Sed-5P	1552	2385	4,000
52	524	2-dr Sed-5P	1664	2405	8,900

NOTE 1: Production totals in chart are estimates based on serial number data.

ENGINE: Inline. Six. Valves in block. Cast iron block. Displacement: 161.04 inches. Bore and stroke: 3.12 x 3.50 inches. Compression ratio: 7.0:1. Brake horsepower: 80 at 3800 rpm. Four main bearings. Solid valve lifters. Carburetor: Carter Type YF one-barrel Model 814S.

CHASSIS FEATURES: Wheelbase: 100 inches. Overall length: (Vagabond four) 1793/8 inches; (Vagabond Six) 181-1/2 inches; (Corsair four) 176-21/32 inches; (Corsair six) 177-21/32. Front tread: 54 inches. Rear tread: 54 inches. Tires: 5.90 x 15.

POWERTRAIN OPTIONS: Three speed manual transmission with column lever control as standard in all models. Overdrive transmission, in Vagabonds ($98); in Corsairs ($107). Hydra-Matic transmission.

OPTIONS: Radio. Antenna. Taillights, on Vagabond (optional); on Corsair (standard). Directional signals. Front and rear bumper guards, on base model with four (standard); on sixes (standard). Wheel trim rings. Full wheelcovers. Heater and defroster. Folding rear seat, on Vagabond (standard); on Corsair (optional). Opening deck lid, on Vagabond (optional); on Corsair (standard). Back-up lights.

1953 HENRY J

CORSAIR — (FOUR) — SERIES K533 — A new hood ornament; new chrome wheel discs and longer, curved wraparound rear bumper characterized the general styling changes in the Henry J for 1953. The standard Corsair four featured the smaller L-head engine; the name Corsair on its front fenders; and a black rubber windshield molding. Bumper guards were optional equipment on the standard four.

I.D. NUMBERS: The numbering system and code locations were the same as on previous models. All production was quartered at Willow Run, Mich. Serial numbers K533-001,001 to 010,226 were used on Corsair fours. Motor numbers were a continuation of 1952, ending at number 3,560,067. Note: This ending Motor number means only that all 1953 engines were included in this series. It does not mean that all numbers in this series were 1953 engines. Due to engine banking, some of these motors appeared in cars built for the 1954 model year.

CORSAIR FOUR

Model Number	Body/Style Number	Body Type & Seating	Factory Price	Shipping Weight	Production Total
K53	33	2-dr Sed-5P	1399	2395	9,333

NOTE 1: Total model year production was 17,505 Henry Js.
NOTE 2: Four-cylinder breakout above is an estimate based on serial numbers.

ENGINE: Inline. Four. Valve in block. Cast iron block. Displacement: 134.2 cid. Bore and stroke: 3-1/8 x 4-3/8 inches. Compression ratio: 7.0:1. Three main bearings. Solid valve lifters. Carburetor: Carter Type YF one-barrel Model 820S.

1953 Henry J, two-door Corsair sedan, 6-cyl

CORSAIR DELUXE — (SIX) — SERIES K534 — Identification features of the Deluxe Henry J included chrome windshield framing; Corsair Deluxe front fender scripts and chrome wheel discs. In standard form, the six was slightly longer than the four, since bumper guards were included at base price. Other standard equipment features included dome lights with switches on both doors; new padded dashboard with dustproof instrument pods; built-in dashboard ashtray and interior trim revisions. Technical highlights were the "Supersonic Six"; waterproof ignition; "Zero-Start" battery; "Follow-Thru" starter; "King-Size" clutch; "Power-House" transmission; pressure lubrication; downdraft carburetion; cellular cored radiator; full-length water jacketing; ball bearing water pump; Hotchkiss drive; independent front wheel suspension; "Sure-Stop" brakes; parking brake; "Long-Life" brake linings; bridge-braced body construction; one-piece top; and "Up-Front" dome lighting.

I.D. NUMBERS: The numbering system and code locations were the same as on previous models. All production was quartered at Willow Run, Mich. Serial numbers K534-001,001 to 010,012 were used on Corsair sixes. Motor numbers were a continuation of 1952, ending at number 3,065,712. Note: This ending motor number means only that all 1953 engines were included in this series. It does not mean that all numbers in this series were 1953 engines. Due to engine banking, some of these motors appeared in cars built for the 1954 model year.

CORSAIR SIX

Model Number	Body/Style Number	Body Type & Seating	Factory Price	Shipping Weight	Production Total
K53	34	2-dr Sed-5P	1561	2445	8,172

NOTE 1: Total model year production was 17,505 Henry Js.
NOTE 2: Six-cylinder breakout above is an estimate based on serial numbers.

ENGINE: Inline. Six. Valves in block. Cast iron block. Displacement: 161.04 inches. Bore and stroke: 3.12 x 3.50 inches. Compression ratio: 7.0:1. Brake horsepower: 80 at 3800 rpm. Four main bearings. Solid valve lifters. Carburetor: Carter Type YF one-barrel model 814S.

CHASSIS FEATURES: Wheelbase: 100 inches. Overall length: (Corsair four) 181-3/4 inches; (Corsair Six) 182-1/8 inches. Front tread: 54 inches. Rear tread: 54 inches. Tires: 5.90 x 15.

POWERTRAIN OPTIONS: Three-speed manual transmission with column lever control was standard in all models. Overdrive transmission ($107).

OPTIONS: Radio. Heater. Windshield washers. White sidewall tires. Chrome wheel disc on Corsair four. Back-up lights. Bumper guards on Corsair four. Directional signals. Wheel trim rings. Folding rear seat.

1954 HENRY J

1954 Henry J, two-door Corsair Deluxe sedan, 6-cyl

CORSAIR — (FOUR) — SERIES K543 — For the last year of production the Henry J was carried over from 1953 with virtually no changes, except for revised serial and motor numbers. Identification features, standard equipment and technical construction principles were unchanged.

I.D. NUMBERS: The numbering system and code locations were the same as on previous models. Corsair fours were numbered K543-001,001 and up. Motor numbers continued from 1953.

CORSAIR FOUR

Model Number	Body/Style Number	Body Type & Seating	Factory Price	Shipping Weight	Production Total
K54	3	2-dr Sed-5P	1404	2405	800

NOTE 1: Production above is an estimate based on serial numbers.

ENGINE: Inline. Four. Valve in head. Cast iron block. Displacement: 134.2 cid. Bore and stroke: 3-1/8 x 4-3/8 inches. Compression ratio: 7.0:1. Brake horsepower: 68 at 4000 rpm. Three main bearings. Solid valve lifters. Carburetor: Carter Type YF one-barrel Model 820S.

CORSAIR DELUXE — (SIX) — SERIES K5444 — As in 1953, the up-market models had Corsair Deluxe front fender scripts; chrome windshield framing; chrome wheel discs; and instrument panel crash pads. Under the hood was the "Super-Sonic Six."

I.D. NUMBERS: The numbering system and code locations were the same as on previous models. Corsair Deluxe sixes were numbered K544-001001 and up. Motor numbers continued from 1953.

CORSAIR DELUXE SIX

Model Number	Body/Style Number	Body Type & Seating	Factory Price	Shipping Weight	Production Total
K54	4	2-dr Sed-5P	1566	2455	325

NOTE 1: Production total in chart based on examination of serial numbers.

ENGINE: Inline. Six. Valves in block. Cast iron block. Displacement: 161.04 cid. Bore and stroke: 3.12 x 3.50 inches. Compression ratio: 7.0:1. Brake horsepower: 80 at 3800 rpm. Four main bearings. Solid valve lifters. Carburetor: Carter Type YF one-barrel Model 814S.

CHASSIS FEATURES: Same as 1953.

CONVENIENCE OPTIONS: Same as 1953.

HISTORICAL FOOTNOTES: A total of 1,119 Henry Js were registered as new cars in 1954. This was the last year that Kaiser offered the Henry J. Approximately 1,071 of the 1954 models were built in 17 days, between Nov. 3, 1953 and Nov. 20, 1953. Model introductions were held on Dec. 1, 1953.

1949-1950 HOPPENSTAND

HOPPENSTAND — This was a small, aluminum-bodied, two-passenger economy car. Company information indicated that it was offered in three different body types: open runabout, coupe and convertible. The two-cylinder engine was apparently the product of the manufacturer. An hydraulic transmission was another unusual Hoppenstand feature. Top speed was 50 mph, but at 35 mph, fuel consumption was 35 mile per gallon.

I.D. NUMBERS: Not available.

HOPPENSTAND

Model Number	Body/Style Number	Body Type & Seating	Factory Price	Shipping Weight	Production Total
690	NA	2-dr Rds-2P	NA	684	NA
690	NA	2-dr Cpe-2P	NA	NA	NA
790	NA	2-dr Conv-2P	1000	NA	NA

1950 Hoppenstand two-door convertible, 2-cyl.

POWERTRAIN: Hydraulic clutch and transmission.

CHASSIS FEATURES: Wheelbase: 90 inches. Overall length: 162 inches. Front tread: 40 inches. Rear tread: 40 Inches. Tire size: 4.50 x 12.

MANUFACTURER: Hoppenstand Motors Inc., Greenville, Pa.

1946 HUMMINGBIRD

1946 Hummingbird, two-door roadster,

HUMMINGBIRD — Talmadge Judd designed this car and built a prototype. He was hoping to interest some manufacturers in volume production. No one was interested enough to make the car, which was interesting, nevertheless. It was a small and light two-passenger roadster built for economical operation. It had an 85 inch wheelbase, and a total weight of only 1,350 pounds. Part of the weight savings was the result of using thin, but weak 8-gauge steel for the body panels. Its small four-cylinder engine got up to 50 mpg and had a top speed of 70 mph.

I.D. NUMBERS: Not available.

HUMMINGBIRD

Model Number	Body/Style Number	Body Type & Seating	Factory Price	Shipping Weight	Production Total
NA	NA	2-dr Rds-2P	NA	1350	1

ENGINE: Four-cylinder. Brake hp: 20.

CHASSIS FEATURES: Wheelbase: 85 inches.

1951 HUNT

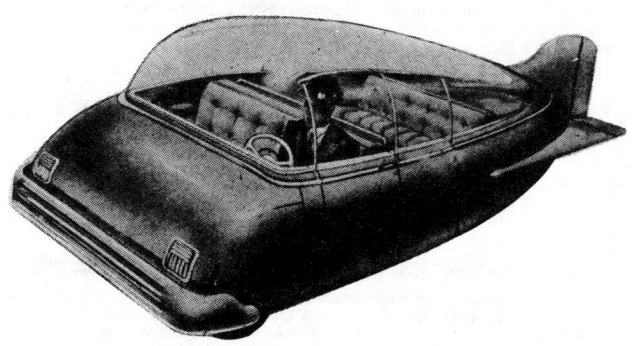

1951 Hunt, dome-top coupe, 4-cyl (CG)

HUNT — (FOUR) — Like many other postwar automotive inventors, Lloyd Hunt had dreams about building his own car. He went as far as to construct a working chassis and sketch studies of the futuristic body he planned to use after reaching the production stage. A chief engineer for Southern California Edison Co., Hunt stuck to automotive basics in a technical sense. His three-wheeled chassis was made of pieces pirated from 10 other cars. Yet, the components were assembled in an unconventional way. Parts were scavenged from wrecking yards and included a 1925 Buick engine with the two middle cylinders cut out to make it a four-cylinder. Pistons came from an Auburn; rods from a Hupmobile; brakes from a Ford; transmission from a Chevy; distributor from a Plymouth; and radiator from a Dodge. The third wheel, at the rear, steered the car via cables linked to a Chrysler steering wheel. All this was mounted, in front-drive fashion, upon a square channel iron frame. The body that Hunt envisioned was clearly aircraft-inspired and was actually intended for mounting on a larger version of the vehicle. Hunt hoped to realize production, or at least build the larger, more complete car. It seems that this dream was never fulfilled.

I.D. NUMBERS: Not applicable.

HUNT

Model Number	Body/Style Number	Body Type & Seating	Factory Price	Shipping Weight	Production Total
NA	NA	4-dr Glasstop-7P	NA	NA	1

NOTE 1: Above data was for the planned car with glass-top and full body.
NOTE 2: Data below applies only to the single prototype made.

ENGINE: Four-cylinder, constructed from a modified 1925 Buick six. Solid billet crankshaft. Auburn pistons. Hupmobile connecting rods. Plymouth distributor (rebuilt to operate in reverse). Dodge cooling system. Engine was mounted, crosswise in front of car.

CHASSIS FEATURES: Wheelbase: 131 inches. Overall length: (not available). Front tread: 66 inches. Square, channel iron frame. Ford mechanical brakes. Single tail wheel mounted in circular steel plate rotated by cable steering system. The wheel rode against roller bearings and could turn 80 degrees left or right. Airplane type shock absorbers.

POWERTRAIN FEATURES: Chevrolet transmission connected to inverted Ford differential for transverse front-wheel-drive. Standard shift with floor-mounted lever control. Drivetrain tilted to rear at 45 degree angle.

CONVENIENCE OPTIONS: Not available.

HISTORICAL FOOTNOTES: The car had a turning circle of approximately 17 feet. Plans called for a four-door body with plastic dome or 'bubble-top' and a large, rear dorsal fin incorporated a rudder that would take over steering control. Square headlamps and a full-width, wraparound bumper were other projected features. A Chrysler Airflow seat was used on the prototype, which realized about the same degree of relative success as the seat donor itself.

1951 Hunt, two-door runabout, 4-cyl (CG)

NOTE1: This type of prototype would have little value unless found in perfect, or near perfect condition.

1961 HYDRAMOTIVE

HYDRAMOTIVE — A great deal of mystery and suspicion surrounds the Hydramotive. Mechanically, it was so unorthodox that it seems almost unbelievable. It was claimed that there was no need for a transmission, universal joints, propeller shaft, differential gears, axles, or brake drums. It did have an engine, which was a diesel. The proposed price was a dubiously low $1,200. The Securities & Exchange Commission took a keen interest in the car. Problems turned up in the investigation regarding fraudulent misrepresentations in the sale of company stock. Whether or not the allegations were true, there was a Hydra-Matic car made. That makes it a part of automotive history.

MANUFACTURER: Hydra-Matic Corp., Charlotte, N.C.

1949-1950 IMP

IMP — Designed for short trips to the grocery store, the Imp was a small open two-passenger car with a parcel compartment under the hood. The fiberglass body was open and doorless and there was a tubular bumper that surrounded the entire car. The little single-cylinder motor was located at the back and reached 60 mpg in fuel consumption.

I.D. NUMBERS: Not available.

1950 Imp, two-passenger open model, one-cyl.

IMP

Model Number	Body/Style Number	Body Type & Seating	Factory Price	Shipping Weight	Production Total
NA	NA	Open-2P	500	475	NA

ENGINE: Gladden. One-cylinder. Air-cooled. Rear-mounted. Brake hp: 7-1/2.

POWERTRAIN: Automatic transmission.

CHASSIS FEATURES: Wheelbase: 63 inches. Overall length: 120 inches.

1951 IMP

IMP — Little or no styling and mechanical change from the previous years.

I.D. NUMBERS: Not available.

IMP

Model Number	Body/Style Number	Body Type & Seating	Factory Price	Shipping Weight	Production Total
NA	NA	Open-2P	795	475	NA

ENGINE: Gladden. One-cylinder. Air-cooled. Rear-mounted. Brake hp: 7-1/2.

POWERTRAIN: Automatic transmission.

CHASSIS FEATURES: Wheelbase: 63 inches. Overall length: 120 inches.

MANUFACTURER: International Motor Products, Glendale, Calif.

1952 JETMOBILE

JETMOBILE — Using three airplane fuel tanks for its body, the Jetmobile looked very unusual, but quite pleasant and very futuristic. It was an open single-passenger car with three wheels. The lone wheel was at front. Originally a Lycoming 75 hp aircraft engine powered the car, but later a Ford-60 flathead V-8 was installed.

I.D. NUMBERS: Not available.

JETMOBILE

Model Number	Body/Style Number	Body Type & Seating	Factory Price	Shipping Weight	Production Total
NA	NA	Open-1P	NA	NA	NA

ENGINE: Ford-60. V-8. L-head. Cast iron block. Displacement: 136 cid. Bore and stroke: 2.6 x 3.2 inches. Compression ratio: 6.6:1. Brake hp: 60 at 3500 rpm. Three main bearings. Solid valve lifters. Carburetor: Ford two-barrel.

CHASSIS FEATURES: Not available.

MANUFACTURER: Richard Harp, Frederick, Md.

1959 JOHNSONMOBILE

JOHNSONMOBILE — This was an early, but futile attempt to make a car in the image of a 1904 horseless carriage. The two-passenger body was made of marine plywood and a small Clinton engine powered the machine.

I.D. NUMBERS: Not available.

JOHNSOMMOBILE

Model Number	Body/Style Number	Body Type & Seating	Factory Price	Shipping Weight	Production Total
NA	NA	Rbt-2P	NA	NA	1

694   Standard Catalog of American Cars

ENGINE: Clinton. Air-cooled. Brake hp: 3.

CHASSIS FEATURES: Not available.

MANUFACTURER: Horton Johnson Inc. Highland Park, Ill.

1955-1960 JOMAR

JOMAR — The Jomar is often confused with the British made TVR. And with good reason! The cars were very similar. Produced by the renowned race car builder Ray Saidel, Jomars had aluminum bodies. They were similar in appearance to the fiberglass TVR. Jomar engines-stock or modified British power plants-were also similar to those used in the TVR. Jomars were offered in three different models, each with its own engine. These cars were different from the Jomar MK II, which was a fiberglass racing car not described here.

I.D. NUMBERS: Not available.

JOMAR

Model Number	Body/Style Number	Body Type & Seating	Factory Price	Shipping Weight	Production Total
NA	NA	2-dr Cpe-2P	2995	1400	NA
NA	NA	2-dr GT Cpe-2P	3495	NA	NA
NA	NA	2-dr Climax Cpe-2P	4195	NA	NA

NOTE 1: The factory prices given above were for the 1958 model year.

ENGINES

(STANDARD SERIES) Ford Anglia 100E. Four-cylinder. L-head. Cast iron block. Displacement: 71.5 cid. Bore and stroke: 2.50 x 3.64 inches. Compression ratio: 7.0:1. Brake hp: 36 at 4500 rpm. Three main bearings. Solid valve lifters. Carburetor: Solex.

(GT SERIES) Ford Anglia 100E (modified). Four-cylinder. L-head. Cast iron block. Super-charged. Displacement: 71.5 cid. Bore and stroke: 2.50 x 3.64 inches. Three main bearings. Solid valve lifters.

(CLIMAX ENGINE) Conventry Climax State 2. Four-cylinder. Overhead valve. Displacement: 70 cid. Bore and stroke: 2.82 x 2.60 inches. Brake hp: 85 at 7000 rpm. Carburetor: Two (2) SUS.

(OPTIONAL CLIMAX ENGINES) Single- or double-overhead cam 1500 cc. Conventry Climax.

1958 Jomar, two-door GT Coupe, 4-cyl.

POWERTRAIN: Four-speed manual transmission.

CHASSIS FEATURES: Wheelbase: 84 inches. Overall length: 138 inches. Front tread: 52 inches. Rear tread: 52 inches. Tire size: 5.00 x 15.

OPTIONS: Close-ratio gearing, except for Climax ($75). Heater and defroster ($65).

MANUFACTURER: Saidel Sports Racing Cars, Division of Merrimack Street Garage, Inc., Manchester, N.H.

1948 KEEN

KEEN — Trying to develop a practical steam car, Charles Keen built one example. It was a 1946 Plymouth convertible, shortened to a three-passenger car. The V-4 steam engine was mounted in the rear, though the boiler was at the front. Operating pressure was 1200 pounds. The car got 16 mpg of kerosene and 25 mpg of water.

1948 Keen Steam, two-door convertible, V-4.

1955-1965

KEEN — Mr. Keen continued his development of the steam car and built another prototype. It used a fiberglass body made by Victress. That has led to the erroneous conclusion that Williams (q.v.) took over Keen's operation. It was about this time that Williams built a car also using the Victress body. Unlike the Williams however, Keen placed his engine in the rear, as on his 148 model. Keen eventually sold out to the Thermal Kinetics Corp. of Rochester, N.Y.

MANUFACTURER: Keen Manufacturing Corp., Madison, Wis.

1948-1950 KELLER

STATION WAGON

1948 Keller, two-door station wagon, 4-cyl (PZ)

KELLER — When Bobbi-Kar was unable, or unwilling, to conform to State of Calif. stock regulations, the company was moved to Ala. and reorganized as the Dixie Motor Car Co. Shortly afterwards, George D. Keller, former sales vice-president of Studebaker, came on the scene and took control of the company. He made some changes to the car and renamed it as the Keller. It was restyled to look more like an honest-to-goodness car. The basic lines of the Bobbi-Kar remained, but the Keller looked much less like a child's play thing. The convertible had its engine in the rear, like the Bobbi-Kar, but the wood-panelled station wagon had its engine up front. A Continental four-cylinder engine was used, but a switch was made to a larger displacement. Thirty-five mpg fuel economy was claimed. The car was offered in two series, the standard Chief and DeLuxe Super Chief. With Keller's sales experience, he, established a network of more than 1,500 dealers. Suddenly, In October 1949, Keller died of a heart attack. For all intents and purposes, the car died too. There was an effort to produce a different style of Keller in Belgium, but that failed to amount to much.

I.D. NUMBERS: Not available.

Keller, two-door convertible, 4-cyl (AA)

695

KELLER

Model Number	Body/Style Number	Body Type & Seating	Factory Price	Shipping Weight	Production Total
CHIEF SERIES					
NA	NA	2-dr Conv-3P	895	1800	Note 1
NA	NA	2-dr Sta Wag-3P	1095	2100	Note 1
NA	NA	2-dr Sup Conv-3P	NA	NA	Note 1
NA	NA	2-dr Sup Sta Wag	1250	NA	Note 1

NOTE 1: Production total for all models was 18 cars.

ENGINES

(EARLY) Continental. Four-cylinder. Rear-mounted in convertible. L-head. Cast iron block. Displacement: 133 cid. Bore and stroke: 3.25 x 4.00 inches. Brake hp: 49 at 3600 rpm. Solid valve lifters.

(LATE) Continental. Four-cylinder. Rear-mounted in convertible. L-head. Cast iron block. Displacement: 162 cid. Bore and stroke: 3.44 x 4.38 inches. Compression ratio: 7.0:1. Brake hp: 58 at 3600 rpm. Solid valve lifters.

POWERTRAIN: Three-speed manual transmission.

CHASSIS FEATURES: Wheelbase: 92 inches. Overall length: 167 inches. Front tread: 50 inches. Rear tread: 50 inches. Tire size: 5.50 x 15.

MANUFACTURER: Keller Motors Corp., Huntsville, Ala.

1947-1950 KING MIDGET

KING MIDGET — In terms of years of continuous production, no American postwar newcomer ever closely matched the longevity of the King Midget, yet it was never commonly seen. Developed by Claud Dry and Dale Orcutt, it was a very economical car. At first, it was a single-passenger open vehicle, which looked much like midget racers of the day. A single-cylinder rear-mounted, Wisconsin engine drove the car. An automatic transmission was developed by the manufacturer after production got underway. The King Midget was only available as a kit for the first year or two. It was advertised as the "World's Lowest Priced Car." At $270 for the kit, it possibly was.

I.D. NUMBERS: Not available.

KING MIDGET

Model Number	Body/Style Number	Body Type & Seating	Factory Price	Shipping Weight	Production Total
NA	NA	Rbt-1P	350-500	330	Note 1

NOTE 1: Total production from 1946 through 1969 was about 5,000 cars.

ENGINE: Wisconsin. One-cylinder. Air-cooled. L-head. Rear-mounted. Brake hp: 6.

POWERTRAIN: (Early models) three-speed manual transmission; (other models) automatic transmission. One forward speed, but no reverse.

1950 King Midget, roadster, one-cyl. (CG)

CHASSIS FEATURES: Front tread: 40 inches. Rear tread: 40 inches. Tire size: 5.50 x 8.

1951-1957 KING MIDGET

KING MIDGET — The second generation King Midget was completely restyled. It became a two-passenger vehicle and had a cloth top. It looked a bit more like a regular car, but in miniature. A more powerful Wisconsin one-cylinder engine was used and kits were still available.

I.D. NUMBERS: Not available.

KING MIDGET

Model Number	Body/Style Number	Body Type & Seating	Factory Price	Shipping Weight	Production Total
NA	NA	Rds-2P	550	450	Note 1

NOTE 1: Total production from 1946 through 1969 was about 5,000 cars.

1952 King-Midget, roadster, one-cyl. (CG)

1955 King-Midget, roadster, one-cyl. (CG)

ENGINE: Wisconsin. One-cylinder. Air-cooled. L-head. Rear-mounted. Displacement: 23 cid. Bore and stroke: 3.00 x 3.25 inches. Brake hp: 7-1/2. (Some of the later models were equipped with a 8-1/2 horsepower engine).

POWERTRAIN: Automatic transmission one forward speed, but no reverse.

CHASSIS FEATURES: Wheelbase: 72 inches. Overall length: 102 inches. Front tread: 42 inches. Rear tread: 42 inches. Tire size: 4.00 x 8 (5.50 x 8 optional).

1956 King-Midget, roadster, one-cyl. (CG)

1958-1955 KING MIDGET

KING MIDGET — The third generation of the King Midget was updated in its styling, with taillights mounted in what could be called fins. Now the King Midget had doors. Also like big American cars, it grew. Still a two-passenger car, it was over a foot longer than before. Another big car feature the King Midget copied was a more powerful engine, although it was still a one-lunger. Economy did not seem to be sacrificed. It was supposed to get up to 60 mpg. In 1961, there was a bodyless version called Driver Training Car. It was marketed for driver education classes.

1958 King Midget, roadster, one-cyl. (CG)

I.D. NUMBERS: Not available.

KING MIDGET

Model Number	Body/Style Number	Body Type & Seating	Factory Price	Shipping Weight	Production Total
NA	NA	2-dr Rds-2P	825-950	675	Note 1

NOTE 1: Total production from 1946 through 1969 was about 5,000 cars.

ENGINE: Wisconsin. One-cylinder. Air-cooled. L-head. Rear mounted. Displacement: 23 cid. Bore and stroke: 3.00 x 3.25 inches. Brake hp: 9-1/4.

1958 King-Midget, two-door roadster, one-cyl.

1961 King Midget, roadster, one-cyl. (CG)

POWERTRAIN: Two-speed automatic transmission.

CHASSIS FEATURES: Wheelbase 76-1/2 inches. Overall length: 117 inches. Front tread: 44 inches. Rear tread: 44 inches. Tire size: 5.70 x 8.

1963 King Midget, roadster, one-cyl. (CG)

1967-1969 KING MIDGET

KING MIDGET — Although there was virtually no styling change, King Midget switched to a Kohler engine. Still a single-cylinder motor, it was a little larger and developed a bit more power. But alas, all good things must come to an end. The last King Midget was built in 1969. It had been in continual production for 24 model years. This record which was the envy of thousands of other car makers, both large and small.

1968 King Midget, two-door roadster, one-cyl.

I.D. NUMBERS: Not available.

KING MIDGET

Model Number	Body/Style Number	Body Type & Seating	Factory Price	Shipping Weight	Production Total
NA	NA	2-dr Rds-2P	1095	800	Note 1

NOTE 1: Total production from 1946 through 1969 was about 5,000 cars.
ADDITIONAL NOTE: The factory price given above is for the 1969 model year.

ENGINE: Kohler. One-cylinder. Four-cycle. Air-cooled. L-head. Rear-mounted. Displacement: 29.1 cid. Bore and stroke: 3.38 x 3.25 inches. Brake hp: 12 at 3600.

POWERTRAIN: Two-speed automatic transmission.

CHASSIS FEATURES: Wheelbase 76-1/2 inches. Overall length: 117 inches. Front tread: 44 inches. Rear tread: 44 inches. Tire size: 5.70 x 8.

MANUFACTURER: Midget Motors Supply Co., (later) Midget Motors Corp., Athens, Ohio.

1948 KNUDSON

KNUDSON — A small, Jeep-type vehicle with one door on the right side and a canvas top was built by James Knudson. Its small, single-cylinder engine was mounted in the rear and gave fuel economy of over 60 mpg.

I.D. NUMBERS: Not available.

KNUDSON

Model Number	Body/Style Number	Body Type & Seating	Factory Price	Shipping Weight	Production Total
NA	NA	1-dr Utl-2P	545	635	1

KNUDSON ENGINE: One-cycle. Air-cooled. Rear-mounted. Brake hp: 4.

POWERTRAIN: Automatic transmission.

CHASSIS FEATURES: Overall length: 90 inches.

MANUFACTURER: Knudson Mfg. & Design Co. Inc., Buffalo, N.Y.

1966-1969 KRIM-GHIA

KRIM-GHIA — A small Detroit firm built and sold two different cars at the same time. Both had custom made Ghia-built bodies. Te 1500 GT used the Italian-built Fiat 1500 chassis and a modified Fiat engine. The larger model used the Plymouth Barracuda chassis and a modified Plymouth engine.

I.D. NUMBERS: Not available.

KRIM-GHIA 1500 GT

Model Number	Body/Style Number	Body Type & Seating	Factory Price	Shipping Weight	Production Total
1500 GT	NA	2-dr Rds-2P	NA	NA	NA

ENGINE: Fiat 1500 (modified). Four-cylinder. Overhead valve. Cast iron block. Displacement: 90.4 cid. Bore and stroke: 3.03 x 3.13 inches. Brake hp: 86. Three main bearings. Solid valve lifters. Carburetor: (not available).

POWERTRAIN: Fiat. Five-speed manual transmission.

CHASSIS FEATURES: Wheelbase: 98.6 inches. Front tread: 48.5 inches. Rear tread: 48.5 inches.

I.D. NUMBERS (BARRACUDA BASED): Not available.

KRIM-GHIA ENGINE (BARRACUDA BASED)

Model Number	Body/Style Number	Body Type & Seating	Factory Price	Shipping Weight	Production Total
NA	NA	2-dr Rds-2P	NA	NA	NA

ENGINE: Plymouth V-8 (modified). Overhead valve. Cast iron block. Displacement: 273 cid. Bore and stroke: 3.63 x 3.31 inches. Brake hp: 245. Five main bearings. Solid valve lifters. Carburetor: (not available).

POWERTRAIN: Not available.

CHASSIS FEATURES: Wheelbase: 106 inches. Front tread: 55.9 inches. Rear tread: 55.6 inches.

MANUFACTURER: Krim Car Import Co., Detroit, Mich.

1949-1950 KURTIS

KURTIS — Frank Kurtis was the builder of many winning Indianapolis cars. He branched out to make high-performance sports cars. His first series had simple and pleasing styling. Fiberglass was used for the body. The engine could be whatever the buyer wanted, but Kurtis often installed a slightly modified Ford flathead V-8. Kits were offered and varied in the number of components the buyer desired. Consequently, kit prices had a rather wide spread from $1,495 to $3,495. Production of the first-generation Kurtis ended in 1950, when Frank Kurtis sold this part of his operation to Earl Muntz. With a few alterations, the Kurtis became the Muntz. Frank Kurtis returned to sports car production a few years later.

Kurtis one-off on 1942 Buick chassis, 8-cyl. (OCW)

1949 Kurtis, two-door roadster, V-8

KURTIS I.D. NUMBERS: Not available.

KURTIS

Model Number	Body/Style Number	Body Type & Seating	Factory Price	Shipping Weight	Production Total
NA	NA	2-dr Rds-2P	3950	2300	36

NOTE 1: The factory price given above is for the 1949 model year.
NOTE 2: The 1950 price, with stock Ford V-8 engine, was $4,700.

POWERTRAIN: Three-speed manual transmission.

CHASSIS FEATURES: Wheelbase: 100 inches. Overall length: 169 inches. Front tread: 56 inches. Rear tread: 56 inches. Tire size: 5.50 x 15.

1950 Kurtis, two-door roadster, V-8 (IMS)

1954-1955 KURTIS

1955 Kurtis, 500M two-door roadster, V-8 (PZ)

KURTIS — Frank Kurtis returned to sports car production in 1954. This effort started when 50 chassis were made. Designed by Kurtis, this tubular chassis was patterned after Bill Vukovitch's winning 1953 Indianapolis 500 race car. It was called 500 KK. Thirty were sold to individuals, who put in an engine of their choice and topped them off with one of several fiberglass bodies available at the time. The remaining 20 chassis were used by Kurtis to assemble complete cars. These cars were given the designation 500 M. They were "guaranteed to out-perform any other sports car or stock car on the road" according to the company's brochures. Again, the buyer could have whatever engine he wanted, but a stock 1955 Cadillac motor was standard. The body was supplied by McCulloch Motors. It was fiberglass. With a Cadillac engine, the Kurtis could reach 95.23 mph in a quarter-mile. Top speed was 135 mph. That was hard to beat. This model marked the end of Kurtis production for the general public.

I.D. NUMBERS: Not available.

KURTIS 500M

Model Number	Body/Style Number	Body Type & Seating	Factory Price	Shipping Weight	Production Total
500M	NA	2-dr Rds-2P	5800	2506	20

NOTE 1: Prices above are for cars with Cadillac engine.

ENGINE (TYPICAL): Cadillac. V-8. Overhead valve. Cast iron block. Displacement: 331.1 cid. Bore and stroke: 3-13/16 x 3-5/8 inches. Compression ratio: 9.75:1. Brake hp: 250 at 4600 rpm. Five main bearings. Hydraulic valve lifters. Carburetor: Carter Model WCFB four-barrel.

POWERTRAIN: Automatic transmission.

CHASSIS FEATURES: Wheelbase: 100 inches. Front tread: 56 inches. Rear tread: 56 inches. Tire size: 5.50 x 15.

MANUFACTURER: Kurtis-Kraft Inc. (1949-1950), Kurtis Sports Car Corp. (1954-1955)), Los Angeles, Calif.

1960 LA DAWRI

LA DAWRI — California of the '50s, and on into the '60s, was a hotbed of retrofit fiberglass auto body manufacturers. One of the best-known and most successful of these was LaDawri Coachcraft, of Los Angeles. LaDawri catered to the do-it-yourself custom car market by offering a variety of body choices for a broad range of available chassis. Their most popular model was the Conquest, a sleek, modern two- or three-passenger roadster.

I.D. NUMBERS: Not available or not used.

1960 LaDawri, two-door convertible-roadster, V-8

LA DAWRI CONQUEST

Model Number	Body/Style Number	Body Type & Seating	Factory Price	Shipping Weight	Production Total
NA	NA	2-dr Rds-2/3P	395	NA	NA

NOTE 1: Price is for the body kit only; donor vehicle additional.
NOTE 2: Buildable using two-passenger bucket seats or three-passenger bench.

ENGINES: Various. Owner's choice.

POWERTRAIN: Various.

CHASSIS FEATURES: Designed for installation on 100 inch chassis such as Willys, Jeepster and Henry J.

1969 LITTLE DUDE

LITTLE DUDE — Styled like an automobile out of the early 1930s, the Little Dude was an attempt to attract buyers from the dune buggy crowd. However, this midget met with little success.

I.D. NUMBERS: Not available.

LITTLE DUDE

Model Number	Body/Style Number	Body Type & Seating	Factory Price	Shipping Weight	Production Total
NA	NA	Rbt-4P	NA	NA	NA

ENGINE: Aichi motor. Two-cylinder. Air-cooled. Horizontally-opposed. Displacement: 21.6 cid. Bore and stroke: 2.5 x 2.2 inches. Compression ratio: 7.5:1. Brake hp: 18.6.

CHASSIS FEATURES: Wheelbase: 77.6 inches. Overall length: 117.9 inches. Front tread: 44.1 inches. Rear tread: 42.7 inches.

MANUFACTURER: Hawaiian Motor Co., Los Angeles, Calif.

1963 LOST CAUSE

LOST CAUSE — This unlikely name was given to an unlikely car conceived by a man with the unlikely name Charles Peaslee Farnsley. The one time mayor of Louisville, Ken., Mr. Farnsley had the famous Derham Body Works of Rosemont, Pa., do some conversion work on a Chevrolet Corvair Monza sedan. Some alterations were done to the body, but most of the work was in equipping the car with the fabulous amount of gadgets. The instrument panel was a maze of gauges and dials, such as altimeter, compass, clock and a full complement of rally timers. The dash itself, door panels and steering wheel were all made of Ken. burl walnut. The seats were upholstered with genuine black leather, which was also used to cover the roof. Some of the many other items included a complete picnic hamper, lap robes, luggage and even vermeil mint julep cups, if you please. The buyer could choose a John Fitch engine conversion to give the car a 115 mph-plus top speed.

I.D. NUMBERS: Not available.

LOST CAUSE

Model Number	Body/Style Number	Body Type & Seating	Factory Price	Shipping Weight	Production Total
NA	NA	4-dr Sed-4P	19,600	NA	NA

1963 Lost Cause, four-door sedan, 6-cyl (PZ)

ENGINES

(STANDARD) Chevrolet Corvair. Six-cylinder. Air-cooled. Horizontally-opposed. Light aluminum alloy. Displacement: 145 cid. Bore and stroke: 3.43 x 2.60 inches. Compression ratio: 9.0:1. Brake hp: 80 at 4400 rpm. Four main bearings. Hydraulic valve lifters. Carburetor: Two Carter Model 7023101 one-barrel.

(OPTIONAL) Chevrolet Corvair modified by John Fitch to produce 120 bhp.

CHASSIS FEATURES: Wheelbase: 108 inches (Chevrolet Corvair chassis). Overall length: 180 inches. Front tread: 54.5 inches. Rear tread: 55.1 inches.

MANUFACTURER: Lost Cause Motors, Louisville, Ken.

1954 MARKETEER

MARKETEER — As its name suggests, this was a car designed for shopping trips. It was a small three-wheeler with the single wheel at the front. A fixed fiberglass top and windshield were featured.

I.D. NUMBERS: Not available.

MARKETEER

Model Number	Body/Style Number	Body Type & Seating	Factory Price	Shipping Weight	Production Total
NA	NA	2-dr Cpe-2P	NA	NA	NA

1954 Marketeer, roadster, electric motor (PZ)

ENGINE: Electric. Brake hp: 3. Six 6-volt batteries. Range between charges: 30 to 35 miles.

CHASSIS FEATURES: Not available.

MANUFACTURER: Electric Marketeer Mfg. Co., Redlands, Calif.

1964 MARKETOUR

MARKETOUR — Another shopper from California was the Marketour. As with most three-wheelers, it had the lone wheel in front. This car was equipped with a detachable leatherette top.

I.D. NUMBERS: Not available.

MARKETOUR

Model Number	Body/Style Number	Body Type & Seating	Factory Price	Shipping Weight	Production Total
NA	NA	2-dr Cpe-2P	NA	NA	NA

ENGINE: Electric. 36-volt motor. Six heavy-duty batteries. Range between charges: 35 to 40 miles.

POWERTRAIN: Four forwards speeds.

CHASSIS FEATURES: Wheelbase: 64 inches. Overall length: 84 inches. Tire size: 4.00 x 8.

MANUFACTURER: Marketour Electric Cars, Long Beach, Calif.

1964 Marketour, roadster, electric motor (PZ)

1967 MARKETTE

MARKETTE — A small electric car was made by Westinghouse with the hopes that it would go into production, but that plan did not materialize. The prototype was a two-passenger coupe, typical of many electrics for urban errands.

I.D. NUMBERS: Not available.

MARKETTE

Model Number	Body/Style Number	Body Type & Seating	Factory Price	Shipping Weight	Production Total
NA	NA	2-dr Cpe-2P	Under 2000	1730	1

ENGINE: Electric. Westinghouse. Twelve 6-volt batteries. Brake hp: 3. Range between charges: 50 miles.

CHASSIS FEATURES: Overall length: 116 inches.

MANUFACTURER: Westinghouse Electric Corp.

1954 MARQUIS

MARQUIS — it was the intention of this company to produce a small luxury car. The prototype had an aluminum body, but fiberglass was to be used on the production model. Renault components were relied upon extensively, including the chassis and rear-mounted engine. A fastback GT type coupe was the only model built. Sometimes this car has been called Plasticar. Though that was the name of the manufacturer, it was erroneously applied to the car.

I.D. NUMBERS: Not available.

MARQUIS

Model Number	Body/Style Number	Body Type & Seating	Factory Price	Shipping Weight	Production Total
NA	NA	2-dr Cpe	3100	NA	1

MARQUIS ENGINE: Renault. (Which engine is uncertain).

CHASSIS FEATURES: Renault chassis (which model chassis is uncertain).

MANUFACTURER: Plasticar, Doylestown, Pa.

1966 MARS II

MARS II — This ambitious electric car program used the Renault 10 body. The electrical system utilized lead-cobalt batteries, rechargable up to 200 times for a 50,000 mile life. Dynamic braking charged the batteries during coasting and deceleration. Top speed was 68 mph. The Mars II was said to be the first electric car to circle the Indianapolis Motor Speedway.

I.D. NUMBERS: Not available.

MARS II

Model Number	Body/Style Number	Body Type & Seating	Factory Price	Shipping Weight	Production Total
NA	NA	4-dr Sed-4P	NA	4260	NA

ENGINE: Electric. DC series-wound traction motor. Four 30-volt battery packs of five lead-cobalt batteries each. Maximum horsepower at peak acceleration: 77. Range between battery charges: 70 to 120 miles. Dynamic braking.

POWERTRAIN: Renault. Four-speed manual transmission.

CHASSIS FEATURES: Wheelbase: 89 inches (Renault 10 chassis). Overall length: 167 1/2 inches. Front tread: 49 inches. Rear tread: 48 inches. Tire size: 165SR15.

MANUFACTURER: Electric Fuel Propulsion, Inc., Ferndale, Mich.

1966 Mars II, four-door sedan, electric motor (PZ)

1948 MARTIN

MARTIN — James Vernon Martin was a persistent proponent of small, three-wheel cars. From 1932 to 1948 he designed, built and revised such a vehicle. This was called the Martinette. It was an aluminum-bodied type with the single wheel at the back. Mr. Martin also designed an interesting automatic transmission which used magnetism to form the lock between the engine and the driveshaft.

1948 Martin, two-door "woodie" coupe, 4-cyl.

I.D. NUMBERS: Not available.

MARTINETTE

Model Number	Body/Style Number	Body Type & Seating	Factory Price	Shipping Weight	Production Total
NA	NA	2-dr Cpe-2P	NA	NA	1

ENGINE: Continental. Four-cylinder. L-head. Rear-mounted. Displacement: 153 cid. Brake hp: 60.

POWERTRAIN: Magnetic fluid-drive transmission.

MANUFACTURER: Martin Development Laboratories, Rochelle Park, N.Y.

1950 MARTIN

MARTIN — The second Martin used the same three-wheel layout as its predecessor, as well as the magnetic automatic transmission. However, this model had an eyecatching wood panel body, which was made in Reading, Pa., by Biehl Autobody. Because the wood panels were similar to those used on wooden station wagons, this Martin was called the Stationette. Mr. Martin was unable to interest anyone in mass production of either his three-wheeler or his magnetic transmission.

I.D. NUMBERS: Not available.

STATIONETTE

Model Number	Body/Style Number	Body Type & Seating	Factory Price	Shipping Weight	Production Total
NA	NA	2-dr Cpe-3P	995	NA	1

ENGINE: Hercules. Four-cylinder. L-head. Rear-mounted. Displacement: 47.3 cid. Brake hp: 24.

POWERTRAIN: Magnetic fluid-drive transmission.

MANUFACTURER: Commonwealth Research Corp., New York, N.Y.

1953-1955 MAVERICK

MAVERICK — Possibly the most aesthetic boattail sports car ever built was the Maverick. Though only a two-passenger car, it was almost as long as the normal sedan of the day. Cleverly integrated into the fiberglass body were such production car parts as the 1940 LaSalle grille, 1949-1951 Lincoln headlight rims and 1949 Mercury parking lights. The buyer could specify whether he wanted two, one or no doors.

I.D. NUMBERS: Not available.

1955 Maverick, roadster, V-8 (PZ)

MAVERICK

Model Number	Body/Style Number	Body Type & Seating	Factory Price	Shipping Weight	Production Total
NA	NA	2-dr Rds-2P	3850	3100	7

NOTE 1: The factory price given above is for the 1953 model year.

ENGINE

(BASE) 1953 Cadillac. V-8. Overhead valves. Displacement: 331.1 cid. Bore and stroke: 3-13/16 x 3-5/8 inches. Compression ratio: 8.25:1. Brake hp: 210.

(OPTIONAL) Buyer had a choice of virtually any engine, but Cadillac power was usually installed.

POWERTRAIN: Three-speed manual transmission.

CHASSIS FEATURES: Wheelbase: 120 to 128 inches (depending on engine requirements). Overall length: Approximately 192 inches. Tire size: 7.60 x 15.

OPTIONS: Motorola radio ($95). Fiberglass top ($200). Overdrive ($200). Hydra-Matic.

MANUFACTURER: Maverick Motors, Mountain View, Calif.

1946 MERCURY SPECIAL

MERCURY SPECIAL — This aluminum-bodied sports roadster, based on the contemporary Mercury, was built in 1946. Only one prototype appeared. It used a Mercury engine, but Cadillac power was planned for production models and, possibly, fiberglass bodies. Volume production never took place.

MANUFACTURER: Paul Omohundro, Los Angeles, Calif.

1946 Mercury Special, two-door sports-roadster, V-8

1958-1962 MERRY OLDS

MERRY OLDS — A replica of the famous Curved Dash Oldsmobile, this car was made of plywood and steel. However it did have such modern equipment as sealed beam headlights (mounted inside lanterns) and an electric starter.

I.D. NUMBERS: Not available.

MERRY OLDS

Model Number	Body/Style Number	Body Type & Seating	Factory Price	Shipping Weight	Production Total
NA	NA	Rbt-2P	1495	425	NA

ENGINE: Clinton. One-cylinder. Air-cooled. Brake hp: 4.

POWERTRAIN: Two-speed manual transmission. Chain-drive.

CHASSIS FEATURES: Overall length: 72 inches.

MANUFACTURER: American Air Products Corp., Fort Lauderdale, Fla.

1959 Merry Oldsmobile, runabout, one-cylinder (PZ)

1960 MERRY RUNABOUT

MERRY RUNABOUT — A half-scale replica of the 1902 Curved Dash Olds.

I.D. NUMBERS: Not available.

MERRY RUNABOUT

Model Number	Body/Style Number	Body Type & Seating	Factory Price	Shipping Weight	Production Total
NA	NA	Rbt-2P	NA	190	NA

ENGINE: Lawson. Four-cycle. Brake hp: 2-1/2.

CHASSIS FEATURES: Wheelbase: 50 inches. Overall length: 65 inches.

MANUFACTURER: Greg-San Klassic Kars, Glendale, Calif.

1969 MINICAR

MINICAR — Designed as a small car, this automobile was equipped with such luxury features as automatic transmission and air conditioning. In spite of its Lilliputian dimensions, legroom was 40 inches.

I.D. NUMBERS: Not available.

MINICAR

Model Number	Body/Style Number	Body Type & Seating	Factory Price	Shipping Weight	Production Total
NA	NA	2-dr Cpe-3P	2500	NA	NA

NOTE 1: Price was projected on basis of annual production of 25,000 cars.

MINICAR ENGINE: Six-cylinder. Air-cooled. Displacement: 164 cid.

POWERTRAIN: Automatic transmission.

CHASSIS FEATURES: Overall length: 108 inches.

MANUFACTURER: Minicars, Inc., Goleta, Calif.

1967-1975 MOHS

MOHS — Mohs was a very unusual car, made even more outstanding by the fact that its many unorthodox features. The high price did not bring about its early demise. It had only one door located at the back. It was hinged in the roof and swung up, much like a lift-back. Side doors were not possible because of a full-length steel rail in each side, for protection in case of a broadside collision. The list of standard equipment must be the longest and most unusual for any car ever built. Sealed beam taillights are just one typical example. An International Havester engine and modified truck chassis were used. This very elaborate car was appropriately called the Ostentatienne Opera sedan.

I.D. NUMBERS: Not available.

OSTENTATIENNE

Model Number	Body/Style Number	Body Type & Seating	Factory Price	Shipping Weight	Production Total
A	NA	1-dr Cpe-4P	19,600	5740	Note 1
B	NA	1-dr Cpe-4P	25,600	6100	Note 1

NOTE 1: Production unknown, but seldom more than three or four cars per year.

1967 Mohs, Ostentatienne Opera sedan, V-8 (PZ)

ENGINES

(MODEL A) International Harvester (truck). V-8. Overhead valves. Cast iron block. Displacement: 304 cid. Bore and stroke: 3.88 x 3.22 inches. Displacement: 304 cid. Compression ratio: 8.2:1. Brake hp: 193 at 4400 rpm. Five main bearings. Hydraulic valve lifters. Carburetor: Holley two-barrel.

(MODEL B) International Harvester (truck). V-8. Overhead valves. Cast iron block. Displacement: 549 cid. Bore and stroke: 4-1/2 x 4-5/16 inches. Brake hp: 250 at 4400 rpm.

POWERTRAIN: Borg-Warner three-speed automatic transmission.

CHASSIS FEATURES: (Chassis made by International Harvester to Mohs specifications.) Wheelbase: 119 inches. Overall length: 246 inches. Front tread: 74 inches. Rear tread: 74 inches. Tire size: 7.50 x 20 (with nitrogen filled inner tubes).

1972-1975 MOHS

MOHS — An additional model was offered by Mohs beginning in 1972. Called the SafariKar, it can be described as a dual cowl phaeton with a retractable metal top. The aluminum body panels were covered with polyurethane foam and Naugahyde on the exterior. Hingeless doors opened and closed by sliding in or out on linear bushings and shafts. Equipped with jump seats, the SafariKar had a total seating capacity of eight. The back seat could convert into a bed to sleep two adults and two children.

SAFARIKAR I.D. NUMBERS: Not available. Cars were built on International Harvester chassis and are believed to carry IH serial numbers. Car in Imperial Palace Auto Collection has serial number 312101H942198.

1972 Mohs, Safarikar convertible, V-8 (PZ)

SAFARIKAR

Model Number	Body/Style Number	Body Type & Seating	Factory Price	Shipping Weight	Production Total
NA	NA	2-dr Conv-8P	14,500	5400	NA

ENGINE: International Harvester (truck). V-8. Overhead valves. Cast iron block. Displacement: 392 cid. Bore and stroke: 4.12 x 3.66 inches. Compression ratio: 8.1:1. Brake hp: 179 at 3600 rpm. Five main bearings. Hydraulic valve lifters. Carburetor: Holley four-barrel.

POWERTRAIN: Three-speed hydraulic torque converter automatic transmission.

CHASSIS FEATURES: Wheelbase: 131 inches (chassis made by International Harvester to Mohs specifications). Overall length: 240.1 inches. Front tread: 63.6 inches. Rear tread: 63.6 inches. Tire size: 8.00 x 17.5

OPTIONS: Four-wheel-drive. Front suspension telescoping dampers. Two-way radio. Stereo. Television. Butane furnace.

MANUFACTURER: Mohs Seaplane Corp., Madison, Wis.

1975 Mohs, two-door SafariKar, V-8 ("The Auction")

1953 MOTA

MOTA — The Mota was a low-slung, fiberglass-bodied sports roadster. Its small gasoline engine drove an alternator, which powered the 'Polade Power' unit. This was located ahead of the rear axle. The manufacturer said this power unit was radically different in concept and performance than conventional electric motors. Acceleration from 0 to 100 mph in just 300 feet was a dubious company claim.

I.D. NUMBERS: Not available.

MOTA

Model Number	Body/Style Number	Body Type & Seating	Factory Price	Shipping Weight	Production Total
NA	NA	2-dr Rds-2P	NA	NA	NA

ENGINE: Air-cooled gasoline engine drove the alternator, which supplied power to an electric motor.

MANUFACTURER: Banning Electric Products Corp., Automotive Division, New York, N.Y.

1953 Mota, two-door roadster

1946-1948 MOTORETTE

MOTORETTE — This small, open-bodied two-seater got off to a far faster start than any other new postwar car, except Kaiser-Frazer. By the fall of 1947, more than 4,000 Motorettes and Truckettes had been made. Buy by the fall of 1948, the company had filed for bankruptcy. The cars themselves had aluminum bodies and three wheels. The single wheel was in front. The Motorette was very economical for use, in good weather, over short runs.

I.D. NUMBERS: Not available.

MOTORETTE

Model Number	Body/Style Number	Body Type & Seating	Factory Price	Shipping Weight	Production Total
20	NA	Rbt2P	495	420	Note 1

NOTE 1: Total production of Motorettes and Truckettes (trucks) from 1946 through 1948 was more than 4,000 units.

ENGINE: Wisconsin. One-cylinder. Air-cooled. Rear-mounted. Displacement: 17.9 cid. Bore and stroke: 2-7.8 x 2-3/4 inches. Brake hp: 4.l.

POWERTRAIN: Two-speed mercury-operated automatic clutch transmission. Roller chain-drive to left rear wheel.

CHASSIS FEATURES: Wheelbase: 60 inches. Overall length: 90 inches. Tire size: 4.00 x 8.

MANUFACTURER: Motorette Corp., Buffalo, N.Y.

1946 Motorette, two-passenger scooter runabout, one-cyl.

1947 Motorette, two-passenger scooter, runabout one-cyl.

1947 Motorette 20, two-door scooter runabout, one-cyl. (PZ)

1952 MULTIPLEX

1952 Multiplex, two-door roadster V-8 (PZ)

MULTIPLEX — This was Multiplex's second entry into the car building business. Their first was in the early teens. The postwar Motorette was a roadster made of Studebaker, Willys and other production car parts. A Willys six-cylinder motor was used.

I.D. NUMBERS: Not available.

MULTIPLEX

Model Number	Body/Style Number	Body Type & Seating	Factory Price	Shipping Weight	Production Total
NA	NA	2-dr Rds-2P	1705	NA	1

ENGINE: Willys. Six-cylinder. F-head. Cast iron block. Displacement: 161 cid. Bore and stroke: 3-1/8 x 3-1/2 inches. Brake hp: Four main bearings. Solid valve lifters. Carburetor: Carter Model YF-924S one-barrel.

CHASSIS FEATURES: Not available.

1953-1954 MULTIPLEX

1954 Multiplex 186, two-door roadster, 4-cyl (PZ)

MULTIPLEX — Multiplex only made three cars during the early 1950s. Their second and third, designated '186' models, were much better and more professional-looking than the first. They had a very strong Italian accent in their styling. Willys F-head engines of four- or six-cylinders were souped-up some before being installed in the fiberglass bodies.

I.D. NUMBERS: Not available.

MULTIPLEX 186

Model Number	Body/Style Number	Body Type & Seating	Factory Price	Shipping Weight	Production Total
186	NA	2-dr Rds-2P	NA	NA	1
186	NA	2-dr HT-2P	4000	1705	1

ENGINES

(ROADSTER) Willys (modified). Four-cylinder. F-head. Cast iron block. Displacement: 121.8 cid. Brake hp: 87 at 4400 rpm. Three main bearings. Solid valve lifters.

(COUPE) Willys (modified). Six-cylinder. F-head. Cast iron block. Displacement: 161 cid. Bore and stroke: 3-1/8 x 3-1/2 inches. Brake hp: 124 at 4500 rpm. Four main bearings.

CHASSIS FEATURES: Wheelbase: (roadster) 85 inches; (coupe) 94 inches. Overall length: (roadster) 140-3/4 inches; (coupe) 148 inches. Front tread: (roadster) 46 inches; (coupe) 49 inches. Rear tread: (roadster) 45.4 inches; (coupe) 50 inches.

OPTIONS: The coupe engine was optional in the roadster.

MANUFACTURER: Multiplex Manufacturing Co., Berwick, Pa.

1951 MUNTZ

MUNTZ — Though previously thought to have originated in 1950, recently discovered information indicates that the first production versions of the Muntz were serial-numbered as 1951 models. Television maker Earl "Madman" Muntz bought the Kurtis-Kraft business. He renamed the car the Muntz and made a few changes. The wheelbase was stretched three inches and turned the car into a four-passenger. Styling of the aluminum-bodied car remained virtually unchanged from its appearance as a Kurtis. Muntz manufacturing operations were moved to Illinois. The Cadillac engine used in the Kurtis was dropped in favor of a Lincoln V-8. It gave the Muntz a top speed of over 108 mph.

I.D. NUMBERS: Serial numbers were located on the right front frame member. Serial numbers were also located under the scuff plate on the left door and also under the right front door jamb. Muntz serial numbers were first listed for the 1951 model year, with M-101 to M-189 used.

1951 Muntz, two-door hardtop, V-8 (HAC)

JET

Model Number	Body/Style Number	Body Type & Seating	Factory Price	Shipping Weight	Production Total
NA	NA	2-dr HT-4P	5210	3400	89

NOTE 1: Production based on actual serial number range.

1951 Muntz Jet, two-door hardtop coupe, V-8 (PZ)

ENGINE: Lincoln. V-8. L-head. Cast iron block. Displacement: 336.7 cid. Bore and stroke: 3.5 x 4.375 inches. Compression ratio: 7.5:1. Brake hp: 154 at 3600 rpm. Three main bearings. Carburetor: Holley dual-downdraft.

POWERTRAIN: GM Hydra-Matic transmission.

CHASSIS FEATURES: Wheelbase: 113 inches. Overall length: 178 inches. Front tread: 56 inches. Rear tread: 56 inches. Tire size: 7.60 x 15.

MANUFACTURER: Muntz Car Co., (1950) Glendale, Calif. (1951 to 1954) Evanston, Ill.

1952 MUNTZ

MUNTZ — Formerly a coupe, the Muntz became a roadster-convertible with a removable hardtop in 1952. Styling remained virtually unchanged and a Lincoln V-8 was used again and had the same horsepower rating. Previously, steel body construction was thought to have started this year. However, this does not agree with contemporary data books, which indicate that the weight of a 1952 Muntz dropped by 100 pounds and the price fell from $5,210.28 to $4,936. Logic suggests that the 1952 model was retained aluminum body construction and was sold in base form without a top. This would account for the lower price and weight. The symbols "52" to identify 1952 models were added to the VIN between the "M" prefix and the sequential production number.

I.D. NUMBERS: Serial numbers were located on the right front frame member. Serial numbers were also located under the scuff plate on the left door and also under the right front door jamb. Muntz serial numbers for the 1952 model year were M-52-190 and up. Ending number was not recorded.

1952 Muntz, two-door hardtop, V-8

JET

Model Number	Body/Style Number	Body Type & Seating	Factory Price	Shipping Weight	Production Total
NA	NA	2-dr Conv-4P	4936	3300	Note 1

NOTE 1: Early catalogs listed 1950 production as 28; 1951 as 230.
NOTE 2: Impossible to integrate data in note 1 with serial numbering data.

ENGINE

POWERTRAIN: GM four-speed Hydra-Matic transmission.

CHASSIS FEATURES: Wheelbase: 116 inches. Overall length: 181 inches. Front tread: 56 inches. Rear tread: 56 inches. Tire size: 7.60 x 15.

OPTIONS: Removable hardtop.

MANUFACTURER: Muntz Car Co., (1950) Glendale, Calif. (1950 to 1954) Evanston, Ill.

1953-1954 MUNTZ

MUNTZ — The 1953 Muntz reflected very little styling change from previous year. However, a 260 pound increase in weight reflects the change to steel body construction. The price also increased by $178. No serial numbering information is available for this year. The base engine listed was the L-head Lincoln V-8 with the same bore and stroke and horsepower rating. Other sources indicate that a modified version of the same motor with almost 220 hp could be had. This is certainly possible, as claims of an increase in top speed to 120 mph were made. Serial numbering ended with 1953 models, although units left in dealer stocks may have been sold and titled as 1954 models.

I.D. NUMBERS: Not available.

JET

Model Number	Body/Style Number	Body Type & Seating	Factory Price	Shipping Weight	Production Total
NA	NA	2-dr Conv-4P	5114	3560	136

ENGINES

(STANDARD) Lincoln. V-8. L-head. Cast iron block. Displacement: 336.7 cid. Bore and stroke: 3-1/2 x 4-3/8 inches. Compression ratio: 7.5:1. Brake hp: 154 at 3600 rpm. Carburetor: Holley Model 587 two-barrel.

(OPTIONAL) Lincoln. V-8. L-head. Cast iron block. Displacement: 336.7 cid. Bore and stroke: 3-1/2 x 4-3/8 inches. Compression ratio: 7.5:1. Brake hp: 218 at 4200 rpm.

POWERTRAIN: GM four-speed Hydra-Matic transmission.

CHASSIS FEATURES: Wheelbase: 116 inches. Overall length: 181 inches. Front tread: 57 inches. Rear tread: 57 inches. Tire size: 7.60 x 15.

MANUFACTURER: Muntz Car Co., Evanston, Ill.

1969-1970 MURENA

MURENA — Something a little different was this GT type station wagon. The front end was styled not too much unlike the Italian Fiat Dino. The cargo area at the back did have some slope, with the back window inset and a bit more upright. Murena used Ford's biggest and most powerful engine to get GT type performance.

I.D. NUMBERS: Not available.

MURENA

Model Number	Body/Style Number	Body Type & Seating	Factory Price	Shipping Weight	Production Total
NA	NA	4-dr Sta Wag-5P	14,950	3770	NA

NOTE 1: Prices were $1,000 more on the West Coast.

ENGINE: Ford. V-8. Overhead. Cast iron block. Displacement: 429 cid. Bore and stroke: 4.36 x 3.59 inches. Compression ratio: 10.5:1. Brake hp: 360 at 4600 rpm. Five main bearings. Hydraulic valve lifters. Carburetor: Autolite Model C8SF-H four-barrel.

CHASSIS FEATURES: Wheelbase: 118 inches. Overall length: 205 inches. Tire size: 205VR x 15. Front and rear tread: 60.5 inches.

POWERTRAIN: Three-speed automatic transmission.

MANUFACTURER: Murena Motors Corp. (Ltd.), New York, N.Y.

1948 MUSTANG

MUSTANG — This was a uniquely styled car. Or, at least, was unique until the Fiat 600D Multipla fastback station wagon appeared eight years later. Designed by Roy C. McCarty, formerly the service manager for the Lincoln-Mercury Div. of Ford, it had an aluminum body that was blunt at the front like a bus. This Mustang had center side doors, like some vans, and a sloping back, like a 1940s GM sedanette. It was a six-passenger vehicle, seating two in front and four in the back bench seat. The engine was in the rear.

I.D. NUMBERS: Not available.

MUSTANG

Model Number	Body/Style Number	Body Type & Seating	Factory Price	Shipping Weight	Production Total
NA	NA	2-dr Sta Wag-6P	1235	NA	1

ENGINE: Hercules. Four-cylinder. L-head. Displacement: 162 cid. Bore and stroke: 37/16 x 4-3/8 inches. Compression ratio: 6.8:1. Brake hp: 59 at 3300 rpm.

POWERTRAIN: Warner, three-speed manual transmission.

CHASSIS FEATURES: Wheelbase: 102 inches.

MANUFACTURER: Mustang Engineering Corp., Renton, Wash.

1953-1954 NAVAJO

1954 Navajo, two-door roadster, V-8 (PZ)

NAVAJO — Overall styling of this car was very similar to a Jaguar XK-120, so the Navajo was a great attention getter. With a light fiberglass body, it had Jaguar-like performance, too. Zero to 100 mph took only 11 seconds. It could do a quarter-mile in just 14 seconds and had a top speed of 125 plus mph, according to company claims. A Mercury flathead V-8 engine was what did the trick.

I.D. NUMBERS: Not available.

NAVAJO

Model Number	Body/Style Number	Body Type & Seating	Factory Price	Shipping Weight	Production Total
NA	NA	2-dr Rds-3P	2895	2300	NA

ENGINE: Mercury (modified). V-8. L-head. Cast iron block. Brake hp: 130. Three main bearings. Solid valve lifters.

CHASSIS FEATURES: Wheelbase: 116 inches.

MANUFACTURER: Navajo Motor Car Co., New York, N.Y.

1959-60 NU-KLEA

1959-1960 NU-KLEA

NU-KLEA — This small, two-passenger fiberglass electric car was offered in either roadster or coupe form. It had two electric motors — one to drive each rear wheel. The driving range claimed, on one battery charge, was an excellent 75 to 80 miles.

I.D. NUMBERS: Not available.

NU-KLEA

Model Number	Body/Style Number	Body Type & Seating	Factory Price	Shipping Weight	Production Total
NA	NA	2-dr HT-2P	NA	NA	NA
NA	NA	2-dr Conv-2P	NA	NA	NA

ENGINE: Electric. Two electric motors (one to drive each rear wheel). Range between battery charges: 75 to 80 miles.

CHASSIS FEATURES: Not available.

MANUFACTURER: Nu-Klea Automobiles Corp., Lansing, Mich.

1959 Nu-Klea, two-door hardtop, electric

1968 OLDS REPLICA

OLDS 1901 REPLICA — Two-passenger, three-quarter scale, likeness of the 1901 Oldsmobile.

MANUFACTURERS: Horseless Carriage Corp., Fort Lauderdale, Fla.

1973 Olds Replica, runabout, one-cylinder (CG)

1967 OMEGA

OMEGA — When the Griffith GT was struggling to get started, the operation was purchased by a company headed by former CAR and DRIVER technical editor, Steve Wilder. The car's name was changed to Omega and the engine was changed from Plymouth to the small Ford V-8. Styling was left virtually untouched, because the steel bodies continued to be built in Italy by Intermeccanica. However, actual assembly of the car was done in Charlotte, N.C., by Holman and Moody.

I.D. NUMBERS: Not available.

OMEGA

Model Number	Body/Style Number	Body Type & Seating	Factory Price	Shipping Weight	Production Total
NA	NA	2-dr HT-2P	8250	2400	NA

ENGINE: Ford. V-8. Overhead valve. Cast iron block. Displacement: 289 cid. Bore and stroke: 4.00 x 2.88 inches. Compression ratio: 9.3:1. Brake hp: 200 at 4400 rpm. Five main bearings. Hydraulic valve lifters. Carburetor: Ford Model C7DF-S two-barrel. The 271 hp 289 cid Ford engine was available as an option with 271 hp at 6000 rpm.; Compression ratio: 10.0:1.

CHASSIS FEATURES: Wheelbase: 94-1/2 inches. Overall length: 175-1/2 inches. Front tread: 58 inches. Rear tread: 57 inches. Tire size: 7.35 x 14.

1968 OMEGA

OMEGA — Very little styling or mechanical change from the previous year, although a larger Ford engine was on the option list. This was the final year for the Omega. Frank Reisner of Intermeccanica continued making virtually the same car, in Italy, using different names and various American and European engines. Meanwhile, Steve Wilder was paid a sum of money, by General Motors, for Oldmobile Div.'s right to use the Omega name.

I.D. NUMBERS: Not available.

OMEGA

Model Number	Body/Style Number	Body Type & Seating	Factory Price	Shipping Weight	Production Total
NA	NA	2-dr HT-2P	8950	2400	NA

ENGINES

(STANDARD) Ford. V-8. Overhead valve. Cast iron block. Displacement: 289 cid. Bore and stroke: 4.00 x 2.88 inches. Compression ratio: 8.7:1. Brake hp: 195 at 4600 rpm. Five main bearings. Hydraulic valve lifters. Carburetor: Autolite two-barrel.

(OPTIONAL) Lincoln. V-8. L-head. Cast iron block. Displacement: 336.7 cid. Bore and stroke: 3-1/2 x 4-3/8 inches. Compression ratio: 7.5:1. Brake hp: 154 at 3600 rpm. Carburetor: Holley Model 587 two-barrel.($400).

(OPTIONAL) Ford V-8. Overhead valve. Cast iron block. Displacement: 302 cid. Bore and stroke: 4.00 x 3.00 inches. Compression ratio: 9.0:1. Brake hp: 21 0 at 4600 rpm. Five main bearings. Hydraulic valve lifters. Carburetor: Autolite Model 9510 C8AF-AK two-barrel.

CHASSIS FEATURES: Wheelbase: 94-1/2 inches. Overall length: 172-1/2 inches. Front tread: 58 inches. Rear tread: 57 inches. Tire size: 7.35 x 14.

MANUFACTURER: Suspensions International Corp., Charlotte, N.C.

1969 PALMERI

1969 Palmeri, two-door touring, V-8

1969 Palmeri, two-door touring, V-8

PALMERI — Antonio (Tony) Palmeri designed and built the Palmeri Touring Car in the two-car garage behind his home in East Detroit, Mich. A tool and die maker by trade and a car lover by inclination, Palmeri also built a number of other distinctive and individual vehicles. While closely resembling contemporary fiberglass "kit cars" of the time, the body and fenders of the neo-classically styled Palmeri were actually hand-built in steel taken from old Cadillacs. Additional styling touches were drawn from other vehicles and the completed package rode on a 1969 Chevrolet Biscayne chassis with V-8 power.

I.D. NUMBERS: Not available.

PALMERI

Model Number	Body/Style Number	Body Type & Seating	Factory Price	Shipping Weight	Production Total
NA	NA	2-dr Trg-4P	10,000	NA	1

ENGINES: Chevrolet V-8. Overhead valve. Cast iron block. Displacement: 326.7 (327) cid, modified.

1955 PANDA

PANDA — This tiny, two-passenger fiberglass car looked not too unlike the American Austin of the 1930s. It had a two-piece roof, which was detachable and storable in the trunk. A Kohler two-cylinder engine was standard, but the smaller Crosley engine was a no-cost option.

I.D. NUMBERS: Not available.

PANDA

Model Number	Body/Style Number	Body Type & Seating	Factory Price	Shipping Weight	Production Total
NA	NA	2-dr Conv-2P	999	900	NA

ENGINES

(BASE) Kohler. Two-cylinder. Horizontally-opposed. L-head. Displacement: 67.1 cid. Bore and stroke: 3.65 x 3.25 inches. Compression ratio: 6.0:1. Brake hp: 26 at 3600 rpm.

(OPTIONAL) Crosley. Overhead cam. Cast iron block. Displacement: 44 cid. Bore and stroke: 2.50 x 2.25 inches. Compression ratio: 7.0:1. Brake hp: 26-1/2 at 5400 rpm. Solid valve lifters. Carburetor: Tillotson Model DY9C one-barrel. (no extra cost).

POWERTRAIN: Three-speed manual transmission.

CHASSIS FEATURES: Wheelbase: 70 inches. Front tread: 40 inches. Rear tread: 40 inches.

1956 PANDA

PANDA — There was a number of minor differences on the 1956 Panda that distinguished it from the previous year's model. Different grillework, an emblem above the grille (instead of the Panda name), different bumper guards and a split windshield were some of the external changes. Mechanically, the biggest change was that the Crosley engine was no longer available as an option. Instead, an Aerojet engine was offered.

I.D. NUMBERS: Not available.

PANDA

Model Number	Body/Style Number	Body Type & Seating	Factory Price	Shipping Weight	Production Total
NA	NA	2-dr Conv-2P	999	900	NA

ENGINES

(BASE) Kohler. Two-cylinder. Air-cooled. Horizontally-opposed. L-head. Displacement: 67.1 cid. Bore and stroke: 3.65 x 3.25 inches. Compression ratio: 6.0:1. Brake hp: 26 at 3600 rpm.

(OPTIONAL) Aerojet. L-head. Displacement: 44 cid. Compression ratio: 7.0:1. Brake hp: 15.

POWERTRAIN: Three-speed manual transmission.

CHASSIS FEATURES: Wheelbase: 70 inches. Front tread: 40 inches. Rear tread: 40 inches.

MANUFACTURER: Small Cars Inc., Kansas City, Mo.

1962-1963 PANTHER

1962 Panther, two-door 2.6 roadster, V-8 (PZ)

PANTHER — The Panther was a beautiful, sleek-looking, fiberglass sports roadster. The very low front had a small oval grille with driving lights in each end. Under the low hood was a Daimler V-8. The Panther came in two versions, Standard and Model M. Both had the Daimler motor, which was slightly modified in the Standard. The Model M had a hotter version of the Daimler motor.

I.D. NUMBERS: Not available.

PANTHER

Model Number	Body/Style Number	Body Type & Seating	Factory Price	Shipping Weight	Production Total
NA	NA	2-dr Std Rds-2P	4250	1200*	NA
M	NA	2-dr Model M Rds-2P	4995	1200*	NA

* Dry weight.

ENGINES

(STANDARD) Daimler (modified). V-8. Overhead valve. Cast iron block. Displacement: 155.9 cid. Bore and stroke: 3.00 x 2.75 inches. Compression ratio: 7.5:1. Brake hp: 145 at 5000 rpm. Five main bearings. Solid valve lifters. Carburetor: Zenith two-barrel.

(OPTIONAL) Daimler (modified). V-8. Overhead valve. Cast iron block. Displacement: 155.9 cid. Compression ratio: 9.0:1. Brake hp: 190 at 6500 rpm. Five main bearings. Solid valve lifters. Carburetor: Two Zenith two-barrel.

POWERTRAIN: Four-speed manual transmission.

CHASSIS FEATURES: Wheelbase: 94 inches. Overall length: 158 inches. Front tread: 50-3/4 inches. Rear tread: 51-1/2 inches. Tire size: 6.00 x 15.

OPTIONS: Radio. Oil temperature gauge (standard). Hardtop. Wire wheels (on standard) 48-spoke type; (on Model M) 60-spoke type.

MANUFACTURER: Panther Automobile Co., Bedford Hills, N.Y.

1973 PEDICAR

PEDICAR — (PEDAL-POWERED) — Does a people-powered vehicle belong in the STANDARD CATALOG OF AMERICAN CARS 1946-1975? In most cases, probably not, but the 1973 Pedicar stands out as a possible exception. It's full-bodied styling certainly places it in the 'car' category, when compared to various powered vehicles that failed to reach such a sophisticated state. As might be expected, it was a single-passenger job designed for low-cost, short-run shopping and commuting trips. The Pedicar had a very unusual shape, looking something like a plastic or fiberglass gondola mounted on four wire-spoke bicycle wheels. It even had doors, which opened front to back in in 'suicide' fashion. The name Pedicar was spelled-out, with large block letters, along the rear side panel. Quite easily passable for an electric, or even gas-powered auto, the Pedicar came with a standard equipment list that was much longer than found on most low-volume alternative cars. It included eight cubic feet of cargo space; a single, cyclops-style headlight; door locks; windows and windshield; driver's seat; pnuematic tires; mid-beltline protective molding; windshield wiper and, even, a rearview mirror. The manufacturer, Environmental Trans-Sport Corp. of Windsor, Conn., advised that most states would probably permit use of the Pedicar on local roads, but not major highways. Of course, two big advantages was that it used no gas and was virtually pollution-free.

1973 Pedi-Car, two-door coupe, peddle-powered (CG)

I.D. NUMBERS: Not available.

CHART SPECIFICATIONS: Not available.

POWER PLANT: Pedal operated by driver.

CHASSIS FEATURES: Five forward and one reverse speed gear transmission. (Overdrive or automatic not available). Bicycle-type tires mounted on wire wheels.

POWERTRAIN OPTIONS: Strong legs.

CONVENIENCE OPTIONS: It is unclear if the features mentioned above were standard or optional equipment.

HISTORICAL FOOTNOTES: The manufacturer was Environmental Trans-Sport Corp., Box 566, Windsor, Conn. 06095.

1959 PIONEER

1959 Pioneer Nic-L-Silver, two-door coupe, electric

PIONEER — This car may also have been known as the Lippencoft Pioneer, or Nic-L-Silver. It was a fiberglass, electric car offered in roadster, hardtop, and one-seat station wagon body types. Each rear wheel had its own electric drive motor. A simple flip of a switch put the car in reverse or forward. The car's range was up to 100 miles between charges.

1959 Pioneer Nic-L-Silver, convertible, electric motor (PZ)

I.D. NUMBERS: Not available.

PIONEER

Model Number	Body/Style Number	Body Type & Seating	Factory Price	Shipping Weight	Production Total
NA	NA	2-dr Rds-3P	NA	1800	NA
NA	NA	2-dr HT-3P	NA	NA	NA
NA	NA	2-dr Sta Wag-3P	NA	NA	NA

ENGINE: Electric. Two electric motors. One to drive each rear wheel. Brake hp: 8 (each). Range between battery charges: 40 to 100 miles (depending on driving conditions).

CHASSIS FEATURES: Wheelbase: 95 inches. Overall length: 157 inches.

MANUFACTURER: Nic-L-Silver Battery Co., Santa Anna, Calif.

1967 PIRANHA

PIRANHA — The maker of this car had produced uncounted millions of cars — the plastic model kind. The Piranha was also made of plastic, but it was a real car. The body was made of a material called Cycolac. Below the beltline, except for hidden headlights, it looked very similar to the CRV (Cycolac Research Vehicle) experimental car made in 1964 by the Marbon Chemical Div. of Borg-Warner. The reason for the similarity is that Marbon Chemical designed the car and AMT built it under license. The body was built out of Cycolac ABS (Acrylonitrile-Butadiene-Styrene) more commonly used for telephones. The two famous Piranhas were the Man From U.N.C.L.E. car and the AMT so-called "Funny Car" that had a blown and injected 426 Chrysler Hemi dragster engine, as well as numerous other modifications including a thicker skinned body. The Piranha was based on the Chevrolet Corvair and used its engine. An option was the turbocharged Corvair engine. This was a two-passenger coupe with gull-wing doors and a tilt steering wheel.

I.D. NUMBERS: Not available.

1967 Piranha, two-door coupe, 6-cyl (CG)

PIRANHA

Model Number	Body/Style Number	Body Type & Seating	Factory Price	Shipping Weight	Production Total
NA	NA	2-dr Cpe-2P	6000	1540	5 or 6

ENGINE: Chevrolet Corvair (1966). Six-cylinders. Horizontally-opposed. Air-cooled. Rear-mounted. Overhead valves. Aluminum block. Displacement: 164 cid. Bore and stroke: 3.44 x 2.94 Inches. Compression ratio: 9.25:1. Brake hp: 140 at 5200 rpm. Four main bearings. Hydraulic valve lifters.

OPTIONAL ENGINE: Chevrolet Corvair (1966). Six-cylinder. Horizontally-opposed. Aircooled. Rear-mounted. Overhead valves. Aluminum block. Displacement: 164 cid. Bore and stroke: 3.44 x 2.94 inches. Compression ratio: 8.25:1. Turbocharged. Brake hp: 180 at 4000 rpm. Four main bearings.

CHASSIS FEATURES: Wheelbase: 95 inches. Overall length: 157 inches. Front tread: 56 inches. Rear tread: 54 inches.

MANUFACTURER: A.M.T. Corp., Phoenix, Ariz.

1947 PLAYBOY

1947 Playboy, two-door retractable hardtop, 4-cyl

PLAYBOY — One of the most promising small postwar cars was the Playboy. Louis Horowitz, a former Packard dealer and Charles D. Thomas, previously with Pontiac, were the president and vice-president of the Playboy company. The original name of the company was Midget Motor Car Co. Playboy was a three-passenger convertible. The top of which was a manual, fold-down, metal affair. It made the car look chic when it was up or down. At least one Playboy had a cloth top, but it was a prototype. A few of the earliest Playboys used a Hercules four-cylinder engine. Top speed was about 75 mph and fuel economy was up to 35 mpg.

I.D. NUMBERS: Not available.

PLAYBOY

Model Number	Body/Style Number	Body Type & Seating	Factory Price	Shipping Weight	Production Total
NA	NA	2-dr Conv-3P	985	2035	NA

ENGINE: Hercules. Four-cylinder. L-head. Cast iron block. Displacement: 133 cid. Bore and stroke: 3.25 x 4.00 inches. Compression ratio: 7.1:1. Brake hp: 40 at 3200 rpm. Solid valve lifters. Three main bearings.

POWERTRAIN: Warner three-speed manual transmission.

CHASSIS FEATURES: Wheelbase: 90 inches. Overall length: 155 inches. Front tread: 47 inches. Rear tread: 47 inches. Tire size: 5.00 x 12.

1948-1950 PLAYBOY

1948 Playboy, two-door retractable hardtop, 4-cyl (PZ)

PLAYBOY — Very little styling change from the previous year. A switch to Continental engines was made, shortly after production began. This was probably around the time production of the 1948 model production began.

I.D. NUMBERS: Not available.

PLAYBOY

Model Number	Body/Style Number	Body Type & Seating	Factory Price	Shipping Weight	Production Total
NA	NA	2-dr Conv-3P	985	2035	NA

NOTE 1: The factory price given above is for the 1948 model year.

PLAYBOY ENGINE: Continental. Four-cylinder. L-head. Cast iron block. Displacement: 91 cid. Bore and stroke: 2.88 x 3.50 inches. Compression ratio: 7.1:1. Brake hp: 40 at 3600 rpm. Solid valve lifters. Three main bearings.

POWERTRAIN: Warner three-speed manual transmission. Overdrive optional.

CHASSIS FEATURES: Wheelbase: 90 inches. Overall length: 155 inches. Front tread: 47 inches. Rear tread: 47 inches. Tire size: 5.90 x 12.

1951 PLAYBOY

PLAYBOY — Very little styling change from the previous year. The final few Playboys made were fitted with Willys four-cylinder engines.

I.D. NUMBERS: Not available.

PLAYBOY

Model Number	Body/Style Number	Body Type & Seating	Factory Price	Shipping Weight	Production Total
NA	NA	2-dr Conv-3P	1600	2035	NA

ENGINE: Willys. Four-cylinder. L-head. Cast iron block. Displacement: 134.2 cid. Bore and stroke: 3-1/8 x 4-3/8 inches. Compression ratio: 6.48:1. Brake hp: 72 at 4000 rpm. Solid valve lifters. Three main bearings. Carburetor: Carter Model YF one-barrel.

POWERTRAIN: Warner three-speed manual transmission. Overdrive optional.

CHASSIS FEATURES: Wheelbase: 90 inches. Overall length: 155 inches. Front tread: 47 inches. Rear tread: 47 inches. Tire size: 5.90 x 12.

MANUFACTURER: Playboy Motor Corp., Buffalo, N.Y.

1955-1956 POWELL

POWELL — Most of this company's production was In pickup trucks, but a few station wagons were also built. Both trucks and wagons used a large number of Plymouth parts. The 1941 chassis was the base, with rebuilt engines of the 1940s and early 1950s. These all-metal wagons (only some of the grille pieces were fiberglass) were offered in Standard and Deluxe versions. The end of production was caused by the drying up of parts sources.

POWELL I.D. NUMBERS: Not available.

POWELL

Model Number	Body/Style Number	Body Type & Seating	Factory Price	Shipping Weight	Production Total
NA	NA	2-dr Sta Wag-6P	1095	2700	Note
NA	NA	2-dr Del Sta Wag-6P	1198	2700	Note

NOTE 1: Approximately 300 station wagons built.
NOTE 2: Approximately 1,000 pickup trucks built.

ENGINE: Plymouth (1941-1950). Six-cylinder. L-head. Cast iron block. Displacement: 217.8 cid; (1941) 201 cid. Bore and stroke: 3-1/4 x 4-3/8 inches; (1941) 3-1/8 x 4-3/8 inches. Compression ratio: (1941) 6.70:1; (1942) 6.80:1; (1946-1948) 6.60:1; (1949-1950) 7.0:1. Brake hp: (1941) 87 at 3800 rpm.; (1942) 95 at 3400 rpm.; (1946-1949) 95 at 3600 rpm.; (1949-1950) 97 at 3600 rpm. Solid valve lifters. Four main bearings.

1955 Powell, two-door sport wagon pickup, 6-cyl (PZ)

POWERTRAIN: Three-speed manual transmission.

CHASSIS FEATURES: Wheelbase: (1941 Plymouth) 117 inches. Overall length: 168 inches. Front tread: 57 inches. Rear tread: 60 inches. Tire size: 6.00 x 16.

MANUFACTURER: Powell Manufacturing Co., Compton, Calif.

1947-1948 PUBLIX

PUBLIX — Ambitious plans were announced for this tiny, economical, three-wheeled car. The single wheel was at the front. Having a smooth, pointed nose, the body was made of aluminum and a cloth or fiberglass top was offered. A variety of aluminum engines were considered and several were offered. The Publix weighed a mere 150 to 250 pounds, depending on the engine used. A number of unusual features were incorporated. The steering wheel was movable to the left or right side, which indicates the company may have been considering exports to countries with left-hand traffic. To save parking space, the car could be tipped onto its back. Production was to have taken place in factories in both Buffalo, N.Y. and across the Niagara River in Fort Erie, Ontario. There seems to be some evidence that all was not above board in the company's activities. The Chambers of Commerce in those two cities knew surprisingly little of Publix operations.

I.D. NUMBERS: Not available.

PUBLIX

Model Number	Body/Style Number	Body Type & Seating	Factory Price	Shipping Weight	Production Total
NA	NA	2-dr Conv-2P	300	150-200	NA

NOTE 1: Price depends on engine used.

1947 Publix, two-door convertible, 1-cyl.

ENGINES: Various aluminum engines were offered. They ranged in bhp from 1.7 to 10.4. Most were single-cylinder, air-cooled motors.

POWERTRAIN: Belt-driven.

CHASSIS FEATURES: Wheelbase: 50 inches. Overall length: 72 inches.

MANUFACTURER: Publix Motor Car Co., Buffalo, N.Y.

1948 PUP

1948 Pup, two-passenger open runabout, one-cyl.

PUP — This unusual, tiny car was made in Wisconsin shortly after the war. It was an open, doorless, two-passenger vehicle. The chassis was made of oak and wood was quite prevalent in the body construction. A rear-mounted, one-cylinder, air-cooled engine powered the Pup through a chain-drive system.

I.D. NUMBERS: Not available.

PUP

Model Number	Body/Style Number	Body Type & Seating	Factory Price	Shipping Weight	Production Total
NA	NA	Open Runbout-2P	595	NA	NA

ENGINE: Briggs & Stratton. One-cylinder. Four cycle. Air-cooled. Rear-mounted. Brake hp: 7-112.

POWERTRAIN: Automatic clutch and chain-drive.

CHASSIS FEATURES: Wheelbase: 72 inches. Overall length: 102 inches.

1949 PUP

PUP — A vastly different Pup model was designed shortly after the first one, which it replaced. Like the original, the latter model was an open, doorless, two-passenger car, but this one had an optional canvas top and side curtains for some protection from the elements. The body was slab sided, because it was made of wood panels. The wheels were hidden by skirts and a rubber bumper, which completely surrounded the vehicle. A two-cylinder engine located in the back, provided power.

I.D. NUMBERS: Not available.

PUP

Model Number	Body/Style Number	Body Type & Seating	Factory Price	Shipping Weight	Production Total
NA	NA	Rbt-2P	595	NA	NA

ENGINE: Briggs & Stratton. Two-cylinder. Air-cooled. Rear-mounted. Brake hp: 10.

POWERTRAIN: Automatic clutch and chain-drive.

CHASSIS FEATURES: Wheelbase: 68 inches. Overall length: 112 inches. Front tread: 44 inches. Rear tread: 44 inches. Tire size: 4.00 x 8.

OPTIONS: Canvas top ($50). Side curtains ($25).

MANUFACTURER: Pup Motor Car Co., Inc., Spencer, Wis.

1962-1963 QUANTUM

QUANTUM — The Swedish built Saab was never a great contender in any beauty contests. Perhaps that is one reason why the Quantum came into existence. It was a Saab that was re-bodied in fiberglass. It had its deep-set headlights covered with clear plastic to reduce air drag, like the early Jaguar XKEs. The change from Saab was quite extensive. The chassis was shortened a foot and the resulting car was a sports roadster — not a sedan like the Saab. The amount of the change from the original car is indicated by the fact that the Quantum's weight was about half that of the Saab. Sales were handied through Saab dealers.

I.D. NUMBERS: Not available.

QUANTUM

Model Number	Body/Style Number	Body Type & Seating	Factory Price	Shipping Weight	Production Total
NA	NA	2-dr Rds-2P	3000	1000	NA

ENGINE: Saab. Three-cylinder. Two stroke. No valves. Cast iron block. Displacement: 52 cid. Bore and stroke: 2.75 x 2.85 inches. Compression ratio: 7.3:1. Brake hp: 42 at 5000 rpm. Four main bearings. Carburetor one-barrel.

POWERTRAIN: Four-speed manual transmission.

CHASSIS FEATURES: Wheelbase: 86 inches (modified Saab). Overall length: 150 inches. Front tread: 48 inches. Rear tread: 48 inches. Tire size: 155 x 15.

MANUFACTURER: Quantum Corp., Rockland, Mass.

1902 RAMBLER REPLICA

RAMBLER 1902 REPLICA — As its name strongly suggests, this car was an imitation of the original 1902 Rambler. It followed the Merry Olds, but was taken over by Gaslight Motors. Evidently the name was changed to Gaslight in 1960.

MANUFACTURER: America Air Products Corp., Ft. Lauderdale, Fla. (Later) Gaslight Motor Corp., Lathrup Village, Mich.

1949-1954 ROCKEFELLER

ROCKEFELLER — A remarkable little sports car was the Rockefeller. Its designer, Warren Shiber, used many Ford components, including engine and shortened chassis. The body consisted of five fiberglass panels and the interior was leather-like plastic. Weighing just one ton, this car was claimed to be capable of 100 mph and 0-to-60 in 12 seconds. It had a fuel consumption rating of 25 mpg. If the buyer so desired, he could order the car without an engine and install one of his own choice. Also the body alone was available.

I.D. NUMBERS: Not available.

ROCKEFELLER YANKEE

Model Number	Body/Style Number	Body Type & Seating	Factory Price	Shipping Weight	Production Total
NA	NA	2-dr Rds-4P	4000	900	NA

ENGINE: Ford. V-8. L-head. Cast iron block. Displacement: 239.4 cid. Bore and stroke: 3.19 x 3.75 inches. Compression ratio: (1949-1951) 6.8:1; (1952-1953) 7.2:1. Brake hp: (1949-1951) 100 at 3600 rpm.; (1952-1953) 110 at 3800 rpm. Solid valve lifters. Three main bearings. Carburetor: two-barrel.

POWERTRAIN: Ford three-speed manual transmission.

CHASSIS FEATURES: Wheelbase: 100 inches (modified Ford). Overall length: 170 at inches (approximate). Tire size: 6.00 x 16. Front tread: 58 inches; rear tread: 56 inches.

MANUFACTURER: Rockefeller Sports Car Corp., Rockville Centre, N.Y.

1948 ROCKET

1948 Rocket, two-door roadster, 4-cyl./6-cyl.

ROCKET — One of the best looking three-wheel cars was the Rocket. It had a 10-panel aluminum body mounted on a tubular, chrome molybdenum steel frame. Styling was smooth and very rounded. Headlights were sunken, something like the 1949-1951 Lincoln. The single wheel was at the back and the front wheels were partially covered by skirts. Three tops were available — cloth, aluminum or clear plastic. The rear-mounted engine could be a four- or six-cylinder powerplant. An automatic transmission was featured with either engine. The four was good for 75 mph. The six could reach 95 mph. An advanced feature of the interior was its padded dash.

I.D. NUMBERS: Not available.

ROCKET

Model Number	Body/Style Number	Body Type & Seating	Factory Price	Shipping Weight	Production Total
NA	NA	2-dr Rds-3P	1500	NA	NA

ENGINES

Four-cylinder. Rear-mounted. Brake hp: 65.

Six-cylinder. Rear-mounted. Brake hp: 95.

POWERTRAIN: Automatic transmission.

CHASSIS FEATURES: Wheelbase: 106 inches. Overall length: 161 inches.

MANUFACTURER: Hewson Pacific Corp., Los Angles Calif.

1949 ROGUE

ROGUE — Robert Monroe and Alexis Dowydoff produced a composite car. The foundation was a modified 1937 Dodge chassis. A modified Cadillac engine, along with Hydra-Matic transmission and two-speed rear axle, gave this car a 0-to-60 time of 6.5 seconds. Hydraulic brakes Lockheeds from a 1936 Auburn. Chrysler steering and Cadillac wheels were also used. The grille came from a 1950 Plymouth, fenders from a 1946 Oldsmobile 98 and bumpers from a 1947-1948 Frazer. The windshield of this roadster was from a 1937 Cord convertible.

1949 Rogue, two-door coupe-roadster, V-8.

I.D. NUMBERS: Not available.

ROGUE

Model Number	Body/Style Number	Body Type & Seating	Factory Price	Shipping Weight	Production Total
NA	NA	2-dr Rds-3P	NA	3000	NA

ENGINE: Cadillac (modified). V-8. Overhead valves. Cast iron block. Brake hp: 200.

POWERTRAIN: GM. Hydra-Matic transmission, with Columbia dual-ratio rear axle.

CHASSIS FEATURES: Wheelbase: 119 inches (modified 1937 Dodge). Overall length: 190 inches. Tire size: 6.00 x 16.

MANUFACTURER: Robert A. Monroe, New York, N.Y.

1958-1960 ROLLSMOBILE

ROLLSMOBILE — Two different models of the Rollsmobile were produced and each was a three-quarter representation of an early car. They aped the 1901 Olds and an early Ford. Mechanics (the same for both models) included a single-cylinder air-cooled engine. Top speed was only a very modest 35 mph, but fuel consumption was claimed to be a whopping 100 mpg.

I.D. NUMBERS: Not available.

ROLLSMOBILE

Model Number	Body/Style Number	Body Type & Seating	Factory Price	Shipping Weight	Production Total
NA	NA	Olds Rbt-2P	1200	NA	NA
NA	NA	Ford Rbt-2P	1200	NA	NA

ROLLSMOBILE ENGINE: Continental. One-cylinder. L-head. Cast iron block. Displacement: 8.4 cid. Bore and stroke: 2.31 x 2.00. Compression ratio: 6.10:1. Brake hp: 3 at 3600 rpm. Carburetor: Carter, Tillotson or Zenith.

POWERTRAIN: Automatic transmission.

CHASSIS FEATURES: Not available.

MANUFACTURER: Starts Mfg. Co. (1958-1960); Horseless Carriage Corp. (1960), Ft. Lauderdale, Fla.

1967-1969 ROWAN

ROWAN — One of the nicest electrics was the Rowan. Although it was basically boxy in shape, it had a sloping front and was rounded enough to have a rather pleasant appearance. It should have looked good, because it was styled by Ghia. It also had a number of mechanical items from DeTomaso of Italy. The Rowan had a tremendous range for an electric — up to 200 miles.

I.D. NUMBERS: Not available.

ROWAN

Model Number	Body/Style Number	Body Type & Seating	Factory Price	Shipping Weight	Production Total
NA	NA	2-dr Cpe-2P	NA	NA	NA

ENGINE: Electric. Two motors. Rear-mounted. Dynamic breaking (deceleration turned the motors into generators). Range between battery charges: 200 miles.

CHASSIS FEATURES: Not available.

MANUFACTURER: Rowan Controller Co., Westminster, Md., (or Oceanport, N.Y.)

1969-1972 RUGER

1969 Ruger, two-door Sports Tourer, V-8 (PZ)

RUGER — Many car makers over the years have been companies already established in some other line of manufacturing. The famous gunmaker, Sturm Ruger, somewhat surprisingly entered the automobile business. He called his car the Sports Tourer. It was built in the likeness of the 4-1/2-litre Bentley of the early 1930s. The car's hood was aluminum, but the rest of the body was fiberglass. All the body panels, except the hood and fenders, were covered with Naugahyde to simulate the leather-covered Bentley. Power came from a big Ford V-8. That gave the not-too-light car very good performance. Zero-to-60 acceleration was reported to be 7.7 seconds and top speed 110 mph.

I.D. NUMBERS: Not available.

SPORTS TOURER

Model Number	Body/Style Number	Body Type & Seating	Factory Price	Shipping Weight	Production Total
NA	NA	2-dr Rds-4P	13,000	3400	NA

ENGINE: Ford (1967). V-8. Overhead valves. Cast iron block. Displacement: 427 cid. Bore and stroke: 4.23 x 3.78 inches. Compression ratio: 11.0:1. Brake hp: 425 at 6000 rpm. Solid valve lifters. Five main bearings. Carburetor: Two Holley four-barrels.

POWERTRAIN: Four-speed manual transmission. Automatic transmission optional on later models.

CHASSIS FEATURES: Wheelbase: 130 inches. Overall length: 185 inches. Front tread: 57 inches. Rear tread: 57 inches. Tire size: 7.00 x 18.

MANUFACTURER: Sturm, Ruger & Co. Inc., Southport, Conn.

1946 RUSSELL

RUSSELL — Hydraulic drive was the primary feature of this car designed by Raymond Russell. The motor supplied oil pressure to four hydraulic motors — one for each wheel. This system eliminated the transmission, driveshaft, differential and the conventional braking system. Seven to 15 forward speeds were provided. After building his prototype, Mr. Russell was hired by the Ford Motor Co. to further research the hydraulic drive principle. Nothing more developed with the Russell car thereafter. The prototype was a crude-looking plywood bodied car, weighing about 2000 pounds. Had it gone into production, it would have been more conventional in appearance and body construction. Mr. Russell also built the Gadabout about this time.

MANUFACTURER: Raymond Russell, Detroit, Mich.

1946 Russell, two-door sedan prototype

1946 Russell, production model design sketch

1968-1969 SAVAGE GT

1969 Savage GT, two-door hardtop sports coupe, V-8 (PZ)

SAVAGE — Modified Plymouth Barracuda basically describes this car. High-performance 340, 383 or 440 cubic inch displacement Chrysler engines were offered. Special grille, wire wheels, exposed chrome exhausts and fiberglass deck lid with a small spoiler were some of the standard exterior features of this car, called the GT.

I.D. NUMBERS: Not available.

GT

Model Number	Body/Style Number	Body Type & Seating	Factory Price	Shipping Weight	Production Total
340	NA	2-dr HT-5P	4600	3300	NA
340	NA	2-dr Conv-5P	NA	3300	NA
383	NA	2-dr HT-5P	4700	3500	NA
383	NA	2-dr Conv-5P	NA	3500	NA
440	NA	2-dr HT-5P	4850	3600	NA
440	NA	2-dr Conv-5P	NA	3600	NA

ENGINES

340 ENGINE: Plymouth (modified). V-8. Overhead valves. Cast iron block. Displacement: 340 cid. Bore and stroke: 4.04 x 3.31 inches. Compression ratio: 10. 5:1. Brake hp: 280 at 5000 rpm. Five main bearings. Hydraulic valve lifters. Carburetor: four-barrel.

383 ENGINE: Plymouth. V-8. Overhead valve. Cast iron block. Displacement: 383 cid. Bore and stroke: 4.25 x 3.38 inches. Compression ratio: 10.0:1. Brake hp: 335 at 5000 rpm. Five main bearings. Hydraulic valve lifters. Carburetor: Carter Model AVS4426S four-barrel.

440 ENGINE: Chrysler Magnum (modified). V-8. Overhead valve. Cast iron block. Displacement: 440 cid. Bore and stroke: 4.32 x 3.75 inches. Compression ratio: 10.0:1. Brake hp: 380 at 4600 rpm. Five main bearings. Hydraulic valve lifters. Carburetor: Carter Model AVS4428S four-barrel.

POWERTRAIN: Four-speed manual transmission.

CHASSIS FEATURES: Wheelbase: 108 inches. Overall length: 192.8 inches. Front tread: 57.4 inches. Rear tread: 55.6 inches. Tire size: 205 x 14.

OPTIONS: TorqueFlite three-speed automatic transmission. Air conditioning. AM/FM push-button radio. Cartridge tape stereo. Power brakes. Front disc brakes. Power steering. Fast manual steering. Center console (standard with automatic transmission). Cold air induction package. High intensity driving lamps.

MANUFACTURER: Auto Craft Co., Fond du Lac, Wis.

1960 SAVIANO

SAVIANO — This economy-utility vehicle was versatile. Seating for four passengers was provided, but the two rear seats could be folded forward for cargo. Made of 12-gauge sheet steel, the Scat (short for Saviano Cargo and Touring) had a solid, forward slanting nose. A top was optional and it was detachable. Doors were removable also.

1960 Saviano, Scat two-door utility wagon, 2-cyl (CG)

I.D. NUMBERS: Not available.

SCAT

Model Number	Body/Style Number	Body Type & Seating	Factory Price	Shipping Weight	Production Total
NA	NA	2-dr Utl-4P	1390	1700	NA

ENGINE: Kohler. Two-cylinder. Air-cooled. Brake hp: 25.

POWERTRAIN: Borg-Warner. Three-speed manual transmission.

CHASSIS FEATURES: Wheelbase: 80 inches. Overall length: 125 inches.

1958 SCARAB

SCARAB — During the mid-'50s, Lance Reventlow, son of heiress Barbara Hutton, undertook development of an American sports racing car that would beat the established European makes at their own game. He brought together a team of the best automotive performance minds on the West Coast and the result was the Scarab. Reportedly, only three examples were built before orders for the very fast and expensive racers dried up. Those who campaigned them were not disappointed, however. They remained front-runners well into the '60s and were standout participants in vintage racing well after that.

SCARAB I.D. NUMBERS: Not available.

SCARAB

Model Number	Body/Style Number	Body Type & Seating	Factory Price	Shipping Weight	Production Total
NA	NA	2-dr Comp Rds-2P	NA	1800	3

ENGINE: Modified Chevrolet Corvette V-8. Overhead valves. 340 cid. 385 hp.

CHASSIS FEATURES: Tubular space frame. DeDion rear end. Independent front suspension. Halibrand quick-change gears. Magnesium racing wheels.

MANUFACTURER: Reventlow Automobile Co., Los Angeles, Calif.

1958 Scarab, two-door competition roadster, V-8 (front view)

1958 Scarab, two-door competition roadster, V-8 (rear view)

1946 SCOOTMOBILE

1946 Scootmobile, two-door coupe, one-cyl.

SCOOTMOBILE — By using a war surplus army bomber auxiliary fuel tank for a body, Norman Anderson made a small economy car. Many other aircraft parts were used as well, such as the wheels. This was a three-wheel car, with the single wheel in the rear. The engine was in the rear as well. Fuel economy of 75 mpg was claimed.

I.D. NUMBERS: Not available.

SCOOTMOBILE

Model Number	Body/Style Number	Body Type & Seating	Factory Price	Shipping Weight	Production Total
NA	NA	2-dr Cpe-2P	350	NA	1

ENGINE: One-cylinder. Air-cooled. Two-cycle: Rear-mounted. Brake hp: 12.

CHASSIS FEATURES: Overall length: 108 inches.

POWERTRAIN: Automatic transmission.

MANUFACTURER: Norman Anderson, Corunna, Mich.

1948 SCOOTMOBILE

SCOOTMOBILE — Another midget economy runabout appeared shortly after World War II. Very little descriptive information about it has remained, however.

I.D. NUMBERS: Not available.

SCOOTMOBILE II

Model Number	Body/Style Number	Body Type & Seating	Factory Price	Shipping Weight	Production Total
NA	NA	2-dr Rbt-2P	265	250	NA

ENGINE: One-cylinder. Brake hp: 4.

CHASSIS FEATURES: Not available.

MANUFACTURER: Jacob Affannato. (Location unknown).

1960 SEAGRAVE

SEAGRAVE — When compact car popularity bloomed, the famous fire apparatus manufacturer, Seagrave, seriously considered jumping on the bandwagon. They built three prototype hardtop coupes on a 93 inch wheelbase. Two were made of fiberglass and one of aluminum. A small four-cylinder engine was used. Seagrave never went beyond the prototype stage, however.

I.D. NUMBERS: Not available.

SEAGRAVE

Model Number	Body/Style Number	Body Type & Seating	Factory Price	Shipping Weight	Production Total
NA	NA	2-dr HT-2P	3000	1700	3

ENGINES: Continental. Four-cylinder. L-head. Displacement: 162 cid. Bore and stroke: 3.44 x 4.38 inches. Brake hp: 65.

CHASSIS FEATURES: Wheelbase: 93 inches. Overall length: 146 inches. Tire size: 5.50 x 12.

MANUFACTURER: Seagrave Fire Apparatus Co., Columbus, Ohio.

NOTE 1: Shelby-American specifications listed here are only for street models and do not include cars especially built for competition.

1962 SHELBY COBRA

SHELBY-AMERICAN — Former race driver Carroll Shelby got the notion that a simple way to make a really hot car would be to slip a small Ford V-8 into the aluminum body of the British-made AC Ace. So that was what he set about to do. The result ultimately led to one of the best performing and best selling American specialty cars ever produced, apart from the major manufacturers' offerings. The AC-bodied Shelbys were called Cobras.

I.D. NUMBERS: Contact Shelby-American Auto Club, 22 Olmstead Rd., West Redding, CT 06896.

SHELBY-AMERICAN COBRA

Model Number	Body/Style Number	Body Type & Seating	Factory Price	Shipping Weight	Production Total
260	NA	2-dr Rds-2P	5995	2020	75

NOTE 1: Production of 289 cid Cobras from 1962 through 1965 totalled 580 cars.

ENGINE: Ford (modified). V-8. Overhead valve. Cast iron block. Displacement: 260 cid. Bore and stroke: 3.80 x 2.88 inches. Compression ratio: 9.2:1. Brake hp: 260 at 5800 rpm. Five main bearings. Hydraulic valve lifters. Carburetor: (not available).

POWERTRAIN: Ford. Four-speed manual transmission.

CHASSIS FEATURES: Wheelbase: 90 inches. Overall length: 151-1/2 inches. Front tread: 51-1/2 inches. Rear tread: 52-1/2 inches. Tire size: 6.50 x 15 or 6.70 x 15.

1963 SHELBY COBRA

SHELBY-AMERICAN — The only significant change for 1963 was the switch to Ford's 289 cid engine from the original 260 V-8.

I.D. NUMBERS: Contact Shelby-American Auto Club, 22 Olmstead Rd., West Redding, CT 06896.

SHELBY-AMERICAN COBRA

Model Number	Body/Style Number	Body Type & Seating	Factory Price	Shipping Weight	Production Total
289	NA	2-dr Rds-2P	5995	2020	Note 1

NOTE 1: Production of 289 cid Cobras from 1962 through 1965 totalled 580 cars.

COBRA ENGINE: Ford (modified). V-8. Overhead valve. Cast iron block. Displacement: 289 cid. Bore and stroke: 4.00 x 2.88 inches. Compression ratio: 10.5:1. Brake hp: 271 at 5800 rpm. Five main bearings. Solid valve lifters. Carburetor: Holley four-barrel.

POWERTRAIN: Ford. Four-speed manual transmission.

CHASSIS FEATURES: Wheelbase: 90 inches. Overall length: 151-1/2 inches. Front tread: 51-1/2 inches. Rear tread: 52-1/2 inches. Tire size: 6.50 x 15 or 6.70 x 15.

1964 SHELBY COBRA

SHELBY-AMERICAN — Very little styling or mechanical change from the previous year.

I.D. NUMBERS: Contact Shelby-American Auto Club, 22 Olmstead Rd., West Redding, CT 06896.

SHELBY-AMERICAN COBRA

Model Number	Body/Style Number	Body Type & Seating	Factory Price	Shipping Weight	Production Total
289	NA	2-dr Rds-2P	5995	2100	Note 1

NOTE 1: Production of 289 cid Cobras from 1962 through 1965 totalled 580 cars.

ENGINE: Ford (modified). V-8. Overhead valve. Cast iron block. Displacement: 289 cid. Bore and stroke: 4.00 x 2.88 inches. Compression ratio: 10.5:1. Brake hp: 271 at 5800 rpm. Five main bearings. Solid valve lifters. Carburetor: Holley four-barrel.

POWERTRAIN: Ford. Four-speed close-ratio manual transmission.

CHASSIS FEATURES: Wheelbase: 90 inches. Overall length: 151-1/2 inches. Front tread: 51-1/2 inches. Rear tread: 52-1/2 inches. Tire size: 7.35 x 15.

1965 SHELBY COBRA

SHELBY-AMERICAN — Very little styling or mechanical change from the previous year. An additional Cobra model was introduced. (Its description follows immediately after this 289 entry). This was the last year for the 289 Cobra.

I.D. NUMBERS: Contact Shelby-American Auto Club, 22 Olmstead Rd., West Redding, CT 06896.

289 COBRA

Model Number	Body/Style Number	Body Type & Seating	Factory Price	Shipping Weight	Production Total
289	NA	2-dr Rds-2P	5995	2550	Note 1

NOTE 1: Production of 289 cid Cobras from 1962 through 1965 totalled 580 cars.

289 COBRA ENGINE: Ford (modified). V-8. Overhead valves. Cast iron block. Displacement: 289 cid. Bore and stroke: 4.00 x 2.88 inches. Compression ratio: 10.5:1. Brake hp: 271 at 5800 rpm. Five main bearings. Solid valve lifters. Carburetor: Holley four-barrel.

POWERTRAIN: Four-speed close-ratio manual transmission.

CHASSIS FEATURES: Wheelbase: 108 inches. Overall length: 181.6 inches. Front tread: 51-1/2 inches. Rear tread: 52-1/2 inches. Tire size: 7.75 x 15.

1965 Shelby-American, Cobra two-door roadster, V-8 (AA)

SHELBY-AMERICAN — If putting a small Ford V-8 into a AC made for excitement, let's see what putting a big V-8 will do, thought Carroll Shelby, so he gave it a try. The Ford 427 cid V-8 was used, so the car was called the 427 Cobra. Its styling was altered very slightly from the 289 Cobra. The honeycomb grillework was replaced by a single horizontal bar. Louvers were placed in the front fenders. Wider track and larger tires necessitated flared out fenders and larger wheel openings.

I.D. NUMBERS: Contact Shelby-American Auto Club, 22 Olmstead Rd., West Redding, CT 06896.

427 COBRA

Model Number	Body/Style Number	Body Type & Seating	Factory Price	Shipping Weight	Production Total
427	NA	2-dr Rds-2P	NA	2529	Note 2

NOTE 2: Production of 427 Cobras 1965-1967 totaled 356 cars.

ENGINE: Ford. V-8. Overhead valve. Cast iron block. Displacement: 427 cid. Bore and stroke: 4.24 x 3.79 inches. Five main bearings. Solid valve lifters. Carburetor: Two Holley four-barrel.

POWERTRAIN: Ford three-speed manual transmission.

CHASSIS FEATURES: Wheelbase: 90 inches. Overall length: 156 inches. Front tread: 56 inches. Rear tread: 56 inches. Tire size: 8.15 x 15.

1965 SHELBY MUSTANG

SHELBY-AMERICAN — The second generation Shelby took a different tack. They discontinued using the AC bodies, and began using the Ford Mustang fastback. Only very slight styling revisions differentiated Shelbys from stock Mustangs at first. Special racing stripes were the most obvious marks of distinction. Modified Ford 289 V-8s powered these Shelby Mustang GT-350s, which were sold through selected Ford dealers.

I.D. NUMBERS: Contact Shelby-American Auto Club, 22 Olmstead Rd., West Redding, CT 06896.

1965 Shelby-Mustang, GT-350 two-door fastback, V-8 (AA)

SHELBY-AMERICAN MUSTANG GT

Model Number	Body/Style Number	Body Type & Seating	Factory Price	Shipping Weight	Production Total
GT-350	NA	2-dr HT-4P	4547	2800	562

ENGINE: Ford (modified). V-8. Overhead valve. Cast iron block. Displacement: 289 cid. Bore and stroke: 4.00 x 2.88 inches. Compression ratio: 11.6:1. Brake hp: 306 at 6000 rpm. Five main bearings. Solid valve lifters. Carburetor: Holley Model 4150 four-barrel.

POWERTRAIN: Borg-Warner. Four-speed manual transmission.

CHASSIS FEATURES: Wheelbase: 108 inches. Overall length: 181.6 inches. Front tread: 57 inches. Rear tread: 57 inches. Tire size: 7.75 x 15.

1966 SHELBY COBRA

SHELBY-AMERICAN — Very little styling change from the previous year. Shelby switched to Ford's 428 cid V-8, because it was more readily available than the 427. Nevertheless the 427 designation was retained by Shelby.

I.D. NUMBERS: Contact Shelby-American Auto Club, 22 Olmstead Rd., West Redding, CT 06896.

1966 Shelby-American, Cobra two-door roadster (OC)

SHELBY-AMERICAN 427 COBRA

Model Number	Body/Style Number	Body Type & Seating	Factory Price	Shipping Weight	Production Total
427	NA	2-dr Rds-2P	NA	2529	Note 2

NOTE 2: Production of 427 Cobras 1965-1967 totaled 356 cars.

ENGINE: Ford (modified). V-8. Overhead valves. Displacement: 428 cid. Bore and stroke: 4.13 x 3.89 inches. Compression ratio: 10.5:1. Brake hp: 355 at 5400 rpm. Five main bearings. Solid valve lifters. Carburetor: Ford four-barrel.

POWERTRAIN: Four-speed manual transmission.

CHASSIS FEATURES: Wheelbase: 90 inches. Overall length: 156 inches. Front tread: 56 inches. Rear tread: 56 inches. Tire size: 8.15 x 15.

1966 SHELBY MUSTANG

SHELBY-AMERICAN — Very little styling or mechanical change from the previous year. Two models were added, though. A few Mustang convertibles were given the Shelby treatment. An ingenious promotion scheme was put into operation when Shelby sold a fleet of their cars to the Hertz car rental company. They were basically the same as the other Shelby coupes, but did have some unique differences. They were black with gold trim, and had full-size triangular rear side windows. These cars were given the GT-350H model designation.

1966 Shelby-Mustang, GT-350H (Hertz) two-door fastback, V-8 (AA)

I.D. NUMBERS: Contact Shelby-American Auto Club, 22 Olmstead Rd., West Redding, CT 06896.

SHELBY-AMERICAN GT-350/350H

Model Number	Body/Style Number	Body Type & Seating	Factory Price	Shipping Weight	Production Total
GT-350	NA	2-dr HT-4P	4600	2800	1438
GT-350H	NA	2-dr HT-4P	Note 1	2800	936
GT-350	NA	2-dr Conv-4P	Note 2	2931	6

NOTE 1: Never sold to the public; only sold to Hertz Car Rental Co.
NOTE 2: Never sold to the public; sold to Carroll Shelby's friends/employees.

ENGINE: Ford (modified). V-8. Overhead valve. Cast iron block. Displacement: 289 cid. Bore and stroke: 4.00 x 2.88 inches. Compression ratio: 11.6:1. Brake hp: 306 at 6000 rpm. Five main bearings. Solid valve lifters. Carburetor: Holley Model 4150 four-barrel.

POWERTRAIN: Four-speed manual transmission.

CHASSIS FEATURES: Wheelbase: 108 inches. Overall length: 186.6 inches. Front tread: 58 inches. Rear tread: 58 inches. Tire size: E70 x 15.

OPTIONS: Heavy-duty Cruise-O-Matic transmission.

1967 SHELBY COBRA/MUSTANG

SHELBY-AMERICAN — Very little styling or mechanical change from the previous year. This was the last of the Shelby Cobras.

I.D. NUMBERS: Contact Shelby-American Auto Club, 22 Olmstead Rd., West Redding, CT 06896.

SHELBY-AMERICAN 427 COBRA

Model Number	Body/Style Number	Body Type & Seating	Factory Price	Shipping Weight	Production Total
427	NA	2-dr Rds-2P	NA	2529	Note 2

NOTE 2: Production of 427 Cobras from 1965 through 1967 totalled 356 cars.

1967 Shelby-America, Cobra two-door roadster (RCA)

ENGINE: Ford (modified). V-8. Overhead valve. Cast iron block. Displacement: 428 cid. Bore and stroke: 4.13 x 3.98 inches. Compression ratio: 11.5:1. Brake hp: 425 at 6000 rpm. Five main bearings. Solid valve lifters. Carburetor: Ford four-barrel.

POWERTRAIN: Four-speed manual transmission.

CHASSIS FEATURES: Wheelbase: 90 inches. Overall length: 156 inches. Front tread: 56 inches. Rear tread: 56 inches. Tire size: 8.50 x 15.

SHELBY-AMERICAN — Contrary to the modest styling changes made to the Ford Mustang's new body for 1967, Shelby introduced greater visual uniqueness. The Mustang grille was removed and a pair of high beam lights were mounted in the center of the cavity. Lock pins Were standard on the hood, as well as a couple of air scoops. Air scoops were also located ahead of the rear wheels and on the roof quarter panels. The Mustang taillights were replaced by long rectangular units. Another model was offered. Called the GT-500, it used the Ford 428 V-8 previously found in the Cobra. Only the fastback was available in either the GT-350 or GT-500.

I.D. NUMBERS: Contact Shelby-American Auto Club, 22 Olmstead Rd., West Redding, CT 06896.

GT-350

Model Number	Body/Style Number	Body Type & Seating	Factory Price	Shipping Weight	Production Total
GT-350	NA	2-dr HT-4P	3995	2723	1175

ENGINE: Ford (modified). V-8. Overhead valve. Cast iron block. Displacement: 289 cid. Bore and stroke: 4.00 x 2.88 inches. Compression ratio: 10.5:1. Brake hp: 306 at 6000 rpm. Five main bearings. Solid valve lifters. Carburetor: Holley Model 4150 four-barrel.

1967 Shelby-Mustang, GT-500 two-door fastback, V8 (AA)

GT-500 I.D. NUMBERS: Not available.

GT-500

Model Number	Body/Style Number	Body Type & Seating	Factory Price	Shipping Weight	Production Total
GT-500	NA	2-dr HT-4P	4195	3286	2050

ENGINE: Ford (modified). V-8. Overhead valve. Cast iron block. Displacement: 328 cid. Bore and stroke: 4.13 x 3.98 inches. Compression ratio: 10.5:1. Brake hp: 355 at 5400 rpm. Five main bearings. Hydraulic valve lifters. Carburetor: Holley models 2604 or 2605 four-barrel.

POWERTRAIN: Four-speed manual transmission.

CHASSIS FEATURES: Wheelbase: 108 inches. Overall length: 186.6 inches. Front tread: 58 inches. Rear tread: 58 inches. Tire size: E70 x 15.

OPTIONS: Cruise-O-Matic SelectShift transmission (C4, GT-250; C6, GT-500).

1968 SHELBY MUSTANG

SHELBY-AMERICAN — The greatest range of models was offered by Shelby for 1968. The convertible was back again in the GT-350, GT-500 and the new GT-500KR. The 'KR' stood for "King of the Road." It was a mid-season replacement for the GT-500 using the 428 engine, modified a bit more than in the GT-500. Interestingly, the 427 cid engine was brought back as an option in the GT-500. The GT-350 moved up from the 289 to Ford's 302. It was modified, of course, and a supercharged version was a GT-350 option. Stylewise, changes for 1968 were the replacement of the high beam lights in the grille opening by widely spaced rectangular fog lights. The taillights were still the same shape, but the lenses were segmented into a strip of squares.

I.D. NUMBERS: Contact Shelby-American Auto Club, 22 Olmstead Rd., West Redding, CT 06896.

GT-350

Model Number	Body/Style Number	Body Type & Seating	Factory Price	Shipping Weight	Production Total
GT-350	NA	2-dr HT-4P	4117	3146	1253
GT-350	NA	2-dr Conv-4P	4238	3332	404

ENGINES

(BASE) Ford. Modified V-8. Overhead valves. Cast iron block. Displacement: 302 cid. Bore and stroke: 4.00 x 3.00 inches. Compression ratio: 10.5:1. Brake hp: 250 at 4800 rpm. Five main bearings. Carburetor: Holley four-barrel.

(OPTIONAL) Ford. Modified V-8. Overhead valve. Cast iron block. Displacement: 302 cid. Bore and stroke: 4.00 x 3.00 inches. Supercharged. Brake hp: 335 at 5200 rpm. Five main bearings. Carburetor: (not available).

1968 Shelby-Mustang, GT-500 two-door fastback, V-8 (AA)

I.D. NUMBERS: Contact Shelby-American Auto Club, 22 Olmstead Rd., West Redding, CT 06896.

GT-500

Model Number	Body/Style Number	Body Type & Seating	Factory Price	Shipping Weight	Production Total
GT-500	NA	2-dr HT-4P	4317	3445	1140
GT-500	NA	2-dr Conv-4P	4439	3631	402

ENGINES

(BASE) Ford. Modified V-8. Overhead valves. Cast iron block. Displacement: 428 cid. Bore and stroke: 4.13 x 3.78 inches. Compression ratio: 10.5:1. Brake hp: 360 at 5400 rpm. Five main bearings. Hydraulic valve lifters. Carburetor: Holley four-barrel.

(OPTIONAL) Ford. V-8. Overhead valves. Cast iron block. Displacement: 427 cid. Bore and stroke: 4.23 x 3.78 inches. Compression ratio: 11.6:1. Brake hp: 400 at 5600 rpm. Five main bearings. Solid valve lifters. Carburetor: Holly four-barrel.

I.D. NUMBERS: Contact Shelby-American Auto Club, 22 Olmstead Rd., West Redding, CT 06896.

GT-500 KR

Model Number	Body/Style Number	Body Type & Seating	Factory Price	Shipping Weight	Production Total
GT-500KRNA		2-dr HT-4P	4473	3545	933
GT-500KRNA		2-dr Conv-4P	4594	3731	318

ENGINE: Ford (modified). V-8. Overhead valves. Cast iron block. Displacement: 428 cid. Bore and stroke: 4.13 x 3.78 inches. Brake hp: 400 (est). Five main bearings. Carburetor: (not available).

POWERTRAIN: Four-speed manual transmission.

CHASSIS FEATURES: Wheelbase: 108 inches. Overall length: 186.6 inches. Front tread: 58.1 inches. Rear tread: 58.1 inches. Tire size: E70 x 15.

OPTIONS: SelectShift transmission ($50). Power disc brakes ($65). Power steering ($57). Shoulder harness ($50). Air conditioning ($356). Tinted glass (with air conditioning only, mandatory) ($30). Tilt steering wheel ($62). AM radio ($58).

1969 SHELBY MUSTANG

SHELBY-AMERICAN — Shelby followed the basic styling changes made by the Ford Mustang for 1969. However, the front deviated from the Mustang considerably. The grille design and hood were copied by Mustang, actually, for its 1970 and 1971 Mach I. The SportsRoof and convertible body types were used by Shelby. The GT-500 returned, but not the GT-500KR. The GT-350 took another step up the engine ladder to Ford's 351 V-8.

I.D. NUMBERS: Contact Shelby-American Auto Club, 22 Olmstead Rd., West Redding, CT 06896.

GT-350

Model Number	Body/Style Number	Body Type & Seating	Factory Price	Shipping Weight	Production Total
GT-350	NA	2-dr HT-4P	4434	3600	1085
GT-350	NA	2-dr Conv-4P	4753	3689	194

ENGINE: Ford (Windsor). V-8. Overhead valve. Cast iron block. Displacement: 351 cid. Bore and stroke: 4.00 x 3.50 inches. Compression ratio: 10.7:1. Brake hp: 290 at 4800 rpm. Five main bearings. Hydraulic valve lifters. Carburetor: Autolite four-barrel.

1969 Shelby-Mustang, GT-500 two-door convertible, V-8 (AA)

I.D. NUMBERS: Contact Shelby-American Auto Club, 22 Olmstead Rd., West Redding, CT 06896.

GT-500

Model Number	Body/Style Number	Body Type & Seating	Factory Price	Shipping Weight	Production Total
GT-500	NA	2-dr HT-4P	4709	3850	1536
GT-500	NA	2-dr Conv-4P	5027	3939	335

ENGINE: Ford. V-8. Overhead valve. Cast iron block. Displacement: 428 cid. Bore and stroke: 4.13 x 3.98 inches. Compression ratio: 10.6:1. Brake hp: 335 at 5200 rpm. Five main bearings. Hydraulic valve lifters. Carburetor: Holley four-barrel.

POWERTRAIN: Four-speed manual transmission.

CHASSIS FEATURES: Wheelbase: 108 inches. Overall length: 186 inches. Front tread: 58.5 inches. Rear tread: 58.5 inches. Tire size: F60 x 15.

OPTIONS: Close-ratio four-speed manual transmission (no charge). SelectShift Cruise-O-Matic transmission ($32). Air conditioning ($398). Tinted glass, recommended with air conditioning, ($16). Tilt steering wheel ($66). AM radio ($61). AM/FM stereo radio ($181). Stereo tape ($134).

1970 SHELBY MUSTANG

SHELBY-AMERICAN — The final year for the Shelby saw no styling or mechanical change from the previous year. Actually, no 1970 production took place. Partially built 1969 models and the stock of 1969 parts were assembled and given 1970 serial numbers.

I.D. NUMBERS: Contact Shelby-American Auto Club, 22 Olmstead Rd., West Redding, CT 06896.

GT-350

Model Number	Body/Style Number	Body Type & Seating	Factory Price	Shipping Weight	Production Total
GT-350	NA	2-dr HT-4P	NA	3600	Note 1
GT-350	NA	2-dr Conv-4P	NA	3689	Note 1

NOTE 1: Production total for all models was 315 cars.

ENGINE: Ford. V-8. Overhead valves. Cast iron block. Displacement: 351 cid. Bore and stroke: 4.00 x 3.50 inches. Compression ratio: 10.7:1. Brake hp: 290 at 4800 rpm. Five main bearings. Hydraulic valve lifters. Carburetor: Autolite four-barrel.

I.D. NUMBERS: Contact Shelby-American Auto Club, 22 Olmstead Rd., West Redding, CT 06896.

GT-500

Model Number	Body/Style Number	Body Type & Seating	Factory Price	Shipping Weight	Production Total
GT-500	NA	2-dr HT-4P	NA	3850	Note 1
GT-500	NA	2-dr Conv-4P	NA	3939	Note 1

NOTE 1: Production total for all models was 286 cars.

ENGINE: Ford. V-8. Overhead valve. Cast iron block. Displacement: 428 cid. Bore and stroke: 4.13 x 3.98 inches. Compression ratio: 10.6:1. Brake hp: 335 at 5200 rpm. Five main bearings. Hydraulic valve lifters. Carburetor: Holley four-barrel.

POWERTRAIN: Fours-speed manual transmission.

CHASSIS FEATURES: Wheelbase: 108 inches. Overall length: 186 inches. Front tread: 58.5 inches. Rear tread: 58.5 inches. Tire size: F60 x 15.

OPTIONS: Close-ratio four-speed manual transmission (no charge). SelectShift Cruise-O-Matic transmission. Air conditioning. Tinted glass (recommended with air conditioning). Tilt steering wheel. Radios: AM, AM/FM stereo and stereo tape.

MANUFACTURER: Shelby-American, Inc. Venice, Calif. (1962-1964); Los Angeles, Calif. (1965-1967); Ionia, Mich. (1968-1970).

1959 SIR VIVAL

1959 Sir Vival, two-door sedan, safety vehicle, 6-cyl.

SIR VIVAL — As its name implies, assuring the survival of its occupants in a crash situation was the primary design purpose of this vehicle. Walter C. Jerome, of Worcester, Mass., conceived the design. It was built in 1959, using a 1948 Hudson sedan as the basis. Jerome hoped to convince the major car makers to purchase his automotive safety ideas and adapt them to their own products. Among these ideas were an articulated, two-section body with engine, drivetrain and steering up front and control and passenger cabin in the rear. Also, both body sections were ringed by heavy-duty bumpers and the driver occupied an elevated, centrally-located seat with a panoramic view of the road. No manufacturers lined up to buy his patents and Jerome also got no orders for complete cars. The lone example built "sir-vives" today in the collection of Edward Moore, in Bellingham, Mass.

I.D. NUMBERS: Unknown.

SIR VIVAL

Model Number	Body/Style Number	Body Type & Seating	Factory Price	Shipping Weight	Production Total
NA	NA	2-dr Articulated Sed-4P	10,000	NA	1

NOTE 1: Only one car was built at a cost of approximately $10,000.

ENGINE: Hudson six. Inline. L-head. Six-cylinder. Chrome alloy block. Displacement: 262 cid. Bore and stroke: 3-9/16 x 4-3/8 inches. Compression ratio: 6.5:1. Brake hp: 128 at 4000 rpm. Four main bearings. Solid valve lifters. Carburetor: Carter two-barrel model WDO 647S.

POWERTRAIN: Hudson three-speed manual transmission.

CHASSIS FEATURES: Articulated, front engine/rear drive with flexible driveshaft.

MANUFACTURER: Walter C. Jerome, Worcester, Mass.

1952-1954 SKORPION

SKORPION — Begun originally in 1950 as a fiberglass body for Crosley chassis and engine, the Skorpion was a pioneer in the drop-on body field. A change of ownership took place in 1951. After the demise of Crosley in 1952, Skorpion had to look further for markets. The bodies were altered slightly to fit modified Ford chassis and Ford or Studebaker engines. Some were even fully assembled.

I.D. NUMBERS: Not available.

SKORPION

Model Number	Body/Style Number	Body Type & Seating	Factory Price	Shipping Weight	Production Total
NA	NA	2-dr Rds-2P	2495	NA	NA

NOTE 1: Kits were offered at $645 and complete bodies for $1200.

ENGINE: Buyer's choice of Ford, Studebaker, Crosley, or other engines.

POWERTRAIN: Three-speed manual transmission.

CHASSIS FEATURES: Dimensions varied, depending on the chassis and engine used.

MANUFACTURER: Viking-Craft Mfg. Co., Anaheim, Calif.

1953 Skorpion, two-door roadster, 4-cyl (PZ)

1953 SKYLINE

1953 Skyline, two-door convertible, 6-cyl.

SKYLINE — Based on the Henry J, this little retractable top convertible featured many advanced items. Padded instrument panel, control knobs on a console between the seats, high-backed seats and seat belts with shoulder straps were some. Styling, below the beltline was like the Henry J, except for a grille like a 1951 Nash and a continental spare tire.

SKYLINE

Model Number	Body/Style Number	Body Type & Seating	Factory Price	Shipping Weight	Production Total
X50	NA	2-dr Conv-2P	under 3000	1050	NA

ENGINE: Henry J (modified). Six-cylinder. L-head. Cast iron block. Displacement: 161 cid. Bore and stroke: 3-1/8 x 3-1/2 inches. Brake hp: 85. Four main bearings. Solid valve lifters.

MANUFACTURER: Skyline Inc., Jamaica, N.Y.

1971-1972 SQUIRE

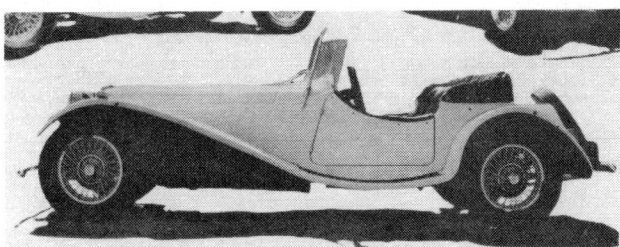

1971 Squire, SS-100 two-door roadster, 6-cyl (PZ)

SQUIRE — The popular SS 100 of the late 1930s was brought back by another replicar, the Squire. Its fiberglass body was made in Italy by Carrozzeria Ramponi. Like its predecessor, the Squire had a six-cylinder overhead valve engine. It used the large Ford six.

I.D. NUMBERS: Not available.

SQUIRE

Model Number	Body/Style Number	Body Type & Seating	Factory Price	Shipping Weight	Production Total
SS 100	NA	2-dr Rds-2P	6795	2000	NA

ENGINE: Ford (modified). Six-cylinders. Overhead valve. Cast iron block. Displacement: 250 cid. Bore and stroke: 3.68 x 3.91 inches. Brake hp: 165 at 4500 rpm. Seven main bearings. Hydraulic valve lifters. Carburetor: Autolite two-barrel.

POWERTRAIN: Ford. Four-speed manual transmission.

OPTIONAL POWERTRAIN: Ford. SelectShift Cruise-O-Matic three-speed automatic transmission.

CHASSIS FEATURES: Wheelbase: 104-1/2 inches. Overall length: 150 inches. Front tread: 59 inches. Rear tread: 59 inches. Tire size: 6.50 x 16.

1973 SQUIRE

SQUIRE — Very little styling or mechanical change from the previous year.

I.D. NUMBERS: Not available.

SQUIRE

Model Number	Body/Style Number	Body Type & Seating	Factory Price	Shipping Weight	Production Total
SS 100	NA	2-dr Rds-2P	NA	2200	NA

ENGINE: Ford (modified). Six-cylinders. Overhead valve. Cast Iron block. Displacement: 250 cid. Bore and stroke: 3.68 x 3.91 inches. Brake hp: 170 at 4500 rpm. Seven main bearings. Hydraulic valve lifters. Carburetor: Autolite two-barrel.

POWERTRAIN: Ford. Four-speed manual transmission.

OPTIONAL POWERTRAIN: Ford. SelectShift Cruise-O-Matic three-speed automatic transmission.

CHASSIS FEATURES: Wheelbase: 104-1/2 inches. Overall length: 150 inches. Front tread: 59 inches. Rear tread: 58.95 inches. Tire size: 6.00 x 16.

1974 SQUIRE

SQUIRE — Very little styling or mechanical change from the prevoius year.

I.D. NUMBERS: Not available.

SQUIRE

Model Number	Body/Style Number	Body Type & Seating	Factory Price	Shipping Weight	Production Total
SS 100	NA	2-dr Rds-2P	9000	2200	NA

ENGINE: Ford (modified). Six-cylinders. Overhead valve. Cast iron block. Displacement: 250 cid. Bore and stroke: 3.68 x 3.91 inches. Brake hp: 170 at 4500 rpm. Seven main bearings. Hydraulic valve lifters. Carburetor: Autolite two-barrel.

POWERTRAIN: Ford. Four-speed manual transmission.

OPTIONAL POWERTRAIN: Ford. Cruise-O-Matic three-speed automatic transmission.

CHASSIS FEATURES: Wheelbase: 104-1/2 inches. Overall length: 150 inches. Front tread: 59 inches. Rear tread: 58.95 inches. Tire size: 185SR x 15.

1975 SQUIRE

SQUIRE — Another car designed to look like a celebrated automobile of the past was the 1975 Squire. It again took inspiration from the British made SS 100 of the latter 1930s — the car for which the Jaguar name was first applied. The Squire used a Ford six-cylinder engine. The fiberglass body was made in Italy by Carrozzeria Ramponi. The Squire's model name was appropriately SS 100.

I.D. NUMBERS: Not available.

SS 100

Model Number	Body/Style Number	Body Type & Seating	Factory Price	Shipping Weight	Production Total
NA	NA	2-dr Rds-2P	9250	2200	NA

ENGINE: Ford (modified). Six-cylinder. Overhead valves. Cast iron block. Displacement: 250 cid. Bore and stroke: 3.68 x 3.91 inches. Brake hp: 170 at 4500 rpm. Seven main bearings. Carburetor: (not available).

POWERTRAIN: Ford. Four-speed manual transmission.

CHASSIS FEATURES: Wheelbase: 104-1/2 inches. Overall length: 150 inches. Front tread: 58 inches. Rear tread: 58.95 inches. Tire size: 6.00 x 16.

MANUFACTURER: Auto Sport Importers, Inc., Philadelphia, Pa.

1953 STAR DUST

1956 Grantham Star Dust, two-door roadster, V-8 (PZ)

STAR DUST — Grantham was one of the largest suppliers of fiberglass bodies in its day. It seems that they also briefly produced some fully-assembled cars themselves, and called them Star Dust. A stock Ford flathead engine was used along with a modified Ford chassis. The engine was situated five inches lower and 19 inches further back than normal.

I.D. NUMBERS: Not available.

STAR DUST

Model Number	Body/Style Number	Body Type & Seating	Factory Price	Shipping Weight	Production Total
NA	NA	2-dr Rds-2P	3750	2650	NA

ENGINE: Ford. V-8. L-head. Cast iron block. Displacement: 239.4 cid. Bore and stroke: 3.19 x 3.75 inches. Brake hp: 110 at 4800 rpm. Solid valve lifters. Three main bearings. Carburetor: Holley Model 2100 two-barrel.

CHASSIS FEATURES: Wheelbase: 110 inches (modified Ford chassis). Overall length: 167 inches.

MANUFACTURER: Grantham Motor Co., Los Angeles, Calif.

1959-1963 STARLITE

STARLITE — The Starlite may also have been called the Kish. It was a small electric, but no details seem to be available about the car's mechanics. A two-passenger roadster, it was offered with either a cloth or transparent plastic top.

I.D. NUMBERS: Not available.

STARLITE

Model Number	Body/Style Number	Body Type & Seating	Factory Price	Shipping Weight	Production Total
NA	NA	2-dr Rds-2P	3000	NA	NA

ENGINE: Electric. (Details unavailable).

CHASSIS FEATURES: Wheelbase: 82 inches. Overall length: 114 inches.

MANUFACTURER: Kish Industries Inc., Lansing, Mich.

1954 STORM

STORM — Only a few brief details are available about this Detroit made car. The hardtop body was supplied by Bertone of Italy. The engine was a Dodge V-8, modified to produce 250 bhp. Evidently that inspired the model designation Z-250.

I.D. NUMBERS: Not available.

Z-250

Model Number	Body/Style Number	Body Type & Seating	Factory Price	Shipping Weight	Production Total
NA	NA	2-dr HT-2P	NA	NA	NA

ENGINE: Dodge V-8 (modified). Brake hp: 250.

CHASSIS FEATURES: Not available.

MANUFACTURER: Sports Car Development Corp., Detroit, Mich.

1954 Storm, two-door hardtop, V-8.

1950 STORY

1950 Story, two-door convertible, V-8.

STORY — Made from parts of several other cars, the Story was a two-passenger sports car. Mercury steering gear and Willys suspension were used. Panels for this low stung roadster included 1949 Chevrolet front fenders and 1949 Pontiac rear fenders. The engine was a Ford "60" highly modified to develop 113 hp. Other V-8 engines could be ordered. However, the standard Ford engine gave the car a top speed of 105 mph.

I.D. NUMBERS: Not available.

STORY

Model Number	Body/Style Number	Body Type & Seating	Factory Price	Shipping Weight	Production Total
NA	NA	2-dr Rds-2P	3500	2080	NA

ENGINES

(STANDARD) Ford V8-60. L-head (Offenhauser heads). Cast iron block. Displacement: 136 cid. Bore and stroke: 2.6 x 3.2 inches. Compression ratio: 10.5:1. Brake hp: 113. Solid valve lifter. Three main bearings.

(OPTIONAL) Stock Mercury, Oldsmobile or Cadillac V-8s.

CHASSIS FEATURES: Wheelbase: 97 inches. Overall length: 148 inches. Front tread: 54 inches. Rear tread: 54 inches.

MANUFACTURER: Tom Story, Portland, Ore.

1961 STUART

STUART — An electric car, the Stuart was a two-passenger station wagon. The fiberglass body looked something like a mini van. Eight 6-volt batteries supplied power to the motor. Range between battery charges was only 40 miles. Barry Stuart was president of this company, though he was only 29 years of age at the time.

I.D. NUMBERS: Not available.

STUART

Model Number	Body/Style Number	Body Type & Seating	Factory Price	Shipping Weight	Production Total
NA	NA	2-dr Sta Wag-2P	1600	1200	Note 1

CHASSIS FEATURES: Overall length: 115 inches. Tire size: 4.00 x 12.

OPTIONS: Radio ($60). Chrome rooftop carrier ($40). Tinted glass ($50).

1961 Stuart Electric, two-door station wagon, electric motor (CG)

MANUFACTURER: Stuart Motors, Kalamazoo, Mich.

1953 STUDILLAC

1953 Studillac, two-door hardtop, V-8

STUDILLAC — After Bill Frick had shoe-horned Cadillac engines under the hoods of Fords and some other cars. In a rather informal way, he began doing this in greater numbers in the new Studebaker Starliner hardtops. Very few other changes were made to these cars. The Cadillac engine was enough, evidently. Studillac acceleration time from 0-to-60 mph was 8.7 seconds, about half what the Studebaker V-8 could do. Cost of the Studillac was $1,500 more than the Studebaker from which it was converted.

I.D. NUMBERS: Not available.

STUDILLAC

Model Number	Body/Style Number	Body Type & Seating	Factory Price	Shipping Weight	Production Total
NA	NA	2-dr HT-SP	3874	3300	NA

ENGINE: Cadillac. V-8. Overhead valves. Cast iron block. Displacement: 331.1 cid. Bore and stroke: 3-13/16 x 3-5/8 inches. Compression ratio: 8.25:1. Brake hp: 210 at 4150 rpm. Hydraulic valve lifters. Five main bearings. Carburetor: Rochester Model 4GC four-barrel.

POWERTRAIN: Three-speed manual transmission.

CHASSIS FEATURES: Wheelbase: 120-1/2 inches. Overall length: 201-15/16 inches. Front tread: 56-1/2 inches. Rear tread: 65-1/2 inches. Tire size: 7.10 x 15.

OPTIONS: Dual-Range Hydra-Matic transmission ($500). Borrani wire wheels.

1954 STUDILLAC

STUDILLAC — Styling changed the same as Studebaker styling changed for 1954. Likewise, the motor had the 1954 Cadillac engine changes.

I.D. NUMBERS: Not available.

STUDILLAC

Model Number	Body/Style Number	Body Type & Seating	Factory Price	Shipping Weight	Production Total
NA	NA	2-dr HT-5P	4002	3300	NA

ENGINE: Cadillac. V-8. Overhead valves. Cast iron block. Displacement: 331.1 cid. Bore and stroke: 3-131/6 x 3-5/8 inches. Compression ratio: 8.25:1. Brake hp: 230 at 4400 rpm. Hydraulic valve lifters. Five main bearings. Carburetor: Rochester Model 4GC four-barrel.

POWERTRAIN: Three-speed manual transmission.

CHASSIS FEATURES: Wheelbase: 120-1/2 inches. Overall length: 202.22 inches. Front tread: 56-1/2 inches. Rear tread: 55-1/2 inches. Tire size: 7.10 x 15.

OPTIONS: Dual-Range Hydra-Matic transmission ($500). Borrani wire wheels.

1955 STUDILLAC

STUDILLAC — Styling changed the same as Studebaker styling changed for 1955. Likewise, the motor had the 1955 Cadillac engine choices.

I.D. NUMBERS: Not available.

STUDILLAC

Model Number	Body/Style Number	Body Type & Seating	Factory Price	Shipping Weight	Production Total
NA	NA	2-dr HT-5P	4002	3300	NA

ENGINES: Cadillac. V-8. Overhead valves. Cast iron block. Displacement: 331.1 cid. Bore and stroke: 3-13/16 x 3-5/8 inches. Compression ratio: 8.25:1. Brake hp: 250 at 4600 rpm. Hydraulic valve lifters. Five main bearings. Rochester Model 4GC four-barrel.

POWERTRAIN: Three-speed manual transmission.

CHASSIS FEATURES: Wheelbase: 120-1/2 inches. Overall length: 204.44 inches. Front tread: 56-1/2 inches. Rear tread: 55-1/2 inches. Tire size: 7.10 x 15.

OPTIONS: Dual-Range Hydra-Matic transmission ($500). Borrani wire wheels.

MANUFACTURER: Bill Frick Motors, Rockville Centre, N.Y.

1969 STUTZ

STUTZ — Sooner or later the replicar field was bound to encompass the Stutz Bearcat. Howard Williams, a House of Representatives member from Oklahoma, was the one who revived the Stutz. He used the international Harvester Scout chassis and engine for his car. His Bearcat was complete with monocle windshield and radiator temperature gauge.

I.D. NUMBERS: Not available.

BEARCAT

Model Number	Body/Style Number	Body Type & Seating	Factory Price	Shipping Weight	Production Total
NA	NA	Open-2P	4950	NA	NA

ENGINE: International Harvester Scout. Four-cylinder (half a V-8). Overhead valves. Cast iron block. Displacement: 195.4 cid. Bore and stroke: 4.13 x 3.66 inches. Compression ratio: 8.1:1. Brake hp: 111 at 4000 rpm. Solid valve lifters. Five main bearings. Carburetor: Holley one-barrel.

POWERTRAIN: Three-speed manual transmission.

CHASSIS FEATURES: Wheelbase: 100 (international Harvester Scout chassis). Front tread: 55.7 inches. Rear tread: 55.7 inches.

MANUFACTURER: Howard D. Williams, Tulsa, Okla.

1970-1971 STUTZ

1971 Stutz, two-door hardtop, V-8 (CG)

STUTZ — Another Stutz has come on the scene, though it was of a modern character. A coupe, called Blackhawk, was the only body type offered initially. The Pontiac Grand Prix provided the base for this car. The engine was a modified big block Pontiac.

I.D. NUMBERS: Not available.

BLACKHAWK

Model Number	Body/Style Number	Body Type & Seating	Factory Price	Shipping Weight	Production Total
NA	NA	2-dr Cpe-5P	22,500	NA	NA

ENGINE: Pontiac (modified). V-8. Overhead valves. Cast iron block. Displacement: 400 cid. Bore and stroke: 4.13 x 3.75 inches. Compression ratio: 10.75:1. Brake hp: 425 at 4000 rpm. Hydraulic valve lifters. Five main bearings. Carburetor: (not available).

POWERTRAIN: GM. Turbo-HydraMatic. Three-speed manual transmission.

CHASSIS FEATURES: Wheelbase: 118 (Pontiac Grand Prix chassis). Overall length: 207 inches. Front tread: 64 inches. Rear tread: 64. Tire size: LXX x 17.

1972 STUTZ

STUTZ — There was very little styling change for the Blackhawk from previous years. The engine was now the 455 cid inch V-8. As before, the engine was modified, and the greater displacement developed more power than before. A new model was introduced. It was a four-door sedan, called the Limousine. The Cadillac Fleetwood Brougham chassis and stock Cadillac engine were used.

I.D. NUMBERS: Not available.

BLACKHAWK

Model Number	Body/Style Number	Body Type & Seating	Factory Price	Shipping Weight	Production Total
NA	NA	2-dr Cpe-5P	24,500	NA	NA

ENGINE: Pontiac (modified). V-8. Overhead valves. Cast iron block. Displacement: 455 cid. Bore and stroke: 4.15 x 4.21 inches. Compression ratio: 10.75:1. Brake hp: 431. Hydraulic valve lifters. Five main bearings. Carburetor: Four-barrel.

POWERTRAIN: GM. Turbo-HydraMatic. Three-speed manual transmission.

CHASSIS FEATURES: Wheelbase: 118 (Pontiac Grand Prix chassis). Overall length: 207 inches. Front tread: 64 inches. Rear tread: 64. Tire size: LXX x 17.

I.D. NUMBERS: Not available.

LIMOUSINE

Model Number	Body/Style Number	Body Type & Seating	Factory Price	Shipping Weight	Production Total
NA	NA	4-dr Sed-6P	32,500	NA	NA

ENGINE: Cadillac. V-8. Overhead valves. Cast iron block. Displacement: 472 cubic inches. Bore and stroke: 4.30 x 4.06 inches. Compression ratio: 8.5:1. Brake hp: 220 at 4000 rpm. Five main bearings. Hydraulic valve lifters. Carburetor: Rochester Model 4MV four-barrel.

POWERTRAIN: GM Turbo-Hydramatic. Three-speed manual transmission.

CHASSIS FEATURES: Wheelbase: 133 (Cadillac Fleetwood Brougham chassis). Overall length: 230 inches. Front tread: 63.3 inches. Rear tread: 63.6 inches.

1973 STUTZ

STUTZ — Very little styling or mechanical change from the previous year. The Limousine name was changed to Duplex.

I.D. NUMBERS: Not available.

BLACKHAWK

Model Number	Body/Style Number	Body Type & Seating	Factory Price	Shipping Weight	Production Total
NA	NA	2-dr Cpe-5P	24,500	NA	Note 1

NOTE 1: Total 1973 production of Blackhawks and Duplex models was 75 cars.

ENGINE: Pontiac (modified). V-8. Overhead valves. Cast iron block. Displacement: 455 cid. Bore and stroke: 4.15 x 4.21 inches. Compression ratio: 10.75:1. Brake hp: 431. Hydraulic valve lifters. Five main bearings. Carburetor: Four-barrel.

POWERTRAIN: GM Turbo-Hydramatic. Three-speed manual transmission.

CHASSIS FEATURES: Wheelbase: 118 (Pontiac Grand Prix chassis). Overall length: 207 inches. Front tread: 64 inches. Rear tread: 64 inches. Tire size: LXX x 17.

I.D. NUMBERS: Not available.

DUPLEX

Model Number	Body/Style Number	Body Type & Seating	Factory Price	Shipping Weight	Production Total
NA	NA	4-dr Sed-6P	32,500	NA	Note 1

NOTE 1: Total 1973 production of Blackhawks and Duplex models was 75 cars.

DUPLEX ENGINE: Cadillac. V-8. Overhead valves. Cast iron block. Displacement: 472 cid. Bore and stroke: 4.30 x 4.06 inches. Compression ratio: 8.5:1. Brake hp: 220 at 4000 rpm. Hydraulic valve lifters. Five main bearings. Carburetor: Rochester Model 4MV four-barrel.

POWERTRAIN: GM Turbo-Hydramatic. Three-speed manual transmission.

CHASSIS FEATURES: Wheelbase: 133 (Cadillac Fleetwood Brougham chassis). Overall length: 230 inches. Front tread: 63.3 inches. Rear tread: 63.6 inches.

1974 STUTZ

STUTZ — Very little styling or mechanical change from the previous year for the Blackhawk. The Duplex sedan was discontinued.

I.D. NUMBERS: Not available.

BLACKHAWK

Model Number	Body/Style Number	Body Type & Seating	Factory Price	Shipping Weight	Production Total
NA	NA	2-dr Cpe-5P	35,000	NA	NA

ENGINE: Pontiac (modified). V-8. Overhead valves. Cast iron block. Displacement: 455 cid. Bore and stroke: 4.15 x 4.21 inches. Compression ratio: 10.75:1. Brake hp: 431. Hydraulic valve lifters. Five main bearings. Carburetor: Four-barrel.

POWERTRAIN: GM Turbo-Hydramatic. Three-speed manual transmission.

CHASSIS FEATURES: Wheelbase: 118 (Pontiac Gran Prix chassis). Overall length: 207 inches. Front tread: 64 inches. Rear tread: 64 inches. Tire size: LXX x 17.

1975 STUTZ

STUTZ — Very little styling or mechanical change from the previous year.

I.D. NUMBERS: Not available.

BLACKHAWK

Model Number	Body/Style Number	Body Type & Seating	Factory Price	Shipping Weight	Production Total
NA	NA	2-dr Cpe-5P	41,500	NA	31

ENGINE: Pontiac (modified). V-8. Overhead valves. Cast iron block.

1974 SUNDANCER

SUNDANCER ELECTRIC — The Sundancer was an experimental electric car constructed by race car builder Bob McKee for the ESB Co. Styling features included a miniature-scale GT-style coupe body manufactured of plastic or fiberglass. Entry to the car was provided by flipping-up the top of the body structure, which opened in hatch-fashion above the beltline. Deep-recessed chrome wheels were used. The Sundancer was small enough to be dwarfed by even the compact Volkswagen Beetle. Power came from an eight horsepower electric motor. There were a dozen six-volt batteries, weighing over 750 pounds. The battery tray was in the car's 'backbone' and was fitted with quick-disconnect type terminals, for easy battery replacements. Power was transmitted through a two-speed, clutchless gearbox. The Sundancer was said to have an excellent cruising range, but was too small to be very practical, even for around-town use.

I.D. NUMBERS: No data available.

SUNDANCER COUPE

Model Number	Body/Style Number	Body Type & Seating	Factory Price	Shipping Weight	Production Total
1974	NA	2-dr Cpe-2P	NA	NA	1

Standard Catalog of American Cars

ENGINE: Eight horsepower electric motor. Uses 12 six-volt batteries.

CHASSIS FEATURES: Two-speed, clutchless transmission.

POWERTRAIN OPTIONS: None.

CONVENIENCE OPTIONS: None.

HISTORICAL FOOTNOTES: H.C. Brown was vice-president and general manager of ESB Inc., Automatic Div. The company, headquartered in Cleveland, Ohio, manufactured Exide brand storage batteries. Apparently, only one Sundancer electric coupe was made, mainly for experimental purposes.

1974 Sundancer, two-door coupe, electric motor (CG)

1946 SUPER KAR

SUPER KAR — Among the countless attempts to build an economy car in the early postwar years was the Super Kar. It was a small three-wheeler, powered by a small rear-mounted air-cooled engine, which drove the single rear wheel.

I.D. NUMBERS: Not available.

SUPER KAR

Model Number	Body/Style Number	Body Type & Seating	Factory Price	Shipping Weight	Production Total
NA	NA	2-dr Rds-2P	550	NA	1

NOTE 1: The car produced appears to have been a prototype.

ENGINE: Air-cooled. Rear-mounted. Brake hp: 15.

MANUFACTURER: Louis Enrod, Cleveland, Ohio.

1954 SUPER WAGON

SUPER STATION WAGON — Henney was associated with Packard for many years. They made ambulance and funeral coach conversions for the firm's chassis. It is not surprising, then, that they undertook to make a Packard station wagon conversion. This was a 12-passenger wagon. There were four seats. The rearmost seat faced backwards and it was curved around a table.

I.D. NUMBERS: Not available.

SUPER STATION WAGON

Model Number	Body/Style Number	Body Type & Seating	Factory Price	Shipping Weight	Production Total
NA	NA	4-dr Sta Wag-12 P	7500	NA	NA

ENGINE: Packard. Eight cylinders. Inline. L-head. Cast iron block. Displacement: 359 cid. Bore and stroke: 3-9/16 x 4-1/4 inches. Compression: 8.0:1. Brake hp: 212 at 4000 rpm. Nine main bearings. Hydraulic valve lifters. Carburetor: Four-barrel.

CHASSIS FEATURES: Wheelbase: 127 inches (Packard Cavalier chassis). Overall length: 252 inches. Front tread: 60 inches. Rear tread: 60.81 inches.

MANUFACTURER: Henney Motor Co., Freeport, Ill.

1958-1960 SURREY

SURREY — Another replica of an early antique car was the Surrey. It was made to look like the 1903 Curved Dash Oldsmobile, which explains its Model Number '03'. Two different single-cylinder, air-cooled engines were used. The Deluxe model had the slightly larger and more powerful motor.

I.D. NUMBERS: Not available.

SURREY

Model Number	Body/Style Number	Body Type & Seating	Factory Price	Shipping Weight	Production Total
03	NA	Surrey-2P	1095	680	NA
03	NA	DeL Surrey-2P	1195	700	NA

ENGINES

STANDARD: Cushman. One-cylinder. Air-cooled. L-head. Displacement: 14.9 cid. Bore and stroke: 2-5/8 x 2-3/4 inches. Compression ratio: 5.1:1. Brake hp: 4. Carburetor: Tillotson.

DELUXE: Cushman. One-cylinder. Air-cooled. L-head. Displacement: 19.5 cid. Bore and stroke: 3.00 x 2.75 inches. Compression ratio: 6.4:1. Brake hp: 8 at 3800 rpm. Carburetor: Tillotson.

POWERTRAIN: Semi-automatic clutch. Two-speed manual transmission. Chain-drive.

CHASSIS FEATURES: Wheelbase: 67 Inches. Overall length: 63 inches. Front tread: 55 inches. Rear tread: 55 inches. Tire size: 28 x 2.125.

OPTIONS: Fringed surrey top. Rear seat. Speedometer. Car cover.

MANUFACTURER: E.W. Bliss Co. for Dyer Products, Canton, Ohio.

1959-1960 SWIFT

SWIFT — A couple of reduced-size cars approximating the appearance of bygone autos were produced under the name of Swift. Some of the earliest examples may have been called Honey Bee. At least two models were offered. The 'T' was intended to resemble a 1910 Model T Ford and the 'Cat' was a vague likeness of the original Stutz Bearcat. These cars only varied in detail. They were basically the same. Stripped down models were available for $595. They had pull cold starters and no windshield. The production totals should be considered approximate.

I.D. NUMBERS: Not available.

1959 Swift, two-door runabout, one-cyl.

SWIFT

Model Number	Body/Style Number	Body Type & Seating	Factory Price	Shipping Weight	Production Total
T	NA	Open-2P	795	230	100
Cat	NA	Open-2P	795	230	100

NOTE 1: Price of stripped-down model was $595.

ENGINE: Clinton. One-cylinder. L-head. Displacement: 8.3 cid. Bore and stroke: 2.38 x 1.88 inches. Compression: 7.0:1. Brake hp: 3 at 3600 rpm.

POWERTRAIN: Two-speed belt drive.

CHASSIS FEATURES: Wheelbase: 66 inches. Overall length: 79 inches. Front tread: 38.2 inches. Rear tread: 38.2 inches. Tire size: 20x2.125.

MANUFACTURER: WM Manufacturing Co., San Diego, Calif. (later) Swift Mfg. Co., El Cajon, Calif.

1948 TASCO

TASCO — It was the intention of the builders to produce a true American sports car. Gordon Buehrig, best known for his styling of the 1936 Cord, was hired to design this car. He incorporated many ideas he thought would be desirable, but it got out of hand. The end result an odd-looking vehicle, too costly to produce. The prototype, built by Derham Body Co., looked like the fuselage of a airplane. Each of the four wheels was enclosed with its own fender. The front fenders turned with the wheels as they were steered. There were two detachable plexiglas roof panels, like those used today on T-tops. Tasco, an acronym of the manufacturer's name, was powered by a modified Mercury motor.

I.D. NUMBERS: Not available.

1948 Tasco Special, two-door T-top coupe, V-8 (ACD)

TASCO

Model Number	Body/Style Number	Body Type & Seating	Factory Price	Shipping Weight	Production Total
NA	NA	2-dr Sed-4P	7500	NA	1

NOTE 1: Only one prototype was built.

ENGINE: Mercury (modified). V-8. L-head.

MANUFACTURER: The American Sports Car Co., Hartford, Conn.

1949-1966 TAYLOR-DUNN

1966 Taylor-Dunn, Model 'R' pickup truck, electric motor (PZ)

TAYLOR-DUNN — Taylor-Dunn has been manufacturing electric industrial vehicles for many years. Some were passenger vehicles with three or four wheels. The former had the single wheel in the front. There were two- and four-passenger models. The four-passenger cars had a rear-facing rear seat. Around 1959 or 1960, some may have been marketed under the Trident name.

I.D. NUMBERS: Not available.

TAYLOR-DUNN

Model Number	Body/Style Number	Body Type & Seating	Factory Price	Shipping Weight	Production Total
NA	NA	2-dr Rbt-2P	NA	965	NA
NA	NA	2-dr Rbt-4P	NA	1125	NA

ENGINE: Electric. 36-volts. Brake hp: (continuous-duty) 2-1/2; (intermittent-duty) 6. Six 6-volt 170 ampere hour batteries. (217 ampere hour batteries optional).

CHASSIS FEATURES: Wheelbase: (3W) 59 inches; (4W) 60 inches. Overall length: (3W) 99 inches; (4W) 102 inches.

MANUFACTURER: Taylor-Dunn Manufacturing Co., Anaheim, Calif.

1947-1955 THRIF-T

1955 Thrift-T, utility vehicle, 2-cyl.

THRIF-T — Ambitious plans were made to produce a lightweight utility vehicle, as well as a pickup and a closed delivery truck. They were all three-wheelers. The single front wheel steered. A small two-cylinder engine was mounted at the rear, where it could be removed in just half an hour for major service.

I.D. NUMBERS: Not available.

THRIF-T

Model Number	Body/Style Number	Body Type & Seating	Factory Price	Shipping Weight	Production Total
NA	NA	2-dr Utl-5P	800	900	NA

ENGINE: Onan. Two-cylinder. Horizontally-opposed. Rear-mounted. Displacement: 62.6 cid. Brake hp: 10.

POWERTRAIN: Three-speed manual transmission.

CHASSIS FEATURES: Wheelbase: 85 inches. Overall length: 126 inches.

MANUFACTURER: Tri-Wheel Motor Corp., Oxford, N.C., (later) Springfield, Mass.

1948 TOWNE SHOPPER

TOWNE SHOPPER — "America's lowest priced automobile" was the slogan of the Town Shopper. It was designed for short shopping trips, with a luggage compartment in front. The small engine was rear-mounted and got up to 50 mpg. The aluminum body had no doors, just cut-down sides for the two passengers to enter.

I.D. NUMBERS: Not available.

1948 Towne Shopper, two-door runabout, 2-cyl.

1948 Towne Shopper, two-door runabout, 2-cyl.

TOWNE SHOPPER

Model Number	Body/Style Number	Body Type & Seating	Factory Price	Shipping Weight	Production Total
NA	NA	Rbt-2P	595	600	NA

ENGINE: Onan. Two-cylinder. Horizontally-opposed. Aluminum block. Rear-mounted. Displacement: 38.8 cid. Bore and stroke: 3.00 x 2.75 inches. Brake hp: 10.6.

CHASSIS FEATURES: Wheelbase: 63 inches. Overall length: 116 inches. Front tread: 32-1/4 inches. Rear tread: 33-1/2 inches. Tire size: 4.00 x 8.

POWERTRAIN: Two-speed transmission with automatic clutch.

MANUFACTURER: International Motor Car Co., San Diego, Calif.

1955 TRI-CAR

TRI-CAR — This little three-wheeler was a fiberglass car with a rear mounted engine that drove the single rear wheel. Goodrich rubber suspension and torque converter were used.

I.D. NUMBERS: Not available.

TRI-CAR

Model Number	Body/Style Number	Body Type & Seating	Factory Price	Shipping Weight	Production Total
NA	NA	2-dr Cpe-3P	995	NA	NA

ENGINE: Lycoming. Vertical twin cylinders. Air-cooled. Rear-mounted. Brake hp: 30 at 3000 rpm.

POWERTRAIN: Westinghouse-Schneider. Torque converter.

CHASSIS FEATURES: Overall length: 117 inches.

MANUFACTURER: The Tri-Car Co., Wheatland, Pa.

1955 Tri-Car, two-door coupe, 2-cyl.

1954-1955 TRIPLEX

TRIPLEX — A slightly revised Chicagoan continued with its fiberglass sports car body. The buyer could choose virtually any V-8 engine of the day, but most installations were flathead Ford V-8s.

I.D. NUMBERS: Not available.

TRIPLEX

Model Number	Body/Style Number	Body Type & Seating	Factory Price	Shipping Weight	Production Total
NA	NA	2-dr Rds-2P	Note 1	NA	NA

NOTE 1: Fully-assembled price unknown. Kits were available at $2000 savings.

ENGINE: Buyer's choice of almost any contemporary V-8. Usually 1942 to 1948 Ford V-8s were used.

CHASSIS FEATURES: Wheelbase: 100 inches.

1954 Triplex Lightning, two-door roadster, V-8 (PZ)

MANUFACTURER: Ketcham's Automotive Corp., Chicago, Ill.

1948 TUCKER

TUCKER — The newcomer that received the most publicity in the American auto industry, except Kaiser, was Preston Tucker. Both his method of financing and the features of his car caused much controversy. The car was styled by the renowned automotive designer Alex Tremulis. The Tucker was easily spotted from any angle. At the front were three headlights. The center one pointed in the direction the car was steered. The long sloping back was accented by fin-like taillights just above the rear grille. It was a rear-engined car. The powerful engine was a pancake six, modified from a helicopter engine made by Air-Cooled Motors (the remaining operations of Franklin Car Co.). A Tucker was clocked at better than 131 mph at Bonneville in 1950.

I.D. NUMBERS: Not available.

TUCKER

Model Number	Body/Style Number	Body Type & Seating	Factory Price	Shipping Weight	Production Total
48	NA	4-dr Sed-6P	2450	4235	51

ENGINE: Air-cooled. Six-cylinder. Horizontally-opposed. Water-cooled. Rear-mounted. L-head. Aluminum alloy block. Displacement: 334.1 cid. Bore and stroke: 41/2 x 3-1/2 inches. Compression ratio: 7.0:1. Brake hp: 166 at 3200 rpm.

POWERTRAIN: Four-speed manual transmission, with Bendix vacuum-electric pre-selector.

CHASSIS FEATURES: Wheelbase: 130 inches. Overall length: 219 inches. Front tread: 64 inches. Rear tread: 65 inches. Tire size: 7.00 x 15.

OPTIONS: Heater and defroster. Radio. Whitewall tires.

MANUFACTURER: Tucker Corp., Chicago, Ill.

1948 Tucker Torpedo, four-door sedan, 6-cyl. (front view)

1948 Tucker Torpedo, four-door sedan, 6-cyl. (rear view)

1956 U.S. MARK II

1956 U.S. Mark II, two-door convertible, V-8

U.S. MARK II — This was a fiberglass two-passenger roadster. Wheelbase was 110 to 118 inches, depending on chassis used. Presumably, engine choice was up to the purchaser. Most were sold in kit form, but some completely assembled cars were available. Specific information is lacking, however.

MANUFACTURER: U.S. Fiberglass Co., Norwood, N.J.

1967-1969 VALKYRIE

VALKYRIE — The Fiberfab company made a reputation for itself by producing many fiberglass bodies for use on owner's chassis. However, they did offer a fully-assembled car using their Valkyrie body and a special ladder-type chassis. It was powered by a souped-up Chevrolet 427 cid engine, mounted in the rear. Zero-to-60 acceleration was said to be 3.9 seconds and top speed 180 plus mph.

I.D. NUMBERS: Not available.

VALKYRIE

Model Number	Body/Style Number	Body Type & Seating	Factory Price	Shipping Weight	Production Total
NA	NA	2-dr Cpe-2P	12,500	NA	NA

ENGINE: Chevrolet (modified). V-8. Rear-mounted. Overhead valve. Cast iron block. Displacement: 427 cid. Bore and stroke: 4.251 x 3.76 inches. Brake hp: 459. Five main bearings. Solid valve lifters. Carburetor: (not available).

POWERTRAIN: ZF. Five-speed transaxle.

MANUFACTURER: Fiberfab, Div. of Velocidad, Inc., Santa Clara, Calif.

1954 VAUGHN

VAUGHN — This brand came in coupe and sports models with an overhead cam V-8 engine. Bodies of the 1500 pound car were made of fiberglass or steel. But very little more has been discovered about the car.

1964-1966 VETTA VENTURA

VETTA VENTURA — It is said that the Vetta Ventura succeeded the Apollo. Evidently there was a short time of overlap, when both cars were in production. The Vetta Ventura was quite similar to the Apollo. The bodies we made in Italy by Intermeccanica — like Apollo. Buick power was used in the Vetta Ventura too. This car is not to be confused with the Warrior, made about the same time, in the same city, by a company with a similar name. There was no connection between the two manufacturers, and their cars are dissimilar.

I.D. NUMBERS: Not available.

VETTA VENTURA

Model Number	Body/Style Number	Body Type & Seating	Factory Price	Shipping Weight	Production Total
GT	NA	2-dr HT-2P	6897	2470	NA
GT	NA	2-dr Conv-2P	7237	NA	NA

ENGINE: Buick. V-8. Overhead valve. Cast iron block. Displacement: 300 cid. Bore and stroke: 3.75 x 3.40 inches. Compression ratio: 11.0:1. Brake hp: 250 at 4800 rpm. Five main bearings. Hydraulic valve lifters. Carburetor: Rochester model 7024044/5 four-barrel.

POWERTRAIN: Four-speed manual transmission.

CHASSIS FEATURES: Wheelbase: 97 inches. Overall length: 178 inches. Front tread: 56 inches. Rear tread: 56 inches. Tire size: 175-400.

OPTIONS: Automatic power-shift transmission. Air conditioning. Borrani chrome plated wire wheels. Magnesium wheels. Pirelli Cinturato high speed tires. AM radio. AM/FM Marine radio.

MANUFACTURER: Vanguard Motors Corp., Dallas, Texas.

1962 VOLTRA

VOLTRA — Very little is known about this electric car. It was outstanding, however, if its weight is correctly reported. Electric cars, fully-equipped with their batteries, are usually quite heavy.

I.D. NUMBERS: Not available.

VOLTRA

Model Number	Body/Style Number	Body Type & Seating	Factory Price	Shipping Weight	Production Total
NA	NA	NA	NA	1600	NA

VOLTRA ENGINE: Electric. General Electric DC motor.

CHASSIS FEATURES: Wheelbase: 106 inches. Overall length: 170 inches.

MANUFACTURER: Voltra Inc., New York, N.Y.

1965 WAGON DE VILLE

WAGON DE VILLE — Cadillac has never produced station wagons, so this has given several opportunists the notion to do what General Motors had not bothered to do. This was a nine-passenger model. It had both an electrically operated roof and a roof rack. Production obviously did not last long. So, what General Motors had not bothered to do is not worth bothering about, at least in this case.

I.D. NUMBERS: Not available.

WAGON DE VILLE

Model Number	Body/Style Number	Body Type & Seating	Factory Price	Shipping Weight	Production Total
NA	NA	4-dr Sta Wag-9P	14,950	NA	NA

WAGON DE VILLE ENGINE: Cadillac. V-8. Overhead valve. Cast iron block. Displacement: 429 cid. Bore and stroke: 4.13 x 4.00 inches. Compression ratio: 10.5:1. Brake hp: 340 at 4600 rpm. Five main bearings. Hydraulic valve lifters. Carburetor: Carter Model AFB 3903-S, or Rochester Model 7025030 four-barrel.

CHASSIS FEATURES: Wheelbase: 129-1/2 inches (Cadillac). Overall length: 224 inches. Front tread: 64-1/2 inches. Rear tread: 64-1/2 inches.

MANUFACTURER: Cadillac Wagons Limited, Linden, N.J.

Standard Catalog of American Cars

1964 WARRIOR

WARRIOR — The similarity of this manufacturers' name and the maker of the Vetta Ventura has caused many to think the Warrior was just another name for the Vetta Ventura. That was not so. The similarity of the manufacturers' names was a coincidence and the cars ware not at all alike. The Warrior was a smaller sports coupe, with a removable roof panel for fresh air touring. A German Ford engine was mounted in the rear of chassis made of rectangular tubing.

I.D. NUMBERS: Not available.

WARRIOR

Model Number	Body/Style Number	Body Type & Seating	Factory Price	Shipping Weight	Production Total
NA	NA	2-dr Cpe-2P	NA	NA	NA

ENGINE: Ford Taunus. V-4. Mounted amidships. Overhead valve. Cast Iron block. Displacement: 103.9 cid. Bore and stroke: 3.31 x 3.02 inches. Compression ratio: 8.4:1. Brake hp: 72 at 4500 rpm. Three main bearings. Solid valve lifters. Carburetor: Solex 32 PDIST one-barrel.

CHASSIS FEATURES: Wheelbase: 95 inches.

MANUFACTURER: Vanguard Products, Dallas, Texas.

1960 WESTCOASTER

WESTCOASTER — This was another fiberglass runabout. It was a three-wheeler with the lone wheel up front. Although it was an electric car, It had no headlights. Because of its 36-volt electrical system, it was called Super 36.

I.D. NUMBERS: Not available.

1960 Westcoaster, Super '36' two-door coupe, electric motor (PZ)

WESTCOASTER

Model Number	Body/Style Number	Body Type & Seating	Factory Price	Shipping Weight	Production Total
36	NA	2-dr Rbt-2P	NA	NA	NA

ENGINE: General Electric. 36-volt system. Built-in battery charger, with automatic voltage control relay.

OPTIONS: Removable fiberglass top.

MANUFACTURER: Westcoast Machinery, Inc., Stockton, Calif.

1957-1969 WILLIAMS

WILLIAMS — Steam-powered conversions of gasoline engines was the work of this company. Using a fiberglass body by Victress, they built a steam-powered car in 1963. It was priced at $7000. In 1966 a Chevrolet Chevelle converted to steam was priced at $10,250.

MANUFACTURER: Williams Engine Co., Inc., Ambler, Pa.

1957 Williams, two-door convertible, (V-8)

1952-1956 WOODILL

1954 Woodill, Wildfire two-door roadster, 6-cyl. (PZ)

WOODILL — Considered the world's first fiberglass production car, Woodill production began about a year before the Chevrolet Corvette or Kaiser-Darrin. This car was conceived by B.R. 'Woody' Woodill, a Dodge dealer. Called the Wildfire, the cars' bodies were supplied by Glasspar for a chassis of Woodill's origin. Most cars used the Willys six, but the buyer could choose almost any other engine. Most Woodills were sold as kits, though some were factory assembled.

I.D. NUMBERS: Not available.

Model Number	Body/Style Number	Body Type & Seating	Factory Price	Shipping Weight	Production Total
NA	NA	2-dr Rds-2P	3263-4500	1620	15

NOTE 1: Prices/production for factory assembled cars only.
NOTE 2: Up to 285 additional cars were sold as kits.

WILDFIRE ENGINE: Willys. Six-cylinder. F-head. Cast iron block. Displacement: 161 cid. Bore and stroke: 3-1/8 x 3-1/2 inches. Compression ratio: 7.6:1. Brake hp: 90 at 4200 rpm. Four main bearings. Solid valve lifters. Carburetor: Carter Model YF-924S one-barrel. (Some later models used flathead Ford V-8 engines).

POWERTRAIN: Three-speed manual transmission with overdrive.

CHASSIS FEATURES: Wheelbase: 101 inches. Overall length: 162 inches. Front tread: 56 inches. Rear tread: 57 inches. Tire size: 6.40 x 15.

MANUFACTURER: Woodill Motor Co. Inc., Downey, Calif.

1964 XR-6

XR-6 — **(SIX)** — In the spring of 1962 LeRoi Smith, associate editor of HOT ROD magazine, announced plans to construct a futuristic street roadster based on a fiberglass body design by Steve Swaja and a Dodge slant six powertrain. Because of a desire to have opening doors, the original plans were modified. An original, steel 1927 Model T Ford body was substituted for the fiberglass type. The XR-6 featured custom sheetmetal work by George Barris on its aluminum nose, hood and fenders. A tube frame was used. Although not intended as a volume production effort, the XR-6 was presented to Inspire readers of the magazine to attempt similar, low-budget projects. In fact, Robert McCreary, of Kansas City, advised HOT ROD editors that his own XR-6 was underway retaining the original fiberglass body concept. Thus, in a sense, the XR-6 served as the prototype for a proposed grass-roots car building program.

I.D. NUMBERS: Not applicable.

XR-6 STREET ROADSTER

Model Number	Body/Style Number	Body Type & Seating	Factory Price	Shipping Weight	Production Total
NA	NA	2-dr Spt Rds-2P	618-1153	NA	1

NOTE 1: Projected cost of building car within guidelines in the chart above.

ENGINE: Modified Dodge slant six. See 1962 Dodge section for basic specifications.

CHASSIS FEATURES: Wheelbase: 105 inches. Overall length: 144 inches. Front tread: 50-3/4 inches. Rear tread: 55-1/2 inches. Tires: (front) 5.00-5.20 x 15; (rear) 7.10 or 7.60 x 15.

POWERTRAIN OPTIONS: Builder's choice.

CONVENIENCE OPTIONS: Builder's choice.

HISTORICAL FOOTNOTES: The XR-6 was introduced at the Miami custom Auto Fair in April, 1963, where it won the Street Rod Sweepstakes trophy. AMT plastics company later offered a scale model kit of the XR-6.

1964 XR-6, two-door sports roadster, 6-cyl (CG)

1950 YANK

YANK — A poor man's sports car might described this attempt. It was a low-cost, Wiilys powered, aluminum-bodied car of fairly good looks. But alas, it failed to succeed, like so many others.

I.D. NUMBERS: Not available.

YANK

Model Number	Body/Style Number	Body Type & Seating	Factory Price	Shipping Weight	Production Total
NA	NA	2-dr Rds-2P	1000	1500	NA

ENGINE: Willys. Four-cylinder. L-head. Cast iron block. Displacement: 134.2 cid. Bore and stroke: 3-1 /8 x 4-3/8 inches. Compression ratio: 6.48:1. Brake hp: 63 at 4000 rpm. Three main bearings. Solid valve lifters. Carburetor: Carter Model 596-S one-barrel.

POWERTRAIN: Three-speed manual transmission.

CHASSIS FEATURES: Wheelbase: 100 inches.

MANUFACTURER: Custom Auto Works, San Diego, Calif.

1954 YANKEE CLIPPER

YANKEE CLIPPER — A Glasspar fiberglass body along with a light original chassis, Ford engine and many other Ford components were put together to make a car called the Yankee Clipper. The body was not unlike the Woodill. All Yankee Clippers were factory assembled. No kits were offered.

I.D. NUMBERS: Not available.

YANKEE CLIPPER

Model Number	Body/Style Number	Body Type & Seating	Factory Price	Shipping Weight	Production Total
NA	NA	2-dr Rds-2P	3400	1900	NA

ENGINE: Ford. V-8. Overhead valve. Cast iron block. Displacement: 239 cid. Bore and stroke: 3.62 x 3.60 inches. Compression ratio: 7.2:1. Brake hp: 130 at 4200 rpm. Five main bearings. Solid valve lifters. Carburetor: Holley two-barrel.

POWERTRAIN: Three-speed manual transmission. Fordomatic (optional).

CHASSIS FEATURES: Wheelbase: 101 inches. Overall length: 159 inches, plus bumpers.

MANUFACTURER: Strassberger Motor Co., Menlo Park, Calif.

1965-1969 YENKO STINGER

YENKO — Chevrolet dealer Don Yenko converted Corvair Corsa coupes for sizzling performance, and appropriately called them Stingers. The Corvair engine was available in various degrees of potency. Only the most powerful, 240 hp version, had a larger than standard displacement.

I.D. NUMBERS: Not available.

STINGER

Model Number	Body/Style Number	Body Type & Seating	Factory Price	Shipping Weight	Production Total
NA	NA	2-dr HT-2P	NA	2153	Note

NOTE 1: Approximately 100-135 Yenko Stingers built.

ENGINES

(STAGE I) Chevrolet Corvair (modified). Six-cylinder. Horizontally-opposed. Rear-mounted. Overhead valve. Light aluminum alloy block. Displacement: 164 cid. Bore and stroke: 3.43 x 2.94 inches. Compression ratio: 8.2:1. Brake hp: 160 at 5500 rpm. Four main bearings.

(STAGE II) Chevrolet Corvair (modified). Six-cylinder. Horizontally-opposed. Rear-mounted. Overhead valve. Light aluminum alloy block. Displacement: 164 cid. Bore and stroke: 3.43 x 2.94 inches. Compression ratio: 10.0:1. Brake hp: 190 at 5500 rpm. Four main bearings.

(STAGE III) Chevrolet Corvair (modified). Six-cylinder. Horizontally-opposed. Rear-mounted. Overhead valve. Light aluminum alloy block. Displacement: 164 cid. Bore and stroke: 3.43 x 2.94 inches. Compression ratio: 10.5:1. Brake hp: 220 at 6000 rpm. (Rated at 240 bhp for 1969). Four main bearings.

(STAGE IV) (Not available for 1969). Chevrolet Corvair (modified). Six-cylinder. Horizontally-opposed. Rear-mounted. Overhead valve. Light aluminum alloy block. Displacement: 176 cid. Bore and stroke: 3.56 x 2.94 inches. Compression ratio: 10.5:1. Brake hp: 240 at 6000 rpm. Four main bearings.

POWERTRAIN: Four-speed manual transmission.

CHASSIS FEATURES: Wheelbase: 108 inches (Chevrolet Corvair chassis). Overall length: 183.3 inches. Front tread: 55 inches. Rear tread: 57.2 inches. Tire size: (Stage III and IV) 7.50 x 14; (other models) 7.50 x 13.

1969 YENKO CAMARO

YENKO — Don Yenko did not give up making high-performance conversions when the Corvair was laid to rest. He began doing the same thing to the Chevrolet Camaros. Big Chevrolet C.O.P.O. (Central OfficeProduction Option) V-8s were installed. These cars were called Camaro 450s. Unfortunately, production lasted only one season.

I.D. NUMBERS: Not available.

CAMARO 450

Model Number	Body/Style Number	Body Type & Seating	Factory Price	Shipping Weight	Production Total
NA	NA	2-dr HT-2P	NA	NA	Note 1

NOTE 1: Approximately 50 Yenko Camaros built.

ENGINES

(BASE) Chevrolet Corvette. V-8. Overhead valves. Cast iron block. Displacement: 427 cid. Bore and stroke: 4.25 x 3.76 inches. Compression ratio: 11.0:1. Brake hp: 435 at 6000 rpm. Five main bearings. Solid valve lifters. Carburetor: Holley four-barrel.

(OPTIONAL) Chevrolet Corvette (modified). V-8. Overhead valves. Cast iron block. Displacement: 427 cid. Bore and stroke: 4.25 x 3.76 inches. Compression ratio: 11.0:1. Brake hp: 450 at 6100 rpm. Five main bearings. Solid valve lifters. Carburetor: Three Rochester two-barrel.

POWERTRAIN: Four-speed manual transmission.

CHASSIS FEATURES: Wheelbase: 108 inches (Chevrolet Camaro chassis). Overall length: 184.7 inches. Front tread: 59 inches. Rear tread: 58.9 inches.

NOTE 1: Total Corvair and Camaro based models was not more than 185. (Possibly as few as 100 Corvairs and 35 Camaros). Don Yenko lost his life in an airplane accident early in 1987.

MANUFACTURER: Yenko Sportscars Inc., Canonsburg, Pa.

DREAM CARS
1946-1975

The term, "Dream Cars," is believed to have been penned in connection with the General Motors Motorama car shows of the early and mid-'50s. Harley Earl, then head of General Motors Styling, used the Motorama shows to bring to the public the stylists' ideas of future automobiles.

All too often the inspired design of a stylist was hacked at and watered down by all the different committees his design passed through on its way to production. Earl used the Motorama to wake up corporate management as to what could be done given a "clean slate" and few restraints. The result brought forth dozens of inspired (and, some not-so-inspired) car designs that influenced future production more than anyone ever imagined.

Practically every auto company jumped onto the Dream Car bandwagon. Chrysler's Virgil Exner began an association with Ghia that lasted for over a decade. Ford's early show cars began their second 50 years with new excitement and flair. But it was GM that really pushed the idea to the fullest. Earl's brilliant Le Sabre and Charles Chayne's Buick XP-300 had the automotive world buzzing with excitement.

The public was starved for anything new. World War II was still a recent memory and Europe, particularly Germany and Italy, was in a huge rebuilding program. Dream Cars caught the public's fancy and millions of people thronged to auto shows all across the nation.

What we are presenting in this section is not all-inclusive. There are numerous holes and omissions in this listing. We certainly hope to expand and complete the section in future editions. You are invited to write in with additions and corrections. We hope to be able to locate all survivors and let you know where to find surviving Dream Cars.

CHRYSLER CORPORATION

Chrysler

1951 K-310. The K-310 was the first of a long string of Virgil Exner designed, Ghia-built show vehicles. It was also the first to have the false tire on the deck lid. The car was built on a Saratoga chassis powered by Chrysler's new 180 hp Hemi V-8 engine.

1952 Chrysler Special. Another Ghia-built show car, the Special was built on a shortened New Yorker chassis. This vehicle was one of two built at the request of then Chrysler export sales department head C.B. Thomas. It made its debut at the Paris Auto Show in 1952. (Chrysler photo)

1952 Chrysler Parade Phaeton. Three of these large parade convertibles were built and used extensively in New York City, Los Angeles and Detroit. Modified in 1955, the original versions were painted black (New York), cream (Los Angeles) and green (Detroit). Each car had a light-weight convertible top in case of rain. All three survive. One is in the Imperial Palace Auto Collection in Las Vegas, Nev.

1952 C-200. This car appears to be a convertible version of the 1951 K-310. It too is built on the Saratoga chassis. The C-200 was painted pale green with a black hood. It had black and green leather upholstery.

1953 C.B. Thomas Special. This is the second of the Thomas-requested, Exner-designed, Ghia-built specials. Though very similar to the 1952 Special, this car differed in several ways. It had a slightly different grille, door handles, rear deck lid and cowl intake outlets. Car is in the Joe Bortz collection.

1954 Le Comte. The only difference between the Le Comte and La Comtesse was the color. This car was painted black and bronze. Chrysler workmen did the conversions on both cars.

1953 D'Elegance. This three-passenger coupe was also Ghia-built. The D'Elegance rode on a shortened 115 inch wheelbase New Yorker chassis. The same 331 cid Hemi V-8 was used along with Chrysler's Fluid-Drive transmission. (Chrysler photo)

1955 Special Corsaire. The Italian designer Boano did this show car. Boano used to work for Ghia, but left after he felt Chrysler's influence was too strong. The chassis was a special tube frame with a Chrysler Hemi V-8 in place.

1954 Custom Imperial Landau Victoria. Chrysler turned to American coach-builder Derham for this tasteful show car. The custom top was covered with white leather and the interior featured four black leather bucket seats.

1955 Parade Phaetons. Chrysler took the three original '52 Phaetons and updated them with '55 Imperial grilles and fenders. The Detroit and New York cars were both painted white, while the Los Angeles car was changed to silver blue metallic.

1954 La Comtesse. This custom built Imperial had clear plexiglass top with white vinyl accents. The La Comtesse was painted pink and white with an interior to match. The wire wheels were by this time production items available on Chrysler products as an option.

1956 Norseman. When the ship Andrea Doria sank in July of 1956, a year of Virgil Exner's design work sunk, too. So did almost 15 months of Ghia's craftsmanship. The Norseman was in the hold on its way to the U.S. Among its unique features was the cantilever roof design which allowed much thinner pillars. The rear window also retracted into the roof.

Standard Catalog of American Cars

1957 Dart or Super Gilda. This Ghia-built car-of-the-future was a retractable hardtop. The top slid back into the rear compartment and could even be retracted while the car was in motion. Engine was the 375 hp 300-C Hemi. It later would be modified and re-named the "Diablo." The car is still in existence in the hands of dream car collector Joe Bortz.

1958 Imperial D'Elegance. This was a body mock-up with no engine or transmission. Exner's design featured a sharply-sloping rear deck and strange eyebrow hidden headlights.

1961 TurboFlite. This was Chrysler's first turbine-powered dream car. As with many of the previous Chrysler dream cars, this one was company-designed and Ghia-of-Italy built. The most unusual styling feature was the canopy top that raised up when the door was opened for entry. Side windows were hinged in the roof and the spoiler on the deck lid was also an air brake that pivoted upward when the brakes were applied. (Chrysler photo)

1963 Turbine. Ghia built a total of 50 identical cars with turbine engines for Chrysler. These cars were loaned out to selected individuals all across the country. The conservatively styled coupes were rated at 130 hp All were painted Turbine Bronze and were most cars were destroyed after evaluation. A few Turbines were donated to museums such as the Henry Ford Museum in Dearborn, Mich. Chrysler still owns one. Chrysler collector Frank Kleptz, of Terre Haute, Ind., has another. (Chrysler Historical Collection photo)

1969 Concept 70X. As was typical when doing a prototype or special show car, this car is a four-door on the driver's side, and a two-door on the passenger side. The doors were hinged with parallelogram hinges that allowed the door(s) to swing out and away from the body. The body was fiberglass. An ultra-sonic device scanned the rear area 180 degrees by 50 feet and warned the driver of any object entering the scanner zone.

1970 Cordoba de Oro. This car has a cantilever roof similar to the ill-fated 1956 Norseman. It was built on the regular 124 inch chassis and powered by a regular Newport engine.

DeSoto

1954 Adventurer I. This car marked the end of the Virgil Exner-designed cars beginning with the Chrysler K-310. Exner considered the Adventurer I to be one of his finest designs. Ghia, of course, built the car. It rested on an 111 inch wheelbase and was almost 190 inches (15.8 feet) long. Exner used the coupe as his personal car for several years.

1954 Adventurer II. Another Ghia-built show car, the Adventurer II was a two-seater. The style was very "Italian," even though it was designed in America. The rear window retracted electrically into the boot. Another curious feature was its bumper-less front end.

1954 Flight-Sweep I. This car was very close to a production-type car. The convertible top was electrically operated and it had fully operating electric side windows. Many show cars didn't have fully operating tops or windows. The Ghia-built car was almost a twin to the Flight-Sweep II, except that it was a hardtop.

1955 Flight-Sweep II. A console between the bucket seats had controls for the PowerFlite transmission, radio, heater, and turn signals. The hooded headlight visors flowed rearward to a upswept fin. As was the Flight-Sweep I, the front fenders, cowl and body were welded as a unit to the frame.

1955 Falcon. The Falcon was a competition-type roadster built with unit body construction. The wheelbase was a relatively short 105 inches. The 170 hp DeSoto Hemi V-8 provided sufficient power for the lightweight roadster. A total of three Falcons were built. One is in the Bortz Collection.

Dodge

1953 Firearrow I. Another separate series of Exner-designed, Ghia-built show cars was the Firearrow series. It began with this roadster mock-up. Very shortly after, the Firearrow II appeared with slight modifications. Firearrow I was painted a brilliant red, offsetting its light yellow leather interior. Note the use of quad headlights and gray moulding entirely circling the car.

1954 Firearrow II. The main difference between Firearrow I and II is the use single headlights in the second version and slightly different side moulding treatment. This Ghia-built roadster was a pale yellow.

1954 Firearrow Coupe. After the two roadster versions, Ghia built this smart coupe with several refined styling touches. The grille was now concave and had the quad headlight system. This was no mock-up version, as it was timed at over 135 mph on the test track.

1954 Firearrow Convertible. This is the final Firearrow. It is very similar to the coupe, with a few subtle styling changes. The grille is less rounded and has an eggcrate pattern to it. Note the wild diamond-patterned black and white leather interior. This version became the pattern for the production of the Dual-Ghia. The Dual-Ghia cars weren't produced for Chrysler Corp. but rather used Chrysler mechanical components in bodies built by Ghia and marketed by Dual Motors of Detroit, Mich.

Standard Catalog of American Cars

1955 Granada. The Granada was billed in a press-release from Dodge, "As the first one-piece, fiberglass car ever developed." This car even had the bumpers, structural members and body-attaching brackets made of fiberglass. This car survives today in the collection of Joseph Bortz, well-known "Dream Car" collector in Illinois. It is unrestored.

1961 Flitewing. On this show car the side windows, which were hinged at the roof, would swing up and out of the way when the doors were opened. A pressure switch was utilized to keep the windows from closing prematurely on someone's head.

1964 Charger. Performance was being stressed in the mid-'60s and the Charger show car epitomized this spirit. The Charger utilized some basic Dodge body panels with special features, such as hood mounted scoop, combination headrest and roll bar and competition-style windscreen. Engine was a 426 cid Hemi.

1965 Charger II. What follows Charger I? Charger II, of course. The direct predecessor of the showroom edition, the Charger II came very close to the production version.

1967 Daroo II. This was a one-off Chrysler Corp. show car on the Dart GT chassis. It was exhibited at key auto shows. "Daroo" is a derivation of the early Anglo-Saxon word Dar-U, meaning "dart or spear." How appropriate. This car survives and was offered for sale at "The Auction," Nov. 1-3, 1991 at the Aladdin Hotel of Las Vegas, Nev.

1968 Charger III. The wildest Charger was the third version. It went all-out to test various design theories. Some thought it had Corvette styling. The ultra-low car sat just 42 inches from the road.

1970 Diamante. This is one of the last true radical "early postwar dream cars," as most show cars made this late were slightly modified production cars. This one was a factory custom two-seater with a Hemi V-8. Dream car collector Joe Bortz (above) has the Diamante in his "Blue Suede Shoes" collection.

Plymouth

1951 XX-500. This was Chrysler's first dream car built in collaboration with the famed Italian coachbuilder Ghia. The car was constructed on a '51 Plymouth chassis. It was a full six-passenger automobile featuring a curved one-piece windshield and fastback rear deck treatment. The car was the work of Ghia stylist Mario Boano, who would eventually go on to establish a coachbuilding firm of his own.

1954 Belmont. The Belmont was constructed of fiberglass by Chrysler engineers at Chrysler's Briggs plant. It was a true roadster with no roll-up windows. The car had a '54 Dodge chassis and engine coupled with Plymouth's Hy-Drive transmission. The color was a light metallic blue.

1954 Explorer. The Plymouth-based Ghia special this year was the Explorer. It was a two-passenger sport coupe styled closely to the Dodge Firearrow Sport Coupe. Main differences were the Explorer's horizontal bumpers, waterfall grille, single headlights and exhaust tips routed through the taillight housings. Power was from Plymouth's reliable flathead six cylinder 110 hp engine coupled to their Hy-Drive semi-automatic transmission. (Chrysler photo)

1956 Plainsman. The Plainsman was more of a corporate exercise than any specific marque. But, it was built on a '55 Plymouth chassis using their new V-8 engine so it counts as a Plymouth. Many of this car's innovative features eventually reached production, including the rear-facing third seat, spare tire carried within the right rear fender, and vinyl-covered roof panel.

1958 Cabana. This nine-passenger wagon joined the show car circuit in '58. It was built by Ghia in Italy and, while utilizing a '58 Plymouth chassis, it had no engine or transmission. A true four-door hardtop, the doors were center locked to floor-height locks giving a full unobstructed entry to either front or rear seat. The tailgate was unique. It was a full-width side-opening door. To make access to the rear seat more convenient, two clear plastic panels slide into the roof for easier entry. And, finally, all the seats except the driver's seat could be folded down to produce a huge carpeted cargo area.

1960 XNR. This wedge-shaped sports car had asymmetrical styling. The hood scoop and headrest faring were inline with the driver's seat. It had a leather-covered glove box that could be removed and used as a camera case. The name of the car, XNR, is a direct derivative of its designer, Virgil Exner. (Chrysler photo)

1961 Plymouth Asymmetrica. "Asymmetric design" (non mirror-image) was catching on in the industrial design field in the early '60s. This Virgil Exner dream cars has some special design elements (bumps and bulges) on the driver's side only. Actually, it appears to be a re-worked edition of the XNR or a closely-related cousin. It survives and was in "The Auction" during November, 1991.

1965 VIP. The VIP was first shown at the 1965 Chicago Auto Show. As the name implies, the VIP was outfitted with many special features for the "very important person" of the business world. A telephone and tape recorder were handy for busy executives while an entertainment center featured, other innovations such as a television, beverage center and stereo. The photochromic glass would get darker with more light and open up in dim light. The T-roof supported two panels that would retract into the rear boot or trunk.

1967 Barracuda Formula SX. A non-functioning show car, the SX was constructed of fiberglass. It had a semi-fastback style with no door handles in sight. Note the unusually thin door pillars.

1969 Duster I. Performance was selling cars. Plymouth's idea car for '69 stressed this to a tee. The Duster had the potent 426 cid Hemi V-8 rated at 425 hp. The car had four moveable "air brakes," two on the rollbar and two on the rear fenders next to the gas filler caps. The dual exhaust exited in the center of the Kamm-styled rear.

Ford

1953 X-100. This is one of Ford's first dream cars. Many of the styling features found their way into production. The torpedo slab-sides were seen on 1961-63 Thunderbirds. The hood ornament is used on '58 Fords. The hooded headlights and front fender outlines would show up on '56 Lincolns. And, the wraparound windshield hit the streets on the '55 Fords and Mercurys.

1954 FX-Atmos. This red, white and blue spaceship made its debut at the '54 Chicago Auto Show. Most of the features were only seen before in styling studio sketches.

1954 Muroc.

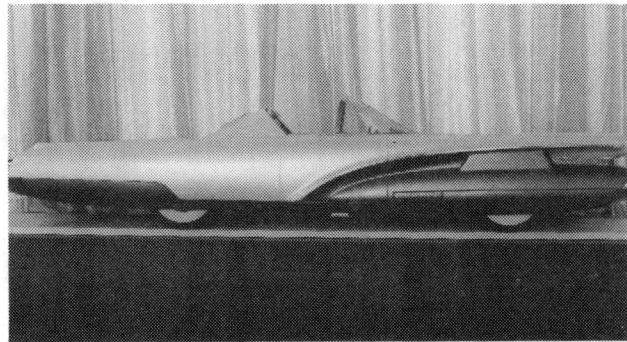

1956 X-1000. Another "spaceship from another planet," the X-1000 was a 3/8 inch scale model. The mode of power was left unnamed.

1956 Mystere. Although a full-sized mock-up, the Mystere was never a serious "idea" car. The power plant was a "mystery," although the large air intakes and perforated panels suggested a gas turbine. Ford, Chrysler and GM were all experimenting with gas turbine engines during this time and each had workable cars or trucks with turbine engines. The steering wheel could be swung to either side, giving either left or right-hand drive.

1956 Syrtis Roof-O-Matic.

1958 La Galaxie. Besides the far-out, space ship styling, Ford stylists let their imaginations run wild on the interior also. Ultra-sophisticated television screen warning devices, all-new steering wheel applications, use of computers, etc. The name La Galaxie lived on in a new Ford Galaxie series.

1959 La Tosca. This 3/8-scale model was radio-controlled so the stylists could see how the car would look while in motion.

1961 Gyron. Many of the "far-out" features of the Gyron are just now being perfected. There was a computer system to give automatic control of driving functions. Plus, a bad weather scanning system that would give a clear picture of the road ahead regardless of fog, snow or rain. The Gyron's name came from the use of only two wheels, one fore and one aft, both driven. Small "training" wheels would keep the car upright at slow speeds or at rest. Once underway, gyroscopes would stabilize the car.

1962 Palomar. The special "flying bridge" for rear passengers inspired the name for this Ford dream car. Mt. Palomar has one of the largest reflecting telescopes for looking into space. The rear part of the roof rolled back, similar to a roll-top desk. There was a second windshield mounted on the roof.

1962 Seattle-ite XXI. Built for display at the Seattle World's Fair in 1962, this 3/8-inch scale model boasted four steering and driving wheels. The power plant could have been anything from an atomic power engine to compact fuel cells driving electric motors. Instead of regular instruments, the Seattle-ite had TV monitors that not only gave details of the operation of the engine and other systems, but gave advanced weather reports and a map display showing exactly where the car was at any given time. (Ford photo)

Standard Catalog of American Cars

1962 Mustang I. This radical little two-seater with a V-4 mounted amidship was a miracle of design and engineering. It was designed from the ground up. Designed by the late Gene Bordinat, the basic layout was done by Ford product planner Roy Lunn. The car was built by well-known West Coast sports car builders Trautman and Barnes (who also built the first Scarab for Lance Reventlow and the Chapparell for Jim Hall). Lee Iacocca, then Ford president, is quoted as saying, "All the buffs said, 'Hey, what a car. It'll be the best car ever built.' But when I looked at the guys saying it - the off-beat crowd, the real buffs, I said 'that's sure not the car we want to build because it can't be a volume car. It's too far out.'" The second Mustang prototype, the Mustang II, was much closer to the final production car.

1963 Mustang II. A much more conventional car than its predecessor, the Mustang I, the II was much closer to the actual production version of the Mustang. (Applegate & Applegate photo)

1965 Techna. Although developed by Ford in 1965, the Techna didn't receive public scrutiny until 1968. Unlike many "idea" cars, the Techna's styling was appealing, but not extreme. Its true significance was as a test bed for dozens of advanced engineering concepts. These included anti-skid brakes, parallel-hinged doors, bonded sheet metal structure and an access hatch in the hood for routine service and fluid checks. (Edward Janecki photo)

1966 Mach 2. This mid-engined prototype was around for many years. The car used a Mustang engine and a German ZF five-speed transaxle. The radiator was front mounted. A tunnel (not for the driveshaft) was used for routing of water hoses, wiring and brake lines. The Mach 2 was studied extensively for several years but ultimately judged to be of no potential sales volume. It did, evidently, open a few eyes at GM because it wasn't too long before the mid-engined Corvette prototypes were developed.

1966 Bordinat Cobra. (Applegate & Applegate photo)

1968 Fiera. The Fiera is a modified version of the '68 Ford XL fastback. The deeply recessed grille features auxiliary driving lights in the center. The headlights and parking lights are hidden. Twin air intakes, located ahead of the rear wheels, provide additional brake cooling. (Ford photo)

1968 Torino Machete. Another "idea" car in the Fiera-vein. This one is a modified version of a '68 Fairlane Torino GT fastback. It has a special two-tone pearlescent white and silver paint scheme. The grille features twin horizontal black air scoops. The Machete's taillights are flush with the lower portion of the deck panel and concealed by white-coated lenses. (Ford photo)

1968 Mustang Mach I. Ford Design came up with this very potent-looking performance machine. The windshield is sloped at a rakish 64 degrees to accentuate the performance-look of the car. Wheel openings are flared to accept special wide-oval racing tires. There are functional air intakes just ahead of the rear wheels for brake cooling. (Ford photo)

1968 Ford Thunderbird Saturn.

1969 Ford Super Cobra. Ford stylists were going through a "Total Performance" era during the late '60s and this "idea" car is typical of their thinking. Hidden headlights, louvers in the rear window, huge scoops for engine and brakes, and rakish-slants to the windshield pillars were all incorporated into the Ford show cars of this era. (Applegate & Applegate photo)

1970 Ford Tridon. This study was done on a Thunderbird chassis. Unusual features included fully-enclosed rear wheels, clear roof panels, a three-element nosepiece, recessed rear window and plastic bumpers.

1972 Mustang Milano. A two-passenger GT car, supposedly Italian-influenced, with scoops, flairs, and wide-oval tires. (Ford photo)

1973 Pinto Sportiva. The Sportiva "sported" a removable roof panel, integrated roll bar and a fully instrumented interior. Sporty wheels, chrome tailpipes and racing mirror add to the sporty feel of this car. The exterior color was silver pearlescent and the interior had silver-colored leather. (Ford photo)

Lincoln

1953 XL-500. The Lincoln XL-500 was introduced in April of 1953. It featured a full-tinted glass roof with a red and white leather interior. The body was fiberglass mounted on a modified 1953 Lincoln chassis. Total height was less than 57 inches. The car was 81.5 inches wide and 216 inches long. The engine was modified for more horsepower. Interior features included a telephone; air conditioner; electric calendar; overhead monitoring lights (for water temperature, generator output, oil pressure, hood and deck ajar and transmission oil level); and a tape recorder. Styling features showed up as soon as 1955. The roof treatment proved very popular on the '55 and '56 Ford Crown Victorias. Front fender treatment of the XL-500 showed up in the '56 Lincolns.

1955 Futura. This has to be probably Ford Motor Co.'s most famous dream car. The Futura went on to become even more famous as the television star of the Batman and Robin epic. George Barris acquired the Futura and did some mild changes, including a black paint job, to turn this show car into a television star. The car was constructed by the Italian coachbuilder, Ghia.

736

1970 Mark III Dual Cowl Phaeton. This garish show car had dual windshields, red leather and corduroy interior, prismatic silver metalflake paint and a Mark III grille that extends under the car. It made its debut at the Detroit Auto Show in November of 1970. (Ford Motor Co. photo)

Mercury

1954 XM-800. Debuting at the February, 1954 Detroit Auto Show, the XM800's hooded headlights and front wheel cutouts later appeared on the '56 Lincoln. The XM-800 body was constructed of fiberglass and was approximately five inches wider than the '54 Mercury Montery. Four vinyl seats, separated by stationary armrests, were installed. Instrumentation included a tachometer and all gauges (which were supplemented by red warning lights). The only modification to the stock '54 Mercury engine was a dual exhaust system.

1956 XM-Turnpike Cruiser. President Eisenhower's grand plan of an Interstate Highway System were well on their way by the mid-'50s. Mercury's Turnpike Cruiser was designed with fast, long-distance driving in mind. Many styling features showed up in the 1957 Mercury, including a "Turnpike Cruiser" model. A special truck-trailer rig was used to haul the XM from city to city. The rig was as much a show on the road as it was at an auditorium.

1964 Super Maurader. This George Barris creation, powered by a 427 cid high-performance V-8, toured the country as part of Mercury's show car fleet. Its twin, torpedo-shaped headrests carried the rear turn signal indicators. A two-handle steering system replaced the customary steering wheel. The exhaust system was integrated into the rocker panels. (Applegate & Applegate photo)

1969 Super Spoiler. Mercury's performance image was being enhanced at this time by many super-speedway wins by the Mercury team in NASCAR. This one-of-a-kind show vehicle carries the image a bit farther. The "spoiler" was more decorative than functional on this canary-yellow car based upon the Cyclone and Cyclone GT production models.

1970 El Gato. The Mercury El Gato is based upon the 1970 Cougar. The steep rake of the windshield and back window give the car a fastback look that is new to Cougar. The custom paint was a shaded green. Lighter at the top and darker as it went down. (Ford Motor Co. photo)

GENERAL MOTORS

Buick

1951 XP-300 The first of two wildly innovative dream cars, the XP-300 was the product of Charles Chayne and Ned Nickles. Most noticeable feature to appear on future production cars were the headlight bezels, which showed up on the '53 Buick line. The car was built on a 116 inch wheelbase, had an overall length of 192.5 inches, was 39.1 inches high to the cowl and 53.4 inches to the top of the windshield. The frame was a box-type steel structure with the body welded on. The body was constructed of aluminum panels, thus reducing overall weight to 3,125 pounds. The engine was a supercharged aluminum V-8 displacing 216 cid. Horsepower was rated at 315. (GM photo)

1951 Le Sabre. The other styling and engineering "tour de force" for '51 was Harley Earl's Le Sabre (Earl was chief of GM styling). Both the XP-300 and the Le Sabre were two-seat roadsters. Both utilized the same 216 cid supercharged aluminum V-8 engine, and both pioneered the panoramic wraparound windshield that was the rage from '54 on. But, that's where the similarity ended. The Le Sabre had wilder styling features and revolutionary suspension layouts. The Le Sabre had rubber springs (working in torsion) in the front and a single-leaf semi-elliptic spring in conjunction with a de Dion rear differential. (Applegate & Applegate photo)

1953 Wildcat I. A fiberglass bodied two-passenger roadster, the first of a series of Wildcat dream cars rode on a 114 inch wheelbase. Note the traditional Buick portholes on top of the fenders. Power was provided by Buick's new V-8 engine that produced 188 hp An unusual feature were the "rotor-static" front wheel discs. They remained stationary while the front wheels revolved. It's in the Bortz Collection today. (GM photo)

1954 Roadmaster Landau. This styling exercise attempted to recapture the Landulettes of the '20s and '30s. It had a blue leather-trimmed chauffeur's compartment with electric division window. The rear of the roof lowered hydraulically like a convertible top, revealing a passenger compartment trimmed in beige leather with mutton carpeting. The rear armrest held a cocktail set and shaker. It has electric windows and a padded deck lid with leather hold-down straps. It is survives in the Bortz/Blue Suede Shoes dream car fleet.

1954 Wildcat II. The smallest (100 inch wheelbase) of the Wildcat roadsters, the Wildcat II is more Corvette-oriented than any. The car had several unique styling features, such as the "flying buttress" front fenders, and, of course, the famous Buick portholes. The Buick V-8 engine sported four carburetors and put out 220 hp. The body was constructed of fiberglass. (GM photo)

1955 Wildcat III. The most conventional of the three Wildcats, the III was a four-passenger convertible with a fiberglass body. It was mounted on a 110 inch wheelbase chassis. There was a floor-mounted transmission lever for the Dynaflow automatic.

1956 Centurion. The Centurion name went on to become a Buick model in 1971. The Centurion was a four-passenger two-door hardtop with a fully transparent roof. When the door was opened, the bucket seat would move back for easier entry. Push on the back of the front seat and the seat would move forward to make exiting the rear easier. Other features included a television screen rearview mirror, and a steering column that passed down the center of the cockpit with the steering wheel suspended on a cantilever arm in front of the driver. (GM photo)

1963 Riviera Sliver Arrow. A modified '63 Riviera, the Silver Arrow's biggest change, other than a new front end treatment, was the chop job on the top. The top was lowered about three inches giving the Arrow a much "leaner" appearance. The front end styling later went into production on the '65 Riviera, complete with hidden headlights in the pods on the front fenders.

1969 Century Cruiser. For '69 Buick dusted off the '64 Firebird IV, changed some details and features, added a new paint job and served it up at the '69 New York Auto Show. Pontiac did basically the same thing with its '69 show car the Cirrus, which originated as the '64 GM-X Stiletto.

Cadillac

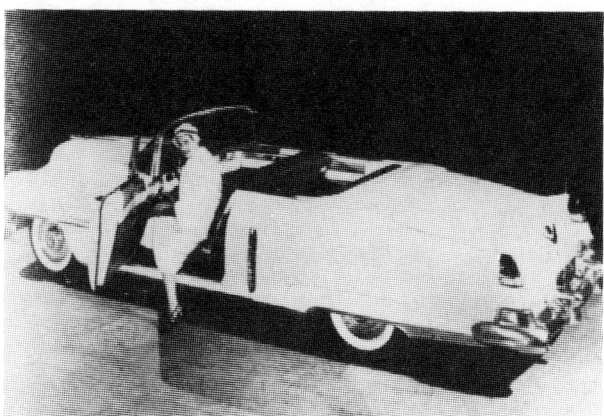

1952 Eldorado. Cadillac built this special convertible for the '52 auto show tour. There was no GM Motorama yet; that came in 1953. This modified Series 62 convertible had several styling features that would show up the next year, notably the wraparound windshield. The exhaust was routed through large pods in the rear bumper.

1953 Le Mans. One of two show cars built expressly for the new GM Motorama shows, the Le Mans had many unique styling features that would show up on '54 and '56 Cadillac production models. The hooded headlights, entire front end and rear fender treatment are examples. The Le Mans was a two-passenger fiberglass roadster powered by a 250 hp Cadillac engine. Factory records suggest that three of these compact little sportsters were built. (Applegate & Applegate photo)

1949 Coupe de Ville. The first of what was to evolve into the famous GM Motoramas of the '50s was a show that took place in January 1949 at the Waldorf Astoria hotel ballroom in New York City. Billed as "Transportation Unlimited," the star of the show was this stunning '49 Cadillac dream car. The Coupe de Ville was built on a 133 inch Sixty Special chassis. Features included a curved, one-piece windshield, hardtop styling, fake air scoops on the rear fenders and chrome scuff plates on the rocker panels. GM president Charles Wilson, used this car for a time and then was given to his secretary. The car survives on the West Coast.

1953 Orleans. This is the second '53 Motorama car. Look closely and you'll see the big feature of the Orleans - it's center-opening four-door hardtop design. Four-door hardtops would make their production debut in the Buick and Oldsmobile line in '55, but not until 1956 would Cadillac get a four-door hardtop. (Applegate & Applegate)

1954 Park Avenue. The '54 Motorama show saw a record three entries from Cadillac division. The Park Avenue had the biggest impact on future production vehicles as the other two were both two-seat sports-type cars. Note the '57 Cadillac-type rear fenders and notch-back roofline. The car was built on the same 133 inch wheelbase as the Fleetwood Sixty Special.

1954 La Espada. A fiberglass two-seat roadster, the La Espada had a 115 inch wheelbase and an overall length of just over 200 inches. It was painted Apollo gold. Note the extreme rake of the wraparound windshield. (GM photo)

1954 El Camino. The third Motorama car in '54 was this rakish coupe. It rode on the same 115 inch chassis that the La Espada did, but had many unique styling features, such as the brushed aluminum top and tinted windows. The rear fender styling would return in the '55 Eldorado convertible and all '58 models. The two sportsters were the first Cadillacs with quad headlights. (GM photo)

1955 Eldorado Brougham. One of the stars of the '55 GM Motorama was this one-of-a-kind predecessor of the exclusive '57-'58 Eldorado Brougham. The Eldorado stood a full seven inches lower than production Cadillacs. GM used the '57 Brougham to counter Lincoln's Mark II Continental, which, ironically, had ceased production by the time the Brougham hit the showrooms. This is the first Cadillac with the troublesome air bag suspension. (Applegate & Applegate photo)

1955 La Salle II Four-Door. The famous La Salle nameplate was revived for use on two '55 Motorama show cars from Cadillac. They both shared V-6 engines and fiberglass bodies. The front ends are also the same. An interesting mechanical feature saw the brake drums and aluminum cast wheels integrated into a single unit.

1955 La Salle II Roadster. The roadster was fiberglass construction. It rested on a very short wheelbase. Note the rear of the car. It looks like it was chopped off. A V-6 engine with fuel-injection produced 150 hp.

1956 Eldorado Brougham Town Car. At the 1956 GM Motorama the '55 Eldorado Brougham four-door hardtop was joined by this new rendition on an old idea. The Town Car, large as it was, was constructed of fiberglass. It stood just 55.5 inches tall and was 219.9 inches long. The passenger compartment housed a bar, a radio-telephone, a cigar humidor, vanity, and air conditioner. The top was covered with black leather. (Applegate & Applegate photo)

Standard Catalog of American Cars

1959 Cyclone. Cadillac traded in their airplane styling ideas for space ship styling in '59. The Cyclone looks every bit like a missile about to be launched, from the "nose cones" on the front fenders (which housed radar to provide the driver with visual and audible warning of obstacles in his path) to the huge fins on the rear fenders (which were toned down in the 1960 version).

1968 Eldorado Biarritz Town Coupe. The interior of the Town Coupe was upholstered in gold velour with the inner door and rear quarter panels made from ornate carved walnut. In the center of the front seat is a medallion embroidered in 14 karat gold thread. There was no roof over the front seat and the landau rear section had no windows.

Chevrolet

1953 Corvette. The Corvette was shown at the New York Auto Show in January of 1953. It was supposedly strictly a show car but public reaction was so great that Chevrolet rushed the car into production. And, on July 1, 1953, the first Corvette rolled off the line at Flint, Mich.

1954 Nomad. One of Chevy's contributions to the 1954 GM Motorama show was this stunning two-door station wagon. The front end resembled the Corvette, and, in fact, used many components of the production Corvette. However, it was built on a standard Chevy chassis and utilized the 150 hp six-cylinder Corvette engine. The '55 Nomad was already past the prototype stage when this beauty went on stage, but it's interesting to note that public reaction was very favorable, thus reinforcing Chevy's foresight in producing a specialty wagon.

1954 Corvair. Like the Nomad, the Corvair utilized many Corvette components, including front end styling, engine and transmission. For 1954 Chevrolet showed three Corvette-styled cars: the Nomad, Corvair and Corvette Hardtop.

1955 Biscayne. A new 4.3 liter V-8 powered this "Dream Car." The unusual inboard headlights and concave door panels were never produced on a regular Chevy. Note the double wraparound windshield. This design eventually showed up on '59 Mercurys of all places. Joe Bortz recovered this car from Warhoop's Salvage several years ago.

1956 Impala. As with the '54 Motorama show cars, this year's entry also had the current Corvette look to it. In addition, the real chrome wire wheels had functional knock-off hubs. The body was again fiberglass and rested on a 116.5 inch chassis with the Corvette V-8 engine.

1958 Corvette XP 700. What began as a personal car for William Mitchell, head of GM styling, became a test bed for future Corvettes. The car started out as a stock '58 Corvette. The rear end treatment found its way to the '61 Corvette. By 1959 the XP 700 was elevated to show car status. (Applegate & Applegate photo)

1960 CERV I. That's Zora Arkus-Duntov, "Mr. Corvette," standing beside the Chevrolet Engineering Research Vehicle (CERV). The vehicle was used mainly for testing of suspension and steering components (at least that's what Duntov told the brass). The car went into the Briggs Cunningham Auto Museum, where it was preserved many years. It`s now owned by the Pro-Team Corvette business.

1963 Corvair Super Spyder. Bill Mitchell carried the Sebring Spyder of 1962 a little farther into the "Dream Car Zone" with the Super Spyder. Note the external exhausts at the rear. The front end received more aggressive styling also. This car, along with the Corvair Monza GT and Monza roadster, made its public debut at various sports car racing facilities across the country.

19

1961 Corvair Sebring Spyder. Chevrolet took the Spyder to many sports car racing tracks around the country. Reaction was favorable for the dolled up roadster. Features included a cut-down windshield, mag wheels, turbocharged engine, racing mirrors and stone guards on the headlights. Another of Bill Mitchell's inspirations.

1963 Corvair Monza SS XP 797. This Corvair was the closest to an out-and-out racing car that Mitchell came up with for the rear-engined Corvair. The air-cooled six cylinder engine had six Dell 'Orto carburetors.

1963 Corvair Testudo. Built by the Italian coachmaker, Bertone, this Corvair-based show car was designed by Giorgio Giugiaro, who gave the world dozens of wild and not-so-wild automobiles. To enter, the entire cockpit cap is swung forward (similar to the Corvair Monza GT).

1962 Corvair Monza GT Coupe. William Mitchell went all out with this version of the Corvair. He named it, like the '61 Sebring Spyder, after a famous sports car racing track: Monza, Italy. Retaining the Corvair rear engine, the fiberglass body had several unusual styling features. Entry to the car was gained when the entire forward part of the passenger compartment hinged forward in one piece. The extreme slant of the windshield was possible when the two seats were moved close together, thus allowing the rakish slant.

1963 Corvette Mako Shark I XP-755. With this design, William Mitchell took the 1958 XP-700 closer to the production Corvette of 1968. The engine is a supercharged version of the new 409 cid power plant. Note the functional external competition exhausts. The plastic roof is both tinted and treated inside with vaporized aluminum to deflect sunlight. The Shark door handles were flush type, with opening handles that flipped out when an integral button was pressed. (GM photo)

1964 Mitchell Corvette. This is one of several "street-modified" styling exercises done by GM styling vice-president William Mitchell in this era. It was introduced at the 1964 Detroit Automobile Show. The car has serial number 40837S106524. It survives and was offered for sale at "The Auction" in the fall of 1991.

1964 Corvette Coupe Rondine. Built by Pininfarina in Italy, this one-of-a-kind features a reverse-slant roofline and much smoother, less aggressive front end treatment. (Applegate & Applegate photo)

1965 Corvette Mako Shark II. With a modifications, the style set forth by the Mako II Corvette dream car became the production 'Vette for 1967. There were no less than 17 electric motors to run such things as headlights, wipers that retracted under the hood, adjustable headrests suspended from the roof, moveable venetian blind rear window shades, adjustable clutch, brake and steering wheel (all electrically-adjustable), adjustable rear spoiler, remote-controlled gas filler, and a retractable rear license plate. None of these features made the production line, except the headlights! (Applegate & Applegate photo)

1967 Corvair Astro II. A bored-out 176 cid Corvair flat six-cylinder engine powered this far out GT coupe. Unlike the earlier 1963 Monza GT, the entire pod over the passenger compartment swung, up and backwards for entry (the GT's pod swung forward). The Astro was built on an 88 inch chassis and the engine put out 240 hp (GM photo)

1967 Astro II XP-880. Frank Winchell and Larry Nies of Chevrolet set about to design the new mid-engined Corvette for the '70s. The Astro II is the result. It had a spot-welded steel backbone frame. The radiator was mounted in the rear so the hot radiator hoses wouldn't have to pass through the passenger compartment. The engine used was the MK IV 390 hp unit with power passing through a two-speed torque converter of a 1963 Pontiac Tempest transaxle. (GM photo)

1968 Astro-Vette. This pearlescent white roadster was unofficially called "Moby Dick," a mythical whale made famous by author Melvile. More for show than go, the Astro-Vette was designed with aerodynamics in mind. The vents scribed on the side were designed to open when pressure reached a predetermined level in the engine compartment. It also had partial belly pans front and rear to further aid streamlining.

1969 Astro III. The Astro III is a two-passenger show car that features a tricycle-type wheel arrangement. It was designed with turbine-power in mind. Closed-circuit television provides rear vision. (Chevrolet photo)

1973 XP-987 GT Corvette 2-Rotor. GM was heavily into the development of the radical Wankle rotary engine in the early '70s. Two famous show cars were developed during this time and this is the first one. Originally, it was not called a Corvette. This snappy two-passenger sports car was also considered a replacement for the German GM division's little "mini-Corvette," the Opel GT. Horsepower from the 2-rotor was about 180. The front end treatment saw production on the Chevy Monza 2+2 in 1975. (Applegate & Applegate photo)

1973 4-rotor or Aero-Vette. Zora Arkus-Duntov decided he wanted a really fast Wankle-engined sports car. He enlisted the aid of Gib Hufstader to build a mid-engined Wankle-powered vehicle utilizing two of the two-rotor rotary engines that powered the XP-987. Horsepower for the 4-rotor was about 350 hp This was the largest Wankle engine ever put into a car. Displacement would have equaled about 585 cid in a conventional engine. The doors were a double-folding gull-wing affair that allowed easy entrance to the passenger compartment. (Applegate & Applegate)

Oldsmobile

1953 Starfire. A fiberglass-bodied four-passenger convertible, the Starfire lent several of its styling ideas to production vehicles. Most notably, the large oval grille ('56 models) and the side trim ('54 models). The wraparound windshield was soon seen on the large series GM cars in 1954 and across the board by 1955. The name Starfire came from the F-94 Starfire jet fighter. For many years to come the name Starfire was attached to all Olds convertibles. It then became the name of a luxury series in the '60s and finally the name Olds called its new small car in 1964. (Olds photo)

1954 Cutlass. One of two Olds show cars built for the '54 GM Motorama show, the Cutlass was also named after a fighter plane. This time it was the Navy's new carrier-based jet. The Cutlass was built on a 110 inch chassis and was 188 inches overall. The engine was the 324 cid Rocket V-8 and put out 250 hp (Olds photo)

1954 F-88. The second show car for '54 was this Corvette-sized sports car made of Fiberglass. The F-88 was built on a 102 inch chassis with a 167 inch overall length. It shared the same basic 324 cid engine that the Cutlass had. The car was painted a metallic gold with a pigskin interior. The rear bumper unit dropped down to reveal the horizontally-stored spare tire. (Olds photo)

1955 Delta. The Delta was Olds' contribution to the GM Motorama for 1955. It was a four-passenger coupe. It used a brushed aluminum roof, wide-set oval recesses housing the headlights, dual fuel tanks in the rear fenders, front seats that swivel for easy entry and cast aluminum wheels. The Delta was finished in two-tone metallic blue with a blue leather interior. The body was constructed of fiberglass. It was built on a 120 inch chassis with a 201 inch overall length. (Olds photo)

1956 Golden Rocket. This two-passenger car is made of fiberglass and painted metallic gold. Projectile-shaped bumper guards are incorporated at the extreme front and rear of the fenders and the extension of this form is carried for the entire length of the car. As either door is opened, the roof panel automatically raises and the seat rises three inches and swivels outwards for easier entry. The Golden Rocket is powered by a 275 hp Olds Rocket V-8. Chassis wheelbase is 105 inches and length is 201. (Olds photo)

1969 Apollo. This space age conception of the 4-4-2 appeared at the 1969 New York Auto Show. It was finished in Fireball red with black accent stripes and hood panels. The interior featured four metallic red and black leather "contour couches" and head restraints. (GM photo)

Pontiac

1953 Parisienne. Pontiac's definition called this a town car, but most town cars are four-doors. This is more of a "landau," as far as definitions go. It had a special wraparound rear window as well as front windshield. Original press releases said it had a plexiglass dome fitted over the driver's compartment in the event of bad weather. However, the car still exists and raises doubts about this claim. The Parisienne rode on a standard 122 inch chassis and was powered by Pontiac's straight eight engine. It was updated in 1954 with a new grille and different paint. Joe Bortz obtained the car and had it restored to its original 1953 format. (GM photo)

1954 Bonneville Special. Harley Earl named this dream car design after the famed Bonneville Salt Flats of Utah. For years it was thought that one car was made, but there are two. Both now survive in the Bortz Collection. The Bonneville Specials were two-seat sports cars on a 100 inch chassis. One was painted a metallic reddish bronze color, the other is green. A transparent plexiglass canopy encloses the entire passenger compartment. Hinged at the center, the canopies raise at each side on springs counter-balanced at the touch of a release catch. The doors are then opened from the inside. The cars have bucket seats, a center console and a modified multi-carbureted straight eight. (GM photo)

1954 Strato Streak. Pontiac called their four-door, four-passenger show car a "sports car." Most people would argue that definition, but the Strato Streak had many far-sighted features. Among them the pillarless four-door (but not hardtop) construction. The doors are hung from the front and from the rear on each side, with strength provided at the center by extra rigidity in the frame. Since the rear doors open into the windstream, they are equipped with special locks to prevent their being opened, except when the car is stopped and in neutral. The front seats swivel 90 degrees for ease of entry and exit. (GM photo)

1954 Firebird I. While not really a Pontiac prototype, the name of this dream car was later given to Pontiac's specialty car of 1967. The original Firebird was a feature attraction at the '54 GM Motorama show. Powered by 379 hp jet aircraft gas turbine engine, the Firebird was one of several experimental gas turbine cars built by GM, Chrysler and Ford, although the GM project was the first American-built gas turbine auto. (GM photo)

1955 `Strato Star.' This six-passenger coupe made its debut at the Jan. 20, 1955 opening of GM's Motorama show in New York City. It featured ultraslim door pillars and lots of glass. For easy access, hinged panels in the roof automatically rose when the doors were opened. Note the unusual parking light pods hanging below the front bumpers. (GM photo)

1956 Club de Mer. Power for this sportscar from Pontiac came from a dual-quad carbureted 300 hp V-8 engine. It used the unusual DeDion rear suspension and rear mounted transmission. All in all a very radical car. It was built on a 104 inch chassis. And, instead of fiberglass, the Club de Mer was constructed of aluminum.

1957 Firebird II. As with Firebird I, the Firebird II wasn't a Pontiac project. It was a GM Engineering project to test the gas turbine engine concept. This version was more family-oriented with room for four passengers. For the first time, titanium was used in an automobile body and the car had a special electro-magnetically controlled four-speed transmission. It also had self-leveling hydro-pneumatic suspension.

1958 Firebird III. Just as Firebird II was starting to look more like a conventional automobile, along comes Firebird III shooting for the stars. GM and Harley Earl pulled out all the stops. There was a single central control lever, accessible from both seats, which controlled steering, acceleration and braking; a speed-hold device (now known as cruise-control); automatic control systems developed from those in Firebird II; remote door-opening by means of ultrasonic control; air-conditioning which maintains the car's interior at a constant temperature (even when it is standing still); automatic illumination of the lamps; a power unit which, though more powerful (225 hp), was also 25 percent more economical; electroluminescent instrument displays; and an anti-skid braking system. Whew!

1959 Bonneville X-400. The '59 model was the first of several X-400 show cars that Pontiac built for the show circuit. This car featured several styling and engineering features, such as supercharged engine, hidden headlights and special interiors.

1960 X-400. The second X-400 again had the Latham supercharged engine. This car was built on a Bonneville chassis but had Catalina rear quarters. Other styling changes included Lucas headlights, fiberglass top boot, blue dot taillights and leather upholstery in a waffle-pattern. The car was painted a metallic blue. It is now in the Joe Bortz "Blue Suede Shoes" collection.

1961 Tempest Monte Carlo. GM Styling boss, William Mitchell, built the Monte Carlo as a companion car to the Corvair Sebring Spyder. The two cars were taken to sportscar racing tracks across the country to test reaction. The Monte Carlo had a Latham supercharged four-cylinder engine, cut-down windshield, head rests for both driver and passenger, and mag wheels. The car survives in the San Antonio Museum of Transportation.

1962 Grand Prix X-400. There was no production Grand Prix convertible for '62 so the X-400 caused quite a stir on the show circuit. Built as a personal car for Bill Mitchell, the engine of the X-400 was again a Latham supercharged unit based on the 421 cid Super Duty engine. Finished in brilliant red, the car was a standout wherever it went.

1963 Grand Prix X-400. The third of the X-400 show cars had a fiberglass hood with scoops, Lathan supercharged engine with four sidedraft Weber carburetors, brushed aluminum rocker panels, rectangular exhaust ports ahead of the rear wheel, special wheels and fiberglass boot. The vertical headlights proved popular at shows. This car survives in the hands of an Arizona collector who is slowly restoring it.

1963 Maharani. Based on a '63 Bonneville convertible, the Maharani's main feature was the special interior. It was created by gluing peacock feathers into patterns to trim the side panels. The pleated leather seats featured a rainbow pattern. The exterior color was a pearlescent turquoise color.

1964 GM-X. Billed as the "sports car of the next decade," the GM-X had enough instrumentation to keep a jet pilot busy. There were 21 dials, 29 switches, 30 warning lights and four control levers. It was built for display at the '64 New York World's Fair.

1964 Firebird IV. The Firebird IV, on display at the '64 New York World's Fair, had a silver "Fire-Frost" body and an all-silver interior. It was designed for fast cross-country trips on automatic highways. An electronic screen provided the driver with a clear view of road/traffic conditions behind his car. The screen also received television programs when the car was on automatic operation. Additional features included a stereo, game table and refrigerator. A narrow light bar served as the Firebird's single headlight.

1964 Runabout. The third GM dream car built for exhibit at the '64 New York World's Fair was this unusual little "Runabout." The Runabout had a single front wheel which could be turned 180 degrees. This allowed it to be parallel parked in one backward and one sideways movement. A lock-out device limited the wheel's turning span in normal driving. Instead of a steering wheel the Runabout was controlled by two linked hand controls. Included in the Runabout's design were two built-in shopping carts. Both the interior and exterior were finished in blue.

1965 Banshee coupe. One of the styling exercises built on the way to the first production Firebird. This car has Opel GT-like headlights and a Corvette-like kickup on the rear door.

1967 Bonneville Le Grand Conchiche. Basically a two-door limousine, the Le Grand was as impractical as it was poorly timed. Built at the height of the muscle car era, the car would have been more in step with the previous decade. The chauffeur's compartment had bucket seats. There was no top provided for the car.

1969 Fiero. Fiero means "fierce," and this Pontiac show car lived up to its name. The racing influence is shown by the two headrests for driver and passenger. GM had finally started producing dream cars that were more realistic than some of the earlier types. The Fiero was billed as the Firebird of tomorrow. It had a 400 cid HO Pontiac V-8 engine and was designed with aerodynamics in mind.

1969 Cirrus. If you see a vague similarity between the '69 Cirrus and the '64 GM-X, congratulations. You've spotted what Pontiac did to come up with a show car for '69. The engine was the 400 HO Pontiac V-8. (Pontiac photo courtesy of Robert Ackerson)

1971 "Firearri." Bill Mitchell was sports car enthusiast of the first degree. Many of his styling exercises are very sports car-oriented (Monza GT/SS/Stingray/Pontiac Monte Carlo, etc.). This Mitchell-designed car has a Ferrari V-12 racing engine along with its very obvious Ferrari-like snout. Needless to say, the car was not exhibited publicly.

1973 Phantom. Bill Mitchell wanted to leave at General Motors a memory of the cars that he loved. The Phantom was the result. Mitchell styled his Phantom with a long hood, V-type windshield ('30s style), modern headlights, flush windows, and front wheel drive. (Pontiac photo)

1974 Banshee III. This John Schinella-designed show car was built on a '74 Firebird chassis. The side windows were fixed, but a small flip-out window was provided for toll booths. The engine was the Super-Duty 455 cid LS-2. The car was painted a metallic maroon with red leather interior.

196? Scorpian. The Scorpian was the platform that John Z. DeLorean (then general manager of Pontiac Motor Div.) used to build the Banshee XP-833.

INDEPENDENTS

AMC/Nash/Hudson

1950 NXI Nash. This cute little prototype was used to test public reaction to a small car. Over 250,000 people were asked their opinions. They must have been all favorable. Soon afterwards, Nash put the Metropolitan hardtop and convertible into production. It was built in England and introduced in April of 1954.

1953 Italia. Hudson's chief designer, Frank Spring, designed the Italia as future Hudson production model. One was built by Carozzeria Touring in Milan, Italy and taken to car shows across the country to test reaction. The public loved it and 25 more were ordered. Price was set at $4,800 each. The engine was an off-the-shelf 114 hp unit that the Hudson Jet used. The Italia had a wraparound windshield, air scoops on the front fenders, Borrani wire wheels, and doors that were cut 14 inches into the top for easy exit and entry.

1956 PininFarina Nash. Soon after the merger of Nash and Hudson, the Italian coachbuilder PininFarina set about to build a new Nash Ambassador design. It was the only one built and is now in private hands.

Standard Catalog of American Cars

1956 Rambler Palm Beach. PininFarina was the designer of the '49 Nash models and also the '52 revamp. He also built the Nash-Healey sports cars of the '50s for Nash. This show car was exhibited at all the major car shows in 1956. It was built on a 101 inch chassis.

1964 AMC Tarpon. This forerunner of the Marlin was built on the 106 inch Rambler American chassis. When AMC's fastback Marlin was built, it used the 112 inch Rambler Classic chassis. The Tarpon was painted a gold metallic. Some critics think AMC should have stuck with the shorter version.

1966 AMX. The forerunner of the production AMX was first displayed at the SAE convention in Detroit, Mich. in January of 1966. It was basically a two-passenger car, except for a unique "Ramble Seat." This feature was a variation on the rumbleseat, used in pre World War II coupes and roadsters. The rear window flipped up to become a windshield for "Ramble Seat" passengers. (AMC photo courtesy of Bob Ackerson)

1966 Project IV Cars: Cavalier. Four idea cars were built and shown to test public reaction to new styling ideas. The Cavalier featured interchangeable panels. The right front fender and left rear fenders were identical. Likewise, the hood and deck lid, along with front and rear bumpers, were interchangeable. The Cavalier was unveiled in June of 1966. Its styling was later adopted for the '70 Hornet, its successor, the Concord and the four-wheel-drive Eagle. (AMC photo courtesy of Bob Ackerson)

1966 Project IV: AMX. This model was custom built by the Italian coachbuilder Vignale. It has the same "Ramble Seat" feature that the original prototype of the AMX had. (AMC photo courtesy of Bob Ackerson)

1966 Project IV: AMX II. A hardtop version had a "V" rear window that blended with rear deck quarters. This modified version of the AMX had a 110 inch wheelbase, overall length of 187 inches and a 51 inch height. Finished in a deep Metallic green paint, the AMX II had gold pinstriping along the lower body section. Safety features included automatic locking of the doors when the engine was started. (AMC photo courtesy Bob Ackerson)

1966 Project IV: Vixen. The Vixen was a sporty, semi-fastback adaptation of the Cavalier with the same features of interchangeability. It also had the same dimensions but its windshield was moved back 12 inches to make the hood longer. A series of louvers, cut at 45 degrees, in the landau-type roof, provided see-through visibility. Non-glare black paint was used for the trunk area with the rest of the car finished in bright sun-yellow paint. (AMC photo courtesy of Bob Ackerson)

1967 AMX III. The '67 show car was painted a silver metallic. It featured four-door hardtop wagon styling like the four-door hardtop Rambler wagons back in 1956. The tailgate lifted up, and through the use of scissor-action hinges, slid horizontally forward to rest on the roof.

1967 Amitron. Basically designed as a three-passenger commuter car, the Amitron was an electric-powered vehicle. AMC and Gulton Industries collaborated on this project.

1969 AMX/GT. AMC chief designer Richard Teague designed many interesting AMX models. This one appears to be more Gremlin-inspired than the rest. Red, white and blue was big at AMC during the '60s and this show car had the appropriate paint job. The top was blue metallic with a red metallic lower section. The difference was shaded between the two colors. A wide white band with red and blue fine-line stripes separates the upper and lower sections. The AMX/GT was a two-passenger vehicle.

1969 AMX/2. Teague really got into the mainstream of modern sports car styling and engineering with the AMX/2. It was a mid-engined V-8 powered sports car in the Pantara-Mangusta tradition.

1970 AMX/3. A further refinement of the AMX/2 was built by Bizzarrini of Italy in 1970. In fact, five of these potent mid-engined sports cars were built. The body is built of hand-rolled steel panels. Engine is the 390 cid 340 hp AMC V-8. It is reported that each of these prototypes cost $250,000 to build. The car had four-wheel disc brakes and a OTO Melara close-ratio four-speed transaxle. Observed top speed was 160 mph. Several of these cars exist, including beautifully restored red and yellow examples.

1975 Pacesetter. This was a Richard Teague design based on the bubble-shaped Pacer two-door station wagon. The main changes are wheelhousing flares and new front and rear fascias. The horizontally ribbed rear bumper was of wraparound style.

Packard

1952 Pan American. Believe it or not, this Packard show car was actually built by the ambulance coachbuilder, Henney Motor Co. Russell Feldman, owner of Henney, approached Packard president Ferry about building a special show car for the 1952 International Motor Sports Show in New York. Ferry gave a 25th series 250 convertible to Feldman. Richard Arbib, a former GM stylist, was the designer. The amount of bodywork needed to convert the stock Packard into the stunning Pan American was mind-boggling. When finished, Packard was so pleased they ordered five more and put them "on the road" in 1952 to auto shows and fairs.

1953 Balboa. James Nance, new president of Packard, decided that people should see Packard innovation first hand. One design innovation result was the Balboa. The Balboa was built on a Caribbean convertible body by using a non-removable hardtop and an unusual rear window treatment. The design never made it to production on Packard models, but in 1958, Lincoln used the unusual reverse-slant rear window on its Continental Mark IIIs. Later, Mercury used the design for many years, calling it "Breezeway" styling.

1954 Panther Daytona. Using a Cavalier chassis and floorpan, Richard Teague and his fellow Packard stylists had very little time to design this fiberglass two-passenger roadster specifically for competing in the Daytona Beach, Florida speed weeks. Teague only had enough time to do a 3/8 inch clay model before Packard management okayed the design and sent it to Creative Industries, of Detroit, for construction. A full-scale mockup was built and from this model four Panthers were made. For competition at Daytona, the Panther's huge straight eight engine was supercharged. It was officially clocked at a rather disappointing 110.9 mph. Driver, Dick Rathman figured the car could do better and had an "unofficial" run at 131 mph. The Panthers were called back to the factory for a styling up-date in the mid-'50s. All of the Panthers are thought to survive. One is in the Bortz Collection, on is in a museum in La Crosse, Wis. and a third is owned by Packard Industries, of Boonton, N.J. (Applegate & Applegate photo)

1955 Request. Over the years Packard had received numerous requests to bring back the vertical radiator associated with Classic prewar Packards back for many years. Packard styling chief Richard Teague took a stock '55 Packard 400 two-door hardtop and restyled it in a classic manner. The result was the Packard Request show car. It made its debut at the Chicago Auto Show in January of 1955. The Request was painted a pearlescent white with a copper top. Speculation had it that the car was scrapped after the show circuit was over. However, it survives. (Applegate & Applegate photo)

1956 Predictor. Originally called "Projector," the name was soon changed to its present title. Built in the incredibly short time of 90 days by Ghia in Italy, the Predictor was the product of styling director Richard Teague. It was finished just in time for the Chicago Auto Show in January of 1956. Many new and innovative styling features were incorporated into the Predictor design. The large vertical grille member was actually an energy-absorbing bumper. When the doors were opened, electric motors automatically retracted aluminum panels in the roof. The rear window slanted, similar to the earlier Packard Balboa of 1953. The interior was done in white leather, while the exterior was done in a pearlescent white color. The car is now part of the Studebaker National Museum in South Bend, Ind. (Studebaker National Museum photo)

Studebaker

1962 Brooks Stevens Prototypes: 1964 Proposal. Independent industrial designer Brooks Stevens had just finished restyling the 1963 Studebaker line, when his company undertook design work for the 1964-1966 Studebakers. All three were built by the little-known Italian coachbuilder Sibona-Bassano. This is the '64 proposal. Its hood was low and flat. Present was the sliding roof design Stevens used on the production 1963-'66 Studebaker station wagons (Wagonaires). Also, the doors were diagonally interchangeable. Note the pillarless construction of the four-door design. (Brooks Stevens Assoc. photo)

1962 Brooks Stevens Prototypes: 1965 Proposal. As was typical of most prototypes, the right side differed from the left. That gave the designer a chance to see how two different trim packages would look. The '65 prototype was more radical than the '64. The doors were again diagonally interchangeable and pillarless. The grille was now recessed and Cibie headlights were used. The front and rear fenders were mated to the hood and trunk respectively and raised as one unit for more access to engine and trunk. Interiors were also radically restyled with orthopedic-styled seats and space-age instrument panels. All three of these cars are on display at the Brooks Stevens Automotive Museum in Mequon, Wis., just north of Milwaukee. (Brooks Stevens Assoc. photo)

1962 Brooks Stevens Prototypes: 1966 Proposal. Pulling out all the stops, Stevens' Studebaker Sceptre was aimed at replacing the aged Hawk lineup. The two-door hardtop had many innovative features. The single-bar headlight system came from Sylvania. The taillight system was a similar single lens unit. The C-pillars were a dark blue polarized glass that allowed passengers to see out but from outward appearances it looked like part of the body work. The interior was rocketship-oriented. The instruments were set into bubbles that were angled towards the driver. Likewise, the center console was also angled towards the driver for more convenient use of gearshift and other controls. (Brooks Stevens Assoc. photo)

1962 Raymond Loewy Prototypes: Notch Back. The Loewy team had just finished the revolutionary Avanti for Studebaker and utilized its radical design theme to produce two prototypes aimed at convincing Studebaker's board members that his design was the one to use. Note that the right side of this prototype is a two-door, while the driver's side is of four-door design. Again, the idea was to get two cars for the price of one prototype. Both cars were built by the French coachbuilder Pichon-Parat of Paris. Luckily, both Loewy cars survived and are on display at the Studebaker National Museum in South Bend, Ind. (Studebaker National Museum photo)

1962 Raymond Loewy Prototypes: Fastback. Again, note the two-door right side and four-door left side construction (see above). This car also is very "Avanti" looking. This car doesn't have the "grille-less" look that the Avanti coupe does. A slight concession to tradition. (Studebaker Nat'l Museum photo)

MISCELLANEOUS

1951 Paxton. Brooks Stevens began work on the Paxton's styling in 1951. Among the many features of this rear-engined vehicle was a retractable hardtop which, when lowered, overlapped the rear deck. Only one operational Paxton, powered by a Porsche engine, was constructed before the project, financed by Robert Paxton (of Paxton/McCulloch supercharger fame) came to an end. (Robert Ackerson photo)

INDY 500 PACE CARS
1946-1975

The Official Pace Car has been a part of the Indianapolis 500-mile race for over 80 years. This pictorial history of postwar pace cars covers the years 1946-1975.

Automakers took the selection of the Official Pace Car very seriously. Advertising and promotional tie-ins accompanied the honor. In many cases, option packages based on the Official Pace Car were developed. Then, a special run of "pace car replicars" was offered to the public.

Modern collectors of vintage automobiles will pay premium prices to obtain genuine Official Pace Cars or pace car replicas.

1949: Oldsmobile 88 convertible (A A)

1946: Lincoln Continental cabriolet (IMS)

1950: Mercury convertible (IMS)

1947: Nash Ambassador four-door sedan (IMS)

1951: Chrysler New Yorker convertible (IMS)

1948: Chevrolet Fleetmaster convertible (IMS)

1952: Studebaker Commander convertible (IMS)

1953: Ford Crestline convertible (IMS)

1954: Dodge Royal 500 convertible (IMS)

1955: Chevrolet Bel Air convertible (IMS)

1956: DeSoto Adventurer two-door hardtop (IMS)
* A DeSoto Pacesetter convertible was the pace car.

1957: Mercury Turnpike Cruiser convertible (A & A)

1958: Pontiac Bonneville Tri-Power convertible (IMS)

1959: Buick Electra 225 convertible (IMS)

1960: Oldsmobile 98 convertible (IMS)

1961: Ford Thunderbird convertible (IMS)

1965: Plymouth Sport Fury convertible (IMS)

1962: Studebaker Lark Daytona convertible (IMS)

1966: Mercury Comet Cyclone GT convertible (IMS)

1963: Chrysler 300 Sport Series convertible (IMS)

1967: Chevrolet Camaro SS convertible (IMS)

1964: Ford Mustang convertible (IMS)

1968: Ford Torino 428 Cobra-Jet convertible (IMS)

Standard Catalog of American Cars

1969: Chevrolet Camaro SS-396 convertible (IMS)

1973: Cadillac Eldorado convertible (IMS)

1970: Oldsmobile 4-4-2 convertible (IMS)

1974: Olds 4-4-2 W-30 convertible (IMS)

1971: Dodge Challenger convertible (IMS)

1975: Buick Century Colonnade T-top (IMS)

1972: Hurst/Oldsmobile 4-4-2 convertible (IMS)

POSTWAR INDY 500 WINNERS

1946 winner George Robson

1950 winner Johnnie Parsons

1947 winner Mauri Rose

1951 winner Lee Wallard

1948 winner Mauri Rose

1952 winner Troy Ruttman

1949 winner Bill Holland

1953 winner Bill Vukovich

Standard Catalog of American Cars

1954 winner Bill Vukovich

1958 winner Jimmy Bryan

1955 winner Bob Sweikert

1959 winner Roger Ward

1956 winner Pat Flaherty

1960 winner Jim Rathmann

1957 winner Sam Hanks

1961 winner A.J. Foyt

Standard Catalog of American Cars

1962 winner Roger Ward

1966 winner Graham Hill

1963 winner Parnelli Jones

1967 winner A.J. Foyt

1964 winner A.J. Foyt

1968 winner Bobby Unser

1965 winner Jimmy Clark

Standard Catalog of American Cars

1969 winner Mario Andretti

1970 winner Al Unser

1971 winner Al Unser

1972 winner Mark Donohue

1973 winner Gordon Johncock

1974 winner Johnny Rutherford

1975 winner Bobby Unser

1976 winner Johnny Rutherford

1977 winner A.J. Foyt

Standard Catalog of American Cars

FACTORY LIGHTWEIGHTS

1946-1975

With the growth of interest in nostalgic drag facing, factory lightweight racing cars have grown hot in the collector market. Asking prices for some such cars have broken the $100,000 barrier. Therefore, it seems logical to include facts about these cars in the ultimate car collector's guide... The Standard Catalog of American Cars 1946-1975.

Factory lightweight cars were built to go fast and win races for manufacturers who competed in the high-performance field. A victory on the race track sent enthusiasts flocking to auto showrooms to purchase look-alike musclecars.

Some of the cars were built at the factory. In other cases, independent contractors -- such as Dearborn Steel Tubing Co. and Automotive Products Co. -- put them together for the factory. Some, like the '64 Galaxie A/Stock Dragster and '65 Comet 289 B/FX were essentially factory kits installed by race-oriented dealers.

Ultra-lightweight cars campaigned by big name drivers usually got "the works," with the complete assortment of lightweight components installed. In other cases, cars were constructed for street-and-strip use, employing only those special parts that were "streetable."

All of these elements factor into what a lightweight factory race car will bring in the collector's market. Then, on top of that, comes the possibility that the car was owned and raced by a well-known driver. A race-documented car will be worth a lot more.

With so many variables, it's virtually impossible to catalog specifications and formulate a specific price guide. What you'll find in this section is a general guide to the best-known factory lightweights and a hint at the price ranges they fall into.

PLYMOUTH

The first Super Stock drag car to break the 12 second barrier was Tom Grove's 1962 Plymouth 413 wedge. Released in the spring of '62, this engine came in 410 and 420 hp formats. In August, Grove's 420 hp car ran an 11.93 at 118.57 mph, setting the stage for 1963.

For '63, the 426 "Max Wedge" introduction was followed by the release of a lightweight package. Then came the "Stage III" version of the engine with 415 or 425 horsepower on tap. These developments gave MoPar drivers the upper hand on the dragstrips. The lightweight package included aluminum alloy front clips, thin gage steel parts and parts deletions that brought the Plymouth two-door sedan down to 3,350 lbs. fighting weight.

About 50 of these "Max Wedge" Plymouths were built. The factory advised that they shouldn't be operated at wide-open throttle for over 15 seconds. That was enough. At a time when a four-speed manual transmission was considered essential to win drag races, the Plymouth Super Stocks came with a three-speed or TorqueFlite automatic. The high-stall-speed TorqueFlite proved a winner and revolutionized drag racing.

Plymouth, like Dodge, got the Super Stock 426 Hemi for 1964. The year's lightweight package started with a Savoy coupe. Sound-deadening materials, radios, heaters, back seats and even sun visors were deleted. The cars had no high-beam headlights, either. Bucket seats from a Dodge van were bolted to the bare floor. Either aluminum or acid-dipped steel body panels were provided. The battery was relocated to the right side of the trunk floor to give better traction. Door windows were plexiglass and the back window was made of lightweight Dow-Corning glass. There was only a single windshield wiper. Light mag wheels were mounted up front.

The Plymouth Super Stockers were among the cheapest race cars available anywhere, pricing out at $4,272.90 for a race-ready Hemi edition. This allowed amateur drivers like Dick Dyke, of Sioux City, Iowa, to run and win against factory-backed teams. Dyke took the 1964 AHRA Stock Eliminator championship and earned a number two national driving rating for the season.

The lightweight package could shave up to 300 lbs. from the 3,200 lb. Savoy. The big Hemi, with two immense Holley four-barrels on an aluminum cross ram intake had a tach-drive distributor and factory headers. Though rated for 425 hp, it put out more like 550. These cars could run in the low 11 second bracket at 125 mph. A four-speed was available for '64s.

According to Chrysler Historical Archives records, only 271 Race Hemi engines were made in 1964. Some went in Plymouths and others in Dodges.

In February, three Hemi-powered Plymouths and a Hemi Dodge took the first four finishing spots in the Daytona 500 stock car race. NASCAR then changed its rules to require higher production to qualify Hemis for Grand National competition. This led to Chrysler retiring from racing for one year, while it developed a "Street Hemi."

During this period, NASCAR champ Richard Petty raced a 1965 Barracuda with a 426 Hemi in B/Altered drag racing. It was one of many altered wheelbase Plymouths that dominated the sport that year. However, it was also the end of an era. Ford refused to race against the MoPars -- which were dubbed "funny cars" -- until a batch of similarly wild Mustangs were ready to run in 1966.

In August, 1965, Ronnie Sox took a nitro-burning Hemi Plymouth to a 9.98 second 136 mph fun, shattering the 10 second barrier in A/FX class and marking a memorable beginning of the end for stock-bodied factory lightweights. Henceforth, the quarter-mile sport would belong to a new breed of machines with fiberglass replica bodies on tube frames with exotic drivetrains.

Today, factory lightweight Plymouth Super Stockers remain one of the best buys in their class. Some models can be purchased for below $25,000 in restored condition. At the top end, expect to pay more like $50,000 to $75,000 for a ready-to-go-racing example that a famous driver once owned. While that sounds high for a Savoy, it's on the affordable scale for an authentic factory lightweight race car.

1963 Plymouth

1963 Plymouth Savoy Hemi

1963 Plymouth Savoy 440

1964 Plymouth Hemi Lightweight

1965 Plymouth 426

1970 Plymouth Hemi Road Runner

DODGE

With their four-speed gearboxes, wider choice of axle ratios and better weight transfer characteristics, GM cars dominated drag racing until 1963. Chrysler reacted to GM's strengths by developing two new power plants. The timing was perfect, as GM banned Chevy and Pontiac from racing in January, 1963, when the new motors bowed.

At the 1963 NHRA Winternationals, the 426 "Max Wedge" Dodge campaigned by Dick Eckstand and the Ramchargers ran a 12.44 second 115.08 mph quarter-mile in Super Stock. The 425 hp engine, linked to a beefy TorqueFlite automatic and 4.56 rear would be running 12s at 117 mph by year's end, thanks to light-weight drag racing components.

MoPar two-door sedans weighed-in at about 3,300 lbs. with all-steel body parts. With aluminum front end sheet metal, gutted interiors and thin gage body panels, they lost about 150 lbs. and started outrunning the hot Fords. These lightweight wedge-powered Dodges could be had with the automatic transmission or with a three-speed manual floor shift. Prices for the cars ranged from $2,600 to $3,200. About 50 were made. All came with disclaimers saying they were built for super-vised acceleration trials and not warranted by the factory.

Working with Automotive Products Co. and Dragmasters, Dodge created a pair of 1964 two-door sedans powered by a blown 480 cid "Stage III" wedge motor that cranked out 800 hp. They were billed as the world's fastest B/FX cars and toured the nation's dragstrips with full factory backing.

Dodge also sponsored the Ramcharger race team again. The deal paid off with an NHRA Top Stock Eliminator title and a new A/FX record of 12.03 seconds and 118.42 mph at Detroit Dragway.

In the spring of 1964, Dodge rolled factory-built lightweights off its Hamtramck, Mich. assembly line. They had the brand new "Maximum Performance" package with a 426 cid/425 hp (actually closer to 500 hp) "Race Hemi." Also featured were aluminum fenders, inner fenders, hood, front bumper and attaching parts. Mag wheels were mounted and, inside, the spartan interior had two racing type bucket seats.

Only 271 Race Hemi engines were built in 1964. Some went in Dodges, the rest in Plymouths. The cars were priced low enough to put them into the hands of anyone who was serious about drag racing, although production was limited by the company's ability to build the special motors. The Super Stock Hemi Dodges sold for just over $4,000 and ran the quarter-mile in the 11.4 second bracket at 125 mph.

In 1965, drag racing rules were changed to create a handicap system and make it harder to qualify factory lightweights for SIS classes. Chrysler found the A/FX class more appealing for its Dodge Ramchargers and Super Stock Plymouths. Before long, these cars started showing up with altered wheelbases with the rear wheels moved up to 15 inches forward.

The AWB Dodges and Plymouths looked strange and the fans nicknamed them "funny cars." In August, Jim Thorton, a member of the Ramcharger Racing Team, broke the nine second barrier with an 8.91 second performance in an ultra-lightweight, AWB, nitro-burning Dodge. It was one of just 360 Dodges and Plymouths made with Race Hemis in 1965.

While the American Hot Rod Association embraced these cars, the NHRA did not. This led to MoPars dominating AHRA races, while Ford became the big name in NHRA competition. Richard Petty was one of the MoPar drivers in the new AHRA SS/X funny car class.

As the interest in funny cars grew, race car builders found that they couldn't get much more out of stock-bodied factory lightweights. The future was in exotic fiberglass bodies on special tube-frame chassis. Ultimately, the S/S and A/FX lightweights gave way to this new kind of machine.

Today, the 1962-1965 factory lightweights have become hot collectibles. Prices as high as $100,000 are being asked for Hemi race cars that were owned by famous drag racers.

1963 Dodge Ramcharger Factory Lightweight Coupe (V-8)

1963 Dodge 880 Ramcharger two-door sedan

1964 Dodge Polara 330 Ramcharger two-door sedan (Hemi)

PONTIAC

Pontiac was the first automaker to build factory lightweight cars. Ever since its NASCAR engine options were issued in mid-1957, the company found that racing sold cars. By 1960, the "Poncho" performance image had made Pontiacs the third most popular U.S. cars for the first time. Chevy's new-for-1962 409 cid engine was a threat, though. Pontiac's best match was the 1961 Super-Duty 389 Catalina (368 hp with Tri-Power), of which maybe 25 were built.

More power and less weight were needed to keep the Pontiacs competitive. So. PMD put its lightest, most powerful car on a diet with a horsepower supplement. Extensive use of aluminum body parts and a special 421 cid/405 hp V-8 created the 3,600 lb. 1962 Super-Duty Catalina.

The new engine featured four-bolt mains, forged pistons and twin Carter four-barrels on a special manifold linked to either a Borg-Warner T-85 three-speed or T-10 four-speed. Actual horsepower was over 500.

Lightweight parts, in addition to front sheet metal, included an aluminum back bumper and dealer-optional plexiglass windows. Many cars used a functional hood scoop that was actually a Ford truck part that Pontiac purchased in quantity and issued a GM parts number for. An unusual Super-Duty option was a set of cast aluminum Tri-Y exhaust headers.

Pontiac racing personality Jim Wangers found the '62 Catalina S-D to his liking and turned in performances like a 12.38 second quarter-mile at 116,23 mph at Detroit Dragway. In all, 225 of the 421 cid motors were built in 1962. They went into 162 cars and 63 engines were made as replacement motors. Not all of the cars that got the 421 S-Ds had factory lightweight body parts.

Pontiac also produced 15 cars with 389 cid Super-Duty V-8s during 1962. Many of these were used as daily drivers and part-time drag racers. Owners say they could run 13 second quarter miles in S/S class with full street equipment.

For 1963, PMD took the 421 Super-Duty program a few steps further. Cylinder heads got higher intake ports and oval-shaped exhaust ports, plus larger valves and higher 12.5:1 compression ratios. A new McKellar no. 10 solid lifter cam was released for use with dual valve springs. A transistorized ignition system was added. A few cars even had 13.0:1 pistons. Official horsepower ratings for the hottest setup went to 410, but actual output was between 540 hp and 550 hp.

The 1963 factory lightweights lost about another 100 pounds through the use of plexiglass windows and aluminum trunk lids. Also available were aluminum splash pans, radiator core supports and bumper attaching parts. In addition, some Catalina frames were "swiss-cheesed," by drilling holes through them. They weighed-in at about 3,325 lbs. in ultimate lightweight format.

Drag racer Arnie Beswick campaigned one of the 15 Swiss-cheese Catalinas built before the GM racing ban fell in January, 1963. His "Passionate Poncho" racked up a low elapsed time of 11.91 seconds in the quarter-mile. With their low production, the Swiss-cheese cars did not qualify for S/S class. Instead, they competed in Factory Experimental racing.

In addition to making a total of 77 Super-Duty Catalinas and Grand Prixs (including the Swiss-cheese units) 11 Super-Duty Tempests were also constructed. This combination was dreamed up by the late Mickey Thompson for A/FX competition. Another pair of A/FX class 421 Tempests -- a coupe and a wagon -- were campaigned by Arnie Beswick.

After GM issued its racing edict, Jim Wangers and the "Young Turks" at PMD Engineering turned their energies in a new, and very successful, direction. Wrapping up a package of performance extras as a LeMans option package, they snuck the first GTOS on the street. The rest is history... Pontiac spun its racing reputation into a winning production vehicle that became a champion in the sales race.

Today, a Super-Duty 421 Catalina factory lightweight car should fetch at least $50,000 in the collectors market. One with a documented race history could bring double that. And an A/FX Tempest or Swiss-Cheese Catalina should top the $100,000 mark. In fact, there were reports of a $150,000 sale from one auction a few years ago.

1962 Pontiac Super-Duty Catalina

1963 Pontiac Super-Duty Catalina hardtop

1964 Pontiac GTO

CHEVROLET

Chevrolets were the dominant force in Super Stock drag racing in 1959-1960. Pontiac was a very close second. Chevrolet's main advantage was that the Bel Air weighed less than a Catalina. The Pontiacs, though, had more horsepower. To stay ahead, Chevrolet put the 409 cid V-8 into production in January, 1961. Less than 150 of the 360 hp engines were made that year, but the one in "Dyno" Don Nicholson's car helped him capture Top Stock Eliminator title at the NHRA Winternationals.

By 1962, Pontiac began building special lightweight drag cars. Chevrolet countered with a Z-11 package including aluminum front fenders, inner fenders and hood, that shaved car weight to 3,360 lbs. There were new engine options, too. The four-barrel 409 was up to 380 hp, while the version with three two-barrel carbs and no air cleaner generated 409 hp.

Hayden Proffitt's '62 Bel Air "bubbletop" coupe took Stock Eliminator honors in A/Stock class at the U.S. Nationals at Indianapolis, with a run of 12.83 seconds at 113.92 mph. In comparison, Don Nicholson's Z-11, running in B/FX turned in 12.93 seconds at 113.63 mph. Another well-known driver was Ronnie Sox, who campaigned two '62 Z-11s.

The Z-11 drag package was upgraded for 1963, with an aluminum front clip, aluminum bumper and insulation-less interior cutting weight to about 3,340 lbs. Only 57 of these cars were built. The first batch of 25 was assembled on Dec. 1, 1962. On Jan. 1, 1963, another 25 were made and seven were added soon after.

The Z-11 cars came without a radio or heater. A heavy-duty clutch was mandatory. It linked the four-speed gearbox to the new-for-1963 engine. A .100 inch stroke increase brought the 409 up to 427 cid. With dual four-barrel carbs on a unique two-piece manifold, high-port heads and 12.5:1 compression it generated 430 hp at 6000 rpm.

Priced at an affordable $1,245 (about half of what the Bel Air coupe sold for), the package also included a special cowl-induction air cleaner, Posi-Traction axle, metallic brake linings and tachometer. The total of 57 produced made the Z-11s "legal" for Super Stock competition.

Chevy had plans to go even further. The new engine was to be the basis of a NASCAR "Mystery Engine" with porcupine heads. However, only five prototype versions of this power plant were put together before GM management brought a halt to the program.

In January, 1963, the corporation announced a total ban on factory racing involvement and the manufacture of special racing parts. No more lightweights were built and Chevy was forced to take a back seat to FoMoCo and MoPar, in drag racing, until the 460 hp Chevelle LS6 showed up in the early '70s.

Today, asking prices for 409/409 Bel Air "bubbletops" are in the $20,000 to $30,000 range. An authentic Z-11 should fetch $50,000 to $75,000 or more.

1962 Chevy "409" Z-11 Factory Lightweight, V-8

1962 Chevrolet Bel Air "409" Factory Lightweight (V-8)

1970 AMT Red Alert Chevelle LS6

FORD

The first factory lightweights made by Ford were Galaxies. Ten cars were built for the National Hot Rod Association (NHRA) 1962 Nationals late that year. They were powered by 406 cid "FE" big-block V-8s and had limited success on the dragstrip in the new Factory Experimental racing class.

In 1963, Ford scheduled production of 50 lightweight Galaxies with a new 427 cid/425 hp dual-quad high-performance engine. The cars used fiberglass hoods, fenders, inner fenders, doors and trunks. A modified Custom 300 frame was employed in at least some of them. They also had aluminum front and rear bumpers. Weighing in at just below 3,500 lbs., the cars could do the quarter-mile in the low 12s at nearly 120 mph. This was not quite fast enough to beat the Super-Duty Pontiacs.

Ford tapped Fred Zimmerman to direct its Special Vehicles drag racing program and the result was the Fairlane Thunderbolt or "T-Bolt." Zimmerman also set up a Ford Drag Council through which race drivers were tied directly to dealerships in certain regions, to generate grassroots support.

Racing rules called for the production of 50 Thunderbolts, but 127 were built. This qualified them as a "production" model that could compete in S/S (Super Stock) race classes and took them out of the A/FX (Factory Experimental) category.

Thunderbolts weighed only 3,200 lbs. They were sold to drag racers, by the factory, for $3,900. Aluminum bumpers and fiberglass body parts were featured. The first eight cars were finalized by the factory, with A/FX competition in mind.

Later, the job of building the cars was turned over to Dearborn Steel Tubing Co. Of the 127 made, about 16-20 percent are thought to survive today.

The engine under the hood of the T-Bolts was the 427 cid/425 hp job with ram air induction. A "power blister" scoop was devised for the fiberglass hood to accommodate the forced air induction system. Actual output in racing tune was around 500 hp, despite the conservative official rating.

Gas Rhonda won the NHRA Winternationals with an 11.78 second 123.4 mph quarter-mile run in a Thunderbolt. He took Top Stock Eliminator honors. In all, T-Bolts took six divisional championships. Other famous Ford pilots included Les Ritchey, Butch Leal, Bill Lawton, Hubert Platt, Phil Bonner and George Newtell. The latter driver's Downtown Ford Thunderbolt once turned an 11.47 second 125.34 mph performance.

In addition to the Fairlane T-Bolts, Ford continued making full-size lightweights in 1964. The Galaxie A/Stock dragster package was offered for two-door models. Also available was a B/Stock package which added a low-riser manifold for the 427 V-8. These cars came in white with red interiors. Body sealer, sound deadening insulation and heaters were deleted. Added were lightweight seats and a fiberglass bubble hood. The grilles were modified with fiberglass air induction vents.

Several A/FX drag cars were also made from restyled 1964 Falcon Futuras. Their boxiness was an aerodynamic disadvantage, but the short wheelbase put the engine and rear axle closer together for improved weight transfer characteristics.

Two 427-powered Falcons with fiberglass front fenders, front bumpers and rear deck lids were made by Dearborn Steel Tubing and shipped to stock car builders Holman & Moody for engineering development. With a high-riser manifold, two big Holleys, 14.0:1 pistons and ram induction, they put out about 550 hp at 7400 rpm. Phil Bonner and Dick Brennan campaigned these cars. Bonner's "Daddy Warbucks" Falcon was the hotter one.

By 1965, Ford Motorsports began to place heavier emphasis on efforts to win at Indianapolis and LeMans. In drag racing, the focus switched from Super Stock 1964 T-Bolts to A/FX class Mustangs fitted with single overhead cam 427s.

Soon, a new type of racer known as a "funny car" evolved for the dragstrip. Using tube frames, full fiberglass bodies and wild power teams, these wheel-standing machines changed the sport of drag racing overnight. Soon, the Ford Y-block and costly-to-build 427 would be gone. The lightweight Galaxies, T-Bolts, 427 Falcons and Cobra-Stangs would pass into history.

Today, the asking prices for restored factory lightweights wearing the Ford blue oval emblem range from about $27,000 for an S/S Galaxie to well over $100,000 for a T-Bolt with a documented race history.

1963 Ford Galaxie Notchback 427

1964 Ford Fairlane T-bolt

1964 Ford Fairlane "Thunderbolt" Factory Lightweight Coupe (V-8)

1963 Ford Galaxie Factory Lightweight "427" two-door hardtop (V-8)

1963 Ford Galaxie Fastback 427 Lightweight

1964 Ford Fairlane T-bolt

1965 Mustang A/FX 427

MERCURY

Mercury entered the Factory Experimental (FX) drag racing wars with a fleet of at least 50 special Comets in 1964. Featuring lightweight body modifications and 427 cid/425 hp big-blocks, these cars were sold as "not for use on public highways." They were meant for drag racing only.

One of the most famous was "Dyno" Don Nicholson's NHRA record holder (serial number 4H23-551846) built in April, 1964. It was one of four factory-backed race cars. The other three belonged to Tom Sturm, Ronnie Sox and Bill Shrewsberry. Below the "power blister" hood scoop was a 427 high-riser linked to a top-loader four-speed and a narrowed rear end with 5.43:1 gears. This Comet established an A/FX record of 11.05 seconds for the quarter and it once did the distance in 10.56 seconds.

Nicolson's Comet has fiberglass doors, in addition to the normal lightweight fiberglass front fenders, hood, bumper and deck lid. However, most of the other '64s had acid-dipped steel doors. Rectangular air intakes on the front edge of the hood proved very beneficial to the Comets in racing. They also featured 10 inch rear tires. About 15-20 of the '64s were assembled by Dearborn Steel Tubing Co. for big name drivers.

In 1965, Mercury returned to the lightweight ranks with smallblock B/FX Comets that relied on high-performance 289 cid/271 hp V-8s for motivation. In addition, about 20 big-block lightweights were made again. The small-engined cars got the big attention, though.

Constructed by Bill Stroppe from 1965 production Comets, the cars featured a B/FX "dealer option" package that included fiberglass doors, front fenders, hoods, front bumper, splash panel, rear seats and dashboard parts. They also received plexiglass windows and windshields.

Two batches of 10 cars were put together, They weighed about 2,600 lbs. The 271 hp engine was the stock high-performance version offered for street cars, although factory and Shelby hardware could be added to pump up as much as 450 hp.

Driver Doug Nash established a B/FX record with a Comet when he covered the quarter-mile in 11.3 seconds at 125 mph.

A famous Comet drag racer was the 1964 Super Cyclone of Jack Christman. This started as a factory lightweight, but it didn't stop there. Christman cut poundage even more and added a blown, nitro-burning 427 that could do 160 mph in the quarter. By 1965, the engine was switched to a single overhead cam 427 'hemi' and Chrisman had the first real "funny car."

During 1966, the Mercury Comet Drag Team won nearly 90 percent of its races with funny cars such as Chrisman's "Cyclone GT-I" and Nicholson's "Eliminator I." That year, Nicholson's car took 130 victories. His 1967 "Eliminator II" ran 8 second 175 mph races. Such Comets changed drag racing forever, but they also brought an end to the era of stock-bodied factory lightweight cars.

According to our sources, the 289 Comet Super Stockers are hard to find, but represent an excellent buy in the under $20,000 category. Expect to pay more than double that for the more desirable "Boss Comets" with 427 power.

1964 Mercury Comet 289 Factory B/FX Car

NASCAR RECORDS

DAYTONA INTERNATIONAL SPEEDWAY, DAYTONA BEACH, FLA.

4.1 Mile Beach/Road Course

Year	Winner	Type Car	Laps	Average Speed	Fastest Qualifier	Type Car	Qual. Speed
1949	Red Byron	Oldsmobile		79.26			
1950	Harold Kite	Lincoln	49	81.75	Bill Blair	Cadillac	98.84
1951	Marshall Teague	Hudson	39	82.39	Tim Flock	Lincoln	82.39
1952	Marshall Teague	Hudson	36	84.65	Pat Kirkwood	'51 Chrysler	110.97
1953	Bill Blair	Oldsmobile	39	89.50	Bob Pronger		115.77
1954	Lee Petty	Chrysler	39	89.14	Lee Petty	'54 Chrysler	123.41
1955	Tim Flock	Chrysler	39	92.056	Tim Flock	'55 Chrysler	130.293
1956	Tim Flock	'56 Chrysler	39	90.836	Tim Flock	'56 Chrysler	135.747
1957	Cotton Owens	'57 Pontiac	39	101.60	Banjo Mathews	'57 Pontiac	134.382
1958	Paul Goldsmith	Pontiac	39	101.18	Paul Goldsmith	'58 Pontiac	40.570

THE FOLLOWING HELD AT NEW 2½-MILE PAVED TRACK

Year	Winner	Type Car	Laps	Average Speed	Fastest Qualifier	Type Car	Qual. Speed
1959	Lee Petty	'59 Oldsmobile	200	135.521	Cotton Owens	'58 Pontiac	143.198
1960	Junior Johnson	'59 Chevrolet	200	124.740	Fireball Roberts	'60 Pontiac	151.556
1961	Marvin Panch	'60 Pontiac	200	149.601	Fireball Roberts	'61 Pontiac	155.709
1962	Fireball Roberts	'62 Pontiac	200	152.529	Fireball Roberts	'62 Pontiac	158.744
1963	Tiny Lund	'63 Ford	200	151.566	John Rutherford	'63 Chevrolet	165.183
1964	Richard Petty	'64 Plymouth	200	154.334	Paul Goldsmith	'64 Plymouth	174.910
1965	Fred Lorenzen	'65 Ford	133*	141.539	Darel Dieringer	'64 Mercury	171.151
1966	Richard Petty	'66 Plymouth	198	160.627	Richard Petty	'66 Plymouth	175.165
1967	Mario Andretti	'67 Ford	200	146.926	Curtis Turner	'66 Chevelle	180.831
1968	Cale Yarborough	'68 Mercury	200	143.251	Cale Yarborough	'68 Mercury	189.222
1969	Lee Roy Yarbrough	'69 Ford	200	157.950	David Pearson	'69 Ford	190.029
1970	Pete Hamilton	'70 Plymouth	200	149.601	Cale Yarborough	'69 Mercury	194.015
1971	Richard Petty	'71 Plymouth	200	144.456	A.J. Foyt	'71 Mercury	182.744
1972	A.J. Foyt	'71 Mercury	200	161.550	Bobby Isaac	'72 Dodge	186.632
1973	Richard Petty	'73 Dodge	200	157.205	Buddy Baker	'73 Dodge	185.662
1974	Richard Petty	'74 Dodge	200	140.894	David Pearson	'73 Mercury	185.017
1975	Benny Parsons	Chevrolet	200	153.649	Donnie Allison	'75 Chevrolet	185.827
1976	David Pearson	Mercury	200	152.181	A.J. Foyt	Chevrolet	185.943
1977	Cale Yarborough	Chevrolet	200	153.218	Donnie Allison	Chevrolet	188.048

Standard Catalog of American Cars

1978	Bobby Allison	Ford	200	159.730	Cale Yarborough	Oldsmobile	187.536
1979	Richard Petty	Oldsmobile	200	143.977	Buddy Baker	Oldsmobile	196.049
1980	Buddy Baker	Oldsmobile	200	177.602	A.J. Foyt	Oldsmobile	195.020
1981	Richard Petty	STP Buick	200	169.651	Bobby Allison	Tuf-Lon Pontiac	194.624

* 1965 race called at 133 laps due to rain.

DAYTONA FIRECRACKER

1959	Fireball Roberts	'59 Pontiac	100*	140.581	Fireball Roberts	'59 Pontiac	144.997
1960	Jack Smith	'60 Pontiac	100*	146.842	Jack Smith	'60 Pontiac	152.129
1961	Dave Pearson	'61 Pontiac	100*	154.294	Fireball Roberts	'61 Pontiac	157.130
1962	Fireball Roberts	'62 Pontiac	100*	153.688	Banjo Matthews	'62 Pontiac	160.490
1963	Fireball Roberts	'63 Ford	160	150.927	Junior Johnson	'63 Chevrolet	166.005
1964	A.J. Foyt	'64 Dodge	160	151.451	Darel Dieringer	'64 Mercury	172.678
1965	A.J. Foyt	'65 Ford	160	150.046	Marvin Panch	'65 Ford	171.510
1966	Sam McQuagg	'66 Dodge	160	153.813	Lee Roy Yarbrough	'66 Dodge	178.660
1967	Cale Yarborough	'67 Ford	160	143.583	Darel Dieringer	'67 Ford	179.802
1968	Cale Yarborough	'68 Mercury	160	167.247	Lee Roy Yarbrough	'68 Mercury	187.049
1969	Lee Roy Yarbrough	'69 Ford	160	160.875	Cale Yarborough	'69 Mercury	190.706
1970	Donnie Allison	'69 Ford	160	162.235	Cale Yarborough	'69 Mercury	191.640
1971	Bobby Isaac	'71 Dodge	160	161.943	Donnie Allison	'71 Mercury	183.228
1972	David Pearson	'71 Mercury	160	134.400	Bobby Isaac	'72 Dodge	192.428
1973	David Pearson	'71 Mercury	160	158.468	Bobby Allison	'73 Chevrolet	179.619
1974	David Pearson	'73 Mercury	160	138.301	David Pearson	'73 Mercury	180.759
1975	Richard Petty	Dodge	160	158.381	Donnie Allison	'75 Chevrolet	186.737
1976	Cale Yarborough	Chevrolet	160	160.966	A.J. Foyt	Chevrolet	183.000
1977	Richard Petty	Dodge	160	142.716	Neil Bonnett	Dodge	187.191
1978	David Pearson	Mercury	160	154.340	Cale Yarborough	Oldsmobile	186.803
1979	Neil Bonnett	Mercury	160	172.890	Buddy Baker	Oldsmobile	193.196
1980	Bobby Allison	Mercury	160	173.473	Cale Yarborough	Oldsmobile	194.670
1981	Cale Yarborough	Buick	160	142.588	Cale Yarborough	Buick	192.852

DARLINGTON INTERNATIONAL SPEEDWAY, DARLINGTON, S.C. — 1⅜ Mile Paved
REBEL 300, 400 AND 500

1957	Fireball Roberts	'57 Ford	219	107.940	Paul Goldsmith	'57 Ford	115.317
1958	Curtis Turner	'58 Ford	219	109.624	Joe Weatherly	'57 Chevrolet	116.841
1959	Fireball Roberts	'59 Chevrolet	219	115.903	Joe Weatherly	'59 T-Bird	120.820
1960	Joe Weatherly	'60 Ford	219	102.646	Fireball Roberts	'60 Pontiac	127.750
1961	Fred Lorenzen	'61 Ford	219	119.529	Fred Lorenzen	'61 Ford	128.965
1962	Nelson Stacy	'62 Ford	219	117.864	Fred Lorenzen	'62 Ford	129.810
1963	Joe Weatherly	'63 Pontiac	220*	121.730	Fred Lorenzen	'63 Ford	131.718
1964	Fred Lorenzen	'64 Ford	219	130.013	Fred Lorenzen	'64 Ford	135.727
1965	Junior Johnson	'65 Ford	219	111.849	Fred Lorenzen	'65 Ford	138.133
1966	Richard Petty	'66 Plymouth	291	131.993	Richard Petty	'66 Plymouth	140.815
1967	Richard Petty	'67 Plymouth	291	125.738	David Pearson	'67 Ford	144.536
1968	David Pearson	'68 Ford	291	132.699	Lee Roy Yarbrough	'68 Ford	148.850
1969	Lee Roy Yarbrough	'69 Mercury	291	131.572	Cale Yarborough	'69 Mercury	152.29
1970	David Pearson	'70 Ford	291	129.668	Charlie Glotzbach	'69 Dodge	153.822
1971**	Buddy Baker	'71 Dodge	293	130.678	Donnie Allison	'71 Mercury	149.826
1972	David Pearson	'71 Mercury	293	124.406	David Pearson	'71 Mercury	148.209
1973	David Pearson	'71 Mercury	293	122.655	David Pearson	'71 Mercury	153.463
1974	David Pearson	'73 Mercury	293	117.543	Donnie Allison	'74 Chevrolet	150.689
1975	Bobby Allison	'75 Matador	293	117.597	David Pearson	'73 Mercury	155.433
1976	David Pearson	Mercury	367	122.973	David Pearson	Mercury	154.171
1977	Darrell Waltrip	Chevrolet	367	128.827	David Pearson	Mercury	151.269
1978	Benny Parsons	Chevrolet	367	127.544	Bobby Allison	Ford	151.862
1979	Darrell Waltrip	Chevrolet	367	121.721	Donnie Allison	Chevrolet	154.797
1980	David Pearson	Chevrolet	189†	112.397	Benny Parsons	Chevrolet	155.866
1981	Darrell Waltrip	Buick	367	126.703	Bill Elliott	Ford	153.896

* 1963 race was split into two events. Petty won 1st part.
** Race changed to 500 miles.
† Race stopped after 189 laps due to darkness. 2 Hours, 19 Minutes rain delay.

SOUTHERN 500

1950	Johnny Mantz	'50 Plymouth	400*	76.26	Wally Campbell	'50 Oldsmobile	82.35
1951	Herb Thomas	'51 Hudson	400*	76.90	Marshall Teague	'51 Hudson	86.21
1952	Fonty Flock	'52 Oldsmobile	400*	74.51	Dick Rathman	'51 Hudson	89.06
1953	Buck Baker	'53 Oldsmobile	364	92.78	Fonty Flock	'53 Hudson	117.40
1954	Herb Thomas	'54 Hudson	364	94.93	Buck Baker	'54 Oldsmobile	108.261
1955	Herb Thomas	'55 Chevrolet	364	92.281	Fonty Flock	'55 Chrysler	112.781
1956	Curtis Turner	'56 Ford	364	95.067	Buck Baker	'56 Chrysler	119.650
1957	Speedy Thompson	'57 Chevrolet	364	100.100	Paul Goldsmith	'57 Ford	119.291
1958	Fireball Roberts	'57 Chevrolet	364	102.590	Fireball Roberts	'57 Chevrolet	118.648
1959	Jim Reed	'59 Chevrolet	364	111.836	Fireball Roberts	'59 Pontiac	123.734
1960	Buck Baker	'60 Pontiac	364	105.901	Cotton Owens	'60 Pontiac	126.461
1961	Nelson Stacy	'61 Ford	364	117.880	Fireball Roberts	'61 Pontiac	128.680
1962	Larry Frank	'62 Ford	364	117.965	Fireball Roberts	'62 Pontiac	130.246
1963	Fireball Roberts	'63 Ford	364	129.784	Fireball Roberts	'63 Ford	133.819
1964	Buck Baker	'64 Dodge	364	117.757	Richard Petty	'64 Plymouth	136.815
1965	Ned Jarrett	'65 Ford	364	115.924	Junior Johnson	'65 Ford	137.528
1966	Darel Dieringer	'66 Mercury	364	114.830	Lee Roy Yarbrough	'66 Dodge	140.058
1967	Richard Petty	'67 Plymouth	364	130.423	Richard Petty	'67 Plymouth	143.436
1968	Cale Yarborough	'68 Mercury	364	126.132	Cale Yarborough	'68 Mercury	144.830
1969	Lee Roy Yarbrough	'69 Ford	230*	105.612	Cale Yarborough	'69 Mercury	151.985
1970	Buddy Baker	'70 Dodge	367	128.817	David Pearson	'70 Ford	150.555
1971	Bobby Allison	'69 Mercury	367	131.398	Bobby Allison	'69 Mercury	147.915
1972	Bobby Allison	'71 Chevrolet	367	128.124	David Pearson	'71 Mercury	152.342
1973	Cale Yarborough	'73 Chevrolet	367	134.033	David Pearson	'71 Mercury	150.366
1974	Cale Yarborough	'74 Chevrolet	367	111.075	Richard Petty	'74 Dodge	150.132
1975	Bobby Allison	Matador	367	116.825	David Pearson	'73 Mercury	153.401

1976	David Pearson	Mercury	367	120.534	David Pearson	Mercury		154.699
1977	David Pearson	Mercury	367	106.797	Darrell Waltrip	Chevrolet		153.493
1978	Cale Yarborough	Oldsmobile	367	116.828	David Pearson	Mercury		153.685
1979	David Pearson	Chevrolet	367	126.259	Bobby Allison	Ford		154.880
1980	Terry Labonte	Chevrolet	367	115.210	Darrell Waltrip	Chevrolet		153.838
1981	Neil Bonnett	Ford	367	126.410	Harry Gant	Pontiac		152.693

*Listed as 1¼ miles thru 1952.

CHARLOTTE MOTOR SPEEDWAY, CHARLOTTE, N.C. — 1.5 Mile Paved
WORLD 600

1960	Joe Lee Johnson	'60 Chevrolet	400	107.752	Fireball Roberts	'60 Pontiac		133.904
1961	David Pearson	'61 Pontiac	400	111.633	David Pearson	'61 Pontiac		138.381
1962	Nelson Stacy	'62 Ford	400	125.552	Fireball Roberts	'62 Pontiac		140.150
1963	Fred Lorenzen	'64 Ford	400	132.418	Junior Johnson	'63 Chevrolet		141.148
1964	Jim Paschal	'64 Plymouth	400	125.772	Junior Johnson	'64 Ford		145.100
1965	Fred Lorenzen	'65 Ford	400	121.772	Fred Lorenzen	'65 Ford		145.268
1966	Marvin Panch	'66 Plymouth	400	135.042	Paul Goldsmith	'66 Plymouth		149.491
1967	Jim Paschal	'67 Plymouth	400	135.832	Cale Yarborough	'67 Ford		154.385
1968	Buddy Baker	'68 Dodge	255*	104.207	Donnie Allison	'68 Ford		159.223
1969	Lee Roy Yarbrough	'69 Mercury	400	134.361	Donnie Allison	'69 Ford		159.296
1970	Donnie Allison	'69 Ford	400	129.680	Bobby Isaac	'69 Dodge		159.277
1971	Bobby Allison	'69 Mercury	400	140.442	Charlie Glotzbach	'71 Chevrolet		157.788
1972	Buddy Baker	'72 Dodge	400	142.255	Bobby Allison	'72 Chevrolet		158.162
1973	Buddy Baker	'73 Dodge	400	134.890	Buddy Baker	'73 Dodge		
1974	David Pearson	'73 Mercury	400	135.720	David Pearson	'73 Mercury		157.498
1975	Richard Petty	Dodge	400	145.327	David Pearson	'73 Mercury		159.353
1976	David Pearson	Mercury	400	137.352	David Pearson	Mercury		159.132
1977	Richard Petty	Dodge	400	137.676	David Pearson	Mercury		161.435
1978	Darrell Waltrip	Chevrolet	400	138.355	David Pearson	Mercury		160.551
1979	Darrell Waltrip	Chevrolet	400	136.674	Neil Bonnett	Mercury	**	160.125
1980	Benny Parsons	Chevrolet	400	119.265	Cale Yarborough	Chevrolet	**	165.194
1981	Bobby Allison	Buick	400	129.326	Neil Bonnett	Ford		158.115

*1962 race shortened by rain.
**Four lap average.

Past Winners Of Indianapolis 500 Race

1911	Ray Harroun	74.59
1912	Joe Dawson	78.72
1913	Jules Goux	75.933
1914	Rene Thomas	82.47
1915	Ralph DePalma	89.84
1916	Dario Resta (300-mile race)	84.00
1917-18	World War I — No race scheduled	
1919	Howard Wilcox	88.05
1920	Gaston Chevrolet	88.62
1921	Tommy Milton	89.62
1922	Jimmy Murphy	94.48
1923 *	Tommy Milton	90.95
1924	Joy Boyer / L.L. Corum	98.23
1925	Peter DePaolo	101.13
1926	Frank Lockhart (400-miles, rain)	95.904
1927	George Souders	97.545
1928	Louis Meyer	99.482
1929	Ray Keech	97.585
1930	Billy Arnold	100.448
1931	Louis Schneider	96.629
1932	Fred Frame	104.144
1933 *	Louis Meyer	104.162
1934	Bill Cummings	104.863
1935	Kelly Petillo	106.240
1936 †	Louis Meyer	109.069
1937	Wilbur Shaw	113.580
1938	Floyd Roberts	117.200
1939 *	Wilbur Shaw	115.035
1940 †	Wilbur Shaw	114.277
1941	Mauri Rose / Floyd Davis	115.117
1942-45	World War II — No races scheduled	
1946	George Robson	114.820
1947 *	Mauri Rose	116.338
1948 †	Mauri Rose	119.814
1949	Bill Holland	121.327

1950	Johnnie Parsons (345-miles, rain)	124.002
1951	Lee Wallard	126.244
1952	Troy Ruttman	128.922
1953	Bill Vukovich	128.740
1954 *	Bill Vukovich	130.840
1955	Bob Sweikert	128.209
1956	Pat Flaherty	128.490
1957	Sam Hanks	135.601
1958	Jim Bryan	133.791
1959	Rodger Ward	135.857
1960	Jim Rathmann	138.767
1961	A.J. Foyt, Jr.	139.130
1962 *	Rodger Ward	140.293
1963	Parnelli Jones	143.137
1964 *	A.J. Foyt, Jr.	147.350
1965	Jim Clark	150.686
1966	Graham Hill	144.317
1967 †	A.J. Foyt, Jr.	151.207
1968	Bobby Unser	152.882
1969	Mario Andretti	156.867
1970	Al Unser	155.749
1971 *	Al Unser	157.735
1972	Mark Donohue	**162.962
1973	Gordon Johncock (332.5 miles, rain)	159.036
1974	Johnny Rutherford	158.589
1975 *	Bobby Unser (435-miles, rain)	149.213
1976 *	Johnny Rutherford (255-miles, rain)	148.725
1977 ‡	A.J. Foyt, Jr.	161.331
1978 †	Al Unser	161.363
1979	Rick Mears	158.899
1980 †	Johnny Rutherford	142.862

* Two-Time Winner
† Three-Time Winner
‡ Four-Time Winner
** Race Record

COLLECTOR CLUB LIST

National Clubs

General Interest

Antique Automobile Club of America, 501 W.Governor Rd., Hershey, PA 17033, (717)534-1910.

Classic Car Club of America, O'Hare Lake Office Plaza, 2300 E. Devon Ave., Suite 126, Des Plaines, IL 60018, (708)390-0443.

Contemporary Historical Vehicle Assoc., 314 Alyssum Circle, Nipomo, CA 93444. Bill Mirken, (805)929-6071.

Horseless Carriage Club of America, 128 S. Cypress St., Orange, CA 92666-1314, (714)538-HCCA.

International Society for Vehicle Preservation, P.O. Box 50046, Tucson, AZ 85703-1046, (602)622-2201.

Milestone Car Society, P.O. Box 24612, Indianapolis, IN 46224.

Society of Automotive Historians, P.O. Box 339, Matamoras, PA 18336.

Veteran Motor Car Club of America, 18840 Pearl Rd., Strongsville, OH 44136.

AMC

AMC World Clubs, Inc., 7963 Depew St., Arvada, CO 80003. Larry Mitchell, (303)428-8760.

American Motors Owners Assoc., 6756 Cornell St., Portage, MI 49002. Darryl Salisbury, (616)323-0369.

American Motors/Rambler Club, 2645 Ashton Rd., Cleveland Heights, OH 44118. Frank Wrenick, (216)371-5946.

Austin

American Austin/Bantam Club, Rt. 1, Box 137 - 351 Wilson Rd. W., Willshire, OH 45898. Helen Jean White, (419)495-2569.

Austin-Healey

Austin-Healey Sports & Touring Club, P.O. Box 3539, York PA 17402. John Morrison, (215)538-3813.

Avanti

Avanti Owners Assoc., Int., P.O. Box 28788, Dallas, TX 75228. 1(800)527-3452.

BMW

BMW Vintage Club of America, Inc., P.O. Box S, San Rafael, CA 94903. (415)897-0220.

Bricklin

Bricklin International Owners Club, Inc., 213 Southwoods Dr., Fredericksburg, TX 78624. Norm Canfield, (512)997-6134.

Buick

Buick Compact Club of America ('61-'62-'63 Specials & Skylarks), Rt. 1, Box 39B, Marion, TX 78124.

Buick Club of America, P.O. Box 898, Garden Grove, CA 92646-0898. Val Ingram, (619)947-2485.

Buick GS Club of America, 1213 Gornto Rd., Valdosta, GA 31602. (912)244-0577.

1950 Buick Registry, 54 Madison St., Pequannock, NV 07440. Bill Braga, (201)696-8418.

1953-'54 Buick Skylark Club, P.O. Box 1281, Frederick, MD 21702. Richard Beckley, Jr., (301)898-5137.

Riviera Owners Assoc., P.O. Box 26344, Lakewood, CO 80226. Ray Knott, (303)987-3712.

Cadillac

Cadillac Drivers Club, 5825 Vista Ave., Sacramento, CA 95824. Wray Tibbs, (916)421-3193.

Cadillac LaSalle Club, Inc., 3083 Howard Rd., Petoskey, MI 49770. (616)347-4611.

Checker

Checker Car Club of America, 469 Tremaine Ave., Kenmore, NY 14217. Donald McHenry, (716)877-3358.

Chevrolet

Chevrolet Nomad Assoc., Rt. 1, Box 166A, Cairo, NE 68824. Bob Maline, (402)393-7281.

Corvair Society of America (CORSA), P.O. Box 607, Lemont, IL 60439-0607. Mike McGowan, (708)257-6530.

Corvettes Ltd., Inc., 11 Liberty Ridge Trail, Totowa, NJ 07512. Neal Ventola, (201)338-4763.

Corvette ZR-1 Registry, 29 Lucille Dr., Sayville, NY 11782.

Cosworth Vega Owners Assoc., P.O. Box 1783, Bloomington, IN 47402. Bob Chin, (812)339-0838.

International Camaro Club, Inc., 2001 Pittston Ave., Scranton, PA 18505-3233, (717)347-5839.

Late Great Chevys, P.O. Box 607824, Orlando, FL 32860. (407)886-1963.

National Chevelle Owners Assoc., 7343-J West Friendly Ave., Greensboro, NC 27410, (919)854-8935.

National Corvette Owners Assoc., 900 S. Washington St., Falls Church, VA 22046. (703)533-7222.

National Corvette Restorers Society, 6291 Day Rd., Cincinnati, OH 45252. (513)385-8526.

National Impala Assoc., P.O. Box 968, Spearfish, SD 57783. (605)642-5864.

National Monte Carlo Owners Assoc., P.O. Box 187, Independence, KY 41051. (606)491-2378.

National Nostalgic Nova, P.O. Box 2344, York, PA 17405. (717)252-4192.

Obsolete Fleet Chevys (1955-'56-'57 Chevys), P.O. Box 554, McMinnville, OR 97128. Jerry Kwiatkowski, (503)472-4382.

'65-'66 Full Size Chevrolet Club, 15615 St. Rd. 23, Granger, IN 46530.

Straight-Axle Corvette Enthusiasts, P.O. Box 2288, North Highlands, CA 95660. (916)729-1165.

Tri-Chevy Assoc., 24862 Ridge Rd., Elwood, IL 60421. (815)478-3633.

Vintage Chevrolet Club of America, P.O. Box 5387, Orange, CA 92613-5387. Dennis Fink, (818)963-0205.

Chrysler/DeSoto/Dodge/Plymouth

Airflow Club of America, 1000 E. Tallmadge Ave., Akron, OH 44310-3516. David Askey, (216)633-6373.

Chrysler 300 Club Int., 19 Donegal Ct., Ann Arbor, MI 48104. Eleanor Riehl, (313)971-3254.

Chrysler Product Owners Club, Inc., 806 Winhall Way, Silver Spring, MD 20904. Ray Montgomery, (301)622-2962.

Chrysler Town & Country Owners Registry, 406 W. 34th, Kansas City, MO 64111. Dennis McLaughlin, (816)931-3341.

D.A.R.T.S. ('67-'72 Dodge Darts & Demons), P.O. Box 9, Wethersfield, CT 06129-0009.

Daytona-Superbird Auto Club, 13717 W. Green Meadow Dr., New Berlin, WI 53151. (414)786-8413.

DeSoto Club of America, 105 E. 96th, Kansas City, MO 64114. Walter O'Kelly, (816)421-6006.

Dodge Brothers Club, Inc., 4451 Wise Rd., Freeland, MI 48623.

Hurst 300 Registry, 5844 W. Eddy St., Chicago, IL 60634. Roman Robaszewski, (312)685-4980.

Mopar Rapid Transit Club, 10705 Old Beatly Ford, Rockwell, NC 28138. Lee Foster, (704)279-7410.

National DeSoto Club, Inc., 412 Cumnock Rd., Inverness, IL 60067.

National Hemi Owners Assoc., 4694 S. Ouray Way, Aurora, CO 80015. Duane Betts, (303)693-7426.

Plymouth Owners Club, Inc., P.O. Box 416, Cavalier, ND 58220. (701)549-3746.

Slant 6 Club of America, P.O. Box 4414, Salem, OR 97302. Jack Poehler, (503)581-2230.

WPC Club (Chrysler Products), P.O. Box 3504, Kalamazoo, MI 49003-3504.

Crosley

Crosley Automobile Club, 217 N. Gilbert, Iowa City, IA 52245. Jim Friday, (319)338-9132.

DAF

DAF Club USA, 293 Hudson St., Hackensack, NJ 07601. Kaz Wysocki, (201)342-3684.

Daimler

Daimler & Lanchester Owners' Club of North America, 135 Kenner Crescent, Stratford, Ontario, Canada M5R 1P8. Linda Simmonds, (519)271-3251.

Durant

Durant Family Registry, 2700 Timber Ln., Green Bay WI 54313-5899.

Ferrari

Ferrari Owners Club, 1708 Seabright Ave., Long Beach, CA 90813. Pat Benz, (213)432-9607.

Ford/Lincoln/Mercury/Edsel

Big M Mercury Club, 5 Robinson Rd., W. Woburn, MA 01801.

Classic Thunderbird Club Int., P.O. Box 4148, Santa Fe Springs, CA 90670. (213)945-6836.

Cougar Club of America, O-4211 N. 120th Ave., Holland, MI 49424. John Baumann (616)396-0390.

Crown Victoria Assoc., P.O. Box 6, Bryan, OH 43506. Sandy Gorny, (419)636-2475.

Cyclone Spoiler/Talladega Registry, P.O. Box 422, Alpharetta, GA 30239-0422.

Early Ford V-8 Club of America, P.O. Box 2122, San Leandro, CA 94577, (510)606-1925.

Edsel Owners Club, Inc., 4713 Queal Dr., Shawnee, KS 66203.

Fabulous Fifties Ford Club of America, P.O. Box 286, Riverside, CA 92502. (714)354-5667.

Fairlane Club of America, 2116 Manville Rd., Muncie, IN 47302-4854.

Ford and Mercury Restorers Club, P.O. Box 2133, Dearborn, MI 48123.

Ford F-100 Truck Club, 1315 Hollis Terrace, Bremerton, WA 98310. John Ramage, (206)377-9828.

Ford Galaxie Club of America, P.O. Box 2206, Bremerton, WA 98310. William Barber, (206)377-4957.

'49-'50-'51 Ford/Mercury Owners, P.O. Box 30647, Midwest City, OK 73140-3647. Mike McCarville, (405)737-6021.

'54 Ford Club of America, 2314 Wakeforest Ct., Arlington, TX 76012. Tom Hoskins, (817)460-8130.

International Edsel Club, P.O. Box 371, Sully, IA 50251. (515)594-4284.

International Mercury Owners Assoc., 6445 W. Grand Ave., Chicago, IL 60635. Jerry Robbin, (312)622-6445.

Lincoln & Continental Owners Club, P.O. Box 68308, Portland, OR 97268. Becky D'Ambrosia, (503)659-3769.

Lincoln Zephyr Owners Club, P.O. Box 165835, Miami, FL 33116. John Murphy, (305)274-3624.

Model A Ford Cabriolet Club, P.O. Box 515, Porter, TX 77365. Larry Macharek, (713)572-2505.

Model A Ford Club of America, 250 S. Cypress, La Habra, CA 90631, (213)697-2712.

Model A Restorers Club, 24822 Michigan Ave., Dearborn, MI 48124. (313)278-1455.

Model T Ford Club Int., P.O. Box 438315, Chicago, IL 60643-8315.

Model T Ford Club of America, Box 579, Ramona, CA 92065, (619)789-3954.

Mustang Club of America, P.O. Box 447, Lithonia, GA 30058. (404)482-4822.

Mustang Owners Club Int., 2720 Tennessee NE, Albuquerque, NM 87110. Paul McLaughlin, (505)296-2554.

Ranchero Club, 1339 Beverly Rd., Port Vue, PA 15133.

Road Race Lincoln Register, 461 Woodland Dr., Wisconsin Rapids, WI 54494. Burr Oxley, (715)423-9579.

Shelby Owners of America, Inc., P.O. Drawer 1429, Great Bend, KS 67530.

Special Interest Fords of the '50s, 246 Silvercreek, Duncanville, TX 75137. Jack Baird, (214)298-4797.

Thunderbirds of America, P.O. Box 2766, Cedar Rapids, IA 52406. John Draxler, (712)884-6546.

Vintage Thunderbird Club Int., P.O. Box 2250, Dearborn, MI 48123-2250. Bea Zastrow, (301)654-7904.

Franklin

The H.H. Franklin Club, Cazenovia College, Cazenovia, NY 13035.

Gardner

Gardner Automobile Register, 341 Fitch Hill Rd., Uncasville, CT 06382. Ed Jacobowitz, (203)848-8934.

Graham

Graham Owners Club, Inc., 2909 13th St., Wausau, WI 54401. Mike Keller, (715)845-1507.

Hudson

Hudson-Essex-Terraplane Club, 100 E. Cross St., Ypsilanti, MI 48198. Jack Miller, (313)482-5200.

Hupmobile

Hupmobile Club, Inc., P.O. Box 3001, Rosemead, CA 91770. Agnes Christie, (203)642-6697.

Isotta Fraschini

Historic Registry of Isotta Fraschini, 1001 Park Ave., New York, NY 10028. Jeff Vogel, (212)517-2899.

Jaguar

Classic Jaguar Assoc., 2860 W. Victoria Dr., Alpine, CA 91901. (619)445-3152.

Jaguar Clubs of North America, Inc., 600 Willow Tree Rd., Leonia, NJ 07605.

Jordan

Jordan Register, 5231 Stratford Ave., Westminster, CA 92683.

Kaiser

Kaiser-Darrin Owners Roster, R.D. 3, Box 36, Somerset, PA 15501. Dave Antram, (814)445-6135.
Kaiser-Frazer Owners Club, Inc., P.O. Box 1251, Wellsville, NY 14895. Dave Choate, (716)593-4751.

Kissel

Kissel Kar Klub, 147 N. Main St., Hartford, WI 53027. Dale Anderson, (414)673-7999.

Locomobile

Locomobile Society of America, 3165 California St., San Francisco, CA 94115-2412, (415)563-1771.

Marmon

Marmon Club, P.O. Box 8031, Canton, OH 44711. Bruce Williams, (216)454-7070.

Mercedes-Benz

Gullwing Group Int., 15875 Oak Glen Ave., Morgan Hill, CA 95037. Barbara Hunt, (408)776-1788.
Mercedes-Benz Club of America, Inc., 1907 Lelaray St., Colorado Springs, CO 80909. (719)633-6427.
Mercedes-Benz 190 SL Group, 16 Theodore Dr., East Brunswick, NJ 08816. Charles Shaw, (908)257-7549.

Mercer

Mercer Associates, 414 Lincoln Ave., Havertown, PA 19083. John Rendemonti, (215)446-0138.

MG

American MGB Assoc., P.O. Box 11401, Chicago, IL 60611. Frank Ochal, 1(800)723-MGMG.
MG Car Club of North America, P.O. Box 1446, Keller, TX 76244-1446. Lou Marchant, (817)431-9322.

Morgan

Morgan +4 Club, 11423 Gradwell, Lakewood, CA 90715. John Willburn, (310)865-2910.

Nash/Metropolitan

Charles W. Nash Assoc., 2412 Lincoln Ave., Alameda, CA 94501.
Metropolitan Owners Club of North America, 5009 Barton Rd., Madison, WI 53711. (608)271-0457.
Nash Car Club of America, 635 Lloyd St., Hubbard, OH 44425.
'35-'36 Nash Registry, 2412 Lincoln Ave., Alameda, CA 94501. Sieg Wroebel (415)523-0454.

Nyberg

Henry Nyberg Society, 35 Fourth Ave., Arlington Heights, IL 60005. (708)956-8595.

Oldsmobile

Curved Dash Oldsmobile Club, 3455 Florida Ave. N, Crystal, MN 55427. Gary Hoonsbeen, (612)533-4280.

Hurst/Olds Club of America, 1600 Knight Rd., Ann Arbor, MI 48103-9303. (313)994-8778.
Oldsmobile Club of America, P.O. Box 16216, Lansing, MI 48901. Russ Yoder, (216)875-5690.
Oldsmobile Club of America-1957 Chapter, P.O. Box 3712, Arcadia, CA 91066.

Packard

Packards Int. Motor Car Club, 302 French St., Santa Ana, CA 92701. (714)541-8431.
The Packard Club, P.O. Box 2808, Oakland, CA 94618. Stella Pyrtek-Blond, (908)738-7859.
1937 Packard Six International Roster, 3174 White Tail Lane, Adel, IA 50003-9724. Kevin Rice, (515)993-4456.

Pierce-Arrow

Pierce-Arrow Society, Inc., 135 Edgerton St., Rochester, NY 14607.

Pontiac/Oakland

All American Oakland Chapter, 22 Washington St., Millinocket, ME 04462. John Armstrong, (614)878-9536.
GTO Assoc. of America, 1634 Briarson Dr., Saginaw, MI 48603.
Oakland/Pontiac Enthusiasts Organization, Inc., P.O. Box 0371, Drayton Plains, MI 48330. (313)623-7573.
Original GTO Club, P.O. Box 18438, Milwaukee, WI 53218. Neil Moderson, (414)691-2627.
Pontiac-Oakland Club Int., Inc., 286 Ahmu Terrace, Vista, CA 92084. Dick Hoyt, 1(800)457-POCI.

Renault

Renault Owners Club of America, 1390 - 156th Ave., NE #240, Bellevue, WA 98007, (208)882-0352.

Reo

Reo Club of America, Inc., P.O. Box 336, Sea Bright, NJ 07760.

Rolls-Royce

The Rolls-Royce Owners Club, 191 Hempt Rd., Mechanicsburg, PA 17055. (717)697-4671.

Saxon

Saxon Registry, 5250 NW Highland Dr., Corvallis, OR 97330. Walter Prichard, (503)752-6231.

Studebaker

Antique Studebaker Club, P.O. Box 28845, Dallas, TX 75228-0845. Sheldon Harrison, 1(800)527-3452.
'53-'54 Studebaker Coupe/Hardtop Owners, 3540 Middlefield Rd., Menlo Park, CA 94025. Dennis Hommel, (415)365-4565.
'56 Studebaker Golden Hawk Owners Club, 1025 Nodding Pines Way, Casselberry, FL 32707.
Studebaker Drivers Club, P.O. Box 28788, Dallas, TX 75228-0788. Sheldon Harrison 1(800)527-3452.

Stutz

Stutz Club, Inc., 7400 Lantern Rd., Indianapolis, IN 46256. Bill Greer, (317)849-3443.

Subaru

Subaru 360 Drivers Club, 1421 N. Grady Ave., Tucson, AZ 85715.

Toyota

Toyota 2000 GT Owners Club, P.O. Box 617, Saco, ME 04072. Bob Tkacik, (207)283-1764.

Triumph

Triumph Register of America, 1641 N. Memorial Dr., Suite TR3, Lancaster, OH 43130. Joe Richards, (614)756-4575.
TR-8 Car Club of America, 266 Linden St., Rochester, NY 14620. Bill Sweeting, (716)244-9693.
Vintage Triumph Register, 15218 W. Warren Ave., Dearborn, MI 48126. Dennis Riley, (404)475-1088.

Tucker

Tucker Automobile Club of America, 311 W. 18th St., Tifton, GA 31794, (912)382-4573.

Volkswagen

Volkswagen Club of America, Inc., P.O. Box 154, North Aurora, IL 60542.

Willys

Willys Club, 719 Lehigh St., Bowmanstown, PA 18030. (215)852-3110.

Foreign

Daimler & Lanchester Owners' Club of Great Britain, 35 Pretoria Ave., London, England E17 7DR. A.C.L. Freeman, (081)521-7647.
Daimler & Lanchester Owners' Club of New Zealand, 24 Glenarchy Rd., Glen Eden, Auckland 7, New Zealand.
Triumph Roadster Club, The Woodlands, Taddington, NE Burton, Derbyshire, England SK179UD. Henry Gillott, 029885308.

Hobby Councils

Arizona Automobile Hobbyist Council, P.O. Box 1945, Phoenix, AZ 85001.
Citizens Against Restrictive Zoning-CARZ, 2510 Haslett Rd., East Lansing, MI 48823.
Connecticut Council of Car Clubs, P.O. Box 340014, Hartford, CT 06134-0014.
DC Council of Car Clubs, 6629 - 32nd St. NW, Washington, D.C. 20015.
Eastern Nebraska/Western Iowa Car Council, 12559 "O" St., Omaha, NE 68137. Paul High, (402)895-0629.
Legislative Council of Motor Vehicles of Pennsylvania, 620 S. 20th St., Harrisburg, PA 17104. Jim Robinson (717)232-3545.
Old Car Council of Colorado, P.O. Box 280042, Lakewood, CO 80228. (303)935-6662.
Texas Vehicle Club Council, Inc., 3715 Durango Dr., Dallas, TX 75220. (214)352-2871.
Wisconsin Automobile Clubs in Association, 4840 St. Rd. 44, Oshkosh, WI 54904. Dick Dorsey, (414)589-4652.
Wisconsin Car Clubs Alliance, P.O. Box 562, Menomonee Falls, WI 53052-0562. Florence Siegel, (414)255-5385.

Racing

Antique Auto Racing Assoc., Inc., P.O. Box 486, Fairview, NC 28730.
Atlantic Coast Old Timers Auto Racing Club, 4 Elm Dr., Newtown, CT 06470. (203)426-0813.
Eastern States Timing Assoc. (vintage drag racing), P.O. Box 176, Lahaska, PA 18931. Charles Gilmour, (215)794-8611.
Nostalgia Drag Racing Assoc., P.O. Box 9438, Anaheim, CA 92802. (714)539-NDRA.
Society of Vintage Racing Enthusiasts, P.O. Box 3816, Federal Way, WA 98063. (206)643-3551.

Vintage Auto Racing Assoc., 3426 N. Knoll Dr., Los Angeles, CA 90068. (213)874-9135.
Vintage Sports Car Club of America, 170 Wethreill Rd., Garden City, NY 11530. Tony Carroll, (516)248-6237.
Vintage Sports Car Drivers Assoc., P.O. Box 490, Lake Forest, IL 60045. Henry Adamson, (708)234-0303.

Related Organizations

American Truck Historical Society, P.O. Box 531168, Birmingham, AL 35253. Larry Scheef, (205)870-0566.
Antique Aviation & Truck Society, 4533 Hwy. 201, Ontario, OR 97914. Mike Anderson, (503)889-2378.
Antique Motorcycle Club of America, 2411 Middle Rd., Davenport, IA 52803. R.B. McClean, (319)359-1545.
Antique Truck Club of America, Inc., P.O. Box 291, Hershey, PA 17033. (717)533-9032.
Cushman Motor Scooter Club of America, P.O. Box 661, Union Springs, AL 36089. Tom O'Hara, (205)738-3874.
'57 Super Cars, 836 Olive St., Lino Lakes, MN 55014.
48 'N Under, Inc., 708 Water St., Sauk City, WI 53583. George Koehler, (608)643-8146.
GM Haulers/Obsolete Fleet Chevys, P.O. Box 554, McMinnville, OR 97128. Jerry Kwiatkowski, (503)472-4382.
Group Ultra Van, 5537 Pioneer Rd., Boulder, CO 80301-3048. W. Christy Barden, (303)530-1288.
Hinkley Car Owners, 1800 Eagle Ridge Dr., Mendota Heights, MN 55118. Jess Liberman, (612)452-2600.
Historical Automobile Assoc., P.O. Box 10313, Fort Wayne, IN 46851-0313.
Indy Pace Car Registry of 1979 Mustangs, P.O. Box 261251, Lakewood, CO 80226.
Inliners Int., RD 3, Box 83, Rte. 44, Pleasant Valley, NY 12569. (914)635-2059
International Bus Collectors Club, 1518 "C" Trailee Dr., Charleston, SC 29407-4144, (803)571-2489.
International Petroliana Collectors' Assoc., Drawer 1000, Westerville, OH 43081.
Light Commercial Vehicle Assoc., 316 Berkley Ct., Jonesboro, TN 37659-5516. Irvin Neubert, (615)753-2838.
Midstates Jeepster Assn., 3123 Magnolia Ct., Bettendorf, IA 52722. Jack Witkowski, (612)447-4064.
Midwest Military Vehicle Assoc., P.O. Box 37596, Milwaukee, WI 53237-0596. Leo Jankowski, (414)483-3787.
Military Vehicle Preservation Assoc., P.O. Box 260607, Lakewood, CO 80226. (303)989-3218.
Miniature Bugattistes Assoc., 2500 University Ave., D3, St. Paul, MN 55114. Andy Martin, (612)729-4680.
Motor Bus Society, Inc., P.O. Box 10503, New Brunswick, NJ 08906.
Motor Wheel & Flyer Club of America, 26289 Schreiner St., New Boston, MI 48164.
National Woodie Club, Inc., 576 Jacobsburg Rd., Nazareth, PA 18064. (215)759-9311.
Professional Car Society, P.O. Box 09636, Columbus, OH 43209.
Sabra Connection, 7040 N. Navajo Ave., Milwaukee, WI 53217. Herb Smith, (414)352-8408.
'60s Auto Touring Club, 836 Olive St., Lino Lakes, MN 55014.
68 Pace Car Registry, 8032 East Haynes, Tucson, AZ 85710. Bill Keller, (602)886-8004.

SPAAMFFA (Society for the Preservation & Appreciation of Antique Motor Fire Apparatus in America), P.O. Box 2005, Syracuse, NY 13220.

Steam Automobile Club of America, Inc., 1227 W. Voorhees St., Danville, IL 61832, (217)442-0268.

Tall Cedars Special Interest Auto Unit, 4906 Mauretania Ave., Harrisburg, PA 17109. Don Usner, (717)545-1694.

Three Rivers Automobiles, 1260 Denison View, Pittsburgh, PA 15205.

Tucson Miniature Auto Club, 264 E. Pastime Rd., Tucson, AZ 85705-3375. Lou Pariseau, (602)293-3178.

World Organization of Automobile Hobbyists, P.O. Box 1331, Palm Desert, CA 92261. (619)346-1984.

REGIONS/LOCAL

Alabama

American Truck Historical Society-Heart of Dixie Chapter, 5417 Caldwell Mill Rd., Birmingham, AL 35242. William Spain, (205)664-1958.

Gadsden Antique Automobile Club, 113 Buckingham Pl., Gadsden, AL 35901. Joan Clements, (205)547-7143.

Alaska

Vernon L. Nash Antique Auto Club of Fairbanks, 285 Old Chena Hot Springs Rd., Fairbanks, AK 99712. Ben Anderson, (907)457-4396.

Arizona

American Truck Historical Society-Arizona Chapter, 1001 E. Roosevelt, Phoenix, AZ 85006. Curt Curtis, (602)257-8788.

Arizona MG Club, P.O. Box 2468, Phoenix, AZ 85002. Jon Nyhus, (602)939-9652.

Arizona MG "T" Roadrunners, 1519 E. Griswold Rd., Phoenix, AZ 85020. Mac Spears, (602)944-7240.

Cactus Corvair Club, P.O. Box 11701, Phoenix, AZ 85061. Sid Stewart, Jr., (602)274-5274.

CARS Clubs of Sun Cities, 12211 Sun Valley Dr., Sun City, AZ 85351. Don Bittenbender, (602)933-3268.

Contemporary Historical Vehicle Assoc.-Southern Arizona Region, 3464 South Manitoba, Tucson, AZ 85730. Bob Jones, (602)298-3528.

Lincoln Continental Owners Club-Southwest Region, 1702 W. Camelback 301, Phoenix, AZ 85015. Bill Gilmore, (602)230-7282.

Prescott Antique Auto Club, 262 San Carlos Rd., Prescott, AZ 86303. Dan Frank (602)778-3604.

Ranchero-Torino Club of Arizona, 8032 East Haynes, Tucson, AZ 85710. Bill Keller, (602)886-8004.

California

American Truck Historical Society-California Central Coast Chapter, 353 Rio Road, Arroyo Grande, CA 93420. Bob King, (805)473-0846.

American Truck Historical Society-Central California Chapter, 3253 Marshall Ave., Carmichael, CA 95608. Bev Davis (916)944-1087.

American Truck Historical Society-San Diego Chapter, 10481 Tatas Place, Escondido, CA 92026. Fred Marinello, (619)743-4266.

American Truck Historical Society-Southern California Cargo Carriers, 901 N. Olive Avenue, Alhambra, CA 91801. Doug Stoner, (818) 284-7063.

American Truck Historical Society-Southern California Chapter, 4403 Picacho Drive, Riverside, CA 92507. Roland O. Smith, (714)683-4563.

California Chrysler Products Club, P.O. Box 2660, Castro Valley, CA 94546, (510)886-0931.

Central Valley Buick, Oldsmobile, Pontiac Club, 2943 "M" St., Merced, CA 95340. Brian Olson, (209)723-0543.

Chrysler 300 Club-Northern California Region, 2337 Byrd Dr., Rancho Cordova, CA 95670.

Classic Car Club of America-SoCal Region, 1232 Highland Ave., Glendale, CA 91202.

Classy Classics Car Club, P.O. Box 268, Los Banos, CA 93635. Chuck Smith, (209)392-6254.

Contemporary Historical Vehicle Assoc.-Klassic Uniques Region, P.O. Box 813, Vacaville, CA 95696-8813. Bob Herring, (707)426-5431.

Contemporary Historical Vehicle Assoc.-SoCal Region, P.O. Box 254, Fullerton, CA 92632. Stan Tilles, (714)777-6656.

Corvair Society of America-San Diego Chapter, P.O. Box 23172, San Diego, CA 92123. Jim Stansbury, (619)268-1050.

Desert Classic Car Assoc., P.O. Box 1331, Palm Desert, CA 92261. (619)346-1984.

Early Ford V-8 Club of America-Cable Car Region, P.O. Box 3551, Hayward, CA 94540.

Early Ford V-8 Club of America-San Diego Region, P.O. Box 881107, San Diego, CA 92168-0023. Jerry Windle, (619)283-8117.

Early Ford V-8 Club of America-SoCal Region, P.O. Box 2294, Costa Mesa, CA 92626.

Fabulous Fifties Ford Club of America-San Diego Chapter, P.O. Box 710632, Santee, CA 92072. Jim Casey, (619)421-1822.

Heartland Model A Ford Club, P.O. Box 3665, Ontario, CA 91761. Jim Forsythe, (714)983-3954.

Jaguar Club of North America-Sacramento Chapter, P.O. Box 161151, Sacramento, CA 95816. Barbara Sweeney, (916)677-1908.

Kern County Corvettes, 1604 Westborne Way, Bakersfield, CA 93309. Gary Fultz, (805)832-7160.

L.A. Classic Chevy Club, P.O. Box 1901, Hawthorne, CA 90251. (213)335-2567.

Lincoln Continental Owners Club-Western Region, 24930 El Dorado Meadow Road, Hidden Hills, CA 91302. Den Fenske, (818)340-1091.

Lincoln Zephyr Owners Club-West, 119 West 36th St., Long Beach, CA 90807. Ray Brez, (714)968-9875.

Mid Peninsula Old Time Auto Club, P.O. Box 525, Belmont, CA 94002. John Rossi, (415)345-1455.

Mid Valley Antique Auto, 1500 Stewart Rd., Yuba City, CA. Dick Johnson, (916)674-7720.

Milestone Car Society of California, 1255 La Brea Dr., Thousand Oaks, CA 91362. Fred Roth, (805)497-1955.

Model T Buffs of Southern California, 1200 N. Rugby Way, Upland, CA 91786. Lester Breeden, (714)985-5105.

Nash Car Club of America-Greater California Region, 2428 Level St., Anaheim, CA 92804. Bob Walker, (714)761-5060.

Nash Car Club of America-NorCal Nash Region, 1215 Pearl St., Alameda, CA 94501, (510)522-2244.

Northern California Imperial Owners Club, Inc., 223 Kent Rd., Pacifica, CA 94044. Tom Johnson, (414)355-5831.

Pacific Bantam Austin Club, 12304 Lambert Ave., El Monte, CA 91732. Lillian Mitchell, (818)444-7869.

Packards Int.-NorCal Region, 1885 Toyon Dr., Concord, CA 94520. Dennis Reinholdt, (510)827-2188.

Plumas Antique Auto Club, P.O. Box 315, Quincy, CA 95971. John Marvin, (916)283-1555.

Rolls-Royce Owners Club-Southern California Region, 10611 Fullbright, Chatsworth, CA 91311. Kathy Decker, (818)882-5324.

Studebaker Drivers Club-Orange Empire Chapter, 7812 Vicksburg Ave., Westchester, CA 90045. Doug Hughes, (310)645-3438.

Thunderbird Circle of Orange County, 21 N. Vista de Catalina, Laguna Beach, CA 92677. Glen Davenport, (714)499-2003.

Vintage Chevrolet Club of America-Foothill Region, 1751 E. Alosta Ave., Glendora, CA 91740. Jean Fink, (818)963-0204.

Vintage Chevrolet Club of America-Northern California Region, P.O. Box 62, San Leandro, CA 94577. Tom Peters, (908)335-4704.

Vintage Chevrolet Club of America-Southern California Region, 5903 Dunrobin Ave., Lakewood, CA 90713, (310)925-5444.

Vintage Corvette of Southern California, P.O. Box 4873, Thousand Oaks, CA 91359.

Vintage Thunderbird Club Int.-SoCal Chapter, 2525 N. Oakmont Ave., Santa Ana, CA 92706. Frank Deleon, (714)496-8154.

Colorado

American Truck Historical Society-Intermountain West Chapter, 5720 De Mott Ave., Commerce City, CO 80022. LeRoy Gurganus, (303)287-6691.

Antique Automobile Club of America-Poudre Valley Chapter, Fort Collins, CO 80522. Robert Ross, (303)223-7658.

Colorado Association of Tiger Owners, 1573 S. Trenton Ct., Denver, CO 80231. Andy Morton, (303)337-3490.

Durango Old Car Club, 215 Riverview Dr., Durango, CO 81301. Steven Wylie, (303)247-8761.

High Country Chevys, 2815 S. Winona Ct., Denver, CO 80236. Stu Aven, (303)936-6416.

High Country Mustang Club, 1441 Melissa Dr., Loveland, CO 80537. Wayne Ellis, (303)669-3277.

Lincoln Continental Owners Club-Rocky Mountain Region, 2458 Ward Dr., Lakewood, CO 80215. Tom Ward, (303)233-2893.

Connecticut

American Truck Historical Society-Nutmeg Chapter, 247 N. Bigelow Rd., Hampton, CT 06247. Ralph Hosford, (203)455-9007.

Blue Script Model A Ford Club, P.O. Box 165, Stafford, CT 06075, (203)684-6532.

Candlewood Valley Corvette Club, P.O. Box 2205, Danbury, CT 06813-2205. Rich Oliveira, (203)744-7334.

Connecticut American Motors Owners, 23 Slade St., Oakville, CT 06779-1225. John Lane, (203)274-6300.

Model A Ford Club of America-Connecticut Region, P.O. Box 339, Stafford Springs, CT 06076.

Pontiac-Oakland Club Int.-Nutmeg Chapter, 10 Church Hill Rd., Washington Depot, CT 06794. Starr Evans, (203)868-7723.

Roaring '20s Antique and Classic Car Club, P.O. Box 1187, Waterbury, CT 06721. Bruce Winter, (203)393-3787.

Delaware

Historical Vintage Car Club of Delaware, P.O. Box 43, Dover, DE 19903. Tom Mercer, (302)734-9912.

Plymouth Owners Club-Delaware Valley Region, 40 E. Edinburgh Dr., New Castle, DE 19720. Phil Volpe, (302)322-5705.

Florida

American Truck Historical Society-Central Florida Chapter, 3233 Hickory Tree Road, St. Cloud, FL 34772. Harry Di Martino, (407)957-8701.

American Truck Historical Society-South Florida Chapter, 9725 SW 146th St., Miami, FL 33176. Cliff Gibson, (305)251-5839.

Antique Classic Auto Club of Titusville, P.O. Box 5837, Titusville, FL 32783. Fred Moats, (407)632-7965.

Antiques Anonymous Car Club, P.O. Box 874, Eustis, FL 32726. Marie Towner, (904)589-5905.

Antique Auto Club of Cape Canaveral, Inc., P.O. Box 1611, Cocoa, FL 32922. Joe Eichner, (407)259-7722.

Bay Mustang, Club, P.O. Box 10118, Panama City, FL 32404. Cesar Matamoros II, (904)265-8975.

Early Ford V-8 Club of America-Palm Beach Region, P.O. Box 12101, Lake Park, FL 33403. Gary Moore, (407)626-1634.

Lincoln Continental Owners Club-Royal Palm Region, 316 NW 42 Terrace, Plantation, FL 33317. Ron Mueller, (305)792-5168.

Model A Restorers Club-Lakeland Region, 419 E. Belmar St., Lakeland, FL 33803-2211. Steve Sopko, (813)683-1129.

Panama City Classic & Antique Club, P.O. Box 1962, Panama City, FL 32402. Bill Crews, (904)769-1745.

Playground Antique & Classic Car Club, P.O. Box 535, Shalimar, FL 32579. Herb Spies (904)651-1074.

Space Coast Mopar Club, 271 Dorado Ave. NE, Palm Bay, FL 32907, (407)729-6236.

Studebaker Drivers Club-Central Florida Chapter, 743 Saddlebrook Dr., Tarpon Springs, FL 34689. Keith Rolleston, (813)938-2164.

Studebaker Drivers Club-Orlando Region, 1025 Nodding Pines Way, Casselberry, FL 32707.

Suncoast Corvair Club, P.O. Box 788, Crystal Beach, FL 34681. Ed Bittman, (813)327-3115.

Sunny Ts of South Florida, 3030 NE 40 Ct., Ft. Lauderdale, FL 33308, Matt Sellers, (305)566-0683.

Georgia

Classic Chevy Club-Dixie Region, P.O. Box 1121, Marietta, GA 30061. Philip Wotring (404)971-5751.

Corvair Atlanta, 218 Cherrywood Dr., Woodstock, GA 30188. (404)928-1550.

Lincoln Continental Owners Club-Southern Region, 9975 Anaheim Dr. Alpharetta, GA 30201. John Bailey, (404)442-8031.

Idaho

Early Ford V-8 Club of America-Gem State Region, 588 Colfax, Boise, ID 83704.

Illinois

American Truck Historical Society-Windy City Chapter, 4606 S. Gee Road, Woodstock, IL 60098. John Wazorick, (708)654-8090.

Automobile Collectors Club of Greater Belleville Area, 7902 W. Main St., Belleville, IL 62223. Bruce Andres, (618)394-0277.

Calumet Corvette Club, 206 East 160th St., South Holland, IL 60473.

Central Illinois Corvettes, 510 Second St., Staunton, IL 62088.

Central Illinois Vintage Car Club, P.O. Box 986, Decatur, IL 62525.

Chicago Corvette Club, 30280 North Darrell Rd., McHenry, IL 60050.

Chicagoland Corvair Enthusiasts, P.O. Box 425, Midlothian, IL 60445, (708)832-VAIR.

Chicagoland Mercury Club, P.O. Box 341, Crete, IL 60417. Carl Hilchen, (708)672-7864.

Chicagoland Thunderbirds, 242 W. Adams, Villa Park, IL 60181-3112. Jerry Bvtak, (708)834-3729.

Classic Chevy Club Int.-Greater Chicago Region, 111 Dato Ct., Streamwood, IL 60107.

Cruzin Knights, P.O. Box 1111, Addison, IL 60101. Wayne Mittlestaedt, (708)682-9651.

Frankfort Car Club, P.O. Box 15, Frankfort, IL 60423.

Golden Glass Vette Club, P.O. Box 94, Orland Park, IL 60462. Helen Zasadny, (708)237-8563.

The H.H. Franklin Club-Midwest Region, 75 Longdale Rd., Elk Grove, IL 60007.

Illinois Valley Oldsmobile Chapter, 816 13th St., Rockford, IL 61104. Bill Wagaman, (815)226-4727.

Jacksonville Area Antique Car Club, P.O. Box 74, Jacksonville, IL 62651. R. Sid Welles, (217)243-5100.

Joliet Antique Auto Club, 1126 Summit St., Joliet, IL 60435. Norma Weibel, (815)726-4422.

Lincoln Continental Owners Club-Lake Shore Region, 1923 Wenonah Ave., Berwyn, IL 60402. Frank J. Monhart III, (708)788-2856.

Lincoln Continental Owners Club-Mid Continent Region, 8455 South Damen, Chicago, IL 60620. William LaFarge, (312)881-1339.

McLean County Antique Car Club, 302 W. Gray, Bloomington, IL 61701. Irene Klink, (309)829-1781.

Midwest Street Rod Assoc. of Illinois, 3747 N. Harding Pk., Chicago, IL 60618. Bob Bacon, (312)539-4415.

Model A Restorers Club-Fox Valley Region, P.O. Box 4, Geneva, IL 60134.

Mississippi Valley Historic Automobile Club, Bayview Dr., Quincy, IL 62301. Brad Grant, (217)224-8197.

North Shore Joliet Rods, 3105 Jo Ann Dr., Joliet, IL 60435. Jim Talaga, (815)436-6081.

Packards of Chicagoland, P.O. Box 1031, Elmhurst, IL 60126.

Past Timers, P.O. Box 1333, North Riverside, IL 60546. Bill Verner, (708)484-5410.

Pontiac Oakland Club Int.-Grand Prix Chapter, 357 Marvin Place, Wheeling, IL 60090. Mike Schaudek, (708)537-0345.

Pontiac Oakland Club Int.-Illinois Chapter, RR1, Box 220, Beecher, IL 60401-9757. Mary Grippo, (708)258-6017.

Rustic Auto Club, P.O. Box 482, Pontaic, IL 61764. Dan Moran, (815)842-2535.

Sunburst Corvette Club, 801 Edgewood Lane, Mt. Prospect, IL 60045.

Studebaker Drivers Club-Blackhawk Chapter, 1801 Burlington, Lisle, IL 60532. Wayne Smida, (708)963-1128.

Tampico Car Club, 4205 Grimes St., Sterling, IL 61081. Ken Bohm, (815)625-3520.

Tri-Chevy Assoc., 24862 Ridge Rd., Elwood, IL 60421. Ron Brockman, (815)478-3633.

Vintage Chevrolet Club of America-Great Lakes Region, 1258 Balmoral Ave., Calumet City, IL 60409.

Wheels Car Club, Ltd., P.O. Box 231, Tuscola, IL 61953. Lois Bodoh, (217)253-2838.

WPC Club-Northern Illinois Region, 327 Highland Ave., Elmhurst, IL 60126.

Indiana

Central Indiana Vintage Vehicles, P.O. Box 635, Noblesville, IN 46060, (317)877-1425.

Early Birds of Hoosierland, 609 East 6th, Alexandria, IN 46001. David Tulowitzky, (317)724-4635.

Hoosier Classic AMX Club, 3420 S. 700 E., Pierceton, IN 46562. Harold Lehman, (219)594-2373.

Hoosier Convertible Club, 3434 E. 136th St., Carmel, IN 46033.

Hoosier Cruisers, RR 6, Box 162, Vincennes, IN 47591. Jay Wolf, (812)882-8666.

Lafayette Historic Auto Club, P.O. Box 191, Lafayette, IN 47902. Howard Joyner, (317)474-5695.

Lincoln Continental Owners Club-Hoosier Region, 3662 Carmel Dr., Carmel, IN 46032. Charles F. Jost, (317)846-9441.

Michiana Antique Auto Club, 910 State St., La Porte, IN 46350. Lars Kneller, (219)324-8830.

Packard Automobile Classics-Indy 500 Packards Region, 613 W. Orchard Ln., Greenwood, IN 46142. Lew Trent (317)881-6293.

Rock n' Roll Cruzers, 6350 W. 133rd Ave., Cedarlake, IN 46303.

Winamac Old Auto Club, P.O. Box 28, Crown Point, IN 46307.

Iowa

American Truck Historical Society-Central Iowa Chapter, Rt. 1, Box 50, Minburn, IA 50167. Lee Snyder, (515)465-2015.

American Truck Historical Society-Heartland Chapter, 1809 Mulberry Avenue, Muscatine, IA 52761. Mike Pagel, (319)263-8586.

Buick Club of America-Hawkeye Chapter, 1610 Douglas Ct., Marion, IA 52302. Alan Oldfield, (319)377-6282.

Cedar Rapids Corvette Club, 8710 Tower Terrace Road, Toddville, IA 52341.

Classic Mustang Club, P.O. Box 659, Hudson, IA 50643. Andy Clough, (319)296-2218.

Corvette Club of Iowa, P.O. Box 344, Nevada, IA 50201.

El-Kahir Vintage Auto Club, P.O. Box 1320, Waterloo, IA 50704. Bob King, (319)283-2294.

Grinnell Vintage Auto Club, 1623 Spencer St., Grinnell, IA 50112. Robert Latting, (515)236-4028.

Iowa Corvair Enthusiasts, 3051 Wayne Ave., Iowa City, IA 52240.

Metro Chevy Club, 1507 Ave. "F", Council Bluffs, IA 51501.

Metropolitan Owners Club-Illinois Chapter, 1325 Lincoln Rd., Bettendorf, IA 52722. Larry Claypool, (815)469-2936.

Packard Automobile Classics-Hawkeye Packards Region, 3174 White Tail Ln., Adel, IA 50003-9724. Kevin Rice, (515)933-4456.

Quad City Antique Ford Club, 3825 Hickory Grove Road, Davenport, IA 52806. Harold Matherly, (309)787-1842.

Kansas

Antique Automobile Club of America-Lawrence Region, 1706 E. 24th, Lawrence, KS 66046. Ray Stone, (913)842-9232.

Buick Club of America-Mid America Chapter, 216 S. Chestnut, Olathe, KS 66061. Richard Sandberg, (913)764-0423.

Camaro Club of Kansas City, P.O. Box 4344, Overland Park, KS 66204-0344. Jim Sharp, (913)962-1559.

Contemporary Historical Vehicle Assoc.-Sunflower Region, 1312 E. 15th, Lawrence, KS 66044. Edna Jewett, (913)843-7224.

Crossroads of Mid-America Auto Club, P.O. Box 8, Iola, KS 66749. Carol Cation, (316)754-3838.

Mid-America Packards, 5308 W. 81st St., Prairie Village, KS 66208. Joe Zacher, (913)648-2639.

Mo-Kan Late Great Chevy Club, P.O. Box 457, Gardner, KS 66030. Ron Beets, (913)294-2613.

Nash Car Club of America-Historic Trails Region, 1312 E. 15th, Lawrence, KS 66044. Steve Jewett, (913)843-7224.

Packard Club-Great Plains Region, 1024 W. 15th St., Wichita, KS 67203-2746.

Performance Ford Club of America-Northeast Kansas Chapter, P.O. Box 8033, Topeka, KS 66608. Keith Hendrix, (913)267-4731.

Vintage Thunderbirds of Kansas City, Inc., 12101 W. 150th Circle, Olathe, KS 66062. Ross Reed, (913)681-3294.

Kentucky

Jaguar Drivers Club-Area 51, 319 Jarvis Ln., Louisville, KY 40207. Jim Graves, (502)897-9982.

Mid-Kentucky Antique Car Club, Inc., 132 Sugartree Ln., Glasgow, KY 42141. Bob Avery (502)678-8932.

National Nostalgic Nova-Kentucky Chapter, 4315 King's Church Rd., Taylorsville, KY 40071. Joe Grom, (502)239-8487.

River City Classics of Kentucky, 3711 Rouge Way, Louisville, KY 40218. Ron Greenwell, (502)459-1730.

Wilderness Road Touring Club, Rt. 1, Box 70-B, East Bernstadt, KY 40729. Viva Casteel, (606)843-7425.

Louisiana

Ark-La-Tex Antique & Classic Car Assoc., P.O. Box 3353, Shreveport, LA 71103. Jan Shavers, (318)746-0159.

Maine

American Truck Historical Society-Pine Tree Chapter, P.O. Box 22, Searsmont, ME 04973. George Sprowl, Sr., (207)342-5211.

Maryland

American Truck Historical Society-Baltimore-Washington Chapter, Rt. 3, Box 695, Hollywood, MD 20636. Gary M. Callis, (301)373-2190.

American Truck Historical Society-Delmarva Chapter, 72 Bonhill Drive, Salisbury, MD 21801. Alan R. Burton, (301)438-3260.

Antique Automobile Club of America-Chesapeake Region, 201 Taplow Rd., Baltimore, MD 21212. Murrell Smith, (410)752-1842.

Antique Automobile Club of America-Harford Region, 219 Princeton Ln., Bel Air, MD 21014.

Capitol Street Rods, 5350 Landing Rd., Elkridge, MD 21227.

D-Dock Antique & Classic Car Club, 1026 Town Point Rd., Chesapeake City, MD 21915. George R. Smith (609)267-6543.

Early Ford V-8 Club of America-National Capitol Region, 2600 Pfefferkorn Rd., West Friendship, MD 21794. Josie O'Donnel, (410)442-1721.

Lincoln Continental Owners Club-Chesapeake Region, P.O. Box 207, Clinton, MD 20735. Norm McDowell, (301) 868-9216.

Plymouth Owners Club-Mid-Atlantic Region, 3345 Florence Rd., Woodbine, MD 21797. Clayton Miller, (410)442-2305.

Ram Rods, Inc., 7901 Queenair Dr., #102, Gaithersburg, MD 20879. (301)840-9190.

Street Cars of Desire Car Club, 9251 Furrow Ave., Ellicott City, MD 21042-1804. Joey Calato, (410)665-7171.

Vintage Chevrolet Club of America-Bay Country Region, 107 Poplar Ave., Glen Burnie, MD 21061. Joe Hyla, (410)766-8981.

Masschusetts

Antique Truck Club of New England, 26 Stearns Road, West Roxbury, MA 02132. Charlie DeRoma, (617)323-1885.

Bay State Camaro Club, 331 Wareham St., Middleborough, MA 02346. Stephen Levenson, (508)946-3529.

Chrome Roamers Cruise Club, P.O. Box 271, Amesbury, MA 01913. Wes Pettengill (603)474-9839.

City Car Club-Corvairs, 23 Ash St., Fairhaven, MA 02719. (508)763-8564.

Classic Thunderbirds of New England, P.O. Box 342, Lynnfield, MA 01940-9998.

Fall River Antique Auto Club, 217 Reed Rd., Westport, MA 02790. Roger Fortier, (508)636-6704.

Massachusetts Cruisers Auto Club, 24 Oak Hill Dr., Walpole, MA 02081. Rocco Guarnagia, (508)668-6268.

Maynard Area Auto Club, 56 A Main St., Ste. 120, Maynard, MA 01754.

MG T Party, 180 Locust St., Danvers, MA 01923. Joe Joslin, (508)774-8998.

Model A Ford Club of America-Worchester County Region, P.O. Box 36, North Oxford, MA 01537. Malcolm Young, Jr., (508)832-9233.

Mustang Modifieds, 138 North St., Medford, MA 02155.

New England/Northeast Mercury Comet Club, 33 Sanaerson Rd., Waltham, MA 02154. Bob Boudrot, (617)891-6097.

Northeast Chevy/GMC Truck Club, 4 Henry St., Apt. 2, Clinton, MA 01510. Wolf Slik, (508)368-1509.

Northeast Mighty Mopar Club, 19 Treasure Island Rd., Plainville, MA 02762. Paul Nagins, (508)695-1583.

North Shore Old Car Club, P.O. Box 55, Danvers, MA 01923.

Old Car Club, Inc., P.O. Box 462, Shrewsbury, MA 01545. Warren Higgins, (508) 842-2161.

Michigan

American Truck Historical Society-Michigan Chapter, 5505 John R. Road, Troy, MI 48098. Larry Brown, (313)828-9325.

Antique Automobile Club of America-Sanilac Region, 4407 French Line Rd., Applegate, MI 48401. Mike Forton, (313)633-9042.

Cadillac Area Rolling Relics, P.O. Box 571, Cadillac, MI 49601. Don Hoitenga, (616)775-4839.

Cadillac-LaSalle Club-Lake St. Clair Region, 25001 Douglas Dr., South Lyon, MI 48178. David Talaga, (313)437-0892.

Central Michigan Old Car Club, Inc., 1786 E. Gordonville Rd., Midland, MI 48640. R. Payne, (517)835-1422.

Early Ford V-8 Club of America-West Michigan Flatheads, 6581 Sunfish Lake, Rockford, MI 49341.

Honey Radio Golden Oldie Car Club, 8736 Lochdale, Dearborn Heights, MI 48127. Tom Lazo, (313)562-7085.

Kalamazoo Antique Auto Restorers Club, P.O. Box 532, Oshtemo, MI 49077. Stan Rakowski, (616)375-3669.

Lincoln Continental Owners Club-Michigan Region, 1780 South Channil Dr., Harsens Island, MI 48028. Albert Schweitzer, (313)882-5083.

Minnesota

American Truck Historical Society-Hiawathaland Chapter, RR1, Box 248, Kasson, MN 55944. Ed Highum, (507)635-5737.

Antique Motorcycle Club-Viking Chapter, 2460 Oxford St., Roseville, MN 55113. Tom Whittles, (612)484-4754.

Auto Restorers Club of Southern Minnesota, P.O. Box 138, Eagle Lake, MN 56024, (507)625-4200.

Bearing Burners Auto Club, 1302 Walter Ave., Red Wing, MN 55066. Dennis Hovde, (612)388-3791.

Central Minnesota Corvette Assoc., P.O. Box 363, St. Cloud, MN 56302.

Classic Corvettes, P.O. Box 32123, Fridley, MN 55432.

Corvair Minnesota, 3370 Library Lane, St. Louis Park, MN 55426.

Corvettes of Minnesota, P.O. Box 8838, Minneapolis, MN 55408.

Early Ford V-8 Club of America-Twin Cities Region, P.O. Box 20236, Minneapolis, MN 55420. John Titus, (612)895-8264.

Gopher State Late Great Chevys, P.O. Box 120561, New Brighton, MN 55112. Don Rohweder, (612)636-2506.

Head of the Lakes Corvair Assoc., 2114 Jefferson St., Duluth, MN 55812.

Land of Lakes GTOs, P.O. Box 9844, North St. Paul, MN 55109-9844.

Lincoln Continental Owners Club-North Star Region, P.O. Box 1408, Minnetonka, MN 55345. Dick Larson, (612)470-0120.

Milestone Car Society-Land of Lakes Chapter, P.O. Box 27348, Golden Valley, MN 55427. Mike Samuels, (612)377-1236.

Minnesota Street Rod Assoc., 1550 - 148th Ln. NE, Ham Lake, MN 55304-6209, (612)641-1992.

Pontiac Oakland Club Int.-Tomahawk Region, 17657 Round Lake Blvd., Andover, MN 55304. John Cary, (612)753-2567.

Red River Wheelers, 503 W. 7th, Crookston, MN 56716.

Southeast Minnesota Classic Chevy Club, 1322 Gage Ct. NW, Rochester, MN 55901, (507)288-2703.

St. Croix Valley Corvette Assoc., P.O. Box 104, Stillwater, MN 55082.

Suburban Corvette Club, P.O. Box 7233, Minneapolis, MN 55407. Christine Hemphill, (612)832-9272.

Thunderbird Midwest, Inc., 4160 Tyler St. NE, Columbia Heights, MN 55421.

T Totalers Model T Ford Club, 4526 Aldrich North, Minneapolis, MN 55412. Monty Naatz, (612)521-1913.

Vintage Chevrolet Club of America-Viking Region, 1620 - 60th St. NE, Buffalo, MN 55313-9417.

Willmar Car Club, P.O. Box 428, Willmar, MN 56201. Joe Shimota, (612)796-6312.

Wright County Car Club, P.O. Box 662, Buffalo, MN 55313. Sandy Glunz, (612)295-2035.

Mississippi

Aberdeen Antique & Classic Car Club, Inc., Rt. 4, Box 204, Aberdeen, MS. Leroy Jones, (601)369-8576.

Antique Vehicle Club of Mississippi, P.O. Box 55792, Jackson, MS 39296-5792. Bob Jackman, (601)957-2442.

Missouri

American Truck Historical Society-Gateway Chapter, Church & Grant Streets, Union, MO 63084. John Lamke, (314)583-8601.

Antique Automobile Club of America-Metro Antique Region, 5308 Phelps Rd., Kansas City, MO 64136. Ken Parker, (913)441-8380.

Buick Club of America-Gateway Chapter, 1967 Alfred, St. Louis, MO 63110. Jeff Watkins, (314)776-7582.

Bootheel Antique Car Klub, Rt. 1, Box 616, Caruthersville, MO 63830. Jim Moore, (314)333-2167.

Classic Car Club of America-Spirit of St. Louis Region, 4429 Bridgeside Ct., St. Louis, MO 63044. Duane Wesche, (314)298-9907.

Golden Triangle Auto Club Inc., P.O. Box 1141, St. Peters, MO 63376. J. Robert Meyer, (314)724-3431.

Horseless Carriage Club of Missouri, 327 Goetz, St. Louis, MO 63125. Phil Reichardt, (314)544-5560.

Oldsmobile Club of America-Archway Chapter, 11366 Birmingham Ct., St. Louis, MO 63138. John Palmberger, (314)355-4864.

Oldsmobile Club of America-Heart of America Chapter, 6025 Woodside, Kansas City, MO 64133. Gary Hartman, (816)737-2675.

Ozark Farm Chevys, Rt. 1, Box 757, Steelville, MO 65565. John Woods, (314)775-5771.

Route 66 Car Club, P.O. Box 130, St. Clair, MO 63077. Jack Wissmann, (314)583-5206.

Vintage Thunderbird Club of America-Heartland Region, 5002 Gardner, Kansas City, MO 64120. Don Kimrey (816)353-6151.

West Central Missouri Vintage Auto Club, P.O. Box 41, Sedalia, MO 65302-0041. Gaylon Alfrey, (816)826-2033.

Montana

Contemporary Historical Vehicle Assoc.-Custer Region, P.O. Box 1139, Baker, MT 59313.

Treasure State Classics, 817 Edith, Missoula, MT 59801, (406)549-5798.

Nebraska

Classic Chevy Club-Omaha/Council Bluffs Region, 6924 Bennington Rd., Omaha, NE 68152. (402)571-0825.

Meadowlark Model A Ford Club, Inc., P.O. Box 6011, Omaha, NE 68106. Don Graves (402)453-7166.

Nevada

Klassic Kruisers Car Club, 7515 Hillview Dr., Reno, NV 89506. Neal Grows, (702)972-7456.

The M.O.B., 825 Brentwood Dr., Reno, NV 89502. M'Lisa Batey, (702)322-3727.

New Hampshire

American Truck Historical Society-Granite State Chapter, Box 113, Barrington, NH 03825. Donald M. Smith, (603)664-9761.

Model A Ford Club of America-White Mountain Region, 16 Martin Rd., Weare, NH 03281.

Mt. Washington Valley Old Car Club, P.O. Box 158, Glen, NH 03838.

Profile Automobile League, Inc., P.O. Box 7267, Concern, NH 03302-7267. Ken Jordan, (603)224-2627.

Society for the Preservation and Appreciation of Antique Motor Fire Apparatus in America-Amoskeag Reserve Engine Co., P.O. Box 307, Lebanon, NH 03766. Charles Harrington, (603)632-4998.

New Jersey

American Truck Historical Society-Metro Jersey Chapter, 269 N. Main St., Wharton, NJ 07885. Jason Wechsler, (201)366-3003.

Antique Automobile Club of America-Garden State Model A Region, 102 Ford Ave., Voorhees, NJ 08043. Jack Markley, (609)795-1280.

Be-Bop Cafe Classic Car Club, 5 E. Railroad Ave., Jamesburg, NJ 08831. Ira Guttman, (908)521-0800.

Buick Club of America-Jersey Shore Chapter, 2425 Cedar St., Manasquan, NJ 08736. Ron Foerster, (908)528-7777.

Central Jersey Antique Car Club, P.O. Box 5282, Trenton, NJ 08638. Jack Widmann, (609)587-9017.

Garden State Chevelle Club, P.O. Box 3805, Union, NJ 07083, (201)428-9356.

Garden State Classic T-Bird Club, 29 Somers Ave., Clarksboro, NJ 08020-1313. John Brickner, (609)224-0044.

Garden State '50s Auto Club, 441 Esibill Ave., Millville, NJ 08332. George Heitz, (609)825-6559.

Packards East, 84 Hoy Ave., Fords, NJ 08863. Stella Pyrtek-Blond, (908)738-7859.

South Jersey Pontiacs, 2848 Menantico Rd., Vineland, NJ 08360. Mike Aumont, (609)582-5444.

Studebaker Drivers Club-Garden State Chapter, 420 Norway Ave., Trenton, NJ 08629. Jack Widmann, (609)587-9017.

The Classic, Antique & Restored Club, 8 Jade Ln., Cherry Hill, NJ 08002. Steve Love, (609)482-0878.

Vintage Chevrolet Club of America-Historic New Jersey Region, 35 Stillhouse Rd., Englishtown, NJ 07726.

Vintage Chevrolet Club of America-Jersey Lakeland Region, P.O. Box 1526, Morristown, NJ 07962-1526. Ron Panicucci, (201)728-2210.

New Mexico

Four Corners Old Car Club, P.O. Box 1881, Farmington, NM 87401.

Lincoln Continental Owners Club-New Mexico Region, 13301 Tierra Montanosa NE, Albuquerque, NM 87112. Charles Venable, (505)296-1099.

Poco Quatros Model As, 3435 Vassar Dr. NE, Albuquerque, NM 87107. Roger Campbell, (505)299-9195.

Rio Grande Corvette Club, P.O. Box 35923, Albuquerque, NM 87176. Al Funke, (505)831-3723.

Tumbleweed V-8 Club, P.O. Box 21429, Albuquerque, NM 87154. Jim Divine, (505)899-0562.

New York

American Truck Historical Society-Hudson Mohawk Chapter, 75 Midline Rd., Ballston Lake, NY 12019. Robert Gocha, (518)399-2890.

American Truck Historical Society-Twin Tiers Chapter, Box 98, Rd 1, Barton, NY 13734. Ed Greene, (607)687-4352.

American Truck Historical Society-Western New York Chapter, P.O. Box 569, Grand Island, NY 14072. Allen Prame, (716)773-5988.

Antique Automobile Club of America-Batavia Region, 47 Corona Rd., Rochester, NY 14615. Marti Kitchen (716)621-6454.

Antique Automobile Club of America-Iroquois Region, 415 W. Wendell St., Endicott, NY 13760. Steve Boettger, (607)754-2351.

Antique Automobile Club of America-Schoharie Valley Region, P.O. Box 232, Middleburgh, NY 12122. Henry Doerge, (518)827-5112.

Antique Automobile Club of America-Staten Island Region, P.O. Box 244 GPO, Staten Island, NY 10314.

Antique Auto Association of Brooklyn, Inc., 824 E. 21st, Brooklyn, NY 11210. Michael Graff, (718)434-0351.

Antique Car Owners of Queens, 51-23 138 St. Flushing, New York, NY 11355.

Automobilists of the Upper Hudson Valley, Inc., P.O. Box 839, Troy, NY 12181. Keith Marvin, (513)273-4352.

British Car Club of Western New York, 108 Mapleleaf Dr., Williamsville, NY 14221. Ed McMahon, (716)689-4991.

Buick Club of America-Long Island Chapter, 25 - 21st St., Jericho, NY 11753-2534. John Heiling, (516)931-4336.

Capitol District Corvair Club, RR 1, Box 1233B, Fort Ann, NY 12827, (518)793-9383.

Central New York Classic Chevy Club, P.O. Box 2864, Syracuse, NY 13220-2864. John Carnowski, (315)469-6541.

Classic Chevy Club-Hudson Valley Region, P.O. Box 1319, Wappingers Falls NY 12590. Ange Carbone (914)562-7392.

Eastern New York MGA Club, 838 West End Ave., New York, NY 10025. Marc Block (212)662-2748.

Glen Regional Corvette Club, P.O. Box 155, Elmira, NY 14902. Tom Markferding, (607)739-2275.

Knight Krusers, P.O. Box 188, Yorkshire, NY 14173. Harold Burch, (716)492-5287.

Lincoln Continental Owners Club-Mid-Atlantic Region, P.O. Box 188, Tivoli, NY 12583. Michael Simco (914)757-4448.

Long Island Chrysler Assoc., 96 Atlantic Ave., Blue Point, NY 11715. Chris Byrne, (516)737-0134.

Long Island Corvair Assoc., P.O. Box 1675, West Babylon, NY 11704. Sean Galvin, (718)847-4642.

Long Island Model A Ford Club, 34 Summit Ave., Northport, NY 11768. Don Corie, (516)261-4833.

MG Car Club-Western New York Chapter, P.O. Box 831, Webster, NY 14580. Dave Wild, (716)223-1065.

Military Vehicle Preservation Assoc.-New York/ Pennsylvania Region, 106 Carl St., Endicott, NY 13760. Mark Snyder, (607)748-2145.

Model A Ford Club of America-Lakeshore Region, 776 Stony Point Rd., Spencerport, NY 14559-9721. Jeff Stoneham, (716)293-1994.

Pontiac Oakland Club Int.-Long Island Chapter, 41 W. Cortland Ave., Oceanside, NY 11572. John Nassour, (516)536-1678.

Rolling Antiquers Old Car Club, P.O. Box 168, Norwich, NY 13815. Ray Hart, (607)334-4044.

Saturday Night Cruisers, 11 Quaker Hill Dr., Hyde Park, NY 12538. Bill Ciangiola, (914)229-9040.

Southern Tier Auto Buffs, P.O. Box 815, Derby, NY 14047. Bill Wallace, (716)825-5249.

Syracuse Shelby Mustang Club, 3271 W. Seneca Turnpike, Syracuse, NY 13215.

Western New York GTO Club, 2229 Third St., Grand Island, NY 14072. Don Chamberlin, (716)773-1507.

North Carolina

American Truck Historical Society-Piedmont Carolina Chapter, 5210 Stokes Ferry Rd., Salisbury, NC 28146. Lester Brown, (704)636-5384.

Blue Ridge Packards, 130 King Gap, Highlands, NC 28741. Emerson Duke, (803)461-8839.

North Dakota

Valley Vintage Car Club, P.O. Box 2682, Fargo, ND 58107. Kurt Ketterl, (218)483-3268.

Ohio

American Cruisers, 12201 Berea Rd., Cleveland, OH 44111. Jerry Skuhrover, (216)476-8300.

American Truck Historical Society-Black Swamp Chapter, 294 County Rd. 193, Fremont, OH 43420. Brent Binkley, (419)363-2900.

American Truck Historical Society-Buckeye Vintage Haulers, 7860 Cook Road, Plain City, OH 43064. Dennis Campbell, (614) 873-3085.

American Truck Historical Society-Northeast Ohio Chapter, 4730 Rt. 7 NE, Burghill, OH 44404. Wallace Yeager, (216)772-4531.

Black Swamp Cruisers, P.O. Box 13093, Toledo, OH 43613.

Buckeye Motorcar Club, P.O. Box 128, Newark, OH 43055. Lew Claggett, (614)345-1282.

Cadillac-LaSalle Club-Western Reserve Region, 5010 Mayfield Rd. #308, Lynd(216)291-0294.

Central Buckeye Corvette Assoc., P.O. Box 30805, Gahanna, OH 43230. Norbert Huner, (614)475-1048.

Central Ohio MG-T Owners, 10260 Covan Drive, Westerville, OH 43081-9219. Jack Smittle, (614)882-6191.

Classic Car Club of America-Northern Ohio Region, 1312 Meadowood Lane, Hudson, OH 44236. Bill Snyder, (216)656-9811.

Cruising The '50s, 4875 Lower Elkton Rd., Leetonia, OH 44431. Bob Darney, (216)482-9297.

Friends of Crawford Auto-Aviation Museum, P.O. Box 751, Willoughby, OH 44094-0751. John Addams, (216)449-6735.

Great Lakes Collector Car Club, P.O. Box 17, Unionville, OH 44088. Tony Barski, (216)354-8639.

Lake Shore Corvettes, Inc., 1124 Wayne St., Sandusky, OH 44870. Dick Howell, (419)625-7698.

Lincoln Continental Owners Club-Ohio Valley Region, 507 Albright-McKay Road, Brookfield, OH 44403. Bob Thompson, (216)448-6217.

Lincoln Continental Owners Club-Southern Ohio Region, 8480 North Piqua Lockington Rd., Piqua, OH 45356. Fred Bauman, (513)773-6262.

Massillon Area Car Club, 7981 Windward Trace Circle NW, Massillon, OH 44646.

North Coast AMC, 5601 Vandalia Ave., Cleveland, OH 44144. Bob Johnson (216)886-3980.

Ohio Chrysler Touring Club, 6735 Hickory Hill Dr., Mayfield Village, OH 44143-1559. John Addams, (216)449-6735.

Packards Int.-Midwest Region, 365 St. Leger Ave., Akron, OH 44305. Bob Zimmerman, (216)784-7155.

Remember Cruisin', P.O. Box 495, Castalia, OH 44824. Penny Zoliniak, (419)625-6174.

Vacationland Corvairs, Inc., 1513 Hayes Ave., Sandusky, OH 44870. Jack Frost, (419)626-6725.

Vintage Thunderbird Club-Heartland Chapter, 6700 Spokane Dr., Huber Heights, OH 45424. Ken Bender, (513)236-4867.

Y-City Custom Car Assoc., 2090 Shady Ln., Zanesville, OH 43701. Ken McPeck, (614)454-0347.

Youngstown Buicks of Yester Year, P.O. Box 8715, Youngstown, OH 44507. Marilyn Fritch, (216)847-9008.

Oklahoma

American Truck Historical Society-Oklahoma Chapter, Box 381, Sulphur, OK 73086. Charles White, (405)622-3089.
Ouachita Model A Club, P.O. Box 463, Broken Bow, OK 74728. M.G. Fisher, (405)494-6614.
Studebaker Drivers Club-Northeast Oklahoma Chapter, 1332 S. Birmingham, Tulsa, OK 74104. Glenn Fetter, (918)592-1562.

Oregon

American Truck Historical Society-Oregon Trail Chapter, 110 SW Iron Mountain Blvd., Lake Oswego, OR 97034. Terrance Dovre, (503)636-4467.
Caveman Vintage Car Club, Box 1394, Grants Pass, OR 97526.
Dream Machines, 251 S. 6th St., Redmond, OR 97756. Jerry Wallace (503)548-5159.
GMC/Chevy Truck Club-GM Haulers, 704 E. North St., Newberg, OR 97123. Steve Van Marter, (503)538-4729.
GMC/Chevy Truck Club-GM Haulers Salem Chapter, P.O. Box 13274, Salem, OR 97309-1274. Rodger Jincks, (503)370-9550.
Obsolete Fleet Chevys-Blue Mountain Chapter, P.O. Box 662, Milton-Freewater, OR 97862. Allen Panraning, (503)529-9672.
Obsolete Fleet Chevys-Capitol City Chapter, P.O. Box 13944, Salem, OR 97309. Tom Nemecek, (503)363-4985.
Obsolete Fleet Chevys-Santiam Chapter, P.O. Box 1955, Albany, OR 97321. Larry Taylor, (503)928-4575.
Pacific Northwest Convertible Club, P.O. Box 16511, Portland, OR 97216. Ron Gibson, (503)524-4107.
Rollin' Oldie's, P.O. Box 194, Lebanon, OR 97355. Carol Peck (503)737-5371.
South Lane Cruisers, 1111 Cooper St., Cottage Grove, OR 97424. Linda Perkins, (503)942-8431.

Pennsylvania

Allentown Area Corvette Club, 2915 Elm Ct., Allentown, PA 18103. Marilyn Gredlics, (215)437-1036.
American Truck Historical Society-Philadelphia Chapter, 404 Longwood Dr., Kennett Square, PA 19348. George Cleves, (215)388-7308.
Antique Automobile Club of America-Butler Old Stone House Region, P.O. Box 2486, Butler, PA 16003. Ray Hughes, (412)586-2660.
Antique Automobile Club of America-Covered Bridge Region, Park Ave., Washington, PA 15307. Sam Post, (412)663-5404.
Antique Automobile Club of America-Hershey Region, 235 N. Chestnut St., Palmyra, PA 17078. Peggy Derr, (717)626-7450.
Central Pennsylvania AMX/AMC Club, 21 Creek Rd., Dauphin, PA 17018. Lee Peterson, (717)921-3363.
Central Pennsylvania Corvair Club, 1751 Chesley Rd., York, PA 17403-4001. Joe Darinsig, (717)845-9347.
Falcon Club of America-Keystone Chapter, 818 W. Callowhill St., Perkasie, PA 18944.
Free Spirit Buick Club, 1424 Elliott Ave., Bethlehem, PA 18018. Dennis Snell (215)867-3711.
Greater Pittsburgh Mustang Club, Rt. 19, Box 373, Wexford, PA 15090-0373. Doris Keefe, (412)935-5350.
Historical Car Club of Pennsylvania, P.O. Box 688, Havertown, PA 19083. Bill Kunett, (215)566-1161.
Keystone Region Crosley Club, R.D. 1, Box 282, Brodbecks, PA 17329. Don Miller, (717)229-2335.

Lehigh Valley Corvair Club, 2304 Main St., Northhampton, PA 18067. Richard Weidner (215)264-9214.
Lincoln Continental Owners Club-Philadelphia Region, 7211 Saul St., Philadelphia, PA 19149. Andrew Goldenberg (215)335-0388.
Pennsylvania Kit Car Club, 3340 Amond St., Philadelphia, PA 19134. Jerry Lisewski, (215)426-7857.
Steel City Classics, 701 Prestley Ave., Carnegie, PA 15106. Bob Boyd, (412)831-1597.
The Classic, Antique & Restored Club, P.O. Box 6255, Philadelphia, PA 19136. Nick LaForgia, (215)332-5455.

Rhode Island

Rhode Island Chevy Owners Assoc., 30 Terrace Ave., Cumberland, RI 02864. Russ Daniels, (401)334-2803.

South Carolina

Antique Automobile Club of America-Coastal Carolina Region, 4 Edenwood Ln., Charleston, SC 29407. Tom Jameson, (803)571-2264.
Antique Automobile Club of America-South Carolina Region, 19 Ward View Ave., Greenville, SC 29611. Ron Pettit, (803)246-8376.
Carolina Mopar Clubs, 742 East Butternut Rd., Summerville, SC 29483. W.S. Larrabee, (803)873-4239.
Charleston Chevrolet Assoc., Inc., P.O. Box 61152, North Charleston, SC 29419-1152. Brenda Jameson, (803)571-2264.
Coastal Classic Ford Club, 110 Adams Ave., Ladson, SC 29456. Charles Hall, (803)871-0130.
CSRA Mopars, 1897 Columbia Hwy.-North, Alken, SC 29801. John Rivinius, (803)648-0673.
Foothills Mopars, 511-B Wilton St., Greenville, SC 29609. Bruce Brown, (803)233-5868.
Grandspan Mopars, 201 N. Lakewood Dr., Florence, SC 29501. Gary Carmichael, (803)669-7222.
Lowcountry Corvettes, 4 Edenwood Ln., Charleston, SC 29407. Brenda Jameson, (803)571-2264.
Lowcountry Mopars, P.O. Box 60934, North Charleston, SC 29419-0934. Betty Harris, (803)797-3246.
Midlands Mopars, 152 Luther Dr., Gaston, SC 29053. Joe Langley, (803)755-9424.
Palmetto Classic Thunderbird Club, 110 Adams Ave., Ladson, SC 29456. Bill Brown, (803)795-1528.

South Dakota

Brookings Area Corvette Club, 1630 Olwein St., Brooking, SD 57006.
Country Travelers, 620 E. 15th Ave., Mitchell, SD 57301. Dick Rozum, (605)996-4974.
Sioux Falls Corvette Club, P.O. Box 90, Sioux Falls, SD 57101.
Sioux-Land Corvairs, 100 South Cliff, Sioux Falls, SD 57103.

Tennessee

American Truck Historical Society-Chattanooga Chapter, 4830 Woodland Circle, Hixson, TN 37343. George A. Grant, (615)875-5191.
American Truck Historical Society-Music City Chapter, 426 Coventry Ct., Nashville, TN 37211. James Waller, (615)781-8611.
Antique Automobile Club of America-Cherokee Valley Region, P.O. Box 2634, Cleveland, TN 37320-2634.
Antique Automobile Club of America-Mid-South Region, 2548 Strathspey Cove, Memphis, TN 38119-7718. H.A. Peanschmidt, (901)761-3548.

Studebaker Drivers Club-West Tennessee Chapter, 2548 Strathsprey Cove, Memphis, TN 38119-7718. H.A. Peanschmidt, (901)761-3548.

Texas

American Motors Club of Houston, 3400 Ocee, #1601, Houston, TX 77063. Ed Stakes, (713)785-1375.

American Truck Historical Society-Dallas Chapter, 502 Vernet, Richardson, TX 75080. Ed Bothe, (214)231-7011.

American Truck Historical Society-Hi-Plains Chapter, 1109 W. 20th, Amarillo, TX 79109. Tom Warren, (806)374-4078.

Antique Automobile Club of America-Central Texas Region, P.O. Box 9234, Austin, TX 78766-9234. G.E. Plocar, (512)892-7442.

Convertibles of Houston, P.O. Box 2412, Houston, TX 77252-2412. Jim Greer, (713)498-5517.

Lincoln Continental Owners Club-Lone Star Region, 1719 Enfield Rd., Austin, TX 78703. Mark Farrari, (512)482-8063.

Lincoln Continental Owners Club-North Texas Region, 3305 Weems Way, Rowlett, TX 75088. Douglas Mattix, (214)412-0754.

Lincoln Continental Owners Club-Texas Gulf Coast Region, 2480 Times Blvd. 203-A, Houston, TX 77005. Ron Stein, (713)988-9343.

Nifty-Fifties Car Club of West Texas, P.O. Box 16711, Lubbock, TX 79490. (806)745-4955.

Red River Valley Honkers, Antique Car Club of Paris, TX. (903)784-3820.

Southwest Street Machines of Houston, 8515 Concho, Houston, TX 77036. Anna Richardson, (713)774-2945.

Vintage Thunderbirds of Houston, 8309-A Augustine, Houston, TX 77036. Cliff Thomas, (713)772-6487.

Utah

Lincoln Continental Owners Club-Bonneville Region, 2688 Sherwood Dr., Salt Lake City, UT 84108. Rowland Cannon, (801)583-8265.

Veteran Motor Car Club of America-Cache Valley Chapter, 557 E. 900 N. #1, Logan, UT 84120. Mike Cazier, (801)753-0758.

Vermont

American Truck Historical Society-Green Mountain Heavy Haulers, 3 Haywood Ave., Rutland, VT 05701. David G. Zsido, (802)747-5297.

Virginia

American Truck Historical Society-Shenandoah Valley Chapter, P.O. Box 35, Dayton, VA 22821. Lewis Clemmer, (703)879-9772.

Antique Automobile Club of America-Accomack-Northampton Region, P.O. Box 55, Atlantic, VA 23303. Herman Chesser, (804)824-4313.

Blue Ridge Model As, 3227 Deer Run Rd., Blacksburg, VA 24060-9075. Don Elson, (703)552-1673.

Potomac Classic Thunderbird Club, 1010 Park St. SE, Vienna, VA 22180. Gary Friedlander, (703)938-8867.

Virginia Classic Thunderbird Club, 311 Farnham Dr., Richmond, VA 23236.

Washington

American Truck Historical Society-Blue Mountain Chapter, Route 2, Box 12, Walla Walla, WA 99362. Ken Goudy, (509)529-0924.

American Truck Historical Society-Inland Empire, 14320 Denver Ct., Spokane, WA 99208. Dave Kappers, (509)468-2556.

American Truck Historical Society-Northwest Chapter, P.O. Box 3795, Federal Way, WA 98003. Robert W. Brown, (206)838-0985.

Antique Automobile Club of America-Evergreen Region, P.O. Box 33904, Seattle, WA 98133. Bill Glass, (206)824-5040.

Inland Northwest Corvair Club, P.O. Box 268, Nine Mile Falls, WA 99026. Don Tilque, (509)299-4835.

Lincoln Continental Owners Club-Pacific Northwest Region, 18617 NE Cedars Dr., Battle Ground, WA 98604. Joseph Sherlock, (206)687-7972.

Rainier Ramblers, 1125 Olympic Ave., Shelton, WA 98584. Dan Corrigan, (206)531-6731.

Southwest Washington Late Great Chevys, 195 Bozarth Heights, Woodland, WA 98674. Karen Whitaker, (206)225-8576.

Sun Country Mustang Club, P.O. Box 556, Moxee, WA 98901. David Haynes, (509)453-2564.

Vintage Chevrolet Club of America-North Cascade Region, 519 S. Davies Rd., Lake Stevens, WA 98258. Dave Kosche, (206)334-3798.

West Coast Cruisers, 2502 S. Anderson, Kennewick, WA 99337. R.E. Lofstrom, (509)375-4264.

West Virginia

Mid-Ohio Valley Mustang Club, Rt. 5, Box 429, Parkersburg, WV 26101. Ron Moncrief, (304)489-9112.

Wisconsin

Algoma Saab Central, 507 Navarino St., Algoma, WI 54201. Brian Davitt, (414)487-5209.

American Truck Historical Society-Beer City Chapter, W234 S6450 Big Bend Dr., Waukesha, WI 53186. John Lyon, (414)662-2086.

American Truck Historical Society-Packerland Chapter, 2707 W. First Ave., Appleton, WI 54914. Dave Falk, (414)734-1113.

American Truck Historical Society-Southern Wisconsin Chapter, P.O. Box 284, Reedsburg, WI 53959. Bill Skinner, (608)524-6605.

Badger State Vettes Ltd., S68 W17323 Rossmar Ct., Muskego, WI 53150.

Badger Wheels Studebaker Club, 327 Lincoln St., Stanley, WI 54768. John Dickson, (715)644-2438.

Buick Club of America-Cream City Chapter, P.O. Box 27372, West Allis, WI 53227. Jerry Whelan, (414)321-8377.

Buick Club of America-Dairyland Chapter, Rt. 4, 1755 Kavanaugh Rd., Kaukauna, WI 54130. Fred Pennings, (414)766-1333.

Capitol City Corvair Club, P.O. Box 14442, Madison, WI 53714.

Central Wisconsin Auto Collectors Ltd., P.O. Box 2132, Oshkosh, WI 54901.

Central Wisconsin Rods & Customs, P.O. Box 1582, Wisconsin Rapids, WI 54495-1582.

Classic Chevy Club-Greater Milwaukee Region, P.O. Box 07372, Milwaukee, WI 53207. Ron Reimer, (414)384-5601.

Corvettes of Indianhead, P.O. Box 713, Eau Claire, WI 57402.

Dells Area Cruisers, 53051 Fox Hill Ct., Baraboo, WI 53913. Cale Good, (608)356-2494.

Early Ford V-8 Club-Badger State Region, 5803 W. North Ave., Milwaukee, WI 53208. Jack Kusch, (414)771-9280.

Fond-de-vettes, West 5081 Maplewood Dr., Fond du Lac, WI 54935.

Fox Valley Street Rod Assoc., P.O. Box 2612, Appleton, WI 54913. Jim Buchman, (414)779-6341.

Good Time Cruisers, Inc., P.O. Box 562, Menomonee Falls, WI 53052, (414)255-5385.

Indianhead Corvairs, P.O. Box 1412, Eau Claire, WI 54702.

Kenosha Car Club, 2112 - 76th St., Kenosha, WI 53140. Ken Hassler, (414)654-4770.

Kettle Moraine Corvette Club, P.O. Box 621, Sheboygan, WI 53082-0621. Jim Schnettler, (414)467-6521.

Klassic Kruisers Car Club, P.O. Box 6333, Madison, WI 53716. Lloyd Larson, (608)244-1965.

Locals Only, 3650 E. Adams, Cudahy, WI 53110. Tom Kruse, (414)744-2639.

Madison Area Street Rods, P.O. Box 14361, Madison, WI 53714. Gene Reineke, (608)837-4920.

Model A Ford Club of America-Wisconsin Chapter, 11728 W. North Ave., Wauwatosa, WI 53226. Robert Heinrich, (414)552-8795.

Milwaukee Corvair Club, 2523 E. Armour Ave., Milwaukee, WI 53235. Ed Thompson, (414)744-0493.

Model A Ford Restorers Club-Chippewa Valley Region, Rt. 2, Box 324, Cornell, WI 54732. Charles Veicht, (715)239-6710.

National DeSoto Club-Northern Adventures Region, S7550 St. Rd. 37, Eau Claire, WI 54701. Mark Waite, (715)832-8690.

Night Shifters of Madison, 533 Dapin Rd., Madison, WI 53704. Ron Peterson (608)249-9854.

Northeast Wisconsin Corvair Club, 2251 Vinland Rd., Oshkosh, WI 54901. Pat Barker, (414)233-0275.

Northeastern Wisconsin Cruisers, Inc., P.O. Box 11441, Green Bay, WI 54307.

Northern Knights Car Club, P.O. Box 1247, Superior, WI 54880. Tom Griffith, (715)392-1833.

Northwoods Classics, 891 Ninth Ave. South, Park Falls, WI 54552. Louis Kelnhofer, (715)762-3589.

Nostalgic Car Club, 3334 S. 13th St., Milwaukee, WI 53215. Jim Wink, (414)645-2758.

Oldsmobile Club of Wisconsin, P.O. Box 435, Sturtevant, WI 53177. Nick Esch, (414)554-1437.

River City Vettes, P.O. Box 2361, La Crosse, WI 54601.

Rods-N-Relics Car Club, Ltd., 4350 W. Pioneer Rd., Cedarburg, WI 53012. Glenn Wille, (414)377-8480.

1000 Islands Auto Group, 224 Franklin St., Little Chute, WI 54140. Randy Vollmer, (414)788-3476.

Tri-County Antique Auto Club, SH1322 Hwy. 98, Spencer, WI 54479. Harold Yost, (715)659-5564.

Vintage Chevrolet Club of America-Packerland Region, 116 Oak St., Brillion, WI 54110-1110.

Warriors Car Club, 510 W. Vine St., West Bend, WI 53095.

Waukesha Olde Car Club, P.O. Box 144, Waukesha, WI 53187.

Waupaca Old Time Auto Club, 519 S. Buchanan St., Appleton, WI 54915. Merl Mangert, (715)258-7004.

Wisconsin Capitol Model T Ford Club, 2123 Jovina St., Cross Plains, WI 53528. Don Chandler, (608)798-3040.

Wisconsin Corvette Club, 2546 No. Summit Ave., Milwaukee, WI 53211.

Wisconsin Early Mustangers, 2511 W. Carrington Ave., Oak Creek, WI 53154. Scott Moen, (414)646-3976.

Wisconsin Jaguars, Ltd., P.O. Box 1745, Milwaukee, WI 53202. Gerald Nell (414)782-3451.

Canada

American Truck Historical Society-Alberta Chapter, 312 Douglasbank Dr. SE, Calgary, AB T2Z 2C7. Harry Reding, (403)279-7562.

American Truck Historical Society-British Columbia Pioneer Chapter, 13091 103 Ave., Surrey, BC V3T 1R4. Norman Thompson, (604)588-2691.

American Truck Historical Society-Quebec Chapter, 5017 St. Denis, Montreal, QU H2J 2L9. Alain Tremblay, (514)849-7759.

American Truck Historical Society-Vancouver Island Chapter, 2170 Anderson Ave., Port Alberni, BC V9Y 2W8. Steve Drybrough, (604)723-5880.

Lincoln Continental Owners Club-Ontario Great Lakes Region, RR 4, Sterling, ON K0K 3E0. Jim Dyson, (613)395-0669.

1946-1975 — CALENDAR YEAR FIGURES

1946

GENERAL MOTORS (all) 827,845
- Chevrolet.................... 397,109
- Buick 156,080
- Pontiac 131,538
- Oldsmobile 114,674
- Cadillac 28,444

CHRYSLER (all) 539,592
- Plymouth 241,656
- Dodge 158,926
- Chrysler/Imperial........ 76,642
- DeSoto 62,368

FORD (all).......................... 457,368
- Ford.......................... 372,917
- Mercury 70,955
- Lincoln/Continental 13,496

AMERICAN MOTORS (all)....... 193,409
- Nash 98,769
- Hudson 94,640

STUDEBAKER (all) 119,668
- Studebaker................ 77,566
- Packard 42,102

KAISER (all) 11,753

1947

GENERAL MOTORS (all) 1,437,727
- Chevrolet.................... 695,992
- Buick 267,830
- Pontiac 223,015
- Oldsmobile 191,454
- Cadillac 59,436

CHRYSLER (all) 776,783
- Plymouth 347,946
- Dodge 237,735
- Chrysler/Imperial........ 108,870
- DeSoto 82,232

FORD (all) 755,552
- Ford.......................... 601,665
- Mercury 124,612
- Lincoln/Continental 29,275

AMERICAN MOTORS (all)....... 217,058
- Nash.......................... 113,315
- Hudson 103,743

STUDEBAKER (all) 179,118
- Studebaker................ 123,641
- Packard...................... 55,477

KAISER (all) 144,506

1948

GENERAL MOTORS (all) 1,565,926
- Chevrolet.................... 775,990
- Buick 275,503
- Pontiac 253,469
- Cadillac 66,209

CHRYSLER (all) 835,154
- Plymouth.................... 381,139
- Dodge 240,547
- Chrysler/Imperial.......... 120,099
- DeSoto...................... 93,369

FORD (all)............................747,467
- Ford.......................... 549,077
- Mercury 154,702
- Lincoln/Continental...... 43,688

STUDEBAKER (all) 263,651
- Studebaker................ 164,754
- Packard 98,897

AMERICAN MOTORS (all).......262,740
- Hudson...................... 144,119
- Nash........................ 118,621

KAISER (all) 181,809

WILLYS (all) 9,968

CHECKER (all) 4,458

1949

GENERAL MOTORS (all)......2,206,827
- Chevrolet.................. 1,109,958
- Buick........................ 398,482
- Pontiac 333,957
- Oldsmobile 282,885
- Cadillac 81,545

CHRYSLER (all) 1,114,941
- Plymouth 569,260
- Dodge...................... 298,053
- Chrysler/Imperial 140,454
- DeSoto 107,174

FORD (all) 1,077,641
- Ford.......................... 841,170
- Mercury 203,339
- Lincoln/Continental...... 33,132

STUDEBAKER (all) 332,995
- Studebaker................ 228,402
- Packard 104,593

AMERICAN MOTORS (all).......285,054
- Nash 142,592
- Hudson...................... 142,462

KAISER (all) 60,405

WILLYS (all) 3,938

CHECKER (all) 1,465

1950

GENERAL MOTORS (all)......3,048,357
- Chevrolet.................. 1,520,583
- Buick........................ 552,827
- Pontiac 467,655
- Oldsmobile 396,757
- Cadillac.................... 110,535

FORD (all) 1,556,688
- Ford.......................... 1,187,122
- Mercury 334,081
- Lincoln/Continental.......... 35,485

CHRYSLER (all) 1,193,456
- Plymouth 567,381
- Dodge...................... 331,220
- Chrysler/Imperial 167,425
- DeSoto 127,430

STUDEBAKER (all) 340,237
- Studebaker.................268,099
- Packard 72,138

AMERICAN MOTORS (all).....331,798
- Nash 167,869
- Hudson 142,255
- Rambler 21,674

KAISER (all) 118,554

HENRY J (all).....................30,947

WILLYS (all)........................5,846

CHECKER (all) 2,715

1951

GENERAL MOTORS (all)......2,255,497
- Chevrolet 1,118,101
- Buick........................404,795
- Pontiac.....................343,795
- Oldsmobile................285,634
- Cadillac....................103,272

CHRYSLER (all) 1,228,645
- Plymouth...................607,691
- Dodge 336,656
- Chrysler/Imperial 163,541
- DeSoto 120,757

FORD (all) 1,165,010
- Ford..........................900,770
- Mercury 238,854
- Lincoln/Continental 25,386

STUDEBAKER (all) 298,075
- Studebaker 222,000
- Packard 76,075

AMERICAN MOTORS (all) 254,473
- Nash 101,438
- Hudson 93,333
- Rambler 59,702

HENRY J (all).....................58,228

KAISER (all)........................41,308

CHECKER (all) 3,085

WILLYS (all)........................2,097

1952

GENERAL MOTORS (all).......1,801,450
- Chevrolet 877,950
- Buick........................321,048
- Pontiac.....................277,156
- Oldsmobile.................228,452
- Cadillac....................96,844

FORD (all) 1,004,784
- Ford..........................777,531
- Mercury 195,261
- Lincoln/Continental 31,992

CHRYSLER (all) 952,660
- Plymouth...................466,289
- Dodge 268,094
- Chrysler/Imperial 120,692
- DeSoto.......................97,585

AMERICAN MOTORS (all)....... 228,440
    Nash.................................. 99,086
    Hudson.............................. 76,354
    Rambler............................. 53,000

STUDEBAKER (all)................ 224,508
    Studebaker....................... 161,520
    Packard............................ 62,988

KAISER (all) 44,570

WILLYS (all) 35,954

HENRY J (all) 30,543

CHECKER (all) 694

1953

GENERAL MOTORS (all) 2,799,615
    Chevrolet....................... 1,477,299
    Buick............................... 485,353
    Pontiac........................... 414,011
    Oldsmobile...................... 319,414
    Cadillac.......................... 103,538

FORD (all)......................... 1,546,518
    Ford.............................. 1,184,187
    Mercury 320,369
    Lincoln/Continental.......... 41,962

CHRYSLER (all) 1,246,577
    Plymouth......................... 654,414
    Dodge............................. 301,827
    Chrysler/Imperial 160,377
    DeSoto 129,959

STUDEBAKER (all)................ 267,215
    Studebaker....................... 186,844
    Packard............................ 80,371

AMERICAN MOTORS (all)....... 212,427
    Nash.................................. 93,504
    Hudson.............................. 77,098
    Rambler............................. 41,825

WILLYS (all) 35,146

KAISER (all) 14,313

HENRY J (all) 7,459

CHECKER (all) 2,974

1954

GENERAL MOTORS (all) 2,874,271
    Chevrolet....................... 1,414,365
    Buick............................... 531,463
    Oldsmobile...................... 433,810
    Pontiac........................... 370,887
    Cadillac.......................... 123,746

FORD (all)......................... 1,687,224
    Ford.............................. 1,394,762
    Mercury 256,729
    Lincoln/Continental.......... 35,733

CHRYSLER (all) 720,051
    Plymouth......................... 396,702
    Dodge............................. 151,761
    Chrysler/Imperial 101,744
    DeSoto 69,844

STUDEBAKER (all)................ 112,967
    Studebaker......................... 85,660
    Packard............................ 27,307

AMERICAN MOTORS (all)........ 95,182
    Rambler............................. 37,779
    Nash.................................. 29,371
    Hudson.............................. 28,032

WILLYS (all) 9,339

KAISER (all) 5,756

CHECKER (all) 2,627

1955

GENERAL MOTORS (all) 3,989,987
    Chevrolet....................... 1,830,038
    Buick............................... 781,296
    Oldsmobile...................... 634,459
    Pontiac........................... 581,860
    Cadillac.......................... 581,334

FORD (all)......................... 2,240,661
    Ford.............................. 1,764,524
    Mercury 434,911
    Lincoln/Continental.......... 41,226

CHRYSLER (all) 1,370,736
    Plymouth......................... 746,361
    Dodge............................. 316,584
    Chrysler/Imperial 176,038
    DeSoto 131,753

STUDEBAKER (all)................ 181,397
    Studebaker....................... 112,723
    Packard............................ 68,674

AMERICAN MOTORS (all)....... 161,790
    Rambler............................. 83,852
    Nash.................................. 51,315
    Hudson.............................. 26,623

WILLYS (all) 4,778

KAISER (all) 1,021

CHECKER (all) 7

1956

GENERAL MOTORS (all) 3,062,426
    Chevrolet....................... 1,621,018
    Buick............................... 535,364
    Oldsmobile...................... 432,903
    Pontiac........................... 332,268
    Cadillac.......................... 140,873

FORD (all)......................... 1,669,165
    Ford.............................. 1,373,542
    Mercury 246,628
    Lincoln/Continental.......... 48,995

CHRYSLER (all) 870,623
    Plymouth......................... 452,918
    Dodge............................. 205,820
    Chrysler/Imperial 107,490
    DeSoto 104,395

AMERICAN MOTORS (all)....... 104,185
    Rambler............................. 79,162
    Nash.................................. 17,841
    Hudson.............................. 7,182

STUDEBAKER (all).................. 96,387
    Studebaker......................... 82,955
    Packard............................ 13,432

CHECKER (all) 3,970

1957

GENERAL MOTORS (all) 2,186,445
    Chevrolet....................... 1,522,549
    Buick............................... 407,271
    Oldsmobile...................... 390,091
    Pontiac........................... 343,298
    Cadillac.......................... 153,236

FORD (all)......................... 1,889,705
    Ford.............................. 1,522,408
    Mercury 274,820
    Edsel 54,607
    Lincoln 37,870

CHRYSLER (all) 1,223,035
    Plymouth......................... 655,006
    Dodge............................. 293,616
    Chrysler 118,718
    DeSoto 117,750
    Imperial 37,945

AMERICAN MOTORS (all)....... 114,084
    Rambler............................ 109,178
    Nash.................................. 3,561
    Hudson.............................. 1,345

STUDEBAKER (all).................. 72,889
    Studebaker......................... 67,394
    Packard............................. 5,495

CHECKER (all) 3,871

1958

GENERAL MOTORS (all) 2,169,186
    Chevrolet....................... 1,255,943
    Oldsmobile...................... 310,795
    Buick............................... 257,124
    Pontiac........................... 219,823
    Cadillac.......................... 125,501

FORD (all)......................... 1,219,422
    Ford.............................. 1,038,560
    Mercury 128,428
    Edsel 26,563
    Lincoln 25,871

CHRYSLER (all) 581,300
    Plymouth......................... 366,758
    Dodge............................. 114,665
    Chrysler 49,504
    DeSoto 36,700
    Imperial 13,673

AMERICAN MOTORS (all)........ 217,332

STUDEBAKER (all).................. 56,920
    Studebaker......................... 55,175
    Packard............................. 1,745

CHECKER (all) 3,267

1959

GENERAL MOTORS (all) 2,555,247
    Chevrolet....................... 1,349,562
    Corvair............................. 79,418
    Chevrolet total 1,428,980
    Pontiac........................... 388,856
    Oldsmobile...................... 366,305
    Buick............................... 232,579
    Cadillac.......................... 138,527

FORD (all)......................... 1,745,409
    Ford.............................. 1,427,835
    Ford Falcon 100,757
    Ford Total 1,528,592
    Mercury 156,756
    Lincoln 30,375
    Edsel 29,677

CHRYSLER (all) 737,799
    Plymouth......................... 393,213
    Valiant............................. 19,991
    Plymouth total 413,204
    Dodge............................. 192,798
    Chrysler 69,411
    DeSoto 42,423
    Imperial 20,963

AMERICAN MOTORS (all)....... 401,446

STUDEBAKER (all) 153,823

CHECKER (all) 5,768

1960

GENERAL MOTORS (all) 3,193,181
Chevrolet.................................. 1,614,342
Corvair 259,276
   Chevrolet total **1,873,618**
Pontiac 418,154
Tempest 32,052
   Pontiac total **450,206**
Oldsmobile 352,861
Olds F-85 39,931
   Oldsmobile total **402,612**
Buick 271,071
Special 36,733
   Buick total **307,804**
Cadillac 158,941

FORD (all) 1,892,005
Ford.. 1,004,305
Ford Falcon 507,199
   Ford total **1,511,504**
Mercury 161,787
Comet 198,031
   Mercury total **359,818**
Lincoln 20,683

CHRYSLER (all) 1,019,295
Plymouth 252,453
Valiant 231,516
   Plymouth total **483,969**
Dodge 362,808
Lancer 48,858
   Dodge total **411,666**
Chrysler....................................... 87,420
DeSoto 19,411
Imperial 16,829

AMERICAN MOTORS (all) 485,745

STUDEBAKER (all) 105,902

CHECKER (all) 6,980

1961

GENERAL MOTORS (all) 1,726,577
Chevrolet.................................... 1,201,811
Corvair 316,679
Chevy II 86,330
   Chevrolet total **1,604,820**
Pontiac 244,391
Tempest 115,945
   Pontiac total **360,336**
Oldsmobile 253,944
Olds F-85 57,894
   Oldsmobile total **321,838**
Buick 191,392
Special 99,893
   Buick total **291,285**
Cadillac 148,298

FORD (all) 1,689,940
Galaxie 710,392
Falcon 486,081
Thunderbird................................ 88,207
Fairlane 60,444
   Ford total **1,345,844**
Mercury Comet 185,844
Monterey 109,755
Meteor 16,037
   Mercury total **311,636**
Lincoln 33,180

CHRYSLER (all) 648,670
Plymouth 188,170
Valiant 122,275
   Plymouth total **310,445**
Dodge 166,158
Lancer 54,621
   Dodge total **220,779**
Chrysler...................................... 104,747
Imperial 12,699

AMERICAN MOTORS (all) 372,485

STUDEBAKER (all) 78,664

CHECKER (all) 5,683

1962

GENERAL MOTORS (all)......3,741,538
Chevrolet.................................... 1,495,476
Chevy II 369,246
Corvair 296,687
   Chevrolet total **2,161,409**
Pontiac 401,674
Tempest 145,676
   Pontiac total **547,350**
Oldsmobile 356,058
Olds F-85..................................... 102,301
   Oldsmobile total **458,359**
Buick.. 256,766
Special 159,126
   Buick total **415,892**
Cadillac...................................... 158,528

FORD (all) 1,935,203
Galaxie 722,642
Fairlane 386,192
Falcon 381,558
Thunderbird 75,536
   Ford total **1,565,928**
Mercury Comet 144,886
Monterey 109,347
Meteor 81,213
   Mercury total **335,446**
Lincoln 33,829

CHRYSLER (all) 716,809
Plymouth 177,651
Valiant 153,248
   Plymouth total **331,079**
Dodge 251,722
Chrysler...................................... 111,958
Imperial 18,051

AMERICAN MOTORS (all) 454,784

STUDEBAKER (all) 86,974

CHECKER (all) 8,029

1963

GENERAL MOTORS (all)......4,077,272
Chevrolet.................................... 1,625,931
Chevy II 312,097
Corvair 251,513
Corvette..................................... 113,774
   Chevrolet total **2,303,315**
Pontiac 481,652
Tempest 143,616
   Pontiac total **625,268**
Oldsmobile 371,033
Olds F-85..................................... 133,522
   Oldsmobile total **504,555**
Buick... 327,173
Special 152,226
Cadillac...................................... 164,735

FORD (all) 1,963,869
Ford.. 911,496
Falcon 341,871
Fairlane 318,018
Thunderbird 66,681
   Ford total **1,638,066**
Mercury 118,815
Mercury Comet 150,694
Meteor 22,577
   Mercury total **292,086**
Lincoln 33,717

CHRYSLER (all) 1,047,722
Plymouth 274,735
Valiant 221,677
   Plymouth total **496,412**
Dodge 246,425
Dart 174,876
   Dodge total **421,301**
Chrysler...................................... 111,958
Imperial 18,051

AMERICAN MOTORS (all) 480,365
Classic 321,916
American 129,655
Ambassador 28,794

STUDEBAKER (all) 67,918

CHECKER (all) 7,231

1964

GENERAL MOTORS (all)......3,956,637
Chevrolet 1,420,304
Chevelle 320,941
Corvair 195,780
Chevy II 157,799
Corvette..................................... 19,894
   Chevrolet total **2,114,718**
Pontiac 443,306
Tempest 250,328
   Pontiac total **693,634**
Oldsmobile 335,637
Olds F-85..................................... 175,294
   Oldsmobile total **510,931**
Buick 257,438
Special 188,980
Riviera 36,313
   Buick total **482,731**
Cadillac...................................... 154,623

FORD (all) 2,145,943
Ford.. 881,061
Mustang..................................... 303,408
Falcon 279,109
Fairlane 233,718
Thunderbird 90,239
   Ford total **1,787,535**
Comet 195,227
Mercury...................................... 125,431
   Mercury total **320,658**
Lincoln 37,750

CHRYSLER (all) 1,242,162
Fury 266,683
Belvedere 63,757
Barracuda 50,110
   Plymouth total **571,339**
Polara 215,896
Dart 208,646
Coronet 80,552
   Dodge total **505,094**
Chrysler...................................... 145,338
Imperial 20,391

AMERICAN MOTORS (all) 393,863
Classic 201,506
American 151,969
Ambassador 40,388

CHECKER (all) 6,310

STUDEBAKER (all) 577

1965

GENERAL MOTORS (all) 4,949,395
- Chevrolet............................. 1,821,266
- Chevelle 370,188
- Corvair 204,007
- Chevy II/Nova....................... 164,348
- Corvette 27,700
  - **Chevrolet total**................... **2,587,509**
- Pontiac 534,633
- Tempest/LeMans 326,019
  - **Pontiac total**......................... **860,652**
- Buick 368,973
- Special/Skylark/Century 243,441
- Riviera 41,424
  - **Buick total**............................ **653,838**
- Oldsmobile 400,664
- Olds F-85/Cutlass 233,154
- Toronado 16,983
  - **Oldsmobile total**................... **650,801**
- Cadillac 196,595

FORD (all).............................. 2,565,776
- Ford..................................... 1,048,388
- Mustang 580,187
- Fairlane/Torino 251,647
- Falcon/Club Wagon 208,970
- Thunderbird 75,710
  - **Ford total** **2,164,902**
- Mercury 193,069
- Comet................................... 162,335
  - **Mercury total** **355,404**
- Lincoln 45,470

CHRYSLER (all) 1,467,553
- Fury, Gran Fury 305,425
- Belvedere/Satellite/Fury 179,823
- Valiant 139,436
- Barracuda 54,855
  - **Plymouth total**...................... **679,539**
- Coronet/Charger 240,199
- Dart...................................... 173,199
- Dodge................................... 134,133
  - **Dodge total** **547,531**
- Chrysler 224,061
- Imperial 16,422

AMERICAN MOTORS (all)....... 346,367
- Classic/Rebel/Matador 173,374
- Rambler/Hornet 100,217
- Ambassador 72,776

CHECKER (all) 6,136

1966

GENERAL MOTORS (all) 4,448,668
- Chevrolet............................. 1,431,022
- Chevelle 423,317
- Chevy II/Nova....................... 155,726
- Camaro 94,426
- Corvair................................... 73,362
- Corvette 24,939
  - **Chevrolet total**................... **2,202,792**
- Pontiac 481,591
- Tempest/LeMans 384,794
  - **Pontiac total** **866,385**
- Oldsmobile 318,667
- Olds F-85/Cutlass 237,982
- Toronado 37,420
  - **Oldsmobile total**................... **594,069**
- Buick 315,639
- Special/Skylark/Century 216,709
- Riviera 48,073
  - **Buick total** **580,421**
- Cadillac 198,797
- Eldorado.................................. 6,204
  - **Cadillac total** **205,001**

Standard Catalog of American Cars

FORD (all)..............................2,425,422
- Ford..................................... 948,462
- Mustang................................ 580,767
- Fairland/Torino 304,659
- Falcon/Club Wagon 131,793
- Thunderbird 72,734
  - **Ford total** **2,038,415**
- Mercury 153,680
- Comet................................... 133,165
- Cougar.................................... 48,013
  - **Mercury total** **334,858**
- Lincoln 52,169

CHRYSLER (all) 1,445,616
- Fury/Gran Fury 289,676
- Belvedere/Satellite/Fury 174,295
- Valiant 134,683
- Barracuda 41,796
  - **Plymouth total** **640,450**
- Coronet/Charger 278,531
- Dart...................................... 146,361
- Dodge................................... 107,134
  - **Dodge total** **532,026**
- Chrysler 255,487
- Imperial 17,653

AMERICAN MOTORS (all)....... 279,225
- Classic/Rebel/Matador 122,036
- Rambler/Hornet 85,107
- Ambassador 68,084
- Marlin...................................... 3,998

CHECKER (all) 5,761

1967

GENERAL MOTORS (all) 4,117,860
- Chevrolet............................. 1,150,264
- Chevelle 375,831
- Camaro 216,210
- Chevy II/Nova....................... 135,884
- Corvette 23,775
- Corvair................................... 18,701
  - **Chevrolet total**................... **1,920,665**
- Pontiac 445,956
- Tempest/LeMans 288,924
- Firebird 122,291
  - **Pontiac total** **857,171**
- Buick 336,366
- Special/Skylark/Century 194,355
- Riviera 43,145
  - **Buick total** **573,866**
- Oldsmobile 277,910
- Olds F-85/Cutlass 256,643
- Toronado 18,444
  - **Oldsmobile total**................... **552,997**
- Cadillac 192,339
- Eldorado................................. 20,822
  - **Cadillac total**....................... **213,161**

FORD (all)............................. 1,696,224
- Ford..................................... 699,356
- Mustang................................ 394,482
- Fairland/Torino 190,383
- Thunderbird 59,640
- Falcon/Club Wagon 33,527
  - **Ford total** **1,377,388**
- Cougar.................................. 131,743
- Mercury 96,309
- Comet.................................... 56,451
  - **Mercury total** **284,503**
- Lincoln 34,133

AMERICAN MOTORS (all)....229,057
- Classic/Rebel/Matador..........88,532
- Rambler/Hornet 63,291
- Ambassador 50,391
- Javelin/AMX..........................26,595
- Marlin..248

CHECKER (all) 5,822

1968

GENERAL MOTORS (all) 4,592,114
- Chevrolet.............................1,217,255
- Chevelle 432,302
- Camaro 229,344
- Chevy II/Nova.......................225,265
- Corvette 32,473
- Corvair 11,490
  - **Chevrolet total**...................**2,148,129**
- Pontiac 484,849
- Tempest/LeMans....................352,878
- Firebird 105,526
  - **Pontiac total**.......................**943,253**
- Buick 384,575
- Special/Skylark/Century 216,594
- Riviera 50,880
  - **Buick total** **652,049**
- Oldsmobile 331,586
- Olds F-85/Cutlass 276,269
- Toronado 29,924
  - **Oldsmobile total** **637,779**
- Cadillac 187,765
- Eldorado 23,139
  - **Cadillac total**....................**210,904**

FORD (all)..............................2,396,924
- Ford.....................................961,839
- Fairlane/Torino 467,069
- Mustang................................345,194
- Thunderbird 76,789
- Falcon/Club Wagon 60,545
  - **Ford total**...........................**1,911,436**
- Montego.................................149,391
- Mercury 142,048
- Cougar.................................129,813
  - **Mercury total**......................**421,252**
- Lincoln 45,774
- Mark III/IV 18,462
  - **Lincoln total**........................**62,236**

CHRYSLER (all) 1,585,591
- Fury/Gran Fury 279,762
- Belvedere/Satellite Fury 250,550
- Valiant...................................114,816
- Barracuda 38,550
  - **Plymouth total** **683,678**
- Coronet/Charger 315,685
- Dart......................................199,780
- Dodge...................................105,671
  - **Dodge total** **621,136**
- Chrysler 263,226
- Imperial 17,551

AMERICAN MOTORS (all).......268,514
- Rambler/Hornet 89,369
- Ambassador 65,770
- Javelin/AMX...........................58,051
- Classic/Rebel/Matador 55,324

CHECKER (all) 5,477

785

1969

GENERAL MOTORS (all) 4,420,442
  Chevrolet.................................. 1,069,544
  Chevelle.................................... 400,460
  Chevy II/Nova 298,738
  Camaro..................................... 159,202
  Monte Carlo 41,342
  Corvette 26,920
  Corvair 3,103
    Chevrolet total **1,999,309**
  Pontiac 453,241
  Tempest/LeMans 269,300
  Firebird 49,563
    Pontiac total **772,104**
  Buick 434,382
  Special/Skylark/Century............. 226,061
  Riviera 53,389
    Buick total **713,832**
  Oldsmobile 373,020
  Olds F-85/Cutlass 265,987
  Toronado 29,392
    Oldsmobile total **668,399**
  Cadillac 239,584
  Eldorado 27,214
    Cadillac total **266,798**

FORD (all) 2,163,109
  Ford.. 876,320
  Fairland/Torino 334,282
  Mustang.................................... 275,391
  Maverick.................................... 130,041
  Falcon/Club Wagon 77,265
  Thunderbird 50,143
    Ford total **1,743,442**
  Mercury 142,509
  Montego 121,597
  Cougar 90,338
    Mercury total **354,444**
  Lincoln 43,290
  Mark III/IV 21,933
    Lincoln total **65,223**

CHRYSLER (all) 1,392,526
  Fury/Gran Fury........................... 259,054
  Belvedere/Satellite/Fury.............. 221,994
  Valiant 120,514
  Barracuda 49,562
    Plymouth total **651,124**
  Coronet/Charger 241,196
  Dart 144,046
  Dodge 57,902
  Challenger................................. 53,041
    Dodge total **496,185**
  Chrysler..................................... 226,590
  Imperial 18,627

AMERICAN MOTORS (all) 242,898
  Rambler/Hornet........................... 87,817
  Ambassador 64,023
  Classic/Rebel/Matador................. 45,733
  Javelin/AMX 45,325

CHECKER (all) 5,417

786

1970

GENERAL MOTORS (all)...... 2,979,248
  Chevrolet................................... 550,596
  Chevelle.................................... 354,839
  Chevy II/Nova 254,245
  Camaro..................................... 143,675
  Monte Carlo 130,659
  Vega 48,005
  Corvette 22,595
    Chevrolet total **1,504,614**
  Buick 287,904
  Special/Skylark/Century 153,334
  Riviera 18,693
    Buick total **459,931**
  Olds F-85/Cutlass 246,567
  Oldsmobile 179,936
  Toronado 13,129
    Oldsmobile total **439,632**
  Pontiac 182,000
  Tempest/LeMans........................ 144,755
  Firebird 58,757
  Grand Prix 36,700
    Pontiac total **422,212**
  Cadillac..................................... 137,365
  Eldorado 15,494
    Cadillac total **152,859**

FORD (all) 2,017,152
  Ford.. 812,617
  Fairland/Torino 327,288
  Maverick.................................... 187,087
  Mustang.................................... 165,414
  Pinto 88,928
  Thunderbird 40,512
  Falcon/Club Wagon 26,972
    Ford total **1,647,918**
  Mercury 124,540
  Montego 82,908
  Cougar...................................... 71,035
  Comet 31,980
    Mercury total **310,463**
  Lincoln 34,503
  Mark III/IV 24,268
    Lincoln total........................... **58,771**

CHRYSLER (all) 1,273,455
  Valiant 279,615
  Fury/Gran Fury........................... 266,116
  Belvedere/Satellite/Fury 123,033
  Barracuda.................................. 30,267
    Plymouth total **699,031**
  Coronet/Charger 154,314
  Dodge 104,402
  Dart.. 104,358
  Challenger 42,625
    Dodge total **405,699**
  Chrysler 158,614
  Imperial 10,111

AMERICAN MOTORS (all)........ 276,127
  Rambler/Hornet 79,670
  Ambassador 56,990
  Classic/Rebel/Matador................. 56,711
  Gremlin 49,539
  Javelin/AMX 33,200

CHECKER (all) 4,146

1971

GENERAL MOTORS (all)...... 4,853,015
  Chevrolet................................... 942,067
  Vega 393,030
  Chevelle.................................... 375,009
  Chevy II/Nova 298,933
  Camaro..................................... 148,379
  Monte Carlo 136,515
  Corvette 26,844
    Chevrolet total **2,320,777**
  Oldsmobile 390,173
  Olds F-85/Cutlass 338,674
  Toronado 46,352
    Oldsmobile total **775,199**
  Buick 463,785
  Special/Skylark/Century 242,612
  Riviera 45,464
    Buick total **751,861**
  Pontiac 300,587
  Tempest/LeMans 195,721
  Grand Prix 89,512
  Ventura 76,708
  Firebird 66,087
    Pontiac total **728,615**
  Cadillac..................................... 236,499
  Eldorado 40,064
    Cadillac total **276,563**

FORD (all) 2,176,335
  Ford 812,923
  Fairlane/Torino 321,487
  Pinto 299,867
  Mustang.................................... 130,488
  Maverick 127,414
  Thunderbird 46,277
  Falcon/Club Wagon 22,656
    Ford total **1,761,112**
  Mercury 134,756
  Comet 78,494
  Montego 76,786
  Cougar...................................... 53,156
    Mercury total **343,192**
  Lincoln 37,801
  Mark II/IV 34,230
    Lincoln total **72,031**

CHRYSLER (all) 1,313,306
  Fury/Gran Fury 291,357
  Valiant....................................... 236,386
  Belvedere/Satellite/Fury 91,836
  Barracuda 17,013
    Plymouth total **636,592**
  Coronet/Charger 159,951
  Dart 152,925
  Dodge 132,054
  Dart 28,901
    Dodge total **473,831**
  Chrysler 188,360
  Imperial 14,523

AMERICAN MOTORS (all) 235,669
  Rambler/Hornet 67,875
  Gremlin 54,615
  Classic/Rebel/Matador 46,489
  Ambassador 42,187
  Javelin/AMX 24,503

CHECKER (all) 5,328

1972

GENERAL MOTORS (all) 4,775,344
   Chevrolet 955,237
   Vega 368,743
   Chevy II/Nova 367,733
   Chevelle 358,568
   Monte Carlo 186,171
   Camaro 35,943
   Corvette 27,376
     Chevrolet total **2,299,771**
   Oldsmobile 389,089
   Olds F-85/Cutlass 341,130
   Toronado 51,267
   Omega 25,708
     Oldsmobile total **807,194**
   Pontiac 304,545
   Tempest/LeMans 198,411
   Grand Prix 98,587
   Ventura 85,200
   Firebird 15,828
     Pontiac total **702,571**
   Buick 425,813
   Special/Skylark/Century 226,534
   Riviera 36,210
     Buick total **688,557**
   Cadillac 233,456
   Eldorado 43,795
     Cadillac total **277,251**

FORD (all) 2,400,871
   Ford 812,718
   Fairlane/Torino 365,532
   Pinto 32,338
   Mustang 118,972
   Maverick 165,934
   Thunderbird 58,582
   Falcon/Club Wagon 23,934
     Ford total **1,868,010**
   Mercury 150,671
   Montego 140,477
   Comet 83,101
   Cougar 53,594
     Mercury total **427,843**
   Mark III/IV 55,561
   Lincoln 49,457
     Lincoln total **105,018**

CHRYSLER (all) 1,367,354
   Fury/Gran Fury 268,724
   Valiant 250,583
   Belvedere/Satellite/Fury 75,089
   Barracuda 19,090
     Plymouth total **613,486**
   Dart 182,122
   Coronet/Charger 178,261
   Dodge 145,441
   Challenger 27,770
     Dodge total **533,594**
   Chrysler 204,881
   Imperial 15,393

AMERICAN MOTORS (all) 279,132
   Rambler/Hornet 83,213
   Gremlin 69,773
   Classic/Rebel/Matador 52,343
   Ambassador 44,698
   Javelin/AMX 29,105

CHECKER (all) 5,504

1973

GENERAL MOTORS (all) 5,252,734
   Chevrolet 866,826
   Chevy II/Nova 395,673
   Vega 359,882
   Chevelle 314,755
   Monte Carlo 246,533
   Camaro 117,828
   Corvette 32,616
     Chevrolet total **2,334,113**
   Olds F-85/Cutlass 422,477
   Oldsmobile 383,623
   Toronado 56,468
     Oldsmobile total **918,119**
   Pontiac 345,214
   Tempest/LeMans 205,135
   Grand Prix 168,803
   Ventura 89,150
   Firebird 58,296
     Pontiac total **866,598**
   Buick 425,207
   Special/Skylark/Century 311,879
   Apollo 59,128
   Riviera 29,992
     Buick total **826,206**
   Cadillac 252,767
   Eldorado 54,931
     Cadillac total **307,698**

FORD (all) 2,495,863
   Ford 752,468
   Pinto 366,748
   Fairlane/Torino 298,545
   Mustang 193,129
   Maverick 184,810
   Thunderbird 90,414
   Falcon/Club Wagon 23,105
     Ford total **1,909,219**
   Montego 146,565
   Mercury 132,896
   Comet 103,275
   Cougar 70,514
     Mercury total **453,250**
   Mark III/IV 76,137
   Lincoln 57,257
     Lincoln total **133,394**

CHRYSLER (all) 1,556,377
   Valiant 335,816
   Fury/Gran Fury 245,058
   Belvedere/Satellite/Fury 140,745
   Barracuda 21,338
     Plymouth total **742,957**
   Dart 239,598
   Coronet/Charger 188,584
   Dodge 134,470
   Challenger 30,211
     Dodge total **592,863**
   Chrysler 205,601
   Imperial 14,956

AMERICAN MOTORS (all) 355,855
   Rambler/Hornet 114,839
   Gremlin 93,597
   Classic/Rebel/Matador 72,476
   Ambassador 43,676
   Javelin/AMX 31,267

CHECKER (all) 6,333

1974

GENERAL MOTORS (all) 3,585,513
   Chevrolet 472,292
   Chevy II/Nova 386,947
   Vega 327,707
   Chevelle 292,719
   Monte Carlo 232,410
   Camaro 157,909
   Corvette 33,869
   Monza 8
     Chevrolet total **1,903,861**
   Olds F-85/Cutlass 312,004
   Oldsmobile 166,424
   Omega 50,751
   Toronado 19,479
     Oldsmobile total **548,658**
   Pontiac 122,037
   Tempest/LeMans 144,786
   Firebird 78,919
   Grand Prix 78,793
   Ventura 78,701
   Astre 28,847
     Pontiac total **502,083**
   Buick 172,562
   Special/Skylark/Century 158,438
   Apollo 52,126
   Riviera 17,136
     Buick total **400,262**
   Cadillac 192,729
   Eldorado 37,920
     Cadillac total **230,649**

CHRYSLER (all) 1,176,662
   Valiant 370,316
   Belvedere/Satellite/Fury 137,636
   Fury/Gran Fury 90,715
   Barracuda 3,939
     Plymouth total **602,606**
   Dart 268,323
   Coronet/Charger 126,432
   Dodge 63,175
   Dart 6,063
     Dodge total **463,993**
   Chrysler 96,630
   Imperial 13,433

AMERICAN MOTORS (all) 352,088
   Rambler/Hornet 127,680
   Gremlin 113,776
   Classic/Rebel/Matador 83,618
   Javelin/AMX 15,953
   Ambassador 11,061

CHECKER (all) 4,996

1975

GENERAL MOTORS (all) 3,679,126
   Chevrolet 318,400
   Citation/Nova 296,413
   Monte Carlo 266,578
   Malibu/Chevelle 246,759
   Vega 193,245
   Monza 82,954
   Chevette 80,394
   Corvette 45,948
     Chevrolet total **1,687,091**
   Cutlass 363,814
   Oldsmobile 226,845
   Omega 37,261
   Toronado 22,535
   Starfire 3,887
   Buick 227,732
   Century/Regal 212,948
   Skylark/Apollo 74,443
   Riviera 16,759
   Skyhawk 3,938
     Buick total **535,820**
   Grand Prix 112,896
   Pontiac 104,073
   Firebird 94,198

LeMans	88,364
Phoenix/Ventura	60,405
Astre	55,805
Sunbird	7,728
Pontiac total	**523,469**
Cadillac	193,444
Eldorado	48,134
Seville	36,826
Cadillac total	**278,404**

FORD (all) 1,808,038

Granada	336,864
Ford	191,405
Mustang	187,554
Pinto	163,510

Torino	153,510
Maverick	105,418
Elite	90,738
Thunderbird	37,776
Club Wagon	34,639
Ford total	**1,301,414**
Monarch	108,103
Mercury	79,507
Bobcat	60,706
Cougar	57,215
Lincoln	55,499
Montego	52,751
Comet	46,822
Mark IV/V/VI	46,021
Lincoln-Mercury total	**506,624**

CHRYSLER (all) 902,902

Valiant	204,426
Fury	122,703
Gran Fury	71,670
Volare	33,416
Voyager	11,299
Plymouth total	**443,550**
Dart	161,615
Coronet	72,417
Dodge	53,463
Sportsman	41,858
Aspen	25,129
Dodge total	**354,482**
Chrysler	102,940
Imperial	1,930

HOW TO USE THE PRICE GUIDE

On the following pages is a **CHEVROLET PRICE GUIDE.** The worth of an old car is a "ballpark" estimate at best. The estimates contained in this book are based upon national and regional data compiled by the editors of *Old Cars News & Marketplace* and *Old Cars Price Guide*. These data include actual bids and prices at collector car auctions and sales, classified and display advertising of such vehicles, verified reports of private sales and input from experts.

Price estimates are listed for cars in six different states of condition. These conditions (1-to-6) are illustrated and explained in the **VEHICLE CONDITION SCALE** on the following pages. Values are for complete vehicles — not parts cars — except as noted. Modified car values are not included, but can be estimated by figuring the cost of restoring the subject vehicle to original condition and adjusting the figures shown here accordingly.

Appearing below is a section of chart taken from the **CHEVROLET PRICE GUIDE** to illustrate the following elements:

A. MAKE The make of car, or marque name, appears in large, boldface type at the beginning of each value section.

B. DESCRIPTION The extreme left-hand column indicates vehicle year, model name, body type, engine configuration and, in some cases, wheelbase.

C. CONDITION CODE The six columns to the right are headed by the numbers one through six (1-6) which correspond to the conditions described in the **VEHICLE CONDITION SCALE** on the following page.

D. PRICE. The price estimates, in dollars, appear below their respective condition code headings and across from the vehicle descriptions.

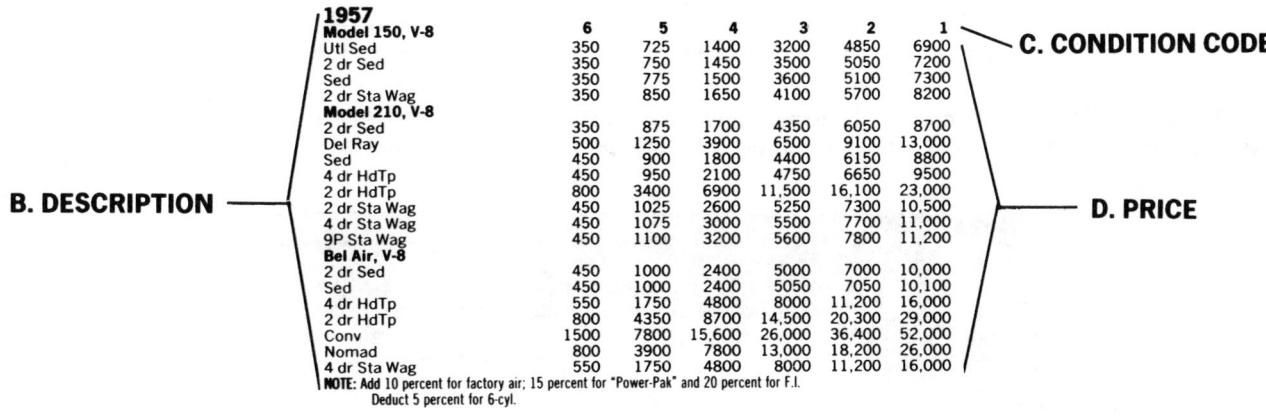

A. MAKE ———— **CHEVROLET**

1957	6	5	4	3	2	1
Model 150, V-8						
Utl Sed	350	725	1400	3200	4850	6900
2 dr Sed	350	750	1450	3500	5050	7200
Sed	350	775	1500	3600	5100	7300
2 dr Sta Wag	350	850	1650	4100	5700	8200
Model 210, V-8						
2 dr Sed	350	875	1700	4350	6050	8700
Del Ray	500	1250	3900	6500	9100	13,000
Sed	450	900	1800	4400	6150	8800
4 dr HdTp	450	950	2100	4750	6650	9500
2 dr HdTp	800	3400	6900	11,500	16,100	23,000
2 dr Sta Wag	450	1025	2600	5250	7300	10,500
4 dr Sta Wag	450	1075	3000	5500	7700	11,000
9P Sta Wag	450	1100	3200	5600	7800	11,200
Bel Air, V-8						
2 dr Sed	450	1000	2400	5000	7000	10,000
Sed	450	1000	2400	5050	7050	10,100
4 dr HdTp	550	1750	4800	8000	11,200	16,000
2 dr HdTp	800	4350	8700	14,500	20,300	29,000
Conv	1500	7800	15,600	26,000	36,400	52,000
Nomad	800	3900	7800	13,000	18,200	26,000
4 dr Sta Wag	550	1750	4800	8000	11,200	16,000

NOTE: Add 10 percent for factory air; 15 percent for "Power-Pak" and 20 percent for F.I. Deduct 5 percent for 6-cyl.

B. DESCRIPTION ————

C. CONDITION CODE

D. PRICE

VEHICLE CONDITION SCALE

Excellent

1) EXCELLENT: Restored to current maxiumum professional standards of quality in every area, or perfect original with components operating and appearing as new. A 95-plus point show vehicle that is not driven.

Fine

2) FINE: Well-restored, or a combination of superior restoration and excellent original. Also, an *extremely* well-maintained original showing very minimal wear.

Very Good

3) VERY GOOD: Completely operable original or "older restoration" showing wear. Also, a good amateur restoration, all presentable and serviceable inside and out. Plus, combinations of well-done restoration and good operable components or a partially restored vehicle with all parts necessary to complete and/or valuable NOS parts.

Good

4) GOOD: A driveable vehicle needing no or only minor work to be functional. Also, a deteriorated restoration or a very poor amateur restoration. All components may need restoration to be "excellent," but the vehicle is mostly useable "as is."

Restorable

5) RESTORABLE: Needs *complete* restoration of body, chassis and interior. May or may not be running, but isn't weathered, wrecked or stripped to the point of being useful only for parts.

Parts Car

6) PARTS VEHICLE: May or may not be running, but is weathered, wrecked and/or stripped to the point of being useful primarily for parts.

PRICING

AMC

1958

Model	6	5	4	3	2	1
American, 6-cyl.						
2 dr DeL	200	500	850	1950	3600	5100
2 dr Super	200	550	900	2000	3600	5200
Rambler DeLuxe, 6-cyl.						
4 dr	200	550	900	2000	3600	5200
Sta Wag	200	550	900	2100	3700	5300
Rambler Super						
4 dr	200	550	900	2100	3700	5300
4 dr HdTp	200	550	900	2150	3800	5400
Sta Wag	200	550	900	2150	3800	5400
Rambler Custom						
4 dr	200	600	950	2150	3850	5500
Sta Wag	200	600	950	2200	3900	5600
Rebel DeLuxe, V8						
4 dr	200	650	1000	2200	4100	5800
Rebel Super						
4 dr	200	650	1050	2250	4200	6000
Sta Wag	200	650	1050	2250	4200	6000
Rebel Custom						
4 dr	200	675	1100	2250	4400	6300
4 dr HdTp	350	700	1100	2300	4500	6400
Sta Wag	200	675	1100	2250	4400	6300
Ambassador Super, V8						
4 dr	200	650	1050	2250	4200	6000
Sta Wag	200	675	1050	2250	4300	6100
Ambassador Custom						
4 dr	200	675	1050	2250	4350	6200
4 dr HdTp	200	675	1100	2250	4400	6300
Sta Wag	200	675	1050	2250	4350	6200
4 dr HdTp Wag	350	700	1150	2300	4550	6500

1959

Model	6	5	4	3	2	1
American DeLuxe, 6-cyl.						
2 dr Sed	200	550	900	2000	3600	5200
Sta Wag	200	550	900	2100	3700	5300
American Super, 6-cyl.						
2 dr Sed	200	550	900	2100	3700	5300
Sta Wag	200	550	900	2150	3800	5400
Rambler DeLuxe, 6-cyl.						
4 dr Sed	200	550	900	2000	3600	5200
Sta Wag	200	500	850	1850	3350	4900
Rambler Super, 6-cyl.						
4 dr Sed	200	500	850	1850	3350	4900
4 dr HdTp	200	500	850	1900	3500	5000
Sta Wag	200	550	900	2150	3800	5400
Rambler Custom, 6-cyl.						
4 dr Sed	200	600	1000	2200	4000	5700
4 dr HdTp	200	650	1000	2200	4150	5900
Sta Wag	200	600	950	2150	3850	5500
Rebel Super V-8						
4 dr Sed	200	650	1000	2200	4100	5800
Sta Wag	200	650	1000	2200	4150	5900
Rebel Custom, V-8						
4 dr Sed	200	650	1000	2200	4150	5900
4 dr HdTp	200	650	1050	2250	4200	6000
Sta Wag	200	650	1050	2250	4200	6000
Ambassador Super, V-8						
4 dr Sed	200	600	1000	2200	4000	5700
Sta Wag	200	650	1000	2200	4100	5800
Ambassador Custom, V-8						
4 dr Sed	200	650	1000	2200	4100	5800
4 dr Hdtp	200	650	1000	2200	4150	5900
Sta Wag	200	650	1000	2200	4150	5900
HdTp Sta Wag	200	675	1050	2250	4300	6100

1960

Model	6	5	4	3	2	1
American DeLuxe, 6-cyl.						
2 dr Sed	200	500	850	1900	3500	5000
4 dr Sed	200	500	850	1850	3350	4900
Sta Wag	200	500	850	1950	3600	5100
American Super, 6-cyl.						
2 dr Sed	200	500	850	1900	3500	5000
4 dr Sed	200	500	850	1950	3600	5100
Sta Wag	200	550	900	2000	3600	5200
American Custom, 6-cyl.						
2 dr Sed	200	500	850	1900	3500	5000
4 dr Sed	200	500	850	1850	3350	4900
Sta Wag	200	500	850	1950	3600	5100
Rambler DeLuxe, 6-cyl.						
4 dr Sed	200	500	850	1850	3350	4900
Sta Wag	200	500	850	1850	3350	4900
Rambler Super, 6-cyl.						
4 dr Sed	200	500	850	1900	3500	5000
6P Sta Wag	200	500	850	1900	3500	5000
8P Sta Wag	200	500	850	1950	3600	5100
Rambler Custom, 6-cyl.						
4 dr Sed	200	500	850	1950	3600	5100
4 dr HdTp	200	550	900	2000	3600	5200
6P Sta Wag	200	500	850	1950	3600	5100
8P Sta Wag	200	550	900	2000	3600	5200
Rebel Super, V-8						
Sed	200	550	900	2100	3700	5300
6P Sta Wag	200	550	900	2000	3600	5200
8P Sta Wag	200	550	900	2100	3700	5300
Rebel Custom, V-8						
Sed	200	550	900	2150	3800	5400
4 dr HdTp	200	600	950	2150	3850	5500
6P Sta Wag	200	550	900	2150	3800	5400
8P Sta Wag	200	600	950	2150	3850	5500
Ambassador Super, V-8						
Sed	200	600	950	2200	3900	5600
6P Sta Wag	200	600	950	2150	3850	5500
8P Sta Wag	200	600	950	2200	3900	5600

Model	6	5	4	3	2	1
Ambassador Custom, V-8						
Sed	200	600	1000	2200	4000	5700
4 dr HdTp	200	650	1000	2200	4100	5800
6P Sta Wag	200	600	1000	2200	4000	5700
HdTp Sta Wag	200	650	1050	2250	4200	6000
8P Sta Wag	200	650	1000	2200	4150	5900

1961

Model	6	5	4	3	2	1
American						
DeL Sed	150	400	750	1600	3100	4400
2 dr DeL Sed	150	400	750	1650	3150	4500
4 dr DeL Sta Wag	150	450	750	1700	3200	4600
2 dr DeL Sta Wag	150	400	750	1650	3150	4500
4 dr Sup Sed	150	400	750	1650	3150	4500
2 dr Sup Sed	150	450	750	1700	3200	4600
4 dr Sup Sta Wag	150	450	800	1750	3250	4700
2 dr Sup Sta Wag	150	450	750	1700	3200	4600
4 dr Cus Sed	150	450	750	1700	3200	4600
2 dr Cus Sed	150	450	800	1750	3250	4700
Cus Conv	200	650	1050	2250	4200	6000
4 dr Cus Sta Wag	150	450	800	1750	3250	4700
2 dr Cus Sta Wag	150	450	800	1800	3300	4800
400 Sed	150	450	800	1750	3250	4700
400 Conv	200	675	1050	2250	4350	6200
Rambler Classic						
DeL Sed	150	400	750	1650	3150	4500
DeL Sta Wag	150	450	750	1700	3200	4600
Sup Sed	150	450	750	1700	3200	4600
Sup Sta Wag	150	450	800	1750	3250	4700
Cus Sed	150	450	800	1750	3250	4700
Cus Sta Wag	150	450	800	1800	3300	4800
400 Sed	150	450	800	1800	3300	4800

NOTE: Add 5 percent for V-8.

Model	6	5	4	3	2	1
Ambassador						
DeL Sed	150	450	750	1700	3200	4600
Sup Sed	150	450	800	1750	3250	4700
5 dr Sup Sta Wag	150	450	800	1800	3300	4800
4 dr Sup Sta Wag	150	450	800	1750	3250	4700
Cus Sed	150	450	800	1800	3300	4800
5 dr Cus Sta Wag	200	500	850	1900	3500	5000
4 dr Cus Sta Wag	200	500	850	1850	3350	4900
400 Sed	200	500	850	1850	3350	4900

1962

Model	6	5	4	3	2	1
American						
DeL Sed	150	350	750	1350	2800	4000
2 dr DeL Sed	150	350	750	1350	2800	4000
4 dr DeL Sta Wag	150	350	750	1450	2900	4100
2 dr DeL Sta Wag	150	350	750	1350	2800	4000
Cus Sed	150	350	750	1450	2900	4100
2 dr Cus Sed	150	350	750	1450	2900	4100
2 dr Cus Sta Wag	150	350	750	1450	3000	4200
4 dr 400	150	350	750	1450	2900	4100
2 dr 400	150	350	750	1450	3000	4200
400 Conv	200	675	1050	2250	4350	6200
400 Sta Wag	150	400	750	1650	3150	4500
Classic						
DeL Sed	150	350	750	1350	2800	4000
2 dr DeL	150	350	750	1450	2900	4100
DeL Sta Wag	150	350	750	1450	3000	4200
Cus Sed	150	400	750	1550	3050	4300
2 dr Cus	150	400	750	1600	3100	4400
4 dr Cus Sta Wag	150	400	750	1550	3050	4300
5 dr Cus Sta Wag	150	400	750	1600	3100	4400
400 Sed	150	400	750	1600	3100	4400
2 dr 400	150	400	750	1650	3150	4500
400 Sta Wag	150	450	750	1700	3200	4600

NOTE: Add 5 percent for V-8.

Model	6	5	4	3	2	1
Ambassador						
4 dr Cus Sed	150	350	750	1450	3000	4200
2 dr Cus Sed	150	400	750	1550	3050	4300
Cus Sta Wag	150	450	800	1750	3250	4700
4 dr 400 Sed	150	400	750	1650	3150	4500
2 dr 400 Sed	150	450	750	1700	3200	4600
4 dr 400 Sta Wag	150	450	800	1750	3250	4700
5 dr 400 Sta Wag	150	450	800	1800	3300	4800

1963

Model	6	5	4	3	2	1
American						
4 dr 220 Sed	125	250	700	1150	2500	3600
2 dr 220 Sed	150	300	700	1250	2600	3700
220 Bus Sed	125	250	700	1150	2450	3500
220 Sta Wag	150	300	700	1250	2600	3700
2 dr 220 Sta Wag	125	250	700	1150	2500	3600
330 Sed	150	300	700	1250	2600	3700
2 dr 330 Sed	125	250	700	1150	2500	3600
330 Sta Wag	150	300	700	1250	2600	3700
330 2 dr Sta Wag	150	300	700	1250	2650	3800
440 Sed	150	300	750	1350	2700	3900
2 dr 440 Sed	150	350	750	1350	2800	4000
440 HdTp	150	400	750	1550	3050	4300
440-H HdTp	200	500	850	1900	3500	5000
440 Conv	200	600	950	2150	3850	5500
440 Sta Wag	150	300	750	1350	2700	3900
Classic						
550 Sed	125	250	700	1150	2450	3500
2 dr 550 Sed	125	250	700	1150	2500	3600
550 Sta Wag	125	250	700	1150	2450	3500
660 Sed	125	250	700	1150	2450	3500
2 dr 660 Sed	125	250	700	1150	2500	3600
660 Sta Wag	150	300	700	1250	2600	3700
770 Sed	150	300	750	1350	2700	3900
2 dr 770 Sed	150	300	700	1250	2650	3800
770 Sta Wag	150	300	700	1250	2600	3700

NOTE: Add 5 percent for V-8 models.

	6	5	4	3	2	1
Ambassador						
800 Sed	150	300	700	1250	2650	3800
2 dr 800 Sed	150	300	750	1350	2700	3900
800 Sta Wag	150	350	750	1350	2800	4000
880 Sed	150	300	750	1350	2700	3900
2 dr 880 Sed	150	350	750	1350	2800	4000
880 Sta Wag	150	350	750	1450	2900	4100
990 Sed	150	350	750	1350	2800	4000
2 dr 990 Sed	150	350	750	1450	2900	4100
5 dr 990 Sta Wag	150	350	750	1450	3000	4200
4 dr 990 Sta Wag	150	350	750	1350	2800	4000
1964						
American						
220 Sed	125	250	700	1150	2500	3600
2 dr 220	150	300	700	1250	2600	3700
220 Sta Wag	150	300	700	1250	2650	3800
330 Sed	150	300	700	1250	2650	3800
2 dr 330	150	300	750	1350	2700	3900
330 Sta Wag	150	300	750	1350	2700	3900
440 Sed	150	300	700	1250	2650	3800
440 HdTp	150	400	750	1550	3050	4300
440-H HdTp	200	500	850	1900	3500	5000
Conv	200	600	950	2150	3850	5500
Classic						
550 Sed	125	250	700	1150	2450	3500
2 dr 550	125	250	700	1150	2500	3600
550 Sta Wag	150	300	700	1250	2600	3700
660 Sed	125	250	700	1150	2500	3600
2 dr 660	150	300	700	1250	2600	3700
660 Sta Wag	150	300	700	1250	2650	3800
770 Sed	150	300	700	1250	2600	3700
2 dr 770	150	300	700	1250	2650	3800
770 Hdtp	150	400	750	1550	3050	4300
770 Typhoon	200	600	950	2150	3850	5500
770 Sta Wag	150	300	700	1250	2650	3800
NOTE: Add 5 percent for V-8 models.						
Ambassador						
Sed	150	400	750	1550	3050	4300
HdTp	150	450	800	1800	3300	4800
990H	200	500	850	1900	3500	5000
Sta Wag	150	350	750	1350	2800	4000
1965						
American						
220 Sed	150	300	700	1250	2600	3700
2 dr 220	150	300	700	1250	2650	3800
220 Sta Wag	150	300	700	1250	2650	3800
330 Sed	150	300	700	1250	2650	3800
2 dr 330	150	350	750	1350	2800	4000
330 Sta Wag	150	350	750	1450	2900	4100
440 Sed	150	350	750	1350	2800	4000
440 HdTp	200	500	850	1900	3500	5000
440-H HdTp	200	550	900	2000	3600	5200
Conv	200	600	950	2200	3900	5600
Classic						
550 Sed	125	250	700	1150	2500	3600
2 dr 550	150	300	700	1250	2600	3700
550 Sta Wag	150	300	700	1250	2600	3700
660 Sed	150	300	750	1350	2700	3900
2 dr 660	150	350	750	1350	2800	4000
660 Sta Wag	150	350	750	1450	2900	4100
770 Sed	150	300	750	1350	2700	3900
770 HdTp	150	350	750	1450	3000	4200
770-H HdTp	200	550	900	2100	3700	5300
770 Conv	200	600	1000	2200	4000	5700
770 Sta Wag	150	350	750	1350	2800	4000
NOTE: Add 5 percent for V-8 models.						
Marlin						
FstBk	200	600	950	2150	3850	5500
Ambassador						
880 Sed	150	350	750	1350	2800	4000
2 dr 880	150	350	750	1450	2900	4100
880 Sta Wag	150	350	750	1450	3000	4200
990 Sed	150	350	750	1450	2900	4100
990 HdTp	150	400	750	1550	3050	4300
990-H HdTp	200	500	850	1900	3500	5000
Conv	200	600	950	2150	3850	5500
Sta Wag	150	350	750	1350	2800	4000
Marlin, V-8						
FstBk	200	550	900	2000	3600	5200
1966						
American						
220 Sed	125	250	700	1150	2450	3500
220 2 dr Sed	125	250	700	1150	2500	3600
220 Wag	150	300	700	1250	2600	3700
440 Sed	150	300	700	1250	2650	3800
440 2 dr Sed	150	300	750	1350	2700	3900
440 Conv	150	450	800	1800	3300	4800
440 Wag	150	300	700	1250	2600	3700
440 HdTp	150	350	750	1350	2800	4000
Rogue	150	400	750	1650	3150	4500
Classic						
550 Sed	125	250	700	1150	2500	3600
550 2 dr Sed	125	250	700	1150	2500	3600
550 Sta Wag	150	300	700	1250	2600	3700
770 Sed	150	300	700	1250	2650	3800
770 HdTp	150	350	750	1450	3000	4200
770 Conv	200	600	950	2150	3850	5500
770 Sta Wag	150	300	700	1250	2600	3700
Rebel						
2 dr HdTp	200	500	850	1900	3500	5000
Marlin						
FsBk Cpe	200	600	950	2150	3850	5500
Ambassador						
880 Sed	150	300	750	1350	2700	3900
880 2 dr Sed	150	350	750	1350	2800	4000
880 Sta Wag	150	350	750	1450	3000	4200
990 Sed	150	350	750	1450	2900	4100
990 HdTp	150	400	750	1650	3150	4500
990 Conv	200	650	1050	2250	4200	6000
990 Sta Wag	125	250	700	1150	2450	3500
DPL (Diplomat)						
DPL HdTp	200	500	850	1900	3500	5000
1967						
American 220						
Sed	125	250	700	1150	2450	3500
2 dr Sed	125	250	700	1150	2450	3500
Sta Wag	125	250	700	1150	2450	3500

	6	5	4	3	2	1
American 440						
Sed	125	250	700	1150	2500	3600
2 dr Sed	125	250	700	1150	2500	3600
HdTp	150	350	750	1350	2800	4000
Sta Wag	125	250	700	1150	2450	3500
American Rogue						
HdTp	200	600	950	2200	3900	5600
Conv	350	700	1150	2300	4550	6500
Rebel 550						
Sed	125	250	700	1150	2450	3500
2 dr Sed	125	250	700	1150	2450	3500
Sta Wag	125	250	700	1150	2450	3500
Rebel 770						
Sed	125	250	700	1150	2500	3600
HdTp	150	350	750	1350	2800	4000
Sta Wag	125	250	700	1150	2450	3500
Rebel SST						
HdTp	150	350	750	1450	3000	4200
Conv	200	650	1050	2250	4200	6000
Rambler Marlin						
FsBk Cpe	200	600	950	2150	3850	5500
Ambassador 880						
Sed	125	250	700	1150	2500	3600
2 dr Sed	125	250	700	1150	2500	3600
Sta Wag	150	300	700	1250	2600	3700
Ambassador 990						
Sed	150	350	750	1350	2800	4000
HdTp	150	450	800	1800	3300	4800
Sta Wag	150	350	750	1450	2900	4100
Ambassador DPL						
HdTp	200	500	850	1950	3600	5100
Conv	350	700	1150	2300	4550	6500
1968						
American 220						
Sed	150	300	700	1250	2600	3700
2 dr Sed	150	300	700	1250	2600	3700
American 440						
Sed	150	300	700	1250	2650	3800
Sta Wag	150	300	700	1250	2600	3700
Rogue						
HdTp	200	650	1050	2250	4200	6000
Rebel 550						
Sed	150	300	700	1250	2600	3700
Conv	150	450	800	1750	3250	4700
Sta Wag	125	250	700	1150	2450	3500
HdTp	150	350	750	1450	3000	4200
Rebel 770						
Sed	150	300	700	1250	2600	3700
Sta Wag	125	250	700	1150	2500	3600
HdTp	150	400	750	1600	3100	4400
Rebel SST						
Conv	200	650	1050	2250	4200	6000
HdTp	150	450	750	1700	3200	4600
Ambassador						
Sed	150	300	700	1250	2650	3800
HdTp	150	400	750	1650	3150	4500
Ambassador DPL						
Sed	150	350	750	1350	2800	4000
HdTp	150	450	800	1750	3250	4700
Sta Wag	150	350	750	1350	2800	4000
Ambassador SST						
Sed	150	350	750	1350	2800	4000
HdTp	200	500	850	1900	3500	5000
Javelin						
FsBk	350	750	1200	2350	4900	7000
Javelin SST						
FsBk	350	900	1550	3050	5900	8500
NOTE: Add 20 percent for GO pkg. Add 30 percent for Big Bad pkg.						
AMX						
FsBk	550	1700	2800	5600	9800	14,000
NOTE: Add 25 percent for Craig Breedlove Edit.						
1969						
Rambler						
Sed	125	250	700	1150	2500	3600
2 dr Sed	125	250	700	1150	2500	3600
Rambler 440						
Sed	150	300	700	1250	2600	3700
2 dr Sed	150	300	700	1250	2600	3700
Rambler Rogue						
HdTp	200	650	1050	2250	4200	6000
Rambler Hurst S/C						
HdTp	500	1550	2600	5200	9100	13,000
Rebel						
Sed	125	250	700	1150	2450	3500
HdTp	150	350	750	1350	2800	4000
Sta Wag	125	250	700	1150	2500	3600
Rebel SST						
Sed	150	300	700	1250	2600	3700
HdTp	150	350	750	1450	3000	4200
Sta Wag	150	300	700	1250	2600	3700
AMX						
FsBk Cpe	550	1700	2800	5600	9800	14,000
NOTE: Add 25 percent for Big Bad Pkg.						
Javelin						
FsBk Cpe	350	750	1200	2350	4900	7000
Javelin SST						
FsBk Cpe	350	900	1550	3050	5900	8500
NOTE: Add 20 percent for GO Pkg. Add 30 percent for Big Bad Pkg.						
Ambassador						
Sed	150	300	700	1250	2650	3800
Ambassador DPL						
Sed	150	350	750	1350	2800	4000
Sta Wag	150	350	750	1350	2800	4000
HdTp	150	350	750	1450	3000	4200
Ambassador SST						
Sed	150	300	700	1250	2650	3800
HdTp	150	400	750	1550	3050	4300
1970						
Hornet						
Sed	125	250	700	1150	2450	3500
2 dr Sed	125	250	700	1150	2450	3500
Hornet SST						
Sed	125	250	700	1150	2500	3600
2 dr Sed	125	250	700	1150	2500	3600

AMC (continued)

	6	5	4	3	2	1
Rebel						
Sed	150	300	700	1250	2600	3700
HdTp	150	400	750	1650	3150	4500
Sta Wag	150	350	750	1450	2900	4100
Rebel SST						
Sed	150	300	700	1250	2650	3800
HdTp	200	650	1050	2250	4200	6000
Sta Wag	150	300	700	1250	2600	3700
Rebel 'Machine'						
HdTp	450	1500	2500	5000	8800	12,500
AMX						
FsBk Cpe	550	1700	2800	5600	9800	14,000
Gremlin						
2 dr Comm	150	300	700	1250	2650	3800
2 dr Sed	150	300	750	1350	2700	3900
Javelin						
FsBk Cpe	350	750	1300	2450	5250	7500
Javelin SST						
FsBk Cpe	450	1000	1600	3300	6250	8900

NOTE: Add 20 percent for GO pkg.
       Add 30 percent for Big Bad pkg.

	6	5	4	3	2	1
'Trans Am'						
FsBk Cpe	400	1200	2000	3950	7000	10,000
'Mark Donahue'						
FsBk Cpe	450	1100	1700	3650	6650	9500
Ambassador						
Sed	150	300	700	1250	2650	3800
Ambassador DPL						
Sed	150	300	750	1350	2700	3900
HdTp	150	350	750	1350	2800	4000
Sta Wag	150	300	700	1250	2650	3800
Ambassador SST						
Sed	150	350	750	1350	2800	4000
HdTp	150	350	750	1450	2900	4100
Sta Wag	150	300	750	1350	2700	3900

1971

	6	5	4	3	2	1
Gremlin						
2 dr Sed	125	250	700	1150	2450	3500
Sed	125	250	700	1150	2450	3500
Hornet						
2 dr Sed	125	250	700	1150	2500	3600
Sed	125	250	700	1150	2500	3600
Hornet SST						
2 dr Sed	125	250	700	1150	2450	3500
Sed	125	250	700	1150	2450	3500
Hornet SC/360						
HdTp	350	800	1450	2750	5600	8000
Javelin						
HdTp	150	400	750	1650	3150	4500
SST HdTp	200	600	950	2150	3850	5500

NOTE: Add 10 percent for 401 V-8.

	6	5	4	3	2	1
Javelin AMX						
HdTp	350	750	1300	2450	5250	7500

NOTE: Add 15 percent for GO Pkg.

	6	5	4	3	2	1
Matador						
Sed	125	250	700	1150	2450	3500
HdTp	150	300	700	1250	2600	3700
Sta Wag	125	250	700	1150	2500	3600
Ambassador DPL						
Sed	125	250	700	1150	2500	3600
Ambassador SST						
Sed	150	300	700	1250	2600	3700
HdTp	150	300	750	1350	2700	3900
Sta Wag	150	300	700	1250	2650	3800

NOTE: Add 10 percent to Ambassador SST for Broughams.

1972

	6	5	4	3	2	1
Hornet SST						
2 dr Sed	125	250	700	1150	2450	3500
Sed	125	250	700	1150	2500	3600
Sta Wag	150	300	700	1250	2600	3700
Gucci	150	400	750	1650	3150	4500
DeL Wag	150	300	700	1250	2650	3800
'X' Wag	150	300	700	1250	2600	3700
Matador						
Sed	150	300	700	1250	2600	3700
HdTp	150	300	750	1350	2700	3900
Sta Wag	150	300	700	1250	2650	3800
Gremlin						
2 dr Sed	125	250	700	1150	2500	3600
'X' Sed	150	400	750	1650	3150	4500
Javelin						
SST	150	400	750	1650	3150	4500
AMX	200	650	1050	2250	4200	6000
Go '360'	350	750	1200	2350	4900	7000
Go '401'	350	800	1350	2700	5500	7900
Cardin	350	725	1200	2350	4800	6800

NOTE: Add 20 percent for 401 V-8.
      Add 25 percent for 401 Police Special V-8.
      Add 30 percent for GO Pkg.

	6	5	4	3	2	1
Ambassador SST						
Sed	150	300	700	1250	2600	3700
HdTp	150	300	750	1350	2700	3900
Sta Wag	150	300	700	1250	2650	3800
Ambassador Brougham						

NOTE: Add 10 percent to SST prices for Brougham.

	6	5	4	3	2	1
Gremlin V8						
2 dr	150	350	750	1450	2900	4100
Hornet V8						
2 dr	150	300	750	1350	2700	3900
4 dr	150	300	700	1250	2650	3800
2 dr Hatchback	150	350	750	1350	2800	4000
Sta Wag	150	300	750	1350	2700	3900
AMX V8						
2 dr HdTp	350	850	1500	2900	5700	8200

NOTE: Add 15 percent for GO Pkg.

	6	5	4	3	2	1
Matador V8						
4 dr Sed	150	300	700	1250	2600	3700
2 dr HdTp	150	300	700	1250	2650	3800
Sta Wag	150	300	700	1250	2600	3700
Ambassador Brgm V8						
4 dr Sed	150	300	700	1250	2650	3800
2 dr HdTp	125	200	600	1100	2300	3300
Sta Wag	150	300	700	1250	2650	3800

1973

	6	5	4	3	2	1
Gremlin V8						
2 dr	150	400	750	1650	3150	4500
Hornet V8						
2 dr	150	300	750	1350	2700	3900
4 dr	150	300	700	1250	2650	3800
2 dr Hatchback	150	350	750	1350	2800	4000
Sta Wag	150	300	750	1350	2700	3900
Javelin V8						
2 dr HdTp	200	500	850	1900	3500	5000
AMX V8						
2 dr HdTp	350	800	1450	2750	5600	8000
Matador V8						
4 dr Sed	150	300	700	1250	2600	3700
2 dr HdTp	150	300	700	1250	2650	3800
Sta Wag	150	300	700	1250	2600	3700
Ambassador Brgm V8						
4 dr Sed	150	300	700	1250	2650	3800
2 dr HdTp	150	300	750	1350	2700	3900
Sta Wag	150	300	700	1250	2650	3800

1974

	6	5	4	3	2	1
Gremlin V8						
2 dr Sed	150	400	750	1650	3150	4500
Hornet						
Sed	125	250	700	1150	2400	3400
2 dr Sed	125	250	700	1150	2450	3500
Hatch	125	250	700	1150	2500	3600
Sta Wag	125	250	700	1150	2450	3500
Javelin						
FsBk	150	350	750	1450	3000	4200
Javelin AMX						
FsBk	350	700	1150	2300	4550	6500
Matador						
Sed	125	200	600	1100	2250	3200
2 dr Sed	125	250	700	1150	2500	3600
Sta Wag	125	200	600	1100	2300	3300
Matador Brougham						
Cpe	150	300	700	1250	2600	3700
Matador 'X'						
Cpe	150	300	700	1250	2650	3800
Ambassador Brougham						
Sed	125	200	600	1100	2300	3300
Sta Wag	125	250	700	1150	2400	3400

NOTE: Add 10 percent for Oleg Cassini coupe.
      Add 12 percent for 'Go-Package'

1975

	6	5	4	3	2	1
Gremlin						
2 dr Sed	150	300	700	1250	2650	3800
Hornet						
Sed	125	250	700	1150	2450	3500
2 dr Sed	125	250	700	1150	2400	3400
Hatch	125	250	700	1150	2450	3500
Sta Wag	125	250	700	1150	2450	3500
Pacer						
2 dr Sed	150	300	750	1350	2700	3900
Matador						
Sed	125	250	700	1150	2400	3400
Cpe	125	250	700	1150	2500	3600
Sta Wag	125	250	700	1150	2450	3500

1976

	6	5	4	3	2	1
Gremlin, V-8						
2 dr Sed	125	250	700	1150	2450	3500
Cus 2 dr Sed	150	300	700	1250	2650	3800
Hornet, V-8						
4 dr Sed	125	200	600	1100	2200	3100
2 dr Sed	100	175	525	1050	2100	3000
2 dr Hatch	125	200	600	1100	2250	3200
4 dr Sptabt	125	200	600	1100	2300	3300
Pacer, 6-cyl.						
2 dr Sed	125	250	700	1150	2450	3500
Matador, V-8						
4 dr Sed	100	175	525	1050	2100	3000
Cpe	125	200	600	1100	2250	3200
Sta Wag	125	200	600	1100	2200	3100

NOTE: Deduct 5 percent for 6 cylinder.

BUICK

1946

	6	5	4	3	2	1
Special Series 40, 8-cyl.						
4 dr Sed	350	750	1350	2600	5400	7700
2 dr S'net	350	750	1300	2500	5300	7600
Super Series 50, 8-cyl.						
Conv	950	3000	5000	10,000	17,500	25,000
2 dr S'net	400	1200	2000	4000	7100	10,100
4 dr Sed	400	1200	2050	4100	7100	10,200
Sta Wag	850	2750	4600	9200	16,100	23,000
Roadmaster Series 70, 8-cyl.						
Conv	1100	3500	5800	11,600	20,300	29,000
2 dr S'net	450	1450	2400	4800	8400	12,000
4 dr Sed	450	1500	2500	5000	8800	12,500

1947

	6	5	4	3	2	1
Special Series 40, 8-cyl.						
2 dr S'net	400	1200	2000	4000	7100	10,100
4 dr Sed	400	1200	2050	4100	7100	10,200
Super Series 50, 8-cyl.						
Conv	1000	3100	5200	10,400	18,200	26,000
2 dr S'net	400	1300	2150	4300	7500	10,700
4 dr Sed	400	1300	2150	4300	7500	10,700
Sta Wag	850	2750	4600	9200	16,100	23,000
Roadmaster Series 70, 8-cyl.						
Conv	1100	3500	5800	11,600	20,300	29,000
2 dr S'net	450	1450	2400	4800	8400	12,000
4 dr Sed	450	1500	2500	5000	8800	12,500
Sta Wag	950	3000	5000	10,000	17,500	25,000

1948

	6	5	4	3	2	1
Special Series 40, 8-cyl.						
2 dr S'net	400	1200	2000	3950	7000	10,000
4 dr Sed	400	1200	2000	4100	7100	10,100
Super Series 50, 8-cyl.						
Conv	1000	3100	5200	10,400	18,200	26,000
2 dr S'net	400	1300	2200	4400	7700	11,000
4 dr Sed	400	1250	2100	4200	7400	10,500
Sta Wag	850	2650	4400	8800	15,400	22,000

	6	5	4	3	2	1
Roadmaster Series 70, 8-cyl.						
Conv	1150	3600	6000	12,000	21,000	30,000
2 dr S'net	450	1450	2400	4800	8400	12,000
4 dr Sed	500	1550	2600	5200	9100	13,000
Sta Wag	1050	3350	5600	11,200	19,600	28,000
1949						
Special Series 40, 8-cyl.						
2 dr S'net	400	1200	2000	4000	7100	10,100
4 dr Sed	400	1200	2050	4100	7100	10,200
Super Series 50, 8-cyl.						
Conv	1000	3250	5400	10,800	18,900	27,000
2 dr S'net	450	1450	2400	4800	8400	12,000
4 dr Sed	450	1450	2400	4800	8400	12,000
Sta Wag	800	2500	4200	8400	14,700	21,000
Roadmaster Series 70, 8-cyl.						
Conv	1300	4100	6800	13,600	23,800	34,000
2 dr Riv HdTp	850	2750	4600	9200	16,100	23,000
2 dr S'net	700	2150	3600	7200	12,600	18,000
4 dr Sed	700	2150	3600	7200	12,600	18,000
Sta Wag	1100	3500	5800	11,600	20,300	29,000

NOTE: Add 10 percent for sweap spear side trim on late 1949 Roadmaster models.

	6	5	4	3	2	1
1950						
Special Series 40, 8-cyl., 121 1/2" wb						
Bus Cpe	350	700	1150	2300	4550	6500
2 dr S'net	350	750	1200	2350	4900	7000
4 dr S'net	350	750	1250	2400	5050	7200
4 dr Tr Sed	350	750	1200	2350	4900	7000
Special DeLuxe Series 40, 8-cyl., 121 1/2" wb						
2 dr S'net	350	750	1250	2350	5000	7100
4 dr S'net	350	750	1300	2400	5200	7400
4 dr Tr Sed	350	750	1250	2400	5050	7200
Super Series 50, 8-cyl.						
Conv	900	2900	4800	9600	16,800	24,000
2 dr Riv HdTp	500	1550	2600	5200	9100	13,000
2 dr S'net	350	750	1300	2400	5200	7400
4 dr Sed	350	750	1250	2400	5100	7300
Sta Wag	950	3000	5000	10,000	17,500	25,000
Roadmaster Series 70, 8-cyl.						
Conv	1000	3250	5400	10,800	18,900	27,000
2 dr Riv HdTp	650	2050	3400	6800	11,900	17,000
2 dr S'net	500	1550	2600	5200	9100	13,000
4 dr Sed 71	350	900	1550	3050	5900	8500
4 dr Sed 72	450	1000	1650	3350	6300	9000
Sta Wag	1000	3250	5400	10,800	18,900	27,000
4 dr Riviera Sed DeLuxe	400	1200	2000	3950	7000	10,000
1951						
Special Series 40, 8-cyl., 121 1/2" wb						
Bus Cpe	350	700	1150	2300	4550	6500
Spt Cpe	350	750	1200	2350	4900	7000
2 dr Sed	200	650	1050	2250	4200	6000
4 dr Sed	200	675	1050	2250	4350	6200
Special DeLuxe Series 40, 8-cyl., 121 1/2" wb						
2 dr Riv HdTp	450	1500	2500	5000	8800	12,500
Conv	750	2400	4000	8000	14,000	20,000
2 dr Sed	200	675	1050	2250	4350	6200
4 dr Sed	350	700	1100	2300	4500	6400
Super Series 50, 8-cyl.						
Conv	900	2900	4800	9600	16,800	24,000
2 dr HdTp	500	1600	2700	5400	9500	13,500
2 dr S'net	400	1200	2000	3950	7000	10,000
4 dr Sed	350	900	1550	3050	5900	8500
Sta Wag	850	2650	4400	8800	15,400	22,000
Roadmaster Series 70, 8-cyl.						
Conv	1000	3250	5400	10,800	18,900	27,000
2 dr HdTp	650	2050	3400	6800	11,900	17,000
4 dr Sed	400	1200	2000	3950	7000	10,000
Sta Wag	950	3000	5000	10,000	17,500	25,000
1952						
Special Series 40, 8-cyl., 121 1/2" wb						
4 dr Sed	200	675	1050	2250	4350	6200
Spt Cpe	350	750	1200	2350	4900	7000
Special DeLuxe Series 40, 8-cyl., 121 1/2" wb						
4 dr Sed	200	675	1100	2250	4400	6300
2 dr Sed	200	675	1050	2250	4350	6200
2 dr Riv HdTp	500	1500	2550	5100	8900	12,700
Conv	700	2300	3800	7600	13,300	19,000
Super Series 50, 8-cyl.						
Conv	800	2500	4200	8400	14,700	21,000
2 dr Riv HdTp	500	1650	2750	5500	9600	13,700
Sta Wag	750	2400	4000	8000	14,000	20,000
4 dr Sed	350	800	1450	2750	5600	8000
Roadmaster Series 70, 8-cyl.						
Conv	900	2900	4800	9600	16,800	24,000
2 dr Riv HdTp	650	2050	3400	6800	11,900	17,000
Sta Wag	950	3000	5000	10,000	17,500	25,000
4 dr Riv Sed	400	1300	2200	4400	7700	11,000
1953						
Special Series 40, 8-cyl.						
4 dr Sed	200	650	1050	2250	4200	6000
2 dr Sed	200	650	1000	2200	4150	5900
2 dr Riv HdTp	500	1550	2600	5200	9000	12,900
Conv	850	2650	4400	8800	15,400	22,000
Super Series 50, V-8						
2 dr Riv HdTp	500	1600	2650	5300	9200	13,200
Conv	900	2900	4800	9600	16,800	24,000
Sta Wag	950	3000	5000	10,000	17,500	25,000
4 dr Riv Sed	350	800	1450	2750	5600	8000
Roadmaster Series 70, V-8						
2 dr Riv HdTp	700	2300	3800	7600	13,300	19,000
Skylark	1900	6000	10,000	20,000	35,000	50,000
Conv	1000	3250	5400	10,800	18,900	27,000
DeL Sta Wag	1000	3250	5400	10,800	18,900	27,000
4 dr Riv Sed	400	1200	2000	3950	7000	10,000
1954						
Special Series 40, V-8						
4 dr Sed	350	700	1150	2300	4550	6500
2 dr Sed	350	700	1100	2300	4500	6400
2 dr Riv HdTp	550	1700	2800	5600	9800	14,000
Conv	950	3000	5000	10,000	17,500	25,000
Sta Wag	400	1200	2000	3950	7000	10,000
Century Series 60, V-8						
4 dr DeL	350	725	1150	2300	4700	6700
2 dr Riv HdTp	550	1800	3000	6000	10,500	15,000
Conv	1250	3950	6600	13,200	23,100	33,000
Sta Wag	400	1300	2200	4400	7700	11,000

	6	5	4	3	2	1
Super Series 50, V-8						
4 dr Sed	350	800	1450	2750	5600	8000
2 dr Riv HdTp	600	2000	3300	6600	11,600	16,500
Conv	950	3000	5000	10,000	17,500	25,000
Roadmaster Series 70, V-8						
4 dr Sed	400	1200	2000	3950	7000	10,000
2 dr Riv HdTp	750	2350	3900	7800	13,700	19,500
Conv	1200	3850	6400	12,800	22,400	32,000
Skylark Series, V-8						
Spt Conv	1800	5750	9600	19,200	33,600	48,000
1955						
Special Series 40, V-8						
4 dr Sed	350	700	1100	2300	4500	6400
4 dr Riv HdTp	400	1250	2100	4200	7400	10,500
2 dr Sed	350	700	1150	2300	4550	6500
2 dr Riv HdTp	650	2050	3400	6800	11,900	17,000
Conv	1100	3500	5800	11,600	20,300	29,000
Sta Wag	400	1200	2050	4100	7100	10,200
Century Series 60, V-8						
4 dr Sed	350	700	1150	2300	4550	6500
4 dr Riv HdTp	450	1400	2300	4600	8100	11,500
2 dr Riv HdTp	750	2400	4000	8000	14,000	20,000
Conv	1350	4300	7200	14,400	25,200	36,000
Sta Wag	400	1250	2100	4200	7300	10,400
Super Series 50, V-8						
4 dr Sed	350	800	1450	2750	5600	8000
2 dr Riv HdTp	700	2300	3800	7600	13,300	19,000
Conv	1250	3950	6600	13,200	23,100	33,000
Roadmaster Series 70, V-8						
4 dr Sed	400	1200	2050	4100	7100	10,200
2 dr Riv HdTp	750	2450	4100	8200	14,400	20,500
Conv	1300	4200	7000	14,000	24,500	35,000
1956						
Special Series 40, V-8						
4 dr Sed	350	750	1300	2450	5250	7500
4 dr Riv HdTp	450	1450	2400	4800	8400	12,000
2 dr Sed	350	700	1100	2300	4500	6400
2 dr Riv HdTp	650	2050	3400	6800	11,900	17,000
Conv	1200	3850	6400	12,800	22,400	32,000
Sta Wag	400	1200	2000	3950	7000	10,000
Century Series 60, V-8						
4 dr Riv HdTp	500	1550	2600	5200	9100	13,000
4 dr Sed	350	800	1450	2750	5600	8000
2 dr Riv HdTp	750	2400	4000	8000	14,000	20,000
Conv	1300	4100	6800	13,600	23,800	34,000
Sta Wag	400	1250	2100	4200	7300	10,400
Super Series 50						
4 dr Sed	350	800	1450	2750	5600	8000
2 dr Riv HdTp	700	2300	3800	7600	13,300	19,000
Conv	1200	3850	6400	12,800	22,400	32,000
4 dr Riv HdTp	550	1800	3000	6000	10,500	15,000
Roadmaster Series 70, V-8						
4 dr Sed	400	1200	2000	4000	7100	10,100
4 dr Riv HdTp	550	1800	3000	6000	10,500	15,000
2 dr Riv HdTp	800	2500	4200	8400	14,700	21,000
Conv	1350	4300	7200	14.400	25.200	36.000
1957						
Special Series 40, V-8						
4 dr Sed	350	700	1150	2300	4550	6500
4 dr Riv HdTp	400	1300	2200	4400	7700	11,000
2 dr Sed	350	700	1100	2300	4500	6400
2 dr Riv HdTp	700	2300	3800	7600	13,300	19,000
Conv	1150	3600	6000	12,000	21,000	30,000
4 dr Sta Wag	450	1450	2400	4800	8400	12,000
4 dr HdTp Wag	700	2150	3600	7200	12,600	18,000
Century Series 60, V-8						
4 dr Sed	350	750	1200	2350	4900	7000
4 dr Riv HdTp	450	1450	2400	4800	8400	12,000
2 dr Riv HdTp	850	2650	4400	8800	15,400	22,000
Conv	1300	4100	6800	13,600	23,800	34,000
4 dr HdTp Wag	750	2400	4000	8000	14,000	20,000
Super Series 50, V-8						
4 dr Riv HdTp	500	1550	2600	5200	9100	13,000
2 dr Riv HdTp	850	2650	4400	8800	15,400	22,000
Conv	1250	3950	6600	13,200	23,100	33,000
Roadmaster Series 70, V-8						
4 dr Riv HdTp	550	1700	2800	5600	9800	14,000
2 dr Riv HdTp	900	2900	4800	9600	16,800	24,000
Conv	1400	4450	7400	14,800	25,900	37,000

NOTE: Add 5 percent for 75 Series.

	6	5	4	3	2	1
1958						
Special Series 40, V-8						
4 dr Sed	200	650	1050	2250	4200	6000
4 dr Riv HdTp	350	900	1550	3050	5900	8500
2 dr Sed	200	650	1050	2250	4200	6000
2 dr Riv HdTp	600	1900	3200	6400	11,200	16,000
Conv	900	2900	4800	9600	16,800	24,000
Sta Wag	350	700	1100	2300	4500	6400
4 dr HdTp Wag	550	1700	2800	5600	9800	14,000
Century Series 60, V-8						
4 dr Sed	200	675	1050	2250	4350	6200
4 dr Riv HdTp	450	1000	1650	3350	6300	9000
2 dr Riv HdTp	650	2050	3400	6800	11,900	17,000
Conv	1000	3100	5200	10,400	18,200	26,000
4 dr HdTp Wag	600	1900	3200	6400	11,200	16,000
Super Series 50, V-8						
4 dr Riv HdTp	350	950	1600	3200	6050	8700
2 dr Riv HdTp	600	1900	3200	6400	11,200	16,000
Roadmaster Series 75, V-8						
4 dr Riv HdTp	450	1100	1700	3650	6650	9500
2 dr Riv HdTp	700	2150	3600	7200	12,600	18,000
Conv	1150	3600	6000	12,000	21,000	30,000
Limited Series 700, V-8						
4 dr Riv HdTp	550	1800	3000	6000	10,500	15,000
2 dr Riv HdTp	750	2400	4000	8000	14,000	20,000
Conv	1550	4900	8200	16,400	28,700	41,000
1959						
LeSabre Series 4400, V-8						
4 dr Sed	200	650	1000	2200	4150	5900
4 dr HdTp	350	700	1150	2300	4600	6600
2 dr Sed	200	650	1050	2250	4200	6000
2 dr HdTp	350	750	1300	2450	5250	7500
Conv	750	2400	4000	8000	14,000	20,000
Sta Wag	200	675	1050	2250	4350	6200

	6	5	4	3	2	1
Invicta Series 4600, V-8						
4 dr Sed	200	675	1050	2250	4300	6100
4 dr HdTp	350	725	1200	2350	4800	6800
2 dr HdTp	350	800	1450	2750	5600	8000
Conv	900	2900	4800	9600	16,800	24,000
Sta Wag	350	700	1150	2300	4550	6500
Electra Series 4700, V-8						
4 dr Sed	350	750	1300	2450	5250	7500
4 dr HdTp	350	900	1550	3050	5900	8500
2 dr HdTp	400	1300	2200	4400	7700	11,000
Electra 225 Series 4800, V-8						
4 dr Riv HdTp 6 window	450	1050	1650	3500	6400	9200
4 dr HdTp 4 window	450	1100	1700	3650	6650	9500
Conv	900	2900	4800	9600	16,800	24,000

1960

	6	5	4	3	2	1
LeSabre Series 4400, V-8						
4 dr Sed	200	650	1050	2250	4200	6000
4 dr HdTp	350	725	1150	2300	4700	6700
2 dr Sed	200	650	1050	2250	4200	6000
2 dr HdTp	350	750	1300	2500	5300	7600
Conv	850	2650	4400	8800	15,400	22,000
Sta Wag	200	650	1050	2250	4200	6000
Invicta Series 4600, V-8						
4 dr Sed	200	675	1050	2250	4300	6100
4 dr HdTp	350	725	1200	2350	4850	6900
2 dr HdTp	450	1000	1650	3400	6350	9100
Conv	1000	3100	5200	10,400	18,200	26,000
Sta Wag	350	700	1150	2300	4550	6500
Electra Series 4700, V-8						
4 dr Riv HdTp 6 window	350	900	1550	3000	5850	8400
4 dr HdTp 4 window	350	950	1600	3200	6050	8700
2 dr HdTp	450	1400	2300	4600	8100	11,500
Electra 225 Series 4800, V-8						
4 dr Riv HdTp 6 window	450	1050	1700	3550	6500	9300
4 dr HdTp 4 window	450	1100	1800	3700	6700	9600
Conv	1000	3100	5200	10,400	18,200	26,000

NOTE: Add 5 percent for bucket seat option.

1961

	6	5	4	3	2	1
Special Series 4000, V-8, 112" wb						
4 dr Sed	200	550	900	2100	3700	5300
Cpe	200	675	1100	2250	4400	6300
Sta Wag	200	550	900	2100	3700	5300
Special DeLuxe Series 4100, V-8, 112" wb						
4 dr Sed	200	550	900	2150	3800	5400
Skylark Cpe	350	700	1100	2300	4500	6400
Sta Wag	200	550	900	2150	3800	5400

NOTE: Deduct 5 percent for V-6.

	6	5	4	3	2	1
LeSabre Series 4400, V-8						
4 dr Sed	200	650	1050	2250	4200	6000
4 dr HdTp	350	750	1200	2350	4900	7000
2 dr Sed	200	675	1050	2250	4300	6100
2 dr HdTp	350	800	1450	2750	5600	8000
Conv	650	2050	3400	6800	11,900	17,000
Sta Wag	200	650	1050	2250	4200	6000
Invicta Series 4600, V-8						
4 dr HdTp	350	750	1300	2450	5250	7500
2 dr HdTp	350	900	1550	3050	5900	8500
Conv	700	2150	3600	7200	12,600	18,000
Electra Series 4700, V-8						
4 dr Sed	350	700	1150	2300	4600	6600
4 dr HdTp	350	800	1450	2750	5600	8000
2 dr HdTp	450	1000	1650	3350	6300	9000
Electra 225 Series 4800, V-8						
4 dr Riv HdTp 6 window	350	800	1450	2750	5600	8000
4 dr Riv HdTp 4 window	350	900	1550	3050	5900	8500
Conv	750	2400	4000	8000	14,000	20,000

1962

	6	5	4	3	2	1
Special Series 4000, V-6, 112.1" wb						
4 dr Sed	200	600	950	2200	3900	5600
Cpe	350	700	1100	2300	4500	6400
Conv	450	1450	2400	4800	8400	12,000
Sta Wag	200	600	950	2200	3900	5600
Special DeLuxe Series 4100, V-8, 112.1" wb						
4 dr Sed	200	650	1000	2200	4100	5800
Conv	550	1700	2800	5600	9800	14,000
Sta Wag	200	650	1000	2200	4100	5800
Special Skylark Series 4300, V-8, 112.1" wb						
2 dr HdTp	200	675	1100	2250	4400	6300
Conv	550	1800	3000	6000	10,500	15,000
LeSabre Series 4400, V-8						
4 dr Sed	200	650	1050	2250	4200	6000
4 dr HdTp	350	750	1200	2350	4900	7000
2 dr Sed	200	650	1000	2200	4100	5800
2 dr HdTp	350	800	1450	2750	5600	8000
Invicta Series 4600, V-8						
4 dr HdTp	350	750	1300	2450	5250	7500
2 dr HdTp	400	1200	2000	4000	7100	10,100
Wildcat 2 dr HdTp	400	1250	2100	4200	7400	10,500
Conv	700	2150	3600	7200	12,600	18,000
Sta Wag*	200	650	1050	2250	4200	6000

NOTE: Add 10 percent for bucket seat option where offered.

	6	5	4	3	2	1
Electra 225 Series 4800, V-8						
4 dr Sed	200	650	1050	2250	4200	6000
4 dr Riv HdTp 6 window	350	800	1450	2750	5600	8000
4 dr HdTp 4 window	350	900	1550	3050	5900	8500
2 dr HdTp	450	1100	1700	3650	6650	9500
Conv	750	2400	4000	8000	14,000	20,000

1963

	6	5	4	3	2	1
Special Series 4000, V-6, 112" wb						
4 dr Sed	200	600	950	2200	3900	5600
Cpe	200	600	1000	2200	4000	5700
Conv	400	1200	2000	4000	7100	10,100
Sta Wag	200	600	950	2150	3850	5500
Special DeLuxe Series 4100, V-6, 112" wb						
4 dr Sed	200	600	1000	2200	4000	5700
Sta Wag	200	600	950	2200	3900	5600
Special DeLuxe Series 4100, V-8, 112" wb						
4 dr Sed	200	650	1000	2200	4100	5800
Sta Wag	200	600	1000	2200	4000	5700
Special Skylark Series 4300, V-8, 112" wb						
2 dr HdTp	350	750	1250	2400	5050	7200
Conv	400	1300	2200	4400	7700	11,000
LeSabre Series 4400, V-8						
4 dr Sed	200	600	1000	2200	4000	5700
4 dr HdTp	350	700	1150	2300	4550	6500
2 dr Sed	200	600	950	2150	3850	5500
2 dr HdTp	350	750	1200	2350	4900	7000
Sta Wag	200	650	1050	2250	4200	6000
Conv	550	1800	3000	6000	10,500	15,000
Invicta Series 4600, V-8						
Sta Wag	350	700	1150	2300	4550	6500
Wildcat Series 4600, V-8						
4 dr HdTp	350	750	1300	2450	5250	7500
2 dr HdTp	350	900	1550	3050	5900	8500
Conv	650	2050	3400	6800	11,900	17,000
Electra 225 Series 4800, V-8						
4 dr Sed	200	550	900	2150	3800	5400
4 dr HdTp 6 window	350	750	1200	2350	4900	7000
4 dr HdTp 4 window	350	750	1300	2450	5250	7500
2 dr HdTp	350	800	1450	2750	5600	8000
Conv	700	2150	3600	7200	12,600	18,000
Riviera Series 4700, V-8						
2 dr HdTp	500	1550	2600	5200	9100	13,000

1964

	6	5	4	3	2	1
Special Series 4000, V-6, 115" wb						
4 dr Sed	200	500	850	1850	3350	4900
Cpe	200	500	850	1950	3600	5100
Conv	400	1300	2200	4400	7700	11,000
Sta Wag	200	500	850	1850	3350	4900
Special Deluxe Series 4100, V-6, 115" wb						
4 dr Sed	200	500	850	1900	3500	5000
Cpe	200	550	900	2000	3600	5200
Sta Wag	200	500	850	1950	3600	5100
Special Skylark Series 4300, V-6, 115" wb						
4 dr Sed	200	550	900	2000	3600	5200
2 dr HdTp	200	600	1000	2200	4000	5700
Conv	500	1550	2600	5200	9100	13,000
Special Series 4000, V-8, 115" wb						
4 dr Sed	200	500	850	1900	3500	5000
Cpe	200	550	900	2000	3600	5200
Conv	450	1450	2400	4800	8400	12,000
Sta Wag	200	550	900	2000	3600	5200
Special DeLuxe Series 4100, V-8, 115" wb						
4 dr Sed	200	500	850	1950	3600	5100
Cpe	200	550	900	2150	3800	5400
Sta Wag	200	600	950	2150	3850	5500
Skylark Series 4300, V-8, 115" wb						
4 dr Sed	200	550	900	2100	3700	5300
2 dr HdTp	350	725	1150	2300	4700	6700
Conv	550	1800	3000	6000	10,500	15,000
Skylark Series 4200, V-8, 120" wb						
4 dr Spt Wag	200	550	900	2150	3800	5400
4 dr Cus Spt Wag	200	600	1000	2200	4000	5700
LeSabre Series 4400, V-8						
4 dr Sed	200	550	900	2000	3600	5200
4 dr HdTp	350	700	1150	2300	4550	6500
2 dr HdTp	350	750	1300	2450	5250	7500
Conv	550	1700	2800	5600	9800	14,000
Spt Wag	200	500	850	1950	3600	5100
Wildcat Series 4600, V-8						
4 dr Sed	200	550	900	2100	3700	5300
4 dr HdTp	350	750	1300	2450	5250	7500
2 dr HdTp	400	1200	2000	3950	7000	10,000
Conv	550	1800	3000	6000	10,500	15,000
Electra 225 Series 4800, V-8						
4 dr Sed	200	550	900	2150	3800	5400
4 dr HdTp 6 window	350	700	1150	2300	4550	6500
4 dr HdTp 4 window	350	750	1200	2350	4900	7000
2 dr HdTp	400	1200	2000	4000	7100	10,100
Conv	600	1900	3200	6400	11,200	16,000
Riviera Series 4700, V-8						
2 dr HdTp	550	1700	2800	5600	9800	14,000

1965

	6	5	4	3	2	1
Special, V-6, 115" wb						
4 dr Sed	150	350	750	1450	3000	4200
Cpe	150	350	750	1350	2800	4000
Conv	400	1300	2200	4400	7700	11,000
Sta Wag	150	350	750	1450	2900	4100
Special DeLuxe, V-6, 115" wb						
4 dr Sed	150	400	750	1600	3100	4400
Sta Wag	150	350	750	1450	3000	4200
Skylark, V-6, 115" wb						
4 dr Sed	150	450	800	1750	3250	4700
Cpe	200	500	850	1900	3500	5000
2 dr HdTp	200	650	1050	2250	4200	6000
Conv	500	1550	2600	5200	9100	13,000
Special, V-8, 115" wb						
4 dr Sed	150	400	750	1600	3100	4400
Cpe	150	350	750	1450	2900	4100
Conv	450	1450	2400	4800	8400	12,000
Sta Wag	150	350	750	1450	3000	4200
Special DeLuxe, V-8, 115" wb						
4 dr Sed	150	450	800	1750	3250	4700
Sta Wag	150	400	750	1600	3100	4400
Skylark, V-8, 115" wb						
4 dr Sed	200	500	850	1900	3500	5000
Cpe	200	550	900	2000	3600	5200
2 dr HdTp	350	725	1150	2300	4700	6700
Conv	550	1700	2800	5600	9800	14,000

NOTE: Add 20 percent for Skylark Gran Sport Series (400 CID/325hp V-8). Deduct 5 percent for V-6.

	6	5	4	3	2	1
Sport Wagon, V-8, 120" wb						
2S Sta Wag	150	400	750	1550	3050	4300
3S Sta Wag	150	400	750	1600	3100	4400
Custom Sport Wagon, V-8, 120" wb						
2S Sta Wag	150	400	750	1650	3150	4500
3S Sta Wag	150	450	750	1700	3200	4600
LeSabre, V-8, 123" wb						
4 dr Sed	150	450	750	1700	3200	4600
4 dr HdTp	200	500	850	1900	3500	5000
2 dr HdTp	200	650	1050	2250	4200	6000
LeSabre Custom, V-8, 123" wb						
4 dr Sed	150	450	800	1800	3300	4800
4 dr HdTp	200	600	950	2150	3850	5500
2 dr HdTp	200	675	1100	2250	4400	6300
Conv	450	1450	2400	4800	8400	12,000
Wildcat, V-8, 126" wb						
4 dr Sed	200	500	850	1850	3350	4900
4 dr HdTp	200	600	1000	2200	4000	5700
2 dr HdTp	350	700	1150	2300	4550	6500
Wildcat DeLuxe, V-8, 126" wb						
4 dr Sed	200	500	850	1900	3500	5000
4 dr HdTp	200	650	1050	2250	4200	6000
2 dr HdTp	350	700	1150	2300	4550	6500
Conv	500	1550	2600	5200	9100	13,000

	6	5	4	3	2	1
Wildcat Custom, V-8, 126" wb						
4 dr HdTp	200	675	1050	2250	4350	6200
2 dr HdTp	350	750	1200	2350	4900	7000
Conv	550	1700	2800	5600	9800	14,000
Electra 225, V-8, 126" wb						
4 dr Sed	200	550	900	2100	3700	5300
4 dr HdTp	350	700	1150	2300	4550	6500
2 dr HdTp	350	750	1200	2350	4900	7000
Electra 225 Custom, V-8, 126" wb						
4 dr Sed	200	600	950	2150	3850	5500
4 dr HdTp	350	725	1150	2300	4700	6700
2 dr HdTp	350	750	1250	2400	5100	7300
Conv	550	1700	2800	5600	9800	14,000
Riviera, V-8, 117" wb						
2 dr HdTp	450	1450	2400	4800	8400	12,000
Gran Sport 2 dr HdTp	500	1550	2600	5200	9100	13,000

NOTE: Add 20 percent for 400.

1966

	6	5	4	3	2	1
Special, V-6, 115" wb						
4 dr Sed	150	300	700	1250	2600	3700
Cpe	125	250	700	1150	2500	3600
Conv	450	1450	2400	4800	8400	12,000
Sta Wag	150	300	700	1250	2600	3700
Special DeLuxe, V-6, 115" wb						
4 dr Sed	150	300	700	1250	2650	3800
Cpe	150	300	700	1250	2600	3700
2 dr HdTp	200	500	850	1900	3500	5000
Sta Wag	150	300	700	1250	2650	3800
Skylark, V-6, 115" wb						
4 dr HdTp	150	350	750	1450	2900	4100
Cpe	150	350	750	1350	2800	4000
2 dr HdTp	200	500	850	1900	3500	5000
Conv	500	1550	2600	5200	9100	13,000
Special, V-8, 115" wb						
4 dr Sed	150	350	750	1350	2800	4000
Cpe	150	300	700	1250	2650	3800
Conv	450	1450	2400	4800	8400	12,000
Sta Wag	150	300	750	1350	2700	3900
Special DeLuxe, V-8						
4 dr Sed	150	350	750	1350	2800	4000
Cpe	150	350	750	1450	2900	4100
2 dr HdTp	200	600	950	2150	3850	5500
Sta Wag	150	300	750	1350	2700	3900
Skylark, V-8						
4 dr HdTp	150	400	750	1550	3050	4300
Cpe	150	350	750	1450	3000	4200
2 dr HdTp	200	650	1050	2250	4200	6000
Conv	550	1700	2800	5600	9800	14,000
Skylark Gran Sport, V-8, 115" wb						
Cpe	350	750	1200	2350	4900	7000
2 dr HdTp	450	1000	1650	3350	6300	9000
Conv	550	1800	3000	6000	10,500	15,000
Sport Wagon, V-8, 120" wb						
2S Sta Wag	150	350	750	1450	3000	4200
3S Sta Wag	150	400	750	1550	3050	4300
Custom 2S Sta Wag	150	400	750	1600	3100	4400
Custom 3S Sta Wag	150	400	750	1650	3150	4500
LeSabre, V-8, 123" wb						
4 dr Sed	150	400	750	1550	3050	4300
4 dr HdTp	200	500	850	1900	3500	5000
2 dr HdTp	200	650	1050	2250	4200	6000
LeSabre Custom, V-8, 123" wb						
4 dr Sed	150	400	750	1600	3100	4400
4 dr HdTp	200	550	900	2000	3600	5200
2 dr Hd Tp	200	675	1050	2250	4350	6200
Conv	450	1450	2400	4800	8400	12,000
Wildcat, V-8, 126" wb						
4 dr Sed	150	400	750	1650	3150	4500
4 dr HdTp	200	600	950	2150	3850	5500
2 dr HdTp	350	700	1150	2300	4550	6500
Conv	500	1550	2600	5200	9100	13,000
Wildcat Custom, V-8, 126" wb						
4 dr Sed	150	450	750	1700	3200	4600
4 dr HdTp	200	650	1000	2200	4150	5900
2 dr HdTp	350	725	1200	2350	4850	6900
Conv	550	1700	2800	5600	9800	14,000

NOTE: Add 20 percent for Wildcat Gran Sport Series.

	6	5	4	3	2	1
Electra 225, V-8, 126" wb						
4 dr Sed	200	550	900	2150	3800	5400
4 dr HdTp	200	650	1050	2250	4200	6000
2 dr HdTp	350	750	1200	2350	4900	7000
Electra 225 Custom, V-8						
4 dr Sed	200	600	950	2150	3850	5500
4 dr HdTp	350	700	1150	2300	4550	6500
2 dr HdTp	350	750	1300	2450	5250	7500
Conv	550	1800	3000	6000	10,500	15,000
Riviera, V-8						
GS 2 dr HdTp	400	1200	2000	3950	7000	10,000
2 dr HdTp	350	750	1300	2450	5250	7500

NOTE: Add 20 percent for 400.

1967

	6	5	4	3	2	1
Special, V-6, 115" wb						
4 dr Sed	150	300	750	1350	2700	3900
Cpe	150	300	700	1250	2650	3800
Sta Wag	150	300	700	1250	2600	3700
Special DeLuxe, V-6, 115" wb						
4 dr Sed	150	350	750	1350	2800	4000
2 dr HdTp	200	500	850	1900	3500	5000
Skylark, V-6, 115" wb						
Cpe	150	450	800	1800	3300	4800
Special, V-8, 115" wb						
4 dr Sed	150	350	750	1450	2900	4100
Cpe	150	400	750	1650	3150	4500
Sta Wag	150	300	750	1350	2700	3900
Special DeLuxe, V-8, 115" wb						
4 dr Sed	150	350	750	1450	3000	4200
2 dr HdTp	200	600	950	2150	3850	5500
Sta Wag	150	350	750	1350	2800	4000
Skylark, V-8, 115" wb						
4 dr Sed	150	400	750	1550	3050	4300
4 dr HdTp	150	400	750	1650	3150	4500
Cpe	200	500	850	1900	3500	5000
2 dr HdTp	200	650	1050	2250	4200	6000
Conv	500	1550	2600	5200	9100	13,000
Sport Wagon, V-8, 120" wb						
2S Sta Wag	150	350	750	1450	2900	4100
3S Sta Wag	150	350	750	1450	3000	4200
Gran Sport 340, V-8, 115" wb						
2 dr HdTp	450	1000	1650	3350	6300	9000
Gran Sport 400, V-8, 115" wb						
Cpe	350	750	1200	2350	4900	7000
2 dr HdTp	450	1100	1700	3650	6650	9500
Conv	550	1700	2800	5600	9800	14,000
LeSabre, V-8, 123" wb						
4 dr Sed	150	400	750	1600	3100	4400
4 dr HdTp	150	400	750	1650	3150	4500
2 dr HdTp	150	450	750	1700	3200	4600
LeSabre Custom, V-8, 123" wb						
4 dr Sed	150	400	750	1650	3150	4500
4 dr HdTp	150	450	750	1700	3200	4600
2 dr HdTp	200	600	950	2150	3850	5500
Conv	450	1450	2400	4800	8400	12,000
Wildcat, V-8, 126" wb						
4 dr Sed	150	450	750	1700	3200	4600
4 dr HdTp	150	450	800	1750	3250	4700
2 dr HdTp	350	700	1150	2300	4550	6500
Conv	500	1550	2600	5200	9100	13,000
Wildcat Custom, V-8, 126" wb						
4 dr HdTp	150	450	800	1800	3300	4800
2 dr HdTp	350	750	1200	2350	4900	7000
Conv	550	1700	2800	5600	9800	14,000
Electra 225, V-8, 126" wb						
4 dr Sed	150	450	800	1750	3250	4700
4 dr HdTp	200	500	850	1850	3350	4900
2 dr HdTp	350	750	1200	2350	4900	7000
Electra 225 Custom, V-8, 126" wb						
4 dr Sed	200	500	850	1950	3600	5100
4 dr HdTp	200	550	900	2100	3700	5300
2 dr HdTp	350	750	1300	2450	5250	7500
Conv	550	1800	3000	6000	10,500	15,000
Riviera Series, V-8						
HdTp GS	350	900	1550	3050	5900	8500
HdTp Cpe	350	800	1450	2750	5600	8000

NOTE: Add 20 percent for 400.

1968

	6	5	4	3	2	1
Special DeLuxe, V-6, 116" wb, 2 dr 112" wb						
4 dr Sed	150	300	700	1250	2600	3700
2 dr Sed	125	250	700	1150	2500	3600
Skylark, V-6, 116" wb, 2 dr 112" wb						
4 dr Sed	150	300	700	1250	2650	3800
2 dr HdTp	150	400	750	1650	3150	4500
Special DeLuxe, V-8, 116" wb, 2 dr 112" wb						
4 dr Sed	150	300	700	1250	2650	3800
2 dr Sed	150	300	700	1250	2600	3700
Sta Wag	150	300	700	1250	2650	3800
Skylark, V-8, 116" wb, 2 dr 112" wb						
4 dr Sed	150	300	750	1350	2700	3900
4 dr HdTp	150	350	750	1350	2800	4000
Skylark Custom, V-8, 116" wb, 2 dr 112" wb						
4 dr Sed	150	350	750	1350	2800	4000
4 dr HdTp	150	350	750	1450	2900	4100
2 dr HdTp	200	500	850	1900	3500	5000
Conv	450	1450	2400	4800	8400	12,000
Sport Wagon, V-8, 121" wb						
2S Sta Wag	150	350	750	1450	2900	4100
3S Sta Wag	150	350	750	1450	3000	4200
Gran Sport GS 350, V-8, 112" wb						
2 dr HdTp	450	1100	1700	3650	6650	9500
Gran Sport GS 400, V-8, 112" wb						
2 dr HdTp	400	1200	2000	3950	7000	10,000
Conv	500	1550	2600	5200	9100	13,000
LeSabre, V-8, 123" wb						
4 dr Sed	150	400	750	1550	3050	4300
4 dr HdTp	150	400	750	1650	3150	4500
2 dr HdTp	200	550	900	2150	3800	5400
LeSabre Custom, V-8, 123" wb						
4 dr Sed	150	400	750	1600	3100	4400
4 dr HdTp	150	450	750	1700	3200	4600
2 dr HdTp	200	650	1050	2250	4200	6000
Conv	450	1450	2400	4800	8400	12,000
Wildcat, V-8, 126" wb						
4 dr Sed	150	400	750	1650	3150	4500
4 dr HdTp	150	450	800	1750	3250	4700
2 dr HdTp	350	700	1150	2300	4550	6500
Wildcat Custom, V-8, 126" wb						
4 dr HdTp	200	500	850	1950	3600	5100
2 dr HdTp	350	750	1200	2350	4900	7000
Conv	550	1700	2800	5600	9800	14,000
Electra 225, V-8, 126" wb						
4 dr Sed	200	500	850	1850	3350	4900
4 dr HdTp	200	500	850	1950	3600	5100
2 dr HdTp	350	750	1250	2400	5100	7300
Electra 225 Custom, V-8, 126" wb						
4 dr Sed	200	500	850	1950	3600	5100
4 dr HdTp	200	600	950	2150	3850	5500
2 dr HdTp	350	750	1300	2450	5250	7500
Conv	550	1800	3000	6000	10,500	15,000
Riviera Series, V-8						
HdTp GS	350	900	1550	3050	5900	8500
HdTp Cpe	350	800	1450	2750	5600	8000

Add 20 percent for 400.
Add 15 percent for Skylark GS Calif. Spl.

1969

	6	5	4	3	2	1
Special DeLuxe, V-6, 116" wb, 2 dr 112" wb						
4 dr Sed	150	300	700	1250	2600	3700
2 dr Sed	125	250	700	1150	2500	3600
Skylark, V-6, 116" wb, 2 dr 112" wb						
4 dr Sed	150	300	700	1250	2650	3800
2 dr HdTp	150	350	750	1350	2800	4000
Special DeLuxe, V-8, 116" wb, 2 dr 112" wb						
4 dr Sed	150	300	700	1250	2650	3800
2 dr Sed	150	300	700	1250	2600	3700
Sta Wag	150	300	700	1250	2650	3800
Skylark, V-8, 116" wb, 2 dr 112" wb						
4 dr Sed	150	300	750	1350	2700	3900
2 dr HdTp	200	500	850	1900	3500	5000
Skylark Custom, V-8, 116" wb, 2 dr 112" wb						
4 dr Sed	150	350	750	1350	2800	4000
4 dr HdTp	150	350	750	1450	2900	4100
2 dr HdTp	200	650	1050	2250	4200	6000
Conv	450	1450	2400	4800	8400	12,000
Gran Sport GS 350, V-8, 112" wb						
2 dr Calif GS	400	1200	2000	3950	7000	10,000
2 dr HdTp	400	1300	2200	4400	7700	11,000

	6	5	4	3	2	1
Gran Sport GS 400, V-8, 112" wb						
2 dr HdTp	450	1450	2400	4800	8400	12,000
Conv	550	1800	3000	6000	10,500	15,000
NOTE: Add 15 percent for Stage I option.						
Sport Wagon, V-8, 121" wb						
2S Sta Wag	150	350	750	1450	2900	4100
3S Sta Wag	150	350	750	1450	3000	4200
LeSabre, V-8, 123.2" wb						
4 dr Sed	150	350	750	1450	3000	4200
4 dr HdTp	150	400	750	1550	3050	4300
2 dr HdTp	150	450	800	1800	3300	4800
LeSabre Custom, V-8, 123.2" wb						
4 dr Sed	150	400	750	1550	3050	4300
4 dr HdTp	150	400	750	1600	3100	4400
2 dr HdTp	200	500	850	1900	3500	5000
Conv	450	1450	2400	4800	8400	12,000
Wildcat, V-8, 123.2" wb						
4 dr Sed	150	400	750	1650	3150	4500
4 dr HdTp	150	450	800	1750	3250	4700
2 dr HdTp	200	600	950	2150	3850	5500
Wildcat Custom, V-8, 123.2" wb						
4 dr Sed	200	500	850	1850	3350	4900
2 dr HdTp	200	650	1050	2250	4200	6000
Conv	500	1550	2600	5200	9100	13,000
Electra 225, V-8, 126.2" wb						
4 dr Sed	150	450	750	1700	3200	4600
4 dr HdTp	150	450	800	1750	3250	4700
2 dr HdTp	350	700	1150	2300	4550	6500
Electra 225 Custom, V-8, 126.2" wb						
4 dr Sed	150	450	800	1800	3300	4800
4 dr HdTp	200	500	850	1950	3600	5100
2 dr HdTp	350	750	1200	2350	4900	7000
Conv	550	1800	3000	6000	10,500	15,000
Riviera Series, V-8						
GS Cpe	350	800	1450	2750	5600	8000
Cpe HdTp	350	900	1550	3050	5900	8500
NOTE: Add 20 percent for 400.						

1970

	6	5	4	3	2	1
Skylark, V-6, 116" wb, 2 dr 112" wb						
4 dr Sed	150	300	700	1250	2650	3800
2 dr HdTp	150	300	700	1250	2600	3700
Skylark 350, V-6, 116" wb, 2 dr 112" wb						
4 dr Sed	150	300	750	1350	2700	3900
2 dr HdTp	150	400	750	1650	3150	4500
Skylark, V-8, 116" wb, 2 dr 112" wb						
4 dr Sed	150	300	750	1350	2700	3900
2 dr HdTp	150	300	700	1250	2650	3800
Skylark 350, V-8, 116" wb, 2 dr 112.2" wb						
4 dr Sed	150	350	750	1350	2800	4000
2 dr HdTp	200	600	950	2150	3850	5500
Skylark Custom, V-8, 116" wb, 2 dr 112" wb						
4 dr Sed	150	350	750	1450	2900	4100
4 dr HdTp	150	350	750	1450	3000	4200
2 dr HdTp	350	700	1150	2300	4550	6500
Conv	450	1450	2400	4800	8400	12,000
Gran Sport GS, V-8, 112" wb						
2 dr HdTp	400	1300	2200	4400	7700	11,000
Gran Sport GS 455, V-8, 112" wb						
2 dr HdTp	450	1450	2400	4800	8400	12,000
Conv	550	1800	3000	6000	10,500	15,000
Gran Sport 455 Stage I						
2 dr HdTp	500	1550	2600	5200	9100	13,000
Conv	700	2150	3600	7200	12,600	18,000
GSX V-8 Stage I						
2 dr HdTp	650	2050	3400	6800	11,900	17,000
GSX, V-8, 112" wb						
2 dr HdTp	600	1900	3200	6400	11,200	16,000
Sport Wagon, V-8, 116" wb						
2S Sta Wag	150	350	750	1450	3000	4200
LeSabre, V-8, 124" wb						
4 dr Sed	150	400	750	1600	3100	4400
4 dr HdTp	150	450	750	1700	3200	4600
2 dr HdTp	200	600	950	2150	3850	5500
LeSabre Custom, V-8, 124" wb						
4 dr Sed	150	400	750	1650	3150	4500
4 dr HdTp	150	450	800	1750	3250	4700
2 dr HdTp	200	650	1050	2250	4200	6000
Conv	450	1450	2400	4800	8400	12,000
LeSabre Custom 455, V-8, 124" wb						
4 dr Sed	150	450	800	1750	3250	4700
4 dr HdTp	200	500	850	1900	3500	5000
2 dr HdTp	200	675	1100	2250	4400	6300
Estate Wagon, V-8, 124" wb						
2S Sta Wag	150	450	800	1750	3250	4700
3S Sta Wag	150	450	800	1800	3300	4800
Wildcat Custom, V-8, 124" wb						
4 dr Sed	200	500	850	1850	3350	4900
2 dr HdTp	350	700	1150	2300	4550	6500
Conv	500	1550	2600	5200	9100	13,000
Electra 225, V-8, 127" wb						
4 dr Sed	150	450	800	1800	3300	4800
4 dr HdTp	200	550	900	2000	3600	5200
2 dr HdTp	350	700	1150	2300	4550	6500
Electra Custom 225, V-8, 127" wb						
4 dr Sed	200	500	850	1850	3350	4900
4 dr HdTp	200	550	900	2150	3800	5400
2 dr HdTp	350	750	1200	2350	4900	7000
Conv	600	1900	3200	6400	11,200	16,000
Riviera Series, V-8						
GS Cpe	350	750	1300	2450	5250	7500
HdTp Cpe	350	800	1450	2750	5600	8000
NOTE: Add 40 percent for 455.						

1971

	6	5	4	3	2	1
Skylark, V-6, 116" wb, 2 dr 112" wb						
4 dr Sed	125	200	600	1100	2250	3200
2 dr Sed	125	200	600	1100	2200	3100
2 dr HdTp	150	350	750	1350	2800	4000
Skylark, V-8, 116" wb, 2 dr 112" wb						
4 dr Sed	150	350	750	1450	2900	4100
2 dr Sed	150	350	750	1350	2800	4000
2 dr HdTp	200	500	850	1900	3500	5000
Skylark Custom, V-8						
4 dr Sed	150	400	750	1550	3050	4300
4 dr HdTp	150	400	750	1650	3150	4500
2 dr HdTp	200	650	1050	2250	4200	6000
Conv	400	1300	2200	4400	7700	11,000

	6	5	4	3	2	1
Gran Sport						
2 dr HdTp	400	1300	2200	4400	7700	11,000
Conv	500	1550	2600	5200	9100	13,000
NOTE: Add 40 percent for GS Stage I & GS-455 options.						
Add 40 percent for GS X option.						
Sport Wagon, V-8, 116" wb						
Sta Wag	125	250	700	1150	2450	3500
LeSabre, V-8, 124" wb						
4 dr Sed	125	250	700	1150	2450	3500
4 dr HdTp	125	250	700	1150	2500	3600
2 dr HdTp	150	300	700	1250	2600	3700
LeSabre Custom, V-8						
4 dr Sed	125	250	700	1150	2500	3600
4 dr HdTp	150	300	700	1250	2600	3700
2 dr HdTp	150	350	750	1350	2800	4000
Conv	400	1200	2000	3950	7000	10,000
Centurion, V-8						
4 dr HdTp	150	300	700	1250	2650	3800
2 dr HdTp	150	350	750	1450	3000	4200
Conv	400	1300	2200	4400	7700	11,000
Electra 225, V-8, 127" wb						
4 dr HdTp	150	300	750	1350	2700	3900
2 dr HdTp	150	400	750	1550	3050	4300
Electra Custom 225, V-8						
4 dr HdTp	150	350	750	1350	2800	4000
2 dr HdTp	150	400	750	1600	3100	4400
Wagons, V-8						
2S	150	300	700	1250	2650	3800
3S	150	300	750	1350	2700	3900
Riviera, V-8						
2 dr HdTp GS	350	700	1150	2300	4550	6500
2 dr HdTp	200	600	950	2150	3850	5500
NOTE: Add 40 percent for 455.						

1972

	6	5	4	3	2	1
Skylark, V-8, 116" wb, 2 dr 112" wb						
4 dr Sed	125	200	600	1100	2250	3200
2 dr Sed	125	200	600	1100	2200	3100
2 dr HdTp	150	350	750	1350	2800	4000
Skylark 350, V-8, 116" wb, 2 dr 112" wb						
4 dr Sed	125	250	700	1150	2400	3400
2 dr HdTp	200	500	850	1900	3500	5000
Skylark Custom, V-8						
4 dr Sed	125	200	600	1100	2300	3300
4 dr HdTp	125	250	700	1150	2450	3500
2 dr HdTp	200	650	1050	2250	4200	6000
Conv	400	1300	2200	4400	7700	11,000
Gran Sport, 350, V-8						
2 dr HdTp	400	1300	2200	4400	7700	11,000
Conv	550	1700	2800	5600	9800	14,000
NOTE: Add 40 percent for Stage I & GS-455 options.						
Add 5 percent for folding sun roof.						
Sport Wagon, V-8, 116" wb						
2S Sta Wag	125	250	700	1150	2400	3400
LeSabre						
4 dr Sed	150	300	700	1250	2650	3800
4 dr HdTp	150	350	750	1350	2800	4000
2 dr HdTp	150	350	750	1450	3000	4200
LeSabre Custom, V-8						
4 dr Sed	150	300	750	1350	2700	3900
4 dr HdTp	150	350	750	1450	2900	4100
2 dr HdTp	150	400	750	1600	3100	4400
Conv	400	1200	2000	3950	7000	10,000
Centurion, V-8						
4 dr Sed	150	400	750	1550	3050	4300
2 dr HdTp	150	450	750	1700	3200	4600
Conv	400	1200	2000	3950	7000	10,000
Estate Wagon, V-8, 124" wb						
2S Sta Wag	150	350	750	1350	2800	4000
3S Sta Wag	150	350	750	1450	2900	4100
Electra 225, V-8, 127" wb						
4 dr HdTp	150	400	750	1600	3100	4400
2 dr HdTp	150	450	800	1750	3250	4700
Electra Custom 225, V-8						
4 dr HdTp	150	400	750	1650	3150	4500
2 dr HdTp	200	500	850	1900	3500	5000
Riviera, V-8						
2 dr HdTp GS	350	700	1150	2300	4550	6500
2 dr HdTp	200	600	950	2150	3850	5500
Wagons						
2S	150	300	700	1250	2650	3800
4S	150	300	750	1350	2700	3900
NOTE: Add 40 percent for 455.						

1973

	6	5	4	3	2	1
Apollo, 6-cyl., 111" wb						
4 dr Sed	125	200	600	1100	2250	3200
2 dr Sed	125	250	700	1150	2400	3400
Hatchback	125	250	700	1150	2500	3600
Apollo, V-8						
4 dr Sed	125	200	600	1100	2300	3300
2 dr Sed	125	250	700	1150	2450	3500
Hatchback	150	300	700	1250	2600	3700
Century, V-8, 116" wb, 2 dr 112" wb						
Cpe	125	250	700	1150	2500	3600
4 dr Sed	125	250	700	1150	2450	3500
3S Sta Wag	125	250	700	1150	2400	3400
Century Luxus, V-8						
4 dr HdTp	125	250	700	1150	2500	3600
Cpe	150	300	700	1250	2600	3700
4 dr Wag 3S	125	250	700	1150	2450	3500
Century Regal, V-8						
2 dr HdTp	150	400	750	1650	3150	4500
NOTE: Add 25 percent for Stage I.						
LeSabre, V-8, 124" wb						
4 dr Sed	125	200	600	1100	2200	3100
4 dr HdTp	125	200	600	1100	2250	3200
2 dr HdTp	125	250	700	1150	2450	3500
LeSabre Custom, V-8						
4 dr Sed	150	300	700	1250	2600	3700
4 dr HdTp	150	300	700	1250	2650	3800
2 dr HdTp	150	400	750	1550	3050	4300
Est Wag 3S	150	300	700	1250	2600	3700
Centurion, V-8						
4 dr Sed	150	300	700	1250	2700	3900
2 dr HdTp	150	400	750	1600	3100	4400
Conv	450	1100	1700	3650	6650	9500

	6	5	4	3	2	1
Electra 225, V-8, 127" wb						
4 dr HdTp	150	350	750	1350	2800	4000
2 dr HdTp	150	450	800	1750	3250	4700
Electra Custom 225, V-8						
4 dr HdTp	150	350	750	1450	2900	4100
2 dr HdTp	150	450	800	1800	3300	4800
Riviera, V-8						
2 dr HdTp GS	200	650	1050	2250	4200	6000
2 dr HdTp	200	500	850	1900	3500	5000

1974

	6	5	4	3	2	1
Apollo, 6-cyl., 111" wb						
4 dr Sed	125	200	600	1100	2200	3100
2 dr Sed	125	200	600	1100	2200	3100
Hatchback	125	200	600	1100	2250	3200
Apollo, V-8, 111" wb						
4 dr Sed	125	200	600	1100	2250	3200
2 dr Sed	125	200	600	1100	2250	3200
Hatchback	125	200	600	1100	2300	3300
Century, V-8						
Cpe	125	250	700	1150	2500	3600
4 dr HdTp	125	250	700	1150	2450	3500
4 dr Sta Wag	125	250	700	1150	2450	3500
Century Luxus, V-8, 112" wb						
2 dr HdTp	125	250	700	1150	2450	3500
4 dr HdTp	125	250	700	1150	2400	3400
4 dr Sta Wag	125	200	600	1100	2250	3200
Gran Sport, V-8						
Cpe	150	350	750	1350	2800	4000
Century Regal, V-8, 112" wb						
2 dr HdTp	150	350	750	1450	2900	4100
4 dr HdTp	150	300	700	1250	2650	3800
LeSabre						
4 dr Sed	100	150	450	1000	1900	2700
4 dr HdTp	100	175	525	1050	1950	2800
2 dr HdTp	100	175	525	1050	2050	2900
LeSabre, V-8, 123" wb						
4 dr Sed	125	250	700	1150	2500	3600
4 dr HdTp	150	300	700	1250	2600	3700
2 dr HdTp	150	300	750	1350	2700	3900
LeSabre Luxus, V-8, 123" wb						
4 dr Sed	150	300	700	1250	2600	3700
4 dr HdTp	150	300	700	1250	2650	3800
2 dr HdTp	150	300	750	1350	2800	4000
Conv	450	1000	1650	3350	6300	9000
Estate Wagon, V-8						
4 dr Sta Wag	150	300	700	1250	2650	3800
Electra 225, V-8						
2 dr HdTp	150	400	750	1650	3150	4500
4 dr HdTp	150	350	750	1350	2800	4000
Electra 225 Custom, V-8						
2 dr HdTp	150	450	750	1700	3200	4600
4 dr HdTp	150	350	750	1450	2900	4100
Electra Limited, V-8						
2 dr HdTp	150	450	800	1750	3250	4700
4 dr HdTp	150	350	750	1450	3000	4200
Riviera, V-8						
2 dr HdTp	150	400	750	1650	3150	4500

NOTES: Deduct 5 percent for Apollo V-8.
Add 10 percent for Apollo GSX.
Add 10 percent for Century Grand Sport.
Add 15 percent for Century GS-455.
Add 20 percent for GS-455 Stage I.
Add 5 percent for sunroof.
Add 15 percent for Riviera GS or Stage I.

1975

	6	5	4	3	2	1
Skyhawk, V-6						
2 dr Hatch 'S'	125	200	600	1100	2300	3300
2 dr Hatch	125	200	600	1100	2300	3300
Apollo, V-8						
4 dr Sed	125	200	600	1100	2250	3200
4 dr 'SR' Sed	125	200	600	1100	2300	3300
Skylark, V-8						
Cpe	125	250	700	1150	2400	3400
2 dr Hatch	125	250	700	1150	2450	3500
'SR' Cpe	125	250	700	1150	2450	3500
2 dr 'SR' Hatch	100	150	450	1000	1800	2600
Century, V-8						
4 dr Sed	125	200	600	1100	2200	3100
Cpe	125	200	600	1100	2200	3100
4 dr Cus Sed	125	250	700	1150	2400	3400
Cus Cpe	125	250	700	1150	2450	3500
2S Sta Wag	125	200	600	1100	2200	3100
3S Sta Wag	125	200	600	1100	2250	3200
Regal, V-8						
4 dr Sed	125	200	600	1100	2300	3300
Cpe	125	250	700	1150	2400	3400
LeSabre, V-8						
4 dr Sed	125	200	600	1100	2300	3300
4 dr HdTp	125	250	700	1150	2450	3500
Cpe	125	250	700	1150	2450	3500
LeSabre Custom, V-8						
4 dr Sed	125	250	700	1150	2450	3500
4 dr HdTp	150	300	700	1250	2650	3800
Cpe	150	300	750	1350	2700	3900
Conv	450	1000	1650	3350	6300	9000
Estate Wagon, V-8						
2S Sta Wag	150	300	700	1250	2600	3700
3S Sta Wag	150	300	750	1350	2700	3900
Electra 225 Custom, V-8						
4 dr HdTp	150	350	750	1350	2800	4000
Cpe	150	350	750	1450	3000	4200
Electra 225 Limited, V-8						
4 dr HdTp	150	350	750	1450	2900	4100
Cpe	150	400	750	1600	3100	4400
Riviera, V-8						
2 dr HdTp	150	400	750	1650	3150	4500

NOTE: Add 15 percent for Park Avenue DeLuxe.
Add 5 percent for Park Avenue, Century, GS or Riviera GS options.
Add 5 percent for Apollo/Skylark V-8.

CADILLAC

1946

	6	5	4	3	2	1
Series 61, V-8, 126" wb						
Clb Cpe	700	2150	3600	7200	12,600	18,000
5P Sed	650	2050	3400	6800	11,900	17,000
Series 62, V-8, 129" wb						
Conv	1300	4200	7000	14,000	24,500	35,000
Clb Cpe	700	2300	3800	7600	13,300	19,000
5P Sed	700	2150	3600	7200	12,600	18,000
Series 60 Special, V-8, 133" wb, Fleetwood						
6P Sed	750	2400	4000	8000	14,000	20,000
Series 75, V-8, 136" wb, Fleetwood						
5P Sed	850	2650	4400	8800	15,400	22,000
7P Sed	850	2750	4600	9200	16,100	23,000
Imp Sed	900	2900	4800	9600	16,800	24,000
9P Bus Sed	850	2750	4600	9200	16,100	23,000
Imp Bus Sed	900	2900	4800	9600	16,800	24,000

1947

	6	5	4	3	2	1
Series 61, V-8, 126" wb						
Clb Cpe	700	2150	3600	7200	12,600	18,000
5P Sed	650	2050	3400	6800	11,900	17,000
Series 62, V-8, 129" wb						
Conv	1300	4100	6800	13,600	23,800	34,000
Clb Cpe	700	2300	3800	7600	13,300	19,000
5P Sed	700	2300	3800	7600	13,300	19,000
Series 60 Special, V-8, 133" wb, Fleetwood						
6P Sed	750	2400	4000	8000	14,000	20,000
Series 75, V-8, 136" wb, Fleetwood						
5P Sed	850	2650	4400	8800	15,400	22,000
7P Sed	850	2750	4600	9200	16,100	23,000
7P Imp Sed	1000	3250	5400	10,800	18,900	27,000
9P Bus Sed	850	2750	4600	9200	16,100	23,000
9P Bus Imp	950	3000	5000	10,000	17,500	25,000

1948

	6	5	4	3	2	1
Series 61, V-8, 126" wb						
Clb Cpe	700	2300	3800	7600	13,300	19,000
5P Sed	700	2300	3800	7600	13,300	19,000
Series 62, V-8, 126" wb						
Conv	1300	4100	6800	13,600	23,800	34,000
Clb Cpe	750	2400	4000	8000	14,000	20,000
5P Sed	750	2400	4000	8000	14,000	20,000
Series 60 Special, V-8, 133" wb, Fleetwood						
5P Sed	800	2500	4200	8400	14,700	21,000
Series 75, V-8, 136" wb, Fleetwood						
5P Sed	850	2650	4400	8800	15,400	22,000
7P Sed	850	2750	4600	9200	16,100	23,000
7P Imp Sed	1000	3250	5400	10,800	18,900	27,000
9P Bus Sed	850	2750	4600	9200	16,100	23,000
9P Bus Imp	950	3000	5000	10,000	17,500	25,000

1949

	6	5	4	3	2	1
Series 61, V-8, 126" wb						
Clb Cpe	750	2400	4000	8000	14,000	20,000
5P Sed	750	2400	4000	8000	14,000	20,000
Series 62, V-8, 126" wb						
5P Sed	800	2500	4200	8400	14,700	21,000
Clb Cpe	800	2500	4200	8400	14,700	21,000
Cpe DeV (2 dr HdTp)	1000	3250	5400	10,800	18,900	27,000
Conv	1300	4200	7000	14,000	24,500	35,000
Series 60 Special, V-8, 133" wb, Fleetwood						
5P Sed	850	2650	4400	8800	15,400	22,000
Series 75, V-8, 136" wb, Fleetwood						
5P Sed	850	2750	4600	9200	16,100	23,000
7P Sed	900	2900	4800	9600	16,800	24,000
7P Imp Sed	1050	3350	5600	11,200	19,600	28,000
9P Bus Sed	900	2900	4800	9600	16,800	24,000
9P Bus Imp	1000	3100	5200	10,400	18,200	26,000

1950

	6	5	4	3	2	1
Series 61, V-8, 122" wb						
5P Sed	600	1900	3200	6400	11,200	16,000
2 dr HdTp Cpe	700	2150	3600	7200	12,600	18,000
Series 62, V-8, 126" wb						
5P Sed	650	2050	3400	6800	11,900	17,000
2 dr HdTp Cpe	850	2750	4600	9200	16,100	23,000
Cpe DeV (2 dr HdTp)	950	3000	5000	10,000	17,500	25,000
Conv	1200	3850	6400	12,800	22,400	32,000
Series 60 Special, V-8, 130" wb, Fleetwood						
5P Sed	900	2900	4800	9600	16,800	24,000
Series 75, V-8, 146- 3/4" wb, Fleetwood						
7P Sed	950	3000	5000	10,000	17,500	25,000
7P Imp	1000	3250	5400	10,800	18,900	27,000

1951

	6	5	4	3	2	1
Series 61, V-8						
5P Sed	600	1900	3200	6400	11,200	16,000
2 dr HdTp Cpe	700	2300	3800	7600	13,300	19,000
Series 62, V-8						
5P Sed	650	2050	3400	6800	11,900	17,000
2 dr HdTp Cpe	850	2750	4600	9200	16,100	23,000
Cpe DeV (2 dr HdTp)	950	3000	5000	10,000	17,500	25,000
Conv	1250	3950	6600	13,200	23,100	33,000
Series 60-S, V-8						
Sed	900	2900	4800	9600	16,800	24,000
Series 75 Fleetwood						
8P Sed	950	3000	5000	10,000	17,500	25,000
8P Imp	1000	3250	5400	10,800	18,900	27,000

1952

	6	5	4	3	2	1
Series 62, V-8						
Sed	650	2050	3400	6800	11,900	17,000
2 dr HdTp	850	2750	4600	9200	16,100	23,000
Cpe DeV (2 dr HdTp)	950	3000	5000	10,000	17,500	25,000
Conv	1300	4100	6800	13,600	23,800	34,000
Series 60-S, V-8						
Sed	900	2900	4800	9600	16,800	24,000
Series 75, V-8, Fleetwood						
Sed	950	3000	5000	10,000	17,500	25,000
Imp Sed	1000	3250	5400	10,800	18,900	27,000

1953

	6	5	4	3	2	1
Series 62, V-8						
Sed	650	2050	3400	6800	11,900	17,000
2 dr HdTp	900	2900	4800	9600	16,800	24,000
Cpe DeV (2 dr HdTp)	1000	3100	5200	10,400	18,200	26,000
Conv	1350	4300	7200	14,400	25,200	36,000
Eldo Conv	3400	10,800	18,000	36,000	63,000	90,000
Series 60-S, V-8						
Sed	950	3000	5000	10,000	17,500	25,000
Series 75, V-8, Fleetwood						
7P Sed	1000	3100	5200	10,400	18,200	26,000
Imp Sed	1050	3350	5600	11,200	19,600	28,000

	6	5	4	3	2	1
1954						
Series 62, V-8						
Sed	600	1900	3200	6400	11,200	16,000
2 dr HdTp	950	3000	5000	10,000	17,500	25,000
Cpe DeV (2 dr HdTp)	1000	3250	5400	10,800	18,900	27,000
Conv	1500	4800	8000	16,000	28,000	40,000
Eldo Conv	2650	8400	14,000	28,000	49,000	70,000
Series 60-S, V-8						
Sed	900	2900	4800	9600	16,800	24,000
Series 75, V-8, Fleetwood						
7P Sed	1000	3250	5400	10,800	18,900	27,000
7P Imp Sed	1100	3500	5800	11,600	20,300	29,000
1955						
Series 62, V-8						
Sed	600	1900	3200	6400	11,200	16,000
2 dr HdTp	1000	3100	5200	10,400	18,200	26,000
Cpe DeV (2 dr HdTp)	1000	3250	5400	10,800	18,900	27,000
Conv	1500	4800	8000	16,000	28,000	40,000
Eldo Conv	1650	5300	8800	17,600	30,800	44,000
Series 60-S, V-8						
Sed	900	2900	4800	9600	16,800	24,000
Series 75, V-8, Fleetwood						
7P Sed	1000	3250	5400	10,800	18,900	27,000
7P Imp Sed	1100	3500	5800	11,600	20,300	29,000
1956						
Series 62, V-8						
Sed	650	2050	3400	6800	11,900	17,000
2 dr HdTp	900	2900	4800	9600	16,800	24,000
Sed DeV (4 dr HdTp)	700	2150	3600	7200	12,600	18,000
Cpe DeV (2 dr HdTp)	950	3000	5000	10,000	17,500	25,000
Conv	1600	5050	8400	16,800	29,400	42,000
Eldo Sev (2 dr HdTp)	1300	4200	7000	14,000	24,500	35,000
Biarritz Conv	1600	5150	8600	17,200	30,100	43,000
Series 60-S, V-8						
Sed	900	2900	4800	9600	16,800	24,000
Series 75, V-8, Fleetwood						
7P Sed	1000	3250	5400	10,800	18,900	27,000
7P Imp Sed	1100	3500	5800	11,600	20,300	29,000
1957						
Series 62, V-8						
4 dr HdTp	550	1700	2800	5600	9800	14,000
2 dr HdTp	950	3000	5000	10,000	17,500	25,000
Cpe DeV (2 dr HdTp)	1000	3250	5400	10,800	18,900	27,000
Sed DeV (4 dr HdTp)	700	2300	3800	7600	13,300	19,000
Conv	1450	4550	7600	15,200	26,600	38,000
Eldorado, V-8						
Sev (2 dr HdTp)	1050	3350	5600	11,200	19,600	28,000
Biarritz Conv	1450	4700	7800	15,600	27,300	39,000
Fleetwood 60 Special, V-8						
4 dr HdTp	750	2400	4000	8000	14,000	20,000
Eldorado Brougham, V-8						
4 dr HdTp	1100	3500	5800	11,600	20,300	29,000
Series 75						
8P Sed	800	2500	4200	8400	14,700	21,000
8P Imp Sed	850	2750	4600	9200	16,100	23,000
1958						
Series 62, V-8						
Sh Dk 4 dr HdTp	450	1450	2400	4800	8400	12,000
6W Sed	500	1550	2600	5200	9100	13,000
4 dr Sed DeV	550	1700	2800	5600	9800	14,000
Cpe	850	2650	4400	8800	15,400	22,000
Cpe DeV	900	2900	4800	9600	16,800	24,000
Conv	1200	3850	6400	12,800	22,400	32,000
Eldorado, V-8						
Sev (2 dr HdTp)	950	3000	5000	10,000	17,500	25,000
Biarritz Conv	1300	4200	7000	14,000	24,500	35,000
Fleetwood 60 Special, V-8						
4 dr HdTp	750	2400	4000	8000	14,000	20,000
Eldorado Brougham, V-8						
4 dr HdTp	1050	3350	5600	11,200	19,600	28,000
Series 75						
8P Sed	700	2300	3800	7600	13,300	19,000
8P Imp Sed	800	2500	4200	8400	14,700	21,000
1959						
Series 62, V-8						
4W 4 dr HdTp	550	1800	3000	6000	10,500	15,000
6W 4 dr HdTp	550	1700	2800	5600	9800	14,000
2 dr HdTp	850	2650	4400	8800	15,400	22,000
Conv	1850	5900	9800	19,600	34,300	49,000
Series 62 DeVille, V-8						
Cpe DeV (2 dr HdTp)	1000	3100	5200	10,400	18,200	26,000
4W 4 dr HdTp	600	1900	3200	6400	11,200	16,000
6W 4 dr HdTp	550	1800	3000	6000	10,500	15,000
Series Eldorado, V-8						
Brgm 4 dr HdTp	1150	3700	6200	12,400	21,700	31,000
Sev 2 dr HdTp	1450	4550	7600	15,200	26,600	38,000
Biarritz Conv	2850	9100	15,200	30,400	53,200	76,000
Fleetwood 60 Special, V-8						
6P Sed	950	3000	5000	10,000	17,500	25,000
Fleetwood Series 75, V-8						
9P Sed	1000	3250	5400	10,800	18,900	27,000
Limo	1100	3500	5800	11,600	20,300	29,000
1960						
Series 62, V-8						
4W 4 dr HdTp	550	1700	2800	5600	9800	14,000
6W 4 dr HdTp	500	1550	2600	5200	9100	13,000
2 dr HdTp	800	2500	4200	8400	14,700	21,000
Conv	1750	5650	9400	18,800	32,900	47,000
Series 62 DeVille, V-8						
4W Sed	550	1800	3000	6000	10,500	15,000
6W Sed	550	1700	2800	5600	9800	14,000
Cpe DeV (2 dr HdTp)	850	2750	4600	9200	16,100	23,000
Eldorado Series, V-8						
Brgm 4 dr HdTp	1150	3700	6200	12,400	21,700	31,000
Sev (2 dr HdTp)	1400	4450	7400	14,800	25,900	37,000
Biarritz Conv	2650	8400	14,000	28,000	49,000	70,000
Fleetwood 60 Special, V-8						
6P 4 dr HdTp	900	2900	4800	9600	16,800	24,000
Fleetwood Series 75, V-8						
9P Sed	950	3000	5000	10,000	17,500	25,000
Limo	1000	3250	5400	10,800	18,900	27,000
1961						
Series 62, V-8						
4W 4 dr HdTp	400	1250	2100	4200	7400	10,500
6W 4 dr HdTp	400	1250	2100	4200	7300	10,400
2 dr HdTp	600	1900	3200	6400	11,200	16,000

	6	5	4	3	2	1
Conv	1150	3600	6000	12,000	21,000	30,000
Series 62 DeVille, V-8						
4W 4 dr HdTp	400	1300	2150	4300	7500	10,700
6W 4 dr HdTp	400	1250	2100	4200	7400	10,600
Sh Dk 4 dr HdTp	400	1250	2100	4200	7400	10,500
Cpe DeV (2 dr HdTp)	700	2150	3600	7200	12,600	18,000
Eldorado Series, V-8						
Biarritz Conv	1150	3700	6200	12,400	21,700	31,000
Fleetwood 60 Special, V-8						
6P 4 dr HdTp	550	1800	3000	6000	10,500	15,000
Fleetwood Series 75, V-8						
9P Sed	650	2050	3400	6800	11,900	17,000
9P Limo	850	2650	4400	8800	15,400	22,000
1962						
Series 62, V-8						
4W 4 dr HdTp	400	1300	2150	4300	7500	10,700
6W 4 dr HdTp	400	1250	2100	4200	7400	10,500
Sh Dk 4 dr HdTp	400	1250	2100	4200	7400	10,500
2 dr HdTp	600	1900	3200	6400	11,200	16,000
Conv	1100	3500	5800	11,600	20,300	29,000
Series 62 DeVille, V-8						
4W 4 dr HdTp	400	1350	2250	4500	7800	11,200
6W 4 dr HdTp	450	1450	2400	4800	8400	12,000
Pk Ave 4 dr HdTp	450	1400	2300	4600	8100	11,500
Cpe DeV (2 dr HdTp)	700	2150	3600	7200	12,600	18,000
Eldorado Series, V-8						
Biarritz Conv	1400	4450	7400	14,800	25,900	37,000
Fleetwood 60 Special, V-8						
6P 4 dr HdTp	600	1900	3200	6400	11,200	16,000
Fleetwood 75 Series, V-8						
9P Sed	650	2050	3400	6800	11,900	17,000
9P Limo	850	2650	4400	8800	15,400	22,000
1963						
Series 62, V-8						
4W 4 dr HdTp	350	750	1350	2650	5450	7800
6W 4 dr HdTp	350	750	1300	2500	5300	7600
2 dr HdTp	450	1450	2400	4800	8400	12,000
Conv	900	2900	4800	9600	16,800	24,000
Series 62 DeVille, V-8						
4W 4 dr HdTp	350	850	1500	2800	5650	8100
6W 4 dr HdTp	350	800	1450	2750	5600	8000
Pk Ave 4 dr HdTp	350	800	1450	2750	5600	8000
Cpe DeV (2 dr HdTp)	500	1550	2600	5200	9100	13,000
Eldorado Series, V-8						
Biarritz Conv	900	2900	4800	9600	16,800	24,000
Fleetwood 60 Special, V-8						
6P 4 dr HdTp	500	1550	2600	5200	9100	13,000
Fleetwood 75 Series, V-8						
9P Sed	550	1800	3000	6000	10,500	15,000
9P Limo	700	2300	3800	7600	13,300	19,000
1964						
Series 62, V-8						
4W 4 dr HdTp	350	800	1450	2750	5600	8000
6W 4 dr HdTp	350	750	1350	2650	5450	7800
2 dr HdTp	500	1550	2600	5200	9100	13,000
Series 62 DeVille, V-8						
4W 4 dr HdTp	350	850	1500	2900	5700	8200
6W 4 dr HdTp	350	800	1450	2750	5600	8000
Cpe DeV (2 dr HdTp)	550	1700	2800	5600	9800	14,000
Conv	850	2650	4400	8800	15,400	22,000
Eldorado Series, V-8						
Conv	950	3000	5000	10,000	17,500	25,000
Fleetwood 60 Special, V-8						
6P 4 dr HdTp	500	1550	2600	5200	9100	13,000
Fleetwood 75 Series, V-8						
9P Sed	550	1800	3000	6000	10,500	15,000
9P Limo	700	2300	3800	7600	13,300	19,000
1965						
Calais Series, V-8						
4 dr Sed	350	750	1350	2650	5450	7800
4 dr HdTp	350	800	1450	2750	5600	8000
2 dr HdTp	400	1200	2000	3950	7000	10,000
DeVille Series, V-8						
6P Sed	350	800	1450	2750	5600	8000
4 dr HdTp	350	900	1550	3000	5850	8400
2 dr HdTp	400	1300	2200	4400	7700	11,000
Conv	700	2300	3800	7600	13,300	19,000
Fleetwood 60 Special, V-8						
6P Sed	450	1400	2300	4600	8100	11,500
Brgm Sed	450	1450	2400	4800	8400	12,000
Fleetwood Eldorado, V-8						
Conv	750	2400	4000	8000	14,000	20,000
Fleetwood 75 Series, V-8						
9P Sed	550	1800	3000	6000	10,500	15,000
9P Limo	700	2300	3800	7600	13,300	19,000
1966						
Calais Series, V-8						
Sed	350	800	1350	2700	5500	7900
4 dr HdTp	350	800	1450	2750	5600	8000
2 dr HdTp	400	1200	2000	3950	7000	10,000
DeVille Series, V-8						
Sed	350	800	1450	2750	5600	8000
4 dr HdTp	350	850	1500	2900	5700	8200
2 dr HdTp	400	1300	2200	4400	7700	11,000
Conv	700	2300	3800	7600	13,300	19,000
Eldorado, V-8						
Conv	800	2500	4200	8400	14,700	21,000
Fleetwood Brougham, V-8						
Sed	400	1300	2200	4400	7700	11,000
Sixty Special, V-8						
Sed	400	1300	2200	4400	7700	11,000
Seventy Five, V-8						
Sed	550	1800	3000	6000	10,500	15,000
Limo	700	2300	3800	7600	13,300	19,000
1967						
Calais, V-8, 129.5" wb						
4 dr HdTp	350	800	1450	2750	5600	8000
2 dr HdTp	450	1100	1700	3650	6650	9500
DeVille, V-8, 129.5" wb						
4 dr HdTp	350	900	1550	3050	5900	8500
2 dr HdTp	400	1200	2000	3950	7000	10,000
Conv	700	2300	3800	7600	13,300	19,000
Fleetwood Eldorado, V-8, 120" wb						
2 dr HdTp	400	1300	2200	4400	7700	11,000
Sixty-Special, V-8, 133" wb						
Sed	400	1200	2000	3950	7000	10,000

	6	5	4	3	2	1
Fleetwood Brougham, V-8, 133" wv						
Sed	400	1200	2000	3950	7000	10,000
Seventy-Five Series, V-8, 149.8" wb						
Sed	400	1300	2200	4400	7700	11,000
Limo	450	1450	2400	4800	8400	12,000

1968
	6	5	4	3	2	1
Calais, V-8, 129.5" wb						
4 dr HdTp	350	850	1500	2800	5650	8100
2 dr HdTp	450	1100	1700	3650	6650	9500
DeVille, V-8 129.5 wb						
4 dr	350	850	1500	2900	5700	8200
4 dr HdTp	350	900	1550	3050	5900	8500
2 dr HdTp	400	1200	2000	3950	7000	10,000
Conv	700	2300	3800	7600	13,300	19,000
Fleetwood Eldorado, V-8, 120" wb						
2 dr HdTp	400	1300	2200	4400	7700	11,000
Sixty-Special, V-8, 133" wb						
Sed	400	1200	2000	3950	7000	10,000
Fleetwood Brougham, V-8, 133" wb						
Sed	400	1200	2000	3950	7000	10,000
Series 75, V-8, 149.8" wb						
Sed	400	1300	2200	4400	7700	11,000
Limo	450	1450	2400	4800	8400	12,000

1969
	6	5	4	3	2	1
Calais, V-8, 129.5" wb						
4 dr HdTp	200	550	900	2100	3700	5300
2 dr HdTp	350	700	1150	2300	4550	6500
DeVille, V-8, 129.5" wb						
4 dr Sed	200	600	950	2150	3850	5500
4 dr HdTp	200	650	1000	2200	4100	5800
2 dr HdTp	350	750	1200	2350	4900	7000
Conv	600	1900	3200	6400	11,200	16,000
Fleetwood Eldorado, V-8, 120.5" wb						
2 dr HdTp	400	1200	2000	3950	7000	10,000
Sixty-Special, V-8, 133" wb						
Sed	350	750	1200	2350	4900	7000
Brgm	350	750	1300	2450	5250	7500
Series 75, V-8, 149.8" wb						
Sed	350	750	1300	2450	5250	7500
Limo	350	800	1450	2750	5600	8000

1970
	6	5	4	3	2	1
Calais, V-8, 129.5" wb						
4 dr HdTp	200	600	950	2150	3850	5500
2 dr HdTp	350	700	1150	2300	4550	6500
DeVille, V-8, 129.5" wb						
4 dr Sed	200	600	950	2200	3900	5600
4 dr HdTp	200	650	1000	2200	4150	5900
2 dr HdTp	350	750	1200	2350	4900	7000
Conv	600	1900	3200	6400	11,200	16,000
Fleetwood Eldorado, V-8, 120" wb						
2 dr HdTp	400	1300	2200	4400	7700	11,000
Sixty-Special, V-8, 133" wb						
Sed	350	750	1200	2350	4900	7000
Brgm	350	750	1300	2450	5250	7500
Series 75, V-8, 149.8" wb						
Sed	350	750	1300	2450	5250	7500
Limo	350	800	1450	2750	5600	8000

1971
	6	5	4	3	2	1
Calais						
4 dr HdTp	200	650	1000	2200	4100	5800
2 dr HdTp	350	750	1200	2350	4900	7000
DeVille						
4 dr HdTp	200	675	1050	2250	4350	6200
2 dr HdTp	350	750	1300	2450	5250	7500
Fleetwood 60 Special						
Brgm	350	750	1200	2350	4900	7000
Fleetwood 75						
9P Sed	350	750	1200	2350	4900	7000
Limo	350	750	1300	2450	5250	7500
Fleetwood Eldorado						
2 dr HdTp	450	1000	1650	3350	6300	9000
Conv	550	1800	3000	6000	10,500	15,000

1972
	6	5	4	3	2	1
Calais						
4 dr HdTp	200	650	1000	2200	4150	5900
2 dr HdTp	350	750	1200	2350	4900	7000
DeVille						
4 dr HdTp	200	675	1100	2250	4400	6300
2 dr HdTp	350	750	1300	2450	5250	7500
Fleetwood 60 Special						
Brgm	350	750	1200	2350	4900	7000
Fleetwood 75						
9P Sed	350	750	1200	2350	4900	7000
Limo	350	750	1300	2450	5250	7500
Fleetwood Eldorado						
2 dr HdTp	450	1000	1650	3350	6300	9000
Conv	550	1800	3000	6000	10,500	15,000

1973
	6	5	4	3	2	1
Calais V8						
2 dr HdTp	200	650	1050	2250	4200	6000
4 dr HdTp	200	650	1000	2200	4100	5800
DeVille V8						
2 dr HdTp	350	700	1150	2300	4550	6500
4 dr HdTp	200	650	1050	2250	4200	6000
Fleetwood 60S V8						
4 dr Brgm Sed	350	700	1100	2300	4500	6400
Fleetwood Eldorado V8						
2 dr HdTp	350	900	1550	3050	5900	8500
Conv	550	1800	3000	6000	10,500	15,000
Fleetwood 75 V8						
4 dr Sed	350	750	1200	2350	4900	7000
Limo	350	750	1300	2450	5250	7500

1974
	6	5	4	3	2	1
Calais V-8						
2 dr HdTp	200	650	1000	2200	4100	5800
4 dr HdTp	200	650	1050	2250	4200	6000
DeVille V-8						
2 dr HdTp	200	650	1050	2250	4200	6000
4 dr HdTp	350	700	1150	2300	4550	6500
Fleetwood Brougham V-8						
4 dr Sed	200	675	1100	2250	4400	6300
Fleetwood Eldorado V-8						
2 dr HdTp	350	900	1550	3050	5900	8500
Conv	600	1900	3200	6400	11,200	16,000

	6	5	4	3	2	1
Fleetwood 75 V-8						
4 dr Sed	350	750	1200	2350	4900	7000
Limo	350	750	1300	2450	5250	7500

NOTES: Add 20 percent for Talisman Brougham.
Add 10 percent for padded top on Series 75.
Add 10 percent for sun roof on DeVille/60/Eldorado.

1975
	6	5	4	3	2	1
Calais V-8						
2 dr HdTp	200	600	1000	2200	4000	5700
4 dr HdTp	200	550	900	2100	3700	5300
DeVille V-8						
2 dr HdTp	200	650	1000	2200	4150	5900
4 dr HdTp	200	600	950	2150	3850	5500
Fleetwood Brougham V-8						
4 dr Sed	200	650	1050	2250	4200	6000
Fleetwood Eldorado V-8						
2 dr HdTp	450	1000	1650	3350	6300	9000
Conv	600	1900	3200	6400	11,200	16,000
Fleetwood 75 V-8						
4 dr Sed	350	750	1200	2350	4900	7000
Limo	350	750	1300	2450	5250	7500

CHECKER

	6	5	4	3	2	1
1960						
Checker Superba Std.						
Sed	350	700	1150	2300	4550	6500
Sta Wag	350	700	1100	2300	4500	6400
Checker Superba Spl.						
Sed	350	700	1150	2300	4600	6600
Sta Wag	350	700	1150	2300	4550	6500
1961						
Checker Superba						
Sed	350	700	1150	2300	4550	6500
Sta Wag	350	700	1100	2300	4500	6400
Checker Marathon						
Sed	350	700	1150	2300	4600	6600
Sta Wag	350	700	1150	2300	4550	6500
1962						
Checker Superba						
Sed	350	700	1150	2300	4550	6500
Sta Wag	350	700	1100	2300	4500	6400
Checker Marathon						
Sed	350	700	1150	2300	4600	6600
Sta Wag	350	700	1150	2300	4550	6500
1963						
Checker Superba						
Sed	350	700	1150	2300	4600	6600
Sta Wag	350	700	1150	2300	4550	6500
Checker Marathon						
Sed	350	700	1150	2300	4600	6600
Sta Wag	350	700	1100	2300	4500	6400
Limo	350	750	1200	2350	4900	7000
1964						
Checker Marathon						
Sed	350	700	1150	2300	4550	6500
Sta Wag	350	700	1100	2300	4500	6400
Limo	350	750	1250	2350	5000	7100
Aerobus	350	725	1150	2300	4700	6700
1965						
Marathon Series						
Sed	350	700	1100	2300	4500	6400
DeL Sed	350	700	1150	2300	4550	6500
Sta Wag	200	675	1100	2250	4400	6300
Limo	350	750	1200	2350	4900	7000
1966						
Marathon Series						
Sed	350	700	1100	2300	4500	6400
DeL Sed	350	700	1150	2300	4550	6500
Sta Wag	200	675	1100	2250	4400	6300
Limo	350	750	1200	2350	4900	7000
1967						
Marathon Series						
Sed	350	700	1100	2300	4500	6400
Sta Wag	350	700	1150	2300	4550	6500
1968						
Marathon Series						
Sed	350	700	1100	2300	4500	6400
Sta Wag	200	675	1100	2250	4400	6300
DeL Sed	350	700	1150	2300	4550	6500
1969						
Marathon Series						
Sed	350	700	1100	2300	4500	6400
Sta Wag	200	675	1100	2250	4400	6300
DeLuxe Series						
Sed	350	700	1150	2300	4550	6500
Limo	350	750	1200	2350	4900	7000
1970						
Marathon Series						
Sed	350	700	1100	2300	4500	6400
Sta Wag	200	675	1100	2250	4400	6300
DeLuxe Series						
Sed	350	700	1150	2300	4550	6500
Limo	350	750	1200	2350	4900	7000
1971						
Marathon Series						
Sed	200	650	1050	2250	4200	6000
Sta Wag	200	650	1000	2200	4150	5900
DeLuxe Series						
Sed	200	675	1050	2250	4350	6200
Limo	350	750	1200	2350	4900	7000

NOTE: Add 5 percent for V8.

	6	5	4	3	2	1
1972						
Marathon Series						
Sed	200	650	1050	2250	4200	6000
Sta Wag	200	650	1000	2200	4150	5900
DeLuxe Series						
Sed	150	400	750	1650	3150	4500

NOTE: Add 5 percent for V8.

1973

	6	5	4	3	2	1
Marathon Series						
Sed	200	650	1000	2200	4150	5900
Sta Wag	200	650	1000	2200	4100	5800
DeLuxe Series						
Sed	200	650	1050	2250	4200	6000

NOTE: Add 5 percent for V8.

1974

	6	5	4	3	2	1
Marathon Series						
Sed	200	650	1000	2200	4150	5900
Sta Wag	200	650	1000	2200	4100	5800
DeLuxe Series						
Sed	200	650	1050	2250	4200	6000

NOTE: Add 5 percent for V8.

1975

	6	5	4	3	2	1
Marathon Series						
Sed	200	650	1000	2200	4150	5900
Sta Wag	200	650	1000	2200	4100	5800
DeLuxe						
Sed	200	650	1050	2250	4200	6000

CHEVROLET

1946

	6	5	4	3	2	1
Stylemaster, 6-cyl.						
Bus Cpe	350	900	1550	3050	5900	8500
Spt Cpe	350	950	1600	3200	6050	8700
Twn Sed	350	750	1300	2450	5250	7500
Spt Sed	350	750	1350	2600	5400	7700
Fleetmaster, 6-cyl.						
Spt Cpe	450	1000	1650	3350	6300	9000
Twn Sed	350	800	1450	2750	5600	8000
Spt Sed	350	850	1500	2900	5700	8200
Conv	800	2500	4200	8400	14,700	21,000
Sta Wag	900	2900	4800	9600	16,800	24,000
Fleetline						
2 dr Aero	350	900	1550	3100	6000	8600
4 dr Spt Mstr	450	950	1600	3250	6150	8800

1947

	6	5	4	3	2	1
Stylemaster, 6-cyl.						
Bus Cpe	350	900	1550	3050	5900	8500
Spt Cpe	350	950	1600	3200	6050	8700
Twn Sed	350	750	1350	2600	5400	7700
Spt Sed	350	800	1350	2700	5500	7900
Fleetmaster, 6-cyl.						
Spt Cpe	450	1000	1650	3350	6300	9000
Twn Sed	350	750	1350	2650	5450	7800
Spt Sed	350	800	1450	2750	5600	8000
Conv	800	2500	4200	8400	14,700	21,000
Sta Wag	950	3000	5000	10,000	17,500	25,000
Fleetline, 6-cyl.						
2 dr Aero	350	950	1600	3200	6050	8700
4 dr Spt Mstr	450	950	1600	3250	6150	8800

1948

	6	5	4	3	2	1
Stylemaster, 6-cyl.						
Bus Cpe	350	900	1550	3050	5900	8500
Spt Cpe	350	950	1600	3200	6050	8700
Twn Sed	350	750	1350	2600	5400	7700
Spt Sed	350	750	1350	2650	5450	7800
Fleetmaster, 6-cyl.						
Spt Cpe	450	1000	1650	3350	6300	9000
Twn Sed	350	750	1350	2650	5450	7800
Spt Sed	350	800	1450	2750	5600	8000
Conv	800	2500	4200	8400	14,700	21,000
Sta Wag	950	3000	5000	10,000	17,500	25,000
Fleetline, 6-cyl.						
2 dr Aero	350	900	1550	3100	6000	8600
4 dr Spt Mstr	450	950	1600	3250	6150	8800

1949

	6	5	4	3	2	1
Styleline Special, 6-cyl.						
Bus Cpe	350	800	1450	2750	5600	8000
Spt Cpe	350	900	1550	3000	5850	8400
2 dr Sed	350	750	1200	2350	4900	7000
Sed	350	750	1250	2350	5000	7100
Fleetline Special, 6-cyl.						
2 dr Sed	350	750	1250	2350	5000	7100
4 dr Sed	350	750	1250	2400	5050	7200
Styleline DeLuxe, 6-cyl.						
Spt Cpe	450	1000	1650	3350	6300	9000
2 dr Sed	350	750	1300	2450	5250	7500
Sed	350	750	1300	2500	5300	7600
Conv	800	2500	4200	8400	14,700	21,000
Mtl Sta Wag	400	1300	2200	4400	7700	11,000
Woodie	600	1900	3200	6400	11,200	16,000
Fleetline DeLuxe, 6-cyl.						
2 dr Sed	350	750	1300	2500	5300	7600
Sed	350	750	1350	2600	5400	7700

1950

	6	5	4	3	2	1
Styleline Special, 6-cyl.						
Bus Cpe	350	800	1450	2750	5600	8000
Spt Cpe	350	900	1550	3000	5850	8400
2 dr Sed	350	750	1200	2350	4900	7000
Sed	350	750	1250	2350	5000	7100
Fleetline Special, 6-cyl.						
2 dr Sed	350	750	1250	2350	5000	7100
4 dr Sed	350	750	1250	2400	5050	7200
Styleline DeLuxe, 6-cyl.						
Spt Cpe	450	1000	1650	3350	6300	9000
2 dr Sed	350	750	1300	2450	5250	7500
Sed	350	750	1300	2500	5300	7600
2 dr HdTp Bel Air	400	1300	2200	4400	7700	11,000
Conv	800	2500	4200	8400	14,700	21,000
Mtl Sta Wag	400	1250	2100	4200	7400	10,500
Fleetline DeLuxe, 6-cyl.						
2 dr Sed	350	750	1300	2500	5300	7600
4 dr Sed	350	750	1350	2600	5400	7700

1951

	6	5	4	3	2	1
Styleline Special, 6-cyl.						
Bus Cpe	350	850	1500	2800	5650	8100
Spt Cpe	350	900	1550	3050	5900	8500
2 dr Sed	350	750	1250	2350	5000	7100
Sed	350	750	1250	2400	5050	7200
Fleetline Special, 6-cyl.						
2 dr Sed	350	750	1250	2400	5050	7200
4 dr Sed	350	750	1250	2400	5100	7300
Styleline DeLuxe, 6-cyl.						
Spt Cpe	450	1000	1650	3400	6350	9100
2 dr Sed	350	750	1300	2500	5300	7600
Sed	350	750	1350	2600	5400	7700
2 dr HdTp Bel Air	400	1300	2200	4400	7700	11,000
Conv	750	2400	4000	8000	14,000	20,000
Sta Wag	400	1300	2200	4400	7700	11,000
Fleetline DeLuxe, 6-cyl.						
2 dr Sed	350	750	1350	2600	5400	7700
4 dr Sed	350	750	1350	2650	5450	7800

1952

	6	5	4	3	2	1
Styleline Special, 6-cyl.						
Bus Cpe	350	850	1500	2800	5650	8100
Spt Cpe	350	900	1550	3050	5900	8500
2 dr Sed	350	750	1250	2350	5000	7100
Sed	350	750	1250	2400	5050	7200
Styleline DeLuxe, 6-cyl.						
Spt Cpe	450	1000	1650	3400	6350	9100
2 dr Sed	350	750	1300	2500	5300	7600
Sed	350	750	1350	2600	5400	7700
2 dr HdTp Bel Air	450	1400	2300	4600	8100	11,500
Conv	800	2500	4200	8400	14,700	21,000
Sta Wag	400	1300	2200	4400	7700	11,000
Fleetline DeLuxe, 6-cyl.						
2 dr Sed	350	800	1450	2750	5600	8000

1953

	6	5	4	3	2	1
Special 150, 6-cyl.						
Bus Cpe	350	700	1100	2300	4500	6400
Clb Cpe	350	700	1150	2300	4550	6500
2 dr Sed	200	650	1050	2250	4200	6000
Sed	200	675	1050	2250	4300	6100
Sta Wag	450	1000	1650	3350	6300	9000
DeLuxe 210, 6-cyl.						
Clb Cpe	350	900	1550	3050	5900	8500
2 dr Sed	350	750	1300	2450	5250	7500
Sed	350	750	1300	2400	5200	7400
2 dr HdTp	400	1300	2200	4400	7700	11,000
Conv	850	2650	4400	8800	15,400	22,000
Sta Wag	450	1000	1650	3350	6300	9000
210 Townsman Sta Wag	450	1050	1650	3500	6400	9200
Bel Air						
2 dr Sed	450	1000	1650	3350	6300	9000
Sed	350	950	1600	3200	6050	8700
2 dr HdTp	450	1450	2400	4800	8400	12,000
Conv	900	2900	4800	9600	16.800	24,000

1954

	6	5	4	3	2	1
Special 150, 6-cyl.						
Utl Sed	200	650	1000	2200	4150	5900
2 dr Sed	200	650	1050	2250	4200	6000
Sed	200	675	1050	2250	4300	6100
Sta Wag	450	1000	1650	3350	6300	9000
Special 210, 6-cyl.						
2 dr Sed	350	750	1300	2450	5250	7500
2 dr Sed Del Rey	450	1000	1650	3350	6300	9000
Sed	350	750	1300	2400	5200	7400
Sta Wag	450	1000	1650	3350	6300	9000
Bel Air, 6-cyl.						
2 dr Sed	350	900	1550	3050	5900	8500
Sed	350	900	1550	3000	5850	8400
2 dr HdTp	450	1450	2400	4800	8400	12,000
Conv	900	2900	4800	9600	16,800	24,000
Sta Wag	400	1300	2200	4400	7700	11,000

1955

	6	5	4	3	2	1
Model 150, V-8						
Utl Sed	350	700	1150	2300	4550	6500
2 dr Sed	350	750	1200	2350	4900	7000
Sed	350	750	1200	2350	4900	7000
Sta Wag	350	900	1550	3050	5900	8500
Model 210, V-8						
2 dr Sed	350	900	1550	3050	5900	8500
2 dr Sed Del Rey	400	1300	2200	4400	7700	11,000
Sed	350	800	1450	2750	5600	8000
2 dr HdTp	650	2050	3400	6800	11,900	17,000
2 dr Sta Wag	450	1100	1700	3650	6650	9500
4 dr Sta Wag	450	1050	1700	3600	6600	9400
Bel Air, V-8						
2 dr Sed	400	1350	2250	4500	7800	11,200
Sed	400	1300	2200	4400	7700	11,000
2 dr HdTp	750	2400	4000	8000	14,000	20,000
Conv	1150	3600	6000	12,000	21,000	30,000
Nomad	700	2150	3600	7200	12,600	18,000
4 dr Sta Wag	450	1350	2300	4600	8000	11,400

NOTE: Add 10 percent for A/C; 15 percent for "Power-Pak".
Deduct 10 percent for 6-cyl.

1956

	6	5	4	3	2	1
Model 150, V-8						
Utl Sed	350	750	1200	2350	4900	7000
2 dr Sed	350	750	1300	2450	5250	7500
Sed	350	750	1250	2400	5100	7300
Sta Wag	350	800	1450	2750	5600	8000
Model 210, V-8						
2 dr Sed	450	1000	1650	3350	6300	9000
2 dr Sed Del Rey	450	1400	2300	4600	8100	11,500
Sed	450	1000	1600	3300	6250	8900
4 dr HdTp	450	1050	1650	3500	6400	9200
2 dr HdTp	550	1800	3000	6000	10,500	15,000
2 dr Sta Wag	400	1200	2000	3950	7000	10,000
4 dr Sta Wag	450	1100	1700	3650	6650	9500
9P Sta Wag	450	1150	1800	3800	6800	9700
Bel Air, V-8						
2 dr Sed	400	1300	2150	4300	7600	10,800
Sed	400	1300	2150	4300	7500	10,700
4 dr HdTp	450	1400	2300	4600	8100	11,500
2 dr HdTp	750	2400	4000	8000	14,000	20,000
Conv	1000	3250	5400	10,800	18,900	27,000
Nomad	550	1800	3000	6000	10,500	15,000
4 dr Sta Wag	400	1300	2200	4400	7700	11,000

NOTE: Add 10 percent for A/C; 15 percent for "Power-Pak".
Deduct 10 percent for 6-cyl.

1957

	6	5	4	3	2	1
Model 150, V-8						
Utl Sed	350	750	1200	2350	4900	7000
2 dr Sed	350	750	1250	2400	5100	7300
Sed	350	750	1250	2400	5100	7300
2 dr Sta Wag	350	800	1450	2750	5600	8000
Model 210, V-8						
2 dr Sed	450	1000	1650	3350	6300	9000
2 dr Sed Del Ray	400	1300	2200	4400	7700	11,000
Sed	450	1000	1600	3300	6250	8900
4 dr HdTp	450	1150	1900	3850	6850	9800
2 dr HdTp	500	1550	2600	5200	9100	13,000
2 dr Sta Wag	400	1200	2000	3950	7000	10,000
4 dr Sta Wag	400	1200	2000	3950	7000	10,000
9P Sta Wag	400	1200	2050	4100	7100	10,200
Bel Air, V-8						
2 dr Sed	450	1400	2300	4600	8100	11,500
Sed	400	1350	2250	4500	7900	11,300
4 dr HdTp	500	1550	2600	5200	9100	13,000
2 dr HdTp	850	2650	4400	8800	15,400	22,000
Conv	1450	4550	7600	15,200	26,600	38,000
Nomad	700	2150	3600	7200	12,600	18,000
4 dr Sta Wag	450	1400	2300	4600	8100	11,500

NOTE: Add 10 percent for A/C; 15 percent for "Power-Pak" and 20 percent for F.I.
Deduct 10 percent for 6-cyl.

1958

	6	5	4	3	2	1
Del-Ray, V-8						
Utl Sed	200	550	900	2100	3700	5300
2 dr Sed	200	600	950	2150	3850	5500
Sed	200	600	950	2150	3850	5500
Biscayne, V-8						
2 dr Sed	200	600	1000	2200	4000	5700
Sed	200	600	950	2200	3900	5600
Bel Air, V-8						
2 dr Sed	350	900	1550	3050	5900	8500
Sed	350	900	1550	3100	6000	8600
4 dr HdTp	450	1000	1650	3350	6300	9000
2 dr HdTp	450	1450	2400	4800	8400	12,000
Impala	900	2900	4800	9600	16,800	24,000
Imp Conv	1400	4450	7400	14,800	25,900	37,000
Station Wagons, V-8						
2 dr Yeo	350	750	1200	2350	4900	7000
4 dr Yeo	350	725	1200	2350	4800	6800
6P Brookwood	350	750	1250	2400	5050	7200
9P Brookwood	350	750	1300	2450	5250	7500
4 dr Nomad	450	1100	1700	3650	6650	9500

NOTE: Add 10 percent for Power-Pak & dual exhaust on 283 V-8.
Add 20 percent for 348.
Add 30 percent for 348 Tri-Power set up.
Add 15 percent for A/C.
Deduct 10 percent for 6-cyl.

1959

	6	5	4	3	2	1
Biscayne, V-8						
Utl Sed	200	500	850	1900	3500	5000
2 dr Sed	200	550	900	2000	3600	5200
Sed	200	550	900	2100	3700	5300
Bel Air, V-8						
2 dr Sed	200	600	1000	2200	4000	5700
Sed	200	650	1000	2200	4100	5800
4 dr HdTp	200	650	1050	2250	4200	6000
Impala, V-8						
Sed	200	650	1050	2250	4200	6000
4 dr HdTp	350	850	1500	2950	5800	8300
2 dr HdTp	550	1800	3000	6000	10,500	15,000
Conv	900	2900	4800	9600	16,800	24,000
Station Wagons, V-8						
Brookwood	200	650	1050	2250	4200	6000
Parkwood	200	675	1100	2250	4400	6300
Kingswood	350	700	1150	2300	4550	6500
4 dr Nomad	350	750	1200	2350	4900	7000

NOTE: Add 20 percent for speed options and 10 percent for A/C.
Add 5 percent for 4-speed transmission.
Deduct 10 percent for 6-cyl.
Add 30 percent for 348 Tri-Power set up.

1960

	6	5	4	3	2	1
Biscayne, V-8						
Utl Sed	150	450	800	1800	3300	4800
2 dr Sed	200	500	850	1950	3600	5100
Sed	200	550	900	2000	3600	5200
Biscayne Fleetmaster, V-8						
2 dr Sed	200	550	900	2100	3700	5300
Sed	200	550	900	2150	3800	5400
Bel Air, V-8						
2 dr Sed	200	650	1000	2200	4100	5800
Sed	200	650	1000	2200	4150	5900
4 dr HdTp	200	675	1100	2250	4400	6300
2 dr HdTp	350	800	1450	2750	5600	8000
Impala, V-8						
Sed	200	675	1100	2250	4400	6300
4 dr HdTp	350	750	1350	2650	5450	7800
2 dr HdTp	500	1550	2600	5200	9100	13,000
Conv	850	2750	4600	9200	16,100	23,000
Station Wagons, V-8						
Brookwood	200	650	1050	2250	4200	6000
4 dr Kingswood	200	675	1100	2250	4400	6300
4 dr Parkwood	350	700	1150	2300	4550	6500
4 dr Nomad	350	750	1200	2350	4900	7000

NOTE: Add 20 percent for speed options and 10 percent for A/C.
Deduct 10 percent for 6-cyl.
Add 30 percent for 348 Tri-Power set up.

1961

	6	5	4	3	2	1
Biscayne, V-8						
Utl Sed	200	500	850	1850	3350	4900
2 dr Sed	200	600	950	2150	3850	5500
Sed	200	500	850	1950	3600	5100
Bel Air, V-8						
2 dr Sed	200	600	1000	2200	4000	5700
Sed	200	600	950	2200	3900	5600
4 dr HdTp	350	750	1200	2350	4900	7000
2 dr HdTp	400	1300	2200	4400	7700	11,000
Impala, V-8						
2 dr Sed	200	650	1050	2250	4200	6000
Sed	200	675	1050	2250	4300	6100
4 dr HdTp	350	750	1300	2450	5250	7500
2 dr HdTp*	450	1450	2400	4800	8400	12,000
Conv*	700	2300	3800	7600	13,300	19,000
Station Wagons, V-8						
Brookwood	200	600	950	2150	3850	5500
Parkwood	200	650	1000	2200	4150	5900
Nomad	350	750	1200	2350	4900	7000

NOTE: Add 10 percent for Power-Pak & dual exhaust on 283 V-8.
Add 15 percent for A/C.
Add 35 percent for 348 CID.
*Add 20 percent for Super Sport option.
Add 50 percent for 409 V-8.
Deduct 10 percent for 6-cyl.

1962

	6	5	4	3	2	1
Chevy II, 4 & 6-cyl.						
2 dr Sed	200	500	850	1900	3500	5000
Sed	200	500	850	1850	3350	4900
2 dr HdTp	350	800	1450	2750	5600	8000
Conv	400	1200	2000	3950	7000	10,000
Sta Wag	200	550	900	2100	3700	5300
Biscayne, V-8						
2 dr Sed	200	550	900	2150	3800	5400
Sed	200	600	950	2150	3850	5500
Sta Wag	200	550	900	2100	3700	5300
Bel Air, V-8						
2 dr Sed	200	600	950	2200	3900	5600
Sed	200	600	1000	2200	4000	5700
2 dr HdTp	450	1450	2400	4800	8400	12,000
Sta Wag	200	600	950	2150	3850	5500
Bel Air 409 muscle car						
2 dr Sed (380 hp)	550	1800	3000	6000	10,500	15,000
2 dr HdTp (380 hp)	950	3000	5000	10,000	17,500	25,000
2 dr Sed (409 hp)	650	2050	3400	6800	11,900	17,000
2 dr HdTp (409 hp)	1000	3250	5400	10,800	18,900	27,000
Impala, V-8						
Sed	200	650	1050	2250	4200	6000
4 dr HdTp	350	800	1450	2750	5600	8000
2 dr HdTp*	600	1900	3200	6400	11,200	16,000
Conv*	800	2500	4200	8400	14,700	21,000
Sta Wag	350	750	1200	2350	4900	7000

***NOTE:** Add 15 percent for Super Sport option.
Add 15 percent for Power-Pak & dual exhaust.
Add 15 percent for A/C.
Add 35 percent for 409 CID.
Deduct 10 percent for 6-cyl except Chevy II.

1963

	6	5	4	3	2	1
Chevy II and Nova, 4 & 6-cyl.						
Sed	200	500	850	1900	3500	5000
2 dr HdTp*	350	800	1450	2750	5600	8000
Conv*	400	1300	2200	4400	7700	11,000
Sta Wag	200	550	900	2150	3800	5400

***NOTE:** Add 15 percent for Super Sport option.

	6	5	4	3	2	1
Biscayne, V-8						
2 dr Sed	200	500	850	1900	3500	5000
Sed	150	450	800	1800	3300	4800
Sta Wag	200	500	850	1850	3350	4900
Bel Air, V-8						
2 dr Sed	200	550	900	2150	3800	5400
Sed	200	600	950	2150	3850	5500
Sta Wag	200	550	900	2100	3700	5300
Impala, V-8						
Sed	200	650	1050	2250	4200	6000
4 dr HdTp	350	800	1450	2750	5600	8000
2 dr HdTp*	600	1900	3200	6400	11,200	16,000
Conv*	800	2500	4200	8400	14,700	21,000
Sta Wag	350	725	1200	2350	4800	6800

NOTE: Add 15 percent for Power-Pak & dual exhaust.
Add 15 percent for A/C.
Add 35 percent for 409 CID.
Add 15 percent for Super Sport option.
Deduct 10 percent for 6-cyl except Chevy II.

1964

	6	5	4	3	2	1
Chevy II and Nova, 4 & 6-cyl.						
2 dr Sed	150	450	800	1800	3300	4800
Sed	200	500	850	1850	3350	4900
2 dr HdTp	350	800	1450	2750	5600	8000
Sta Wag	200	600	950	2150	3850	5500

NOTE: Add 10 percent for 6-cyl.

	6	5	4	3	2	1
Nova Super Sport Series, 6-cyl.						
2 dr HdTp	400	1300	2200	4400	7700	11,000

NOTE: Add 25 percent for V8.
Add 10 percent for 4 speed trans.

	6	5	4	3	2	1
Chevelle						
2 dr Sed	150	300	700	1250	2650	3800
Sed	150	300	700	1250	2650	3800
2 dr Sta Wag	150	400	750	1600	3100	4400
4 dr Sta Wag	150	400	750	1550	3050	4300
Malibu Series, V-8						
Sed	150	450	800	1800	3300	4800
2 dr HdTp*	500	1550	2600	5200	9100	13,000
Conv*	750	2400	4000	8000	14,000	20,000
4 dr Sta Wag	200	500	850	1900	3500	5000

NOTE: Add 15 percent for Super Sport option.
Deduct 10 percent for 6-cyl.

	6	5	4	3	2	1
Biscayne, V-8						
2 dr Sed	200	500	850	1900	3500	5000
Sed	200	500	850	1950	3600	5100
Sta Wag	200	550	900	2000	3600	5200
Bel Air, V-8						
2 dr Sed	200	550	900	2150	3800	5400
Sed	200	600	950	2150	3850	5500
Sta Wag	200	550	900	2150	3800	5400
Impala, V-8						
Sed	350	700	1100	2300	4500	6400
4 dr HdTp	350	800	1450	2750	5600	8000
2 dr HdTp*	550	1800	3000	6000	10,500	15,000
Conv*	800	2500	4200	8400	14,700	21,000
Sta Wag	350	700	1150	2300	4550	6500

***NOTE:** Add 15 percent for Super Sport option.
Add 15 percent for Power-Pak & dual exhaust.
Add 15 percent for A/C.
Add 35 percent for 409 CID.
Deduct 10 percent for 6-cyl.

1965

	6	5	4	3	2	1
Chevy II, V-8						
Sed	150	450	750	1700	3200	4600
2 dr Sed	150	400	750	1650	3150	4500
Sta Wag	150	400	750	1600	3100	4400
Nova Series, V-8						
Sed	150	450	800	1750	3250	4700

	6	5	4	3	2	1
2 dr HdTp	350	800	1450	2750	5600	8000
Sta Wag	150	450	800	1750	3250	4700
Nova Super Sport, V-8						
Spt Cpe	400	1300	2200	4400	7700	11,000
Chevelle						
2 dr Sed	150	400	750	1600	3100	4400
Sed	150	400	750	1650	3150	4500
2 dr Sta Wag	200	500	850	1900	3500	5000
Sta Wag	150	400	750	1650	3150	4500
Malibu, V-8						
Sed	150	450	800	1800	3300	4800
2 dr HdTp	400	1300	2200	4400	7700	11,000
Conv	650	2050	3400	6800	11,900	17,000
Sta Wag	150	450	800	1750	3250	4700
Malibu Super Sport, V-8						
2 dr HdTp	700	2150	3600	7200	12,600	18,000
Conv	900	2900	4800	9600	16,800	24,000

NOTE: Add 50 percent for RPO Z16 SS-396 option.

	6	5	4	3	2	1
Biscayne, V-8						
2 dr Sed	150	400	750	1600	3100	4400
Sed	150	400	750	1650	3150	4500
Sta Wag	150	400	750	1650	3150	4500
Bel Air, V-8						
2 dr Sed	150	450	800	1800	3300	4800
Sed	200	500	850	1850	3350	4900
Sta Wag	200	500	850	1850	3350	4900
Impala, V-8						
Sed	200	650	1050	2250	4200	6000
4 dr HdTp*	350	750	1300	2450	5250	7500
2 dr HdTp	400	1300	2200	4400	7700	11,000
Conv	700	2150	3600	7200	12,600	18,000
Sta Wag	200	600	950	2150	3850	5500
Impala Super Sport, V-8						
2 dr HdTp	450	1450	2400	4800	8400	12,000
Conv	700	2300	3800	7600	13,300	19,000

NOTE: Add 20 percent for Power-Pak & dual exhaust.
Add 15 percent for A/C.
Add 35 percent for 409 CID.
Add 35 percent for 396 CID.
Deduct 10 percent for 6-cyl.
Add 15 percent for Caprice models.

1966

	6	5	4	3	2	1
Chevy II Series 100						
2 dr Sed	150	450	750	1700	3200	4600
Sed	150	450	800	1750	3250	4700
Sta Wag	150	450	800	1750	3250	4700
Nova Series, V-8						
2 dr HdTp	350	750	1200	2350	4900	7000
Sed	150	450	800	1800	3300	4800
Sta Wag	150	450	800	1800	3300	4800
Nova Super Sport						
2 dr HdTp	350	800	1450	2750	5600	8000

NOTE: Add 60 percent for High Performance pkg.

	6	5	4	3	2	1
Chevelle						
2 dr Sed	150	400	750	1600	3100	4400
Sed	150	400	750	1650	3150	4500
Sta Wag	150	400	750	1650	3150	4500
Malibu, V-8						
Sed	150	450	800	1800	3300	4800
4 dr HdTp	200	500	850	1900	3500	5000
2 dr HdTp	450	1450	2400	4800	8400	12,000
Conv	700	2150	3600	7200	12,600	18,000
Sta Wag	200	500	850	1900	3500	5000
Super Sport, '396' V-8						
2 dr HdTp	800	2500	4200	8400	14,700	21,000
Conv	1000	3100	5200	10,400	18,200	26,000

NOTE: Deduct 10 percent for 6-cyl. Chevelle.

	6	5	4	3	2	1
Biscayne, V-8						
2 dr Sed	200	500	850	1850	3350	4900
Sed	150	450	750	1700	3200	4600
Sta Wag	150	450	750	1700	3200	4600
Bel Air, V-8						
2 dr Sed	200	500	850	1900	3500	5000
Sed	150	450	800	1750	3250	4700
3S Wag	150	450	800	1750	3250	4700
Impala, V-8						
Sed	200	600	950	2150	3850	5500
4 dr HdTp	350	750	1200	2350	4900	7000
2 dr HdTp	450	1450	2400	4800	8400	12,000
Conv	700	2300	3800	7600	13,300	19,000
Sta Wag	200	650	1050	2250	4200	6000
Impala Super Sport, V-8						
2 dr HdTp	550	1800	3000	6000	10,500	15,000
Conv	800	2500	4200	8400	14,700	21,000
Caprice, V-8						
4 dr HdTp	350	900	1550	3050	5900	8500
2 dr HdTp	500	1550	2600	5200	9100	13,000
Sta Wag	350	725	1150	2300	4700	6700

NOTE: Add 40 percent for 396 CID.
Add approx. 40 percent for 427 CID engine when available.
Add 15 percent for A/C.

1967

	6	5	4	3	2	1
Chevy II, 100, V-8, 110" wb						
2 dr Sed	150	400	750	1550	3050	4300
4 dr Sed	150	400	750	1600	3100	4400
Sta Wag	150	400	750	1600	3100	4400
Chevy II Nova, V-8, 110" wb						
4 dr Sed	150	400	750	1650	3150	4500
2 dr HdTp	350	900	1550	3050	5900	8500
Sta Wag	150	400	750	1650	3150	4500
Chevy II Nova SS, V-8, 110" wb						
2 dr HdTp	450	1100	1700	3650	6650	9500

NOTE: Add 60 percent for High Performance pkg.

	6	5	4	3	2	1
Chevelle 300, V-8, 115" wb						
2 dr Sed	150	400	750	1600	3100	4400
4 dr Sed	150	400	750	1650	3150	4500
Chevelle 300 DeLuxe, V-8, 115" wb						
2 dr Sed	150	450	800	1750	3250	4700
4 dr Sed	150	450	800	1800	3300	4800
Sta Wag	200	500	850	1900	3500	5000
Chevelle Malibu, V-8, 115" wb						
4 dr Sed	200	500	850	1900	3500	5000
4 dr HdTp	200	650	1050	2250	4200	6000
2 dr HdTp	400	1200	2000	3950	7000	10,000
Conv	500	1550	2600	5200	9100	13,000
Sta Wag	200	600	950	2150	3850	5500

	6	5	4	3	2	1
Chevelle Concours, V-8, 115" wb						
Sta Wag	200	600	950	2200	3900	5600
Chevelle Super Sport 396, 115" wb						
2 dr HdTp	750	2400	4000	8000	14,000	20,000
Conv	850	2650	4400	8800	15,400	22,000
Biscayne, V-8, 119" wb						
2 dr Sed	200	500	850	1900	3500	5000
4 dr Sed	200	500	850	1950	3600	5100
Sta Wag	200	500	850	1950	3600	5100
Bel Air, V-8, 119" wb						
2 dr Sed	200	650	1050	2250	4200	6000
4 dr Sed	200	600	950	2200	3900	5600
3S Sta Wag	200	600	950	2200	3900	5600
Impala, V-8, 119" wb						
4 dr Sed	200	650	1050	2250	4200	6000
4 dr HdTp	350	700	1150	2300	4550	6500
2 dr HdTp	400	1200	2000	3950	7000	10,000
Conv	650	2050	3400	6800	11,900	17,000
3S Sta Wag	200	600	950	2150	3850	5500
Impala SS, V-8, 119" wb						
2 dr HdTp	400	1300	2200	4400	7700	11,000
Conv	700	2150	3600	7200	12,600	18,000
Caprice, V-8, 119" wb						
2 dr HdTp	450	1450	2400	4800	8400	12,000
4 dr HdTp	350	800	1450	2750	5600	8000
3S Sta Wag	350	750	1200	2350	4900	7000

NOTE: Add approximately 40 percent for SS-427 engine options when available in all series.
Add 40 percent for SS-396 option.
Add 15 percent for A/C.

	6	5	4	3	2	1
Camaro						
Indy Pace Car	950	3000	5000	10,000	17,500	25,000
Cpe	550	1700	2800	5600	9800	14,000
Conv	700	2150	3600	7200	12,600	18,000
Z-28	1300	4100	6800	13,600	23,800	34,000
Yenko Cpe	2850	9100	15,200	30,400	53,200	76,000

NOTE: Deduct 5 percent for Six, (when available).
Add 10 percent for Rally Sport Package (when available; except incl. w/Indy Pace Car).
Add 5 percent for SS-350 (when available; except incl. w/Indy Pace Car).
Add 15 percent for SS-396 (L-35/325 hp; when available).
Add 35 percent for SS-396 (L-78/375 hp; when available).
Add 10 percent for A/C.
Add 35 percent for the 375 horsepower 396, (L78 option).
Add 25 percent for 396 CID-L35.

1968

	6	5	4	3	2	1
Nova Four						
Cpe	200	500	850	1900	3500	5000
Sed	150	400	750	1650	3150	4500

NOTE: Only 1,270 Nova 4's were built in 1968.

	6	5	4	3	2	1
Nova Six						
Cpe	200	600	950	2150	3850	5500
Sed	150	450	800	1750	3250	4700

NOTE: Add 20 percent for "SS" equipment pkg.
Add 25 percent for 327 CID.
Add 30 percent for 350 CID.
Add 35 percent for 396 CID engine.

	6	5	4	3	2	1
Chevelle 300						
2 dr Sed	150	300	750	1350	2700	3900
Sta Wag	150	350	750	1350	2800	4000
Chevelle 300 DeLuxe						
Sed	150	350	750	1350	2800	4000
4 dr HdTp	150	400	750	1550	3050	4300
Cpe	150	350	750	1350	2800	4000
Sta Wag	150	300	750	1350	2700	3900
Chevelle Malibu						
Sed	150	350	750	1450	2900	4100
4 dr HdTp	150	400	750	1650	3150	4500
2 dr HdTp	450	1000	1650	3350	6300	9000
Conv	450	1450	2400	4800	8400	12,000
Sta Wag	150	400	750	1650	3150	4500
Chevelle Concours Estate						
Sta Wag	150	300	750	1350	2700	3900
Chevelle SS-396						
2 dr HdTp	700	2300	3800	7600	13,300	19,000
Conv	800	2500	4200	8400	14,700	21,000
Biscayne						
2 dr Sed	150	350	750	1350	2800	4000
Sed	150	300	750	1350	2700	3900
Sta Wag	150	350	750	1450	2900	4100
Bel Air						
2 dr Sed	150	350	750	1450	2900	4100
Sed	150	350	750	1350	2800	4000
2S Sta Wag	150	350	750	1450	3000	4200
3S Sta Wag	150	400	750	1550	3050	4300
Impala						
Sed	150	400	750	1650	3150	4500
4 dr HdTp	200	600	950	2150	3850	5500
2 dr HdTp	350	750	1300	2450	5250	7500
Cus Cpe	350	800	1450	2750	5600	8000
Conv	650	2050	3400	6800	11,900	17,000
2S Sta Wag	150	400	750	1550	3050	4300
3S Sta Wag	150	400	750	1600	3100	4400
Caprice						
4 dr HdTp	350	700	1150	2300	4550	6500
2 dr HdTp	450	1000	1650	3350	6300	9000
2S Sta Wag	200	600	950	2150	3850	5500
3S Sta Wag	200	650	1050	2250	4200	6000
Chevelle 300						

NOTE: Only 1,270 Nova 4's were built in 1968.

	6	5	4	3	2	1
Camaro						
Cpe	500	1550	2600	5200	9100	13,000
Conv	650	2050	3400	6800	11,900	17,000
Z-28	750	2400	4000	8000	14,000	20,000
Yenko Cpe	2200	6950	11,600	23,200	40,600	58,000

NOTE: Deduct 5 percent for Six, (when available).
Add 10 percent for A/C.
Add 10 percent for Rally Sport Package (when available).
Add 5 percent for SS-350 (when available; except Z-28).
Add 15 percent for SS-396 (L35/325 hp; when available).
Add 35 percent for SS-396 (L78/375 hp; when available).
Add 40 percent for SS-396 (L89; when available).
Add approx. 40 percent for 427 engine options when availble.

1969

	6	5	4	3	2	1
Nova Four						
Cpe	150	400	750	1550	3050	4300
Sed	150	350	750	1450	3000	4200

	6	5	4	3	2	1
Nova Six						
Cpe	150	400	750	1600	3100	4400
Sed	150	400	750	1550	3050	4300
Chevy II, Nova V-8						
Cpe	150	400	750	1650	3150	4500
Sed	150	400	750	1600	3100	4400
Yenko Cpe	2200	6950	11,600	23,200	40,600	58,000

NOTES: Add 25 percent for Nova SS.
Add 30 percent for 350 CID.
Add 35 percent for 396 CID.
Add 25 percent for Impala "SS".
Add 25 percent for other "SS" equipment pkgs.

	6	5	4	3	2	1
Chevelle 300 DeLuxe						
Sed	150	350	750	1350	2800	4000
2 dr HdTp	350	700	1150	2300	4550	6500
Cpe	150	400	750	1650	3150	4500
Nomad	150	450	800	1750	3250	4700
Dual Nomad	200	500	850	1900	3500	5000
GB Wag	150	400	750	1650	3150	4500
GB Dual Wag-6P	150	400	750	1650	3150	4500
GB Dual Wag-9P	150	450	750	1700	3200	4600
Chevelle Malibu, V-8						
Sed	150	400	750	1650	3150	4500
4 dr HdTp	200	500	850	1900	3500	5000
2 dr HdTp	400	1300	2200	4400	7700	11,000
Conv	450	1450	2400	4800	8400	12,000
Estate-9P	150	350	750	1450	2900	4100
Estate-6P	150	350	750	1350	2800	4000

NOTE: Add 10 percent for Concours 4-dr hardtop.

	6	5	4	3	2	1
Chevelle Malibu SS-396						
2 dr HdTp	750	2400	4000	8000	14,000	20,000
Conv	850	2650	4400	8800	15,400	22,000

NOTE: Add 60 percent for Yenko Hardtop.

	6	5	4	3	2	1
Biscayne						
2 dr Sed	150	350	750	1350	2800	4000
Sed	150	300	750	1350	2700	3900
Sta Wag	150	300	750	1350	2700	3900
Bel Air						
2 dr Sed	150	400	750	1650	3150	4500
Sed	150	350	750	1350	2800	4000
Sta Wag-6P	150	350	750	1350	2800	4000
Sta Wag-9P	150	350	750	1450	2900	4100
Impala, V-8						
Sed	150	400	750	1650	3150	4500
4 dr HdTp	200	600	950	2150	3850	5500
2 dr HdTp	350	750	1200	2350	4900	7000
2 dr Cus Cpe	350	750	1250	2400	5050	7200
Conv	500	1550	2600	5200	9100	13,000
Sta Wag-6P	150	350	750	1450	2900	4100
Sta Wag-9P	150	350	750	1450	3000	4200

NOTE: Add 35 percent for Impala SS 427 option.

	6	5	4	3	2	1
Caprice, V-8						
4 dr HdTp	350	700	1150	2300	4550	6500
Cus Cpe	350	800	1450	2750	5600	8000
Sta Wag-6P	150	400	750	1650	3150	4500
Sta Wag-9P	150	450	800	1750	3250	4700
Camaro						
Spt Cpe	450	1450	2400	4800	8400	12,000
Conv	550	1800	3000	6000	10,500	15,000
Z-28	750	2400	4000	8000	14,000	20,000
Pace Car	650	2050	3400	6800	11,900	17,000
ZL-1*	1750	5650	9400	18,800	32,900	47,000
RS Yenko	1750	5650	9400	18,800	32,900	47,000

NOTE: Deduct 5 percent for Six, (when available).
Add 5 percent for Rally Sport (except incl. w/Indy Pace Car).
Add 15 percent for SS-350 (when avail.; except incl. w/Indy Pace Car).
Add 15 percent for SS-396 (L78/375 hp; when available).
Add 35 percent for SS-396 (L89/375 hp, alum. heads; when available).
Add approx. 40 percent for 427 engine options when availble.

*The specially trimmed coupe with the aluminum block 427.

1970

	6	5	4	3	2	1
Nova Four						
Cpe	150	350	750	1350	2800	4000
Sed	150	300	750	1350	2700	3900
Nova Six						
Cpe	150	350	750	1450	2900	4100
Sed	150	350	750	1350	2800	4000
Nova, V-8						
Cpe	150	350	750	1450	3000	4200
Sed	150	350	750	1450	2900	4100
Yenko Cpe	750	2400	4000	8000	14,000	20,000
Chevelle						
Cpe	200	650	1000	2200	4100	5800
Sed	150	400	750	1650	3150	4500
Nomad	200	500	850	1900	3500	5000
Greenbrier						
Sta Wag-6P	150	400	750	1650	3150	4500
Sta Wag-8P	150	400	750	1650	3150	4500
Malibu, V-8						
Sed	150	450	750	1700	3200	4600
4 dr HdTp	200	500	850	1900	3500	5000
2 dr HdTp	400	1200	2000	3950	7000	10,000
Conv	500	1550	2600	5200	9100	13,000
Concours	200	600	950	2150	3850	5500
Estate	200	600	950	2200	3900	5600
Chevelle Malibu SS 396						
2 dr HdTp	550	1700	2800	5600	9800	14,000
Conv	950	3000	5000	10,000	17,500	25,000
Chevelle Malibu SS 454						
2 dr HdTp	1000	3100	5200	10,400	18,200	26,000
Conv	1100	3500	5800	11,600	20,300	29,000

NOTE: Add 30 percent for SS 396 engine option.
Add 35 percent for SS 454-LS6 engine option.

	6	5	4	3	2	1
Monte Carlo						
2 dr HdTp	400	1300	2200	4400	7700	11,000

NOTE: Add 35 percent for SS 454.

	6	5	4	3	2	1
Biscayne						
Sed	150	300	700	1250	2600	3700
Sta Wag	150	300	700	1250	2650	3800
Bel Air						
Sed	150	350	750	1450	2900	4100
Sta Wag-6P	150	350	750	1350	2800	4000
Sta Wag-9P	150	350	750	1450	2900	4100
Impala, V-8						
Sed	150	400	750	1650	3150	4500
4 dr HdTp	200	600	950	2150	3850	5500
Spt Cpe	350	700	1150	2300	4550	6500
Cus Cpe	350	750	1200	2350	4900	7000
Conv	400	1200	2000	3950	7000	10,000
Sta Wag-6P	150	400	750	1650	3150	4500
Sta Wag-9P	150	450	750	1700	3200	4600
Caprice, V-8						
4 dr HdTp	350	700	1150	2300	4550	6500
Cus Cpe	350	800	1450	2750	5600	8000
Sta Wag-6P	150	450	800	1800	3300	4800
Sta Wag-9P	200	500	850	1850	3350	4900

NOTE: Add 35 percent for SS 454 option.
Add 25 percent for Rally Sport and/or Super Sport options.

	6	5	4	3	2	1
Camaro						
Cpe	400	1300	2200	4400	7700	11,000
Z-28	600	1900	3200	6400	11,200	16,000
Sup Spt	550	1700	2800	5600	9800	14,000
Rally Spt	550	1700	2800	5600	9800	14,000

NOTE: Deduct 5 percent for Six, (except Z-28).
Add 35 percent for the 375 horsepower 396, (L78 option).

1971

	6	5	4	3	2	1
Vega						
2 dr	125	250	700	1150	2450	3500
Hatchback	125	250	700	1150	2500	3600
Kammback	150	300	700	1250	2600	3700

NOTE: Add 5 percent for GT.

	6	5	4	3	2	1
Nova, V-8						
4 dr	125	250	700	1150	2450	3500
2 dr	150	300	700	1250	2600	3700
SS 2 dr	450	1000	1650	3350	6300	9000
Chevelle						
2 dr HdTp	450	1000	1650	3350	6300	9000
2 dr Malibu HdTp	500	1550	2600	5200	9100	13,000
Malibu Conv	650	2050	3400	6800	11,900	17,000
4 dr HdTp	200	650	1050	2250	4200	6000
4 dr Sed	150	400	750	1650	3150	4500
Est Wag	200	500	850	1900	3500	5000
Chevelle Malibu SS-350						
2 dr HdTp	600	1900	3200	6400	11,200	16,000
Conv	750	2400	4000	8000	14,000	20,000
Chevelle Malibu SS-454						
2 dr HdTp	700	2300	3800	7600	13,300	19,000
Conv	850	2750	4600	9200	16,100	23,000
Monte Carlo						
2 dr HdTp	450	1450	2400	4800	8400	12,000

NOTE: Add 35 percent for SS 454.

	6	5	4	3	2	1
Biscayne, V-8, 121" wb						
4 dr Sed	125	200	600	1100	2300	3300
Bel Air, V-8, 121" wb						
4 dr Sed	150	350	750	1350	2800	4000
Impala, V-8, 121" wb						
4 dr Sed	150	350	750	1450	3000	4200
4 dr HdTp	200	500	850	1900	3500	5000
2 dr HdTp	200	600	950	2150	3850	5500
2 dr HdTp Cust	200	600	1000	2200	4000	5700
Conv	400	1300	2200	4400	7700	11,000
Caprice, V-8, 121" wb						
4 dr HdTp	200	650	1050	2250	4200	6000
2 dr HdTp	350	750	1200	2350	4900	7000
Station Wags, V-8, 125" wb						
Brookwood 2-S	125	250	700	1150	2400	3400
Townsman 3-S	150	300	700	1250	2600	3700
Kingswood 3-S	150	300	750	1350	2700	3900
Estate 3-S	150	350	750	1350	2800	4000

NOTE: Add 35 percent for SS 454 option.

	6	5	4	3	2	1
Camaro						
Cpe	400	1200	2000	3950	7000	10,000
Z-28	550	1700	2800	5600	9800	14,000

NOTE: Add 15 percent for V-8, (except Z-28).
Add 35 percent for Rally Sport and/or Super Sport options.

1972

	6	5	4	3	2	1
Vega						
2 dr	125	250	700	1150	2450	3500
Hatchback	125	250	700	1150	2500	3600
Kammback	150	300	700	1250	2600	3700

NOTE: Add 15 percent for GT.

	6	5	4	3	2	1
Nova						
4 dr	150	300	700	1250	2600	3700
2 dr	150	300	700	1250	2650	3800

NOTE: Add 25 percent for SS.

	6	5	4	3	2	1
Chevelle						
Malibu Spt Cpe	500	1550	2600	5200	9100	13,000
Malibu Conv	650	2050	3400	6800	11,900	17,000
4 dr HdTp	200	650	1050	2250	4200	6000
4 dr Sed	150	400	750	1650	3150	4500
Est Wag	150	450	750	1700	3200	4600
Chevelle Malibu SS-350						
2 dr HdTp	600	1900	3200	6400	11,200	16,000
Conv	750	2400	4000	8000	14,000	20,000
Chevelle Malibu SS-454						
2 dr HdTp	700	2150	3600	7200	12,600	18,000
Conv	850	2750	4600	9200	16,100	23,000
Monte Carlo						
2 dr HdTp	500	1550	2600	5200	9100	13,000

NOTE: Add 35 percent for 454 CID engine.
Add 25 percent for 402 LT CID engine.

	6	5	4	3	2	1
Biscayne, V-8, 121" wb						
4 dr Sed	125	200	600	1100	2300	3300
Bel Air, V-8, 121" wb						
4 dr Sed	125	250	700	1150	2400	3400
Impala, V-8, 121" wb						
4 dr Sed	150	350	750	1350	2800	4000
4 dr HdTp	200	500	850	1900	3500	5000
2 dr HdTp Custom	200	550	900	2000	3600	5200
2 dr HdTp	150	450	800	1800	3300	4800
Conv	400	1250	2100	4200	7400	10,500
Caprice, V-8, 121" wb						
4 dr Sed	150	350	750	1450	3000	4200
4 dr HdTp	200	600	950	2150	3850	5500
2 dr HdTp	200	650	1050	2250	4200	6000
Station Wagons, V-8, 125" wb						
Brookwood 2-S	125	250	700	1150	2400	3400
Townsman 3-S	150	300	700	1250	2600	3700
Kingswood 3-S	150	350	750	1350	2800	4000
Estate 3-S	150	400	750	1650	3150	4500

NOTE: Add 35 percent for 454 option.
Add 30 percent for 402 option.

	6	5	4	3	2	1
Camaro						
Cpe	400	1200	2000	3950	7000	10,000
Z-28	550	1700	2800	5600	9800	14,000

NOTE: Add 20 percent for V-8, (except Z-28). Add 35 percent for Rally Sport and/or Super Sport options.

1973

	6	5	4	3	2	1
Vega						
2 dr	125	250	700	1150	2500	3600
Hatchback	150	300	700	1250	2600	3700
Sta Wag	150	300	700	1250	2650	3800
Nova Custom V8						
Cpe	150	300	750	1350	2700	3900
4 dr	150	300	700	1250	2650	3800
Hatchback	150	350	750	1350	2800	4000
Chevelle Malibu V8						
Cpe	150	350	750	1450	2900	4100
4 dr	150	350	750	1350	2800	4000
NOTE: Add 15 percent for SS option.						
Laguna V8						
4 dr	150	350	750	1450	2900	4100
Cpe	350	700	1150	2300	4550	6500
DeL Sta Wag 3S	125	250	700	1150	2450	3500
Malibu Sta Wag 3S	125	250	700	1150	2500	3600
Malibu Est 3S	150	300	700	1250	2600	3700
Laguna 3S	150	350	750	1350	2800	4000
Laguna Est 3S	150	350	750	1450	3000	4200
Monte Carlo V8						
Cpe	200	650	1050	2250	4200	6000
Cpe Landau	350	700	1150	2300	4550	6500
Bel Air						
4 dr	150	350	750	1450	2900	4100
Bel Air 2S	150	300	750	1350	2700	3900
Bel Air 3S	150	350	750	1350	2800	4000
Impala V8						
Cpe Sport	200	500	850	1900	3500	5000
Cpe Custom	200	550	900	2000	3600	5200
4 dr	150	350	750	1450	3000	4200
4 dr HdTp	150	400	750	1650	3150	4500
Impala 3S Wag	150	400	750	1600	3100	4400
Caprice Classic V8						
Cpe	200	600	950	2150	3850	5500
4 dr	150	400	750	1550	3050	4300
4 dr HdTp	150	450	800	1750	3250	4700
Conv	400	1250	2100	4200	7400	10,500
Caprice Est 3S	150	450	800	1800	3300	4800
Camaro						
Cpe	400	1200	2000	3950	7000	10,000
Z-28	500	1550	2600	5200	9100	13,000
NOTE: Add 20 percent for V-8, (except Z-28).						

1974

	6	5	4	3	2	1
Vega						
Cpe	150	300	700	1250	2600	3700
Hatch	150	300	700	1250	2650	3800
Sta Wag	150	300	750	1350	2700	3900
Nova						
Cpe	150	300	750	1350	2700	3900
Hatch	150	350	750	1450	2900	4100
Sed	150	300	750	1350	2700	3900
Nova Custom						
Cpe	150	350	750	1350	2800	4000
Hatch	150	350	750	1450	2900	4100
Sed	150	350	750	1350	2800	4000
NOTE: Add 10 percent for Spirit of America option where applied.						
Malibu						
Col Cpe	150	400	750	1650	3150	4500
Col Sed	150	350	750	1450	2900	4100
Sta Wag	150	300	700	1250	2600	3700
Malibu Classic						
Col Cpe	150	450	800	1750	3250	4700
Lan Cpe	150	400	750	1600	3100	4400
Col Sed	150	350	750	1450	2900	4100
Sta Wag	125	250	700	1150	2500	3600
Malibu Classic Estate						
Sta Wag	150	350	750	1450	2900	4100
Laguna						
Type S3	350	750	1300	2450	5250	7500
Monte Carlo						
'S' Cpe	200	600	950	2150	3850	5500
Landau	200	650	1050	2250	4200	6000
Bel Air						
Sed	150	350	750	1350	2800	4000
Sta Wag	150	350	750	1350	2800	4000
Impala						
Sed	150	400	750	1550	3050	4300
HdTp Sed	150	400	750	1600	3100	4400
Spt Cpe	200	500	850	1900	3500	5000
Cus Cpe	200	600	1000	2200	4000	5700
Sta Wag	150	350	750	1450	2900	4100
Caprice Classic						
Sed	150	400	750	1600	3100	4400
HdTp Sed	150	450	800	1750	3250	4700
Cus Cpe	200	650	1050	2250	4200	6000
Conv	400	1250	2100	4200	7400	10,500
Sta Wag	150	400	750	1650	3150	4500
NOTES: Add 20 percent for Nova SS package.						
Add 12 percent for Malibu with canopy roof.						
Add 35 percent for 454 V-8.						
Add 15 percent for Nova with 185 horsepower V-8.						
Add 25 percent for Impala 'Spirit of America' Sport Coupe.						
Camaro						
Cpe	450	1100	1700	3650	6650	9500
LT Cpe	400	1200	2000	3950	7000	10,000
Z-28						
Cpe	400	1300	2200	4400	7700	11,000

1975

	6	5	4	3	2	1
Vega						
Cpe	125	200	600	1100	2250	3200
Hatch	125	200	600	1100	2300	3300
Lux Cpe	125	250	700	1150	2400	3400
Sta Wag	125	250	700	1150	2400	3400
Estate	125	250	700	1150	2450	3500
Cosworth	350	800	1450	2750	5600	8000
Nova						
'S' Cpe	125	250	700	1150	2500	3600
Cpe	125	250	700	1150	2500	3600
Hatch	150	300	700	1250	2600	3700
Sed	150	300	700	1250	2600	3700
Nova Custom						
Cpe	150	300	700	1250	2600	3700
Hatch	150	300	700	1250	2650	3800
Sed	150	300	700	1250	2600	3700
Nova LN, V-8						
4 dr	150	300	700	1250	2650	3800

	6	5	4	3	2	1
Cpe	150	300	750	1350	2700	3900
Monza						
2 plus 2	150	350	750	1350	2800	4000
Twn Cpe	150	300	700	1250	2600	3700
Malibu						
Col Cpe	150	350	750	1350	2800	4000
Col Sed	125	250	700	1150	2450	3500
Sta Wag	125	250	700	1150	2500	3600
Malibu Classic						
Col Cpe	150	400	750	1650	3150	4500
Landau	150	450	800	1750	3250	4700
Col Sed	150	300	700	1250	2600	3700
Sta Wag	125	250	700	1150	2500	3600
Estate Wag	150	300	700	1250	2600	3700
Laguna						
Type S3 2 dr	350	750	1300	2450	5250	7500
Monte Carlo						
'S' Cpe	200	600	950	2150	3850	5500
Landau	200	650	1050	2250	4200	6000
Bel Air						
Sed	125	250	700	1150	2500	3600
Sta Wag	125	250	700	1150	2450	3500
Impala						
Sed	150	300	700	1250	2650	3800
4 dr HdTp	150	300	750	1350	2700	3900
Spt Cpe	150	400	750	1650	3150	4500
Cus Cpe	150	450	750	1700	3200	4600
Landau	200	500	850	1900	3500	5000
Sta Wag	150	300	750	1350	2700	3900
Caprice Classic						
Sed	150	300	750	1350	2700	3900
4 dr HdTp	150	350	750	1350	2800	4000
Cus Cpe	200	500	850	1900	3500	5000
Landau	200	600	950	2150	3850	5500
Conv	500	1550	2600	5200	9100	13,000
Sta Wag	150	350	750	1350	2800	4000
NOTES: Add 10 percent for Nova SS.						
Add 15 percent for SS option on Chevelle wagon.						
Add 20 percent for Monte Carlo or Laguna 454.						
Add 15 percent for canopy top options.						
Add 10 percent for Monza V-8.						
Camaro						
Cpe	350	750	1200	2350	4900	7000
Type LT	350	800	1450	2750	5600	8000
NOTE: Add 30 percent for Camaro R/S.						

CORVAIR

	6	5	4	3	2	1
1960						
Standard, 6-cyl.						
Sed	200	600	950	2150	3850	5500
Cpe	200	650	1050	2250	4200	6000
DeLuxe, 6-cyl.						
Sed	200	600	950	2200	3900	5600
Cpe	200	675	1050	2250	4350	6200
Monza, 6-cyl.						
Cpe	350	900	1550	3050	5900	8500
1961						
Series 500, 6-cyl.						
Sed	200	600	950	2150	3850	5500
Cpe	200	650	1050	2250	4200	6000
Sta Wag	200	650	1000	2200	4100	5800
Series 700, 6-cyl.						
Sed	200	650	1000	2200	4150	5900
Cpe	350	700	1150	2300	4550	6500
Sta Wag	200	675	1050	2250	4350	6200
Monza, 6-cyl.						
Sed	200	675	1050	2250	4300	6100
Cpe	350	750	1350	2600	5400	7700
Greenbrier, 6-cyl.						
Spt Wag	350	700	1150	2300	4550	6500
NOTE: Add $1,200. for A/C.						
1962						
Series 500, 6-cyl.						
Cpe	200	650	1000	2200	4150	5900
Series 700, 6-cyl.						
Sed	200	600	1000	2200	4000	5700
Cpe	350	700	1150	2300	4550	6500
Sta Wag	200	675	1050	2250	4350	6200
Series 900 Monza, 6-cyl.						
Sed	200	675	1050	2250	4300	6100
Cpe	350	750	1300	2500	5300	7600
Conv	450	950	1600	3250	6150	8800
Sta Wag	350	700	1150	2300	4600	6600
Monza Spyder, 6-cyl.						
Cpe	350	850	1500	2800	5650	8100
Conv	450	1100	1700	3650	6650	9500
NOTE: Add $1,600. for K.O. wire wheels.						
Add $800. for A/C.						
Greenbrier, 6-cyl.						
Sta Wag	200	675	1100	2250	4400	6300
1963						
Series 500, 6-cyl.						
Cpe	200	675	1050	2250	4300	6100
Series 700, 6-cyl.						
Sed	200	675	1050	2250	4300	6100
Cpe	350	700	1150	2300	4600	6600
Series 900 Monza, 6-cyl.						
Sed	350	700	1150	2300	4600	6600
Cpe	350	850	1500	2800	5650	8100
Conv	450	1150	1900	3850	6850	9800
Monza Spyder, 6-cyl.						
Cpe	350	900	1550	3100	6000	8600
Conv	450	1100	1800	3700	6700	9600
Greenbrier, 6-cyl.						
Spt Wag	200	675	1100	2250	4400	6300
NOTE: Add $1,600. for K.O. wire wheels.						
Add $800. for A/C.						
1964						
Series 500, 6-cyl.						
Cpe	200	675	1100	2250	4400	6300

	6	5	4	3	2	1
Series 700, 6-cyl.						
Sed	200	675	1050	2250	4300	6100
Series 900 Monza, 6-cyl.						
Sed	350	700	1150	2300	4550	6500
Cpe	350	850	1500	2800	5650	8100
Conv	450	1000	1650	3350	6300	9000
Monza Spyder, 6-cyl.						
Cpe	350	900	1550	3100	6000	8600
Conv	400	1200	2000	3950	7000	10,000
Greenbrier, 6-cyl.						
Spt Wag	350	700	1150	2300	4600	6600

NOTE: Add $1,600. for K.O. wire wheels.
Add $800. for A/C except Spyder.

1965

	6	5	4	3	2	1
Series 500, 6-cyl.						
4 dr HdTp	150	450	800	1800	3300	4800
2 dr HdTp	200	600	950	2150	3850	5500
Monza Series, 6-cyl.						
4 dr HdTp	200	600	950	2150	3850	5500
2 dr HdTp	350	750	1300	2450	5250	7500
Conv	450	1100	1700	3650	6650	9500

NOTE: Add 20 percent for 140 hp engine.

	6	5	4	3	2	1
Corsa Series, 6-cyl.						
2 dr HdTp	350	750	1300	2450	5250	7500
Conv	450	1100	1700	3650	6650	9500
Greenbrier, 6-cyl.						
Spt Wag	200	650	1050	2250	4200	6000

NOTE: Add $1,000. for A/C.

1966

	6	5	4	3	2	1
Series 500, 6-cyl.						
4 dr HdTp	200	500	850	1900	3500	5000
2 dr HdTp	200	600	950	2200	3900	5600
Monza Series, 6-cyl.						
4 dr HdTp	200	600	1000	2200	4000	5700
2 dr HdTp	350	750	1300	2450	5250	7500
Conv	450	1100	1700	3650	6650	9500

NOTE: Add 20 percent for 140 hp engine.

	6	5	4	3	2	1
Corsa Series, 6-cyl.						
2 dr HdTp	350	850	1500	2800	5650	8100
Conv	450	1100	1700	3650	6650	9500

NOTE: Add $1,000. for A/C.

1967

	6	5	4	3	2	1
Series 500, 6-cyl.						
2 dr HdTp	200	600	950	2150	3850	5500
4 dr HdTp	200	500	850	1900	3500	5000
Monza, 6-cyl.						
4 dr HdTp	200	600	1000	2200	4000	5700
2 dr HdTp	350	750	1300	2450	5250	7500
Conv	450	1100	1700	3650	6650	9500

NOTE: Add $1,000. for A/C.

1968

	6	5	4	3	2	1
Series 500, 6-cyl.						
2 dr HdTp	200	600	950	2150	3850	5500
Monza, 6-cyl.						
2 dr HdTp	350	750	1300	2450	5250	7500
Conv	450	1100	1700	3650	6650	9500

NOTE: Add $1,000. for A/C.

1969

	6	5	4	3	2	1
Series 500, 6-cyl.						
2 dr HdTp	350	700	1150	2300	4550	6500
Monza						
2 dr HdTp	450	1000	1650	3350	6300	9000
Conv	450	1150	1800	3800	6800	9700

CORVETTE

	6	5	4	3	2	1
1953						
6-cyl. Conv	1600	5150	8600	17,200	30,100	43,000

1954
(Add $1,800. & up for access. HdTp.)

	6	5	4	3	2	1
6-cyl. Conv	1600	5050	8400	16,800	29,400	42,000

1955
(Add $1,800. & up for access. HdTp.)

	6	5	4	3	2	1
6-cyl. Conv	1550	4900	8200	16,400	28,700	41,000
8-cyl. Conv	1600	5150	8600	17,200	30,100	43,000

1956
NOTE: All post 1956 Corvettes are V-8 powered.
(Add $1,500. & up for removable HdTp.)

	6	5	4	3	2	1
Conv	1700	5400	9000	18,000	31,500	45,000

Add 20 percent for two 4 barrel carbs.

1957
(Add $1,500. for HdTp; 20 percent for F.I.)
(Add 20 percent for two 4 barrel carbs.)

	6	5	4	3	2	1
Conv	1700	5400	9000	18,000	31,500	45,000

1958
(Add $1,500. for HdTp; 20 percent for F.I.)
(Add 20 percent for two 4 barrel carbs.)

	6	5	4	3	2	1
Conv	1400	4450	7400	14,800	25,900	37,000

1959
(Add $1,500. for HdTp; 20 percent for F.I.)
(Add 15 percent for two 4 barrel carbs.)

	6	5	4	3	2	1
Conv	1250	3950	6600	13,200	23,100	33,000

1960
(Add $1,500. for HdTp; 20 percent for F.I.)
(Add 15 percent for two 4 barrel carbs.)

	6	5	4	3	2	1
Conv	1300	4100	6800	13,600	23,800	34,000

1961
(Add $1,600. for HdTp; 20 percent for F.I.)
(Add 15 percent for two 4 barrel carbs.)

	6	5	4	3	2	1
Conv	1250	3950	6600	13,200	23,100	33,000

1962
(Add $1,600. for HdTp; 20 percent for F.I.)

	6	5	4	3	2	1
Conv	1300	4200	7000	14,000	24,500	35,000

1963
(Add 20 percent for F.I.; $4,500. for A/C. $3,000. for knock off wheels.)
(Add $1,200. for hardtop.)

	6	5	4	3	2	1
Spt Cpe	1050	3350	5600	11,200	19,600	28,000

	6	5	4	3	2	1
Conv	1250	3950	6600	13,200	23,100	33,000
Grand Sport				value not estimable		

1964
(Add 20 percent for F.I. $4,500. for A/C. $3,000. for knock off wheels.)
(Add $1,200. for hardtop.)

	6	5	4	3	2	1
Spt Cpe	1000	3100	5200	10,400	18,200	26,000
Conv	1200	3850	6400	12,800	22,400	32,000

1965
(Add 20 percent for F.I. $4,500. for A/C.)
(Add $3,000. for knock off wheels; 50 percent for 396 engine.)
(Add $1,200. for hardtop.)

	6	5	4	3	2	1
Spt Cpe	1000	3100	5200	10,400	18,200	26,000
Conv	1150	3700	6200	12,400	21,700	31,000

1966
(Add $4,500. for A/C, 20 percent for 427 engine - 390 hp, 50 percent for 427 engine - 425 hp. $3,000. for knock off wheels.)
(Add $1,200. for hardtop.)

	6	5	4	3	2	1
Spt Cpe	1000	3100	5200	10,400	18,200	26,000
Conv	1150	3700	6200	12,400	21,700	31,000

1967
(Add $4,500. for A/C. L88 & L89 option not estimable. 20 percent for 427 engine - 390 hp. Add 40 percent for 427 engine - 400 hp, 60 percent for 427 engine - 435 hp. $4,000. for aluminum wheels.)
(Add $1,200. for hardtop.)

	6	5	4	3	2	1
Spt Cpe	1600	5050	8400	16,800	29,400	42,000
Conv	1500	4800	8000	16,000	28,000	40,000

1968
(Add 30 percent for 427 engine - 435 hp. L88 & L89 option not estimable.)

	6	5	4	3	2	1
Spt Cpe	800	2500	4200	8400	14,700	21,000
Conv	1000	3250	5400	10,800	18,900	27,000

1969
(Add 30 percent for 427 engine - 435 hp. L88 & L89 option not estimable.)

	6	5	4	3	2	1
Spt Cpe	750	2400	4000	8000	14,000	20,000
Conv	1000	3100	5200	10,400	18,200	26,000

1970
(Add 20 percent for LT-1 option.)

	6	5	4	3	2	1
Spt Cpe	700	2300	3800	7600	13,300	19,000
Conv	800	2500	4200	8400	14,700	21,000

1971
(Add 20 percent for LT-1 option. Add 20 percent for LS 6 option.)

	6	5	4	3	2	1
Spt Cpe	700	2150	3600	7200	12,600	18,000
Conv	750	2400	4000	8000	14,000	20,000

1972
(Add 20 percent for LT-1 option).

	6	5	4	3	2	1
Spt Cpe	650	2050	3400	6800	11,900	17,000
Conv	750	2400	4000	8000	14,000	20,000

1973

	6	5	4	3	2	1
Spt Cpe	650	2050	3400	6800	11,900	17,000
Conv	750	2400	4000	8000	14,000	20,000

1974

	6	5	4	3	2	1
Spt Cpe	600	1900	3200	6400	11,200	16,000
Conv	700	2300	3800	7600	13,300	19,000

1975

	6	5	4	3	2	1
Spt Cpe	600	1900	3200	6400	11,200	16,000
Conv	750	2400	4000	8000	14,000	20,000

CHRYSLER

	6	5	4	3	2	1
1946						
Royal Series, 6-cyl., 121.5" wb						
3P Cpe	450	1050	1700	3550	6500	9300
6P Cpe	450	1150	1900	3850	6850	9800
2 dr Brgm	350	750	1350	2650	5450	7800
4 dr Sed	350	750	1350	2650	5450	7800
Royal, Series C-38S, 6-cyl., 139.5" wb						
8P Sed	400	1250	2100	4200	7400	10,500
Sed Limo	450	1500	2500	5000	8800	12,500
Windsor Series, 6-cyl., 121.5" wb						
Conv Cpe	850	2650	4400	8800	15,400	22,000
3P Cpe	450	1050	1700	3550	6500	9300
6P Cpe	450	1150	1900	3850	6850	9800
2 dr Brgm	350	750	1250	2400	5100	7300
4 dr Sed	350	750	1350	2650	5450	7800
Windsor Series, 6-cyl., 121.5" wb						
8P Sed	400	1300	2200	4400	7700	11,000
8P Sed Limo	500	1550	2600	5200	9100	13,000
Saratoga Series, 8-cyl., 127.5" wb						
3P Cpe	450	1100	1700	3650	6650	9500
6P Cpe	450	1100	1800	3700	6700	9600
2 dr Brgm	350	750	1250	2400	5050	7200
4 dr Sed	350	750	1300	2500	5300	7600
New Yorker Series, 8-cyl., 127.5" wb						
Conv Cpe	950	3000	5000	10,000	17,500	25,000
3P Cpe	450	1100	1800	3700	6700	9600
6P Cpe	450	1150	1900	3850	6850	9800
2 dr Brgm	350	750	1250	2400	5100	7300
4 dr Sed	350	750	1350	2650	5450	7800
Town & Country						
Conv	2700	8650	14,400	28,800	50,400	72,000
4 dr Sed	1450	4550	7600	15,200	26,600	38,000

NOTE: Add 3 percent for 8-cyl. sedan.

	6	5	4	3	2	1
Crown Imperial, 8-cyl., 145.5" wb						
Limo	550	1800	3000	6000	10,500	15,000
4 dr Sed	500	1550	2600	5200	9100	13,000
1947						
Royal Series, 6-cyl., 121.5" wb						
Cpe	450	1050	1700	3550	6500	9300
Clb Cpe	450	1100	1700	3650	6650	9500
Brgm	350	750	1250	2400	5100	7300
4 dr Sed	350	750	1300	2400	5200	7400
Royal Series, 6-cyl., 139.5" wb						
4 dr Sed	400	1250	2100	4200	7400	10,500
Limo	450	1500	2500	5000	8800	12,500
Windsor Series, 6-cyl., 121.5" wb						
Cpe	450	1100	1700	3650	6650	9500
Clb Cpe	450	1100	1800	3700	6700	9600
Conv	850	2750	4600	9200	16,100	23,000
Brgm	350	750	1350	2650	5450	7800
Windsor Series, 6-cyl., 139.5" wb						
4 dr Sed	400	1300	2200	4400	7700	11,000
Limo	500	1550	2600	5200	9100	13,000

	6	5	4	3	2	1
Saratoga Series, 8-cyl., 127.5" wb						
Cpe	450	1150	1800	3800	6800	9700
Clb Cpe	450	1150	1900	3850	6850	9800
Brgm	350	850	1500	2950	5800	8300
4 dr Sed	350	900	1550	3000	5850	8400
New Yorker, 8-cyl., 127.5" wb						
Cpe	450	1150	1900	3850	6850	9800
Clb Cpe	400	1250	2050	4100	7200	10,300
Conv	950	3000	5000	10,000	17,500	25,000
Brgm	350	900	1550	3100	6000	8600
4 dr Sed	450	950	1600	3250	6150	8800
Town & Country						
Conv	2700	8650	14,400	28,800	50,400	72,000
4 dr Sed	1450	4550	7600	15,200	26,600	38,000
Crown Imperial, 8-cyl., 145.5" wb						
Limo	600	1900	3200	6400	11,200	16,000
4 dr Sed	500	1550	2600	5200	9100	13,000

1948

	6	5	4	3	2	1
Royal Series, 6-cyl., 121.5" wb						
4 dr Sed	350	750	1300	2450	5250	7500
2 dr Sed	350	750	1250	2400	5100	7300
Clb Cpe	450	1050	1700	3600	6600	9400
Cpe	450	1050	1700	3550	6500	9300
Royal Series, 6-cyl., 139.5" wb						
4 dr Sed	400	1250	2100	4200	7400	10,500
Limo	450	1500	2500	5000	8800	12,500
Windsor Series, 6-cyl., 121.5" wb						
4 dr Sed	350	750	1300	2500	5300	7600
Trav Sed	350	750	1350	2650	5450	7800
2 dr Sed	350	750	1300	2450	5250	7500
Clb Cpe	450	1100	1800	3700	6700	9600
Cpe	450	1100	1700	3650	6650	9500
Conv	900	2900	4800	9600	16,800	24,000
Windsor Series, 6-cyl., 139.5" wb						
4 dr Sed	400	1300	2200	4400	7700	11,000
Limo	500	1550	2600	5200	9100	13,000
Saratoga Series, 8-cyl., 127.5" wb						
4 dr Sed	350	850	1500	2950	5800	8300
2 dr Sed	350	850	1500	2900	5700	8200
Clb Cpe	450	1150	1800	3800	6800	9700
3P Cpe	450	1100	1800	3700	6700	9600
New Yorker, 8-cyl., 127.5" wb						
4 dr Sed	450	950	1600	3250	6150	8800
2 dr Sed	350	950	1600	3200	6050	8700
Clb Cpe	400	1300	2200	4400	7700	11,000
Cpe	400	1250	2100	4200	7400	10,500
Conv	1000	3250	5400	10,800	18,900	27,000
Town & Country						
Conv	2700	8650	14,400	28,800	50,400	72,000
4 dr Sed	1450	4550	7600	15,200	26,600	38,000
Imperial C-40						
Limo	600	1900	3200	6400	11,200	16,000
8P Sed	500	1550	2600	5200	9100	13,000

1949

First Series 1949 is the same as 1948

	6	5	4	3	2	1
Royal - Second Series, 6-cyl., 125.5" wb						
4 dr Sed	350	750	1300	2500	5300	7600
Clb Cpe	450	1000	1650	3350	6300	9000
Sta Wag	800	2500	4200	8400	14,700	21,000
Royal - Second Series, 6-cyl., 139.5" wb						
4 dr Sed	350	900	1550	3000	5850	8400
Windsor - Second Series, 6-cyl., 125.5" wb						
4 dr Sed	350	950	1600	3200	6050	8700
Clb Cpe	450	1050	1650	3500	6400	9200
Conv	750	2400	4000	8000	14,000	20,000
Windsor - Second Series, 6-cyl., 139.5" wb						
4 dr Sed	400	1200	2000	3950	7000	10,000
Limo	400	1300	2200	4400	7700	11,000
Saratoga - Second Series, 8-cyl., 131.5" wb						
4 dr Sed	350	800	1450	2750	5600	8000
Clb Cpe	450	1100	1700	3650	6650	9500
New Yorker - Second Series, 8-cyl., 131.5" wb						
4 dr Sed	450	1000	1650	3350	6300	9000
Clb Cpe	450	1150	1800	3800	6800	9700
Conv	800	2500	4200	8400	14,700	21,000
Town & Country - Second Series, 8-cyl., 131.5" wb						
Conv	1900	6000	10,000	20,000	35,000	50,000
Imperial - Second Series, 8-cyl., 131.5" wb						
Sed - Der	450	1450	2400	4800	8400	12,000
Crown Imperial, 8-cyl., 145.5" wb						
8P Sed	500	1550	2600	5200	9100	13,000
Limo	600	2000	3300	6600	11,600	16,500

1950

	6	5	4	3	2	1
Royal Series, 6-cyl., 125.5" wb						
4 dr Sed	350	750	1250	2400	5100	7300
Clb Cpe	350	800	1450	2750	5600	8000
T&C Sta Wag	700	2150	3600	7200	12,600	18,000
Sta Wag	800	2500	4200	8400	14,700	21,000
Royal Series, 6-cyl., 139.5" wb						
4 dr Sed	450	1000	1650	3350	6300	9000
Windsor Series, 6-cyl., 125.5" wb						
4 dr Sed	350	750	1300	2400	5200	7400
Trav Sed	350	750	1300	2500	5300	7600
Clb Cpe	350	900	1550	3050	5900	8500
HdTp	500	1550	2600	5200	9100	13,000
Conv	750	2400	4000	8000	14,000	20,000
Windsor Series, 6-cyl., 139.5" wb						
4 dr Sed	400	1200	2000	3950	7000	10,000
Limo	450	1450	2400	4800	8400	12,000
Saratoga, 8-cyl., 131.5" wb						
4 dr Sed	350	750	1300	2500	5300	7600
Clb Cpe	450	1000	1650	3350	6300	9000
New Yorker, 8-cyl., 131.5" wb						
4 dr Sed	450	1000	1650	3350	6300	9000
Clb Cpe	450	1100	1700	3650	6650	9500
HdTp	550	1700	2800	5600	9800	14,000
Conv	800	2500	4200	8400	14,700	21,000
Town & Country, 8-cyl., 131.5" wb						
HdTp	1550	4900	8200	16,400	28,700	41,000
Imperial , 8-cyl., 131.5" wb						
4 dr Sed	400	1300	2200	4400	7700	11,000
Crown Imperial, 8-cyl., 145.5" wb						
4 dr Sed	450	1450	2400	4800	8400	12,000
Limo	600	1850	3100	6200	10,900	15,500

1951

	6	5	4	3	2	1
Windsor Series, 6-cyl., 125.5" wb						
4 dr Sed	350	750	1250	2400	5100	7300
Clb Cpe	350	800	1450	2750	5600	8000
T&C Sta Wag	650	2050	3400	6800	11,900	17,000
Windsor Series, 6-cyl., 139.5" wb						
4 dr Sed	350	750	1300	2450	5250	7500
Windsor DeLuxe, 6-cyl., 125.5" wb						
4 dr Sed	350	750	1300	2450	5250	7500
Trav Sed	350	750	1350	2600	5400	7700
Clb Cpe	350	900	1550	3050	5900	8500
HdTp	450	1450	2400	4800	8400	12,000
Conv	700	2300	3800	7600	13,300	19,000
Windsor DeLuxe, 6-cyl., 139.5" wb						
4 dr Sed	350	800	1450	2750	5600	8000
Limo	350	900	1550	3050	5900	8500
Saratoga, 8-cyl., 125.5" wb						
4 dr Sed	350	750	1350	2650	5450	7800
Clb Cpe	450	1000	1650	3350	6300	9000
T&C Sta Wag	700	2300	3800	7600	13,300	19,000
Saratoga, 8-cyl., 139.5" wb						
4 dr Sed	400	1300	2200	4400	7700	11,000
Limo	450	1450	2400	4800	8400	12,000
New Yorker, 8-cyl., 131.5" wb						
4 dr Sed	350	850	1500	2950	5800	8300
Clb Cpe	450	950	1600	3250	6150	8800
HdTp	550	1700	2800	5600	9800	14,000
Conv	850	2650	4400	8800	15,400	22,000
T&C Sta Wag	700	2300	3800	7600	13,300	19,000
Imperial, 8-cyl., 131.5" wb						
4 dr Sed	450	950	1600	3250	6150	8800
Clb Cpe	450	1100	1700	3650	6650	9500
HdTp	500	1550	2600	5200	9100	13,000
Conv	700	2150	3600	7200	12,600	18,000
Crown Imperial, 8-cyl., 145.5" wb						
4 dr Sed	450	1450	2400	4800	8400	12,000
Limo	600	1900	3200	6400	11,200	16,000

1952

	6	5	4	3	2	1
Windsor, 6-cyl., 125.5" wb						
4 dr Sed	350	750	1250	2400	5100	7300
Clb Cpe	350	800	1450	2750	5600	8000
T&C Sta Wag	650	2050	3400	6800	11,900	17,000
Windsor, 6-cyl., 139.5" wb						
4 dr Sed	350	750	1300	2500	5300	7600
Windsor DeLuxe, 6-cyl., 125.5" wb						
4 dr Sed	350	750	1300	2500	5300	7600
HdTp	400	1200	2000	3950	7000	10,000
Conv	700	2300	3800	7600	13,300	19,000
Saratoga, 8-cyl., 125.5" wb						
4 dr Sed	350	750	1350	2650	5450	7800
Clb Cpe	350	900	1550	3050	5900	8500
T&C Sta Wag	650	2050	3400	6800	11,900	17,000
Saratoga, 8-cyl., 139.5" wb						
4 dr Sed	400	1200	2000	3950	7000	10,000
New Yorker, 8-cyl., 131.5" wb						
4 dr Sed	350	900	1550	3050	5900	8500
HdTp	550	1800	3000	6000	10,500	15,000
Conv	850	2650	4400	8800	15,400	22,000
Imperial, 8-cyl., 131.5" wb						
4 dr Sed	450	1000	1650	3350	6300	9000
Clb Cpe	450	950	1600	3250	6150	8800
HdTp	650	2050	3400	6800	11,900	17,000
Crown Imperial, 8-cyl., 145.5" wb						
4 dr Sed	450	1450	2400	4800	8400	12,000
Limo	550	1800	3000	6000	10,500	15,000

1953

	6	5	4	3	2	1
Windsor Series, 6-cyl., 125.5" wb						
4 dr Sed	350	750	1200	2350	4900	7000
Clb Cpe	350	800	1450	2750	5600	8000
T&C Sta Wag	650	2050	3400	6800	11,900	17,000
Windsor Series, 6-cyl., 139.5" wb						
4 dr Sed	350	750	1250	2350	5000	7100
Windsor DeLuxe Series, 6-cyl., 125.5" wb						
4 dr Sed	350	750	1250	2400	5100	7300
HdTp	400	1200	2000	3950	7000	10,000
Conv	600	1900	3200	6400	11,200	16,000
New Yorker, 8-cyl., 125.5" wb						
4 dr Sed	350	750	1350	2650	5450	7800
Clb Cpe	350	900	1550	3050	5900	8500
HdTp	450	1450	2400	4800	8400	12,000
T&C Sta Wag	600	1900	3200	6400	11,200	16,000
New Yorker, 8-cyl., 139.5" wb						
4 dr Sed	350	850	1500	2950	5800	8300
New Yorker Deluxe, 8-cyl., 125.5" wb						
4 dr Sed	350	850	1500	2800	5650	8100
Clb Cpe	450	1000	1650	3350	6300	9000
HdTp	550	1700	2800	5600	9800	14,000
Conv	850	2650	4400	8800	15,400	22,000
Custom Imperial Series, 8-cyl., 133.5" wb						
4 dr Sed	350	900	1550	3050	5900	8500
Twn Limo	450	1450	2400	4800	8400	12,000
Custom Imperial, 8-cyl., 131.5" wb						
HdTp	600	1900	3200	6400	11,200	16,000
Crown Imperial, 8-cyl., 145.5" wb						
4 dr Sed	450	1450	2400	4800	8400	12,000
Limo	550	1700	2800	5600	9800	14,000

1954

	6	5	4	3	2	1
Windsor DeLuxe Series, 6-cyl., 125.5" wb						
4 dr Sed	350	750	1200	2350	4900	7000
Clb Cpe	350	750	1300	2450	5250	7500
HdTp	550	1700	2800	5600	9800	14,000
Conv	850	2650	4400	8800	15,400	22,000
T&C Sta Wag	500	1550	2600	5200	9100	13,000
Windsor DeLuxe Series, 6-cyl., 139.5" wb						
4 dr Sed	350	900	1550	3050	5900	8500
New Yorker Series, 8-cyl., 125.5" wb						
4 dr Sed	350	800	1450	2750	5600	8000
Clb Cpe	450	1000	1650	3350	6300	9000
HdTp	700	2150	3600	7200	12,600	18,000
T&C Sta Wag	550	1700	2800	5600	9800	14,000
New Yorker Series, 8-cyl., 139.5" wb						
4 dr Sed	450	1000	1650	3350	6300	9000
New Yorker DeLuxe Series, 8-cyl., 125.5" wb						
4 dr Sed	350	900	1550	3050	5900	8500
Clb Cpe	450	1100	1700	3650	6650	9500
HdTp	750	2400	4000	8000	14,000	20,000
Conv	1000	3250	5400	10,800	18,900	27,000
Custom Imperial Line, 8-cyl., 133.5" wb						
4 dr Sed	400	1300	2200	4400	7700	11,000
Limo	550	1800	3000	6000	10,500	15,000

	6	5	4	3	2	1
Custom Imperial Line, 8-cyl., 131" wb						
2 dr HdTp Newport	600	1900	3200	6400	11,200	16,000
Crown Imperial Line, 8-cyl., 145.5" wb						
4 dr Sed	450	1450	2400	4800	8400	12,000
Limo	600	1900	3200	6400	11,200	16,000

1955

	6	5	4	3	2	1
Windsor DeLuxe Series, V-8, 126" wb						
4 dr Sed	350	750	1300	2450	5250	7500
2 dr HdTp Nassau	550	1800	3000	6000	10,500	15,000
2 dr HdTp Newport	600	1900	3200	6400	11,200	16,000
Conv	850	2750	4600	9200	16,100	23,000
T&C Sta Wag	400	1300	2200	4400	7700	11,000
New Yorker Deluxe Series, V-8, 126" wb						
4 dr Sed	350	900	1550	3050	5900	8500
2 dr HdTp Newport	600	1900	3200	6400	11,200	16,000
2 dr HdTp St Regis	650	2050	3400	6800	11,900	17,000
Conv	1000	3250	5400	10,800	18,900	27,000
T&C Sta Wag	450	1450	2400	4800	8400	12,000
300 Series, V-8, 126" wb						
Spt Cpe	1350	4300	7200	14,400	25,200	36,000
Imperial Series, V-8						
4 dr Sed	400	1300	2200	4400	7700	11,000
2 dr HdTp Newport	700	2150	3600	7200	12,600	18,000
Crown Imperial Series, V-8						
8P 4 dr Sed	550	1700	2800	5600	9800	14,000
8P Limo	750	2400	4000	8000	14,000	20,000

1956

	6	5	4	3	2	1
Windsor Series, V-8						
4 dr Sed	350	750	1350	2600	5400	7700
4 dr HdTp	350	900	1550	3050	5900	8500
2 dr HdTp Nassau	550	1800	3000	6000	10,500	15,000
2 dr HdTp Newport	600	1900	3200	6400	11,200	16,000
Conv	1000	3100	5200	10,400	18,200	26,000
T&C Sta Wag	450	1400	2300	4600	8100	11,500
New Yorker Series, V-8						
4 dr Sed	350	900	1550	3050	5900	8500
4 dr HdTp	450	1450	2400	4800	8400	12,000
2 dr HdTp Newport	700	2150	3600	7200	12,600	18,000
2 dr HdTp St Regis	700	2300	3800	7600	13,300	19,000
Conv	1100	3500	5800	11,600	20,300	29,000
T&C Sta Wag	450	1450	2400	4800	8400	12,000
300 Letter Series "B", V-8						
2 dr HdTp	1350	4300	7200	14,400	25,200	36,000
Imperial Line, V-8						
4 dr Sed	400	1300	2200	4400	7700	11,000
4 dr HdTp S Hamp	550	1700	2800	5600	9800	14,000
2 dr HdTp S Hamp	700	2300	3800	7600	13,300	19,000
Crown Imperial Line, V-8						
8P 4 dr Sed	550	1800	3000	6000	10,500	15,000
8P Limo	700	2300	3800	7600	13,300	19,000

1957

	6	5	4	3	2	1
Windsor Series, V-8						
4 dr Sed	350	750	1200	2350	4900	7000
4 dr HdTp	350	900	1550	3050	5900	8500
2 dr HdTp	600	1900	3200	6400	11,200	16,000
T&C Sta Wag	350	800	1450	2750	5600	8000
Saratoga Series, V-8						
4 dr Sed	350	750	1300	2450	5250	7500
4 dr HdTp	400	1300	2200	4400	7700	11,000
2 dr HdTp	650	2050	3400	6800	11,900	17,000
New Yorker Series, V-8						
4 dr Sed	350	750	1300	2450	5250	7500
4 dr HdTp	450	1450	2400	4800	8400	12,000
2 dr HdTp	750	2400	4000	8000	14,000	20,000
Conv	1000	3100	5200	10,400	18,200	26,000
T&C Sta Wag	450	1000	1650	3350	6300	9000
300 Letter Series "C", V-8						
2 dr HdTp	1600	5050	8400	16,800	29,400	42,000
Conv	2050	6500	10,800	21,600	37,800	54,000
Imperial Line, V-8						
4 dr Sed	400	1200	2000	3950	7000	10,000
4 dr HdTp S Hamp	500	1550	2600	5200	9100	13,000
2 dr HdTp S Hamp	800	2500	4200	8400	14,700	21,000
Crown Imperial Line, V-8						
4 dr Sed	400	1300	2200	4400	7700	11,000
4 dr HdTp S Hamp	550	1700	2800	5600	9800	14,000
2 dr HdTp S Hamp	850	2650	4400	8800	15,400	22,000
Conv	1150	3600	6000	12,000	21,000	30,000
Imperial LeBaron Line, V-8						
4 dr Sed	500	1550	2600	5200	9100	13,000
4 dr HdTp S Hamp	550	1800	3000	6000	10,500	15,000
Crown Imperial Ghia, V-8						
8P Limo	1000	3100	5200	10,400	18,200	26,000

1958

	6	5	4	3	2	1
Windsor Series, V-8						
4 dr Sed	350	750	1300	2450	5250	7500
4 dr HdTp	400	1200	2000	3950	7000	10,000
2 dr HdTp	550	1700	2800	5600	9800	14,000
T&C Sta Wag	350	750	1300	2450	5250	7500
T&C Sta Wag	350	750	1350	2600	5400	7700
Saratoga Series, V-8						
4 dr Sed	350	750	1300	2450	5250	7500
4 dr HdTp	400	1200	2000	3950	7000	10,000
2 dr HdTp	550	1800	3000	6000	10,500	15,000
New Yorker Series, V-8						
4 dr Sed	350	800	1450	2750	5600	8000
4 dr HdTp	400	1300	2200	4400	7700	11,000
2 dr HdTp	600	1900	3200	6400	11,200	16,000
Conv	950	3000	5000	10,000	17,500	25,000
6P T&C Sta Wag	350	900	1550	3050	5900	8500
9P T&C Sta Wag	350	950	1600	3200	6050	8700
300 Letter Series "D"						
2 dr HdTp	1650	5300	8800	17,600	30,800	44,000
Conv	2050	6600	11,000	22,000	38,500	55,000
NOTE: Add 40 percent for EFI.						
Imperial Line, V-8						
4 dr Sed	400	1200	2000	3950	7000	10,000
4 dr HdTp S Hamp	450	1450	2400	4800	8400	12,000
2 dr HdTp S Hamp	800	2500	4200	8400	14,700	21,000
Crown Imperial Line, V-8						
4 dr Sed	400	1300	2200	4400	7700	11,000
4 dr HdTp S Hamp	500	1550	2600	5200	9100	13,000
2 dr HdTp S Hamp	750	2400	4000	8000	14,000	20,000
Conv	950	3000	5000	10,000	17,500	25,000
Imperial LeBaron Line, V-8						
4 dr Sed	450	1450	2400	4800	8400	12,000
4 dr HdTp S Hamp	600	1900	3200	6400	11,200	16,000
Crown Imperial Ghia, V-8						
Limo	950	3000	5000	10,000	17,500	25,000

1959

	6	5	4	3	2	1
Windsor Series, V-8						
4 dr Sed	350	750	1200	2350	4900	7000
4 dr HdTp	450	1000	1650	3350	6300	9000
2 dr HdTp	550	1700	2800	5600	9800	14,000
Conv	700	2300	3800	7600	13,300	19,000
Town & Country Series, V-8						
6P Sta Wag	350	750	1200	2350	4900	7000
9P Sta Wag	350	750	1250	2400	5050	7200
Saratoga Series, V-8						
4 dr Sed	350	750	1300	2450	5250	7500
4 dr HdTp	400	1200	2000	3950	7000	10,000
2 dr HdTp	550	1700	2800	5600	9800	14,000
New Yorker Series, V-8						
4 dr Sed	350	800	1450	2750	5600	8000
4 dr HdTp	400	1300	2200	4400	7700	11,000
2 dr HdTp	550	1800	3000	6000	10,500	15,000
Conv	850	2650	4400	8800	15,400	22,000
Town & Country, V-8						
6P Sta Wag	350	750	1300	2450	5250	7500
9P Sta Wag	350	750	1350	2600	5400	7700
300 Letter Series "E", V-8						
2 dr HdTp	1650	5300	8800	17,600	30,800	44,000
Conv	1950	6250	10,400	20,800	36,400	52,000
Imperial Custom Line, V-8						
Sed	450	1100	1700	3650	6650	9500
4 dr HdTp S Hamp	400	1300	2200	4400	7700	11,000
2 dr HdTp S Hamp	550	1800	3000	6000	10,500	15,000
Crown Imperial Line, V-8						
4 dr Sed	400	1200	2000	3950	7000	10,000
4 dr HdTp S Hamp	450	1450	2400	4800	8400	12,000
2 dr HdTp S Hamp	600	1900	3200	6400	11,200	16,000
Conv	950	3000	5000	10,000	17,500	25,000
Imperial LeBaron Line, V-8						
4 dr Sed	400	1300	2200	4400	7700	11,000
4 dr HdTp S Hamp	500	1550	2600	5200	9100	13,000
Crown Imperial Ghia, V-8						
Limo	950	3000	5000	10,000	17,500	25,000

1960

	6	5	4	3	2	1
Windsor Series, V-8						
4 dr Sed	200	600	950	2150	3850	5500
4 dr HdTp	200	650	1050	2250	4200	6000
2 dr HdTp	350	800	1450	2750	5600	8000
Conv	550	1700	2800	5600	9800	14,000
Town & Country Series, V-8						
9P Sta Wag	200	600	950	2150	3850	5500
6P Sta Wag	200	600	950	2150	3850	5500
Saratoga Series, V-8						
4 dr Sed	200	600	1000	2200	4000	5700
4 dr HdTp	350	750	1200	2350	4900	7000
2 dr HdTp	450	1000	1650	3350	6300	9000
New Yorker Series, V-8						
4 dr Sed	200	650	1000	2200	4150	5900
4 dr HdTp	350	750	1300	2450	5250	7500
2 dr HdTp	400	1200	2000	3950	7000	10,000
Conv	600	1900	3200	6400	11,200	16,000
Town & Country Series, V-8, 126" wb						
9P Sta Wag	350	725	1150	2300	4700	6700
6P Sta Wag	350	725	1150	2300	4700	6700
300 Letter Series "F", V-8						
2 dr HdTp	1600	5050	8400	16,800	29,400	42,000
Conv	1900	6100	10,200	20,400	35,700	51,000
NOTE: Add 50 percent for 4 speed trans. short Ram engine.						
Custom Imperial Line, V-8						
4 dr Sed	350	750	1300	2450	5250	7500
4 dr HdTp S Hamp	400	1200	2000	3950	7000	10,000
2 dr HdTp S Hamp	450	1450	2400	4800	8400	12,000
Crown Imperial Line, V-8						
4 dr Sed	350	800	1450	2750	5600	8000
4 dr HdTp S Hamp	400	1300	2200	4400	7700	11,000
2 dr HdTp S Hamp	500	1550	2600	5200	9100	13,000
Conv	750	2400	4000	8000	14,000	20,000
Imperial LeBaron Line						
4 dr Sed	450	1000	1650	3350	6300	9000
4 dr HdTp S Hamp	450	1450	2400	4800	8400	12,000
Crown Imperial Ghia, V-8						
Limo	950	3000	5000	10,000	17,500	25,000

1961

	6	5	4	3	2	1
Newport Series, V-8						
4 dr Sed	150	450	750	1700	3200	4600
4 dr HdTp	200	600	950	2150	3850	5500
2 dr HdTp	200	650	1050	2250	4200	6000
Conv	450	1450	2400	4800	8400	12,000
9P Sta Wag	150	450	750	1700	3200	4600
6P Sta Wag	150	450	750	1700	3200	4600
Windsor Series, V-8						
4 dr Sed	150	450	800	1800	3300	4800
4 dr HdTp	200	650	1050	2250	4200	6000
2 dr HdTp	350	750	1200	2350	4900	7000
New Yorker Series, V-8						
4 dr Sed	200	500	850	1900	3500	5000
4 dr HdTp	350	700	1150	2300	4550	6500
2 dr HdTp	350	750	1300	2450	5250	7500
Conv	550	1800	3000	6000	10,500	15,000
9P Sta Wag	200	500	850	1900	3500	5000
6P Sta Wag	200	500	850	1900	3500	5000
300 Letter Series "G", V-8						
2 dr HdTp	1500	4800	8000	16,000	28,000	40,000
Conv	1950	6250	10,400	20,800	36,400	52,000
NOTE: Add 20 percent for 400HP engine.						
Custom Imperial Line, V-8						
4 dr HdTp S Hamp	350	750	1300	2450	5250	7500
2 dr HdTp S Hamp	350	900	1550	3050	5900	8500
Crown Imperial Line, V-8						
4 dr HdTp S Hamp	350	800	1450	2750	5600	8000
2 dr HdTp S Hamp	450	1000	1650	3350	6300	9000
Conv	700	2300	3800	7600	13,300	19,000
Imperial LeBaron Line, V-8						
4 dr HdTp S Hamp	400	1200	2000	3950	7000	10,000
Crown Imperial Ghia, V-8						
Limo	900	2900	4800	9600	16,800	24,000

1962

	6	5	4	3	2	1
Newport Series, V-8						
4 dr Sed	150	450	750	1700	3200	4600
4 dr HdTp	200	500	850	1900	3500	5000

	6	5	4	3	2	1
2 dr HdTp	350	700	1150	2300	4550	6500
Conv	400	1300	2200	4400	7700	11,000
9P HdTp Wag	200	650	1050	2250	4200	6000
6P HdTp Wag	200	650	1000	2200	4150	5900
300 Series						
4 dr HdTp	350	700	1150	2300	4550	6500
2 dr HdTp	450	1000	1650	3350	6300	9000
Conv	550	1800	3000	6000	10,500	15,000
300 Letter Series "H", V-8						
2 dr HdTp	1450	4700	7800	15,600	27,300	39,000
Conv	1900	6100	10,200	20,400	35,700	51,000
New Yorker Series, V-8						
4 dr Sed	200	500	850	1900	3500	5000
4 dr HdTp	350	700	1150	2300	4550	6500
9P HdTp Wag	350	750	1200	2350	4900	7000
6P HdTp Wag	350	750	1200	2350	4900	7000
Custom Imperial Line, V-8						
4 dr HdTp S Hamp	350	800	1450	2750	5600	8000
2 dr HdTp S Hamp	450	1000	1650	3350	6300	9000
Crown Imperial Line, V-8						
4 dr HdTp S Hamp	350	900	1550	3050	5900	8500
2 dr HdTp S Hamp	450	1100	1700	3650	6650	9500
Conv	700	2150	3600	7200	12,600	18,000
Imperial LeBaron Line, V-8						
4 dr HdTp S Hamp	400	1200	2000	3950	7000	10,000
Crown Imperial Ghia, V-8						
8P 4 dr Sed	450	1450	2400	4800	8400	12,000
Limo	700	2150	3600	7200	12,600	18,000

1963

	6	5	4	3	2	1
Newport Series, V-8						
4 dr Sed	150	350	750	1350	2800	4000
4 dr HdTp	200	500	850	1900	3500	5000
2 dr HdTp	200	650	1050	2250	4200	6000
Conv	400	1300	2200	4400	7700	11,000
9P Sta Wag	150	350	750	1350	2800	4000
6P Sta Wag	150	350	750	1350	2800	4000
300 Series, "383" V-8						
4 dr HdTp	350	700	1150	2300	4550	6500
2 dr HdTp	350	900	1550	3050	5900	8500
Conv	550	1700	2800	5600	9800	14,000
300 "Pacesetter" Series, "383" V-8						
2 dr HdTp	350	800	1450	2750	5600	8000
Conv	550	1800	3000	6000	10,500	15,000
300 Letter Series "J", "413" V-8						
2 dr HdTp	1050	3350	5600	11,200	19,600	28,000
New Yorker Series, V-8						
4 dr Sed	150	400	750	1550	3050	4300
4 dr HdTp	200	600	950	2150	3850	5500
4 dr HdTp Salon	200	650	1050	2250	4200	6000
9P HdTp Wag	200	600	950	2150	3850	5500
6P HdTp Wag	200	600	950	2150	3850	5500
Custom Imperial Line, V-8						
4 dr HdTp S Hamp	200	600	950	2150	3850	5500
2 dr HdTp S Hamp	350	750	1200	2350	4900	7000
Crown Imperial Line, V-8						
4 dr HdTp S Hamp	350	750	1200	2350	4900	7000
2 dr HdTp S Hamp	350	800	1450	2750	5600	8000
Conv	600	1900	3200	6400	11,200	16,000
Imperial LeBaron Line, V-8						
4 dr HdTp S Hamp	350	750	1300	2450	5250	7500
Crown Imperial Ghia, V-8						
8P 4 dr Sed	450	1450	2400	4800	8400	12,000
8P Limo	700	2150	3600	7200	12,600	18,000

1964

	6	5	4	3	2	1
Newport Series, V-8						
4 dr Sed	125	250	700	1150	2450	3500
4 dr HdTp	150	450	750	1700	3200	4600
2 dr HdTp	200	600	950	2150	3850	5500
Conv	450	1100	1700	3650	6650	9500
Town & Country Series, V-8						
9P Sta Wag	150	400	750	1650	3150	4500
6P Sta Wag	150	400	750	1650	3150	4500
300 Series						
4 dr HdTp	200	600	950	2150	3850	5500
2 dr HdTp	350	750	1300	2450	5250	7500
Conv	550	1700	2800	5600	9800	14,000
300 Letter Series "K", V-8						
2 dr HdTp	1050	3350	5600	11,200	19,600	28,000
Conv	1300	4100	6800	13,600	23,800	34,000
New Yorker Series, V-8						
4 dr Sed	200	500	850	1900	3500	5000
4 dr HdTp	200	650	1050	2250	4200	6000
4 dr HdTp Salon	350	700	1150	2300	4550	6500
Town & Country Series, V-8						
9P HdTp Wag	200	650	1050	2250	4200	6000
6P HdTp Wag	200	650	1050	2250	4200	6000
Imperial Crown, V-8						
4 dr HdTp	350	750	1200	2350	4900	7000
2 dr HdTp	350	750	1300	2450	5250	7500
Conv	600	1900	3200	6400	11,200	16,000
Imperial LeBaron, V-8						
4 dr HdTp	350	800	1450	2750	5600	8000
Crown Imperial Ghia, V-8						
Limo	700	2150	3600	7200	12,600	18,000

1965

	6	5	4	3	2	1
Newport Series, V-8						
4 dr Sed	125	250	700	1150	2450	3500
6W 4 dr Sed	125	250	700	1150	2450	3500
4 dr HdTp	150	400	750	1650	3150	4500
2 dr HdTp	200	600	950	2150	3850	5500
Conv	450	1100	1700	3650	6650	9500
Town & Country Series, V-8						
9P HdTp Wag	200	500	850	1900	3500	5000
6P HdTp Wag	200	500	850	1900	3500	5000
300 Series						
4 dr HdTp	200	600	950	2150	3850	5500
2 dr HdTp	350	750	1200	2350	4900	7000
Conv	500	1550	2600	5200	9100	13,000
300 Letter Series "L", V-8						
2 dr HdTp	1000	3250	5400	10,800	18,900	27,000
Conv	1200	3850	6400	12,800	22,400	32,000
New Yorker Series, V-8						
6W 4 dr Sed	150	350	750	1350	2800	4000
4 dr HdTp	200	500	850	1900	3500	5000
2 dr HdTp	350	700	1150	2300	4550	6500
Town & Country Series, V-8						
9P HdTp Wag	200	650	1050	2250	4200	6000
6P HdTp Wag	200	650	1050	2250	4200	6000
Crown Imperial Line, V-8						
4 dr HdTp	200	650	1050	2250	4200	6000
2 dr HdTp	350	750	1200	2350	4900	7000
Conv	550	1800	3000	6000	10,500	15,000
Imperial LeBaron Line, V-8						
4 dr HdTp	350	750	1300	2450	5250	7500
Crown Imperial Ghia, V-8						
Limo	650	2050	3400	6800	11,900	17,000

1966

	6	5	4	3	2	1
Newport Series, V-8						
4 dr Sed	150	350	750	1350	2800	4000
6W 4 dr Sed	150	350	750	1350	2800	4000
4 dr HdTp	200	600	950	2150	3850	5500
2 dr HdTp	350	700	1150	2300	4550	6500
Conv	450	1100	1700	3650	6650	9500
Town & Country Series, V-8						
9P Sta Wag	200	500	850	1900	3500	5000
6P Sta Wag	200	500	850	1900	3500	5000
Chrysler 300, V-8						
4 dr HdTp	200	650	1050	2250	4200	6000
2 dr HdTp	400	1300	2200	4400	7700	11,000
Conv	650	2050	3400	6800	11,900	17,000
New Yorker, V-8						
6W 4 dr Sed	200	600	950	2150	3850	5500
4 dr HdTp	200	650	1000	2200	4100	5800
2 dr HdTp	350	700	1150	2300	4550	6500
Imperial, V-8						
4 dr HdTp	200	650	1050	2250	4200	6000
2 dr HdTp	350	750	1200	2350	4900	7000
Conv	550	1800	3000	6000	10,500	15,000
Imperial Lebaron, V-8						
4 dr HdTp	350	800	1450	2750	5600	8000

1967

	6	5	4	3	2	1
Newport, V-8, 124" wb						
4 dr Sed	150	350	750	1450	2900	4100
4 dr HdTp	200	600	950	2150	3850	5500
2 dr HdTp	350	700	1150	2300	4550	6500
Conv	400	1200	2000	3950	7000	10,000
Sta Wag	200	500	850	1900	3500	5000
Newport Custom, V-8, 124" wb						
4 dr Sed	150	350	750	1450	3000	4200
4 dr HdTp	200	600	950	2150	3850	5500
2 dr HdTp	350	700	1150	2300	4550	6500
300, V-8, 124" wb						
2 dr HdTp	350	750	1300	2450	5250	7500
4 dr HdTp	200	650	1050	2250	4200	6000
Conv	550	1800	3000	6000	10,500	15,000
New Yorker, V-8, 124" wb						
4 dr Sed	150	400	750	1650	3150	4500
2 dr HdTp	350	750	1200	2350	4900	7000
4 dr HdTp	200	650	1050	2250	4200	6000
Imperial, V-8, 127" wb						
4 dr Sed	350	700	1150	2300	4550	6500
Conv	650	2050	3400	6800	11,900	17,000
Imperial Crown						
4 dr HdTp	350	750	1200	2350	4900	7000
2 dr HdTp	450	1100	1700	3650	6650	9500
Imperial Lebaron						
4 dr HdTp	350	750	1300	2450	5250	7500

1968

	6	5	4	3	2	1
Newport, V-8, 124" wb						
2 dr HdTp	350	700	1150	2300	4550	6500
4 dr Sed	150	400	750	1650	3150	4500
4 dr HdTp	200	600	950	2150	3850	5500
Conv	400	1200	2000	3950	7000	10,000
Newport Custom, V-8, 124" wb						
4 dr Sed	150	450	800	1750	3250	4700
4 dr HdTp	200	600	950	2200	3900	5600
2 dr HdTp	350	750	1200	2350	4900	7000
300, V-8, 124" wb						
4 dr HdTp	200	650	1050	2250	4200	6000
2 dr HdTp	350	750	1300	2450	5250	7500
Conv	550	1800	3000	6000	10,500	15,000
Town & Country, V-8, 122" wb						
Sta Wag	200	600	950	2150	3850	5500
New Yorker, V-8, 124" wb						
4 dr Sed	200	500	850	1900	3500	5000
4 dr HdTp	350	700	1150	2300	4550	6500
2 dr HdTp	350	750	1300	2450	5250	7500
Imperial, V-8, 127" wb						
4 dr Sed	200	600	950	2150	3850	5500
4 dr HdTp	350	750	1200	2350	4900	7000
2 dr HdTp	450	1100	1700	3650	6650	9500
Conv	650	2050	3400	6800	11,900	17,000
Imperial LeBaron						
4 dr HdTp	350	900	1550	3050	5900	8500

1969

	6	5	4	3	2	1
Newport, V-8, 124" wb						
4 dr Sed	125	200	600	1100	2250	3200
4 dr HdTp	125	250	700	1150	2400	3400
2 dr HdTp	150	450	750	1700	3200	4600
Conv	450	1000	1650	3350	6300	9000
Newport Custom, V-8, 124" wb						
4 dr Sed	125	200	600	1100	2300	3300
4 dr HdTp	125	250	700	1150	2450	3500
2 dr HdTp	150	350	750	1450	3000	4200
300, V-8, 124" wb						
2 dr HdTp	200	500	850	1900	3500	5000
4 dr HdTp	150	400	750	1650	3150	4500
Conv	400	1200	2000	3950	7000	10,000
New Yorker, V-8, 124" wb						
4 dr Sed	150	300	700	1250	2650	3800
4 dr HdTp	150	350	750	1350	2800	4000
2 dr HdTp	200	500	850	1900	3500	5000
Town & Country, V-8, 122" wb						
Sta Wag	125	250	700	1150	2450	3500
Imperial Crown, V-8, 127" wb						
4 dr Sed	150	350	750	1350	2800	4000
4 dr HdTp	150	400	750	1650	3150	4500
2 dr HdTp	200	500	850	1900	3500	5000
Imperial LeBaron						
4 dr HdTp	150	400	750	1650	3150	4500
2 dr HdTp	200	600	950	2150	3850	5500

1970

	6	5	4	3	2	1
Newport, V-8, 124" wb						
4 dr Sed	150	300	700	1250	2600	3700
4 dr HdTp	150	350	750	1350	2800	4000

	6	5	4	3	2	1
2 dr HdTp	150	400	750	1650	3150	4500
Conv	350	900	1550	3050	5900	8500
Newport Custom						
4 dr Sed	150	350	750	1350	2800	4000
4 dr HdTp	150	450	800	1750	3250	4700
2 dr HdTp	200	500	850	1900	3500	5000
300, V-8, 124" wb						
4 dr HdTp	200	600	950	2150	3850	5500
2 dr HdTp	200	650	1050	2250	4200	6000
2 dr HdTp Hurst	400	1200	2000	3950	7000	10,000
Conv Hurst	700	2300	3800	7600	13,300	19,000
Conv	400	1300	2200	4400	7700	11,000
New Yorker, V-8, 124" wb						
4 dr Sed	150	400	750	1650	3150	4500
4 dr HdTp	200	500	850	1900	3500	5000
2 dr HdTp	200	600	950	2150	3850	5500
Town & Country, V-8, 122" wb						
Sta Wag	150	400	750	1650	3150	4500
Imperial Crown, V-8, 127" wb						
4 dr HdTp	200	600	950	2150	3850	5500
2 dr HdTp	200	650	1050	2250	4200	6000
Imperial LeBaron, V-8, 127" wb						
4 dr HdTp	200	650	1050	2250	4200	6000
2 dr HdTp	350	700	1150	2300	4550	6500
1971						
Newport Royal, V-8, 124" wb						
4 dr Sed	150	300	700	1250	2650	3800
4 dr HdTp	150	300	750	1350	2700	3900
2 dr HdTp	150	350	750	1350	2800	4000
Newport, V-8, 124" wb						
4 dr Sed	150	300	750	1350	2700	3900
4 dr HdTp	150	350	750	1450	3000	4200
2 dr HdTp	200	500	850	1900	3500	5000
Newport Custom						
4 dr Sed	150	350	750	1350	2800	4000
4 dr HdTp	150	400	750	1650	3150	4500
2 dr HdTp	200	600	950	2150	3850	5500
300						
4 dr HdTp	150	350	750	1450	3000	4200
2 dr HdTp	150	450	800	1750	3250	4700
New Yorker						
4 dr Sed	150	350	750	1450	2900	4100
4 dr HdTp	200	500	850	1900	3500	5000
2 dr HdTp	200	650	1050	2250	4200	6000
Town & Country						
Sta Wag	150	300	750	1350	2700	3900
Imperial						
4 dr HdTp	200	600	950	2150	3850	5500
2 dr HdTp	350	700	1150	2300	4550	6500
1972						
Newport Royal						
4 dr Sed	125	250	700	1150	2400	3400
4 dr HdTp	150	350	750	1350	2800	4000
2 dr HdTp	150	400	750	1650	3150	4500
Newport Custom						
4 dr Sed	125	250	700	1150	2450	3500
4 dr HdTp	150	400	750	1650	3150	4500
2 dr HdTp	200	500	850	1900	3500	5000
New Yorker Brougham						
4 dr Sed	150	300	750	1350	2700	3900
4 dr HdTp	200	500	850	1900	3500	5000
2 dr HdTp	200	600	950	2150	3850	5500
Town & Country						
Sta Wag	150	300	700	1250	2650	3800
Imperial						
4 dr HdTp	200	600	950	2150	3850	5500
2 dr HdTp	200	650	1050	2250	4200	6000
1973						
Newport, V-8, 124" wb						
4 dr Sed	125	200	600	1100	2300	3300
4 dr HdTp	125	250	700	1150	2450	3500
2 dr HdTp	125	250	700	1150	2500	3600
Newport Custom V-8						
4 dr	125	250	700	1150	2450	3500
4 dr HdTp	125	250	700	1150	2500	3600
2 dr HdTp	150	300	700	1250	2600	3700
New Yorker Brgm V-8						
4 dr	125	250	700	1150	2500	3600
4 dr HdTp	150	350	750	1350	2800	4000
2 dr HdTp	150	400	750	1650	3150	4500
Town & Country V-8						
Sta Wag 3S	125	200	600	1100	2300	3300
Imperial LeBaron V-8						
2 dr HdTp	150	400	750	1550	3050	4300
4 dr HdTp	150	350	750	1450	3000	4200
1974						
Newport V-8						
4 dr	125	250	700	1150	2400	3400
4 dr HdTp	125	250	700	1150	2450	3500
2 dr HdTp	150	300	700	1250	2650	3800
Newport Custom V-8						
4 dr	125	250	700	1150	2500	3600
4 dr HdTp	150	300	700	1250	2600	3700
2 dr HdTp	150	350	750	1350	2800	4000
New Yorker V-8						
4 dr	150	300	700	1250	2600	3700
4 dr HdTp	150	350	750	1450	3000	4200
New Yorker Brgm V-8						
4 dr	150	300	750	1350	2700	3900
4 dr HdTp	150	350	750	1350	2800	4000
2 dr HdTp	150	350	750	1450	3000	4200
Town & Country V-8						
3S Sta Wag	150	300	750	1350	2700	3900
Imperial LeBaron						
HdTp	150	400	750	1600	3100	4400
4 dr HdTp	150	400	750	1550	3050	4300

NOTE: Add 20 percent for Crown Coupe package (Orig. price $542.).

	6	5	4	3	2	1
1975						
Cordoba V-8						
2 dr HdTp	150	400	750	1650	3150	4500
Newport V-8						
4 dr	125	250	700	1150	2400	3400
4 dr HdTp	125	250	700	1150	2450	3500
2 dr HdTp	125	250	700	1150	2450	3500
Newport Custom V-8						
4 dr	125	250	700	1150	2450	3500
4 dr HdTp	125	250	700	1150	2500	3600

	6	5	4	3	2	1
2 dr HdTp	125	250	700	1150	2500	3600
New Yorker Brgm V-8						
4 dr	125	250	700	1150	2500	3600
4 dr HdTp	150	300	700	1250	2650	3800
2 dr HdTp	150	300	700	1250	2650	3800
Town & Country V-8						
3S Sta Wag	125	250	700	1150	2500	3600
Imperial LeBaron						
HdTp	150	350	750	1450	2900	4100
4 dr HdTp	150	350	750	1350	2800	4000

NOTE: Add 20 percent for Crown Coupe package (Orig. price $569.).

DESOTO

	6	5	4	3	2	1
1946						
S-11 DeLuxe, 6-cyl.						
Cpe	350	750	1300	2450	5250	7500
Clb Cpe	350	800	1450	2750	5600	8000
2 dr Sed	200	650	1050	2250	4200	6000
Sed	200	675	1100	2250	4400	6300
S-11 Custom, 6-cyl.						
Conv	850	2650	4400	8800	15,400	22,000
Clb Cpe	350	900	1550	3050	5900	8500
2 dr Sed	200	675	1100	2250	4400	6300
Sed	200	675	1100	2250	4400	6300
7P Sed	350	750	1200	2350	4900	7000
Limo	350	750	1250	2400	5100	7300
Sub	450	1050	1700	3550	6500	9300
1947						
S-11 DeLuxe, 6-cyl.						
Cpe	350	750	1300	2450	5250	7500
Clb Cpe	350	800	1450	2750	5600	8000
2 dr Sed	200	650	1050	2250	4200	6000
Sed	200	675	1100	2250	4400	6300
S-11 Custom, 6-cyl.						
Conv	850	2650	4400	8800	15,400	22,000
Clb Cpe	350	900	1550	3050	5900	8500
2 dr Sed	200	675	1100	2250	4400	6300
Sed	350	700	1150	2300	4550	6500
7P Sed	350	750	1200	2350	4900	7000
Limo	350	750	1250	2400	5100	7300
Sub	450	1050	1700	3550	6500	9300
1948						
S-11 DeLuxe, 6-cyl.						
Cpe	350	750	1300	2450	5250	7500
Clb Cpe	350	800	1450	2750	5600	8000
2 dr Sed	200	650	1050	2250	4200	6000
Sed	200	675	1100	2250	4400	6300
S-11 Custom, 6-cyl.						
Conv	850	2650	4400	8800	15,400	22,000
Clb Cpe	350	900	1550	3050	5900	8500
2 dr Sed	200	675	1100	2250	4400	6300
Sed	350	700	1150	2300	4550	6500
7P Sed	350	750	1200	2350	4900	7000
Limo	350	750	1250	2400	5100	7300
Sub	450	1050	1700	3550	6500	9300
1949						

First series values same as 1947-48

	6	5	4	3	2	1
SECOND SERIES						
S-13 DeLuxe, 6-cyl.						
Clb Cpe	350	800	1450	2750	5600	8000
Sed	200	675	1100	2250	4400	6300
C-A Sed	200	675	1050	2250	4350	6200
Sta Wag	450	1450	2400	4800	8400	12,000
S-13 Custom, 6-cyl.						
Conv	700	2150	3600	7200	12,600	18,000
Clb Cpe	350	900	1550	3050	5900	8500
Sed	200	675	1050	2250	4300	6100
8P Sed	350	700	1100	2300	4500	6400
Sub	350	750	1350	2650	5450	7800
1950						
S-14 DeLuxe, 6-cyl.						
Clb Cpe	350	750	1300	2450	5250	7500
Sed	200	650	1050	2250	4200	6000
C-A Sed	350	700	1100	2300	4500	6400
8P Sed	350	725	1200	2350	4850	6900
S-14 Custom, 6-cyl.						
Conv	650	2050	3400	6800	11,900	17,000
Sptman 2 dr HdTp	400	1300	2200	4400	7700	11,000
Clb Cpe	350	800	1450	2750	5600	8000
Sed	200	675	1050	2250	4300	6100
6P Sta Wag	400	1300	2200	4400	7700	11,000
Stl Sta Wag	450	1050	1700	3550	6500	9300
8P Sed	350	725	1200	2350	4800	6800
Sub Sed	350	750	1250	2400	5100	7300
1951						
DeLuxe, 6-cyl., 125.5" wb						
Sed	200	650	1000	2200	4100	5800
Clb Cpe	350	750	1200	2350	4900	7000
C-A Sed	200	675	1050	2250	4300	6100
DeLuxe, 6-cyl., 139.5" wb						
Sed	200	675	1050	2250	4350	6200
Custom, 6-cyl., 125.5" wb						
Sed	200	650	1000	2200	4100	5800
Clb Cpe	350	750	1300	2450	5250	7500
Sptman 2 dr HdTp	400	1200	2000	3950	7000	10,000
Conv	650	2050	3400	6800	11,900	17,000
Sta Wag	450	950	1600	3250	6150	8800
Custom, 6-cyl., 139.5" wb						
Sed	200	650	1000	2200	4100	5800
Sub	200	675	1050	2250	4300	6100
1952						
DeLuxe, 6-cyl., 125.5" wb						
Sed	200	650	1000	2200	4100	5800
Clb Cpe	350	750	1200	2350	4900	7000
C-A Sed	200	675	1050	2250	4300	6100
DeLuxe, 6-cyl., 139.5" wb						
Sed	200	675	1050	2250	4350	6200
Custom, 6-cyl., 125.5" wb						
Sed	200	650	1000	2200	4100	5800
Clb Cpe	350	750	1300	2450	5250	7500
Sptman 2 dr HdTp	400	1200	2000	3950	7000	10,000

	6	5	4	3	2	1
Conv	650	2050	3400	6800	11,900	17,000
Sta Wag	350	750	1250	2400	5100	7300
Custom, 6-cyl., 139.5" wb						
Sed	200	650	1050	2250	4200	6000
Sub	200	675	1100	2250	4400	6300
Firedome, V-8, 125.5" wb						
Sed	350	700	1150	2300	4550	6500
Clb Cpe	350	800	1450	2750	5600	8000
Sptman 2 dr HdTp	400	1300	2200	4400	7700	11,000
Conv	700	2150	3600	7200	12,600	18,000
Sta Wag	350	900	1550	3050	5900	8500
Firedome, V-8, 139.5" wb						
8P Sed	350	725	1200	2350	4800	6800
1953						
Powermaster Six, 6-cyl., 125.5" wb						
Sed	200	675	1050	2250	4300	6100
Clb Cpe	350	700	1150	2300	4550	6500
Sptman 2 dr HdTp	450	1000	1650	3350	6300	9000
Sta Wag	350	725	1200	2350	4800	6800
Powermaster Six, 6-cyl., 139.5" wb						
Sed	200	675	1100	2250	4400	6300
Firedome, V-8, 125.5" wb						
Sed	350	700	1150	2300	4600	6600
Clb Cpe	350	750	1200	2350	4900	7000
Sptman 2 dr HdTp	400	1300	2200	4400	7700	11,000
Conv	700	2150	3600	7200	12,600	18,000
Sta Wag	350	750	1250	2400	5100	7300
Firedome, V-8, 139.5" wb						
Sed	350	700	1150	2300	4600	6600
1954						
Powermaster Six, 6-cyl., 125.5" wb						
Sed	200	675	1050	2250	4350	6200
Clb Cpe	350	700	1150	2300	4550	6500
Sta Wag	350	700	1150	2300	4600	6600
Powermaster Six, 6-cyl., 139.5" wb						
Sed	200	650	1050	2250	4200	6000
Firedome, V-8, 125.5" wb						
Sed	350	700	1150	2300	4600	6600
Clb Cpe	350	750	1200	2350	4900	7000
Sptman 2 dr HdTp	450	1450	2400	4800	8400	12,000
Conv	800	2500	4200	8400	14,700	21,000
Sta Wag	350	750	1200	2350	4900	7000
Firedome, V-8, 139.5" wb						
Sed	350	700	1150	2300	4550	6500
1955						
Firedome, V-8						
Sed	200	650	1050	2250	4200	6000
2 dr HdTp	400	1300	2200	4400	7700	11,000
Sptman 2 dr HdTp	550	1800	3000	6000	10,500	15,000
Conv	900	2900	4800	9600	16,800	24,000
Sta Wag	350	750	1200	2350	4900	7000
Fireflite, V-8						
Sed	350	700	1150	2300	4550	6500
Sptman 2 dr HdTp	650	2050	3400	6800	11,900	17,000
Conv	1000	3100	5200	10,400	18,200	26,000
1956						
Firedome, V-8						
Sed	200	650	1050	2250	4200	6000
4 dr HdTp Sev	350	900	1550	3050	5900	8500
4 dr HdTp Sptman	450	1100	1700	3650	6650	9500
2 dr HdTp Sev	500	1550	2600	5200	9100	13,000
2 dr HdTp Sptman	550	1700	2800	5600	9800	14,000
Conv	850	2650	4400	8800	15,400	22,000
Sta Wag	350	800	1450	2750	5600	8000
Fireflite, V-8						
Sed	350	700	1150	2300	4550	6500
4 dr HdTp Sptman	400	1200	2000	3950	7000	10,000
2 dr HdTp Sptman	550	1800	3000	6000	10,500	15,000
Conv	900	2900	4800	9600	16,800	24,000
Conv Pace Car	1000	3250	5400	10,800	18,900	27,000
Adventurer						
HdTp	550	1800	3000	6000	10,500	15,000
1957						
Firesweep, V 8, 122" wb						
Sed	200	600	950	2150	3850	5500
4 dr HdTp Sptman	450	1000	1650	3350	6300	9000
2 dr HdTp Sptman	450	1450	2400	4800	8400	12,000
2S Sta Wag	200	650	1050	2250	4200	6000
3S Sta Wag	200	675	1050	2250	4300	6100
Firedome, V-8, 126" wb						
Sed	200	600	1000	2200	4000	5700
4 dr HdTp Sptman	450	1100	1700	3650	6650	9500
2 dr HdTp Sptman	500	1550	2600	5200	9100	13,000
Conv	800	2500	4200	8400	14,700	21,000
Fireflite, V-8, 126" wb						
Sed	200	650	1000	2200	4150	5900
4 dr HdTp Sptman	400	1200	2000	3950	7000	10,000
2 dr HdTp Sptman	550	1700	2800	5600	9800	14,000
Conv	850	2750	4600	9200	16,100	23,000
2S Sta Wag	200	675	1050	2250	4350	6200
3S Sta Wag	200	675	1100	2250	4400	6300
Fireflite Adventurer, 126" wb						
2 dr HdTp	550	1800	3000	6000	10,500	15,000
Conv	900	2900	4800	9600	16,800	24,000

NOTE: A DeSoto Fireflite convertible placed the Indy 500 this year.

	6	5	4	3	2	1
1958						
Firesweep, V-8						
Sed	200	600	950	2200	3900	5600
4 dr HdTp Sptman	450	1000	1650	3350	6300	9000
2 dr HdTp Sptman	400	1300	2200	4400	7700	11,000
Conv	800	2500	4200	8400	14,700	21,000
2S Sta Wag	200	650	1000	2200	4100	5800
3S Sta Wag	200	650	1000	2200	4150	5900
Firedome, V-8						
Sed	200	650	1000	2200	4100	5800
4 dr HdTp Sptman	450	1100	1700	3650	6650	9500
2 dr HdTp Sptman	450	1450	2400	4800	8400	12,000
Conv	850	2650	4400	8800	15,400	22,000
Fireflite, V-8						
Sed	200	650	1050	2250	4200	6000
4 dr HdTp Sptman	400	1200	2000	3950	7000	10,000
2 dr HdTp Sptman	550	1700	2800	5600	9800	14,000
Conv	900	2900	4800	9600	16,800	24,000
2S Sta Wag	200	650	1050	2250	4200	6000
3S Sta Wag	200	675	1050	2250	4350	6200
Adventurer, V-8						
2 dr HdTp	550	1800	3000	6000	10,500	15,000
Conv	1000	3100	5200	10,400	18,200	26,000
1959						
Firesweep, V-8						
Sed	200	600	950	2150	3850	5500
4 dr HdTp Sptman	350	800	1450	2750	5600	8000
2 dr HdTp Sptman	450	1100	1700	3650	6650	9500
Conv	700	2150	3600	7200	12,600	18,000
2S Sta Wag	200	550	900	2100	3700	5300
3S Sta Wag	200	550	900	2150	3800	5400
Firedome, V-8						
Sed	200	600	950	2200	3900	5600
4 dr HdTp Sptman	350	750	1300	2450	5250	7500
2 dr HdTp Sptman	400	1200	2000	3950	7000	10,000
Conv	700	2300	3800	7600	13,300	19,000
Fireflite, V-8						
Sed	200	600	950	2200	3900	5600
4 dr HdTp Sptman	450	1100	1700	3650	6650	9500
2 dr HdTp Sptman	400	1300	2200	4400	7700	11,000
Conv	750	2400	4000	8000	14,000	20,000
2S Sta Wag	200	600	950	2150	3850	5500
3S Sta Wag	200	600	1000	2200	4000	5700
Adventurer, V-8						
2 dr HdTp	450	1450	2400	4800	8400	12,000
Conv	800	2500	4200	8400	14,700	21,000
1960						
Fireflite, V-8						
Sed	200	500	850	1900	3500	5000
4 dr HdTp	200	650	1050	2250	4200	6000
2 dr HdTp	350	800	1450	2750	5600	8000
Adventurer, V-8						
Sed	200	550	900	2000	3600	5200
4 dr HdTp	350	750	1300	2450	5250	7500
2 dr HdTp	450	1100	1700	3650	6650	9500
1961						
Fireflite, V-8						
4 dr HdTp	350	800	1450	2750	5600	8000
2 dr HdTp	400	1200	2000	3950	7000	10,000

DODGE

	6	5	4	3	2	1
1946						
DeLuxe Series D24, 6-cyl., 119.5" wb						
Cpe	350	750	1300	2450	5250	7500
2 dr Sed	350	725	1150	2300	4700	6700
4 dr Sed	350	725	1200	2350	4800	6800
Custom Series D24, 6-cyl., 119.5" wb - 137.5" wb, (*)						
Conv	850	2650	4400	8800	15,400	22,000
Clb Cpe	350	800	1450	2750	5600	8000
Sed	350	750	1200	2350	4900	7000
Twn Sed	350	750	1250	2350	5000	7100
7P Sed (*)	350	750	1350	2650	5450	7800
1947						
DeLuxe Series D24, 6-cyl., 119.5" wb						
Cpe	350	750	1300	2450	5250	7500
2 dr Sed	350	725	1150	2300	4700	6700
4 dr Sed	350	725	1200	2350	4800	6800
Custom Series D24, 6-cyl., 119.5" wb - 137.5" wb, (*)						
Conv	850	2650	4400	8800	15,400	22,000
Clb Cpe	350	800	1450	2750	5600	8000
Sed	350	750	1200	2350	4900	7000
Twn Sed	350	750	1250	2350	5000	7100
7P Sed (*)	350	750	1350	2650	5450	7800
1948						
DeLuxe Series D24, 6-cyl., 119.5" wb						
Cpe	350	750	1300	2450	5250	7500
2 dr Sed	350	725	1150	2300	4700	6700
4 dr Sed	350	725	1200	2350	4800	6800
Custom Series D24, 6-cyl., 119.5" wb - 137.5" wb, (*)						
Conv	850	2650	4400	8800	15,400	22,000
Clb Cpe	350	800	1450	2750	5600	8000
Sed	350	750	1200	2350	4900	7000
Twn Sed	350	750	1250	2350	5000	7100
7P Sed (*)	350	750	1350	2650	5450	7800
1949						
First Series 1949 is the same as 1948						
Second Series						
Series D29 Wayfarer, 6-cyl., 115" wb						
Rds	800	2500	4200	8400	14,700	21,000
Bus Cpe	350	750	1200	2350	4900	7000
2 dr Sed	200	675	1100	2250	4400	6300
Series D30 Meadowbrook, 6-cyl., 123.5" wb						
Sed	350	700	1150	2300	4550	6500
Series D30 Coronet, 6-cyl., 123.5" wb - 137.5" wb, (*)						
Conv	750	2400	4000	8000	14,000	20,000
Clb Cpe	350	750	1300	2450	5250	7500
Sed	350	725	1200	2350	4800	6800
Twn Sed	350	750	1200	2350	4900	7000
Sta Wag	400	1300	2200	4400	7700	11,000
8P Sed (*)	350	800	1450	2750	5600	8000
1950						
Series D33 Wayfarer, 6-cyl., 115" wb						
Rds	800	2500	4200	8400	14,700	21,000
Cpe	350	750	1300	2450	5250	7500
2 dr Sed	200	675	1100	2250	4400	6300
Series D34 Meadowbrook, 6-cyl., 123.5" wb						
Sed	350	700	1150	2300	4550	6500
Series D34 Coronet, 123.5" wb - 137.5" wb, (*)						
Conv	750	2400	4000	8000	14,000	20,000
Clb Cpe	350	750	1300	2450	5250	7500
Dipl 2 dr HdTp	400	1300	2200	4400	7700	11,000
Sed	350	725	1150	2300	4700	6700
Twn Sed	350	725	1200	2350	4850	6900
Sta Wag	400	1300	2200	4400	7700	11,000
Mtl Sta Wag	400	1200	2000	3950	7000	10,000
8P Sed (*)	350	850	1500	2800	5650	8100
1951						
Wayfarer Series D41, 6-cyl., 115" wb						
2 dr Sed	200	675	1100	2250	4400	6300
Cpe	350	750	1200	2350	4900	7000

	6	5	4	3	2	1
Rds	800	2500	4200	8400	14,700	21,000
Meadowbrook Series D42, 6-cyl., 123.5" wb						
Sed	350	700	1150	2300	4550	6500
Coronet Series D42, 6-cyl., 123.5" wb - 137.5" wb, (*)						
4 dr Sed	350	700	1150	2300	4600	6600
Clb Cpe	350	750	1250	2400	5100	7300
Dipl 2 dr HdTp	400	1200	2000	3950	7000	10,000
Conv	750	2400	4000	8000	14,000	20,000
Mtl Sta Wag	450	1150	1900	3850	6850	9800
8P Sed (*)	350	750	1250	2400	5100	7300
1952						
Wayfarer Series D41, 6-cyl., 115" wb						
2 dr Sed	350	700	1150	2300	4550	6500
Cpe	350	725	1200	2350	4800	6800
Meadowbrook Series D42, 6-cyl., 123.5" wb						
Sed	200	675	1100	2250	4400	6300
Coronet Series D42, 6-cyl., 123.5" wb						
Sed	350	700	1150	2300	4600	6600
Clb Cpe	350	750	1300	2450	5250	7500
Dipl 2 dr HdTp	400	1200	2000	3950	7000	10,000
Conv	750	2400	4000	8000	14,000	20,000
Mtl Sta Wag	450	1150	1900	3850	6850	9800
8P Sed	350	750	1250	2400	5100	7300
1953						
Meadowbrook Special, 6-cyl., disc 4/53						
Sed	200	675	1100	2250	4400	6300
Clb Cpe	350	700	1150	2300	4550	6500
Series D46 Meadowbrook, 6-cyl., 119" wb						
Sed	350	700	1150	2300	4550	6500
Clb Cpe	350	700	1150	2300	4600	6600
Sub	200	675	1100	2250	4400	6300
Coronet, 6-cyl., 119" wb						
Sed	350	725	1150	2300	4700	6700
Clb Cpe	350	725	1200	2350	4800	6800
Series D44 Coronet, V-8, 119" wb						
Sed	350	750	1200	2350	4900	7000
Clb Cpe	350	750	1250	2350	5000	7100
Series D48 Coronet, V-8, 119" wb - 114" wb, (*)						
Dipl 2 dr HdTp	400	1300	2200	4400	7700	11,000
Conv	700	2150	3600	7200	12,600	18,000
Sta Wag (*)	350	750	1350	2650	5450	7800
1954						
Series D51-1 Meadowbrook, 6-cyl., 119" wb						
Sed	350	725	1150	2300	4700	6700
Clb Cpe	350	725	1200	2350	4800	6800
Series D51-2 Coronet, 6-cyl., 119" wb						
Sed	350	725	1200	2350	4850	6900
Clb Cpe	350	750	1200	2350	4900	7000
Series D52 Coronet, 6-cyl., 114" wb						
2 dr Sub	350	750	1250	2400	5050	7200
6P Sta Wag	350	750	1250	2400	5100	7300
8P Sta Wag	350	750	1300	2400	5200	7400
Series D50-1 Meadowbrook, V-8, 119" wb						
Sed	350	725	1200	2350	4800	6800
Clb Cpe	350	750	1200	2350	4900	7000
Series D50-2 Coronet, V-8, 119" wb						
Sed	350	750	1250	2400	5100	7300
Clb Cpe	350	750	1300	2450	5250	7500
Series D53-2 Coronet, V-8, 114" wb						
Sub	350	750	1250	2400	5100	7300
2S Sta Wag	350	750	1300	2400	5200	7400
3S Sta Wag	350	750	1300	2450	5250	7500
Series D50-3 Royal, V-8, 119" wb						
Sed	350	850	1500	2800	5650	8100
Clb Cpe	350	800	1450	2750	5600	8000
Series D53-3 Royal, V-8, 114" wb						
HdTp	450	1450	2400	4800	8400	12,000
Conv	700	2300	3800	7600	13,300	19,000
Pace Car Replica	950	3000	5000	10,000	17,500	25,000
1955						
Coronet, V-8, 120" wb						
Sed	350	725	1200	2350	4800	6800
2 dr Sed	350	725	1150	2300	4700	6700
Clb Sed	350	725	1200	2350	4850	6900
2 dr HdTp	400	1300	2200	4400	7700	11,000
2 dr Sub	350	700	1150	2300	4550	6500
6P Sta Wag	350	725	1150	2300	4700	6700
8P Sta Wag	350	725	1200	2350	4800	6800
NOTE: Deduct 5 percent for 6-cyl. models.						
Royal, V-8, 120" wb						
Sed	350	725	1200	2350	4800	6800
2 dr HdTp	450	1450	2400	4800	8400	12,000
6P Sta Wag	350	725	1200	2350	4800	6800
8P Sta Wag	350	725	1200	2350	4850	6900
Custom Royal, V-8, 120" wb						
Sed	350	750	1250	2350	5000	7100
4 dr Lancer	350	900	1550	3050	5900	8500
2 dr HdTp	550	1800	3000	6000	10,500	15,000
Conv	850	2750	4600	9200	16,100	23,000
NOTE: Deduct 5 percent for 6-cyl. models. Add 5 percent for La-Femme.						
1956						
Coronet, V-8, 120" wb						
Sed	350	700	1150	2300	4550	6500
4 dr HdTp	350	750	1200	2350	4900	7000
Clb Sed	200	650	1050	2250	4200	6000
2 dr HdTp	450	1450	2400	4800	8400	12,000
Conv	900	2900	4800	9600	16,800	24,000
2 dr Sub	200	650	1050	2250	4200	6000
6P Sta Wag	200	675	1050	2250	4350	6200
8P Sta Wag	350	700	1100	2300	4500	6400
NOTE: Deduct 5 percent for 6-cyl. models.						
Royal, V-8, 120" wb						
Sed	350	750	1300	2500	5300	7600
4 dr HdTp	350	800	1450	2750	5600	8000
2 dr HdTp	500	1550	2600	5200	9100	13,000
2 dr Sub	200	675	1050	2250	4350	6200
6P Sta Wag	350	700	1100	2300	4500	6400
8P Sta Wag	350	700	1150	2300	4600	6600
Custom Royal, V-8, 120" wb						
Sed	350	750	1350	2600	5400	7700
4 dr HdTp	450	1000	1650	3350	6300	9000
2 dr HdTp	600	1900	3200	6400	11,200	16,000
Conv	1000	3250	5400	10,800	18,900	27,000
NOTE: Add 30 percent for D500 option. Add 10 percent for Golden Lancer. Add 5 percent for La-Femme or Texan options.						

	6	5	4	3	2	1
1957						
Coronet, V-8, 122" wb						
Sed	200	600	950	2150	3850	5500
4 dr HdTp	350	750	1300	2450	5250	7500
2 dr Sed	200	600	950	2150	3850	5500
2 dr HdTp	450	1450	2400	4800	8400	12,000
NOTE: Deduct 5 percent for 6-cyl. models.						
Coronet Lancer						
Conv	950	3000	5000	10,000	17,500	25,000
Royal, V-8, 122" wb						
Sed	200	600	1000	2200	4000	5700
4 dr HdTp	350	800	1450	2750	5600	8000
2 dr HdTp	550	1800	3000	6000	10,500	15,000
Royal Lancer						
Conv	1000	3250	5400	10,800	18,900	27,000
Custom Royal, V-8, 122" wb						
4 dr Sed	200	650	1050	2250	4200	6000
4 dr HdTp	350	900	1550	3050	5900	8500
2 dr HdTp	650	2050	3400	6800	11,900	17,000
6P Sta Wag	200	650	1050	2250	4200	6000
9P Sta Wag	200	675	1050	2250	4300	6100
2 dr Sub	200	650	1050	2250	4200	6000
NOTE: Add 30 percent for D500 option.						
Custom Royal Lancer						
Conv	1100	3500	5800	11,600	20,300	29,000
1958						
Coronet, V-8, 122" wb						
4 dr Sed	200	600	950	2200	3900	5600
4 dr HdTp	350	750	1300	2450	5250	7500
2 dr Sed	200	600	950	2200	3900	5600
2 dr HdTp	500	1550	2600	5200	9100	13,000
Conv	900	2900	4800	9600	16,800	24,000
NOTE: Deduct 5 percent for 6-cyl. models.						
Royal						
4 dr Sed	200	650	1050	2250	4200	6000
4 dr HdTp	350	800	1450	2750	5600	8000
2 dr HdTp	550	1700	2800	5600	9800	14,000
Custom Royal						
NOTE: Add 30 percent for D500 option and 30 percent for E.F.I. Super D500. Add 20 percent for Regal Lancer.						
4 dr Sed	350	700	1150	2300	4600	6600
4 dr HdTp	350	900	1550	3050	5900	8500
2 dr HdTp	650	2050	3400	6800	11,900	17,000
Conv	1000	3250	5400	10,800	18,900	27,000
6P Sta Wag	200	600	950	2200	3900	5600
9P Sta Wag	200	600	1000	2200	4000	5700
6P Cus Wag	200	650	1000	2200	4100	5800
9P Cus Wag	200	650	1000	2200	4100	5800
2 dr Sub	200	600	1000	2200	4000	5700
1959						
Eight cylinder models						
Coronet						
4 dr Sed	200	600	950	2200	3900	5600
4 dr HdTp	200	675	1050	2250	4350	6200
2 dr Sed	200	600	950	2200	3900	5600
2 dr HdTp	450	1450	2400	4800	8400	12,000
Conv	950	3000	5000	10,000	17,500	25,000
NOTE: Deduct 10 percent for 6-cyl. models.						
Royal						
4 dr Sed	200	600	1000	2200	4000	5700
4 dr HdTp	350	750	1200	2350	4900	7000
2 dr HdTp	550	1700	2800	5600	9800	14,000
NOTE: Add 30 percent for D500 option.						
Custom Royal						
4 dr Sed	200	650	1000	2200	4150	5900
4 dr HdTp	350	750	1300	2450	5250	7500
2 dr HdTp	600	1900	3200	6400	11,200	16,000
Conv	1050	3350	5600	11,200	19,600	28,000
Sierra						
6P Sta Wag	200	600	950	2200	3900	5600
9P Sta Wag	200	600	1000	2200	4000	5700
6P Cus Wag	200	600	950	2200	3900	5600
9P Cus Wag	200	600	1000	2200	4000	5700
1960						
Dart Series						
Seneca, V-8, 118" wb						
4 dr Sed	200	550	900	2000	3600	5200
2 dr Sed	200	500	850	1950	3600	5100
Sta Wag	200	500	850	1950	3600	5100
Pioneer, V-8, 118" wb						
4 dr Sed	200	550	900	2100	3700	5300
2 dr Sed	200	550	900	2000	3600	5200
2 dr HdTp	450	1000	1650	3350	6300	9000
9P Sta Wag	200	500	850	1950	3600	5100
6P Sta Wag	200	500	850	1900	3500	5000
Phoenix, V-8, 118" wb						
4 dr Sed	200	600	950	2150	3850	5500
4 dr HdTp	400	1200	2000	3950	7000	10,000
2 dr HdTp	450	1450	2400	4800	8400	12,000
Conv	600	1900	3200	6400	11,200	16,000
Dodge Series						
Matador						
4 dr Sed	200	600	950	2200	3900	5600
4 dr HdTp	400	1250	2100	4200	7400	10,500
2 dr HdTp	500	1550	2600	5200	9100	13,000
9P Sta Wag	200	550	900	2000	3600	5200
6P Sta Wag	200	550	900	2100	3700	5300
Polara						
4 dr Sed	200	600	1000	2200	4000	5700
4 dr HdTp	400	1300	2150	4300	7500	10,700
2 dr HdTp	550	1700	2800	5600	9800	14,000
Conv	700	2300	3800	7600	13,300	19,000
9P Sta Wag	200	600	950	2150	3850	5500
6P Sta Wag	200	600	950	2200	3900	5600
NOTE: Deduct 5 percent for 6-cyl. models. Add 30 percent for D500 option.						
1961						
Lancer, 6-cyl., 106.5" wb						
Sed	200	550	900	2100	3700	5300
HdTp	200	650	1050	2250	4200	6000
Spt Cpe	350	700	1100	2300	4500	6400
Lancer 770						
Sta Wag	200	500	850	1950	3600	5100
Dart Series						
Seneca, V-8, 118" wb						
4 dr Sed	200	550	900	2000	3600	5200

	6	5	4	3	2	1
2 dr Sed	200	500	850	1950	3600	5100
Sta Wag	200	500	850	1950	3600	5100
Pioneer, V-8, 118" wb						
4 dr Sed	200	550	900	2100	3700	5300
2 dr Sed	200	500	850	1950	3600	5100
2 dr HdTp	350	700	1150	2300	4550	6500
9P Sta Wag	200	550	900	2150	3800	5400
6P Sta Wag	200	550	900	2000	3600	5200
Phoenix, V-8, 118" wb						
4 dr Sed	200	550	900	2100	3700	5300
4 dr HdTp	200	600	950	2150	3850	5500
2 dr HdTp	350	750	1200	2350	4900	7000
Conv	450	1450	2400	4800	8400	12,000
Polara						
4 dr Sed	200	600	1000	2200	4000	5700
4 dr HdTp	200	650	1050	2250	4200	6000
2 dr HdTp	350	750	1300	2450	5250	7500
Conv	500	1550	2600	5200	9100	13,000
9P Sta Wag	200	550	900	2100	3700	5300
6P Sta Wag	200	550	900	2000	3600	5200

NOTE: Deduct 5 percent for 6-cyl. models.
   Add 30 percent for D500 option.
   Add 30 percent for Ram Charger "413".

1962

Lancer, 6-cyl., 106.5" wb	6	5	4	3	2	1
4 dr Sed	150	450	800	1750	3250	4700
2 dr Sed	150	450	800	1800	3300	4800
4 dr Sta Wag	150	450	800	1750	3250	4700
Lancer 770, 6-cyl., 106.5" wb						
4 dr Sed	200	500	850	1900	3500	5000
2 dr Sed	200	500	850	1850	3350	4900
Sta Wag	150	450	800	1800	3300	4800
GT Cpe	350	750	1200	2350	4900	7000

Dart Series

Dart, V-8, 116" wb	6	5	4	3	2	1
4 dr Sed	200	500	850	1950	3600	5100
2 dr Sed	200	500	850	1900	3500	5000
2 dr HdTp	200	600	950	2150	3850	5500
9P Sta Wag	200	500	850	1900	3500	5000
6P Sta Wag	200	500	850	1850	3350	4900
Dart 440, V-8, 116" wb						
4 dr Sed	200	550	900	2000	3600	5200
4 dr HdTp	200	550	900	2100	3700	5300
2 dr HdTp	200	650	1050	2250	4200	6000
Conv	400	1200	2000	3950	7000	10,000
9P Sta Wag	200	500	850	1950	3600	5100
6P Sta Wag	200	500	850	1900	3500	5000
Polara 500, V-8, 116" wb						
4 dr HdTp	200	600	950	2150	3850	5500
2 dr HdTp	350	700	1150	2300	4550	6500
Conv	400	1300	2200	4400	7700	11,000

NOTE: Add 20 percent for Daytona 500 Pace Car.

Custom 880, V-8, 122" wb	6	5	4	3	2	1
4 dr Sed	200	550	900	2100	3700	5300
4 dr HdTp	200	600	950	2150	3850	5500
2 dr HdTp	350	750	1200	2350	4900	7000
Conv	450	1450	2400	4800	8400	12,000
9P Sta Wag	200	500	850	1850	3350	4900
6P Sta Wag	200	500	850	1950	3600	5100

NOTE: Deduct 5 percent for 6-cyl. models.
   Add 50 percent for Ram Charger "413".

1963

Dart 170, 6-cyl., 111" wb	6	5	4	3	2	1
4 dr Sed	150	350	750	1450	3000	4200
2 dr Sed	150	350	750	1450	2900	4100
Sta Wag	150	350	750	1450	3000	4200
Dart 270, 6-cyl., 111" wb						
4 dr Sed	150	400	750	1550	3050	4300
2 dr Sed	150	350	750	1450	3000	4200
Conv	350	700	1150	2300	4600	6600
Sta Wag	150	400	750	1550	3050	4300
Dart GT						
HdTp	350	800	1450	2750	5600	8000
Conv	450	1000	1650	3350	6300	9000
Dodge, V-8, 119" wb						
4 dr Sed	150	450	750	1700	3200	4600
2 dr Sed	150	450	800	1750	3250	4700
2 dr HdTp	200	650	1050	2250	4200	6000
9P Sta Wag	150	400	750	1650	3150	4500
6P Sta Wag	150	400	750	1600	3100	4400
Polara, 318 CID V-8, 119" wb						
4 dr Sed	200	500	850	1850	3350	4900
4 dr HdTp	200	550	900	2150	3800	5400
2 dr HdTp	350	700	1150	2300	4550	6500
Conv	450	1000	1650	3350	6300	9000
Polara 500, 383 CID V-8, 122" wb						
2 dr HdTp	350	750	1300	2450	5250	7500
Conv	450	1100	1700	3650	6650	9500
880, V-8, 122" wb						
4 dr Sed	200	550	900	2150	3800	5400
4 dr HdTp	200	650	1050	2250	4200	6000
2 dr HdTp	350	750	1200	2350	4900	7000
Conv	450	1000	1650	3350	6300	9000
9P Sta Wag	200	500	850	1900	3500	5000
6P Sta Wag	150	450	800	1800	3300	4800

NOTE: Deduct 5 percent for 6-cyl. models.
   Add 100 percent for Ram Charger 426.

1964

Dart 170, 6-cyl., 111" wb	6	5	4	3	2	1
4 dr Sed	150	350	750	1450	3000	4200
2 dr Sed	150	350	750	1450	2900	4100
Sta Wag	150	350	750	1450	3000	4200
Dart 270, 6-cyl., 106" wb						
4 dr Sed	150	400	750	1550	3050	4300
2 dr Sed	150	350	750	1450	3000	4200
Conv	350	750	1300	2400	5200	7400
Sta Wag	150	400	750	1550	3050	4300
Dart GT						
HdTp	350	750	1300	2450	5250	7500
Conv	450	1100	1700	3650	6650	9500
Dodge, V-8, 119" wb						
4 dr Sed	150	450	750	1700	3200	4600
2 dr Sed	150	450	800	1750	3250	4700
2 dr HdTp	200	650	1050	2250	4200	6000
9P Sta Wag	150	400	750	1650	3150	4500
6P Sta Wag	150	400	750	1600	3100	4400

Polara, V-8, 119" wb	6	5	4	3	2	1
4 dr Sed	200	500	850	1850	3350	4900
4 dr HdTp	200	550	900	2150	3800	5400
2 dr HdTp	350	750	1300	2450	5250	7500
Conv	400	1200	2000	3950	7000	10,000
880, V-8, 122" wb						
4 dr Sed	200	500	850	1950	3600	5100
4 dr HdTp	200	600	950	2200	3900	5600
2 dr HdTp	350	800	1450	2750	5600	8000
Conv	400	1250	2100	4200	7400	10,500
9P Sta Wag	200	500	850	1900	3500	5000
6P Sta Wag	200	500	850	1850	3350	4900

NOTE: Add 50 percent for 426 wedge and 60 percent
   for 415 hp Hemi and 100 percent for 425 hp Hemi.
   Add 30 percent for Polara 500 option.
   Deduct 5 percent for 6-cyl. models.

1965

Dart, V8, 106" wb	6	5	4	3	2	1
4 dr Sed	150	350	750	1450	3000	4200
2 dr Sed	150	350	750	1450	2900	4100
Sta Wag	150	350	750	1450	3000	4200
Dart 270, V-8, 106" wb						
4 dr Sed	150	400	750	1550	3050	4300
2 dr Sed	150	350	750	1450	3000	4200
HdTp	200	650	1050	2250	4200	6000
Conv	350	700	1150	2300	4600	6600
Sta Wag	150	400	750	1550	3050	4300
Dart GT						
HdTp	350	800	1450	2750	5600	8000
Conv	400	1200	2000	3950	7000	10,000
Coronet, V-8, 117" wb						
4 dr Sed	150	300	750	1350	2700	3900
2 dr Sed	150	300	700	1250	2650	3800
Coronet, V-8, 117" wb						
4 dr Sed	150	350	750	1450	2900	4100
2 dr Sed	150	350	750	1350	2800	4000
Sta Wag	150	350	750	1450	2900	4100
Coronet 440, V-8, 117" wb						
4 dr Sed	150	350	750	1450	3000	4200
2 dr HdTp	350	800	1450	2750	5600	8000
Conv	400	1250	2100	4200	7400	10,500
9P Sta Wag	150	350	750	1450	2900	4100
6P Sta Wag	150	350	750	1350	2800	4000
Coronet 500, V-8, 117" wb						
2 dr HdTp	350	900	1550	3050	5900	8500
Conv	400	1300	2200	4400	7700	11,000
Polara, V-8, 121" wb						
4 dr Sed	150	350	750	1450	3000	4200
4 dr HdTp	150	400	750	1600	3100	4400
2 dr HdTp	350	700	1150	2300	4550	6500
Conv	450	1450	2400	4800	8400	12,000
9P Sta Wag	150	350	750	1450	2900	4100
6P Sta Wag	150	350	750	1350	2800	4000
Custom 880, V-8, 121" wb						
4 dr Sed	150	400	750	1550	3050	4300
4 dr HdTp	200	500	850	1900	3500	5000
2 dr HdTp	350	750	1200	2350	4900	7000
Conv	450	1500	2500	5000	8800	12,500
9P Sta Wag	150	400	750	1550	3050	4300
6P Sta Wag	150	350	750	1450	3000	4200
Monaco, V-8, 121" wb						
2 dr HdTp	350	750	1200	2350	4900	7000

NOTE: Deduct 5 percent for 6-cyl. models.
   Add 50 percent for 426 wedge and 60 percent
   for 415 hp Hemi and 100 percent for 425 hp Hemi.

1966

Dart, 6-cyl., 111" wb	6	5	4	3	2	1
4 dr Sed	150	350	750	1450	3000	4200
2 dr Sed	150	350	750	1450	2900	4100
Sta Wag	150	350	750	1450	3000	4200
Dart 270, V-8, 111" wb						
4 dr Sed	150	400	750	1550	3050	4300
2 dr Sed	150	350	750	1450	3000	4200
2 dr HdTp	350	700	1150	2300	4550	6500
Conv	350	800	1450	2750	5600	8000
Sta Wag	150	400	750	1550	3050	4300
Dart GT, V-8, 111" wb						
2 dr HdTp	350	750	1300	2450	5250	7500
Conv	450	1100	1700	3650	6650	9500
Coronet, V-8, 117" wb						
4 dr Sed	150	350	750	1350	2800	4000
2 dr Sed	150	300	750	1350	2700	3900
Coronet DeLuxe, V-8, 117" wb						
4 dr Sed	150	350	750	1450	3000	4200
2 dr Sed	150	350	750	1450	2900	4100
Sta Wag	150	350	750	1450	3000	4200
Coronet 440, V-8, 117" wb						
4 dr Sed	150	400	750	1550	3050	4300
2 dr HdTp	350	900	1550	3050	5900	8500
Conv	400	1200	2000	3950	7000	10,000
Sta Wag	150	400	750	1550	3050	4300
Coronet 500, V-8, 117" wb						
Sed	150	400	750	1550	3050	4300
HdTp	450	1000	1650	3350	6300	9000
Conv	400	1300	2200	4400	7700	11,000
Coronet R/T, V-8, 117" wb						
2 dr HdTp	600	1900	3200	6400	11,200	16,000
Conv	750	2400	4000	8000	14,000	20,000

NOTE: Deduct 5 percent for all Dodge 6-cyl.

Polara, V-8, 121" wb	6	5	4	3	2	1
4 dr Sed	150	400	750	1600	3100	4400
4 dr HdTp	200	500	850	1850	3350	4900
2 dr HdTp	350	700	1150	2300	4550	6500
Conv	450	1000	1650	3350	6300	9000
Sta Wag	150	350	750	1450	3000	4200
Monaco, V-8, 121" wb						
4 dr Sed	200	550	900	2150	3800	5400
4 dr HdTp	200	650	1050	2250	4200	6000
2 dr HdTp	350	700	1150	2300	4600	6600
Sta Wag	200	550	900	2150	3800	5400
Monaco 500						
2 dr Hdtp	350	750	1250	2350	5000	7100
Charger, 117" wb						
2 dr HdTp	550	1700	2800	5600	9800	14,000

NOTE: Add 100 percent for 425 hp 426 Hemi.

1967

Dart, 6-cyl., 111" wb	6	5	4	3	2	1
4 dr Sed	150	350	750	1450	3000	4200

	6	5	4	3	2	1
4 dr 9P Vill	450	1150	1800	3800	6800	9700
4 dr 9P Ber	400	1200	2000	3950	7000	10,000
2 dr Rdup	350	800	1450	2750	5600	8000
1959						
Ranger Series, V-8, 120" wb						
Sed	350	750	1300	2450	5250	7500
4 dr HdTp	350	800	1450	2750	5600	8000
2 dr Sed	350	750	1300	2450	5250	7500
2 dr HdTp	450	1450	2400	4800	8400	12,000
Corsair Series, V-8, 120" wb						
Sed	350	800	1450	2750	5600	8000
4 dr HdTp	350	900	1550	3050	5900	8500
2 dr HdTp	500	1550	2600	5200	9100	13,000
Conv	850	2650	4400	8800	15,400	22,000
Station Wagons, V-8, 118" wb						
Vill	350	900	1550	3050	5900	8500
9P Vill	450	1000	1650	3350	6300	9000
NOTE: Deduct 5 percent for 6 cyl.						
1960						
Ranger Series, V-8, 120" wb						
Sed	350	750	1300	2450	5250	7500
4 dr HdTp	350	900	1550	3050	5900	8500
2 dr Sed	350	750	1300	2450	5250	7500
2 dr HdTp	550	1800	3000	6000	10,500	15,000
Conv	1000	3100	5200	10,400	18,200	26,000
Station Wagons, V-8, 120" wb						
9P Vill	450	1050	1650	3500	6400	9200
6P Vill	450	1000	1650	3350	6300	9000
NOTE: Deduct 5 percent for 6 cyl.						

FORD

	6	5	4	3	2	1
1946						
Series 69A DeLuxe, V-8						
Cpe	350	900	1550	3050	5900	8500
Tudor	350	750	1200	2350	4900	7000
Fordor	350	750	1200	2350	4900	7000
Super DeLuxe						
Conv	850	2750	4600	9200	16,100	23,000
Sptman Conv	1800	5750	9600	19,200	33,600	48,000
3P Cpe	450	1000	1650	3350	6300	9000
5P Cpe	450	1050	1650	3500	6400	9200
Tudor	350	750	1300	2450	5250	7500
Fordor	350	750	1300	2450	5250	7500
Sta Wag	850	2650	4400	8800	15,400	22,000
NOTE: Deduct 5 percent avg. for 6-cyl.						
1947						
Model 79A DeLuxe, V-8						
3P Cpe	450	1100	1700	3650	6650	9500
Tudor	350	750	1200	2350	4900	7000
Fordor	350	750	1200	2350	4900	7000
Super DeLuxe						
Conv	900	2900	4800	9600	16,800	24,000
Sptman Conv	1800	5750	9600	19,200	33,600	48,000
3P Cpe	400	1200	2000	3950	7000	10,000
5P Cpe	400	1200	2000	3950	7000	10,000
2 dr Sed	350	750	1300	2450	5250	7500
4 dr Sed	350	750	1300	2450	5250	7500
Sta Wag	850	2750	4600	9200	16,100	23,000
NOTE: Deduct 5 percent average for 6-cyl.						
1948						
Model 89A DeLuxe, V-8						
3P Cpe	450	1100	1700	3650	6650	9500
2 dr Sed	350	750	1200	2350	4900	7000
Sed	350	750	1200	2350	4900	7000
Model 89A Super DeLuxe, V-8						
Conv	900	2900	4800	9600	16,800	24,000
Sptman Conv	1800	5750	9600	19,200	33,600	48,000
3P Cpe	400	1200	2000	3950	7000	10,000
5P Cpe	400	1200	2000	3950	7000	10,000
2 dr Sed	350	750	1300	2450	5250	7500
4 dr Sed	350	750	1300	2450	5250	7500
Sta Wag	850	2750	4600	9200	16,100	23,000
NOTE: Deduct 5 percent avg. for 6-cyl.						
1949						
Model 8BA DeLuxe, V-8						
Cpe	350	800	1450	2750	5600	8000
Clb Cpe	350	850	1500	2900	5700	8200
2 dr Sed	350	725	1200	2350	4850	6900
4 dr Sed	350	725	1200	2350	4800	6800
Custom						
Conv	700	2300	3800	7600	13,300	19,000
Clb Cpe	450	1000	1650	3350	6300	9000
2 dr Sed	350	750	1300	2450	5250	7500
4 dr Sed	350	750	1300	2400	5200	7400
Sta Wag	700	2150	3600	7200	12,600	18,000
NOTE: Deduct 5 percent avg. for 6-cyl.						
1950						
DeLuxe, V-8, 114" wb						
4 dr Sed	350	725	1200	2350	4800	6800
2 dr Sed	350	725	1200	2350	4850	6900
Bus Cpe	350	800	1450	2750	5600	8000
Custom DeLuxe, V-8, 114" wb						
4 dr Sed	350	750	1300	2400	5200	7400
2 dr Sed	350	750	1300	2450	5250	7500
Crest	400	1250	2100	4200	7400	10,500
Conv	750	2400	4000	8000	14,000	20,000
Sta Wag	700	2300	3800	7600	13,300	19,000
Clb Cpe	450	1100	1700	3650	6650	9500
NOTE: Deduct 5 percent average for 6-cyl.						
1951						
DeLuxe, V-8, 114" wb						
4 dr Sed	350	725	1150	2300	4700	6700
2 dr Sed	350	700	1150	2300	4550	6500
Bus Cpe	350	750	1350	2600	5400	7700
Custom DeLuxe, V-8, 114" wb						
4 dr Sed	350	750	1300	2400	5200	7400
2 dr Sed	350	750	1300	2450	5250	7500
Crest	400	1250	2100	4200	7400	10,500
Clb Cpe	450	1050	1650	3500	6400	9200

	6	5	4	3	2	1
2 dr HdTp	400	1300	2200	4400	7700	11,000
Conv	800	2500	4200	8400	14,700	21,000
Sta Wag	750	2400	4000	8000	14,000	20,000
NOTE: Deduct 5 percent average for 6-cyl.						
1952						
Mainline, V-8, 115" wb						
4 dr Sed	200	600	950	2200	3900	5600
2 dr Sed	200	600	950	2150	3850	5500
Bus Cpe	350	700	1150	2300	4550	6500
Sta Wag	350	725	1200	2350	4800	6800
Customline, V-8, 115" wb						
4 dr Sed	350	725	1200	2350	4800	6800
2 dr Sed	350	725	1150	2300	4700	6700
Clb Cpe	350	750	1300	2450	5250	7500
Ctry Sed	350	750	1350	2650	5450	7800
Crestline, V-8, 115" wb						
2 dr HdTp	400	1300	2200	4400	7700	11,000
Conv	650	2050	3400	6800	11,900	17,000
Sta Wag	450	1000	1650	3350	6300	9000
NOTE: Deduct 5 percent average for 6-cyl.						
1953						
Mainline, V-8, 115" wb						
4 dr Sed	200	550	900	2150	3800	5400
2 dr Sed	200	550	900	2100	3700	5300
Bus Cpe	350	700	1150	2300	4550	6500
Sta Wag	350	750	1200	2350	4900	7000
Customline, V-8, 115" wb						
4 dr Sed	350	725	1200	2350	4850	6900
2 dr Sed	350	700	1150	2300	4600	6600
Clb Cpe	350	750	1250	2400	5050	7200
Sta Wag	350	800	1450	2750	5600	8000
Crestline, 8-cyl., 115" wb						
2 dr HdTp	400	1300	2200	4400	7700	11,000
Conv	650	2050	3400	6800	11,900	17,000
Sta Wag	450	1000	1650	3350	6300	9000
NOTE: Deduct 5 percent average for 6-cyl. Add 50 percent for Indy Pace Car replica convertible.						
1954						
Mainline, 8-cyl., 115.5" wb						
4 dr Sed	200	600	950	2150	3850	5500
2 dr Sed	200	550	900	2150	3800	5400
Bus Cpe	350	700	1150	2300	4550	6500
Sta Wag	350	700	1150	2300	4600	6600
Customline, V-8, 115.5" wb						
4 dr Sed	350	725	1200	2350	4800	6800
2 dr Sed	350	725	1150	2300	4700	6700
Clb Cpe	350	750	1250	2350	5000	7100
Sta Wag	350	750	1200	2350	4900	7000
Crestline, V-8, 115.5" wb						
4 dr Sed	350	750	1200	2350	4900	7000
Sky Cpe	500	1550	2600	5200	9100	13,000
2 dr HdTp	400	1200	2000	3950	7000	10,000
Conv	700	2150	3600	7200	12,600	18,000
Sta Wag	450	1100	1700	3650	6650	9500
NOTE: Deduct 5 percent average for 6-cyl.						
1955						
Mainline, V-8, 115.5" wb						
4 dr Sed	200	650	1000	2200	4100	5800
Bus Sed	200	600	950	2200	3900	5600
2 dr Sed	200	600	1000	2200	4000	5700
Customline, V-8, 115.5" wb						
4 dr Sed	200	675	1050	2250	4300	6100
2 dr Sed	200	650	1050	2250	4200	6000
Fairlane, V-8, 115.5" wb						
4 dr Sed	350	750	1300	2400	5200	7400
2 dr Sed	350	750	1250	2400	5050	7200
2 dr HdTp	500	1550	2600	5200	9100	13,000
Crn Vic	850	2650	4400	8800	15,400	22,000
Crn Vic Plexi-top	950	3000	5000	10,000	17,500	25,000
Conv	1050	3350	5600	11,200	19,600	28,000
Station Wagon, V-8, 115.5" wb						
Ran Wag	350	750	1200	2350	4900	7000
Ctry Sed	350	800	1450	2750	5600	8000
Ctry Sq	400	1300	2200	4400	7700	11,000
NOTE: Deduct 5 percent average for 6-cyl.						
Thunderbird, 102" wb						
Conv	1600	5050	8400	16,800	29,400	42,000
NOTE: Add $1,800. for hardtop.						
1956						
Mainline, V-8, 115.5" wb						
4 dr Sed	200	650	1000	2200	4150	5900
2 dr Sed	200	650	1000	2200	4100	5800
Bus Sed	200	600	1000	2200	4000	5700
Customline, V-8, 115.5" wb						
4 dr Sed	200	675	1100	2250	4400	6300
2 dr Sed	200	675	1050	2250	4350	6200
2 dr HdTp Vic	400	1200	2000	3950	7000	10,000
Fairlane, V-8, 115.5" wb						
4 dr Sed	350	725	1150	2300	4700	6700
4 dr HdTp Vic	350	900	1550	3050	5900	8500
2 dr Sed	350	700	1150	2300	4600	6600
2 dr HdTp Vic	650	2050	3400	6800	11,900	17,000
Crn Vic	800	2500	4200	8400	14,700	21,000
Crn Vic Plexi-top	950	3000	5000	10,000	17,500	25,000
Conv	1100	3500	5800	11,600	20,300	29,000
Station Wagons, V-8, 115.5" wb						
Ran Wag	350	750	1350	2600	5400	7700
Parklane	500	1550	2600	5200	9100	13,000
Ctry Sed	350	950	1600	3200	6050	8700
Ctry Sq	400	1300	2200	4400	7700	11,000
NOTE: Deduct 5 percent average for 6-cyl. Add 10 percent for "T-Bird Special" V-8.						
Thunderbird						
Conv	1600	5150	8600	17,200	30,100	43,000
NOTE: Add $1,800. for hardtop.						
1957						
Custom, V-8, 116" wb						
Sed	200	650	1000	2200	4150	5900
2 dr Sed	200	650	1000	2200	4100	5800
Bus Cpe	200	600	950	2200	3900	5600
Custom 300, V-8, 116" wb						
4 dr Sed	200	675	1050	2250	4300	6100
2 dr Sed	200	650	1050	2250	4200	6000
Fairlane, V-8, 118" wb						
4 dr Sed	350	700	1100	2300	4500	6400
4 dr HdTp Vic	350	750	1200	2350	4900	7000
2 dr Sed	200	675	1100	2250	4400	6300

	6	5	4	3	2	1
2 dr Vic HdTp	450	1100	1700	3650	6650	9500
Fairlane 500, V-8, 118" wb						
4 dr Sed	350	725	1150	2300	4700	6700
4 dr HdTp Vic	350	750	1300	2450	5250	7500
2 dr Sed	350	700	1150	2300	4600	6600
2 dr HdTp Vic	450	1450	2400	4800	8400	12,000
Conv	850	2750	4600	9200	16,100	23,000
Sky HdTp Conv	1000	3250	5400	10,800	18,900	27,000
Station Wagons, 8-cyl., 116" wb						
Ctry Sed	350	900	1550	3050	5900	8500
Ctry Sq	400	1200	2000	3950	7000	10,000
Ran Wag	350	750	1300	2450	5250	7500
DeL Rio Ran	350	800	1450	2750	5600	8000
NOTE: Deduct 5 percent average for 6-cyl. Add 20 percent for "T-Bird Special" V-8 (Code E). Add 30 percent for Supercharged V-8 (Code F).						
Thunderbird, 102" wb						
Conv	1650	5300	8800	17,600	30,800	44,000
NOTE: Add $1,800. for hardtop. Add 30 percent for super charged V-8 (Code F). Add 20 percent for "T-Bird Special" V-8 (Code E).						
1958						
Custom 300, V-8, 116.03" wb						
4 dr Sed	200	650	1000	2200	4100	5800
2 dr Sed	200	600	1000	2200	4000	5700
Bus Cpe	200	550	900	2000	3600	5200
Fairlane, V-8, 116.03" wb						
4 dr Sed	200	650	1000	2200	4150	5900
4 dr HdTp	200	675	1050	2250	4350	6200
2 dr Sed	200	650	1000	2200	4100	5800
2 dr HdTp	450	1100	1700	3650	6650	9500
Fairlane 500, V-8, 118.04" wb						
4 dr Sed	350	700	1100	2300	4500	6400
4 dr HdTp	350	750	1300	2450	5250	7500
2 dr Sed	200	675	1050	2250	4350	6200
2 dr HdTp	450	1450	2400	4800	8400	12,000
Sun Conv	700	2300	3800	7600	13,300	19,000
Sky HdTp Conv	850	2650	4400	8800	15,400	22,000
Station Wagons, V-8, 116.03" wb						
Ctry Sed	350	800	1450	2750	5600	8000
Ctry Sq	450	1000	1650	3350	6300	9000
4 dr Ran	350	750	1200	2350	4900	7000
2 dr Ran	350	750	1250	2400	5050	7200
DeL Rio Ran	350	750	1350	2600	5400	7700
NOTE: Deduct 5 percent average for 6-cyl.						
Thunderbird						
2 dr HdTp	750	2400	4000	8000	14,000	20,000
Conv	1000	3250	5400	10,800	18,900	27,000
1959						
Custom 300, V-8, 118" wb						
Sed	200	550	900	2000	3600	5200
2 dr Sed	200	675	1050	2250	4300	6100
Bus Cpe	200	650	1050	2250	4200	6000
Fairlane, V-8, 118" wb						
4 dr Sed	200	550	900	2100	3700	5300
2 dr Sed	200	550	900	2000	3600	5200
Fairlane 500, V-8, 118" wb						
4 dr Sed	200	600	950	2150	3850	5500
4 dr HdTp	200	650	1000	2200	4150	5900
2 dr Sed	200	550	900	2150	3800	5400
2 dr HdTp	350	900	1550	3050	5900	8500
Sun Conv	750	2400	4000	8000	14,000	20,000
Sky HdTp Conv	900	2900	4800	9600	16,800	24,000
Galaxie, V-8, 118" wb						
4 dr Sed	200	600	1000	2200	4000	5700
4 dr HdTp	200	675	1050	2250	4350	6200
2 dr Sed	200	600	950	2200	3900	5600
2 dr HdTp	450	1100	1700	3650	6650	9500
Sun Conv	750	2400	4000	8000	14,000	20,000
Sky HdTp Conv	900	2900	4800	9600	16,800	24,000
Station Wagons, V-8, 118" wb						
4 dr Ran	200	650	1000	2200	4100	5800
Ctry Sed	350	800	1450	2750	5600	8000
Ctry Sq	350	900	1550	3050	5900	8500
2 dr Ran	200	650	1050	2250	4200	6000
DeL Rio Ran	350	750	1200	2350	4900	7000
NOTE: Deduct 5 percent average for 6-cyl.						
Thunderbird						
2 dr HdTp	700	2300	3800	7600	13,300	19,000
Conv	950	3000	5000	10,000	17,500	25,000
1960						
Falcon, 6-cyl., 109.5" wb						
4 dr Sed	200	550	900	2000	3600	5200
2 dr Sed	200	500	850	1950	3600	5100
4 dr Sta Wag	200	550	900	2100	3700	5300
2 dr Sta Wag	200	550	900	2000	3600	5200
Fairlane, V-8, 119" wb						
Sed	200	550	900	2000	3600	5200
2 dr Sed	200	500	850	1950	3600	5100
Bus Cpe	200	500	850	1900	3500	5000
Fairlane 500, V-8, 119" wb						
4 dr Sed	200	550	900	2150	3800	5400
2 dr Sed	200	550	900	2100	3700	5300
Galaxie, V-8, 119" wb						
4 dr Sed	200	650	1000	2200	4100	5800
4 dr HdTp	200	650	1050	2250	4200	6000
2 dr HdTp	400	1200	2000	3950	7000	10,000
2 dr Sed	200	600	1000	2200	4000	5700
Galaxie Special, V-8, 119" wb						
2 dr HdTp	450	1450	2400	4800	8400	12,000
Sun Conv	700	2150	3600	7200	12,600	18,000
Station Wagons, V-8, 119" wb						
4 dr Ran	200	600	950	2150	3850	5500
2 dr Ran	200	650	1000	2200	4100	5800
Ctry Sed	200	650	1050	2250	4200	6000
Ctry Sq	350	700	1150	2300	4550	6500
NOTE: Deduct 5 percent average for 6-cyl.						
Thunderbird, 113" wb						
SR HdTp	800	2500	4200	8400	14,700	21,000
2 dr HdTp	700	2300	3800	7600	13,300	19,000
Conv	950	3000	5000	10,000	17,500	25,000
1961						
Falcon, 6-cyl., 109.5" wb						
4 dr Sed	200	550	900	2100	3700	5300
2 dr Sed	200	550	900	2000	3600	5200
Futura	350	800	1450	2750	5600	8000
4 dr Sta Wag	200	550	900	2100	3700	5300
2 dr Sta Wag	200	550	900	2000	3600	5200
Fairlane, V-8, 119" wb						
4 dr Sed	200	550	900	2150	3800	5400
2 dr Sed	200	550	900	2100	3700	5300
Galaxie, V-8, 119" wb						
4 dr Sed	200	600	950	2150	3850	5500
4 dr Vic HdTp	350	700	1150	2300	4550	6500
2 dr Sed	200	550	900	2150	3800	5400
2 dr Vic HdTp	450	1100	1700	3650	6650	9500
2 dr Star HdTp	400	1300	2200	4400	7700	11,000
Sun Conv	550	1700	2800	5600	9800	14,000
Station Wagons, V-8, 119" wb						
4 dr Ran	200	600	950	2150	3850	5500
2 dr Ran	200	600	1000	2200	4000	5700
6P Ctry Sed	200	650	1050	2250	4200	6000
Ctry Sq	350	700	1150	2300	4550	6500
Thunderbird, 113" wb						
2 dr HdTp	500	1550	2600	5200	9100	13,000
Conv	900	2900	4800	9600	16,800	24,000
NOTE: Deduct 5 percent average for 6-cyl.						
1962						
Falcon, 6-cyl., 109.5" wb						
4 dr Sed	200	500	850	1900	3500	5000
2 dr	200	500	850	1850	3350	4900
Fut Spt Cpe	450	1100	1700	3650	6650	9500
Sq Wag	200	600	950	2150	3850	5500
Falcon Station Bus, 6-cyl., 109.5" wb						
Sta Bus	150	450	800	1800	3300	4800
Clb Wag	200	500	850	1850	3350	4900
DeL Wag	200	500	850	1900	3500	5000
Fairlane, V-8, 115.5" wb						
4 dr Sed	200	500	850	1850	3350	4900
2 dr Sed	150	450	800	1800	3300	4800
Spt Sed	200	550	900	2150	3800	5400
Galaxie 500, V-8, 119" wb						
4 dr Sed	200	500	850	1950	3600	5100
4 dr HdTp	200	550	900	2100	3700	5300
2 dr Sed	200	500	850	1900	3500	5000
2 dr HdTp	400	1200	2000	3950	7000	10,000
Conv	450	1450	2400	4800	8400	12,000
Galaxie 500 XL, V-8, 119" wb						
2 dr HdTp	400	1300	2200	4400	7700	11,000
Conv	550	1800	3000	6000	10,500	15,000
Station Wagons, V-8, 119" wb						
Ranch	200	600	950	2150	3850	5500
Ctry Sed	200	650	1050	2250	4200	6000
Ctry Sq	350	700	1150	2300	4550	6500
NOTE: Deduct 5 percent for 6-cyl.						
Thunderbird						
2 dr HdTp	550	1700	2800	5600	9800	14,000
2 dr Lan HdTp	550	1800	3000	6000	10,500	15,000
Conv	900	2900	4800	9600	16,800	24,000
Spt Rds	1100	3500	5800	11,600	20,300	29,000
NOTE: Add 30 percent for 406 V-8.						
1963						
Falcon, 6-cyl., 109.5" wb						
4 dr Sed	200	550	900	2000	3600	5200
2 dr Sed	200	500	850	1950	3600	5100
2 dr Spt Sed	200	600	950	2200	3900	5600
2 dr HdTp	450	1000	1650	3350	6300	9000
2 dr Spt HdTp	450	1100	1700	3650	6650	9500
Conv	400	1300	2200	4400	7700	11,000
Spt Conv	450	1450	2400	4800	8400	12,000
Squire Wag	200	600	950	2150	3850	5500
4 dr Sta Wag	200	500	850	1850	3350	4900
2 dr Sta Wag	150	450	800	1800	3300	4800
Station Buses, 6-cyl., 90" wb						
Sta Bus	150	450	800	1800	3300	4800
Clb Wag	200	500	850	1850	3350	4900
DeL Clb Wag	200	500	850	1900	3500	5000
Sprint, V-8, 109.5" wb						
HdTp	400	1200	2000	3950	7000	10,000
Conv	550	1700	2800	5600	9800	14,000
Fairlane, V-8, 115.5" wb						
4 dr Sed	200	500	850	1850	3350	4900
2 dr Sed	150	450	800	1800	3300	4800
2 dr HdTp	200	650	1050	2250	4200	6000
Spt Cpe	350	750	1200	2350	4900	7000
Sq Wag	200	500	850	1900	3500	5000
Cus Ran	200	500	850	1850	3350	4900
NOTE: Add 20 percent for 271 hp V-8.						
Ford 300, V-8, 119" wb						
Sed	200	500	850	1900	3500	5000
2 dr Sed	200	500	850	1850	3350	4900
Galaxie 500, V-8, 119" wb						
Sed	200	500	850	1950	3600	5100
4 dr HdTp	200	500	850	1900	3500	5000
2 dr Sed	200	500	850	1900	3500	5000
2 dr HdTp	400	1200	2000	3950	7000	10,000
FsBk	450	1450	2400	4800	8400	12,000
Conv	500	1550	2600	5200	9100	13,000
Galaxie 500 XL, V-8, 119" wb						
4 dr HdTp	350	700	1150	2300	4550	6500
2 dr HdTp	400	1300	2200	4400	7700	11,000
FsBk	500	1550	2600	5200	9100	13,000
Conv	600	1900	3200	6400	11,200	16,000
Station Wagons, V-8, 119" wb						
Squire	200	650	1050	2250	4200	6000
Ctry Sed	200	600	950	2150	3850	5500
NOTE: Deduct 5 percent average for 6-cyl.						
Thunderbird, 113.2 wb						
2 dr HdTp	550	1700	2800	5600	9800	14,000
2 dr Lan HdTp	550	1800	3000	6000	10,500	15,000
Conv	900	2900	4800	9600	16,800	24,000
Spt Rds	1100	3500	5800	11,600	20,300	29,000
NOTE: Add 5 percent for Monaco option. Add 30 percent for 406 & add 40 percent for 427.						
1964						
NOTE: Add 5 percent for V-8 except Sprint.						
Falcon, 6-cyl., 109.5" wb						
4 dr Sed	200	500	850	1950	3600	5100
2 dr Sed	200	500	850	1900	3500	5000
2 dr HdTp	350	750	1300	2450	5250	7500
2 dr Spt HdTp	450	1100	1700	3650	6650	9500
Conv	400	1250	2100	4200	7400	10,500
Spt Conv	450	1400	2300	4600	8100	11,500
Squire Wag	200	600	950	2150	3850	5500
DeL Wag	150	400	750	1650	3150	4500

	6	5	4	3	2	1
4 dr Sta	150	400	750	1650	3150	4500
2 dr Sta	150	450	800	1800	3300	4800
Station Bus, 6-cyl, 90" wb						
Sta Bus	150	400	750	1650	3150	4500
Clb Wag	150	450	750	1700	3200	4600
DeL Clb	150	450	800	1800	3300	4800
Sprint, V-8, 109.5" wb						
2 dr HdTp	400	1250	2100	4200	7400	10,500
Conv	450	1450	2400	4800	8400	12,000
Fairlane, V-8, 115.5" wb						
Sed	200	550	900	2000	3600	5200
2 dr Sed	200	500	850	1950	3600	5100
2 dr HdTp	350	900	1550	3050	5900	8500
2 dr Spt HdTp	450	1100	1700	3650	6650	9500
Ran Cus	200	675	1050	2250	4300	6100

NOTE: Add 20 percent for 271 hp V-8.

	6	5	4	3	2	1
Fairlane Thunderbolt						
2 dr Sed				value not estimable		
Custom, V-8, 119" wb						
Sed	200	550	900	2000	3600	5200
2 dr Sed	200	500	850	1950	3600	5100
Custom 500, V-8, 119" wb						
Sed	200	550	900	2100	3700	5300
2 dr Sed	200	550	900	2000	3600	5200
Galaxie 500, V-8, 119" wb						
Sed	200	600	950	2150	3850	5500
4 dr HdTp	200	600	950	2150	3850	5500
2 dr Sed	200	550	900	2150	3800	5400
2 dr HdTp	400	1300	2200	4400	7700	11,000
Conv	500	1550	2600	5200	9100	13,000
Galaxie 500XL, V-8, 119" wb						
4 dr HdTp	350	700	1150	2300	4550	6500
2 dr HdTp	450	1450	2400	4800	8400	12,000
Conv	700	2150	3600	7200	12,600	18,000
Station Wagons, V-8, 119" wb						
Ctry Sq	200	650	1050	2250	4200	6000
Ctry Sed	200	600	950	2150	3850	5500
Thunderbird, 113.2" wb						
2 dr HdTp	400	1300	2200	4400	7700	11,000
2 dr Lan HdTp	450	1450	2400	4800	8400	12,000
Conv	800	2500	4200	8400	14,700	21,000

NOTE: Add 25 percent for Tonneau convertible option.
Add 40 percent for 427 V-8.

1965

	6	5	4	3	2	1
Falcon, 6-cyl., 109.5" wb						
4 dr Sed	150	450	800	1800	3300	4800
2 dr Sed	150	450	800	1750	3250	4700
2 dr HdTp	200	650	1050	2250	4200	6000
Conv	450	1100	1700	3650	6650	9500
Squire Wag	200	500	850	1900	3500	5000
DeL Wag	150	450	800	1750	3250	4700
4 dr Sta	150	450	800	1750	3250	4700
2 dr Sta	150	450	750	1700	3200	4600
Sprint V-8, 109.5" wb						
2 dr HdTp	450	1000	1650	3350	6300	9000
Conv	400	1300	2200	4400	7700	11,000
Falcon Station Buses, 6-cyl., 90" wb						
Sta Bus	200	500	850	1850	3350	4900
Clb Wag	200	500	850	1950	3600	5100
DeL Wag	200	550	900	2100	3700	5300
Fairlane, V-8, 116" wb						
Sed	200	500	850	1950	3600	5100
2 dr Sed	200	500	850	1900	3500	5000
2 dr HdTp	200	650	1050	2250	4200	6000
2 dr Spt HdTp	350	900	1550	3050	5900	8500
Sta Wag	200	500	850	1900	3500	5000

NOTE: Add 10 percent for 271 hp V-8.
Add 50 percent for 427 Thunderbolt.

	6	5	4	3	2	1
Custom, V-8, 119" wb						
Sed	150	450	800	1800	3300	4800
2 dr Sed	150	450	800	1750	3250	4700
Custom 500, V-8, 119" wb						
Sed	200	500	850	1850	3350	4900
2 dr Sed	150	450	800	1800	3300	4800
Galaxie 500, V-8, 119" wb						
Sed	200	500	850	1900	3500	5000
4 dr HdTp	200	550	900	2000	3600	5200
2 dr HdTp	350	800	1450	2750	5600	8000
Conv	400	1200	2000	3950	7000	10,000
Galaxie 500 XL, V-8, 119" wb						
2 dr HdTp	350	900	1550	3050	5900	8500
Conv	450	1450	2400	4800	8400	12,000
Galaxie 500 LTD, V-8, 119" wb						
4 dr HdTp	200	650	1050	2250	4200	6000
2 dr HdTp	450	1000	1650	3350	6300	9000
Station Wagons, V-8, 119" wb						
9P Ctry Sq	200	600	950	2150	3850	5500
9P Ctry Sed	200	500	850	1900	3500	5000
Ran	150	450	800	1800	3300	4800
Thunderbird						
2 dr HdTp	400	1300	2200	4400	7700	11,000
2 dr Lan HdTp	450	1450	2400	4800	8400	12,000
Conv	800	2500	4200	8400	14,700	21,000

NOTE: Add 5 Special Landau option.
Add 40 percent for 427 V-8.

1966

NOTE: Add 5 percent for V-8.

	6	5	4	3	2	1
Falcon, 6-cyl., 110.9" wb						
Sed	150	450	800	1800	3300	4800
Clb Cpe	150	450	800	1750	3250	4700
Spt Cpe	200	500	850	1950	3600	5100
6P Wag	150	450	800	1750	3250	4700
Squire Wag	200	600	950	2150	3850	5500
Falcon Station Bus, 6-cyl., 90" wb						
Clb Wag	150	450	750	1700	3200	4600
Cus Clb Wag	150	450	800	1750	3250	4700
DeL Clb Wag	150	450	800	1800	3300	4800
Fairlane, V-8, 116" wb						
Sed	200	500	850	1850	3350	4900
Clb Cpe	150	450	800	1800	3300	4800
2 dr HdTp Cpe	200	600	950	2150	3850	5500
Conv	350	800	1450	2750	5600	8000
Fairlane 500 XL, V-8, 116" wb						
2 dr HdTp	350	750	1300	2450	5250	7500
Conv	400	1200	2000	3950	7000	10,000
Fairlane 500 GT, V-8, 116" wb						
2 dr HdTp	350	800	1450	2750	5600	8000

	6	5	4	3	2	1
Conv	400	1300	2200	4400	7700	11,000
Station Wagons, V-8, 113" wb						
6P DeL	150	450	800	1800	3300	4800
Squire	200	500	850	1900	3500	5000
Custom, V-8, 119" wb						
Sed	200	500	850	1900	3500	5000
2 dr Sed	200	500	850	1850	3350	4900
Galaxie 500, V-8, 119" wb						
Sed	200	500	850	1950	3600	5100
4 dr HdTp	200	550	900	2100	3700	5300
2 dr HdTp	350	750	1300	2450	5250	7500
Conv	450	1100	1700	3650	6650	9500
Galaxie 500, XL, V-8, 119" wb						
2 dr HdTp	350	900	1550	3050	5900	8500
Conv	450	1450	2400	4800	8400	12,000
LTD, V-8, 119" wb						
4 dr HdTp	200	600	950	2150	3850	5500
2 dr HdTp	350	750	1300	2450	5250	7500
Galaxie 500 7-litre, V-8, 119" wb						
2 dr HdTp	450	1450	2400	4800	8400	12,000
Conv		1800	3000	6000	10,500	15,000

NOTE: Add 50 percent for 427 engine option on 7-litre models.

	6	5	4	3	2	1
Station Wagons, V-8, 119" wb						
Ran Wag	150	450	800	1800	3300	4800
Ctry Sed	200	500	850	1900	3500	5000
Ctry Sq	200	550	900	2000	3600	5200
Thunderbird, 113" wb						
2 dr HdTp Cpe	450	1450	2400	4800	8400	12,000
2 dr Twn Lan	550	1700	2800	5600	9800	14,000
2 dr HdTp Twn	500	1550	2600	5200	9100	13,000
Conv	700	2200	3800	7600	13,300	19,000

NOTE: Add 40 percent for 427 or 30 percent for 428 engine option.

1967

	6	5	4	3	2	1
Falcon, 6-cyl, 111" wb						
4 dr	150	450	800	1800	3300	4800
2 dr	150	450	800	1750	3250	4700
Sta Wag	150	450	800	1800	3300	4800
Futura						
Sed	200	500	850	1850	3350	4900
Clb Cpe	150	450	800	1800	3300	4800
2 dr HdTp	200	500	850	1950	3600	5100
Fairlane						
4 dr Sed	150	450	800	1800	3300	4800
Cpe	150	450	800	1750	3250	4700
Fairlane 500, V-8, 116" wb						
4 dr Sed	200	500	850	1850	3350	4900
Cpe	150	450	800	1800	3300	4800
2 dr HdTp	350	700	1150	2300	4550	6500
Conv	450	1100	1700	3650	6650	9500
Wagon	150	450	800	1800	3300	4800
Fairlane 500 XL V-8						
2 dr HdTp	350	750	1200	2350	4900	7000
Conv	400	1300	2200	4400	7700	11,000
2 dr GT HdTp	350	800	1450	2750	5600	8000
Conv GT	450	1450	2400	4800	8400	12,000
Fairlane Wagons						
Sta Wag	150	450	800	1800	3300	4800
500 Wag	200	500	850	1850	3350	4900
Squire	200	500	850	1950	3600	5100
Ford Custom						
4 dr Sed	150	450	800	1800	3300	4800
2 dr Sed	150	450	800	1750	3250	4700
Ford Custom 500						
4 dr Sed	200	500	850	1850	3350	4900
2 dr Sed	150	450	800	1800	3300	4800
Galaxie 500, V-8, 119" wb						
4 dr Sed	200	500	850	1950	3600	5100
4 dr HdTp	200	550	900	2100	3700	5300
2 dr HdTp	350	900	1550	3050	5900	8500
Conv	450	1450	2400	4800	8400	12,000
Galaxie 500 XL						
2 dr HdTp	450	1100	1700	3650	6650	9500
Conv	500	1550	2600	5200	9100	13,000
LTD, V-8, 119" wb						
4 dr HdTp	200	650	1050	2250	4200	6000
2 dr HdTp	400	1200	2000	3950	7000	10,000
Wagons						
Ranch	150	450	800	1800	3300	4800
Ctry Sq	200	600	950	2150	3850	5500
Ctry Sed	200	500	850	1900	3500	5000
Thunderbird, 115" wb						
4 dr Lan	350	750	1300	2450	5250	7500
2 dr Lan	450	1000	1650	3350	6300	9000
2 dr HdTp	450	1050	1650	3500	6400	9200

NOTE: Add 5 percent for V-8.
Add 40 percent for 427 or 428 engine option.

1968

NOTE: Add 5 percent for V-8.

	6	5	4	3	2	1
Standard Falcon						
Sed	150	400	750	1650	3150	4500
2 dr Sed	150	400	750	1600	3100	4400
Sta Wag	150	400	750	1550	3050	4300
Falcon Futura, 6-cyl., 110.0" wb						
Sed	150	450	750	1700	3200	4600
2 dr Sed	150	400	750	1650	3150	4500
Spt Cpe	150	450	800	1800	3300	4800
Sta Wag	150	400	750	1550	3050	4300
Fairlane						
4 dr Sed	150	450	750	1700	3200	4600
2 dr HdTp	200	550	900	2100	3700	5300
Sta Wag	150	400	750	1600	3100	4400
Fairlane 500, V-8, 116" wb						
4 dr Sed	150	450	800	1750	3250	4700
2 dr HdTp	200	650	1050	2250	4200	6000
2 dr FsBk	350	700	1150	2300	4550	6500
Conv	450	1100	1700	3650	6650	9500
Sta Wag	150	400	750	1550	3050	4300
Torino, V-8, 116" wb						
4 dr Sed	150	400	750	1550	3050	4300
2 dr HdTp	350	700	1150	2300	4550	6500
Wagon	150	400	750	1550	3050	4300
Torino GT V-8						
2 dr HdTp	350	800	1450	2750	5600	8000
FsBk	450	1000	1650	3350	6300	9000
Conv	450	1400	2300	4600	8100	11,500
Custom						
4 dr Sed	150	400	750	1650	3150	4500
2 dr Sed	150	400	750	1600	3100	4400

	6	5	4	3	2	1
Custom 500						
4 dr Sed	150	450	750	1700	3200	4600
2 dr Sed	150	400	750	1650	3150	4500
Galaxie 500, V-8, 119" wb						
4 dr Sed	150	450	800	1750	3250	4700
4 dr HdTp	150	450	800	1800	3300	4800
2 dr HdTp	350	750	1200	2350	4900	7000
FsBk	450	1000	1650	3350	6300	9000
Conv	400	1300	2200	4400	7700	11,000
XL						
Fsbk	400	1200	2000	3950	7000	10,000
Conv	450	1450	2400	4800	8400	12,000
LTD						
4 dr Sed	200	500	850	1900	3500	5000
4 dr HdTp	200	600	950	2150	3850	5500
2 dr HdTp	350	750	1300	2450	5250	7500
Ranch Wag						
Std Wag	150	400	750	1550	3050	4300
500 Wag	150	400	750	1600	3100	4400
DeL 500 Wag	150	400	750	1650	3150	4500
Country Sedan						
Std Wag	150	450	750	1700	3200	4600
DeL Wag	150	450	800	1750	3250	4700
Country Squire						
Sta Wag	200	500	850	1900	3500	5000
DeL Wag	200	550	900	2000	3600	5200

NOTE: Add 50 percent for 429 engine option.

	6	5	4	3	2	1
Thunderbird, 115" wb						
HdTp	450	1000	1650	3350	6300	9000
Lan Cpe	450	1050	1650	3500	6400	9200
Lan Sed	350	750	1300	2400	5200	7400

NOTE: Add 40 percent for 427 or 428 engine option.

1969

NOTE: Add 10 percent for V-8.

	6	5	4	3	2	1
Falcon Futura, 6-cyl, 111" wb						
Spt Cpe	150	350	750	1450	2900	4100
2 dr	150	300	700	1250	2600	3700
Fairlane 500, V-8, 116" wb						
4 dr	125	250	700	1150	2500	3600
2 dr HdTp	200	600	950	2150	3850	5500
FsBk	200	650	1050	2250	4200	6000
Conv	350	900	1550	3050	5900	8500
Wagon	150	350	750	1350	2800	4000
Torino, V-8, 116" wb						
4 dr	150	350	750	1350	2800	4000
2 dr HdTp	200	600	950	2150	3850	5500
Torino GT V-8						
2 dr HdTp	350	750	1200	2350	4900	7000
FsBk	450	1000	1650	3350	6300	9000
Conv	400	1300	2200	4400	7700	11,000
Cobra						
2 dr HdTp	550	1700	2800	5600	9800	14,000
FsBk	550	1800	3000	6000	10,500	15,000
Galaxie 500, V-8, 121" wb						
4 dr HdTp	150	350	750	1450	3000	4200
2 dr HdTp	150	450	800	1750	3250	4700
FsBk	350	750	1200	2350	4900	7000
Conv	450	1000	1650	3350	6300	9000
XL						
FsBk	350	900	1550	3050	5900	8500
Conv	400	1200	2000	3950	7000	10,000
LTD						
4 dr HdTp	200	500	850	1900	3500	5000
2 dr HdTp	350	700	1150	2300	4550	6500
Thunderbird, 117.2" wb						
4 dr Lan	200	550	900	2100	3700	5300
2 dr Lan	350	725	1150	2300	4700	6700
2 dr HdTp	350	700	1150	2300	4550	6500

NOTE: Add 40 percent for 428 engine option.
Add 50 percent for 429 engine option.

1970

	6	5	4	3	2	1
Falcon, 6-cyl, 110" wb						
4 dr Sed	150	300	750	1350	2700	3900
2 dr Sed	150	300	700	1250	2650	3800
Sta Wag	150	300	700	1250	2650	3800
1970-1/2 Falcon, 6-cyl, 117" wb						
4 dr Sed	150	350	750	1450	2900	4100
2 dr Sed	150	300	750	1350	2700	3900
Sta Wag	150	350	750	1350	2800	4000
Futura, 6-cyl, 110" wb						
4 dr Sed	150	350	750	1450	3000	4200
2 dr Sed	150	350	750	1350	2800	4000
Sta Wag	150	350	750	1350	2800	4000

NOTE: Add 10 percent for V-8.

	6	5	4	3	2	1
Maverick						
2 dr	150	300	700	1250	2600	3700
Fairlane 500, V-8, 117" wb						
4 dr Sed	150	400	750	1550	3050	4300
2 dr HdTp	200	600	950	2150	3850	5500
Sta Wag	150	350	750	1450	3000	4200
Torino, V-8, 117" wb						
4 dr Sed	150	400	750	1600	3100	4400
4 dr HdTp	150	400	750	1650	3150	4500
2 dr HdTp	350	700	1150	2300	4550	6500
2 dr HdTp Sports Roof	350	750	1300	2450	5250	7500
Sta Wag	150	400	750	1650	3150	4500
Torino Brougham, V-8, 117" wb						
4 dr HdTp	150	400	750	1650	3150	4500
2 dr HdTp	350	700	1150	2300	4550	6500
Sta Wag	150	400	750	1550	3050	4300
Torino GT, V-8, 117" wb						
2 dr HdTp	350	800	1450	2750	5600	8000
Conv	400	1200	2000	3950	7000	10,000
Cobra, V-8, 117" wb						
2 dr HdTp	700	2300	3800	7600	13,300	19,000
Custom, V-8, 121" wb						
4 dr Sed	150	350	750	1350	2800	4000
Sta Wag	150	350	750	1350	2800	4000
Custom 500, V-8, 121" wb						
4 dr Sed	150	350	750	1450	2900	4000
Sta Wag	150	350	750	1450	2900	4100
Galaxie 500, V-8, 121" wb						
4 dr Sed	150	350	750	1450	3000	4200
4 dr HdTp	150	400	750	1650	3150	4500
2 dr HdTp	200	600	950	2150	3850	5500
Sta Wag	150	400	750	1650	3150	4500
2 dr FsBk HdTp	350	750	1200	2350	4900	7000

	6	5	4	3	2	1
XL, V-8, 121" wb						
2 dr FsBk HdTp	350	750	1300	2450	5250	7500
Conv	450	1100	1700	3650	6650	9500
LTD, V-8, 121" wb						
4 dr Sed	150	400	750	1550	3050	4300
4 dr HdTp	150	450	750	1750	3250	4700
2 dr HdTp	200	600	950	2150	3850	5500
Sta Wag	150	450	750	1700	3200	4600
LTD Brougham, V-8, 121" wb						
4 dr Sed	150	400	750	1600	3100	4400
4 dr HdTp	200	500	850	1900	3500	5000
2 dr HdTp	200	650	1050	2250	4200	6000
Thunderbird, 117" wb						
4 dr Lan	200	675	1100	2250	4400	6300
2 dr Lan	350	700	1100	2300	4500	6400
2 dr HdTp	350	725	1150	2300	4700	6700

NOTE: Add 40 percent for 429 engine option.
Add 50 percent for 429 engine option.

1971

	6	5	4	3	2	1
Pinto						
Rbt	150	300	700	1250	2600	3700
Maverick						
2 dr	150	300	700	1250	2600	3700
4 dr	150	300	700	1250	2650	3800
Grabber	150	300	750	1350	2700	3900
Torino, V-8, 114" wb, Sta Wag 117" wb						
4 dr Sed	150	300	750	1350	2700	3900
2 dr HdTp	200	500	850	1900	3500	5000
Sta Wag	150	300	700	1250	2650	3800
Torino 500, V-8, 114" wb, Sta Wag 117" wb						
4 dr Sed	150	350	750	1350	2800	4000
4 dr HdTp	150	350	750	1450	2900	4100
2 dr HdTp Formal Roof	350	750	1300	2450	5250	7500
2 dr HdTp Sports Roof	350	800	1450	2750	5600	8000
Sta Wag	150	300	700	1250	2600	3700
4 dr HdTp Brougham	150	350	750	1450	2900	4100
2 dr HdTp Brougham	200	650	1050	2250	4200	6000
Squire Sta Wag	125	250	700	1150	2500	3600
2 dr HdTp Cobra	700	2150	3600	7200	12,600	18,000
2 dr HdTp GT	400	1200	2000	3950	7000	10,000
Conv	450	1500	2500	5000	8800	12,500
Custom, V-8, 121" wb						
4 dr Sed	125	250	700	1150	2500	3600
Sta Wag	125	250	700	1150	2500	3600
Custom 500, V-8, 121" wb						
4 dr Sed	150	300	700	1250	2600	3700
Sta Wag	150	300	700	1250	2600	3700
Galaxie 500, V-8, 121" wb						
4 dr Sed	150	300	700	1250	2650	3800
4 dr HdTp	150	350	750	1350	2800	4000
2 dr HdTp	150	450	800	1750	3250	4700
Sta Wag	150	300	700	1250	2650	3800
LTD						
4 dr	150	300	750	1350	2700	3900
2 dr HdTp	150	350	750	1450	2900	4100
Conv	350	800	1450	2750	5600	8000
Ctry Sq	150	350	750	1350	2800	4000
LTD Brougham, V-8, 121" wb						
4 dr Sed	150	350	750	1450	2900	4100
4 dr HdTp	150	400	750	1600	3100	4400
2 dr HdTp	200	600	950	2150	3850	5500
Thunderbird						
4 dr HdTp	200	650	1000	2200	4150	5900
2 dr HdTp	200	675	1050	2250	4300	6100
2 dr Lan HdTp	200	675	1050	2250	4350	6200

NOTE: Add 40 percent for 429 engine option.

1972

	6	5	4	3	2	1
Pinto						
2 dr	125	250	700	1150	2400	3400
3 dr	125	250	700	1150	2450	3500
Wagon	125	250	700	1150	2500	3600
Maverick						
4 dr	125	250	700	1150	2400	3400
2 dr	125	250	700	1150	2450	3500
Grabber	150	300	750	1350	2700	3900

NOTE: Deduct 20 percent for 6-cyl.

	6	5	4	3	2	1
Torino, V-8, 118" wb, 2 dr 114" wb						
4 dr Sed	125	250	700	1150	2400	3400
2 dr HdTp	150	400	750	1650	3150	4500
Sta Wag	125	250	700	1150	2400	3400
Gran Torino						
4 dr	125	250	700	1150	2450	3500
2 dr HdTp	200	650	1050	2250	4200	6000
Custom, V-8, 121" wb						
4 dr Sed	125	250	700	1150	2500	3600
Sta Wag	125	250	700	1150	2500	3600
Custom 500, V-8, 121" wb						
4 dr Sed	150	300	700	1250	2600	3700
Sta Wag	150	300	700	1250	2600	3700
Galaxie 500, V-8, 121" wb						
4 dr Sed	150	300	700	1250	2650	3800
4 dr HdTp	150	350	750	1350	2800	4000
2 dr HdTp	200	600	950	2150	3850	5500
Sta Wag	150	300	700	1250	2650	3800
LTD, V-8, 121" wb						
4 dr Sed	150	300	750	1350	2700	3900
4 dr HdTp	150	350	750	1450	3000	4200
2 dr HdTp	200	600	1050	2250	4200	6000
Conv	450	1000	1650	3350	6300	9000
Sta Wag	150	350	750	1350	2800	4000
LTD Brougham, V-8, 121" wb						
4 dr Sed	150	350	750	1350	2800	4000
4 dr HdTp	150	450	800	1750	3250	4700
2 dr HdTp	350	700	1150	2300	4550	6500
Thunderbird						
2 dr HdTp	350	700	1100	2300	4500	6400

NOTE: Add 40 percent for 429 engine option.
Add 30 percent for 460 engine option.

1973

	6	5	4	3	2	1
Pinto, 4-cyl.						
2 dr	125	250	700	1150	2450	3500
Rbt	125	250	700	1150	2500	3600
Sta Wag	150	300	700	1250	2600	3700
Maverick V8						
2 dr	125	250	700	1150	2500	3600
4 dr	150	300	700	1250	2600	3700
2 dr Grabber	150	350	750	1450	3000	4200

	6	5	4	3	2	1
Torino V8						
4 dr	125	250	700	1150	2400	3400
2 dr HdTp	150	400	750	1650	3150	4500
Sta Wag	125	250	700	1150	2500	3600
Gran Torino V8						
4 dr	125	250	700	1150	2450	3500
2 dr HdTp	200	500	850	1900	3500	5000
Sta Wag	150	300	700	1250	2600	3700
Gran Torino Sport V8						
2 dr SR HdTp	350	700	1150	2300	4550	6500
2 dr FR HdTp	350	750	1200	2350	4900	7000
Sq Wag	150	350	750	1350	2800	4000
Gran Torino Brgm V8						
4 dr	125	250	700	1150	2500	3600
2 dr HdTp	350	700	1150	2300	4550	6500
Custom 500 V8						
4 dr	125	250	700	1150	2500	3600
Sta Wag	150	300	700	1250	2600	3700
Galaxie 500 V8						
4 dr	150	300	700	1250	2600	3700
2 dr HdTp	150	450	750	1700	3200	4600
4 dr HdTp	150	300	700	1250	2650	3800
Sta Wag	150	300	700	1250	2600	3700
LTD V8						
4 dr	150	300	700	1250	2650	3800
2 dr HdTp	150	450	800	1800	3300	4800
4 dr HdTp	150	300	750	1350	2700	3900
Sta Wag	150	300	700	1250	2650	3800
LTD Brgm V8						
4 dr	150	300	750	1350	2700	3900
2 dr HdTp	200	500	850	1950	3600	5100
4 dr HdTp	150	350	750	1350	2800	4000
Thunderbird						
2 dr HdTp	200	600	950	2150	3850	5500

NOTE: Add 30 percent for 429 engine option.
Add 30 percent for 460 engine option.

1974
Pinto

	6	5	4	3	2	1
Cpe	125	250	700	1150	2500	3600
Htchbk	150	300	700	1250	2600	3700
Sta Wag	125	250	700	1150	2500	3600
Maverick, V-8						
Cpe	125	250	700	1150	2500	3600
Sed	150	300	700	1250	2600	3700
Grabber	150	300	750	1350	2700	3900
Torino, V-8						
4 dr Sed	125	250	700	1150	2500	3600
HdTp	150	450	800	1750	3250	4700
Sta Wag	125	250	700	1150	2450	3500
Gran Torino, V-8						
4 dr Sed	125	250	700	1150	2500	3600
2 dr HdTp	150	450	800	1750	3250	4700
Sta Wag	125	250	700	1150	2500	3600
Gran Torino Sport, V-8						
2 dr HdTp	200	600	950	2150	3850	5500
Gran Torino Brgm, V-8						
4 dr Sed	150	300	700	1250	2650	3800
2 dr HdTp	200	500	850	1900	3500	5000
Gran Torino Elite, V-8						
2 dr HdTp	200	550	900	2000	3600	5200
Gran Torino Squire, V-8						
Sta Wag	150	300	700	1250	2600	3700
Custom 500						
4 dr Sed	125	250	700	1150	2450	3500
Sta Wag	125	250	700	1150	2450	3500
Galaxie 500, V-8						
4 dr Sed	125	250	700	1150	2500	3600
2 dr HdTp	150	300	750	1350	2700	3900
4 dr HdTp	150	300	700	1250	2600	3700
Sta Wag	125	250	700	1150	2500	3600
LTD, V-8						
2 dr HdTp	150	350	750	1450	2900	4100
4 dr Sed	150	300	700	1250	2600	3700
4 dr HdTp	150	300	700	1250	2650	3800
Sta Wag	150	300	700	1250	2600	3700
Ltd Brgm, V-8						
4 dr Sed	150	300	700	1250	2600	3700
2 dr HdTp	150	350	750	1450	3000	4200
4 dr HdTp	150	300	700	1250	2650	3800
Thunderbird						
HdTp	200	600	950	2150	3850	5500

NOTE: Add 30 percent for 460 engine option.

1975
Pinto

	6	5	4	3	2	1
Cpe	125	200	600	1100	2300	3300
Htchbk	125	250	700	1150	2400	3400
Sta Wag	125	200	600	1100	2300	3300
Maverick						
Cpe	125	250	700	1150	2400	3400
4 dr Sed	125	250	700	1150	2450	3500
Grabber	125	250	700	1150	2500	3600
Torino						
o/w Cpe	125	250	700	1150	2450	3500
4 dr Sed	100	175	525	1050	2100	3000
Sta Wag	125	200	600	1100	2200	3100
Gran Torino						
o/w Cpe	125	250	700	1150	2500	3600
4 dr Sed	125	200	600	1100	2250	3200
Sta Wag	125	200	600	1100	2250	3200
Gran Torino Brougham						
o/w Cpe	150	300	700	1250	2650	3800
4 dr Sed	125	200	600	1100	2250	3200
Gran Torino Sport						
2 dr HdTp	150	350	750	1350	2800	4000
Torino Squire						
Sta Wag	125	200	600	1100	2300	3300
Elite						
2 dr HdTp	150	350	750	1450	3000	4200
Granada						
Cpe	125	200	600	1100	2300	3300
4 dr Sed	100	150	450	1000	1750	2500
Ghia Cpe	125	250	700	1150	2500	3600
Ghia Sed	125	250	700	1150	2450	3500
Custom 500						
4 dr Sed	125	200	600	1100	2200	3100
Sta Wag	125	200	600	1100	2200	3100
LTD						
o/w Cpe	125	250	700	1150	2400	3400

	6	5	4	3	2	1
4 dr Sed	125	200	600	1100	2250	3200
LTD Brougham						
o/w Cpe	125	250	700	1150	2450	3500
4 dr Sed	125	200	600	1100	2300	3300
LTD Landau						
o/w Cpe	150	300	700	1250	2600	3700
4 dr Sed	125	250	700	1150	2400	3400
LTD Station Wagon						
Sta Wag	125	200	600	1100	2250	3200
Ctry Squire	125	200	600	1100	2300	3300
Thunderbird						
HdTp	200	500	850	1950	3600	5100

NOTE: Add 30 percent for 460 engine option.

MUSTANG

	6	5	4	3	2	1
1964						
2 dr HdTp	450	1450	2400	4800	8400	12,000
Conv	850	2750	4600	9200	16,100	23,000

NOTE: Deduct 10 percent for 6-cyl.
Add 20 percent for Challenger Code "K" V-8.
First Mustang introduced April 17, 1964 at N.Y. World's Fair.

	6	5	4	3	2	1
1965						
2 dr HdTp	450	1450	2400	4800	8400	12,000
Conv	850	2750	4600	9200	16,100	23,000
FsBk	700	2150	3600	7200	12,600	18,000

NOTE: Add 30 percent for 271 hp Hi-perf engine.
Add 10 percent for "GT" Package.
Add 10 percent for original "pony interior".
Deduct 10 percent for 6-cyl.

	6	5	4	3	2	1
1965 Shelby GT						
GT-350 FsBk	1600	5150	8600	17,200	30,100	43,000
1966						
2 dr HdTp	450	1450	2400	4800	8400	12,000
Conv	850	2750	4600	9200	16,100	23,000
FsBk	700	2150	3600	7200	12,600	18,000

NOTE: Same as 1965.

	6	5	4	3	2	1
1966 Shelby GT						
GT-350 FsBk	1400	4450	7400	14,800	25,900	37,000
GT-350H FsBk	1450	4700	7800	15,600	27,300	39,000
GT-350 Conv	1600	5150	8600	17,200	30,100	43,000
1967						
2 dr HdTp	450	1450	2400	4800	8400	12,000
Conv	750	2400	4000	8000	14,000	20,000
FsBk	550	1800	3000	6000	10,500	15,000

NOTES: Same as 1964-65, plus:
Add 10 percent for 390 cid V-8 (code "Z").
Deduct 10 percent for 6-cyl.

	6	5	4	3	2	1
1967 Shelby GT						
GT-350 FsBk	1150	3600	6000	12,000	21,000	30,000
GT-500 FsBk	1600	5050	8400	16,800	29,400	42,000
1968						
2 dr HdTp	450	1450	2400	4800	8400	12,000
Conv	750	2400	4000	8000	14,000	20,000
FsBk	550	1800	3000	6000	10,500	15,000

NOTES: Same as 1964-67, plus;
Add 10 percent for GT-390.
Add 50 percent for 427 cid V-8 (code "W").
Add 30 percent for 428 cid V-8 (code "Q").
Add 15 percent for "California Special" trim.

	6	5	4	3	2	1
1968 Shelby GT						
350 Conv	1900	6000	10,000	20,000	35,000	50,000
350 FsBk	1050	3350	5600	11,200	19,600	28,000
500 Conv	2500	7900	13,200	26,400	46,200	66,000
500 FsBk	1500	4800	8000	16,000	28,000	40,000

NOTE: Add 30 percent for KR models.

	6	5	4	3	2	1
1969						
2 dr HdTp	450	1450	2400	4800	8400	12,000
Conv	600	1900	3200	6400	11,200	16,000
FsBk	500	1550	2600	5200	9100	13,000

NOTE: Deduct 10 percent for 6-cyl.

	6	5	4	3	2	1
Mach I	650	2050	3400	6800	11,900	17,000
Boss 302	1000	3100	5200	10,400	18,200	26,000
Boss 429	1900	6000	10,000	20,000	35,000	50,000
Grande	550	1700	2800	5600	9800	14,000

NOTES: Same as 1968; plus;
Add 30 percent for Cobra Jet V-8.
Add 40 percent for "Super Cobra Jet" engine.

	6	5	4	3	2	1
1969 Shelby GT						
350 Conv	1900	6000	10,000	20,000	35,000	50,000
350 FsBk	1100	3500	5800	11,600	20,300	29,000
500 Conv	2550	8150	13,600	27,200	47,600	68,000
500 FsBk	1300	4200	7000	14,000	24,500	35,000
1970						
2 dr HdTp	450	1450	2400	4800	8400	12,000
Conv	600	1900	3200	6400	11,200	16,000
FsBk	500	1550	2600	5200	9100	13,000
Mach I	650	2050	3400	6800	11,900	17,000
Boss 302	1000	3100	5200	10,400	18,200	26,000
Boss 429	1900	6000	10,000	20,000	35,000	50,000
Grande	550	1700	2800	5600	9800	14,000

NOTE: Add 30 percent for Cobra Jet V-8.
Add 40 percent for "Super Cobra Jet".
Deduct 10 percent for 6-cyl.

	6	5	4	3	2	1
1970 Shelby GT						
350 Conv	1900	6000	10,000	20,000	35,000	50,000
350 FsBk	1100	3500	5800	11,600	20,300	29,000
500 Conv	2550	8150	13,600	27,200	47,600	68,000
500 FsBk	1300	4200	7000	14,000	24,500	35,000
1971						
2 dr HdTp	450	1100	1700	3650	6650	9500
Grande	400	1200	2000	3950	7000	10,000
Conv	600	1900	3200	6400	11,200	16,000
FsBk	550	1700	2800	5600	9800	14,000
Mach I	550	1800	3000	6000	10,500	15,000
Boss 351	1100	3500	5800	11,600	20,300	29,000

NOTE: Same as 1970.
Deduct 10 percent for 6-cyl.

Standard Catalog of American Cars

1972

	6	5	4	3	2	1
2 dr HdTp	450	1100	1700	3650	6650	9500
Grande	400	1200	2000	3950	7000	10,000
FsBk	550	1700	2800	5600	9800	14,000
Mach I	550	1800	3000	6000	10,500	15,000
Conv	600	1900	3200	6400	11,200	16,000

NOTE: Add 5 percent for engine and decor options.
Deduct 10 percent for 6-cyl.

1973

	6	5	4	3	2	1
2 dr HdTp	450	1000	1650	3350	6300	9000
Grande	400	1200	2000	3950	7000	10,000
FsBk	500	1550	2600	5200	9100	13,000
Mach I	550	1700	2800	5600	9800	14,000
Conv	650	2050	3400	6800	11,900	17,000

NOTE: Add 10 percent for engine and decor options.

1974
Mustang II
Mustang Four

	6	5	4	3	2	1
HdTp Cpe	150	350	750	1350	2800	4000
FsBk	150	350	750	1450	2900	4100
Ghia	150	350	750	1450	3000	4200
Mustang Six						
HdTp Cpe	150	350	750	1350	2800	4000
FsBk	150	350	750	1450	2900	4100
Ghia	150	350	750	1450	3000	4200
Mach I Six						
FsBk	200	500	850	1900	3500	5000

1975
Mustang

	6	5	4	3	2	1
HdTp Cpe	150	350	750	1350	2800	4000
FsBk	150	350	750	1450	2900	4100
Ghia	150	350	750	1450	3000	4200
Mustang Six						
HdTp Cpe	150	350	750	1450	2900	4100
FsBk	150	350	750	1450	3000	4200
Ghia	150	400	750	1550	3050	4300
Mach I	150	400	750	1650	3150	4500
Mustang, V-8						
HdTp Cpe	200	600	950	2200	3900	5600
FsBk Cpe	200	600	1000	2200	4000	5700
Ghia	200	650	1050	2250	4200	6000
Mach I	350	700	1150	2300	4550	6500

FRAZER

1947

	6	5	4	3	2	1
Sed	450	1050	1700	3550	6500	9300
Manhattan, 6-cyl.						
Sed	450	1100	1800	3700	6700	9600

1948

	6	5	4	3	2	1
Sed	450	1050	1700	3550	6500	9300
Manhattan, 6-cyl.						
Sed	450	1100	1800	3700	6700	9600

1949-1950

	6	5	4	3	2	1
Sed	400	1200	2000	3950	7000	10,000
Manhattan, 6-cyl.						
Sed	400	1250	2100	4200	7400	10,500
Conv	1000	3100	5200	10,400	18,200	26,000

1951
Manhattan, 6-cyl.

	6	5	4	3	2	1
Sed	450	1050	1700	3550	6500	9300
Vag	450	1100	1700	3650	6650	9500
4 dr Sed HdTp	700	2300	3800	7600	13,300	19,000
4 dr Del Sed HdTp	750	2400	4000	8000	14,000	20,000
Conv	1000	3100	5200	10,400	18,200	26,000
Del Conv Sed	1000	3250	5400	10,800	18,900	27,000

HUDSON

1946
Super Series 51, 6-cyl., 121" wb

	6	5	4	3	2	1
Conv	850	2650	4400	8800	15,400	22,000
Cpe	350	800	1350	2700	5500	7900
Clb Cpe	350	800	1450	2750	5600	8000
2 dr Sed	350	700	1150	2300	4600	6600
Sed	350	750	1300	2400	5200	7400
Commodore Series 52, 6-cyl., 121" wb						
Clb Cpe	350	900	1550	3050	5900	8500
Sed	350	800	1450	2750	5600	8000
Super Series 53, 8-cyl., 121" wb						
Clb Cpe	350	900	1550	3100	6000	8600
Sed	350	850	1500	2900	5700	8200
Commodore Custom Series 54, 8-cyl., 121" wb						
Conv	950	3000	5000	10,000	17,500	25,000
Clb Cpe	450	1100	1700	3650	6650	9500
Sed	450	1000	1650	3350	6300	9000

1947
Super Series 171, 6-cyl., 121" wb

	6	5	4	3	2	1
Conv	850	2750	4600	9200	16,100	23,000
Cpe	350	800	1350	2700	5500	7900
Clb Cpe	350	800	1450	2750	5600	8000
2 dr Sed	350	700	1150	2300	4600	6600
Sed	350	725	1200	2350	4850	6900
Commodore Series 172, 6-cyl., 121" wb						
Clb Cpe	350	900	1550	3100	6000	8600
Sed	350	800	1450	2750	5600	8000
Super Series 173, 8-cyl., 121" wb						
Clb Cpe	350	950	1600	3200	6050	8700
Sed	350	850	1500	2900	5700	8200
Commodore Series 174, 8-cyl., 121" wb						
Conv	1050	3350	5600	11,200	19,600	28,000
Clb Cpe	450	1050	1700	3550	6500	9300
Sed	450	950	1600	3250	6150	8800

1948
Super Series 481, 6-cyl., 124" wb

	6	5	4	3	2	1
Conv	850	2750	4600	9200	16,100	23,000
Cpe	350	900	1550	3050	5900	8500
Clb Cpe	450	950	1600	3250	6150	8800
2 dr Sed	350	800	1450	2750	5600	8000
Sed	350	800	1350	2700	5500	7900
Commodore Series 482, 6-cyl., 124" wb						
Conv	950	3000	5000	10,000	17,500	25,000
Clb Cpe	450	1050	1650	3500	6400	9200
Sed	450	950	1600	3250	6150	8800
Super Series 483, 8-cyl., 124" wb						
Clb Cpe	450	1050	1700	3550	6500	9300
Sed	450	1000	1600	3300	6250	8900
Commodore Series 484, 8-cyl., 124" wb						
Conv	1000	3250	5400	10,800	18,900	27,000
Clb Cpe	400	1250	2100	4200	7300	10,400
Sed	400	1200	2000	4000	7100	10,100

1949
Super Series 491, 6-cyl., 124" wb

	6	5	4	3	2	1
Sed	450	1050	1700	3550	6500	9300
Conv	950	3000	5000	10,000	17,500	25,000
Cpe	450	1100	1700	3650	6650	9500
Clb Cpe	450	1150	1800	3800	6800	9700
2 dr Sed	450	1050	1650	3500	6400	9200
Commodore Series 492, 6-cyl., 124" wb						
Conv	1050	3350	5600	11,200	19,600	28,000
Clb Cpe	450	1150	1900	3850	6850	9800
Sed	450	1100	1700	3650	6650	9500
Super Series 493, 8-cyl., 124" wb						
Clb Cpe	450	1150	1900	3900	6900	9900
2 dr Sed	450	1050	1700	3550	6500	9300
Sed	450	750	1300	2500	5300	7600
Commodore Series 494, 8-cyl., 124" wb						
Conv	1150	3600	6000	12,000	21,000	30,000
Clb Cpe	400	1300	2200	4400	7700	11,000
Sed	400	1200	2000	3950	7000	10,000

1950
Pacemaker Series 500, 6-cyl., 119" wb

	6	5	4	3	2	1
Conv	950	3000	5000	10,000	17,500	25,000
Bus Cpe	450	1050	1700	3600	6600	9400
Clb Cpe	450	1150	1800	3800	6800	9700
2 dr Sed	450	1050	1700	3500	6500	9300
Sed	450	1000	1650	3400	6350	9100
DeLuxe Series 50A, 6-cyl., 119" wb						
Conv	1000	3100	5200	10,400	18,200	26,000
Clb Cpe	450	1150	1900	3850	6850	9800
2 dr Sed	450	1150	1800	3800	6800	9700
Sed	450	1100	1700	3650	6650	9500
Super Six Series 501, 6-cyl., 124" wb						
Conv	1000	3250	5400	10,800	18,900	27,000
Clb Cpe	450	1150	1900	3900	6900	9900
2 dr Sed	450	1150	1900	3850	6850	9800
Sed	450	1100	1800	3700	6700	9600
Commodore Series 502, 6-cyl., 124" wb						
Conv	1050	3350	5600	11,200	19,600	28,000
Clb Cpe	400	1300	2200	4400	7700	11,000
Sed	400	1200	2000	3950	7000	10,000
Super Series 503, 8-cyl., 124" wb						
Clb Cpe	450	1400	2300	4600	8100	11,500
2 dr Sed	400	1300	2200	4400	7700	11,000
Sed	400	1250	2100	4200	7400	10,500
Commodore Series 504, 8-cyl., 124" wb						
Conv	1150	3600	6000	12,000	21,000	30,000
Clb Cpe	450	1450	2400	4800	8400	12,000
Sed	400	1300	2200	4400	7700	11,000

1951
Pacemaker Custom Series 4A, 6-cyl., 119" wb

	6	5	4	3	2	1
Conv	900	2900	4800	9600	16,800	24,000
Cpe	450	1150	1900	3900	6900	9900
Clb Cpe	400	1200	2000	4000	7100	10,100
2 dr Sed	450	1150	1800	3800	6800	9700
Sed	450	1150	1900	3850	6850	9800
Super Custom Series 5A, 6-cyl., 124" wb						
Conv	950	3000	5000	10,000	17,500	25,000
Clb Cpe	400	1250	2100	4200	7400	10,500
2 dr Sed	450	1150	1900	3850	6850	9800
Sed	400	1200	2000	3950	7000	10,000
Hlywd	450	1450	2400	4800	8400	12,000
Commodore Custom Series 6A, 6-cyl., 124" wb						
Conv	1000	3100	5200	10,400	18,200	26,000
Clb Cpe	400	1250	2100	4200	7300	10,400
Sed	400	1200	2000	4000	7100	10,100
Hlywd	500	1550	2600	5200	9100	13,000
Hornet Series 7A, 6-cyl., 124" wb						
Conv	1100	3500	5800	11,600	20,300	29,000
Clb Cpe	400	1250	2100	4200	7400	10,600
Sed	400	1250	2100	4200	7300	10,400
Hlywd	550	1700	2800	5600	9800	14,000
Commodore Custom Series 8A, 8-cyl., 124" wb						
Conv	1150	3600	6000	12,000	21,000	30,000
Clb Cpe	400	1300	2200	4400	7700	11,000
Sed	400	1250	2100	4200	7400	10,600
Hlywd	550	1800	3000	6000	10,500	15,000

1952
Pacemaker Series 4B, 6-cyl., 119" wb

	6	5	4	3	2	1
Cpe	450	1150	1800	3800	6800	9700
Clb Cpe	450	1150	1900	3850	6850	9800
2 dr Sed	450	1100	1700	3650	6650	9500
Sed	450	1100	1800	3700	6700	9600
Wasp Series 5B, 6-cyl., 119" wb						
Conv	950	3000	5000	10,000	17,500	25,000
Hlywd	400	1300	2200	4400	7700	11,000
Clb Cpe	400	1200	2000	3950	7000	10,000
2 dr Sed	450	1100	1800	3700	6700	9600
Sed	450	1150	1800	3800	6800	9700
Commodore Series 6B, 6-cyl., 124" wb						
Conv	1000	3100	5200	10,400	18,200	26,000
Hlywd	500	1550	2600	5200	9100	13,000
Clb Cpe	400	1200	2050	4100	7100	10,200
Sed	400	1200	2000	3950	7000	10,000
Hornet Series 7B, 6-cyl., 124" wb						
Conv	1000	3250	5400	10,800	18,900	27,000
Hlywd	550	1700	2800	5600	9800	14,000
Clb Cpe	400	1250	2100	4200	7300	10,400
Sed	400	1200	2000	4000	7100	10,100

	6	5	4	3	2	1
Commodore Series 8B, 8-cyl., 124" wb						
Conv	1050	3350	5600	11,200	19,600	28,000
Hlywd	550	1800	3000	6000	10,500	15,000
Clb Cpe	400	1250	2100	4200	7300	10,400
Sed	400	1200	2000	4000	7100	10,100
1953						
Jet Series 1C, 6-cyl., 105" wb						
4 dr Sed	350	750	1200	2350	4900	7000
Super Jet Series 2C, 6-cyl., 105" wb						
2 dr Clb Sed	350	750	1300	2500	5300	7600
4 dr Sed	350	750	1300	2450	5250	7500
Wasp Series 4C, 6-cyl., 119" wb						
Clb Cpe	450	950	1600	3250	6150	8800
2 dr Sed	350	900	1550	3050	5900	8500
Sed	350	900	1550	3100	6000	8600
Super Wasp Series 5C, 6-cyl., 119" wb						
Conv	900	2900	4800	9600	16,800	24,000
Hlywd	400	1300	2200	4400	7700	11,000
Clb Cpe	450	1000	1650	3350	6300	9000
2 dr Sed	350	900	1550	3100	6000	8600
4 dr Sed	350	950	1600	3200	6050	8700
Hornet Series 7C, 6-cyl., 124" wb						
Conv	1000	3100	5200	10,400	18,200	26,000
Clb Cpe	400	1250	2100	4200	7400	10,500
Sed	400	1200	2000	3950	7000	10,000
Hlywd	500	1550	2600	5200	9100	13,000
1954						
Jet Series 1D, 6-cyl., 105" wb						
2 dr Utl Sed	350	750	1200	2350	4900	7000
2 dr Clb Sed	350	750	1250	2400	5050	7200
4 dr Sed	350	750	1250	2350	5000	7100
Super Jet Series 2D, 6-cyl., 105" wb						
2 dr Clb Sed	350	750	1300	2450	5250	7500
4 dr Sed	350	750	1300	2500	5300	7600
Jet Liner Series 3D, 6-cyl., 105" wb						
2 dr Sed	350	750	1350	2600	5400	7700
4 dr Sed	350	800	1450	2750	5600	8000
Wasp Series 4D, 6-cyl., 119" wb						
Clb Cpe	350	750	1300	2450	5250	7500
Clb Sed	350	750	1250	2400	5100	7300
Sed	350	750	1300	2400	5200	7400
Super Wasp Series 5D, 6-cyl., 119" wb						
Conv	850	2750	4600	9200	16,100	23,000
Hlywd	450	1450	2400	4800	8400	12,000
Clb Cpe	350	900	1550	3050	5900	8500
Clb Sed	350	750	1350	2650	5450	7800
Sed	350	800	1450	2750	5600	8000
Hornet Special Series 6D, 6-cyl., 124" wb						
Clb Cpe	400	1200	2000	3950	7000	10,000
Clb Sed	450	1000	1650	3400	6350	9100
Sed	450	1050	1700	3600	6600	9400
Hornet Series 7D, 6-cyl., 124" wb						
Brgm Conv	1000	3100	5200	10,400	18,200	26,000
Hlywd	550	1700	2800	5600	9800	14,000
Clb Cpe	400	1300	2200	4400	7700	11,000
Sed	450	1100	1800	3700	6700	9600
Italia, 6-cyl.						
2 dr	1050	3350	5600	11,200	19,600	28,000
1955						
Super Wasp, 6-cyl., 114" wb						
Sed	350	700	1150	2300	4550	6500
Custom Wasp, 6-cyl., 114" wb						
Hlywd	400	1300	2200	4400	7700	11,000
Sed	350	700	1150	2300	4600	6600
Hornet Super, 6-cyl., 121" wb						
Sed	350	725	1200	2350	4850	6900
Hornet Custom, 6-cyl., 121" wb						
Hlywd	450	1450	2400	4800	8400	12,000
Sed	350	750	1300	2450	5250	7500
Italia, 6-cyl.						
2 dr	1050	3350	5600	11,200	19,600	28,000

NOTE: Add 5 percent for V-8.
For Hudson Rambler prices see AMC.

	6	5	4	3	2	1
1956						
Super Wasp, 6-cyl., 114" wb						
Sed	350	700	1150	2300	4550	6500
Super Hornet, 6-cyl., 121" wb						
Sed	350	750	1200	2350	4900	7000
Custom Hornet, 6-cyl., 121" wb						
Hlywd	450	1400	2300	4600	8100	11,500
Sed	350	800	1450	2750	5600	8000
Hornet Super Special, 8-cyl., 114" wb						
Hlywd	450	1500	2500	5000	8800	12,500
Sed	350	850	1500	2900	5700	8200
Hornet Custom, 8-cyl., 121" wb						
Hlywd	500	1600	2700	5400	9500	13,500
Sed	350	900	1550	3050	5900	8500

NOTE: For Hudson Rambler prices see AMC.

	6	5	4	3	2	1
1957						
Hornet Super, 8-cyl., 121" wb						
Hlywd	450	1450	2400	4800	8400	12,000
Sed	450	1100	1700	3650	6650	9500
Hornet Custom, 8-cyl., 121" wb						
Hlywd	550	1700	2800	5600	9800	14,000
Sed	400	1250	2100	4200	7400	10,500

NOTE: For Hudson Rambler prices see AMC.

KAISER

	6	5	4	3	2	1
1947						
Special, 6-cyl.						
Sed	450	1000	1650	3350	6300	9000
Custom, 6-cyl.						
Sed	450	1100	1700	3650	6650	9500
1948						
Special, 6-cyl.						
Sed	450	1000	1650	3350	6300	9000
Custom, 6-cyl.						
Sed	450	1100	1700	3650	6650	9500

	6	5	4	3	2	1
1949						
Special, 6-cyl.						
4 dr Sed	450	1050	1700	3600	6600	9400
Traveler, 6-cyl.						
4 dr Sed	400	1200	2000	3950	7000	10,000
DeLuxe, 6-cyl.						
4 dr Sed	400	1250	2050	4100	7200	10,300
Conv	1000	3100	5200	10,400	18,200	26,000
Vagabond, 6-cyl.						
4 dr Sed	400	1250	2100	4200	7400	10,500
Virginian, 6-cyl.						
4 dr Sed HdTp	750	2400	4000	8000	14,000	20,000
1950						
Special, 6-cyl.						
4 dr Sed	450	1150	1900	3850	6850	9800
Traveler, 6-cyl.						
4 dr Sed	400	1200	2000	3950	7000	10,000
DeLuxe, 6-cyl.						
4 dr Sed	400	1250	2050	4100	7200	10,300
Conv	1000	3100	5200	10,400	18,200	26,000
Vagabond, 6-cyl.						
4 dr Sed	400	1250	2100	4200	7400	10,500
Virginian, 6-cyl.						
4 dr Sed HdTp	750	2400	4000	8000	14,000	20,000
1951						
Special, 6-cyl.						
4 dr Sed	400	1200	2000	3950	7000	10,000
4 dr Trav Sed	400	1250	2050	4100	7200	10,300
2 dr Sed	400	1200	2000	4000	7100	10,100
2 dr Trav Sed	400	1250	2100	4200	7400	10,500
Bus Cpe	400	1300	2150	4300	7500	10,700
DeLuxe						
4 dr Sed	400	1250	2100	4200	7400	10,400
4 dr Trav Sed	400	1250	2100	4200	7400	10,600
2 dr Sed	400	1250	2100	4200	7400	10,500
2 dr Trav Sed	400	1300	2150	4300	7500	10,700
Clb Cpe	400	1300	2200	4400	7700	11,000
1952						
Kaiser DeLuxe, 6-cyl.						
4 dr Sed	400	1200	2000	3950	7000	10,000
Trav Sed	400	1200	2000	4000	7100	10,100
2 dr Sed	400	1200	2000	3950	7000	10,000
2 dr Trav	400	1200	2000	4000	7100	10,100
Bus Cpe	400	1250	2100	4200	7400	10,500
Kaiser Manhattan, 6-cyl.						
4 dr Sed	400	1250	2050	4100	7200	10,300
2 dr Sed	400	1250	2100	4200	7400	10,500
Clb Cpe	400	1300	2150	4300	7600	10,800
Virginian, 6-cyl.						
4 dr Sed	400	1250	2100	4200	7400	10,500
2 dr Sed	400	1250	2100	4200	7400	10,600
Clb Cpe	400	1300	2200	4400	7700	11,000
1953						
Carolina, 6-cyl.						
2 dr Sed	400	1250	2050	4100	7200	10,300
4 dr Sed	400	1200	2050	4100	7100	10,200
Deluxe						
Clb Sed	400	1250	2100	4200	7400	10,500
Trav Sed	400	1250	2100	4200	7400	10,600
4 dr Sed	400	1250	2100	4200	7300	10,400
Manhattan, 6-cyl.						
Clb Sed	400	1300	2150	4300	7500	10,700
4 dr Sed	400	1250	2100	4200	7400	10,600
Dragon 4 dr Sed, 6-cyl.						
4 dr Sed	500	1550	2600	5200	9100	13,000
1954						
Special, 6-cyl.						
(Add 5 percent for late Special).						
4 dr Sed	400	1300	2200	4400	7700	11,000
Clb Sed	400	1350	2200	4400	7800	11,100
Manhattan, 6-cyl.						
4 dr Sed	450	1450	2400	4800	8400	12,000
Clb Sed	450	1450	2450	4900	8500	12,200
Kaiser Darrin Spts Car, 6-cyl.						
Spt Car	1000	3250	5400	10,800	18,900	27,000
1955						
Manhattan, 6-cyl.						
4 dr Sed	450	1450	2400	4800	8400	12,000
Clb Sed	450	1450	2400	4800	8500	12,100

LINCOLN

	6	5	4	3	2	1
1946						
V-12, 125" wb						
Clb Cpe	550	1800	3000	6000	10,500	15,000
Conv	1400	4450	7400	14,800	25,900	37,000
4 dr Sed	500	1550	2600	5200	9100	13,000
Cont Cpe	1300	4200	7000	14,000	24,500	35,000
Cont Conv	1700	5400	9000	18,000	31,500	45,000
1947						
V-12, 125" wb						
Clb Cpe	550	1800	3000	6000	10,500	15,000
Conv	1400	4450	7400	14,800	25,900	37,000
4 dr Sed	500	1550	2600	5200	9100	13,000
Cont Cpe	1300	4200	7000	14,000	24,500	35,000
Cont Conv	1700	5400	9000	18,000	31,500	45,000
1948						
8th Series, V-12, 125" wb						
Clb Cpe	550	1800	3000	6000	10,500	15,000
Conv	1400	4450	7400	14,800	25,900	37,000
4 dr Sed	500	1550	2600	5200	9100	13,000
Cont Cpe	1300	4200	7000	14,000	24,500	35,000
Cont Conv	1700	5400	9000	18,000	31,500	45,000
1949						
Model 9-EL, V-8, 121" wb						
Spt Sed	400	1200	2000	3950	7000	10,000
Cpe	500	1550	2600	5200	9100	13,000
Conv	700	2300	3800	7600	13,300	19,000

	6	5	4	3	2	1
Cosmopolitan, V-8, 125" wb						
Twn Sed	400	1300	2200	4400	7700	11,000
Spt Sed	450	1400	2300	4600	8100	11,500
Cpe	550	1700	2800	5600	9800	14,000
Conv	1000	3250	5400	10,800	18,900	27,000
1950						
Model OEL, V-8, 121" wb						
Spt Sed	400	1200	2000	3950	7000	10,000
Cpe	550	1800	3000	6000	10,500	15,000
Lido Cpe	600	1900	3200	6400	11,200	16,000
Cosmopolitan, V-8, 125" wb						
Spt Sed	400	1300	2200	4400	7700	11,000
Cpe	600	1900	3200	6400	11,200	16,000
Capri	650	2050	3400	6800	11,900	17,000
Conv	950	3000	5000	10,000	17,500	25,000
1951						
Model Del, V-8, 121" wb						
Spt Sed	400	1200	2000	3950	7000	10,000
Cpe	550	1800	3000	6000	10,500	15,000
Lido Cpe	600	1900	3200	6400	11,200	16,000
Cosmopolitan, V-8, 125" wb						
Spt Sed	400	1300	2200	4400	7700	11,000
Cpe	600	1900	3200	6400	11,200	16,000
Capri	650	2050	3400	6800	11,900	17,000
Conv	1000	3100	5200	10,400	18,200	26,000
1952						
Model 2H, V-8, 123" wb						
Cosmopolitan						
4 dr Sed	400	1200	2000	3950	7000	10,000
2 dr HdTp	550	1800	3000	6000	10,500	15,000
Capri, V-8, 123" wb						
4 dr Sed	400	1300	2200	4400	7700	11,000
2 dr HdTp	600	1900	3200	6400	11,200	16,000
Conv	1000	3100	5200	10,400	18,200	26,000
1953						
Model BH, V-8, 123" wb						
Cosmopolitan						
4 dr Sed	400	1200	2000	3950	7000	10,000
2 dr HdTp	550	1800	3000	6000	10,500	15,000
Capri, V-8, 123" wb						
4 dr Sed	400	1300	2200	4400	7700	11,000
2 dr HdTp	600	1900	3200	6400	11,200	16,000
2 dr Conv	1000	3100	5200	10,400	18,200	26,000
1954						
V-8, 123" wb						
4 dr Sed	450	1150	1800	3800	6800	9700
2 dr HdTp	550	1800	3000	6000	10,500	15,000
Capri, V-8, 123" wb						
4 dr Sed	400	1200	2000	3950	7000	10,000
2 dr HdTp	600	1900	3200	6400	11,200	16,000
Conv	1000	3250	5400	10,800	18,900	27,000
1955						
V-8, 123" wb						
4 dr Sed	400	1200	2000	3950	7000	10,000
HdTp	600	1900	3200	6400	11,200	16,000
Capri, V-8, 123" wb						
4 dr Sed	400	1250	2100	4200	7400	10,500
2 dr HdTp	650	2050	3400	6800	11,900	17,000
Conv	950	3000	5000	10,000	17,500	25,000
1956						
Capri, V-8, 126" wb						
4 dr Sed	450	1450	2400	4800	8400	12,000
2 dr HdTp	650	2050	3400	6800	11,900	17,000
Premiere, V-8, 126" wb						
4 dr Sed	500	1550	2600	5200	9100	13,000
2 dr HdTp	700	2150	3600	7200	12,600	18,000
Conv	1050	3350	5600	11,200	19,600	28,000
Lincoln Continental Mark II, V-8, 126" wb						
2 dr HdTp	1100	3500	5800	11,600	20,300	29,000
1957						
Capri, V-8, 126" wb						
4 dr Sed	400	1250	2100	4200	7400	10,500
4 dr HdTp	500	1550	2600	5200	9100	13,000
2 dr HdTp	550	1800	3000	6000	10,500	15,000
Premiere, V-8, 126" wb						
4 dr Sed	450	1400	2300	4600	8100	11,500
4 dr HdTp	550	1700	2800	5600	9800	14,000
2 dr HdTp	600	1900	3200	6400	11,200	16,000
Conv	1050	3350	5600	11,200	19,600	28,000
Lincoln Continental, V-8, 126" wb						
2 dr HdTp	1100	3500	5800	11,600	20,300	29,000
1958						
Lincoln Capri, V-8, 131" wb						
4 dr Sed	350	750	1350	2600	5400	7700
4 dr HdTp	350	750	1350	2650	5450	7800
2 dr HdTp	350	900	1550	3050	5900	8500
Lincoln Premiere, V-8, 131" wb						
4 dr Sed	350	800	1450	2750	5600	8000
4 dr HdTp	350	900	1550	3050	5900	8500
2 dr HdTp	400	1200	2000	3950	7000	10,000
Lincoln Continental Mark III, V-8, 131" wb						
4 dr Sed	450	1100	1700	3650	6650	9500
4 dr HdTp	400	1200	2000	3950	7000	10,000
2 dr HdTp	500	1550	2600	5200	9100	13,000
Conv	1000	3100	5200	10,400	18,200	26,000
1959						
Capri, V-8, 131" wb						
4 dr Sed	350	800	1450	2750	5600	8000
4 dr HdTp	350	900	1550	3050	5900	8500
2 dr HdTp	400	1200	2000	3950	7000	10,000
Premiere, V-8, 131" wb						
4 dr Sed	350	900	1550	3050	5900	8500
4 dr HdTp	450	1000	1650	3350	6300	9000
2 dr HdTp	400	1300	2200	4400	7700	11,000
Continental Mark IV, V-8, 131" wb						
4 dr Sed	400	1200	2000	3950	7000	10,000
4 dr HdTp	400	1250	2100	4200	7400	10,500
2 dr HdTp	550	1800	3000	6000	10,500	15,000
Conv	1000	3250	5400	10,800	18,900	27,000
TwnC	550	1700	2800	5600	9800	14,000
Limo	550	1800	3000	6000	10,500	15,000
1960						
Lincoln, V-8, 131" wb						
4 dr Sed	350	900	1550	3050	5900	8500
4 dr HdTp	450	1000	1650	3350	6300	9000

	6	5	4	3	2	1
2 dr HdTp	400	1300	2200	4400	7700	11,000
Premiere, V-8, 131" wb						
4 dr Sed	450	1000	1650	3350	6300	9000
4 dr HdTp	450	1100	1700	3650	6650	9500
2 dr HdTp	500	1550	2600	5200	9100	13,000
Continental Mark V, V-8, 131" wb						
4 dr Sed	400	1300	2200	4400	7700	11,000
4 dr HdTp	450	1450	2400	4800	8400	12,000
2 dr HdTp	550	1700	2800	5600	9800	14,000
Conv	1050	3350	5600	11,200	19,600	28,000
TwnC	550	1700	2800	5600	9800	14,000
Limo	550	1800	3000	6000	10,500	15,000
1961						
Lincoln Continental, V-8, 123" wb						
4 dr Sed	350	800	1450	2750	5600	8000
4 dr Conv	500	1550	2600	5200	9100	13,000
1962						
Lincoln Continental, V-8, 123" wb						
4 dr Sed	350	800	1450	2750	5600	8000
4 dr Conv	550	1700	2800	5600	9800	14,000
1963						
Lincoln Continental, V-8, 123" wb						
4 dr Sed	350	800	1450	2750	5600	8000
4 dr Conv	550	1700	2800	5600	9800	14,000
Exec Limo	450	1450	2400	4800	8400	12,000
1964						
Lincoln Continental, V-8, 126" wb						
4 dr Sed	350	800	1450	2750	5600	8000
4 dr Conv	550	1700	2800	5600	9800	14,000
Exec Limo	450	1450	2400	4800	8400	12,000
1965						
Lincoln Continental, V-8, 126" wb						
4 dr Sed	350	800	1450	2750	5600	8000
4 dr Conv	550	1700	2800	5600	9800	14,000
Exec Limo	450	1450	2400	4800	8400	12,000
1966						
Lincoln Continental, V-8, 126" wb						
4 dr Sed	350	800	1450	2750	5600	8000
2 dr HdTp	350	850	1500	2900	5700	8200
4 dr Conv	550	1700	2800	5600	9800	14,000
1967						
Lincoln Continental, V-8, 126" wb						
4 dr Sed	350	800	1450	2750	5600	8000
2 dr HdTp	350	850	1500	2900	5700	8200
4 dr Conv	550	1700	2800	5600	9800	14,000
1968						
Lincoln Continental, V-8, 126" wb						
4 dr Sed	350	800	1450	2750	5600	8000
2 dr HdTp	350	850	1500	2900	5700	8200
Continental Mark III, V-8, 117" wb						
2 dr HdTp	450	1450	2400	4800	8400	12,000
1969						
Lincoln Continental, V-8, 126" wb						
4 dr Sed	350	750	1200	2350	4900	7000
2 dr HdTp	350	750	1300	2450	5250	7500
Continental Mark III, V-8, 117" wb						
2 dr HdTp	450	1450	2400	4800	8400	12,000
1970						
Lincoln Continental						
4 dr Sed	350	750	1200	2350	4900	7000
2 dr HdTp	350	750	1300	2450	5250	7500
Continental Mark III, V-8, 117" wb						
2 dr HdTp	450	1450	2400	4800	8400	12,000
1971						
Continental						
4 dr Sed	350	700	1150	2300	4550	6500
2 dr	350	750	1200	2350	4900	7000
Mark III						
2 dr	400	1300	2200	4400	7700	11,000
1972						
Continental						
4 dr Sed	350	700	1150	2300	4600	6600
2 dr	350	750	1200	2350	4900	7000
Mark IV						
2 dr	400	1300	2200	4400	7700	11,000
1973						
Continental V-8						
2 dr HdTp	350	725	1200	2350	4850	6900
4 dr HdTp	350	700	1100	2300	4500	6400
Mark IV V-8						
2 dr HdTp	400	1300	2200	4400	7700	11,000
1974						
Continental, V-8						
4 dr Sed	200	675	1050	2250	4350	6200
2 dr Cpe	350	725	1200	2350	4800	6800
Mark IV, V-8						
2 dr HdTp	450	1100	1700	3650	6650	9500
1975						
Continental, V-8						
4 dr Sed	200	675	1050	2250	4300	6100
2 dr Cpe	350	700	1150	2300	4550	6500
Mark IV, V-8						
2 dr HdTp	450	1000	1650	3350	6300	9000

MERCURY

	6	5	4	3	2	1
1946						
Series 69M, V-8, 118" wb						
Conv	850	2750	4600	9200	16,100	23,000
6P Cpe	450	1100	1700	3650	6650	9500
2 dr Sed	350	850	1500	2900	5700	8200
4 dr Sed	350	800	1450	2750	5600	8000
Sta Wag	900	2900	4800	9600	16,800	24,000
Sptsman Conv	1750	5500	9200	18,400	32,200	46,000
1947						
Series 79M, V-8, 118" wb						
Conv	850	2750	4600	9200	16,100	23,000
6P Cpe	450	1100	1700	3650	6650	9500
2 dr Sed	350	850	1500	2900	5700	8200

	6	5	4	3	2	1
4 dr Sed	350	800	1450	2750	5600	8000
Sta Wag	950	3000	5000	10,000	17,500	25,000
Sptsman Conv	1750	5500	9200	18,400	32,200	46,000
1948						
Series 89M, V-8, 118" wb						
Conv	900	2900	4800	9600	16,800	24,000
Cpe	450	1100	1700	3650	6650	9500
2 dr Sed	350	850	1500	2900	5700	8200
4 dr Sed	350	800	1450	2750	5600	8000
Sta Wag	950	3000	5000	10,000	17,500	25,000
1949						
Series 9CM, V-8, 118" wb						
Conv	700	2150	3600	7200	12,600	18,000
Cpe	400	1200	2000	3950	7000	10,000
4 dr Sed	350	750	1350	2600	5400	7700
Sta Wag	750	2400	4000	8000	14,000	20,000
1950						
Series OCM, V-8, 118" wb						
Conv	700	2300	3800	7600	13,300	19,000
Cpe	400	1200	2000	3950	7000	10,000
Clb Cpe	400	1250	2100	4200	7400	10,500
Mon Cpe	400	1300	2200	4400	7700	11,000
4 dr Sed	350	750	1350	2650	5450	7800
Sta Wag	750	2400	4000	8000	14,000	20,000
1951						
Mercury, V-8, 118" wb						
4 dr Sed	350	750	1300	2450	5250	7500
Cpe	400	1200	2000	3950	7000	10,000
Conv	750	2400	4000	8000	14,000	20,000
Sta Wag	800	2500	4200	8400	14,700	21,000
Monterey, V-8, 118" wb						
Clth Cpe	450	1400	2300	4600	8100	11,500
Lthr Cpe	450	1450	2400	4800	8400	12,000
1952						
Mercury Custom, V-8, 118" wb						
4 dr Sed	200	650	1050	2250	4200	6000
2 dr Sed	200	650	1000	2200	4150	5900
2 dr HdTp	400	1250	2100	4200	7400	10,500
Sta Wag	450	1000	1650	3350	6300	9000
Mercury Monterey, V-8, 118" wb						
4 dr Sed	350	750	1200	2350	4900	7000
2 dr HdTp	400	1300	2200	4400	7700	11,000
Conv	750	2400	4000	8000	14,000	20,000
1953						
Mercury Custom, V-8, 118" wb						
4 dr Sed	200	675	1050	2250	4300	6100
2 dr Sed	200	650	1050	2250	4200	6000
2 dr HdTp	400	1250	2100	4200	7400	10,500
Monterey Special Custom, V-8, 118" wb						
4 dr Sed	350	750	1250	2350	5000	7100
2 dr HdTp	400	1300	2200	4400	7700	11,000
Conv	750	2400	4000	8000	14,000	20,000
Sta Wag	450	1000	1650	3350	6300	9000
1954						
Mercury Custom, V-8, 118" wb						
4 dr Sed	350	700	1100	2300	4500	6400
2 dr Sed	200	675	1100	2250	4400	6300
2 dr HdTp	450	1450	2400	4800	8400	12,000
Monterey Special Custom, V-8, 118" wb						
4 dr Sed	350	750	1300	2400	5200	7400
SV Cpe	650	2050	3400	6800	11,900	17,000
2 dr HdTp	500	1550	2600	5200	9100	13,000
Conv	850	2650	4400	8800	15,400	22,000
Sta Wag	400	1200	2000	3950	7000	10,000
NOTE: Overhead valve V-8 introduced.						
1955						
Custom Series, V-8, 119" wb						
4 dr Sed	350	700	1100	2300	4500	6400
2 dr Sed	200	675	1100	2250	4400	6300
2 dr HdTp	550	1800	3000	6000	10,500	15,000
Sta Wag	350	750	1300	2450	5250	7500
Monterey Series, V-8, 119" wb						
4 dr Sed	350	750	1350	2600	5400	7700
2 dr HdTp	600	1900	3200	6400	11,200	16,000
Sta Wag	350	800	1450	2750	5600	8000
Montclair Series, V-8, 119" wb						
4 dr Sed	350	900	1550	3050	5900	8500
2 dr HdTp	700	2300	3800	7600	13,300	19,000
2 dr HdTp SV	850	2750	4600	9200	16,100	23,000
Conv	1050	3350	5600	11,200	19,600	28,000
1956						
Medalist Series, V-8, 119" wb						
4 dr Sed	200	650	1050	2250	4200	6000
2 dr Sed	200	650	1050	2250	4200	6000
2 dr HdTp	500	1550	2600	5200	9100	13,000
Custom Series, V-8, 119" wb						
4 dr Sed	350	700	1150	2300	4550	6500
2 dr Sed	350	700	1150	2300	4550	6500
2 dr HdTp	550	1800	3000	6000	10,500	15,000
4 dr HdTp	400	1300	2200	4400	7700	11,000
Conv	1000	3100	5200	10,400	18,200	26,000
4 dr Sta Wag	350	750	1300	2450	5250	7500
2 dr Sta Wag	350	800	1450	2750	5600	8000
Monterey Series, V-8, 119" wb						
4 dr Sed	350	750	1250	2400	5100	7300
4 dr Spt Sed	350	750	1300	2450	5250	7500
2 dr HdTp	600	1900	3200	6400	11,200	16,000
4 dr HdTp	450	1400	2300	4600	8100	11,500
4 dr Sta Wag	350	900	1550	3050	5900	8500
Montclair Series, V-8, 119" wb						
4 dr Spt Sed	450	1100	1700	3650	6650	9500
2 dr HdTp	700	2150	3600	7200	12,600	18,000
4 dr HdTp	450	1450	2400	4800	8400	12,000
Conv	1100	3500	5800	11,600	20,300	29,000
1957						
Monterey Series, V-8, 122" wb						
4 dr Sed	350	700	1100	2300	4500	6400
4 dr HdTp	350	800	1450	2750	5600	8000
2 dr Sed	200	675	1100	2250	4400	6300
2 dr HdTp	550	1700	2800	5600	9800	14,000
Conv	750	2400	4000	8000	14,000	20,000
Montclair Series, V-8, 122" wb						
4 dr Sed	350	700	1150	2300	4550	6500
4 dr HdTp	350	900	1550	3050	5900	8500
2 dr HdTp	600	1900	3200	6400	11,200	16,000

	6	5	4	3	2	1
Conv	900	2900	4800	9600	16,800	24,000
Turnpike Cruiser, V-8, 122" wb						
4 dr HdTp	500	1550	2600	5200	9100	13,000
2 dr HdTp	700	2300	3800	7600	13,300	19,000
Conv	1050	3350	5600	11,200	19,600	28,000
Station Wagons, V-8, 122" wb						
Voy 2 dr HdTp	450	1450	2400	4800	8400	12,000
Voy 4 dr HdTp	450	1450	2400	4800	8400	12,000
Com 2 dr HdTp	500	1550	2600	5200	9100	13,000
Com 4 dr HdTp	500	1550	2600	5200	9100	13,000
Col Pk 4 dr HdTp	550	1700	2800	5600	9800	14,000
1958						
Mercury, V-8, 122" wb						
4 dr Sed	200	675	1050	2250	4300	6100
2 dr Sed	200	650	1050	2250	4200	6000
Monterey, V-8, 122" wb						
4 dr Sed	200	675	1050	2250	4350	6200
4 dr HdTp	350	725	1200	2350	4800	6800
2 dr Sed	200	675	1050	2250	4300	6100
2 dr HdTp	450	1450	2400	4800	8400	12,000
Conv	750	2400	4000	8000	14,000	20,000
Montclair, V-8, 122" wb						
4 dr Sed	200	675	1100	2250	4400	6300
4 dr HdTp	350	750	1250	2400	5100	7300
2 dr HdTp	500	1550	2600	5200	9100	13,000
Conv	850	2650	4400	8800	15,400	22,000
Turnpike Cruiser, V-8, 122" wb						
4 dr HdTp	450	1450	2400	4800	8400	12,000
2 dr HdTp	650	2050	3400	6800	11,900	17,000
Station Wagons, V-8, 122" wb						
Voy 2 dr HdTp	400	1300	2200	4400	7700	11,000
Voy 4 dr HdTp	400	1300	2200	4400	7700	11,000
Com 2 dr HdTp	450	1450	2400	4800	8400	12,000
Col Pk 4 dr HdTp	450	1450	2400	4800	8400	12,000
Com 4 dr HdTp	500	1550	2600	5200	9100	13,000
Parklane, V-8, 125" wb						
4 dr HdTp	500	1550	2600	5200	9100	13,000
2 dr HdTp	600	1900	3200	6400	11,200	16,000
Conv	1000	3250	5400	10,800	18,900	27,000
1959						
Monterey, V-8, 126" wb						
4 dr Sed	200	675	1050	2250	4350	6200
4 dr HdTp	350	750	1200	2350	4900	7000
2 dr Sed	200	675	1050	2250	4300	6100
2 dr HdTp	500	1550	2600	5200	9100	13,000
Conv	700	2150	3600	7200	12,600	18,000
Montclair, V-8, 126" wb						
4 dr Sed	350	700	1100	2300	4500	6400
4 dr HdTp	350	750	1300	2450	5250	7500
2 dr HdTp	550	1800	3000	6000	10,500	15,000
Parklane, V-8, 128" wb						
4 dr HdTp	450	1100	1700	3650	6650	9500
2 dr HdTp	600	1900	3200	6400	11,200	16,000
Conv	800	2500	4200	8400	14,700	21,000
Country Cruiser Station Wagons, V-8, 126" wb						
Com 2 dr HdTp	400	1300	2200	4400	7700	11,000
Com 4 dr HdTp	400	1300	2200	4400	7700	11,000
Voy 4 dr HdTp	450	1450	2400	4800	8400	12,000
Col Pk 4 dr HdTp	500	1550	2600	5200	9100	13,000
1960						
Comet, 6-cyl., 114" wb						
4 dr Sed	350	700	1100	2300	4500	6400
2 dr Sed	200	675	1100	2250	4400	6300
4 dr Sta Wag	200	675	1050	2250	4350	6200
2 dr Sta Wag	200	675	1050	2250	4350	6200
Monterey, V-8, 126" wb						
4 dr Sed	200	675	1050	2250	4300	6100
4 dr HdTp	350	750	1300	2450	5250	7500
2 dr Sed	200	650	1050	2250	4200	6000
2 dr HdTp	400	1300	2200	4400	7700	11,000
Conv	700	2150	3600	7200	12,600	18,000
Country Cruiser Station Wagons, V-8, 126" wb						
Com 4 dr HdTp	400	1200	2000	3950	7000	10,000
Col Pk 4 dr HdTp	400	1300	2200	4400	7700	11,000
Montclair, V-8, 126" wb						
4 dr Sed	350	700	1150	2300	4550	6500
4 dr HdTp	450	1000	1650	3350	6300	9000
2 dr HdTp	450	1450	2400	4800	8400	12,000
Parklane, V-8, 126" wb						
4 dr HdTp	450	1100	1700	3650	6650	9500
2 dr HdTp	550	1700	2800	5600	9800	14,000
Conv	850	2650	4400	8800	15,400	22,000
1961						
Comet, 6-cyl., 114" wb						
4 dr Sed	200	550	900	2150	3800	5400
2 dr Sed	200	550	900	2100	3700	5300
S-22 Cpe	350	900	1550	3050	5900	8500
4 dr Sta Wag	200	550	900	2150	3800	5400
2 dr Sta Wag	200	550	900	2100	3700	5300
Meteor 600, V-8, 120" wb						
4 dr Sed	200	550	900	2100	3700	5300
2 dr Sed	200	550	900	2000	3600	5200
Meteor 800, V-8, 120" wb						
4 dr Sed	200	600	950	2150	3850	5500
4 dr HdTp	200	600	950	2200	3900	5600
2 dr Sed	200	550	900	2150	3800	5400
2 dr HdTp	200	650	1050	2250	4200	6000
Monterey, V-8, 120" wb						
4 dr Sed	200	650	1000	2200	4150	5900
4 dr HdTp	200	650	1050	2250	4200	6000
2 dr HdTp	350	750	1200	2350	4900	7000
Conv	400	1200	2000	3950	7000	10,000
Station Wagon, V-8, 120" wb						
Col Pk	200	650	1000	2200	4100	5800
Com	200	600	1000	2200	4000	5700
1962						
Comet, 6-cyl.						
(Add 10 percent for Custom line)						
4 dr Sed	200	550	900	2150	3800	5400
2 dr Sed	200	550	900	2100	3700	5300
4 dr Sta Wag	200	550	900	2100	3700	5300
2 dr Sta Wag	200	550	900	2150	3800	5400
S-22 Cpe	350	900	1550	3050	5900	8500
Vill Sta Wag	200	600	950	2150	3850	5500
Meteor, 8-cyl.						
(Deduct 10 percent for 6-cyl. Add 10 percent for Custom line).						

	6	5	4	3	2	1
4 dr Sed	200	600	950	2150	3850	5500
2 dr Sed	200	550	900	2150	3800	5400
S-33 Cpe	350	750	1300	2450	5250	7500
Monterey, V-8						
(Add 10 percent for Custom line)						
4 dr Sed	200	600	950	2200	3900	5600
4 dr HdTp Sed	200	600	1000	2200	4000	5700
2 dr Sed	200	550	900	2150	3800	5400
2 dr HdTp	200	650	1050	2250	4200	6000
Sta Wag	200	600	950	2150	3850	5500
Custom S-55 Sport Series, V-8						
2 dr HdTp	350	900	1550	3050	5900	8500
Conv	450	1450	2400	4800	8400	12,000
NOTE: Add 30 percent for 406.						

1963
Comet, 6-cyl.
(Add 10 percent for Custom line)

	6	5	4	3	2	1
4 dr Sed	200	550	900	2150	3800	5400
2 dr Sed	200	550	900	2100	3700	5300
Cus HdTp	350	750	1200	2350	4900	7000
Cus Conv	450	1000	1650	3350	6300	9000
S-22 Cpe	350	900	1550	3050	5900	8500
S-22 HdTp	450	1000	1650	3350	6300	9000
S-22 Conv	450	1450	2400	4800	8400	12,000
4 dr Sta Wag	200	550	900	2100	3700	5300
2 dr Sta Wag	200	550	900	2100	3700	5300
Vill Sta Wag	200	600	1000	2200	4000	5700

Meteor, V-8
(Deduct 10 percent for 6-cyl. Add 10 percent for Custom line).

	6	5	4	3	2	1
4 dr Sed	200	600	950	2150	3850	5500
2 dr Sed	200	550	900	2150	3800	5400
Sta Wag	200	550	900	2100	3700	5300
Cus HdTp	200	650	1050	2250	4200	6000
S-33 HdTp	350	750	1300	2450	5250	7500

Monterey, V-8
(Add 10 percent for Custom line)

	6	5	4	3	2	1
4 dr Sed	200	600	1000	2200	4000	5700
4 dr HdTp	200	650	1050	2250	4200	6000
2 dr Sed	200	600	950	2200	3900	5600
2 dr HdTp	200	675	1050	2250	4300	6100
Cus Conv	350	750	1250	2400	5050	7200
S-55 2 dr HdTp	450	1000	1650	3350	6300	9000
S-55 Conv	500	1550	2600	5200	9100	13,000
Maraud FsBk	350	800	1450	2750	5600	8000
Mar S-55 FsBk	450	1100	1700	3650	6650	9500
Col Pk	200	650	1050	2250	4200	6000
NOTES: Add 30 percent for 406.						
Add 40 percent for 427.						

1964
Comet, 6-cyl., 114" wb

	6	5	4	3	2	1
4 dr Sed	200	500	850	1900	3500	5000
2 dr Sed	200	500	850	1850	3350	4900
Sta Wag	150	450	800	1800	3300	4800
Comet 404, 6-cyl., 114" wb						
4 dr Sed	200	500	850	1950	3600	5100
2 dr Sed	200	500	850	1900	3500	5000
2 dr HdTp	200	650	1050	2250	4200	6000
Conv	450	1100	1700	3650	6650	9500
DeL Wag	150	450	800	1800	3300	4800
Sta Wag	150	450	800	1750	3250	4700
Comet Caliente, V-8 cyl., 114" wb						
4 dr Sed	200	550	900	2000	3600	5200
2 dr HdTp	350	900	1550	3050	5900	8500
Conv	400	1300	2200	4400	7700	11,000
Comet Cyclone, V-8 cyl., 114" wb						
2 dr HdTp	400	1250	2100	4200	7400	10,500
NOTE: Deduct 25 percent for 6-cyl. Caliente.						
Monterey, V-8						
4 dr Sed	200	500	850	1850	3350	4900
4 dr HdTp	200	500	850	1950	3600	5100
2 dr Sed	150	450	800	1800	3300	4800
2 dr HdTp	200	550	900	2100	3700	5300
FsBk	200	650	1000	2200	4100	5800
Conv	450	1100	1700	3650	6650	9500
Montclair, V-8, 120" wb						
4 dr Sed	200	500	850	1900	3500	5000
4 dr HdTp	200	550	900	2100	3700	5300
2 dr HdTp	350	700	1150	2300	4550	6500
FsBk	350	750	1200	2350	4900	7000
Parklane, V-8, 120" wb						
4 dr Sed	200	550	900	2000	3600	5200
4 dr HdTp	200	600	950	2150	3850	5500
4 dr FsBk	350	700	1150	2300	4550	6500
2 dr HdTp	350	750	1300	2450	5250	7500
2 dr FsBk	350	900	1550	3050	5900	8500
Conv	450	1450	2400	4800	8400	12,000
Station Wagon, V-8, 120" wb						
Col Pk	200	550	900	2150	3800	5400
Com	200	550	900	2100	3700	5300
NOTES: Add 10 percent for Marauder.						
Add 40 percent for 427 Super Marauder.						

1965
Comet 202, V-8, 114" wb
(Deduct 20 percent for 6 cyl.)

	6	5	4	3	2	1
4 dr Sed	200	500	850	1950	3600	5100
2 dr Sed	200	500	850	1900	3500	5000
Sta Wag	200	500	850	1950	3600	5100
Comet 404						
4 dr Sed	200	550	900	2000	3600	5200
2 dr Sed	200	500	850	1950	3600	5100
Vill Wag	200	550	900	2000	3600	5200
Sta Wag	200	500	850	1950	3600	5100
Comet Caliente, V-8, 114" wb						
(Deduct 20 percent for 6 cyl.)						
4 dr Sed	200	550	900	2100	3700	5300
2 dr HdTp	350	750	1200	2350	4900	7000
Conv	400	1200	2000	3950	7000	10,000
Comet Cyclone, V-8, 114" wb						
2 dr HdTp	400	1300	2200	4400	7700	11,000
Monterey, V-8, 123" wb						
4 dr Sed	200	600	950	2150	3850	5500
4 dr HdTp	200	650	1000	2200	4100	5800
Brzwy	200	650	1000	2200	4150	5900
2 dr Sed	200	550	900	2150	3800	5400
2 dr HdTp	200	650	1050	2250	4200	6000
Conv	450	1100	1700	3650	6650	9500

	6	5	4	3	2	1
Montclair, V-8, 123" wb						
Brzwy	200	675	1050	2250	4350	6200
4 dr HdTp	200	650	1050	2250	4200	6000
2 dr HdTp	350	700	1150	2300	4550	6500
Parklane, V-8, 123" wb						
Brzwy	350	700	1150	2300	4550	6500
4 dr HdTp	200	650	1050	2250	4200	6000
2 dr HdTp	350	750	1200	2350	4900	7000
Conv	400	1250	2100	4200	7400	10,500
Station Wagon, V-8, 119" wb						
Col Pk	200	600	950	2150	3850	5500
Com	200	550	900	2150	3800	5400
NOTE: Add 20 percent for 427 CI engine.						

1966
Comet Capri, V8, 116" wb

	6	5	4	3	2	1
4 dr Sed	200	550	900	2000	3600	5200
2 dr HdTp	200	650	1000	2200	4100	5800
Sta Wag	200	550	900	2100	3700	5300
Comet Caliente, V8, 116" wb						
4 dr Sed	200	550	900	2100	3700	5300
2 dr HdTp	350	800	1450	2750	5600	8000
Conv	400	1200	2000	3950	7000	10,000
Comet Cyclone, V8, 116" wb						
2 dr HdTp	350	900	1550	3050	5900	8500
Conv	400	1300	2200	4400	7700	11,000
Comet Cyclone GT/GTA, V8, 116" wb						
2 dr HdTp	400	1300	2200	4400	7700	11,000
Conv	500	1550	2600	5200	9100	13,000
Comet 202, V8, 116" wb						
4 dr Sed	200	500	850	1900	3500	5000
2 dr Sed	200	550	900	2000	3600	5200
Sta Wag	200	500	850	1900	3500	5000
Monterey, V-8, 123" wb						
4 dr Sed	200	550	900	2100	3700	5300
4 dr Brzwy Sed	200	600	950	2150	3850	5500
4 dr HdTp	200	550	900	2100	3700	5300
2 dr Sed	200	550	900	2100	3700	5300
2 dr HdTp FsBk	200	650	1050	2250	4200	6000
Conv	450	1100	1700	3650	6650	9500
Montclair, V-8, 123" wb						
4 dr Sed	200	550	900	2100	3700	5300
4 dr HdTp	200	550	900	2150	3800	5400
2 dr HdTp	200	600	950	2200	3900	5600
Parklane, V-8, 123" wb						
4 dr Brzwy Sed	200	650	1050	2250	4200	6000
4 dr HdTp	200	600	950	2200	3900	5600
2 dr HdTp	200	675	1050	2250	4350	6200
Conv	400	1200	2000	3950	7000	10,000
S-55, V-8, 123" wb						
2 dr HdTp	350	800	1450	2750	5600	8000
Conv	400	1200	2000	3950	7000	10,000
Station Wagons, V-8, 123" wb						
Comm	200	600	950	2150	3850	5500
Col Pk	200	600	1000	2200	4000	5700
NOTE: Add 18 percent for 410 CI engine.						
Add 40 percent for 428 CI engine.						

1967
Comet 202, V-8, 116" wb

	6	5	4	3	2	1
2 dr Sed	200	550	900	2100	3700	5300
4 dr Sed	200	550	900	2150	3800	5400
Capri, V-8, 116" wb						
2 dr HdTp	200	600	1000	2200	4000	5700
4 dr Sdn	200	550	900	2100	3700	5300
Caliante, V-8, 116" wb						
4 dr Sed	200	650	1000	2200	4100	5800
2 dr HdTp	350	750	1300	2450	5250	7500
Conv	400	1250	2100	4200	7400	10,500
Cyclone, V-8, 116" wb						
2 dr HdTp	400	1200	2000	3950	7000	10,000
Conv	500	1550	2600	5200	9100	13,000
Station Wagons, V-8, 113" wb						
Voyager	200	550	900	2100	3700	5300
Villager	200	550	900	2150	3800	5400
Cougar, V-8, 11" wb						
2 dr HdTp	400	1200	2000	3950	7000	10,000
X-R7 HdTp	400	1300	2200	4400	7700	11,000
Monterey, V-8, 123" wb						
4 dr Sed	200	550	900	2100	3700	5300
4 dr Brzwy	200	550	900	2150	3800	5400
Conv	450	1000	1650	3350	6300	9000
2 dr HdTp	200	600	950	2200	3900	5600
2 dr HdTp	200	550	900	2150	3800	5400
4 dr HdTp	200	550	900	2150	3800	5400
Montclair, V-8, 123" wb						
4 dr Sed	200	550	900	2150	3800	5400
4 dr Brzwy	200	600	950	2150	3850	5500
2 dr HdTp	200	600	1000	2200	4000	5700
4 dr HdTp	200	600	950	2150	3850	5500
Parklane, V-8, 123" wb						
4 dr Brzwy	200	600	950	2200	3900	5600
Conv	400	1200	2000	3950	7000	10,000
2 dr HdTp	200	650	1000	2200	4100	5800
4 dr HdTp	200	650	1000	2200	4150	5900
Brougham, V-8, 123" wb						
4 dr Brzwy	200	650	1050	2250	4200	6000
4 dr HdTp	200	600	1000	2200	4000	5700
Marquis, V-8, 123" wb						
2 dr HdTp	350	700	1150	2300	4550	6500
Station Wagons, 119" wb						
Commuter	200	600	950	2150	3850	5500
Col Park	200	600	1000	2200	4000	5700
NOTES: Add 10 percent for GT option.						
Add 15 percent for S-55 performance package.						
Add 40 percent for 427 C.I. engine.						
Add 50 percent for 428 cubic inch V-8.						

1968
Comet, V-8

	6	5	4	3	2	1
2 dr Hdtp	200	650	1050	2250	4200	6000
Montego, V-8						
4 dr Sed	150	350	750	1450	3000	4200
2 dr Hdtp	150	400	750	1650	3150	4500
Montego MX						
Sta Wag	150	400	750	1550	3050	4300
Sed	150	400	750	1550	3050	4300
2 dr HdTp	200	600	950	2150	3850	5500
Conv	350	800	1450	2750	5600	8000

	6	5	4	3	2	1
Cyclone, V-8						
Fsbk Cpe	450	1000	1650	3350	6300	9000
2 dr HdTp	350	900	1550	3050	5900	8500
Cyclone GT 427, V-8						
Fsbk Cpe	700	2300	3800	7600	13,300	19,000
2 dr HdTp	700	2150	3600	7200	12,600	18,000
Cyclone GT 428, V-8						
Fsbk Cpe	500	1550	2600	5200	9100	13,000
Cougar, V-8						
HdTp Cpe	400	1200	2000	3950	7000	10,000
XR-7 Cpe	450	1450	2400	4800	8400	12,000
NOTE: Add 10 percent for GTE package.						
Monterey, V-8						
4 dr Sed	150	400	750	1550	3050	4300
Conv	450	1000	1650	3350	6300	9000
2 dr HdTp	150	400	750	1650	3150	4500
4 dr HdTp	150	400	750	1550	3050	4300
Montclair, V-8						
4 dr Sed	150	400	750	1600	3100	4400
2 dr HdTp	150	450	800	1750	3250	4700
4 dr HdTp	150	400	750	1650	3150	4500
Parklane, V-8						
4 dr Sed	150	400	750	1650	3150	4500
Conv	400	1250	2100	4200	7400	10,500
2 dr HdTp	200	650	1050	2250	4200	6000
4 dr HdTp	150	450	800	1800	3300	4800
Marquis, V-8						
2 dr HdTp	200	650	1050	2250	4200	6000
Station Wagons, V-8						
Commuter	150	400	750	1650	3150	4500
Col Pk	150	450	800	1750	3250	4700
NOTES: Deduct 5 percent for six-cylinder engine.						
Add 5 percent for Brougham package.						
Add 5 percent for 'yacht paneling'.						
Add 40 percent for '427'.						
Add 50 percent for 428.						

1969

	6	5	4	3	2	1
Comet, 6-cyl.						
2 dr HdTp	200	500	850	1900	3500	5000
Montego, 6-cyl.						
Sed	150	300	700	1250	2650	3800
2 dr HdTp	150	350	750	1350	2800	4000
Montego MX, V8						
Sed	150	300	750	1350	2700	3900
2 dr HdTp	200	500	850	1900	3500	5000
Conv	350	700	1150	2300	4550	6500
Sta Wag	150	300	700	1250	2650	3800
Cyclone, V-8						
2 dr HdTp	350	800	1450	2750	5600	8000
Cyclone CJ, V-8						
2 dr HdTp	450	1000	1650	3350	6300	9000
Cougar, V-8						
2 dr HdTp	450	1000	1650	3350	6300	9000
Conv	400	1250	2100	4200	7400	10,500
XR-7	400	1200	2000	3950	7000	10,000
XR-7 Conv	450	1400	2300	4600	8100	11,500
NOTE: Add 45 percent for Eliminator 428 V-8 option.						
Monterey, V-8						
Sed	150	300	700	1250	2650	3800
4 dr HdTp	150	300	750	1350	2700	3900
2 dr HdTp	150	350	750	1450	3000	4200
Conv	200	600	950	2150	3850	5500
Sta Wag	150	300	700	1250	2650	3800
Marauder, V-8						
2 dr HdTp	200	650	1050	2250	4200	6000
X-100 HdTp	350	800	1450	2750	5600	8000
Marquis, V-8						
Sed	150	300	750	1350	2700	3900
4 dr HdTp	150	350	750	1350	2800	4000
2 dr HdTp	200	600	950	2150	3850	5500
Conv	400	1200	2000	3950	7000	10,000
Sta Wag	150	300	750	1350	2700	3900
Marquis Brgm, V-8						
Sed	150	350	750	1350	2800	4000
4 dr HdTp	150	400	750	1650	3150	4500
2 dr HdTp	200	650	1050	2250	4200	6000
NOTES: Add 10 percent for Montego/Comet V-8.						
Add 15 percent for GT option.						
Add 20 percent for GT Spoiler II.						
Add 10 percent for bucket seats (except Cougar).						
Add 10 percent for bench seats (Cougar only).						
Add 40 percent for 'CJ' 428 V-8.						
Add 50 percent for 429.						

1970

	6	5	4	3	2	1
Montego						
4 dr	150	300	750	1350	2700	3900
2 dr	150	350	750	1350	2800	4000
Montego MX, V-8						
4 dr	150	400	750	1550	3050	4300
2 dr HdTp	150	400	750	1550	3050	4300
Sta Wag	150	350	750	1350	2800	4000
Montego MX Brgm, V-8						
4 dr	150	350	750	1450	3000	4200
4 dr HdTp	150	400	750	1550	3050	4300
2 dr HdTp	150	450	800	1800	3300	4800
Vill Sta Wag	150	350	750	1450	2900	4100
Cyclone, V-8						
2 dr HdTp	350	750	1300	2450	5250	7500
Cyclone GT, V-8						
2 dr HdTp	350	900	1550	3050	5900	8500
Cyclone Spoiler, V-8						
2 dr HdTp	450	1100	1700	3650	6650	9500
NOTE: Add 40 percent for 429 V-8 GT and Spoiler. .						
Cougar, V-8						
2 dr HdTp	350	900	1550	3050	5900	8500
Conv	400	1200	2000	3950	7000	10,000
Cougar XR-7, V-8						
2 dr HdTp	450	1100	1700	3650	6650	9500
Conv	450	1400	2300	4600	8100	11,500
NOTE: Add 45 percent for Eliminator 428 V-8 option.						
Monterey, V-8						
4 dr	150	300	750	1350	2700	3900
4 dr HdTp	150	350	750	1350	2800	4000
2 dr HdTp	150	350	750	1450	2900	4100

	6	5	4	3	2	1
Conv	350	700	1150	2300	4550	6500
Sta Wag	150	350	750	1350	2800	4000
Monterey Custom, V-8						
4 dr	150	350	750	1350	2800	4000
4 dr HdTp	150	350	750	1450	2900	4100
2 dr HdTp	150	350	750	1450	3000	4200
Marauder, V-8						
2 dr HdTp	200	650	1050	2250	4200	6000
Marauder X-100, V-8						
2 dr HdTp	350	750	1200	2350	4900	7000
Marquis, V-8						
4 dr	150	350	750	1450	2900	4100
4 dr HdTp	150	350	750	1450	3000	4200
2 dr HdTp	150	400	750	1600	3100	4400
Conv	400	1200	2000	3950	7000	10,000
Sta Wag	150	350	750	1450	2900	4100
Col Pk	150	350	750	1450	3000	4200
Marquis Brgm, V-8						
4 dr	150	350	750	1450	3000	4200
4 dr HdTp	150	400	750	1550	3050	4300
2 dr HdTp	200	500	850	1900	3500	5000
NOTE: Add 30 percent for any 429 engine option.						

1971

	6	5	4	3	2	1
Comet, V-8						
4 dr	125	200	600	1100	2200	3100
2 dr	125	200	600	1100	2250	3200
2 dr GT	150	350	750	1350	2800	4000
Montego, V-8						
4 dr	100	175	525	1050	2100	3000
2 dr HdTp	125	250	700	1150	2400	3400
Montego MX						
4 dr	125	200	600	1100	2200	3100
2 dr HdTp	150	300	700	1250	2600	3700
Sta Wag	125	200	600	1100	2200	3100
Montego MX Brgm						
4 dr	125	200	600	1100	2250	3200
4 dr HdTp	125	250	700	1150	2400	3400
2 dr HdTp	150	300	750	1350	2700	3900
Villager Sta Wag	125	200	600	1100	2250	3200
Cyclone, V-8						
2 dr HdTp	200	650	1050	2250	4200	6000
Cyclone GT, V-8						
2 dr HdTp	350	750	1200	2350	4900	7000
Cyclone Spoiler, V-8						
2 dr HdTp	350	750	1300	2450	5250	7500
NOTE: Add 40 percent for 429 V-8 GT and Spoiler.						
Cougar, V-8						
2 dr HdTp	350	750	1200	2350	4900	7000
Conv	350	800	1450	2750	5600	8000
Cougar XR-7, V-8						
2 dr HdTp	350	900	1550	3050	5900	8500
Conv	450	1100	1700	3650	6650	9500
Monterey, V-8						
4 dr	100	175	525	1050	2100	3000
4 dr HdTp	125	200	600	1100	2200	3100
2 dr HdTp	125	200	600	1100	2250	3200
Sta Wag	100	175	525	1050	2100	3000
Monterey Custom, V-8						
4 dr	125	200	600	1100	2200	3100
4 dr HdTp	125	200	600	1100	2250	3200
2 dr HdTp	125	250	700	1150	2450	3500
Marquis, V-8						
4 dr	125	200	600	1100	2200	3100
4 dr HdTp	125	250	700	1150	2450	3500
2 dr HdTp	150	350	750	1350	2800	4000
Sta Wag	100	175	525	1050	2100	3000
Marquis Brgm						
4 dr	125	200	600	1100	2250	3200
4 dr HdTp	125	250	700	1150	2450	3500
2 dr HdTp	150	400	750	1650	3150	4500
Col Pk	125	250	700	1150	2450	3500
NOTE: Add 30 percent for 429.						

1972

	6	5	4	3	2	1
Comet, V-8						
4 dr	125	200	600	1100	2200	3100
2 dr	125	250	700	1150	2450	3500
Montego, V-8						
4 dr	100	175	525	1050	2100	3000
2 dr HdTp	125	250	700	1150	2400	3400
Montego MX, V-8						
4 dr	125	200	600	1100	2250	3200
2 dr HdTp	150	300	750	1350	2700	3900
Sta Wag	125	200	600	1100	2250	3200
Montego Brgm, V-8						
4 dr	125	200	600	1100	2300	3300
2 dr HdTp	150	350	750	1350	2800	4000
Sta Wag	125	200	600	1100	2300	3300
Montego GT, V-8						
2 dr HdTp Fsbk	150	400	750	1650	3150	4500
Cougar, V-8						
2 dr HdTp	350	750	1200	2350	4900	7000
Conv	350	900	1550	3050	5900	8500
Cougar XR-7, V-8						
2 dr HdTp	350	900	1550	3050	5900	8500
Conv	400	1200	2000	3950	7000	10,000
Monterey, V-8						
4 dr	125	200	600	1100	2300	3300
4 dr HdTp	125	250	700	1150	2450	3500
2 dr HdTp	150	350	750	1350	2800	4000
Sta Wag	125	250	700	1150	2450	3500
Monterey Custom, V-8						
4 dr	125	250	700	1150	2400	3400
4 dr HdTp	150	350	750	1350	2800	4000
2 dr HdTp	150	400	750	1650	3150	4500
Marquis, V-8						
4 dr	125	250	700	1150	2450	3500
4 dr HdTp	150	400	750	1650	3150	4500
2 dr HdTp	200	500	850	1900	3500	5000
Sta Wag	125	250	700	1150	2450	3500
Marquis Brgm, V-8						
4 dr	125	250	700	1150	2500	3600
4 dr HdTp	150	300	700	1250	2600	3700
2 dr HdTp	150	450	800	1800	3300	4800
Col Pk	125	250	700	1150	2500	3600

	6	5	4	3	2	1
1973						
Comet, V-8						
4 dr	125	200	600	1100	2200	3100
2 dr	125	250	700	1150	2450	3500
Montego, V-8						
4 dr	100	175	525	1050	2100	3000
2 dr HdTp	150	300	700	1250	2650	3800
Montego MX, V-8						
4 dr	125	200	600	1100	2200	3100
2 dr HdTp	150	350	750	1350	2800	4000
Montego MX Brgm, V-8						
4 dr	125	200	600	1100	2250	3200
2 dr HdTp	150	350	750	1450	3000	4200
Montego GT, V-8						
2 dr HdTp	200	500	850	1900	3500	5000
Montego MX						
Village Wag	125	200	600	1100	2250	3200
Cougar, V-8						
2 dr HdTp	350	750	1200	2350	4900	7000
Conv	350	800	1450	2750	5600	8000
Cougar XR-7, V-8						
2 dr HdTp	350	800	1450	2750	5600	8000
Conv	450	1000	1650	3350	6300	9000
Monterey, V-8						
4 dr	100	175	525	1050	2100	3000
2 dr HdTp	125	200	600	1100	2200	3100
Monterey Custom, V-8						
4 dr	125	200	600	1100	2200	3100
2 dr HdTp	150	350	750	1350	2800	4000
Marquis, V-8						
4 dr	125	200	600	1100	2300	3300
4 dr HdTp	125	250	700	1150	2450	3500
2 dr HdTp	150	400	750	1650	3150	4500
Marquis Brgm, V-8						
4 dr	125	250	700	1150	2400	3400
4 dr HdTp	150	350	750	1350	2800	4000
2 dr HdTp	200	500	850	1900	3500	5000
Station Wagon, V-8						
Monterey	125	200	600	1100	2300	3300
Marquis	125	250	700	1150	2400	3400
Col Pk	125	250	700	1150	2450	3500
1974						
Comet, V-8						
4 dr	125	200	600	1100	2200	3100
2 dr	125	250	700	1150	2450	3500
Montego, V-8						
4 dr	125	200	600	1100	2250	3200
2 dr HdTp	125	250	700	1150	2500	3600
Montego MX, V-8						
4 dr	125	200	600	1100	2300	3300
2 dr HdTp	150	300	700	1250	2600	3700
Montego MX Brgm, V-8						
4 dr	125	250	700	1150	2400	3400
2 dr HdTp	150	300	750	1350	2700	3900
Villager	125	250	700	1150	2400	3400
Cougar, V-8						
2 dr	200	600	950	2150	3850	5500
Monterey, V-8						
4 dr	125	200	600	1100	2200	3100
2 dr HdTp	150	350	750	1350	2800	4000
Monterey Custom, V-8						
4 dr	125	200	600	1100	2250	3200
2 dr HdTp	150	400	750	1650	3150	4500
Marquis, V-8						
4 dr	125	200	600	1100	2300	3300
4 dr HdTp	125	250	700	1150	2450	3500
2 dr HdTp	150	450	800	1800	3300	4800
Marquis Brgm, V-8						
4 dr	125	250	700	1150	2400	3400
4 dr HdTp	150	350	750	1350	2800	4000
2 dr HdTp	200	500	850	1900	3500	5000
Station Wagons, V-8						
Monterey	125	250	700	1150	2450	3500
Marquis	125	250	700	1150	2500	3600
Col Pk	150	300	700	1250	2600	3700
1975						
Bobcat 4-cyl.						
Htchbk	125	250	700	1150	2500	3600
Sta Wag	125	250	700	1150	2450	3500
Comet, V-8						
4 dr	125	200	600	1100	2200	3100
2 dr	125	200	600	1100	2250	3200
Monarch, V-8						
4 dr	125	250	700	1150	2400	3400
2 dr	125	250	700	1150	2450	3500
Monarch Ghia, V-8						
4 dr	125	250	700	1150	2450	3500
2 dr	125	250	700	1150	2500	3600
Monarch Grand Ghia, V-8						
4 dr	150	300	700	1250	2600	3700
Montego, V-8						
4 dr	125	200	600	1100	2300	3300
2 dr	125	250	700	1150	2400	3400
Montego MX, V-8						
4 dr	125	250	700	1150	2400	3400
2 dr	125	250	700	1150	2450	3500
Montego Brgm, V-8						
4 dr	125	250	700	1150	2450	3500
2 dr	125	250	700	1150	2500	3600
Station Wagons, V-8						
Villager	125	250	700	1150	2400	3400
Cougar, V-8						
2 dr HdTp	125	250	700	1150	2500	3600
Marquis, V-8						
4 dr	125	250	700	1150	2400	3400
2 dr	125	250	700	1150	2450	3500
Marquis Brgm, V-8						
4 dr	125	250	700	1150	2450	3500
2 dr	125	250	700	1150	2500	3600
Grand Marquis, V-8						
4 dr	125	250	700	1150	2500	3600
2 dr	150	300	700	1250	2600	3700
Station Wagons, V-8						
Marquis	150	300	700	1250	2600	3700
Col Pk	150	300	700	1250	2650	3800

NASH

	6	5	4	3	2	1
1946						
600, 6-cyl.						
2 dr Brgm	200	500	850	1950	3600	5100
4 dr Sed	200	500	850	1900	3500	5000
4 dr Trk Sed	200	550	900	2100	3700	5300
Ambassador, 6-cyl.						
2 dr Brgm	350	750	1300	2450	5250	7500
4 dr Sed	350	750	1300	2450	5250	7500
4 dr Trk Sed	350	750	1300	2500	5300	7600
4 dr Sub Sed	850	2750	4600	9200	16,100	23,000
1947						
600, 6-cyl.						
2 dr Brgm	200	550	900	2000	3600	5200
4 dr Sed	200	500	850	1950	3600	5100
4 dr Trk Sed	200	600	950	2150	3850	5500
Ambassador, 6-cyl.						
2 dr Brgm	350	750	1300	2450	5250	7500
4 dr Sed	350	750	1300	2500	5300	7600
4 dr Trk Sed	350	750	1350	2600	5400	7700
4 dr Sub Sed	850	2750	4600	9200	16,100	23,000
1948						
600, 6-cyl.						
DeL Bus Cpe	200	600	950	2200	3900	5600
4 dr Super Sed	200	600	950	2150	3850	5500
4 dr Super Trk Sed	200	600	950	2150	3850	5500
2 dr Super Brgm	200	600	1000	2200	4000	5700
4 dr Cus Sed	200	650	1000	2200	4150	5900
4 dr Cus Trk Sed	200	675	1050	2250	4300	6100
2 dr Cus Brgm	200	650	1050	2250	4200	6000
Ambassador, 6-cyl.						
4 dr Sed	350	750	1250	2400	5050	7200
4 dr Trk Sed	350	750	1250	2400	5100	7300
2 dr Brgm	350	750	1250	2350	5000	7100
4 dr Sub Sed	900	2900	4800	9600	16,800	24,000
Custom Ambassador, 6-cyl.						
4 dr Sed	350	750	1300	2450	5250	7500
4 dr Trk Sed	350	750	1300	2500	5300	7600
2 dr Brgm	350	750	1300	2450	5250	7500
2 dr Cabr	950	3000	5000	10,000	17,500	25,000
1949						
600 Super, 6-cyl.						
4 dr Sed	200	600	950	2200	3900	5600
2 dr Sed	200	600	950	2200	3900	5600
2 dr Brgm	200	600	950	2200	3900	5600
600 Super Special, 6-cyl.						
4 dr Sed	200	675	1050	2250	4300	6100
2 dr Sed	200	650	1000	2200	4150	5900
2 dr Brgm	200	600	1000	2200	4000	5700
600 Custom, 6-cyl.						
4 dr Sed	200	650	1000	2200	4100	5800
2 dr Sed	200	600	1000	2200	4000	5700
2 dr Brgm	200	650	1000	2200	4100	5800
Ambassador Super, 6-cyl.						
4 dr Sed	350	750	1200	2350	4900	7000
2 dr Sed	350	725	1200	2350	4850	6900
2 dr Brgm	350	750	1200	2350	4900	7000
Ambassador Super Special, 6-cyl.						
4 dr Sed	350	750	1250	2350	5000	7100
2 dr Sed	350	750	1200	2350	4900	7000
2 dr Brgm	350	750	1250	2350	5000	7100
Ambassador Custom, 6-cyl.						
4 dr Sed	350	750	1250	2400	5050	7200
2 dr Sed	350	750	1250	2350	5000	7100
2 dr Brgm	350	750	1250	2400	5050	7200
1950						
Rambler Custom, 6-cyl.						
2 dr Conv Lan	350	700	1150	2300	4550	6500
2 dr Sta Wag	200	600	950	2150	3850	5500
Nash Super Statesman, 6-cyl.						
2 dr DeL Cpe	200	675	1050	2250	4300	6100
4 dr Sed	200	600	950	2200	3900	5600
2 dr Sed	200	600	950	2200	3900	5600
2 dr Clb Cpe	350	700	1150	2300	4600	6600
Nash Custom Statesman, 6-cyl.						
4 dr Sed	200	600	950	2200	3900	5600
2 dr Sed	200	600	1000	2200	4000	5700
2 dr Clb Cpe	200	650	1000	2200	4100	5800
Ambassador, 6-cyl.						
4 dr Sed	350	725	1150	2300	4700	6700
2 dr Sed	350	725	1200	2350	4800	6800
2 dr Clb Cpe	350	725	1200	2350	4850	6900
Ambassador Custom, 6-cyl.						
4 dr Sed	350	725	1200	2350	4800	6800
2 dr Sed	350	725	1200	2350	4850	6900
2 dr Clb Cpe	350	750	1200	2350	4900	7000
1951						
Rambler, 6-cyl.						
2 dr Utl Wag	200	600	950	2200	3900	5600
2 dr Cus Clb Sed	200	600	1000	2200	4000	5700
2 dr Cus Conv Sed	350	750	1200	2350	4900	7000
2 dr Cus Sta Wag	200	600	1000	2200	4000	5700
Nash Statesman, 6-cyl.						
2 dr DeL Bus Cpe	200	600	1000	2200	4000	5700
4 dr Sup Sed	200	650	1000	2200	4100	5800
2 dr Sup	200	600	1000	2200	4000	5700
2 dr Sup Cpe	200	650	1000	2200	4100	5800
2 dr Cus Cpe	200	675	1050	2250	4300	6100
2 dr Cus	200	650	1000	2200	4150	5900
Ambassador, 6-cyl.						
4 dr Sup Sed	350	725	1200	2350	4850	6900
2 dr Sup	350	725	1200	2350	4800	6800
2 dr Sup Cpe	350	725	1200	2350	4850	6900
4 dr Cus Sed	350	750	1250	2350	5000	7100
2 dr Cus	350	750	1250	2400	5050	7200
2 dr Cus Cpe	350	750	1250	2400	5100	7300
Nash-Healy						
Spt Car	1200	3850	6400	12,800	22,400	32,000
1952						
Rambler, 6-cyl.						
2 dr Utl Wag	200	600	950	2150	3850	5500
2 dr Cus Clb Sed	200	650	1000	2200	4100	5800
2 dr Cus Sta Wag	200	600	950	2200	3900	5600
2 dr Cus Conv Sed	350	750	1300	2450	5250	7500

	6	5	4	3	2	1
Nash Statesman, 6-cyl.						
(Add 10 percent for Custom)						
2 dr Sed	200	600	1000	2200	4000	5700
2 dr Cus Ctry Clb	350	800	1450	2750	5600	8000
Ambassador, 6-cyl.						
(Add 10 percent for Custom)						
2 dr Sed	350	750	1200	2350	4900	7000
2 dr Ctry Clb	400	1200	2000	3950	7000	10,000
Nash-Healey, 6-cyl.						
Spt Car	1500	4800	8000	16,000	28,000	40,000

1953

	6	5	4	3	2	1
Rambler, 6-cyl.						
2 dr Utl Wag	200	600	950	2150	3850	5500
2 dr Cus Clb Sed	200	600	1000	2200	4000	5700
2 dr Cus Conv Sed	350	750	1300	2450	5250	7500
2 dr Cus Sta Wag	200	600	950	2150	3850	5500
Nash Statesman, 6-cyl.						
(Add 10 percent for Custom)						
2 dr Sed	200	600	1000	2200	4000	5700
2 dr Cus Ctry Clb	350	750	1300	2450	5250	7500
Ambassador, 6-cyl.						
(Add 10 percent for Custom)						
2 dr Sed	350	750	1250	2350	5000	7100
2 dr Cus Ctry Clb	450	1100	1700	3650	6650	9500
Nash-Healey						
Spt Car	1500	4800	8000	16,000	28,000	40,000

1954

	6	5	4	3	2	1
Rambler, 6-cyl.						
2 dr DeL Clb Sed	200	600	950	2150	3850	5500
2 dr Sup Clb Sed	200	600	950	2200	3900	5600
2 dr Ctry Clb Sed	200	600	1000	2200	4000	5700
2 dr Utl Wag	200	600	1000	2200	4000	5700
4 dr Sup Sed (108")	200	600	950	2150	3850	5500
2 dr Cus Ctry Clb	350	750	1200	2350	4900	7000
2 dr Cus Conv	350	800	1450	2750	5600	8000
2 dr Cus Sta Wag	200	600	950	2150	3850	5500
4 dr Cus Sed (108")	200	600	950	2150	3850	5500
2 dr Cus Wag (108")	200	600	1000	2200	4000	5700
Nash Statesman, 6-cyl.						
4 dr Sup Sed	200	650	1050	2250	4200	6000
2 dr Sup Sed	200	675	1050	2250	4300	6100
4 dr Cus Sed	200	675	1050	2250	4350	6200
2 dr Cus Ctry Clb	450	1000	1650	3350	6300	9000
Nash Ambassador, 6-cyl.						
(Add 5 percent for LeMans option).						
4 dr Sup Sed	350	750	1250	2400	5050	7200
2 dr Sup Sed	350	750	1250	2400	5100	7300
4 dr Cus Sed	350	750	1300	2450	5250	7500
2 dr Cus Ctry Clb	400	1300	2200	4400	7700	11,000
Nash-Healey						
Spt Car	1600	5050	8400	16,800	29,400	42,000

1955

	6	5	4	3	2	1
Rambler, 6-cyl.						
2 dr DeL Clb Sed	200	600	950	2200	3900	5600
2 dr DeL Bus Sed	200	600	950	2150	3850	5500
4 dr DeL Sed (108")	200	600	950	2150	3850	5500
2 dr Sup Clb Sed	200	600	950	2200	3900	5600
2 dr Utl Wag	200	600	1000	2200	4000	5700
4 dr Sup Sed (108")	200	600	950	2200	3900	5600
4 dr Sup Crs Ctry (108")	200	600	1000	2200	4000	5700
2 dr Cus Ctry Clb	350	725	1200	2350	4850	6900
4 dr Cus Sed (108")	200	600	1000	2200	4000	5700
4 dr Cus Crs Ctry (108")	200	650	1000	2200	4100	5800
Nash Statesman, 6-cyl.						
2 dr Sup Sed	200	600	950	2150	3850	5500
2 dr Cus Sed	200	600	950	2200	3900	5600
2 dr Cus Ctry Clb	350	750	1300	2450	5250	7500
Nash Ambassador, 6-cyl.						
4 dr Sup Sed	350	700	1150	2300	4600	6600
4 dr Cus Sed	350	725	1150	2300	4700	6700
2 dr Cus Ctry Clb	450	1450	2400	4800	8400	12,000
Nash Ambassador, 8-cyl.						
4 dr Sup Sed	350	725	1150	2300	4700	6700
4 dr Cus Sed	350	750	1200	2350	4900	7000
2 dr Cus Ctry Clb	500	1550	2600	5200	9100	13,000

1956

	6	5	4	3	2	1
Rambler, 6-cyl.						
4 dr DeL Sed	200	500	850	1850	3350	4900
4 dr Sup Sed	200	500	850	1900	3500	5000
4 dr Sup Crs Ctry	200	650	1000	2200	4100	5800
4 dr Cus Sed	200	500	850	1850	3350	4900
4 dr Cus HdTp	200	600	950	2200	3900	5600
4 dr Cus Crs Ctry	200	675	1100	2250	4400	6300
4 dr HdTp Wag	350	725	1150	2300	4700	6700
Nash Statesman, 6-cyl.						
4 dr Sup Sed	200	550	900	2150	3800	5400
Nash Ambassador, 6-cyl.						
4 dr Sup Sed	350	700	1150	2300	4600	6600
Nash Ambassador, 8-cyl.						
4 dr Sup Sed	350	725	1150	2300	4700	6700
4 dr Cus Sed	350	725	1200	2350	4800	6800
2 dr Cus HdTp	500	1550	2600	5200	9100	13,000

1957

	6	5	4	3	2	1
Rambler, 6-cyl.						
4 dr DeL Sed	200	500	850	1900	3500	5000
4 dr Sup Sed	200	550	900	2000	3600	5200
4 dr Sup HdTp	200	600	950	2200	3900	5600
4 dr Sup Crs Ctry	200	650	1000	2200	4100	5800
4 dr Cus Sed	200	500	850	1950	3600	5100
4 dr Cus Crs Ctry	200	650	1000	2200	4150	5900
Rambler, 8-cyl.						
4 dr Sup Sed	200	550	900	2000	3600	5200
4 dr Sup Crs Ctry Wag	200	650	1000	2200	4150	5900
4 dr Cus Sed	200	550	900	2100	3700	5300
4 dr Cus HdTp	200	650	1050	2250	4200	6000
4 dr Cus Crs Ctry Wag	200	675	1050	2250	4300	6100
4 dr Cus Crs Ctry HdTp	350	700	1150	2300	4600	6600
Rebel, 8-cyl.						
4 dr HdTp	450	1000	1650	3350	6300	9000
Nash Ambassador, 8-cyl.						
4 dr Sup Sed	350	725	1150	2300	4700	6700
4 dr Sup HdTp	350	800	1450	2750	5600	8000
4 dr Cus Sed	350	750	1200	2350	4900	7000
2 dr Cus HdTp	500	1600	2700	5400	9500	13,500

OLDSMOBILE

1946

	6	5	4	3	2	1
Special Series 66, 6-cyl.						
Conv	750	2400	4000	8000	14,000	20,000
Clb Cpe	350	725	1150	2300	4700	6700
Clb Sed	350	700	1150	2300	4550	6500
Sed	350	700	1100	2300	4500	6400
Sta Wag	700	2150	3600	7200	12,600	18,000
Dynamic Series 76, 6-cyl.						
Clb Sed	350	700	1150	2300	4550	6500
Sed	350	700	1150	2300	4600	6600
Dynamic Series 78, 8-cyl.						
Clb Sed	350	725	1200	2350	4850	6900
Sed	350	750	1200	2350	4900	7000
Custom Cruiser 98, 8-cyl.						
Conv	900	2900	4800	9600	16,800	24,000
Clb Sed	350	750	1250	2400	5050	7200
Sed	350	750	1250	2400	5100	7300

1947

	6	5	4	3	2	1
Special Series 66, 6-cyl.						
Conv	700	2300	3800	7600	13,300	19,000
Clb Cpe	350	700	1150	2300	4600	6600
Clb Sed	350	700	1100	2300	4500	6400
Sed	200	675	1100	2250	4400	6300
Sta Wag	700	2150	3600	7200	12,600	18,000
Special Series 68, 8-cyl.						
Conv	750	2400	4000	8000	14,000	20,000
Clb Cpe	350	725	1200	2350	4800	6800
Clb Sed	350	700	1150	2300	4550	6500
Sed	350	700	1100	2300	4500	6400
Sta Wag	700	2300	3800	7600	13,300	19,000
Dynamic Cruiser, Series 76, 6-cyl.						
Clb Sed	350	700	1100	2300	4500	6400
DeL Clb Sed	350	725	1150	2300	4700	6700
Sed	350	700	1150	2300	4550	6500
DeL Sed	350	700	1150	2300	4600	6600
Dynamic Cruiser Series 78, 8-cyl.						
Clb Sed	350	725	1150	2300	4700	6700
DeL Clb Sed	350	725	1200	2350	4850	6900
Sed	350	725	1200	2350	4800	6800
DeL Sed	350	750	1200	2350	4900	7000
Custom Cruiser Series 98, 8-cyl.						
Conv	850	2650	4400	8800	15,400	22,000
Clb Sed	450	1050	1650	3500	6400	9200
Sed	450	1000	1650	3350	6300	9000

1948

	6	5	4	3	2	1
Dynamic Series 66, 6-cyl., 119" wb						
Conv	700	2300	3800	7600	13,300	19,000
Clb Cpe	350	700	1150	2300	4550	6500
Clb Sed	200	675	1050	2250	4350	6200
Sed	200	675	1100	2250	4400	6300
Sta Wag	700	2150	3600	7200	12,600	18,000
Dynamic Series 68, 8-cyl., 119" wb						
Conv	750	2400	4000	8000	14,000	20,000
Clb Cpe	350	750	1200	2350	4900	7000
Clb Sed	350	700	1150	2300	4550	6500
Sed	350	700	1150	2300	4600	6600
Sta Wag	700	2300	3800	7600	13,300	19,000
Dynamic Series 76, 6-cyl., 125" wb						
2 dr Club Sed	350	700	1150	2300	4550	6500
4 dr Sed	350	700	1150	2300	4600	6600
Dynamic Series 78, 8-cyl., 125" wb						
Clb Sed	350	725	1150	2300	4700	6700
Sed	350	725	1200	2350	4800	6800
Futuramic Series 98, 8-cyl., 125" wb						
Conv	850	2650	4400	8800	15,400	22,000
Clb Sed	350	900	1550	3050	5900	8500
Sed	350	900	1550	3050	5900	8500

1949

	6	5	4	3	2	1
Futuramic 76, 6-cyl., 119.5" wb						
Conv	750	2400	4000	8000	14,000	20,000
Clb Cpe	450	1050	1700	3600	6600	9400
2 dr Sed	200	650	1050	2250	4200	6000
4 dr Sed	200	675	1050	2250	4300	6100
Sta Wag	550	1700	2800	5600	9800	14,000
Futuramic Series 88, V-8, 119.5" wb						
NOTE: Deduct 10 percent for 6-cyl. models.						
Conv	1000	3100	5200	10,400	18,200	26,000
Clb Cpe	400	1200	2000	3950	7000	10,000
2 dr Clb Sed	350	750	1200	2350	4900	7000
4 dr Sed	350	750	1250	2350	5000	7100
Sta Wag	550	1800	3000	6000	10,500	15,000
Futuramic Series 98, V-8, 125" wb						
Conv	1000	3100	5200	10,400	18,200	26,000
Holiday	700	2300	3800	7600	13,300	19,000
Clb Sed	450	1000	1650	3350	6300	9000
Sed	450	1000	1650	3350	6300	9000

1950

(All factory prices for top-line models)

	6	5	4	3	2	1
Futuramic 76, 6-cyl., 119.5" wb						
Conv	850	2750	4600	9200	16,100	23,000
Holiday	650	2050	3400	6800	11,900	17,000
Clb Cpe	350	800	1450	2750	5600	8000
2 dr Sed	200	675	1050	2250	4350	6200
Clb Sed	350	750	1200	2350	4900	7000
Sed	200	675	1100	2250	4400	6300
Sta Wag	600	1900	3200	6400	11,200	16,000
Futuramic 88, 8-cyl., 119.5" wb						
Conv	1000	3250	5400	10,800	18,900	27,000
DeL Holiday	650	2050	3400	6800	11,900	17,000
DeL Clb Cpe	400	1300	2200	4400	7700	11,000
DeL 2 dr	450	1000	1650	3350	6300	9000
DeL Clb Sed	450	1100	1700	3650	6650	9500
DeL Sed	350	900	1550	3100	6000	8600
DeL Sta Wag	650	2050	3400	6800	11,900	17,000
Futuramic 98, V-8, 122" wb						
DeL Conv	900	2900	4800	9600	16,800	24,000
2 dr HdTp DeL Holiday	600	1900	3200	6400	11,200	16,000
2 dr HdTp Holiday	550	1800	3000	6000	10,500	15,000
2 dr DeL Clb Sed	350	850	1500	2900	5700	8200
4 dr DeL FsBk	350	800	1450	2750	5600	8000
4 dr DeL Sed	350	850	1500	2800	5650	8100
4 dr DeL Town Sed	350	800	1450	2750	5600	8000

Deduct 10 percent for 6-cyl.

830

Standard Catalog of American Cars

1951

	6	5	4	3	2	1
Standard 88, V-8, 119.5" wb						
2 dr Sed	350	900	1550	3050	5900	8500
4 dr Sed	350	900	1550	3100	6000	8600
DeLuxe 88, V-8, 120" wb						
2 dr Sed	350	750	1250	2350	5000	7100
4 dr Sed	350	750	1250	2400	5050	7200
Super 88, V-8, 120" wb						
Conv	900	2900	4800	9600	16,800	24,000
2 dr HdTp Holiday	500	1550	2600	5200	9100	13,000
Clb Cpe	350	800	1350	2700	5500	7900
2 dr Sed	350	750	1250	2400	5100	7300
4 dr Sed	350	750	1300	2400	5200	7400
Series 98, V-8, 122" wb						
Conv	1000	3250	5400	10,800	18,900	27,000
2 dr DeL Holiday HdTp	550	1800	3000	6000	10,500	15,000
2 dr Holiday HdTp	550	1700	2800	5600	9800	14,000
4 dr Sed	350	750	1350	2650	5450	7800

1952

	6	5	4	3	2	1
DeLuxe 88, V-8, 120" wb						
2 dr Sed	350	750	1250	2350	5000	7100
4 dr Sed	350	750	1250	2400	5050	7200
Super 88, V-8, 120" wb						
Conv	950	3000	5000	10,000	17,500	25,000
2 dr Holiday HdTp	500	1550	2600	5200	9100	13,000
Clb Cpe	350	800	1450	2750	5600	8000
2 dr Sed	350	750	1250	2400	5100	7300
4 dr Sed	350	750	1300	2400	5200	7400
Classic 98, V-8, 124" wb						
Conv	1100	3500	5800	11,600	20,300	29,000
2 dr Holiday HdTp	550	1800	3000	6000	10,500	15,000
4 dr Sed	350	750	1350	2650	5450	7800

1953

	6	5	4	3	2	1
Series 88, V-8, 120" wb						
2 dr Sed	350	700	1100	2300	4500	6400
4 dr Sed	350	700	1150	2300	4550	6500
Conv	1000	3250	5400	10,800	18,900	27,000
2 dr Holiday HdTp	600	1900	3200	6400	11,200	16,000
2 dr Sed	350	700	1150	2300	4550	6500
4 dr Sed	350	700	1150	2300	4600	6600
Series Super 88, V-8, 120" wb						
Classic 98, V-8, 124" wb						
Conv	1150	3600	6000	12,000	21,000	30,000
2 dr Holiday HdTp	700	2150	3600	7200	12,600	18,000
4 dr Sed	350	800	1450	2750	5600	8000
Fiesta 98, V-8, 124" wb						
Conv	1700	5400	9000	18,000	31,500	45,000

1954

	6	5	4	3	2	1
Series 88, V-8, 122" wb						
2 dr Holiday HdTp	600	1900	3200	6400	11,200	16,000
2 dr Sed	350	750	1250	2350	5000	7100
4 dr Sed	350	750	1200	2350	4900	7000
Series Super 88, V-8, 122" wb						
Conv	1100	3500	5800	11,600	20,300	29,000
2 dr Holiday HdTp	700	2150	3600	7200	12,600	18,000
2 dr Sed	350	750	1300	2500	5300	7600
4 dr Sed	350	750	1300	2450	5250	7500
Classic 98, V-8, 126" wb						
Starfire Conv	1400	4450	7400	14,800	25,900	37,000
2 dr DeL Holiday HdTp	900	2900	4800	9600	16,800	24,000
2 dr Holiday HdTp	850	2650	4400	8800	15,400	22,000
4 dr Sed	400	1200	2000	3950	7000	10,000

1955

	6	5	4	3	2	1
Series 88, V-8, 122" wb						
2 dr DeL Holiday HdTp	500	1550	2600	5200	9100	13,000
4 dr Holiday HdTp	400	1200	2000	3950	7000	10,000
2 dr Sed	350	750	1250	2350	5000	7100
4 dr Sed	350	750	1200	2350	4900	7000
Series Super 88, V-8, 122" wb						
Conv	1000	3250	5400	10,800	18,900	27,000
2 dr DeL Holiday HdTp	600	1900	3200	6400	11,200	16,000
4 dr Holiday HdTp	400	1250	2100	4200	7400	10,500
2 dr Sed	350	750	1300	2500	5300	7600
4 dr Sed	350	750	1300	2450	5250	7500
Classic 98, V-8, 126" wb						
Starfire Conv	1300	4200	7000	14,000	24,500	35,000
2 dr DeL Holiday HdTp	800	2500	4200	8400	14,700	21,000
4 dr DeL Holiday HdTp	450	1450	2400	4800	8400	12,000
4 dr Sed	400	1200	2000	3950	7000	10,000

1956

	6	5	4	3	2	1
Series 88, V-8, 122" wb						
2 dr Holiday HdTp	500	1600	2700	5400	9500	13,500
4 dr Holiday HdTp	400	1250	2100	4200	7400	10,500
2 dr Sed	350	750	1250	2400	5100	7300
4 dr Sed	350	750	1250	2400	5050	7200
Series Super 88, V-8, 122" wb						
Conv	1050	3350	5600	11,200	19,600	28,000
2 dr Holiday HdTp	600	1900	3200	6400	11,200	16,000
4 dr Holiday HdTp	400	1300	2200	4400	7700	11,000
2 dr Sed	450	1100	1700	3650	6650	9500
4 dr Sed	350	800	1450	2750	5600	8000
Series 98, V-8, 126" wb						
Starfire Conv	1350	4300	7200	14,400	25,200	36,000
2 dr DeL Holiday HdTp	750	2400	4000	8000	14,000	20,000
4 dr DeL Holiday HdTp	500	1550	2600	5200	9100	13,000
4 dr Sed	400	1250	2100	4200	7400	10,500

1957

(Add 10 percent for J-2 option).

	6	5	4	3	2	1
Series 88, V-8, 122" wb						
Conv	1100	3500	5800	11,600	20,300	29,000
2 dr Holiday HdTp	550	1800	3000	6000	10,500	15,000
4 dr Holiday HdTp	400	1250	2100	4200	7400	10,500
2 dr Sed	350	850	1500	2800	5650	8100
4 dr Sed	350	800	1450	2750	5600	8000
4 dr HdTp Wag	450	1450	2400	4800	8400	12,000
4 dr Sta Wag	400	1200	2000	3950	7000	10,000
Series Super 88, V-8, 122" wb						
Conv	1300	4100	6800	13,600	23,800	34,000
2 dr Holiday HdTp	700	2150	3600	7200	12,600	18,000
4 dr Holiday HdTp	450	1450	2400	4800	8400	12,000
2 dr Sed	450	1000	1650	3350	6300	9000
4 dr Sed	350	950	1600	3200	6050	8700
4 dr HdTp Wag	550	1700	2800	5600	9800	14,000
Series 98, V-8, 126" wb						
Starfire Conv	1400	4450	7400	14,800	25,900	37,000
2 dr Holiday HdTp	750	2400	4000	8000	14,000	20,000
4 dr Holiday HdTp	550	1700	2800	5600	9800	14,000
4 dr Sed	400	1250	2100	4200	7400	10,500

1958

NOTE: Add 10 percent for J-2 option.

	6	5	4	3	2	1
Series 88, V-8, 122.5" wb						
Conv	750	2400	4000	8000	14,000	20,000
2 dr Holiday HdTp	550	1700	2800	5600	9800	14,000
4 dr Holiday HdTp	450	1100	1700	3650	6650	9500
2 dr Sed	350	750	1300	2450	5250	7500
4 dr Sed	350	750	1300	2400	5200	7400
4 dr HdTp Wag	450	1450	2400	4800	8400	12,000
4 dr Sta Wag	450	1000	1650	3350	6300	9000
Series Super 88, V-8, 122.5" wb						
Conv	1000	3100	5200	10,400	18,200	26,000
2 dr Holiday HdTp	550	1700	2800	5600	9800	14,000
4 dr Holiday HdTp	400	1300	2200	4400	7700	11,000
4 dr Sed	350	800	1450	2750	5600	8000
4 dr HdTp Wag	450	1450	2400	4800	8400	12,000
Series 98, V-8, 126.5" wb						
Conv	1200	3850	6400	12,800	22,400	32,000
2 dr Holiday HdTp	700	2300	3800	7600	13,300	19,000
4 dr Holiday HdTp	450	1400	2300	4600	8100	11,500
4 dr Sed	450	1100	1700	3650	6650	9500

1959

(Add 10 percent for hp option).

	6	5	4	3	2	1
Series 88, V-8, 123" wb						
Conv	850	2650	4400	8800	15,400	22,000
2 dr Holiday HdTp	400	1250	2100	4200	7400	10,500
4 dr Holiday HdTp	450	1000	1650	3350	6300	9000
4 dr Sed	200	650	1050	2250	4200	6000
Sta Wag	200	675	1050	2250	4350	6200
Series Super 88, V-8, 123" wb						
Conv	950	3000	5000	10,000	17,500	25,000
2 dr Holiday HdTp	450	1400	2300	4600	8100	11,500
4 dr Holiday HdTp	400	1200	2000	3950	7000	10,000
4 dr Sed	350	750	1200	2350	4900	7000
Sta Wag	350	725	1150	2300	4700	6700
Series 98, V-8, 126.3" wb						
Conv	1100	3500	5800	11,600	20,300	29,000
2 dr Holiday HdTp	450	1500	2500	5000	8800	12,500
4 dr Holiday HdTp	400	1300	2200	4400	7700	11,000
4 dr Sed	450	1000	1650	3350	6300	9000

1960

	6	5	4	3	2	1
Series 88, V-8, 123" wb						
Conv	850	2650	4400	8800	15,400	22,000
2 dr Holiday HdTp	400	1250	2100	4200	7400	10,500
4 dr Holiday HdTp	350	900	1550	3050	5900	8500
4 dr Sed	200	650	1050	2250	4200	6000
Sta Wag	200	675	1050	2250	4350	6200
Series Super 88, V-8, 123" wb						
Conv	950	3000	5000	10,000	17,500	25,000
2 dr Holiday HdTp	450	1400	2300	4600	8100	11,500
4 dr Holiday HdTp	450	1100	1700	3650	6650	9500
4 dr Sed	350	750	1200	2350	4900	7000
Wagon	350	750	1250	2400	5050	7200
Series 98, V-8, 126.3" wb						
Conv	1000	3250	5400	10,800	18,900	27,000
2 dr Holiday HdTp	450	1500	2500	5000	8800	12,500
4 dr Holiday HdTp	400	1250	2100	4200	7400	10,500
4 dr Sed	350	900	1550	3050	5900	8500

1961

Deduct 10 percent for std. line values; add 10 percent for Cutlass.
(All factory prices for top-line models).

	6	5	4	3	2	1
F-85, V-8, 112" wb						
4 dr Sed	150	400	750	1600	3100	4400
Clb Cpe	200	600	950	2150	3850	5500
Sta Wag	150	400	750	1650	3150	4500
Dynamic 88, V-8, 123" wb						
4 dr Sed	200	600	950	2150	3850	5500
4 dr Holiday HdTp	350	750	1200	2350	4900	7000
2 dr Sed	200	550	900	2150	3800	5400
2 dr Holiday HdTp	350	900	1550	3050	5900	8500
Conv	700	2300	3800	7600	13,300	19,000
Sta Wag	350	700	1150	2300	4550	6500
Super 88, V-8, 123" wb						
4 dr Sed	200	650	1050	2250	4200	6000
4 dr Holiday HdTp	350	800	1450	2750	5600	8000
2 dr Holiday HdTp	450	1100	1700	3650	6650	9500
Conv	750	2400	4000	8000	14,000	20,000
Sta Wag	350	750	1200	2350	4900	7000
Starfire Conv	1150	3600	6000	12,000	21,000	30,000
Series 98, V-8, 126" wb						
4 dr Twn Sed	350	900	1550	3050	5900	8500
4 dr Spt Sed	350	950	1600	3200	6050	8700
4 dr Holiday HdTp	450	1000	1650	3350	6300	9000
2 dr Holiday HdTp	400	1250	2100	4200	7400	10,500
Conv	850	2750	4600	9200	16,100	23,000

1962

	6	5	4	3	2	1
F-85 Series, V-8, 112" wb						
4 dr Sed	150	400	750	1650	3150	4500
Cutlass Cpe	200	650	1050	2250	4200	6000
Cutlass Conv	350	800	1450	2750	5600	8000
Sta Wag	200	500	850	1900	3500	5000
Jetfire Turbo-charged, V-8, 112" wb						
2 dr HdTp	450	1000	1650	3350	6300	9000
Dynamic 88, V-8, 123" wb						
4 dr Sed	200	600	950	2150	3850	5500
4 dr Holiday HdTp	350	750	1200	2350	4900	7000
2 dr Holiday HdTp	450	1000	1650	3350	6300	9000
Conv	700	2150	3600	7200	12,600	18,000
Sta Wag	200	650	1050	2250	4200	6000
Super 88, V-8, 123" wb						
4 dr Sed	200	650	1050	2250	4200	6000
4 dr Holiday HdTp	350	800	1450	2750	5600	8000
2 dr Holiday HdTp	400	1200	2000	3950	7000	10,000
Sta Wag	350	700	1150	2300	4550	6500
Starfire, 345 hp V-8, 123" wb						
2 dr HdTp	650	2050	3400	6800	11,900	17,000
Conv	1050	3350	5600	11,200	19,600	28,000
Series 98, V-8, 126" wb						
4 dr Twn Sed	350	750	1300	2450	5250	7500
4 dr Spt Sed	350	750	1350	2600	5400	7700

	6	5	4	3	2	1
4 dr Holiday HdTp	450	1000	1650	3350	6300	9000
2 dr Holiday Spt HdTp	400	1300	2200	4400	7700	11,000
Conv	850	2750	4600	9200	16,100	23,000

1963

	6	5	4	3	2	1
F-85 Series, V-8, 112" wb						
4 dr Sed	200	500	850	1900	3500	5000
Cutlass Cpe	200	650	1050	2250	4200	6000
Cutlass Conv	450	1000	1650	3350	6300	9000
Sta Wag	200	600	950	2150	3850	5500
Jetfire Series, V-8, 112" wb						
2 dr HdTp	350	950	1600	3200	6050	8700
Dynamic 88, V-8, 123" wb						
4 dr Sed	200	650	1050	2250	4200	6000
4 dr Holiday HdTp	350	700	1150	2300	4550	6500
2 dr Holiday HdTp	450	1000	1650	3350	6300	9000
Conv	500	1550	2600	5200	9100	13,000
Sta Wag	200	675	1050	2250	4350	6200
Super 88, V-8, 123" wb						
4 dr Sed	350	700	1150	2300	4550	6500
4 dr Holiday HdTp	350	750	1300	2450	5250	7500
2 dr Holiday HdTp	400	1200	2000	3950	7000	10,000
Sta Wag	350	725	1150	2300	4700	6700
Starfire, V-8, 123" wb						
Cpe	600	1900	3200	6400	11,200	16,000
Conv	1000	3100	5200	10,400	18,200	26,000
Series 98, V-8, 126" wb						
4 dr Sed	350	750	1200	2350	4900	7000
4 dr 4W Holiday HdTp	350	900	1550	3050	5900	8500
4 dr 6W Holiday HdTp	350	750	1350	2600	5400	7700
2 dr Holiday HdTp	400	1300	2200	4400	7700	11,000
2 dr Spt HdTp	400	1300	2200	4400	7700	11,000
Conv	850	2650	4400	8800	15,400	22,000

1964

	6	5	4	3	2	1
F-85 Series, V-8, 115" wb						
4 dr Sed	150	450	800	1750	3250	4700
Sta Wag	200	500	850	1900	3500	5000
Cutlass 3200, V-8						
Spt Cpe	200	600	950	2150	3850	5500
2 dr HdTp	350	700	1150	2300	4550	6500
Conv	400	1200	2000	3950	7000	10,000
Cutlass 4-4-2						
2 dr Sed	350	700	1150	2300	4600	6600
2 dr HdTp	350	750	1350	2650	5450	7800
Conv	400	1300	2200	4400	7700	11,000
Vista Cruiser, V-8, 120" wb						
Sta Wag	200	600	950	2150	3850	5500
Cus Wag	200	600	1000	2200	4000	5700
Jetstar, V-8, 123" wb						
4 dr Sed	200	650	1050	2250	4200	6000
4 dr HdTp	350	700	1150	2300	4550	6500
2 dr HdTp	350	800	1450	2750	5600	8000
Conv	650	2050	3400	6800	11,900	17,000
Jetstar I, V-8, 123" wb						
HdTp Cpe	400	1300	2200	4400	7700	11,000
Dynamic 88, V-8, 123" wb						
4 dr Sed	350	700	1150	2300	4550	6500
4 dr HdTp	350	750	1200	2350	4900	7000
2 dr HdTp	350	800	1450	2750	5600	8000
Conv	650	2100	3500	7000	12,300	17,500
Sta Wag	350	700	1150	2300	4600	6600
Super 88, V-8, 123" wb						
4 dr Sed	350	750	1200	2350	4900	7000
4 dr HdTp	350	750	1300	2450	5250	7500
Starfire, 123" wb						
2 dr HdTp	550	1800	3000	6000	10,500	15,000
Conv	800	2500	4200	8400	14,700	21,000
Series 98, V-8, 126" wb						
4 dr Sed	350	750	1300	2450	5250	7500
4 dr 6W HdTp	350	800	1450	2750	5600	8000
4 dr 4W HdTp	350	800	1450	2750	5600	8000
2 dr HdTp	400	1200	2000	3950	7000	10,000
Conv	750	2400	4000	8000	14,000	20,000
2 dr Cus Spt HdTp	450	1400	2300	4600	8100	11,500

1965

	6	5	4	3	2	1
F-85 Series, V-8, 115" wb						
4 dr Sed	150	450	750	1700	3200	4600
Cpe	200	500	850	1900	3500	5000
Sta Wag	150	450	800	1750	3250	4700
DeL Sed	150	450	800	1750	3250	4700
DeL Wag	200	500	850	1900	3500	5000
Cutlass Series, V-8, 115" wb						
Cpe	350	700	1150	2300	4550	6500
2 dr HdTp	350	750	1200	2350	4900	7000
Conv	350	950	1600	3200	6050	8700
Cutlass 4-4-2						
2 dr Sed	350	750	1350	2650	5450	7800
2 dr HdTp	350	900	1550	3000	5850	8400
Conv	450	1450	2400	4800	8400	12,000
Vista Cruiser, V-8, 120" wb						
Sta Wag	200	600	950	2150	3850	5500
Jetstar Series, V-8, 123" wb						
4 dr Sed	200	500	850	1950	3600	5100
4 dr HdTp	200	600	950	2150	3850	5500
2 dr HdTp	350	700	1150	2300	4550	6500
Conv	400	1200	2000	3950	7000	10,000
Dynamic 88, V-8, 123" wb						
4 dr Sed	200	600	950	2150	3850	5500
4 dr HdTp	200	650	1000	2200	4150	5900
2 dr HdTp	350	750	1200	2350	4900	7000
Conv	400	1300	2200	4400	7700	11,000
Delta 88, V-8, 123" wb						
4 dr Sed	200	600	950	2200	3900	5600
4 dr HdTp	200	650	1050	2250	4200	6000
2 dr HdTp	350	750	1300	2450	5250	7500
Jetstar I, V-8, 123" wb						
2 dr HdTp	450	1000	1650	3350	6300	9000
Starfire, 123" wb						
2 dr HdTp	400	1300	2200	4400	7700	11,000
Conv	550	1800	3000	6000	10,500	15,000
Series 98, V-8, 126" wb						
4 dr Twn Sed	200	650	1000	2200	4150	5900
4 dr Lux Sed	200	675	1050	2250	4300	6100
4 dr HdTp	350	700	1150	2300	4550	6500
2 dr HdTp	350	800	1450	2750	5600	8000
Conv	550	1800	3000	6000	10,500	15,000

1966

	6	5	4	3	2	1
F-85 Series, Standard V-8, 115" wb						
4 dr Sed	150	450	750	1700	3200	4600
Cpe	200	500	850	1900	3500	5000
Sta Wag	200	500	850	1900	3500	5000
F-85 Series, Deluxe, V-8, 115" wb						
4 dr Sed	150	450	800	1750	3250	4700
4 dr HdTp	200	500	850	1900	3500	5000
2 dr HdTp	200	600	950	2150	3850	5500
Sta Wag	200	550	900	2000	3600	5200
Cutlass, V-8, 115" wb						
4 dr Sed	150	450	800	1800	3300	4800
4 dr HdTp	200	500	850	1900	3500	5000
Cpe	200	500	850	1950	3600	5100
2 dr HdTp	350	700	1150	2300	4550	6500
Conv	400	1250	2100	4200	7400	10,500
Cutlass 4-4-2						
2 dr Sed	200	675	1050	2250	4300	6100
2 dr HdTp	350	750	1350	2650	5450	7800
Conv	450	1450	2400	4800	8400	12,000

NOTE: Add 10 percent for triple two-barrel carbs.
Add 30 percent for W-30.
Add 10 percent for tri power.

	6	5	4	3	2	1
Sta Was 3S	200	600	950	2150	3850	5500
Sta Wag 2S	200	550	900	2100	3700	5300
Cus Sta Wag 3S	200	600	1000	2200	4000	5700
Cus Sta Wag 2S	200	600	950	2150	3850	5500
Jetstar 88, V-8, 123" wb						
4 dr Sed	200	500	850	1900	3500	5000
4 dr HdTp	200	550	900	2150	3800	5400
2 dr HdTp	350	700	1150	2300	4550	6500
Dynamic 88, V-8, 123" wb						
4 dr Sed	200	550	900	2000	3600	5200
4 dr HdTp	200	600	950	2150	3850	5500
2 dr HdTp	350	725	1200	2350	4800	6800
Conv	400	1200	2000	3950	7000	10,000
Delta 88, V-8, 123" wb						
4 dr Sed	200	600	950	2150	3850	5500
4 dr HdTp	200	650	1050	2250	4200	6000
2 dr HdTp	350	750	1200	2350	4900	7000
Conv	400	1200	2000	3950	7000	10,000
Starfire, V-8, 123" wb						
2 dr HdTp	400	1200	2000	3950	7000	10,000
Ninety-Eight, V-8, 126" wb						
4 dr Twn Sed	200	600	1000	2200	4000	5700
4 dr Lux Sed	200	650	1000	2200	4100	5800
4 dr HdTp	350	700	1150	2300	4550	6500
2 dr HdTp	350	800	1450	2750	5600	8000
Conv	450	1400	2300	4600	8100	11,500
Toronado, FWD V-8, 119" wb						
2 dr Spt HdTp	400	1200	2000	3950	7000	10,000
2 dr Cus HdTp	400	1250	2100	4200	7400	10,500

1967

	6	5	4	3	2	1
F-85 Series, Standard, V-8, 115" wb						
4 dr Sed	150	450	750	1700	3200	4600
Cpe	200	500	850	1900	3500	5000
Sta Wag 2S	150	450	750	1700	3200	4600
Cutlass, V-8, 115" wb						
4 dr Sed	150	450	800	1800	3300	4800
4 dr HdTp	200	500	850	1900	3500	5000
2 dr HdTp	200	650	1050	2250	4200	6000
Conv	450	1100	1700	3650	6650	9500
Sta Wag 2S	200	500	850	1900	3500	5000

NOTE: Deduct 20 percent for 6-cyl.

	6	5	4	3	2	1
Cutlass-Supreme, V-8, 115" wb						
4 dr Sed	200	500	850	1900	3500	5000
4 dr HdTp	200	550	900	2150	3800	5400
Cpe	200	600	950	2200	3900	5600
2 dr HdTp	450	1000	1600	3300	6250	8900
Conv	400	1300	2200	4400	7700	11,000
Cutlass 4-4-2						
2 dr Sed	350	900	1550	3050	5900	8500
2 dr HdTp	450	1450	2400	4800	8400	12,000
Conv	600	1900	3200	6400	11,200	16,000

NOTE: Add 30 percent for W-30.

	6	5	4	3	2	1
Vista Cruiser, V-8, 120" wb						
Sta Wag 3S	200	500	850	1900	3500	5000
Cus Sta Wag 2S	200	550	900	2150	3800	5400
Cus Sta Wag 3S	200	600	1000	2200	4000	5700
Delmont 88, 330 V-8, 123" wb						
4 dr Sed	150	350	750	1350	2800	4000
4 dr HdTp	150	400	750	1600	3100	4400
2 dr HdTp	200	600	950	2150	3850	5500
Delmont 88, 425 V-8, 123" wb						
4 dr Sed	150	400	750	1600	3100	4400
4 dr HdTp	200	500	850	1850	3350	4900
2 dr HdTp	200	650	1050	2250	4200	6000
Conv	400	1200	2000	3950	7000	10,000
Delta 88, V-8, 123" wb						
4 dr Sed	150	450	800	1800	3300	4800
4 dr HdTp	200	550	900	2100	3700	5300
2 dr HdTp	350	700	1150	2300	4550	6500
Conv	450	1400	2300	4600	8100	11,500
Delta 88, Custom V-8, 123" wb						
4 dr HdTp	200	650	1050	2250	4200	6000
2 dr HdTp	350	750	1200	2350	4900	7000
Ninety-Eight, V-8, 126" wb						
4 dr Sed Twn	200	650	1000	2200	4100	5800
4 dr Sed Lux	200	650	1000	2200	4150	5900
4 dr HdTp	350	750	1200	2350	4900	7000
2 dr HdTp	350	750	1300	2450	5250	7500
Conv	450	1500	2500	5000	8800	12,500
Toronado, V-8, 119" wb						
2 dr HdTp	450	1100	1700	3650	6650	9500
2 dr HdTp Custom	400	1200	2000	3950	7000	10,000

NOTE: Add 10 percent for "425" Delmont Series.
Add 30 percent for W-30.

1968

	6	5	4	3	2	1
F-85, V-8, 116" wb, 2 dr 112" wb						
4 dr Sed	150	450	800	1750	3250	4700
Cpe	200	500	850	1900	3500	5000
Cutlass, V-8, 116" wb, 2 dr 112" wb						
4 dr Sed	150	450	800	1800	3300	4800
4 dr HdTp	200	500	850	1850	3350	4900
Cpe S	200	550	900	2000	3600	5200
2 dr HdTp S	350	700	1150	2300	4550	6500

	6	5	4	3	2	1
Conv S	350	900	1550	3050	5900	8500
Sta Wag	200	500	850	1900	3500	5000
Cutlass Supreme, V-8, 116" wb, 2 dr 112" wb						
4 dr Sed	200	500	850	1900	3500	5000
4 dr HdTp	200	550	900	2150	3800	5400
2 dr HdTp	350	750	1300	2450	5250	7500
NOTE: Deduct 5 percent for 6-cyl.						
4-4-2, V-8, 112" wb						
Cpe	450	1000	1650	3350	6300	9000
2 dr HdTp	450	1450	2400	4800	8400	12,000
Conv	650	2050	3400	6800	11,900	17,000
Hurst/Olds						
2 dr HdTp	600	1900	3200	6400	11,200	16,000
2 dr HdTp	550	1700	2800	5600	9800	14,000
Vista Cruiser, V-8, 121" wb						
Sta Wag 2-S	200	550	900	2000	3600	5200
Sta Wag 3-S	200	600	950	2150	3850	5500
Delmont 88, V-8, 123" wb						
4 dr Sed	200	600	950	2150	3850	5500
4 dr HdTp	200	600	1000	2200	4000	5700
2 dr HdTp	350	700	1150	2300	4550	6500
Conv	400	1300	2200	4400	7700	11,000
Delta 88, V-8, 123" wb						
4 dr Sed	200	600	1000	2200	4000	5700
2 dr HdTp	350	750	1200	2350	4900	7000
4 dr HdTp	200	650	1050	2250	4200	6000
Ninety-Eight, V-8, 126" wb						
4 dr Sed	200	650	1050	2250	4200	6000
4 dr Lux Sed	200	675	1050	2250	4350	6200
4 dr HdTp	350	700	1150	2300	4550	6500
2 dr HdTp	350	800	1450	2750	5600	8000
Conv	450	1450	2400	4800	8400	12,000
Toronado, V-8, 119" wb						
Cus Cpe	350	900	1550	3050	5900	8500
NOTE: Add 30 percent for W-30.						
Add 20 percent for 455.						

1969

F-85, V-8, 116" wb, 2 dr 112" wb	6	5	4	3	2	1
Cpe	200	500	850	1900	3500	5000
Cutlass, V-8, 116" wb, 2 dr 112" wb						
4 dr Sed	150	450	750	1700	3200	4600
4 dr HdTp	150	450	800	1800	3300	4800
Sta Wag	150	450	750	1700	3200	4600
Cutlass - S						
Cpe	200	600	950	2150	3850	5500
2 dr HdTp	350	750	1450	2750	5600	8000
Conv	400	1300	2200	4400	7700	11,000
Cutlass Supreme, V-8, 116" wb, 2 dr 112" wb						
4 dr Sed	200	500	850	1950	3600	5100
4 dr HdTp	200	600	950	2150	3850	5500
2 dr HdTp	400	1300	2200	4400	7700	11,000
4-4-2, V-8 112" wb						
Cpe	400	1200	2000	3950	7000	10,000
2 dr HdTp	500	1550	2600	5200	9100	13,000
Conv	700	2150	3600	7200	12,600	18,000
Hurst/Olds						
2 dr HdTp	650	2050	3400	6800	11,900	17,000
Vista Cruiser						
Sta Wag 2-S	200	550	900	2000	3600	5200
Sta Wag 3-S	200	550	900	2100	3700	5300
Delta 88, V-8, 124" wb						
4 dr Sed	200	650	1050	2250	4200	5700
Conv	400	1200	2000	3950	7000	10,000
4 dr HdTp	350	700	1150	2300	4550	6500
2 dr HdTp	350	750	1200	2350	4900	7000
Delta 88 Custom, V-8, 124" wb						
4 dr Sed	200	650	1000	2200	4100	5800
4 dr HdTp	350	750	1200	2350	4900	7000
2 dr HdTp	350	750	1300	2450	5250	7500
Delta 88 Royale, V-8, 124" wb						
2 dr HdTp	350	750	1350	2600	5400	7700
Ninety Eight, V-8, 127" wb						
4 dr Sed	350	700	1150	2300	4550	6500
4 dr Lux Sed	350	700	1150	2300	4600	6600
4 dr Lux HdTp	350	750	1300	2500	5300	7600
4 dr HdTp	350	750	1300	2450	5250	7500
2 dr HdTp	350	800	1450	2750	5600	8000
Conv	450	1450	2400	4800	8400	12,000
Cus Cpe	350	750	1350	2600	5400	7700
Toronado, V-8, 119" wb						
2 dr HdTp	350	900	1550	3050	5900	8500
NOTE: Add 30 percent for W-30.						
Add 20 percent for 455.						

1970

F-85, V-8, 116" wb, 2 dr 112" wb	6	5	4	3	2	1
Cpe	200	600	950	2150	3850	5500
Cutlass, V-8, 116" wb, 2 dr 112" wb						
4 dr Sed	200	500	850	1900	3500	5000
4 dr HdTp	200	600	950	2150	3850	5500
Sta Wag	200	550	900	2000	3600	5200
NOTE: Deduct 5 percent for 6-cyl.						
Cutlass-S, V-8, 112" wb						
Cpe	350	750	1200	2350	4900	7000
2 dr HdTp	450	1100	1700	3650	6650	9500
NOTE: Add 25 percent for W45-W30-W31.						
Cutlass-Supreme, V-8, 112" wb						
4 dr HdTp	200	600	950	2150	3850	5500
2 dr HdTp	450	1400	2300	4600	8100	11,500
Conv	650	2050	3400	6800	11,900	17,000
442, V-8, 112" wb						
Cpe	450	1450	2400	4800	8400	12,000
2 dr HdTp	650	2050	3400	6800	11,900	17,000
Conv	750	2400	4000	8000	14,000	20,000
Vista Cruiser, V-8, 121" wb						
Sta Wag 2-S	200	550	900	2000	3600	5200
Sta Wag 3-S	200	550	900	2100	3700	5300
Delta 88, V-8, 124" wb						
4 dr Sed	200	550	900	2100	3700	5300
4 dr HdTp	200	600	950	2150	3850	5500
2 dr HdTp	200	650	1050	2250	4200	6000
Conv	400	1200	2000	3950	7000	10,000
Delta 88 Custom, V-8, 124" wb						
4 dr Sed	200	600	950	2150	3850	5500
4 dr HdTp	200	600	950	2200	3900	5600
2 dr HdTp	350	700	1150	2300	4550	6500

Delta 88 Royale, V-8, 124" wb	6	5	4	3	2	1
2 dr HdTp	350	750	1200	2350	4900	7000
Ninety Eight, V-8, 127" wb						
4 dr Sed	200	600	950	2200	3900	5600
4 dr Lux Sed	200	650	1000	2200	4100	5800
4 dr Lux HdTp	200	675	1050	2250	4300	6100
4 dr HdTp	200	650	1050	2250	4200	6000
2 dr HdTp	350	750	1200	2350	4900	7000
Conv	400	1300	2200	4400	7700	11,000
Toronado, V-8, 119" wb						
Std Cpe	350	900	1550	3050	5900	8500
Cus Cpe	450	1000	1650	3350	6300	9000
NOTE: Add 20 percent for SX Cutlass Supreme option.						
Add 35 percent for Y-74 Indy Pace Car option.						
Add 30 percent for W-30.						
Add 20 percent for 455.						
Add 15 percent for Toronado GT W-34 option.						

1971

F-85, V-8, 116" wb	6	5	4	3	2	1
4 dr Sed	125	250	700	1150	2400	3400
Cutlass, V-8, 116" wb, 2 dr 112" wb						
4 dr Sed	125	250	700	1150	2450	3500
2 dr HdTp	350	700	1150	2300	4550	6500
Sta Wag	125	250	700	1150	2400	3400
Cutlass-S, V-8, 112" wb						
Cpe	200	650	1050	2250	4200	6000
2 dr HdTp	350	800	1450	2750	5600	8000
NOTE: Deduct 5 percent for 6 cyl.						
Cutlass Supreme, V-8, 116" wb, 2 dr 112" wb						
4 dr Sed	150	450	750	1700	3200	4600
2 dr HdTp	400	1200	2000	3950	7000	10,000
Conv	700	2150	3600	7200	12,600	18,000
NOTE: Add 15 percent for SX Cutlass Supreme option.						
4-4-2, V-8, 112" wb						
2 dr HdTp	650	2050	3400	6800	11,900	17,000
Conv	800	2500	4200	8400	14,700	21,000
Vista Cruiser, 121" wb						
Sta Wag 2-S	125	250	700	1150	2450	3500
Sta Wag 3-S	125	250	700	1150	2500	3600
Delta 88, V-8, 124" wb						
4 dr Sed	125	250	700	1150	2450	3500
4 dr HdTp	150	350	750	1350	2800	4000
2 dr HdTp	150	400	750	1650	3150	4500
Delta 88 Custom V-8, 124" wb						
4 dr Sed	125	250	700	1150	2500	3600
4 dr HdTp	150	350	750	1450	3000	4200
2 dr HdTp	150	450	800	1750	3250	4700
Delta 88 Royale, V-8, 124" wb						
2 dr HdTp	200	500	850	1900	3500	5000
Conv	350	900	1550	3050	5900	8500
Ninety Eight, V-8, 127" wb						
2 dr HdTp	200	600	950	2150	3850	5500
4 dr HdTp	150	400	750	1650	3150	4500
4 dr Lux HdTp	150	450	800	1750	3250	4700
2 dr Lux HdTp	200	600	1000	2200	4000	5700
Custom Cruiser, V-8, 127" wb						
Sta Wag 2-S	150	400	750	1650	3150	4500
Sta Wag 3-S	150	400	750	1650	3150	4500
Toronado, 122" wb						
2 dr HdTp	350	750	1200	2350	4900	7000
NOTES: Add 30 percent for W-30.						
Add 20 percent for 455.						

1972

F-85, V-8, 116" wb	6	5	4	3	2	1
4 dr Sed	125	250	700	1150	2400	3400
Cutlass, V-8, 116" wb, 2 dr 112" wb						
4 dr Sed	125	250	700	1150	2450	3500
2 dr HdTp	200	600	950	2150	3850	5500
Sta Wag	125	250	700	1150	2400	3400
Cutlass -S, V-8, 112" wb						
Cpe	200	650	1050	2250	4200	6000
2 dr HdTp	400	1200	2000	3950	7000	10,000
NOTE: Deduct 5 percent for 6-cyl.						
Cutlass Supreme, V-8, 116" wb, 2 dr 112" wb						
4 dr Sed	200	600	950	2150	3850	5500
2 dr HdTp	400	1300	2200	4400	7700	11,000
Conv	700	2150	3600	7200	12,600	18,000
NOTE: Add 40 percent for 442 option.						
Add 20 percent for Hurst option.						
Vista Cruiser, 121" wb						
Sta Wag 2-S	125	250	700	1150	2450	3500
Sta Wag 3-S	125	250	700	1150	2500	3600
Delta 88, V-8, 124" wb						
4 dr Sed	125	200	600	1100	2300	3300
4 dr HdTp	150	350	750	1350	2800	4000
2 dr HdTp	150	400	750	1650	3150	4500
Delta 88 Royale, 124" wb						
4 dr Sed	125	250	700	1150	2400	3400
4 dr HdTp	150	350	750	1450	3000	4200
2 dr HdTp	150	450	800	1750	3250	4700
Conv	350	750	1200	2350	4900	7000
Custom Cruiser, 127" wb						
Sta Wag 2-S	150	350	750	1350	2800	4000
Sta Wag 3-S	150	350	750	1350	2800	4000
Ninety-Eight, 127" wb						
4 dr HdTp	150	350	750	1450	3000	4200
2 dr HdTp	150	400	750	1650	3150	4500
Ninety-Eight Luxury, 127" wb						
4 dr HdTp	150	400	750	1650	3150	4500
2 dr HdTp	200	500	850	1900	3500	5000
Toronado, 122" wb						
2 dr HdTp	350	750	1200	2350	4900	7000
NOTES: Add 30 percent for W-30.						
Add 20 percent for 455.						

1973

Omega, V-8, 111" wb	6	5	4	3	2	1
Sed	125	250	700	1150	2400	3400
Cpe	125	250	700	1150	2500	3600
Hatch	150	300	750	1350	2700	3900
Cutlass, 112" - 116" wb						
2 dr Col HdTp	125	250	700	1150	2500	3600
4 dr Col HdTp	150	300	700	1250	2600	3700
Cutlass S, 112" wb						
Cpe	150	300	750	1350	2700	3900

	6	5	4	3	2	1
Cutlass Supreme, 112" - 116" wb						
2 dr Col HdTp	150	350	750	1350	2800	4000
4 dr Col HdTp	150	300	700	1250	2650	3800
NOTE: Add 10 percent for 442 option.						
Vista Cruiser, 116" wb						
2S Sta Wag	150	300	700	1250	2650	3800
3S Sta Wag	150	300	750	1350	2700	3900
Delta 88, 124" wb						
4 dr Sed	125	200	600	1100	2300	3300
4 dr HdTp	150	350	750	1350	2800	4000
2 dr HdTp	150	400	750	1650	3150	4500
Delta 88 Royale, 124" wb						
4 dr Sed	125	250	700	1150	2400	3400
4 dr HdTp	150	350	750	1450	3000	4200
2 dr HdTp	200	600	1000	2200	4000	5700
Conv	350	750	1200	2350	4900	7000
Custom Cruiser, 127" wb						
3S Sta Wag	150	350	750	1350	2800	4000
2S Sta Wag	150	350	750	1350	2800	4000
3S Roy Wag	150	350	750	1450	3000	4200
2S Roy Wag	150	350	750	1450	3000	4200
Ninety-Eight, 127" wb						
4 dr HdTp	150	350	750	1350	2800	4000
2 dr HdTp	150	350	750	1450	3000	4200
4 dr HdTp Lux	150	400	750	1600	3100	4400
2 dr HdTp Lux	150	450	800	1750	3250	4700
4 dr HdTp Reg	150	400	750	1650	3150	4500
Toronado, 122" wb						
HdTp Cpe	350	700	1150	2300	4550	6500
NOTE: Add 20 percent for Hurst/Olds.						
1974						
Omega, 111" wb						
Cpe	150	300	700	1250	2600	3700
Hatch	150	350	750	1350	2800	4000
4 dr Sed	125	250	700	1150	2450	3500
Cutlass, 112" - 116" wb						
Cpe	125	250	700	1150	2500	3600
4 dr Sed	125	250	700	1150	2450	3500
Cutlass S, 112" wb						
Cpe	125	250	700	1150	2500	3600
Cutlass Supreme, 112" - 116" wb						
4 dr Sed	150	300	700	1250	2600	3700
Cpe	125	250	700	1150	2450	3500
NOTE: Add 10 percent for 442 option.						
Vista Cruiser, 116" wb						
Sta Wag-6P	100	175	525	1050	2100	3000
Sta Wag-8P	125	200	600	1100	2200	3100
Delta 88, 124" wb						
2 dr HdTp	150	350	750	1350	2800	4000
4 dr HdTp	150	300	750	1350	2700	3900
4 dr Sed	125	250	700	1150	2450	3500
Custom Cruiser, 127" wb						
Sta Wag-6P	150	300	700	1250	2650	3800
Sta Wag-8P	150	300	700	1250	2650	3800
Delta 88 Royale, 124" wb						
2 dr HdTp	150	350	750	1450	3000	4200
4 dr HdTp	150	350	750	1450	2900	4100
4 dr Sed	125	250	700	1150	2500	3600
Conv	350	750	1200	2350	4900	7000
NOTE: Add 20 percent for Indy Pace car.						
Ninety-Eight, 127" wb						
4 dr HdTp	150	350	750	1450	3000	4200
2 dr HdTp Lux	150	400	750	1650	3150	4500
4 dr HdTp Lux	150	400	750	1600	3100	4400
2 dr HdTp Reg	150	400	750	1650	3150	4500
4 dr Reg Sed	150	450	750	1700	3200	4600
Toronado, 122" wb						
2 dr Cpe	350	700	1150	2300	4550	6500
1975						
Starfire, 97" wb						
Cpe 'S'	125	200	600	1100	2200	3100
Cpe	125	200	600	1100	2250	3200
Omega, 111" wb						
Cpe	125	200	600	1100	2200	3100
Hatch	125	250	700	1150	2450	3500
4 dr Sed	125	200	600	1100	2250	3200
Omega Salon, 111" wb						
Cpe	125	250	700	1150	2400	3400
Hatch	125	250	700	1150	2500	3600
4 dr Sed	125	250	700	1150	2450	3500
Cutlass, 112" - 116" wb						
Cpe	125	200	600	1100	2300	3300
4 dr Sed	125	200	600	1100	2250	3200
Cpe 'S'	125	200	600	1100	2300	3300
Cutlass Supreme, 112" - 116" wb						
Cpe	125	250	700	1150	2400	3400
4 dr Sed	125	250	700	1150	2450	3500
Cutlass Salon, 112" - 116" wb						
Cpe	125	250	700	1150	2450	3500
4 dr Sed	125	250	700	1150	2500	3600
NOTE: Add 10 percent for 442 option.						
Vista Cruiser, 116" wb						
Sta Wag	125	250	700	1150	2400	3400
Delta 88, 124" wb						
Cpe	125	250	700	1150	2450	3500
4 dr Twn Sed	125	200	600	1100	2200	3100
4 dr HdTp	150	350	750	1350	2800	4000
Delta 88 Royale, 124" wb						
Cpe	125	250	700	1150	2500	3600
4 dr Twn Sed	125	200	600	1100	2250	3200
4 dr HdTp	150	350	750	1450	3000	4200
Conv	350	750	1200	2350	4900	7000
Ninety-Eight, 127" wb						
2 dr Lux Cpe	150	450	800	1800	3300	4800
4 dr HdTp Lux	150	400	750	1650	3150	4500
2 dr Reg Cpe	200	500	850	1850	3350	4900
4 dr HdTp Reg	150	450	800	1750	3250	4700
Toronado, 122" wb						
Cus Cpe	200	650	1050	2250	4200	6000
Brm Cpe	350	700	1150	2300	4550	6500
Custom Cruiser, 127" wb						
Sta Wag	125	250	700	1150	2500	3600
NOTE: Add 20 percent for Hurst/Olds.						

PACKARD

	6	5	4	3	2	1
1946 21st Series						
Clipper, 6-cyl., 120" wb, 2100						
Clb Sed	400	1300	2200	4400	7700	11,000
Sed	450	1450	2400	4800	8400	12,000
Clipper, 6-cyl., 120" wb, 2130						
4 dr Taxi				value not estimable		
Clipper, 8-cyl., 120" wb, 2101						
Tr Sed	450	1450	2400	4800	8400	12,000
Clipper, DeLuxe, 8-cyl., 120" wb, 2111						
Clb Sed	500	1550	2600	5200	9100	13,000
Tr Sed	550	1700	2800	5600	9800	14,000
Clipper, Super 8, 127" wb, 2103						
Clb Sed	550	1700	2800	5600	9800	14,000
Tr Sed	550	1800	3000	6000	10,500	15,000
Clipper, Super 8, 127" wb, 2106 Custom						
Clb Sed	600	1900	3200	6400	11,200	16,000
Tr Sed	650	2050	3400	6800	11,900	17,000
Clipper, Super, 148" wb, 2126 Custom						
8P Sed	900	2900	4800	9600	16,800	24,000
Limo	1100	3500	5800	11,600	20,300	29,000
1947 21st Series						
Clipper, 6-cyl., 120" wb, 2100						
Clb Sed	400	1300	2200	4400	7700	11,000
Tr Sed	450	1450	2400	4800	8400	12,000
Clipper, DeLuxe, 8-cyl., 120" wb, 2111						
Clb Sed	450	1450	2400	4800	8400	12,000
Tr Sed	500	1550	2600	5200	9100	13,000
Clipper, Super 8, 127" wb, 2103						
Clb Sed	500	1550	2600	5200	9100	13,000
Tr Sed	550	1700	2800	5600	9800	14,000
Clipper, Super 8, 127" wb, 2106 Custom						
Clb Sed	600	1900	3200	6400	11,200	16,000
Tr Sed	650	2050	3400	6800	11,900	17,000
Clipper, Super 8, 148" wb, 2126 Custom						
7P Sed	900	2900	4800	9600	16,800	24,000
Limo	1100	3500	5800	11,600	20,300	29,000
1948 & Early 1949 22nd Series						
Series 2201, 8-cyl., 120" wb						
Clb Sed	400	1300	2200	4400	7700	11,000
Sed	450	1450	2400	4800	8400	12,000
Sta Wag	1300	4100	6800	13,600	23,800	34,000
Series 2211, DeLuxe, 8-cyl., 120" wb						
Clb Sed	450	1450	2400	4800	8400	12,000
Tr Sed	500	1550	2600	5200	9100	13,000
Super 8, 120" wb, 2202						
Clb Sed	550	1700	2800	5600	9800	14,000
Sed	550	1800	3000	6000	10,500	15,000
Super 8, 120" wb, 2232						
Conv	1300	4200	7000	14,000	24,500	35,000
Super 8, 141" wb, 2222						
Sed	850	2750	4600	9200	16,100	23,000
Limo	1050	3350	5600	11,200	19,600	28,000
Super 8, DeLuxe, 141" wb						
Sed	900	2900	4800	9600	16,800	24,000
Limo	1100	3500	5800	11,600	20,300	29,000
Custom 8, 127" wb, 2206						
Clb Sed	700	2300	3800	7600	13,300	19,000
Tr Sed	750	2400	4000	8000	14,000	20,000
Custom 8, 127" wb, 2233						
Conv	1450	4550	7600	15,200	26,600	38,000
Custom 8, 148" wb, 2226						
7P Sed	1100	3500	5800	11,600	20,300	29,000
Limo	1150	3600	6000	12,000	21,000	30,000
1949-1950 23rd Series						
Series 2301, 120" wb						
Clb Sed	550	1700	2800	5600	9800	14,000
Sed	550	1750	2900	5800	10,200	14,500
Sta Wag	1200	3850	6400	12,800	22,400	32,000
2301 DeLuxe, 120" wb						
Clb Sed	550	1800	3000	6000	10,500	15,000
Sed	600	1850	3100	6200	10,900	15,500
Super 8, 127" wb, 2302						
Clb Sed	600	1900	3200	6400	11,200	16,000
Sed	600	2000	3300	6600	11,600	16,500
Super 8, 2302 DeLuxe						
Clb Sed	650	2050	3400	6800	11,900	17,000
Sed	650	2100	3500	7000	12,300	17,500
Super 8, Super DeLuxe, 127" wb, 2332						
Conv	1150	3700	6200	12,400	21,700	31,000
Super 8, 141" wb, 2322						
7P Sed	950	3000	5000	10,000	17,500	25,000
Limo	1150	3600	6000	12,000	21,000	30,000
Custom 8, 127" wb, 2306						
Sed	600	1900	3200	6400	11,200	16,000
Custom 8, 127" wb, 2333						
Conv	1300	4200	7000	14,000	24,500	35,000
1951 24th Series						
200, Standard, 122" wb, 2401						
Bus Cpe	400	1200	2000	3950	7000	10,000
2 dr Sed	400	1250	2100	4200	7400	10,500
Sed	400	1300	2200	4400	7700	11,000
200, DeLuxe						
2 dr Sed	400	1300	2200	4400	7700	11,000
Sed	450	1400	2300	4600	8100	11,500
122" wb, 2402						
M.F HdTp	550	1700	2800	5600	9800	14,000
Conv	750	2400	4000	8000	14,000	20,000
300, 127" wb; 2402						
Sed	450	1450	2400	4800	8400	12,000
Patrician, 400, 127" wb, 2406						
Sed	550	1700	2800	5600	9800	14,000
1952 25th Series						
200, Std., 122" wb, 2501						
2 dr Sed	450	1100	1700	3650	6650	9500
Sed	450	1150	1800	3800	6800	9700
200, DeLuxe						
2 dr Sed	450	1150	1800	3800	6800	9700
Sed	450	1150	1900	3850	6850	9800
122" wb, 2531						
Conv	700	2300	3800	7600	13,300	19,000
M.F HdTp	550	1800	3000	6000	10,500	15,000

	6	5	4	3	2	1
300, 122" wb, 2502						
Sed	450	1400	2300	4600	8100	11,500
Patrician, 400, 127" wb, 2506						
Sed	550	1700	2800	5600	9800	14,000
Der Cus Sed	550	1800	3000	6000	10,500	15,000
1953 26th Series						
Clipper, 122" wb, 2601						
2 dr HdTp	550	1700	2800	5600	9800	14,000
2 dr Sed	400	1200	2000	3950	7000	10,000
Sed	400	1200	2000	4000	7100	10,100
Clipper DeLuxe						
2 dr Sed	400	1300	2200	4400	7700	11,000
Sed	400	1350	2200	4400	7800	11,100
Cavalier, 127" wb, 2602						
Cav Sed	450	1450	2400	4800	8400	12,000
Packard 8, 122" wb, 2631						
Conv	850	2650	4400	8800	15,400	22,000
Carr Conv	1050	3350	5600	11,200	19,600	28,000
M.F HdTp	550	1800	3000	6000	10,500	15,000
Patrician, 127" wb, 2606						
Sed	550	1800	3000	6000	10,500	15,000
Der Fml Sed	650	2050	3400	6800	11,900	17,000
149" wb, 2626						
Exec Sed	600	1900	3200	6400	11,200	16,000
Corp Limo	700	2150	3600	7200	12,600	18,000
1954 54th Series						
Clipper, 122" wb, DeLuxe 5401						
2 dr HdTp	550	1700	2800	5600	9800	14,000
Clb Sed	400	1300	2200	4400	7700	11,000
Sed	400	1350	2200	4400	7800	11,100
Clipper Super 5411						
Pan HdTp	550	1800	3000	6000	10,500	15,000
Clb Sed	450	1450	2400	4800	8400	12,000
Sed	450	1450	2400	4800	8500	12,100
Cavalier, 127" wb, 5402						
Sed	500	1550	2600	5200	9100	13,000
Packard 8, 122" wb, 5431						
Pac HdTp	600	1900	3200	6400	11,200	16,000
Conv	900	2900	4800	9600	16,800	24,000
Carr Conv	1100	3500	5800	11,600	20,300	29,000
Patrician, 127" wb, 5406						
Sed	550	1700	2800	5600	9800	14,000
Der Cus Sed	600	1900	3200	6400	11,200	16,000
149" wb, 5426						
8P Sed	650	2050	3400	6800	11,900	17,000
Limo	700	2150	3600	7200	12,600	18,000
1955 55th Series						
Clipper, DeLuxe, 122" wb, 5540						
Sed	450	1000	1650	3350	6300	9000
Clipper, Super, 5540						
Pan HdTp	500	1550	2600	5200	9100	13,000
Sed	450	1100	1700	3650	6650	9500
Clipper Custom 5560 (352 cid V-8)						
Con HdTp	550	1800	3000	6000	10,500	15,000
Sed	400	1200	2000	3950	7000	10,000
Packard, 400, 127" wb, 5580						
"400" HdTp	750	2400	4000	8000	14,000	20,000
Caribbean 5580						
Conv	1300	4200	7000	14,000	24,500	35,000
Patrician 5580						
Sed	550	1700	2800	5600	9800	14,000
1956 56th Series						
Clipper, DeLuxe, 122" wb, 5640						
Sed	450	1100	1700	3650	6650	9500
Clipper, Super, 5640						
HdTp	550	1700	2800	5600	9800	14,000
Sed	400	1200	2000	3950	7000	10,000
Clipper, Custom, 5660						
Con HdTp	550	1800	3000	6000	10,500	15,000
Sed	400	1300	2200	4400	7700	11,000
Clipper Executive						
HdTp	600	1900	3200	6400	11,200	16,000
Sed	450	1450	2400	4800	8400	12,000
Packard, 400, 127" wb, 5680						
"400" HdTp	750	2400	4000	8000	14,000	20,000
Caribbean, 5688						
Conv	1300	4200	7000	14,000	24,500	35,000
HdTp	1000	3250	5400	10,800	18,900	27,000
Patrician, 5680						
Sed	550	1800	3000	6000	10,500	15,000
1957 57th L Series						
Clipper						
Sed	350	750	1300	2450	5250	7500
Sta Wag	350	750	1300	2400	5200	7400
1958 58th L Series						
HdTp	400	1300	2200	4400	7700	11,000
Sed	350	750	1300	2500	5300	7600
Sta Wag	350	750	1300	2450	5250	7500
Hawk	700	2150	3600	7200	12,600	18,000

PLYMOUTH

	6	5	4	3	2	1
1946						
P15 DeLuxe, 6-cyl., 117" wb						
Cpe	350	950	1600	3200	6050	8700
Clb Cpe	450	1050	1650	3500	6400	9200
2 dr Sed	200	600	950	2150	3850	5500
Sed	200	600	950	2200	3900	5600
P15 Special DeLuxe, 6-cyl., 117" wb						
Conv	750	2400	4000	8000	14,000	20,000
Cpe	450	1000	1650	3350	6300	9000
Clb Cpe	450	1100	1700	3650	6650	9500
2 dr Sed	200	650	1000	2200	4100	5800
Sed	200	650	1050	2250	4200	6000
Sta Wag	600	1900	3200	6400	11,200	16,000
1947						
P15 DeLuxe, 6-cyl., 117" wb						
Cpe	350	900	1550	3050	5900	8500

	6	5	4	3	2	1
Clb Cpe	450	1000	1650	3350	6300	9000
2 dr Sed	200	600	950	2150	3850	5500
Sed	200	600	950	2200	3900	5600
P15 Special DeLuxe, 6-cyl., 117" wb						
Conv	750	2400	4000	8000	14,000	20,000
Cpe	450	1000	1650	3350	6300	9000
Clb Cpe	450	1100	1700	3650	6650	9500
2 dr Sed	200	650	1000	2200	4100	5800
Sed	200	650	1050	2250	4200	6000
Sta Wag	600	1900	3200	6400	11,200	16,000
1948						
P15 DeLuxe, 6-cyl., 117" wb						
Cpe	350	900	1550	3050	5900	8500
Clb Cpe	450	1000	1650	3350	6300	9000
2 dr Sed	200	600	950	2150	3850	5500
Sed	200	600	950	2200	3900	5600
P15 Special DeLuxe, 6-cyl., 117" wb						
Conv	750	2400	4000	8000	14,000	20,000
Cpe	450	1000	1650	3350	6300	9000
Clb Cpe	450	1100	1700	3650	6650	9500
2 dr Sed	200	650	1000	2200	4100	5800
Sed	200	650	1050	2250	4200	6000
Sta Wag	600	1900	3200	6400	11,200	16,000
1949						
First Series values same as 1948						
Second Series						
DeLuxe, 6-cyl., 111" wb						
Cpe	350	900	1550	3050	5900	8500
2 dr Sed	200	675	1050	2250	4300	6100
Sta Wag	350	900	1550	3050	5900	8500
DeLuxe, 6-cyl., 118.5" wb						
Clb Cpe	350	950	1600	3200	6050	8700
Sed	350	700	1150	2300	4550	6500
Special DeLuxe, 6-cyl., 118.5" wb						
Conv	700	2300	3800	7600	13,300	19,000
Clb Cpe	450	1000	1650	3350	6300	9000
Sed	350	725	1200	2350	4800	6800
Sta Wag	500	1550	2600	5200	9100	13,000
1950						
DeLuxe, 6-cyl., 111" wb						
Cpe	350	750	1350	2650	5450	7800
2 dr Sed	200	675	1050	2250	4300	6100
Sta Wag	350	900	1550	3050	5900	8500
DeLuxe, 6-cyl., 118.5" wb						
Clb Cpe	350	800	1450	2750	5600	8000
Sed	200	675	1100	2250	4400	6300
Special DeLuxe, 6-cyl., 118.5" wb						
Conv	700	2300	3800	7600	13,300	19,000
Clb Cpe	350	900	1550	3050	5900	8500
Sed	350	725	1200	2350	4800	6800
Sta Wag	500	1550	2600	5200	9100	13,000
NOTE: Add 5 percent for P-19 Special DeLuxe Suburban.						
1951						
P22 Concord, 6-cyl., 111" wb						
2 dr Sed	200	600	950	2200	3900	5600
Cpe	350	750	1300	2450	5250	7500
Sta Wag	350	750	1300	2450	5250	7500
P23 Cambridge, 6-cyl., 118.5" wb						
Sed	200	650	1000	2200	4150	5900
Clb Cpe	350	800	1450	2750	5600	8000
P23 Cranbrook, 6-cyl., 118.5" wb						
Sed	200	675	1050	2250	4300	6100
Clb Cpe	350	900	1550	3050	5900	8500
HdTp	400	1200	2000	3950	7000	10,000
Conv	700	2150	3600	7200	12,600	18,000
1952						
P22 Concord, 6-cyl., 111" wb						
2 dr Sed	200	600	950	2200	3900	5600
Cpe	350	750	1300	2450	5250	7500
Sta Wag	350	750	1300	2450	5250	7500
P23 Cambridge, 6-cyl., 118.5" wb						
Sed	200	675	1050	2250	4300	6100
Clb Cpe	350	800	1450	2750	5600	8000
P23 Cranbrook, 6-cyl., 118.5" wb						
Sed	350	700	1150	2300	4550	6500
Clb Cpe	350	900	1550	3050	5900	8500
HdTp	400	1200	2050	4100	7100	10,200
Conv	700	2150	3600	7200	12,600	18,000
1953						
P24-1 Cambridge, 6-cyl., 114" wb						
Sed	200	600	1000	2200	4000	5700
2 dr Sed	200	600	950	2200	3900	5600
Bus Cpe	200	650	1000	2200	4100	5800
Sta Wag	200	600	1000	2200	4000	5700
P24-2 Cranbrook, 6-cyl., 114" wb						
Sed	200	650	1050	2250	4200	6000
Clb Cpe	350	700	1150	2300	4550	6500
HdTp	400	1200	2000	3950	7000	10,000
Sta Wag	350	750	1300	2450	5250	7500
Conv	650	2050	3400	6800	11,900	17,000
1954						
P25-1 Plaza, 6-cyl., 114" wb						
4 dr Sed	200	650	1000	2200	4100	5800
2 dr Sed	200	650	1000	2200	4150	5900
Bus Cpe	200	650	1050	2250	4200	6000
Sta Wag	350	750	1250	2400	5050	7200
P25-2 Savoy, 6-cyl., 114" wb						
4 dr Sed	200	650	1050	2250	4200	6000
2 dr Sed	200	675	1050	2250	4300	6100
Clb Cpe	350	700	1150	2300	4550	6500
P25-3 Belvedere, 6-cyl., 114" wb						
4 dr Sed	350	700	1150	2300	4550	6500
2 dr HdTp	450	1450	2400	4800	8400	12,000
Conv	700	2150	3600	7200	12,600	18,000
Sta Wag	350	800	1450	2750	5600	8000
1955						
Plaza, V-8, 115" wb						
4 dr Sed	200	650	1000	2200	4150	5900
2 dr Sed	200	650	1050	2250	4200	6000
2 dr Sta Wag	200	650	1000	2200	4100	5800
4 dr Sta Wag	200	600	1000	2200	4000	5700
Savoy, V-8, 115" wb						
4 dr Sed	200	650	1050	2250	4200	6000
2 dr Sed	200	675	1050	2250	4300	6100
Belvedere, V-8, 115" wb						
4 dr Sed	350	700	1150	2300	4550	6500

	6	5	4	3	2	1
2 dr Sed	350	700	1100	2300	4500	6400
2 dr HdTp	500	1550	2600	5200	9100	13,000
Conv	700	2300	3800	7600	13,300	19,000
Sta Wag	350	750	1300	2450	5250	7500

NOTE: Deduct 10 percent for 6-cyl. models.

1956

	6	5	4	3	2	1
Plaza, V-8, 115" wb						
4 dr Sed	200	650	1000	2200	4150	5900
2 dr Sed	200	650	1050	2250	4200	6000
Bus Cpe	200	600	1000	2200	4000	5700
Savoy, V-8, 115" wb						
4 dr Sed	200	650	1050	2250	4200	6000
2 dr Sed	200	675	1050	2250	4300	6100
2 dr HdTp	400	1250	2100	4200	7400	10,500
Belvedere, V-8, 115" wb (conv. avail. as 8 cyl. only)						
4 dr Sed	350	700	1150	2300	4550	6500
4 dr HdTp	350	800	1450	2750	5600	8000
2 dr Sed	350	700	1150	2300	4550	6500
2 dr HdTp	550	1700	2800	5600	9800	14,000
Conv	700	2300	3800	7600	13,300	19,000
Suburban, V-8, 115" wb						
DeL Sta Wag	200	650	1050	2250	4200	6000
Cus Sta Wag	350	700	1150	2300	4550	6500
4 dr Spt Sta Wag	350	750	1200	2350	4900	7000
Fury, V-8, (avail. as 8-cyl. only)						
2 dr HdTp	700	2150	3600	7200	12,600	18,000

NOTE: Deduct 10 percent for 6-cyl. models.

1957

	6	5	4	3	2	1
Plaza, V-8, 118" wb						
4 dr Sed	200	550	900	2100	3700	5300
2 dr Sed	200	550	900	2000	3600	5200
Bus Cpe	200	500	850	1950	3600	5100
Savoy, V-8						
4 dr Sed	200	550	900	2150	3800	5400
4 dr HdTp	200	650	1050	2250	4200	6000
2 dr Sed	350	700	1100	2300	4500	6400
2 dr HdTp	400	1200	2000	3950	7000	10,000
Belvedere, V-8, 118" wb (conv. avail. as 8-cyl. only)						
4 dr Sed	200	675	1050	2250	4300	6100
4 dr Spt HdTp	350	750	1300	2450	5250	7500
2 dr Sed	200	650	1050	2250	4200	6000
2 dr HdTp	550	1700	2800	5600	9800	14,000
Conv	750	2400	4000	8000	14,000	20,000
Suburban, V-8, 122" wb						
4 dr Cus Sta Wag	200	600	950	2150	3850	5500
2 dr Cus Sta Wag	200	600	950	2200	3900	5600
4 dr Spt Sta Wag	200	600	1000	2200	4000	5700
Fury, V-8, 118" wb (avail. as 8 cyl. only: 290 hp)						
2 dr HdTp	700	2300	3800	7600	13,300	19,000

NOTE: Deduct 10 percent for 6-cyl. model.

1958

	6	5	4	3	2	1
Plaza, V-8, 118" wb						
4 dr Sed	200	550	900	2000	3600	5200
2 dr Sed	200	500	850	1950	3600	5100
Bus Cpe	200	500	850	1900	3500	5000
Savoy, V-8, 118" wb						
4 dr Sed	200	500	850	1950	3600	5100
4 dr HdTp	200	650	1050	2250	4200	6000
2 dr Sed	200	500	850	1950	3600	5100
2 dr HdTp	450	1100	1700	3650	6650	9500
Belvedere, V-8, 118" wb (conv. avail. as 8-cyl. only)						
4 dr Sed	200	600	950	2150	3850	5500
4 dr HdTp	350	700	1150	2300	4550	6500
2 dr Sed	200	550	900	2150	3800	5400
2 dr HdTp	500	1550	2600	5200	9100	13,000
Conv	700	2300	3800	7600	13,300	19,000
Suburban, V-8, 122" wb						
4 dr Cus Sta Wag	200	550	900	2150	3800	5400
2 dr Cus Sta Wag	200	600	950	2150	3850	5500
4 dr Spt Sta Wag	200	600	950	2200	3900	5600
Fury, V-8, 118" wb (avail. as 8-cyl. only)						
2 dr HdTp	650	2050	3400	6800	11,900	17,000

NOTE: Deduct 20 percent for 6-cyl. models.

1959

	6	5	4	3	2	1
Savoy, 6-cyl., 118" wb						
4 dr Sed	200	500	850	1950	3600	5100
2 dr Sed	200	500	850	1900	3500	5000
Belvedere, V-8, 118" wb						
4 dr Sed	200	500	850	1900	3500	5000
4 dr HdTp	200	650	1050	2250	4200	6000
2 dr Sed	200	500	850	1850	3350	4900
2 dr HdTp	450	1100	1700	3650	6650	9500
Conv	500	1550	2600	5200	9100	13,000
Fury, V-8, 118" wb						
4 dr Sed	200	500	850	1900	3500	5000
4 dr HdTp	350	700	1150	2300	4550	6500
2 dr HdTp	400	1200	2000	3950	7000	10,000
Sport Fury, V-8, 118" wb (260 hp - V-8 offered)						
2 dr HdTp	450	1450	2400	4800	8400	12,000
Conv	600	1900	3200	6400	11,200	16,000
Suburban, V-8, 122" wb						
4 dr Spt Sta Wag	200	550	900	2000	3600	5200
2 dr Cus Sta Wag	200	500	850	1950	3600	5100
4 dr Cus Sta Wag	200	500	850	1900	3500	5000

NOTE: Deduct 10 percent for 6-cyl. models.

1960

	6	5	4	3	2	1
Valiant 100, 6-cyl., 106.5" wb						
4 dr Sed	150	450	800	1750	3250	4700
Sta Wag	150	450	800	1800	3300	4800
Valiant 200, 6-cyl., 106" wb						
4 dr Sed	150	450	800	1800	3300	4800
Sta Wag	200	500	850	1850	3350	4900
Fleet Special, V8, 118" wb						
4 dr Sed	150	350	750	1450	3000	4200
2 dr Sed	150	350	750	1450	3000	4200
Savoy, V-8, 118" wb						
4 dr Sed	150	450	800	1750	3250	4700
2 dr Sed	150	450	750	1700	3200	4600
Belvedere, V-8, 118" wb						
4 dr Sed	150	450	800	1800	3300	4800
2 dr Sed	150	450	800	1750	3250	4700
4 dr HdTp	200	600	950	2150	3850	5500
Fury, V-8, 118" wb (conv. avail. as 8-cyl. only)						
4 dr Sed	200	500	850	1900	3500	5000
4 dr HdTp	200	650	1050	2250	4200	6000
2 dr HdTp	400	1200	2000	3950	7000	10,000
Conv	450	1450	2400	4800	8400	12,000
Suburban, V-8, 122" wb						
4 dr DeL Sta Wag	150	450	800	1750	3250	4700
2 dr DeL Sta Wag	150	450	750	1700	3200	4600
4 dr Cus 9P Sta Wag	150	450	800	1750	3250	4700
9P Spt Sta Wag	150	450	800	1800	3300	4800

NOTE: Deduct 20 percent for 6-cyl. model except Valiant.

1961

	6	5	4	3	2	1
Valiant 100, 6-cyl., 106.5" wb						
4 dr Sed	200	500	850	1850	3350	4900
2 dr Sed	150	450	800	1800	3300	4800
Sta Wag	150	450	800	1800	3300	4800
Valiant 200, 6-cyl., 106.5" wb						
4 dr Sed	200	500	850	1900	3500	5000
2 dr HdTp	200	600	950	2150	3850	5500
Sta Wag	150	450	800	1750	3250	4700
Fleet Special, V8, 118" wb						
4 dr Sed	150	450	800	1750	3250	4700
2 dr Sed	150	450	750	1700	3200	4600
Savoy, V-8, 118" wb						
4 dr Sed	150	450	800	1800	3300	4800
2 dr Sed	150	450	800	1750	3250	4700
Belvedere, V-8, 118" wb						
4 dr Sed	150	450	800	1750	3250	4700
Clb Sed	150	450	800	1750	3250	4700
HdTp Cpe	200	600	950	2150	3850	5500
Fury, V-8, 118" wb						
4 dr Sed	200	500	850	1850	3350	4900
4 dr HdTp	200	500	850	1900	3500	5000
2 dr HdTp	350	800	1450	2750	5600	8000
Conv	400	1250	2100	4200	7400	10,500
Suburban, V-8, 122" wb						
4 dr 6P DeL Sta Wag	150	450	800	1750	3250	4700
2 dr 6P DeL Sta Wag	150	450	750	1700	3200	4600
6P Cus Sta Wag	150	450	800	1750	3250	4700
9P Spt Sta Wag	150	450	800	1800	3300	4800

NOTE: Deduct 10 percent for 6-cyl. models.
Add 30 percent for 330, 340, 350, 375 hp engines.

1962

	6	5	4	3	2	1
Valiant 100, 6-cyl., 106.5" wb						
4 dr Sed	150	450	800	1750	3250	4700
2 dr Sed	150	450	750	1700	3200	4600
Sta Wag	150	450	800	1800	3300	4800
Valiant 200, 6-cyl., 106.5" wb						
4 dr Sed	150	450	800	1800	3300	4800
2 dr Sed	150	450	800	1750	3250	4700
Sta Wag	200	500	850	1850	3350	4900
Valiant Signet, 6-cyl., 106.5" wb						
2 dr HdTp	200	550	900	2000	3600	5200
Fleet Special, V8, 116" wb						
4 dr Sed	150	450	750	1700	3200	4600
2 dr Sed	150	400	750	1650	3150	4500
Savoy, V-8, 116" wb						
4 dr Sed	150	450	800	1750	3250	4700
2 dr Sed	150	450	750	1700	3200	4600
Belvedere, V-8, 116" wb						
4 dr Sed	150	450	800	1800	3300	4800
2 dr Sed	150	450	800	1750	3250	4700
2 dr HdTp	200	550	900	2100	3700	5300
Fury, V-8, 116" wb						
4 dr Sed	200	500	850	1850	3350	4900
4 dr HdTp	150	450	800	1800	3300	4800
2 dr HdTp	350	750	1200	2350	4900	7000
Conv	400	1200	2000	3950	7000	10,000
Sport Fury, V-8, 116" wb						
2 dr HdTp	350	750	1300	2450	5250	7500
Conv	400	1250	2100	4200	7400	10,500
Suburban, V-8, 116" wb						
6P Savoy Sta Wag	150	450	800	1750	3250	4700
6P Belv Sta Wag	150	450	800	1800	3300	4800
9P Fury Sta Wag	200	500	850	1850	3350	4900

NOTE: Deduct 10 percent for 6-cyl. models.
Add 30 percent for Golden Comando 410 hp engine.

1963

	6	5	4	3	2	1
Valiant 100, 6-cyl., 106.5" wb						
4 dr Sed	150	350	750	1450	2900	4100
2 dr Sed	150	350	750	1350	2800	4000
Sta Wag	150	350	750	1450	2900	4100
Valiant 200, 6-cyl., 106.5" wb						
4 dr Sed	150	350	750	1450	3000	4200
2 dr Sed	150	350	750	1450	2900	4100
Conv	350	750	1200	2350	4900	7000
Sta Wag	150	350	750	1450	2900	4100
Valiant Signet, 6-cyl., 106.5" wb						
HdTp Sed	200	600	950	2150	3850	5500
Conv	350	750	1300	2450	5250	7500
Savoy, V-8, 116" wb						
4 dr Sed	150	400	750	1650	3150	4500
2 dr Sed	150	450	750	1700	3200	4600
6P Sta Wag	150	400	750	1600	3100	4400
Belvedere, V-8, 116" wb						
4 dr Sed	150	450	750	1700	3200	4600
2 dr Sed	150	450	750	1700	3200	4600
4 dr HdTp	200	500	850	1850	3350	4900
6P Sta Wag	150	400	750	1600	3100	4400
Fury, V-8, 116" wb						
4 dr Sed	150	450	800	1750	3250	4700
4 dr HdTp	200	500	850	1900	3500	5000
2 dr HdTp	350	750	1200	2350	4900	7000
Conv	450	1000	1650	3350	6300	9000
9P Sta Wag	150	450	750	1700	3200	4600
Sport Fury, V-8, 116" wb						
2 dr HdTp	450	1000	1650	3350	6300	9000
Conv	400	1200	2000	3950	7000	10,000

NOTES: Deduct 10 percent for 6-cyl. models.
Add 80 percent for Max Wedge II 426 engine.
Add 40 percent for 413.

1964

	6	5	4	3	2	1
Valiant 100, 6-cyl., 106.5" wb						
4 dr Sed	150	350	750	1450	2900	4100
2 dr Sed	150	350	750	1350	2800	4000
Sta Wag	150	350	750	1450	2900	4100
Valiant 200, 6 or V-8, 106.5" wb						
4 dr Sed	150	350	750	1450	3000	4200
2 dr Sed	150	350	750	1450	2900	4100
Conv	350	800	1450	2750	5600	8000
Sta Wag	150	350	750	1450	2900	4100

	6	5	4	3	2	1
Valiant Signet, V-8 cyl., 106.5" wb						
2 dr HdTp	350	750	1200	2350	4900	7000
Barracuda	400	1250	2100	4200	7400	10,500
Conv	500	1550	2600	5200	9100	13,000
Savoy, V-8, 116" wb						
4 dr Sed	150	400	750	1650	3150	4500
2 dr Sed	150	450	750	1700	3200	4600
6P Sta Wag	150	400	750	1600	3100	4400
Belvedere, V-8, 116" wb						
4 dr Sed	150	450	750	1700	3200	4600
2 dr Sed	150	450	750	1700	3200	4600
6P Sta Wag	150	400	750	1600	3100	4400
Fury, V-8, 116" wb						
4 dr Sed	150	450	800	1750	3250	4700
4 dr HdTp	150	450	800	1800	3300	4800
2 dr HdTp	350	800	1450	2750	5600	8000
Conv	400	1200	2000	3950	7000	10,000
9P Sta Wag	150	450	750	1700	3200	4600
Sport Fury, V-8, 116" wb						
2 dr HdTp	350	900	1550	3050	5900	8500
Conv	450	1100	1700	3650	6650	9500

NOTES: Deduct 10 percent for 6-cyl. models.
Add 90 percent for Max Wedge III 426-425 engine.
Add 80 percent for 426-415 MW II.
Add 100 percent for 426 Hemi 425 hp.

1965

	6	5	4	3	2	1
Valiant 100, 6 or V8, 106.5" wb						
4 dr Sed	150	350	750	1450	2900	4100
2 dr Sed	150	350	750	1350	2800	4000
Sta Wag	150	350	750	1450	2900	4100
Valiant 200, 6 or V-8, 106" wb						
4 dr Sed	150	350	750	1450	3000	4200
2 dr Sed	150	350	750	1450	2900	4100
Conv	350	750	1200	2350	4900	7000
Sta Wag	150	350	750	1450	2900	4100
Valiant Signet, V8, 106" wb						
HdTp	450	1000	1650	3350	6300	9000
Conv	500	1550	2600	5200	9100	13,000
Barracuda	400	1300	2200	4400	7700	11,000
Belvedere I, V-8, 116" wb						
NOTE: Add 10 percent for Formula S option.						
4 dr Sed	150	300	700	1250	2650	3800
2 dr Sed	150	300	700	1250	2600	3700
Sta Wag	150	300	700	1250	2650	3800
Belvedere II, V8, 116" wb						
4 dr Sed	150	350	750	1350	2800	4000
2 dr HdTp	200	600	950	2150	3850	5500
Conv	350	750	1300	2450	5250	7500
9P Sta Wag	150	350	750	1350	2800	4000
6P Sta Wag	150	300	750	1350	2700	3900
Satellite, V8, 116"wb						
2 dr	350	900	1550	3050	5900	8500
Conv	500	1550	2600	5200	9100	13,000
Fury, V-8, 119" wb.; 121" Sta. Wag.						
4 dr Sed	150	350	750	1450	3000	4200
2 dr Sed	150	350	750	1450	2900	4100
Sta Wag	150	300	750	1350	2700	3900
Fury II, V8, 119" wb, Sta Wag 121" wb						
4 dr Sed	150	400	750	1550	3050	4300
2 dr Sed	150	400	750	1550	3050	4300
9P Sta Wag	150	350	750	1350	2800	4000
6P Sta Wag	150	300	750	1350	2700	3900
Fury III, V8, 119" wb, Sta Wag 121" wb						
4 dr Sed	150	400	750	1600	3100	4400
4 dr HdTp	150	400	750	1650	3150	4500
2 dr HdTp	350	750	1300	2450	5250	7500
Conv	400	1200	2000	3950	7000	10,000
9P Sta Wag	150	350	750	1450	2900	4100
6P Sta Wag	150	350	750	1350	2800	4000
Sport Fury, V-8						
2 dr HdTp	450	1100	1700	3650	6650	9500
Conv	400	1300	2200	4400	7700	11,000

NOTES: Deduct 5 percent for 6-cyl. models.
Add 80 percent for 426 Commando engine option.
Add 100 percent for 426 Hemi 425 hp.

1966

	6	5	4	3	2	1
Valiant 100, V8, 106" wb						
4 dr Sed	150	350	750	1450	3000	4200
2 dr Sed	150	350	750	1450	2900	4100
Sta Wag	150	350	750	1450	3000	4200
Valiant 200, V8, 106" wb						
4 dr Sed	150	400	750	1550	3050	4300
Sta Wag	150	350	750	1450	3000	4200
Valiant Signet						
2 dr HdTp	350	750	1300	2450	5250	7500
Conv	450	1100	1700	3650	6650	9500
Valiant Barracuda, V8, 106" wb						
2 dr HdTp	400	1200	2000	3950	7000	10,000
NOTE: Add 10 percent for Formula S.						
Belvedere I, V-8, 116" wb						
4 dr Sed	150	300	750	1350	2700	3900
2 dr Sed	150	300	700	1250	2650	3800
Sta Wag	150	300	750	1350	2700	3900
Belvedere II, V8, 116" wb						
4 dr Sed	150	350	750	1450	2900	4100
2 dr HdTp	350	700	1150	2300	4550	6500
Conv	350	900	1550	3050	5900	8500
Sta Wag	150	350	750	1450	2900	4100
Satellite, V-8, 116" wb						
2 dr HdTp	450	1100	1700	3650	6650	9500
Conv	400	1300	2200	4400	7700	11,000
Fury I, V-8, 119" wb						
Sed	150	350	750	1350	2800	4000
2 dr Sed	150	300	750	1350	2700	3900
6P Sta Wag	150	350	750	1350	2800	4000
NOTE: Deduct 5 percent for 6-cyl. models.						
Fury II, V-8, 119" wb						
Sed	150	350	750	1450	2900	4100
2 dr Sed	150	350	750	1350	2800	4000
9P Sta Wag	150	350	750	1450	2900	4100
Fury III, V8, 119" wb						
Sed	150	350	750	1450	3000	4200
2 dr HdTp	350	750	1200	2350	4900	7000
4 dr HdTp	150	450	750	1700	3200	4600
Conv	400	1300	2200	4400	7700	11,000
9P Sta Wag	150	350	750	1450	3000	4200
Sport Fury, V-8, 119" wb						
2 dr HdTp	350	800	1450	2750	5600	8000
Conv	450	1450	2400	4800	8400	12,000
VIP, V-8, 119" wb						
4 dr HdTp	350	700	1150	2300	4550	6500
2 dr HdTp	350	800	1450	2750	5600	8000

NOTES: Add 100 percent for 426 Street Hemi, 426 hp.
Add 125 percent for 426 Race Hemi, 425 hp.

1967

	6	5	4	3	2	1
Valiant 100, V8, 108" wb						
4 dr Sed	150	350	750	1450	3000	4200
2 dr Sed	150	350	750	1450	2900	4100
Valiant Signet, V-8, 108" wb						
4 dr Sed	150	400	750	1550	3050	4300
2 dr Sed	150	350	750	1450	3000	4200
Barracuda, V-8, 108" wb						
2 dr HdTp	400	1200	2000	3950	7000	10,000
2 dr FsBk	400	1300	2200	4400	7700	11,000
Conv	550	1700	2800	5600	9800	14,000
NOTE: Add 10 percent for Formula S and 40 percent for 383 CID.						
Belvedere I, V-8, 116" wb						
4 dr Sed	150	300	750	1350	2700	3900
2 dr Sed	150	300	700	1250	2650	3800
6P Sta Wag	150	300	750	1350	2700	3900
Belvedere II, V8, 116" wb						
4 dr Sed	150	350	750	1450	2900	4100
2 dr HdTp	200	675	1050	2250	4300	6100
Conv	450	1100	1700	3650	6650	9500
9P Sta Wag	150	350	750	1450	2900	4100
Satellite, V-8, 116" wb						
2 dr HdTp	400	1300	2200	4400	7700	11,000
Conv	500	1550	2600	5200	9100	13,000
GTX, V8, 116" wb						
2 dr HdTp	600	1900	3200	6400	11,200	16,000
Conv	650	2050	3400	6800	11,900	17,000
Fury I, V8, 122" wb						
4 dr Sed	150	350	750	1350	2800	4000
2 dr Sed	150	300	750	1350	2700	3900
6P Sta Wag	150	350	750	1350	2800	4000
Fury II, V8, 122" wb						
4 dr Sed	150	350	750	1450	2900	4100
2 dr Sed	150	350	750	1350	2800	4000
9P Sta Wag	150	350	750	1450	2900	4100
Fury III, V8, 122" wb						
4 dr Sed	150	350	750	1450	3000	4200
4 dr HdTp	150	400	750	1600	3100	4400
2 dr HdTp	350	700	1150	2300	4550	6500
Conv	450	1100	1700	3650	6650	9500
9P Sta Wag	150	350	750	1450	3000	4200
Sport Fury, V-8, 119" wb						
2 dr HdTp	350	750	1200	2350	4900	7000
2 dr FsBk	350	750	1300	2450	5250	7500
Conv	400	1200	2000	3950	7000	10,000
VIP, V-8, 119" wb						
4 dr HdTp	350	700	1150	2300	4550	6500
2 dr HdTp	350	750	1300	2450	5250	7500

NOTES: Add 50 percent for 440 engine.
Add 100 percent for 426 Hemi 425 hp.

1968

	6	5	4	3	2	1
Valiant 100, V8, 108" wb						
4 dr Sed	150	350	750	1450	2900	4100
2 dr Sed	150	350	750	1350	2800	4000
Valiant Signet, V-8, 108" wb						
4 dr Sed	150	400	750	1600	3100	4400
2 dr Sed	150	450	750	1700	3200	4600
Barracuda, V-8, 108" wb						
2 dr HdTp	400	1200	2000	3950	7000	10,000
2 dr FsBk	400	1300	2200	4400	7700	11,000
Conv	600	1900	3200	6400	11,200	16,000
Add 20 percent for Barracuda/Formula S' and 40 percent for 383 CID.						
Belvedere, V8, 116" wb						
4 dr Sed	150	350	750	1450	3000	4200
2 dr Sed	150	350	750	1450	2900	4100
6P Sta Wag	150	350	750	1450	3000	4200
Satellite, V8, 116" wb						
4 dr Sed	150	400	750	1550	3050	4300
2 dr HdTp	450	1000	1650	3350	6300	9000
Conv	400	1300	2200	4400	7700	11,000
Sta Wag	150	400	750	1650	3150	4500
Sport Satellite, V8, 116" wb						
2 dr HdTp	450	1450	2400	4800	8400	12,000
Conv	550	1700	2800	5600	9800	14,000
Sta Wag	150	400	750	1600	3100	4400
Road Runner, V8, 116" wb						
Cpe	550	1800	3000	6000	10,500	15,000
2 dr HdTp	650	2050	3400	6800	11,900	17,000
GTX, V8, 116" wb						
2 dr HdTp	700	2150	3600	7200	12,600	18,000
Conv	800	2500	4200	8400	14,700	21,000
Fury I, V8, 119" & 122" wb						
4 dr Sed	150	400	750	1550	3050	4300
2 dr Sed	150	350	750	1450	3000	4200
6P Sta Wag	150	400	750	1550	3050	4300
Fury II, V8, 119" & 122" wb						
4 dr Sed	150	400	750	1600	3100	4400
2 dr Sed	150	400	750	1550	3050	4300
6P Sta Wag	150	400	750	1600	3100	4400
Fury III, V8, 119" & 122" wb						
4 dr Sed	150	400	750	1650	3150	4500
4 dr HdTp	200	600	1000	2200	4000	5700
2 dr HdTp	350	800	1450	2750	5600	8000
2 dr HdTp FsBk	350	900	1550	3050	5900	8500
Conv	400	1200	2000	3950	7000	10,000
6P Sta Wag	150	400	750	1650	3150	4500
Suburban, V-8, 121" wb						
6P Cust Sta Wag	150	450	750	1700	3200	4600
9P Cust Sta Wag	150	450	800	1750	3250	4700
6P Spt Sta Wag	150	450	800	1800	3300	4800
9P Spt Sta Wag	200	500	850	1850	3350	4900
Sport Fury, V8, 119" wb						
2 dr HdTp	350	800	1450	2750	5600	8000
2 dr HdTp FsBk	350	900	1550	3050	5900	8500
Conv	400	1300	2200	4400	7700	11,000
VIP, V8, 119" wb						
4 dr HdTp	350	750	1300	2450	5250	7500

	6	5	4	3	2	1
2 dr FsBk	350	900	1550	3050	5900	8500

NOTES: Add 50 percent for 440 engine.
Add 100 percent for 426 Hemi 425 hp.

1969

	6	5	4	3	2	1
Valiant 100, V8, 108" wb						
4 dr Sed	150	300	750	1350	2700	3900
2 dr Sed	150	300	700	1250	2650	3800
Valiant Signet, V-8, 108" wb						
4 dr Sed	150	350	750	1350	2800	4000
2 dr Sed	150	300	750	1350	2700	3900
Barracuda, V-8, 108" wb						
2 dr HdTp	400	1300	2200	4400	7700	11,000
FsBk	450	1450	2400	4800	8400	12,000
Conv	550	1800	3000	6000	10,500	15,000

NOTE: Add 40 percent for Formula S 383 CID option.

	6	5	4	3	2	1
Belvedere, V-8, 117" wb						
4 dr Sed	150	300	700	1250	2600	3700
2 dr Sed	125	250	700	1150	2500	3600
6P Sta Wag	150	300	700	1250	2600	3700
Satellite, V8, 116" & 117" wb						
4 dr Sed	150	300	750	1350	2700	3900
2 dr HdTp	450	1000	1650	3350	6300	9000
Conv	500	1550	2600	5200	9100	13,000
6P Sta Wag	150	350	750	1350	2800	4000
Sport Satellite, V8, 116" & 117" wb						
4 dr Sed	150	350	750	1350	2800	4000
2 dr HdTp	400	1200	2000	3950	7000	10,000
Conv	550	1700	2800	5600	9800	14,000
9P Sta Wag	150	350	750	1350	2800	4000
Road Runner, V8, 116" wb						
2 dr Sed	550	1800	3000	6000	10,500	15,000
2 dr HdTp	650	2050	3400	6800	11,900	17,000
Conv	850	2650	4400	8800	15,400	22,000
GTX, V8, 116" wb						
2 dr HdTp	650	2050	3400	6800	11,900	17,000
Conv	700	2300	3800	7600	13,300	19,000
Fury I, V-8, 120" & 122" wb						
4 dr Sed	150	300	700	1250	2650	3800
2 dr Sed	150	300	700	1250	2600	3700
6P Sta Wag	150	300	700	1250	2650	3800
Fury II, V8, 120" & 122" wb						
4 dr Sed	150	300	750	1350	2700	3900
2 dr Sed	150	300	700	1250	2650	3800
6P Sta Wag	150	300	750	1350	2700	3900
Fury III, V8, 120" & 122" wb						
4 dr Sed	150	350	750	1350	2800	4000
4 dr HdTp	150	350	750	1450	3000	4200
2 dr HdTp	350	750	1200	2350	4900	7000
Conv	350	900	1550	3100	6000	8600
9P Sta Wag	150	350	750	1350	2800	4000
Sport Fury						
2 dr HdTp	350	750	1300	2450	5250	7500
Conv	450	1100	1700	3650	6650	9500
VIP						
4 dr HdTp	200	600	950	2150	3850	5500
2 dr HdTp	350	800	1450	2750	5600	8000

NOTES: Add 70 percent for 440 6 pack.
Add 100 percent for 426 Hemi 425 hp.
Add 40 percent for 'Cuda 340.
Add 40 percent for 'Cuda 383 (not avail. on conv.).

1970

	6	5	4	3	2	1
Valiant						
Sed	150	300	700	1250	2650	3800
Valiant Duster						
HdTp	200	500	850	1900	3500	5000
Duster '340'						
HdTp	350	750	1300	2450	5250	7500
Barracuda						
HdTp	550	1700	2800	5600	9800	14,000
Conv	550	1800	3000	6000	10,500	15,000
Gran Coupe						
HdTp	700	2150	3600	7200	12,600	18,000
Conv	650	2050	3400	6800	11,900	17,000
Cuda						
HdTp	700	2150	3600	7200	12,600	18,000
Conv	700	2300	3800	7600	13,300	19,000
Hemi Cuda Conv					value inestimable	
Cuda AAR						
2 dr HdTp	1000	3100	5200	10,400	18,200	26,000
Belvedere						
Sed	125	250	700	1150	2500	3600
Cpe	150	300	700	1250	2650	3800
Wag	125	250	700	1150	2500	3600
Road Runner						
Cpe	600	1900	3200	6400	11,200	16,000
HdTp	700	2150	3600	7200	12,600	18,000
Superbird	2050	6600	11,000	22,000	38,500	55,000
Conv	900	2900	4800	9600	16,800	24,000
Satellite						
Sed	150	300	700	1250	2650	3800
HdTp	450	1000	1650	3350	6300	9000
Conv	450	1450	2400	4800	8400	12,000
Wag-6P	150	300	700	1250	2650	3800
Wag-9P	150	300	700	1250	2650	3800
Sport Satellite						
Sed	150	350	750	1350	2800	4000
HdTp	500	1550	2600	5200	9100	13,000
Wag-6P	150	300	750	1350	2700	3900
Wag-9P	150	350	750	1350	2800	4000
GTX						
HdTp	650	2050	3400	6800	11,900	17,000
Fury I						
Sed	150	300	700	1250	2650	3800
2 dr Sed	150	300	700	1250	2600	3700
Fury II						
Sed	150	300	750	1350	2700	3900
2 dr Sed	150	300	700	1250	2650	3800
Wag-9P	150	300	750	1350	2700	3900
Wag-6P	150	300	700	1250	2650	3800
Gran Coupe						
2 dr Sed	350	750	1200	2350	4900	7000
Fury III						
Sed	150	400	750	1550	3050	4300
HdTp	200	600	950	2150	3850	5500
4 dr HdTp	150	400	750	1650	3150	4500
Formal	200	675	1050	2250	4350	6200
Conv	400	1200	2000	3950	7000	10,000
Wag-9P	150	350	750	1350	2800	4000
Wag-6P	150	300	750	1350	2700	3900
Sport Fury						
Sed	150	400	750	1600	3100	4400
HdTp	350	700	1150	2300	4550	6500
4 dr HdTp	200	500	850	1900	3500	5000
Formal	350	750	1200	2350	4900	7000
Wag	150	350	750	1350	2800	4000
Fury S-23						
HdTp	450	1100	1700	3650	6650	9500
Fury GT						
HdTp	400	1200	2000	3950	7000	10,000

NOTES: Add 80 percent for 440 6 pack.
Add 100 percent for 426 Hemi 425 hp.

1971

	6	5	4	3	2	1
Valiant						
Sed	150	300	700	1250	2600	3700
Duster						
Cpe	150	350	750	1350	2800	4000
Duster '340'						
Cpe	350	750	1300	2500	5300	7600
Scamp						
HdTp	200	600	950	2150	3850	5500
Barracuda						
Cpe	400	1300	2200	4400	7700	11,000
HdTp	450	1450	2400	4800	8400	12,000
Conv	550	1800	3000	6000	10,500	15,000
Gran Coupe						
HdTp	550	1700	2800	5600	9800	14,000
'Cuda						
HdTp	550	1800	3000	6000	10,500	15,000
Conv	650	2050	3400	6800	11,900	17,000
Satellite						
Sed	125	250	700	1150	2500	3600
Cpe	200	500	850	1950	3600	5100
Sta Wag	125	250	700	1150	2500	3600
Satellite Sebring						
HdTp	450	1100	1700	3650	6650	9500
Satellite Custom						
Sed	150	300	700	1250	2600	3700
Sta Wag-9P	150	300	700	1250	2600	3700
Sta Wag-6P	125	250	700	1150	2500	3600
Road Runner						
HdTp	550	1800	3000	6000	10,500	15,000
Sebring Plus						
HdTp	400	1200	2000	3950	7000	10,000
Satellite Brougham						
Sed	150	300	700	1250	2650	3800
Regent Wagon						
Sta Wag-9P	150	300	700	1250	2650	3800
Sta Wag-6P	150	300	700	1250	2650	3800
GTX						
HdTp	400	1300	2200	4400	7700	11,000
Fury I						
Sed	150	300	700	1250	2650	3800
2 dr Sed	150	300	700	1250	2600	3700
Fury Custom						
Sed	150	300	700	1250	2650	3800
2 dr Sed	150	300	700	1250	2600	3700
Fury II						
Sed	150	300	700	1250	2600	3700
HdTp	200	650	1050	2250	4200	6000
Sta Wag-9P	150	300	700	1250	2600	3700
Sta Wag-6P	125	250	700	1150	2500	3600
Fury III						
Sed	150	300	700	1250	2600	3700
HdTp	350	700	1150	2300	4550	6500
4 dr HdTp	150	300	750	1350	2700	3900
Formal Cpe	350	725	1200	2350	4800	6800
Sta Wag-9P	150	300	700	1250	2600	3700
Sta Wag-6P	125	250	700	1150	2500	3600
Sport Fury						
Sed	150	300	700	1250	2600	3700
4 dr HdTp	150	400	750	1650	3150	4500
Formal Cpe	200	650	1050	2250	4200	6000
HdTp	200	600	950	2150	3850	5500
Sta Wag-9P	150	300	700	1250	2600	3700
Sta Wag-6P	125	250	700	1150	2500	3600
Sport Fury 'GT'						
2 dr HdTp	350	900	1550	3050	5900	8500

NOTES: Add 60 percent for 440 engine.
Add 70 percent for 440 6 pack.
Add 100 percent for 426 Hemi 425 hp.

1972

	6	5	4	3	2	1
Valiant						
Sed	150	300	700	1250	2600	3700
Duster						
2 dr Cpe	200	600	950	2150	3850	5500
'340' Cpe	350	750	1300	2450	5250	7500
Scamp						
HdTp	350	700	1150	2300	4550	6500
Barracuda						
HdTp	450	1450	2400	4800	8400	12,000
'Cuda'						
HdTp	500	1550	2600	5200	9100	13,000
Satellite						
Sed	150	300	750	1350	2700	3900
2 dr Cpe	200	600	950	2150	3850	5500
6P Wag	125	250	700	1150	2400	3400
Satellite Sebring						
HdTp	350	900	1550	3050	5900	8500
Satellite Custom						
Sed	150	350	750	1350	2800	4000
6P Wag	400	1200	2000	3950	7000	10,000
9P Wag	125	250	700	1150	2450	3500
Sebring-Plus						
HdTp	450	1000	1650	3350	6300	9000
Regent						
6P Wag	125	250	700	1150	2400	3400
9P Wag	125	250	700	1150	2450	3500
Road Runner						
HdTp	400	1300	2200	4400	7700	11,000
Fury I						
Sed	125	250	700	1150	2500	3600
Fury II						
Sed	150	300	700	1250	2600	3700
HdTp	200	600	950	2150	3850	5500

	6	5	4	3	2	1
Fury III						
Sed	125	250	700	1150	2500	3600
4 dr HdTp	150	300	700	1250	2650	3800
Formal Cpe	200	550	900	2100	3700	5300
HdTp	350	700	1150	2300	4550	6500
Gran Fury						
4 dr HdTp	150	450	750	1700	3200	4600
Formal Cpe	200	600	950	2150	3850	5500
Suburban						
6P Sta Wag	125	250	700	1150	2400	3400
9P Sta Wag	125	250	700	1150	2450	3500
6P Cus Wag	125	250	700	1150	2450	3500
9P Cus Wag	125	250	700	1150	2500	3600
6P Spt Wag	125	250	700	1150	2500	3600
9P Spt Wag	150	300	700	1250	2600	3700

1973
	6	5	4	3	2	1
Valiant, V-8						
4 dr	125	250	700	1150	2500	3600
Duster, V-8						
Cpe Sport	150	350	750	1450	2900	4100
340 Cpe Sport	200	600	950	2150	3850	5500
Scamp, V-8						
2 dr HdTp	150	450	800	1750	3250	4700
Barracuda, V-8						
2 dr HdTp	400	1200	2000	3950	7000	10,000
2 dr 'Cuda HdTp	400	1300	2200	4400	7700	11,000
Satellite Custom, V-8						
4 dr	125	250	700	1150	2400	3400
3S Sta Wag	125	250	700	1150	2400	3400
3S Sta Wag Regent	125	250	700	1150	2450	3500
Satellite Cpe	150	300	700	1250	2650	3800
Road Runner, V-8						
Cpe	500	1550	2600	5200	9100	13,000
Sebring Plus, V-8						
2 dr HdTp	400	1300	2200	4400	7700	11,000
Fury, V-8						
I 4 dr	125	250	700	1150	2450	3500
II 4 dr	125	250	700	1150	2500	3600
III 4 dr	150	300	700	1250	2600	3700
2 dr HdTp	200	600	950	2150	3850	5500
4 dr HdTp	150	300	700	1250	2650	3800
Gran Fury, V-8						
2 dr HdTp	200	650	1050	2250	4200	6000
4 dr HdTp	150	300	700	1250	2650	3800
Fury Suburban, V-8						
3S Sport Sta Wag	125	200	600	1100	2300	3300

1974
	6	5	4	3	2	1
Valiant						
Sed	125	250	700	1150	2450	3500
Duster						
Cpe	125	250	700	1150	2500	3600
Scamp						
HdTp	150	350	750	1450	2900	4100
Duster '360'						
Cpe	150	450	800	1750	3250	4700
Valiant Brougham						
Sed	125	250	700	1150	2500	3600
HdTp	200	500	850	1900	3500	5000
Barracuda						
Spt Cpe	450	1000	1650	3350	6300	9000
'Cuda						
Spt Cpe	400	1200	2000	3950	7000	10,000
Satellite						
Sed	125	250	700	1150	2400	3400
Cpe	125	250	700	1150	2450	3500
Satellite Custom						
Sed	125	250	700	1150	2450	3500
Sebring						
HdTp	350	725	1200	2350	4800	6800
Sebring-Plus						
HdTp	350	750	1250	2350	5000	7100
Road Runner						
Cpe	350	900	1550	3050	5900	8500
Satellite Wagon						
Std Wag	125	250	700	1150	2400	3400
6P Cus Wag	125	250	700	1150	2450	3500
9P Cus Wag	125	250	700	1150	2500	3600
6P Regent	125	250	700	1150	2450	3500
9P Regent	125	250	700	1150	2500	3600
Fury I						
Sed	125	250	700	1150	2400	3400
Fury II						
Sed	125	250	700	1150	2450	3500
Fury III						
Sed	125	250	700	1150	2500	3600
HdTp	150	300	750	1350	2700	3900
4 dr HdTp	150	300	700	1250	2600	3700
Gran Fury						
HdTp	150	350	750	1350	2800	4000
4 dr HdTp	150	300	700	1250	2600	3700
Suburban						
Std	125	200	600	1100	2200	3100
6P Cus	125	200	600	1100	2250	3200
9P Cus	125	200	600	1100	2300	3300
6P Spt	125	200	600	1100	2300	3300
9P Spt	125	250	700	1150	2400	3400

1975
	6	5	4	3	2	1
Valiant						
Sed	125	250	700	1150	2450	3500
Custom	125	250	700	1150	2500	3600
Brougham						
4 dr Sed	125	250	700	1150	2500	3600
2 dr HdTp	150	400	750	1550	3050	4300
Duster						
Cpe	125	200	600	1100	2200	3100
Custom	125	200	600	1100	2250	3200
'360' Cpe	150	350	750	1350	2800	4000
Scamp						
HdTp	125	250	700	1150	2450	3500
Brghm	150	300	700	1250	2600	3700
Fury						
HdTp	125	250	700	1150	2450	3500
Cus HdTp	125	250	700	1150	2500	3600
Spt HdTp	150	300	700	1250	2600	3700
Sed	125	250	700	1150	2400	3400
Cus Sed	125	250	700	1150	2450	3500

	6	5	4	3	2	1
Suburban						
Std Wag	125	200	600	1100	2200	3100
6P Cus	125	200	600	1100	2250	3200
9P Cus	125	250	700	1150	2400	3400
6P Spt	125	200	600	1100	2300	3300
9P Spt	125	250	700	1150	2450	3500
Road Runner						
HdTp	150	350	750	1450	2900	4100
Gran Fury						
Sed	125	200	600	1100	2300	3300
Gran Fury Custom						
Sed	125	250	700	1150	2400	3400
4 dr HdTp	125	250	700	1150	2450	3500
2 dr HdTp	125	250	700	1150	2500	3600
Gran Fury Brougham						
4 dr HdTp	125	250	700	1150	2500	3600
2 dr HdTp	150	300	700	1250	2600	3700
Suburban						
Std	125	200	600	1100	2200	3100
6P Cus	125	200	600	1100	2250	3200
9P Cus	125	200	600	1100	2300	3300
6P Spt	125	200	600	1100	2300	3300
9P Spt	125	250	700	1150	2400	3400

PONTIAC

1946
	6	5	4	3	2	1
Torpedo, 8-cyl.						
Conv	800	2500	4200	8400	14,700	21,000
Bus Cpe	200	675	1100	2250	4400	6300
Spt Cpe	350	725	1200	2350	4800	6800
5P Cpe	350	700	1150	2300	4600	6600
2 dr Sed	350	700	1150	2300	4550	6500
4 dr Sed	350	700	1150	2300	4600	6600

NOTE: All 1946-1954 Pontiacs are sometimes called "Silver Streaks". On some models nameplates bearing this designation appear on the cars, but it is not a true model name. The true model names are "Torpedo" (for conventional styles) and "Streamliner" (for fastbacks and station wagons).

	6	5	4	3	2	1
Streamliner, 8-Cyl.						
5P Cpe	350	725	1200	2350	4850	6900
4 dr Sed	350	725	1200	2350	4800	6800
Sta Wag	700	2300	3800	7600	13,300	19,000
DeL Sta Wag	750	2400	4000	8000	14,000	20,000

NOTE: Deduct 5 percent for 6-cyl. models.

1947
	6	5	4	3	2	1
Torpedo, 8-cyl.						
Conv	800	2500	4200	8400	14,700	21,000
DeL Conv	850	2750	4600	9200	16,100	23,000
Bus Cpe	200	675	1100	2250	4400	6300
Spt Cpe	350	725	1200	2350	4800	6800
5P Cpe	350	700	1150	2300	4600	6600
2 dr Sed	350	700	1150	2300	4550	6500
4 dr Sed	350	700	1150	2300	4600	6600
Streamliner, 8-cyl.						
Cpe	350	725	1200	2350	4850	6900
Sed	350	725	1200	2350	4800	6800
Sta Wag	700	2300	3800	7600	13,300	19,000
DeL Sta Wag	750	2400	4000	8000	14,000	20,000

NOTE: Deduct 5 percent for 6-cyl. models.

1948
	6	5	4	3	2	1
Torpedo, 8-cyl.						
Bus Cpe	200	675	1100	2250	4400	6300
Spt Cpe	350	725	1200	2350	4800	6800
5P Cpe	350	700	1150	2300	4600	6600
2 dr Sed	350	700	1150	2300	4550	6500
4 dr Sed	350	700	1150	2300	4600	6600
DeLuxe Torpedo, 8-cyl.						
Conv	850	2650	4400	8800	15,400	22,000
Spt Cpe	350	750	1200	2350	4900	7000
5P Cpe	350	725	1200	2350	4800	6800
4 dr Sed	350	725	1150	2300	4700	6700
DeLuxe Streamliner, 8-cyl.						
Cpe	350	725	1200	2350	4800	6800
4 dr Sed	350	725	1200	2350	4850	6900
Sta Wag	750	2400	4000	8000	14,000	20,000

NOTE: Deduct 5 percent for 6-cyl. models.

1949
	6	5	4	3	2	1
Streamliner, 8-cyl.						
Cpe Sed	200	675	1050	2250	4350	6200
4 dr Sed	200	675	1050	2250	4350	6200
Sta Wag	450	1100	1700	3650	6650	9500
Wood Sta Wag	500	1550	2600	5200	9100	13,000
Streamliner DeLuxe, 8-cyl.						
4 dr Sed	200	675	1100	2250	4400	6300
Cpe Sed	350	700	1100	2300	4500	6400
Stl Sta Wag	450	1000	1650	3350	6300	9000
Woodie	500	1600	2700	5400	9500	13,500
Sed Dely	450	1000	1650	3350	6300	9000
Chieftain, 8-cyl.						
4 dr Sed	350	700	1100	2300	4500	6400
2 dr Sed	200	675	1050	2250	4350	6200
Cpe Sed	350	700	1100	2300	4600	6600
Bus Cpe	350	700	1150	2300	4550	6500
Chieftain DeLuxe, 8-cyl.						
4 dr Sed	350	700	1150	2300	4550	6500
2 dr Sed	200	675	1100	2250	4400	6300
Bus Cpe	350	700	1150	2300	4600	6600
Cpe Sed	350	725	1150	2300	4700	6700
Conv	750	2400	4000	8000	14,000	20,000

NOTE: Deduct 5 percent for 6-cyl. models.

1950
	6	5	4	3	2	1
Streamliner, 8-cyl.						
4 dr Sed	200	675	1050	2250	4300	6100
Cpe	200	675	1100	2250	4400	6300
Sta Wag	450	1000	1650	3350	6300	9000
Streamliner DeLuxe fastback, 8-cyl.						
4 dr Sed	200	675	1100	2250	4400	6300
Cpe	350	700	1150	2300	4600	6600
Sta Wag	450	1100	1700	3650	6650	9500
Sed Dely	450	1100	1700	3650	6650	9500

	6	5	4	3	2	1
Chieftain, 8-cyl.						
4 dr Sed	350	700	1150	2300	4550	6500
2 dr Sed	200	675	1050	2250	4350	6200
Cpe Sed	350	725	1150	2300	4700	6700
Bus Cpe	350	700	1150	2300	4550	6500
Chieftain DeLuxe, 8-cyl.						
4 dr Sed	350	700	1150	2300	4600	6600
2 dr Sed	200	675	1100	2250	4400	6300
Cpe Sed	350	725	1200	2350	4800	6800
2 dr HdTp	400	1200	2000	3950	7000	10,000
2 dr HdTp Super	400	1300	2200	4400	7700	11,000
Conv	700	2150	3600	7200	12,600	18,000

NOTE: Deduct 5 percent for 6-cyl. models.

1951

	6	5	4	3	2	1
Streamliner, 8-cyl.						
Cpe Sed	200	675	1100	2250	4400	6300
Sta Wag	450	1100	1700	3650	6650	9500
Streamliner DeLuxe, 8-cyl.						
Cpe Sed	350	700	1150	2300	4550	6500
Sta Wag	400	1200	2000	3950	7000	10,000
Sed Dely	450	1100	1700	3650	6650	9500
Chieftain, 8-cyl.						
4 dr Sed	350	700	1150	2300	4550	6500
2 dr Sed	200	675	1100	2250	4400	6300
Cpe Sed	350	700	1150	2300	4600	6600
Bus Cpe	350	700	1150	2300	4600	6600
Chieftain DeLuxe, 8-cyl.						
4 dr Sed	350	700	1150	2300	4600	6600
2 dr Sed	350	700	1150	2300	4550	6500
Cpe Sed	350	725	1200	2350	4850	6900
2 dr HdTp	400	1200	2000	3950	7000	10,000
2 dr HdTp Super	400	1300	2200	4400	7700	11,000
Conv	700	2150	3600	7200	12,600	18,000

NOTE: Deduct 5 percent for 6-cyl. models.

1952

	6	5	4	3	2	1
Chieftain, 8-cyl., 120" wb						
4 dr Sed	350	700	1150	2300	4550	6500
2 dr Sed	350	700	1100	2300	4500	6400
Sta Wag	450	1100	1700	3650	6650	9500
Sed Dely	450	1150	1800	3800	6800	9700
Chieftain DeLuxe, 8-cyl.						
4 dr Sed	350	700	1150	2300	4600	6600
2 dr Sed	350	700	1150	2300	4550	6500
2 dr HdTp	400	1200	2000	3950	7000	10,000
Conv	700	2150	3600	7200	12,600	18,000
Sta Wag	450	1150	1800	3800	6800	9700
Chieftain Super, 8-cyl., 122" wb						
2 dr HdTp	400	1300	2200	4400	7700	11,000

NOTE: Deduct 5 percent for 6-cyl. models.

1953

	6	5	4	3	2	1
Chieftain, 8-cyl., 122" wb						
4 dr Sed	350	700	1150	2300	4600	6600
2 dr Sed	350	700	1150	2300	4550	6500
Paint Sta Wag	450	1100	1700	3650	6650	9500
Wood grain Sta Wag	450	1150	1900	3850	6850	9800
Sed Dely	400	1200	2000	3950	7000	10,000
Chieftain DeLuxe, 8-cyl.						
4 dr Sed	350	725	1150	2300	4700	6700
2 dr Sed	350	700	1150	2300	4600	6600
2 dr HdTp	400	1300	2200	4400	7700	11,000
Conv	850	2650	4400	8800	15,400	22,000
Mtl Sta Wag	450	1000	1650	3350	6300	9000
Sim W Sta Wag	450	1100	1700	3650	6650	9500
Custom Catalina, 8-cyl.						
2 dr HdTp	450	1450	2400	4800	8400	12,000

NOTE: Deduct 5 percent for 6-cyl. models.

1954

	6	5	4	3	2	1
Chieftain, 8-cyl., 122" wb						
4 dr Sed	350	725	1200	2350	4800	6800
2 dr Sed	350	725	1150	2300	4700	6700
Sta Wag	400	1200	2000	3950	7000	10,000
Chieftain DeLuxe, 8-cyl.						
4 dr Sed	350	725	1200	2350	4850	6900
2 dr Sed	350	725	1200	2350	4800	6800
2 dr HdTp	450	1450	2400	4800	8400	12,000
Sta Wag	400	1250	2100	4200	7400	10,500
Custom Catalina, 8-cyl.						
2 dr HdTp	500	1550	2600	5200	9100	13,000
Star Chief DeLuxe, 8-cyl.						
4 dr Sed	350	800	1450	2750	5600	8000
Conv	850	2750	4600	9200	16,100	23,000
Custom Star Chief, 8-cyl.						
4 dr Sed	450	1000	1650	3350	6300	9000
2 dr HdTp	500	1600	2700	5400	9500	13,500

NOTE: Deduct 5 percent for 6-cyl. models.

1955

	6	5	4	3	2	1
Chieftain 860, V-8						
4 dr Sed	200	650	1050	2250	4200	6000
2 dr Sed	200	650	1000	2200	4150	5900
2 dr Sta Wag	350	750	1200	2350	4900	7000
4 dr Sta Wag	350	700	1150	2300	4550	6500
Chieftain 870, V-8, 122" wb						
4 dr Sed	350	700	1150	2300	4550	6500
2 dr Sed	200	675	1050	2250	4350	6200
2 dr HdTp	450	1450	2400	4800	8400	12,000
4 dr Sta Wag	350	750	1200	2350	4900	7000
Star Chief Custom Safari, 122" wb						
2 dr Sta Wag	550	1800	3000	6000	10,500	15,000
Star Chief, V-8, 124" wb						
4 dr Sed	350	750	1300	2450	5250	7500
Conv	950	3000	5000	10,000	17,500	25,000
Custom Star Chief, V-8, 124" wb						
4 dr Sed	350	900	1550	3050	5900	8500
2 dr HdTp	550	1750	2900	5800	10,200	14,500

1956

	6	5	4	3	2	1
Chieftain 860, V-8, 122" wb						
4 dr Sed	200	650	1050	2250	4200	6000
4 dr HdTp	350	750	1200	2350	4900	7000
2 dr Sed	200	650	1050	2250	4200	6000
2 dr HdTp	450	1400	2300	4600	8100	11,500
2 dr Sta Wag	350	750	1250	2350	5000	7100
4 dr Sta Wag	350	700	1150	2300	4600	6600
Chieftain 870, V-8, 122" wb						
4 dr Sed	200	675	1100	2250	4400	6300
4 dr HdTp	350	800	1450	2750	5600	8000
2 dr HdTp	450	1500	2500	5000	8800	12,500
4 dr Sta Wag	350	750	1300	2450	5250	7500
Custom Star Chief Safari, V-8, 122" wb						
2 dr Sta Wag	600	1850	3100	6200	10,900	15,500
Star Chief, V-8, 124" wb						
4 dr Sed	350	750	1200	2350	4900	7000
Conv	1000	3100	5200	10,400	18,200	26,000
Custom Star Chief, V-8, 124" wb						
4 dr HdTp	450	1000	1650	3350	6300	9000
2 dr HdTp	550	1800	3000	6000	10,500	15,000

NOTE: (Add 10 percent for optional 285 hp V-8 speed engine).

1957

	6	5	4	3	2	1
Chieftain, V-8, 122" wb						
4 dr Sed	200	675	1100	2250	4400	6300
4 dr HdTp	350	750	1200	2350	4900	7000
2 dr Sed	200	675	1050	2250	4350	6200
2 dr HdTp	400	1250	2100	4200	7400	10,500
4 dr Sta Wag	350	750	1200	2350	4900	7000
2 dr Sta Wag	350	750	1250	2400	5050	7200
Super Chief, V-8, 122" wb						
4 dr Sed	350	725	1200	2350	4800	6800
4 dr HdTp	350	800	1450	2750	5600	8000
2 dr HdTp	450	1400	2300	4600	8100	11,500
4 dr Sta Wag	350	750	1300	2450	5250	7500
Star Chief Custom Safari, V-8, 122" wb						
4 dr Sta Wag	450	1450	2400	4800	8400	12,000
2 dr Sta Wag	600	1900	3200	6400	11,200	16,000
Star Chief, V-8, 124" wb						
4 dr Sed	350	900	1550	3050	5900	8500
Conv	900	2900	4800	9600	16,800	24,000
Bonneville Conv*	2050	6500	10,800	21,600	37,800	54,000
Custom Star Chief, V-8, 124" wb						
4 dr Sed	450	1000	1650	3350	6300	9000
4 dr HdTp	450	1100	1700	3650	6650	9500
2 dr HdTp	600	1900	3200	6400	11,200	16,000

*Available on one-to-a-dealer basis.

1958

	6	5	4	3	2	1
Chieftain, V-8, 122" wb						
4 dr Sed	200	600	950	2200	3900	5600
4 dr HdTp	350	700	1150	2300	4550	6500
2 dr Sed	200	600	1000	2200	4000	5700
2 dr HdTp	450	1000	1650	3350	6300	9000
Conv	800	2500	4200	8400	14,700	21,000
4 dr Safari - 9P	350	750	1200	2350	4900	7000
Super-Chief, V-8, 122" wb						
4 dr Sed	200	675	1050	2250	4300	6100
4 dr HdTp	350	750	1300	2450	5250	7500
2 dr HdTp	400	1200	2000	3950	7000	10,000
Star Chief, V-8, 124" wb						
4 dr Cus Sed	350	700	1150	2300	4550	6500
4 dr HdTp	350	900	1550	3050	5900	8500
2 dr HdTp	450	1450	2400	4800	8400	12,000
4 dr Cus Safari	450	1000	1650	3350	6300	9000
Bonneville, V-8, 122" wb						
2 dr HdTp	1050	3350	5600	11,200	19,600	28,000
Conv	1350	4300	7200	14,400	25,200	36,000

NOTE: Add 20 percent for fuel-injection Bonneville.
Add 5 percent for bucket seats.

1959

	6	5	4	3	2	1
Catalina, V-8, 122" wb						
4 dr Sed	200	650	1000	2200	4150	5900
4 dr HdTp	350	750	1200	2350	4900	7000
2 dr Sed	200	600	950	2150	3850	5500
2 dr HdTp	450	1100	1700	3650	6650	9500
Conv	750	2400	4000	8000	14,000	20,000
Safari, V-8, 124" wb						
4 dr Sta Wag - 6P	200	650	1050	2250	4200	6000
4 dr Sta Wag - 9P	200	675	1050	2250	4350	6200
Star Chief, V-8, 124" wb						
4 dr Sed	200	600	950	2200	3900	5600
4 dr HdTp	350	800	1450	2750	5600	8000
2 dr Sed	350	750	1300	2450	5250	7500
Bonneville, V-8, 124" wb						
4 dr HdTp	450	1000	1650	3350	6300	9000
2 dr HdTp	450	1450	2400	4800	8400	12,000
Conv	950	3000	5000	10,000	17,500	25,000
Custom Safari, V-8, 122" wb						
4 dr Sta Wag	350	750	1300	2450	5250	7500

NOTE: Add 10 percent for engine options (incl. economy V-8) or bucket seats.

1960

	6	5	4	3	2	1
Catalina, V-8, 122" wb						
4 dr Sed	200	600	950	2200	3900	5600
4 dr HdTp	350	700	1150	2300	4550	6500
2 dr Sed	200	600	950	2200	3900	5600
2 dr HdTp	350	800	1450	2750	5600	8000
Conv	800	2500	4200	8400	14,700	21,000
Safari, V-8, 122" wb						
4 dr Sta Wag	200	650	1050	2250	4200	6000
4 dr Sta Wag - 6P	200	650	1050	2250	4200	6000
Ventura, V-8, 122" wb						
4 dr HdTp	350	750	1300	2450	5250	7500
2 dr HdTp	400	1200	2000	3950	7000	10,000
Star Chief, V-8, 124" wb						
4 dr Sed	350	750	1300	2450	5250	7500
4 dr HdTp	350	900	1550	3050	5900	8500
2 dr Sed	350	800	1450	2750	5600	8000
Bonneville, V-8, 124" wb						
4 dr HdTp	450	1000	1650	3350	6300	9000
2 dr HdTp	400	1300	2200	4400	7700	11,000
Conv	1000	3100	5200	10,400	18,200	26,000
Bonneville Safari, V-8, 122" wb						
4 dr Sta Wag	350	750	1300	2500	5300	7600

(Add 5 percent for S-D motor).

1961

	6	5	4	3	2	1
Tempest Compact, 4-cyl.						
4 dr Sed	150	450	800	1750	3250	4700
Cpe	150	450	800	1800	3300	4800
Cus Cpe	200	500	850	1900	3500	5000
Safari Wag	200	500	850	1900	3500	5000
Catalina, V-8, 119" wb						
4 dr Sed	200	550	900	2150	3800	5400
4 dr HdTp	200	675	1050	2250	4350	6200
2 dr Sed	200	650	1050	2250	4200	6000
2 dr HdTp	350	750	1200	2350	4900	7000
Conv	550	1700	2800	5600	9800	14,000
Safari Wag	200	650	1050	2250	4200	6000
Ventura, V-8, 119" wb						
4 dr HdTp	350	750	1200	2350	4900	7000

	6	5	4	3	2	1
2 dr HdTp	450	1000	1650	3350	6300	9000
Star Chief, V-8, 123" wb						
4 dr Sed	200	650	1050	2250	4200	6000
4 dr HdTp	350	750	1250	2400	5050	7200
Bonneville, V-8, 123" wb						
4 dr HdTp	350	750	1300	2450	5250	7500
2 dr HdTp	450	1000	1650	3350	6300	9000
Conv	700	2150	3600	7200	12,600	18,000
Bonneville Safari, V-8, 119" wb						
4 dr Sta Wag	350	800	1450	2750	5600	8000

NOTE: Add 5 percent for Tempest V-8.
(Add 10 percent for S-D motor).

1962

	6	5	4	3	2	1
Tempest Series, 4-cyl., 122" wb						
4 dr Sed	150	450	800	1750	3250	4700
Cpe	150	450	800	1800	3300	4800
2 dr HdTp	200	650	1050	2250	4200	6000
Conv	450	1000	1650	3350	6300	9000
Safari	200	500	850	1900	3500	5000

NOTE: Add 10 percent for Tempest V-8.

	6	5	4	3	2	1
Catalina Series, V-8, 120" wb						
4 dr Sed	200	500	850	1950	3600	5100
4 dr HdTp	350	700	1150	2300	4550	6500
2 dr Sed	200	600	950	2150	3850	5500
2 dr HdTp	350	750	1300	2450	5250	7500
Conv	450	1450	2400	4800	8400	12,000
Sta Wag	200	600	950	2150	3850	5500

NOTES: Add 5 percent for Catalina Ventura.

	6	5	4	3	2	1
Catalina Super-Duty						
2 dr HdTp (421/405)	2850	9100	15,200	30,400	53,200	76,000
2 dr Sed (421/405)	2850	9100	15,200	30,400	53,200	76,000

NOTE: Add 5 percent for four-speed.
Add 5 percent for bucket seats.
Add 10 percent for factory lightweight package.

	6	5	4	3	2	1
Star Chief Series, V-8, 123" wb						
4 dr Sed	200	650	1050	2250	4200	6000
4 dr HdTp	350	750	1300	2450	5250	7500
Bonneville Series, V-8, 123" wb, Sta Wag 119" wb						
4 dr HdTp	350	800	1450	2750	5600	8000
2 dr HdTp	400	1200	2000	3950	7000	10,000
Conv	600	1900	3200	6400	11,200	16,000
Sta Wag	350	700	1150	2300	4550	6500
Grand Prix Series, V-8, 120" wb						
2 dr HdTp	400	1300	2200	4400	7700	11,000

NOTE: Add 30 percent for 421.
Add 30 percent for "421" S-D models.

1963

	6	5	4	3	2	1
Tempest (Compact) Series, 4-cyl., 112" wb						
4 dr Sed	150	400	750	1650	3150	4500
Cpe	200	500	850	1850	3350	4900
2 dr HdTp	200	600	950	2150	3850	5500
Conv	350	900	1550	3050	5900	8500
Sta Wag	200	500	850	1900	3500	5000
LeMans Series, 8-cyl., "326" option.						
2 dr HdTp	350	750	1200	2350	4900	7000
Conv	450	1100	1700	3650	6650	9500
Catalina Series, V-8, 119" wb						
4 dr Sed	200	500	850	1950	3600	5100
4 dr HdTp	350	700	1150	2300	4600	6600
2 dr Sed	200	600	950	2200	3900	5600
2 dr HdTp	350	900	1550	3050	5900	8500
Conv	500	1550	2600	5200	9100	13,000
Sta Wag	350	700	1150	2300	4550	6500
Catalina Super-Duty						
2 dr HdTp (421/405)	2850	9100	15,200	30,400	53,200	76,000
2 dr HdTp (421/400)	2950	9350	15,600	31,200	54,600	78,000
2 dr Sed (421/405)	2850	9100	15,200	30,400	53,200	76,000
2 dr Sed (421/410)	2850	9100	15,200	30,400	53,200	76,000

NOTE: Add 5 percent for four-speed.
Add 5 percent for bucket seats.
Add 10 percent for factory lightweight package.

	6	5	4	3	2	1
Star Chief Series, V-8, 123" wb						
4 dr Sed	200	550	900	2150	3800	5400
4 dr HdTp	350	750	1300	2450	5250	7500
Bonneville Series, V-8, 123" wb						
2 dr HdTp	400	1200	2000	3950	7000	10,000
4 dr HdTp	350	900	1550	3050	5900	8500
Conv	600	1900	3200	6400	11,200	16,000
Sta Wag	350	700	1150	2300	4550	6500
Grand Prix Series, V-8, 120" wb						
2 dr HdTp	400	1200	2000	3950	7000	10,000

NOTE: Add 5 percent for Tempest V-8.
Add 5 percent for Catalina Ventura.
Add 30 percent for "421" S-D models.

1964

	6	5	4	3	2	1
Tempest Custom 21, V-8, 115" wb						
4 dr Sed	150	450	800	1750	3250	4700
2 dr HdTp	200	600	950	2150	3850	5500
Conv	450	1000	1650	3350	6300	9000
Sta Wag	200	500	850	1900	3500	5000
LeMans Series, V-8, 115" wb						
2 dr HdTp	450	1100	1700	3650	6650	9500
Cpe	350	900	1550	3050	5900	8500
Conv	450	1450	2400	4800	8400	12,000
GTO Cpe	550	1700	2800	5600	9800	14,000
GTO Conv	700	2150	3600	7200	12,600	18,000
GTO HdTp	550	1800	3000	6000	10,500	15,000

NOTE: Deduct 10 percent for Tempest 6-cyl.

	6	5	4	3	2	1
Catalina Series, V-8, 120" wb						
4 dr Sed	200	550	900	2150	3800	5400
4 dr HdTp	350	700	1150	2300	4550	6500
2 dr Sed	200	600	950	2150	3850	5500
2 dr HdTp	450	1000	1650	3350	6300	9000
Conv	450	1450	2400	4800	8400	12,000
Sta Wag	200	650	1050	2250	4200	6000
Star Chief Series, 123" wb						
4 dr Sed	200	600	950	2150	3850	5500
4 dr HdTp	350	750	1300	2450	5250	7500
Bonneville Series, V-8, 123" wb						
4 dr HdTp	350	900	1550	3050	5900	8500
2 dr HdTp	400	1200	2000	3950	7000	10,000
Conv	650	2050	3400	6800	11,900	17,000
Sta Wag	350	750	1200	2350	4900	7000
Grand Prix Series, V-8, 120" wb						
2 dr HdTp	400	1200	2000	3950	7000	10,000

NOTES: Add 20 percent for tri power.
Add 5 percent for Catalina-Ventura option.
Add 10 percent for 2 plus 2, 7,998 built.

1965

	6	5	4	3	2	1
Tempest Series, V-8, 115" wb						
4 dr Sed	150	450	750	1700	3200	4600
2 dr Sport Cpe	200	500	850	1950	3600	5100
2 dr HdTp	200	600	950	2150	3850	5500
Conv	450	1000	1650	3350	6300	9000
Sta Wag	200	500	850	1850	3350	4900
LeMans Series, V-8, 115" wb						
4 dr Sed	200	500	850	1900	3500	5000
Cpe	350	700	1150	2300	4550	6500
2 dr HdTp	350	750	1300	2450	5250	7500
Conv	550	1700	2800	5600	9800	14,000
GTO Conv	650	2050	3400	6800	11,900	17,000
GTO HdTp	550	1800	3000	6000	10,500	15,000
GTO Cpe	450	1450	2400	4800	8400	12,000

NOTE: Deduct 5 percent for Tempest 6-cyl.

	6	5	4	3	2	1
Catalina Series, V-8, 121" wb						
4 dr Sed	150	450	800	1800	3300	4800
4 dr HdTp	200	650	1050	2250	4200	6000
2 dr Sed	200	600	950	2150	3850	5500
2 dr HdTp	350	700	1150	2300	4550	6500
Conv	400	1200	2000	3950	7000	10,000
Sta Wag	200	600	950	2150	3850	5500
Star Chief Series, V-8, 123" wb						
4 dr Sed	200	500	850	1900	3500	5000
4 dr HdTp	350	700	1150	2300	4550	6500
Bonneville Series, V-8, 123" wb						
4 dr HdTp	350	750	1300	2450	5250	7500
2 dr HdTp	450	1100	1700	3650	6650	9500
Conv	550	1700	2800	5600	9800	14,000
2S Sta Wag	350	700	1150	2300	4550	6500
Grand Prix Series, 120" wb						
2 dr HdTp	400	1200	2000	3950	7000	10,000

NOTE: Add 30 percent for "421" H.O. Tri-power V-8.
Add 20 percent for tri power.
Add 10 percent for 2 plus 2.
Add 10 percent for Catalina-Ventura option.
Add 10 percent for Ram Air.

1966

	6	5	4	3	2	1
Tempest Custom, OHC-6, 115" wb						
4 dr Sed	150	450	750	1700	3200	4600
4 dr HdTp	150	450	800	1750	3250	4700
2 dr HdTp	200	675	1100	2250	4400	6300
Cpe	200	650	1050	2250	4200	6000
Conv	350	800	1450	2750	5600	8000
Sta Wag	150	400	750	1650	3150	4500
Lemans Series, OHC-6, 115" wb						
4 dr HdTp	200	500	850	1850	3350	4900
Cpe	200	650	1000	2200	4100	5800
2 dr HdTp	350	700	1150	2300	4550	6500
Conv	450	1100	1700	3650	6650	9500

NOTE: Add 20 percent for 326 V-8.

	6	5	4	3	2	1
GTO Series, V-8, 115" wb						
2 dr HdTp	550	1800	3000	6000	10,500	15,000
Cpe	450	1450	2400	4800	8400	12,000
Conv	650	2050	3400	6800	11,900	17,000
Catalina, V-8, 121" wb						
4 dr Sed	150	450	800	1750	3250	4700
4 dr HdTp	200	650	1050	2250	4200	6000
2 dr Sed	200	600	950	2150	3850	5500
2 dr HdTp	350	750	1200	2350	4900	7000
Conv	450	1450	2400	4800	8400	12,000
Sta Wag	200	500	850	1950	3600	5100
2 Plus 2, V-8, 121" wb						
2 dr HdTp	350	800	1450	2750	5600	8000
Conv	500	1550	2600	5200	9100	13,000
Executive, V-8, 124" wb						
4 dr Sed	200	600	950	2150	3850	5500
4 dr HdTp	350	700	1150	2300	4550	6500
2 dr HdTp	450	1100	1700	3650	6650	9500
Bonneville, V-8, 124" wb						
4 dr HdTp	350	750	1300	2450	5250	7500
2 dr HdTp	450	1100	1700	3650	6650	9500
Conv	550	1700	2800	5600	9800	14,000
Sta Wag	200	650	1050	2250	4200	6000
Grand Prix, V-8, 121" wb						
2 dr HdTp	400	1200	2000	3950	7000	10,000

NOTE: Add 30 percent for 421.
Add 20 percent for Ram Air.
Add 20 percent for tri power.
Add 10 percent for Ventura Custom trim option.

1967

	6	5	4	3	2	1
Tempest, 6-cyl., 115" wb						
4 dr Sed	150	400	750	1650	3150	4500
Cpe	200	500	850	1900	3500	5000
Sta Wag	200	600	950	2200	3900	5600
Tempest Custom, 6-cyl., 115" wb						
Cpe	200	500	850	1950	3600	5100
2 dr HdTp	200	600	950	2200	3900	5600
Conv	350	800	1450	2750	5600	8000
4 dr HdTp	200	550	900	2000	3600	5200
4 dr Sed	150	450	750	1700	3200	4600
Sta Wagon	200	500	850	1900	3500	5000
Lemans, 6-cyl., 115" wb						
4 dr HdTp	200	500	850	1900	3500	5000
Cpe	200	550	900	2000	3600	5200
2 dr HdTp	200	650	1050	2250	4200	6000
Conv	450	1000	1650	3350	6300	9000
Tempest Safari, 6-cyl., 115" wb						
Sta Wag	200	500	850	1900	3500	5000
GTO, V-8, 115" wb						
Cpe	450	1450	2400	4800	8400	12,000
2 dr HdTp	550	1700	2800	5600	9800	14,000
Conv	700	2150	3600	7200	12,600	18,000
Catalina, V-8, 121" wb						
4 dr Sed	150	450	800	1750	3250	4700
4 dr HdTp	200	650	1050	2250	4200	6000
2 dr Sed	200	600	950	2200	3900	5600
2 dr HdTp	350	750	1200	2350	4900	7000
Conv	450	1100	1700	3650	6650	9500
3S Sta Wag	200	500	850	1900	3500	5000
Executive, V-8, 124" wb, Sta Wag 121" wb						
4 dr Sed	200	500	850	1900	3500	5000
4 dr HdTp	350	700	1150	2300	4550	6500
2 dr HdTp	350	800	1450	2750	5600	8000
3S Sta Wag	200	650	1050	2250	4200	6000

	6	5	4	3	2	1
Bonneville, V-8, 124" wb						
4 dr HdTp	350	750	1200	2350	4900	7000
2 dr HdTp	350	900	1550	3050	5900	8500
Conv	450	1450	2400	4800	8400	12,000
Sta Wag	200	600	950	2150	3850	5500
Grand Prix, V-8, 121" wb						
2 dr HdTp	450	1000	1650	3350	6300	9000
Conv	550	1700	2800	5600	9800	14,000

NOTES: Add 10 percent for Tempest 326.
Add 30 percent for 428.
Add 10 percent for Sprint option.
Add 15 percent for 2 plus 2 option.
Add 10 percent for Ventura Custom trim option.
Add 5 percent for Brougham trim.

	6	5	4	3	2	1
Firebird, V-8, 108" wb						
Cpe	350	800	1450	2750	5600	8000
Conv	450	1100	1700	3650	6650	9500

NOTES: Add 10 percent for V-8 Sprint option.
Add 15 percent for 350 HO.
Add 20 percent for the Ram Air 400 Firebird.

1968

	6	5	4	3	2	1
Tempest, 6-cyl., 112" wb						
Spt Cpe	200	500	850	1900	3500	5000
Cus "S" Cpe	200	600	950	2150	3850	5500
Cus "S" HdTp	200	650	1050	2250	4200	6000
Cus "S" Conv	350	750	1200	2350	4900	7000
2 dr LeMans	200	500	850	1900	3500	5000
LeMans Spt Cpe	200	650	1050	2250	4200	6000
LeMans Conv	450	1000	1650	3350	6300	9000
GTO, V-8, 112" wb						
2 dr HdTp	500	1550	2600	5200	9100	13,000
Conv	600	1900	3200	6400	11,200	16,000
Catalina, V-8, 122" wb						
4 dr Sed	150	400	750	1650	3150	4500
4 dr HdTp	200	500	850	1900	3500	5000
2 dr Sed	200	600	1000	2200	4000	5700
2 dr HdTp	200	650	1050	2250	4200	6000
Conv	350	900	1550	3050	5900	8500
Sta Wag	200	500	850	1900	3500	5000
Executive, V-8, 124" wb, Sta Wag 121" wb						
4 dr Sed	200	600	950	2150	3850	5500
4 dr HdTp	200	650	1050	2250	4200	6000
2 dr HdTp	350	750	1200	2350	4900	7000
3S Sta Wag	200	550	900	2100	3700	5300
Bonneville, V-8, 125" wb						
4 dr Sed	200	600	1000	2200	4000	5700
4 dr HdTp	350	700	1150	2300	4550	6500
2 dr HdTp	350	750	1300	2450	5250	7500
Conv	450	1450	2400	4800	8400	12,000
Sta Wagon	200	600	950	2150	3850	5500
Grand Prix, V-8, 118" wb						
2 dr HdTp	350	800	1450	2750	5600	8000

NOTES: Add 10 percent for Sprint option.
Add 30 percent for 428.
Add 20 percent for Ram Air I or II.
Add 20 percent for 350 (Tempest) or 428 V-8's.
Add 10 percent for Ventura Custom trim option.
Add 5 percent for Brougham trim.

	6	5	4	3	2	1
Firebird, V-8, 108" wb						
Cpe	350	800	1450	2750	5600	8000
Conv	450	1100	1700	3650	6650	9500

NOTE: Add 10 percent for V-8 or SOHC six Sprint option.
Add 10 percent for 350 HO.
Add 25 percent for the Ram Air 400 Firebird.

1969

	6	5	4	3	2	1
Tempest, 6-cyl., 116" wb, 2 dr 112" wb						
4 dr Sed	150	350	750	1450	2900	4100
Cpe	150	350	750	1450	3000	4200
Tempest 'S' Custom, 6-cyl., 116" wb, 2 dr 112" wb						
4 dr Sed	150	350	750	1450	3000	4200
4 dr HdTp	150	400	750	1600	3100	4400
Cpe	150	400	750	1550	3050	4300
2 dr HdTp	200	500	850	1900	3500	5000
Conv	350	700	1150	2300	4550	6500
Sta Wag	150	400	750	1650	3150	4500
Tempest Lemans, 6-cyl., 116" wb, 2 dr 112" wb						
4 dr HdTp	150	400	750	1650	3150	4500
Cpe	150	400	750	1650	3150	4500
2 dr HdTp	200	600	950	2150	3850	5500
Conv	350	750	1200	2350	4900	7000
Tempest Safari, 6-cyl., 116" wb						
Sta Wag	150	45C	800	1750	3250	4700
GTO, V-8, 112" wb						
2 dr HdTp	550	1700	2800	5600	9800	14,000
Conv	600	1900	3200	6400	11,200	16,000
Catalina, V-8, 122" wb						
4 dr Sed	150	400	750	1650	3150	4500
4 dr HdTp	150	450	800	1750	3250	4700
2 dr HdTp	200	600	950	2150	3850	5500
Conv	350	900	1550	3050	5900	8500
3S Sta Wag	200	500	850	1900	3500	5000
Executive, V-8, 125" wb, Sta Wag 122" wb						
4 dr Sed	150	450	750	1700	3200	4600
4 dr HdTp	150	450	800	1800	3300	4800
2 dr HdTp	200	650	1050	2250	4200	6000
3S Sta Wag	200	550	900	2000	3600	5200
Bonneville, V-8, 125" wb						
4 dr Sed	150	450	750	1700	3200	4600
4 dr HdTp	200	500	850	1900	3500	5000
2 dr HdTp	350	700	1150	2300	4550	6500
Conv	450	1100	1700	3650	6650	9500
Sta Wag	200	600	950	2150	3850	5500
Grand Prix, V-8, 118" wb						
2 dr HdTp	350	750	1200	2350	4900	7000

NOTES: Add 10 percent for LeMans Rally E Pkg.
Add 30 percent for 428 CID V-8.
Add 20 percent for Ram Air III.
Add 5 percent for Brougham trim.
Add 25 percent for Ram Air IV.
Add 40 percent for GTO Judge option.
Add 10 percent for Tempest V-8.
Add 25 percent for Ram Air IV.

	6	5	4	3	2	1
Firebird, V-8, 108" wb						
Cpe	350	900	1550	3050	5900	8500
Conv	400	1200	2000	3950	7000	10,000

	6	5	4	3	2	1
Trans Am Cpe	550	1700	2800	5600	9800	14,000
Trans Am Conv	850	2650	4400	8800	15,400	22,000

NOTE: Add 10 percent for V-8 or SOHC six Sprint option.
Add 15 percent for "HO" 400 Firebird.
Add 20 percent for Ram Air IV Firebird.
Add 50 percent for '303' V-8 SCCA race engine.
The Trans Am was a mid-year model.

1970

	6	5	4	3	2	1
Tempest, 6-cyl., 116" wb, 2 dr 112" wb						
4 dr Sed	150	400	750	1550	3050	4300
2 dr HdTp	200	500	850	1900	3500	5000
Cpe	150	400	750	1650	3150	4500
LeMans, 6 cyl., 116" wb, 2 dr 112" wb						
4 dr Sed	150	400	750	1600	3100	4400
4 dr HdTp	200	500	850	1900	3500	5000
Cpe	150	450	750	1700	3200	4600
2 dr HdTp	200	600	950	2150	3850	5500
Sta Wag	150	450	800	1800	3300	4800
LeMans Sport, 6 cyl., 116" wb, 2 dr 112" wb						
4 dr HdTp	200	550	900	2000	3600	5200
Cpe	200	600	950	2150	3850	5500
2 dr HdTp	200	650	1050	2250	4200	6000
Conv	350	750	1300	2450	5250	7500
Sta Wag	200	500	850	1900	3500	5000
LeMans GT 37, V-8, 112" wb						
Cpe	350	750	1200	2350	4900	7000
2 dr HdTp	350	750	1300	2450	5250	7500
GTO, V-8, 112" wb						
HdTp	500	1550	2600	5200	9100	13,000
Conv	600	1900	3200	6400	11,200	16,000
Catalina, V-8, 122" wb						
4 dr Sed	150	400	750	1650	3150	4500
4 dr HdTp	200	500	850	1900	3500	5000
2 dr HdTp	200	650	1050	2250	4200	6000
Conv	350	800	1450	2750	5600	8000
3S Sta Wag	200	500	850	1900	3500	5000
Executive, V-8, 125" wb, Sta Wag 122" wb						
4 dr Sed	150	450	750	1700	3200	4600
4 dr HdTp	200	650	1050	2250	4200	6000
2 dr HdTp	350	700	1150	2300	4550	6500
3S Sta Wag	200	550	900	2000	3600	5200
Bonneville, V-8, 125" wb, Sta Wag 122" wb						
4 dr Sed	200	500	850	1900	3500	5000
4 dr HdTp	350	700	1150	2300	4550	6500
2 dr HdTp	350	750	1200	2350	4900	7000
Conv	450	1100	1700	3650	6650	9500
3S Sta Wag	200	600	950	2150	3850	5500
Grand Prix, V-8, 118" wb						
Hurst "SSJ" HdTp	450	1100	1700	3650	6650	9500
	350	750	1300	2450	5250	7500

NOTES: Add 10 percent for V-8 LeMans Rally Pkg.
Add 40 percent for GTO Judge.
Add 30 percent for 428.
Add 5 percent for Brougham trim.
Add 10 percent for Grand Prix S.J.
Add 20 percent for Ram Air IV.

	6	5	4	3	2	1
Firebird, V-8, 108" wb						
Firebird	450	1000	1650	3350	6300	9000
Esprit	450	1100	1700	3650	6650	9500
Formula 400	400	1300	2200	4400	7700	11,000
Trans Am	550	1700	2800	5600	9800	14,000

NOTES: Add 10 percent for V-8, (Firebird).
Add 25 percent for Trans Am with 4-speed.
Add 25 percent for Ram Air IV Firebird.

1971

	6	5	4	3	2	1
Ventura II, 6 cyl., 111" wb						
Cpe	150	350	750	1350	2800	4000
4 dr Sed	150	350	750	1450	3000	4200
Ventura II, V-8, 111" wb						
Cpe	125	250	700	1150	2500	3600
4 dr Sed	150	300	700	1250	2650	3800
LeMans T37, 6 cyl., 116" wb, 2 dr 112" wb						
2 dr Sed	150	400	750	1650	3150	4500
4 dr Sed	150	350	750	1350	2800	4000
2 dr HdTp	200	500	850	1900	3500	5000
LeMans, 6 cyl., 116" wb, 2 dr 112" wb						
2 dr Sed	150	350	750	1350	2800	4000
4 dr Sed	150	350	750	1450	2900	4100
4 dr HdTp	150	400	750	1600	3100	4400
2 dr HdTp	200	650	1050	2250	4200	6000
3S Sta Wag	150	350	750	1350	2800	4000
LeMans Sport, 6 cyl., 116" wb, 2 dr 112" wb						
4 dr HdTp	150	400	750	1550	3050	4300
2 dr HdTp	350	700	1150	2300	4550	6500
Conv	450	1100	1700	3650	6650	9500

NOTE: Add 10 percent for 8 cyl.

	6	5	4	3	2	1
LeMans GT 37, V-8, 112" wb						
2 dr HdTp	450	1000	1650	3350	6300	9000
GTO						
2 dr HdTp	500	1550	2600	5200	9100	13,000
Conv	650	2050	3400	6800	11,900	17,000

NOTE: Add 40 percent for GTO Judge option.

	6	5	4	3	2	1
Catalina						
4 dr	125	250	700	1150	2500	3600
4 dr Sed	150	300	700	1250	2600	3700
2 dr HdTp	150	400	750	1650	3150	4500
Conv	350	800	1450	2750	5600	8000
Safari, V-8, 127" wb						
2S Sta Wag	150	300	700	1250	2600	3700
3S Sta Wag	150	300	700	1250	2650	3800
Catalina Brougham, V-8, 123" wb						
4 dr Sed	150	300	700	1250	2600	3700
4 dr HdTp	150	300	700	1250	2650	3800
2 dr HdTp	150	450	800	1750	3250	4700
Grand Safari, V-8, 127" wb						
2S Sta Wag	150	350	750	1350	2800	4000
3S Sta Wag	150	350	750	1450	2900	4100
Bonneville						
4 dr Sed	150	300	700	1250	2650	3800
4 dr HdTp	150	350	750	1450	2900	4100
2 dr HdTp	200	500	850	1900	3500	5000
Grandville						
4 dr HdTp	150	350	750	1350	2800	4000
2 dr HdTp	200	550	900	2000	3600	5200
Conv	450	1000	1650	3350	6300	9000
Grand Prix						
2 dr HdTp	200	650	1050	2250	4200	6000

Standard Catalog of American Cars

	6	5	4	3	2	1
Hurst "SSJ" Cpe	350	900	1550	3050	5900	8500
Firebird, V-8, 108" wb						
Firebird	450	1100	1700	3650	6650	9500
Esprit	450	1000	1650	3350	6300	9000
Formula	400	1200	2000	3950	7000	10,000
Trans Am	500	1550	2600	5200	9100	13,000

NOTES: Add 20 percent for V-8, (Firebird).
Add 25 percent for Formula 455.
Add 25 percent for 455 HO V-8.
(Formula Series – 350, 400, 455).

1972

	6	5	4	3	2	1
Ventura, 6 cyl., 111" wb						
4 dr Sed	150	300	700	1250	2600	3700
Cpe	125	250	700	1150	2450	3500

NOTE: Add 20 percent for V-8.

	6	5	4	3	2	1
LeMans, 6 cyl., 116" wb, 2 dr 112" wb						
Cpe	150	350	750	1350	2800	4000
4 dr Sed	150	300	700	1250	2600	3700
2 dr HdTp	350	700	1150	2300	4550	6500
Conv	450	1100	1700	3650	6650	9500
3S Sta Wag	150	350	750	1350	2800	4000
GTO 2 dr HdTp	400	1300	2200	4400	7700	11,000
Luxury LeMans, V-8						
4 dr HdTp	150	350	750	1450	3000	4200
2 dr HdTp	350	750	1200	2350	4900	7000

NOTE: Add 20 percent for V-8.

	6	5	4	3	2	1
Catalina, V-8, 123" wb						
4 dr Sed	125	250	700	1150	2450	3500
4 dr HdTp	150	300	700	1250	2600	3700
2 dr HdTp	150	400	750	1650	3150	4500
Conv	350	750	1300	2450	5250	7500
Catalina Brougham, V-8, 123" wb						
4 dr Sed	125	250	700	1150	2500	3600
4 dr HdTp	150	350	750	1350	2800	4000
2 dr HdTp	200	500	850	1900	3500	5000
Bonneville						
4 dr Sed	150	300	700	1250	2600	3700
4 dr HdTp	150	400	750	1650	3150	4500
2 dr HdTp	200	600	950	2150	3850	5500
Grandville						
4 dr HdTp	150	400	750	1650	3150	4500
2 dr HdTp	200	600	1000	2200	4000	5700
Conv	350	900	1550	3050	5900	8500
Safari, V-8, 127" wb						
2S Sta Wag	125	250	700	1150	2500	3600
3S Sta Wag	150	300	700	1250	2600	3700
Grand Safari, V-8, 127" wb						
2S Sta Wag	150	300	700	1250	2650	3800
3S Sta Wag	150	300	750	1350	2700	3900
Grand Prix						
Hurst "SSJ" HdTp	350	700	1150	2300	4550	6500
2 dr HdTp	200	550	900	2000	3600	5200
Firebird, V-8, 108" wb						
Firebird	450	1100	1700	3650	6650	9500
Esprit	450	1000	1650	3350	6300	9000
Formula	400	1200	2000	3950	7000	10,000
Trans Am	500	1550	2600	5200	9100	13,000

NOTES: Add 20 percent for V-8, (Firebird).
Add 10 percent for Trans Am with 4-speed.

1973

	6	5	4	3	2	1
Ventura						
4 dr Sed	150	300	700	1250	2600	3700
Cpe	125	250	700	1150	2400	3400
Hatch Cpe	150	300	700	1250	2650	3800
Ventura Custom						
4 dr Sed	150	300	700	1250	2650	3800
Cpe	150	300	750	1350	2700	3900
Hatch Cpe	125	250	700	1150	2500	3600

NOTE: Deduct 5 percent for 6-cyl.

	6	5	4	3	2	1
LeMans						
4 dr Sed	150	350	750	1350	2800	4000
2 dr HdTp	150	350	750	1450	3000	4200
LeMans Spt						
Cpe	150	400	750	1650	3150	4500
Luxury LeMans						
Cpe	150	450	800	1750	3250	4700
4 dr HdTp	150	400	750	1650	3150	4500
LeMans Safari, V-8, 116" wb						
2S Sta Wag	150	350	750	1350	2800	4000
3S Sta Wag	150	350	750	1350	2800	4000
Grand AM						
2 dr HdTp	350	750	1200	2350	4900	7000
4 dr HdTp	200	500	850	1900	3500	5000
GTO Spt Cpe	350	700	1150	2300	4550	6500
Deduct 5 percent for 6-cyl.						
Catalina						
4 dr HdTp	125	250	700	1150	2500	3600
2 dr HdTp	150	350	750	1350	2800	4000
Bonneville						
4 dr Sed	125	250	700	1150	2500	3600
4 dr HdTp	150	350	750	1350	2800	4000
2 dr HdTp	150	400	750	1600	3100	4400
Safari, V-8, 127" wb						
2S Sta Wag	150	350	750	1350	2800	4000
3S Sta Wag	150	350	750	1450	2900	4100
Grand Safari, V-8, 127" wb						
2S Sta Wag	150	350	750	1450	3000	4200
3S Sta Wag	150	400	750	1550	3050	4300
Grandville						
4 dr HdTp	150	350	750	1450	3000	4200
2 dr HdTp	150	450	750	1700	3200	4600
Conv	350	800	1450	2750	5600	8000
Grand Prix						
2 dr HdTp	200	500	850	1900	3500	5000
2 dr 'SJ' HdTp	200	550	900	2000	3600	5200
Firebird, V-8, 108" wb						
Cpe	350	900	1550	3050	5900	8500
Esprit	450	1000	1650	3350	6300	9000
Formula	450	1100	1700	3650	6650	9500
Trans Am	400	1200	2000	3950	7000	10,000

NOTE: Add 10 percent for V-8, (Firebird).
Add 50 percent for 455 SD V-8 (Formula & Trans Am only).

1974

	6	5	4	3	2	1
Ventura						
4 dr Sed	150	300	700	1250	2600	3700
Cpe	125	250	700	1150	2400	3400
Hatch	150	300	700	1250	2650	3800
Ventura Custom						
4 dr Sed	150	300	700	1250	2650	3800
Cpe	125	250	700	1150	2450	3500
Hatch	150	300	750	1350	2700	3900
GTO	200	600	950	2150	3850	5500

NOTE: Deduct 4 percent for 6-cyl.

	6	5	4	3	2	1
LeMans						
4 dr HdTp	125	200	600	1100	2250	3200
2 dr HdTp	150	300	700	1250	2600	3700
Sta Wag	125	250	700	1150	2450	3500
LeMans Sport						
2 dr Cpe	150	350	750	1350	2800	4000
Luxury LeMans						
4 dr HdTp	150	300	700	1250	2650	3800
2 dr HdTp	150	350	750	1450	3000	4200
Safari	150	350	750	1350	2800	4000

NOTE: Add 10 percent for GT option.

	6	5	4	3	2	1
Grand AM						
2 dr HdTp	350	750	1200	2350	4900	7000
4 dr HdTp	150	450	800	1800	3300	4800
Catalina						
4 dr HdTp	150	300	700	1250	2650	3800
2 dr HdTp	150	350	750	1350	2800	4000
4 dr Sed	100	175	525	1050	2100	3000
Safari	150	300	700	1250	2650	3800
Bonneville						
4 dr Sed	125	200	600	1100	2250	3200
4 dr HdTp	150	350	750	1350	2800	4000
2 dr HdTp	150	400	750	1600	3100	4400
Grandville						
4 dr HdTp	150	350	750	1450	2900	4100
2 dr HdTp	150	400	750	1650	3150	4500
Conv	350	800	1450	2750	5600	8000
Grand Prix						
2 dr HdTp	200	500	850	1900	3500	5000
'SJ' Cpe	200	550	900	2000	3600	5200
Firebird, V-8, 108" wb						
Firebird	350	750	1300	2450	5250	7500
Esprit	350	800	1450	2750	5600	8000
Formula	450	1100	1700	3650	6650	9500
Trans Am	400	1200	2000	3950	7000	10,000

NOTE: Add 10 percent for V-8, (Firebird).
Add 40 percent for 455-SD V-8 (Formula & Trans Am only).

1975

	6	5	4	3	2	1
Astre S						
2 dr Cpe	100	175	525	1050	1950	2800
2 dr Hatch	100	175	525	1050	2050	2900
Safari	100	175	525	1050	2100	3000
Astre						
2 dr Hatch	125	200	600	1100	2200	3100
Safari	125	200	600	1100	2250	3200

NOTE: Add 10 percent for Astre 'SJ'.

	6	5	4	3	2	1
Ventura						
4 dr Sed	125	200	600	1100	2300	3300
2 dr Cpe	125	250	700	1150	2450	3500
2 dr Hatch	125	250	700	1150	2500	3600

NOTES: Deduct 5 percent for Ventura 'S'.
Add 15 percent for Ventura 'SJ'.
Add 5 percent for Ventura Custom.

	6	5	4	3	2	1
LeMans						
4 dr HdTp	100	175	525	1050	2100	3000
2 dr HdTp	125	250	700	1150	2450	3500
Safari	125	250	700	1150	2400	3400

NOTE: Add 10 percent for Grand LeMans.

	6	5	4	3	2	1
LeMans Sport						
2 dr HdTp Cpe	150	300	700	1250	2600	3700
Grand AM						
4 dr HdTp	125	250	700	1150	2500	3600
2 dr HdTp	150	350	750	1350	2800	4000

NOTE: Add 5 percent for four-speed and bucket seats.
Add 20 percent for 455 H.O. V-8.

	6	5	4	3	2	1
Catalina						
4 dr Sed	125	200	600	1100	2200	3100
2 dr Cpe	125	250	700	1150	2450	3500
Safari	100	175	525	1050	2100	3000
Bonneville						
4 dr HdTp	125	200	600	1100	2300	3300
2 dr Cpe	125	250	700	1150	2500	3600
Gr. Safari	125	250	700	1150	2400	3400
Grand Ville Brougham						
4 dr HdTp	125	200	600	1100	2300	3300
2 dr Cpe	150	300	700	1250	2650	3800
Conv	350	800	1450	2750	5600	8000

NOTE: Add 20 percent for 455 V-8.

	6	5	4	3	2	1
Grand Prix						
Cpe	150	400	750	1650	3150	4500
'LJ' Cpe	150	450	750	1700	3200	4600
'SJ' Cpe	150	450	800	1750	3250	4700

NOTE: Add 12 percent for 455 V-8.
Add 5 percent for Custom interior.

	6	5	4	3	2	1
Firebird, V-8, 108" wb						
Cpe	350	700	1150	2300	4550	6500
Esprit	350	750	1300	2450	5250	7500
Formula	350	750	1300	2450	5250	7500
Trans Am	350	900	1550	3050	5900	8500

NOTE: Add 18 percent for 455 H.O. V-8.
Add 5 percent for four speed.
Add $150.00 for Honeycomb wheels.

STUDEBAKER

1946

	6	5	4	3	2	1
Skyway Champion, 6-cyl., 109.5" wb						
3P Cpe	350	700	1150	2300	4550	6500
5P Cpe	350	725	1150	2300	4700	6700
2 dr Sed	350	725	1150	2300	4700	6700
Sed	350	725	1200	2350	4850	6900

1947

	6	5	4	3	2	1
Champion, 6-cyl., 112" wb						
3P Cpe	200	650	1000	2200	4100	5800

	6	5	4	3	2	1
5P Cpe Starlite	350	750	1200	2350	4900	7000
2 dr Sed	200	650	1000	2200	4150	5900
Sed	200	650	1050	2250	4200	6000
Conv	650	2050	3400	6800	11,900	17,000
Commander, 6-cyl., 119" wb						
3P Cpe	200	650	1050	2250	4200	6000
5P Cpe Starlite	350	750	1300	2450	5250	7500
2 dr Sed	200	650	1050	2250	4200	6000
Sed	200	675	1100	2250	4400	6300
Conv	700	2150	3600	7200	12,600	18,000
Land Cruiser, 6-cyl., 123" wb						
Ld Crs	350	750	1300	2450	5250	7500

1948

	6	5	4	3	2	1
Champion, 6-cyl., 112" wb						
3P Cpe	200	650	1000	2200	4100	5800
5P Cpe Starlight	350	750	1300	2400	5200	7400
2 dr Sed	200	650	1000	2200	4150	5900
Sed	200	650	1050	2250	4200	6000
Conv	700	2150	3600	7200	12,600	18,000
Commander, 6-cyl., 119" wb						
3P Cpe	200	650	1050	2250	4200	6000
5P Cpe Starlight	350	750	1350	2650	5450	7800
2 dr Sed	200	650	1050	2250	4200	6000
Sed	200	675	1100	2250	4400	6300
Conv	700	2300	3800	7600	13,300	19,000
Land Cruiser, 6-cyl., 123" wb						
Ld Crs Sed	350	750	1350	2600	5400	7700

1949

	6	5	4	3	2	1
Champion, 6-cyl., 112" wb						
3P Cpe	200	600	1000	2200	4000	5700
5P Cpe Starlight	350	750	1300	2400	5200	7400
2 dr Sed	200	600	1000	2200	4000	5700
Sed	200	650	1000	2200	4100	5800
Conv	700	2150	3600	7200	12,600	18,000
Commander, 6-cyl., 119" wb						
3P Cpe	200	675	1050	2250	4300	6100
5P Cpe Starlight	350	750	1350	2650	5450	7800
2 dr Sed	200	675	1050	2250	4300	6100
Sed	200	675	1100	2250	4400	6300
Conv	700	2300	3800	7600	13,300	19,000
Land Cruiser, 6-cyl., 123" wb						
Ld Crs Sed	350	750	1350	2600	5400	7700

1950

	6	5	4	3	2	1
Champion, 6-cyl., 113" wb						
3P Cpe	200	675	1050	2250	4300	6100
5P Cpe Starlight	350	750	1300	2450	5250	7500
2 dr Sed	200	675	1050	2250	4300	6100
Sed	200	675	1100	2250	4400	6300
Conv	700	2300	3800	7600	13,300	19,000
Commander, 6-cyl., 120" - 124" wb						
3P Cpe	200	675	1100	2250	4400	6300
5P Cpe Starlight	350	800	1450	2750	5600	8000
2 dr Sed	200	675	1100	2250	4400	6300
Sed	350	700	1100	2300	4500	6400
Conv	750	2400	4000	8000	14,000	20,000
Land Cruiser, 6-cyl., 124" wb						
Ld Crs Sed	350	800	1450	2750	5600	8000

1951

	6	5	4	3	2	1
Champion Custom, 6-cyl., 115" wb						
Sed	200	600	950	2200	3900	5600
2 dr Sed	200	600	950	2150	3850	5500
5P Cpe Starlight	350	750	1300	2450	5250	7500
3P Cpe	200	550	900	2100	3700	5300
Champion DeLuxe, 6-cyl., 115" wb						
Sed	200	600	1000	2200	4000	5700
2 dr Sed	200	600	950	2200	3900	5600
5P Cpe Starlight	350	750	1350	2600	5400	7700
3P Cpe	200	550	900	2150	3800	5400
Champion Regal, 6-cyl., 115" wb						
Sed	200	650	1000	2200	4100	5800
2 dr Sed	200	600	1000	2200	4000	5700
5P Cpe Starlight	350	800	1450	2750	5600	8000
3P Cpe	200	600	950	2150	3850	5500
Conv	700	2300	3800	7600	13,300	19,000
Commander Regal, V-8, 115" wb						
Sed	200	650	1000	2200	4100	5800
2 dr Sed	200	600	950	2200	3900	5600
5P Cpe Starlight	450	1000	1650	3350	6300	9000
Commander State, V-8, 115" wb						
Sed	200	675	1100	2250	4400	6300
2 dr Sed	200	675	1050	2250	4350	6200
5P Cpe Starlight	450	1050	1700	3600	6600	9400
Conv	800	2500	4200	8400	14,700	21,000
Land Cruiser, V-8, 119" wb						
Sed	350	850	1500	2900	5700	8200

1952

	6	5	4	3	2	1
Champion Custom, 6-cyl., 115" wb						
Sed	200	600	950	2200	3900	5600
2 dr Sed	200	600	950	2150	3850	5500
5P Cpe Starlight	350	750	1300	2450	5250	7500
Champion DeLuxe, 6-cyl., 115" wb						
Sed	200	600	1000	2200	4000	5700
2 dr Sed	200	600	950	2200	3900	5600
5P Cpe Starlight	350	750	1350	2600	5400	7700
Champion Regal, 6-cyl., 115" wb						
Sed	200	650	1000	2200	4100	5800
2 dr Sed	200	600	1000	2200	4000	5700
5P Cpe Starlight	350	800	1450	2750	5600	8000
Star Cpe	350	900	1550	3050	5900	8500
Conv	700	2150	3600	7200	12,600	18,000
Commander Regal, V-8, 115" wb						
Sed	200	650	1050	2250	4200	6000
2 dr Sed	200	650	1000	2200	4100	5800
5P Cpe Starlight	350	900	1550	3050	5900	8500
Commander State, V-8, 115" wb						
Sed	200	675	1050	2250	4300	6100
2 dr Sed	200	650	1000	2200	4150	5900
Cpe Starlight	450	950	1600	3250	6150	8800
Star HdTp	400	1200	2000	3950	7000	10,000
Conv	700	2300	3800	7600	13,300	19,000
Land Cruiser, V-8, 119" wb						
Sed	350	850	1500	2800	5650	8100

1953

	6	5	4	3	2	1
Champion Custom, 6-cyl., 116.5" wb						
4 dr Sed	200	500	850	1900	3500	5000
2 dr Sed	150	450	800	1750	3250	4700
Champion DeLuxe, 6-cyl., 116.5" - 120.5" wb						
4 dr Sed	200	500	850	1950	3600	5100
2 dr Sed	150	450	800	1800	3300	4800
5P Cpe	350	800	1450	2750	5600	8000
Champion Regal, 6-cyl., 116.5" - 120.5" wb						
4 dr Sed	200	550	900	2000	3600	5200
2 dr Sed	200	500	850	1850	3350	4900
Cpe	450	1000	1650	3350	6300	9000
HdTp	400	1200	2000	3950	7000	10,000
Commander DeLuxe, V-8, 116.5" - 120.5" wb						
4 dr Sed	200	550	900	2100	3700	5300
2 dr Sed	200	500	850	1900	3500	5000
Cpe	400	1200	2000	3950	7000	10,000
Commander Regal, V-8, 116.5" - 120.5" wb						
4 dr Sed	200	600	950	2150	3850	5500
Cpe	400	1300	2200	4400	7700	11,000
HdTp	450	1450	2400	4800	8400	12,000
Land Cruiser, V-8, 120.5" wb						
4 dr Sed	350	750	1250	2400	5050	7200

1954

	6	5	4	3	2	1
Champion Custom, 6-cyl., 116.5" wb						
4 dr Sed	150	450	800	1800	3300	4800
2 dr Sed	150	450	750	1700	3200	4600
Champion DeLuxe, 6-cyl., 116.5" - 120.5" wb						
4 dr Sed	200	500	850	1850	3350	4900
2 dr Sed	150	450	750	1700	3200	4600
Cpe	350	800	1450	2750	5600	8000
Sta Wag	200	550	900	2000	3600	5200
Champion Regal, 6-cyl., 116.5" - 120.5" wb						
4 dr Sed	200	500	850	1900	3500	5000
2 dr Sed	150	450	800	1750	3250	4700
5P Cpe	450	1000	1650	3350	6300	9000
HdTp	400	1200	2000	3950	7000	10,000
Sta Wag	200	600	950	2150	3850	5500
Commander DeLuxe, V-8, 116.5" - 120.5" wb						
4 dr Sed	200	550	900	2100	3700	5300
2 dr Sed	200	550	900	2000	3600	5200
Cpe	400	1200	2000	3950	7000	10,000
Sta Wag	200	600	1000	2200	4000	5700
Commander Regal, V-8, 116.5" - 120.5" wb						
4 dr Sed	200	600	950	2150	3850	5500
Cpe	400	1300	2200	4400	7700	11,000
HdTp	450	1450	2400	4800	8400	12,000
Sta Wag	200	650	1050	2250	4200	6000
Land Cruiser, V-8, 120.5" wb						
4 dr Sed	350	725	1200	2350	4800	6800
4 dr Reg Sed	350	750	1200	2350	4900	7000

1955

	6	5	4	3	2	1
Champion Custom, 6-cyl., 116.5" wb						
4 dr Sed	150	450	800	1750	3250	4700
2 dr Sed	150	450	750	1700	3200	4600
Champion DeLuxe, 6-cyl., 116.5" wb, 120.5" wb						
4 dr Sed	200	500	850	1850	3350	4900
2 dr Sed	150	450	800	1750	3250	4700
Cpe	450	1000	1650	3350	6300	9000
Champion Regal, 6-cyl., 116.5" wb, 120.5" wb						
4 dr Sed	200	500	850	1950	3600	5100
Cpe	450	1100	1700	3650	6650	9500
2 dr HdTp	400	1200	2000	3950	7000	10,000
Sta Wag	200	600	950	2150	3850	5500
Commander Custom, V-8, 116.5" wb						
4 dr Sed	200	550	900	2000	3600	5200
2 dr Sed	200	500	850	1950	3600	5100
Commander DeLuxe, V-8, 116.5" - 120.5" wb						
4 dr Sed	200	550	900	2100	3700	5300
2 dr Sed	200	550	900	2000	3600	5200
Cpe	400	1250	2100	4200	7400	10,500
Sta Wag	200	600	1000	2200	4000	5700
Commander Regal, V-8, 116.5" - 120.5" wb						
4 dr Sed	200	550	900	2150	3800	5400
Cpe	400	1300	2200	4400	7700	11,000
HdTp	450	1450	2400	4800	8400	12,000
Sta Wag	200	650	1050	2250	4200	6000
President DeLuxe, V-8, 120.5" wb						
4 dr Sed	200	650	1050	2250	4200	6000
President State, V-8, 120.5" wb						
4 dr Sed	200	675	1050	2250	4350	6200
Cpe	450	1450	2400	4800	8400	12,000
HdTp	550	1700	2800	5600	9800	14,000
Spds HdTp	600	1900	3200	6400	11,200	16,000

NOTE: Deduct $200. for Champion models in all series.

1956

	6	5	4	3	2	1
Champion, 6-cyl., 116.5" wb						
4 dr Sed	150	450	750	1700	3200	4600
2 dr S'net	150	400	750	1600	3100	4400
2 dr Sed	150	400	750	1650	3150	4500
Flight Hawk, 6-cyl., 120.5" wb						
Cpe	450	1100	1700	3650	6650	9500
Champion Pelham, 6-cyl., 116.5" wb						
Sta Wag	200	600	950	2150	3850	5500
Commander, V-8, 116.5" wb						
4 dr Sed	200	550	900	2100	3700	5300
2 dr S'net	200	550	900	2000	3600	5200
2 dr Sed	200	550	900	2100	3700	5300
Power Hawk, V-8, 120.5" wb						
Cpe	400	1250	2100	4200	7400	10,500
Commander Parkview, V-8, 116.5" wb						
2 dr Sta Wag	200	600	950	2150	3850	5500
President, V-8, 116.5" wb						
4 dr Sed	200	600	950	2150	3850	5500
4 dr Classic	200	650	1000	2200	4100	5800
2 dr Sed	200	550	900	2150	3800	5400
Sky Hawk, V-8, 120.5" wb						
HdTp	500	1550	2600	5200	9100	13,000
President Pinehurst, V-8, 116.5" wb						
Sta Wag	200	675	1050	2250	4350	6200
Golden Hawk, V-8, 120.5" wb						
HdTp	700	2150	3600	7200	12,600	18,000

	6	5	4	3	2	1
1957						
Champion Scotsman, 6-cyl., 116.5" wb						
4 dr Sed	150	400	750	1600	3100	4400
2 dr Sed	150	400	750	1600	3100	4400
Sta Wag	150	400	750	1650	3150	4500
Champion Custom, 6-cyl., 116.5" wb						
4 dr Sed	150	400	750	1650	3150	4500
2 dr Clb Sed	150	400	750	1650	3150	4500
Champion DeLuxe, 6-cyl., 116.5" wb						
4 dr Sed	150	450	750	1700	3200	4600
2 dr Clb Sed	150	400	750	1600	3100	4400
Silver Hawk, 6-cyl., 120.5" wb						
Cpe	350	800	1450	2750	5600	8000
Champion Pelham, 6-cyl., 116.5" wb						
Sta Wag	200	500	850	1900	3500	5000
Commander Custom, V-8, 116.5" wb						
4 dr Sed	150	450	750	1700	3200	4600
2 dr Clb Sed	150	400	750	1650	3150	4500
Commander DeLuxe, V-8, 116.5" wb						
4 dr Sed	200	500	850	1900	3500	5000
2 dr Clb Sed	150	450	800	1800	3300	4800
Commander Station Wagons, V-8, 116.5" wb						
Park	200	650	1000	2200	4100	5800
Prov	200	675	1050	2250	4350	6200
President, V-8, 116.5" wb						
4 dr Sed	200	650	1000	2200	4150	5900
4 dr Classic	200	650	1050	2250	4200	6000
2 dr Clb Sed	200	650	1000	2200	4100	5800
Silver Hawk, V-8, 120.5" wb						
Cpe	450	1450	2400	4800	8400	12,000
President Broadmoor, V-8, 116.5" wb						
4 dr Sta Wag	350	700	1150	2300	4550	6500
Golden Hawk, V-8, 120.5" wb						
Spt HdTp	700	2150	3600	7200	12,600	18,000
1958						
Champion Scotsman, 6-cyl., 116.5" wb						
4 dr Sed	150	350	750	1450	3000	4200
2 dr Sed	150	350	750	1450	2900	4100
Sta Wag	150	400	750	1550	3050	4300
Champion, 6-cyl., 116.5" wb						
4 dr Sed	150	400	750	1550	3050	4300
2 dr Sed	150	350	750	1450	3000	4200
Silver Hawk, 6-cyl., 120.5" wb						
Cpe	450	1000	1650	3350	6300	9000
Commander, V-8, 116.5" wb						
4 dr Sed	150	400	750	1600	3100	4400
HdTp	200	650	1050	2250	4200	6000
Sta Wag	150	450	800	1750	3250	4700
President, V-8, 120.5" & 116.5" wb						
4 dr Sed	150	450	800	1750	3250	4700
HdTp	200	675	1050	2250	4350	6200
Silver Hawk, V-8, 120.5" wb						
Cpe	450	1450	2400	4800	8400	12,000
Golden Hawk, V-8, 120.5" wb						
Spt HdTp	600	1900	3200	6400	11,200	16,000
1959						
Lark DeLuxe, 6-cyl., 108" wb						
4 dr Sed	150	400	750	1550	3050	4300
2 dr Sed	150	400	750	1550	3050	4300
Sta Wag	150	400	750	1550	3050	4300
Lark Regal, 6-cyl., 108" wb						
4 dr Sed	150	400	750	1550	3050	4300
2 dr HdTp	200	600	950	2150	3850	5500
Sta Wag	150	400	750	1550	3050	4300
Lark Regal, V-8, 108.5" wb						
4 dr Sed	150	400	750	1650	3150	4500
HdTp	200	650	1050	2250	4200	6000
Sta Wag	150	450	750	1700	3200	4600
Silver Hawk, V-8, 108.5" wb						
Spt Cpe	400	1300	2200	4400	7700	11,000
NOTE: Deduct 10 percent for 6 cyl. models.						
1960						
Lark DeLuxe, V-8, 108.5" wb						
4 dr Sed	150	400	750	1550	3050	4300
2 dr Sed	150	400	750	1600	3100	4400
4 dr Sta Wag	150	400	750	1600	3100	4400
2 dr Sta Wag	150	450	750	1700	3200	4600
Lark Regal, V-8, 108.5" wb						
4 dr Sed	150	400	750	1650	3150	4500
HdTp	200	650	1050	2250	4200	6000
Conv	400	1300	2200	4400	7700	11,000
Sta Wag	150	450	800	1800	3300	4800
NOTE: Deduct 5 percent for 6 cyl. models.						
Hawk, V-8, 120.5" wb						
Spt Cpe	450	1450	2400	4800	8400	12,000
1961						
Lark DeLuxe, V-8, 108.5" wb						
4 dr Sed	150	400	750	1550	3050	4300
2 dr Sed	150	400	750	1600	3100	4400
Lark Regal, V-8, 108.5" wb						
4 dr Sed	150	400	750	1650	3150	4500
HdTp	200	650	1050	2250	4200	6000
Conv	400	1300	2200	4400	7700	11,000
Lark Cruiser, V-8, 113" wb						
4 dr Sed	150	450	800	1750	3250	4700
Station Wagons, V-8, 113" wb						
4 dr DeL	150	400	750	1550	3050	4300
2 dr	150	400	750	1550	3050	4300
4 dr Reg	150	400	750	1600	3100	4400
Hawk, 8-cyl., 120.5" wb						
Spt Cpe	500	1550	2600	5200	9100	13,000
NOTE: Deduct 5 percent for 6 cyl. models. First year for 4-speed Hawks.						
1962						
Lark DeLuxe, V-8, 109" - 113" wb						
4 dr Sed	150	400	750	1550	3050	4300
2 dr Sed	150	400	750	1550	3050	4300
Sta Wag	150	450	800	1800	3300	4800
Lark Regal, V-8, 109" - 113" wb						
4 dr Sed	150	400	750	1550	3050	4300
2 dr HdTp	350	750	1200	2350	4900	7000
Conv	400	1200	2000	3950	7000	10,000
Sta Wag	200	500	850	1900	3500	5000
Lark Daytona, V-8, 109" wb						
HdTp	350	800	1450	2750	5600	8000

	6	5	4	3	2	1
Conv	400	1250	2100	4200	7400	10,500
Lark Cruiser, V-8, 113" wb						
4 dr Sed	200	550	900	2100	3700	5300
Gran Turismo Hawk, V-8, 120.5" wb						
HdTp	500	1550	2600	5200	9100	13,000
NOTE: Deduct 5 percent for 6 cyl. models.						
1963						
Lark Standard, V-8, 109" - 113" wb						
4 dr Sed	150	400	750	1550	3050	4300
2 dr Sed	150	400	750	1550	3050	4300
Sta Wag	200	500	850	1900	3500	5000
Lark Regal, V-8, 109" - 113" wb						
4 dr Sed	150	400	750	1550	3050	4300
2 dr Sed	150	400	750	1550	3050	4300
Sta Wag	200	550	900	2000	3600	5200
Lark Custom, V-8, 109" - 113" wb						
4 dr Sed	150	400	750	1550	3050	4300
2 dr Sed	150	400	750	1600	3100	4400
Lark Daytona, V-8, 109" - 113" wb						
2 dr HdTp	350	900	1550	3050	5900	8500
Conv	400	1250	2100	4200	7400	10,500
Sta Wag	350	700	1100	2300	4500	6400
Cruiser, V-8, 113" wb						
4 dr Sed	350	700	1100	2300	4500	6400
Gran Turismo Hawk, V-8, 120.5" wb						
2 dr HdTp	550	1700	2800	5600	9800	14,000
NOTE: Deduct 5 percent for 6 cyl.						
Add 10 percent for R1 engine option.						
Add 20 percent for R2 engine option.						
Add 30 percent for R3 engine option.						
1964						
Challenger V-8, 109" - 113" wb						
4 dr Sed	150	400	750	1600	3100	4400
2 dr Sed	150	400	750	1650	3150	4500
Sta Wag	150	450	800	1750	3250	4700
Commander, V-8, 109" - 113" wb						
4 dr Sed	150	450	750	1700	3200	4600
2 dr Sed	150	450	800	1750	3250	4700
Sta Wag	200	500	850	1900	3500	5000
Daytona, V-8, 109" - 113" wb						
4 dr Sed	200	500	850	1900	3500	5000
HdTp	450	1000	1650	3350	6300	9000
Conv	400	1250	2100	4200	7400	10,500
Sta Wag	350	700	1150	2300	4550	6500
Cruiser, V-8, 113" wb						
4 dr Sed	350	700	1150	2300	4550	6500
Gran Turismo Hawk, V-8, 120.5" wb						
HdTp	550	1700	2800	5600	9800	14,000
NOTE: Deduct 5 percent for 6 cyl. models.						
Add 10 percent for R1 engine option.						
Add 20 percent for R2 engine option.						
Add 30 percent for R3 engine option.						
1965						
Commander, V-8, 109" - 113" wb						
4 dr Sed	150	450	800	1750	3250	4700
2 dr Sed	150	450	800	1800	3300	4800
Sta Wag	200	500	850	1850	3350	4900
Daytona, V-8, 109" - 113" wb						
Spt Sed	200	500	850	1950	3600	5100
Sta Wag	200	550	900	2150	3800	5400
Cruiser, V-8, 113" wb						
4 dr Sed	200	600	1000	2200	4000	5700
NOTE: Deduct 10 percent for 6 cyl. models.						
1966						
Commander, V-8, 109" wb						
4 dr Sed	150	450	800	1800	3300	4800
2 dr Sed	200	500	850	1850	3350	4900
Daytona, V-8, 109" - 113" wb						
2 dr Spt Sed	200	600	950	2200	3900	5600
Cruiser, V-8, 113" wb						
4 dr Sed	200	600	1000	2200	4000	5700
Wagonaire, V-8, 113" wb						
Sta Wag	200	650	1000	2200	4100	5800

AVANTI

	6	5	4	3	2	1
1963						
Avanti, V-8, 109" wb						
2 dr Spt Cpe	750	2400	4000	8000	14,000	20,000
NOTE: Add 20 percent for R2 engine option.						
1964						
Avanti, V-8, 109" wb						
2 dr Spt Cpe	700	2300	3800	7600	13,300	19,000
NOTE: Add 20 percent for R2 engine option.						
Add 60 percent for R3 engine option.						

WILLYS

	6	5	4	3	2	1
1946-47						
Willys 4-63, 4-cyl., 104" wb, 63 hp						
Sta Wag	350	700	1150	2300	4550	6500
1948						
Willys 4-63, 4-cyl., 104" wb, 63 hp						
Sta Wag	350	700	1150	2300	4550	6500
Jeepster	450	1000	1650	3350	6300	9000
Willys 6-63, 6-cyl., 104" wb, 75 hp						
Sta Sed	350	700	1150	2300	4550	6500
Jeepster	450	1100	1700	3650	6650	9500
1949						
Willys 4X463, 4-cyl., 104.5" wb, 63 hp						
FWD Sta Wag	350	700	1150	2300	4550	6500

	6	5	4	3	2	1
Willys VJ3, 4-cyl., 104" wb, 63 hp						
Phae	450	1000	1650	3350	6300	9000
Willys 463, 4-cyl., 104" wb, 63 hp						
Sta Wag	200	650	1050	2250	4200	6000
Willys Six, 6-cyl., 104" wb, 75 hp						
Phae	450	1100	1700	3650	6650	9500
Willys Six, 6-cyl., 104" wb, 75 hp						
Sta Sed	350	725	1200	2350	4800	6800
Sta Wag	350	700	1150	2300	4550	6500

1950-51
	6	5	4	3	2	1
Willys 473SW, 4-cyl., 104" wb, 63 hp						
Sta Wag	200	600	950	2150	3850	5500
Willys 4X473SW, 4-cyl., 104.5" wb, 63 hp						
FWD Sta Wag	200	650	1050	2250	4200	6000
Willys 473VJ, 4-cyl., 104" wb, 63 hp						
Phae	450	1100	1700	3650	6650	9500

NOTE: Add 10 percent for six cylinder models.

1952
	6	5	4	3	2	1
Willys Aero, 6-cyl., 108" wb, 75 hp						
2 dr Lark	150	400	750	1650	3150	4500
2 dr Wing	150	450	800	1750	3250	4700
2 dr Ace	200	500	850	1950	3600	5100
2 dr HdTp Eagle	200	600	950	2150	3850	5500
Willys Four, 4-cyl., 104"-104.5" wb, 63 hp						
FWD Sta Wag	200	650	1050	2250	4200	6000
Sta Wag	200	600	950	2150	3850	5500
Willys Six, 6-cyl., 104" wb, 75 hp						
Sta Wag	200	650	1000	2200	4100	5800

NOTE: Deduct 10 percent for standard models.

1953
	6	5	4	3	2	1
Willys Aero, 6-cyl., 108" wb, 90 hp						
4 dr H.D. Aero	200	550	900	2100	3700	5300
4 dr DeL Lark	150	450	800	1800	3300	4800
2 dr DeL Lark	200	500	850	1900	3500	5000
4 dr Falcon	200	500	850	1950	3600	5100
2 dr Falcon	200	500	850	1900	3500	5000
4 dr Ace	200	550	900	2100	3700	5300
2 dr Ace	200	500	850	1950	3600	5100
2 dr HdTp Eagle	350	700	1150	2300	4550	6500
Willys Four, 4-cyl., 104"-104.5" wb, 72 hp						
FWD Sta Wag	200	650	1050	2250	4200	6000
Sta Wag	200	600	950	2150	3850	5500
Willys Six, 6-cyl., 104" wb, 90 hp						
Sta Wag	200	650	1000	2200	4100	5800

1954
	6	5	4	3	2	1
Willys, 6-cyl., 108" wb, 90 hp						
4 dr DeL Ace	200	500	850	1850	3350	4900
2 dr DeL Ace	150	450	800	1750	3250	4700
2 dr HdTp Eagle	200	600	950	2200	3900	5600
2 dr HdTp Cus Eagle	200	650	1050	2250	4200	6000
4 dr Lark	150	450	800	1750	3250	4700
2 dr Lark	150	450	750	1700	3200	4600
4 dr Ace	150	450	800	1750	3250	4700
2 dr Ace	150	450	750	1700	3200	4600
2 dr HdTp Eagle	350	700	1150	2300	4550	6500
Willys Four, 4-cyl., 104"-104.5" wb, 72 hp						
Sta Wag	200	600	950	2150	3850	5500
Willys Six, 6-cyl., 104" wb, 90 hp						
FWD Sta Wag	200	650	1050	2250	4200	6000
Sta Wag	200	650	1000	2200	4100	5800

1955
	6	5	4	3	2	1
Willys Six, 6-cyl., 108" wb, 90 hp						
4 dr Cus Sed	200	550	900	2100	3700	5300
2 dr Cus	200	650	1000	2200	4100	5800
2 dr HdTp Bermuda	400	1200	2000	3950	7000	10,000
Willys Six, 6-cyl., 104"-104.5" wb, 90 hp						
FWD Sta Wag	200	650	1050	2250	4200	6000
Sta Wag	200	600	950	2150	3850	5500

ALTERNATIVE CARS

AIRSCOOT
	6	5	4	3	2	1
1947						
Airscoot, 1-cyl						
2P	125	250	700	1150	2450	3500

AIRWAY
	6	5	4	3	2	1
1949-1950						
Sedan, 100" wb						
2d, 3P	150	350	750	1350	2800	4000
Town Traveler, 100" wb						
2d Cpe, 2P	150	350	750	1450	2900	4100

ALLSTATE
	6	5	4	3	2	1
1952						
Series 4, 4-cyl, 100" wb, 134.2 cid						
Model 110						
2d Sed	450	1000	1650	3350	6300	9000
Model 111, Std.						
2d Sed	450	1050	1650	3500	6400	9200

	6	5	4	3	2	1
Model 113, DeL						
2d Sed	450	1050	1700	3550	6500	9300
Series 6, 6-cyl, 100" wb, 161 cid						
Model 115						
2d Sed	450	1050	1650	3500	6400	9200
2d DeL Sed	450	1050	1700	3600	6600	9400
1953						
Series 4, 4-cyl, 100" wb, 134.2 cid						
Model 210, Std.						
2d Sed	450	1000	1650	3400	6350	9100
Model 213, DeL						
2d Sed	450	1050	1700	3550	6500	9300
Series 6, 6-cyl, 100" wb, 161 cid						
Model 215						
2d DeL Sed	450	1050	1700	3600	6600	9400

AMERICAN BUCKBOARD
	6	5	4	3	2	1
1955						
2-cyl, 70" wb						
2d Rds	125	200	600	1100	2250	3200

APACHE
	6	5	4	3	2	1
1966						
Apache						
2d Conv	150	400	750	1650	3150	4500

APOLLO
	6	5	4	3	2	1
1962						
GT, V-8, 97" wb, 215.5 cid						
2d Cpe	400	1200	2000	3950	7000	10,000
1963						
GT, V-8, 97" wb, 215.5 cid						
2d Cpe	400	1200	2000	3950	7000	10,000
1964-1965						
GT 5000, V-8, 97" wb, 300.4 cid						
2d Cpe	450	1450	2400	4800	8400	12,000
2d Conv	550	1800	3000	6000	10,500	15,000

ARGONAUT
	6	5	4	3	2	1
1959						
Argonaut, 126.5" wb						
Chassis Only	450	1450	2400	4800	8400	12,000

ARNOLT
	6	5	4	3	2	1
1953-1954						
MG, 4-cyl, 94" wb, 76.3 cid						
2d Cpe	450	1450	2400	4800	8400	12,000
2d Conv	550	1700	2800	5600	9800	14,000

ARNOLT-BRISTOL
	6	5	4	3	2	1
1955-1963						
6-cyl, 96.25" wb, 120.2 cid						
Mk II 2d Cpe	1200	3850	6400	12,800	22,400	32,000
2d Bol Rds	1300	4200	7000	14,000	24,500	35,000
2d DeL Rds	1400	4450	7400	14,800	25,900	37,000
2d Cpe	1250	3950	6600	13,200	23,100	33,000

ASARDO
	6	5	4	3	2	1
1959						
1500 AR-S, 4-cyl, 88" wb, 91.3 cid						
2d Cpe	450	1100	1700	3650	6650	9500

ASTRA
	6	5	4	3	2	1
1955						
V-8, 102" wb						
2d HT	550	1800	3000	6000	10,500	15,000

AUBURN I

	6	5	4	3	2	1
1967-1970						
Model 866, V-8, 127" wb, 428 cid						
2d Rds	950	3000	5000	10,000	17,500	25,000
NOTE: Pricing for 1967 Auburn I.						
1971-1975						
V-8, 127" wb, 429 cid						
866, 2d Rds	1000	3100	5200	10,400	18,200	26,000
4d Phae (1975)	900	2900	4800	9600	16,800	24,000
NOTE: Pricing for Model 866 Roadster is for 1971 model.						

AUBURN II

	6	5	4	3	2	1
1973						
Auburn II						
V-8, 351 cid						
2d Rds	900	2900	4800	9600	16,800	24,000
NOTE: Optional V-8, 400 cid. engine was available.						

AUBURN III

	6	5	4	3	2	1
1974-1975						
Auburn III						
V-8, 351 cid						
2d Rds	1300	4200	7000	14,000	24,500	35,000
NOTE: See also Romulus II.						

AUTO CUB

	6	5	4	3	2	1
1956						
Rbt	100	125	450	900	1550	2200

AUTOETTE

	6	5	4	3	2	1
1952-1957						
Runabout, Electric						
24V DC motor						
Model 800	100	125	450	900	1550	2200
Model 850	100	125	450	900	1550	2200
Model 875	100	125	450	900	1550	2200

AVANTI II

	6	5	4	3	2	1
Avanti II, V-8, 109" wb						
2 dr Spt Cpe						
1965 - 5 Prototypes Made	900	2900	4800	9600	16,800	24,000
1966	750	2400	4000	8000	14,000	20,000
1967	750	2400	4000	8000	14,000	20,000
1968	750	2400	4000	8000	14,000	20,000
1969	750	2400	4000	8000	14,000	20,000
1970	750	2400	4000	8000	14,000	20,000
1971	750	2400	4000	8000	14,000	20,000
1972	750	2400	4000	8000	14,000	20,000
1973	750	2400	4000	8000	14,000	20,000
1974	750	2400	4000	8000	14,000	20,000
1975	850	2650	4400	8800	15,400	22,000
NOTE: Add 5 percent for leather upholstery.						
Add 5 percent for sun roof.						
Add 6 percent for wire wheels.						

BANGERT

	6	5	4	3	2	1
1955						
V-8, 96"-104" wb, 331 cid						
2d Rds	350	750	1300	2450	5250	7500
NOTE: Fiberglass kit.						

BANNER BOY

	6	5	4	3	2	1
Banner Boy (replicar)						
Buckboard	100	125	450	900	1550	2200

BASSON'S STAR

	6	5	4	3	2	1
1956						
1-cyl						
Rbt	350	750	1300	2450	5250	7500

BEARCAT

	6	5	4	3	2	1
1956						
2-cyl (motorcycle), 70" wb						
2d Rds	100	150	450	1000	1900	2700

BEECHCRAFT

	6	5	4	3	2	1
1946						
Plainsman						
4-cyl, (Franklin-aircraft type)						
4d Sed	350	750	1300	2450	5250	7500

BLOOMQUIST

	6	5	4	3	2	1
1959						
Sports Car, 6-cyl						
2d Rds	200	600	950	2150	3850	5500

BMC

	6	5	4	3	2	1
1952						
4-cyl, 91.3 cid						
2d Rds	350	700	1150	2300	4550	6500

BOARDMAN

	6	5	4	3	2	1
1948						
6-cyl, 119" wb, 226.2 cid						
2d Rds	350	750	1200	2350	4900	7000

BOBBI-KAR

	6	5	4	3	2	1
1945-1947						
4-cyl, 80" wb, 64.9 cid						
2d Cpe	200	600	950	2150	3850	5500
2d Sed	200	500	850	1900	3500	5000
4-cyl, 100" wb, 64.9 cid						
2d Sta Wag	350	700	1150	2300	4550	6500

BOCAR

	6	5	4	3	2	1
1958						
XP-4, V-8, 90" wb, 283 cid						
2d Rds	650	2050	3400	6800	11,900	17,000
1959						
XP-5, V-8, 91" wb, 283 cid						
2d Rds	650	2050	3400	6800	11,900	17,000
1960						
XP-6, V-8, 104" wb, 283 cid						
2d Rds	700	2150	3600	7200	12,600	18,000

BOLIDE

	6	5	4	3	2	1
1970						
Can Am I						
V-8, 90" wb, 351 cid						
Rds	350	700	1150	2300	4550	6500
XJ002, V-6, 225 cid						
Spt Utl						6000

BOSLEY

	6	5	4	3	2	1
1955						
V-8, 102" wb, 331.1 cid						
2d Spt Cpe				value not estimable		

BRICKLIN

	6	5	4	3	2	1
1974-1975						
SV-1, V-8, 96" wb, 351 or 360 cid						
2d GW Spt Cpe	700	2150	3600	7200	12,600	18,000

BROGAN

	6	5	4	3	2	1
1946-1946 2-cyl, 60" wb Rbt	125	200	600	1100	2250	3200
1949-1950 Broganette, 120" wb 2d Rbt	125	250	700	1150	2450	3500

BUCKAROO

	6	5	4	3	2	1
1957						

NOTE: Details and pricing not available on this tiny car which reportedly was made in Cleveland in 1957.

BUCKBOARD

	6	5	4	3	2	1
1956 Ariel 'Square 4', 94" wb Open-2P	150	300	700	1250	2600	3700

BUGETTA

	6	5	4	3	2	1
1968 V-8, 302 cid Open-2P	150	400	750	1650	3150	4500
Open-4P	150	400	750	1650	3150	4500

CENTAUR

	6	5	4	3	2	1
1950 Inline 4, 120 cid 2d Rds	125	200	600	1100	2250	1500

CHADWICK

	6	5	4	3	2	1
1960 300, 1-cyl, 58" wb Open-2P	100	125	500	950	1700	2400

CHARLES

	6	5	4	3	2	1
1958-1959 Electric, 2 motor, 94.5" wb 2d HT	150	300	700	1250	2600	3700

CHICAGOAN

	6	5	4	3	2	1
1952-1953 6-cyl, 161 cid 2d Rds	150	450	800	1750	3250	4700

CITICAR

	6	5	4	3	2	1
1974 Electric, 65.5" wb 2d Cpe	125	250	700	1150	2450	3500
1975 Electric, 65.5" wb 2d Cpe	125	250	700	1150	2450	3500

COLT

	6	5	4	3	2	1
1958 1-cyl, 77" wb, 23 cid 2d Cpe	100	150	450	1000	1750	2500

COMET I

	6	5	4	3	2	1
1946-1948 Comet I Rbt, 2P	100	125	450	900	1550	2200

COMET II

	6	5	4	3	2	1
1951 Kit Car 2d Rds	100	150	450	1000	1750	2500

CORD I

	6	5	4	3	2	1
1964-1966 8/10, 6-cyl, 100" wb, 164 cid 2d Conv	850	2650	4400	8800	15,400	22,000

CORD II

	6	5	4	3	2	1
1968-1970 Warrior V-8, 108" wb, 302 cid 2d Conv	550	1800	3000	6000	10,500	15,000
Royal V-8, 108" wb, 440 cid 2d Conv	450	1450	2400	4800	8400	12,000

CROFTON

	6	5	4	3	2	1
1959-1961 Bug, 4-cyl, 63" wb, 44 cid 2d Utl	150	300	750	1350	2700	3900

CROSLEY

	6	5	4	3	2	1
1946-47-48 4-cyl., 80" wb						
Conv	150	400	750	1650	3150	4500
Sed	150	350	750	1350	2800	4000
Sta Wag	150	400	750	1550	3050	4300
1949 4-cyl., 80" wb						
Conv	150	400	750	1650	3150	4500
Sed	150	350	750	1350	2800	4000
Sta Wag	150	400	750	1550	3050	4300
1950 Standard, 4-cyl., 80" wb						
Conv	150	400	750	1650	3150	4500
Sed	150	350	750	1350	2800	4000
Sta Wag	150	400	750	1550	3050	4300
Super, 4-cyl., 80" wb						
Conv.	150	450	750	1700	3200	4600
Sed	150	350	750	1450	2900	4100
Sta Wag	150	400	750	1600	3100	4400
Hot Shot, 4-cyl, 85" wb						
Rdst	200	650	1050	2250	4200	6000
1951 Standard, 4-cyl., 80" wb						
Cpe	150	350	750	1350	2800	4000
Sta Wag	150	400	750	1550	3050	4300
Super, 4-cyl., 80" wb						
Conv	150	400	750	1650	3150	4500
Sed	150	350	750	1450	3000	4200
Sta Wag	150	400	750	1600	3100	4400
Hot Shot, 4-cyl., 85" wb						
Rdst	200	650	1050	2250	4200	6000
1952 Standard, 4-cyl., 80" wb						
Cpe	150	350	750	1350	2800	4000
Sta Wag	150	400	750	1550	3050	4300
Super, 4-cyl., 80" wb						
Conv	150	450	750	1700	3200	4600
Sed	150	350	750	1450	2900	4100
Sta Wag	150	400	750	1600	3100	4400
Hot Shot, 4-cyl., 85" wb						
Rdst	200	650	1050	2250	4200	6000

CUNNINGHAM

	6	5	4	3	2	1
1951 C-2, V-8, 105" wb, 331.1 cid 2d Rds	1750	5500	9200	18,400	32,200	46,000

	6	5	4	3	2	1
1952						
C-4R, V-8, 100" wb, 331.1 cid						
2d Rds	1750	5500	9200	18,400	32,200	46,000
1953						
Continental						
C-3, V-8, 105" wb, 331.1 cid						
2d HT	1700	5400	9000	18,000	31,500	45,000
1954						
C-5R, V-8, 100" wb, 331.1 cid						
2d Rds	1800	5750	9600	19,200	33,600	48,000
Continental						
C-3, V-8, 105" wb, 331.1 cid						
2d HT	1750	5500	9200	18,400	32,200	46,000
1955						
C-6R, 4-cyl, 100" wb, 179.5 cid						
2d Rds	1900	6000	10,000	20,000	35,000	50,000

CUSTER

	6	5	4	3	2	1
1953-1960						
Custer, (Gasoline)						
4 cycle, 70" wb						
Rbt	100	125	450	900	1550	2200
Special, (Electric), 70" wb						
Rbt	100	125	450	900	1550	2200

DARRIN

	6	5	4	3	2	1
1946						
6-cyl, 115" wb, 187 cid						
2d Conv	650	2050	3400	6800	11,900	17,000
1955						
V-8, 100" wb, 331.1 cid						
2d HT Cpe	1050	3350	5600	11,200	19,600	28,000
1956						
V-8, 100" wb, 365 cid						
2d HT Spt Cpe	1050	3350	5600	11,200	19,600	28,000
1957						
V-8, 100" wb, 365 cid						
2d HT Spt Cpe	1050	3350	5600	11,200	19,600	28,000
1958						
V-8, 100" wb, 365 cid						
2d HT	1050	3350	5600	11,200	19,600	28,000

DAVIS

	6	5	4	3	2	1
1947-1949						
Early, 4-cyl, 108" wb, 132.7 cid						
Late, 4-cyl, 109.5" wb, 162 cid						
482A, 2d Cpe	550	1800	3000	6000	10,500	15,000
484X, 1/4 Ton Jeep	450	1450	2400	4800	8400	12,000

DAYTONA

	6	5	4	3	2	1
1956						
Minicar						
Rbt	75	100	400	750	1350	1900

DELCAR

	6	5	4	3	2	1
1947						
4-cyl, 60" wb						
2d Sta Wag	100	150	450	1000	1750	2500

DEL MAR

	6	5	4	3	2	1
1949						
4-cyl, 100"-104" wb, 162 cid						
2d Conv	125	200	600	1100	2250	3200

DeLOREAN

	6	5	4	3	2	1
1981						
DMC-12, V-6, 95" wb, 174 cid						
2d GW Spt Cpe	1200	3850	6400	12,800	22,400	32,000
1982						
DMC-12, V-6, 95" wb, 174 cid						
2d GW Spt Cpe	1200	3850	6400	12,800	22,400	32,000

DETRICK

	6	5	4	3	2	1
1957						
Steam, 2-cyl, 127" wb, 125.7 cid						
Chassis only	75	100	400	750	1350	1900

DETROITER

	6	5	4	3	2	1
1953						
V-8, 115" wb, 239.4 cid						
2d Conv	125	250	700	1150	2500	3600

DEVIN

	6	5	4	3	2	1
1958-1961						
Super Sport						
V-8, 92" wb, 283 cid						
2d Rds	400	1300	2200	4400	7700	11,000
1959-1964						
Model D, 4-cyl, 82" wb, 72.7 cid						
2d Rds	450	1100	1700	3650	6650	9500
1961-1964						
Model C, 6-cyl, 82" wb, 145 cid						
2d Rds	400	1200	2000	3950	7000	10,000

DIEHLMOBILE

	6	5	4	3	2	1
1961						
1-cyl, 3 hp						
Std Rbt	75	100	400	750	1350	1900
DeL Rbt	75	100	400	750	1350	1900

DORAY

	6	5	4	3	2	1
1950						
6-cyl, 104" wb						
2d Rds	150	400	750	1650	3150	4500

DTL

	6	5	4	3	2	1
1960						
Electric, (2) 1/3 hp motors						
47" wb						
Rbt	100	150	450	1000	1750	2500

DUAL-GHIA

	6	5	4	3	2	1
1956-1958						
D500, V-8, 115" wb, 315 cid						
2d HT	2050	6600	11,000	22,000	38,500	55,000
2d Conv	2250	7200	12,000	24,000	42,000	60,000

NOTE: Optional D500 V-8, 325 cid engine was available.

DUESENBERG I

	6	5	4	3	2	1
1959						
8-cyl, 435 cid						
2d Rds					value not estimable	

DUESENBERG II

	6	5	4	3	2	1
1966						
V-8, 137.5" wb, 440 cid						
4d Sed					value not estimable	

DUESENBERG III

	6	5	4	3	2	1
1970-1973						
SSJ, V-8, 128" wb, 383 cid						
2d Rds, SC					value not estimable	

1974-1975
SSJ, V-8, 128" wb, 440 cid

	6	5	4	3	2	1
2d Rds			value not estimable			

EDWARDS

	6	5	4	3	2	1

1954
V-8, 107" wb, 317 cid

	6	5	4	3	2	1
2d Conv	750	2400	4000	8000	14,000	20,000

1955
V-8, 107" wb, 331.1 cid

2d Conv	750	2400	4000	8000	14,000	20,000

ELECTRA

	6	5	4	3	2	1

1974
Electric, 3 motors, 77.8" wb

2d Rds	125	250	700	1150	2450	3500

ELECTRA-KING

	6	5	4	3	2	1

1961-1966
Electric

P100, 2d Cpe, 2P	100	150	450	1000	1750	2500
2d Cpe, 4P	100	150	450	1000	1750	2500

1967-1971
Electric, PF100
68.5" wb, 3 wheel

2d Cpe	100	150	450	1000	1750	2500

65" wb, 4 wheel

2d Cpe	100	150	450	1000	1800	2600

1972-1973
Electric
PFS100, 68.5" wb, 3 wheel

2d Cpe	100	150	450	1000	1750	2500

PFS110, 65" wb, 4 wheel

2d Cpe	100	150	450	1000	1800	2600

1974-1975
Electric, 68.5" wb, 3 wheel
65" wb, 4 wheel

2d Cpe (all styles)	100	150	450	1000	1800	2600

ELECTRICAR

	6	5	4	3	2	1

1950-1966
Electric
Cutie Junior

2d Rds	100	125	475	900	1600	2300

Cutie

Rds	100	125	500	950	1700	2400

Boulevard

Rds	100	150	450	1000	1750	2500

ELECTRIC SHOPPER

	6	5	4	3	2	1

1952-1962
Electric, 61" wb

Rbt	100	125	450	900	1550	2200

ELECTRO-MASTER

	6	5	4	3	2	1

1962-1964
Electric, 2 hp

2d Rbt	100	125	450	900	1550	2200

ELECTROMOTION

	6	5	4	3	2	1

1974
Electric

2d Van	125	200	600	1100	2250	3200

ELECTRONIC

	6	5	4	3	2	1

1955
LaSaetta, turbo-electric
110" wb

2d Rds	100	125	475	900	1600	2300

EL MOROCCO

	6	5	4	3	2	1

1956
V-8, 115" wb, 265 cid

2d HT	850	2650	4400	8800	15,400	22,000
4d HT	700	2300	3800	7600	13,300	19,000
2d Conv	1150	3600	6000	12,000	21,000	30,000

1957
V-8, 115" wb, 283 cid

2d HT	900	2900	4800	9600	16,800	24,000
4d HT	800	2500	4200	8400	14,700	21,000
2d Conv	1200	3850	6400	12,800	22,400	32,000

ESHELMAN

	6	5	4	3	2	1

1953-1958
Sportabout, 1-cyl

2d Rds	100	125	450	900	1550	2200

1955-1960
1-cyl

Open-1P	100	125	450	900	1550	2200

ESTATE CARRIAGE

	6	5	4	3	2	1

1960
V-8, 130" wb, 390 cid

4d Sta Wag	450	1450	2400	4800	8400	12,000

EXCALIBUR I

	6	5	4	3	2	1

1952
J, 6-cyl, 100" wb, 161 cid

2d Rds				value not estimable		

EXCALIBUR II

	6	5	4	3	2	1

1965
V-8, 109" wb, 327 cid

SS 2d Phae	1500	4800	8000	16,000	28,000	40,000

1966
V-8, 109" wb, 327 cid

SSK 2d Rds	1500	4800	8000	16,000	28,000	40,000
SS 2d Rds	1600	5050	8400	16,800	29,400	42,000

1967
V-8, 109" wb, 327 cid

SSK 2d Rds	1500	4800	8000	16,000	28,000	40,000
SS 2d Rds	1600	5050	8400	16,800	29,400	42,000
SS 2d Phae	1450	4550	7600	15,200	26,600	38,000

NOTE: Optional supercharged engine available.

1968
V-8, 109" wb, 327 cid

SSK 2d Rds	1500	4800	8000	16,000	28,000	40,000
SS 2d Rds	1600	5050	8400	16,800	29,400	42,000
SS 2d Phae	1450	4550	7600	15,200	26,600	38,000

NOTE: Optional supercharged engine available.

1969
V-8, 109" wb, 327 cid

SSK 2d Rds	1500	4800	8000	16,000	28,000	40,000
SS 2d Rds	1600	5050	8400	16,800	29,400	42,000
SS 2d Phae	1450	4550	7600	15,200	26,600	38,000

NOTE: Optional supercharged engine available.

1970
V-8, 111" wb, 350 cid

SSK 2d Rds	1550	4900	8200	16,400	28,700	41,000
SS 2d Rds	1600	5150	8600	17,200	30,100	43,000
SS 2d Phae	1450	4700	7800	15,600	27,300	39,000

1971
V-8, 111" wb, 350 cid

SSK 2d Rds	1550	4900	8200	16,400	28,700	41,000
SS 2d Rds	1600	5150	8600	17,200	30,100	43,000
SS 2d Phae	1450	4700	7800	15,600	27,300	39,000

1972
V-8, 111" wb, 454 cid

SSK 2d Rds	1550	4900	8200	16,400	28,700	41,000
SS 2d Rds	1600	5150	8600	17,200	30,100	43,000
SS 2d Phae	1450	4700	7800	15,600	27,300	39,000

1973
V-8, 112" wb, 454 cid

SSK 2d Rds	1550	4900	8200	16,400	28,700	41,000
SS 2d Rds	1600	5150	8600	17,200	30,100	43,000
SS 2d Phae	1450	4700	7800	15,600	27,300	39,000

1974
V-8, 112" wb, 454 cid

SS 2d Rds	1500	4800	8000	16,000	28,000	40,000
SS 2d Phae	1450	4550	7600	15,200	26,600	38,000

1975
V-8, 112" wb, 454 cid

SS 2d Rds	1500	4800	8000	16,000	28,000	40,000
SS 2d Phae	1450	4550	7600	15,200	26,600	38,000

FAGEOL

	6	5	4	3	2	1

1948
Supersonic
124" wb, 404 cid

4d Sed				value not estimable		

Standard Catalog of American Cars

FERGUS

	6	5	4	3	2	1
1949 4-cyl, 73.1 cid 2d Rds	125	200	600	1100	2250	3200

FERRER

	6	5	4	3	2	1
1966 GT, 4-cyl, 94.5" wb, 78.4 cid 2d Cpe	350	700	1150	2300	4550	6500

FIBERSPORT

	6	5	4	3	2	1
1953-1954 4-cyl, 85" wb 2d Rds	125	200	600	1100	2250	3200

FINA SPORT

	6	5	4	3	2	1
1953-1955 V-8, 115" wb, 331.1 cid 2d HT	700	2300	3800	7600	13,300	19,000

FISHER

	6	5	4	3	2	1
1961 Electric, 80" wb, 4 hp 2d Rds	100	175	525	1050	1950	2800

FITCH

	6	5	4	3	2	1
1949-1951 Type B, V-8, 95" wb, 136 cid 2d Rds	350	900	1550	3050	5900	8500
1966 Fitch-Phoenix II 6-cyl, 95" wb, 164 cid 2d Conv	1450	4550	7600	15,200	26,600	38,000

FLINTRIDGE-DARRIN

	6	5	4	3	2	1
1957 3-cyl, 92" wb, 54.8 cid Standard 2d HT	350	800	1450	2750	5600	8000
Deluxe 2d HT	450	1000	1650	3350	6300	9000

FORERUNNER

	6	5	4	3	2	1
1955 6-cyl, 100" wb, 210 cid 2d HT	1450	4550	7600	15,200	26,600	38,000

FRANCE JET

	6	5	4	3	2	1
1961 1-cyl, 74" wb 2d Rds	150	350	750	1350	2800	4000

NOTE: Optional 2-cyl engine available.

FRAZEN

	6	5	4	3	2	1
1951-1962 6-cyl, 100" wb, 161 cid 2d Rds	125	250	700	1150	2450	3500

FRICK

	6	5	4	3	2	1
1955 V-8, 110" wb, 331.1 cid 2d Cpe	550	1800	3000	6000	10,500	15,000

GADABOUT

	6	5	4	3	2	1
1946 4-cyl, 80" wb, 76.3 cid 2d Rds	100	125	450	900	1550	2200

GASLIGHT

	6	5	4	3	2	1
1960-1961 1-cyl, 77" wb Rbt	100	175	525	1050	2100	3000

GAYLORD

	6	5	4	3	2	1
1955 V-8, 100" wb, 331.1 cid 2d Cpe					value not estimable	
1956 V-8, 100" wb, 365 cid 2d Cpe					value not estimable	

GLASCAR

	6	5	4	3	2	1
1956 V-8, 100" wb 2d Rds	—	—	—	—	—	11,000

GLASSIC

	6	5	4	3	2	1
1966-1967 4-cyl, 100" wb, 151.8 cid 2d Rds	450	1100	1700	3650	6650	9500
1968 4-cyl, 100" wb, 151.8 cid 2d Rds	450	1100	1700	3650	6650	9500
2d Phae	450	1000	1650	3350	6300	9000
1969 4-cyl, 100" wb, 195.4 cid 2d Rds	450	1100	1700	3650	6650	9500
2d Phae	450	1000	1650	3350	6300	9000
1970 4-cyl, 100" wb, 195.4 cid 2d Rds	450	1100	1700	3650	6650	9500
1971 4-cyl, 100" wb, 195.4 cid 2d Rds	450	1100	1700	3650	6650	9500
2d Phae	450	1000	1650	3350	6300	9000
1972 V-8, 102" wb, 302 cid 2d Rds	450	1150	1800	3800	6800	9700
2d Phae	450	1100	1700	3650	6650	9500
1973 V-8, 102" wb, 302 cid 2d Rds	450	1150	1800	3800	6800	9700
2d Phae	450	1100	1700	3650	6650	9500
1974 V-8, 102" wb, 302 cid 2d Rds	450	1150	1800	3800	6800	9700
1975 V-8, 102" wb, 302 cid 2d Rds	450	1150	1800	3800	6800	9700
2d Phae	450	1100	1700	3650	6650	9500

GLASSIC-ROMULUS

	6	5	4	3	2	1
1975 V-8, 127" wb, 302 cid 2d Rds	750	2400	4000	8000	14,000	20,000

GLASSPAR

	6	5	4	3	2	1
1950 G-2, V-8, 100" wb 2d Spts Rds	400	1300	2200	4400	7700	11,000
1955 Ascot, 4-cyl, 94" wb 2d Rds	450	1100	1700	3650	6650	9500

GOFF

	6	5	4	3	2	1
1956 V-8, 221 cid 2d Rds	350	750	1200	2350	4900	7000

GORDON

	6	5	4	3	2	1
1948						
Diamond, V-8, 156" wb, 239 cid						
2d Sed	200	650	1050	2250	4200	6000

GREGORY I

	6	5	4	3	2	1
1948						
4-cyl, 94" wb, 119.8 cid						
2d Sed	150	350	750	1350	2800	4000

GREGORY II

	6	5	4	3	2	1
1956						
4-cyl, 90" wb, 97 cid						
2d Rds	200	500	850	1900	3500	5000

GRIFFITH

	6	5	4	3	2	1
1964						
Series 200						
V-8, 85.5" wb, 289 cid						
2d Cpe	1050	3350	5600	11,200	19,600	28,000
NOTE: Optional V-8 engine available.						
1965						
V-8, 85.5" wb, 289 cid						
2d Cpe	1050	3350	5600	11,200	19,600	28,000
NOTE: Optional V-8 engine available.						
1966						
V-8, 94.5" wb, 273 cid						
2d Cpe	1100	3500	5800	11,600	20,300	29,000

HENNEY

	6	5	4	3	2	1
1960-1964						
Electric						
Kilowatt, 89" wb						
4d Sed	100	175	525	1050	2100	3000

HENRY J

	6	5	4	3	2	1
1951						
Four						
2 dr Sed	350	850	1500	2800	5650	8100
DeLuxe six						
2 dr Sed	350	850	1500	2950	5800	8300
1952						
Vagabond (4 cyl.)						
2 dr Sed	350	900	1550	3050	5900	8500
Vagabond (6 cyl.)						
2 dr Sed	350	950	1600	3200	6050	8700
Corsair (4 cyl.)						
2 dr Sed	450	1000	1650	3350	6300	9000
Corsair (6 cyl.)						
2 dr Sed	450	1050	1650	3500	6400	9200
Allstate						
4 Cyl	450	1000	1650	3400	6350	9100
DeL Six	450	1050	1700	3550	6500	9300
1953						
Corsair (4 cyl.)						
2 dr Sed	450	1000	1600	3300	6250	8900
Corsair (6 cyl.)						
DeL 2 dr Sed	450	1000	1650	3400	6350	9100
Allstate						
4 Cyl	450	1000	1650	3400	6350	9100
DeL Six	450	1050	1700	3550	6500	9300
1954						
Corsair (4 cyl.)						
2 dr	450	1000	1650	3350	6300	9000
Corsair Deluxe (6 cyl.)						
2 dr	450	1050	1650	3500	6400	9200

HOPPENSTAND

	6	5	4	3	2	1
1949-1950						
2-cyl, 90" wb						
690, 2d Rds	100	150	450	1000	1750	2500
690, 2d Cpe	100	125	450	900	1550	2200
790, 2d Conv	100	150	450	1000	1800	2600

HUMMINGBIRD

	6	5	4	3	2	1
1946						
4-cyl, 85" wb						
2d Rds	100	150	450	1000	1750	2500

852

HUNT

	6	5	4	3	2	1
1951						
Glass-Top, 4-cyl, 131" wb						
4d Sed					value not estimable	

HYDRAMOTIVE

	6	5	4	3	2	1
1961						
Diesel	100	175	525	1050	2100	3000

IMP

	6	5	4	3	2	1
1949-1950						
1-cyl, 63" wb						
Open 2P	100	150	450	1000	1750	2500
1951						
1-cyl, 63" wb						
Open 2P	100	150	450	1000	1750	2500

JETMOBILE

	6	5	4	3	2	1
1952						
V-8, 136 cid						
Open 1P	125	200	600	1100	2250	3200

JOHNSONMOBILE

	6	5	4	3	2	1
1959						
Clinton Engine						
Rbt	100	150	450	1000	1750	2500

JOMAR

	6	5	4	3	2	1
1955-1960						
4-cyl, 84" wb, 71.5 cid						
2d Cpe	200	500	850	1900	3500	5000
4-cyl, 84" wb, SC 71.5 cid						
2d GT Cpe	200	550	900	2000	3600	5200
4-cyl, 84" wb, 70 cid						
Climax 2d Cpe	200	600	950	2150	3850	5500

KEEN

	6	5	4	3	2	1
1948						
V-4 Steam Engine						
3P Conv	125	250	700	1150	2450	3500

KELLER

	6	5	4	3	2	1
1948-1950						
4-cyl, 92" wb, 133 cid - 162 cid						
Standard Chief						
2d Conv	200	600	950	2150	3850	5500
2d Sta Wag	200	500	850	1900	3500	5000
Deluxe Super Chief						
2d Conv	200	650	1050	2250	4200	6000
2d Sta Wag	200	600	950	2150	3850	5500

KING MIDGET

	6	5	4	3	2	1
1947-1950						
1-cyl						
Rbt	125	200	600	1100	2250	3200
1951-1957						
1-cyl, 72" wb, 23 cid						
Rds	125	200	600	1100	2250	3200
1958-1966						
1-cyl, 76.5" wb, 23 cid						
2d Rds	125	250	700	1150	2450	3500
1967-1969						
1-cyl, 76.5" wb, 29.1 cid						
2d Rds	125	250	700	1150	2450	3500

KNUDSON

	6	5	4	3	2	1
1948 90" wb 1d Utl	100	175	525	1050	1950	2800

KRIM-GHIA

	6	5	4	3	2	1
1966-1969 1500 GT, 4-cyl, 98.6" wb, 90.4 cid 2d Rds	350	900	1550	3050	5900	8500
(Barracuda Based) V-8, 106" wb, 273 cid 2d Rds	450	1100	1700	3650	6650	9500

KURTIS

	6	5	4	3	2	1
1949-1950 V-8, 100" wb, 239.4 cid 2d Rds	1200	3850	6400	12,800	22,400	32,000
1954-1955 500M, V-8, 100" wb, 331.1 cid 2d Rds	2050	6600	11,000	22,000	38,500	55,000

LITTLE DUDE

	6	5	4	3	2	1
1969 2-cyl, 77.6" wb, 21.6 cid Rbt, 4P	100	150	450	1000	1750	2500

LOST CAUSE

	6	5	4	3	2	1
1963 6-cyl, 108" wb, 145 cid 4d Sed	350	700	1150	2300	4550	6500

MARKETEER

	6	5	4	3	2	1
1954 Electric 2d Cpe	100	125	475	900	1600	2300

MARKETOUR

	6	5	4	3	2	1
1964 Electric, 64" wb 2d Cpe	100	125	475	900	1600	2300

MARKETTE

	6	5	4	3	2	1
1967 Electric 2d Cpe	100	125	475	900	1600	2300

MARQUIS

	6	5	4	3	2	1
1954 Marquis 2d Cpe	150	300	700	1250	2650	3800

MARS II

	6	5	4	3	2	1
1966 Electric, 89" wb 4d Sed	125	250	700	1150	2450	3500

MARTIN

	6	5	4	3	2	1
1948 Martinette, 4-cyl 153 cid, 3 wheel 2d Cpe	100	150	450	1000	1750	2500
1950 Stationette, 4-cyl 47.3 cid, 3 wheel 2d Cpe	100	150	450	1000	1750	2500

MAVERICK

	6	5	4	3	2	1
1953-1955 V-8, 120"-128" wb, 331.1 cid BT 2d Rds	950	3000	5000	10,000	17,500	25,000

MERCURY SPECIAL

	6	5	4	3	2	1
1946 Mercury Special Spt Rds					value not estimable	

MERRY OLDS

	6	5	4	3	2	1
1958-1962 1-cyl Rbt	150	350	750	1350	2800	4000

MERRY RUNABOUT

	6	5	4	3	2	1
1960 50" wb Rbt	100	175	525	1050	2100	3000

MINICAR

	6	5	4	3	2	1
1969 6-cyl, 164 cid 2d Cpe	100	175	525	1050	2100	3000

MOHS

	6	5	4	3	2	1
1967-1975 Model A, V-8, 119" wb, 304 cid 1d Cpe	1150	3600	6000	12,000	21,000	30,000
Model B, V-8, 119" wb, 549 cid 1d Cpe	1150	3650	6100	12,200	21,400	30,500
1972-1975 Safari Kar, DC Phae V-8, 131" wb, 392 cid 2d Conv	1000	3200	5300	10,600	18,600	26,000

MOTA

	6	5	4	3	2	1
1953 Electric 2d Rds	100	150	450	1000	1750	2500

MOTORETTE

	6	5	4	3	2	1
1946-1948 Model 20, 1-cyl, 60" wb Rbt, 2P	100	125	450	900	1550	2200

MULTIPLEX

	6	5	4	3	2	1
1952 6-cyl, 161 cid 2d Rds	150	300	700	1250	2650	3800

1953-1954
4-cyl, 85" wb, 121.8 cid

	6	5	4	3	2	1
2d Rds	150	300	750	1350	2700	3900

NOTE: Optional 6-cyl, 161 cid engine available.
6-cyl, 94" wb, 161 cid

	6	5	4	3	2	1
2d HT	150	350	750	1350	2800	4000

MUNTZ

1950
Jet, V-8, 113" wb, 331.1 cid

	6	5	4	3	2	1
2d HT	950	3000	5000	10,000	17,500	25,000

1951-1952
Jet, V-8, 116" wb, 336.7 cid

	6	5	4	3	2	1
2d HT	—	—	—	—	—	27,000

1953-1954
Jet, V-8, 116" wb, 336.7 cid

	6	5	4	3	2	1
2d HT	1000	3250	5400	10,800	18,900	27,000

MURENA

1969-1970
V-8, 118" wb, 429 cid

	6	5	4	3	2	1
4d Sta Wag	600	1900	3200	6400	11,200	16,000

MUSTANG

1948
4-cyl, 102" wb, 162 cid

	6	5	4	3	2	1
2d Sta Wag	350	750	1200	2350	4900	7000

NAVAJO

1953-1954
V-8, 116" wb

	6	5	4	3	2	1
2d Rds	550	1800	3000	6000	10,500	15,000

NU-KLEA

1959-1960
Electric

	6	5	4	3	2	1
2d HT	100	125	450	900	1550	2200
2d Conv	100	150	450	1000	1750	2500

OLDS REPLICA

1968
1901 Replica

	6	5	4	3	2	1
2P	125	200	600	1100	2200	3100

OMEGA

1967
V-8, 94.5" wb, 289 cid

	6	5	4	3	2	1
2d HT	550	1800	3000	6000	10,500	15,000

1968
V-8, 94.5" wb, 289 cid

	6	5	4	3	2	1
2d HT	600	1900	3200	6400	11,200	16,000

NOTE: Optional V-8, 302 cid engine was available.

PANDA

1955
2-cyl, 70" wb, 67.1 cid

	6	5	4	3	2	1
2d Conv	200	500	850	1900	3500	5000

1956
2-cyl, 70" wb, 67.1 cid

	6	5	4	3	2	1
2d Conv	200	500	850	1900	3500	5000

PANTHER

1962-1963
Std, V-8, 94" wb, 155.9 cid

	6	5	4	3	2	1
2d Rds	450	1450	2400	4800	8400	12,000

Model M, V-8, 94" wb, 155.9 cid

	6	5	4	3	2	1
2d Rds	500	1550	2600	5200	9100	13,000

NOTE: Model M contained a hotter version of the V-8 engine.

PEDICAR

1973
People pedal-powered

	6	5	4	3	2	1
2d Cpe	75	100	400	750	1350	1900

PIONEER

1959
Electric, 95" wb

	6	5	4	3	2	1
2d Rds	200	600	950	2150	3850	5500
2d HT	150	400	750	1650	3150	4500
2d Sta Wag	150	350	750	1350	2800	4000

PIRANHA

1967
6-cyl, 95" wb, 164 cid

	6	5	4	3	2	1
2d GW Cpe	700	2150	3600	7200	12,600	18,000

NOTE: Optional V-6 turbocharged engine was available.

PLAYBOY

1947
4-cyl, 90" wb, 133 cid

	6	5	4	3	2	1
2d Conv	450	1450	2400	4800	8400	12,000

1948-1950
4-cyl, 90" wb, 91 cid

	6	5	4	3	2	1
2d Conv	450	1450	2400	4800	8400	12,000

1951
4-cyl, 90" wb, 134.2 cid

	6	5	4	3	2	1
2d Conv	450	1450	2400	4800	8400	12,000

POWELL

1955-1956
6-cyl, 117" wb, 217.8 cid

	6	5	4	3	2	1
2d Sta Wag	350	800	1450	2750	5600	8000
DeL 2d Sta Wag	350	900	1550	3050	5900	8500

PUBLIX

1947-1948
50" wb

	6	5	4	3	2	1
2d Conv	100	150	450	1000	1750	2500

PUP

1948
1-cyl, 72" wb

	6	5	4	3	2	1
Open Rbt	100	150	450	1000	1750	2500

1949
2-cyl, 68" wb

	6	5	4	3	2	1
Rbt, 2P	100	150	450	1000	1800	2600

QUANTUM

1962-1963
3-cyl, 86" wb, 52 cid

	6	5	4	3	2	1
2d Rds	125	250	700	1150	2450	3500

RAMBLER REPLICAR

(1959-1960)
1902 Replica

	6	5	4	3	2	1
Rbt	125	250	700	1150	2450	3500

854

ROCKEFELLER

	6	5	4	3	2	1
1949-1954 Yankee, V-8, 100" wb, 239.4 cid						
2d Rds	350	750	1200	2350	4900	7000

ROCKET

	6	5	4	3	2	1
1948 4-cyl or 6-cyl, 106" wb						
2d Rds	200	600	950	2150	3850	5500

ROGUE

	6	5	4	3	2	1
1949 V-8, 119" wb						
2d Rds	125	250	700	1150	2450	3500

ROLLSMOBILE

	6	5	4	3	2	1
1958-1960 1-cyl						
Olds Rbt	125	250	700	1150	2450	3500
Ford Rbt	125	250	700	1150	2450	3500

ROWAN

	6	5	4	3	2	1
1967-1969 Electric						
2d Cpe	125	200	600	1100	2250	3200

RUGER

	6	5	4	3	2	1
1969-1972 Sports Tourer V-8, 130" wb, 427 cid						
2d Rds	400	1300	2200	4400	7700	11,000

RUSSELL

	6	5	4	3	2	1
1946 Hydraulic Drive						
Prototype	100	150	450	1000	1750	2500

SAVAGE GT

	6	5	4	3	2	1
1968-1969 Model 340, V-8, 108" wb, 340 cid						
2d HT	400	1300	2200	4400	7700	11,000
2d Conv	550	1700	2800	5600	9800	14,000

NOTE: Add 5 percent for 383 cubic inch V-8 or add 10 percent for 440 cubic inch V-8.

SAVIANO

	6	5	4	3	2	1
1960 Scat, 2-cyl, 80" wb						
2d Utl Wag	125	200	600	1100	2250	3200

SCOOTMOBILE I

	6	5	4	3	2	1
1946 3 Wheel						
2d Cpe	100	150	450	1000	1750	2500

SCOOTMOBILE II

	6	5	4	3	2	1
1948 1-cyl						
2d Rbt	100	150	450	1000	1750	2500

SEAGRAVE

	6	5	4	3	2	1
1960 4-cyl, 93" wb, 162 cid						
2d HT	150	350	750	1450	2900	4100

SHELBY COBRA

	6	5	4	3	2	1
1962 V-8, 90" wb, 260 cid						
2d Rds	7150	22,800	38,000	76,000	133,000	190,000
1963 V-8, 90" wb, 289 cid						
2d Rds	7500	24,000	40,000	80,000	140,000	200,000
1964 V-8, 90" wb, 289 cid						
2d Rds	7500	24,000	40,000	80,000	140,000	200,000
1965 V-8, 108" wb, 289 cid						
2d Rds	7500	24,000	40,000	80,000	140,000	200,000
V-8, 90" wb, 427 cid						
2d Rds	12,000	38,400	64,000	128,000	224,000	320,000
1966 V-8, 90" wb, 428 cid						
2d Rds	13,150	42,000	70,000	140,000	245,000	350,000
1967 V-8, 90" wb, 428 cid						
2d Rds	13,150	42,000	70,000	140,000	245,000	350,000

SHELBY MUSTANG

	6	5	4	3	2	1
1965-1970 NOTE: See Ford-Mustang.						

SKORPION

	6	5	4	3	2	1
1952-1954 Kit Car						
2d Rds	150	350	750	1450	3000	4200

SKYLINE

	6	5	4	3	2	1
1953 X50, 6-cyl, 161 cid						
2d Conv	150	400	750	1650	3150	4500

SQUIRE

	6	5	4	3	2	1
1971-1972 SS 100, 6-cyl, 104.5" wb, 250 cid						
2d Rds	450	1100	1700	3650	6650	9500
1973 SS 100, 6-cyl, 104.5" wb, 250 cid						
2d Rds	450	1100	1700	3650	6650	9500
1974 SS 100, 6-cyl, 104.5" wb, 250 cid						
2d Rds	450	1100	1700	3650	6650	9500
1975 SS 100, 6-cyl, 104.5" wb, 250 cid						
2d Rds	450	1100	1700	3650	6650	9500

STAR DUST

	6	5	4	3	2	1
1953 V-8, 110" wb, 239.4 cid						
2d Rds	200	500	850	1900	3500	5000

STARLITE

	6	5	4	3	2	1
1959-1963 Electric, 82" wb						
2d Rds	100	175	525	1050	1950	2800

STORM

	6	5	4	3	2	1
1954 Z-250, V-8 2d HT	200	500	850	1900	3500	5000

STORY

	6	5	4	3	2	1
1950 V-8, 97" wb, 136 cid 2d Rds	150	300	700	1250	2650	3800

STUART

	6	5	4	3	2	1
1961 Electric 2d Sta Wag, 2P	100	175	525	1050	1950	2800

STUDILLAC

	6	5	4	3	2	1
1953 V-8, 120.5" wb, 331.1 cid 2d HT	400	1250	2100	4200	7400	10,500
1954 V-8, 120.5" wb, 331.1 cid 2d HT	400	1250	2100	4200	7400	10,500
1955 V-8, 120.5" wb, 331.1 cid 2d HT	400	1250	2100	4200	7400	10,500

STUTZ I

	6	5	4	3	2	1
1969 Bearcat 4-cyl, 100" wb, 195.4 cid Open, 2P	450	1450	2400	4800	8400	12,000

STUTZ II

	6	5	4	3	2	1
1970-1971 Blackhawk V-8, 118" wb, 400 cid 2d Cpe	1300	4200	7000	14,000	24,500	35,000
1972 Blackhawk V-8, 118" wb, 455 cid 2d Cpe	1300	4200	7000	14,000	24,500	35,000
Limousine V-8, 133" wb, 472 cid 4d Sed	1900	6000	10,000	20,000	35,000	50,000
1973 Blackhawk V-8, 118" wb, 455 cid 2d Cpe	1300	4200	7000	14,000	24,500	35,000
Duplex V-8, 133" wb, 472 cid 4d Sed	1900	6000	10,000	20,000	35,000	50,000
1974 Blackhawk V-8, 118" wb, 455 cid 2d Cpe	1300	4200	7000	14,000	24,500	35,000
1975 Blackhawk V-8, 118" wb 2d Cpe	1300	4200	7000	14,000	24,500	35,000

SUNDANCER

	6	5	4	3	2	1
1974 Electric 2d Cpe	100	175	525	1050	2100	3000

SUPER KAR

	6	5	4	3	2	1
1946 3 Wheel 2d Rds	100	175	525	1050	1950	2800

SUPER WAGON

	6	5	4	3	2	1
1954 8-cyl, 127" wb, 369 cid 4d Sup Sta Wag	550	1800	3000	6000	10,500	15,000

SURREY

	6	5	4	3	2	1
1958-1960 Model 03, 1-cyl, 67" wb Std 2P	100	175	525	1050	2100	3000
DeL 2P	125	200	600	1100	2200	3100

SWIFT

	6	5	4	3	2	1
1959-1960 T, 1-cyl, 66" wb Open, 2P	100	175	525	1050	2100	3000
Cat, 1-cyl, 66" wb Open, 2P	125	200	600	1100	2200	3100

TASCO

	6	5	4	3	2	1
1948 V-8, Prototype 2d Sed						value not estimable

TAYLOR-DUNN

	6	5	4	3	2	1
1949-1966 Electric 2d Rbt, 2P	100	150	450	1000	1750	2500
2d Rbt, 4P	100	150	450	1000	1800	2600

THRIF-T

	6	5	4	3	2	1
1947-1955 2-cyl, 85" wb, 62.6 cid 2d Utl	100	150	450	1000	1750	2500

TOWNE SHOPPER

	6	5	4	3	2	1
1948 2-cyl, 63" wb, 38.8 cid Rbt, 2P	100	150	450	1000	1750	2500

TRI-CAR

	6	5	4	3	2	1
1955 2-cyl, 3 Wheel 2d Cpe	100	150	450	1000	1750	2500

TRIPLEX

	6	5	4	3	2	1
1954-1955 Any V-8, 100" wb 2d Rds	125	250	700	1150	2450	3500

TUCKER

	6	5	4	3	2	1
1948 Model 48 6-cyl, 130" wb, 334.1 cid 4d Sed	10,300	33,000	55,000	110,000	192,500	275,000

U.S. MARK II

	6	5	4	3	2	1
1956 110"-118" wb						
2P Rds	125	250	700	1150	2450	3500

VALKYRIE

	6	5	4	3	2	1
1967-1969 V-8, 427 cid						
2d Cpe	450	1450	2400	4800	8400	12,000

VAUGHN

	6	5	4	3	2	1
1954 V-8						
Cpe	125	200	600	1100	2250	3200
Spt	150	300	700	1250	2600	3700

VETTA VENTURA

	6	5	4	3	2	1
1964-1966 V-8, 97" wb, 300 cid						
2d HT	450	1450	2400	4800	8400	12,000
2d Conv	550	1700	2800	5600	9800	14,000

VOLTRA

	6	5	4	3	2	1
1962 Electric, 106" wb	100	150	450	1000	1750	2500

WAGON DE VILLE

	6	5	4	3	2	1
1965 V-8, 129.5" wb, 429 cid						
4d Sta Wag	700	2150	3600	7200	12,600	18,000

WARRIOR

	6	5	4	3	2	1
1964 V-4, 95" wb, 103.9 cid						
2d Cpe	150	300	700	1250	2600	3700

WESTCOASTER

	6	5	4	3	2	1
1960 Model 36, Electric						
2d Rbt	100	150	450	1000	1750	2500

WILLIAMS

	6	5	4	3	2	1
1957-1969 Steam-powered	450	1450	2400	4800	8400	12,000

WOODHILL

	6	5	4	3	2	1
1952-1956 Wildfire 6-cyl, 101" wb, 161 cid						
2d Rds	900	2900	4800	9600	16,800	24,000

XR-6

	6	5	4	3	2	1
1964 Slant Six, 105" wb						
2d Spt Rds	1150	3600	6000	12,000	21,000	30,000

YANK

	6	5	4	3	2	1
1950 4-cyl, 100" wb, 134.2 cid						
2d Rds	150	350	750	1350	2800	4000

YANKEE CLIPPER

	6	5	4	3	2	1
1954 V-8, 101" wb, 239 cid						
2d Rds	—	—	—	—	—	5500

YENKO STINGER

	6	5	4	3	2	1
1965-1969 6-cyl, 108" wb, 164 cid & 176 cid						
2d HT	850	2750	4600	9200	16,100	23,000

YENKO CAMARO

	6	5	4	3	2	1

1969
NOTE: See Chevrolet-Camaro.

1970 AMC, Javelin SST two-door fastback coupe, V-8

1970 AMC, Hornet two-door sedan, 6-cyl

1974 Checker, four-door taxicab, V-8

1968 Checker, four-door taxicab, V-8

1973 Imperial, LeBaron four-door hardtop, V-8

1973 Imperial, LeBaron four-door hardtop, V-8

1973 Corvette, Stingray two-door T-top coupe, V-8

1975 Corvette, Stingray two-door T-top coupe, V-8

Standard Catalog of American Cars

CONTRIBUTORS

David C. Antram has a lifetime membership in the Kaiser-Frazer Owners Club (KFOC) and serves as the organization's secretary. His letterhead indicates a special interest in the Kaiser-Darrin KF161. The Somerset, Pa. resident has belonged to the club for 16 years. He is also a member of the Society of Automotive Historians (SAH). He helped update the Kaiser section in this third edition of *THE STANDARD CATALOG of AMERICAN CARS 1946-1975 (SCAC II)*.

Dick Bachman's interest is postwar Packards, specifically the 22nd and 23rd Series models. Dick has owned a "bathtub" Packard, of one type or another, since 1971. He is currently restoring a 1950 Custom Eight Touring Sedan. Bachman has compiled "genealogical" charts on these Packards. You'll find more information about his research in the Packard section.

Terry V. Boyce is an automotive historian, author, photo archivist and collector of automotive literature. His numerous contributions to the old car hobby include hundreds of authoritative articles and two outstanding books. His book *CAR INTERIOR RESTORATION* is now in its third printing. It has helped thousands of hobbyists through this most difficult phase of bringing a vintage automobile back to life. Terry also wrote *CHEVY SUPER SPORTS 1961-1976*, which covers both historical and technical aspects of one of the hottest postwar collector cars. A former editor of *OLD CARS* and *CLASSIC SIXTIES*, Terry now lives in Mt. Clemmons, Mich. and works for Chevrolet's advertising agency in Detroit. His contributions to this book include the Buick chapter and portions of the Chevrolet section.

Arch Brown is a prolific automotive journalist and contributes to numerous magazines. His specialized knowledge of Nash history is reflected in the improvements he made to the Nash chapter in this third edition. Arch lives in Stockton, Calif.

Ken Buttolph is the editor of *OLD CARS PRICE GUIDE* and research editor for *OLD CARS WEEKLY*. His contributions to this catalog include photographic research and creation of the price guide to current collector car values.

Dennis Casteele is a free-lance automotive writer whose work has appeared in numerous magazines including *OLD CARS WEEKLY* and *CAR EXCHANGE*. In his authoritative history book, *THE CARS of OLDSMOBILE*, Casteele described himself as an automotive collector, restorer, merchant, mechanic and racer. He has also authored the *OLDSMOBILE SOURCE BOOK* and serves as the editor of *JOURNEY WITH OLDS*, published by the Oldsmobile Club of America. Dennis has also worked as sports writer for the *ATHENS OHIO MESSENGER*, automotive editor for the *SAGINAW MICHIGAN NEWS* and chief photographer and writer for Oldsmobile's public relations department. He was also public relations director for the Lansing Board of Power & Light. His contribution to this catalog is the original chapter covering postwar Oldsmobiles.

Pat Chappell has written *THE HOT ONES* and served as editor of *THE STANDARD CATALOG of CHEVROLET 1912-1990*. She lives in Wilmington, Del. with her '55 Chevy hardtop, '56 Nomad and '59 Impala convertible. Pat helped with the Chevrolet and Corvair sections of this third edition.

John R. Chevedden is a talented fact finder in the ranks of automotive historical writers. The Redondo Beach, Calif. resident reflects a great knowledge of a vast variety of cars and trucks. Chevedden contributed to the Oldsmobile section of this catalog.

Linda Clark is a freelance automotive writer and an automotive radio personality. Clark's lively stories and articles about antique and special-interest cars have appeared in dozens of hobby publications including *OLD CARS WEEKLY*, *CAR EXCHANGE*, *AUTOWEEK*, *CAR COLLECTOR* and *SPECIAL-INTEREST AUTOS*. Linda has applied her witty and bouncy writing style to several of the chapter introductions in this catalog, namely those on postwar Hudsons and Plymouths. She is also a member of the Society of Automotive Historians, Antique Automobile Club of America and Camaro Owners Club.

J.B. "Joe" Coyle is the president of the Chrysler Product Owners Club and a member of the Society of Automotive Historians. Coyle's father owned a Chrysler franchise from 1938 to 1964. His collection of 27 vehicles currently includes eight Imperials, although he has owned 18 over the years. No wonder the native of Chevy Chase, Md. did a great job fine-tuning the chapter on postwar Imperials.

Larry Daum has studied the automotive industry, as a hobby, since the early 1970s. He has a particular interest in American Motors Corp., Nash Motors and other independent manufacturers. A member of the Wisconsin Chapter, Society of Automotive Historians, Daum has served as editor for the American Motors Owners Association and has also written a number of articles for *OLD CARS WEEKLY*, *CAR EXCHANGE* and other national automotive magazines. Larry graduated from Illinois Central College. Frank Wrenick of the AMC Rambler Club and Nash Car Club Historian Bob Aaron aided Larry in researching and compiling the data covering Nash, AMC and Rambler in this catalog. Taylor & Son AMC, of Kewanee, Ill., provided invaluable help through use of their parts books for serial number and code breakdowns.

Helen Early spent many years working for Oldsmobile and fell in love with the company's rich and robust history. Helen has been among the recipients of the SAH's "Friends of Automotive History Award," which is a rare honor. She contributed to the Oldsmobile chapter in the third edition.

Fred K. Fox is a freelance automotive writer who contributes to *OLD CARS WEEKLY* and other old car hobby magazines. Fox also writes the "Literature in Review" column for the Studebaker Drivers Club publication *TURNING WHEELS*. He is a member of the Studebaker Drivers Club, the Avanti Owners Association, the Antique Studebaker Club and the National Studebaker Family Association. In conjunction with William Cannon, Fred Fox co-authored the book *STUDEBAKER: THE COMPLETE STORY*. He has researched and compiled the original Studebaker chapter of this catalog and did an extensive update for edition number three.

John Gunnell resides in Iola, Wis. with his 1936 and 1953 Pontiacs. There he works as Director of Editorial for *OLD CARS WEEKLY* publications. For over 20 years, "Gunner" has specialized in writing about Pontiacs. Gunnell served as editor of the previous editions of this book, as well as this edition.

Phil Hall is a collector of automotive photos, magazines and catalogs, as well as the owner of eight collector cars and trucks. He works for *MIDWEST RACING NEWS* and also as a racetrack announcer. A resident of Wawatosa, Wis., Hall's facts and photos are seen throughout this catalog.

Phil Hanson operates Twin Brooke Appraisal Service in Holden, Mass. We asked him to "appraise" the Corvair section of this catalog and increase its "value" to Corvair hobbyists. We think he did a great job.

Bob Hovorka's outstanding automotive artwork is familiar to thousands of automotive hobbyists and enthusiasts through its regular appearances in *OLD CARS WEEKLY* and *SPECIAL-INTEREST AUTOS*. Other samples have been presented in publications, such as *CAR CLASSICS*. Hovorka also has done limited-edition posters and prints of popular postwar cars. An avowed Hudson lover and Jeep enthusiast, Bob's projects have included helping with the restoration of a 1957 Chevrolet in his rare hours away from a drawingboard. The art plates covering the 1-6 Vehicle Grading System and the Body I.D. Guides located in the rear of this catalog are representative of the high-quality artwork that Bob Hovorka has gifted the old car hobby with.

F.L. Johnson, of Seattle, Wash., is a member of the Society of Automotive Historians with a deep interest in Ford Motor Co.'s fabulous Thunderbird. He's added many refinements to that particular section of this book.

Sherwood Kahlenberg's name is well-known to Chrysler enthusiasts coast-to-coast. He has served hard and well as the president of the Walter P. Chrysler Club, Inc., a non-profit organization dedicated to the preservation and enjoyment of Plymouth, Dodge, DeSoto, Chrysler, Imperial and related automobiles. As a contributing editor to the *WPC NEWS*, Kahlenberg has researched and written some of the best historical articles ever printed about Chrysler Corp. cars. He has also been instrumental in supplying hobbyists with technical and restoration aid for Chrysler brand automobiles. Sherwood's own fleet of Chrysler collectibles includes a number of exceptional rarities, such as a 1958 Chrysler 300D complete with the Bendix electronic fuel-injection system, which was installed in less than 30 cars. His original contributions to this catalog were the sections covering Chrysler and DeSoto. This time around, he also updated the Imperial data.

Richard M. Langworth's contributions to the hobby and to automotive historical research are immense. Langworth penned dozens of books and hundreds of columns and articles. He operates Dragonwyck Publishing Co., in Contoocook, N.H. His contribution to this edition was an outstanding re-working of the Kaiser and Frazer sections.

John Lee has been a Krause Publications contributor for over 15 years. He also authored articles about collector cars, customs and hot rods in numerous magazines. The Lincoln, Neb. native was a member of the National Automotive Journalists Assoc. and currently produces *THE NOMAD POST* for the Chevrolet Nomad Association. Lee is an active member of the Kustom Kemps of America. John works for a firm that produces maps of local communities. In this edition, he "re-mapped" the Chrysler, DeSoto, Dodge and Plymouth sections.

James T. Lenzke is technical editor of *OLD CARS WEEKLY* and associate editor of *OLD CARS PRICE GUIDE*. In addition to editing our pricing section, Jim wrote several new histories of "alternative" automobiles. He resides in Iola, Wis.

Robert L. Lichty is responsible for the body style illustrations in this catalog. Bob has worked for *OLD CARS WEEKLY*, *CARS & PARTS*, *HEMMINGS MOTOR NEWS*, Lucas Tire Co., Kruse International and Carlisle Productions. He is currently employed as a media specialist with the Blackhawk Collection of world-class automobiles.

John F. Mack, of Madison, Wis., is listed in the *SAH ROSTER* as a DeSoto buff. His interest in the marque shows through in his excellent contributions to our DeSoto section.

Paul G. McLaughlin operates the Mustang Owners Club International, based in his hometown of Albuquerque, N.M. He also does the "Light-Duty Trucking" column for *OLD CARS WEEKLY*. In this edition of SCAC II, Paul stuck to reviewing and updating the Mustang chapter. The results are impressive.

Jack Miller is the owner of Miller Motor Sales in Ypsilanti, Mich. His dealership, located in the city's historic section, is a virtual museum of Hudson Motor Car Co. with a circa-1957 atmosphere. Jack has served as business manager for the Hudson-Essex-Terraplane Club, an organization that has been a cornerstone of the club movement within the old car hobby. It has been more than 35 years since Hudson Motor Car Co. built its last models and people have been collecting examples of the marque ever since. This explains the popularity of the H-E-T Club. Miller's base of operations is the former Hudson dealership once operated by his father. In 1980, we asked Jack Miller if H-E-T would be willing to share its remarkable archives for the purpose of compiling the first edition of SCAC. Fortunately, the idea was acceptable. With the invaluable help of H-E-T Club librarian Charles Liskow and Jack Miller's photo and literature collection, we discovered a wealth of heretofore unpublished facts about the outstanding postwar history of Hudson Motor Car Co. For the third edition, Jack contributed more facts and photos to the chapter on Hudsons.

Joel R. Miller operates Miller's Dodge Garage in Portland, Ore. He is also a Dodge columnist and technical advisor on 1954-1960 Dodge trucks for the Light Commercial Vehicle Association. We asked him to peruse our Dodge information for accuracy and he did an outstanding job.

Jack Mueller maintains the Kaiser-Frazer Archives in Cambridge, Wis. He has spent many years researching the lavish history of both marques made in Willow Run, Mich. Our Kaiser section reflects his valued input.

G. Marshall Naul is a co-founder of the Society of Automotive Historians. He has served as President of this organization, editor of the *SAH NEWSLETTER* and chairman of the group's oral history committee. Naul has written countless articles for hobby periodicals including *OLD CARS WEEKLY*. He has also authored or contributed to a number of important automotive books including *THE SPECIFICATION BOOK FOR U.S. CARS 1930-1969* and *THE COMPLETE ENCYCLOPEDIA of COMMERCIAL VEHICLES*, the latter a winner of the 1980 Cugnot Award for outstanding automotive history books. The sections in this catalog covering Checker, Kaiser-Frazer and Packard were researched and compiled by G. Marshall Naul in 1980.

John O'Halloran's main interest is Hudson. He added facts and photos about the marque to the third edition of *THE STANDARD CATALOG of AMERICAN CARS 1946-1975*. A member of the Society of Automotive Historians, O'Halloran hails from Chicago, Ill.

Byron D. Olsen works for a law firm in Minneapolis, Minn. and collects automotive literature. He has sales brochures for every American car made from 1950 on, plus many from the '30s and '40s. Byron's Kaiser-Frazer literature helped him make significant changes to our chapter about Frazers.

Vaughn W. Oswald, of Howell, Mich., listed an interest in Chrysler products in the *SAH ROSTER*. As a result, he became involved as a contributor to the Chrysler-Imperial section of SCAC II, edition three.

Joseph L. Parker is an automotive historian from Chesapeake Beach, Md. He's one of the specialists who helped update and improve the Packard section of edition number three.

Gerald Perschbacher is a frequent contributor to *OLD CARS WEEKLY*. A collector of Packards, Packard literature and Packard filmstrips, Perschbacher made major enhancements to our Packard information and supplied photos of other marques.

Dale Rapp is an avowed Edsel lover and the owner of 32 examples of the rare marque, which was produced for only three short years in the late-1950s. Dale explains that Edsels are one of many interests in his life, even if the most obvious. He has taught industrial education classes and is a licensed aircraft mechanic specializing in the sport plane field. When he's not out fixing or driving Edsels, Dale spends most of the time harvesting crops on his farm. He is a member of both the Edsel Owners Club and the International Edsel Club and frequently writes technical articles for the *INTERNATIONAL EDSELETTER*, a highly respected hobby publication. Dale compiled the original chapter on Edsels for this catalog.

Darryl A. Salisbury plays active roles in the American Motors Owners Club (AMO) and the Milestone Car Society (MCS). The Portage, Mich. resident is an AMX enthusiast and helped update the AMC and AMC-Rambler pages.

John M. Sawruk works as a product engineer for General Motors. He is a collector of toy cars and model trains, although he's famous among car collectors as the Official Historian for Pontiac Motor Div. He helped "re-engineer" the Pontiac section in this third edition.

Phil Skinner is a freelance automotive journalist and a Hollywood screenwriter for such shows as "Alf" and "Mannix." When not behind a typewriter, Phil is often behind the wheel of his Edsel station wagon tooling across America. The Fullerton, Calif. native did a major update of our Edsel section.

When **John Smith** was five years old his father brought home a "Golden Anniversary 1953 Ford Country Sedan. It proved to be a very good car. Since then, John has been a Ford man. He even has a Ford snowblower! A draftsman by trade, Smith is a freelance writer and photographer for eight different automotive magazines. Besides photography, his current fascination is truck and tractor pulling. John served as regional director of the Northeastern Ohio Region of the Performance Ford Club of America, a group devoted to the promotion of Ford Motor Co. and its products. The club has a current roster of more than 3,000 members internationally. John has also compiled the Mustang and Dodge sections of this catalog and admits to checking-out Chargers and Challengers since. In addition, he applied his professional research abilities to covering the postwar history of Willys-Overland.

R.J. Stoltzfus is a member of the Society of Automotive Historians from Denver, Pa. A love of Packards and interest in the marque's history shows through his work on the Packard section of this book.

Dale O. Stouch, Jr., has rare knowledge of the postwar years of Willys-Overland and contributed to that section of this catalog. He lives in Durham, N.C. and belongs to the Society of Automotive Historians.

Charles Webb writes a nationally syndicated column for Copely News Service (San Diego). He is co-author of *THE INVESTOR'S ILLUSTRATED GUIDE to AMERICAN CONVERTIBLES* and *SPECIAL-INTEREST AUTOMOBILES 1946-1976*. Webb owns three special-interest cars, a 1956 Chevrolet 210 station wagon (with factory power pack), a 1963 Chevy II Nova convertible and a 1965 Corvair Monza coupe. In addition, he collects vintage automobile TV commercials and sales promotion movies. Webb is a member of the Wisconsin Chapter, Society of Automotive Historians. His work in this catalog includes research and compilation of the Corvette, Imperial, Lincoln and Mercury chapters.

J. Francis Werneth lives in Baltimore, Md. He is a member of the Society of Automotive Historians with an interest in DeSoto. That interest is reflected in updates he made to our DeSoto chapter.

R. Perry Zavitz is an acknowledged expert on postwar cars and has written numerous specialized articles and book sections covering alternative automobiles and Canadian cars built after World War II. His "Postwar Scripts" column has been a popular feature of *OLD CARS WEEKLY* for many years. Zavitz's special interests include collecting sales literature, factory photos and historical items related to passenger cars, station wagons and crew cab trucks built from 1945 on. He has served as secretary and director of the Society of Automotive Historians and was the first Director of the Society's Canadian Chapter. Perry is employed as a television production staff executive. His contributions in the catalog include a number of chapter introductions and, the section on alternative cars.

PHOTO CREDITS

Whenever possible, throughout SCAC II, we have strived to picture all cars with photographs that show them in their most original form. All photos gathered from reliable outside sources have an alphabetical code, following the caption, which indicates the photo source. An explanation of these codes is given below. Photos without such a credit code are from the **Old Cars Publications'** photo archives.

(AA)	Applegate & Applegate
(AB)	Arch Brown
(ACD)	ACD Museum, Auburn, Ind.
(CG)	Catherine Gunnell
(DAB)	Donald A. Bougher
(DC)	Dennis Casteele
(FF)	Fred Fox
(GP)	Gerald Perschbacher
(HAC)	Harrah's Automobile Collection
(HET)	Hudson Essex Terraplane Club/(Jack Miller)
(IB)	Stern Walters/Earle Ludgin Inc./(Ira Brichta)
(IMS)	Indianapolis Motor Speedway Photo Dept.
(IP)	Imperial Palace
(JFW)	J. Francis Werneth
(JL)	John Lee
(JO)	John O'Halloran
(JTL)	James T. Lenzke
(LL)	Lew Lazarus
(MC)	Micheal Carbonella
(NAHC)	National Automotive History Collection
(PH)	Phil Hall
(RCA)	Rick Cole Auctions
(RPZ)	R. Perry Zavitz
(SS)	Sam Shields
(TVB)	Terry V. Boyce
(WB)	William Bailey

ACKNOWLEDGEMENTS

SPECIAL THANKS TO: Bob Adams (Union Grove, Wis.); D.E. Allen (Buick Motor Div.); Automotive History Collection (Detroit Public Library); George Berg (Chrysler 300 Club); Joe Bortz/Blue Suede Shoes (Highland Park, Mich.); Sally Boyce (Mt. Clemmons, Mich.); the late James Bradley, (Detroit Public Library); Buick Motor Div. (Flint, Mich.); Jack Carew (Green Lake, Wis.); Chevrolet Motor Div. (Detroit, Mich.); Chrysler Historical Archives (Detroit, Mich.); Derek Cottier (Ford Motor Co.); David R. Crippin (Ford Archives); Gil Cunningham (Chrysler 300 Club); Dianne Davis (Pennsylvania); Ford Motor Co. (Dearborn, Mich.); Robert J. Gary (Stevens Point, Wis.); Jim Gill (General Motors); William F. Hamilton, Sr. (Iola, Wis.); Bill Hebal (Stevens Point, Wis.); Bob Hensel/Chevy Acres (Brillion, Wis.); Tony Hossain (Rochester Hills, Mich.), Indianapolis Motor Speedway Corporation (IMSC); Chuck Licari (GMC); Robert Manning Strozier Library (Florida State University); Jack L. Martin (Indianapolis, Ind.); Bruce McDonald (Pontiac Motor Div.; T. McGee (General Motors); Ron McQueeney (Official Photographer IMSC); Joan Morris (Florida State University); Roy Nagel (GM Tech Center); Oldsmobile Div. (Lansing, Mich.); H.A. Pfanschmidt (Kansas City, Kan.); Pontiac Motor Div. (Pontiac, Mich.); Sam Shields (Bookman Dan); Ben E. Scheiwe (Pontiac Motor Div.); James W. Sponsellar (Fisher Body Div.); Dick Thompson (Pontiac Motor Div.); Ben Walker (Kaiser-Frazer); Jill Witzenberg (Pontiac Motor Div.).

Standard Catalog of American Cars

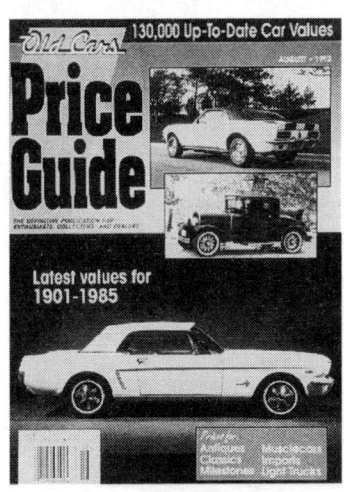